THE
MACMILLAN
NAUTICAL ALMANAC
INCORPORATING REED'S

1999

EDITOR
Commander Neville Featherstone RN

First published 1980
This edition published 1998 by Macmillan
an imprint of Macmillan Publishers Limited
25 Eccleston Place, London SW1W 9NF
and Basingstoke

Associated companies throughout the world

ISBN 0-333-719719

9 8 7 6 5 4 3 2 1

A CIP catalogue record for this book is available from the British
Library

CORRESPONDENCE
Letters on nautical matters should be addressed to:

Cdr N Featherstone, The Editor, Macmillan Nautical Almanac,
Edington House, Trent, Sherborne, Dorset DT9 4SR, England

☎ +44 (0) 1935 850737. e-mail: MacAlman@aol.com

Enquiries about despatch, invoicing or commercial matters
should be addressed to:

Customer Services Department
Macmillan Press Ltd, Houndmills, Basingstoke,
Hampshire RG21 2XS

Enquiries about advertising space should be addressed to:

Communications Management International
Chiltern House, 120 Eskdale Avenue, Chesham,
Buckinghamshire HP5 3BD

Chapters 1-7 Page preparation by
          Wyvern 21 Limited, Bristol

Chapter 8   Cartography and page preparation by
          Lovell Johns Limited, Oxford

Printed and bound in Great Britain by
          Bath Press Colourbooks, Glasgow

IMPROVEMENTS IN THE 1999 EDITION

NEW for 1999

Quick Page Reference re-introduced by popular demand

Personal Index re-introduced by popular demand

Sun's Declination table provided to enable a compass check by sun's azimuth

Cruise Planning Proforma appears in Chapter 2 (Navigation)

Internet a mini-directory of nautical Web sites and email addresses is provided

The National Coastwatch Institution is described alongside HM Coastguard

Search & Rescue Data for Belgium, Netherlands and Germany have been added to Chapter 6 (Safety)

Tidal Predictions Standard Ports of Wick, Stornoway and Dunkerque are added

Tidal Streams new hourly chartlets for off Land's End, Rathlin Island and the Mull of Kintyre

CHANGED for 1999

New and revised Introduction (based on old Chapter 1)

Glossary has been split into French, Dutch and German, and placed in areas 15, 20 and 21 respectively

Sun and Moon Tables now in Chapter 2

Former Chapters 2 to 9 have been much revised, simplified and streamlined – they are re-numbered as Chapters 1 to 7

DGPS beacons are listed separately

Traffic Separation Schemes each scheme is now depicted in its relevant geographic area

NEW ports, anchorages and data

New or enhanced chartlets and text are shown below by geographic areas

England, *South Coast*
Passage information in Area 1 now includes more information on tidal gates at:
- *Land's End*
- *Lizard and Start Point*

New Chartlets of:
- *Lulworth Ranges*
- *Poole Quay to Cobbs Quay*
- *Poole tidal curve*
- *Buckler's Hard inset*
- *Port Solent*

Subfacts diagram:
- *Start Point to Selsey Bill*

England, *East Coast*
- *Mersea Quarters (River Blackwater)*
- *Scarborough at larger scale*
- *Whitby extended*
- *Royal Quays marina on River Tyne*

England, *West Coast* and Wales
Chartlets of:
- *Fleetwood (Wyre Dock marina)*
- *Preston marina*
- *Cardiff barrage*
- *Severn bridges*
- *the marinas being built at Watchet and Portishead*

Scotland
- *Eyemouth*
- *Shetland: Fair Isle, Scalloway and Foula*
- *West coast: Loch Inver*

Channel Islands
A complete overhaul of this popular area:
- *new Area Maps*
- *expanded Passage Information*
- *more detailed information on minor harbours and anchorages*

New chartlets include:
- *Braye Harbour*
- *Herm*
- *enlarged chartlet of Sark*
- *the new marina at St Helier*

Ireland
- *Ballycastle*
- *Rathlin Island*
- *the new marina at Waterford*

France, *Channel coast*
- *Lezardrieux inset*
- *Primel-Tregastel*

France, *Atlantic Coast*
- *diagram of Landes firing range*

The symbol of the **CHART AND NAUTICAL INSTRUMENT TRADE ASSOCIATION**, founded in 1918. With the full support of the Hydrographer of the Navy and leading manufacturers of nautical instruments, members of the Association are able to place their experience and service at the disposal of the shipping industry and all navigators.

CHART SUPPLY AND CORRECTION SERVICES

The CNITA counts among its members many of the leading Admiralty Chart Agents who can supply your requirements from a single chart or publication to a worldwide outfit and special folio requirements from comprehensive stocks in all the major ports. Carefully trained chart correctors are available to examine and correct all Admiralty charts.

THE CNITA TRACING SERVICE

Although tracings have been in use by the Royal Navy and Admiralty Chart Agents for many years, it was the Chart Committee of the Chart Nautical Instrument Trade Association that successfully negotiated with the Hydrographer of the Navy for them to become available to the merchant navigator and private user.

The CNITA tracing overlay correction service is available from all Admiralty Chart Agents who are members of the Association, and is now supplied to more than 5,000 vessels each week. Each tracing wallet contains the weekly "Notices to Mariners" and the tracings printed with much of the relevant details of the area surrounding the correction, making the correction of each chart a simpler operation. All that the user has to do is match the tracing to the chart, pierce through the small circle showing the exact position of the correction, in conjunction with the "Notices to Mariners", and then transfer the information onto the chart. Navigating Officers welcome the tracings systems for its accuracy and speed. Onboard chart correction time can be cut by up to 80% and Masters can now rest assured that their charts can be kept continually up to date. Reasonably priced, these tracings are an economical and invaluable contribution to safety at sea.

COMPASS ADJUSTING AND NAUTICAL INSTRUMENTS

The CNITA insists that its Compass Adjusters are thoroughly trained to its own high standards, and independently examined by the Department of Trade. For yacht or super tanker our compass adjusters can advise you on the type of compass you need, its siting, and any adjustments needed. CNITA Compass Adjusters are based in all the major ports and are available day and night to "swing" ships.

Members of the CNITA, many with a life long experience in this field, can advise you when purchasing all your nautical instruments. Most suppliers provide an instrument repair service combining traditional craftsmanship with modern methods to ensure that instruments are serviced and tested to a high standard.

ARE YOU COMPLYING WITH THE LATEST INTERNATIONAL REGULATIONS?

Chart and Nautical Instrument Trade Association members established in most UK ports and overseas are able to advise you. For full details of the Association, its activities and its services to the Navigator, write to:

The Secretaries,
CHART AND NAUTICAL INSTRUMENT TRADE ASSOCIATION,
Dalmore House, 310 Vincent Street, GLASGOW G2 5QR.

PORTS WHERE SHIPS' COMPASSES ARE ADJUSTED

Names of member firms. Those marked * have DoT Certified Compass Adjusters available for Adjustment of Compasses, day or night.

Port or District	Name and Address	Telephone
ABERDEEN	*Thomas Gunn Navigation Services, Anchor House, 62 Regents Quay, Aberdeen AB11 5AR.	01224 595045
BANGOR (N Ireland)	Todd Chart Agency Ltd., 4 Seacliff Road, The Harbour, Bangor, N Ireland BT20 5EY.	01247 466640
BRISTOL	*W F Price & Co Ltd., Northpoint House, Wapping Wharf, Bristol BS1 6UD.	0117-929 2229
FALMOUTH	*Marine Instruments, The Bosun's Locker, Upton Slip, Falmouth TR11 3DQ.	01326 312414
GLASGOW	Brown, Son & Ferguson, Ltd., 4-10 Darnley Street, Glasgow G41 2SD.	0141-429 1234
HULL	*B Cooke & Son, Ltd., Kingston Observatory, 58-59 Market Place, Hull HU1 1RH.	01482 223454
KENT	*SIRS Navigation Ltd., 186a Milton Road, Swanscombe, Kent DA10 0LX.	01322 383672
LIVERPOOL	Dubois-Phillips & McCallum Ltd. Oriel Chambers, Covent Garden, Liverpool L2 8UD.	0151-236 2776
LONDON	*Kelvin Hughes Charts and Maritime Supplies New North Road, Hainault, Ilford, Essex IG6 2UR.	0181-500 6166
	A M Smith (Marine) Ltd., 33 Epping Way, Chingford, London E4 7PB.	0181-529 6988
LOWESTOFT	*Seath Instruments (1992) Ltd., Unit 30, Colville Works, Colville Road, Lowestoft NR33 9QS.	01502 573811
NORTH SHIELDS (Newcastle)	*John Lilley & Gillie Ltd., Clive Street, North Shields, Tyne & Wear NE29 6LF.	0191-257 2217

Port or District	Name and Address	Telephone
SOUTHAMPTON	*R J Muir, 22 Seymour Close, Chandlers Ford, Eastleigh, Southampton SO5 2JE.	01703 261042
	Wessex Marine Equipment Ltd., Logistics House, 2nd Avenue Business Park, Millbrook Road East, Southampton SO1 0LP.	01703 510570

OVERSEAS MEMBERS

Port or District	Name and Address
ANTWERP	Bogerd Navtec NV, Oude Leenwnrui 37 Antwerp 2000.
	*Martin & Co. Oude Leewenrui 37, Antwerp 2000.
COPENHAGEN	Iver C Weilbach & Co. A/S, 35 Toldbodgade, Postbox 1560, DK-1253 Copenhagen K.
GOTHENBURG	A B Ramantenn, Knipplagatan 12 S-414 74, Gothenburg.
HONG KONG	George Falconer (Nautical) Ltd., The Hong Kong Jewellery Building, 178-180 Queen's Road, Central Hong Kong.
	Hong Kong Ship's Supplies Co. Room 1614, Melbourne Plaza, 33 Queen's Road, Central Hong Kong.
LISBON	J Garraio & Co. Ltd., Avenida 24 de Julho, 2-1°, D-1200, Lisbon.
ROTTERDAM	*Kelvin Hughes Observator B.V., Nieuwe Langeweg 41, 3194 DC, Hoogvliet (Rt), The Netherlands.
SINGAPORE	Motion Smith, 78 Shenton Way #01-03, Singapore 0207.
SKYTTA	A/S Navicharts, Masteveien 3, N-1483 Skytta, Norway.
URUGUAY	Captain Stephan Nedelchev Soc. Col. Port of Montevideo, Florida 1562, 11100 Montevideo.
VARNA	Captain Lyudmil N. Jordanov, 13A Han Omurtag Str. 9000 Bulgaria.

1918 - 1999
OVER 80 YEARS OF SERVING THE MARINER

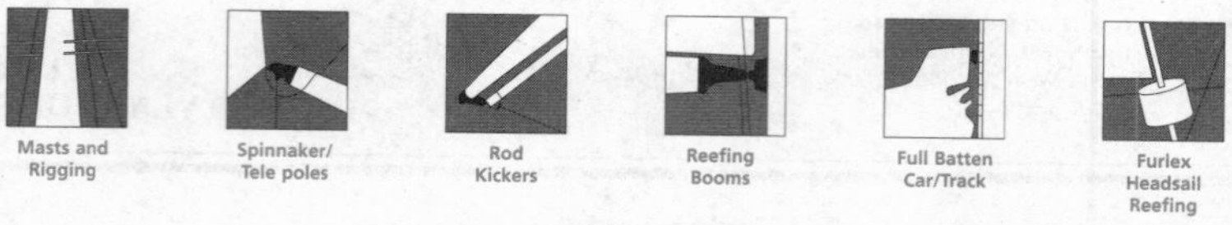

Contents

IMPROVEMENTS IN THIS EDITION **Prelim**

QUICK PAGE REFERENCE
AND PERSONAL INDEX **Overleaf**

DIRECTORY OF MARINE SUPPLIES
AND SERVICES BY TYPE AND AREA **Page i**

INTRODUCTION **Page 1**
Numbering system, index, acknowledgments,
suggestions for improvements, supplements,
abbreviations and symbols.

CHAPTER 1 **7**
GENERAL INFORMATION
Rules of the road, documentation of yachts,
HM Customs, useful addresses.

COLOUR PLATES **15**
Buoyage, chart symbols, lights & shapes,
signal flags, ensigns, port traffic signals,
notes on flag etiquette.

CHAPTER 2 **25**
COASTAL NAVIGATION
Definitions and terms, IALA buoyage, light
characteristics, passage planning, calculator
navigation. Tables giving: distance of horizon
for various heights of eye, distance of lights
when rising/dipping, distance off by Vertical
Sextant Angle, time/speed/distance, speed
over measured mile, true bearing of Sun at
sunrise/sunset, Sun's declination, phases
of the Moon, eclipse notes, sunrise/set,
twilights, moonrise/set, conversion tables.

CHAPTER 3 **47**
RADIO NAVIGATIONAL AIDS
Position fixing systems – GPS, Decca, and
Loran-C, Waypoints, RDF beacons, Radar,
Racons.

CHAPTER 4 **65**
COMMUNICATIONS
International Code, radio, link calls, Inmarsat,
port operations, VTS, navigational warnings,
coast radio stations, Internet, time.

CHAPTER 5 **81**
WEATHER
Shipping forecast, Beaufort scale, conversion
scales, weather terms, BBC broadcasts,
Navtex, recorded weather, coast radio stations.

CHAPTER 6 **101**
SAFETY
Safety equipment, emergency signals,
GMDSS, EPIRBs, HM Coastguard, VHF DF,
Subfacts and Gunfacts, UK SAR procedures,
SAR organisation on the Continent.

CHAPTER 7 **117**
TIDES
Explanation, definitions, calculating times and
heights of HW and LW, intermediate times and
heights of tide, factors, rule of twelfths,
clearance under bridges, tidal prediction by
computer, tidal streams, meteorological
conditions, Standard ports.

CHAPTER 8 **127**
HARBOUR, COASTAL AND
TIDAL INFORMATION
Contents, map of areas, general and harbour
information, TSS, high speed craft, ferries,
distance tables, harbours, tidal predictions, list
of lights and waypoints, passage information.

Area			
1	South West England, including Isles of Scilly		137
2	Central Southern England		181
3	South East England		245
4	East England		269
5	North East England		323
6	South East Scotland		355
7	North East Scotland		383
8	North West Scotland		415
9	South West Scotland		451
10	North West England, Isle of Man and North Wales		479
11	South Wales and Bristol Channel		509
12	South Ireland		545
13	North Ireland		583
14	Channel Islands		617
15	Central North France		643
16	North Brittany		675
17	South Brittany		707
18	South Biscay		737
19	North East France		769
20	Belgium and Netherlands		807
21	Germany		853

LATE CORRECTIONS **892**

INDEX **894**

QUICK PAGE REFERENCE

(For main index see page 894)

Abandon ship	113	International code flags (Plates 6 & 7)	20-21
Abbreviations & symbols	3-6	Late corrections	892
Beaufort wind scale	84	Link calls (R/T)	68
Buoyage (Plate 1)	15, 27	Map of geographic areas	128
Chart symbols (Plates 2 & 3)	16-17	**MAYDAY** call	104
Coastguard, HM	108	Morse code	20-21
Coast Radio Stations	67, 72, 91	Navigation lights & shapes (Plates 4 & 5)	18-19
Conversion factors/scales	46	Navtex	86-87
Customs, HM	12	**PAN PAN** call	104
Distance tables	134-136 & Areas	Phonetic alphabet	20-21
Distress signals (R/T)	103	Racons (Radar beacons)	60-63
Dover HW	264-266	RDF beacons	53-59
Dover Range	Crewsaver card	Rules of the road	8-11
Emergency signals	112	Shipping forecast	82, 86
Emergency VHF DF service	110	Single letter signals	20-21
Glossary: French	653-655	Sound signals	11
Dutch	817-819	Tidal calculations	119-122
German	862-864	Tidal coefficients (Brest)	698
Harbour, coastal and tidal information	127-891	Traffic signals (Plate 9)	22, 652, 822, 867
Helicopter rescue	113	Visual and audible emergency signals	103

PERSONAL INDEX OF IMPORTANT PAGES

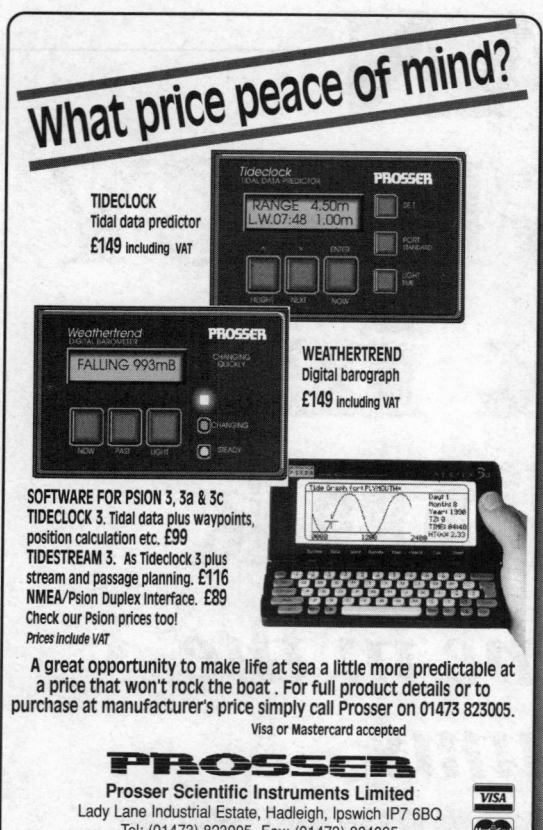

THE PINK PAGE SECTION

Marine Supplies & Services Guide
Coastal & Waterways Services
Directory - area by area

This section provides readers with a quick reference to harbours, marinas, companies and organisations currently delivering services - including emergency services, equipment and supplies to boat owners and the boating industry. Each entry carries concise information for guidance.

Pages I-XXXI lists by types of service and products and XXXII-LIV by coastal location.

AIR CONDITIONING II	LEGAL SERVICES XV
ANCHORS & CHAINS II	LIFERAFT/INFLATABLES & REPAIRS XVI
ANENOMETERS/AUTOPILOTS II	MAIL ORDER XVI
ASSOCIATIONS II	MARINA DEVELOPMENT CONSULTANTS XVII
ASTRO NAVIGATION II	MARINAS XVII
BERTHS & MOORINGS II	MARINE ACTIVITY CENTRES XXI
BINOCULARS/REPAIRS IV	MARINE ARTISTS/CARTOONISTS XXI
BOAT BUILDERS & REPAIRS IV	MARINE ENGINEERS XXI
BOAT NAMING SYSTEMS V	MARINE PHOTOGRAPHERS/LIBRARIES XXII
BOAT STORAGE V	MASTS/SPARS & RIGGING XXII
BOATYARD SERVICES & SUPPLIES VI	MOISTURE METRES XXIII
BOOKS & CHARTS/PUBLISHERS VII	NAVIGATION EQUIPMENT - GENERAL XXIII
BREAKDOWN VIII	NAVIGATION LIGHT SWITCHES & MONITORS XXIII
CANVAS GOODS VIII	PAINT & OSMOSIS XXIII
CHANDLERS VIII	PROPELLERS & STERNGEAR/REPAIRS XXIV
CLEANING AGENTS IX	QUAY SERVICES XXIV
CLOTHING IX	RADIO COURSES/SCHOOLS XXIV
COMMUNICATIONS EQUIPMENT X	REPAIR MATERIALS & ACCESSORIES XXIV
COMPASS ADJUSTERS/MANUFACTURERS X	SAFETY EQUIPMENT XXIV
COMPUTERS & SOFTWARE X	SAILMAKERS & REPAIRS XXV
CORPORATE PROMOTIONS XI	SEA DELIVERIES XXV
CORPORATE YACHT OWNERSHIP XI	SKIPPERED CHARTERS/CRUISING XXV
DECK EQUIPMENT XI	SLIPWAYS XXVI
DIESEL MARINE FUEL ADDITIVES XI	SOLAR POWER XXVI
DIVING TUITION XI	SPEED LOGS XXVI
ELECTRICAL & ELECTRONIC ENGINEERS XI	SPRAYHOODS & DODGERS XXVI
ELECTRONIC DEVICES & EQUIPMENT XII	STAINLESS STEEL FITTINGS XXVI
EMERGENCY REPAIRS XII	SURVEYORS & NAUTICAL ARCHITECTS XXVI
ENGINES & ACCESSORIES XII	TANKS XXVII
FABRICATIONS & REPAIRS XII	TAXI SERVICE XXVII
FIRST AID XII	TRANSPORT/ YACHT DELIVERIES XXVII
FLAGS, FLAGSTAFFS & PENNANTS XII	TUITION/SAILING SCHOOLS XXVII
FLOTILLA HOLIDAYS XIII	UPHOLSTERY & COVERS XXVIII
GENERAL MARINE EQUIPMENT XIII	WATERSIDE ACCOMMODATION & RESTAURANTS XXX
GENERATORS XIII	WEATHER INFORMATION XXVIII
GLASS FIBRE MARINE SPECIALISTS XIII	WIND POWER XXVIII
GRAPHICS XIII	WOOD FITTINGS XXVIII
HARBOURS XIII	YACHT BROKERS XXVIII
HYDRAULIC MARINE EQUIPMENT XIV	YACHT CHARTERS & HOLIDAYS XXVIII
INSTRUMENTATION & POSITION FIXING XIV	YACHT CLUB FACILITIES XXIX
INSURANCE & FINANCE XV	YACHT MANAGEMENT XXIX
INTERIOR LIGHTS XV	YACHT REGISTRATION XXIX

AIR CONDITIONING

CRUISAIR UK LTD
26 Old Wareham Road, Poole,
Dorset BH12 4QR.
Tel (01202) 716469 Fax (01202) 716478
Marine air conditioning.

ANCHORS & CHAINS

GRIFF CHAINS LTD
Quarry Road, Dudley Wood, Dudley,
West Midlands DY2 0ED.
Tel (01384) 569415 Fax (01384) 410580
Manufacturers of mooring systems and
equipment. For over 150 years Griff Chains
has been synonymous with chain, anchor
and chain component development for
marine applications. Quality chains to meet
all markets.

griff CHAINS
ANCHOR CHAINS AND CABLES
SHACKLES
SWIVELS
MOORING CHAINS
ANCHORS
Manufacturers since 1835 to
British Defence Standards
Griff Chains Ltd
Quarry Road, Dudley Wood,
Dudley,
West Midlands DY2 0ED.
England.
Tel: (01384) 569415
Fax: (01384) 410580

ANENOMETERS/ AUTOPILOTS

THOMAS WALKER GROUP LTD
37-41 Bissell Street,
Birmingham B5 7HR.
Tel 0121-622 4475 Fax 0121-622 4478
Manufacturer of marine instruments
including, Neco Autopilots, Walker Logs
and Towing Logs, Walker Anemometers,
Chernikeeff Logs.

ASSOCIATIONS

CHART & NAUTICAL INSTRUMENT
TRADE ASSOCIATION (C N I T A)
The Secretaries, Dalmore House
310 St Vincent Street, Glasgow G2 5QR.
Tel 0141-226 8000 Fax 0141-228 8310
Members of the Association are able to
place their experience and service at the
disposal of the shipping industry and all
navigators.

ROYAL INSTITUTE OF NAVIGATION
1 Kensington Gore, London SW7 2AT.
Tel 0171-591 3130 Fax 0171-591 3131
Forum for all interested in navigation - Air:
Sea: Land: Space.

ASTRO NAVIGATION

REED'S NAUTICAL BOOKS
The Barn, Ford Farm, Bradford Leigh,
Bradford on Avon, Wiltshire BA15 2RP.
Tel 0181-941 7878 Fax 0181-941 8787
From 1st January 1999
Tel (01225) 868821 Fax (01225) 868831
THE HEAVENLY BODIES - Annual astro-
navigation tables for yachtsmen edited by
Lt Cdr H J Baker. Price £10.95 incl p&p.
Showing monthly pages for Sun, Moon,
Planets and Stars accompanied by examples
and all necessary tables. Complete SIGHT
REDUCTION PACKAGE with programmed
calculator also available together with book
and chart catalogues, for world wide mail

BERTHS & MOORINGS

ARDENTINNY HOTEL
Ardentinny, Loch Long,
By Dunoon, Argyll PA23 8TR.
Tel (01369) 810209 Fax (01369) 810241
A warm Scottish welcome awaits you at the
Ardentinny. Delightful dinners to a very
high standard are prepared by our chef
complemented by a choice of over 50
selections of French and New World wines.
Excellent casual lunches served in the
garden or buttery. Friendly bar, frequented
by yachtsmen, with a good selection of
beer. 7 moorings available.

BALTIC WHARF
WATER LEISURE CENTRE
Bristol Harbour,
Underfall Yard, Bristol BS1 6XG.
Tel 0117-929 7608 Fax 0117-929 4454
Tuition: 0117-952 5202
Sailing school and centre, with qualified
instruction in most watersports. Also
moorings available throughout the Bristol
harbour for all types of leisurecraft.

W BATES & SON BOATBUILDERS LTD
Bridge Wharf,
Chertsey, Surrey KT16 8LG.
Tel (01932) 562255 Fax (01932) 571161
110-berth marina in quiet picturesque area
and additional riverside moorings. Full
facilities including electricity to most berths,
toilets and showers. 12-ton crane and hard
standing for winter storage. Always a
welcome to visitors from our friendly staff.
Sales office open seven days a week.

BRIGHTON MARINA
Brighton Marina Village,
Brighton, East Sussex BN2 5UF.
Tel (01273) 819919 Fax (01273) 675082
Britain's largest marina (1600 pontoon
berths) with marina village under
development. TYHA Five-Gold Anchors. Full
boatyard and shore facilities. Brokerage
and boat sales. Club racing throughout the
year. Group visits, rallies welcome.

BURGH CASTLE MARINA
Butt Lane, Burgh Castle,
Norfolk, Norwich NR31 9PZ.
Tel (01493) 780331 Fax (01493) 780163
100 serviced pontoons and quay moorings
accessible at all tides. Secure car and boat
parking. Adjoining boatyard services, access
to holiday park showers, laundry and heated
pool. Riverside pub and shop. Complex
open all year.

CARRICKFERGUS MARINA
Rodger's Quay, Carrickfergus,
Co Antrim, N Ireland BT38 8BE.
Tel (01960) 366666 Fax (01960) 350505
300 fully serviced pontoon berths with
excellent full on-shore facilities (half a mile
from town centre). Steeped in a wealth of
historical legend. Carrickfergus has
excellent restaurants, hotels, pubs, shops
and a host of recreational leisure facilities.

CHELSEA HARBOUR LTD
108 The Chambers,
Chelsea Harbour, London SW10 0XF.
Tel 0171-351 4433 Fax 0171-352 7868
A tranquil and intimate marina of 55 berths
close to the heart of the west end of London.
5-Star hotel, restaurants and bars. Overnight
pontoon and amenities. 24-hour security
patrols and CCTV.

THE CREGGANS INN
Strachur, Argyll PA27 8BX.
Tel (01369) 860279 Fax (01369) 860637
Approximately 18 nautical miles from
Ardrishaig the Creggans Inn makes a useful
stop for lunch, dinner or overnight respite!
5 moorings available. Bar lunches from 12
noon and excellent restaurant serving from
7 to 9pm. Shower and changing facilities
for our travelling yachtsmen.

CRINAN BOATS LTD
Crinan, Lochgilphead, Argyll PA31 8SP.
Tel (01546) 830232 Fax (01546) 830281
Boatbuilders, chandlers, engineers, slipping, repairs, charts, electricians, pontoon, moorings, showers, laundry and basic stores.

DART MARINA
Sandquay, Dartmouth, Devon TQ6 9PH.
Tel (01803) 833351 Fax (01803) 832307
High quality 110-berth marina on the fabulous river Dart, opposite the Dart Marina hotel. A superb situation with all amenities, 24-hour security, hotel and restaurant, showers, baths and laundry, fuel berth, holding tank pump-out facility and a warm welcome to all visitors.

DEAN & REDDYHOFF LTD - EAST COWES MARINA
Clarence Road,
East Cowes, Isle of Wight PO32 6HA.
Tel (01983) 293983 Fax (01983) 299276
This existing marina (but new to Dean and Reddyhoff) is undergoing a facelift which will include dredging, new pontoons, toilets and showers and possibly a clubhouse. Regular yachtsmen, visitors and rallies will be welcome as before.

DEAN & REDDYHOFF LTD - HASLAR MARINA
Haslar Road,
Gosport, Hampshire PO12 1NU.
Tel (01705) 601201 Fax (01705) 602201
Haslar Marina is just inside the entrance of Portsmouth harbour on the Gosport side. Included in the 600 berths is a visitors' area which is adjacent to a converted lightship with bar facilities and excellent toilets and showers.

DEAN & REDDYHOFF LTD - WEYMOUTH MARINA
70 Commercial Road,
Weymouth, Dorset DT4 8NA.
Tel (01305) 767576 Fax (01305) 767575
This new marina in the inner harbour of Weymouth provides facilities for visitors which are proving very popular. The marina is right next to Weymouth's high street, and the area has a multitude of pubs and restaurants.

DUCHY OF CORNWALL
Harbour Office, St Mary's,
Isles of Scilly, Cornwall TR21 0HU.
Tel/Fax (01720) 422768
Port of St Mary's, Isles of Scilly - 38 visitor moorings. New visitor centre, hot showers, toilets, launching facilities, winter storage, security lockers, fuel and fresh water. 5 minutes from town centre. Ferry terminal and airport close by. Contact Harbour Master for more information.

ELKINS BOATYARD
Tidesreach, 18 Convent Meadow,
The Quay, Christchurch,
Dorset BH23 1BD.
Tel (01202) 483141
All boatyard facilities. Moorings alongside, water and electricity, storage ashore, repairs. Boats up to 45', 10 tons maximum, haul-out.

EMSWORTH YACHT HARBOUR LTD
Thorney Road, Emsworth,
Hampshire PO10 8BP.
Tel (01243) 377727 Fax (01243) 373432
Friendly marina in Chichester harbour. Water, electricity, diesel, Calor gas, 25-tonne mobile crane, slipways, hard-standing and storage areas. Showers and toilets, car parking, chandlery, engineers and boat repairs.

FIDDLERS FERRY YACHT HAVEN
Off Station Road, Penketh,
Warrington, Cheshire WA5 2UJ.
Tel (01925) 727519
Sheltered moorings upto 6'6" draught, 50' long. Access through lock from river Mersey 1½ hours either side of high tide. Signed from A652. Boatyard and lift-out facilities. Annual rate per foot £8.25.

THE GUNFIELD
Castle Road, Dartmouth, Devon TQ6 0JN.
Tel (01803) 834843 Fax (01803) 834772
e-mail: enquiry@gunfield.co.uk
VHF Ch M2 or Ch 37.
Waterfront position with 10 impressive en suite bedrooms, central heating etc, all command fantastic river views. Restaurant offers modestly priced, delicious Mediterranean cuisine. Continental bar and lounge open to non-residents. Large terraces and gardens, BBQs during summer. Pontoon and deep water moorings.

HAFAN PWLLHELI
Glan Don, Pwllheli, Gwynedd LL53 5YT.
Tel (01758) 701219 Fax (01758) 701443
Hafan Pwllheli has over 400 pontoon berths and offers access at virtually all states of the tide. Ashore, its modern purpose-built facilities include luxury toilets, showers, landerette, a secure boat park for winter storage, 40-ton travel hoist, mobile crane and plenty of space for car parking. Open 24-hours a day, 7 days a week.

HALCON MARINE LTD
The Point, Canvey Island, Essex SS8 7TL.
Tel (01268) 511611 Fax (01268) 510044
Marine engineers, repairs and full boatyard services in this quiet and picturesque area. Berths, moorings, slipping facilities. Summer and winter storage. Dry dock (70t max), diesel. 1 to 2 hours ± HW. Water, electric, toilets and showers. A friendly welcome awaits you.

HIGHWAY MARINE LTD
Pillory Gate Wharf, Strand Street,
Sandwich, Kent CT13 9EU.
Tel (01304) 613925 Fax (01304) 614814
Pontoon moorings available in town of Sandwich. Lift-out facilities and hard standing, water, electricity. OMC main dealer with full service centre. New engine sales. Brokerage and chandlery. Excellent waterside apartments available, call (01304) 611433 for details.

ISLE OF ANGLESEY COUNTY COUNCIL
Highways & Technical Services
Department, Council Offices,
Llangefni, Anglesey LL77 7TW
Tel (01248) 752331 Fax (01248) 724839
Berths and moorings available at Menai bridge, Amlwch harbour and north east Menai Straits (Beaumaris). Winter storage at competitive rates available at Beaumaris and Amlwch. Contact Maritime Officer 01248 752331 for details.

JERSEY HARBOURS
Harbour Office, Weighbridge,
St Helier, Jersey JE4 9XF.
Tel (01534) 885588 Fax (01534) 885599
A warm welcome to visiting yachtsmen! Elizabeth Marina opens in April 1998. Berths available on lease - £184.86 per metre. St Helier marina continues to cater for visitng yachts. Both marinas offer excellent facilities.

KAMES HOTEL
Kames,
By Tighnabruaich, Argyll PA21 2AF.
Tel (01700) 811489 Fax (01700) 811283
On the Kyles of Bute, with 15 free moorings. Good food, real ales, fine malts. Showers available for visitors. 10 en-suite bedrooms. Regular music nights. Fresh local seafood in season.

KINSALE YACHT CLUB MARINA
Kinsale, Co Cork, Ireland.
Tel +353 21 772196 Fax +353 21 774455
Marina Manager +353 87 449471
Magnificent deep water yacht club marina offering Kinsale hospitality to visiting yachtsmen. Full facilities include berths up to 20 metres, fresh water, electricity, diesel on pier. Club bar and wealth of pubs and restaurants in Kinsale. Enter Kinsale Harbour - lit at night - no restrictions.

LANGSTONE HARBOUR BOARD
Harbour Office, Ferry Road,
Hayling Island, Hampshire PO11 0DG.
Tel (01705) 463419 Fax (01705) 467144
All boatyard facilities. Deep water and tidal moorings available. Water, electricity and diesel. Summer and winter storage. Public slipways. 6-ton crane. Landrover vessel and trailer recovery services.

THE MAYFLOWER INTERNATIONAL MARINA
Ocean Quay, Richmond Walk,
Plymouth, Devon PL1 4LS.
Tel (01752) 556633/567106
Fax (01752) 606896
Plymouth's only Five-Gold Anchor Marina. Known for its extensive facilities, courtesy and security. Owned by berth holders and run to a very high standard.

MILFORD MARINA
The Docks, Milford Haven,
Pembrokeshire, West Wales SA73 3AE.
Tel (01646) 696312 Fax (01646) 696314
Safe sheltered haven, 250 berths, 5 minutes from shopping, rail and bus services. Water and electricity to all berths. Staff available 24 hours. Restaurant, chandlery, electronics, boat repair, lifting and storage available on-site.

NOSS-ON-DART MARINA
Noss Quay, Dartmouth, Devon TQ6 0EA.
Tel (01803) 833351 Fax (01803) 832307
Peacefully located on the east shore of the river Dart, this relaxing marina is the perfect base for cruising yachtsmen. Extensive parking, chandlery, repair and lift-out facilities, easy access from London and the Midlands. Boat taxi to Dartmouth.

THE OYSTERCATCHER RESTAURANT
Otter Ferry, Argyll PA21 2DH.
Tel (01700) 821229 Fax (01700) 821300
Situated on Loch Fyne, just north of the Otter Spit, about one hour's sailing from the Crinan canal. Moorings (insured to 12t) free to patrons. French chef and superb food, seafood our speciality. 1996 Tourist Board winner 'BEST PLACE TO EAT'. Children's play area.

THE PANDORA INN
**Restronguet Creek, Mylor,
Falmouth, Cornwall TR11 5ST.**
Tel (01326) 372678 Fax (01326) 372678
Thatched creek-side inn with floating pontoon. Morning coffee, delicious bar meals, cream teas and fine dining in the superb Andrew Miller restaurant (entitles yachtsmen to free mooring). Telephone, showers and water available. Open all day in the summer.

PARKSTONE YACHT CLUB
**Pearce Avenue, Parkstone,
Poole, Dorset BH14 8EH.**
Tel (01202) 743610 Fax (01202) 716394
Deep water club haven facilities in Poole harbour. Access at all states of the tide. Berths for yachts up to 15 metres. Facilities include electricity, fresh water, toilets and showers. Visitors welcome by appointment. Club bar and restaurant.

PORT FLAIR LTD
**Bradwell Marina, Waterside,
Bradwell-on-Sea, Essex CM0 7RB.**
Tel (01621) 776235/776391
300 pontoon berths with water and electricity, petrol and diesel, chandlery, marine slip/hoistage to 20 tons. Repairs, winter lay-ups, licensed club, yacht brokerage.

PORT OF TRURO
**Harbour Office, Town Quay,
Truro, Cornwall.**
Tel (01872) 272130 Fax (01872) 225346
VHF Ch. 12.
Facilities for the yachtsman include visitor pontoons located at Turnaware Bar, Ruan Creek and Boscawen Park. Visitor moorings at Woodbury. Quay facilities at Truro with free showers and toilets. Chemical toilet disposal, fresh water, electricity and garbage disposal.

RAMSGATE ROYAL HARBOUR MARINA
**Harbour Office, Military Road,
Ramsgate, Kent CT11 9LQ.**
Tel (01843) 592277 Fax (01843) 590941
Ramsgate Royal Harbour is situated on the south east coast, making an ideal base for crossing to the Continent. 24-hour access to finger pontoons. Comprehensive security systems. Amenities: Launderette, repairs,

slipways, boatpark. Competitive rates for permanent berths and discount for visitors' group bookings.

RHU MARINA LTD
Helensburgh, Dunbartonshire G84 8LN.
Tel (01436) 820238 Fax (01436) 821039
Berths accessible at all times and moorings available situated in an area of outstanding natural beauty, by the Garsloch and 10 minutes from Loch Lomond. Hotels, shops, yacht clubs all adjacent.

ROYAL HOTEL - TIGHNABRUAICH
Tighnabruaich, Argyll PA21 2BE.
Tel (01700) 811239 Fax (01700) 811300
On the Kyles of Bute. Fully licensed individual family run hotel. Superb food, venison, game, prawns, scallops and lobster served in our cosy bars and restaurant. *Taste of Scotland* recommended. 12 moorings, slipway, showers, hairdryers.

RUDDERS BOATYARD & MOORINGS
**Church Road, Burton, Milford Haven,
Pembrokeshire SA73 1NU.**
Tel (01646) 600288
Moorings, pontoon, storage. All repairs.

SOUTH DOCK MARINA
**South Lock Office, Rope Street,
Plough Way, London SE16 1AA.**
Tel 0171-252 2244 Fax 0171-237 3806
London's largest marina. 200+ berths. Spacious, tranquil setting. Manned 24 hours. Lift-out for 20 tonnes. Competitve mooring rates.

SWANSEA MARINA
**Lockside, Maritime Quarter,
Swansea, West Glamorgan SA1 1WG.**
Tel (01792) 470310 Fax (01792) 463948
Access all states of the tide except LWST. City centre marina, restaurants, theatres etc. Call us on Ch 18 or 80 to check locking times. Visitors always welcome - a good destination for your annual trip.

WEIR QUAY BOATYARD
**Heron's Reach,
Bere Alston, Devon PL20 7BT.**
Tel (01822) 840474 Fax (01822) 840948
Deepwater swinging moorings, shore storage, full boatyard facilities and services, cranage to 12 tons, repairs, maintenance, slipway. A traditional boatyard at affordable rates in *a superb setting* on the Tamar, with excellent security.

WHITEHAVEN HARBOUR MARINA
**Harbour Commissioners,
Pears House, 1 Duke Street,
Whitehaven, Cumbria CA28 7HW.**
Tel (01946) 692435 Fax (01946) 691135
Long and short-term berths available at newly created 100 capacity marina, maximum length 12m. 11 hectare permanent locked harbour with 45 tonne boat hoist, access at least HW $\pm$ 3hours. Sheltered historic location adjacent to town centre.

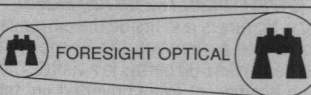

WORCESTER YACHT CHANDLERS LTD
**Unit 7, 75 Waterworks Road,
Barbourne, Worcester WR1 3EZ.**
Tel (01905) 22522 & 27949
Chandlery, paints, ropes, cables, chain, clothing, footwear, shackles, books, bottled gas, anti-foul, fastenings, oakam, fenders. Hard storage, crane, haulage, engine service, oils, navigation aids, buoyancy aids, life jackets, distress flares, **small boat hire**.

BINOCULARS/REPAIRS

B P S C MARINE SERVICES
**Logistics House,
Second Avenue, Millbrook,
Southampton, Hampshire SO15 0LP.**
Tel (01703) 510561 Fax (01703) 510560
BPSC offer a fast efficient repair service on a wide range of nautical and survey instruments. Free estimates and advice. A comprehensive range of spares are carried, most of which can be despatched same day. Instruments commissioned. Compass adjusting service.

FORESIGHT OPTICAL
**13 New Road, Banbury,
Oxfordshire OX16 9PN.**
Tel (01295) 264365
Suppliers of general purpose and nautical binoculars, spotting scopes, astronomical telescopes, night vision equipment, microscopes, magnifiers, spotlights, tripods and accessories. National mail order service.

BOAT BUILDERS & REPAIRS

AILSA-TROON LTD
**Harbour Road,
Troon, Ayrshire KA10 6DN.**
Tel (01292) 311311 Fax (01292) 317613
Boatyard with full repair and maintenance facilities for GRP, steel, aluminium, timber and inflatable craft. Ship repair, fabrication and new building work also undertaken in Ailsa's extensive 15 acre covered facilities.

ARDFERN YACHT CENTRE
Ardfern by Lochgilphead,
Argyll PA31 8QN.
Tel (01852) 500247/636
Fax (01852) 500624 and 07000
Ardfern Boatyard with full repair and maintenance facilities. Timber and GRP repairs, painting and engineering. Sheltered moorings and pontoon berthing. Winter storage, chandlery, showers, fuel, Calor, brokerage, 20-ton boat hoist, rigging. Hotel, bars and restaurant.

BOATWORKS + LTD
Castle Emplacement, St Peter Port,
Guernsey, Channel Islands GY1 1AU.
Tel (01481) 726071 Fax (01481) 714224
Boatworks+ provides a comprehensive range of services including boatbuilding and repairs, chandlery, clothing and fuel supplies.

CRINAN BOATS LTD
Crinan, Lochgilphead, Argyll PA31 8SP.
Tel (01546) 830232 Fax (01546) 830281
Boatbuilders, chandlers, engineers, slipping, repairs, charts, electricians, pontoon, moorings, showers, laundry and basic stores.

DARTHAVEN MARINA LTD
Brixham Road, Kingswear,
Dartmouth, Devon TQ6 0SG.
Tel (01803) 752242 Fax (01803) 752722
Marina Office: (01803) 752545
Chandlery: (01803) 752733
Fax: (01803) 752790
All types of repair facilities available. Fully trained staff. 30-ton mobile hoist available all states of tide. Extensive chandlery open 7 days a week. Agents for Autohelm/Raytheon, Cetrek, B&G, Simrad Stowe, Navico, Simpson Lawrence, Sowester, International Paint, Webasto, Yanmar Main Agents, Volvo Penta ASW and Vetus sales and service. Visitors welcome. 24-hour engineering call-out service. Mobile numbers 0411 404 259 and 0467 250 787

ELKINS BOATYARD
Tidesreach, 18 Convent Meadow,
The Quay, Christchurch,
Dorset BH23 1BD.
Tel (01202) 483141
All boatyard facilities. Moorings alongside, water and electricity, storage ashore, repairs. Boats up to 45', 10 tons maximum, haul-out.

HULL MARINA LTD
Warehouse 13,
Kingston Street, Hull HU1 2DQ.
Tel (01482) 613451 Fax (01482) 224148
Four-Anchor Marina. Situated 5 minues from the centre of Hull and all national and international transport systems. First class leisure, boatyard and brokerage facilities. 4-Star hotel and quayside restaurants. Professional and caring staff. Competitive rates.

LANGNEY MARINE SERVICES LTD
Sovereign Harbour Marina,
Pevensey Bay Road, Eastbourne,
East Sussex BN23 6JH.
Tel (01323) 470244 Fax (01323) 470255
We offer a complete service to the boat owner offering repairs on all types of engines, GRP, steel, wood, electronics, rigging, cleaning, etc. We are also contractors to the RNLI.

MILFORD MARINA
The Docks, Milford Haven,
Pembrokeshire, West Wales SA73 3AE.
Tel (01646) 696312 Fax (01646) 696314
Safe sheltered haven, 250 berths, 5 minutes from shopping, rail and bus services. Water and electricity to all berths. Staff available 24 hours. Restaurant, chandlery, electronics, boat repair, lifting and storage available on-site.

ROSDEN GLASS FIBRE
La Rue Durell, La Collette,
St Helier, Jersey JE2 3NB.
Tel (01534) 625418 Fax (01534) 625419
Specialists in all types of glass fibre marine works, structural repairs, alterations, re-flow coating, GEL coat work, Blakes Osmosis Treatment Centre. Manufacturers of fuel tanks, bathing platforms and boat builders. General refurbishment and polishing. A division of Precision Plastics (Jersey) Ltd.

SLEAT MARINE SERVICES
Ardvasar, Isle of Skye IV45 8RU.
Tel (01471) 844216/844387
Yacht charter (bareboat and skippered) from Armadale Bay, Isle of Skye. Six yachts 34' to 40' LOA. All medium to heavy displacement blue water cruisers. Fuel, water and emergency services for passing yachts with problems.

SOUTHDOWN MARINA
Southdown Quay,
Millbrook, Cornwall PL10 1HG.
Tel/Fax (01752) 823084
32-berth marina on edge of river Tamar in quiet location behind Rame Peninsula. Plymouth is just across the river. Quayside berths available for large vessels. Dry Berthing. 24-hour security. DIY facilities available.

WINTERS MARINE LTD
(Lincombe Boatyard)
Lincombe, Salcombe, Devon TQ8 8NQ.
Tel (01548) 843580
e-mail: lincombeboatyard@eclipse.co.uk
Deep water pontoon moorings. Winter storage for 150 boats. All maintenance and repair facilities. Slipway capacity 30 tonnes. Inflatable craft sales and service. Liferaft surveys and repairs. Short and long-term liferaft hire.

WET & WILD GRAPHICS
7 Firefly Road, Hamble Point Marina,
Hamble, Southampton,
Hampshire SO31 4NB.
Tel (01703) 458332 Fax (01703) 456830
Supply and application of vinyl graphics, signboards, banners and flags. Specialist materials for sails and spinnakers. Brochure available for mail order boat names. Deadlines never a problem!!!

CALEY MARINA
Canal Road, Inverness IV3 6NF.
Tel (01463) 236539 Fax (01463) 238323
Open 08.30 - 17.30. Berths: 50 Pontoons (visitors available). Facilities: Fuel, water, pump-out facilities, provisions (nearby shops), repair, cranage, secure storage afloat and ashore. Comprehensive chandlery, showers, workshop. Situated at eastern end of Caledonian canal above Muirtown locks. Access via sea locks 4 hours either side of high water.

DUCHY OF CORNWALL
Harbour Office, St Mary's, Isles of Scilly,
Cornwall TR21 0HU.
Tel/Fax (01720) 422768
Port of St Mary's, Isles of Scilly - 38 visitor moorings. New visitor centre, hot showers, toilets, launching facilities, winter storage, security lockers, fuel and fresh water. 5 minutes from town centre. Ferry terminal and airport close by. Contact Harbour Master for more information.

ELKINS BOATYARD
Tidesreach, 18 Convent Meadow,
The Quay, Christchurch,
Dorset BH23 1BD.
Tel (01202) 483141
All boatyard facilities. Moorings alongside, water and electricity, storage ashore, repairs. Boats up to 45', 10 tons maximum, haul-out.

EMSWORTH YACHT HARBOUR LTD
Thorney Road,
Emsworth, Hampshire PO10 8BP.
Tel (01243) 377727 Fax (01243) 373432
Friendly marina in Chichester harbour. Water, electricity, diesel, Calor gas, 25-tonne mobile crane, slipways, hard-standing and storage areas. Showers and toilets, car parking, chandlery, engineers and boat repairs.

HALCON MARINE LTD
The Point, Canvey Island, Essex SS8 7TL.
Tel (01268) 511611 Fax (01268) 510044
Marine engineers, repairs and full boatyard services in this quiet and picturesque area. Berths, moorings, slipping facilities. Summer and winter storage. Dry dock (70t max), diesel 1 to 2 hours ± HW. Water, electric, toilets and showers. A friendly welcome awaits you.

ISLE OF ANGLESEY COUNTY COUNCIL
**Highways & Technical Services
Department, Council Offices,
Llangefni, Anglesey LL77 7TW**
Tel (01248) 752331 Fax (01248) 724839
Berths and moorings available at Menai bridge, Amlwch harbour and north east Menai Straits (Beaumaris). Winter storage at competitive rates available at Beaumaris and Amlwch. Contact Maritime Officer 01248 752331 for details.

SOUTHDOWN MARINA
**Southdown Quay,
Millbrook, Cornwall PL10 1HG.**
Tel/Fax (01752) 823084
32-berth marina on edge of river Tamar in quiet location behind Rame Peninsula. Plymouth is just across the river. Quayside berths available for large vessels. Dry berthing. 24-hour security. DIY facilities available.

SPARKES YACHT HARBOUR LTD
**38 Wittering Road,
Hayling Island, Hampshire PO11 9SR.**
Tel (01705) 463572 Fax (01705) 465741
Sparkes Marina - a small friendly, family run business offering all the facilities you require including access at all states of the tide to a depth of 2 metres at lowest low water springs. In addition to marina berths, accessible through a security gate, we also offer dry boat sailing, moorings, storage ashore plus full maintenance facilities, new boat sales and brokerage, chandlery and restaurant.

BOATYARD SERVICES & SUPPLIES

ARDORAN MARINE
Lerags, Oban, Argyll PA34 4SE.
Tel (01631) 566123 Fax (01631) 566611
All marine services. Winter storage and moorings.

BIRDHAM SHIPYARD LTD
**Birdham Pool,
Chichester, West Sussex PO20 7BG.**
Tel (01243) 512310 Fax (01243) 513163
Quiet, picturesque marina in Chichester harbour. Moorings available for boats up to 55' overall and 5'6' draught. Chandlery and all boatyard sevices available. Visitors welcome.

BURGH CASTLE MARINA
**Butt Lane, Burgh Castle,
Norfolk, Norwich NR31 9PZ.**
Tel (01493) 780331 Fax (01493) 780163
100 serviced pontoons and quay moorings accessible at all tides. Secure car and boat parking. Adjoining boatyard services, access to holiday park showers, laundry and heated pool. Riverside pub and shop. Complex open all year.

CHALLENGER MARINE
**Freeman's Wharf, Falmouth Road,
Penryn, Cornwall TR10 8AS.**
Tel (01326) 377222 Fax (01326) 377800
Marine engineers, chandlery, boatyard. Main Volvo Penta dealer, marina berths, brokerage, Bombard and Zodiac inflatables' dealer.

CRAOBH MARINA
By Lochgilphead, Argyll PA31 8UD.
Tel (01852) 500222 Fax (01852) 500252
250-berth marina on Loch Shuna. Water, electricity, diesel and gas. Full boatyard services. Chandlery. Brokerage. Insurance. Shops, bar. 24-hour access. VHF Ch37 and 80 (M).

DALE SAILING COMPANY
**Brunel Quay, Neyland Marina,
Neyland, Pembrokeshire SA73 1PY.**
Tel (01646) 601636 Fax (01646) 601061
Engine service and repair, hull repair, chandlery. Boatyard, lifting, boat building, sea school and new and used boat sales.

DART MARINA
Sandquay, Dartmouth, Devon TQ6 9PH.
Tel (01803) 833351 Fax (01803) 832307
High quality 110-berth marina on the fabulous river Dart, opposite the Dart Marina hotel. A superb situation with all amenities, 24-hour security, hotel and restaurant, showers, baths and laundry, fuel berth, holding tank pump-out facility and a warm welcome to all visitors.

DEACONS BOATYARD LTD
**Bursledon Bridge,
Southampton, Hampshire SO31 8AZ.**
Tel (01703) 402253 Fax (01703) 405665
This yard has all major services for yachtsmen. Moorings, hardstanding, repairs, marine engineers, riggers, chandlery and brokerage - new yacht sales. Deacons are UK importers for Feeling Yachts.

FIDDLERS FERRY YACHT HAVEN
**Off Station Road, Penketh,
Warrington, Cheshire WA5 2UJ.**
Tel (01925) 727519
Sheltered moorings upto 6'6" draught, 50' long. Access through lock from river Mersey 1½ hours either side of high tide. Signed from A652. Boatyard and lift-out facilities. Annual rate per foot £8.25.

HALCON MARINE LTD
The Point, Canvey Island, Essex SS8 7TL.
Tel (01268) 511611 Fax (01268) 510044
Marine engineers, repairs and full boatyard services in this quiet and picturesque area. Berths, moorings, slipping facilities. Summer and winter storage. Dry dock (70t max), diesel 1 to 2 hours ± HW. Water, electric, toilets and showers. A friendly welcome awaits you.

JACKSON YACHT SERVICES
**Le Boulevard, St Aubin,
Jersey, Channel Islands JE3 8AB.**
Tel (01534) 743819 Fax (01534) 745952
Boatyard, chandler, sailoft, liferaft service, yacht management and brokerage.

KIP MARINA
**The Yacht Harbour,
Inverkip, Renfrewshire PA16 0AS.**
Tel (01475) 521485 Fax (01475) 521298
Marina berths for vessels up to 65' LOA. Full boatyard facilities including travel hoist, crane, on-site engineers, GRP repairs etc. Bar, restaurant, saunas, launderette and chandlery. Distributors for Moody Yachts, Northshore and Searanger Motor Yachts.

LANGSTONE HARBOUR BOARD
**Harbour Office, Ferry Road,
Hayling Island, Hampshire PO11 0DG.**
Tel (01705) 463419 Fax (01705) 467144
All boatyard facilities. Deep water and tidal moorings available. Water, electricity and diesel. Summer and winter storage. Public slipways. 6-ton crane. Landrover vessel and trailer recovery services.

LOCH NESS CHARTERS
**The Boatyard,
Dochgarroch, Inverness IV3 6JY.**
Tel (01463) 861303 Fax (01463) 861353
Yacht and cruiser charter. Boat services and repairs. Hardstanding and slipway. Diesel supply. Boat finishing.

THE MAYFLOWER INTERNATIONAL MARINA
**Ocean Quay, Richmond Walk,
Plymouth, Devon PL1 4LS.**
*Tel (01752) 556633/567106
Fax (01752) 606896*
Plymouth's only Five-Gold Anchor Marina. Known for its extensive facilities, courtesy and security. Owned by berth holders and run to a very high standard.

NOSS-ON-DART MARINA
Noss Quay, Dartmouth, Devon TQ6 0EA.
Tel (01803) 833351 Fax (01803) 832307
Peacefully located on the east shore of the river Dart, this relaxing marina is the perfect base for cruising yachtsmen. Extensive parking, chandlery, repair and lift-out facilities, easy access from London and the Midlands. Boat taxi to Dartmouth.

PORT FALMOUTH BOATYARD
**North Parade,
Falmouth, Cornwall TR11 2TB.**
Tel (01326) 313248 Fax (01326) 319395
Powered hoist and slipway. Cradle with 100 tons capacity. Shipwrights, marine engineering, hard standing and friendly efficient service.

SHOTLEY MARINA LTD
Shotley Gate, Ipswich, Suffolk IP9 1QJ.
Tel (01473) 788982 Fax (01473) 788868
A modern state of the art marina with 350 berths offering all the services expected. Open 24-hours with full security. Access all states of tide, ideal cruising base. Well stocked chandlery and general store, repair facilities, laundry and ironing centre, showers/baths and toilets. Restaurants, bar, children's room, TV/video and function rooms with dance floor and bar. Disabled facilities.

SPARKES YACHT HARBOUR LTD
**38 Wittering Road,
Hayling Island, Hampshire PO11 9SR.**
Tel (01705) 463572 Fax (01705) 465741
Sparkes Marina - a small friendly, family run business offering all the facilities you require including access at all states of the tide to a depth of 2 metres at lowest low water springs. In addition to marina berths, accessible through a security gate, we also offer dry boat sailing, moorings, storage ashore plus full maintenance facilities, new boat sales and brokerage, chandlery and restaurant.

MARINECALL®

THE LOCAL AUTHORITY
UP TO DATE COASTAL WEATHER INFORMATION BY PHONE OR FAX

FOR A DETAILED 2-5 DAY LOCAL FORECAST
PHONE 0891 500 4 + area number

FOR A 48 HOUR LOCAL FORECAST WITH SYNOPTIC CHARTS
FAX 0897 300 2 + area number

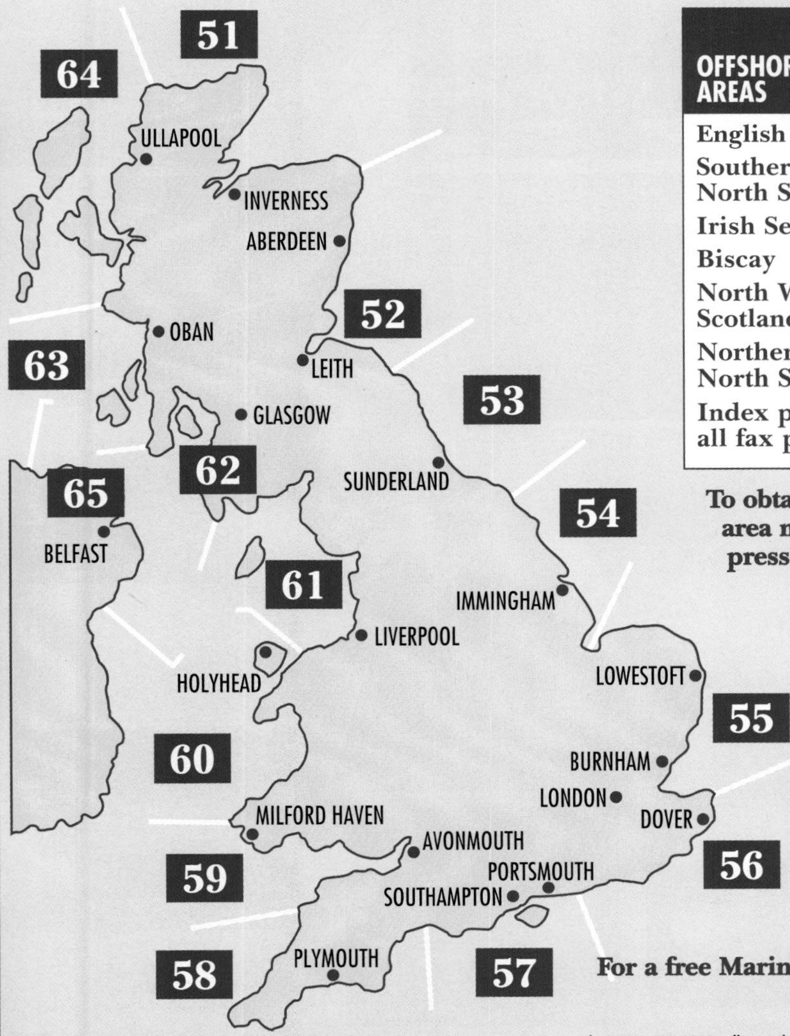

OFFSHORE AREAS	Telephone 2-5 Day Planner 0891 500 PLUS	Fax 2-5 Day Planner 0897 300 PLUS
English Channel	992	270
Southern North Sea	991	271
Irish Sea	954	273
Biscay	953	274
North West Scotland	955	275
Northern North Sea	985	276
Index page to all fax products	-	0891 24 66 80

To obtain fax - simply dial 0897 300 plus area number on your fax machine and press the start button when prompted

FOR CURRENT WEATHER CONDITIONS BY PHONE, UPDATED HOURLY CALL 0891 226 4 + area number

Map labels:
64, 51, ULLAPOOL, INVERNESS, ABERDEEN, OBAN, 52, LEITH, 63, GLASGOW, 53, 65, 62, SUNDERLAND, BELFAST, 54, 61, IMMINGHAM, LIVERPOOL, HOLYHEAD, LOWESTOFT, 60, 55, BURNHAM, LONDON, MILFORD HAVEN, DOVER, AVONMOUTH, 59, PORTSMOUTH, 56, SOUTHAMPTON, 58, PLYMOUTH, 57

Information Supplied by
The Met. Office

For a free Marinecall card or customer helpline call
0171 729 8811

TITCHMARSH MARINA
Coles Lane,
Walton-on-the-Naze, Essex CO14 8SL.
Tel (01255) 672185 Fax (01255) 851901
Friendly service in the peaceful backwaters.
Visiting yachtsmen welcome. Sheltered
marina berths. Full marina facilities: Travel-
lift, cranage, 16 amp electricity, diesel.
Winter storage. Restaurant and bar open
every day. (See Harbour Lights Restaurant.)

TOLLESBURY MARINA
The Yacht Harbour,
Tollesbury, Maldon, Essex CM9 8SE.
Tel (01621) 869202 Fax (01621) 868489
e-mail: marina@woodrolfe.demon.co.uk
Dedicated to customer service, this family-
run marina can offer 240 marina berths
with water and electricity on all pontoons.
Cruising club with bar, restaurant,
swimming pool and tennis courts. Repair
workshop, osmosis treatment centre. Full
brokerage service listing over 200 boats.
VHF Ch37 and 80.

WEIR QUAY BOATYARD
Heron's Reach,
Bere Alston, Devon PL20 7BT.
Tel (01822) 840474 Fax (01822) 840948
Deepwater swinging moorings, shore
storage, full boatyard facilities and services,
cranage to 12 tons, repairs, maintenance,
slipway. A traditional boatyard at affordable
rates in *a superb setting* on the Tamar, with
excellent security.

BOOKS & CHARTS/ PUBLISHERS

BLUNDELL HARLING LTD
Lynch Lane,
Weymouth, Dorset DT4 9DW.
Tel (01305) 206007 Fax (01305) 760598
e-mail: sales@blundellharling.co.uk
Manufacturer of chart table navigation
equipment.

BOGERD NAVTEC NV
Oude Leeuwenrui 37,
Antwerp 2000, Belgium.
Books and charts.

BOOK CABIN
Unit 20, Canutes Pavilion, Ocean Village,
Southampton, Hampshire SO14 3JS.
Tel (01703) 211199 Fax (01703) 338488
Nautical and general booksellers.

BROWN SON & FERGUSON LTD
4-10 Darnley Street, Glasgow G41 2SD.
Tel 0141-429 1234
Books and charts.

W & H CHINA
Howley Properties Ltd,
PO Box 149, Warrington WA1 2DW.
Tel (01925) 634621 Fax (01925) 418009
Manufacturer of China chart dividers.

B COOKE & SON LTD
Kingston Observatory,
58-59 Market Place, Hull HU1 1RH.
Tel (01482) 223454
Books and Charts. DTp Certificated.

DUBOIS-PHILLIPS & McCALLUM LTD
Oriel Chambers,
Covent Garden, Liverpool L2 8UD.
Tel 0151-236 2776
Books and charts.

IVER C WEILBACH & CO., A/S
35 Toldbodgade,
Postbox 1560, DK-1253
Copenhagen K, Denmark.
Books and charts.

JOHN LILLEY & GILLIE LTD
Clive Street, North Shields,
Tyne & Wear NE29 6LF.
Tel 0191-257 2217
Books and Charts. DTp Certificated.

KELVIN HUGHES CHARTS & MARITIME SUPPLIES
New North Road,
Hainault, Ilford, Essex IG6 2UR.
Tel 0181-500 6166
Books and charts. DTp Certificated.

KELVIN HUGHES OBSERVATOR
Nieuwe Langeweg 41, 3194
DC Hoogvliet (Rt), The Netherlands.
Books and charts. DTp Certificated.

LONDON YACHT CENTRE LTD - LYC
13 Artillery Lane, London E1 7LP.
Tel 0171-247 2047 Fax 0171-377 5680
Two minutes from Liverpool Street Railway
Station. Four floors with 8000 top name
product lines including Musto, Henri Lloyd
and Douglas Gill. Extensive range of
chandlery, inflatables, outboards, liferafts,
electronics, software, books, charts, optics,
rope and chain. All at discount prices.

MARINE INSTRUMENTS
The Bosun's Locker, Upton Slip,
Falmouth, Cornwall TR11 3DQ.
Tel (01326) 312414
Books and charts. DTp Certificated.

MARTIN & CO
Oude Leeuwenrui 37,
Antwerp 2000, Belgium.
Books and charts. DTp Certificated.

R J MUIR
22 Seymour Close, Chandlers Ford,
Eastleigh, Southampton SO5 2JE.
Tel (01703) 261042
Books and Charts. DTp Certificated.

OCEAN LEISURE LTD
11-14 Northumberland Avenue,
London WC2N 5AQ.
Tel 0171-930 5050 Fax 0171-930 3032
Complete range of sailing clothing, swim
and beachwear stocked all year round.
Chandlery includes marine electronic
equipment, marine antiques, books and
charts. Also canoeing, underwater
photography, diving and waterskiing
specialists. Learn to scuba dive.

W F PRICE & CO LTD
Wapping Wharf, Bristol BS1 6UD.
Tel 0117-929 2229
Books and charts. DTp Certificated.

REED'S NAUTICAL BOOKS
The Barn, Ford Farm, Bradford Leigh,
Bradford on Avon, Wiltshire BA15 2RP.
Tel 0181-941 7878 Fax 0181-941 8787
From 1st January 1999
Tel (01225) 868821 Fax (01225) 868831
THE HEAVENLY BODIES - Annual astro-
navigation tables for yachtsmen edited by
Lt Cdr H J Baker. Price £10.95 incl p&p.
Showing monthly pages for Sun, Moon,
Planets and Stars accompanied by examples
and all necessary tables. Complete SIGHT
REDUCTION PACKAGE with programmed
calculator also available together with book
and chart catalogues, for world wide mail
order.

S I R S NAVIGATION LTD
186a Milton Road,
Swanscombe, Kent DA10 0LX.
Tel (01322) 383672
Books and charts. DTp Certificated.

THE SEA CHEST NAUTICAL BOOKS & CHARTS
Queen Anne's Battery Marina,
Plymouth, Devon PL4 0LP.
Tel (01752) 222012 Fax (01752) 252679
Admiralty Chart Agent. Worldwide mail
order service.

SEATH INSTRUMENTS (1992) LTD
Unit 30, Colville Road Works,
Colville Road, Lowestoft NR33 9QS.
Tel (01502) 573811
Books and charts. DTp Certificated.

SHAMROCK CHANDLERY
Shamrock Quay, William Street,
Northam, Southampton,
Hampshire SO14 5QL.
Tel (01703) 632725 Fax (01703) 225611
e-mail: sales@shamrock.co.uk
Website: http://www.shamrock.co.uk
Situated on Shamrock Quay, a busy working
yard with a pub, restaurant and boutiques.
Shamrock Chandlery is renowned for
extensive quality stocks and service, and is
widely used by both the trade and boat
owners. Excellent mail order facilities - Order
Hotline 01703 225746.

SIMPSON LAWRENCE LTD
218-228 Edmiston Drive,
Glasgow G51 2YT.
Tel 0141-300 9100 Fax 0141-427 5419
e-mail: info@simpson-lawrence.co.uk
Simpson Lawrence are manufacturers and
the UK's largest wholesale distributor of
quality marine equipment.

A M SMITH (MARINE) LTD
33 Epping Way, Chingford E4 7PB.
Tel 0181-529 6988
Books and charts.

SOFTWAVE
4 Aranmor House, Kingston Hill,
Kingston, Surrey KT2 7LY.
Tel 0181-549 0650 Fax 0181-546 1090
Website: www:softwave.co.uk.
Specialist supplier of PC based electronics
navigation systems and high quality
vectorized charts drawn from Admiralty
and other official sources. Also tide
computing, simulations, hardware and on-
board installations. (See advertisement first
left hand page in this volume.)

THOMAS GUNN NAVIGATION SERVICES
Anchor House, 62 Regents Quay,
Aberdeen AB11 5AR.
Tel (01224) 595045
Books and charts. DTp Certificated.

TODD CHART AGENCY LTD
4 Seacliff Road, The Harbour, Bangor,
Northern Ireland BT20 5EY.
Tel (01247) 466640 Fax (01247) 471070
e-mail: admiralty@toddchart.co.uk
International Admiralty Chart Agent, chart
correction service and nautical booksellers.
Stockist of Imray charts and books,
navigation and chartroom instruments,
binoculars, clocks etc. UK agent for Icelandic
Hydrographic Service. Mail order - Visa,
Mastercard, American Express and Switch/
Delta accepted.

WARSASH NAUTICAL BOOKSHOP
6 Dibles Road, Warsash,
Southampton, Hampshire SO31 9HZ.
Tel (01489) 572384 Fax (01489) 885756
e-mail: alan@nauticalbooks.co.uk
Website: http://www.nautical books.co.uk
Nautical bookseller and chart agent. Callers
and mail order. Free new and secondhand
book lists. Credit cards taken. Publishers of
the Bibliography of Nautical books.

WESSEX MARINE EQUIPMENT LTD
Logistics House,
2nd Avenue Business Park,
Millbrook Road East,
Southampton, Hampshire SO1 0LP.
Tel (01703) 510570
Books and charts.

BREAKDOWN

DARTHAVEN MARINA LTD
Brixham Road, Kingswear,
Dartmouth, Devon TQ6 0SG.
Tel (01803) 752242 Fax (01803) 752722
Marina Office: (01803) 752545
Chandlery: (01803) 752733
Fax: (01803) 752790
All types of repair facilities available. Fully
trained staff. 30-ton mobile hoist available
all states of tide. Extensive chandlery open
7 days a week. Agents for Autohelm/
Raytheon, Cetrek, B&G, Simrad Stowe,
Navico, Simpson Lawrence, Sowester,
International Paint, Webasto, Yanmar Main
Agents, Volvo Penta ASW and Vetus sales
and service. Visitors welcome. 24-hour
engineering call-out service. Mobile
numbers 0411 404 259 and 0467 250 787

SEA START
Unit 13, Hamble Point Marina,
Southampton SO31 4JD.
Tel 0800 88 55 00 or (01703) 458000
Fax (01703) 452666
Sea Start is the 24-hour marine breakdown
service on both sides of the English Channel
and the Channel Islands. Membership cost
from as little as £9 per month. Join now
using your credit card on 0800 88 55 00 or
ring for our colour brochure.

CANVAS GOODS

THE CANVAS FACTORY
5 Foss Street,
Dartmouth, Devon TQ6 9DW.
Tel/Fax (01803) 832186
Custom-made sailcloth canvas goods for
the boat and home. Traditional patterns and
one-offs in a range of distinctive colours in
both 100% cotton and weatherproof acrylic.
Also wide range of smocks, fleeces and
fisherman's jumpers.

CHANDLERS

**AQUA-MARINE
MANUFACTURING (UK) LTD**
216 Fair Oak Road, Bishopstoke,
Eastleigh, Hampshire SO50 8NJ.
Tel (01703) 694949
Fax (01703) 601381
Sales Fax Hotline: (01703) 601188
e-mail: sales@aqua-marine.co.uk
Manufacturers and distributors of
chandlery, including: Engel refrigeration,
Dutton-Lainson winches, Anchor fenders,
Rule pumps, Aquaflow water systems, TFX
steering and controls. Admiralty small craft
charts, Aquameter compasses, POWER 1st
battery charges, Danforth anchors, Aqua-
Signal lights, Techimpex cookers.

ARDFERN YACHT CENTRE
Ardfern by Lochgilphead,
Argyll PA31 8QN.
Tel (01852) 500247/636
Fax (01852) 500624 and 07000
Ardfern Boatyard with full repair and
maintenance facilities. Timber and GRP
repairs, painting and engineering. Sheltered
moorings and pontoon berthing. Winter
storage, chandlery, showers, fuel, Calor,
brokerage, 20-ton boat hoist, rigging. Hotel,
bars and restaurant.

BOATWORKS + LTD
Castle Emplacement, St Peter Port,
Guernsey, Channel Islands GY1 1AU.
Tel (01481) 726071 Fax (01481) 714224
Boatworks+ provides a comprehensive
range of services including boatbuilding
and repairs, chandlery, clothing and fuel
supplies.

BRIXHAM YACHT SUPPLIES LTD
72 Middle Street, Brixham,
Devon TQ5 8EJ.
Tel (01803) 882290
We stock a complete range of sailing and
leisure clothing. English and Continental
pure wool traditional knitwear. Camping
accessories.

CALEY MARINA
Canal Road, Inverness IV3 6NF.
Tel (01463) 236539 Fax (01463) 238323
Open 08.30 - 17.30. Berths: 50 Pontoons
(visitors available). Facilities: Fuel, water,
pump-out facilities, provisions (nearby
shops), repair, cranage, secure storage
afloat and ashore. Comprehensive
chandlery, showers, workshop. Situated at
eastern end of Caledonian canal above
Muirtown locks. Access via sea locks 4
hours either side of high water.

CHALLENGER MARINE
Freeman's Wharf, Falmouth Road,
Penryn, Cornwall TR10 8AS.
Tel (01326) 377222 Fax (01326) 377800
Marine engineers, chandlery, boatyard.
Main Volvo Penta dealer, marina berths,
brokerage, Bombard and Zodiac inflatables'
dealer.

CRINAN BOATS LTD
Crinan, Lochgilphead, Argyll PA31 8SP.
Tel (01546) 830232 Fax (01546) 830281
Boatbuilders, chandlers, engineers,
slipping, repairs, charts, electricians,
pontoon, moorings, showers, laundry and
basic stores.

DARTHAVEN MARINA LTD
Brixham Road, Kingswear,
Dartmouth, Devon TQ6 0SG.
Tel (01803) 752242 Fax (01803) 752722
Marina Office: (01803) 752545
Chandlery: (01803) 752733
Fax: (01803) 752790
All types of repair facilities available. Fully
trained staff. 30-ton mobile hoist available
all states of tide. Extensive chandlery open
7 days a week. Agents for Autohelm/
Raytheon, Cetrek, B&G, Simrad Stowe,
Navico, Simpson Lawrence, Sowester,
International Paint, Webasto, Yanmar Main
Agents, Volvo Penta ASW and Vetus sales
and service. Visitors welcome. 24-hour
engineering call-out service. Mobile
numbers 0411 404 259 and 0467 250 787.

FOX'S MARINA IPSWICH LTD
The Strand, Wherstead,
Ipswich, Suffolk IP2 8SA.
Tel (01473) 689111 Fax (01473) 601737
The most comprehensive boatyard facility
on the east coast. Extensive chandlery.
Marina access 24-hours. Diesel dock, two
travel hoists to 45 tons, 10 ton crane. Full
electronics, rigging, engineering, stainless
steel services. Specialists in osmosis and
spray painting.

JOSEPH P LAMB & SONS
Maritime Building
(opposite Albert Dock),
Wapping, Liverpool L1 8DQ.
Tel 0151-709 4861 Fax 0151-709 2786
Situated in the centre of Liverpool, J P
Lamb have provided a service to world
shipping for over 200 years. All chandlery
supplies, clothing, rope, paint and flags are
available. Full sailmaking and repairs. Kemp
Retail Outlet for spars and rigging. Open
Mon to Fri 8am to 5.30pm - Sat 9am to
12.30pm.

LIVERPOOL MARINA
**Coburg Dock,
Sefton Street, Liverpool L3 4BP.**
*Tel 0151-709 0578 (2683 after 5pm)
Fax 0151-709 8731*
300-berth yacht harbour. All serviced pontoons. Tidal access HW±2½ hours approximately, depending on draught. 60-ton hoist, workshops, bar and restaurant, toilets and showers. City centre one mile. Open all year. Active yacht club and yacht brokerage.

LONDON YACHT CENTRE LTD - LYC
13 Artillery Lane, London E1 7LP.
Tel 0171-247 2047 Fax 0171-377 5680
Two minutes from Liverpool Street Railway Station. Four floors with 8000 top name product lines including Musto, Henri Lloyd and Douglas Gill. Extensive range of chandlery, inflatables, outboards, liferafts, electronics, software, books, charts, optics, rope and chain. All at discount prices.

MANX MARINE
**35 North Quay, Douglas,
Isle of Man IM1 4LB.**
Tel/Fax (01624) 674842
The Island's leading and most established yacht chandlery. Stockists of quality foul-weather clothing and thermal wear. Large stock holdings of stainless steel fixtures and fittings and a comprehensive range of general chandlery including rigging facilities.

MARQUAND BROS LTD
**- Yacht Chandlers
North Quay, St Peter Port,
Guernsey, Channel Islands.**
Tel (01481) 720962 Fax (01481) 713974
Yacht chandlers, stockists of a comprehensive range of marine products. Guernsey distributor for International Paint. Extensive leisure and marine clothing department including Barbour, Driza-Bone, Dubarry and Quayside.

NORTH QUAY MARINE
**North Side, St Sampson's Harbour,
Guernsey, Channel Islands.**
Tel (01481) 46561 Fax (01481) 43488
The complete boating centre. Full range of chandlery, rope, chain, lubricants, paint, boatwear and shoes. Fishing tackle for on-shore and on-board. Inflatables and safety equipment. Electronics and small outboard engines.

OCEAN LEISURE LTD
**11-14 Northumberland Avenue,
London WC2N 5AQ.**
Tel 0171-930 5050 Fax 0171-930 3032
Complete range of sailing clothing, swim and beachwear stocked all year round. Chandlery includes marine electronic equipment, marine antiques, books and charts. Also canoeing, underwater photography, diving and waterskiing specialists. Learn to scuba dive.

SHAMROCK CHANDLERY
**Shamrock Quay, William Street,
Northam, Southampton,
Hampshire SO14 5QL.**
*Tel (01703) 632725 Fax (01703) 225611
e-mail: sales@shamrock.co.uk
Website: http://www.shamrock.co.uk*
Situated on Shamrock Quay, a busy working yard with a pub, restaurant and boutiques. Shamrock Chandlery is renowned for extensive quality stocks and service, and is widely used by both the trade and boat owners. Excellent mail order facilities - Order Hotline 01703 225746.

UPPER DECK MARINE/OUTRIGGERS
Albert Quay, Fowey, Cornwall PL23 1AQ.
Tel (01726) 832287 Fax (01726) 833265
Chandlery, fastenings, paints, cords, fenders, anchors, compasses, lifejackets, Gaz. Leading names in waterproofs and warm wear.

WEYMOUTH OLD HARBOUR
**Weymouth & Portland Borough Council,
Borough Engineers Department,
Municipal Offices, North Quay,
Weymouth, Dorset DT4 8TA.**
*Tel (01305) 206363/206423
Fax (01305) 206276
e-mail: cflowers@weymouth.gov.uk
Website: http://www.weymouth.gov.uk/marine.htm*
Access at all stages of tide. Visitor berths in the centre of prime tourist resort with shops, restaurants and night life all at hand. Diesel fuelling from pontoon or tanker. Chandlery and repair facilities available.

WORCESTER YACHT CHANDLERS LTD
**Unit 7, 75 Waterworks Road,
Barbourne, Worcester WR1 3EZ.**
Tel (01905) 22522 & 27949
Chandlery, paints, ropes, cables, chain, clothing, footwear, shackles, books, bottled gas, anti-foul, fastenings, oakam, fenders. Hard storage, crane, haulage, engine service, oils, navigation aids, buoyancy aids, life jackets, distress flares, **small boat hire**.

EARTHCARE MARKETING SALES
**P O Box 68, Newtownards,
Northern Ireland BT22 2FY.**
*Tel/Fax (012477) 58171
Mobile 0410 649767*
Skipper's Choice is an all-purpose cleaner

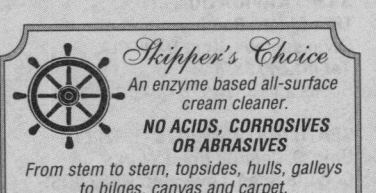

meeting every requirement from stern to stem. Totally non-toxic. Organic and biodegradable and contains no bleaches, solvents or abrasives. Removes heavy staines from upholstery and carpets and yet ideal for stainless steel and fibre glass. An Earthcare BC Canadian product. Reliable mail order service available.

BOATWORKS + LTD
**Castle Emplacement, St Peter Port,
Guernsey, Channel Islands GY1 1AU.**
Tel (01481) 726071 Fax (01481) 714224
Boatworks+ provides a comprehensive range of services including boatbuilding and repairs, chandlery, clothing and fuel supplies.

THE CANVAS FACTORY
**5 Foss Street,
Dartmouth, Devon TQ6 9DW.**
Tel/Fax (01803) 832186
Custom-made sailcloth canvas goods for the boat and home. Traditional patterns and one-offs in a range of distinctive colours in both 100% cotton and weatherproof acrylic. Also wide range of smocks, fleeces and fisherman's jumpers.

COMPASS WATERSPORTS
**Ridout Yard, Great Cheverell, Devizes,
Wiltshire SN10 5XZ.**
Tel (01380) 813100 Fax (01380) 813900
Direct marine mail order of hardware, electronics and clothing at very competitive prices.

OCEAN LEISURE LTD
**11-14 Northumberland Avenue,
London WC2N 5AQ.**
Tel 0171-930 5050 Fax 0171-930 3032
Complete range of sailing clothing, swim and beachwear stocked all year round. Chandlery includes marine electronic equipment, marine antiques, books and charts. Also canoeing, underwater photography, diving and waterskiing specialists. Learn to scuba dive.

OUTRIGGERS/UPPER DECK MARINE
Albert Quay, Fowey, Cornwall PL23 1AQ.
Tel (01726) 833233 Fax (01726) 833265
'Outriggers' casual and marine clothing, footwear, nautical gifts, Admiralty chart agent and marine books.

SHAMROCK CHANDLERY
**Shamrock Quay, William Street,
Northam, Southampton,
Hampshire SO14 5QL.**
*Tel (01703) 632725 Fax (01703) 225611
e-mail: sales@shamrock.co.uk
Website: http://www.shamrock.co.uk*
Situated on Shamrock Quay, a busy working yard with a pub, restaurant and boutiques. Shamrock Chandlery is renowned for extensive quality stocks and service, and is widely used by both the trade and boat owners. Excellent mail order facilities - Order Hotline 01703 225746.

COMMUNICATIONS EQUIPMENT

NORTH QUAY MARINE
North Side, St Sampson's Harbour,
Guernsey, Channel Islands.
Tel (01481) 46561 Fax (01481) 43488
The complete boating centre. Full range of chandlery, rope, chain, lubricants, paint, boatwear and shoes. Fishing tackle for on-shore and on-board. Inflatables and safety equipment. Electronics and small outboard engines.

RADIO & ELECTRONIC SERVICES LTD
Les Chenes, Rohais, St Peter Port,
Guernsey, Channel Islands GY1 1FB.
Tel (01481) 728837 Fax (01481) 714379
Chart plotters, GPS, C-Map and Navionics charting, radars, VHF fixed and portable radios and autopilots. We offer full electronic supply and service. Sales and service dealers for Furuno, Icom, Shipmate, Cetrek, Autohelm, Robertson and AP Navigator.

RADIO SCHOOL LTD
33 Island Close,
Hayling Island, Hampshire PO11 0NJ.
Tel/Fax (01705) 466450
Regular weekend courses/exams for the NEW GMDSS VHF and SSB/Sat. Radio-telephone Operator's Certificates in UK's only permanent, fully equipped classroom solely dedicated to training small-boat sailors on a full-time, professional basis. Established 1980.

ROWLANDS MARINE ELECTRONICS LTD
Pwllheli Marina Centre, Glan Don,
Pwllheli, Gwynedd LL53 5YT.
Tel (01758) 613193 Fax (01758) 613617
BEMA and BMIF members, dealer for Autohelm, B&G, Cetrek, ICOM, Kelvin Hughes, Marconi, Nasa, Navico, Navstar, Neco, Seafarer, Shipmate, Stowe, Racal-Decca, V-Tronix, Ampro, Walker. Equipment supplied installed and serviced.

COMPASS ADJUSTERS/ MANUFACTURERS

B P S C MARINE SERVICES
Logistics House, Second Avenue,
Millbrook, Southampton,
Hampshire SO15 0LP.
Tel (01703) 510561 Fax (01703) 510560
BPSC offer a fast efficient repair service on a wide range of nautical and survey instruments. Free estimates and advice. A comprehensive range of spares are carried,

most of which can be despatched same day. Instruments commissioned. Compass adjusting service.

B COOKE & SON LTD
Kingston Observatory,
58-59 Market Place, Hull HU1 1RH.
Tel (01482) 223454
Books and Charts. DTp Certificated.

JOHN LILLEY & GILLIE LTD
Clive Street, North Shields,
Tyne & Wear NE29 6LF.
Tel 0191-257 2217
Books and Charts. DTp Certificated.

KELVIN HUGHES CHARTS & MARITIME SUPPLIES
New North Road, Hainault,
Ilford, Essex IG6 2UR.
Tel 0181-500 6166
Books and charts. DTp Certificated.

KELVIN HUGHES OBSERVATOR
Nieuwe Langeweg 41, 3194 DC
Hoogvliet (Rt), The Netherlands.
Books and charts. DTp Certificated.

MARINE INSTRUMENTS
The Bosun's Locker, Upton Slip,
Falmouth, Cornwall TR11 3DQ.
Tel (01326) 312414
Books and charts. DTp Certificated.

MARTIN & CO
Oude Leeuwenrui 37,
Antwerp 2000, Belgium.
Books and charts. DTp Certificated.

R J MUIR
22 Seymour Close, Chandlers Forge,
Eastleigh, Southampton,
Hampshire SO5 2JE.
Tel (01703) 261042
Books and Charts. DTp Certificated.

W F PRICE & CO LTD
Wapping Wharf, Bristol BS1 6UD.
Tel 0117-929 2229
Books and charts. DTp Certificated.

S I R S NAVIGATION LTD
186a Milton Road,
Swanscombe, Kent DA10 0LX.
Tel (01322) 383672
Books and Charts. DTp Certificated.

SEATH INSTRUMENTS (1992) LTD
Unit 30, Colville Road Works,
Colville Road, Lowestoft NR33 9QS.
Tel (01502) 573811
Books and charts. DTp Certificated.

THOMAS GUNN NAVIGATION SERVICES
Anchor House,
62 Regents Quay, Aberdeen AB11 5AR.
Tel (01224) 595045
Books and charts. DTp Certificated.

COMPUTERS & SOFTWARE

DOLPHIN MARITIME SOFTWARE LTD
713 Cameron House, White Cross,
Lancaster LA1 4XQ.
Tel/Fax (01524) 841946
e-mail: 100417.744@compuserve.com
Website:http://ourworld.compuserve.
com/homepages/Dolphin_software
Marine computer programs for IBM PC, Psion and Sharp pocket computers. Specialists in navigation, tidal prediction and other programs for both yachting and commercial uses.

EURONAV NAVIGATION
20 The Slipway, Port Solent,
Portsmouth, Hampshire PO6 4TR.
Tel (01705) 373855 Fax (01705) 325800
Electronic charting specialists, offering the seaPro 2000 range of PC-based chart plotting systems, ARCS, Livechart 'B' and BSB top quality electronic charts. Products are available from good chandlers or direct from Euronav e-mail:http://www.euronav.
co.uk

NEPTUNE NAVIGATIONAL SOFTWARE
P O Box 5106,
Riseley, Berkshire RG7 1FD.
Tel 0118-988 5309
www.neptunenav.demon.co.uk
Passage planning, tides and tidal stream prediction software for the PCs. Providing course to steer calculations, point and click planning, waypoint upload to GPS, chart plotter and many more functions. Intuitively easy to use Windows programs.

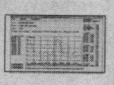
PROSSER SCIENTIFIC INSTRUMENTS LTD
Lady Lane Industrial Estate,
Hadleigh, Ipswich, Suffolk IP7 6BQ.
Tel (01473) 823005 Fax (01473) 824095
Manufacturers of a range of marine instruments, including the WEATHER-TREND digital barometer, with full 24-hour history, the unique TIDECLOCK tidal data predictor and tidal software for the PSION 3 series.

SOFTWAVE
4 Aranmor House, Kingston Hill,
Kingston, Surrey KT2 7LY.
Tel 0181-549 0650 Fax 0181-546 1090
Website: www.softwave.co.uk.
Specialist supplier of PC based electronics navigation systems and high quality vectorized charts drawn from Admirality and other official sources. Also tide computing, simulations, hardware and on-board installations. *(See advertisement first left hand page in this volume.)*

CORPORATE PROMOTIONS

MARK ANTONY PHOTOGRAPHY
Station Road Industrial Estate,
Mauchline, Ayrshire KA5 5EU.
Tel (07071) 203203 Fax (07071) 503503
Still life table photography. For all your advertising needs Mark Antony can photograph all types of products for your brochures and promotional literature. £50 for film, developing and prints (more than one subject on each film). *Mail order service.*

SEA VENTURES YACHT CHARTER
Lymington Yacht Haven, Lymington,
Hampshire SO41 3QD.
Tel (01590) 672472 Fax (01590) 671924
Website: www.c-ventures.co.uk
Based in Lymington our large modern fleet offers both skippered and bareboat charters to Greece, Guernsey and the Canaries. A large selection of yachts from 29' to 52'. Corporate and team building and yacht management also available.

CORPORATE YACHT OWNERSHIP

WARD & McKENZIE LTD
3 Wherry Lane, Ipswich, Suffolk IP4 1LG.
Tel (01473) 255200 Fax (01473) 255044
National and International Marine Surveyors, Technical and Legal Consultants - offering a comprehensive service to boat owners and those seeking to acquire pleasure yachts. All aspects of title/lien check, registration. Survey, purchase and ownership undertaken, including insurance surveys, finance and disputes. See regional offices in Area Directory.

WILDE MARINE SERVICES LTD
Frances House, Sir William Place,
St Peter Port, Guernsey,
Channel Islands GY1 4HQ.
Tel (01481) 723573 Fax (01481) 711353
British yacht registration, corporate yacht ownership and management, marine insurance, crew placement and management. Wilde Marine Services aims to provide a personal and individual service to its clients.

DECK EQUIPMENT

GRIFF CHAINS LTD
Quarry Road, Dudley Wood,
Dudley, West Midlands DY2 0ED.
Tel (01384) 569415 Fax (01384) 410580
Manufacturers of mooring systems and equipment. For over 150 years Griff Chains has been synonymous with chain, anchor and chain component development for marine applications. Quality chains to meet all markets.

HARKEN - DISTRIBUTED BY
SIMPSON LAWRENCE
218-228 Edmiston Drive,
Glasgow G51 2YT.
Tel 0141-300 9100 Fax 0141-427 5419
e-mail: info@simpson-lawrence.co.uk
Distributors of **Harken** deck hardware, ball bearing blocks in all sizes from micros to maxis, jib reefing and furling systems, from dinghies to 150 footers, winches, backstay tensioners, power sheet jammers and deck shoes. We also distribute **Spinlock** and **Barton** quality racing deck hardware products.

LEWMAR MARINE LTD
Southmoor Lane,
Havant, Hampshire PO9 1JJ.
Tel (01705) 471841 Fax (01705) 476043
Manufacturers of winches, windlasses, hatches, hardware, hydraulics and marine thrusters for boats ranging in size from 25' to 300' LOA.

SHAMROCK CHANDLERY
Shamrock Quay, William Street,
Northam, Southampton,
Hampshire SO14 5QL.
Tel (01703) 632725 Fax (01703) 225611
e-mail: sales@shamrock.co.uk
Website: http://www.shamrock.co.uk
Situated on Shamrock Quay, a busy working yard with a pub, restaurant and boutiques. Shamrock Chandlery is renowned for extensive quality stocks and service, and is widely used by both the trade and boat owners. Excellent mail order facilities - Order Hotline 01703 225746.

DIESEL MARINE FUEL ADDITIVES

CHICK'S MARINE LTD/VOLVO PENTA
Collings Road, St Peter Port,
Guernsey, Channel Islands GY1 1FL.
Tel (01481) 723716 Fax (01481) 713632
Distributor of diesel fuel biocide used to treat and protect contamination in fuel tanks where an algae (bug) is present. Most owners do not realise what the problem is, loss of power, blocked fuel filter, exhaust smoking, resulting in expensive repairs to injectors - fuel pump - or complete engine overhaul. Marine engineers, engines, spares, service - VAT free. Honda outboards, pumps and generators. Volvo Penta specialists.

DIVING TUITION

OCEAN LEISURE LTD
11-14 Northumberland Avenue,
London WC2N 5AQ.
Tel 0171-930 5050 Fax 0171-930 3032
Complete range of sailing clothing, swim and beachwear stocked all year round.

Chandlery includes marine electronic equipment, marine antiques, books and charts. Also canoeing, underwater photography, diving and waterskiing specialists. Learn to scuba dive.

ELECTRICAL & ELECTRONIC ENGINEERS

LANGNEY MARINE SERVICES LTD
Sovereign Harbour Marina,
Pevensey Bay Road, Eastbourne,
East Sussex BN23 6JH.
Tel (01323) 470244 Fax (01323) 470255
We offer a complete service to the boat owner offering repairs on all types of engines, GRP, steel, wood, electronics, rigging, cleaning, etc. We are also contractors to the RNLI.

MARINE RADIO SERVICES LTD
50 Merton Way,
East Molesley, Surrey KT8 1PQ.
Tel 0181-979 2929 Fax 0181-783 1032
Maritime Electronics: Service, sales and repair of marine radio, radar and electronic equipment.

REGIS ELECTRONICS LTD
Regis House, Quay Hill,
Lymington, Hampshire SO41 3AR.
Tel (01590) 679251/679176
Fax (01590) 679910
(also at Cowes, Southampton & Chichester). Sales, service and installation of marine electronic equipment. Leading south coast agents for AUTOHELM, FURUNO, RAYTHEON, CETREK, STOWE, ROBERTSON, A.P. NAVIGATOR, GARMIN, KELVIN HUGHES and other manufacturers of quality marine electronic equipment. Competitively priced quotations (including owner familiarisation and sea trials) forwarded by return of post.

ROWLANDS MARINE ELECTRONICS LTD
Pwllheli Marina Centre, Glan Don,
Pwllheli, Gwynedd LL53 5YT.
Tel (01758) 613193 Fax (01758) 613617
BEMA and BMIF members, dealer for Autohelm, B&G, Cetrek, ICOM, Kelvin Hughes, Marconi, Nasa, Navico, Navstar, Neco, Seafarer, Shipmate, Stowe, Racal-Decca, V-Tronix, Ampro, Walker. Equipment supplied installed and serviced.

SWALE MARINE (ELECTRICAL)
The Old Stable, North Road,
Queenborough, Kent ME11 5EH.
Tel (01795) 580930 Fax (01795) 667280
For all your electrical and electronic needs. Authorised agents for: Furuno, Autohelm, Raytheon and most major manufacturers. Fight crime with Harbourguard monitored security: Medway and Swale coverage - Boatmark registration centre.

ELECTRONIC DEVICES & EQUIPMENT

COMPASS WATERSPORTS
Ridout Yard, Great Cheverell,
Devizes, Wiltshire SN10 5XZ.
Tel (01380) 813100 Fax (01380) 813900
Direct marine mail order of hardware, electronics and clothing at very competitive prices.

DIVERSE YACHT SERVICES
Unit 12, Hamble Yacht Services, Port Hamble, Hamble, Hampshire SO31 4NN.
Tel (01703) 453399 Fax (01703) 455288
Marine electronics and electrics. Supplied and installed. Specialists in racing yachts. Suppliers of 'Loadsense' Loadcells for marine applications.

GREENHAM MARINE
King's Saltern Road,
Lymington, Hampshire SO41 9QD.
Tel (01590) 671144 Fax (01590) 679517
Greenham Marine can offer yachtsmen one of the most comprehensive selections of marine electronic equipment currently available. Also at Poole/Weymouth 01202 676363 and Emsworth/Chichester 01243 378314.

LONDON YACHT CENTRE LTD - LYC
13 Artillery Lane, London E1 7LP.
Tel 0171-247 2047 Fax 0171-377 5680
Two minutes from Liverpool Street Railway Station. Four floors with 8000 top name product lines including Musto, Henri Lloyd and Douglas Gill. Extensive range of chandlery, inflatables, outboards, liferafts, electronics, software, books, charts, optics, rope and chain. All at discount prices.

RADIO & ELECTRONIC SERVICES LTD
Les Chenes, Rohais, St Peter Port,
Guernsey, Channel Islands GY1 1FB.
Tel (01481) 728837 Fax (01481) 714379
Chart plotters, GPS, C-Map and Navionics charting, radars, VHF fixed and portable radios and autopilots. We offer full electronic supply and service. Sales and service dealers for Furuno, Icom, Shipmate, Cetrek, Autohelm, Robertson and AP Navigator.

REGIS ELECTRONICS LTD
Regis House, Quay Hill, Lymington,
Hampshire SO41 3AR.
Tel (01590) 679251/679176
Fax (01590) 679910
(also at Cowes, Southampton & Chichester). Sales, service and installation of marine electronic equipment. Leading south coast agents for AUTOHELM, FURUNO, RAYTHEON, CETREK, STOWE, ROBERT-SON, A.P. NAVIGATOR, GARMIN, KELVIN HUGHES and other manufacturers of quality marine electronic equipment. Competitively priced quotations (including owner familiarisation and sea trials) forwarded by return of post.

ROWLANDS MARINE ELECTRONICS LTD
Pwllheli Marina Centre, Glan Don,
Pwllheli, Gwynedd LL53 5YT.
Tel (01758) 613193 Fax (01758) 613617
BEMA and BMIF members, dealer for Autohelm, B&G, Cetrek, ICOM, Kelvin Hughes, Marconi, Nasa, Navico, Navstar, Neco, Seafarer, Shipmate, Stowe, Racal-Decca, V-Tronix, Ampro, Walker. Equipment supplied installed and serviced.

SIMPSON LAWRENCE LTD
218-228 Edmiston Drive,
Glasgow G51 2YT.
Tel 0141-300 9100 Fax 0141-427 5419
e-mail: info@simpson-lawrence.co.uk
Simpson Lawrence are manufacturers and the UK's largest wholesale distributor of quality marine equipment.

SOFTWAVE
4 Aranmor House, Kingston Hill,
Kingston, Surrey KT2 7LY.
Tel 0181-549 0650 Fax 0181-546 1090
Website: www.softwave.co.uk.
Specialist supplier of PC based electronics navigation systems and high quality vectorized charts drawn from Admiralty and other official sources. Also tide computing, simulations, hardware and on-board installations. *(See advertisement first left hand page in this volume.)*

TOLLEY MARINE LTD
Unit 7, Blackhill Road West,
Holton Heath Trading Park,
Poole, Dorset BH16 6LS.
Tel (01202) 632644 Fax (01202) 632622
Branches at Salterns Marina (01202) 706040 and Plymouth (01752) 222530. Agents for all major marine electronics manufacturers. Autohelm, B&G, Cetrek, Furuno, Garmin, Icom, Koden, Lo-Kata, MLR, Magnavox, Navico, Panasonic, Raytheon, Robertson, Sailor, Shipmate, Trimble.

EMERGENCY REPAIRS

D C G BANBURY
1 Longfellow Road,
Banbury, Oxon OX16 9LB.
Tel/Fax (01295) 257707
e-mail: subrella97@aol.com
Website: http://members.aol.com.
subrella97
Makers of *Subrella* the only quick and reliable way to close off a hole in the hull below the water line from the safety of the inside. *Subrella* celebrates its 25th birthday in 1999.

ENGINES & ACCESSORIES

CHICK'S MARINE LTD/VOLVO PENTA
Collings Road, St Peter Port,
Guernsey, Channel Islands GY1 1FL.
Tel (01481) 723716 Fax (01481) 713632
Distributor of diesel fuel biocide used to treat and protect contamination in fuel tanks where an algae (bug) is present. Most owners do not realise what the problem is, loss of power, blocked fuel filter, exhaust smoking, resulting in expensive repairs to injectors - fuel pump - or complete engine overhaul. Marine engineers, engines, spares, service - VAT free. Honda outboards, pumps and generators. Volvo Penta specialists.

LANGNEY MARINE SERVICES LTD
Sovereign Harbour Marina,
Pevensey Bay Road,
Eastbourne, East Sussex BN23 6JH.
Tel (01323) 470244 Fax (01323) 470255
We offer a complete service to the boat owner offering repairs on all types of engines, GRP, steel, wood, electronics, rigging, cleaning, etc. We are also contractors to the RNLI.

SILLETTE SONIC LTD
182 Church Hill Road, North Cheam,
Sutton, Surrey SM3 8NF.
Tel 0181-715 0100 Fax 0181-288 0742
Mobile 0410 270107
Sillette manufactures a range of propulsion systems - stern drive, saildrives etc and sterngear. Markets Radice & Gori fixed and folding propellers. Acts as agents for Morse Controls, Yanmar and Lombardini marine engines, and Fuji Robin generators. See distribution depot Poole, Dorset - Area 2.

VOLVO PENTA LTD
Otterspool Way, Watford,
Hertfordshire WD2 8HW.
Tel (01923) 28544
Volvo Penta's leading marine power-petrol and diesel for leisurecraft and workboats - is supported by an extensive network of parts and service dealers.

FABRICATIONS & REPAIRS

AILSA-TROON LTD
Harbour Road,
Troon, Ayrshire KA10 6DN.
Tel (01292) 311311 Fax (01292) 317613
Boatyard with full repair and maintenance facilities for GRP, steel, aluminium, timber and inflatable craft. Ship repair, fabrication and new building work also undertaken in Ailsa's extensive 15 acre covered facilities.

FIRST AID

K T Y YACHTS
Unit 12, Universal Marina,
Crableck Lane, Sarisbury Green,
Southampton, Hampshire SO31 7ZN.
Tel (0385) 335189 Fax (01489) 570302
First aid at sea and ship captain's medical courses. Qualified, practical instruction from a sailor and paramedic.

FLAGS, FLAGSTAFFS & PENNANTS

JOSEPH P LAMB & SONS
Maritime Building
(opposite Albert Dock),
Wapping, Liverpool L1 8DQ.
Tel 0151-709 4861 Fax 0151-709 2786
Situated in the centre of Liverpool, J P Lamb have provided a service to world shipping for over 200 years. All chandlery supplies, clothing, rope, paint and flags are available. Full sailmaking and repairs. Kemp Retail Outlet for spars and rigging. Open Mon to Fri 8am to 5.30pm - Sat 9am to 12.30pm.

SARNIA FLAGS
8 Belmont Road, St Peter Port,
Guernsey, Channel Islands GY1 1PY.
Tel (01481) 725995 Fax (01481) 729335
Flags and pennants made to order. National flags, house, club and battle flags, and burgees made to order. Any size, shape or design. Prices on request.

FLOTILLA HOLIDAYS

GREEK SAILS YACHT CHARTER
21 The Mount, Kippax, Leeds LS25 7NG.
Tel/Fax 0113-232 0926
Freephone 0800 731 8580
e-mail: greek_sails_uk@msn.com
Bareboat yacht charter throughout Greece and the islands. Flotilla based in Corfu and the Ionian Islands. Family dinghy sailing holidays in Corfu. Skippered charter and sail training.

GENERAL MARINE EQUIPMENT

A B MARINE LTD
Castle Walk, St Peter Port, Guernsey,
Channel Islands GY1 1AU.
Tel (01481) 722378 (Fax 01481) 711080
We specialise in safety and survival equipment and are a DoT approved service station for liferafts including R.F.D., Beaufort/Dunlop, Zodiac, Plastimo amd Lifeguard. We also carry a full range of new liferafts, dinghies and lifejackets, and are agents for Bukh marine engines.

AQUA-MARINE
MANUFACTURING (UK) LTD
216 Fair Oak Road, Bishopstoke,
Eastleigh, Hampshire SO50 8NJ.
Tel (01703) 694949
Fax (01703) 601381
Sales Fax Hotline: (01703) 601188
e-mail: sales@aqua-marine.co.uk
Manufacturers and distributors of chandlery, including: Engel refrigeration, Dutton-Lainson winches, Anchor fenders, Rule pumps, Aquaflow water systems, TFX steering and controls. Admiralty small craft charts, Aquameter compasses, POWER 1st battery charges, Danforth anchors, Aqua-Signal lights, Techimpex cookers.

COMPASS WATERSPORTS
Ridout Yard, Great Cheverell,
Devizes, Wiltshire SN10 5XZ.
Tel (01380) 813100 Fax (01380) 813900
Direct marine mail order of hardware, electronics and clothing at very competitive prices.

LEWMAR MARINE LTD
Southmoor Lane, Havant,
Hampshire PO9 1JJ.
Tel (01705) 471841 Fax (01705) 476043
Manufacturers of winches, windlasses, hatches, hardware, hydraulics and marine thrusters for boats ranging in size from 25' to 300' LOA.

SIMPSON LAWRENCE LTD
218-228 Edmiston Drive,
Glasgow G51 2YT.
Tel 0141-300 9100 Fax 0141-427 5419
e-mail: info@simpson-lawrence.co.uk
Simpson Lawrence are manufacturers and the UK's largest wholesale distributor of quality marine equipment.

VETUS DEN OUDEN LTD
39 South Hants Industrial Park, Totton,
Southampton, Hampshire SO40 3SA.
Tel (01703) 861033 Fax (01703) 663142
Suppliers of marine diesel equipment, exhaust systems, steering systems, bow propellers, propellers and shafts, hatches, portlights, windows, electronic instruments, batteries, ventilators, windlasses, water and fuel tanks, chandlery items and much much more.

WORCESTER YACHT CHANDLERS LTD
Unit 7, 75 Waterworks Road,
Barbourne, Worcester WR1 3EZ.
Tel (01905) 22522 & 27949
Chandlery, paints, ropes, cables, chain, clothing, footwear, shackles, books, bottled gas, anti-foul, fastenings, oakam, fenders. Hard storage, crane, haulage, engine service, oils, navigation aids, buoyancy aids, life jackets, distress flares, **small boat hire**.

GENERATORS

GenACis
Power House, Gordon Road,
Winchester, Hampshire SO23 7DD.
Tel (01962) 841828 Fax (01962) 841834
Dolphin water cooled diesel generators, 3 - 16 KVA.

GLASS FIBRE MARINE SPECIALISTS

ROSDEN GLASS FIBRE
La Rue Durell, La Collette,
St Helier, Jersey JE2 3NB.
Tel (01534) 625418 Fax (01534) 625419
Specialists in all types of glass fibre marine works, structural repairs, alterations, re-flow coating, GEL coat work, Blakes Osmosis Treatment Centre. Manufacturers of fuel tanks, bathing platforms and boat builders. General refurbishment and polishing. A division of Precision Plastics (Jersey) Ltd.

GRAPHICS

WET & WILD GRAPHICS
7 Firefly Road, Hamble Point Marina,
Hamble, Southampton,
Hampshire SO31 4NB.
Tel (01703) 458332 Fax (01703) 456830
Supply and application of vinyl graphics, signboards, banners and flags. Specialist materials for sails and spinnakers. Brochure available for mail order boat names. Deadlines never a problem!!!

HARBOURS

BALTIC WHARF
WATER LEISURE CENTRE
Bristol Harbour,
Underfall Yard, Bristol BS1 6XG.
Tel 0117-929 7608 Fax 0117-929 4454
Tuition: 0117-952 5202
Sailing school and centre, with qualified instruction in most watersports. Also moorings available throughout the Bristol harbour for all types of leisurecraft.

BEAULIEU RIVER MANAGEMENT LTD
Harbour Master's Office,
Bucklers Hard Yacht Harbour,
Beaulieu, Hampshire SO42 7XB.
Tel (01590) 616200 Fax (01590) 616211
110-berth yacht harbour (pontoon berths), fully serviced with back-up facilities of historic Bucklers Hard village. Agamemnon boatyard - 290 swinging moorings let on annual basis. Visiting craft welcome. Capacity 100+ pile/pontoon.

CHELSEA HARBOUR LTD
108 The Chambers,
Chelsea Harbour, London SW10 0XF.
Tel 0171-351 4433
Fax 0171-352 7868
A tranquil and intimate marina of 55 berths close to the heart of the west end of London. 5-Star hotel, restaurants and bars. Overnight pontoon and amenities. 24-hour security patrols and CCTV.

CLYDE MARINA - ARDROSSAN
The Harbour,
Ardrossan, Ayrshire KA22 8DB.
Tel (01294) 607077 Fax (01294) 607076
e-mail: clydemarina@aol.com
Located on the north Ayrshire coast within easy cruising reach of Arran, the Cumbrae Islands, Bute and the Kintyre Peninsula. Deep draught harbour with 200 pontoon berths and quayside for vessels up to 120'. 20-ton hoist, undercover storage and most services and facilities. Ancasta Scotland brokerage, also Beneteau, Nimbus-Maxi, Westerly Yachts, SeaRay and Marlin RIBs.

DUCHY OF CORNWALL
Harbour Office, St Mary's,
Isles of Scilly, Cornwall TR21 0HU.
Tel/Fax (01720) 422768
Port of St Mary's, Isles of Scilly - 38 visitor moorings. New visitor centre, hot showers, toilets, launching facilities, winter storage, security lockers, fuel and fresh water. 5 minutes from town centre. Ferry terminal and airport close by. Contact Harbour Master for more information.

HAFAN PWLLHELI
Glan Don, Pwllheli, Gwynedd LL53 5YT.
Tel (01758) 701219 Fax (01758) 701443
Hafan Pwllheli has over 400 pontoon berths and offers access at virtually all states of the tide. Ashore, its modern purpose-built facilities include luxury toilets, sho... landerette, a secure boat park for... storage, 40-ton travel hoist, mob... and plenty of space for car park... 24-hours a day, 7 days a week...

JERSEY HARBOURS
Harbour Office, Weighbridge,
St Helier, Jersey JE4 9XF.
Tel (01534) 885588 Fax (01534) 885599
A warm welcome to visiting yachtsmen! Elizabeth Marina opens in April 1998. Berths available on lease - £184.86 per metre. St Helier marina continues to cater for visitng yachts. Both marinas offer excellent facilities.

LANGSTONE HARBOUR BOARD
Harbour Office, Ferry Road, Hayling Island, Hampshire PO11 0DG.
Tel (01705) 463419 Fax (01705) 467144
All boatyard facilities. Deep water and tidal moorings available. Water, electricity and diesel. Summer and winter storage. Public slipways. 6-ton crane. Landrover vessel and trailer recovery services.

THE MAYFLOWER INTERNATIONAL MARINA
Ocean Quay, Richmond Walk, Plymouth, Devon PL1 4LS.
Tel (01752) 556633/567106
Fax (01752) 606896
Plymouth's only Five-Gold Anchor Marina. Known for its extensive facilities, courtesy and security. Owned by berth holders and run to a very high standard.

PETERHEAD BAY AUTHORITY
Bath House,
Bath Street, Peterhead AB42 1DX.
Tel (01779) 474020 Fax (01779) 475712
Contact: Stephen Paterson. Peterhead Bay Marina offers fully serviced pontoon berthing for local and visiting boat owners. Local companies provide a comprehensive range of supporting services. Ideal stopover for vessels heading to/from Scandinavia or the Caledonian canal.

PORT DINORWIC MARINA
N W S Dock Management Ltd,
Port Dinorwic, Gwynedd LL56 4JN.
Tel (01248) 671500/670620
Fax (01248) 671252
250-berths in lock basin or tidal pontoon basin. Toilets, showers and restaurant facilities. Visitors always welcome. Call Ch 80.

PORT OF TRURO
Harbour Office,
Town Quay, Truro, Cornwall.
Tel (01872) 272130 Fax (01872) 225346
VHF Ch. 12.
Facilities for the yachtsman include visitor pontoons located at Turnaware Bar, Ruan Creek and Boscawen Park. Visitor moorings at Woodbury. Quay facilities at Truro with free showers and toilets. Chemical toilet disposal, fresh water, electricity and garbage disposal.

QUEENBOROUGH HARBOUR
Town Quay, South Street,
Queenborough,
Isle of Sheppey, Kent ME11 5AF.
Tel/Fax (01795) 662051
Moorings available in sought after position close to Thames and Medway estuaries.

RAMSGATE ROYAL HARBOUR MARINA
Harbour Office, Military Road,
Ramsgate, Kent CT11 9LQ.
Tel (01843) 592277 Fax (01843) 590941
Ramsgae Royal Harbour is situated on the south east coast, making an ideal base for crossing to the Continent. 24-hour access to finger pontoons. Comprehensive security systems. Amenities: Launderette; repairs; slipways; boatpark. Competitive rates for permanent berths and discounts for visitors' group bookings.

SUFFOLK YACHT HARBOUR LTD
Levington, Ipswich, Suffolk IP10 0LN.
Tel (01473) 659240 Fax (01473) 659632
500-berths - access at all states of tide (dredged to 2.5 meters at LW Springs). Boat hoist facilities up to 60 tons. Full boatyard services, chandlery, gas, diesel, petrol, engineering, sailmaking, electronics. Club house and restaurant.

SUTTON HARBOUR MARINA
Sutton Harbour,
Plymouth, Devon PL4 0RA.
Tel (01752) 204186 Fax (01752) 205403
A superb sheltered marina with 24-hour access and fully serviced visitor berths with full on-shore facilities in the city's historic Elizabethan quarter. Just a few minutes stroll from the shops, restaurants and entertainment of the city centre.

WEYMOUTH OLD HARBOUR
Weymouth & Portland Borough Council,
Borough Engineers Department,
Municipal Offices, North Quay,
Weymouth, Dorset DT4 8TA.
Tel (01305) 206363/206423
Fax (01305) 206276
e-mail: cflowers@weymouth.gov.uk
Website: http://www.weymouth.gov.uk/marine.htm
Access at all stages of tide. Visitor berths in the centre of prime tourist resort with shops, restaurants and night life all at hand. Diesel fuelling from pontoon or tanker. Chandlery and repair facilities available.

WHITEHAVEN HARBOUR MARINA
Harbour Commissioners,
Pears House, 1 Duke Street,
Whitehaven, Cumbria CA28 7HW.
Tel (01946) 692435 Fax (01946) 691135
Long and short-term berths available at newly created 100 capacity marina, maximum length 12m. 11 hectare permanent locked harbour with 45 tonne boat hoist, access at least HW ± 3hours. Sheltered historic location adjacent to town centre.

VOSPER THORNYCROFT MARINE PRODUCTS LTD
Northarbour Road,
Cosham, Hampshire PO6 3TL.
Tel (01705) 383311 Fax (01705) 325133
Manufacturer and supplier of Fin stabilizers, Transverse thrusters and Vospower water jets to the luxury, commercial and naval markets worldwide.

W & H CHINA
Howley Properties Ltd,
PO Box 149, Warrington WA1 2DW.
Tel (01925) 634621 Fax (01925) 418009
Manufacturer of China chart dividers.

DIVERSE YACHT SERVICES
Unit 12, Hamble Yacht Services,
Port Hamble, Hamble,
Hampshire SO31 4NN.
Tel (01703) 453399 Fax (01703) 455288
Marine electronics and electrics. Supplied and installed. Specialists in racing yachts. Suppliers of 'Loadsense' Loadcells for marine applications.

GREENHAM MARINE
King's Saltern Road,
Lymington, Hampshire SO41 9QD.
Tel (01590) 671144 Fax (01590) 679517
Greenham Marine can offer yachtsmen one of the most comprehensive selections of marine electronic equipment currently available. Also at Poole/Weymouth 01202 676363 and Emsworth/Chichester 01243 378314.

SOFTWAVE
4 Aranmor House, Kingston Hill,
Kingston, Surrey KT2 7LY.
Tel 0181-549 0650 Fax 0181-546 1090
Website: www:softwave.co.uk.
Specialist supplier of PC based electronics navigation systems and high quality vectorized charts drawn from Admirality and other official sources. Also tide computing, simulations, hardware and on-board installations. *(See advertisement first left hand page in this volume.)*

SWALE MARINE (ELECTRICAL)
The Old Stable, North Road,
Queenborough, Kent ME11 5EH.
Tel (01795) 580930 Fax (01795) 667280
For all your electrical and electronic needs. Authorised agents for: Furuno, Autohelm, Raytheon and most major manufacturers. Fight crime with Harbourguard monitored security: Medway and Swale coverage - Boatmark registration centre.

INSURANCE & FINANCE

ARDEN INSURANCE SERVICES
29 Stourton Close, Knowle, West Midlands B93 9NP.
Tel (01564) 777833 Fax (01564) 774499
Marine insurance specialist - from the smallest dinghy to the largest ocean vessels. We offer highly competitive prices, first class security and service.

BISHOP SKINNER
INTERNATIONAL INSURANCE BROKERS
Oakley Crescent,
City Road, London EC1V 1NU.
Tel 0171-566 5800 Fax 0171-608 2171
Dinghy Insurance - As insurance brokers to the RYA we offer cover for accidental damage, racing risks, 30-days European extension, discounts for dinghy instructors, third party indemnity of £2,000,000, no claim bonus (transferable) and first class security. Immediate quotation and instant cover all at competitive rates.

C CLAIMS (Marine Loss Adjusters)
PO Box 8, Romford, Essex RM4 1UY.
Tel Helpline: 0181-502 6999
Fax 0181-500 1005
C Claims are specialist marine and small craft claims adjusters with a central record of stolen vessels and equipment. They have provided a unique service to marine insurers since 1979 and welcome trade and private enquiries. They are represented throughout the world.

CRAVEN HODGSON ASSOCIATES
Suite 15,
30-38 Dock Street, Leeds LS10 1JF.
Tel 0113-243 8443
As an independent intermediary, we are in a position to advise you in relation to all major marine insurers and consequently act as your agent.

DESMOND CHEERS & PARTNERS
INSURANCE SERVICES
44 High Street,
Hampton Hill, Middlesex TW12 1PD.
Tel 0181-943 5333 Fax 0181-943 5444
Marine insurance specialists with over 30 years' experience in arranging tailor-made policies through leading marine underwriters. For all your insurance enquiries for yachts, motorcruisers and speedboats call Tim Cheers or Daphne Bamberger.

GENERAL ACCIDENT
FIRE & LIFE ASSURANCE
CORPORATION plc
Head Office: Pitheavlis, Perth PH2 0NH.
Tel (01738) 621202 Fax (01738) 621843
Pleasurecraft insurance for small craft, yachts and motor boats. Contact your local GA office for details of our Sailplan policies.

KENDALL BECKER LTD
Kendalls, West Bracklesham,
Bracklesham Bay,
Chichester, Sussex PO20 8PH.
Tel (01243) 672142 Fax (01243) 672068
Freephone: 0800 975 5795
Marine insurance specialists for yachts and motor cruisers throughout the world. Vessels over 20 years old a speciality (surveys not required). Immediate quotes and cover. Call us now.

LOMBARD GENERAL
INSURANCE CO LTD
Lombard House, 182 High Street,
Tonbridge, Kent TN9 1BY.
Tel (01732) 376317 Fax (01732) 773117
One of the UK's largest specialist yacht underwriters and risk carriers. For full details of the range of insurance products available for all types of pleasurecraft, please contact your local marine insurance broker or intermediary.

J & H MARSH & McLENNAN (UK) LTD
Yacht Practice, Havelock Chambers,
Queens Terrace, Southampton,
Hampshire SO14 3PP.
Tel (01703) 318300 Fax (01703) 318391
A member of the largest insurance broking firm in the world with associated offices in Antibes and Fort Lauderdale. Specialists in yacht insurance for craft cruising UK, Mediterranean, Caribbean and US waters.

NORTHERN STAR INSURANCE CO LTD
London Road, Gloucester GL1 3NS.
Tel (01452) 393000
Yacht Department Direct Line: 01452 393109. Founded over four decades ago and now part of the worldwide Generali Group, Northern Star underwrites most classes of insurance but specialises in insurances for homeworkers, pleasurecraft, holiday and travel, property owners and householders.

WARD & McKENZIE LTD
3 Wherry Lane, Ipswich, Suffolk IP4 1LG.
Tel (01473) 255200 Fax (01473) 255044
National and International Marine Surveyors. Technical and legal consultants - offering a comprehensive service to boat owners and those seeking to acquire pleasure yachts. All aspects of title/lien check, registration. Survey, purchase and ownership undertaken, including insurance surveys, finance and disputes. See regional offices in Area Directory.

WILDE MARINE SERVICES LTD
Frances House, Sir William Place,
St Peter Port, Guernsey,
Channel Islands GY1 4HQ.
Tel (01481) 723573 Fax (01481) 711353
British yacht registration, corporate yacht ownership and management, marine insurance, crew placement and manage-ment. Wilde Marine Services aims to provide a personal and individual service to its clients.

INTERIOR LIGHTS

TOOMER & HAYTER LTD
74 Green Road, Winton,
Bournemouth, Dorset BH9 1EB.
Tel (01202) 515789 Fax (01202) 538771
Marine upholstery manufacturers. Cabin and cockpit upholstery made to any shape or size. Sprung interior mattresses made to measure. Foam backed cabin lining always in stock, also carpet side lining. Visit our factory and showroom.

LEGAL SERVICES

SHOOSMITHS & HARRISON
Russell House, 1550 Parkway
Solent Business Park,
Fareham, Hampshire PO15 7AG.
Tel (01489) 881010/616960
Fax (01489) 881000
Marine solicitors advising on yacht sales, purchase and charter, insurance claims, disputes, debt recovery and general advice for the yachting community. Contact: Jonathan Hadley-Piggin.

WARD & McKENZIE LTD
3 Wherry Lane, Ipswich, Suffolk IP4 1LG.
Tel (01473) 255200 Fax (01473) 255044
National and International Marine Survey-ors. Technical and legal consultants - offering a comprehensive service to boat owners and those seeking to acquire pleasure yachts. All aspects of title/lien check, registration. Survey, purchase and ownership undertaken, including insurance surveys, finance and disputes. See regional offices in Area Directory.

LIFERAFT/INFLATABLES & REPAIRS

A B MARINE LTD
Castle Walk, St Peter Port,
Guernsey, Channel Islands GY1 1AU.
Tel (01481) 722378 (Fax 01481) 711080
We specialise in safety and survival equipment and are a DoT approved service station for liferafts including R.F.D., Beaufort/Dunlop, Zodiac, Plastimo amd Lifeguard. We also carry a full range of new liferafts, dinghies and lifejackets, and are agents for Bukh marine engines.

ADEC MARINE LTD
4 Masons Avenue,
Croydon, Surrey CR0 1EH.
Tel 0181-686 9717 Fax 0181-680 9912
e-mail: adecmarine@ukbusiness.com
Approved liferaft service station for south east UK. Additionally we hire and sell new rafts and sell a complete range of safety equipment for yachts including pyrotechnics, fire extinguishers, lifejackets, buoys and a buoyancy bag system.

PREMIUM LIFERAFT SERVICES
Liferaft House, Burnham Business Park,
Burnham-on-Crouch, Essex CM0 8TE.
Tel (01621) 784858 Fax (01621) 785934
Freephone 0800 243673
e-mail:liferaftuk@aol.com
Hire and sales of DoT and RORC approved liferafts. Long and short-term hire from 18 depots nationwide. Servicing and other safety equipment available.

THROUGHOUT THE UK AND EIRE
Liferaft and Dinghy Servicing
For free information pack
and depot list
ring 0800 243673
Fax us on 01621 785934

OR USE OUR E-MAIL ADDRESS
liferaftuk@aol.com
THE LIFERAFT HIRE COMPANY
LIFERAFT HOUSE
BURNHAM-ON-CROUCH
ESSEX CM0 8TE

SOUTH EASTERN MARINE SERVICES LTD
Units 13 & 25, Olympic Business Centre,
Paycocke Road,
Basildon, Essex SS14 3EX.
Tel (01268) 534427 Fax (01268) 281009
e-mail: sems@bt.internet.com
Liferaft service, sales and hire, 1-65 persons. Approved by major manufacturers and MSA. Callers welcome. View your own raft. Family owned and operated. Inflatable boat repairs and spares. WE WANT YOU TO COME BACK. www.sems.com

MAIL ORDER

B P S C MARINE SERVICES
Logistics House, Second Avenue,
Millbrook, Southampton,
Hampshire SO15 0LP.
Tel (01703) 510561 Fax (01703) 510560
BPSC offer a fast efficient repair service on a wide range of nautical and survey instruments. Free estimates and advice. A comprehensive range of spares are carried, most of which can be despatched same day. Instruments commissioned. Compass adjusting service.

THE CARTOON GALLERY
(Wavelength Design)
37 Lower Street,
Dartmouth, Devon TQ6 9AN.
Tel/Fax (01803) 834466
Tel (01803) 834425 Evenings
Rick, the International Cartoonist specialises in hand coloured and personalised sailing cartoon prints (eg A3 £10). Commissions are carried out in Rick's Dartmouth gallery and studio. Prints available by mail order. Telephone or fax for details.

COMPASS WATERSPORTS
Ridout Yard, Great Cheverell,
Devizes, Wiltshire SN10 5XZ.
Tel (01380) 813100 Fax (01380) 813900
Direct marine mail order of hardware, electronics and clothing at very competitive prices.

EARTHCARE MARKETING SALES
P O Box 68, Newtownards,
Northern Ireland BT22 2FY.
Tel/Fax (012477) 58171
Mobile 0410 649767
Skipper's Choice is an all-purpose cleaner meeting every requirement from stern to stem. Totally non-toxic. Organic and biodegradable and contains no bleaches, solvents or abrasives. Removes heavy staines from upholstery and carpets and yet ideal for stainless steel and fibre glass. An Earthcare BC Canadian product. Reliable mail order service available.

EURONAV NAVIGATION
20 The Slipway, Port Solent,
Portsmouth, Hampshire PO6 4TR.
Tel (01705) 373855 Fax (01705) 325800
Electronic charting specialists, offering the seaPro 2000 range of PC-based chart plotting systems, ARCS, Livechart 'B' and BSB top quality electronic charts. Products are available from good chandlers or direct from Euronav-mail:http://www.euronav.co.uk

FORESIGHT OPTICAL
13 New Road,
Banbury, Oxfordshire OX16 9PN.
Tel (01295) 264365
Suppliers of general purpose and nautical binoculars, spotting scopes, astronomical telescopes, night vision equipment, microscopes, magnifiers, spotlights, tripods and accessories. National mail order service.

MARK ANTONY PHOTOGRAPHY
Station Road Industrial Estate,
Mauchline, Ayrshire KA5 5EU.
Tel (07071) 203203 Fax (07071) 503503
Still life table photography. For all your advertising needs Mark Antony can photograph all types of products for your brochures and promotional literature. £50 for film, developing and prints (more than one subject on each film). *Mail order service.*

REED'S NAUTICAL BOOKS
The Barn, Ford Farm, Bradford Leigh,
Bradford on Avon, Wiltshire BA15 2RP.
Tel 0181-941 7878 Fax 0181-941 8787
From 1st January 1999
Tel (01225) 868821 Fax (01225) 868831
THE HEAVENLY BODIES - Annual astro-navigation tables for yachtsmen edited by Lt Cdr H J Baker. Price £10.95 incl p&p. Showing monthly pages for Sun, Moon, Planets and Stars accompanied by examples and all necessary tables. Complete SIGHT REDUCTION PACKAGE with programmed calculator also available together with book and chart catalogues, for world wide mail order.

SARNIA FLAGS
8 Belmont Road, St Peter Port,
Guernsey, Channel Islands GY1 1PY.
Tel (01481) 725995 Fax (01481) 729335
Flags and pennants made to order. National flags, house, club and battle flags, and burgees made to order. Any size, shape or design. Prices on request.

SHAMROCK CHANDLERY
Shamrock Quay, William Street,
Northam, Southampton,
Hampshire SO14 5QL.
Tel (01703) 632725 Fax (01703) 225611
e-mail: sales@shamrock.co.uk
Website: http://www.shamrock.co.uk
Situated on Shamrock Quay, a busy working yard with a pub, restaurant and boutiques. Shamrock Chandlery is renowned for extensive quality stocks and service, and is widely used by both the trade and boat owners. Excellent mail order facilities - Order Hotline 01703 225746.

TODD CHART AGENCY LTD
4 Seacliff Road, The Harbour, Bangor,
Northern Ireland BT20 5EY.
Tel (01247) 466640 Fax (01247) 471070
e-mail: admiralty@toddchart.co.uk
International Admiralty Chart Agent, chart correction service and nautical booksellers. Stockist of Imray charts and books, navigation and chartroom instruments, binoculars, clocks etc. UK agent for Icelandic Hydrographic Service. Mail order - Visa, Mastercard, American Express and Switch/Delta accepted.

TOOMER & HAYTER LTD
74 Green Road, Winton,
Bournemouth, Dorset BH9 1EB.
Tel (01202) 515789 Fax (01202) 538771
Marine upholstery manufacturers. Cabin and cockpit upholstery made to any shape or size. Sprung interior mattresses made to measure. Foam backed cabin lining always in stock, also carpet side lining. Visit our factory and showroom.

PLEASE MENTION THE MACMILLAN NAUTICAL ALMANAC WHEN MAKING ENQUIRIES

WARSASH NAUTICAL BOOKSHOP
6 Dibles Road, Warsash,
Southampton, Hampshire SO31 9HZ.
Tel (01489) 572384 Fax (01489) 885756
e-mail: alan@nauticalbooks.co.uk
*Website: http://www.nautical books.
co.uk*
Nautical bookseller and chart agent. Callers
and mail order. Free new and secondhand
book lists. Credit cards taken. Publishers of
the Bibliography of Nautical books.

WET & WILD GRAPHICS
7 Firefly Road, Hamble Point Marina,
Hamble, Southampton,
Hampshire SO31 4NB.
Tel (01703) 458332 Fax (01703) 456830
Supply and application of vinyl graphics,
signboards, banners and flags. Specialist
materials for sails and spinnakers. Brochure
available for mail order boat names. Deadlines never a problem!!!

MARINA DEVELOPMENT CONSULTANTS

CREST NICHOLSON
MARINAS LTD - BRISTOL
Parklands,
Stoke Gifford, Bristol BS12 6QU.
Tel 0117-923 6466 Fax 0117-923 6508
Marina development management and
consultancy.

MARINAS

ARDFERN YACHT CENTRE
Ardfern by Lochgilphead,
Argyll PA31 8QN.
Tel (01852) 500247/636
Fax (01852) 500624 and 07000
Ardfern Boatyard with full repair and
maintenance facilities. Timber and GRP
repairs, painting and engineering. Sheltered
moorings and pontoon berthing. Winter
storage, chandlery, showers, fuel, Calor,
brokerage, 20-ton boat hoist, rigging. Hotel,
bars and restaurant.

W BATES & SON BOATBUILDERS LTD
Bridge Wharf,
Chertsey, Surrey KT16 8LG.
Tel (01932) 562255 Fax (01932) 571161
110-berth marina in quiet picturesque area
and additional riverside moorings. Full
facilities including electricity to most berths,
toilets and showers. 12-ton crane and hard
standing for winter storage. Always a
welcome to visitors from our friendly staff.
Sales office open seven days a week.

BEAUCETTE MARINA
Vale, Guernsey,
Channel Islands GY3 5BQ.
Tel (01481) 45000 Fax (01481) 47071
Situated on the north east coast, Beaucette
is one of Europe's most charming deep
water marinas. With 140 berths, the marina
offers all the services and facilities you
would expect. Beaucette is a PREMIER
marina.

BEAULIEU RIVER MANAGEMENT LTD
Harbour Master's Office,
Bucklers Hard Yacht Harbour,
Beaulieu, Hampshire SO42 7XB.
Tel (01590) 616200 Fax (01590) 616211
110-berth yacht harbour (pontoon berths),
fully serviced with back-up facilities of
historic Bucklers Hard village. Agamemnon
boatyard - 290 swinging moorings let on
annual basis. Visiting craft welcome.
Capacity 100+ pile/pontoon.

BIRDHAM SHIPYARD LTD
Birdham Pool, Chichester,
West Sussex PO20 7BG.
Tel (01243) 512310 Fax (01243) 513163
Quiet, picturesque marina in Chichester
harbour. Moorings available for boats up to
55' overall and 5'6' draught. Chandlery and
all boatyard sevices available. Visitors
welcome.

BRIGHTON MARINA
Brighton Marina Village,
Brighton, East Sussex BN2 5UF.
Tel (01273) 819919 Fax (01273) 675082
Britain's largest marina (1600 pontoon
berths) with marina village under
development. TYHA Five-Gold Anchors. Full
boatyard and shore facilities. Brokerage
and boat sales. Club racing throughout the
year. Group visits, rallies welcome.

BURGH CASTLE MARINA
Butt Lane, Burgh Castle,
Norfolk, Norwich NR31 9PZ.
Tel (01493) 780331 Fax (01493) 780163
100 serviced pontoons and quay moorings
accessible at all tides. Secure car and boat
parking. Adjoining boatyard services, access
to holiday park showers, laundry and heated
pool. Riverside pub and shop. Complex
open all year.

BURNHAM YACHT HARBOUR
MARINA LTD
Burnham Yacht Harbour,
Burnham-on-Crouch, Essex CM0 8BL.
Tel (01621) 782150 Fax (01621) 785848
VHF Ch 80
The only Five-Gold Anchor marina in Essex.
350 fully serviced pontoon berths and 120
deep water swing moorings. Marina access
at all states of tide with minimum 2.5m
depth at low water.

CALEY MARINA
Canal Road, Inverness IV3 6NF.
Tel (01463) 236539 Fax (01463) 238323
Open 08.30 - 17.30. Berths: 50 Pontoons
(visitors available). Facilities: Fuel, water,
pump-out facilities, provisions (nearby
shops), repair, cranage, secure storage
afloat and ashore. Comprehensive
chandlery, showers, workshop. Situated at
eastern end of Caledonian canal above
Muirtown locks. Access via sea locks 4
hours either side of high water.

CARLINGFORD MARINA
CLUB - IRELAND
Carlingford, Co Louth, Ireland.
Tel/Fax +353 42 73492
Superb location in beautiful setting close to
historic village of Carlingford, our friendly
marina provides a top class service for all

boat users. Moorings, chandlery, slipway,
16-ton cranage, power, diesel, water,
laundry, showers and coffee shop. Visitors
always welcome. VHF Ch16 and 37 (M).
Sailing Holidays in Ireland - Only the Best.

CARRICKFERGUS MARINA
Rodger's Quay, Carrickfergus,
Co Antrim, N Ireland BT38 8BE.
Tel (01960) 366666 Fax (01960) 350505
300 fully serviced pontoon berths with
excellent full on-shore facilities (half a mile
from town centre). Steeped in a wealth of
historical legend, Carrickfergus has
excellent restaurants, hotels, pubs, shops
and a host of recreational leisure facilities.

CASTLEPARK MARINA - IRELAND
Kinsale, Co Cork, Ireland.
Tel +353 21 774959 Fax +353 21 774958
100-berth fully serviced marina with
restaurant, laundry, showers and toilets.
Waterside hostel-type accommodation
available. New restaurant catering for both
breakfast and evening meals. Access at all
stages of the tide. *Sailing Holidays in Ireland
- Only the Best.*

CHELSEA HARBOUR LTD
108 The Chambers,
Chelsea Harbour, London SW10 0XF.
Tel 0171-351 4433
Fax 0171-352 7868
A tranquil and intimate marina of 55 berths
close to the heart of the west end of London.
5-Star hotel, restaurants and bars. Overnight
pontoon and amenities. 24-hour security
patrols and CCTV.

CHICHESTER MARINA
Birdham, Chichester,
West Sussex PO20 7EJ.
Tel (01243) 512731 Fax (01243) 513472
Situated in the north east corner of
Chichester harbour, Chichester Marina
enjoys one of the most attractive locations
in the country. With 1100 berths, Chichester
offers a unique combination of service,
facilities, security and friendliness,
unparalleled in UK marinas. Chichester
Marina is a PREMIER Marina.

CHISWICK QUAY MARINA LTD
Marina Office,
Chiswick Quay, London W4 3UR.
Tel 0181-994 8743
Small, secluded, peaceful marina on tidal
Thames at Chiswick. Slipway, marine
engineers and electricians, power, water,
toilets and sluice. Some residential
moorings.

CLYDE MARINA - ARDROSSAN
The Harbour,
Ardrossan, Ayrshire KA22 8DB.
Tel (01294) 607077 Fax (01294) 607076
e-mail: clydemarina@aol.com
Located on the north Ayrshire coast within
easy cruising reach of Arran, the Cumbrae
Islands, Bute and the Kintyre Peninsula.
Deep draught harbour with 200 pontoon
berths and quayside for vessels up to 120'.
20-ton hoist, undercover storage and most
services and facilities. Ancasta Scotland
brokerage, also Beneteau, Nimbus-Maxi,
Westerly Yachts, SeaRay and Marlin RIBs.

COLERAINE MARINA
64 Portstewart Road,
Coleraine, Co Londonderry,
Northern Ireland BT52 1RS.
Tel (01265) 44768
Wide range of facilities.

COWES YACHT HAVEN
Vectis Yard, High Street,
Cowes, Isle of Wight PO31 7BD.
Tel (01983) 299975 Fax (01983) 200332
Cowes Yacht Haven is the Solent's premier sailing event centre offering 200 fully serviced berths right in the heart of Cowes. Our improved facilities, capability and location ensures the perfect venue and profile for every kind of boating event.

CRAOBH MARINA
By Lochgilphead, Argyll PA31 8UD.
Tel (01852) 500222 Fax (01852) 500252
250-berth marina on Loch Shuna. Water, electricity, diesel and gas. Full boatyard services. Chandlery. Brokerage. Insurance. Shops, bar. 24-hour access. VHF Ch37 and 80 (M).

CREST NICHOLSON MARINAS LTD - BANGOR
Bangor Marina, Bangor,
Co Down, Northern Ireland BT20 5ED.
Tel (01247) 453297 Fax (01247) 453450
Situated on the south shore of Belfast Lough, Bangor is Ireland's largest and most comprehensive yachting facility. The marina is within convenient walking distance of all the town's amenities and may be accessed at any time of day or state of the tide.

CREST NICHOLSON MARINAS LTD - CONWY
Conwy Marina, Conwy Morfa,
Conwy, Gwynedd LL32 8EP.
Tel (01492) 593000 Fax (01492) 572111
Conwy Marina is ideally placed on the south shore of the Conwy estuary. The marina is set within idyllic surroundings and has comprehensive facilities. Road access is extremely convenient, with the A55 dual carriageway passing close by.

CREST NICHOLSON MARINAS LTD - MALAHIDE
(Marketing Agents) Malahide Marina,
Malahide, Co Dublin, Ireland.
+353 1 845 4129 Fax +353 1 845 4255
Situated within Malahide's estuary north of Dublin Bay. Full range of marina facilities available.

CREST NICHOLSON MARINAS LTD - NORTH SHIELDS
Royal Quays Marina, Coble Dene Road,
North Shields NE29 6DU.
Tel 0191-272 8282 Fax 0191-272 8288
Situated 2 miles from the entrance of the river Tyne. 24-hour lock access. Extensive range of facilities.

CREST NICHOLSON MARINAS LTD - PENARTH
Portway Village,
Penarth, South Glamorgan CF64 1TQ.
Tel (01222) 705021 Fax (01222) 712170
Situated within the sheltered waters of Cardiff Bay the marina provides fully serviced, secure berths and wide ranging ancilliary services. Open 24-hours, year round, we can assure visitors of a warm welcome. Please apply for details.

CROSSHAVEN BOATYARD MARINA - IRELAND
Crosshaven, Co Cork, Ireland.
Tel +353 21 831161 Fax +353 21 831603
All facilities at this 100-berth marina situated 12 miles from Cork City and close to ferryport and airport. Travel lift, full repair and maintenance services, spray painting and approved International Gelshield centre. Storage undercover and outside for 250 boats. Brokerage. RNLI and Defence contractors. *Sailing Holidays in Ireland - Only the Best.*

DART MARINA
Sandquay, Dartmouth, Devon TQ6 9PH.
Tel (01803) 833351 Fax (01803) 832307
High quality 110-berth marina on the fabulous river Dart, opposite the Dart Marina hotel. A superb situation with all amenities, 24-hour security, hotel and restaurant, showers, baths and laundry, fuel berth, holding tank pump-out facility and a warm welcome to all visitors.

DARTHAVEN MARINA LTD
Brixham Road, Kingswear
Dartmouth, Devon TQ6 0SG.
Tel (01803) 752242 Fax (01803) 752722
Marina Office: (01803) 752545
Chandlery: (01803) 752733
Fax: (01803) 752790
All types of repair facilities available. Fully trained staff. 30-ton mobile hoist available all states of tide. Extensive chandlery open 7 days a week. Agents for Autohelm/Raytheon, Cetrek, B&G, Simrad Stowe, Navico, Simpson Lawrence, Sowester, International Paint, Webasto, Yanmar Main Agents, Volvo Penta ASW and Vetus sales and service. Visitors welcome. 24-hour engineering call-out service. Mobile numbers 0411 404 259 and 0467 250 787

DEAN & REDDYHOFF LTD - EAST COWES MARINA
Clarence Road,
East Cowes, Isle of Wight PO32 6HA.
Tel (01983) 293983 Fax (01983) 299276
This existing marina (but new to Dean and Reddyhoff) is undergoing a facelift which will include dredging, new pontoons, toilets and showers and possibly a clubhouse. Regular yachtsmen, visitors and rallies will be welcome as before.

DEAN & REDDYHOFF LTD - HASLAR MARINA
Haslar Road, Gosport,
Hampshire PO12 1NU.
Tel (01705) 601201 Fax (01705) 602201
Haslar Marina is just inside the entrance of Portsmouth harbour on the Gosport side. Included in the 600 berths is a visitors' area which is adjacent to a converted lightship with bar facilities and excellent toiltes and showers.

DEAN & REDDYHOFF LTD - WEYMOUTH MARINA
70 Commercial Road,
Weymouth, Dorset DT4 8NA.
Tel (01305) 767576 Fax (01305) 767575
This new marina in the inner harbour of Weymouth provides facilities for visitors which are proving very popular. The marina is right next to Weymouth's high street, and the area has a multitude of pubs and restaurants.

DINGLE MARINA - IRELAND
Harbour Master, Strand Street,
Dingle, Co Kerry, Ireland.
Tel +353 66 51629 Fax +353 66 52629
Europe's most westerly marina on the beautiful south west coast of Ireland in the heart of the old sheltered fishing port of Dingle. Visitor berths, fuel and water. Shops, 52 pubs and many restaurants with traditional music and hospitality. Harbour easily navigable day or night. *Sailing Holidays in Ireland - Only the Best.*

EMSWORTH YACHT HARBOUR LTD
Thorney Road, Emsworth,
Hampshire PO10 8BP.
Tel (01243) 377727 Fax (01243) 373432
Friendly marina in Chichester harbour. Water, electricity, diesel, Calor gas, 25-tonne mobile crane, slipways, hard-standing and storage areas. Showers and toilets, car parking, chandlery, engineers and boat repairs.

FALMOUTH MARINA
North Parade, Falmouth,
Cornwall TR11 2TD.
Tel (01326) 316620 Fax (01326) 313939
The most westerly marina in England, Falmouth is an ideal starting point for a cruise to the Channel Islands, Brittany or the Scilly Isles. The marina offers fully serviced permanent and visitor berths with a professional and friendly service you would expect from a PREMIER marina.

FENIT HARBOUR MARINA - IRELAND
Fenit, Co Kerry, Ireland.
Tel/Fax +353 66 36231
A new marina opened in July 1997 with 104 berths for all sizes of boat up to 15m x 3m draught, with one berth available for larger vessels up to 30m. Access at all tides. Minimum approach depth 5m. Facilities include smartcard access, toilets, showers, laundry and harbour office. Visitors are welcome to use the superb clubhouse facilities of the Tralee Sailing Club and participate in races. Sailing Holidays in - only the best.

FIDDLERS FERRY YACHT HAVEN
Off Station Road, Penketh,
Warrington, Cheshire WA5 2UJ.
Tel (01925) 727519
Sheltered moorings upto 6'6" draught, 50' long. Access through lock from river Mersey 1½ hours either side of high tide. Signed from A652. Boatyard and lift-out facilities. Annual rate per foot £8.25.

FOX'S MARINA IPSWICH LTD
The Strand, Wherstead,
Ipswich, Suffolk IP2 8SA.
Tel (01473) 689111 Fax (01473) 601737
The most comprehensive boatyard facility on the east coast. Extensive chandlery. Marina access 24-hours. Diesel dock, two travel hoists to 45 tons, 10 ton crane. Full electronics, rigging, engineering, stainless steel services. Specialists in osmosis and spray painting.

HAFAN PWLLHELI
Glan Don, Pwllheli, Gwynedd LL53 5YT.
Tel (01758) 701219 Fax (01758) 701443
Hafan Pwllheli has over 400 pontoon berths and offers access at virtually all states of the tide. Ashore, its modern purpose-built facilities include luxury toilets, showers, landerette, a secure boat park for winter storage, 40-ton travel hoist, mobile crane and plenty of space for car parking. Open 24-hours a day, 7 days a week.

HOWTH MARINA - IRELAND
Howth, Co Dublin, Ireland.
Tel +353 1 8392777 Fax +353 1 8392430
Modern marina in beautiful sheltered location. Fully serviced berths with every facility and 24-hour security. Very popular marina for traffic in the Irish Sea. Is available at all states of the tide with extremely easy access. *Sailing Holidays in Ireland - Only the Best.*

HULL MARINA LTD
Warehouse 13,
Kingston Street, Hull HU1 2DQ.
Tel (01482) 613451 Fax (01482) 224148
Four-Anchor Marina. Situated 5 minues from the centre of Hull and all national and international transport systems. First class leisure, boatyard and brokerage facilities. 4-Star hotel and quayside restaurants. Professional and caring staff. Competitive rates.

JERSEY HARBOURS
Harbour Office, Weighbridge,
St Helier, Jersey JE4 9XF.
Tel (01534) 885588 Fax (01534) 885599
A warm welcome to visiting yachtsmen! Elizabeth Marina opens in April 1998. Berths available on lease - £184.86 per metre. St Helier marina continues to cater for visitng yachts. Both marinas offer excellent facilities.

KILMORE QUAY MARINA - IRELAND
Kilmore Quay, Co Wexford, Ireland.
Tel/Fax +353 53 29955
Kilmlore Quay in the south east of Ireland has a new marina with 20 pontoon visitor berths. This friendly fishing port has pleasant hotel facilities, pubs and restaurants offering a traditional Irish welcome. Rosslare ferryport is only 15 miles away. *Sailing Holidays in Ireland - Only the Best.*

KILRUSH CREEK MARINA - IRELAND
Kilrush, Co Clare, Ireland.
Tel +353 65 52072 Fax +353 65 51692
Mobile +353 87 2313870 VHF Ch 80
Kilrush Creek Marina on Ireland's beautiful west coast, is a new marina with 120 fully serviced berths. The marina has all shore facilities including a modern boatyard with 45-ton hoist. It adjoins the busy market town of Kilrush which has every facility required by the visiting yachtsman. *Sailing Holidays in Ireland - Only the best.*

KIP MARINA
The Yacht Harbour,
Inverkip, Renfrewshire PA16 0AS.
Tel (01475) 521485 Fax (01475) 521298
Marina berths for vessels up to 65' LOA. Full boatyard facilities including travel hoist, crane, on-site engineers, GRP repairs etc. Bar, restaurant, saunas, launderette and chandlery. Distributors for Moody Yachts, Northshore and Searanger Motor Yachts.

LARGS YACHT HAVEN
Irvine Road, Largs, Ayrshire KA30 8EZ.
Tel (01475) 675333 Fax (01475) 672245
Perfectly located 600-berth marina with full services afloat and ashore. 45-ton travel hoist operational 7 days; fuel (diesel and petrol); gas and ice on sale 24-hours. Bar, coffee shop, dive shop plus usual marine services.

LAWRENCE COVE MARINA - IRELAND
Bere Island, Bantry Bay,
Co Cork, Ireland.
Tel/Fax +353 27 75044
Lawrence Cove Marina is situated in Bantry Bay in the south west corner of Ireland in the heart of the best cruising ground in Europe. It is a new marina, family run with full facilities and a very safe haven to leave a boat. It is 2 hours from Cork airport with good connections. *Sailing Holidays in Ireland - Only the Best.*

LIVERPOOL MARINA
Coburg Dock,
Sefton Street, Liverpool L3 4BP.
Tel 0151-709 0578 (2683 after 5pm)
Fax 0151-709 8731
300-berth yacht harbour. All serviced pontoons. Tidal access HW ± 2½ hours approximately, depending on draught. 60-ton hoist, workshops, bar and restaurant, toilets and showers. City centre one mile. Open all year. Active yacht club and yacht brokerage.

LYMINGTON YACHT HAVEN
King's Saltern Road, Lymington,
Hampshire SO4 9XY.
Tel (01590) 677071 Fax (01590) 678186
Perfectly situated at the mouth of the Lymington river giving instant access to the Western Solent. Full marina services, boatyard, brokerage, diesel, petrol and gas.

MALAHIDE MARINA - IRELAND
Malahide, Co Dublin, Ireland.
Tel +353 1 8454129 Fax +353 1 8454255
Located next to the picturesque village of Malahide our marina village is the ideal spot to enjoy and relax. There are 150 fully serviced berths, petrol and diesel available, 30-ton hoist with full boatyard facilities with winter storage ashore or afloat. A fine selection of shops, and friendly pubs and restaurants serving good food are close by. *Sailing Holidays in Ireland - Only the Best.*

THE MAYFLOWER INTERNATIONAL MARINA
Ocean Quay, Richmond Walk,
Plymouth, Devon PL1 4LS.
Tel (01752) 556633/567106
Fax (01752) 606896
Plymouth's only Five-Gold Anchor Marina. Known for its extensive facilities, courtesy and security. Owned by berth holders and run to a very high standard.

MILFORD MARINA
The Docks, Milford Haven,
Pembrokeshire, West Wales SA73 3AE.
Tel (01646) 696312 Fax (01646) 696314
Safe sheltered haven, 250 berths, 5 minutes from shopping, rail and bus services. Water and electricity to all berths. Staff available 24 hours. Restaurant, chandlery, electronics, boat repair, lifting and storage available on-site.

NEYLAND YACHT HAVEN LTD
Brunel Quay,
Neyland, Pembrokeshire SA73 1PY.
Tel (01646) 601601 Fax (01646) 600713
Marina operators with all facilities. 360 fully serviced pontoon berths in a sheltered, tree lined marina. On-site services include boatyard, sailmaker, sailing school, chandlery, cafe, lounge/bar, launderette, showers and toilets. 30 visitor berths. 24-hour access and security.

NOSS-ON-DART MARINA
Noss Quay, Dartmouth, Devon TQ6 0EA.
Tel (01803) 833351 Fax (01803) 832307
Peacefully located on the east shore of the river Dart, this relaxing marina is the perfect base for cruising yachtsmen. Extensive parking, chandlery, repair and lift-out facilities, easy access from London and the Midlands. Boat taxi to Dartmouth.

PETERHEAD BAY AUTHORITY
Bath House,
Bath Street, Peterhead AB42 1DX.
Tel (01779) 474020 Fax (01779) 475712
Contact: Stephen Paterson. Peterhead Bay Marina offers fully serviced pontoon berthing for local and visiting boat owners. Local companies provide a comprehensive range of supporting services. Ideal stopover for vessels heading to/from Scandinavia or the Caledonian canal.

PLYMOUTH YACHT HAVEN
Shaw Way, Mount Batten
Plymouth, Devon PL9 9XH.
Tel (01752) 404231 Fax (01752) 484177
Position: Southern side of cattewater, sheltered from prevailing winds by Mountbatten Peninsula. Open: All year, 24 hours. Radio: VHF Ch37 and 80. Callsign: Clovelly Bay. **Berths:** 180 berths, vessels up to 150', some fore and afts, visitors welcome. **Facilities:** electricity, water, 24-hour security, workshop, chandlery, brokerage, showers, laundry, diesel. Calor gas. NEW MARINA NOW OPEN.

VOLVO PENTA

PORT DINORWIC MARINA
N W S Dock Management Ltd,
Port Dinorwic, Gwynedd LL56 4JN.
Tel (01248) 671500/670620
Fax (01248) 671252
250-berths in lock basin or tidal pontoon basin. Toilets, showers and restaurant facilities. Visitors always welcome. Call Ch 80.

PORT FLAIR LTD
Bradwell Marina, Waterside,
Bradwell-on-Sea, Essex CM0 7RB.
Tel (01621) 776235/776391
300 pontoon berths with water and electricity, petrol and diesel, chandlery, marine slip/hoistage to 20 tons. Repairs, winter lay-ups, licensed club, yacht brokerage.

PORT OF TRURO
Harbour Office, Town Quay,
Truro, Cornwall.
Tel (01872) 272130 Fax (01872) 225346
VHF Ch. 12.
Facilities for the yachtsman include visitor pontoons located at Turnaware Bar, Ruan Creek and Boscawen Park. Visitor moorings at Woodbury. Quay facilities at Truro with free showers and toilets. Chemical toilet disposal, fresh water, electricity and garbage disposal.

PORT SOLENT
South Lockside, Port Solent,
Portsmouth, Hampshire PO6 4TJ.
Tel (01705) 210765 Fax (01705) 324241
From a marine superstore and outstanding slipway services to restaurants, bars and multiscreen cinema, Port Solent offers visitors and berth holders superb facilities, unsurpassed by any other UK marina. Port Solent is a PREMIER Marina.

PREMIER MARINAS LTD
South Lockside, Port Solent,
Portsmouth, Hampshire PO6 4TJ.
Tel (01705) 214145 Fax (01705) 221876
At our marinas we're always on hand to help you. PREMIER GROUP MARINAS - Beaucette - Chichester - Falmouth - Port Solent.

RAMSGATE ROYAL HARBOUR MARINA
Harbour Office, Military Road,
Ramsgate, Kent CT11 9LQ.
Tel (01843) 592277 Fax (01843) 590941
Ramsgate Royal Harbour is situated on the south east coast, making an ideal base for crossing to the Continent. 24-hour access to finger pontoons. Comprehensive security systems. Amenities: Launderette, repairs, slipways, boatpark. Competitive rates for permanent berths and discount for visitors' group bookings.

RHU MARINA LTD
Helensburgh, Dunbartonshire G84 8LN.
Tel (01436) 820238 Fax (01436) 821039
Berths accessible at all times and moorings available situated in an area of outstanding natural beauty, by the Garsloch and 10 minutes from Loch Lomond. Hotels, shops, yacht clubs all adjacent.

RIDGE WHARF YACHT CENTRE
Ridge, Wareham, Dorset BH20 5BG.
Tel (01929) 552650 Fax (01929) 554434
Marina with full boatyard facilities. Winter lay-up and fuels etc.

SALVE MARINE LTD - IRELAND
Crosshaven, Co Cork, Ireland.
Tel +353 21 831145 Fax +353 21 831747
The marina is situated just 20 minutes from Cork City, Cork airport and Ringaskiddy ferry port. Located yards from Royal Cork Yacht Club and Crosshaven village centre. Facilities for yachts up to 140' x 14' draught including mains electricity 240/380 volts, telephone, fax, toilets and showers. Welding and machining in stainless steel, aluminium and bronze. Repairs and maintenance to hulls and rigging. Routine and detailed engine maintenance. Slip. Sailing Holidays in Ireland - Only the Best

SHOTLEY MARINA LTD
Shotley Marina Ltd, Shotley Gate,
Ipswich, Suffolk IP9 1QJ.
Tel (01473) 788982 Fax (01473) 788868
Fully equipped yard and repair service. Heated workshop (up to 90' LOA). Experts in wood, GRP and steel fabricated vessels from small repairs to full refits. Registered Blakes osmosis centre. Full marine engineering service. Commissioning of new vessels. Please call for further information or a free quotation.

SOUTH DOCK MARINA
South Lock Office, Rope Street,
Plough Way, London SE16 1AA.
Tel 0171-252 2244 Fax 0171-237 3806
London's largest marina. 200+ berths. Spacious, tranquil setting. Manned 24 hours. Lift-out for 20 tonnes. Competitve mooring rates.

SOUTHDOWN MARINA
Southdown Quay,
Millbrook, Cornwall PL10 1HG.
Tel/Fax (01752) 823084
32-berth marina on edge of river Tamar in quiet location behind Rame Peninsula. Plymouth is just across the river. Quayside berths available for large vessels. Dry berthing. 24-hour security. DIY facilities available.

SPARKES YACHT HARBOUR LTD
38 Wittering Road,
Hayling Island, Hampshire PO11 9SR.
Tel (01705) 463572 Fax (01705) 465741
Sparkes Marina - a small friendly, family run business offering all the facilities you require including access at all states of the tide to a depth of 2 metres at lowest low water springs. In addition to marina berths, accessible through a security gate, we also offer dry boat sailing, moorings, storage ashore plus full maintenance facilities, new boat sales and brokerage, chandlery and restaurant.

ST KATHARINE HAVEN
50 St Katharine's Way, London E1 9LB.
Tel 0171-264 5312 Fax 0171-702 2252
In the heart of London, St Katharine's 200-berth Haven offers facilities for 100'+ vessels, access to the West End and City, its own shops, restaurants, health club and yacht club, plus water, electric, showers and sewerage disposal. Entry via a lock. Operational HW - 2hrs to HW±1½ hours London Bridge. October-March 0800-1800. April-August 0600-2030 or by arrangement.

SUFFOLK YACHT HARBOUR LTD
Levington, Ipswich, Suffolk IP10 0LN.
Tel (01473) 659240 Fax (01473) 659632
500-berths - access at all states of tide (dredged to 2.5 meters at LW Springs). Boat hoist facilities up to 60 tons. Full boatyard services, chandlery, gas, diesel, petrol, engineering, sailmaking, electronics. Club house and restaurant.

SUTTON HARBOUR MARINA
Sutton Harbour,
Plymouth, Devon PL4 0RA.
Tel (01752) 204186 Fax (01752) 205403
A superb sheltered marina with 24-hour access and fully serviced visitor berths with full on-shore facilities in the city's historic Elizabethan quarter. Just a few minutes stroll from the shops, restaurants and entertainment of the city centre.

SWANSEA MARINA
Lockside, Maritime Quarter,
Swansea, West Glamorgan SA1 1WG.
Tel (01792) 470310 Fax (01792) 463948
Access all states of the tide except LWST. City centre marina, restaurants, theatres etc. Call us on Ch 18 or 80 to check locking times. Visitors always welcome - a good destination for your annual trip.

TITCHMARSH MARINA
Coles Lane,
Walton-on-the-Naze, Essex CO14 8SL.
Tel (01255) 672185 Fax (01255) 851901
Friendly service in the peaceful backwaters. Visiting yachtsmen welcome. Sheltered marina berths. Full marina facilities: Travel-lift, cranage, 16 amp electricity, diesel. Winter storage. Restaurant and bar open every day. (See Harbour Lights Restaurant.)

TOLLESBURY MARINA
The Yacht Harbour,
Tollesbury, Maldon, Essex CM9 8SE.
Tel (01621) 869202 Fax (01621) 868489
e-mail: marina@woodrolfe.demon.co.uk
Dedicated to customer service, this family-run marina can offer 240 marina berths with water and electricity on all pontoons. Cruising club with bar, restaurant, swimming pool and tennis courts. Repair workshop, osmosis treatment centre. Full brokerage service listing over 200 boats. VHF Ch37 and 80.

TROON YACHT HAVEN
The Harbour, Troon, Ayrshire KA10 6DJ.
Tel (01292) 315553 Fax (01292) 312836
Sheltered harbour for 350 berths. Well placed for those on passage to and from the Clyde. Bar, restaurant, marine services.

Attractive seafront town with good beaches and championship golf.

WATERFORD CITY MARINA - IRELAND
Waterford City, Ireland.
Tel +353 51 873501 Fax +353 51 870813
Located right in the heart of the historic city centre. There are 80 fully serviced berths available. The marina has full security, with CCTV in operation. Showers available on shore in adjoining hostel. Wide range of shops, restaurants, pubs and other amenities available on the doorstep of the marina because of its unique city-centre location. Open all year with both winter and summer season rates available. Sailing Holidays in Ireland - Only the Best

WEYMOUTH OLD HARBOUR
Weymouth & Portland Borough Council,
Borough Engineers Department,
Municipal Offices, North Quay,
Weymouth, Dorset DT4 8TA.
Tel (01305) 206363/206423
Fax (01305) 206276
e-mail: cflowers@weymouth.gov.uk
Website: http://www.weymouth.gov.uk/marine.htm
Access at all stages of tide. Visitor berths in the centre of prime tourist resort with shops, restaurants and night life all at hand. Diesel fuelling from pontoon or tanker. Chandlery and repair facilities available.

WHITEHAVEN HARBOUR MARINA
Harbour Commissioners,
Pears House, 1 Duke Street,
Whitehaven, Cumbria CA28 7HW.
Tel (01946) 692435 Fax (01946) 691135
Long and short-term berths available at newly created 100 capacity marina, maximum length 12m. 11 hectare permanent locked harbour with 45 tonne boat hoist, access at least HW ± 3hours. Sheltered historic location adjacent to town centre.

HIGHWAY MARINE LTD
Pillory Gate Wharf, Strand Street,
Sandwich, Kent CT13 9EU.
Tel (01304) 613925 Fax (01304) 614814
Pontoon moorings available in town of Sandwich. Lift-out facilities and hard standing, water, electricity. OMC main dealer with full service centre. New engine sales. Brokerage and chandlery. Excellent waterside apartments available, call (01304) 611433 for details.

JEFFREY WOOD MARINE LTD
26 Rectory Gardens,
Granham, Essex RM14 3YJ.
Tel (01708) 641300 Fax (01708) 641110
Consultant forensic marine engineers, boat designers and surveyors, naval architects. Osmosis and Ferro cement specialists - wood or steel boats of all types.

R K MARINE LTD
Hamble River Boatyard,
Bridge Road, Swanwick,
Southampton, Hampshire SO31 7EB.
Tel (01489) 583572 Fax (01489) 583172
Volvo Penta main dealer with all marina facilities.

ROB PERRY MARINE
Monmouth Beach,
Lyme Regis, Dorset DT7 3LE.
Tel (01297) 445816 Fax (01297) 445886
Outboard and inboard sales and service. Wetsuits, lifejackets. Some chandlery. Fast efficient service. Marine surveys and insurance.

WARD & McKENZIE LTD
3 Wherry Lane,
Upswich, Suffolk IP4 1LG.
Tel (01473) 255200 Fax (01473) 255044
National and International Marine Surveyors. Technical and legal Consultants - offering a comprehensive service to boat owners and those seeking to acquire pleasure yachts. All aspects of title/lien check, registration. Survey, purchase and ownership undertaken, including insurance surveys, finance and disputes. See regional offices in Area Directory.

MARINE PHOTOGRAPHERS/ LIBRARIES

MARK ANTONY PHOTOGRAPHY
Station Road Industrial Estate,
Mauchline, Ayrshire KA5 5EU.
Tel (07071) 203203 Fax (07071) 503503
Still life table photography. For all your advertising needs Mark Antony can photograph all types of products for your brochures and promotional literature. £50 for film, developing and prints (more than one subject on each film). Mail order service available.

PETER CUMBERLIDGE PHOTO LIBRARY
Sunways, Slapton,
Kingsbridge, Devon TQ7 2PR.
Tel (01548) 580461 Fax (01548) 580588
Large selection of nautical, travel and coastal colour transparencies. Specialities boats, harbours, lighthouses, marinas and inland waterways in Britain, Northern Europe, the Mediterranean and the Baltic. Commissions undertaken.

MASTS/SPARS & RIGGING

ALL SPARS (KEMP SOUTHWEST)
The Boathouse, Commercial Road,
Penryn, Falmouth, Cornwall TR10 8AE.
Tel (01326) 374177 Fax (01326) 377696
Regional centre for SELDÉN and KEMP integrated sailing systems. Full range of rigging services on-site and mobile. Large and comprehensively stocked chandlery to cover all yachting requirements. Support and back-up for retail and trade alike.

ATLANTIC SPARS (KEMP WEST)
The Loft, Mayors Avenue,
Dartmouth, Devon TQ6 9NG.
Tel (01803) 833322 Fax (01803) 835855
Regional centre for SELDÉN and KEMP integrated sailing systems. Services include standing and running rigging, repairs, custom spars and furling systems. Aluminium design and fabrications for industry. Official suppliers to the BT Global Challenge.

CALIBRA MARINE INTERNATIONAL
26 Foss Street,
Dartmouth, Devon TQ6 9DR.
Tel (01803) 833094 Fax (01803) 833615
e-mail: calibra1@aol.com
A complete boating centre. Marine and architectural rigging service. Sail makers, repairs and valeting. All types of canvas work. Boat brokerage, new and used. Yacht management services. Agents for Nemo, Z-Spar, Whitlock, Lewmar, Norseman and many others.

CARBOSPARS LTD
Hamble Point, School Lane, Hamble,
Southampton, Hampshire SO31 4JD.
Tel (01703) 456736 Fax (01703) 455361
e-mail: carbospars@compuserve.com
Design and manufacture of carbon spars for racing and cruising and the award-winning AeroRig ®.

FOX'S SPARS & RIGGING (KEMP EAST)
Fox's Marina, The Strand, Wherstead,
Ipswich, Suffolk IP2 8SA.
Tel (01473) 691235 Fax (01473) 601737
Regional centre for SELDÉN and KEMP integrated sailing systems. Fox's experience in world girdling racing and cruising yachts provides testimony to products and skills. The No 1 choice for yachtsmen everywhere. Supplier to the OYSTER range.

GUY BROOKE MASTS & RIGGING
(KEMP NORTHWEST)
Conwy Marina, Conwy,
Gwynedd, North Wales LL32 8GU.
Tel/Fax (01492) 592909
Mobile 0589 108860
Regional centre for SELDÉN and KEMP integrated sailing systems. Specialists in mast build and maintenance. Full rigging service for swaging, splicing and rig surveys. Personal, professional and mobile along the north Wales and north west coasts.

HARKEN - DISTRIBUTED BY
SIMPSON LAWRENCE
218-228 Edmiston Drive,
Glasgow G51 2YT.
Tel 0141-300 9100 Fax 0141-427 5419
e-mail: info@simpson-lawrence.co.uk
Distributors of **Harken** deck hardware, ball bearing blocks in all sizes from micros to maxis, jib reefing and furling systems, from dinghies to 150 footers, winches, backstay tensioners, power sheet jammers and deck shoes. We also distribute **Spinlock** and **Barton** quality racing deck hardware products.

IRISH SPARS & RIGGING
(KEMP IRELAND)
52 Whiterock Road, Killinchy,
Co Down, Northern Ireland BT23 6PT.
Tel/Fax (01238) 541727
Regional centre for SELDÉN and KEMP integrated sailing systems. The complete and fully mobile rigging service for yachtsmen in Ireland with outlets in Dublin and Cork. A comprehensive stock of all KEMP/SELDÉN products always available.

JOSEPH P LAMB & SONS
Maritime Building
(opposite Albert Dock),
Wapping, Liverpool L1 8DQ.
Tel 0151-709 4861 Fax 0151-709 2786
Situated in the centre of Liverpool, J P Lamb have provided a service to world shipping for over 200 years. All chandlery supplies, clothing, rope, paint and flags are available. Full sailmaking and repairs. Kemp Retail Outlet for spars and rigging. Open Mon to Fri 8am to 5.30pm - Sat 9am to 12.30pm.

KEMP MASTS LTD
(Seldén Masts Ltd)
Duncan Road, Park Gate,
Southampton, Hampshire SO31 1BX.
Tel (01489) 484000 Fax (01489) 487487
Now renamed Seldén, this is the UK manufacturing and supply base for the Seldén range of masts, booms, poles, kickers, mainsail-furling and headsail-furling to suit production yachts upto 45' and custom yachts from upto 70'.

MANX MARINE
35 North Quay,
Douglas, Isle of Man IM1 4LB.
Tel/Fax (01624) 674842
The Island's leading and most established yacht chandlery. Stockists of quality foul-weather clothing and thermal wear. Large stock holdings of stainless steel fixtures and fittings and a comprehensive range of general chandlery including rigging facilities.

**MAST & RIGGING SERVICES LTD
(KEMP SCOTLAND)
Kip Marina,
Inverkip, Renfrewshire PA16 0AS.**
Tel (01475) 522700 Fax (01475) 522800
Regional centre for SELDÉN and KEMP integrated sailing systems. Specialist mast and rigging service offering - splicing, swaging, spar maintenance and repairs throughout Scotland. Suppliers of main and headsail furling gears, spinnaker poles and rod kickers.

**NORTHERN SPAR SERVICES
(KEMP NORTHWEST)
M R Coates Marine,
The Marina Boatyard,
Whitby, North Yorkshire YO21 1EU.**
Tel (01947) 604486 Fax (01947) 600580
Regional centre for SELDÉN and KEMP integrated sailing systems. 25 years' experience of mast and rigging manufacturing. Surveys undertaken. UK and export mail order service. Roll-swaging, Talurits, wire and rope splicing. Suppliers of furling systems.

**OFFSHORE SPARS & RIGGING
(KEMP CHANNEL ISLANDS)
Boatworks+, Castle Emplacement,
St Peter Port, Guernsey,
Channel Islands GY1 1AU.**
Tel (01481) 726071 Fax (01481) 714224
Regional centre for SELDÉN and KEMP integrated sailing systems. Specialist in new mast builds and maintenance for the Channel Islands. Complete retrofit and rigging services including FURLEX genoa and mainsail furling, rod kickers, spinnaker poles etc.

**SELDÉN MASTS LTD
Duncan Road, Park Gate,
Southampton, Hampshire SO31 1BX.**
Tel (01489) 484000 Fax (01489) 487487
Formerly Kemp Masts this is the UK manufacturing arm of the Seldén Group. Now incorporating PROCTOR, and relocated at Park Gate, Seldén the UK's largest spar maker - covering the whole range from performance dinghies up to 70' yachts.

**SIMPSON LAWRENCE LTD
218-228 Edmiston Drive,
Glasgow G51 2YT.**
Tel 0141-300 9100 Fax 0141-427 5419
e-mail: info@simpson-lawrence.co.uk
Simpson Lawrence are manufacturers and the UK's largest wholesale distributor of quality marine equipment.

**SOUTHERN MAST & RIGGING
(KEMP SOUTHEAST)
Unit B The Boatyard, Brighton Marina,
Brighton, East Sussex BN2 5UF.**
Tel (01273) 818189
Fax (01273) 818188 Mobile 0802 284088
Regional centre for SELDÉN and KEMP integrated sailing systems. Builders of masts and spars, standing and running rigging. Rig surveyors. Suppliers of rope, wire, mast and deck hardware, booms, kickers and reefing systems. Mobile service available.

**SOUTHERN SPAR SERVICES
(KEMP SOUTH)
Shamrock Quay, William Street,
Northam, Southampton,
Hampshire SO14 5QL.**
Mobile 0850 736540
Tel (01703) 331714 Fax (01703) 230559
Regional centre for SELDÉN and KEMP integrated sailing systems. Convectional and furling spars for UK and abroad. Also headsail and mainsail reefing, deck equipment, toe rails and stanchion bases. All forms of repairs and modifications undertaken.

MOISTURE METRES

**TRAMEX LTD
Shankill Business Centre,
Shankill, Co Dublin, Ireland.**
Tel+353 1 282 3688 Fax +353 1 282 7880
e-mail: tramex@iol.ie
Website: www.tramexltd.com
Manufacturers of Moisture Metre and osmosis detection instruments for boats.

NAVIGATION EQUIPMENT - GENERAL

**BLUNDELL HARLING LTD
Lynch Lane,
Weymouth, Dorset DT4 9DW.**
Tel (01305) 206007 Fax (01305) 760598
e-mail: sales@blundellharling.co.uk
Manufacturer of chart table navigation equipment.

**DOLPHIN MARITIME SOFTWARE LTD
713 Cameron House, White Cross,
Lancaster LA1 4XQ**
Tel/Fax (01524) 841946
e-mail: 100417.744@compuserve.com
Website:http://ourworld.compuserve.
com/homepages/Dolphin_software
Marine computer programs for IBM PC, Psion and Sharp pocket computers. Specialists in navigation, tidal prediction and other programs for both yachting and commercial uses.

**EURONAV NAVIGATION
20 The Slipway, Port Solent,
Portsmouth, Hampshire PO6 4TR.**
Tel (01705) 373855 Fax (01705) 325800
Electronic charting specialists, offering the seaPro 2000 range of PC-based chart plotting systems, ARCS, Livechart 'B' and BSB top quality electronic charts. Products are available from good chandlers or direct from Euronav e-mail:http://www.euronav. co.uk

**NEPTUNE NAVIGATIONAL SOFTWARE
P O Box 5106,
Riseley, Berkshire RG7 1FD.**
Tel 0118-988 5309
www.neptunenav.demon.co.uk
Passage planning, tides and tidal stream prediction software for the PCs. Providing course to steer calculations, point and click planning, waypoint upload to GPS, chart plotter and many more functions. Intuitively easy to use Windows programs.

**RADIO & ELECTRONIC SERVICES LTD
Les Chenes, Rohais, St Peter Port,
Guernsey, Channel Islands GY1 1FB.**
Tel (01481) 728837 Fax (01481) 714379
Chart plotters, GPS, C-Map and Navionics charting, radars, VHF fixed and portable radios and autopilots. We offer full electronic supply and service. Sales and service dealers for Furuno, Icom, Shipmate, Cetrek, Autohelm, Robertson and AP Navigator.

**ROYAL INSTITUTE OF NAVIGATION
1 Kensington Gore, London SW7 2AT.**
Tel 0171-591 3130 Fax 0171-591 3131
Forum for all interested in navigation - Air: Sea: Land: Space.

**SWALE MARINE (ELECTRICAL)
The Old Stable, North Road,
Queenborough, Kent ME11 5EH.**
Tel (01795) 580930 Fax (01795) 667280
For all your electrical and electronic needs. Authorised agents for: Furuno, Autohelm, Raytheon and most major manufacturers. Fight crime with Harbourguard monitored security: Medway and Swale coverage - Boatmark registration centre.

NAVIGATION LIGHT SWITCHES & MONITORS

**MECTRONICS MARINE
PO Box 8,
Newton Abbot, Devon TQ12 1FF.**
Tel (01626) 334453
LIGHT ACTIVATED SWITCHES, rugged solid state devices to automatically switch anchor lights at sunset and sunrise. NAVLIGHT SELECTORS, protected enclosed rotary switches internally connected to ensure approved navigation light combination on auxiliary sailing vessels. NAVLIGHT STATUS MONITORS, diagnostic displays on which the appropriate indicator flashes quickly or slowly in the event of a short or open circuit fault. Also drives an optional audible warning device.

PAINT & OSMOSIS

**FOX'S MARINA IPSWICH LTD
The Strand, Wherstead,
Ipswich, Suffolk IP2 8SA.**
Tel (01473) 689111 Fax (01473) 601737
The most comprehensive boatyard facility on the east coast. Extensive chandlery. Marina access 24-hours. Diesel dock, two travel hoists to 45 tons, 10 ton crane. Full electronics, rigging, engineering, stainless steel services. Specialists in osmosis and spray painting.

**INTERNATIONAL PAINT
24-30 Canute Road, Southampton,
Hampshire SO14 3PB.**
Tel (01703) 226722 Fax (01703) 335975
International Paint is the leading supplier of quality paints, epoxies, varnishes and anti-foulings to the marine industry. Over half the world's pleasure craft are protected by International products.

JEFFREY WOOD MARINE LTD
26 Rectory Gardens,
Granham, Essex RM14 3YJ.
Tel (01708) 641300 Fax (01708) 641110
Consultant forensic marine engineers, boat designers and surveyors, naval architects. Osmosis and Ferro cement specialists - wood or steel boats of all types.

NORTH QUAY MARINE
North Side, St Sampson's Harbour,
Guernsey, Channel Islands.
Tel (01481) 46561 Fax (01481) 43488
The complete boating centre. Full range of chandlery, rope, chain, lubricants, paint, boatwear and shoes. Fishing tackle for on-shore and on-board. Inflatables and safety equipment. Electronics and small outboard engines.

ROSDEN GLASS FIBRE
La Rue Durell, La Collette,
St Helier, Jersey JE2 3NB.
Tel (01534) 625418 Fax (01534) 625419
Specialists in all types of glass fibre marine works, structural repairs, alterations, re-flow coating, GEL coat work, Blakes Osmosis Treatment Centre. Manufacturers of fuel tanks, bathing platforms and boat builders. General refurbishment and polishing. A division of Precision Plastics (Jersey) Ltd.

S P SYSTEMS
Love Lane,
Cowes, Isle of Wight PO31 7EU.
Tel (01983) 284000 Fax (01983) 298453
Epoxy resins for laminating, bonding, coating and filling. Usable with wood, GRP, concrete. GRP/FRP materials including glass, carbon and Kevlar fibres. Structural engineering of GRP and composite materials. Technical advice service.

TRAMEX LTD
Shankill Business Centre, Shankill, Co Dublin, Ireland.
Tel +353 1 282 3688 Fax +353 1 282 7880
e-mail: tramex@iol.ie
Website: www.tramexltd.com
Manufacturers of Moisture Metre and osmosis detection instruments for boats.

PROP PROTECTOR
74 Abingdon Road,
Maidstone, Kent ME16 9EE.
Tel (01622) 728738 Fax (01622) 727973
Prevention is better than cure when it comes to avoiding a fouled propeller. Prop Protectors are now accepted worldwide as the first line of defence against stray rope, netting, weed and plastic bags.

SILLETTE SONIC LTD
182 Church Hill Road,
North Cheam, Sutton, Surrey SM3 8NF.
Tel 0181-715 0100 Fax 0181-288 0742
Mobile 0410 270107
Sillette manufactures a range of propulsion systems - stern drive, saildrives etc and sterngear. Markets Radice & Gori fixed and folding propellers. Acts as agents for Morse

Controls, Yanmar and Lombardini marine engines, and Fuji Robin generators. See distribution depot Poole, Dorset - Area 2.

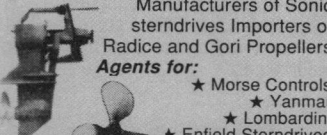

SILLETTE - SONIC LTD
182 CHURCH HILL ROAD
NORTH CHEAM SUTTON SURREY SM3 8NF
TEL: 0181-715 0100 FAX: 0181-288 0742
MOBILE: 0410 270107
Manufacturers of Sonic sterndrives Importers of Radice and Gori Propellers
Agents for:
★ Morse Controls
★ Yanmar
★ Lombardini
★ Enfield Sterndrives
★ Lake Sterngear
Manufacturing depot based at Poole.

VETUS DEN OUDEN LTD
39 South Hants Industrial Park, Totton, Southampton, Hampshire SO40 3SA.
Tel (01703) 861033 Fax (01703) 663142
Suppliers of marine diesel equipment, exhaust systems, steering systems, bow propellers, propellers and shafts, hatches, portlights, windows, electronic instruments, batteries, ventilators, windlasses, water and fuel tanks, chandlery items and much much more.

CHISWICK QUAY MARINA LTD
Marina Office,
Chiswick Quay, London W4 3UR.
Tel 0181-994 8743
Small, secluded, peaceful marina on tidal Thames at Chiswick. Slipway, marine engineers and electricians, power, water, toilets and sluice. Some residential moorings.

HOYLAKE SAILING SCHOOL
43a Market Street,
Hoylake, Wirral L47 2BG.
Tel 0151-632 4664 Fax 0151-632 4776
RYA recognised shorebased teaching establishment offering a wide range of courses including Day Skipper to Yachtmaster Ocean, VHF and First Aid. Day, evening or intensive classes. Pratical courses by arrangement. Books, charts and gifts available.

RADIO SCHOOL LTD
33 Island Close,
Hayling Island, Hampshire PO11 0NJ.
Tel/Fax (01705) 466450
Regular weekend courses/exams for the NEW GMDSS VHF and SSB/Sat. Radio-telephone Operator's Certificates in UK's only permanent, fully equipped classroom solely dedicated to training small-boat sailors on a full-time, professional basis. Established 1980.

D C G BANBURY
1 Longfellow Road,
Banbury, Oxon OX16 9LB.
Tel/Fax (01295) 257707
e-mail: subrella97@aol.com
Website: http://members.aol.com. subrella97
Makers of *Subrella* the only quick and reliable way to close off a hole in the hull below the water line from the safety of the inside. *Subrella* celebrates its 25th birthday in 1999.

ROSDEN GLASS FIBRE
La Rue Durell,
La Collette,
St Helier, Jersey JE2 3NB.
Tel (01534) 625418 Fax (01534) 625419
Specialists in all types of glass fibre marine works, structural repairs, alterations, re-flow coating, GEL coat work, Blakes Osmosis Treatment Centre. Manufacturers of fuel tanks, bathing platforms and boat builders. General refurbishment and polishing. A division of Precision Plastics (Jersey) Ltd.

S P SYSTEMS
Love Lane,
Cowes,
Isle of Wight PO31 7EU.
Tel (01983) 284000 Fax (01983) 298453
Epoxy resins for laminating, bonding, coating and filling. Usable with wood, GRP, concrete. GRP/FRP materials including glass, carbon and Kevlar fibres. Structural engineering of GRP and composite materials. Technical advice service.

A B MARINE LTD
Castle Walk, St Peter Port,
Guernsey, Channel Islands GY1 1AU.
Tel (01481) 722378 (Fax 01481) 711080
We specialise in safety and survival equipment and are a DoT approved service station for liferafts including R.F.D., Beaufort/Dunlop, Zodiac, Plastimo amd Lifeguard. We also carry a full range of new liferafts, dinghies and lifejackets, and are agents for Bukh marine engines.

ADEC MARINE LTD
4 Masons Avenue,
Croydon, Surrey CR0 1EH.
Tel 0181-686 9717 Fax 0181-680 9912
e-mail: adecmarine@ukbusiness.com
Approved liferaft service station for south east UK. Additionally we hire and sell new rafts and sell a complete range of safety equipment for yachts including pyro-technics, fire extinguishers, lifejackets, buoys and a buoyancy bag system.

CREWSAVER LTD
Crewsaver House, Mumby Road,
Gosport, Hampshire PO12 1AQ.
Tel (01705) 528621
MARLIN - Leading manufacturer of stylish, comfortable, hardwearing wetsuits, lifejackets, buoyancy aids and accessories for all seasons and all-surface watersports. YAK - Catering for all canoeing needs from cags and decks to long johns and buoyancy aids.

PREMIUM LIFERAFT SERVICES
Liferaft House, Burnham Business Park,
Burnham-on-Crouch, Essex CM0 8TE.
Tel (01621) 784858 Fax (01621) 785934
Freephone 0800 243673
e-mail:liferaftuk@aol.com
Hire and sales of DoT and RORC approved liferafts. Long and short-term hire from 18 depots nationwide. Servicing and other safety equipment available.

SHAMROCK CHANDLERY
Shamrock Quay,
William Street, Northam,
Southampton, Hampshire SO14 5QL.
Tel (01703) 632725 Fax (01703) 225611
e-mail: sales@shamrock.co.uk
Website: http://www.shamrock.co.uk
Situated on Shamrock Quay, a busy working yard with a pub, restaurant and boutiques. Shamrock Chandlery is renowned for extensive quality stocks and service, and is widely used by both the trade and boat owners. Excellent mail order facilities - Order Hotline 01703 225746.

SOUTH EASTERN
MARINE SERVICES LTD
Units 13 & 25, Olympic Business Centre,
Paycocke Road, Basildon,
Essex SS14 3EX.
Tel (01268) 534427 Fax (01268) 281009
e-mail: sems@bt.internet.com
Liferaft service, sales and hire, 1-65 persons. Approved by major manufacturers and MSA. Callers welcome. View your own raft. Family owned and operated. Inflatable boat repairs and spares. WE WANT YOU TO COME BACK. www.sems.com

WINTERS MARINE LTD
(Lincombe Boatyard)
Lincombe, Salcombe, Devon TQ8 8NQ.
Tel (01548) 843580
e-mail:
lincombeboatyard@eclipse.co.uk
Deep water pontoon moorings. Winter storage for 150 boats. All maintenance and repair facilities. Slipway capacity 30 tonnes. Inflatable craft sales and service. Liferaft surveys and repairs. Short and long-term liferaft hire.

SAILMAKERS & REPAIRS

CALIBRA MARINE INTERNATIONAL
26 Foss Street,
Dartmouth, Devon TQ6 9DR.
Tel (01803) 833094 Fax (01803) 833615
e-mail: calibra1@aol.com
A complete boating centre. Marine and architectural rigging service. Sail makers, repairs and valeting. All types of canvas

work. Boat brokerage, new and used. Yacht management services. Agents for Nemo, Z-Spar, Whitlock, Lewmar, Norseman and many others.

KEMP SAILS LTD
Unit 2, Sandford Lane Industrial Estate,
Wareham, Dorset BH20 4DY.
Tel (01929) 554308 Fax (01929) 554350
e-mail: kemp@eluk.co.ukwww.eluk.co.
uk/kemp
Sailmakers and reefing system. Suppliers of sail handling equipment.

PARKER & KAY SAILMAKERS - EAST
Suffolk Yacht Harbour,
Levington, Ipswich, Suffolk IP10 0LN.
Tel (01473) 659878 Fax (01473) 659197
A complete sailmaking service, from small repairs to the construction of custom designed sails for racing or cruising yachts. Covers constructed for sail and powercraft, plus the supply of all forms of sail handling hardware.

PARKER & KAY SAILMAKERS - SOUTH
Port Hamble Marina,
Satchell Lane, Hamble,
Southampton, Hampshire SO31 5QD.
Tel (01703) 458213 Fax (01703) 458228
A complete sailmaking service, from small repairs to the construction of custom designed sails for racing or cruising yachts. Covers constructed for sail and powercraft, plus the supply of all forms of sail handling hardware.

UK/McWILLIAM SAILMAKERS
Crosshaven, Co Cork, Ireland.
Tel +353 21 831505 Fax +353 21 831700
Ireland's premier sailmaker, prompt repairs and service.

SEA DELIVERIES

CARDINAL YACHTS
12A Grafton Court, Grafton Road,
Torquay, Devon TQ1 1UP.
Tel/Fax (01803) 212954
Mobile: 0860 906390
e-mail: cardinal.yachts@eclipse.co.uk
Sail and power deliveries worldwide by experienced, commercial yachtmasters. Take the cheapest Mediterranean route with our combined sea and road service. Owners welcome. As an RYA recognised sea school we offer tuition at all levels.

MAX WALKER YACHT DELIVERIES
Zinderneuf Sailing, PO Box 105,
Macclesfield, Cheshire SK10 2EY.
Tel (01625) 431712 Fax (01625) 619704
Fixed price deliveries. Sailing yachts delivered with care in north west European, UK and Eire waters by RYA/DoT yachtmaster and crew - 30 years' experience. Owners welcome. Tuition if required. References available. Your enquiries welcome 24 hours.

PETERS & MAY LTD
18 Canute Road, Ocean Village,
Southampton, Hampshire SO14 3FJ.
Tel (01703) 480480 Fax (01703) 480400
The 'Round the World' specialists in shipping, transporting, cradling yachts and

powerboats. Weekly service to USA, Far East, Mediterranean, Middle East and Caribbean.

SEALAND BOAT DELIVERIES LTD
Tower, Liverpool Marina, Coburg Wharf,
Liverpool L3 4BP.
Tel (01254) 705225 Fax (01254) 776582
Website: http://www.btx.co.uk
e-mail: ros@mcr1.poptel.org.uk
Nationwide and European road transporters of all craft. No weight limit. We never close. Irish service. Worldwide shipping agents. Extrication of yachts from workshops and building yards. Salvage contractors. Established 25 years.

TREVOR VINCETT DELIVERIES
Coombe Cottage, 9 Swannaton Road,
Dartmouth, Devon TQ6 9RL.
Tel/Fax (01803) 833757
Mobile 07970 208799
Worldwide delivery of yachts and commercial vessels undertaken at short notice by RYA/DoT Yachtmaster Ocean (with commercial endorsement). Over 28 years' experience including three masted schooners, tugs, motor yachts and hi-tec racers. For instant quotes call/fax 01803 833757.

SKIPPERED CHARTERS/ CRUISING

DINGLE SEA VENTURES
YACHT CHARTER
Dingle, Co Kerry, Ireland.
Tel +353 66 52244 Fax +353 66 52313
e-mail: jgreany@iol.ie
Bareboat charter, skippered charter, sailing tuition on south west coast of Ireland: One way charter Dingle-Kinsale-Dingle - 1997 and 1998 fleet of eight boats 31' - 44'. Close to all ferries and airports. Personal, friendly service. PINTS OF PEACE.

ISLAND SEA SCHOOL
7 Church View,
South Milford, Leeds LS25 5BM.
Tel/Fax (01977) 685394
e-mail: sea.school@mcmail.com
RYA practical courses from our base at Port Dinorwic on the Menai Strait: Competent Crew, Day Skipper, Coastal Skipper, Yachtmaster Preparatory, Ocean Yachtmaster Qualifying Passages. Own boat tuition. Skippered charter.

ISLANDER YACHT CHARTERS
& ISLANDER SAILING SCHOOL
7 Torinturk, Argyll PA29 6YE.
Tel (01880) 820012
Fax (01880) 821143/820012
e-mail: r.fleck@virgin.net
Sail the spectacular and uncrowded waters of the Scottish west coast and Hebrides from our base at Aberdeen Yacht Centre, Argyll. Bareboat or skippered yachts from 33' to 44', all Dtp certificated. RYA recognised sailing school, YM, CS, DS and CC courses from March to October.

SLIPWAYS

RAMSGATE ROYAL HARBOUR MARINA
Harbour Office,
Military Road, Ramsgate, Kent CT11 9LQ.
Tel (01843) 592277 Fax (01843) 590941
Ramsgate Royal Harbour is situated on the south east coast, making an ideal base for crossing to the Continent. 24-hour access to finger pontoons. Comprehensive security systems. Amenities: Launderette, repairs, slipways, boatpark. Competitive rates for permanent berths and discount for visitors' group bookings.

RIVERSFORD HOTEL
Limers Lane, Bideford, Devon EX39 2RG.
Tel (01237) 474239
Peace and tranquility in gardens beside the river Torridge. A relaxing retreat with convenient slipway close by. Excellent restaurant with efficient, friendly service with a choice of imaginative food and wine from our extensive menu and wine list. Comfortable, flexible lounge bar.

ROYAL AIR FORCE YACHT CLUB
Riverside House, Rope Walk, Hamble,
Southampton, Hampshire SO31 4HD.
Tel (01703) 452208 Fax (01703) 458001
Superb club, open to non-service members, on the river Hamble. Offers many amenities. New waterfront, dock, scrubbing pile, bar and restaurant, showers and laundry. Excellent accommodation available - 3 bedrooms and 1 en suit - bookings essential. Full programme of racing, cruising and rallies. Welcomes visiting yachtsmen.

ST MAWES SAILING CLUB
No 1 The Quay,
St Mawes, Cornwall TR2 5DG.
Tel (01326) 270686 Fax (01326) 270040
Quayside sailing club in centre of village. Visitor moorings in harbour. Private slip, launching and recovery facilities. Dinghy park, post box, showers. Visitors encouraged. Chandlery and sail repairs to order. No marina but a warm welcome awaits.

WEIR QUAY BOATYARD
Heron's Reach,
Bere Alston, Devon PL20 7BT.
Tel (01822) 840474 Fax (01822) 840948
Deepwater swinging moorings, shore storage, full boatyard facilities and services, cranage to 12 tons, repairs, maintenance, slipway. A traditional boatyard at affordable rates *in a superb setting* on the Tamar, with excellent security.

WINTERS MARINE LTD
(Lincombe Boatyard)
Lincombe, Salcombe, Devon TQ8 8NQ.
Tel (01548) 843580
e-mail: lincombeboatyard@eclipse.
co.uk
Deep water pontoon moorings. Winter storage for 150 boats. All maintenance and repair facilities. Slipway capacity 30 tonnes. Inflatable craft sales and service. Lifecraft surveys and repairs. Short and long-term lifecraft hire.

SOLAR POWER

MARLEC ENGINEERING CO LTD
Rutland House, Trevithick Road,
Corby, Northamptonshire NN17 5XY.
Tel (01536) 201588 Fax (01536) 400211
For wind and solar powered battery charging on board talk to Marlec. We manufacture the Rutland Marine range of wind windchargers, and import and distribute Solarex photovoltaic modules. Manufacturer of Leisurelights - IOW energy high efficiency 12v lamps.

SPEED LOGS

THOMAS WALKER GROUP LTD
37-41 Bissell Street,
Birmingham B5 7HR.
Tel 0121-622 4475 Fax 0121-622 4478
Manufacturer of marine instruments including, Neco Autopilots, Walker Logs and Towing Logs, Walker Anemometers, Chernikeeff Logs.

SPRAYHOODS & DODGERS

MARTELLO YACHT SERVICES
Mulberry House, Mulberry Road,
Canvey Island, Essex SS8 0PR.
Tel/Fax (01268) 681970
Manufacturers and suppliers of made-to-measure upholstery, covers, hoods, dodgers, sailcovers, curtains and cushions etc. Repairs undertaken. DIY materials, chandlery and fitting-out supplies.

STAINLESS STEEL FITTINGS

MANX MARINE
35 North Quay,
Douglas, Isle of Man IM1 4LB.
Tel/Fax (01624) 674842
The Island's leading and most established yacht chandlery. Stockists of quality foul-weather clothing and thermal wear. Large stock holdings of stainless steel fixtures and fittings and a comprehensive range of general chandlery including rigging facilities.

SURVEYORS & NAUTICAL ARCHITECTS

ANDREW POTTER MA AMYDSA YACHT SURVEYOR
Penrallt Cottage, Cichle Hill,
Llandegfan, Anglesey LL59 5TD.
Tel/Fax (01248) 712358
Mobile 0374 411681
Prompt and professional surveys prior to purchase and for insurance purposes throughout Wales, the north west and Midlands. Services also include valuations, osmosis inspections and consultancy.

JEFFREY WOOD MARINE LTD
26 Rectory Gardens,
Granham, Essex RM14 3YJ.
Tel (01708) 641300 Fax (01708) 641110
Consultant forensic marine engineers, boat designers and surveyors, naval architects. Osmosis and Ferro cement specialists - wood or steel boats of all types.

LIONSTAR YACHT & MOTORBOAT SURVEYS
The Lawn, Ashbrooke Road,
Sunderland, Tyne & Wear SR2 7HQ.
Tel 0191-528 6422
Lionstar Yacht Services, Sunderland - Surveys of sailing and motor yachts by chartered marine engineers and naval architects with full PI and PL insurance. Northern England and southern Scotland. Telephone Derek May on 0191-528 6422 for quote.

N W SEAWAYS DOCK MANAGEMENT LTD
Port Dinorwic Marina,
Y Felinheli, Gwynedd LL56 4JN.
Tel (01248) 670620 Fax (01248) 671252
Mobile 0468 794361
Condition and pre-purchase surveys and insurance valuations, damage and repair reports, underwater dive inspections. Repair and dry dock facilities available. Call in or phone your requirement for prompt, professionl service at competitive rates.

ROB PERRY MARINE
Monmouth Beach,
Lyme Regis, Dorset DT7 3LE.
Tel (01297) 445816 Fax (01297) 445886
Outboard and inboard sales and service. Wetsuits, lifejackets. Some chandlery. Fast efficient service. Marine surveys and insurance.

RUPERT SMITH B.Eng.(Hons)
16 Manor Road North,
Seaford, East Sussex BN25 3RB.
Tel/Fax (01323) 898782
Yacht and powercraft surveys, design and consultancy. Pre-purchase insurance and damage surveys.

WARD & McKENZIE LTD

3 Wherry Lane, Ipswich, Suffolk IP4 1LG.
Tel (01473) 255200 Fax (01473) 255044
National and International Marine Surveyors, Technical and Legal Consultants - offering a comprehensive service to boat owners and those seeking to acquire pleasure yachts. All aspects of title/lien check, registration. Survey, purchase and ownership undertaken, including insurance surveys, finance and disputes. See regional offices in Area Directory.

TANKS

TEK-TANKS
Units 5A - 5B Station Approach,
Four Marks, Nr Alton,
Hampshire GU34 5HN.
Tel (01420) 564359 Fax (01420) 561605
e-mail: tek_tanks@compuserve.com
Manufacturers and suppliers of made-to-measure and standard polypropylene water, waste and HDPE diesel tanks.

TAXI SERVICE

ADMIRAL PRIVATE HIRE TAXIS
2 The Stables, Northford Road,
Dartmouth, Devon TQ6 9EP.
Tel (01803) 834315
Private hire taxi service nationwide from the South Hams.

TRANSPORT/ YACHT DELIVERIES

CARDINAL YACHTS
12A Grafton Court, Grafton Road,
Torquay, Devon TQ1 1UP.
Tel/Fax (01803) 212954
Mobile: 0860 906390
e-mail: cardinal.yachts@eclipse.co.uk
Sail and power deliveries worldwide by experienced, commercial yachtmasters. Take the cheapest Mediterranean route with our combined sea and road service. Owners welcome. As an RYA recognised sea school we offer tuition at all levels.

CONVOI EXCEPTIONNEL
Castleton House, High Street, Hamble,
Southampton, Hampshire SO31 4HA.
Tel (01703) 453045 Fax (01703) 454551
International marine haulage and abnormal load consultants. Specialist services up to 40 tons.

EAST SUSSEX SAILING
4 Arun Path,
Uckfield, East Sussex TN22 1NL.
Tel/Fax (01825) 769578
Mobile 0402 275165
Based in the heart of East Sussex, we conduct RYA recognised shorebased navigation and VHF courses which can be tailored to suit your individual requirements. Own boat tuition and yacht/power deliveries are also available.

EXONIA EUROPEAN MARINE TRANSPORT

The Sidings, Heathfield, Newton Abbot, Devon TQ12 0JB.
Tel (01626) 836688 Fax (01626) 836831
Europe's premier overland marine transport company, 25 years' experience, expertise cross border formalities, documentation, notifications, escorts, permits and schedules. Highly experienced well briefed drivers with a fully qualified back-up team. *Indubitably the best.*

MAX WALKER YACHT DELIVERIES
Zinderneuf Sailing, PO Box 105,
Macclesfield, Cheshire SK10 2EY.
Tel (01625) 431712 Fax (01625) 619704
Fixed price deliveries. Sailing yachts delivered with care in north west European, UK and Eire waters by RYA/DoT yachtmaster and crew - 30 years' experience. Owners welcome. Tuition if required. References available. Your enquiries welcome 24 hours.

PETERS & MAY LTD
18 Canute Road, Ocean Village,
Southampton, Hampshire SO14 3FJ.
Tel (01703) 480480 Fax (01703) 480400
The 'Round the World' specialists in shipping, transporting, cradling yachts and powerboats. Weekly service to USA, Far East, Mediterranean, Middle East and Caribbean.

SEALAND BOAT DELIVERIES LTD
Tower, Liverpool Marina,
Coburg Wharf, Liverpool L3 4BP.
Tel (01254) 705225 Fax (01254) 776582
Website: http://www.btx.co.uk
e-mail: ros@mcr1.poptel.org.uk
Nationwide and European road transporters of all craft. No weight limit. We never close. Irish service. Worldwide shipping agents. Extrication of yachts from workshops and building yards. Salvage contractors. Established 25 years.

TREVOR VINCETT DELIVERIES
Coombe Cottage,
9 Swannaton Road,
Dartmouth, Devon TQ6 9RL.
Tel/Fax (01803) 833757
Mobile 07970 208799
Worldwide delivery of yachts and commercial vessels undertaken at short notice by RYA/DoT Yachtmaster Ocean (with commercial endorsement). Over 28 years' experience including three masted schooners, tugs, motor yachts and hi-tec racers. For instant quotes call/fax 01803 833757.

WARD & McKENZIE LTD

3 Wherry Lane, Ipswich, Suffolk IP4 1LG.
Tel (01473) 255200 Fax (01473) 255044
National and International Marine Surveyors, Technical and Legal Consultants - offering a comprehensive service to boat owners and those seeking to acquire pleasure yachts. All aspects of title/lien check, registration. Survey, purchase and ownership undertaken, including insurance surveys, finance and disputes. See regional offices in Area Directory.

TUITION/SAILING SCHOOLS

CARDINAL YACHTS
12A Grafton Court, Grafton Road,
Torquay, Devon TQ1 1UP.
Tel/Fax (01803) 212954
Mobile: 0860 906390
e-mail: cardinal.yachts@eclipse.co.uk
Sail and power deliveries worldwide by experienced, commercial yachtmasters. Take the cheapest Mediterranean route with our combined sea and road service. Owners welcome. As an RYA recognised sea school we offer tuition at all levels.

DINGLE SEA VENTURES
YACHT CHARTER
Dingle, Co Kerry, Ireland.
Tel +353 66 52244 Fax +353 66 52313
e-mail: jgreany@iol.ie
Bareboat charter, skippered charter, sailing tuition on south west coast of Ireland: One way charter Dingle-Kinsale-Dingle - 1997 and 1998 fleet of eight boats 31' - 44'. Close to all ferries and airports. Personal, friendly service. PINTS OF PEACE.

EAST SUSSEX SAILING
4 Arun Path,
Uckfield, East Sussex TN22 1NL.
Tel/Fax (01825) 769578
Mobile 0402 275165
Based in the heart of East Sussex, we conduct RYA recognised shorebased navigation and VHF courses which can be tailored to suit your individual requirements. Own boat tuition and yacht/power deliveries are also available.

HOYLAKE SAILING SCHOOL
43a Market Street,
Hoylake, Wirral L47 2BG.
Tel 0151-632 4664 Fax 0151-632 4776
RYA recognised shorebased teaching establishment offering a wide range of courses including Day Skipper to Yachtmaster Ocean, VHF and First Aid. Day, evening or intensive classes. Pratical courses by arrangement. Books, charts and gifts available.

ISLAND SEA SCHOOL
7 Church View,
South Milford, Leeds LS25 5BM.
Tel/Fax (01977) 685394
e-mail: sea.school@mcmail.com
RYA practical courses from our base at Port Dinorwic on the Menai Strait: Competent Crew, Day Skipper, Coastal Skipper, Yachtmaster Preparatory, Ocean Yachtmaster Qualifying Passages. Own boat tuition. Skippered charter.

**ISLANDER YACHT CHARTERS
& ISLANDER SAILING SCHOOL**
7 Torinturk, Argyll PA29 6YE.
Tel (01880) 820012
Fax (01880) 821143/820012
e-mail: r.fleck@virgin.net
Sail the spectacular and uncrowded waters of the Scottish west coast and Hebrides from our base at Aberdeen Yacht Centre, Argyll. Bareboat or skippered yachts from 33' to 44', all Dtp certificated. RYA recognised sailing school, YM, CS, DS and CC courses from March to October.

UPHOLSTERY & COVERS

MARTELLO YACHT SERVICES
Mulberry House, Mulberry Road,
Canvey Island, Essex SS8 0PR.
Tel/Fax (01268) 681970
Manufacturers and suppliers of made-to-measure upholstery, covers, hoods, dodgers, sailcovers, curtains and cushions etc. Repairs undertaken. DIY materials, chandlery and fitting-out supplies.

TOOMER & HAYTER LTD
74 Green Road,
Winton, Bournemouth, Dorset BH9 1EB.
Tel (01202) 515789 Fax (01202) 538771
Marine upholstery manufacturers. Cabin and cockpit upholstery made to any shape or size. Sprung interior mattresses made to measure. Foam backed cabin lining always in stock, also carpet side lining. Visit our factory and showroom.

WEATHER INFORMATION

**MARINECALL - TELEPHONE
INFORMATION SERVICES**
Avalon House, London EC2A 4PJ.
Tel 0171-631 6000
Marinecall provides detailed coastal weather forecasts for 17 different regions up to 5 days ahead from the Met Office. For a full fax list of services dial 0891 24 66 80. Telephone forecasts are updated daily, morning and afternoon.

**PROSSER SCIENTIFIC
INSTRUMENTS LTD**
Lady Lane Industrial Estate,
Hadleigh, Ipswich, Suffolk IP7 6BQ.
Tel (01473) 823005 Fax (01473) 824095
Manufacturers of a range of marine instruments, including the WEATHER-TREND digital barometer, with full 24-hour history, the unique TIDECLOCK tidal data predictor and tidal software for the PSION 3 series.

WIND POWER

MARLEC ENGINEERING CO LTD
Rutland House, Trevithick Road, Corby,
Northamptonshire NN17 5XY.
Tel (01536) 201588 Fax (01536) 400211
For wind and solar powered battery charging on board talk to Marlec. We manufacture the Rutland Marine range of wind windchargers, and import and distribute Solarex photovoltaic modules. Manufacturer of Leisurelights - IOW energy high efficiency 12v lamps.

WOOD FITTINGS

SHERATON MARINE CABINET
White Oak Green,
Hailey, Witney, Oxfordshire OX8 5XP.
Tel/Fax (01993) 868275
Manufacturers of quality teak and mahogany marine fittings, louvre doors, gratings and tables. Special fitting-out items to customer specification. Colour catalogue available on request.

YACHT BROKERS

ARDFERN YACHT CENTRE
Ardfern By Lochgilphead,
Argyll PA31 8QN.
Tel (01852) 500247/636
Fax (01852) 500624 and 07000
Ardfern Boatyard with full repair and maintenance facilities. Timber and GRP repairs, painting and engineering. Sheltered moorings and pontoon berthing. Winter storage, chandlery, showers, fuel, Calor, brokerage, 20-ton boat hoist, rigging. Hotel, bars and restaurant.

CALIBRA MARINE INTERNATIONAL
26 Foss Street,
Dartmouth, Devon TQ6 9DR.
Tel (01803) 833094 Fax (01803) 833615
e-mail: calibra1@aol.com
A complete boating centre. Marine and architectural rigging service. Sail makers, repairs and valeting. All types of canvas work. Boat brokerage, new and used. Yacht management services. Agents for Nemo, Z-Spar, Whitlock, Lewmar, Norseman and many others.

CRAOBH MARINA
By Lochgilphead, Argyll PA31 8UD.
Tel (01852) 500222 Fax (01852) 500252
250-berth marina on Loch Shuna. Water, electricity, diesel and gas. Full boatyard services. Chandlery. Brokerage. Insurance. Shops, bar. 24-hour access. VHF Ch37 and 80 (M).

DEACONS BOATYARD LTD
Bursledon Bridge,
Southampton, Hampshire SO31 8AZ.
Tel (01703) 402253 Fax (01703) 405665
This yard has all major services for yachtsmen. Moorings, hardstanding, repairs, marine engineers, riggers, chandlery and brokerage - new yacht sales. Deacons are UK importers for Feeling Yachts.

YACHT CHARTERS & HOLIDAYS

**DINGLE SEA VENTURES
YACHT CHARTER**
Dingle, Co Kerry, Ireland.
Tel +353 66 52244 Fax +353 66 52313
e-mail: jgreany@iol.ie
Bareboat charter, skippered charter, sailing tuition on south west coast of Ireland: One way charter Dingle-Kinsale-Dingle - 1997 and 1998 fleet of eight boats 31' - 44'. Close to all ferries and airports. Personal, friendly service. PINTS OF PEACE.

GREEK SAILS YACHT CHARTER
21 The Mount, Kippax, Leeds LS25 7NG.
Tel/Fax 0113-232 0926
Freephone 0800 731 8580
e-mail: greek_sails_uk@msn.com
Bareboat yacht charter throughout Greece and the islands. Flottilla based in Corfu and the Ionian Islands. Family dinghy sailing holidays in Corfu. Skippered charter and sail   training.

ISLAND SEA SCHOOL
7 Church View,
South Milford, Leeds LS25 5BM.
Tel/Fax (01977) 685394
e-mail: sea.school@mcmail.com
RYA practical courses from our base at Port Dinorwic on the Menai Strait: Competent Crew, Day Skipper, Coastal Skipper, Yachtmaster Preparatory, Ocean Yacht-master Qualifying Passages. Own boat tuition. Skippered charter.

ISLANDER YACHT CHARTERS & ISLANDER SAILING SCHOOL
7 Torinturk, Argyll PA29 6YE.
Tel (01880) 820012
Fax (01880) 821143/820012
e-mail: r.fleck@virgin.net
Sail the spectacular and uncrowded waters of the Scottish west coast and Hebrides from our base at Aberdeen Yacht Centre, Argyll. Bareboat or skippered yachts from 33' to 44', all Dtp certificated. RYA recognised sailing school, YM, CS, DS and CC courses from March to October.

ISLANDER YACHT CHARTERS & ISLANDER SAILING SCHOOL
7 Torinturk,
Argyll PA29 6YE.
Tel: 01880 820012
Fax: 01880 821143
e-mail: r.fleck@virgin.net
Based at Ardfern Yacht Centre, Argyll. Come and explore the spectacular and uncrowded waters of the west coast and Hebrides. Quality yachts ranging from 33'- to 44'- all Dtp certified.
RYA Courses available at our Sailing School.

LOCH NESS CHARTERS
The Boatyard,
Dochgarroch, Inverness IV3 6JY.
Tel (01463) 861303 Fax (01463) 861353
Yacht and cruiser charter. Boat services and repairs. Hardstanding and slipway. Diesel supply. Boat finishing.

OCEAN SPIRIT SAILING CHARTERS LTD
The Canvas Factory, 5 Foss Street,
Dartmouth, Devon TQ6 9DW.
Tel/Fax (0)1803 832186
e-mail: ADBriscoe@compuserve.com
MALDIVES SAIL/DIVE - Beautiful 61' yacht, with experienced crew await your arrival. Over 1000 unspoiled islands and virgin diving are on offer from the Maldives oldest luxury yacht operator.

ODYSSEUS YACHTING HOLIDAYS
33 Grand Parade,
Brighton, East Sussex BN2 2QA.
Tel (01273) 695094 Fax (01273) 688855
Templecraft Yacht Charters are bonded tour operators specialising in independent yacht charter holidays in the Mediterranean and in the Caribbean, and as Odysseus Yachting Holidays in flotilla sailing holidays in Corfu and the Ionian islands.

SEA VENTURES YACHT CHARTER
Lymington Yacht Haven,
Lymington, Hampshire SO41 3QD.
Tel (01590) 672472 Fax (01590) 671924
Website: www.c-ventures.co.uk
Based in Lymington our large modern fleet offers both skippered and bareboat charters to Greece, Guernsey and the Canaries. A large selection of yachts from 29' to 52'. Corporate and team building and yacht management also available.

SLEAT MARINE SERVICES
Ardvasar, Isle of Skye IV45 8RU.
Tel (01471) 844216/844387
Yacht charter (bareboat and skippered) from Armadale Bay, Isle of Skye. Six yachts 34' to 40' LOA. All medium to heavy displacement blue water cruisers. Fuel, water and emergency services for passing yachts with problems.

TEMPLECRAFT YACHT CHARTERS
33 Grand Parade,
Brighton, East Sussex BN2 2QA.
Tel (01273) 695094 Fax (01273) 688855
Templecraft Yacht Charters are bonded tour operators specialising in independent yacht charter holidays in the Mediterranean and in the Caribbean, and as Odysseus Yachting Holidays in flotilla sailing holidays in Corfu and the Ionian islands.

YACHT CLUB FACILITIES

KINSALE YACHT CLUB MARINA
Kinsale, Co Cork, Ireland.
Tel +353 21 772196 Fax +353 21 774455
Marina Manager +353 87 449471
Magnificent deep water yacht club marina offering Kinsale hospitality to visiting yachtsmen. Full facilities include berths up to 20 metres, fresh water, electricity, diesel on pier. Club bar and wealth of pubs and restaurants in Kinsale. Enter Kinsale Harbour - lit at night - no restrictions.

PARKSTONE YACHT CLUB
Pearce Avenue,
Parkstone, Poole, Dorset BH14 8EH.
Tel (01202) 743610 Fax (01202) 716394
Deep water club haven facilities in Poole harbour. Access at all states of the tide. Berths for yachts up to 15 metres. Facilities include electricity, fresh water, toilets and showers. Visitors welcome by appointment. Club bar and restaurant.

ROYAL AIR FORCE YACHT CLUB
Riverside House, Rope Walk, Hamble,
Southampton, Hampshire SO31 4HD.
Tel (01703) 452208 Fax (01703) 458001
Superb club, open to non-service members, on the river Hamble. Offers many amenities. New waterfront, dock, scrubbing pile, bar and restaurant, showers and laundry. Excellent accommodation available - 3 bedrooms and 1 en suit - bookings essential. Full programme of racing, cruising and rallies. Welcomes visiting yachtsmen.

ROYAL WESTERN YACHT CLUB
Queen Anne's Battery,
Plymouth, Devon PL4 0TW.
Tel (01752) 660077 Fax (01752) 224299
Home of shorthanded sailing. Visiting yachtsmen welcome. Mooring facilities available.

ST MAWES SAILING CLUB
No 1 The Quay,
St Mawes, Cornwall TR2 5DG.
Tel (01326) 270686 Fax (01326) 270040
Quayside sailing club in centre of village. Visitor moorings in harbour. Private slip, launching and recovery facilities. Dinghy park, post box, showers. Visitors

encouraged. Chandlery and sail repairs to order. No marina but a warm welcome awaits.

YACHT MANAGEMENT

LOCH NESS CHARTERS
The Boatyard,
Dochgarroch, Inverness IV3 6JY.
Tel (01463) 861303 Fax (01463) 861353
Yacht and cruiser charter. Boat services and repairs. Hardstanding and slipway. Diesel supply. Boat finishing.

SEA VENTURES YACHT CHARTER
Lymington Yacht Haven,
Lymington, Hampshire SO41 3QD.
Tel (01590) 672472 Fax (01590) 671924
Website: www.c-ventures.co.uk
Based in Lymington our large modern fleet offers both skippered and bareboat charters to Greece, Guernsey and the Canaries. A large selection of yachts from 29' to 52'. Corporate and team building and yacht management also available.

WILDE MARINE SERVICES LTD
Frances House, Sir William Place,
St Peter Port, Guernsey,
Channel Islands GY1 4HQ.
Tel (01481) 723573 Fax (01481) 711353
British yacht registration, corporate yacht ownership and management, marine insurance, crew placement and management. Wilde Marine Services aims to provide a personal and individual service to its clients.

YACHT REGISTRATION

WARD & McKENZIE LTD
3 Wherry Lane, Ipswich, Suffolk IP4 1LG.
Tel (01473) 255200 Fax (01473) 255044
National and International Marine Surveyors. Technical and legal consultants - offering a comprehensive service to boat owners and those seeking to acquire pleasure yachts. All aspects of title/lien check, registration. Survey, purchase and ownership undertaken, including insurance surveys, finance and disputes. See regional offices in Area Directory.

WILDE MARINE SERVICES LTD
Frances House, Sir William Place,
St Peter Port, Guernsey,
Channel Islands GY1 4HQ.
Tel (01481) 723573 Fax (01481) 711353
British yacht registration, corporate yacht ownership and management, marine insurance, crew placement and manage-ment. Wilde Marine Services aims to provide a personal and individual service to its clients.

WATERSIDE ACCOMMODATION & RESTAURANTS

Sometimes after a long haul, or at the end of an arduous day carrying out necessary maintenance on your boat, or indeed as part of your holiday you may wish to enjoy the luxury of haute cuisine or simply a good meal cooked by somebody else, followed maybe, by a comfortable bed for the night. The following list guides you to hotels, restaurants and accommodation with their own private berths, or moorings close by.

ARDENTINNY HOTEL
Ardentinny, Loch Long,
By Dunoon, Argyll PA23 8TR.
Tel (01369) 810209 Fax (01369) 810241
A warm Scottish welcome awaits you at the Ardentinny. Delightful dinners to a very high standard are prepared by our chef complemented by a choice of over 50 selections of French and New World wines. Excellent casual lunches served in the garden or buttery. Friendly bar, frequented by yachtsmen, with a good selection of beer. 7 moorings available.

THE CREGGANS INN
Strachur, Argyll PA27 8BX.
Tel (01369) 860279 Fax (01369) 860637
Approximately 18 nautical miles from Ardrishaig the Creggans Inn makes a useful stop for lunch, dinner or overnight respite! 5 moorings available. Bar lunches from 12 noon and excellent restaurant serving from 7 to 9pm. Shower and changing facilities for our traveling yachtsmen.

THE CREGGANS INN
Strachur, Argyll PA27 8BX
"THE INN ON THE ROAD TO THE ISLES"
5 moorings available - Lat 56 10 3'N - Long 005 04 9'W
Approx 18 nautical miles from Ardrishaig, Creggans makes a useful stop for lunch, dinner or an overnight respite. Bar Lunch 12 noon - 2.30 Supper 6pm - 9pm Restaurant 7pm - 9pm We do not have a dress code but for guests who prefer to change we can provide shower and changing facilities.
AA ***
RAC ***
Tel: 01369 860279   Fax: 01369 860637

THE GUNFIELD
Castle Road,
Dartmouth, Devon TQ6 0JN.
Tel (01803) 834843 Fax (01803) 834772
e-mail: enquiry@gunfield.co.uk
VHF Ch M2 or Ch 37.
Waterfront position with 10 impressive en suite bedrooms, central heating etc, all command fantastic river views. Restaurant offers modestly priced, delicious Mediterranean cuisine. Continental bar and lounge open to non-residents. Large terraces and gardens, BBQs during summer. Pontoon and deep water moorings.

THE GUNFIELD
HOTEL·RESTAURANT·BAR

The Gunfield
Hotel·Restaurant·Bar

Unique position at the mouth of the River Dart with stunning views of Dartmouth Deep Water and Pontoon Moorings for Visitors

Tel:01803 834843
VHF Ch.M2 or Ch.37

THE HARBOUR LIGHTS
RESTAURANT (Walton-on-the-Naze)
Titchmarsh Marina, Coles Lane,
Walton-on-the-Naze, Essex CO14 8SL.
Tel (01255) 851887 Fax (01255) 677300
Open 7 days a week the Harbour Lights offers a welcome to yachtsmen and land-lubbers alike. Fine views over the marina and Walton Backwaters. Hearty breakfasts are served 8am - 10am, and extensive bar meals are available all day. Sizzling summer weekend barbecues, weather permitting. Silver service restaurant wuth traditional English fare.

HIGHWAY MARINE LTD
Pillory Gate Wharf, Strand Street, Sandwich, Kent CT13 9EU.
Tel (01304) 613925 Fax (01304) 614814
Pontoon moorings available in town of Sandwich. Lift-out facilities and hard standing, water, electricity. OMC main dealer with full service centre. New engine sales. Brokerage and chandlery. Excellent waterside apartments available, call (01304) 611433 for details.

HULL MARINA LTD
Warehouse 13,
Kingston Street, Hull HU1 2DQ.
Tel (01482) 613451 Fax (01482) 224148
Four-Anchor Marina. Situated 5 minues from the centre of Hull and all national and international transport systems. First class leisure, boatyard and brokerage facilities. 4-Star hotel and quayside restaurants. Professional and caring staff. Competitive rates.

KAMES HOTEL
Kames,
By Tighnabruaich, Argyll PA21 2AF.
Tel (01700) 811489 Fax (01700) 811 283
On the Kyles of Bute with 15 free moorings. Good food, real ales, fine malts. Showers available for visitors. 10 en-suite bedrooms. Regular music nights. Fresh local seafood in season.

KAMES HOTEL
Kames, Nr Tighnabruaich, Argyll PA21 2AF.
Tel: 01700 811489
Fax: 01700 811283
Situated on the beautiful Kyles of Bute.
Free moorings - excellent food
real ale - fine malts.
A traditional Scottish welcome awaits you.

KING SITRIC FISH RESTAURANT
East Pier,
Howth, Co Dublin, Ireland.
Tel +353 1 832 5235 & 6729
Fax +353 1 839 2442
Lovely location on the harbour front. Marina and Howth Yacht Club 3 minutes walk. Established 1971, Aidan and Joan MacManus have earned an international reputation for superb, fresh seafood, service and hospitality. Wine conoisseurs take note! Quality accommodation April 1999. Informal summer lunch - dinner all year.

THE OYSTERCATCHER RESTAURANT
Otter Ferry, Argyll PA21 2DH.
Tel (01700) 821229 Fax (01700) 821300
Situated on Loch Fyne, just north of the Otter Spit, about one hour's sailing from the Crinan canal. Moorings (insured to 12t) free to patrons. French chef and superb food, seafood our speciality. 1996 Tourist Board winner 'BEST PLACE TO EAT'. Children's play area.

THE PANDORA INN
Restronguet Creek, Mylor Bridge,
Falmouth, Cornwall TR11 5ST.
Tel/Fax (01326) 372678
Thatched creek-side inn with floating pontoon. Morning coffee, delicious bar meals, cream teas and fine dining in the superb Andrew Miller restaurant (entitles yachtsmen to free mooring). Telephone, showers and water available. Open all day in the summer.

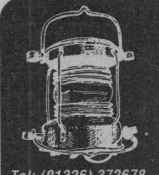
RAMSGATE - JARVIS MARINA HOTEL
Harbour Parade,
Ramsgate, Kent CT11 8LZ.
Tel (01843) 588276 Fax (01843) 586866
Situated on the edge of Ramsgate's Marina, the ideal accommodation venue for the travelling yachtsman. Club bar open all day serving drinks and snacks. Hobson's restaurant offers an extensive menu. Leisure club open to non-residents.

RIVERSFORD HOTEL
Limers Lane, Bideford,
Devon EX39 2RG.
Tel (01237) 474239
Peace and tranquility in gardens beside the river Torridge. A relaxing retreat with convenient slipway close by. Excellent restaurant with efficient, friendly service with a choice of imaginative food and wine from our extensive menu and wine list. Comfortable, flexible lounge bar.

ROYAL AIR FORCE YACHT CLUB
Riverside House, Rope Walk, Hamble, Southampton,
Hampshire SO31 4HD.
Tel (01703) 452208 Fax (01703) 458001
Superb club, open to non-service members, on the river Hamble. Offers many amenities. New waterfront, dock, scrubbing pile, bar and restaurant, showers and laundry. Excellent accommodation available - 3 bedrooms and 1 en suit - bookings essential. Full programme of racing, cruising and rallies. Welcomes visiting yachtsmen.

ROYAL HOTEL - TIGHNABRUAICH
Tighnabruaich, Argyll PA21 2BE.
Tel (01700) 811239 Fax (01700) 811300
On the Kyles of Bute. Fully licensed individual family run hotel. Superb food, venison, game, prawns, scallops and lobster served in our cosy bars and restaurant. *Taste of Scotland* recommended. 12 moorings, slipway, showers, hairdryers.

TIGH AN EILEAN HOTEL
Shieldaig by Strathcaron,
Ross-shire IV54 8XN.
Tel (01520) 755251 Fax (01520) 755321
On the edge of the sea amongst some of the most dramatic landscapes in the Highlands, this friendly 12-bedroom hotel is run under the personal supervision of the proprietors. Our restaurant serves local produce cooked with flair and complemented with good wine. Excellent drying room for those wet clothes!!

TOLLESBURY MARINA
The Yacht Harbour,
Tollesbury, Maldon, Essex CM9 8SE.
Tel (01621) 869202 Fax (01621) 868489
e-mail: marina@woodrolfe.demon.co.uk
 Dedicated to customer service, this family-run marina can offer 240 marina berths with water and electricity on all pontoons. Cruising club with bar, restaurant, swimming pool and tennis courts. Repair workshop, osmosis treatment centre. Full brokerage service listing over 200 boats. VHF Ch37 and 80.

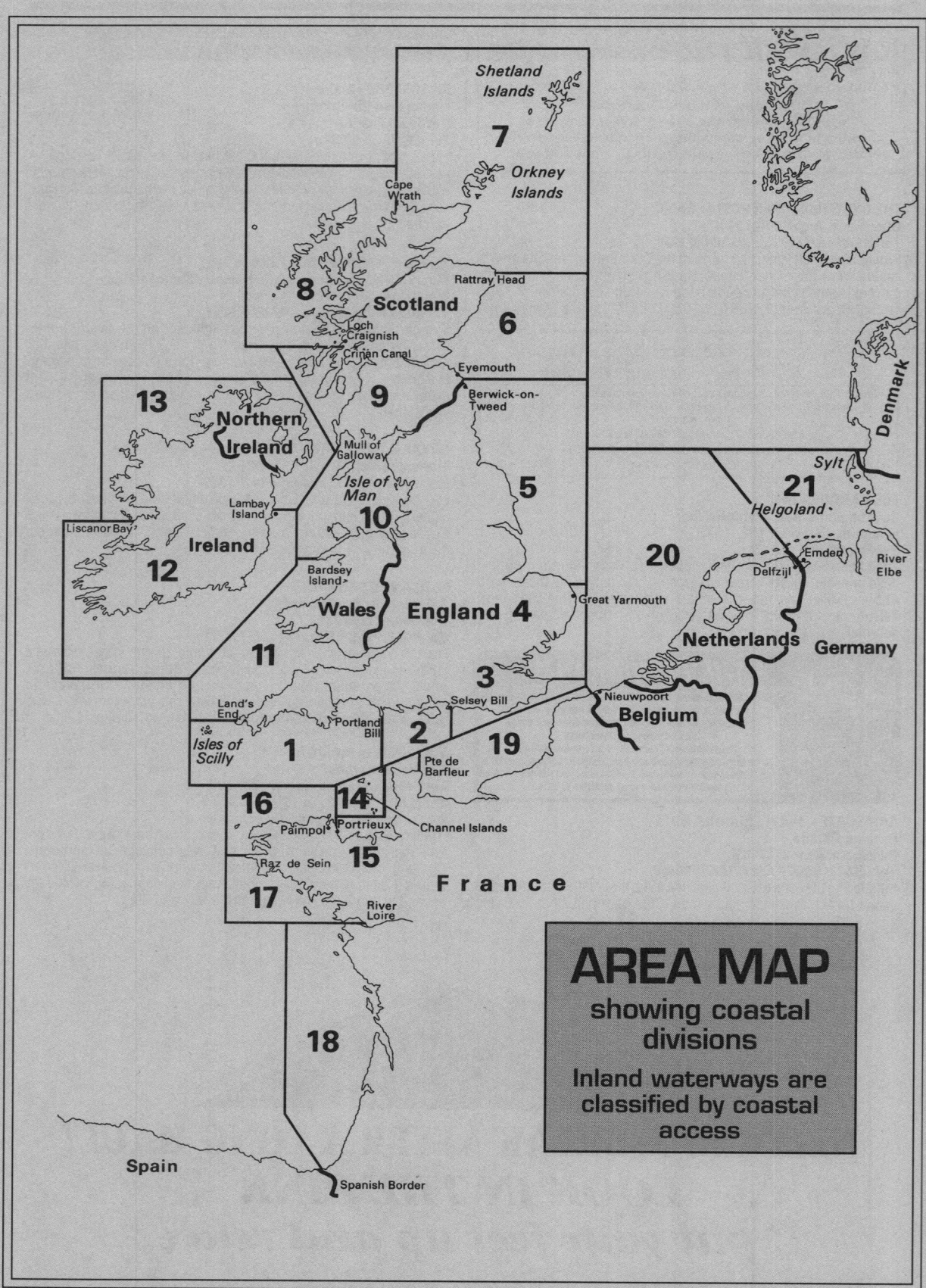

AREA MAP

showing coastal divisions

Inland waterways are classified by coastal access

Coastal and Waterways Services Directory - Area by Area

SOUTH WEST ENGLAND (AREA 1)
Scilly Isles to Portland Bill

ADMIRAL PRIVATE HIRE TAXIS
2 The Stables, Northford Road, Dartmouth, Devon TQ6 9EP. Tel (01803) 834315 Private hire taxi service nationwide from the South Hams.

ALL SPARS (KEMP SOUTHWEST)
The Boathouse, Commercial Road, Penryn, Falmouth, Cornwall TR10 8AE. Tel (01326) 374177 Fax (01326) 377696 Regional centre for SELDÉN and KEMP integrated sailing systems. Full range of rigging services on-site and mobile. Large and comprehensively stocked chandlery to cover all yachting requirements. Support and back-up for retail and trade alike.

ATLANTIC SPARS (KEMP WEST)
The Loft, Mayors Avenue, Dartmouth, Devon TQ6 9NG. Tel (01803) 833322 Fax (01803) 835855 Regional centre for SELDÉN and KEMP integrated sailing systems. Services include standing and running rigging, repairs, custom spars and furling systems. Aluminium design and fabrications for industry. Official suppliers to the BT Global Challenge.

BRIXHAM YACHT SUPPLIES LTD
72 Middle Street, Brixham, Devon TQ5 8EJ. Tel (01803) 882290 We stock a complete range of sailing and leisure clothing. English and Continental pure wool traditional knitwear. Camping accessories.

CALIBRA MARINE INTERNATIONAL
26 Foss Street, Dartmouth, Devon TQ6 9DR. Tel (01803) 833094 Fax (01803) 833615 e-mail: calibra1@aol.com A complete boating centre. Marine and architectural rigging service. Sail makers, repairs and valeting. All types of canvas work. Boat brokerage, new and used. Yacht management services. Agents for Nemo, Z-Spar, Whitlock, Lewmar, Norseman and many others.

THE CANVAS FACTORY
5 Foss Street, Dartmouth, Devon TQ6 9DW. Tel/Fax (01803) 832186 Custom-made sailcloth canvas goods for the boat and home. Traditional patterns and one-offs in a range of distinctive colours in both 100% cotton and weatherproof acrylic. Also wide range of smocks, fleeces and fisherman's jumpers.

CARDINAL YACHTS
12A Grafton Court, Grafton Road, Torquay, Devon TQ1 1UP. Tel/Fax (01803) 212954 Mobile: 0860 906390 e-mail: cardinal.yachts@eclipse.co.uk Sail and power deliveries worldwide by experienced, commercial yachtmasters. Take the cheapest Mediterranean route with our combined sea and road service. Owners welcome. As an RYA recognised sea school we offer tuition at all levels.

THE CARTOON GALLERY (Wavelength Design)
37 Lower Street, Dartmouth, Devon TQ6 9AN. Tel/Fax (01803) 834466 Tel (01803) 834425 Evenings Rick, the International Cartoonist specialises in hand coloured and personalised sailing cartoon prints (eg A3 £10). Commissions are carried out in Rick's Dartmouth gallery and studio. Prints available by mail order. Telephone or fax for details.

CHALLENGER MARINE
Freeman's Wharf, Falmouth Road, Penryn, Cornwall TR10 8AS. Tel (01326) 377222 Fax (01326) 377800 Marine engineers, chandlery, boatyard. Main Volvo Penta dealer, marina berths, brokerage, Bombard and Zodiac inflatables' dealer.

DART MARINA
Sandquay, Dartmouth, Devon TQ6 9PH. Tel (01803) 833351 Fax (01803) 832307 High quality 110-berth marina on the fabulous river Dart, opposite the Dart Marina hotel. A superb situation with all amenities, 24-hour security, hotel and restaurant, showers, baths and laundry, fuel berth, holding tank pump-out facility and a warm welcome to all visitors.

DARTHAVEN MARINA LTD
Brixham Road, Kingswear, Dartmouth, Devon TQ6 0SG. Tel (01803) 752242 Fax (01803) 752722 Marina Office: (01803) 752545 Chandlery: (01803) 752733 Fax: (01803) 752790 All types of repair facilities available. Fully trained staff. 30-ton mobile hoist available all states of tide. Extensive chandlery open 7 days a week. Agents for Autohelm/Raytheon, Cetrek, B&G, Simrad Stowe, Navico, Simpson Lawrence, Sowester, International Paint, Webasto, Yanmar Main Agents, Volvo Penta ASW and Vetus sales and service. Visitors welcome. 24-hour engineering call-out service. Mobile numbers 0411 404 259 and 0467 250 787

DUCHY OF CORNWALL

Harbour Office, St Mary's, Isles of Scilly, Cornwall TR21 0HU. Tel/Fax (01720) 422768 Port of St Mary's, Isles of Scilly - 38 visitor moorings. New visitor centre, hot showers, toilets, launching facilities, winter storage, security lockers, fuel and fresh water. 5 minutes from town centre. Ferry terminal and airport close by. Contact Harbour Master for more information.

EXONIA EUROPEAN MARINE TRANSPORT

The Sidings, Heathfield, Newton Abbot, Devon TQ12 0JB. Tel (01626) 836688 Fax (01626) 836831 Europe's premier overland marine transport company, 25 years' experience, expertise cross border formalities, documentation, notifications, escorts, permits and schedules. Highly experienced well briefed drivers with a fully qualified back-up team. *Indubitably the best.*

FALMOUTH MARINA

North Parade, Falmouth, Cornwall TR11 2TD. Tel (01326) 316620 Fax (01326) 313939 The most westerly marina in England, Falmouth is an ideal starting point for a cruise to the Channel Islands, Brittany or the Scilly Isles. The marina offers fully serviced permanent and visitor berths with a professional and friendly service you would expect from a PREMIER marina.

THE GUNFIELD

Castle Road, Dartmouth, Devon TQ6 0JN. Tel (01803) 834843 Fax (01803) 834772 e-mail: enquiry@gunfield.co.uk VHF Ch M2 or Ch 37. Waterfront position with 10 impressive en suite bedrooms, central heating etc, all command fantastic river views. Restaurant offers modestly priced, delicious Mediterranean cuisine. Continental bar and lounge open to non-residents. Large terraces and gardens, BBQs during summer. Pontoon and deep water moorings.

MARINE INSTRUMENTS

The Bosun's Locker, Upton Slip, Falmouth, Cornwall TR11 3DQ. Tel (01326) 312414 Books and charts. DTp Certificated.

THE MAYFLOWER INTERNATIONAL MARINA

Ocean Quay, Richmond Walk, Plymouth, Devon PL1 4LS. Tel (01752) 556663/567106 Fax (01752) 606896 Plymouth's only Five-Gold Anchor Marina. Known for its extensive facilities, courtesy and security. Owned by berth holders and run to a very high standard.

MECTRONICS MARINE

PO Box 8, Newton Abbot, Devon TQ12 1FF. Tel (01626) 334453 LIGHT ACTIVATED SWITCHES, rugged solid state devices to automatically switch anchor lights at sunset and sunrise. NAVLIGHT SELECTORS, protected enclosed rotary switches internally connected to ensure approved navigation light combination on auxiliary sailing vessels. NAVLIGHT STATUS MONITORS, diagnostic displays on which the appropriate indicator flashes quickly or slowly in the event of a short or open circuit fault. Also drives an optional, audible warning device.

NOSS-ON-DART MARINA

Noss Quay, Dartmouth, Devon TQ6 0EA. Tel (01803) 833351 Fax (01803) 832307 Peacefully located on the east shore of the river Dart, this relaxing marina is the perfect base for cruising yachtsmen. Extensive parking, chandlery, repair and lift-out facilities, easy access from London and the Midlands. Boat taxi to Dartmouth.

OCEAN SPIRIT SAILING CHARTERS LTD

The Canvas Factory, 5 Foss Street, Dartmouth, Devon TQ6 9DW. Tel/Fax (0)1803 832186 e-mail: ADBriscoe@compu serve.com MALDIVES SAIL/DIVE - Beautiful 61' yacht, with experienced crew await your arrival. Over 1000 unspoiled islands and virgin diving are on offer from the Maldives oldest luxury yacht operator.

OUTRIGGERS/UPPER DECK MARINE

Albert Quay, Fowey, Cornwall PL23 1AQ. Tel (01726) 833233 Fax (01726) 833265 'Outriggers' casual and marine clothing, footwear, nautical gifts, Admiralty chart agent and marine books.

THE PANDORA INN

Restronguet Creek, Mylor, Falmouth, Cornwall TR11 5ST. Tel (01326) 372678 Fax (01326) 372678 Thatched creek-side inn with floating pontoon. Morning coffee, delicious bar meals, cream teas and fine dining in the superb Andrew Miller restaurant (entitles yachtsmen to free mooring). Telephone, showers and water available. Open all day in the summer.

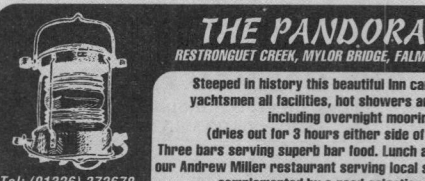
PETER CUMBERLIDGE PHOTO LIBRARY

Sunways, Slapton, Kingsbridge, Devon TQ7 2PR. Tel (01548) 580461 Fax (01548) 580588 Large selection of nautical, travel and coastal colour transparencies. Specialities boats, harbours, lighthouses, marinas and inland waterways in Britain, Northern Europe, the Mediterranean and the Baltic. Commissions undertaken.

PLYMOUTH YACHT HAVEN
Shaw Way, Mount Batten, Plymouth, Devon PL9 9XH. Tel (01752) 404231 Fax (01752) 484177 Position: Southern side of cattewater, sheltered from prevailing winds by Mountbatten Peninsula. Open: All year, 24 hours. Radio: VHF Ch37 and 80. Callsign: Clovelly Bay. Berths: 180 berths, vessels up to 150', some fore and afts, visitors welcome. Facilities: electricity, water, 24-hour security, workshop, chandlery, brokerage, showers, laundry, diesel. Calor gas, etc. NEW MARINA NOW OPEN.

PORT FALMOUTH BOATYARD
North Parade, Falmouth, Cornwall TR11 2TB. Tel (01326) 313248 Fax (01326) 319395 Powered hoist and slipway. Cradle with 100 tons capacity. Shipwrights, marine engineering, hard standing and friendly efficient service.

PORT OF TRURO
Harbour Office, Town Quay, Truro, Cornwall. Tel (01872) 272130 Fax (01872) 225346 VHF Ch. 12. Facilities for the yachtsman include visitor pontoons located at Turnaware Bar, Ruan Creek and Boscawen Park. Visitor moorings at Woodbury. Quay facilities at Truro with free showers and toilets. Chemical toilet disposal, fresh water, electricity and garbage disposal.

RIVERSFORD HOTEL
Limers Lane, Bideford, Devon EX39 2RG. Tel (01237) 474239 Peace and tranquility in gardens beside the river Torridge. A relaxing retreat with convenient slipway close by. Excellent restaurant with efficient, friendly service with a choice of imaginative food and wine from our extensive menu and wine list. Comfortable, flexible lounge bar.

ROYAL WESTERN YACHT CLUB
Queen Anne's Battery, Plymouth, Devon PL4 0TW. Tel (01752) 660071 Fax (01752) 224299 Home of shorthanded sailing. Visiting yachtsmen welcome. Mooring facilities available.

THE SEA CHEST NAUTICAL BOOKS & CHARTS
Queen Anne's Battery Marina, Plymouth, Devon PL4 0LP. Tel (01752) 222012 Fax (01752) 252679 Admiralty Chart Agent. Worldwide mail order service.

SOUTHDOWN MARINA
Southdown Quay, Millbrook, Cornwall PL10 1HG. Tel/Fax (01752) 823084 32-berth marina on edge of river Tamar in quiet location behind Rame Peninsula. Plymouth is just across the river. Quayside berths available for large vessels. Dry Berthing. 24-hour security. DIY facilities available.

ST MAWES SAILING CLUB
No 1 The Quay, St Mawes, Cornwall TR2 5DG. Tel (01326) 270686 Fax (01326) 270040 Quayside sailing club in centre of village. Visitor moorings in harbour. Private slip, launching and recovery facilities. Dinghy park, post box, showers. Visitors encouraged. Chandlery and sail repairs to order. No marina but a warm welcome awaits.

SUTTON HARBOUR MARINA
Sutton Harbour, Plymouth, Devon PL4 0RA. Tel (01752) 204186 Fax (01752) 205403 A superb sheltered marina with 24-hour access and fully serviced visitor berths with full on-shore facilities in the city's historic Elizabethan quarter. Just a few minutes stroll from the shops, restaurants and entertainment of the city centre.

TREVOR VINCETT DELIVERIES
Coombe Cottage, 9 Swannaton Road, Dartmouth, Devon TQ6 9RL. Tel/Fax (01803) 833757 Mobile 07970 208799 Worldwide delivery of yachts and commercial vessels undertaken at short notice by RYA/DoT Yachtmaster Ocean (with commercial endorsement). Over 28 years' experience including three masted schooners, tugs, motor yachts and hi-tec racers. For instant quotes call/fax 01803 833757.

UPPER DECK MARINE/OUTRIGGERS
Albert Quay, Fowey, Cornwall PL23 1AQ. Tel (01726) 832287 Fax (01726) 833265 Chandlery, fastenings, paints, cords, fenders, anchors, compasses, lifejackets, Gaz. Leading names in waterproofs and warm wear.

WARD & McKENZIE (South West) LTD
Little Brook Cottage, East Portlemouth, Salcombe, Devon TQ8 8PW. Tel (01548) 511590 Fax (01548) 511539 National and International Marine Surveyors, Technical and Legal Consultants. Contact: Chris Olsen - Mobile 0370 758505,

WEIR QUAY BOATYARD
Heron's Reach, Bere Alston, Devon PL20 7BT. Tel (01822) 840474 Fax (01822) 840948 Deepwater swinging moorings, shore storage, full boatyard facilities and services, cranage to 12 tons, repairs, maintenance, slipway. A traditional boatyard at affordable rates in *a superb setting* on the Tamar, with excellent security.

WINTERS MARINE LTD (Lincombe Boatyard)
Lincombe, Salcombe, Devon TQ8 8NQ. Tel (01548) 843580 e-mail: lincombeboatyard@eclipse.co.uk Deep water pontoon moorings. Winter storage for 150 boats. All maintenance and repair facilities. Slipway capacity 30 tonnes. Inflatable craft sales and service. Liferaft surveys and repairs. Short and long-term liferaft hire.

CENTRAL SOUTHERN ENGLAND
(AREA 2)
Portland Bill to Selsey Bill

AQUA-MARINE MANUFACTURING (UK) LTD
216 Fair Oak Road, Bishopstoke, Eastleigh, Hampshire SO50 8NJ. Tel (01703) 694949 Fax (01703) 601381 Sales Fax Hotline: (01703) 601188 e-mail: sales@aqua-marine.co.uk Manufacturers and distributors of chandlery, including: Engel refrigeration, Dutton-Lainson winches, Anchor fenders, Rule pumps, Aquaflow water systems, TFX steering and controls. Admiralty small craft charts, Aquameter compasses, POWER 1st battery charges, Danforth anchors, Aqua-Signal lights, Techimpex cookers.

B P S C MARINE SERVICES
Logistics House, Second Avenue, Millbrook, Southampton, Hampshire SO15 0LP. Tel (01703) 510561 Fax (01703) 510560 BPSC offer a fast efficient repair service on a wide range of nautical and survey instruments. Free estimates and advice. A comprehensive range of spares are carried, most of which can be despatched same day. Instruments commissioned. Compass adjusting service.

BEAULIEU RIVER MANAGEMENT LTD
Harbour Master's Office, Bucklers Hard Yacht Harbour, Beaulieu, Hampshire SO42 7XB. Tel (01590) 616200 Fax (01590) 616211 110-berth yacht harbour (pontoon berths), fully serviced with back-up facilities of historic Bucklers Hard village. Agamemnon boatyard - 290 swinging moorings let on annual basis. Visiting craft welcome. Capacity 100+ pile/pontoon.

BIRDHAM SHIPYARD LTD
Birdham Pool, Chichester, West Sussex PO20 7BG. Tel (01243) 512310 Fax (01243) 513163 Quiet, picturesque marina in Chichester harbour. Moorings available for boats up to 55' overall and 5'6' draught. Chandlery and all boatyard sevices available. Visitors welcome.

BLUNDELL HARLING LTD
Lynch Lane, Weymouth, Dorset DT4 9DW. Tel (01305) 206007 Fax (01305) 760598 e-mail: sales@blundellharling.co.uk Manufacturer of chart table navigation equipment.

BOOK CABIN
Unit 20, Canutes Pavilion, Ocean Village, Southampton, Hampshire SO14 3JS. Tel (01703) 211199 Fax (01703) 338488 Nautical and general booksellers.

CARBOSPARS LTD
Hamble Point, School Lane, Hamble, Southampton, Hampshire SO31 4JD. Tel (01703) 456736 Fax (01703) 455361 e-mail: carbospars@compuserve.com Design and manufacture of carbon spars for racing and cruising and the award-winning AeroRig ®.

CHICHESTER MARINA
Birdham, Chichester, West Sussex PO20 7EJ. Tel (01243) 512731 Fax (01243) 513472 Situated in the north east corner of Chichester harbour, Chichester Marina enjoys one of the most attractive locations in the country. With 1100 berths, Chichester offers a unique combination of service, facilities, security and friendliness, unparalleled in UK marinas. Chichester Marina is a PREMIER Marina.

COMPASS WATERSPORTS
Ridout Yard, Great Cheverell, Devizes, Wiltshire SN10 5XZ. Tel (01380) 813100 Fax (01380) 813900 Direct marine mail order of hardware, electronics and clothing at very competitive prices.

CONVOI EXCEPTIONNEL
Castleton House, High Street, Hamble, Southampton, Hampshire SO31 4HA. Tel (01703) 453045 Fax (01703) 454551 International marine haulage and abnormal load consultants. Specialist services up to 40 tons.

COWES YACHT HAVEN
Vectis Yard, High Street, Cowes, Isle of Wight PO31 7BD. Tel (01983) 299975 Fax (01983) 200332 Cowes Yacht Haven is the Solent's premier sailing event centre offering 200 fully serviced berths right in the heart of Cowes. Our improved facilities, capability and location ensures the perfect venue and profile for every kind of boating event.

CREWSAVER LTD
Crewsaver House, Mumby Road, Gosport, Hampshire PO12 1AQ. Tel (01705) 528621 MARLIN - Leading manufacturer of stylish, comfortable, hardwearing wetsuits, lifejackets, buoyancy aids and accessories for all seasons and all-surface watersports. YAK - Catering for all canoeing needs from cags and decks to long johns and buoyancy aids.

CRUISAIR UK LTD
26 Old Wareham Road, Poole, Dorset BH12 4QR. Tel (01202) 716469 Fax (01202) 716478 Marine air conditioning.

DEACONS BOATYARD LTD
Bursledon Bridge, Southampton, Hampshire SO31 8AZ. Tel (01703) 402253 Fax (01703) 405665 This yard has all major services for yachtsmen. Moorings, hardstanding, repairs, marine engineers, riggers, chandlery and brokerage - new yacht sales. Deacons are UK importers for Feeling Yachts.

DEAN & REDDYHOFF LTD - EAST COWES MARINA
Clarence Road, East Cowes, Isle of Wight PO32 6HA. Tel (01983) 293983 Fax (01983) 299276 This existing marina (but new to Dean and Reddyhoff) is undergoing a facelift which will include dredging, new pontoons, toilets and showers and possibly a clubhouse. Regular yachtsmen, visitors and rallies will be welcome as before.

DEAN & REDDYHOFF LTD - HASLAR MARINA
Haslar Road, Gosport, Hampshire PO12 1NU. Tel (01705) 601201 Fax (01705) 602201 Haslar Marina is just inside the entrance of Portsmouth harbour on the Gosport side. Included in the 600 berths is a visitors' area which is adjacent to a converted lightship with bar facilities and excellent toilets and showers.

DEAN & REDDYHOFF LTD - WEYMOUTH MARINA
70 Commercial Road, Weymouth, Dorset DT4 8NA. Tel (01305) 767576 Fax (01305) 767575 This new marina in the inner harbour of Weymouth provides facilities for visitors which are proving very popular. The marina is right next to Weymouth's high street, and the area has a multitude of pubs and restaurants.

DIVERSE YACHT SERVICES
Unit 12, Hamble Yacht Services, Port Hamble, Hamble, Hampshire SO31 4NN. Tel (01703) 453399 Fax (01703) 455288 Marine electronics and electrics. Supplied and installed. Specialists in racing yachts. Suppliers of 'Loadsense' Loadcells for marine applications.

ELKINS BOATYARD
Tidesreach, 18 Convent Meadow, The Quay, Christchurch, Dorset BH23 1BD. Tel (01202) 483141 All boatyard facilities. Moorings alongside, water and electricity, storage ashore, repairs. Boats up to 45', 10 tons maximum, haul-out.

EMSWORTH YACHT HARBOUR LTD

Thorney Road, Emsworth, Hampshire PO10 8BP. Tel (01243) 377727 Fax (01243) 373432 Friendly marina in Chichester harbour. Water, electricity, diesel, Calor gas, 25-tonne mobile crane, slipways, hard-standing and storage areas. Showers and toilets, car parking, chandlery, engineers and boat repairs.

EURONAV NAVIGATION

20 The Slipway, Port Solent, Portsmouth, Hampshire PO6 4TR. Tel (01705) 373855 Fax (01705) 325800 Electronic charting specialists, offering the seaPro 2000 range of PC-based chart plotting systems, ARCS, Livechart 'B' and BSB top quality electronic charts. Products are available from good chandlers or direct from Euronav e-mail:http://www.euronav.co.uk

GREENHAM MARINE

King's Saltern Road, Lymington, Hampshire SO41 9QD. Tel (01590) 671144 Fax (01590) 679517 Greenham Marine can offer yachtsmen one of the most comprehensive selections of marine electronic equipment currently available. Also at Poole/Weymouth 01202 676363 and Emsworth/Chichester 01243 378314.

GenACis

Power House, Gordon Road, Winchester, Hampshire SO23 7DD. Tel (01962) 841828 Fax (01962) 841834 Dolphin water cooled diesel generators, 3 - 16 KVA.

INTERNATIONAL PAINT

24-30 Canute Road, Southampton, Hampshire SO14 3PB. Tel (01703) 226722 Fax (01703) 335975 International Paint is the leading supplier of quality paints, epoxies, varnishes and antifoulings to the marine industry. Over half the world's pleasure craft are protected by International products.

K T Y YACHTS

Unit 12, Universal Marina, Crableck Lane, Sarisbury Green, Southampton, Hampshire SO31 7ZN. Tel (0385) 335189 Fax (01489) 570302 First aid at sea and ship captain's medical courses. Qualified, practical instruction from a sailor and paramedic.

KEMP MASTS LTD (Seldén Masts Ltd)

Duncan Road, Park Gate, Southampton, Hampshire SO31 1BX. Tel (01489) 484000 Fax (01489) 487487 Now renamed Seldén, this is the UK manufacturing and supply base for the Seldén range of masts, booms, poles, kickers, mainsail-furling and headsail-furling to suit production yachts upto 45' and custom yachts from upto 70'.

KEMP SAILS LTD

Unit 2, Sandford Lane Industrial Estate, Wareham, Dorset BH20 4DY. Tel (01929) 554308 Fax (01929) 554350 e-mail: kemp@eluk.co.uk www.eluk.co.uk/kemp Sailmakers and reefing system. Suppliers of sail handling equipment.

KENDALL BECKER LTD

Kendalls, West Bracklesham, Bracklesham Bay, Chichester, Sussex PO20 8PH. Tel (01243) 672142 Fax (01243) 672068 Freephone: 0800 975 5795 Marine insurance specialists for yachts and motor cruisers throughout the world. Vessels over 20 years old a speciality (surveys not required). Immediate quotes and cover. Call us now.

LANGSTONE HARBOUR BOARD

Harbour Office, Ferry Road, Hayling Island, Hampshire PO11 0DG. Tel (01705) 463419 Fax (01705) 467144 All boatyard facilities. Deep water and tidal moorings available. Water, electricity and diesel. Summer and winter storage. Public slipways. 6-ton crane. Landrover vessel and trailer recovery services.

LEWMAR MARINE LTD

Southmoor Lane, Havant, Hampshire PO9 1JJ. Tel (01705) 471841 Fax (01705) 476043 Manufacturers of winches, windlasses, hatches, hardware, hydraulics and marine thrusters for boats ranging in size from 25' to 300' LOA.

LYMINGTON YACHT HAVEN

King's Saltern Road, Lymington, Hampshire SO4 9XY. Tel (01590) 677071 Fax (01590) 678186 Perfectly situated at the mouth of the Lymington river giving instant access to the Western Solent. Full marina services, boatyard, brokerage, diesel, petrol and gas.

J & H MARSH & McLENNAN (UK) LTD

Yacht Practice, Havelock Chambers, Queens Terrace, Southampton, Hampshire SO14 3PP. Tel (01703) 318300 Fax (01703) 318391 A member of the largest insurance broking firm in the world with associated offices in Antibes and Fort Lauderdale. Specialists in yacht insurance for craft cruising UK, Mediterranean, Caribbean and US waters.

R J MUIR

22 Seymour Close, Chandlers Ford, Eastleigh, Southampton SO5 2JE. Tel (01703) 261042 Books and Charts. DTp Certificated.

PARKER & KAY SAILMAKERS - SOUTH

Port Hamble Marina, Satchell Lane, Hamble, Southampton, Hampshire SO31 5QD. Tel (01703) 458213 Fax (01703) 458228 A complete sailmaking service, from small repairs to the construction of custom designed sails for racing or cruising yachts. Covers constructed for sail and powercraft, plus the supply of all forms of sail handling hardware.

PARKSTONE YACHT CLUB

Pearce Avenue, Parkstone, Poole, Dorset BH14 8EH. Tel (01202) 743610 Fax (01202) 716394 Deep water club haven facilities in Poole harbour. Access at all states of the tide. Berths for yachts up to 15 metres. Facilities include electricity, fresh water, toilets and showers. Visitors welcome by appointment. Club bar and restaurant.

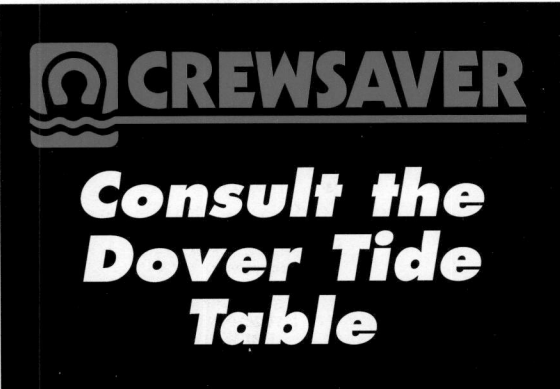

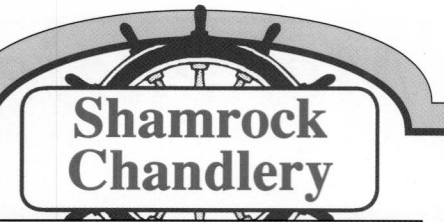

PETERS & MAY LTD
18 Canute Road, Ocean Village, Southampton, Hampshire SO14 3FJ. Tel (01703) 480480 Fax (01703) 480400 The 'Round the World' specialists in shipping, transporting, cradling yachts and powerboats. Weekly service to USA, Far East, Mediterranean, Middle East and Caribbean.

PORT SOLENT
South Lockside, Port Solent, Portsmouth, Hampshire PO6 4TJ. Tel (01705) 210765 Fax (01705) 324241 From a marine superstore and outstanding slipway services to restaurants, bars and multiscreen cinema, Port Solent offers visitors and berth holders superb facilities, unsurpassed by any other UK marina. Port Solent is a PREMIER Marina.

PREMIER MARINAS LTD
South Lockside, Port Solent, Portsmouth, Hampshire PO6 4TJ. Tel (01705) 214145 Fax (01705) 221876 At our marinas we're always on hand to help you. PREMIER GROUP MARINAS - Beaucette - Chichester - Falmouth - Port Solent.

R K MARINE LTD
Hamble River Boatyard, Bridge Road, Swanwick, Southampton, Hampshire SO31 7EB. Tel (01489) 583572 Fax (01489) 583172 Volvo Penta main dealer with all marina facilities.

RADIO SCHOOL LTD
33 Island Close, Hayling Island, Hampshire PO11 0NJ. Tel/Fax (01705) 466450 Regular weekend courses/exams for the NEW GMDSS VHF and SSB/Sat. Radiotelephone Operator's Certificates in UK's only permanent, fully equipped classroom solely dedicated to training small-boat sailors on a full-time, professional basis. Established 1980.

REGIS ELECTRONICS LTD
Regis House, Quay Hill, Lymington, Hampshire SO41 3AR. Tel (01590) 679251/679176 Fax (01590) 679910 (also at Cowes, Southampton & Chichester). Sales, service and installation of marine electronic equipment. Leading south coast agents for AUTOHELM, FURUNO, RAYTHEON, CETREK, STOWE, ROBERTSON, A.P. NAVIGATOR, GARMIN, KELVIN HUGHES and other manufacturers of quality marine electronic equipment. Competitively priced quotations (including owner familiarisation and sea trials) forwarded by return of post.

RIDGE WHARF YACHT CENTRE
Ridge, Wareham, Dorset BH20 5BG. Tel (01929) 552650 Fax (01929) 554434 Marina with full boatyard facilities. Winter lay-up and fuels etc.

ROB PERRY MARINE
Monmouth Beach, Lyme Regis, Dorset DT7 3LE. Tel (01297) 445816 Fax (01297) 445886 Outboard and inboard sales and service. Wetsuits, lifejackets. Some chandlery. Fast efficient service. Marine surveys and insurance.

ROYAL AIR FORCE YACHT CLUB
Riverside House, Rope Walk, Hamble, Southampton, Hampshire SO31 4HD. Tel (01703) 452208 Fax (01703) 458001 Superb club, open to non-service members, on the river Hamble. Offers many amenities. New waterfront, dock, scrubbing pile, bar and restaurant, showers and laundry. Excellent accommodation available - 3 bedrooms and 1 en suit - bookings essential. Full programme of racing, cruising and rallies. Welcomes visiting yachtsmen.

S P SYSTEMS
Love Lane, Cowes, Isle of Wight PO31 7EU. Tel (01983) 284000 Fax (01983) 298453 Epoxy resins for laminating, bonding, coating and filling. Usable with wood, GRP, concrete. GRP/FRP materials including glass, carbon and Kevlar fibres. Structural engineering of GRP and composite materials. Technical advice service.

SEA VENTURES YACHT CHARTER
Lymington Yacht Haven, Lymington, Hampshire SO41 3QD. Tel (01590) 672472 Fax (01590) 671924 Website: www.c-ventures.co.uk Based in Lymington our large modern fleet offers both skippered and bareboat charters to Greece, Guernsey and the Canaries. A large selection of yachts from 29' to 52'. Corporate and team building and yacht management also available.

SELDÉN MASTS LTD
Duncan Road, Park Gate, Southampton, Hampshire SO31 1BX. Tel (01489) 484000 Fax (01489) 487487 Formerly Kemp Masts this is the UK manufacturing arm of the Seldén Group. Now incorporating PROCTOR, and relocated at Park Gate, Seldén is the UK's largest spar maker - covering the whole range from performance dinghies up to 70' yachts.

SHAMROCK CHANDLERY
Shamrock Quay, William Street, Northam, Southampton, Hampshire SO14 5QL. Tel (01703) 632725 Fax (01703) 225611 e-mail: sales@shamrock.co.uk Website: http://www.shamrock.co.uk Situated on Shamrock Quay, a busy working yard with a pub, restaurant and boutiques. Shamrock Chandlery is renowned for extensive quality stocks and service, and is widely used by both the trade and boat owners. Excellent mail order facilities - Order Hotline 01703 225746.

SHOOSMITHS & HARRISON
Russell House, 1550 Parkway, Solent Business Park, Fareham, Hampshire PO15 7AG. Tel (01489) 881010/616960 Fax (01489) 881000 Marine solicitors advising on yacht sales, purchase and charter, insurance claims, disputes, debt recovery and general advice for the yachting community. Contact: Jonathan Hadley-Piggin.

SILLETTE SONIC LTD
Unit 5 Stepnell Reach, 541 Blandford Road, Hamworthy, Poole, Dorset BH16 5BW. Tel (01202) 621631 Fax (01202) 625877 Distribution Depot: Sillette manufactures a range of propulsion systems - stern drive, saildrives etc and sterngear. Markets Radice and Gori fixed and folding propellers. Acts as agents for Morse Controls, Yanmar and Lombardini marine engines, and Fuji Robin generators. See Area 4.

SOUTHERN SPAR SERVICES (KEMP SOUTH)
Shamrock Quay, William Street, Northam, Southampton, Hampshire SO14 5QL. Mobile 0850 736540 Tel (01703) 331714 Fax (01703) 230559 Regional centre for SELDEN and KEMP integrated sailing systems. Convectional and furling spars for UK and abroad. Also headsail and mainsail reefing, deck equipment, toe rails and stanchion bases. All forms of repairs and modifications undertaken.

SPARKES YACHT HARBOUR LTD
38 Wittering Road, Hayling Island, Hampshire PO11 9SR. Tel (01705) 463572 Fax (01705) 465741 Sparkes Marina - a small friendly, family run business offering all the facilities you require including access at all states of the tide to a depth of 2 metres at lowest low water springs. In addition to marina berths, accessible through a security gate, we also offer dry boat sailing, moorings, storage ashore plus full maintenance facilities, new boat sales and brokerage, chandlery and restaurant.

Sparkes Yacht Harbour and Boatyard
Hayling Island
Based at the entrance to Chichester Harbour, a small family run marina offering full Marina and Boatyard facilities with access at all states of the tide. Marina Berths - Visitors' Berths - Dry Boat Sailing - Deep Water Moorings - Drying Moorings - Pontoon Drying Berths, Marina Type Tidal Berths - Boat Movement - Storage Ashore - Brokerage - New Boat Sales -Chandlery - Restaurant
Tel: 01705 463572 Fax: 01705 465741 for more details.

SEA START
Unit 13, Hamble Point Marina, Southampton SO31 4JD. Tel 0800 88 55 00 or (01703) 458000 Fax (01703) 452666 Sea Start is the 24-hour marine breakdown service on both sides of the English Channel and the Channel Islands. Membership cost from as little as £9 per month. Join now using your credit card on 0800 88 55 00 or ring for our colour brochure.

SEA START
MEMBERSHIP
Sea Start Sales Office, Unit 13, Hamble Point Marina, Southampton SO31 4JD

24 HOURS, 365 DAYS A YEAR MECHANICAL BREAKDOWN ASSISTANCE
FREEPHONE 0800 88 55 00

TEK-TANKS
Units 5A - 5B Station Approach, Four Marks, Nr Alton, Hampshire GU34 5HN. Tel (01420) 564359 Fax (01420) 561605 e-mail: tek_tanks@compuserve.com Manufacturers and suppliers of made-to-measure and standard polypropylene water, waste and HDPE diesel tanks.

TOLLEY MARINE LTD
Unit 7, Blackhill Road West, Holton Heath Trading Park, Poole, Dorset BH16 6LS. Tel (01202) 632644 Fax (01202) 632622 Branches at Salterns Marina (01202) 706040 and Plymouth (01752) 222530. Agents for all major marine electronics manufacturers. Autohelm, B&G, Cetrek, Furuno, Garmin, Icom, Koden, Lo-Kata, MLR, Magnavox, Navico, Panasonic, Raytheon, Robertson, Sailor, Shipmate, Trimble.

TOOMER & HAYTER LTD
74 Green Road, Winton, Bournemouth, Dorset BH9 1EB. Tel (01202) 515789 Fax (01202) 538771 Marine upholstery manufacturers. Cabin and cockpit upholstery made to any shape or size. Sprung interior mattresses made to measure. Foam backed cabin lining always in stock, also carpet side lining. Visit our factory and showroom.

Quality marine upholstery manufacturers of helmsman seats, carpet lining, interior lighting, cabin lining, replacement cushions and recovering service. Reliable mail order service available by cheque or credit card. For full details and colour brochure call:
Toomer and Hayter Ltd
74 Green Road Winton Bournemouth BH9 1EB
Tel: 01202 515789 or Fax: 01202 538771

VETUS DEN OUDEN LTD
39 South Hants Industrial Park, Totton, Southampton, Hampshire SO40 3SA. Tel (01703) 861033 Fax (01703) 663142 Suppliers of marine diesel equipment, exhaust systems, steering systems, bow propellers, propellers and shafts, hatches, portlights, windows, electronic instruments, batteries, ventilators, windlasses, water and fuel tanks, chandlery items and much much more.

vetus
BOAT EQUIPMENT
VETUS DEN OUDEN LTD
39 South Hants Industrial Park, Totton, Southampton, Hants SO40 3SA
FOR VETUS BOAT EQUIPMENT INCLUDING DIESEL EQUIPMENT, HYDRAULIC STEERING, BOW PROPELLERS AND HUNDREDS OF OTHER PRODUCTS - ASK FOR FREE COLOUR CATALOGUE
TEL: SOUTHAMPTON (01703) 861033 FAX: (01703) 663142

VOSPER THORNYCROFT MARINE PRODUCTS LTD
Northarbour Road, Cosham, Hampshire PO6 3TL. Tel (01705) 383311 Fax (01705) 325133 Manufacturer and supplier of Fin stabilizers, Transverse thrusters and Vospower water jets to the luxury, commercial and naval markets worldwide.

WARD & McKENZIE (Dorset) LTD
69 Alexander Road, Parkstone, Poole, Dorset BH14 9EL. Tel (01202) 718440 National and International Marine Surveyors, Technical and Legal Consultants. Contact: Tony McGrail - Mobile 0411 329314.

WARD & McKENZIE (Portsmouth) LTD
25 Wilby Lane, Anchorage Park, Portsmouth, Hampshire PO3 5UP. Tel (01705) 655228 Fax (01705) 652570 National and International Marine Surveyors, Technical and Legal Consultants. Contact: Kevin Read.

WARD & McKENZIE (W Solent) LTD
Old Rectory, Beatrice Avenue, Whippingham, East Cowes, Isle of Wight. Tel (01983) 280010 Fax (01983) 281988 National and International Marine Surveyors, Technical and Legal Consultants. Contact: Gillian Tobin.

WARSASH NAUTICAL BOOKSHOP
6 Dibles Road, Warsash, Southampton, Hampshire SO31 9HZ. Tel (01489) 572384 Fax (01489) 885756 e-mail: alan@nautical books.co.uk Website: http://www.nautical books.co.uk Nautical bookseller and chart agent. Callers and mail order. Free new and secondhand book lists. Credit cards taken. Publishers of the Bibliography of Nautical books.

WESSEX MARINE EQUIPMENT LTD
Logistics House, 2nd Avenue Business Park, Millbrook Road East, Southampton, Hampshire SO1 0LP. Tel (01703) 510570 Books and charts.

WET & WILD GRAPHICS
7 Firefly Road, Hamble Point Marina, Hamble, Southampton, Hampshire SO31 4NB. Tel (01703) 458332 Fax (01703) 456830 Supply and application of vinyl graphics, signboards, banners and flags. Specialist materials for sails and spinnakers. Brochure available for mail order boat names. Deadlines never a problem!!!

WEYMOUTH OLD HARBOUR
Weymouth & Portland Borough Council, Borough Engineers Department, Municipal Offices, North Quay, Weymouth, Dorset DT4 8TA. Tel (01305) 206363/206423 Fax (01305) 206276 e-mail: cflowers@weymouth.gov.uk Website: http://www.weymouth.gov.uk/marine.htm Access at all stages of tide. Visitor berths in the centre of prime tourist resort with shops, restaurants and night life all at hand. Diesel fuelling from pontoon or tanker. Chandlery and repair facilities available.

SOUTH EAST ENGLAND   (AREA 3)
Selsey Bill to North Foreland

ADEC MARINE LTD
4 Masons Avenue, Croydon, Surrey CR0 1EH. Tel 0181-686 9717 Fax 0181-680 9912 e-mail: adecmarine@ukbusiness.com Approved liferaft service station for south east UK. Additionally we hire and sell new rafts and sell a complete range of safety equipment for yachts including pyrotechnics, fire extinguishers, lifejackets, buoys and a buoyancy bag system.

BRIGHTON MARINA
Brighton Marina Village, Brighton, East Sussex BN2 5UF. Tel (01273) 819919 Fax (01273) 675082 Britain's largest marina (1600 pontoon berths) with marina village under development. TYHA Five-Gold Anchors. Full boatyard and shore facilities. Brokerage and boat sales. Club racing throughout the year. Group visits, rallies welcome.

EAST SUSSEX SAILING
4 Arun Path, Uckfield, East Sussex TN22 1NL. Tel/Fax (01825) 769578 Mobile 0402 275165 Based in the heart of East Sussex, we conduct RYA recognised shorebased navigation and VHF courses which can be tailored to suit your individual requirements. Own boat tuition and yacht/power deliveries are also available.

HIGHWAY MARINE LTD
Pillory Gate Wharf, Strand Street, Sandwich, Kent CT13 9EU. Tel (01304) 613925 Fax (01304) 614814 Pontoon moorings available in town of Sandwich. Lift-out facilities and hard standing, water, electricity. OMC main dealer with full service centre. New engine sales. Brokerage and chandlery. Excellent waterside apartments available, call (01304) 611433 for details.

LANGNEY MARINE SERVICES LTD
Sovereign Harbour Marina, Pevensey Bay Road, Eastbourne, East Sussex BN23 6JH. Tel (01323) 470244 Fax (01323) 470255 We offer a complete service to the boat owner offering repairs on all types of engines, GRP, steel, wood, electronics, rigging, cleaning, etc. We are also contractors to the RNLI.

LOMBARD GENERAL INSURANCE CO LTD
Lombard House, 182 High Street, Tonbridge, Kent TN9 1BY. Tel (01732) 376317 Fax (01732) 773117 One of the UK's largest specialist yacht underwriters and risk carriers. For full details of the range of insurance products available for all types of pleasurecraft, please contact your local marine insurance broker or intermediary.

ODYSSEUS YACHTING HOLIDAYS
33 Grand Parade, Brighton, East Sussex BN2 2QA. Tel (01273) 695094 Fax (01273) 688855 Templecraft Yacht Charters are bonded tour operators specialising in independent yacht charter holidays in the Mediterranean and in the Caribbean, and as Odysseus Yachting Holidays in flotilla sailing holidays in Corfu and the Ionian islands.

PROP PROTECTOR
74 Abingdon Road, Maidstone, Kent ME16 9EE. Tel (01622) 728738 Fax (01622) 727973 Prevention is better than cure when it comes to avoiding a fouled propeller. Prop Protectors are now accepted worldwide as the first line of defence against stray rope, netting, weed and plastic bags.

QUEENBOROUGH HARBOUR
Town Quay, South Street, Queenborough, Isle of Sheppey, Kent ME11 5AF. Tel/Fax (01795) 662051 Moorings available in sought after position close to Thames and Medway estuaries.

RAMSGATE ROYAL HARBOUR MARINA
Harbour Office, Military Road, Ramsgate, Kent CT11 9LQ. Tel (01843) 592277 Fax (01843) 590941 Ramsgate Royal Harbour is situated on the south east coast, making an ideal base for crossing to the Continent. 24-hour access to finger pontoons. Comprehensive security systems. Amenities: Launderette; repairs; slipways; boatpark. Competitive rates for permanent berths and discounts for visitors' group bookings.

RUPERT SMITH B.Eng.(Hons)
16 Manor Road North, Seaford, East Sussex BN25 3RB. Tel/Fax (01323) 898782 Yacht and powercraft surveys, design and consultancy. Pre-purchase insurance and damage surveys.

SOUTHERN MAST & RIGGING (KEMP SOUTHEAST)
Unit B The Boatyard, Brighton Marina, Brighton, East Sussex BN2 5UF. Tel (01273) 818189 Fax (01273) 818188 Mobile 0802 284088 Regional centre for SELDÉN and KEMP integrated sailing systems. Builders of masts and spars, standing and running rigging. Rig surveyors. Suppliers of rope, wire, mast and deck hardware, booms, kickers and reefing systems. Mobile service available.

SWALE MARINE (ELECTRICAL)
The Old Stable, North Road, Queenborough, Kent ME11 5EH. Tel (01795) 580930 Fax (01795) 667280 For all your electrical and electronic needs. Authorised agents for: Furuno, Autohelm, Raytheon and most major manufacturers. Fight crime with Harbourguard monitored security: Medway and Swale coverage - Boatmark registration centre.

TEMPLECRAFT YACHT CHARTERS
33 Grand Parade, Brighton, East Sussex BN2 2QA. Tel (01273) 695094 Fax (01273) 688855 Templecraft Yacht Charters are bonded tour operators specialising in independent yacht charter holidays in the Mediterranean and in the Caribbean, and as Odysseus Yachting Holidays in flotilla sailing holidays in Corfu and the Ionian islands.

WARD & McKENZIE (Kent) LTD
26 Station Road, Meopham, Gravesend, Kent DA13 0LX. Tel (01474) 815800 Fax (01474) 815850 National and International Marine Surveyors, Technical and Legal Consultants. Contact: Nick Redfern - Mobile 0411 665345.

WARD & McKENZIE (Sussex) LTD
Oak Bend, Pook Reed Lane, Heathfield, Sussex TN21 0AU. Tel (01435) 866410 Fax (01435) 863310 National and International Marine Surveyors, Technical and Legal Consultants. Contact: Guy Steven.

THAMES ESTUARY   (AREA 4)
North Foreland to Great Yarmouth

BURNHAM YACHT HARBOUR MARINA LTD
Burnham Yacht Harbour, Burnham-on-Crouch, Essex CM0 8BL. Tel (01621) 782150 Fax (01621) 785848 VHF Ch 80 The only Five-Gold Anchor marina in Essex. 350 fully serviced pontoon berths and 120 deep water swing moorings. Marina access at all states of tide with minimum 2.5m depth at low water

C CLAIMS (Marine Loss Adjusters)
PO Box 8, Romford, Essex RM4 1UY. Tel Helpline: 0181-502 6999 Fax 0181-500 1005 C Claims are specialist marine and small craft claims adjusters with a central record of stolen vessels and equipment. They have provided a unique service to marine insurers since 1979 and welcome trade and private enquiries. They are represented throughout the world.

CHELSEA HARBOUR LTD
108 The Chambers, Chelsea Harbour, London SW10 0XF. Tel 0171-351 4433 Fax 0171-352 7868 A tranquil and intimate marina of 55 berths close to the heart of the west end of London. 5-Star hotel, restaurants and bars. Overnight pontoon and amenities. 24-hour security patrols and CCTV.

FOX'S MARINA IPSWICH LTD
The Strand, Wherstead, Ipswich, Suffolk IP2 8SA. Tel (01473) 689111 Fax (01473) 601737 The most comprehensive boatyard facility on the east coast. Extensive chandlery. Marina access 24-hours. Diesel dock, two travel hoists to 45 tons, 10 ton crane. Full electronics, rigging, engineering, stainless steel services. Specialists in osmosis and spray painting.

FOX'S SPARS & RIGGING (KEMP EAST)
Fox's Marina, The Strand, Wherstead, Ipswich, Suffolk IP2 8SA. Tel (01473) 691235 Fax (01473) 601737 Regional centre for SELDÉN and KEMP integrated sailing systems. Fox's experience in world girdling racing and cruising yachts provides testimony to products and skills. The No 1 choice for yachtsmen everywhere. Supplier to the OYSTER range.

HALCON MARINE LTD
The Point, Canvey Island, Essex SS8 7TL. Tel (01268) 511611 Fax (01268) 510044 Marine engineers, repairs and full boatyard services in this quiet and picturesque area. Berths, moorings, slipping facilities. Summer and winter storage. Dry dock (70t max), diesel 1 to 2 hours ±. Water, electric, toilets and showers. A friendly welcome awaits you.

THE HARBOUR LIGHTS RESTAURANT (Walton-on-the Naze)
Titchmarsh Marina, Coles Lane, Walton-on-the-Naze, Essex CO14 8SL. Tel (01255) 851887 Fax (01255) 677300 Open 7 days a week the Harbour Lights offers a welcome to yachtsmen and land-lubbers alike. Fine views over the marina and Walton Backwaters. Hearty breakfasts are served 8am - 10am, and extensive bar meals are available all day. Sizzling summer weekend barbecues, weather permitting. Silver service restaurant with traditional English fare.

JEFFREY WOOD MARINE LTD
26 Rectory Gardens, Granham, Essex RM14 3YJ. Tel (01708) 641300 Fax (01708) 641110 Consultant forensic marine engineers, boat designers and surveyors, naval architects. Osmosis and Ferro cement specialists - wood or steel boats of all types.

KELVIN HUGHES CHARTS & MARITIME SUPPLIES
New North Road, Hainault, Ilford, Essex IG6 2UR. Tel 0181-500 6166 Books and charts. DTp Certificated.

LONDON YACHT CENTRE LTD - LYC
13 Artillery Lane, London E1 7LP. Tel 0171-247 2047 Fax 0171-377 5680 Two minutes from Liverpool Street Railway Station. Four floors with 8000 top name product lines including Musto, Henri Lloyd and Douglas Gill. Extensive range of chandlery, inflatables, outboards, liferafts, electronics, software, books, charts, optics, rope and chain. All at discount prices.

MARINECALL - TELEPHONE INFORMATION SERVICES
Avalon House, London EC2A 4PJ. Tel 0171-631 6000 Marinecall provides detailed coastal weather forecasts for 17 different regions up to 5 days ahead from the Met Office. For a full fax list of services dial 0891 24 66 80. Telephone forecasts are updated daily, morning and afternoon.

MARTELLO YACHT SERVICES
Mulberry House, Mulberry Road, Canvey Island, Essex SS8 0PR. Tel/Fax (01268) 681970 Manufacturers and suppliers of made-to-measure upholstery, covers, hoods, dodgers, sailcovers, curtains and cushions etc. Repairs undertaken. DIY materials, chandlery and fitting-out supplies.

OCEAN LEISURE LTD
11-14 Northumberland Avenue, London WC2N 5AQ. Tel 0171-930 5050 Fax 0171-930 3032 Complete range of sailing clothing, swim and beachwear stocked all year round. Chandlery includes marine electronic equipment, marine antiques, books and charts. Also canoeing, underwater photography, diving and waterskiing specialists. Learn to scuba dive.

PARKER & KAY SAILMAKERS - EAST
Suffolk Yacht Harbour, Levington, Ipswich, Suffolk IP10 0LN. Tel (01473) 659878 Fax (01473) 659197 A complete sailmaking service, from small repairs to the construction of custom designed sails for racing or cruising yachts. Covers constructed for sail and powercraft, plus the supply of all forms of sail handling hardware.

PORT FLAIR LTD
Bradwell Marina, Waterside, Bradwell-on-Sea, Essex CM0 7RB. Tel (01621) 776235/776391 300 pontoon berths with water and electricity, petrol and diesel, chandlery, marine slip/hoistage to 20 tons. Repairs, winter lay-ups, licensed club, yacht brokerage.

PREMIUM LIFERAFT SERVICES
Liferaft House, Burnham Business Park, Burnham-on-Crouch, Essex CM0 8TE. Tel (01621) 784858 Fax (01621) 785934 Freephone 0800 243673 e-mail:liferaftuk@aol.com Hire and sales of DoT and RORC approved liferafts. Long and short-term hire from 18 depots nationwide. Servicing and other safety equipment available.

PROSSER SCIENTIFIC INSTRUMENTS LTD
Lady Lane Industrial Estate, Hadleigh, Ipswich, Suffolk IP7 6BQ. Tel (01473) 823005 Fax (01473) 824095 Manufacturers of a range of marine instruments, including the WEATHERTREND digital barometer, with full 24-hour history, the unique TIDECLOCK tidal data predictor and tidal software for the PSION 3 series.

S I R S NAVIGATION LTD
186a Milton Road, Swanscombe, Kent DA10 0LX. Tel (01322) 383672 Books and charts. DTp Certificated.

SEATH INSTRUMENTS (1992) LTD
Unit 30, Colville Road Works, Colville Road, Lowestoft NR33 9QS. Tel (01502) 573811 Books and charts. DTp Certificated.

SHOTLEY MARINA LTD
Shotley Gate, Ipswich, Suffolk IP9 1QJ. Tel (01473) 788982 Fax (01473) 788868 A modern state of the art marina with 350 berths offering all the services expected. Open 24-hours with full security. Access all states of tide, ideal cruising base. Well stocked chandlery and general store, repair facilities, laundry and ironing centre, showers/baths and toilets. Restaurants, bar, children's room, TV/video and function rooms with dance floor and bar. Disabled facilities.

A M SMITH (MARINE) LTD
33 Epping Way, Chingford E4 7PB. Tel 0181-529 6988 Books and charts.

SOUTH DOCK MARINA
South Lock Office, Rope Street, Plough Way, London SE16 1AA. Tel 0171-252 2244 Fax 0171-237 3806 London's largest marina. 200+ berths. Spacious, tranquil setting. Manned 24 hours. Lift-out for 20 tonnes. Competitve mooring rates.

SOUTH EASTERN MARINE SERVICES LTD
Units 13 & 25, Olympic Business Centre, Paycocke Road, Basildon, Essex SS14 3EX. Tel (01268) 534427 Fax (01268) 281009 e-mail: sems@bt.internet.com Liferaft service, sales and hire, 1-65 persons. Approved by major manufacturers and MSA. Callers welcome. View your own raft. Family owned and operated. Inflatable boat repairs and spares. WE WANT YOU TO COME BACK. www.sems.com

ST KATHARINE HAVEN
50 St Katharine's Way, London E1 9LB. Tel 0171-264 5312 Fax 0171-702 2252 In the heart of London, St Katharine's 200-berth Haven offers facilities for 100'+ vessels, access to the West End and City, its own shops, restaurants, health club and yacht club, plus water, electric, showers and sewerage disposal. Entry via a lock. Operational HW - 2hrs to HW ± 1½ hrs London Bridge. October-March 0800-1800. April-August 0600-2030 or by arrangement.

SUFFOLK YACHT HARBOUR LTD
Levington, Ipswich, Suffolk IP10 0LN. Tel (01473) 659240 Fax (01473) 659632 500-berths - access at all states of tide (dredged to 2.5 meters at LW Springs). Boat hoist facilities up to 60 tons. Full boatyard services, chandlery, gas, diesel, petrol, engineering, sailmaking, electronics. Club house and restaurant.

TITCHMARSH MARINA
Coles Lane, Walton-on-the-Naze, Essex CO14 8SL. Tel (01255) 672185 Fax (01255) 851901 Friendly service in the peaceful backwaters. Visiting yachtsmen welcome. Sheltered marina berths. Full marina facilities: Travel-lift, cranage, 16 amp electricity, diesel. Winter storage. Restaurant and bar open every day. (See Harbour Lights Restaurant.)

TOLLESBURY MARINA
The Yacht Harbour, Tollesbury, Maldon, Essex CM9 8SE. Tel (01621) 869202 Fax (01621) 868489 e-mail: marina@wood rolfe.demon.co.uk Dedicated to customer service, this family-run marina can offer 240 marina berths with water and electricity on all pontoons. Cruising club with bar, restaurant, swimming pool and tennis courts. Repair workshop, osmosis treatment centre. Full brokerage service listing over 200 boats. VHF Ch37 and 80.

WARD & McKENZIE (East Anglia) LTD
3 Wherry Lane, Ipswich, Suffolk IP4 1LG. Tel (01473) 255200 Fax (01473) 255044 National and International Marine Surveyors, Technical and Legal Consultants. Contact: Clive Brown - Mobile 0585 190357, Mike Williamson - Mobile 0498 578312 and Ian Collett - Mobile 0370 655306.

UPPER THAMES (AREA 4)
Navigable west of Westminster Bridge

W BATES & SON BOATBUILDERS LTD
Bridge Wharf, Chertsey, Surrey KT16 8LG. Tel (01932) 562255 Fax (01932) 571161 110-berth marina in quiet picturesque area and additional riverside moorings. Full facilities including electricity to most berths, toilets and showers. 12-ton crane and hard standing for winter storage. Always a welcome to visitors from our friendly staff. Sales office open seven days a week.

BISHOP SKINNER INTERNATIONAL INSURANCE BROKERS
Oakley Crescent, City Road, London EC1V 1NU. Tel 0171-566 5800 Fax 0171-608 2171 Dinghy Insurance - As insurance brokers to the RYA we offer cover for accidental damage, racing risks, 30-days European extension, discounts for dinghy instructors, third party indemnity of £2,000,000, no claim bonus (transferable) and first class security. Immediate quotation and instant cover all at competitive rates.

CHISWICK QUAY MARINA LTD
Marina Office, Chiswick Quay, London W4 3UR. Tel 0181-994
8743 Small, secluded, peaceful marina on tidal Thames at Chiswick.
Slipway, marine engineers and electricians, power, water, toilets
and sluice. Some residential moorings.

**DESMOND CHEERS & PARTNERS
INSURANCE SERVICES**
44 High Street, Hampton Hill, Middlesex TW12 1PD. Tel 0181-
943 5333 Fax 0181-943 5444 Marine insurance specialists with
over 30 years' experience in arranging tailor-made policies through
leading marine underwriters. For all your insurance enquiries for
yachts, motorcruisers and speedboats call Tim Cheers or Daphne
Bamberger.

FORESIGHT OPTICAL
13 New Road, Banbury, Oxfordshire OX16 9PN. Tel (01295)
264365 Suppliers of general purpose and nautical binoculars,
spotting scopes, astronomical telescopes, night vision equipment,
microscopes, magnifiers, spotlights, tripods and accessories.
National mail order service.

MARINE RADIO SERVICES LTD.
50 Merton Way, East Molesley, Surrey KT8 1PQ. Tel 0181-979
2929 Fax 0181-783 1032 Maritime Electronics: Service, sales and
repair of marine radio, radar and electronic equipment.

NEPTUNE NAVIGATIONAL SOFTWARE
P O Box 5106, Riseley, Berkshire RG7 1FD. Tel 0118-988 5309
www.neptunenav.demon.co.uk Passage planning, tides and tidal
stream prediction software for the PCs. Providing course to steer
calculations, point and click planning, waypoint upload to GPS,
chart plotter and many more functions. Intuitively easy to use
Windows programs.

ROYAL INSTITUTE OF NAVIGATION
1 Kensington Gore, London SW7 2AT. Tel 0171-591 3130
Fax 0171-591 3131 Forum for all interested in navigation - Air: Sea:
Land: Space.

SHERATON MARINE CABINET
White Oak Green, Hailey, Witney, Oxfordshire OX8 5XP.
Tel/Fax (01993) 868275 Manufacturers of quality teak and
mahogany marine fittings, louvre doors, gratings and tables. Special
fitting-out items to customer specification. Colour catalogue
available on request.

SILLETTE SONIC LTD
182 Church Hill Road, North Cheam, Sutton, Surrey SM3 8NF.
Tel 0181-715 0100 Fax 0181-288 0742 Mobile 0410 270107 Sillette
manufactures a range of propulsion systems - stern drive, saildrives
etc and sterngear. Markets Radice & Gori fixed and folding
propellers. Acts as agents for Morse Controls, Yanmar and
Lombardini marine engines, and Fuji Robin generators. See
distribution depot Poole, Dorset - Area 2.

SOFTWAVE
4 Aranmor House, Kingston Hill, Kingston, Surrey KT2 7LY.
Tel 0181-549 0650 Fax 0181-546 1090 Website: www:softwave
.co.uk. Specialist supplier of PC based electronics navigation
systems and high quality vectorized charts drawn from Admirality
and other official sources. Also tide computing, simulations,
hardware and on-board installations. (See advertisement first left
hand page in this volume.)

EAST ENGLAND   (AREA 5)
Blakeney to Berwick-on-Tweed

BURGH CASTLE MARINA
Butt Lane, Burgh Castle, Norfolk, Norwich NR31 9PZ. Tel (01493)
780331 Fax (01493) 780163 100 serviced pontoons and quay
moorings accessible at all tides. Secure car and boat parking.
Adjoining boatyard services, access to holiday park showers,
laundry and heated pool. Riverside pub and shop. Complex open
all year.

B COOKE & SON LTD
Kingston Observatory, 58-59 Market Place, Hull HU1 1RH.
Tel (01482) 223454 Books and Charts. DTp Certificated.

**CREST NICHOLSON MARINAS LTD
- NORTH SHIELDS**
Royal Quays Marina, Coble Dene Road, North Shields
NE29 6DU. Tel 0191-272 8282 Fax 0191-272 8288
Situated 2 miles from the entrance of the river Tyne. 24-
hour lock access. Extensive range of facilities.

HULL MARINA LTD
Warehouse 13, Kingston Street, Hull HU1 2DQ. Tel (01482)
613451 Fax (01482) 224148 Four-Anchor Marina. Situated 5 minues
from the centre of Hull and all national and international transport
systems. First class leisure, boatyard and brokerage facilities. 4-
Star hotel and quayside restaurants. Professional and caring staff.
Competitive rates.

JOHN LILLEY & GILLIE LTD
Clive Street, North Shields, Tyne & Wear NE29 6LF. Tel 0191-257 2217 Books and Charts. DTp Certificated.

LIONSTAR YACHT & MOTORBOAT SURVEYS
The Lawn, Ashbrooke Road, Sunderland, Tyne & Wear SR2 7HQ. Tel 0191-528 6422 Lionstar Yacht Services, Sunderland - Surveys of sailing and motor yachts by chartered marine engineers and naval architects with full PI and PL insurance. Northern England and southern Scotland. Telephone Derek May on 0191-528 6422 for quote.

NORTHERN SPAR SERVICES (KEMP NORTHWEST)
M R Coates Marine, The Marina Boatyard, Whitby, North Yorkshire YO21 1EU. Tel (01947) 604486 Fax (01947) 600580 Regional centre for SELDÉN and KEMP integrated sailing systems. 25 years' experience of mast and rigging manufacturing. Surveys undertaken. UK and export mail order service. Roll-swaging, Talurits, wire and rope splicing. Suppliers of furling systems.

WARD & McKENZIE (North East) LTD
11 Sherbuttgate Drive, Pocklington, York YO4 2ED. Tel (01759) 304322 Fax (01759) 303194 National and International Marine Surveyors, Technical and Legal Consultants. Contact: Neville Styles - Mobile 0831 335943.

SOUTH EAST SCOTLAND   (AREA 6)
Eyemouth to Rattray Head

PETERHEAD BAY AUTHORITY
Bath House, Bath Street, Peterhead AB42 1DX. Tel (01779) 474020 Fax (01779) 475712 *Contact: Stephen Paterson.* Peterhead Bay Marina offers fully serviced pontoon berthing for local and visiting boat owners. Local companies provide a comprehensive range of supporting services. Ideal stopover for vessels heading to/from Scandinavia or the Caledonian canal.

THOMAS GUNN NAVIGATION SERVICES
Anchor House, 62 Regents Quay, Aberdeen AB11 5AR. Tel (01224) 595045 Books and charts. DTp Certificated.

NORTH EAST SCOTLAND   (AREA 7)
Rattray Head to Cape Wrath including Orkney and Shetland

CALEY MARINA
Canal Road, Inverness IV3 6NF. Tel (01463) 236539 Fax (01463) 238323 Open 08.30 - 17.30. Berths: 50 Pontoons (visitors available). Facilities: Fuel, water, pump-out facilities, provisions (nearby shops), repair, cranage, secure storage afloat and ashore. Comprehensive chandlery, showers, workshop. Situated at eastern end of Caledonian canal above Muirtown locks. Access via sea locks 4 hours either side of high water.

LOCH NESS CHARTERS
The Boatyard, Dochgarroch, Inverness IV3 6JY. Tel (01463) 861303 Fax (01463) 861353 Yacht and cruiser charter. Boat services and repairs. Hardstanding and slipway. Diesel supply. Boat finishing.

NORTH WEST/CENTRAL WEST SCOTLAND   (AREA 8)
Cape Wrath to Crinan Canal

ARDENTINNY HOTEL
Ardentinny, Loch Long, By Dunoon, Argyll PA23 8TR. Tel (01369) 810209 Fax (01369) 810241 A warm Scottish welcome awaits you at the Ardentinny. Delightful dinners to a very high standard are prepared by our chef complemented by a choice of over 50 selections of French and New World wines. Excellent casual lunches served in the garden or buttery. Friendly bar, frequented by yachtsmen, with a good selection of beer. 7 moorings available.

ARDFERN YACHT CENTRE
Ardfern By Lochgilphead, Argyll PA31 8QN. Tel (01852) 500247/636 Fax (01852) 500624 and 07000 Ardfern Boatyard with full repair and maintenance facilities. Timber and GRP repairs, painting and engineering. Sheltered moorings and pontoon berthing. Winter storage, chandlery, showers, fuel, Calor, brokerage, 20-ton boat hoist, rigging. Hotel, bars and restaurant.

ARDORAN MARINE
Lerags, Oban, Argyll PA34 4SE. Tel (01631) 566123 Fax (01631) 566611 All marine services. Winter storage and moorings.

CRAOBH MARINA
By Lochgilphead, Argyll PA31 8UD. Tel (01852) 500222 Fax (01852) 500252 250-berth marina on Loch Shuna. Water, electricity, diesel and gas. Full boatyard services. Chandlery. Brokerage. Insurance. Shops, bar. 24-hour access. VHF Ch37 and 80 (M).

THE CREGGANS INN
Strachur, Argyll PA27 8BX. Tel (01369) 860279 Fax (01369) 860637 Approximately 18 nautical miles from Ardrishaig the Creggans Inn makes a useful stop for lunch, dinner or overnight respite! 5 moorings available. Bar lunches from 12 noon and excellent restaurant serving from 7 to 9pm. Shower and changing facilities for our travelling yachtsmen.

In an EMERGENCY You may be able to get help through the PINK PAGES

CRINAN BOATS LTD

Crinan, Lochgilphead, Argyll PA31 8SP. Tel (01546) 830232 Fax (01546) 830281 Boatbuilders, chandlers, engineers, slipping, repairs, charts, electricians, pontoon, moorings, showers, laundry and basic stores.

ISLANDER YACHT CHARTERS & ISLANDER SAILING SCHOOL

7 Torinturk, Argyll PA29 6YE. Tel (01880) 820012 Fax (01880) 821143/820012 e-mail: r.fleck@virgin.net Sail the spectacular and uncrowded waters of the Scottish west coast and Hebrides from our base at Aberdeen Yacht Centre, Argyll. Bareboat or skippered yachts from 33' to 44', all Dtp certificated. RYA recognised sailing school, YM, CS, DS and CC courses from March to October.

KAMES HOTEL

Kames, By Tighnabruaich, Argyll PA21 2AF. Tel (01700) 811489 Fax (01700) 811283 On the Kyles of Bute, with 15 free moorings. Good food, real ales, fine malts. Showers available for visitors. 10 en-suite bedrooms. Regular music nights. Fresh local seafood in season.

SLEAT MARINE SERVICES

Ardvasar, Isle of Skye IV45 8RU. Tel (01471) 844216/844387 Yacht charter (bareboat and skippered) from Armadale Bay, Isle of Skye. Six yachts 34' to 40' LOA. All medium to heavy displacement blue water cruisers. Fuel, water and emergency services for passing yachts with problems.

TIGH AN EILEAN HOTEL

Shieldaig by Strathcaron, Ross-shire IV54 8XN. Tel (01520) 755251 Fax (01520) 755321 On the edge of the sea amongst some of the most dramatic landscapes in the Highlands, this friendly 12-bedroom hotel is run under the personal supervision of the proprietors. Our restaurant serves local produce cooked with flair and complemented with good wine. Excellent drying room for those wet clothes!!

AILSA-TROON LTD

Harbour Road, Troon, Ayrshire KA10 6DN. Tel (01292) 311311 Fax (01292) 317613 Boatyard with full repair and maintenance facilities for GRP, steel, aluminium, timber and inflatable craft. Ship repair, fabrication and new building work also undertaken in Ailsa's extensive 15 acre covered facilities.

BROWN SON & FERGUSON LTD

4-10 Darnley Street, Glasgow G41 2SD. Tel 0141-429 1234 Books and charts.

CLYDE MARINA - ARDROSSAN

The Harbour, Ardrossan, Ayrshire KA22 8DB. Tel (01294) 607077 Fax (01294) 607076 e-mail: clydemarina@aol.com Located on the north Ayrshire coast within easy cruising reach of Arran, the Cumbrae Islands, Bute and the Kintyre Peninsula. Deep draught harbour with 200 pontoon berths and quayside for vessels up to 120'. 20-ton hoist, undercover storage and most services and facilities. Ancasta Scotland brokerage, also Beneteau, Nimbus-Maxi, Westerly Yachts, SeaRay and Marlin RIBs.

HARKEN - DISTRIBUTED BY SIMPSON LAWRENCE

218-228 Edmiston Drive, Glasgow G51 2YT. Tel 0141-300 9100 Fax 0141-427 5419 e-mail: info@simpson-lawrence.co.uk Distributors of Harken deck hardware, ball bearing blocks in all sizes from micros to maxis, jib reefing and furling systems, from dinghies to 150 footers, winches, backstay tensioners, power sheet jammers and deck shoes. We also distribute Spinlock and Barton quality racing deck hardware products.

KIP MARINA

The Yacht Harbour, Inverkip, Renfrewshire PA16 0AS. Tel (01475) 521485 Fax (01475) 521298 Marina berths for vessels up to 65' LOA. Full boatyard facilities including travel hoist, crane, on-site engineers, GRP repairs etc. Bar, restaurant, saunas, launderette and chandlery. Distributors for Moody Yachts, Northshore and Searanger Motor Yachts.

LARGS YACHT HAVEN

Irvine Road, Largs, Ayrshire KA30 8EZ. Tel (01475) 675333 Fax (01475) 672245 Perfectly located 600-berth marina with full services afloat and ashore. 45-ton travel hoist operational 7 days; fuel (diesel and petrol); gas and ice on sale 24-hours. Bar, coffee shop, dive shop plus usual marine services.

MARK ANTONY PHOTOGRAPHY

Station Road Industrial Estate, Mauchline, Ayrshire KA5 5EU. Tel (07071) 203203 Fax (07071) 503503 Still life table photography. For all your advertising needs Mark Antony can photograph all types of products for your brochures and promotional literature. £50 for film, developing and prints (more than one subject on each film). Mail order service available.

MAST & RIGGING SERVICES LTD (KEMP SCOTLAND)

Kip Marina, Inverkip, Renfrewshire PA16 0AS. Tel (01475) 522700 Fax (01475) 522800 Regional centre for SELDÉN and KEMP integrated sailing systems. Specialist mast and rigging service offering - splicing, swaging, spar maintenance and repairs throughout Scotland. Suppliers of main and headsail furling gears, spinnaker poles and rod kickers.

THE OYSTERCATCHER RESTAURANT

Otter Ferry, Argyll PA21 2DH. Tel (01700) 821229 Fax (01700) 821300 Situated on Loch Fyne, just north of the Otter Spit, about one hour's sailing from the Crinan canal. Moorings (insured to 12t) free to patrons. French chef and superb food, seafood our speciality. 1996 Tourist Board winner 'BEST PLACE TO EAT'. Children's play area.

RHU MARINA LTD

Helensburgh, Dunbartonshire G84 8LN. Tel (01436) 820238 Fax (01436) 821039 Berths accessible at all times and moorings available situated in an area of outstanding natural beauty, by the Garsloch and 10 minutes from Loch Lomond. Hotels, shops, yacht clubs all adjacent.

ROYAL HOTEL - TIGHNABRUAICH

Tighnabruaich, Argyll PA21 2BE. Tel (01700) 811239 Fax (01700) 811300 On the Kyles of Bute. Fully licensed individual family run hotel. Superb food, venison, game, prawns, scallops and lobster served in our cosy bars and restaurant. *Taste of Scotland* recommended. 12 moorings, slipway, showers, hairdryers.

SIMPSON LAWRENCE LTD

218-228 Edmiston Drive, Glasgow G51 2YT. Tel 0141-300 9100 Fax 0141-427 5419 e-mail: info@simpson-lawrence.co.uk Simpson Lawrence are manufacturers and the UK's largest wholesale distributor of quality marine equipment.

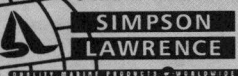
TROON YACHT HAVEN

The Harbour, Troon, Ayrshire KA10 6DJ. Tel (01292) 315553 Fax (01292) 312836 Sheltered harbour for 350 berths. Well placed for those on passage to and from the Clyde. Bar, restaurant, marine services. Attractive seafront town with good beaches and championship golf.

NORTH WEST ENGLAND   (AREA 10)
Isle of Man and North Wales, Mull of Galloway to Bardsey Island

ANDREW POTTER MA AMYDSA YACHT SURVEYOR

Penrallt Cottage, Cichle Hill, Llandegfan, Anglesey LL59 5TD. Tel/Fax (01248) 712358 Mobile 0374 411681 Prompt and professional surveys prior to purchase and for insurance purposes throughout Wales, the north west and Midlands. Services also include valuations, osmosis inspections and consultancy.

CREST NICHOLSON MARINAS LTD - CONWY

Conwy Marina, Conwy Morfa, Conwy, Gwynedd LL32 8EP. Tel (01492) 593000 Fax (01492) 572111 Conwy Marina is ideally placed on the south shore of the Conwy estuary. The marina is set within idyllic surroundings and has comprehensive facilities. Road access is extremely convenient, with the A55 dual carriageway passing close by.

DOLPHIN MARITIME SOFTWARE LTD

713 Cameron House, White Cross, Lancaster LA1 4XQ. Tel/Fax (01524) 841946 e-mail: 100417.744@compuserve.com Website:http://ourworld.compuserve.com/homepages/Dolphin_software Marine computer programs for IBM PC, Psion and Sharp pocket computers. Specialists in navigation, tidal prediction and other programs for both yachting and commercial uses.

DUBOIS-PHILLIPS & McCALLUM LTD

Oriel Chambers, Covent Garden, Liverpool L2 8UD. Tel 0151-236 2776 Books and charts.

FIDDLERS FERRY YACHT HAVEN

Off Station Road, Penketh, Warrington, Cheshire WA5 2UJ. Tel (01925) 727519 Sheltered moorings upto 6'6" draught, 50' long. Access through lock from river Mersey 1½ either side of high tide. Signed from A652. Boatyard and lift-out facilities. Annual rate per foot £8.25.

GUY BROOKE MASTS & RIGGING (KEMP NORTHWEST)

Conwy Marina, Conwy, Gwynedd, North Wales LL32 8GU. Tel/Fax (01492) 592909 Mobile 0589 108860 Regional centre for SELDÉN and KEMP integrated sailing systems. Specialists in mast build and maintenance. Full rigging service for swaging, splicing and rig surveys. Personal, professional and mobile along the north Wales and north west coasts.

HAFAN PWLLHELI

Glan Don, Pwllheli, Gwynedd LL53 5YT. Tel (01758) 701219 Fax (01758) 701443 Hafan Pwllheli has over 400 pontoon berths and offers access at virtually all states of the tide. Ashore, its modern purpose-built facilities include luxury toilets, showers, landerette, a secure boat park for winter storage, 40-ton travel hoist, mobile crane and plenty of space for car parking. Open 24-hours a day, 7 days a week.

HOYLAKE SAILING SCHOOL

43a Market Street, Hoylake, Wirral L47 2BG. Tel 0151-632 4664 Fax 0151-632 4776 RYA recognised shorebased teaching establishment offering a wide range of courses including Day Skipper to Yachtmaster Ocean, VHF and First Aid. Day, evening or intensive classes. Pratical courses by arrangement. Books, charts and gifts available.

ISLAND SEA SCHOOL
7 Church View, South Milford, Leeds LS25 5BM. Tel/Fax (01977) 685394 e-mail: sea.school@mcmail.com RYA practical courses from our base at Port Dinorwic on the Menai Strait: Competent Crew, Day Skipper, Coastal Skipper, Yachtmaster Preparatory, Ocean Yachtmaster Qualifying Passages. Own boat tuition. Skippered charter.

ISLE OF ANGLESEY COUNTY COUNCIL
Highways & Technical Services Department, Council Offices, Llangefni, Anglesey LL77 7TW Tel (01248) 752331 Fax (01248) 724839 Berths and moorings available at Menai bridge, Amlwch harbour and north east Menai Straits (Beaumaris). Winter storage at competitive rates available at Beaumaris and Amlwch. Contact Maritime Officer 01248 752331 for details.

JOSEPH P LAMB & SONS
Maritime Building (opposite Albert Dock), Wapping, Liverpool L1 8DQ. Tel 0151-709 4861 Fax 0151-709 2786 Situated in the centre of Liverpool, J P Lamb have provided a service to world shipping for over 200 years. All chandlery supplies, clothing, rope, paint and flags are available. Full sailmaking and repairs. Kemp Retail Outlet for spars and rigging. Open Mon to Fri 8am to 5.30pm - Sat 9am to 12.30pm.

LIVERPOOL MARINA
Coburg Dock, Sefton Street, Liverpool L3 4BP. Tel 0151-709 0578 (2683 after 5pm) Fax 0151-709 8731 300-berth yacht harbour. All serviced pontoons. Tidal access HW ± 2½ approximately, depending on draught. 60-ton hoist, workshops, bar and restaurant, toilets and showers. City centre one mile. Open all year. Active yacht club and yacht brokerage.

MANX MARINE
35 North Quay, Douglas, Isle of Man IM1 4LB. Tel/Fax (01624) 674842 The Island's leading and most established yacht chandlery. Stockists of quality foul-weather clothing and thermal wear. Large stock holdings of stainless steel fixtures and fittings and a comprehensive range of general chandlery including rigging facilities.

MAX WALKER YACHT DELIVERIES
Zinderneuf Sailing, PO Box 105, Macclesfield, Cheshire SK10 2EY. Tel (01625) 431712 Fax (01625) 619704 Fixed price deliveries. Sailing yachts delivered with care in north west European, UK and Eire waters by RYA/DoT yachtmaster and crew - 30 years' experience. Owners welcome. Tuition if required. References available. Your enquiries welcome 24 hours.

SEALAND BOAT DELIVERIES LTD
Tower, Liverpool Marina, Coburg Wharf, Liverpool L3 4BP. Tel (01254) 705225 Fax (01254) 776582 Website: http://www.btx. co.uk e-mail: ros@mcr1.poptel.org.uk Nationwide and European road transporters of all craft. No weight limit. We never close. Irish service. Worldwide shipping agents. Extrication of yachts from workshops and building yards. Salvage contractors. Established 25 years.

WARD & McKENZIE (North West) LTD
2 Healey Court, Burnley, Lancashire BB11 2QJ. Tel/Fax (01282) 420102 National and International Marine Surveyors, Technical and Legal Consultants. Contact: Bob Sheffield - Mobile 0370 667457.

WHITEHAVEN HARBOUR MARINA
Harbour Commissioners, Pears House, 1 Duke Street, Whitehaven, Cumbria CA28 7HW. Tel (01946) 692435 Fax (01946) 691135 Long and short-term berths available at newly created 100 capacity marina, maximum length 12m. 11 hectare permanent locked harbour with 45 tonne boat hoist, access at least HW ± 3hours. Sheltered historic location adjacent to town centre.

WEST WALES, SOUTH WALES AND BRISTOL CHANNEL   (AREA 11)
Bardsey Island to Lands End

BALTIC WHARF WATER LEISURE CENTRE
Bristol Harbour, Underfall Yard, Bristol BS1 6XG. Tel 0II7-929 7608 Fax 0117-929 4454 Tuition: 0117-952 5202 Sailing school and centre, with qualified instruction in most watersports. Also moorings available throughout the Bristol harbour for all types of leisurecraft.

CREST NICHOLSON MARINAS LTD · BRISTOL
Parklands, Stoke Gifford, Bristol BS12 6QU. Tel 0117-923 6466 Fax 0117-923 6508 Marina development management and consultancy.

CREST NICHOLSON MARINAS LTD · PENARTH
Portway Village, Penarth, South Glamorgan CF64 1TQ. Tel (01222) 705021 Fax (01222) 712170 Situated within the sheltered waters of Cardiff Bay the marina provides fully serviced, secure berths and wide ranging ancilliary services. Open 24-hours, year round, we can assure visitors of a warm welcome. Please apply for details.

DALE SAILING COMPANY
Brunel Quay, Neyland Marina, Neyland, Pembrokeshire SA73 1PY. Tel (01646) 601636 Fax (01646) 601061 Engine service and repair, hull repair, chandlery. Boatyard, lifting, boat building, sea school and new and used boat sales.

MILFORD MARINA
The Docks, Milford Haven, Pembrokeshire, West Wales SA73 3AE. Tel (01646) 696312 Fax (01646) 696314 Safe sheltered haven, 250 berths, 5 minutes from shopping, rail and bus services. Water and electricity to all berths. Staff available 24 hours. Restaurant, chandlery, electronics, boat repair, lifting and storage available onsite.

N W SEAWAYS DOCK MANAGEMENT LTD
Port Dinorwic Marina, Y Felinheli, Gwynedd LL56 4JN. Tel (01248) 670620 Fax (01248) 671252 Mobile 0468 794361 Condition and pre-purchase surveys and insurance valuations, damage and repair reports, underwater dive inspections. Repair and dry dock facilities available. Call in or phone your requirement for prompt, professionl service at competitive rates.

NEYLAND YACHT HAVEN LTD
Brunel Quay, Neyland, Pembrokeshire SA73 1PY. Tel (01646) 601601 Fax (01646) 600713 Marina operators with all facilities. 360 fully serviced pontoon berths in a sheltered, tree lined marina. On-site services include boatyard, sailmaker, sailing school, chandlery, cafe, lounge/bar, launderette, showers and toilets. 30 visitor berths. 24-hour access and security.

PORT DINORWIC MARINA
N W S Dock Management Ltd, Port Dinorwic, Gwynedd LL56 4JN. Tel (01248) 671500/670620 Fax (01248) 671252 250-berths in lock basin or tidal pontoon basin. Toilets, showers and restaurant facilities. Visitors always welcome. Call Ch 80.

W F PRICE & CO LTD
Wapping Wharf, Bristol BS1 6UD. Tel 0117-929 2229 Books and charts. DTp Certificated.

ROWLANDS MARINE ELECTRONICS LTD
Pwllheli Marina Centre, Glan Don, Pwllheli, Gwynedd LL53 5YT. Tel (01758) 613193 Fax (01758) 613617 BEMA and BMIF members, dealer for Autohelm, B&G, Cetrek, ICOM, Kelvin Hughes, Marconi, Nasa, Navico, Navstar, Neco, Seafarer, Shipmate, Stowe, Racal-Decca, V-Tronix, Ampro, Walker. Equipment supplied installed and serviced.

RUDDERS BOATYARD & MOORINGS
Church Road, Burton, Milford Haven, Pembrokeshire SA73 1NU. Tel (01646) 600288 Moorings, pontoon, storage. All repairs.

SWANSEA MARINA
Lockside, Maritime Quarter, Swansea, West Glamorgan SA1 1WG. Tel (01792) 470310 Fax (01792) 463948 Access all states of the tide except LWST. City centre marina, restaurants, theatres etc. Call us on Ch 18 or 80 to check locking times. Visitors always welcome - a good destination for your annual trip.

WARD & McKENZIE (South Wales) LTD
58 The Meadows, Marshfield, Cardiff CF3 8AY. Tel (01633) 680280 National and International Marine Surveyors, Technical and Legal Consultants. Contact: Kevin Ashworth - Mobile 0498 843594.

WORCESTER YACHT CHANDLERS LTD
Unit 7, 75 Waterworks Road, Barbourne, Worcester WR1 3EZ. Tel (01905) 22522 & 27949 Chandlery, paints, ropes, cables, chain, clothing, footwear, shackles, books, bottled gas, anti-foul, fastenings, oakam, fenders. Hard storage, crane, haulage, engine service, oils, navigation aids, buoyancy aids, life jackets, distress flares, *small boat hire.*

SOUTHERN IRELAND (AREA 12)
Malahide, south to Liscanor Bay

CARLINGFORD MARINA CLUB - IRELAND
Carlingford, Co Louth, Ireland. Tel/Fax +353 42 73492 Superb location in beautiful setting close to historic village of Carlingford, our friendly marina provides a top class service for all boat users. Moorings, chandlery, slipway, 16-ton cranage, power, diesel, water, laundry, showers and coffee shop. Visitors always welcome. VHF Ch16 and 37 (M). *Sailing Holidays in Ireland - Only the Best.*

CASTLEPARK MARINA - IRELAND
Kinsale, Co Cork, Ireland. Tel +353 21 774959 Fax +353 21 774958 100-berth fully serviced marina with restaurant, laundry, showers and toilets. Waterside hostel-type accommodation available. New restaurant catering for both breakfast and evening meals. Access at all stages of the tide. *Sailing Holidays in Ireland - Only the Best.*

CROSSHAVEN BOATYARD MARINA - IRELAND
Crosshaven, Co Cork, Ireland. Tel +353 21 831161 Fax +353 21 831603 All facilities at this 100-berth marina situated 12 miles from Cork City and close to ferryport and airport. Travel lift, full repair and maintenance services, spray painting and approved International Gelshield centre. Storage undercover and outside for 250 boats. Brokerage. RNLI and Defence contractors. *Sailing Holidays in Ireland - Only the Best.*

DINGLE MARINA - IRELAND
Harbour Master, Strand Street, Dingle, Co Kerry, Ireland. Tel +353 66 51629 Fax +353 66 52629 Europe's most westerly marina on the beautiful south west coast of Ireland in the heart of the old sheltered fishing port of Dingle. Visitor berths, fuel and water. Shops, 52 pubs and many restaurants with traditional music and hospitality. Harbour easily navigable day or night. *Sailing Holidays in Ireland - Only the Best.*

DINGLE SEA VENTURES YACHT CHARTER
Dingle, Co Kerry, Ireland. Tel +353 66 52244 Fax +353 66 52313 e-mail: jgreany@iol.ie Bareboat charter, skippered charter, sailing tuition on south west coast of Ireland: One way charter Dingle-Kinsale-Dingle - 1997 and 1998 fleet of eight boats 31' - 44'. Close to all ferries and airports. Personal, friendly service. PINTS OF PEACE.

FENIT HARBOUR MARINA - IRELAND
Fenit, Co Kerry, Ireland. Tel/Fax +353 66 36231 A new marina opened in July 1997 with 104 berths for all sizes of boat up to 15m x 3m draught, with one berth available for larger vessels up to 30m. Access at all tides. Minimum approach depth 5m. Facilities include smartcard access, toilets, showers, laundry and harbour office. Visitors are welcome to use the superb clubhouse facilities of the Tralee Sailing Club and participate in races Tuesdays. *Sailing Holidays in Ireland - Only the Best.*

HOWTH MARINA - IRELAND
Howth, Co Dublin, Ireland. Tel +353 1 8392777 Fax +353 1 8392430 Modern marina in beautiful sheltered location. Fully serviced berths with every facility and 24-hour security. Very popular marina for traffic in the Irish Sea. Is available at all states of the tide with extremely easy access. *Holidays in Ireland - Only the Best.*

KILMORE QUAY MARINA - IRELAND
Kilmore Quay, Co Wexford, Ireland. Tel/Fax +353 53 29955 Kilmlore Quay in the south east of Ireland has a new marina with 20 pontoon visitor berths. This friendly fishing port has pleasant hotel facilities, pubs and restaurants offering a traditional Irish welcome. Rosslare ferryport is only 15 miles away. *Sailing Holidays in Ireland - Only the Best.*

KILRUSH CREEK MARINA - IRELAND
Kilrush, Co Clare, Ireland. Tel +353 65 52072 Fax +353 65 51692 Mobile +353 87 2313870 VHF Ch 80 Kilrush Creek Marina on Ireland's beautiful west coast, is a new marina with 120 fully serviced berths. The marina has all shore facilities including a modern boatyard with 45-ton hoist. It adjoins the busy market town of Kilrush which has every facility required by the visiting yachtsman. *Sailing Holidays in Ireland - Only the best.*

KING SITRIC FISH RESTAURANT
East Pier, Howth, Co Dublin, Ireland. Tel +353 1 832 5235 & 6729 Fax +353 1 839 2442 Lovely location on the harbour front. Marina and Howth Yacht Club 3 minutes walk. Established 1971, Aidan and Joan MacManus have earned an international reputation for superb, fresh seafood, service and hospitality. Wine conoisseurs take note! Quality accommodation April 1999. Informal summer lunch - dinner all year.

KINSALE YACHT CLUB MARINA
Kinsale, Co Cork, Ireland. Tel +353 21 772196 Fax +353 21 774455 Marina Manager +353 87 449471 Magnificent deep water yacht club marina offering Kinsale hospitality to visiting yachtsmen. Full facilities include berths up to 20 metres, fresh water, electricity, diesel on pier. Club bar and wealth of pubs and restaurants in Kinsale. Enter Kinsale Harbour - lit at night - no restrictions.

LAWRENCE COVE MARINA - IRELAND
Bere Island, Bantry Bay, Co Cork, Ireland. Tel/Fax +353 27 75044 Lawrence Cove Marina is situated in Bantry Bay in the south west corner of Ireland in the heart of the best cruising ground in Europe. It is a new marina, family run with full facilities and a very safe haven to leave a boat. It is 2 hours from Cork airport with good connections. *Sailing Holidays in Ireland - Only the Best.*

MALAHIDE MARINA - IRELAND
Malahide, Co Dublin, Ireland. Tel +353 1 8454129 Fax +353 1 8454255 Located next to the picturesque village of Malahide our marina village is the ideal spot to enjoy and relax. There are 150 fully serviced berths, petrol and diesel available, 30-ton hoist with full boatyard facilities with winter storage ashore or afloat. A fine selection of shops, and friendly pubs and restaurants serving good food are close by. *Sailing Holidays in Ireland - Only the Best.*

SALVE MARINE LTD - IRELAND
Crosshaven, Co Cork, Ireland. Tel +353 21 831145 Fax +353 21 831747 The marina is situated just 20 minutes from Cork City, Cork airport and Ringaskiddy ferry port. Located yards from Royal Cork Yacht Club and Crosshaven village centre. Facilities for yachts up to 140' x 14' draught including mains electricity 240/380 volts, telephone, fax, toilets and showers. Welding and machining in stainless steel, aluminium and bronze. Repairs and maintenance to hulls and rigging. Routine and detailed engine maintenance. Slip. *Sailing Holidays in Ireland - Only the Best.*

TRAMEX LTD
Shankill Business Centre, Shankill, Co Dublin, Ireland. Tel+353 1 282 3688 Fax +353 1 282 7880 e-mail: tramex@iol.ie Website: www.tramexltd.com Manufacturers of Moisture Metre and osmosis detection instruments for boats.

UK/McWILLIAM SAILMAKERS
Crosshaven, Co Cork, Ireland. Tel +353 21 831505 Fax +353 21 831700 Ireland's premier sailmaker, prompt repairs and service.

WATERFORD CITY MARINA - IRELAND
Waterford City, Ireland. Tel +353 51 873501 Fax +353 51 870813 Located right in the heart of the historic city centre. There are 80 fully serviced berths available. The marina has full security, with CCTV in operation. Showers available on shore in adjoining hostel. Wide range of shops, restaurants, pubs and other amenities available on the doorstep of the marina because of its unique city-centre location. Open all year with both winter and summer season rates available. *Sailing Holidays in Ireland - Only the Best.*

NORTHERN IRELAND   (AREA 13)
Lambay Island, north to Liscanor Bay

CARRICKFERGUS MARINA
Rodger's Quay, Carrickfergus, Co Antrim, N Ireland BT38 8BE. Tel (01960) 366666 Fax (01960) 350505 300 fully serviced pontoon berths with excellent full on-shore facilities (half a mile from town centre). Steeped in a wealth of historical legend. Carrickfergus has excellent restaurants, hotels, pubs, shops and a host of recreational leisure facilities.

COLERAINE MARINA
64 Portstewart Road, Coleraine, Co Londonderry, Northern Ireland BT52 1RS. Tel (01265) 44768 Wide range of facilities.

CREST NICHOLSON MARINAS LTD - BANGOR
Bangor Marina, Bangor, Co Down, Northern Ireland BT20 5ED. Tel (01247) 453297 Fax (01247) 453450 Situated on the south shore of Belfast Lough, Bangor is Ireland's largest and most comprehensive yachting facility. The marina is within convenient walking distance of all the town's amenities and may be accessed at any time of day or state of the tide.

EARTHCARE MARKETING SALES
P O Box 68, Newtownards, Northern Ireland BT22 2FY. Tel/Fax (012477) 58171 Mobile 0410 549767 Skipper's Choice is an all-purpose cleaner meeting every requirement from stern to stem. Totally non-toxic. Organic and biodegradable and contains no bleaches, solvents or abrasives. Removes heavy staines from upholstery and carpets and yet ideal for stainless steel and fibre glass. An Earthcare BC Canadian product. Reliable mail order service available.

IRISH SPARS & RIGGING (KEMP IRELAND)
52 Whiterock Road, Killinchy, Co Down, Northern Ireland BT23 6PT. Tel/Fax (01238) 541727 Regional centre for SELDÉN and KEMP integrated sailing systems. The complete and fully mobile rigging service for yachtsmen in Ireland with outlets in Dublin and Cork. A comprehensive stock of all KEMP/SELDÉN products always available.

TODD CHART AGENCY LTD
4 Seacliff Road, The Harbour, Bangor, Northern Ireland BT20 5EY. Tel (01247) 466640 Fax (01247) 471070 e-mail: admiralty @toddchart.co.uk International Admiralty Chart Agent, chart correction service and nautical booksellers. Stockist of Imray charts and books, navigation and chartroom instruments, binoculars, clocks etc. UK agent for Icelandic Hydrographic Service. Mail order - Visa, Mastercard, American Express and Switch/Delta accepted.

CHANNEL ISLANDS   (AREA 14)
Guernsey, Jersey, Alderney.

A B MARINE LTD
Castle Walk, St Peter Port, Guernsey, Channel Islands GY1 1AU. Tel (01481) 722378 (Fax 01481) 711080 We specialise in safety and survival equipment and are a DoT approved service station for liferafts including R.F.D., Beaufort/Dunlop, Zodiac, Plastimo amd Lifeguard. We also carry a full range of new liferafts, dinghies and lifejackets, and are agents for Bukh marine engines.

BEAUCETTE MARINA
Vale, Guernsey, Channel Islands GY3 5BQ. Tel (01481) 45000 Fax (01481) 47071 Situated on the north east coast, Beaucette is one of Europe's most charming deep water marinas. With 140 berths, the marina offers all the services and facilities you would expect. Beaucette is a PREMIER marina.

BOATWORKS + LTD
Castle Emplacement, St Peter Port, Guernsey, Channel Islands GY1 1AU. Tel (01481) 726071 Fax (01481) 714224 Boatworks+ provides a comprehensive range of services including boatbuilding and repairs, chandlery, clothing and fuel supplies.

CHICK'S MARINE LTD/VOLVO PENTA
Collings Road, St Peter Port, Guernsey, Channel Islands GY1 1FL. Tel (01481) 723716 Fax (01481) 713632 Distributor of diesel fuel biocide used to treat and protect contamination in fuel tanks where an algae (bug) is present. Most owners do not realise what the problem is, loss of power, blocked fuel filter, exhaust smoking, resulting in expensive repairs to injectors - fuel pump - or complete engine overhaul. Marine engineers, engines, spares, service - VAT free. Honda outboards, pumps and generators. Volvo Penta specialists.

CREST NICHOLSON MARINAS LTD - MALAHIDE
(Marketing Agents) Malahide Marina, Malahide, Co Dublin, Ireland. +353 1 845 4129 Fax +353 1 845 4255 Situated within Malahide's estuary north of Dublin Bay. Full range of marina facilities available.

JACKSON YACHT SERVICES
Le Boulevard, St Aubin, Jersey, Channel Islands JE3 8AB. Tel (01534) 743819 Fax (01534) 745952 Boatyard, chandler, sailoft, liferaft service, yacht management and brokerage.

JERSEY HARBOURS
Harbour Office, Weighbridge, St Helier, Jersey JE4 9XF. Tel (01534) 885588 Fax (01534) 885599 A warm welcome to visiting yachtsmen! Elizabeth Marina opens in April 1998. Berths available on lease - £184.86 per metre. St Helier marina continues to cater for visitng yachts. Both marinas offer excellent facilities.

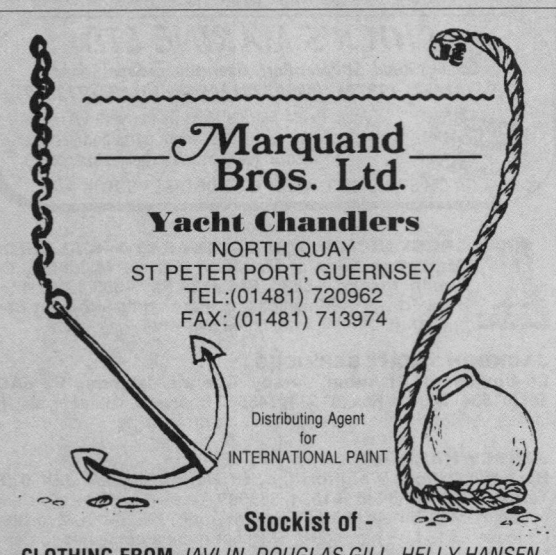
MARQUAND BROS LTD - Yacht Chandlers
North Quay, St Peter Port, Guernsey, Channel Islands.
Tel (01481) 720962 Fax (01481) 713974 Yacht chandlers, stockists
of a comprehensive range of marine products. Guernsey distributor
for International Paint. Extensive leisure and marine clothing
department including Barbour, Driza-Bone, Dubarry and Quayside.

NORTH QUAY MARINE
North Side, St Sampson's Harbour, Guernsey, Channel Islands.
Tel (01481) 46561 Fax (01481) 43488 The complete boating centre.
Full range of chandlery, rope, chain, lubricants, paint, boatwear
and shoes. Fishing tackle for on-shore and on-board. Inflatables
and safety equipment. Electronics and small outboard engines.

OFFSHORE SPARS & RIGGING
(KEMP CHANNEL ISLANDS)
Boatworks+, Castle Emplacement, St Peter Port, Guernsey,
Channel Islands GY1 1AU. Tel (01481) 726071 Fax (01481)
714224 Regional centre for SELDÉN and KEMP integrated sailing
systems. Specialist in new mast builds and maintenance for the
Channel Islands. Complete retrofit and rigging services including
FURLEX genoa and mainsail furling, rod kickers, spinnaker poles
etc.

RADIO & ELECTRONIC SERVICES LTD
Les Chenes, Rohais, St Peter Port, Guernsey, Channel Islands
GY1 1FB. Tel (01481) 728837 Fax (01481) 714379 Chart plotters,
GPS, C-Map and Navionics charting, radars, VHF fixed and portable
radios and autopilots. We offer full electronic supply and service.
Sales and service dealers for Furuno, Icom, Shipmate, Cetrek,
Autohelm, Robertson and AP Navigator.

ROSDEN GLASS FIBRE
La Rue Durell, La Collette, St Helier, Jersey JE2 3NB. Tel (01534)
625418 Fax (01534) 625419 Specialists in all types of glass fibre
marine works, structural repairs, alterations, re-flow coating, GEL
coat work, Blakes Osmosis Treatment Centre. Manufacturers of fuel
tanks, bathing platforms and boat builders. General refurbishment
and polishing. A division of Precision Plastics (Jersey) Ltd.

SARNIA FLAGS
8 Belmont Road, St Peter Port, Guernsey, Channel Islands GY1
1PY. Tel (01481) 725995 Fax (01481) 729335 Flags and pennants
made to order. National flags, house, club and battle flags, and
burgees made to order. Any size, shape or design. Prices on
request.

WILDE MARINE SERVICES LTD
Frances House, Sir William Place, St Peter Port, Guernsey,
Channel Islands GY1 4HQ. Tel (01481) 723573 Fax (01481)
711353 British yacht registration, corporate yacht ownership and
management, marine insurance, crew placement and management.
Wilde Marine Services aims to provide a personal and individual
service to its clients.

BELGIUM AND THE NETHERLANDS (AREA 20)
Nieuwpoort to Delfzijl

BOGERD NAVTEC NV
Oude Leeuwenrui 37, Antwerp 2000, Belgium. Books and charts.

KELVIN HUGHES OBSERVATOR
Nieuwe Langeweg 41, 3194 DC Hoogvliet (Rt), The Netherlands.
Book and charts. DTp Certificated.

MARTIN & CO
Oude Leewenrui 37, Antwerp 2000, Belgium. Books and charts.
DTp Certificated.

GERMANY (AREA 21)
Emden to the Danish Border

IVER C WEILBACH & CO., A/S
35 Toldbodgade, Postbox 1560, DK-1253 Copenhagen K,
Denmark. Books and charts.

GREEK IRELANDS
Not within the areas designated in this volume

GREEK SAILS YACHT CHARTER
21 The Mount, Kippax, Leeds LS25 7NG. Tel/Fax 0113-232 0926
Freephone 0800 731 8580 e-mail: greek_sails_uk@msn.com
Bareboat yacht charter throughout Greece and the islands. Flotilla
based in Corfu and the Ionian Islands. Family dinghy sailing holidays
in Corfu. Skippered charter and sail training.

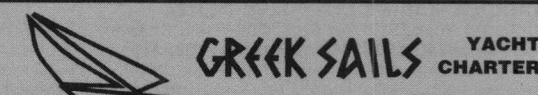

FEEL THE COMFORT
of our waterside hotels & restaurants

From the coast of Cornwall to Mull and beyond - there is always the opportunity to take a break and stay or eat at some of the most beautiful locations in the British Isles and Ireland.

A welcome change after a long haul, to let somebody else do the work and be wined and dined in the comfort of a hotel which caters for the needs and desires of travelling yachtsmen and their families.

The Idle Rocks Hotel - St Mawes
50° 9.4' north, 05° 1.5' west

The Pandora Inn - Restronguet Creek - Falmouth
50° 12' north, 05° 04' west

Falmouth harbour
50° 9.3' north, 05° 04' west

The Tobermory Hotel - Mull
56° 37.3' north, 06° 04' west

Look in the Pink Pages under Waterside Accommodation & Restaurants

With thanks to the proprietors of: The Idle Rocks Hotel - St Mawes, The Pandora Inn - Falmouth, The Galley of Lorne Inn - Ardfern, The Tobermory Hotel - Mull.

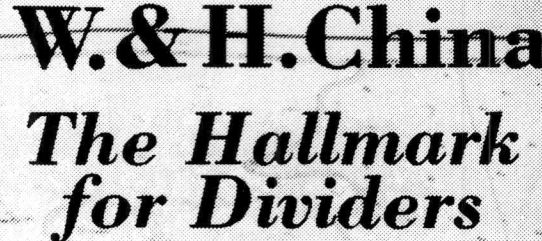

INTRODUCTION

The Almanac and associated publications

The 1999 Macmillan Nautical Almanac contains in one volume all the nautical information needed by yachtsmen navigating the waters around the United Kingdom, Ireland and the coast of Europe from the North Sea border of Germany and Denmark to the Franco-Spanish Atlantic border.

The Macmillan & Silk Cut Yachtsman's Handbook is an enduring and valuable reference work which complements the Almanac. It covers matters of a permanent or semi-permanent nature in as much detail as a single volume permits. The Handbook is not published annually, but is revised as necessary; a new third edition was published in 1995.

Two free Supplements are issued each year in January and May to update the above publications.

THE ALMANAC

Numbering system

There are eight chapters. For ease of reference each chapter is divided into numbered sections, prefaced by the number of the chapter. Thus the sections in Chapter 7, for example, are numbered 7.1, 7.2, etc.

Within each section the key paragraphs are numbered. Thus in section 7.2 (say) the main paragraphs are numbered 7.2.1, 7.2.2, 7.2.3, etc.

Diagrams carry the chapter number and a figure in brackets, thus: Fig 7(1), Fig 7(2), Fig 7(3), etc.

Tables carry the chapter number and a figure in brackets, thus: Table 7(1), Table 7(2), etc.

Chapter 8 is divided into 21 geographic areas.

Contents and Index

The main paragraph headings and the page numbers of each section are listed on the contents page at the start of each chapter and geographical area. A full index is located at the back of the Almanac.

General acknowledgments

The Editor thanks the many individuals and official bodies who have kindly provided essential information and much advice in the preparation of this Almanac. They include the UK Hydrographic Office, Trinity House, Northern Lighthouse Board, Irish Lights, HM Nautical Almanac Office, HM Stationery Office, HM Customs, Meteorological Office, HM Coastguard, British Telecom, BBC and IBA, Marine Safety Agency, Royal National Lifeboat Institution, Koninklijke Nederlandse Redding Maatschappij (KNRM), Deutsche Gesellschaft zur Rettung Schiffbrüchiger (DGzRS), Port of London Authority, Associated British Ports, countless Harbour Masters and our many individual agents.

Chartlets, tidal stream diagrams and tidal curves are reproduced from Admiralty Charts and Publications with permission of the UK Hydrographic Office (Licence No HO 313/961001/01) and the Controller of HMSO.

The tidal stream arrows on the S and W coasts of Ireland are printed in 8.12.3 and 8.13.3 by kind permission of the Irish Cruising Club.

Information from the Admiralty List of Lights, Admiralty Sailing Directions, Admiralty Tide Tables, and the Admiralty List of Radio Signals is reproduced with the permission of the UK Hydrographic Office and the Controller of HMSO.

WARNING: No National Hydrographic Office has verified the information in this product and none accept liability for the accuracy of reproduction or any modifications made thereafter. No National Hydrographic Office warrants that this product satisfies national or international regulations regarding the use of the appropriate products for navigation.

Chartlets are only intended for reference and should not be used for navigation. Always consult navigational charts updated for the latest information.

Extracts from the following are published by permission of the Controller of HM Stationery Office: *International Code of Signals, 1969; Meteorological Office Weather Services for Shipping*.

Phases of the Moon and Sun/Moon rising and setting times in Chapter 2 are derived from the current edition of the *Nautical Almanac*, and are included by permission of HM Nautical Almanac Office and of the Particle Physics and Astronomy Research Council.

Acknowledgments – tidal predictions

UK and foreign tidal predictions are supplied by the UK Hydrographic Office, Taunton TA1 2DN, England to whom grateful acknowledgement is made.

Acknowledgment is made to the following authorities for permission to use the tidal predictions stated:

Service Hydrographique et Océanographique de la Marine, France: Dieppe, Le Havre, Cherbourg, St Malo, Brest, Pointe de Grave (authorisation No 828/97); and Dunkerque (authorisation No 101/98).

Rijkswaterstaat, The Netherlands: Vlissingen (Flushing), and Hoek van Holland.

Bundesamt für Seeschiffahrt und Hydrographie, Hamburg and Rostock: Helgoland, Wilhelmshaven and Cuxhaven (BSH 8095·02/97-Z1102).

IMPROVING THE ALMANAC

Suggestions for improvements

The Editor welcomes suggestions, however minor, for improving the content or layout of the Almanac. Ideas based on experience and practical use at sea are especially welcome. It is not always feasible to implement every suggestion received, but all will be very carefully considered.

Please write your comments on the Supplement application card, or send them by letter, fax or e-mail direct to:

The Editor, The Macmillan Nautical Almanac, Edington House, Trent, Sherborne, Dorset DT9 4SR; ✆ 01935 850737; MacAlman@aol.com. Please do not write to Macmillan General Books in London on purely nautical matters.

Notification of errors

Although very great care has been taken in compiling all the information from innumerable sources, it is recognised that in a publication of this nature some errors may occur. Please notify the Editor in writing at the above address of any such lapses.

KEEPING IT UP TO DATE

It is most important that charts and other navigational publications – such as this Almanac – are kept up to date. The body of the Almanac is corrected up to and including *Admiralty Notices to Mariners*, Weekly Edition No 17/98.

Late corrections

Subsequent corrections up to *Admiralty Notices to Mariners*, Weekly Edition No 24/98 are contained in Late corrections at the back of the Almanac, before the Index.

Free Supplements

Further corrections up to November 1998 are given in the first of two free Supplements, published in January 1999. The second Supplement containing corrections up to April 1999, is published in May 1999. The Supplements may also include important corrections to The *Macmillan & Silk Cut Yachtsman's Handbook*.

As information contained in this Almanac is subject to constant change throughout the year, it is essential that users should **immediately** apply for the correcting Supplements in order to bring the Almanac fully up to date before using it for planning or at sea.

To obtain these Supplements please complete, stamp and post the enclosed addressed postcard. They will be sent to you as soon as possible after publication.

Notices to Mariners

Corrections to Admiralty charts and publications are issued weekly in *Admiralty Notices to Mariners*. These can be obtained from Admiralty Chart Agents (by post if required), or they can be seen at Customs Houses or Mercantile Marine Offices.

An alternative service is given by the *Admiralty Notices to Mariners, Small Craft Edition*, published quarterly in February, May, July and September. These contain reprinted notices for the British Isles and the continental coast from the Gironde to the Elbe. Notices concerning depths greater than 7 metres (23ft) are excluded, as are those which do not affect small craft for other reasons. They are available from Admiralty Chart Agents and the Royal Yachting Association.

In Oct 1997 the Hydrographic Office published NP 294 *How to correct your charts the Admiralty Way*, (£7.95). This useful guide deals not only with charts but with the whole range of Admiralty publications.

Record of amendments

The amendment sheet below is intended to assist you in keeping the Almanac up to date; it can also be used to record corrections to charts or other publications. Tick where indicated when the appropriate amendments have been made.

Weekly Notices to Mariners		Small Craft Notices to Mariners	
1	27	1 Feb 1998	....
2	28		
3	29	1 May 1998	....
4	30		
5	31	1 July 1998	....
6	32		
7	33	1 Sept 1998	....
8	34		
9	35	1 Feb 1999	....
10	36		
11	37	1 May 1999	....
12	38		
13	39	1 July 1999	....
14	40		
15	41	1 Sept 1999	....
16	42		
17	43	**Late corrections**	
18	44	(see back of Almanac,	
19	45	before index)	....
20	46		
21	47	**Macmillan**	
22	48	**Supplement**	
23	49	First	
24	50	(Jan 1999)	....
25	51	Second	
26	52	(May 1999)	....

ABBREVIATIONS AND SYMBOLS

The following selected abbreviations and symbols may be found in this Almanac, in the Supplements, and in Admiralty publications and charts. The margin tab A helps to locate the pages. The loose-leaf card bookmark for Dover HW and Range also contains abbreviations and symbols for those harbour facilities given in Chapter 8.

NOTE: *   Not shown for Marinas

AB*	Alongside berth
Abm	Abeam
ABP	Associated British Ports
abt	About
AC	220-250v AC electrical supplies
AC	Admiralty Chart
ACA	Admiralty Chart Agent
✈	Airport
Aff Mar	Affaires Maritimes
ALL	Admiralty List of Lights
ALRS	Admiralty List of Radio Signals
Alt	Altitude
Al	Alternating light
AM	Amplitude Modulation
anch, ⚓	Anchorage
annly	Annually
ANWB	Dutch Tourist Association of Road & Waterway Users
App	Apparent
Appr.	Approaches
ARCC	Aeronautical Rescue Co-ordination Centre
ATT	Admiralty Tide Tables
Auto	Météo Répondeur Automatique
Az	Azimuth
B.	Bay
B	Black
Ⓑ	Bank (£)
Bar	Licensed bar, public house
Bcst	Broadcast
BFO	Beat Frequency Oscillator
BH	Boat Hoist (tons)
Bk.	Bank (shoal)
bk	Broken
Bkwtr	Breakwater
Bldg	Building
Bn(s)	Beacon, beacon(s)
Bol	Bollard
brg	Bearing
BS	British Standard
BSH	German Hydrographic chart(s)
BST	British Summer Time
BT	British Telecom
Bu	Blue
BWB	British Waterways Board

By(s)	Buoy, buoys
BY	Boatyard
C.	Cape, Cabo, Cap
C	Crane (tons)
c	Coarse
ca	Cable
Cas	Castle
CD	Chart datum
CEVNI	Code Européen de Voies de la Navigation Intérieure
CG	Coastguard
🄲🄶, ⚓	Coastguard MRCC, MRSC
CH	Chandlery
Ch	Channel (VHF)
Ch, ⛪	Church, chapel
chan.	Channel (navigational)
Chy	Chimney
cm	Centimetre(s)
Col, Ⅰ	Column, pillar, obelisk
conspic	Conspicuous
const	Construction
cont	Continuous
Corr	Correction
cov	Covers
Cr.	Creek
CROSS	Centre Régional Opérationnel de Surveillance et Sauvetage
CRS, ✆, ☎	Coast Radio Station
Cup	Cupola
⌗	Customs (see HMC)
Cy	Clay
D	Diesel fuel
Dec	Declination
decrg	Decreasing
dest	Destroyed
DF	Direction finding
DG Range	Degaussing Range
DGPS	Differential GPS
Dia	Diaphone
◆ ◇	Diamond
Dir Lt	Directional light
discont	Discontinued
dist	Distance, distant
Dk	Dock
DLR	Dockland Light Railway
dm	Decimetre(s)
Dn(s)	Dolphin(s)
DOP	Dilution of precision (GPS)
Dr	Doctor
dr	Dries
DR	Dead reckoning
DSC	Digital selective calling
DST	Daylight Saving time
DW	Deep water, Deep-draught route
DYC	Dutch Yacht Chart(s)

DZ	Danger Zone (buoy)		H_e	Height of eye
			HF	High Frequency
E	East		HFP	High Focal Plane Buoy
EC	Early closing		HIE	Highlands & Islands Enterprise
ECM _	East Cardinal Mark		HJ	Day Service only, Sunrise to Sunset
ECM	Éditions Cartographiques Maritimes		HMC, ⌗	HM Customs
ED	Existence doubtful, European datum		HMSO	Her Majesty's Stationery Office
EEA	European Economic Area		HN	Night Service only, Sunset to Sunrise
El	Electrical repairs		Hn.	Haven
Ⓔ	Electronics repairs		Ho	House
Ent.	Entrance		HO	Office hours, Hydrographic Office
EP	Estimated position		H_o	Height of object
Est.	Estuary			Holding tank pumpout
ETA	Estimated Time of Arrival		(hor)	Horizontally disposed
ETD	Estimated Time of Departure		Ⓗ	Hospital
exper	Experimental		Hbr	Harbour
explos	Explosive		Hrs	Hours
ext	Extension		Hr Mr, Ⓗ	Harbour Master
			ht	Height
F&A	Fore and aft berth		HW	High Water
, Fax	Facsimile		HX	No fixed hrs
⠕⠕	Fog signal		Hz	Hertz
F	Fixed light			
f	Fine		Ⓘ	Harbour information/tidal data
F&A	Fore and aft berth		I	Island, islet
Fcst	Forecast		IALA	International Association of Lighthouse Authorities
FFL	Fixed and Flashing light			
Fl	Flashing light		Ident	Identification signal
FM	Frequency Modulation		IDM _	Isolated Danger Mark
Fog Det Lt	Fog detector light		IHO	International Hydrographic Organisation
Freq, Fx	Frequency			
FS	Flagstaff, Flagpole		(illum)	Illuminated
ft	Foot, feet		IMO	International Maritime Organisation
Ft	Fort		incrg	Increasing
FV(s)	Fishing vessel(s)		info	Information
FW, ⌐	Fresh water supply		INMARSAT	International Maritime Satellite Organisation
			inop	Inoperative
G	Gravel		INT	International
G, Ⓖ	Green, Green Fixed light		intens	Intensified
Gas	Calor Gas		IPTS	International Port Traffic Signals
Gaz	Camping Gaz		IQ	Interrupted quick flashing light
GC	Great-circle		IRPCS	International Regulations for Prevention of Collision at Sea
GDOP (GPS)	Geometrical Dilution of Precision			
GHA	Greenwich Hour Angle		Iso	Isophase light
GMDSS	Global Maritime Distress and Safety System		ITU	International Telecommunications Union
GPS	Global Positioning System		ITZ	Inshore Traffic Zone
grt	Gross Registered Tonnage		IUQ	Interrupted ultra quick flashing light
Gt	Great		IVQ	Interrupted very quick flashing light
Gy	Grey			
			kHz	Kilohertz
⌖ ⌖	Hearing-impaired facilities		km	Kilometre(s)
h	Hard, Hour		kn	knot(s)
H+, H–	Minutes past/before each hour		Kos	Kosangas
H24	Continuous		kW	Kilowatts
HAT	Highest Astronomical Tide			
Hd.	Head, Headland			

L	Lake, Loch, Lough
L*, Lndg, ⬎	Landing place
⬚	Launderette
Lat	Latitude
LAT	Lowest Astronomical Tide
Lanby ⌐	Large Automatic Navigational Buoy
LB, ⬚, △	Lifeboat, inshore lifeboat
Ldg	Leading
L Fl	Long-flashing light
Le.	Ledge
LF	Low frequency
LHA	Local Hour Angle
LH	Left hand
LL	List of lights
Lndg	Landing place
LOA	Length overall
Long	Longitude
LT	Local time
Lt(s)	Light(s)
Lt By	Light buoy
Lt F ⌐	Light float
Lt Ho	Lighthouse
Lt V ⌐	Light vessel
LW	Low Water
M*	Moorings available
M	Sea mile(s)
M	Mud
m	Metre(s)
mm	Millimetre(s)
Mag	Magnetic, magnitude (of Star)
ME	Marine engineering repairs
Météo	Météorologie/Weather
MF	Medium Frequency
MHWN	Mean High Water Neaps
MHWS	Mean High Water Springs
MHz	Megahertz
min(s)	Minute(s) of time
Mk	Mark
ML	Mean Level
MLWN	Mean Low Water Neaps
MLWS	Mean Low Water Springs
MMSI	Maritime Mobile Service Call Identity Code
Mo	Morse
Mon	Monument, Monday
MRCC	Maritime Rescue Co-ordination Centre
MRSC	Maritime Rescue Sub-Centre
ms	Millisecond(s); minutes, seconds
MSL	Mean Sea Level
Mt.	Mountain, Mount
N	North
NB	Notice Board
NCM ↓	North Cardinal Mark
NGS	Naval Gunfire Support
NM	Notice(s) to Mariners
No	Number

NON	Unmodulated continuous wave emission
np	Neap tides
NP	Naval Publication
NRT	Net registered tonnage
NT	National Trust
Obscd	Obscured
Obstn	Obstruction
Oc	Occulting light
(occas)	Occasional
ODAS	Ocean Data Acquisition System
Off	Office
Or	Orange
OSGB	Ordnance Survey GB Datum (1936)
OT	Other times
⬚	Partial-sighted facilities
P	Petrol
P.	Port (harbour)
P	Pebbles
(P)	Preliminary (NM)
PA	Position approximate
Pass.	Passage
Pax	Passengers
PC	Portuguese chart
PD	Position doubtful
PHM ⬚ ⬚	Port-hand Mark
Pk.	Peak
↑ ↑	Perch, Stake (PHM & SHM)
PLA	Port of London Authority
PO, ⬚	Post Office
⬚	Port Radio
pos	Position
△	Precautionary Area
(priv)	Private
Prog	Prognosis (weather charts)
prohib	Prohibited
proj	Projected
prom	Prominent
Pt.	Point
Pta	Punta
PV	Pilot Vessel
Pyl	Pylon
Q	Quick flashing light
QHM	Queen's Harbour Master
R, ⬚	Red, Red Fixed light, Rock
R.	River
R	Restaurant
R, Rk, Rky	Rock, Rocky
Ra	Coast Radar Station
⬚	Marine RDF Beacon
⬚ Aero	Aeronautical RDF Beacon
Racon ⬚	Radar Transponder Beacon
Radome	Radar dome
Ramark	Radar Beacon
RC	Non-directional radiobeacon
RCC	Rescue Co-ordination Centre

RDF	Radio direction-finding
Rds.	Roads, Roadstead
Rep	Reported
Rf.	Reef
RG	Radio direction finding station
RH	Right hand
⇌	Railway station
RNLI	Royal National Lifeboat Institution
Ro-Ro	Roll-on Roll-off (ferry terminal)
● ○	Round, circular; Ball
RPN	Reverse Polish notation
RT	Radiotelephony
Rtg	Rating (harbour)
Ru	Ruins
S	South
S	Sand
S, St, Ste	Saint(s)
SAE	Stamped, addressed envelope
SAR	Search and Rescue
⛑	SAR helicopter base
SBM	Single buoy mooring
SC	Sailing Club, Spanish chart
Sch	School
SCM ↓	South Cardinal Mark
Sd.	Sound
SD	Sailing Directions, Semi-Diameter
SD	Sounding of doubtful depth
sec(s)	Second(s) (of time)
Sem	Semaphore
Seq	Sequence
sf	Stiff
Sh	Shells, Shoal
Sh	Shipwright, hull repairs, etc
SHA	Sidereal Hour Angle (Stars)
SHM ▲ ◬	Starboard-hand Mark
SHOM	French hydrographic charts
Si	Silt
Sig	Signal
SIGNI	Signalisation de Navigation Intérieure (Dutch inland buoyage)
SM	Sailmaker
SMG	Speed made good
◣	Slip for launching, scrubbing
SNSM	Société Nationale de Sauvetage en Mer (Lifeboats)
so	Soft
Sp	Spire
sp	Spring tides
SPM ⌂ ◬ ↓	Special Mark, Single Point Mooring
SPS	Standard Positioning Service (GPS)
■ □	Square
SR	Sunrise
SS	Sunset, Signal Station
SSB	Single Sideband
St	Stones
Stbd	Starboard
Sta	Station
Str.	Strait
subm	Submerged
SWM ⊛ ↓	Safe Water Mark
sy	Sticky
sync	Synchronised
(T), (temp)	Temporary (NM)
t	Ton, tonne
TD	Fog signal temp discontinued
TE	Light temp extinguished
☎, Tel	Telephone
Tfc	Traffic
Tr	Tower
▼ ▲ ▽ △	Triangle, cone
TSS	Traffic Separation Scheme
Twi	Twilight
≠	In transit with
ufn	Until further notice
uncov	Uncovers
Unintens	Unintensified
unexam	Unexamined
UQ	Ultra quick flashing light
UT	Universal Time
V	Victuals, food stores, etc
Ⓥ, ⊘	Visitors berth/mooring
Var	Variation
Vel	Velocity
(vert)	Vertically disposed
VHF	Very High Frequency
Vi	Violet
vis	Visibility, visible
VLCC	Very large crude carrier
Volmet	Weather broadcasts for aviation
VTM	Vessel Traffic Management
VTS	Vessel Traffic Service
VQ	Very quick flashing light
W	West
W, Ⓦ	White, White Fixed light
WCM ↓	West Cardinal Mark
Wd	Weed
wef	With effect from
WGS	World Geodetic System (datum)
♿	Wheelchair access
Whf	Wharf
Whis	Whistle
WIP	Work in progress
⚲ ⚲	Withy (SHM & PHM)
Wk	Wreck
WMO	World Meteorological Organisation
WPT, ⊕	Waypoint
☁, Wx	Weather (☎ or times)
Y, Ⓨ	Yellow, Amber, Orange, Yellow fixed lt
YC, ⚑	Yacht Club
⚓	Yacht harbour, Marina
⚐	Where to report, or yacht berths

Chapter 1

General Information

Contents

1.1 INTERNATIONAL REGULATIONS FOR PREVENTING COLLISIONS AT SEA Page 8
1.1.1 General
1.1.2 Traffic Separation Schemes
1.1.3 Vessels in sight of each other
1.1.4 Restricted visibility
1.1.5 Lights and shapes
1.1.6 Sound signals
1.1.7 Annexes to IRPCS
1.1.8 Distress signals

1.2 DOCUMENTATION 12
1.2.1 Cruising formalities
1.2.2 Registration
1.2.3 Insurance
1.2.4 International Certificate of Competence

1.3 HM CUSTOMS 12
1.3.1 The European Union
1.3.2 Regulations
1.3.3 Stores
1.3.4 Notice of departure
1.3.5 Arrival from an EU country
1.3.6 Arrival from a non-EU country

1.3.7 Immigration
1.3.8 Customs offices – telephone numbers
1.3.9 Drug smuggling

1.4 FOREIGN CUSTOMS – PROCEDURES 13
1.4.1 General

1.5 VAT AND THE SINGLE MARKET 13
1.5.1 General
1.5.2 Temporary importation (TI)

1.6 USEFUL ADDRESSES 14

1.7 COLOUR PLATES 15
Plate 1 IALA buoyage
2/3 Admiralty chart symbols
4/5 Navigation lights and shapes 18
6/7 Signal flags, morse, phonetic alphabet
8 National ensigns
9 International Port traffic signals 22

1.7.1 Ensigns 23
1.7.2 International Port traffic signals
1.7.3 Notes on flag etiquette 24

C1

Summary

This chapter contains notes on interpreting the *International Regulations for Preventing Collisions at Sea (IRPCS)*, together with documentation, Customs procedures, useful addresses and nine colour plates. The full text of the IRPCS is given in *The Macmillan & Silk Cut Yachtsman's Handbook*.

The following subjects are described in detail in Chapter 2 of *The Macmillan & Silk Cut Yachtsman's Handbook*:

Limits and dangers – eg territorial waters; fishing limits; measured distances; hovercraft; warships on exercises; practice and exercise areas; submarines; minefields; wrecks; offshore oil and gas fields; power cables; traffic schemes; HM Customs – notice of departure; immigration; full and quick reports; Customs regulations in European countries; yacht tonnage measurement – net and gross tonnages; Lloyd's Register tonnage; dead weight tonnage; One Ton Cup etc; units and conversions; glossaries of nautical terms; yachting organisations – Royal Yachting Association; Seamanship Foundation; British Marine Industries Federation; Trinity House; useful addresses.

Chapter 6 of *The Macmillan & Silk Cut Yachtsman's Handbook* contains more detailed notes on flag etiquette, with colour plates of 217 selected yacht club burgees and the maritime flags of 165 nations.

1.1   INTERNATIONAL REGULATIONS FOR PREVENTING COLLISIONS AT SEA

1.1.1   General

a.   The 1972 International Regulations for Preventing Collisions at Sea (IRPCS), also referred to as Colregs or Rule of the Road, are given in full in *The Macmillan & Silk Cut Yachtsman's Handbook* (2.1), together with supporting diagrams and explanatory notes; also in RYA booklet G2. The exact wording of the IRPCS is important. The following notes on some of the provisions of special interest to yachtsmen are only to be used to help understand the Rules.

b.   The rules must be interpreted in a seamanlike way if collisions are to be avoided (Rule 2). The rules do not give any vessel right of way over another, completely regardless of special circumstances – eg other vessels under way or at anchor, shallow water, poor visibility, traffic separation schemes, fishing fleets, etc – or the handling characteristics of the vessels concerned in the prevailing conditions. Sometimes vessels may need to depart from the rules to avoid immediate danger (2 b).

c.   A sailing vessel is so defined (Rule 3) when she is under sail only.

d.   Keep a good lookout (Rule 5; the most important rule) at all times, using eyes and ears as well as radar and VHF, particularly at night or in poor visibility.

e.   Safe speed (Rule 6) is dictated by visibility, traffic density, including concentrations of fishing or other vessels, depth of water, the state of wind, sea and current, proximity of navigational dangers, and the manoeuvrability of the boat with special reference to stopping distance and turning ability in the prevailing conditions. Excessive speed gives less time to assess the situation, less time to take avoiding action, and produces a worse collision if such action fails.

f.   When faced with closing vessel(s), a skipper/crew must always answer the following three questions and take action if required.

    1. Is there a risk of collision?
    2. If there is, am I the give-way vessel?
    3. If I am, what action must I take?

g.   If there is any doubt, assume that there is a risk (Rule 7). A yacht should take a series of compass bearings on a converging ship; see Fig 1(1). Unless the bearings change appreciably, there is a risk of collision. Radar offers early warning of risk of collision. Take special care with large ships.

h.   Take early, positive and seamanlike action to avoid collision (Rule 8). Large alterations of course and/or speed are more evident to the other skipper, particularly at night or on radar. Slow down, stop (or even go astern, under power). While keeping clear of one vessel, watch out for others.

j.   In narrow channels (Rule 9), keep to starboard and as near to the outer limit of the channel or fairway as

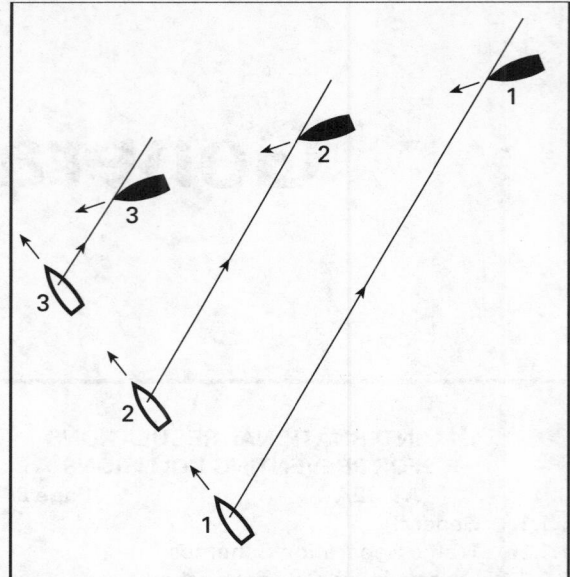

Fig 1(1) Rule 7. The bearing of black from white is steady. Before position 2 white should have altered to starboard by at least 45° to pass under black's stern.

is safe and practicable whether under power or sail. A yacht <20m LOA shall not impede larger vessels confined to a channel. A yacht should not cross a narrow channel if such crossing would impede a vessel which can only safely navigate within the channel, and should avoid anchoring in such channels.

1.1.2   Traffic Separation Schemes (TSS)

TSS (Rule 10) are essential to the safety of larger vessels and, whilst inconvenient for yachtsmen, must be accepted as another element of passage planning, or be avoided where possible. They are shown on most charts and those covered by this Almanac are depicted in the relevant geographic areas of Chapter 8.

All vessels, including yachts, must conform to TSS. However, when two vessels meet or converge in a TSS with a risk of collision, Rule 10 does not modify any other provisions of the IRPCS. But note that craft <20m LOA, and any sailing yacht, shall not impede a power vessel using a traffic lane (10 j). They should preferably use inshore traffic zones (ITZ) – often the most sensible action for a yacht, rather than using the main lanes. If, unusually, obliged to join or leave a lane, do so at its extremity; if joining or leaving at the side, do so at as shallow an angle as possible. Follow the general direction of traffic in the correct lane.

If obliged to cross a traffic lane, do so on a heading at 90° to the lane (10 c).

The best advice for yachtsmen is:

a.   Keep a sharp lookout.

b.   Use a good radar reflector.

c.   Monitor VHF Ch 16 and/or any TSS information broadcasts.

d. Use the engine if that makes the crossing quicker or if speed over the ground falls below about 3 knots.

e. Bear in mind that a yacht may not easily be seen by a big vessel, especially in rough seas or bad weather.

f. Use your common sense. In poor visibility a small craft has every disadvantage imaginable.

Some TSS are under surveillance by radar, aircraft or patrol vessels. There are heavy penalties for breaking the rules. 'YG' in the International Code means 'You appear not to be complying with the traffic separation scheme'. See Plates 6 and 7 on pages 20 and 21.

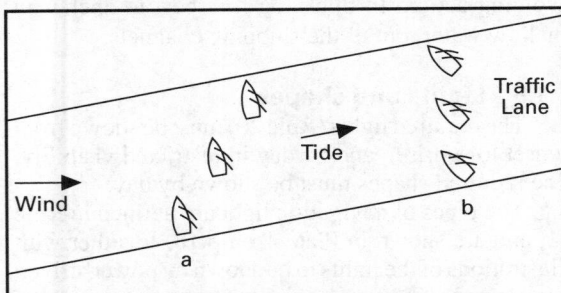

Fig 1(2) Rule 10. When crossing a traffic lane, the heading of the yacht must be at right angles to the traffic flow as shown in (a) above, regardless of the course made good which is affected by tidal streams. The yacht at (b) above is not heading at right angles and is therefore on an incorrect course.

1.1.3   Vessels in sight of one another

a. When two sailing vessels (Rule 12) are at risk of collision and on opposite tacks, the one on the port tack keeps clear. If on the same tack, the windward yacht keeps clear. If a yacht with the wind on the port side sees a yacht to windward and cannot determine with certainty whether the other yacht has the wind on the port or starboard side, then keep out of the way of the other. The windward side is deemed to be the side opposite to that on which the mainsail is carried. Rule 12 does not apply when either yacht is motor sailing. Fig 1(3) illustrates the practical application of the rules in the three cases mentioned above.

There are two other practical situations which might give cause for doubt about the application of Rule 12:

i. When running downwind under spinnaker alone. In this case windward would be the side on which the spinnaker boom is set (normally opposite to the mainsail).

ii. When hove-to. This would depend on the most likely position of the mainsail if it were set.

f. Using the arcs of visibility of the sidelights and sternlight to illustrate the rules, Fig 1(4) allots names to each arc. The arc of the sternlight is called the 'overtaking sector'; the arc of the starboard (Green) sidelight is called the 'give-way sector'; and the arc of the port (Red) sidelight is called the 'stand-on sector'.

b. Any overtaking vessel, whether power or sail, shall keep out of the way of the vessel being overtaken

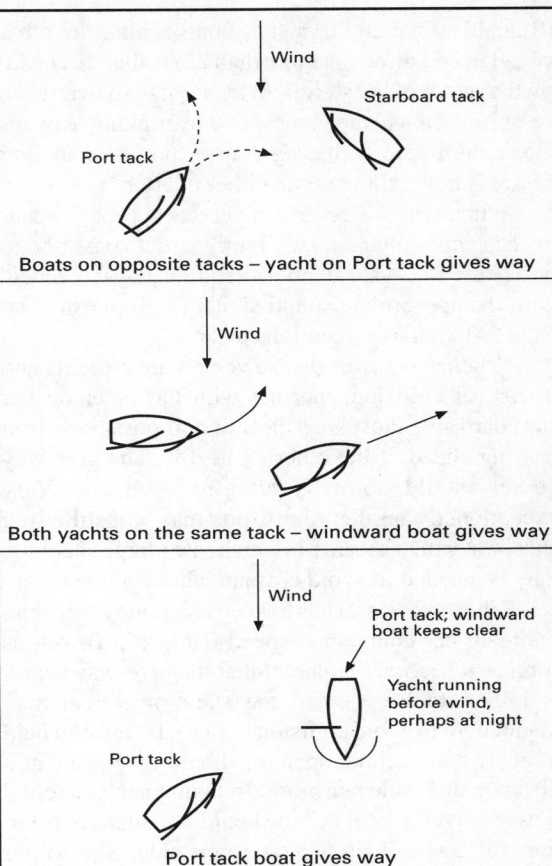

Fig 1(3) Rule 12. Conduct between sailing vessels. In all cases the yacht on the port tack keeps clear; if both yachts are on the same tack the windward boat keeps clear. If in doubt, always keep clear.

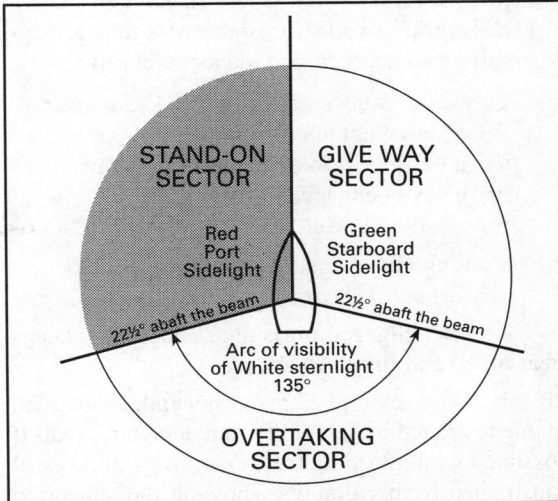

Fig 1(4) Rules 11 to 17. These rules apply only to vessels in sight of one another and do not apply when vessels can only see each other on radar.

(Rule 13). Overtaking means approaching the other vessel from a direction more than 22½° abaft her beam (in the sector of her sternlight by night). An overtaken vessel must not hamper one that is overtaking. Always look astern before altering course to ensure another vessel is not coming up on either quarter.

c.   When two power-driven vessels approach head-on, each must alter course to starboard, to pass port to port (Rule 14). A substantial alteration may be needed, with the appropriate sound signal (see opposite and Rule 34), to make intentions clear.

d.   When two power-driven vessels are crossing and in risk of collision, the one with the other on her starboard side must keep clear and, if possible, avoid passing ahead of the other (Rule 15). The give-way vessel should normally alter to starboard. Very exceptionally, an alteration to port may be justified (eg shoal water to starboard), in which case a large alteration may be needed to avoid crossing ahead of the other.

e.   When one vessel has to keep clear, the other shall maintain her course and speed (Rule 17a i). But as soon as it becomes apparent that the give-way vessel is failing to keep clear, the stand-on vessel may manoeuvre to avoid collision (17a ii). It has been held in court that such manoeuvre should take place at a distance of 2 miles or more. In taking such action, a power-driven vessel (17 c) should not alter course to port for a vessel on her own port side. She would normally alter substantially to starboard, thus minimising the risk of both vessels turning towards each other.

f.   Under Rule 17(b), when the stand-on vessel finds herself so close that collision cannot be avoided by the action of the give-way vessel alone, the stand-on vessel <u>shall</u> take such action as will best aid to avoid a collision.

g.   Rule 18, except where Rules 9 (narrow channels), 10 (TSS) and 13 (overtaking) otherwise require, lays down priorities according to manoeuvrability:

(a)   A power-driven vessel under way keeps clear of:
    (i)   a vessel not under command;
    (ii)   a vessel restricted in manoeuvrability;
    (iii)   a vessel engaged in fishing;
    (iv)   a sailing vessel.

(b)   A sailing vessel under way keeps clear of:
    (i)-(iii) in (a) above.

(c)   A vessel engaged in fishing, under way, keeps clear of: (i) and (ii) in (a) above.

(d)   (i)   Any vessel, except one not under command or one restricted in her ability to manoeuvre, shall if possible avoid impeding the safe passage of a vessel constrained by her draught, showing the signals in Rule 28 (see Plate 5, page 19).

    (ii)   A vessel constrained by her draught shall navigate with particular caution.

1.1.4   Restricted visibility

In poor visibility vessels must proceed at a safe speed (Rules 19 and 6). On hearing a fog signal ahead of the beam, be prepared to reduce speed or stop. If a vessel is detected by radar, take early action to avoid collision. If the other vessel is ahead of the beam, avoid altering course to port, unless the other vessel is being overtaken. If the other vessel is abaft the beam, do not alter course towards it. Sound the appropriate fog signal; keep a good lookout; have an efficient radar reflector; keep clear of shipping lanes; and be ready to take drastic avoiding action. In thick fog it is best to anchor in shallow water, out of the shipping channels.

1.1.5   Lights and shapes

a.   The required lights (Rule 20) must be shown from sunset to sunrise, and by day in restricted visibility. The required shapes must be shown by day.

b.   The types of navigation light are defined in Rule 21, and are shown in Plate 4 on p 18, together with illustrations of the lights to be shown by power-driven vessels and sailing vessels under way. A summary of further lights and shapes to be shown by various classes of vessel is given in Plate 5 on page 19.

c.   A power-driven vessel under 12m in length may combine her masthead light and sternlight in one all-round white light (Rule 23).

d.   Lights required for vessels towing and being towed (Rule 24) include a special yellow towing light above the sternlight of the towing vessel. But this is not required by a yacht or other small craft not normally used for towing.

e.   In a sailing yacht < 20m LOA, the sidelights and sternlight may be combined in one tricolour lantern at the masthead (Rule 25 b). This gives excellent visibility for the lights, and maximum brightness for minimum battery drain. A tricolour light should not be switched on at the same time as the normal sidelights and sternlight, and must not be used when under power.

f.   A sailing vessel under way may, in addition to her normal sidelights and sternlight, show near the masthead two all-round lights in a vertical line, red over green (25 c). But these lights must not be shown in conjunction with the tricolour lantern described in paragraph d above.

g.   A yacht when being driven by engine (25 e), even with sails set, must show the lights of a power-driven vessel, and by day, a cone, point-down, forward.

h.   In broad terms special lights indicate types and classes of vessel. Commonly encountered all-round lights, displayed vertically, include: fishing vessels = red over white; trawlers = green over white; vessels which cannot manoeuvre = red, over white, over red; a vessel constrained by her draught = three red lights. A hovercraft shows an all-round flashing yellow light.

j.   Rule 27 (vessels not under command, or restricted in their ability to manoeuvre), does not apply to vessels <12m LOA, except for flying flag 'A' when engaged in diving operations.

SUMMARY OF IMPORTANT SOUND SIGNALS – RULES 34 AND 35

Note: • indicates a short blast, of about one second's duration, on the foghorn.
       — indicates a prolonged blast, of four to six seconds' duration, on the foghorn.

Manoeuvring and warning signals (Rule 34)

•	I am altering course to starboard (power-driven vessel).
••	I am altering course to port (power-driven vessel).
•••	I am operating astern propulsion (power-driven vessel).
——•	(In a narrow channel) I intend to overtake you on your starboard side.
——••	(In a narrow channel) I intend to overtake you on your port side.
—•—•	Agreement with the overtaking signal above.
•••••	I fail to understand your intentions or actions/I doubt if you are taking sufficient action to avoid collision.
—	Warning signal by vessel(s) approaching a bend in channel.

Sound signals in restricted visibility (Rule 35, a-f)

—	Power-driven vessel making way through the water.
——	Power-driven vessel under way, but stopped and not making way through the water.
—••	Vessel not under command, or restricted in her ability to manoeuvre, or constrained by her draught, or engaged in fishing, or towing or pushing, or a **sailing vessel**.
—•••	Vessel being towed, or if more than one vessel is towed, the last vessel in the tow.
••••	Pilot vessel engaged on pilotage duties (Rule 35, h, ii).

The maximum interval between sound signals for vessels under way in restricted visibility is two minutes, but they should be sounded more frequently if other craft are near.

Sound signals by vessels at anchor or aground in restricted visibility (Rule 35 g & h)

Bell rung rapidly for about 5 seconds, every minute.	= Vessel at anchor; the bell being sounded in the fore part of the vessel.
Gong sounded rapidly for about 5 seconds following above signal, every minute.	= Vessel of 100m or more in length at anchor; the gong being sounded in the aft part of the vessel.
•—• short, prolonged, short blasts	= Vessel at anchor (optional additional warning signal).
Rapid ringing of a bell (and gong if required) for 5 secs every minute, with 3 separate and distinct strokes on the bell before and after the rapid ringing.	= Vessel aground.

C1

k.   A yacht <7m LOA, when at anchor not in or near a narrow channel, fairway or anchorage, or where other vessels normally navigate, is not required to show an anchor light or ball (Rule 30 e). Apart from this minor exemption, yachts at anchor, like other vessels, <u>shall</u> show an anchor light or ball. This requirement has safety and insurance implications, assists other mariners and is often enforced abroad. A vessel <12m LOA, when aground, is not required to show the lights or shapes prescribed by Rule 30 f.

1.1.6 Sound signals

Sound signals (Rules 34 and 35) are summarised in the table above. Vessels >12m LOA must be provided with a whistle (foghorn) and a bell. A boat <12m LOA is not obliged to carry these sound-signalling appliances, but must have some means of making an efficient sound signal. The effectiveness of a yacht's sound signal should be judged against its audibility from the bridge of a large ship, with conflicting noises from other sources.

1.1.7 Annexes to IRPCS

Annexes I and III give tecnical details of lights, shapes and sound signals. Annex II gives additional lights which may be shown by fishing vessels working in close proximity to one another.

1.1.8   Distress signals

Annex IV of the IRPCS gives details of all the signals which may be used either together or separately to indicate distress and need of assistance. Those most suited to use by yachts are described in more detail in Chapter 6 (6.3.3). For those flag and sound signals having a special meaning under IRPCS, see also Plates 6 – 7 on pages 20 and 21. For lesser emergencies use 'V' International Code = 'I require assistance'.

1.2   DOCUMENTATION

1.2.1   Cruising formalities

Before, or while cruising abroad, certain formalities are necessary, as summarised below. It creates a favourable impression, especially abroad, and saves time if ship's and owner's documents are smartly presented in a readily available file.

(1) **Yacht documents**
Registration certificate (1.2.2). Proof of VAT status (1.5.1). Marine insurance covering the intended cruising area, including third-party cover (1.2.3).
Ship's radio licence (4.2.2). Ship's Log and yacht's itinerary.

(2) **Personal documents**
Valid passports and Forms E.111. Crew list.
Certificate of Competence, eg ICC or Yachtmaster (1.2.4). Radio Operator's certificate of competence and authority to operate (4.2.2).

(3) Comply with health regulations (eg report any infectious disease); exceptionally, vaccination certificates may be needed.

(4) The yacht should wear the national ensign and fly a courtesy ensign of the country visited at starboard crosstree. Carry flag 'Q'.

(5) Conform to HM Customs regulations (1.3).

(6) Conform to Customs regulations in countries visited (1.4). If in doubt about specific items or procedures, ask. All countries are sensitive to the importation (including carriage on board) of illegal quantities of alcohol and tobacco, and any drugs.

(7) In most countries it is illegal to use a visiting cruising yacht for a commercial purpose (eg charter).

1.2.2   Registration

British-owned yachts can be registered under the Merchant Shipping Act 1995 and the Merchant Shipping (Registration of Ships) Regulations 1993. The Register is in four parts:

Part I   for merchant ships and pleasure vessels
Part II   for fishing vessels
Part III   for small ships (Small Ships Register)
Part IV   for bareboat charter ships

The procedures for all types of registration are fully described in a booklet *Registering British Ships in the United Kingdom* issued by the RSS/MSA/DoT, and obtainable from:
Registry of Shipping and Seamen (RSS), PO Box 165, Cardiff CF4 5FU. ☎ 01222 747333; ✆ 747877. There is a ☎ help line available on 0891 615353.

a.   Registration under Part I is a relatively complex and expensive business, since a yacht has to follow the same procedure as a large merchant vessel. The certificate establishes the ship's nationality and tonnage. It does **not** prove ownership nor show mortgages. It costs £46 to renew for 5 years.

b.   Part III, commonly called The Small Ships Register (SSR), is for ships which only want a simple registration. This is sufficient for most purposes. A small ship is deemed to be < 24 metres LOA. It satisfies the law that a British yacht proceeding abroad

must be registered, and it also meets the registration requirement for a privileged ensign. Part III registration registers neither 'Title' nor mortgages.

The cost is £10 for a five-year period, and measurement is a simple matter of taking the LOA of the boat. An application form is obtainable from: The RSS, PO Box 508, Cardiff CF4 5FH. ☎: 01222-761911 or 747333 ext 289; ✆: 01222 747877.

1.2.3   Insurance

Any cruising boat represents a large capital investment, which should be protected against possible loss or damage by adequate insurance. It is also essential to insure against third-party risks, and cover for at least £1,000,000 is now normal.

The value for which a boat is insured should be the replacement cost of the boat and all equipment. Abide by the nominated period in commission and cruising area. Note the various warranties which are implied or expressed in the policy. For example, the owner is required to keep the boat in a seaworthy condition; theft is only covered if forcible entry or removal can be shown; engines and other mechanical items are only covered in exceptional circumstances; charter and loss of personal effects are not covered, unless specially arranged.

1.2.4   International Certificate of Competence

The International Certificate of Competence (ICC) (Pleasure Craft) replaces the former Helmsman's Overseas Certificate of Competence (HOCC) and is valid for five years. If a suitable RYA Certificate (eg Yachtmaster offshore) is not held, the ICC will be issued by the RYA to British Citizens or bonafide UK residents who either:
(a) pass a test at an RYA recognised sea school or participating Club; or
(b) already hold a HOCC, or a professional or military seagoing qualification.

1.3   HM CUSTOMS

1.3.1   The European Union (EU)

EU yachtsmen can move freely within the EU, provided that all taxes due, such as Customs duty, VAT, or any other Customs charges, have been paid in one of the EU countries. But most nations still carry out random checks on yachts to stop illegal goods, especially drugs, from entering their country.

EU and EEA countries are: Austria, Belgium, Denmark, Finland, France, Germany, Greece, Holland, Iceland, Italy, Luxembourg, Norway, Portugal (including the Azores and Madeira), Republic of Ireland, Spain (including the Balearic Islands, but not the Canary Islands), Sweden, and the UK (including Gibraltar, but not the Isle of Man and the Channel Islands).

The Channel Islands and the Canary Islands do not operate a VAT system under EU rules, and are therefore treated as being outside the EU single market.

1.3.2   Regulations

All yachts sailing beyond UK Territorial Waters must

comply with Customs Notice No 8 (April 1996), *Sailing your pleasure craft to/from the UK* which is summarised below. This Notice and further information may be obtained from any Customs and Excise Office, or from HM Customs and Excise, OAS at the address overleaf.

Yachtsmen are warned that a boat may be searched at any time. There are severe penalties for non-declaration of prohibited or restricted goods, and the carriage and non-declaration of prohibited drugs and firearms will incur the forfeiture of your boat and all its equipment. It is a good idea to have a copy of Notice No 8 aboard.

1.3.3   Stores
Duty-free stores may be allowed on vessels going south of Brest (France) or north of the north bank of the Eider (Germany), by prior application to a Customs office, and subject to certain conditions. Duty-free stores cannot be taken to the Republic of Ireland or the Channel Islands. Details on how to ship stores, or re-ship previously landed surplus duty-free stores, can be obtained from any Customs office. Stores being shipped under bond, or on which repayment of Customs charges is being claimed, are normally placed under a Customs seal on board. Such goods cannot be used in UK waters without paying duty, and duty may be liable if the voyage is abandoned or interrupted.

1.3.4   Notice of departure
a. To another EU country: No report is needed , unless requested by a Customs Officer.
b. To a place outside the EU: Each intended departure must be notified to HM Customs on Part 1 of Form C1331, copies of which are available at Customs offices and from most marinas and yacht clubs. Failure to give notice of departure may result in delay and inconvenience on return, and possible prosecution.

The completed Part 1 should be handed to a Customs Officer, taken to the Customs office nearest the place of departure, or put in a Customs post box, so that the form arrives before departure. Form C1331 is valid for up to 48 hours from the stated time of departure. Retain Part 2 on board for use on your return. If the voyage is abandoned, Part 2 should be delivered to the same office marked 'voyage abandoned'.

1.3.5   Arrival from an EU country
If arriving directly from another EU country there is no need to fly flag 'Q', complete any paperwork, or contact Customs. You must, however, contact Customs if you have goods to declare, or have non-EU nationals on board. You must declare any animals or birds; any prohibited or restricted goods such as controlled drugs, firearms, or radio transmitters not approved for use in UK; counterfeit goods; any duty-free stores; or the boat itself if duty and VAT are owed on it. Further details on which goods are classified as prohibited or restricted are given in Notice 8.

1.3.6   Arrival from a non-EU country
If arriving directly from a country outside the EU (including the Channel Islands), yachts are subject to Customs control. As soon as UK Territorial Waters are entered, ie the 12-mile limit, complete Part 2 of Form C1331 and fly the flag 'Q' where it can easily be seen until formalities are complete. On arrival contact a Customs Officer in person or by telephone. If an officer boards your vessel, you must hand Form C1331 to him. You must declare any tobacco goods, alcoholic drinks, perfumes and toilet waters in excess of your duty-free allowance; animals or birds; prohibited or restricted goods; duty-free stores; or the boat itself if duty and VAT are owed on it. You must also declare any goods that are to be left in the UK. You must not land any persons or goods, or transfer them to another vessel until a Customs Officer says that you may.

1.3.7   Immigration
In most yachting centres the Customs Officer also acts as the Immigration Officer. Anyone aboard who is not an EU national must get an Immigration Officer's permission to enter the UK from any country other than the Isle of Man, the Channel Islands, or Eire. The skipper is responsible for ensuring that this is done.

1.3.8   Customs offices – telephone numbers
The telephone number of the appropriate Customs office (#) is given under the heading 'Telephone' for each British harbour in Chapter 8.

1.3.9   Drug smuggling
The prevention of drug smuggling is a key role for HM Customs. Public support is very important. If you see a suspicious incident or know of suspicious activity, telephone 0800 59 5000. This is a 24 hours, free and confidential Action line. There may be a reward.

1.4   FOREIGN CUSTOMS
1.4.1   General
Other EU countries should follow the same regulations as described in 1.3.1 to 1.3.6 above, and any Customs formalities are likely to be minimal. However, before departure, skippers are recommended to check the procedures in force in their destination country. Currently, both the Netherlands and Belgium require a vessel to report on arrival even if coming from another EU country.

1.5.   VAT AND THE SINGLE MARKET
1.5.1   General
An EU resident can move a yacht between member states without restriction, providing evidence is available that VAT has been paid.

1.5.2   Temporary importation (TI)
A boat can only be permitted into an EU country under TI arrangements if: (1) The owner is not an EU resident (ie lives outside the EU for at least 185 days in any 12-month period), and
(2)   The owner does not keep the boat in the EU for more than six months in a continuous 12-month period, within the EU as a whole. The period of TI cannot be extended by moving the boat to another EU member state. It may, however, be extended by written application to the member state where the yacht is at present. For the UK, this is the National Unit for Personal Transport; see overleaf for address.

C1

1.6   USEFUL ADDRESSES

See also page 80 for selected e-mail addresses.

British Marine Industries Federation (BMIF).
Boating Industry House, Mead Lake Place,
Thorpe Lea Road, Egham, Surrey TW20 8HE.
☎ 01784 473377. 🕿 01784 439678.

British Sub-Aqua Club.
Telford's Quay, Ellesmere Port, South Wirral,
Cheshire L65 4FY.
☎ 0151-357 1951. 🕿 0151-357 1250.

British Waterways Board.
Willow Grange, Church Road, Watford WD1 3QA.
☎ 01923 226422. 🕿 01923 226081.

Clyde Cruising Club.
Suite 408, The Pentagon Centre, 36 Washington
Street, Glasgow G3 8AZ.
☎ 0141-221 2774. 🕿 0141-221 2775.

Commissioners of Irish Lights.
16 Lower Pembroke Street, Dublin 2.
☎ 00-353-1-6624525. 🕿 00-353-1-6618094.

Cowes Combined Clubs.
18 Bath Road, Cowes, Isle of Wight PO31 7QN.
☎ 01983 295744. 🕿 01983 295329.

Cruising Association (CA).
CA House, 1 Northey Street, Limehouse Basin,
London E14 8BT.
☎ 0171-537 2828. 🕿 0171-537 2266.

HM Customs and Excise.
OAS, 5th Floor East, New King's Beam House,
22 Upper Ground, London SE1 9PJ.
☎ 0171-865 4742. 🕿 0171-865 4744.

Hydrographic Office.
Admiralty Way, Taunton, Somerset TA1 2DN.
☎ 01823 337900. 🕿 01823 284077.

Inmarsat.
99 City Road, London EC1Y 1AX.
☎ 0171-728 1000. 🕿 0171-728 1044.

International Maritime Organisation (IMO).
4 Albert Embankment, London SE1 7SR.
☎ 0171-735 7611. 🕿 0171-587 3210.

Irish Cruising Club.
Hon Sec, 8 Heidelberg, Ardlea, Dublin 14.
☎ +353 1 2884733.

Junior Offshore Group.
43 Parklands Ave, Cowes, Isle of Wight PO31 7NH.
☎ 01983 280279. 🕿 01983 292962.

Little Ship Club.
Bell Wharf Lane, Upper Thames Street,
London EC4R 3TB.
☎ 0171-236 7729. 🕿 0171-236 9100.

Lloyd's Register of Shipping.
71 Fenchurch St, London EC3M 4BS.
☎ 0171 709 9166. 🕿 0171 488 4796.

Maritime and Coastguard Agency.
Spring Place, 105 Commercial Road,
Southampton SO1 0ZD.
☎ 01703 329100. 🕿 01703 329351.

Maritime Trust.
2 Greenwich Church Street, London SE10 9BG.
☎ 0181-858 2698. 🕿 0181-858 6976.

Meteorological Office.
London Road, Bracknell, Berks RG12 2SZ.
☎ 01344 420242. 🕿 01344 855921.

National Unit for Personal Transport (See 1.5.2)
HM Customs and Excise, PO Box 242, Dover, CT17 9GP.
☎ 01304 224372; 🕿 01304 215786

Northern Lighthouse Board.
84 George Street, Edinburgh EH2 3DA.
☎ 0131 226 7051. 🕿 0131 220 2093.

Radiocommunications Agency.
New King's Beam House, 22 Upper Ground,
London SE1 9SA.
☎ 0171 211 0215. 🕿 0171 211 0507.

Radio Licensing Centre. (See 4.2.3)
Subscription Services Ltd, Barton House,
Bond Street, Bristol BS98 1TI.
☎ 0117 9258333. 🕿 0117 9219026.

Registry of Shipping and Seamen (RSS).
Part I registration: PO Box 165, Cardiff CF4 5FU.
☎ 01222 747333 Extn 289. 🕿 01222 747877.
Part III registration (Small Ships Register):
RSS, PO Box 508, Cardiff CF4 5FH.
☎ 01222 761911 or 747333 x289. 🕿 01222 747877.

Royal Cruising Club (RCC).
At the Royal Thames Yacht Club (see below).

Royal Institute of Navigation.
At the Royal Geographical Society,
1 Kensington Gore, London SW7 2AT.
☎ 0171-589 5021. 🕿 0171-823 8671.

Royal National Lifeboat Institution (RNLI).
West Quay Road, Poole, Dorset BH15 1HZ.
☎ 01202 663000. 🕿 01202 663167.

Royal Naval Sailing Association (RNSA).
17 Pembroke Road, Portsmouth, Hants PO1 2NT.
☎ 01705 823524. 🕿 01705 870654.

Royal Ocean Racing Club (RORC).
20 St James's Place, London SW1A 1NN.
☎ 0171-493 2248. 🕿 0171-493 5252.

Royal Thames Yacht Club (RTYC).
60 Knightsbridge, London SW1A 7LF.
☎ 0171-235 2121. 🕿 0171-235 5672.

Royal Yachting Association (RYA).
RYA House, Romsey Road, Eastleigh SO50 9YA.
☎ 01703 629962. 🕿 01703 629924.

Royal Yachting Association (Scotland).
Caledonia House, South Gyle,
Edinburgh EH12 9DQ.
☎ 0131-317 7388. 🕿 0131-317 8566.

Ship Radio Licensing Unit.
Wray Castle Ltd, Ship Radio Licensing,
PO Box 5, Ambleside LA22 0BF.
☎ 015394 34662. 🕿 015394 34663.

Solent Cruising and Racing Association.
18 Bath Road, Cowes, Isle of Wight PO31 7QN.
☎ 01983 295744. 🕿 01983 295329.

Sports Council.
16 Upper Woburn Place, London WC1H 0OP.
☎ 0171-388 1277. 🕿 0171-383 5740.

Trinity House, Corporation of.
Trinity House, Tower Hill, London EC3N 4DH.
☎ 0171-480 6601. 🕿 0171-480 7662.

UK Offshore Boating Association.
1 Carbis Close, Port Solent, Portsmouth PO6 4TW.
☎ 01705 219949. 🕿 01705 219969.

Yacht Brokers, Designers and Surveyors Assoc'n.
Wheel House, Petersfield Rd, Bordon GU35 9BU.
☎ 01420 473862. 🕿 01420 488328.

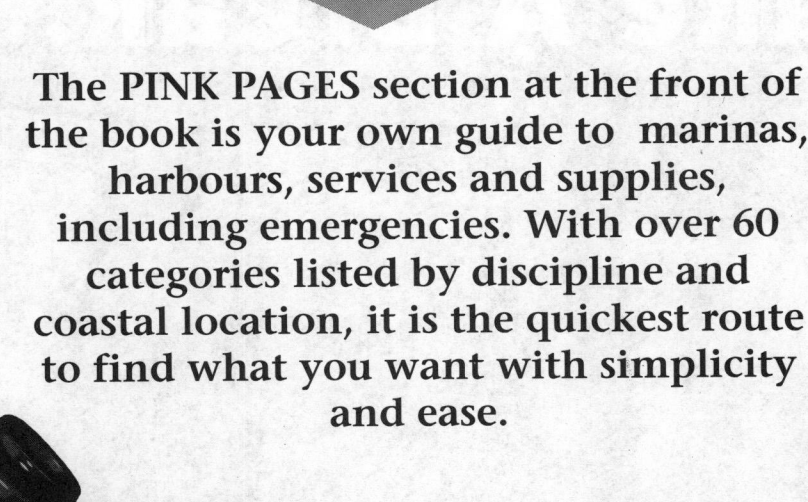

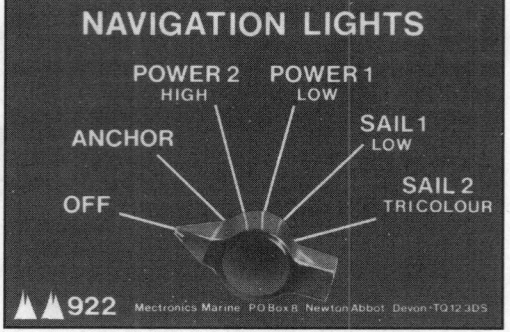
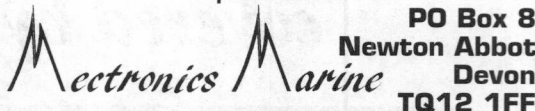

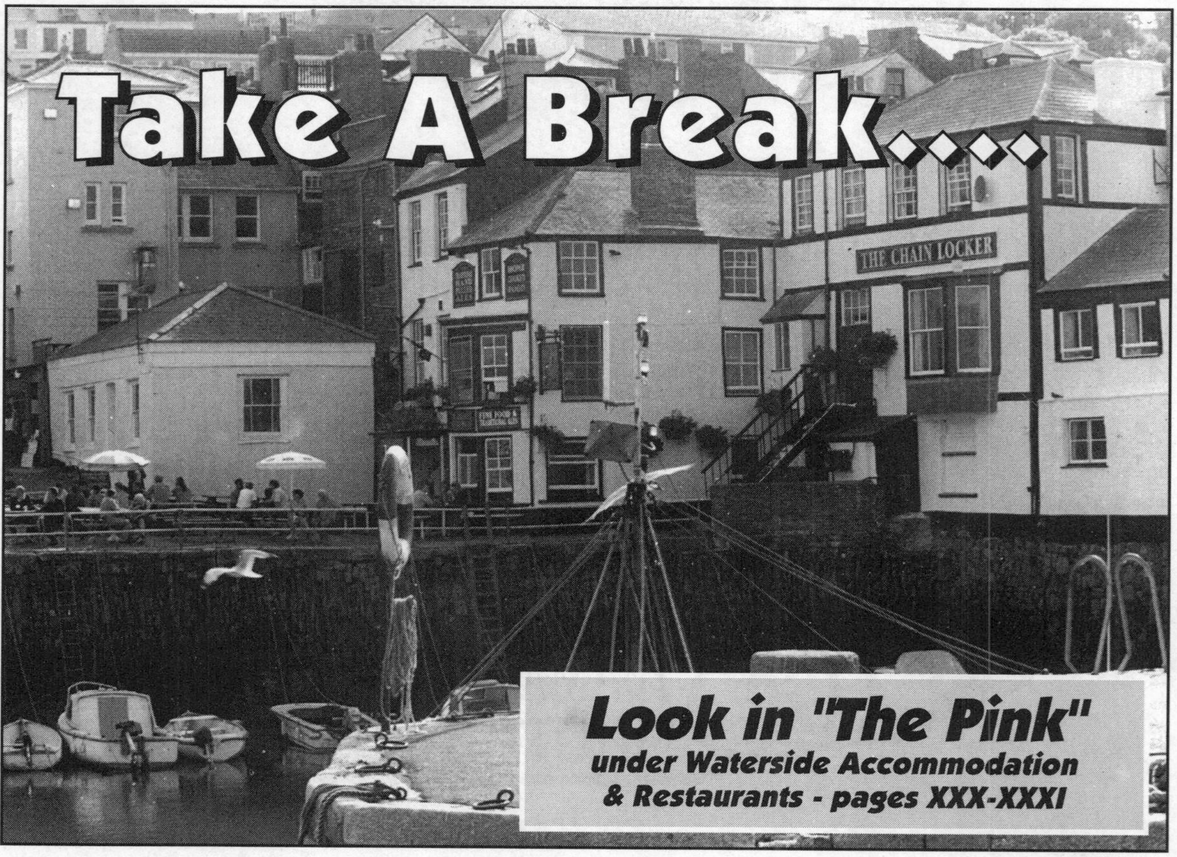

PLATE 5 – NAVIGATION LIGHTS

Port sidelight (red) shows from ahead to 22½° abaft the beam

112½°

Abeam

For yachts 12-50m overall, visibility – 2 miles. For yachts under 12m – 1 mile

(May be combined with starboard sidelight in one centreline lantern in boats under 20m overall)

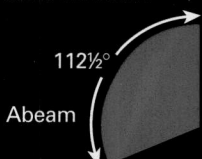

White masthead light shows over arc of 225° – from ahead to 22½° abaft the beam each side. Shown by vessels under power only

Ahead

225°

(Masthead light and sternlight may be combined in one all-round white light in boats under 12m overall)

Astern

White sternlight shows over arc of 135°, 67½° on each side of vessel

135°

For yachts under 50m overall, visibility – 2 miles

For yachts 20-50m overall, visibility – 5 miles. For yachts 12-20m – 3 miles. For yachts under 12m – 2 miles

Starboard sidelight (green) shows from ahead to 22½° abaft the beam

112½°

Abeam

For yachts 12-50m overall, visibility – 2 miles. For yachts under 12m – 1 mile

(May be combined with port sidelight in one centreline lantern in boats under 20m overall)

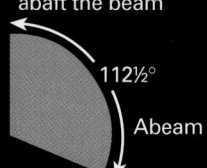

Lights for power-driven vessels underway (plan views)

Note: Also apply to sailing yachts or other sailing craft when under power

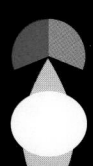

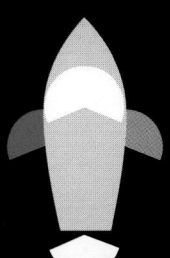
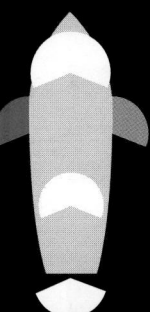

Motor boat under 7m, less than 7 knots

Motor boat under 12m (combined masthead & sternlight)

Motor yacht under 20m (combined lantern for sidelights)

Motor yacht over 20m

Larger vessel, over 50m, with two masthead lights – the aft one higher

Lights for sailing vessels underway (plan views)

Note: These lights apply to sailing craft when under sail ONLY. If motor-sailing, the appropriate lights for a power-driven vessel must be shown, as above

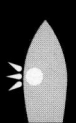
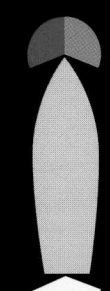
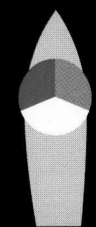
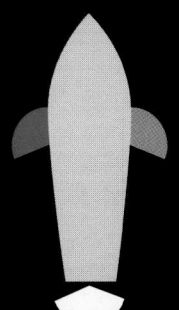

Masthead tricolour lantern

or

Sailing boat under 7m shows white light to prevent collision. If practicable, she should show sidelights and sternlight

Combined sidelights plus sternlight

Tricolour lantern at masthead

Sailing yacht under 20m

Separate sidelights and sternlight for sailing vessel over 20m

Bow view

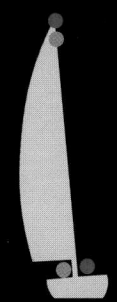

If *not* using tricolour masthead lantern, a sailing yacht may show (in addition to other lights) two all-round lights near masthead, the upper red and the lower green

PLATES 6-7 – INTERNATIONAL CODE OF SIGNALS, CODE FLAGS, PHONETIC ALPHABET, MORSE SYMBOLS AND SINGLE-LETTER SIGNALS

Notes:
1. Single-letter signals may be made by any method of signalling. Those marked * when made by sound must comply with the *International Regulations for Preventing Collisions at Sea,* Rules 34 and 35.
2. Signals 'K' and 'S' have special meanings as landing signals for small boats with persons in distress.
3. In the phonetic alphabet, the syllables to be emphasised are in italics.

A Alfa (*AL* FAH)

I have a diver down, keep well clear at slow speed

*B Bravo (*BRA* VOH)

I am taking in, discharging, or carrying dangerous goods

*C Charlie (*CHAR* LEE)

Yes (affirmative or 'The significance of the previous group should be read in the affirmative)

*D Delta (*DELL* TAH)

Keep clear of me; I am manoeuvring with difficulty

*E Echo (*ECK* OH)

I am altering my course to starboard

F Foxtrot (*FOKS* TROT)

I am disabled, communicate with me

*G Golf (*GOLF*)

I require a pilot. When made by fishing vessels operating in close proximity on the fishing grounds it means: I am hauling nets

*H Hotel (HOH *TELL*)

I have a pilot on board

Code and Answering Pendant

*I India (*IN* DEE AH)

I am altering my course to port

J Juliet (JEW LEE *ETT*)

I am on fire and have dangerous cargo on board: keep well clear of me

K Kilo (*KEY* LOH)

I wish to communicate with you

L Lima (*LEE* MAH)

You should stop your vessel instantly

*M Mike (MIKE)

My vessel is stopped and making no way through the water

N November (NO *VEM* BER)

No (negative or 'The significance of the previous group should be read in the negative'). This signal may be given only visually or by sound

O Oscar (*OSS* CAH)

Man overboard

P Papa (PAH *PAH*)

In harbour: all persons should report on board as the vessel is about to proceed to sea. **At sea:** it may be used by fishing vessels to mean 'My nets have come fast upon an obstruction'

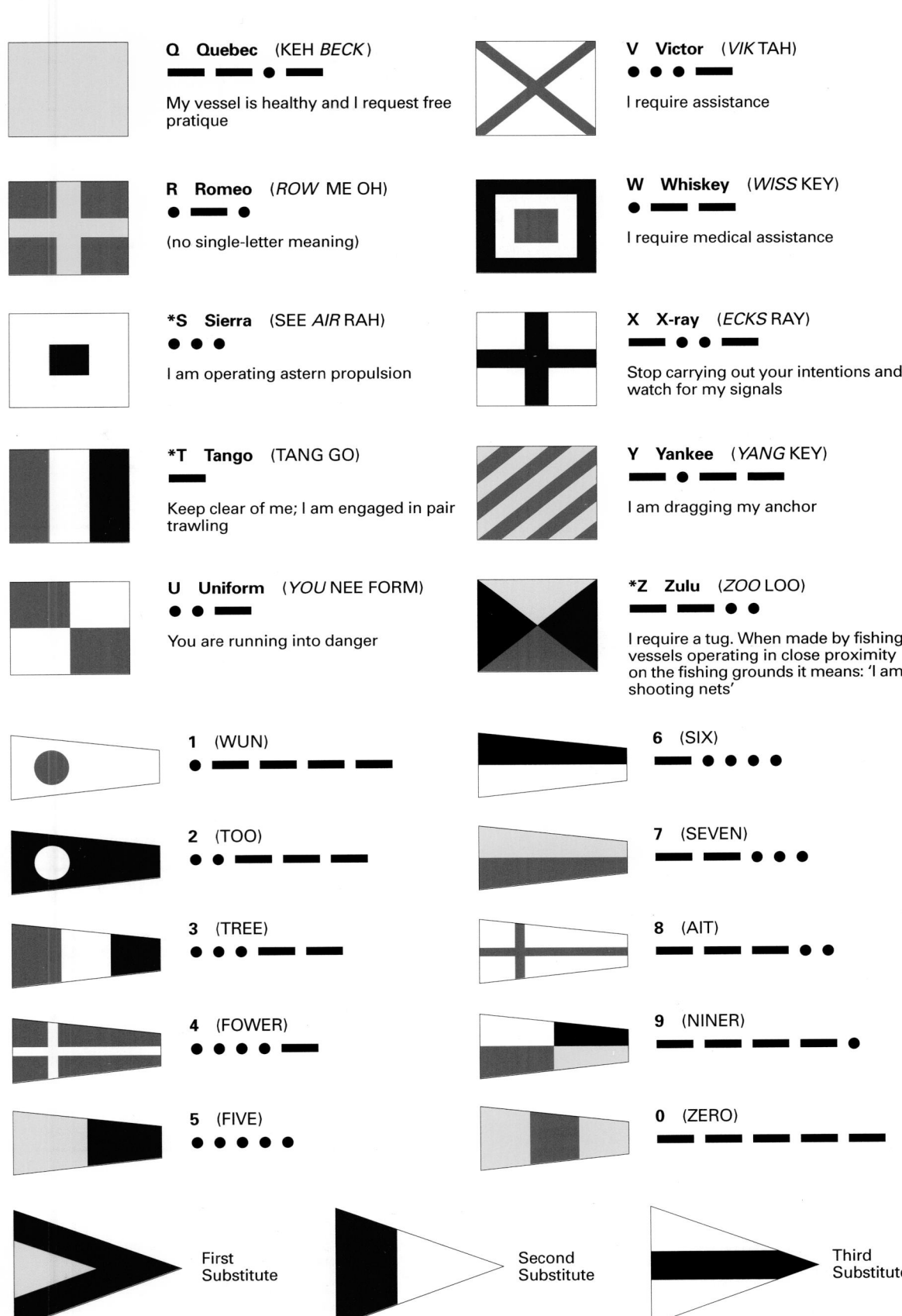

Q Quebec (KEH *BECK*)
━ ━ ●

My vessel is healthy and I request free pratique

R Romeo (*ROW* ME OH)
● ━ ●

(no single-letter meaning)

*S Sierra (SEE *AIR* RAH)
● ● ●

I am operating astern propulsion

*T Tango (TANG GO)
━

Keep clear of me; I am engaged in pair trawling

U Uniform (*YOU* NEE FORM)
● ● ━

You are running into danger

V Victor (*VIK* TAH)
● ● ● ━

I require assistance

W Whiskey (*WISS* KEY)
● ━ ━

I require medical assistance

X X-ray (*ECKS* RAY)
━ ● ● ━

Stop carrying out your intentions and watch for my signals

Y Yankee (*YANG* KEY)
━ ● ━ ━

I am dragging my anchor

*Z Zulu (*ZOO* LOO)
━ ━ ● ●

I require a tug. When made by fishing vessels operating in close proximity on the fishing grounds it means: 'I am shooting nets'

1 (WUN)
● ━ ━ ━ ━

2 (TOO)
● ● ━ ━ ━

3 (TREE)
● ● ● ━ ━

4 (FOWER)
● ● ● ● ━

5 (FIVE)
● ● ● ● ●

6 (SIX)
━ ● ● ● ●

7 (SEVEN)
━ ━ ● ● ●

8 (AIT)
━ ━ ━ ● ●

9 (NINER)
━ ━ ━ ━ ●

0 (ZERO)
━ ━ ━ ━ ━

First Substitute

Second Substitute

Third Substitute

PLATE 8 – NATIONAL ENSIGNS

UK WHITE ENSIGN

FINLAND

UK BLUE ENSIGN

SWEDEN

UK RED ENSIGN

NORWAY

IRELAND

DENMARK

GUERNSEY

GERMANY

FRANCE

NETHERLANDS

SPAIN

BELGIUM

PORTUGAL

GREECE

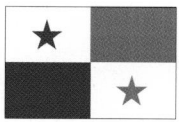

PANAMA

LIBERIA

PLATE 9 – INTERNATIONAL PORT TRAFFIC SIGNALS

No	Lights		Main message
1	(three flashing red lights)	Flashing	Serious emergency – all vessels to stop or divert according to instructions
2	(three red lights)	Fixed or Slow Occulting	Vessels shall not proceed (*Note:* Some ports may use an exemption signal, as in 2a below)
3	(green, green, green)	Fixed or Slow Occulting	Vessels may proceed. One-way traffic
4	(green, green, white)	Fixed or Slow Occulting	Vessels may proceed. Two-way traffic
5	(green, white, green)	Fixed or Slow Occulting	A vessel may proceed only when she has received specific orders to do so. (*Note:* Some ports may use an exemption signal, as in 5a below)
	Exemption signals and messages		
2a	(yellow + red, red, red)	Fixed or Slow Occulting	Vessels shall not proceed, except that vessels which navigate outside the main channel need not comply with the main message
5a	(yellow + green, white, green)	Fixed or Slow Occulting	A vessel may proceed when she has received specific orders to do so, except that vessels which navigate outside the main channel need not comply with the main message
	Auxiliary signals and messages		
	White and/or yellow lights, displayed to the right of the main lights		Local meanings, as promulgated in local port orders

1.7.1   ENSIGNS

1.7.1.1   Introduction

All countries have national flags and some have maritime versions (ensigns), normally based on the national flag (e.g. the United Kingdom's Red Ensign). Some countries use their national flag unaltered (eg France's tricolore or the Dutch flag which is also the civil and naval ensign).

On the facing page are some of the ensigns most likely to be seen in the areas covered by this Almanac.

See overleaf at 1.7.3.1 for further information on the wearing of ensigns and notes on flag etiquette

1.7.1.2   United Kingdom

The United Kingdom has three principal ensigns. The White worn by ships and shore establishments of the Royal Navy. Members of the Royal Yacht Squadron may also wear the White Ensign (subject to permit) in vessels of a certain size. The Blue may be worn by British Merchant Ships commanded by a RNR officer and, more commonly, by members of certain privileged yacht clubs (subject to permit). In its defaced form (i.e. with a badge) it is used by various government organisations and certain other yacht clubs (see 1.7.3.2). The Red is worn by other British vessels not mentioned above, not least by merchant ships and the vast majority of yachts and motor cruisers. The defaced Red Ensign is used by a small number of privileged yacht clubs (see 1.7.3.2).

The Guernsey ensign is included as it is the only Channel Island with an approved ensign. It can be worn by any yacht based within the bailiwick of Guernsey and can be worn as an alternative to the Red Ensign as the courtesy flag by visiting yachts. The national flag of Guernsey should not be worn. UK yachts need not fly a courtesy flag in the Channel Islands.

1.7.1.3   Other countries

Most countries have a common national and maritime flag, but there are exceptions – usually for the senior yacht club which administers the sport. For instance the Royal Danish Yacht Club may use the split flag (swallow-tail) ensign of their navy with the letters YF and three golden stars in their canton. The ensign of the Royal Norwegian Yacht Club (KNS) has a swallow-tail with a tongue and a royal cypher in gold beneath the crown of the state arms. Similar privileges are accorded to the Yacht Club Italiano and the Yacht Club of Poland.

1.7.1.4   Flags of convenience

The flags of Liberia and Panama are included since many ships are registered in these two countries by owners who are not their nationals. Known as flags of convenience, they are used to avoid the much more stringent inspections and regulations imposed by traditional maritime countries.

1.7.2   INTERNATIONAL PORT TRAFFIC SIGNALS

The international system is gradually being introduced, but its general adoption is likely to take many years.

(a) The main movement message given by a port traffic signal always comprises three lights, disposed vertically. No additional light shall be added to the column carrying the main message. (The fact that the main message always consists of three vertical lights allows the mariner to recognise it as a traffic signal, and not lights of navigational significance.) The signals may also be used to control traffic at locks and bridges.

(b) Red lights indicate 'Do not proceed'.

(c) Green lights indicate 'Proceed, subject to the conditions stipulated'. (For examples, see opposite.) Note that, to avoid confusion, red and green lights are never displayed together.

(d) Some signals may be omni-directional – i.e. exhibited to all vessels simultaneously: others must be directional, and be shown either to vessels entering or to vessels leaving harbour.

(e) The 'Serious Emergency' signal must be flashing, at least 60 flashes per minute. All other signals must be either fixed or slow occulting (the latter useful when background glare is a problem). A mixture of fixed and occulting lights must not be used.

(f) Signal No 5 is based on the assumption that another means of communication such as VHF radio, signal lamp, loud-hailer, or auxiliary signal will be used to inform a vessel that she may specifically proceed.

(g) A single yellow light, displayed to the left of the column carrying main messages Nos 2 or 5, at the level of the upper light, may be used to indicate that 'Vessels which can safely navigate outside the main channel need not comply with the main message'. This signal, as shown at Nos 2a and 5a, is of obvious significance to yachtsmen.

(h) Signals which are auxiliary to the main message may be devised by local authorities. Such auxiliary signals should employ only white and/or yellow lights, and should be displayed to the right of the column carrying the main message. Ports with complex entrances and much traffic may need many auxiliary signals, which will have to be documented. Smaller harbours with less traffic may only need one or two of the basic signals, such as Nos 2 and 4.

See also 8.15.9 for traffic signals which may still be shown at some French ports.

C1

1.7.3   NOTES ON FLAG ETIQUETTE

For many years flags were the only way to pass messages at sea, and although this function has now been largely superseded by radio, flags remain a useful way of expressing identity – by national ensigns, club burgees, etc. The following notes offer brief guidance on how they should be used.

1.7.3.1   Ensign

A yacht's ensign is the national maritime flag corresponding to the nationality of her owner. Thus a British yacht should wear the Red Ensign, unless she qualifies for a special ensign (see 1.7.3.2). It goes without saying that the national ensign should be kept clean and in good repair. *Nothing betokens the landsman more than slovenly colours.*

At sea the ensign must be worn when meeting other vessels, entering or leaving foreign ports. Increasingly it has become the practice to leave the ensign (and burgee) flying at all times in foreign waters – even at night in harbour, assuming that the boat is not unattended. In British harbours it is customary for the ensign to be hoisted at 0800LT (0900 from 1 Nov to 14 Feb) or as soon after that time as people come on board; and lowered at sunset (or 2100LT if earlier) or before that time if the crew is leaving the boat.

The ensign should normally be worn at the stern, but if this is not possible the nearest position should be used, eg at the peak in a gaff-rigged boat, at the mizzen masthead in a ketch or yawl, or about two-thirds up the leech of the mainsail. In harbour or at anchor the proper position is at the stern.

The ensign should not be worn when racing (after the five minute gun). It should be hoisted on finishing or when retiring.

1.7.3.2   Special ensigns

Members of certain clubs may apply for permission to wear a special ensign (e.g. Blue Ensign, defaced Blue Ensign, or defaced Red Ensign). For this purpose the yacht must either be a registered ship under Part I of the Merchant Shipping Act 1995 and of at least 2 tons gross tonnage, or be registered under the Merchant Shipping Act 1993 (Part III, Small Ships Register) and of at least 7 metres LOA. The owner or owners must be British subjects, and the yacht must not be used for any professional, business or commercial purpose. Full details are available from yacht clubs concerned.

A special ensign must only be worn when the owner is on board or ashore in the vicinity, and only when the yacht is flying the burgee (or a Flag Officer's flag) of the club concerned.

1.7.3.3   Burgee

A burgee shows that a yacht is in the charge of a member of the club indicated, and does not necessarily indicate ownership. It should be flown at the masthead.

Should this be impossible due to wind sensors, radio antennae etc, the burgee may be flown at the starboard spreader, but this should be avoided unless absolutely necessary. A yacht should not fly more than one burgee. A burgee is not flown when a yacht is racing. If the yacht is on loan, or is chartered, it is correct to use the burgee of the skipper or charterer – not that of the absent owner. Normal practice has been to lower the burgee at night, at the same time as the ensign, but nowadays many owners leave the burgee flying if they are on board or ashore in the vicinity.

1.7.3.4   Choice of burgee

An owner who is not a Flag Officer, and who belongs to more than one club, should normally fly the burgee (and if authorised the special ensign) of the senior club in the harbour where the yacht is lying. An exception may be if another club is staging a regatta or similar function.

1.7.3.5   Flag Officer's flag

Clubs authorise their Flag Officers to fly special swallow-tailed flags, with the same design as the club burgee and in place of it. The flags of a vice-commodore and a rear-commodore carry one and two balls respectively.

1.7.3.6   Courtesy ensign

It is customary when abroad to fly a small maritime ensign of the country concerned at the starboard spreader. A courtesy ensign must not be worn below any other flag on the same halyard. Thus a club burgee, if usually flown at the starboard spreader, must be shifted to the port spreader when abroad, permitting the courtesy ensign to be close up at the starboard spreader. The correct courtesy flag for a foreign yacht in British waters is the Red Ensign. British yachts do not fly a courtesy flag in the Channel Islands.

1.7.3.7   House flag

An owner may fly his personal flag when he is on board in harbour, provided it does not conflict with the design of some existing flag. A house flag is normally rectangular, and is flown at the crosstrees in a sloop or cutter, at the mizzen masthead in a ketch or yawl, or at the foremast head in a schooner.

1.7.3.8   Salutes

Yachts should salute all Royal Yachts, and all warships of whatever nationality. A salute is made by dipping the ensign (only). The vessel saluted responds by dipping her ensign, and then re-hoisting it, whereupon the vessel saluting re-hoists hers. It is customary for a Flag Officer to be saluted (not more than once a day) by a yacht flying the burgee of that club.

1.7.3.9   Dressing ship

Dressing overall (as opposed to dressing with masthead flags) is normally only done in harbour and marks national festivals. The international code flags and pennants (Plates 6/7, pp 20/1) are flown in the following order from stem to masthead(s) to stern:
E, Q, p 3, G, p 8, Z, p 4, W, p 6, P, p 1, Code, T, Y, B, X, 1st Sub, H, 3rd Sub, D, F, 2nd Sub, U, A, O, M, R, p 2, J, p 0, N, p 9, K, p 7, V, p 5, L, C, S.

Chapter 2

Coastal Navigation

Contents

2.1	**DEFINITIONS AND TERMS Page 26**	
2.1.1	Time	
2.1.2	Position	
2.1.3	Direction	
2.1.4	Compass variation and deviation	
2.1.5	Distance	
2.1.6	Speed	
2.1.7	Depth	
2.2	**IALA BUOYAGE**	27
2.2.1	IALA Buoyage System (Region A) (See also Plate 1 on page 15)	
2.3	**LIGHTS**	28
2.3.1	Light characteristics	
2.3.2	Light sectors, arcs of visibility	
2.4	**PASSAGE PLANNING**	29
2.4.1	General	
2.4.2	Passage planning check list	
2.4.3	Planning proforma	
2.5	**CALCULATOR NAVIGATION**	31
2.5.1	Formulae and working	

2.6	**NAVIGATION TABLES**	32
2.6.1	Explanation of the following Tables	
2(1)	Distance of horizon	33
2(2)	Lights: distance off when rising or dipping	33
2(3)	Distance off by vertical sextant angle	34
2(4)	Distance, speed and time	36
2(5)	Speed over measured mile	38
2(6)	True bearing of Sun at sunrise/set	39
2(7)	Sun's declination	40
2(8)	Phases of the Moon	
2.6.2	Eclipse notes	
2.7	**SUN AND MOON TABLES**	41
2.7.1	Explanation of the following Tables:	
2(9)	Sun rise/set and twilights	42
2(10)	Sun: latitude corrections	
2(11)	Moon rise/set	44
2.8	**CONVERSION TABLES**	46
2.8.1	Conversion factors	
2.8.2	Metres-feet-metres	

C2

Summary

This chapter serves as both a primer and an aide memoire on basic navigational considerations and practical techniques. It provides navigational tables to meet most needs, including sunrise/set, the sun's declination, phases of the moon and moonrise/set.

The following subjects are described in more detail in Chapters 3 and 15 of *The Macmillan & Silk Cut Yachtsman's Handbook*:

The terms and definitions used in coastal navigation; magnetic variation and deviation; compass checks; compass adjusting and compass swinging; charts and their symbols; lights and fog signals; methods of laying-off courses and position fixing; time, speed and distance; measured mile table; pilotage; IALA Buoyage System; passage planning; the use of calculators; practical passage making; sailing directions.

2.1   DEFINITIONS AND TERMS

Introduction

This chapter introduces basic coastal navigation in simplified form and includes useful tables and data.

2.1.1   Time

Times are quoted as Universal Time (UT) or Local time (LT), unless otherwise stated. The 24-hour clock convention is used throughout, ie 0001 to 2359. See 4.12.2 for the Standard times adopted by nations. Daylight Saving time (DST), or BST in the UK, has been standardised amongst the maritime nations in this Almanac as applying between the last Sundays in March and October each year.

2.1.2   Position

Position on the Earth's surface can be expressed in two ways: by latitude and longitude, or by a bearing and distance from a known position.

The latitude of a place is its angular distance, measured in degrees (°), minutes (') and decimals of a minute from 0° to 90°, north or south of the equator.

The longitude of a place is measured in degrees (°), minutes ('), and decimals of a minute from 0° to 180° east or west of the Greenwich meridian.

2.1.3   Direction

Direction is measured clockwise from north in a three-digit group, ie 000° to 359°. Thus east is written as 090°, and west 270°. Direction may be referenced to three different norths, namely:

(1)   **True North** as measured from the Geographic North Pole.

(2)   **Magnetic North** as measured from the Magnetic North Pole.

(3)   **Compass North** as measured from the north-seeking end of the compass needle.

Bearings and tracks as given on charts, or quoted in publications, are normally True bearings.

The direction from which the wind is blowing is normally given in points of the compass, clockwise from a cardinal or quadrantal point rather than in degrees, ie N, NNE, NE by N, etc. There are 32 points of the compass, with each point equal to 11¼°.

Tidal streams are always expressed as the direction towards which they are running.

2.1.4   Compass variation and deviation

The magnetic compass is the most vital navigational instrument in a cruising boat. It is affected by:
Variation (the angular difference between True and Magnetic North), which alters from place to place and year to year, and is shown on the chart, normally at the compass rose; and by
Deviation (the angular difference between Magnetic and Compass North) which is caused by the boat's own magnetic field. Deviation varies according to the boat's heading. Following a compass swing and adjustment of the compass, any residual deviation is shown, for different headings, on a deviation card. With a properly adjusted compass, deviation should not be more than about 2° on any heading, in which case it can often be ignored except on long passages.

When converting a True course or a True bearing to Magnetic: add westerly variation or deviation and subtract easterly.

When converting a Magnetic course or bearing to True: subtract westerly variation or deviation, and add easterly.

2.1.5   Distance

Distance at sea is measured in nautical miles (M). A nautical mile is defined as the length of one minute of latitude. The length of a nautical mile varies with latitude and measures 6,108 feet at the Pole and 6,046 at the Equator. For practical purposes the nautical mile is taken as being 6,076 feet or 1,852 metres.

Shorter distances are measured in cables. A cable is one tenth of a nautical mile, and for practical purposes approximates to 200 yards, 600 feet or 100 fathoms in length and is always used for navigational purposes irrespective of the latitude.

Distances must always be measured from the latitude scale of a chart, never from the longitude scale because the length of one minute of longitude on the earth varies from being roughly equal to a minute of latitude at the Equator, to zero length at the Pole. The longitude scale is therefore of no value as a measure of distance.

Metric dimensions are given in this Almanac for more general purposes, the Imperial equivalent being included where appropriate.

2.1.6   Speed

Speed at sea is measured in knots. A knot is 1 nautical mile per hour. The important relationship between speed, time and distance is given in basic formulae used to find one quantity when the other two are known (see 2.5.1). A convenient speed, time and distance table is also given in Table 2 (4).

A log measures distance run through the water and most logs today also incorporate a speed indicator. Course and speed made good over the ground can be obtained directly from electronic position-fixing receivers such as GPS, Decca or Loran-C.

2.1.7   Depth

Depths and heights are given in metres (m). The depth of water is usually important and is measured by echo sounder (or lead line). It is important to know whether an echo sounder indicates depth below the water level, the transducer or the base of the keel. Chart Datum (CD) is the level below which the tide never, or very rarely, falls. Charted depths and drying heights shown on charts are always referenced to CD. The height of tide is the height of the sea surface above Chart Datum at any instant. See chapter 7 for tidal calculations.

2.2   IALA BUOYAGE

2.2.1   IALA Buoyage System (Region A)
(See also Plate 1 on page 15.)

International buoyage is harmonised into a single system which, applied to Regions A and B, differs only in the use of red and green lateral marks. In Region A (which includes all Europe) lateral marks are red on the port hand, and in Region B red on the starboard hand, related to direction of buoyage. Five types of marks are used, as illustrated in Plate 1, on page 15.

(1) *Lateral marks:* are used in conjunction with a direction of buoyage, shown by a special arrow on the chart. Around the British Isles the general direction is from SW to NE in open waters, but from seaward when approaching a harbour, river or estuary. Where port or starboard lateral marks do not rely on can or conical buoy shapes for identification, they carry, where practicable, the appropriate topmarks. Any numbering or lettering follows the direction of buoyage, evens to port and odds to starboard.

In Region A, port-hand marks are coloured red, and port-hand buoys are can or spar shaped. Any topmark fitted is a single red can. Any light fitted is red, any rhythm. Starboard-hand marks are coloured green, and starboard-hand buoys are conical or spar shaped. Any topmark fitted is a single green cone, point up. Any light fitted is green, any rhythm. In exceptional cases starboard-hand marks may be coloured black.

At a division, the preferred channel may be shown by lateral marks with red or green bands:

Preferred channel	Indicated by	Light (if any)
To starboard	Port lateral mark with green band	Flashing red (2 + 1)
To port	Starboard lateral mark with red band	Flashing green (2 + 1)

(2) *Cardinal marks:* are named after the quadrant in which the mark is placed, in relation to the danger or point indicated. The four quadrants (north, east, south and west) are bounded by the True bearings NW-NE, NE-SE, SE-SW and SW-NW, taken from the point of interest. The name of a cardinal mark indicates that it should be passed on the named side. For example, a NCM (situated in the quadrant between NW and NE from the point of interest) should be passed on its north side; an ECM on its E side, and so on.

A cardinal mark may indicate the safe side on which to pass a danger, or that the deepest water is on the named side of the mark, or it may draw attention to a feature in a channel such as a bend, junction or fork, or the end of a shoal.

Cardinal marks are pillar or spar shaped, painted black and yellow, and always carry black double cone topmarks, one cone above the other. Their lights are white, and are either VQ or Q. VQ lights flash at a rate of 80 to 159 flashes per minute, usually either 100 or 120, and Q flash at a rate of between 50 to 79 flashes per minute, usually either 50 or 60. A long flash is one of not less than two seconds' duration.

North cardinal mark

Two black cones	— Points up
Colour	— Black above yellow
Light (if fitted)	— White; Q or VQ

East cardinal mark

Two black cones	— Base to base
Colour	— Black, with horizontal yellow band
Light (if fitted)	— White; Q (3) 10 sec or VQ (3) 5 sec

South cardinal mark

Two black cones	— Points down
Colour	— Yellow above black
Light (if fitted)	— White; VQ (6) plus long flash 10 sec or Q (6) plus long flash 15 sec

West cardinal mark

Two black cones	— Point to point
Colour	— Yellow, with horizontal black band
Light (if fitted)	— White; VQ (9) 10 sec or Q (9) 15 sec

(3) *Isolated danger marks:* are placed on or above an isolated danger such as a rock or a wreck which has navigable water all around it. The marks are black, with one or more broad horizontal red bands. Buoys are pillar or spar shaped. Any light is white, flashing twice. Topmark = two black spheres.

(4) *Safe water marks:* indicate that there is navigable water all round the mark, and are used for mid-channel or landfall marks. Buoys are spherical, pillar, with spherical topmark or spar, and are coloured with red and white vertical stripes. Any topmark fitted is a single red sphere. Any light fitted is white, either isophase, occulting or long-flash every 10 seconds.

(5) *Special marks:* do not primarily assist navigation, but indicate a special area or feature (e.g. spoil grounds, exercise areas, water-ski areas, cable or pipeline marks, outfalls, Ocean Data Acquisition Systems (ODAS), or traffic separation marks where conventional channel marks may cause confusion). Special marks are yellow, and any shape not conflicting with lateral or safe water marks. If can, spherical or conical are used they indicate the side on which to pass. Any topmark fitted is a yellow X. Any light fitted is yellow, and may have any rhythm not used for white lights.

New dangers (which may be natural obstructions such as a sandbank, or a wreck) are marked in accordance with the rules above, and lit accordingly. For a very grave danger one of the marks may be duplicated.

C2

2.3   LIGHTS

2.3.1   Light characteristics (Metric and Fathoms charts)

CLASS OF LIGHT	International abbreviations	National abbreviations	Illustration Period shown ⊢———⊣
FIXED	F		
OCCULTING (total duration of light longer than dark)			
Single-occulting	Oc	Occ	
Group-occulting eg	Oc(2)	Gp Occ(2)	
Composite group-occulting eg	Oc(2+3)	Gp Occ(2+3)	
Isophase (light and dark equal)	Iso		
FLASHING (total duration of light shorter than dark)			
Single-flashing	Fl		
Long-flashing (flash 2s or longer)	L Fl		
Group-flashing eg	Fl(3)	Gp Fl(3)	
Composite group-flashing eg	Fl(2+1)	Gp Fl(2+1)	
QUICK (50 to 79, usually either 50 or 60, flashes per minute)			
Continuous quick	Q	Qk Fl	
Group quick eg	Q(3)	Qk Fl(3)	
Interrupted quick	IQ	Int Qk Fl	
VERY QUICK (80 to 159, usually either 100 or 120, flashes per minute)			
Continuous very quick	VQ	V Qk Fl	
Group very quick eg	VQ(3)	V Qk Fl(3)	
Interrupted very quick	IVQ	Int V Qk Fl	
ULTRA QUICK (160 or more, usually 240 to 300, flashes per minute)			
Continuous ultra quick	UQ		
Interrupted ultra quick	IUQ		
MORSE CODE eg	Mo(K)		
FIXED and FLASHING	F Fl		
ALTERNATING eg	Al. WR	Alt. WR	

COLOUR	International abbreviations
White	W (may be omitted)
Red	R
Green	G
Blue	Bu
Violet	Vi
Yellow	Y
Orange	Y
Amber	Y

NOMINAL RANGE in miles		International abbreviations
Light with single range	eg	15M
Light with two different ranges	eg	15/10M
Light with three or more ranges	eg	15-7M
PERIOD is given in seconds	eg	90s
DISPOSITION horizontally disposed		(hor)
vertically disposed		(vert)
ELEVATION is given in metres (m) or feet (ft) above MHWS		

2.3.2 Light sectors, arcs of visibility

The abbreviations for, and characteristics of, lights are shown opposite and in AC 5011 (a booklet).

In this Almanac details of lights are listed in section 8.AA.4 for each area, where the day-time appearance of the light is also described, eg W ○ tr, R bands.The limits of light sectors and arcs of visibility, and the alignment of directional and leading lights, are always given as seen from seaward by an observer aboard ship. For example, the sector of a white light listed as W090°–180° would be seen over an arc of 90° by any vessel between due West and due North of that light.

Coloured sector lights are often used to guide vessels up narrow channels or warn of a dangerous area. The navigable portion of a channel may be covered by a white pencil beam, flanked by red and green sectors. If you stray to port you see red; if to starboard you see green.

A typical example of a simple sectored light occurs with the Ouistreham main light, listed as Oc WR 4s 37m **W17M**, R13M, vis R115°-151°,W151°-115°. This is depicted in Fig. 2(1) below.

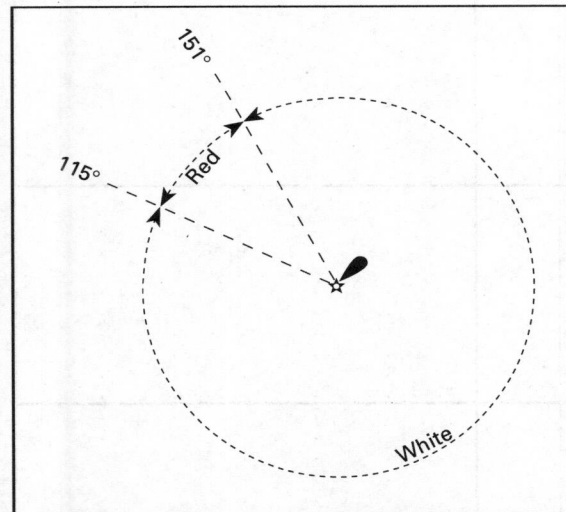

Fig 2(1)

The light occults every 4s and is 37 metres above the level of MHWS. It has red and white sectors. The red sector has a nominal range of 13M and is visible between 115° (WNW of the light) and 151° (NNW of the light), an arc of 36°. The white sector has a nominal range of 17M and is visible from 151° clockwise right round to 115°, an angular coverage of the remaining 324°. **Bold** type indicates a light with a nominal range of more than 15M.

A slightly more complex example of a sectored light is shown below in Fig 2(2). It is listed as:
Q WRG 9m 10M, vis G015°-058°(43°), W058°-065°(7°), R065°-103°(38°), G103°-143·5°(40·5°), W143·5°-145·5°(3°), R146·5°-015° (129·5°).

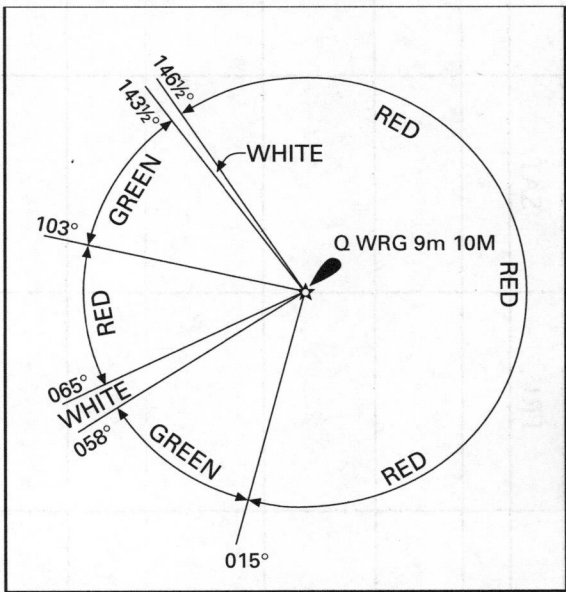

Fig 2(2)

It is a quick flashing light, with an elevation of 9 metres above MHWS, and a nominal range of 10M. It has white, red and green sectors – in fact two sectors of each colour. After plotting these sectors, it will be seen that there are two sets of WRG directional sectors, such that in each case a narrow white sector is flanked by a red sector to port and a green sector to starboard. These sectors provide the guidance described in paragraph 3 of the text of 2.3.2.

2.4   PASSAGE PLANNING

2.4.1   General

Any passage, however short, must be pre-planned. Even in very familiar waters you should at the very least know the state of the tide (springs/neaps; HW/LW times and heights), tidal streams and have studied an up-to-date forecast. The necessary chart(s) should be aboard.

Decide where you intend going, then study the relevant charts in conjunction with yachtsman's sailing directions (Pilots) and cruising guides.

Much of the navigational work such as laying-off courses on the chart, measuring distances, selecting waypoints and tidal calculations can be done in advance. Use a check list which as far as possible schools you into a carefully orchestrated procedure, thus minimising the risk of careless errors and omissions (see overleaf).

C2

DAY/DATE	MON	TUE	WED	THU	FRI	SAT	SUN
SUN RISE/SET							
HW DOVER Sp/Nps/Coeff							
STANDARD PORT HW/LW							
DEPARTURE PORT HW/LW							
Exit Window Bar/lock/sill							
ARRIVAL PORT HW/LW							
Arrival window Bar/lock/sill							
TIME 0000							
PLAN 0400							
0800							
1200							
1600							
2000							
2359							

2.4.2   Passage planning check list

The following is a suggested list of navigational items which need to be considered before departure. (Other key items such as the boat, crew, watch-keeping and feeding arrangements must also be taken into account).

a.   Note times of HW at the reference port(s).

b.   Insert the dates and times of HW applicable on each page of the tidal stream atlas.

c.   Note when the streams turn fair and foul. Be aware of tidal stream gates, typically off headlands and in narrow channels.

d.   Note any critical times and heights of tides which may affect the departure and destination harbours, eg crossing bars, sills.

e.   Study potential dangers en route: clearing lines, distance-off dangers, traffic separation schemes, busy shipping lanes, etc.

f.   Consider visual and radio aids to be used.

g.   Prepare a detailed pilotage plan for entry to any unfamiliar harbour, final destination or refuge port.

h.   Ensure that charts for the intended route and alternative harbours are up to date and on board, together with the current Almanac, Yachtsman's Handbook, correcting supplement and pilotage information.

j.   Study the weather pattern over several days before leaving. It is likely to have a considerable impact on your original plans. Stay flexible.

2.4.3 Planning proforma

A planning proforma, such as that opposite, is a useful aide memoire and worksheet which helps to organise the navigational plan. It can also save much repetitive referring to the Almanac. It is largely self-explanatory, but note the following:

a. It covers a week's cruise, ie THE BIG PICTURE.

b. Times of sun rise/set, HW Dover and whether it is springs or neaps can be filled in for the whole week. French tidal coefficients (8.16.25) are a quick and quantitative way of checking springs/neaps.

c. Times and heights of HW/LW at the relevant Standard Port can probably be inserted for the whole week (item a in 2.4.2 above).

d. The tidal blocks for the departure and intended arrival ports also prompt calculation of constraints, if any, imposed by bars, locks or sills (item d in 2.4.2).

e. The 24 hours Time Plan can be variously used to show tidal streams (items b & c in 2.4.2), shade in hours of darkness, plan a watch keeping system, act as a mini-diary or illustrate passage times and the sea/shore ratio.

2.5   CALCULATOR NAVIGATION

2.5.1   Speed, time and distance formulae

$$\text{Speed (in kn)} = \frac{\text{Distance (M)} \times 60}{\text{Time (mins)}}$$

$$\text{Time (in mins)} = \frac{\text{Distance (M)} \times 60}{\text{Speed (kn)}}$$

$$\text{Distance (in M)} = \frac{\text{Speed (kn)} \times \text{Time (mins)}}{60}$$

$$\text{Speed (kn) over measured M} = \frac{3600}{\text{time in seconds}}$$

Distances

Distance of horizon (in M) = $2 \cdot 072 \times \sqrt{\text{Ht of eye (m)}}$

Distance a light is visible (M) = $2 \cdot 072 \times (\sqrt{h_o} + \sqrt{h_e})$ where h_o and h_e are heights of object and eye (m).

Distance of mountains etc beyond horizon, (in M) =

$$\sqrt{3 \cdot 71(h_o - h_e) + (a' - 1 \cdot 76 \times \sqrt{h_e})^2} - (a' - 1 \cdot 76 \times \sqrt{h_e})$$

where h_o and h_e are in metres, and a' is the sextant angle in minutes.

Distance to radar horizon (M)
$$= 2 \cdot 21 \times \sqrt{\text{Ht of scanner (m)}}$$

2.5.2   Sextant angles

a.   Horizontal sextant angle

Radius of position circle (in M) =

$$\frac{D}{2 \times \sin A}$$

where D is distance between objects in M, and A is the angle between them in degrees.

b.   Vertical sextant angle

$$\text{Distance off} = \frac{\text{Ht of object (above MHWS in m)}}{1852 \times \tan(\text{sextant angle})}$$

Note: sextant angle above is in degrees and minutes, and must be corrected for index error.

c.   Distance off

An approximate distance off, in M, adequate for most purposes is given by:

$$\text{Distance} = \frac{h_o \text{ (in metres)} \times 1 \cdot 854}{\text{sextant angle (in minutes)}}$$

2.5.3   Coastal navigation

To find the DR/EP, as bearing and distance from start position; example using algebraic calculator. Key in:

1st distance run   5·2 x < > t
1st course (°T)   230 →R STO 0 x< >t STO 6
2nd distance run   1·9 x< >t
2nd course (°T)   255 →R SUM 0 x< >t SUM 6

Repeat for each subsequent Co (°T) and distance. For EP, treat Set/Drift as for Co (°T) and distance.

C2

To display bearing and distance from start:

RCL 6 x < >t RCL 0 →P 236·6 (°T)
x< >t   6·97 (M)

Note: to find EP, treat Set/Drift as for Co (°T) and distance run.

Example: using RPN calculator. Key in:

1st course (°T)	230 ENTER
1st distance run	5·2 →R Σ+
2nd course (°T)	255 ENTER
2nd distance run	1·9 →R Σ+

Repeat for each subsequent Co (°T) and distance.

To display distance and bearing from start:

RCL 13[1] RCL 11[1]   →P   6·97   M
x ↔ y   236·6[2] (°T)

Notes: (l) Check the actual stores used for vector summation in your calculator.
(2) If display negative (–), add 360.

To find EP, treat Set/Drift as for Co (°T) and distance run.

Distance (D, in M) of object at second bearing

$$= \frac{R \times \sin A}{\sin (B - A)}$$

Predicted distance (in M) object will be off when abeam = D x sin B, where R is distance run (M) between two relative bearings of an object, first A degrees and then B degrees.

2.5.4   Course to steer and speed made good

Co (°T) = Tr (°T) – sin⁻¹ – ((Drift ÷ Speed) × sin (Set – Track))

SMG = Speed × cos (Co.T – Track) + Drift × cos (Set – Track)

Note: the drift must be less than the yacht's speed.

2.5.5   Conversion angle (half convergency)

Radio bearings follow great circles, and become curved lines when plotted on a Mercator chart. A correction may be needed for bearings of beacons more than about 60M away, and can be calculated from the formula:

Conversion angle = ½ d.Long × sin mid Latitude

A great circle always lies on the polar side of the rhumb line, and conversion angle is applied towards the Equator.

2.5.6   Short distance sailing

(Note: these formulae should not be used for distances over 600M.)

Departure	=	Distance × sin Course
	=	d.Long × cos Mean Latitude
	=	tan Course × d.Lat
d.Lat	=	Distance × cos Course
d.Long	=	Departure ÷ cos Mean Latitude
Distance	=	Departure ÷ sin Course
	=	d.Lat × sec Course
sin Course	=	Departure ÷ Distance
cos Course	=	d.Lat ÷ Distance
tan Course	=	Departure ÷ d.Lat

2.6   NAVIGATION TABLES

2.6.1   Explanations

Brief explanations are given below, where necessary, of the use of tables on pages 33-40.

Table 2(1)   Distance of horizon

Enter with height of eye (m), and extract distance of horizon (M). The actual distance may be affected by abnormal refraction.

Table 2(2)   Lights, rising/dipping distance

Enter with height of eye and height of light to extract the range of a light when rising/dipping.

Table 2(3)   Distance off by Vertical Sextant Angle

Enter with the height of the object (m) and read across the page until the required sextant angle (corrected for index error) is met. Extract the distance of the object (M) at the head of the column. Caution is needed when the base of the object (eg a lighthouse) is below the horizon. For precise ranges the distance that sea level is below MHWS must be added to the height of the object (above MHWS) before entering the table.

Table 2(4)   Distance, speed and time

Enter with time (in decimals of an hour, or in minutes) and speed (kn) to determine distance run (M).

Table 2(5)   Speed over measured mile

Enter with minutes at the top of columns and seconds at the side of the table, to extract speed (kn).

Table 2(6)   True bearing of the Sun

A compass can be checked against the azimuth of the Sun when rising or setting. The Sun's bearing should be taken when its lower limb is a little over half a diameter above the horizon.

Enter with the approximate latitude and declination of the Sun (obtained from Table 2(7)). The tabulated figure is the True bearing, measured from north if declination is north or from south if declination is south, towards the east if rising or towards the west if setting; see examples below.

Lat	Dec	Sun	Tab brg	True brg	
33°	9°N	Rising	79°	N79°E	= 079°
33°	9°N	Setting	79°	N79°W	= 281°
33°	9°S	Rising	79°	S79°E	= 101°
33°	9°S	Setting	79°	S79°W	= 259°

Having determined the True bearing, apply variation, then compare with the compass to determine deviation on course steered.

Table 2(7)   Declination of the Sun

Enter the appropriate date band and read across to the centre column. Extract declination (bold type) noting whether it is North or South. See previous paragraph.

TABLE 2(1)   Distance of horizon for various heights of eye

Height of eye		Horizon distance	Height of eye		Horizon distance	Height of eye		Horizon distance
metres	feet	M	metres	feet	M	metres	feet	M
1	3·3	2·1	21	68·9	9·5	41	134·5	13·3
2	6·6	2·9	22	72·2	9·8	42	137·8	13·5
3	9·8	3·6	23	75·5	10·0	43	141·1	13·7
4	13·1	4·1	24	78·7	10·2	44	144·4	13·8
5	16·4	4·7	25	82·0	10·4	45	147·6	14·0
6	19·7	5·1	26	85·3	10·6	46	150·9	14·1
7	23·0	5·5	27	88·6	10·8	47	154·2	14·3
8	26·2	5·9	28	91·9	11·0	48	157·5	14·4
9	29·6	6·2	29	95·1	11·2	49	160·8	14·6
10	32·8	6·6	30	98·4	11·4	50	164·0	14·7
11	36·1	6·9	31	101·7	11·6	51	167·3	14·9
12	39·4	7·2	32	105·0	11·8	52	170·6	15·0
13	42·7	7·5	33	108·3	12·0	53	173·9	15·2
14	45·9	7·8	34	111·6	12·1	54	177·2	15·3
15	49·2	8·1	35	114·8	12·3	55	180·4	15·4
16	52·5	8·3	36	118·1	12·5	56	183·7	15·6
17	55·8	8·6	37	121·4	12·7	57	187·0	15·7
18	59·1	8·8	38	124·7	12·8	58	190·3	15·9
19	62·3	9·1	39	128·0	13·0	59	193·6	16·0
20	65·6	9·3	40	131·2	13·2	60	196·9	16·1

C2

TABLE 2(2)   Lights – distance off when rising or dipping (M)

Height of light		Height of eye									
		metres	1	2	3	4	5	6	7	8	9	10
metres	feet	feet	3	7	10	13	16	20	23	26	30	33
10	33		8·7	9·5	10·2	10·8	11·3	11·7	12·1	12·5	12·8	13·2
12	39		9·3	10·1	10·8	11·4	11·9	12·3	12·7	13·1	13·4	13·8
14	46		9·9	10·7	11·4	12·0	12·5	12·9	13·3	13·7	14·0	14·4
16	53		10·4	11·2	11·9	12·5	13·0	13·4	13·8	14·2	14·5	14·9
18	59		10·9	11·7	12·4	13·0	13·5	13·9	14·3	14·7	15·0	15·4
20	66		11·4	12·2	12·9	13·5	14·0	14·4	14·8	15·2	15·5	15·9
22	72		11·9	12·7	13·4	14·0	14·5	14·9	15·3	15·7	16·0	16·4
24	79		12·3	13·1	13·8	14·4	14·9	15·3	15·7	16·1	16·4	17·0
26	85		12·7	13·5	14·2	14·8	15·3	15·7	16·1	16·5	16·8	17·2
28	92		13·1	13·9	14·6	15·2	15·7	16·1	16·5	16·9	17·2	17·6
30	98		13·5	14·3	15·0	15·6	16·1	16·5	16·9	17·3	17·6	18·0
32	105		13·9	14·7	15·4	16·0	16·5	16·9	17·3	17·7	18·0	18·4
34	112		14·2	15·0	15·7	16·3	16·8	17·2	17·6	18·0	18·3	18·7
36	118		14·6	15·4	16·1	16·7	17·2	17·6	18·0	18·4	18·7	19·1
38	125		14·9	15·7	16·4	17·0	17·5	17·9	18·3	18·7	19·0	19·4
40	131		15·3	16·1	16·8	17·4	17·9	18·3	18·7	19·1	19·4	19·8
42	138		15·6	16·4	17·1	17·7	18·2	18·6	19·0	19·4	19·7	20·1
44	144		15·9	16·7	17·4	18·0	18·5	18·9	19·3	19·7	20·0	20·4
46	151		16·2	17·0	17·7	18·3	18·8	19·2	19·6	20·0	20·3	20·7
48	157		16·5	17·3	18·0	18·6	19·1	19·5	19·9	20·3	20·6	21·0
50	164		16·8	17·6	18·3	18·9	19·4	19·8	20·2	20·6	20·9	21·3
55	180		17·5	18·3	19·0	19·6	20·1	20·5	20·9	21·3	21·6	22·0
60	197		18·2	19·0	19·7	20·3	20·8	21·2	21·6	22·0	22·3	22·7
65	213		18·9	19·7	20·4	21·0	21·5	21·9	22·3	22·7	23·0	23·4
70	230		19·5	20·3	21·0	21·6	22·1	22·5	22·9	23·2	23·6	24·0
75	246		20·1	20·9	21·6	22·2	22·7	23·1	23·5	23·9	24·2	24·6
80	262		20·7	21·5	22·2	22·8	23·3	23·7	24·1	24·5	24·8	25·2
85	279		21·3	22·1	22·8	23·4	23·9	24·3	24·7	25·1	25·4	25·8
90	295		21·8	22·6	23·3	23·9	24·4	24·8	25·2	25·6	25·9	26·3
95	312		22·4	23·2	23·9	24·5	25·0	25·4	25·8	26·2	26·5	26·9
metres	feet	metres	1	2	3	4	5	6	7	8	9	10
Height of light		feet	3	7	10	13	16	20	23	26	30	33
							Height of eye					

TABLE 2(3)   Distance off by Vertical Sextant Angle

Distance of object (nautical miles) — values given in degrees and minutes (° ')

Height ft	m	0·1	0·2	0·3	0·4	0·5	0·6	0·7	0·8	0·9	1·0	1·1	1·2	1·3	1·4	1·5	1·6
33	10	3 05	1 33	1 02	0 46	0 37	0 31	0 27	0 23	0 21	0 19	0 17	0 15	0 14	0 13	0 12	0 12
39	12	3 42	1 51	1 14	0 56	0 45	0 37	0 32	0 28	0 25	0 22	0 20	0 19	0 17	0 16	0 15	0 14
46	14	4 19	2 10	1 27	1 05	0 52	0 43	0 37	0 32	0 29	0 26	0 24	0 22	0 20	0 19	0 17	0 16
53	16	4 56	2 28	1 39	1 14	0 59	0 49	0 42	0 37	0 33	0 30	0 27	0 25	0 23	0 21	0 20	0 19
59	18	5 33	2 47	1 51	1 24	1 07	0 56	0 48	0 42	0 37	0 33	0 30	0 28	0 26	0 24	0 22	0 21
66	20	6 10	3 05	2 04	1 33	1 14	1 02	0 53	0 46	0 41	0 37	0 34	0 31	0 29	0 27	0 25	0 23
72	22	6 46	3 24	2 16	1 42	1 22	1 08	0 58	0 51	0 45	0 41	0 37	0 34	0 31	0 29	0 27	0 26
79	24	7 23	3 42	2 28	1 51	1 29	1 14	1 04	0 56	0 49	0 45	0 40	0 37	0 34	0 32	0 30	0 28
85	26	7 59	4 01	2 41	2 01	1 36	1 20	1 09	1 00	0 54	0 48	0 44	0 40	0 37	0 34	0 32	0 30
92	28	8 36	4 19	2 53	2 10	1 44	1 27	1 14	1 05	0 58	0 52	0 47	0 43	0 40	0 37	0 35	0 32
98	30	9 12	4 38	3 05	2 19	1 51	1 33	1 20	1 10	1 02	0 56	0 51	0 46	0 43	0 40	0 37	0 35
105	32	9 48	4 56	3 18	2 28	1 58	1 39	1 25	1 14	1 06	0 59	0 54	0 49	0 46	0 42	0 40	0 37
112	34	10 24	5 15	3 30	2 38	2 06	1 45	1 30	1 19	1 10	1 03	0 57	0 53	0 49	0 45	0 42	0 39
118	36	11 00	5 33	3 42	2 47	2 14	1 51	1 35	1 24	1 14	1 07	1 01	0 56	0 51	0 48	0 45	0 42
125	38	11 36	5 41	3 55	2 56	2 21	1 58	1 41	1 28	1 18	1 11	1 04	0 59	0 54	0 50	0 47	0 44
131	40	12 11	6 10	4 07	3 05	2 28	2 04	1 46	1 33	1 22	1 14	1 07	1 02	0 57	0 53	0 49	0 46
138	42	12 47	6 28	4 19	3 15	2 36	2 10	1 51	1 37	1 27	1 18	1 11	1 05	1 00	0 56	0 52	0 49
144	44	13 22	6 46	4 32	3 24	2 43	2 16	1 57	1 42	1 31	1 22	1 14	1 08	1 03	0 58	0 54	0 51
151	46	13 57	7 05	4 44	3 33	2 51	2 22	2 02	1 47	1 35	1 25	1 18	1 11	1 06	1 01	0 57	0 53
157	48	14 32	7 23	4 56	3 42	2 58	2 28	2 07	1 51	1 39	1 29	1 21	1 14	1 09	1 04	0 59	0 56
164	50	15 07	7 41	5 09	3 52	3 05	2 35	2 13	1 56	1 43	1 33	1 24	1 17	1 11	1 06	1 02	0 58
171	52	15 41	7 59	5 21	4 01	3 13	2 41	2 18	2 01	1 47	1 36	1 28	1 20	1 14	1 09	1 04	1 00
177	54	16 15	8 18	5 33	4 10	3 20	2 47	2 23	2 05	1 51	1 40	1 31	1 23	1 17	1 12	1 07	1 03
184	56	16 49	8 36	5 45	4 19	3 28	2 53	2 28	2 10	1 55	1 44	1 34	1 27	1 20	1 14	1 09	1 05
190	58	17 23	8 54	5 58	4 29	3 35	2 59	2 34	2 15	2 00	1 48	1 38	1 30	1 23	1 17	1 12	1 07
197	60	17 57	9 12	6 10	4 38	3 42	3 05	2 39	2 19	2 04	1 51	1 41	1 33	1 26	1 20	1 14	1 10
203	62	18 31	9 30	6 22	4 47	3 50	3 12	2 44	2 24	2 08	1 55	1 45	1 36	1 29	1 22	1 17	1 12
210	64	19 04	9 48	6 34	4 56	3 57	3 18	2 50	2 28	2 12	1 59	1 48	1 39	1 31	1 25	1 19	1 14
217	66	19 37	10 06	6 46	5 05	4 05	3 24	2 53	2 33	2 16	2 02	1 51	1 42	1 34	1 27	1 22	1 17
223	68	20 10	10 24	6 59	5 15	4 12	3 30	3 00	2 38	2 20	2 06	1 55	1 45	1 37	1 30	1 24	1 19
230	70	20 42	10 42	7 11	5 24	4 19	3 36	3 05	2 42	2 24	2 09	1 58	1 48	1 40	1 33	1 27	1 21
236	72	21 15	11 00	7 23	5 33	4 27	3 42	3 11	2 47	2 28	2 14	2 01	1 51	1 43	1 35	1 29	1 24
246	75	22 03	11 27	7 41	5 47	4 38	3 52	3 19	2 54	2 35	2 19	2 07	1 56	1 47	1 39	1 33	1 27
256	78	22 50	11 54	7 59	6 01	4 49	4 01	3 27	3 01	2 41	2 24	2 12	2 01	1 51	1 43	1 36	1 30
266	81	23 37	12 20	8 18	6 14	5 00	4 10	3 35	3 08	2 47	2 30	2 17	2 05	1 56	1 47	1 40	1 34
276	84	24 24	12 47	8 36	6 28	5 11	4 19	3 42	3 15	2 53	2 36	2 22	2 10	2 00	1 51	1 44	1 37
289	88	25 25	13 22	9 00	6 46	5 26	4 32	3 53	3 24	3 01	2 43	2 28	2 16	2 06	1 57	1 49	1 42
302	92	26 25	13 57	9 24	7 05	5 40	4 44	4 04	3 33	3 10	2 51	2 35	2 22	2 11	2 02	1 54	1 47
315	96	27 24	14 32	9 48	7 23	5 55	4 56	4 14	3 42	3 18	2 58	2 42	2 28	2 17	2 07	1 59	1 51
328	100	28 22	15 07	10 12	7 41	6 10	5 09	4 25	3 52	3 26	3 05	2 49	2 35	2 23	2 13	2 04	1 56
341	104	29 19	15 41	10 36	7 59	6 24	5 21	4 35	4 01	3 34	3 13	2 55	2 41	2 28	2 18	2 09	2 01
358	109	30 29	16 24	11 06	8 22	6 43	5 36	4 48	4 12	3 44	3 22	3 04	2 48	2 36	2 24	2 15	2 06
374	114	31 37	17 06	11 36	8 45	7 01	5 51	5 02	4 24	3 55	3 31	3 12	2 56	2 43	2 31	2 21	2 12
394	120	32 56	17 57	12 11	9 12	7 23	6 10	5 17	4 38	4 07	3 42	3 22	3 05	2 51	2 39	2 28	2 19
427	130	35 04	19 20	13 10	9 57	8 00	6 40	5 44	5 01	4 28	4 01	3 39	3 21	3 05	2 52	2 41	2 31
459	140	37 05	20 42	14 09	10 42	8 36	7 11	6 10	5 24	4 48	4 19	3 56	3 36	3 20	3 05	2 53	2 42
492	150	39 00	22 03	15 07	11 27	9 12	7 41	6 36	5 47	5 09	4 38	4 13	3 52	3 34	3 19	3 05	2 54
574	175			25 17	17 29	13 17	10 42	8 57	7 41	6 44	6 00	5 24	4 55	4 30	4 09	3 52	3 36
656	200			28 22	19 48	15 07	12 11	10 12	8 46	7 41	6 51	6 10	5 36	5 09	4 45	4 25	4 07
738	225			22 03	16 54	13 39	11 27	9 51	8 38	7 41	6 56	6 18	5 47	5 20	4 58	4 38	4 21
820	250			24 14	18 39	15 07	12 41	10 55	9 35	8 32	7 41	7 00	6 25	5 56	5 30	5 09	4 49
902	275			26 20	20 22	16 32	13 54	11 59	10 31	9 22	8 27	7 41	7 03	6 31	6 03	5 39	5 18
984	300				22 03	17 57	15 07	13 02	11 27	10 12	9 12	8 23	7 41	7 06	6 36	6 10	5 47
1148	350					20 42	17 29	15 07	13 17	11 51	10 42	9 45	8 57	8 16	7 41	7 11	6 44
1312	400						19 48	17 09	15 07	13 30	12 11	11 07	10 12	9 26	8 46	8 12	7 41
ft	m	0·1	0·2	0·3	0·4	0·5	0·6	0·7	0·8	0·9	1·0	1·1	1·2	1·3	1·4	1·5	1·6

Height of object — Distance of object (nautical miles)

TABLE 2(3) Distance off by Vertical Sextant Angle (continued)

Height of object ft	m	\multicolumn{16}{c}{Distance of object (nautical miles)}

ft	m	1·8	2·0	2·2	2·4	2·6	2·8	3·0	3·2	3·4	3·6	3·8	4·0	4·2	4·4	4·6	5·0
		° ′	° ′	° ′	° ′	° ′	° ′	° ′	° ′	° ′	° ′	° ′	° ′	° ′	° ′	° ′	° ′
33	10	0 10															
39	12	0 12	0 11	0 10	0 10												
46	14	0 14	0 13	0 12	0 11	0 10											
53	16	0 16	0 15	0 13	0 12	0 11	0 11	0 10									
59	18	0 19	0 17	0 15	0 14	0 13	0 12	0 11	0 10	0 10							
66	20	0 21	0 19	0 17	0 15	0 14	0 13	0 12	0 12	0 11	0 10	0 10					
72	22	0 23	0 20	0 19	0 17	0 16	0 15	0 14	0 13	0 12	0 11	0 11	0 10				
79	24	0 25	0 22	0 20	0 19	0 17	0 16	0 15	0 14	0 13	0 12	0 12	0 11	0 11	0 10		
85	26	0 27	0 24	0 22	0 20	0 19	0 17	0 16	0 15	0 14	0 13	0 13	0 12	0 11	0 11	0 10	
92	28	0 29	0 26	0 24	0 22	0 20	0 19	0 17	0 16	0 15	0 14	0 14	0 13	0 12	0 12	0 11	0 10
98	30	0 31	0 28	0 25	0 23	0 21	0 20	0 19	0 17	0 16	0 15	0 15	0 14	0 13	0 13	0 12	0 11
105	32	0 33	0 30	0 27	0 25	0 23	0 21	0 20	0 19	0 17	0 16	0 16	0 15	0 14	0 13	0 13	0 12
112	34	0 35	0 31	0 29	0 26	0 24	0 23	0 21	0 20	0 19	0 17	0 17	0 16	0 15	0 14	0 14	0 13
118	36	0 37	0 33	0 30	0 28	0 26	0 24	0 22	0 21	0 20	0 19	0 18	0 17	0 16	0 15	0 14	0 13
125	38	0 39	0 35	0 32	0 29	0 27	0 25	0 24	0 22	0 21	0 20	0 19	0 18	0 17	0 16	0 15	0 14
131	40	0 41	0 37	0 34	0 31	0 29	0 27	0 25	0 23	0 22	0 21	0 20	0 19	0 18	0 17	0 16	0 15
138	42	0 43	0 40	0 35	0 32	0 30	0 28	0 26	0 24	0 23	0 22	0 21	0 19	0 19	0 18	0 17	0 16
144	44	0 45	0 41	0 37	0 34	0 31	0 29	0 27	0 25	0 24	0 23	0 22	0 20	0 19	0 19	0 18	0 16
151	46	0 47	0 43	0 39	0 36	0 33	0 30	0 28	0 27	0 25	0 24	0 22	0 21	0 20	0 19	0 19	0 17
157	48	0 49	0 45	0 40	0 37	0 34	0 32	0 30	0 28	0 26	0 25	0 23	0 22	0 21	0 20	0 19	0 18
164	50	0 52	0 46	0 42	0 39	0 36	0 33	0 31	0 29	0 27	0 26	0 24	0 23	0 22	0 21	0 20	0 19
171	52	0 54	0 48	0 44	0 40	0 37	0 34	0 32	0 30	0 28	0 27	0 25	0 24	0 23	0 22	0 21	0 19
177	54	0 56	0 50	0 46	0 42	0 39	0 36	0 33	0 31	0 29	0 28	0 26	0 25	0 24	0 23	0 22	0 20
184	56	0 58	0 52	0 47	0 43	0 40	0 37	0 35	0 32	0 31	0 29	0 27	0 26	0 25	0 24	0 23	0 21
190	58	1 00	0 54	0 49	0 45	0 41	0 38	0 36	0 34	0 32	0 30	0 28	0 27	0 26	0 24	0 23	0 21
197	60	1 02	0 56	0 51	0 46	0 43	0 40	0 37	0 35	0 33	0 31	0 29	0 28	0 26	0 25	0 24	0 22
203	62	1 04	0 58	0 52	0 48	0 44	0 41	0 38	0 36	0 34	0 32	0 30	0 29	0 27	0 26	0 25	0 23
210	64	1 06	0 59	0 54	0 49	0 46	0 42	0 40	0 37	0 35	0 33	0 31	0 30	0 28	0 27	0 26	0 24
217	66	1 08	1 01	0 56	0 51	0 47	0 44	0 41	0 38	0 36	0 34	0 32	0 31	0 29	0 28	0 27	0 25
223	68	1 10	1 03	0 57	0 53	0 49	0 45	0 42	0 39	0 37	0 35	0 33	0 32	0 30	0 29	0 27	0 25
230	70	1 12	1 05	0 59	0 54	0 50	0 46	0 43	0 41	0 38	0 36	0 34	0 32	0 31	0 29	0 28	0 26
236	72	1 14	1 07	1 01	0 56	0 51	0 48	0 45	0 42	0 39	0 37	0 35	0 33	0 32	0 30	0 29	0 27
246	75	1 17	1 10	1 03	0 58	0 54	0 50	0 46	0 44	0 41	0 39	0 37	0 35	0 33	0 32	0 30	0 28
256	78	1 20	1 12	1 06	1 00	0 56	0 52	0 48	0 45	0 43	0 40	0 38	0 36	0 34	0 33	0 31	0 29
266	81	1 23	1 15	1 08	1 03	0 58	0 54	0 50	0 47	0 44	0 42	0 40	0 38	0 36	0 34	0 33	0 30
276	84	1 27	1 18	1 11	1 05	1 00	0 56	0 52	0 49	0 46	0 43	0 41	0 39	0 37	0 35	0 34	0 31
289	88	1 31	1 22	1 14	1 08	1 03	0 58	0 54	0 51	0 48	0 45	0 43	0 41	0 39	0 37	0 36	0 33
302	92	1 35	1 25	1 18	1 11	1 06	1 01	0 57	0 53	0 50	0 47	0 45	0 43	0 41	0 39	0 37	0 34
315	96	1 39	1 29	1 21	1 14	1 09	1 04	0 59	0 56	0 52	0 49	0 47	0 45	0 42	0 41	0 39	0 36
328	100	1 43	1 33	1 24	1 17	1 11	1 06	1 02	0 58	0 55	0 52	0 49	0 46	0 44	0 42	0 40	0 37
341	104	1 47	1 36	1 28	1 20	1 14	1 09	1 04	1 00	0 57	0 54	0 51	0 48	0 46	0 44	0 42	0 39
358	109	1 52	1 41	1 32	1 24	1 18	1 12	1 07	1 03	1 00	0 56	0 53	0 51	0 48	0 46	0 44	0 40
374	114	1 58	1 46	1 36	1 28	1 21	1 16	1 11	1 06	1 02	0 59	0 56	0 53	0 50	0 48	0 46	0 42
394	120	2 04	1 51	1 41	1 33	1 26	1 20	1 14	1 10	1 06	1 02	0 59	0 56	0 53	0 51	0 48	0 45
427	130	2 14	2 01	1 50	1 41	1 33	1 26	1 20	1 15	1 11	1 07	1 03	1 00	0 57	0 55	0 52	0 48
459	140	2 24	2 10	1 58	1 48	1 40	1 33	1 27	1 21	1 16	1 12	1 08	1 05	1 02	0 59	0 56	0 52
492	150	2 35	2 19	2 07	1 56	1 47	1 39	1 33	1 27	1 22	1 17	1 13	1 10	1 06	1 03	1 01	0 56
574	175	3 00	2 42	2 28	2 15	2 05	1 56	1 48	1 41	1 36	1 30	1 25	1 21	1 17	1 14	1 11	1 05
656	200	3 26	3 05	2 49	2 35	2 23	2 13	2 04	1 56	1 49	1 43	1 38	1 33	1 28	1 24	1 21	1 14
738	225	3 52	3 29	3 10	2 54	2 41	2 29	2 19	2 10	2 03	1 56	1 50	1 44	1 39	1 35	1 31	1 24
820	250	4 17	3 52	3 31	3 13	2 58	2 46	2 35	2 25	2 16	2 09	2 02	1 56	1 50	1 45	1 41	1 33
902	275	4 43	4 15	3 52	3 32	3 16	3 02	2 50	2 39	2 30	2 22	2 14	2 08	2 01	1 56	1 51	1 42
984	300	5 09	4 38	4 13	3 52	3 34	3 19	3 05	2 54	2 44	2 35	2 26	2 19	2 13	2 07	2 01	1 51
1148	350	6 00	5 24	4 55	4 30	4 09	3 52	3 36	3 23	3 11	3 00	2 51	2 42	2 35	2 28	2 21	2 10
1312	400	6 51	6 10	5 36	5 09	4 45	4 25	4 07	3 52	3 38	3 26	3 15	3 05	2 57	2 49	2 41	2 28
ft	m	1·8	2·0	2·2	2·4	2·6	2·8	3·0	3·2	3·4	3·6	3·8	4·0	4·2	4·4	4·6	5·0

Height of object

Distance of object (nautical miles)

C2

Table 2(4) Distance for a given speed and time

Decimal of hr	Mins	2·5	3·0	3·5	4·0	4·5	5·0	5·5	6·0	6·5	7·0	7·5	8·0	8·5	9·0	9·5	10·0	Mins	Decimal of hr
·0167	1				0·1	0·1	0·1	0·1	0·1	0·1	0·1	0·1	0·1	0·1	0·2	0·2	0·2	1	·0167
·0333	2	0·1	0·1	0·1	0·1	0·1	0·2	0·2	0·2	0·2	0·2	0·2	0·3	0·3	0·3	0·3	0·3	2	·0333
·0500	3	0·1	0·1	0·2	0·2	0·2	0·2	0·3	0·3	0·3	0·3	0·4	0·4	0·4	0·4	0·5	0·5	3	·0500
·0667	4	0·1	0·2	0·2	0·3	0·3	0·3	0·4	0·4	0·4	0·5	0·5	0·5	0·6	0·6	0·6	0·7	4	·0667
·0833	5	0·2	0·2	0·3	0·3	0·4	0·4	0·5	0·5	0·5	0·6	0·6	0·7	0·7	0·7	0·8	0·8	5	·0833
·1000	6	0·2	0·3	0·3	0·4	0·4	0·5	0·5	0·6	0·6	0·7	0·7	0·8	0·8	0·9	0·9	1·0	6	·1000
·1167	7	0·3	0·4	0·4	0·5	0·5	0·6	0·6	0·7	0·8	0·8	0·9	0·9	1·0	1·1	1·1	1·2	7	·1167
·1333	8	0·3	0·4	0·5	0·5	0·6	0·7	0·7	0·8	0·9	0·9	1·0	1·1	1·1	1·2	1·3	1·3	8	·1333
·1500	9	0·4	0·4	0·5	0·6	0·7	0·7	0·8	0·9	1·0	1·0	1·1	1·2	1·3	1·3	1·4	1·5	9	·1500
·1667	10	0·4	0·5	0·6	0·7	0·8	0·8	0·9	1·0	1·1	1·2	1·3	1·3	1·4	1·5	1·6	1·7	10	·1667
·1833	11	0·5	0·5	0·6	0·7	0·8	0·9	1·0	1·1	1·2	1·3	1·4	1·5	1·6	1·6	1·7	1·8	11	·1833
·2000	12	0·5	0·6	0·7	0·8	0·9	1·0	1·1	1·2	1·3	1·4	1·5	1·6	1·7	1·8	1·9	2·0	12	·2000
·2167	13	0·5	0·6	0·8	0·9	1·0	1·1	1·2	1·3	1·4	1·5	1·6	1·7	1·8	2·0	2·0	2·2	13	·2167
·2333	14	0·6	0·7	0·8	0·9	1·0	1·2	1·3	1·4	1·5	1·6	1·7	1·9	2·0	2·1	2·2	2·3	14	·2333
·2500	15	0·6	0·7	0·9	1·0	1·1	1·2	1·4	1·5	1·6	1·8	1·9	2·0	2·1	2·2	2·4	2·5	15	·2500
·2667	16	0·7	0·8	0·9	1·1	1·2	1·3	1·5	1·6	1·7	1·9	2·0	2·1	2·3	2·4	2·5	2·7	16	·2667
·2833	17	0·7	0·8	1·0	1·1	1·3	1·4	1·6	1·7	1·8	2·0	2·1	2·3	2·4	2·5	2·7	2·8	17	·2833
·3000	18	0·7	0·9	1·0	1·2	1·3	1·5	1·6	1·8	1·9	2·1	2·2	2·4	2·5	2·7	2·8	3·0	18	·3000
·3167	19	0·8	1·0	1·1	1·3	1·4	1·6	1·7	1·9	2·1	2·1	2·4	2·5	2·7	2·9	3·0	3·2	19	·3167
·3333	20	0·8	1·0	1·2	1·3	1·5	1·7	1·8	2·0	2·2	2·3	2·5	2·7	2·8	3·0	3·2	3·3	20	·3333
·3500	21	0·9	1·0	1·2	1·4	1·6	1·7	1·9	2·1	2·3	2·4	2·6	2·8	3·0	3·1	3·3	3·5	21	·3500
·3667	22	0·9	1·1	1·3	1·5	1·7	1·8	2·1	2·2	2·4	2·6	2·8	2·9	3·1	3·3	3·5	3·7	22	·3667
·3833	23	1·0	1·1	1·3	1·5	1·7	1·9	2·1	2·3	2·5	2·7	2·9	3·1	3·3	3·4	3·6	3·8	23	·3833
·4000	24	1·0	1·2	1·4	1·6	1·8	2·0	2·2	2·4	2·6	2·8	3·0	3·2	3·4	3·6	3·8	4·0	24	·4000
·4167	25	1·0	1·3	1·5	1·7	1·9	2·1	2·3	2·5	2·7	2·9	3·1	3·3	3·5	3·8	4·0	4·2	25	·4167
·4333	26	1·1	1·3	1·5	1·7	1·9	2·2	2·4	2·6	2·8	3·0	3·2	3·5	3·7	3·9	4·1	4·3	26	·4333
·4500	27	1·1	1·3	1·6	1·8	2·0	2·2	2·5	2·7	2·9	3·1	3·4	3·6	3·8	4·0	4·3	4·5	27	·4500
·4667	28	1·2	1·4	1·6	1·9	2·1	2·3	2·6	2·8	3·0	3·3	3·5	3·7	4·0	4·2	4·4	4·7	28	·4667
·4833	29	1·2	1·5	1·7	1·9	2·2	2·4	2·7	2·9	3·1	3·4	3·6	3·9	4·1	4·3	4·6	4·8	29	·4833
·5000	30	1·2	1·5	1·7	2·0	2·2	2·5	2·7	3·0	3·2	3·5	3·7	4·0	4·2	4·5	4·7	5·0	30	·5000
·5167	31	1·3	1·6	1·8	2·1	2·3	2·6	2·8	3·1	3·4	3·6	3·9	4·1	4·4	4·7	4·9	5·2	31	·5167
·5333	32	1·3	1·6	1·9	2·1	2·4	2·7	2·9	3·2	3·5	3·7	4·0	4·3	4·5	4·8	5·1	5·3	32	·5333
·5500	33	1·4	1·6	1·9	2·2	2·5	2·7	3·0	3·3	3·6	3·8	4·1	4·4	4·7	4·9	5·2	5·5	33	·5500
·5667	34	1·4	1·7	2·0	2·3	2·6	2·8	3·1	3·4	3·7	4·0	4·3	4·5	4·8	5·1	5·4	5·7	34	·5667
·5833	35	1·5	1·7	2·0	2·3	2·6	2·9	3·2	3·5	3·8	4·1	4·4	4·7	5·0	5·2	5·5	5·8	35	·5833
·6000	36	1·5	1·8	2·1	2·4	2·7	3·0	3·3	3·6	3·9	4·2	4·5	4·8	5·1	5·4	5·7	6·0	36	·6000
·6117	37	1·6	1·8	2·1	2·4	2·8	3·1	3·4	3·7	4·0	4·3	4·6	4·9	5·2	5·5	5·8	6·1	37	·6117
·6333	38	1·6	1·9	2·2	2·5	2·8	3·2	3·5	3·8	4·1	4·4	4·7	5·1	5·4	5·7	6·0	6·3	38	·6333
·6500	39	1·6	1·9	2·3	2·6	2·9	3·2	3·6	3·9	4·2	4·5	4·9	5·2	5·5	5·8	6·2	6·5	39	·6500
·6667	40	1·7	2·0	2·3	2·7	3·0	3·3	3·7	4·0	4·3	4·7	5·0	5·3	5·7	6·0	6·3	6·7	40	·6667
·6833	41	1·7	2·0	2·4	2·7	3·1	3·4	3·8	4·1	4·4	4·8	5·1	5·5	5·8	6·1	6·5	6·8	41	·6833
·7000	42	1·7	2·1	2·4	2·8	3·1	3·5	3·8	4·2	4·5	4·9	5·2	5·6	5·9	6·3	6·6	7·0	42	·7000
·7167	43	1·8	2·2	2·5	2·9	3·2	3·6	3·9	4·3	4·7	5·0	5·4	5·7	6·1	6·5	6·8	7·2	43	·7167
·7333	44	1·8	2·2	2·6	2·9	3·3	3·7	4·0	4·4	4·8	5·1	5·5	5·9	6·2	6·6	7·0	7·3	44	·7333
·7500	45	1·9	2·2	2·6	3·0	3·4	3·7	4·1	4·5	4·9	5·2	5·6	6·0	6·4	6·7	7·1	7·5	45	·7500
·7667	46	1·9	2·3	2·7	3·1	3·5	3·8	4·2	4·6	5·0	5·4	5·8	6·1	6·5	6·9	7·3	7·7	46	·7667
·7833	47	2·0	2·3	2·7	3·1	3·5	3·9	4·3	4·7	5·1	5·5	5·9	6·3	6·7	7·0	7·4	7·8	47	·7833
·8000	48	2·0	2·4	2·8	3·2	3·6	4·0	4·4	4·8	5·2	5·6	6·0	6·4	6·8	7·2	7·6	8·0	48	·8000
·8167	49	2·0	2·5	2·9	3·3	3·7	4·1	4·5	4·9	5·3	5·7	6·1	6·5	6·9	7·4	7·8	8·2	49	·8167
·8333	50	2·1	2·5	2·9	3·3	3·7	4·2	4·6	5·0	5·4	5·8	6·2	6·7	7·1	7·5	7·9	8·3	50	·8333
·8500	51	2·1	2·5	3·0	3·4	3·8	4·2	4·7	5·1	5·5	5·9	6·4	6·8	7·2	7·6	8·1	8·5	51	·8500
·8667	52	2·2	2·6	3·0	3·5	3·9	4·3	4·8	5·2	5·6	6·1	6·5	6·9	7·4	7·8	8·2	8·7	52	·8667
·8833	53	2·2	2·6	3·1	3·5	4·0	4·4	4·9	5·3	5·7	6·2	6·6	7·1	7·5	7·9	8·4	8·8	53	·8833
·9000	54	2·2	2·7	3·1	3·6	4·0	4·5	4·9	5·4	5·8	6·3	6·7	7·2	7·6	8·1	8·5	9·0	54	·9000
·9167	55	2·3	2·8	3·2	3·7	4·1	4·6	5·0	5·5	6·0	6·4	6·9	7·3	7·8	8·3	8·7	9·2	55	·9167
·9333	56	2·3	2·8	3·3	3·7	4·2	4·7	5·1	5·6	6·1	6·5	7·0	7·5	7·9	8·4	8·9	9·3	56	·9333
·9500	57	2·4	2·8	3·3	3·8	4·3	4·7	5·2	5·7	6·2	6·6	7·1	7·6	8·1	8·5	9·0	9·5	57	·9500
·9667	58	2·4	2·9	3·4	3·9	4·4	4·8	5·3	5·8	6·3	6·8	7·3	7·7	8·2	8·7	9·2	9·7	58	·9667
·9833	59	2·5	2·9	3·4	3·9	4·4	4·9	5·4	5·9	6·4	6·9	7·4	7·9	8·4	8·8	9·3	9·8	59	·9833
1·0000	60	2·5	3·0	3·5	4·0	4·5	5·0	5·5	6·0	6·5	7·0	7·5	8·0	8·5	9·0	9·5	10·0	60	1·0000

Table 2(4)   Distance for a given speed and time (continued)

Time Decimal of hr	Mins	10·5	11·0	11·5	12·0	12·5	13·0	13·5	14·0	14·5	15·0	15·5	16·0	17·0	18·0	19·0	20·0	Mins	Time Decimal of hr
·0167	1	0·2	0·2	0·2	0·2	0·2	0·2	0·2	0·2	0·2	0·3	0·3	0·3	0·3	0·3	0·3	0·3	1	·0167
·0333	2	0·3	0·4	0·4	0·4	0·4	0·4	0·4	0·5	0·5	0·5	0·5	0·5	0·6	0·6	0·6	0·7	2	·0333
·0500	3	0·5	0·5	0·6	0·6	0·6	0·6	0·7	0·7	0·7	0·7	0·8	0·8	0·8	0·8	0·9	1·0	3	·0500
·0667	4	0·7	0·7	0·8	0·8	0·8	0·9	0·9	0·9	1·0	1·0	1·0	1·1	1·1	1·2	1·3	1·3	4	·0667
·0833	5	0·9	0·9	1·0	1·0	1·0	1·1	1·1	1·2	1·2	1·2	1·3	1·3	1·4	1·5	1·6	1·7	5	·0833
·1000	6	1·0	1·1	1·1	1·2	1·2	1·3	1·3	1·4	1·4	1·5	1·5	1·6	1·7	1·8	1·9	2·0	6	·1000
·1167	7	1·2	1·3	1·3	1·4	1·5	1·5	1·6	1·6	1·7	1·8	1·8	1·9	2·0	2·1	2·2	2·3	7	·1167
·1333	8	1·4	1·5	1·5	1·6	1·7	1·7	1·8	1·9	1·9	2·0	2·1	2·1	2·3	2·4	2·5	2·7	8	·1333
·1500	9	1·6	1·6	1·7	1·8	1·9	1·9	2·0	2·1	2·1	2·2	2·3	2·4	2·5	2·7	2·8	3·0	9	·1500
·1667	10	1·8	1·8	1·9	2·0	2·1	2·2	2·3	2·3	2·4	2·5	2·6	2·7	2·8	3·0	3·2	3·3	10	·1667
·1833	11	1·9	2·0	2·1	2·2	2·3	2·4	2·5	2·6	2·7	2·7	2·8	2·9	3·1	3·3	3·5	3·7	11	·1833
·2000	12	2·1	2·2	2·3	2·4	2·5	2·6	2·7	2·8	2·9	3·0	3·1	3·2	3·4	3·6	3·8	4·0	12	·2000
·2167	13	2·3	2·4	2·5	2·6	2·7	2·8	2·9	3·0	3·1	3·2	3·3	3·5	3·7	3·9	4·1	4·3	13	·2167
·2333	14	2·4	2·6	2·7	2·8	2·9	3·0	3·1	3·3	3·4	3·5	3·6	3·7	4·0	4·2	4·4	4·7	14	·2333
·2500	15	2·6	2·7	2·9	3·0	3·1	3·2	3·4	3·5	3·6	3·7	3·9	4·0	4·2	4·5	4·7	5·0	15	·2500
·2667	16	2·8	2·9	3·1	3·2	3·3	3·5	3·6	3·7	3·9	4·0	4·1	4·3	4·5	4·8	5·1	5·3	16	·2667
·2833	17	3·0	3·1	3·3	3·4	3·5	3·7	3·8	4·0	4·1	4·2	4·4	4·5	4·8	5·1	5·4	5·7	17	·2833
·3000	18	3·1	3·3	3·4	3·6	3·7	3·9	4·0	4·2	4·3	4·5	4·6	4·8	5·1	5·4	5·7	6·0	18	·3000
·3167	19	3·3	3·5	3·6	3·8	4·0	4·1	4·3	4·4	4·6	4·8	4·9	5·1	5·4	5·7	6·0	6·3	19	·3167
·3333	20	3·5	3·7	3·8	4·0	4·2	4·3	4·5	4·7	4·8	5·0	5·2	5·3	5·7	6·0	6·3	6·7	20	·3333
·3500	21	3·7	3·8	4·0	4·2	4·4	4·5	4·7	4·9	5·1	5·2	5·4	5·6	5·9	6·3	6·6	7·0	21	·3500
·3667	22	3·9	4·0	4·2	4·4	4·6	4·8	5·0	5·1	5·3	5·5	5·7	5·9	6·2	6·6	7·0	7·3	22	·3667
·3833	23	4·0	4·2	4·4	4·6	4·8	5·0	5·2	5·4	5·6	5·7	5·9	6·1	6·5	6·9	7·3	7·7	23	·3833
·4000	24	4·2	4·4	4·6	4·8	5·0	5·2	5·4	5·6	5·8	6·0	6·2	6·4	6·8	7·2	7·6	8·0	24	·4000
·4167	25	4·4	4·6	4·8	5·0	5·2	5·4	5·6	5·8	6·0	6·3	6·5	6·7	7·1	7·5	7·9	8·3	25	·4167
·4333	26	4·5	4·8	5·0	5·2	5·4	5·6	5·8	6·1	6·3	6·5	6·7	6·9	7·4	7·8	8·2	8·7	26	·4333
·4500	27	4·7	4·9	5·2	5·4	5·6	5·8	6·1	6·3	6·5	6·7	7·0	7·2	7·6	8·1	8·5	9·0	27	·4500
·4667	28	4·9	5·1	5·4	5·6	5·8	6·1	6·3	6·5	6·8	7·0	7·2	7·5	7·9	8·4	8·9	9·3	28	·4667
·4833	29	5·1	5·3	5·6	5·8	6·0	6·3	6·5	6·8	7·0	7·2	7·5	7·7	8·2	8·7	9·2	9·7	29	·4833
·5000	30	5·2	5·5	5·7	6·0	6·2	6·5	6·7	7·0	7·2	7·5	7·7	8·0	8·5	9·0	9·5	10·0	30	·5000
·5167	31	5·4	5·7	5·9	6·2	6·5	6·7	7·0	7·2	7·5	7·8	8·0	8·3	8·8	9·3	9·8	10·3	31	·5167
·5333	32	5·6	5·9	6·1	6·4	6·7	6·9	7·2	7·5	7·7	8·0	8·3	8·5	9·1	9·6	10·1	10·7	32	·5333
·5500	33	5·8	6·0	6·3	6·6	6·9	7·1	7·4	7·7	8·0	8·2	8·5	8·8	9·3	9·9	10·4	11·0	33	·5500
·5667	34	6·0	6·2	6·5	6·8	7·1	7·4	7·7	7·9	8·2	8·5	8·8	9·1	9·6	10·2	10·8	11·3	34	·5667
·5833	35	6·1	6·4	6·7	7·0	7·3	7·6	7·9	8·2	8·5	8·7	9·0	9·3	9·9	10·5	11·1	11·7	35	·5833
·6000	36	6·3	6·6	6·9	7·2	7·5	7·8	8·1	8·4	8·7	9·0	9·3	9·6	10·2	10·8	11·4	12·0	36	·6000
·6117	37	6·4	6·7	7·0	7·3	7·6	8·0	8·3	8·6	8·9	9·2	9·5	9·8	10·4	11·0	11·6	12·2	37	·6117
·6333	38	6·6	7·0	7·3	7·6	7·9	8·2	8·5	8·9	9·2	9·5	9·8	10·1	10·8	11·4	12·0	12·7	38	·6333
·6500	39	6·8	7·1	7·5	7·8	8·1	8·4	8·8	9·1	9·4	9·7	10·1	10·4	11·0	11·7	12·3	13·0	39	·6500
·6667	40	7·0	7·3	7·7	8·0	8·3	8·7	9·0	9·3	9·7	10·0	10·3	10·7	11·3	12·0	12·7	13·3	40	·6667
·6833	41	7·2	7·5	7·9	8·2	8·5	8·9	9·2	9·6	9·9	10·2	10·6	10·9	11·6	12·3	13·0	13·7	41	·6833
·7000	42	7·3	7·7	8·0	8·4	8·7	9·1	9·4	9·8	10·1	10·5	10·8	11·2	11·9	12·6	13·3	14·0	42	·7000
·7167	43	7·5	7·9	8·2	8·6	9·0	9·3	9·7	10·0	10·4	10·8	11·1	11·5	12·2	12·9	13·6	14·3	43	·7167
·7333	44	7·7	8·1	8·4	8·8	9·2	9·5	10·0	10·3	10·6	11·0	11·4	11·7	12·5	13·2	13·9	14·7	44	·7333
·7500	45	7·9	8·2	8·6	9·0	9·4	9·7	10·1	10·5	10·9	11·2	11·6	12·0	12·7	13·5	14·2	15·0	45	·7500
·7667	46	8·1	8·4	8·8	9·2	9·6	10·0	10·4	10·7	11·1	11·5	11·9	12·3	13·0	13·8	14·6	15·3	46	·7667
·7833	47	8·2	8·6	9·0	9·4	9·8	10·2	10·6	11·0	11·4	11·7	12·1	12·5	13·3	14·1	14·9	15·7	47	·7833
·8000	48	8·4	8·8	9·2	9·6	10·0	10·4	10·8	11·2	11·6	12·0	12·4	12·8	13·6	14·4	15·2	16·0	48	·8000
·8167	49	8·6	9·0	9·4	9·8	10·2	10·6	11·0	11·4	11·8	12·2	12·7	13·1	13·9	14·7	15·5	16·3	49	·8167
·8333	50	8·7	9·2	9·6	10·0	10·4	10·8	11·2	11·7	12·1	12·5	12·9	13·3	14·2	15·0	15·8	16·7	50	·8333
·8500	51	8·9	9·3	9·8	10·2	10·6	11·0	11·5	11·9	12·3	12·7	13·2	13·6	14·4	15·3	16·1	17·0	51	·8500
·8667	52	9·1	9·5	10·0	10·4	10·8	11·3	11·7	12·1	12·6	13·0	13·4	13·9	14·7	15·6	16·5	17·3	52	·8667
·8833	53	9·3	9·7	10·2	10·6	11·0	11·5	11·9	12·4	12·8	13·2	13·7	14·1	15·0	15·9	16·8	17·7	53	·8833
·9000	54	9·4	9·9	10·3	10·8	11·2	11·7	12·1	12·6	13·0	13·5	13·9	14·4	15·3	16·2	17·1	18·0	54	·9000
·9167	55	9·6	10·1	10·5	11·0	11·5	11·9	12·4	12·8	13·3	13·8	14·2	14·7	15·6	16·5	17·4	18·3	55	·9167
·9333	56	9·8	10·3	10·7	11·2	11·7	12·1	12·6	13·1	13·5	14·0	14·5	14·9	15·9	16·8	17·7	18·7	56	·9333
·9500	57	10·0	10·4	10·9	11·4	11·9	12·3	12·8	13·3	13·8	14·2	14·7	15·2	16·1	17·1	18·0	19·0	57	·9500
·9667	58	10·2	10·6	11·1	11·6	12·1	12·6	13·1	13·5	14·0	14·5	15·0	15·5	16·4	17·4	18·4	19·3	58	·9667
·9833	59	10·3	10·8	11·3	11·8	12·3	12·8	13·3	13·8	14·3	14·7	15·2	15·7	16·7	17·7	18·7	19·7	59	·9833
1·0000	60	10·5	11·0	11·5	12·0	12·5	13·0	13·5	14·0	14·5	15·0	15·5	16·0	17·0	18·0	19·0	20·0	60	1·0000
Decimal of hr Mins		10·5	11·0	11·5	12·0	12·5	13·0	13·5	14·0	14·5	15·0	15·5	16·0	17·0	18·0	19·0	20·0	Mins	Decimal of hr

Time · · · Speed in knots · · · Time

C2

Table 2(5) Speed (knots) over measured nautical mile

Secs	1 min	2 min	3 min	4 min	5 min	6 min	7 min	8 min	9 min	10 min	11 min
	60·00	30·00	20·00	15·00	12·00	10·00	8·57	7·50	6·67	6·00	5·45
1	59·02	29·75	19·89	14·94	11·96	9·97	8·55	7·48	6·66	5·99	5·45
2	58·06	29·51	19·78	14·88	11·92	9·94	8·53	7·47	6·64	5·98	5·44
3	57·14	29·27	19·67	14·81	11·88	9·92	8·51	7·45	6·63	5·97	5·43
4	56·25	29·03	19·57	14·75	11·84	9·89	8·49	7·44	6·62	5·96	5·42
5	55·38	28·80	19·46	14·69	11·80	9·86	8·47	7·42	6·61	5·95	5·41
6	54·55	28·57	19·35	14·63	11·76	9·84	8·45	7·41	6·59	5·94	5·41
7	53·73	28·35	19·25	14·57	11·73	9·81	8·43	7·39	6·58	5·93	5·40
8	52·94	28·12	19·15	14·52	11·69	9·78	8·41	7·38	6·57	5·92	5·39
9	52·17	27·91	19·05	14·46	11·65	9·76	8·39	7·36	6·56	5·91	5·38
10	51·43	27·69	18·95	14·40	11·61	9·73	8·37	7·35	6·55	5·90	5·37
11	50·70	27·48	18·85	14·34	11·58	9·70	8·35	7·33	6·53	5·89	5·37
12	50·00	27·27	18·75	14·29	11·54	9·68	8·33	7·32	6·52	5·88	5·36
13	49·32	27·07	18·65	14·23	11·50	9·65	8·31	7·30	6·51	5·87	5·35
14	48·65	26·87	18·56	14·17	11·46	9·63	8·29	7·29	6·50	5·86	5·34
15	48·00	26·67	18·46	14·12	11·43	9·60	8·28	7·27	6·49	5·85	5·33
16	47·37	26·47	18·37	14·06	11·39	9·58	8·26	7·26	6·47	5·84	5·33
17	46·75	26·28	18·27	14·01	11·36	9·55	8·24	7·24	6·46	5·83	5·32
18	46·15	26·09	18·18	13·95	11·32	9·52	8·22	7·23	6·45	5·83	5·31
19	45·57	25·90	18·09	13·90	11·29	9·50	8·20	7·21	6·44	5·82	5·30
20	45·00	25·71	18·00	13·85	11·25	9·47	8·18	7·20	6·43	5·81	5·29
21	44·44	25·53	17·91	13·79	11·21	9·45	8·16	7·19	6·42	5·80	5·29
22	43·90	25·35	17·82	13·74	11·18	9·42	8·14	7·17	6·41	5·79	5·28
23	43·37	25·17	17·73	13·69	11·15	9·40	8·13	7·16	6·39	5·78	5·27
24	42·86	25·00	17·65	13·64	11·11	9·37	8·11	7·14	6·38	5·77	5·26
25	42·35	24·83	17·56	13·58	11·08	9·35	8·09	7·13	6·37	5·76	5·26
26	41·86	24·66	17·48	13·53	11·04	9·33	8·07	7·11	6·36	5·75	5·25
27	41·38	24·49	17·39	13·48	11·01	9·30	8·05	7·10	6·35	5·74	5·24
28	40·91	24·32	17·31	13·43	10·98	9·28	8·04	7·09	6·34	5·73	5·23
29	40·45	24·16	17·22	13·38	10·94	9·25	8·02	7·07	6·33	5·72	5·22
30	40·00	24·00	17·14	13·33	10·91	9·23	8·00	7·06	6·32	5·71	5·22
31	39·56	23·84	17·06	13·28	10·88	9·21	7·98	7·04	6·30	5·71	5·21
32	39·13	23·68	16·98	13·24	10·84	9·18	7·96	7·03	6·29	5·70	5·20
33	38·71	23·53	16·90	13·19	10·81	9·16	7·95	7·02	6·28	5·69	5·19
34	38·30	23·38	16·82	13·14	10·78	9·14	7·93	7·00	6·27	5·68	5·19
35	37·89	23·23	16·74	13·09	10·75	9·11	7·91	6·99	6·26	5·67	5·18
36	37·50	23·08	16·67	13·04	10·71	9·09	7·89	6·98	6·25	5·66	5·17
37	37·11	22·93	16·59	13·00	10·68	9·07	7·88	6·96	6·24	5·65	5·16
38	36·73	22·78	16·51	12·95	10·65	9·05	7·86	6·95	6·23	5·64	5·16
39	36·36	22·64	16·44	12·90	10·62	9·02	7·84	6·94	6·22	5·63	5·15
40	36·00	22·50	16·36	12·86	10·59	9·00	7·83	6·92	6·21	5·62	5·14
41	35·64	22·36	16·29	12·81	10·56	8·98	7·81	6·91	6·20	5·62	5·13
42	35·29	22·22	16·22	12·77	10·53	8·96	7·79	6·90	6·19	5·61	5·13
43	34·95	22·09	16·14	12·72	10·50	8·93	7·78	6·89	6·17	5·60	5·12
44	34·62	21·95	16·07	12·68	10·47	8·91	7·76	6·87	6·16	5·59	5·11
45	34·29	21·82	16·00	12·63	10·43	8·89	7·74	6·86	6·15	5·58	5·10
46	33·96	21·69	15·93	12·59	10·40	8·87	7·72	6·84	6·14	5·57	5·10
47	33·64	21·56	15·86	12·54	10·37	8·85	7·71	6·83	6·13	5·56	5·09
48	33·33	21·43	15·79	12·50	10·34	8·82	7·69	6·82	6·12	5·56	5·08
49	33·03	21·30	15·72	12·46	10·32	8·80	7·68	6·80	6·11	5·55	5·08
50	32·73	21·18	15·65	12·41	10·29	8·78	7·66	6·79	6·10	5·54	5·07
51	32·43	21·05	15·58	12·37	10·26	8·76	7·64	6·78	6·09	5·53	5·06
52	32·14	20·93	15·52	12·33	10·23	8·74	7·63	6·77	6·08	5·52	5·06
53	31·86	20·81	15·45	12·29	10·20	8·72	7·61	6·75	6·07	5·51	5·05
54	31·58	20·69	15·38	12·24	10·17	8·70	7·59	6·74	6·06	5·50	5·04
55	31·30	20·57	15·32	12·20	10·14	8·67	7·58	6·73	6·05	5·50	5·04
56	31·03	20·45	15·25	12·16	10·11	8·65	7·56	6·72	6·04	5·49	5·03
57	30·77	20·34	15·19	12·12	10·08	8·63	7·55	6·70	6·03	5·48	5·02
58	30·51	20·22	15·13	12·08	10·06	8·61	7·53	6·69	6·02	5·47	5·01
59	30·25	20·11	15·06	12·04	10·03	8·59	7·52	6·68	6·01	5·46	5·00
Secs	1 min	2 min	3 min	4 min	5 min	6 min	7 min	8 min	9 min	10 min	11 min

TABLE 2(6)   TRUE BEARING OF SUN AT SUNRISE AND SUNSET

LAT	0°	1°	2°	3°	4°	5°	6°	7°	8°	9°	10°	11°	LAT
	°	°	°	°	°	°	°	°	°	°	°	°	
30°	90	88·8	87·7	86·5	85·4	84·2	83·1	81·9	80·7	79·6	78·4	77·3	30°
31°	90	88·8	87·7	86·5	85·3	84·2	83·0	81·9	80·6	79·5	78·3	77·1	31°
32°	90	88·8	87·6	86·5	85·3	84·1	82·9	81·7	80·5	79·4	78·2	77·0	32°
33°	90	88·8	87·6	86·4	85·2	84·0	82·8	81·6	80·4	79·2	78·0	76·8	33°
34°	90	88·8	87·6	86·4	85·2	84·0	82·7	81·5	80·3	79·1	77·9	76·7	34°
35°	90	88·8	87·5	86·3	85·1	83·9	82·7	81·4	80·2	79·0	77·8	76·5	35°
36°	90	88·8	87·5	86·3	85·0	83·8	82·6	81·3	80·1	78·8	77·6	76·3	36°
37°	90	88·7	87·5	86·2	85·0	83·7	82·5	81·2	80·0	78·7	77·4	76·2	37°
38°	90	88·7	87·5	86·2	84·9	83·6	82·4	81·1	79·8	78·5	77·3	76·0	38°
39°	90	88·7	87·4	86·1	84·8	83·6	82·3	81·0	79·7	78·4	77·1	75·8	39°
40°	90	88·7	87·4	86·1	84·8	83·5	82·1	80·8	79·5	78·2	76·9	75·6	40°
41°	90	88·7	87·3	86·0	84·7	83·4	82·0	80·7	79·4	78·0	76·7	75·3	41°
42°	90	88·6	87·3	86·0	84·6	83·3	81·9	80·6	79·2	77·8	76·5	75·1	42°
43°	90	88·6	87·3	85·9	84·5	83·1	81·8	80·4	79·0	77·6	76·3	74·9	43°
44°	90	88·6	87·2	85·8	84·4	83·0	81·6	80·2	78·8	77·4	76·0	74·6	44°
45°	90	88·6	87·2	85·7	84·3	82·9	81·5	80·1	78·6	77·2	75·8	74·3	45°
46°	90	88·6	87·1	85·7	84·2	82·8	81·3	79·9	78·4	77·0	75·5	74·0	46°
47°	90	88·5	87·1	85·6	84·1	82·6	81·2	79·7	78·2	76·7	75·2	73·7	47°
48°	90	88·5	87·0	85·5	84·0	82·5	81·0	79·5	78·0	76·5	75·0	73·4	48°
49°	90	88·5	86·9	85·4	83·9	82·4	80·8	79·3	77·7	76·2	74·6	73·1	49°
50°	90	88·4	86·9	85·3	83·8	82·2	80·6	79·1	77·5	75·9	74·3	72·7	50°
51°	90	88·4	86·8	85·2	83·6	82·0	80·4	78·8	77·2	75·6	74·0	72·4	51°
52°	90	88·4	86·7	85·1	83·5	81·9	80·2	78·6	76·9	75·3	73·6	71·9	52°
53°	90	88·3	86·7	85·0	83·3	81·7	80·0	78·3	76·6	74·9	73·2	71·5	53°
54°	90	88·3	86·6	84·9	83·2	81·5	79·8	78·0	76·3	74·6	72·8	71·1	54°
55°	90	88·2	86·5	84·8	83·0	81·3	79·5	77·7	76·0	74·2	72·4	70·6	55°
56°	90	88·2	86·4	84·6	82·8	81·0	79·2	77·4	75·6	73·8	71·9	70·0	56°
57°	90	88·2	86·3	84·5	82·6	80·8	78·9	77·0	75·2	73·3	71·4	69·5	57°
58°	90	88·1	86·2	84·3	82·4	80·5	78·6	76·7	74·8	72·8	70·9	68·9	58°
59°	90	88·1	86·1	84·2	82·2	80·3	78·3	76·3	74·3	72·3	70·3	68·3	59°
60°	90	88·0	86·0	84·0	82·0	80·0	77·9	75·9	73·8	71·8	69·7	67·6	60°

LAT	12°	13°	14°	15°	16°	17°	18°	19°	20°	21°	22°	23°	LAT
	°	°	°	°	°	°	°	°	°	°	°	°	
30°	76·1	74·9	73·8	72·6	71·4	70·3	69·1	67·9	66·7	65·5	64·4	63·2	30°
31°	76·0	74·8	73·6	72·4	71·2	70·0	68·9	67·7	66·5	65·3	64·1	62·9	31°
32°	75·8	74·6	73·4	72·2	71·0	69·8	68·6	67·4	66·2	65·0	63·8	62·6	32°
33°	75·6	74·4	73·2	72·1	70·8	69·6	68·4	67·1	65·9	64·7	63·5	62·2	33°
34°	75·5	74·2	73·0	71·8	70·6	69·3	68·1	66·9	65·6	64·4	63·1	61·9	34°
35°	75·3	74·1	72·8	71·6	70·3	69·1	67·8	66·6	65·3	64·1	62·8	61·5	35°
36°	75·1	73·8	72·6	71·3	70·1	68·8	67·5	66·3	65·0	63·7	62·4	61·1	36°
37°	74·9	73·6	72·4	71·1	69·8	68·5	67·2	65·9	64·6	63·3	62·0	60·7	37°
38°	74·7	73·4	72·0	70·8	69·5	68·2	66·9	65·6	64·3	62·9	61·6	60·3	38°
39°	74·5	73·2	71·9	70·5	69·2	67·9	66·6	65·2	63·9	62·5	61·2	59·8	39°
40°	74·2	72·9	71·6	70·2	68·9	67·6	66·2	64·8	63·5	62·1	60·7	59·3	40°
41°	74·0	72·7	71·3	69·9	68·6	67·2	65·8	64·4	63·0	61·6	60·2	58·8	41°
42°	73·7	72·4	71·0	69·6	68·2	66·8	65·4	64·0	62·6	61·2	59·7	58·3	42°
43°	73·5	72·1	70·7	69·3	67·9	66·4	65·0	63·6	62·1	60·7	59·2	57·7	43°
44°	73·2	71·8	70·3	68·9	67·5	66·0	64·6	63·1	61·6	60·1	58·6	57·1	44°
45°	72·9	71·4	70·0	68·5	67·0	65·6	64·1	62·6	61·1	59·5	58·0	56·4	45°
46°	72·6	71·1	69·6	68·1	66·6	65·1	63·6	62·0	60·5	58·9	57·4	55·8	46°
47°	72·2	70·7	69·2	67·7	66·2	64·6	63·1	61·5	59·9	58·3	56·7	55·0	47°
48°	71·9	70·3	68·8	67·2	65·7	64·1	62·5	60·9	59·3	57·6	55·9	54·3	48°
49°	71·5	69·9	68·4	66·8	65·1	63·5	61·9	60·2	58·6	56·9	55·2	53·4	49°
50°	71·1	69·5	67·9	66·2	64·6	62·9	61·3	59·6	57·8	56·1	54·3	52·6	50°
51°	70·7	69·1	67·4	65·7	64·0	62·3	60·6	58·8	57·1	55·3	53·5	51·6	51°
52°	70·3	68·6	66·9	65·1	63·4	61·6	59·9	58·1	56·3	54·4	52·5	50·6	52°
53°	69·8	68·1	66·3	64·5	62·7	60·9	59·1	57·3	55·4	53·5	51·5	49·5	53°
54°	69·3	67·5	65·7	63·9	62·0	60·2	58·3	56·4	54·4	52·4	50·4	48·3	54°
55°	68·7	66·9	65·1	63·2	61·3	59·4	57·4	55·4	53·4	51·3	49·2	47·1	55°
56°	68·2	66·3	64·4	62·4	60·5	58·5	56·5	54·4	52·3	50·1	47·9	45·7	56°
57°	67·6	65·6	63·6	61·6	59·6	57·5	55·4	53·3	51·1	48·9	46·5	44·2	57°
58°	66·9	64·9	62·8	60·8	58·7	56·5	54·3	52·1	49·8	47·4	45·0	42·5	58°
59°	66·2	64·1	62·0	59·8	57·6	55·4	53·1	50·8	48·4	45·9	43·3	40·7	59°
60°	65·4	63·3	61·1	58·8	56·5	54·2	51·8	49·4	46·8	44·2	41·5	38·6	60°

TABLE 2 (7)   DECLINATION OF THE SUN

SOUTH		DECLINATION	NORTH	
Dec 07 – Jan 05		**23°**	Jun 05 – Jul 07	
Jan 06 – Jan 12	Nov 30 – Dec 06	**22°**	May 29 – Jun 04	Jul 08 – Jul 15
Jan 13 – Jan 18	Nov 24 – Nov 29	**21°**	May 23 – May 28	Jul 16 – Jul 20
Jan 19 – Jan 22	Nov 20 – Nov 23	**20°**	May 18 – May 22	Jul 21 – Jul 25
Jan 23 – Jan 26	Nov 16 – Nov 19	**19°**	May 14 – May 17	Jul 26 – Jul 30
Jan 27 – Jan 30	Nov 12 – Nov 15	**18°**	May 10 – May 13	Jul 31 – Aug 03
Jan 31 – Feb 03	Nov 08 – Nov 11	**17°**	May 06 – May 09	Aug 04 – Aug 06
Feb 04 – Feb 06	Nov 05 – Nov 07	**16°**	May 03 – May 05	Aug 07 – Aug 10
Feb 07 – Feb 09	Nov 02 – Nov 04	**15°**	Apr 30 – May 02	Aug 11 – Aug 13
Feb 10 – Feb 12	Oct 30 – Nov 01	**14°**	Apr 27 – Apr 29	Aug 14 – Aug 16
Feb 13 – Feb 15	Oct 27 – Oct 29	**13°**	Apr 23 – Apr 26	Aug 17 – Aug 19
Feb 16 – Feb 18	Oct 24 – Oct 26	**12°**	Apr 21 – Apr 22	Aug 20 – Aug 22
Feb 19 – Feb 21	Oct 21 – Oct 23	**11°**	Apr 18 – Apr 20	Aug 23 – Aug 25
Feb 22 – Feb 23	Oct 18 – Oct 20	**10°**	Apr 15 – Apr 17	Aug 26 – Aug 28
Feb 24 – Feb 26	Oct 16 – Oct 17	**9°**	Apr 12 – Apr 14	Aug 29 – Aug 31
Feb 27 – Mar 01	Oct 13 – Oct 15	**8°**	Apr 09 – Apr 11	Sep 01 – Sep 03
Mar 02 – Mar 03	Oct 10 – Oct 12	**7°**	Apr 07 – Apr 08	Sep 04 – Sep 05
Mar 04 – Mar 06	Oct 08 – Oct 09	**6°**	Apr 04 – Apr 06	Sep 06 – Sep 08
Mar 07 – Mar 09	Oct 05 – Oct 07	**5°**	Apr 01 – Apr 03	Sep 09 – Sep 11
Mar 10 – Mar 11	Oct 02 – Oct 04	**4°**	Mar 30 – Mar 31	Sep 12 – Sep 13
Mar 12 – Mar 14	Sep 30 – Oct 01	**3°**	Mar 27 – Mar 29	Sep 14 – Sep 16
Mar 15 – Mar 16	Sep 27 – Sep 29	**2°**	Mar 25 – Mar 26	Sep 17 – Sep 19
Mar 17 – Mar 19	Sep 25 – Sep 26	**1°**	Mar 22 – Mar 24	Sep 20 – Sep 21
Mar 20 – Mar 21	Sep 22 – Sep 24	**0°**	Mar 20 – Mar 21	Sep 22 – Sep 24

TABLE 2(8)   PHASES OF THE MOON 1999 – Times in UT

New Moon ●	d	h	m	First Quarter ◑	d	h	m	Full Moon ○	d	h	m	Last Quarter ◐	d	h	m
								Jan	02	02	49	Jan	09	14	22
Jan	17	15	46	Jan	24	19	15	Jan	31	16	06	Feb	08	11	58
Feb	16	06	39	Feb	23	02	43	Mar	02	06	58	Mar	10	08	40
Mar	17	18	48	Mar	24	10	18	Mar	31	22	49	Apr	09	02	51
Apr	16	04	22	Apr	22	19	01	Apr	30	14	55	May	08	17	28
May	15	12	05	May	22	05	34	May	30	06	40	Jun	07	04	20
Jun	13	19	03	Jun	20	18	13	Jun	28	21	37	Jul	06	11	57
Jul	13	02	24	Jul	20	09	00	Jul	28	11	25	Aug	04	17	27
Aug	11	11	08	Aug	19	01	47	Aug	26	23	48	Sep	02	22	17
Sept	09	22	02	Sept	17	20	06	Sep	25	10	51	Oct	02	04	02
Oct	09	11	34	Oct	17	15	00	Oct	24	21	02	Oct	31	12	04
Nov	08	03	53	Nov	16	09	03	Nov	23	07	04	Nov	29	23	18
Dec	07	22	32	Dec	16	00	50	Dec	22	17	31	Dec	29	14	04

2.6.2 ECLIPSE NOTES 1999

1. Annular Eclipse of the Sun, 16 February.   Not visible from Europe.
2. Total Eclipse of the Sun, 11 August.   Visible from Europe including the British Isles.

Path of totality passes through extreme SW England including the Channel Islands and Central Europe.
Immediately prior to the total eclipse, road traffic in Cornwall will be at a standstill; harbours will be full.

2.7 SUN AND MOON TABLES — RISING, SETTING AND TWILIGHTS

2.7.1 Rising and Setting Phenomena

The tables of Sunrise, Sunset and Twilights, Moonrise and Moonset and Phases of the Moon (see Table 2(8)) enable the degree of darkness around twilight and throughout the night to be estimated.

2.7.2 Contents of Tables 2(9), 2(10) and 2(11)

Table 2(9) provides Local Mean Times (LMT) for every third day of the year, of morning Nautical Twilight, Sunrise, Sunset and evening Civil Twilight for latitude 50°N and latitude variations (v). Use the left-hand sign in the tabular entry for v for Sunrise, and the right-hand sign for Sunset. The latitude corrections in Table 2(10) for Sunrise, Sunset and Twilights, enable the LMT for latitudes in the range 30°N to 60°N to be found.

Table 2(11) gives times of Moonrise and Moonset for each day for latitude 50°N and latitude variations (v). The latitude correction table enables the LMT for latitudes in the range 30°N to 60°N to be found.

The tabular values are for the Greenwich Meridian, and are approximately the LMT of the corresponding phenomena for the other meridians. Expressing the longitude in time, the UT is obtained from:

$$UT = LMT \begin{array}{c} + \text{ west} \\ - \text{ east} \end{array} \text{longitude}$$

For Moonrise and Moonset a further small correction of one minute for every seven degrees of longitude is also required, which is added to the LMT if west, subtracted if east.

At Sunrise and Sunset the upper limb of the Sun is on the horizon at sea level. The Sun's zenith distance is 96° for Civil Twilight and 102° for Nautical Twilight. At Civil Twilight the brightest stars are visible and the horizon is clearly defined. At Nautical Twilight the horizon is not visible.

At Moonrise and Moonset the Moon's upper limb is on the horizon at sea level.

2.7.3 Example (a): The Sun – rising, setting and twilights

Find the UT of the beginning of morning Nautical Twilight, Sunrise, Sunset and the end of evening Civil Twilight on 22 January, 1999 for latitude 36°07'N, longitude 18°20'E.

From table 2(9), for 22 January, $v = +30$ for the beginning of Nautical Twilight, $v = +52$ for Sunrise; $v = -52$ for Sunset and $v = -41$ for the end of Civil Twilight. The latitude corrections for Nautical Twilight, Sunrise, Sunset and Civil Twilight are –21 mins, –39 mins, +39 mins and +31 mins respectively. Note that for Sunset, the sign of the correction has to be reversed because v is minus.

Convert longitude from degrees and minutes of arc to whole minutes of time, by multiplying the degrees of longitude by 4 and adding a further correction of 0 mins, 1 min, 2 mins, 3 mins or 4 mins when the minutes of longitude are in the range 0' to 7', 8' to 22', 23' to 37', 38' to 52' or 53' to 59', respectively.

The longitude equivalent in time of 18°20'E is – $(18 \times 4 + 1) = -73m$.

Remarks	Naut Twilight		Sunrise		Sunset		Civil Twilight	
Tabular value, 22 Jan	06h	31m	07h	47m	16h	37m	17h	13m
Corr'n for latitude		–21m		–39m		+39m		+31m
LMT	06h	10m	07h	08m	17h	16m	17h	44m
Corr'n for longitude	–1h	13m	–1h	13m	–1h	13m	–1h	13m
UT of phenomenon	04h	57m	05h	55m	16h	03m	16h	31m

2.7.4 Example (b): The Moon – rising and setting

Find the UT of Moonrise and Moonset on 30 January, 1999 for latitude 36°07'N, longitude 06°30'W.

From Table 2(11) for 30 January, $v = -51$ for Moonrise and $v = +53$ for Moonset. The latitude correction for Moonrise and Moonset is +38 mins and –40 mins, respectively. Note the reversal of the sign of the correction for Moonrise, because v is minus.

Using the method in example (a), the longitude equivalent in time of 06°30'W is +26mins.

Remarks	Moonrise		Moonset	
Tabular value, 30 Jan	15h	45m	06h	33m
Corr'n for latitude		+38m		–40m
LMT	16h	23m	05h	53m
Corr'n for longitude		+26m		+26m
UT of phenomenon	16h	49m	06h	19m

These times can be increased by +1min to allow for the effect of longitude on the LMT of the phenomenon. See text at end of Table 2(11) for the instructions.

TABLE 2(9)   **1999 — SUNRISE, SUNSET and TWILIGHTS**

Date	Naut Twi	v	Sun-rise	v	Sun-set	Civil Twi	v	Date	Naut Twi	v	Sun-rise	v	Sun-set	Civil Twi	v
	h m		h m		h m	h m			h m		h m		h m	h m	
Jan 1	06 39	+39	07 59	+63−	16 08	16 47	−51	Jul 3	02 08	−115	03 56	−67+	20 12	20 56	+83
4	06 39	38	07 58	62	16 12	16 50	50	6	02 12	112	03 58	66	20 11	20 54	82
7	06 39	38	07 57	61	16 15	16 53	49	9	02 16	110	04 01	65	20 09	20 52	81
10	06 38	36	07 56	59	16 19	16 56	48	12	02 20	107	04 04	63	20 07	20 49	79
13	06 37	35	07 54	57	16 23	17 00	46	15	02 26	104	04 07	62	20 04	20 46	77
16	06 35	+34	07 52	+56−	16 27	17 04	−44	18	02 31	−100	04 10	−60+	20 01	20 43	+74
19	06 33	32	07 50	54	16 32	17 09	43	21	02 37	97	04 14	58	19 58	20 39	72
22	06 31	30	07 47	52	16 37	17 13	41	24	02 42	93	04 18	56	19 54	20 35	70
25	06 28	28	07 43	49	16 42	17 17	39	27	02 48	89	04 22	54	19 50	20 30	67
28	06 25	26	07 40	47	16 47	17 22	37	30	02 54	86	04 26	52	19 46	20 25	64
31	06 22	+24	07 36	+45−	16 52	17 27	−34	Aug 2	03 00	− 82	04 30	−49+	19 42	20 20	+61
Feb 3	06 18	22	07 31	42	16 57	17 32	32	5	03 07	78	04 34	47	19 37	20 15	58
6	06 14	20	07 27	39	17 02	17 36	30	8	03 13	74	04 38	44	19 32	20 09	55
9	06 10	17	07 22	37	17 07	17 41	27	11	03 19	70	04 43	42	19 27	20 03	52
12	06 05	15	07 17	34	17 12	17 46	24	14	03 25	66	04 47	39	19 21	19 57	49
15	06 00	+12	07 11	+31−	17 18	17 51	−22	17	03 31	− 63	04 52	−36+	19 15	19 51	+46
18	05 55	10	07 06	28	17 23	17 56	19	20	03 37	59	04 56	34	19 10	19 45	43
21	05 50	7	07 00	26	17 28	18 01	16	23	03 42	55	05 01	31	19 04	19 38	40
24	05 44	5	06 54	23	17 33	18 06	14	26	03 48	52	05 05	28	18 58	19 32	37
27	05 39	+ 2	06 48	20	17 38	18 11	11	29	03 54	48	05 10	25	18 51	19 25	34
Mar 2	05 33	− 1	06 42	+17−	17 43	18 15	− 8	Sep 1	03 59	− 44	05 14	−23+	18 45	19 19	+31
5	05 27	4	06 36	14	17 48	18 20	5	4	04 04	41	05 19	20	18 39	19 12	28
8	05 20	7	06 30	11	17 53	18 25	− 2	7	04 10	38	05 23	17	18 32	19 05	25
11	05 14	10	06 23	8	17 58	18 30	+ 1	10	04 15	34	05 28	14	18 26	18 59	22
14	05 07	13	06 17	5	18 03	18 35	4	13	04 20	31	05 32	11	18 19	18 52	19
17	05 01	− 16	06 11	+ 2−	18 07	18 40	+ 6	16	04 25	− 28	05 36	− 8+	18 13	18 45	+16
20	04 54	19	06 04	− 1+	18 12	18 44	9	19	04 30	24	05 41	5	18 06	18 38	13
23	04 47	22	05 58	3	18 17	18 49	12	22	04 35	21	05 45	− 3+	17 59	18 32	10
26	04 40	25	05 51	6	18 22	18 54	15	25	04 40	18	05 50	0	17 53	18 25	7
29	04 33	29	05 44	9	18 26	18 59	18	28	04 45	15	05 55	+ 3−	17 46	18 18	5
Apr 1	04 26	− 32	05 38	−12+	18 31	19 04	+21	Oct 1	04 49	− 12	05 59	+ 6−	17 40	18 12	+ 2
4	04 19	35	05 31	15	18 36	19 09	24	4	04 54	9	06 04	9	17 33	18 05	− 1
7	04 12	39	05 25	18	18 40	19 14	28	7	04 59	6	06 08	12	17 27	17 59	4
10	04 04	42	05 19	21	18 45	19 19	31	10	05 03	− 3	06 13	15	17 20	17 53	7
13	03 57	46	05 12	24	18 50	19 24	34	13	05 08	0	06 18	18	17 14	17 47	10
16	03 50	− 49	05 06	−26+	18 55	19 29	+37	16	05 12	+ 2	06 23	+20−	17 08	17 41	−12
19	03 43	53	05 00	29	19 00	19 34	40	19	05 17	5	06 27	23	17 02	17 35	15
22	03 36	57	04 54	32	19 04	19 39	43	22	05 22	8	06 32	26	16 56	17 29	18
25	03 28	60	04 48	35	19 09	19 44	46	25	05 26	10	06 37	29	16 50	17 24	20
28	03 21	64	04 43	38	19 13	19 49	49	28	05 31	13	06 42	32	16 45	17 18	23
May 1	03 14	− 68	04 37	−40+	19 18	19 55	+52	31	05 35	+ 15	06 47	+34−	16 39	17 13	−26
4	03 07	72	04 32	43	19 22	20 00	55	Nov 3	05 40	18	06 52	37	16 34	17 08	28
7	03 01	76	04 27	46	19 27	20 05	58	6	05 44	20	06 57	40	16 30	17 04	31
10	02 54	80	04 22	48	19 31	20 10	61	9	05 48	22	07 02	42	16 25	17 00	33
13	02 48	83	04 18	51	19 36	20 15	64	12	05 53	25	07 07	45	16 21	16 56	35
16	02 41	− 87	04 13	−53+	19 40	20 20	+67	15	05 57	+ 27	07 12	+47−	16 17	16 52	−37
19	02 35	91	04 10	55	19 44	20 25	70	18	06 01	29	07 17	50	16 13	16 49	39
22	02 30	95	04 06	57	19 48	20 29	72	21	06 05	30	07 21	52	16 10	16 46	41
25	02 24	99	04 03	59	19 52	20 33	74	24	06 09	32	07 26	54	16 07	16 43	43
28	02 19	102	04 00	61	19 55	20 38	77	27	06 13	34	07 30	56	16 04	16 41	45
31	02 15	−105	03 57	−63+	19 59	20 41	+79	30	06 17	+ 35	07 35	+58−	16 02	16 39	−47
Jun 3	02 11	108	03 55	64	20 02	20 45	81	Dec 3	06 20	36	07 39	59	16 00	16 38	48
6	02 07	111	03 53	66	20 05	20 48	82	6	06 23	38	07 42	61	15 59	16 37	49
9	02 04	113	03 52	67	20 07	20 51	84	9	06 26	39	07 46	62	15 58	16 36	50
12	02 02	115	03 51	68	20 09	20 53	85	12	06 29	39	07 49	63	15 58	16 36	51
15	02 01	−117	03 50	−68+	20 11	20 55	+85	15	06 32	+ 40	07 52	+64−	15 58	16 37	−52
18	02 00	118	03 50	69	20 12	20 57	86	18	06 34	40	07 54	64	15 59	16 37	52
21	02 00	118	03 51	69	20 13	20 58	86	21	06 36	40	07 56	64	16 00	16 39	52
24	02 01	118	03 51	69	20 13	20 58	86	24	06 37	40	07 57	64	16 02	16 40	52
27	02 03	117	03 52	68	20 13	20 58	85	27	06 38	40	07 58	64	16 04	16 42	52
30	02 05	−116	03 54	−68+	20 13	20 57	+85	30	06 39	+ 40	07 59	+63−	16 06	16 45	−51
Jul 3	02 08	−115	03 56	−67+	20 12	20 56	+83	Jan 2	06 39	+ 39	07 59	+63−	16 09	16 47	−51

TABLE 2(10)   **1999 — SUNRISE, SUNSET AND TWILIGHTS**

Corrections to Sunrise and Sunset

N.Lat	30°	35°	40°	45°	50°	52°	54°	56°	58°	60°
v	m	m	m	m	m	m	m	m	m	m
0	0	0	0	0	0	0	0	0	0	0
2	−2	−2	−1	−1	0	0	+1	+1	+2	+2
4	4	3	2	1	0	+1	1	2	3	4
6	6	5	4	2	0	1	2	3	4	6
8	8	6	5	3	0	1	2	4	6	7
10	−10	−8	−6	−3	0	+1	+3	+5	+7	+9
12	12	10	7	4	0	2	4	6	8	11
14	14	11	8	4	0	2	4	7	10	13
16	16	13	9	5	0	2	5	8	11	15
18	18	14	10	6	0	3	6	9	12	16
20	−20	−16	−12	−6	0	+3	+6	+10	+14	+18
22	22	18	13	7	0	3	7	11	15	20
24	24	19	14	8	0	4	7	12	16	22
26	26	21	15	8	0	4	8	13	18	24
28	28	22	16	9	0	4	9	14	19	26
30	−30	−24	−17	−10	0	+4	+9	+15	+21	+28
32	32	26	19	10	0	5	10	16	22	30
34	34	27	20	11	0	5	11	17	24	32
36	36	29	21	11	0	5	11	18	25	34
38	38	31	22	12	0	6	12	19	27	36
40	−40	−32	−23	−13	0	+6	+13	+20	+28	+38
42	42	34	24	13	0	6	13	21	30	40
44	44	35	26	14	0	7	14	22	31	42
46	46	37	27	15	0	7	15	23	33	44
48	48	39	28	15	0	7	15	24	35	47
50	−50	−40	−29	−16	0	+8	+16	+26	+36	+49
52	52	42	30	17	0	8	17	27	38	51
54	54	44	32	17	0	8	17	28	40	54
56	56	45	33	18	0	9	18	29	42	56
58	58	47	34	19	0	9	19	30	43	59
60	−60	−49	−35	−19	0	+9	+20	+32	+45	+62
62	62	50	36	20	0	10	20	33	47	64
64	64	52	38	21	0	10	21	34	49	67
66	66	53	39	22	0	10	22	36	51	70
68	68	55	40	22	0	11	23	37	54	74
70	−70	−57	−41	−23	0	+11	+24	+38	+56	+77

If v is negative reverse the sign of the correction

Corrections to Nautical Twilight

N.Lat	30°	35°	40°	45°	50°	52°	54°	56°	58°	60°
v	m	m	m	m	m	m	m	m	m	m
+40	−40	−31	−22	−12	0	+5	+11	+17	+24	+31
30	30	23	16	9	0	4	8	12	17	22
20	20	15	10	5	0	2	5	7	10	13
+10	−10	−7	−5	−2	0	+1	+2	+3	+3	+4
0	0	+1	+1	+1	0	−1	−1	−2	−3	−4
−10	+10	+9	+7	+4	0	−2	−4	−7	−10	−13
20	20	17	13	7	0	3	7	12	17	23
30	30	25	18	10	0	5	11	17	24	33
40	40	33	24	14	0	7	14	23	33	44
50	50	41	30	17	0	−8	18	29	42	57
−60	+60	+49	+37	+21	0	−10	−22	−36	−52	−73
70	70	58	43	24	0	12	27	44	65	95
80	80	66	49	28	0	15	32	54	83	−136
90	90	75	56	32	0	17	39	67	−116	TAN
100	100	83	63	37	0	20	47	−88	TAN	TAN
−110	+110	+92	+70	+42	0	−24	−59	TAN	TAN	TAN
−120	+120	+101	+78	+47	0	−29	−81	TAN	TAN	TAN

Corrections to Civil Twilight

N.Lat	30°	35°	40°	45°	50°	52°	54°	56°	58°	60°
v	m	m	m	m	m	m	m	m	m	m
−50	+50	+40	+28	+15	0	−7	−15	−24	−33	−44
40	40	32	23	12	0	6	12	18	26	34
30	30	24	17	9	0	4	8	13	19	25
20	20	16	11	6	0	3	5	8	12	15
−10	+10	+8	+5	+3	0	−1	−2	−4	−5	−7
0	0	0	0	0	0	0	+1	+1	+2	+2
+10	−10	−8	−6	−4	0	+2	4	6	8	11
20	20	16	12	7	0	3	7	11	15	20
30	30	24	18	10	0	5	10	16	22	30
40	40	33	24	13	0	6	13	21	30	41
+50	−50	−41	−30	−17	0	+8	+17	+27	+39	+52
60	60	49	36	20	0	10	21	33	48	66
70	70	57	42	24	0	12	25	41	60	84
80	80	66	49	27	0	14	30	49	74	110
83	83	68	50	29	0	14	32	52	80	121
+86	−86	−71	−52	−30	0	+15	+33	+56	+86	+137

C2

The times on the opposite page are the local mean times (LMT) of morning nautical twilight, sunrise, sunset and evening civil twilight for latitude N 50°, together with their variations v. The variations are the differences in minutes of time between the time of the phenomenon for latitudes N 50° and N 30°. The sign on the left-hand side of v (between sunrise and sunset) applies to sunrise, and the sign on the right-hand side applies to sunset. The LMT of the phenomenon for latitudes between N 30° and N 60° is found by applying the corrections in the tables above to the tabulated times as follows:

Sunrise and sunset To determine the LMT of sunrise or sunset, take out the tabulated time and v corresponding to the required date. Using v and latitude as arguments in the table of "Corrections to Sunrise and Sunset", extract the correction. This table is for positive v. If v is minus, reverse the sign of the correction. Apply the correction to the tabulated time.

Nautical twilight To determine the LMT of morning nautical twilight, follow the same method as for sunrise and sunset, but use the table of "Corrections to Nautical Twilight". This table includes both positive and negative values of v. The entry TAN stands for Twilight All Night, because the Sun does not reach an altitude of −12°.

Civil twilight To determine the LMT of evening civil twilight follow the same method as for nautical twilight, but use the table of "Corrections to Civil Twilight". This table includes both positive and negative values of v.

Convert LMT to UT by adding the longitude in time if west, or subtracting if east.

Examples of the use of these tables are given in 2.7.3

TABLE 2(11) 1999 — MOONRISE AND MOONSET

Day	JANUARY Rise	v	Set	v	MARCH Rise	v	Set	v	MAY Rise	v	Set	v	JULY Rise	v	Set	v
	h m		h m		h m		h m		h m		h m		h m		h m	
1	15 58	−55	06 52	+54	16 54	−29	06 28	+33	20 05	+38	05 29	−32	21 52	+46	06 23	−51
2	16 59	54	07 53	54	18 02	18	06 57	23	21 06	46	05 57	41	22 24	37	07 27	43
3	18 06	48	08 44	50	19 09	− 7	07 23	12	22 04	52	06 29	48	22 53	26	08 34	33
4	19 15	40	09 27	43	20 14	+ 4	07 47	+ 2	22 59	56	07 07	54	23 19	15	09 44	22
5	20 24	30	10 01	34	21 18	15	08 10	− 9	23 48	56	07 50	56	23 44	+ 3	10 55	− 9
6	21 32	−19	10 30	+24	22 21	+25	08 34	−19	24 33	+53	08 41	−56	24 10	− 9	12 08	+ 3
7	22 37	− 8	10 56	13	23 23	34	08 59	29	00 33	53	09 37	52	00 10	9	13 24	16
8	23 41	+ 3	11 20	+ 3	24 23	43	09 26	38	01 11	47	10 40	45	00 38	21	14 41	29
9	24 44	13	11 42	− 8	00 23	43	09 57	45	01 45	39	11 47	35	01 09	33	15 59	41
10	00 44	13	12 05	18	01 22	50	10 34	51	02 16	29	12 58	24	01 46	44	17 15	50
11	01 46	+23	12 30	−27	02 18	+54	11 17	−55	02 44	+17	14 13	−12	02 31	−53	18 27	+56
12	02 48	33	12 57	36	03 10	55	12 07	55	03 12	+ 5	15 30	+ 1	03 25	57	19 30	57
13	03 49	42	13 28	44	03 57	53	13 04	51	03 39	− 8	16 50	15	04 29	56	20 22	52
14	04 49	49	14 04	50	04 39	47	14 09	45	04 09	21	18 11	29	05 39	50	21 05	44
15	05 47	53	14 47	54	05 16	39	15 19	35	04 42	33	19 33	41	06 52	40	21 40	34
16	06 40	+55	15 37	−55	05 48	+28	16 33	−24	05 21	−45	20 52	+50	08 05	−29	22 09	+23
17	07 28	53	16 35	52	06 19	17	17 50	−11	06 08	53	22 04	56	09 16	18	22 35	+11
18	08 11	48	17 39	45	06 47	+ 4	19 08	+ 2	07 03	56	23 05	56	10 24	− 6	22 58	0
19	08 48	40	18 48	36	07 16	− 8	20 28	15	08 06	55	23 56	51	11 30	+ 5	23 20	−11
20	09 21	30	19 59	25	07 46	21	21 47	28	09 13	49	24 37	44	12 35	16	23 43	21
21	09 50	+19	21 12	−13	08 19	−33	23 04	+40	10 23	−40	00 37	+44	13 38	+27	24 08	−31
22	10 17	+ 7	22 26	− 1	08 56	43	24 18	48	11 32	30	01 10	34	14 41	37	00 08	31
23	10 44	− 5	23 41	+12	09 39	51	00 18	48	12 39	19	01 38	24	15 42	45	00 35	40
24	11 12	17	24 56	24	10 30	55	01 25	54	13 45	− 8	02 03	13	16 41	52	01 06	48
25	11 42	29	00 56	24	11 27	54	02 24	55	14 49	+ 3	02 25	+ 2	17 36	56	01 43	54
26	12 17	−39	02 12	+35	12 30	−50	03 14	+52	15 53	+14	02 47	− 8	18 27	+57	02 27	−57
27	12 58	48	03 25	45	13 36	42	03 56	45	16 56	25	03 10	19	19 13	54	03 17	57
28	13 46	53	04 35	52	14 43	33	04 31	36	17 58	35	03 34	29	19 52	48	04 14	53
29	14 42	54	05 39	55	15 50	22	05 00	27	18 59	43	04 00	38	20 27	40	05 18	46
30	15 45	51	06 33	53	16 56	−11	05 26	16	19 59	51	04 31	46	20 57	30	06 25	36
31	16 53	−44	07 19	+47	18 02	0	05 50	+ 5	20 55	+55	05 06	−52	21 24	+19	07 35	−25

Day	FEBRUARY Rise	v	Set	v	APRIL Rise	v	Set	v	JUNE Rise	v	Set	v	AUGUST Rise	v	Set	v
1	18 03	−35	07 57	+39	19 06	+11	06 13	− 5	21 47	+57	05 47	−56	21 50	+ 7	08 46	−13
2	19 12	24	08 29	29	20 10	21	06 36	15	22 33	55	06 35	57	22 15	− 5	09 59	− 1
3	20 19	13	08 57	18	21 12	31	07 01	25	23 13	50	07 30	54	22 42	17	11 13	+12
4	21 25	− 2	09 22	+ 8	22 13	40	07 27	35	23 49	43	08 30	48	23 11	29	12 28	25
5	22 29	+ 8	09 45	− 3	23 13	48	07 56	43	24 19	33	09 35	39	23 45	40	13 43	37
6	23 32	+19	10 08	−13	24 10	+53	08 30	−50	00 19	+33	10 43	−29	24 25	−50	14 58	+47
7	24 34	29	10 32	23	00 10	53	09 10	54	00 47	22	11 54	17	00 25	50	16 10	54
8	00 34	29	10 58	32	01 03	56	09 56	56	01 14	+11	13 08	− 5	01 13	55	17 15	57
9	01 35	38	11 27	41	01 51	50	10 50	54	01 40	− 2	14 24	+ 8	02 11	57	18 11	55
10	02 36	46	12 00	48	02 34	51	11 50	49	02 07	14	15 43	22	03 17	53	18 58	48
11	03 34	+52	12 40	−53	03 12	+43	12 56	−40	02 37	−27	17 03	+35	04 29	−45	19 36	+39
12	04 29	55	13 26	55	03 45	34	14 07	30	03 12	39	18 23	46	05 42	35	20 08	28
13	05 20	54	14 21	53	04 16	23	15 22	18	03 54	49	19 40	54	06 55	23	20 35	17
14	06 05	50	15 23	48	04 45	+11	16 40	− 5	04 45	55	20 48	57	08 05	−11	21 00	+ 5
15	06 45	43	16 30	40	05 13	− 2	18 00	+ 9	05 45	57	21 46	55	09 14	0	21 23	− 6
16	07 20	+34	17 42	−30	05 42	−15	19 21	+22	06 52	−53	22 32	+48	10 20	+12	21 46	−17
17	07 51	23	18 57	18	06 14	28	20 42	35	08 03	45	23 10	39	11 25	23	22 10	27
18	08 20	+11	20 13	− 5	06 50	39	22 01	46	09 15	35	23 41	28	12 28	33	22 36	36
19	08 48	− 1	21 29	+ 8	07 32	49	23 14	53	10 25	24	24 08	17	13 30	42	23 06	45
20	09 16	13	22 46	20	08 22	54	24 19	56	11 33	12	00 08	17	14 30	50	23 40	52
21	09 46	−25	24 02	+32	09 18	−56	00 19	+56	12 39	− 1	00 31	+ 6	15 27	+55	24 21	−56
22	10 19	36	00 02	32	10 21	52	01 13	54	13 43	+10	00 54	− 4	16 20	57	00 21	56
23	10 57	45	01 16	42	11 27	45	01 58	48	14 47	21	01 16	15	17 07	56	01 08	57
24	11 42	52	02 26	50	12 35	36	02 35	40	15 49	31	01 39	25	17 49	51	02 03	55
25	12 34	54	03 31	54	13 42	26	03 05	30	16 51	40	02 04	35	18 26	43	03 04	49
26	13 33	−53	04 27	+54	14 48	−15	03 32	+20	17 51	+48	02 33	−43	18 58	+34	04 10	−40
27	14 38	−47	05 15	+50	15 53	− 4	03 56	+ 9	18 49	54	03 06	50	19 27	23	05 21	30
28	15 46	−39	05 55	+42	16 57	+ 7	04 19	− 1	19 43	57	03 46	55	19 53	+11	06 33	18
29					18 01	18	04 41	12	20 32	56	04 31	57	20 19	− 1	07 47	− 5
30					19 03	+28	05 04	−22	21 15	+52	05 24	−56	20 46	14	09 02	+ 8
31													21 14	−26	10 18	+21

TABLE 2(11) *continued*   **1999 — MOONRISE AND MOONSET**

SEPTEMBER / NOVEMBER

Day	Rise	v	Set	v	Rise	v	Set	v
	h m		h m		h m		h m	
1	21 46	−37	11 34	+33	24 12	−37	14 13	+40
2	22 24	47	12 49	44	00 12	37	14 44	30
3	23 09	54	14 01	52	01 22	25	15 10	19
4	24 02	57	15 07	57	02 31	14	15 33	+7
5	00 02	57	16 04	56	03 39	−2	15 55	−4
6	01 04	−55	16 53	+51	04 45	+10	16 17	−15
7	02 12	49	17 33	43	05 50	21	16 41	26
8	03 23	40	18 07	33	06 55	32	17 06	36
9	04 35	28	18 35	22	07 58	42	17 35	45
10	05 46	17	19 01	+10	08 59	50	18 08	52
11	06 56	−5	19 24	−1	09 57	+56	18 46	−57
12	08 04	+7	19 48	12	10 50	59	19 31	59
13	09 10	18	20 11	23	11 38	58	20 22	58
14	10 14	29	20 36	33	12 19	54	21 20	53
15	11 17	39	21 05	42	12 55	48	22 22	45
16	12 18	+47	21 37	−49	13 26	+39	23 29	−35
17	13 17	54	22 14	55	13 54	28	24 38	23
18	14 11	57	22 58	57	14 20	16	00 38	23
19	15 00	57	23 50	57	14 45	+4	01 51	−11
20	15 44	54	24 48	52	15 11	−9	03 06	+2
21	16 23	+47	00 48	−52	15 39	−22	04 25	+16
22	16 57	38	01 52	45	16 11	35	05 46	30
23	17 27	28	03 01	35	16 49	47	07 08	43
24	17 54	16	04 13	23	17 35	55	08 28	53
25	18 21	+4	05 27	−10	18 31	59	09 41	59
26	18 47	−9	06 44	+3	19 36	−57	10 44	+59
27	19 15	22	08 02	16	20 47	51	11 35	53
28	19 46	34	09 20	29	22 00	41	12 16	45
29	20 23	45	10 38	41	23 12	30	12 49	34
30	21 06	53	11 53	51	24 22	18	13 16	23

OCTOBER / DECEMBER

Day	Rise	v	Set	v	Rise	v	Set	v
1	21 57	−57	13 01	+56	00 22	−18	13 40	+11
2	22 56	57	14 02	57	01 30	−6	14 02	0
3	24 01	52	14 53	54	02 37	+6	14 24	−11
4	00 01	52	15 34	46	03 42	18	14 46	22
5	01 11	43	16 09	37	04 46	29	15 10	33
6	02 21	−33	16 38	+26	05 50	+39	15 37	−42
7	03 32	21	17 04	15	06 52	48	16 08	50
8	04 41	−9	17 27	+3	07 51	55	16 44	56
9	05 49	+3	17 50	−8	08 47	59	17 27	59
10	06 56	14	18 13	19	09 36	59	18 16	59
11	08 01	+25	18 37	−29	10 20	+57	19 12	−55
12	09 05	36	19 04	39	10 57	51	20 12	48
13	10 08	45	19 35	47	11 30	43	21 16	39
14	11 07	52	20 10	54	11 58	33	22 23	29
15	12 03	57	20 51	58	12 24	22	23 32	17
16	12 55	+58	21 38	−58	12 48	+10	24 43	−4
17	13 40	56	22 33	55	13 12	−2	00 43	−4
18	14 20	51	23 33	49	13 37	15	01 58	+9
19	14 55	43	24 39	40	14 06	28	03 15	23
20	15 25	33	00 39	40	14 39	40	04 35	36
21	15 53	+22	01 49	−29	15 20	−51	05 55	+48
22	16 20	+10	03 02	17	16 11	58	07 13	56
23	16 46	−3	04 18	−4	17 12	59	08 24	60
24	17 13	16	05 36	+10	18 22	55	09 23	57
25	17 43	29	06 56	24	19 37	46	10 10	50
26	18 18	−41	08 17	+37	20 53	−35	10 48	+39
27	18 59	51	09 37	48	22 07	23	11 19	28
28	19 49	57	10 51	56	23 18	−10	11 45	16
29	20 47	58	11 57	58	24 26	+2	12 08	+4
30	21 52	55	12 52	56	00 26	2	12 30	−7
31	23 01	−47	13 37	+50	01 33	+13	12 52	−18

Corrections to Moonrise and Moonset

N Lat v	30°	35°	40°	45°	50°	52°	54°	56°	58°	60°
v	m	m	m	m	m	m	m	m	m	m
0	0	0	0	0	0	0	0	0	0	0
2	−2	−2	−1	−1	0	0	+1	+1	+1	+2
4	4	3	2	1	0	+1	1	2	3	4
6	6	5	3	2	0	1	2	3	4	5
8	8	6	5	3	0	1	2	4	5	7
10	−10	−8	−6	−3	0	+1	+3	+5	+7	+9
12	12	10	7	4	0	2	4	6	8	11
14	14	11	8	4	0	2	4	7	9	12
16	16	13	9	5	0	2	5	8	11	14
18	18	14	10	6	0	3	5	9	12	16
20	−20	−16	−12	−6	0	+3	+6	+10	+14	+18
22	22	18	13	7	0	3	7	11	15	20
24	24	19	14	8	0	3	7	12	16	22
26	26	21	15	8	0	4	8	13	18	23
28	28	22	16	9	0	4	9	14	19	25
30	−30	−24	−17	−9	0	+4	+9	+15	+21	+27
32	32	26	18	10	0	5	10	16	22	29
34	34	27	20	11	0	5	10	17	23	31
36	36	29	21	11	0	5	11	18	25	33
38	38	31	22	12	0	6	12	19	26	35
40	−40	−32	−23	−13	0	+6	+12	+20	+28	+37
42	42	34	24	13	0	6	13	21	30	39
44	44	35	26	14	0	7	14	22	31	42
46	46	37	27	15	0	7	15	23	33	44
48	48	39	28	15	0	7	15	24	34	46
50	−50	−40	−29	−16	0	+8	+16	+25	+36	+48
52	52	42	30	17	0	8	17	26	38	51
54	54	44	32	17	0	8	17	28	39	53
56	56	45	33	18	0	9	18	29	41	56
58	58	47	34	19	0	9	19	30	43	58
60	−60	−48	−35	−19	0	+9	+20	+31	+45	+61
62	62	50	36	20	0	10	20	33	47	64
64	64	52	38	21	0	10	21	34	49	67
66	66	53	39	22	0	10	22	35	51	70
68	68	55	40	22	0	11	23	37	53	73
70	−70	−57	−41	−23	0	+11	+24	+38	+55	+76
72	72	58	43	24	0	11	24	40	58	80
74	74	60	44	24	0	12	25	41	60	83
76	76	62	45	25	0	12	26	43	62	87
78	78	63	46	26	0	13	27	44	65	91
80	−80	−65	−48	−27	0	+13	+28	+46	+68	+96
82	82	67	49	27	0	13	29	48	70	101
84	84	68	50	28	0	14	30	49	73	106
86	86	70	51	29	0	14	31	51	77	112
88	88	72	53	30	0	15	32	53	80	119
90	−90	−73	−54	−30	0	+15	+33	+55	+84	+127

If *v* is minus reverse the sign of the correction

The daily times of moonrise and moonset given above are the local mean times (LMT) of the phenomena for latitude N 50°, together with their variations *v*. The variations are the differences in minutes between the time of the phenomenon for latitudes N 50° and N 30°. The LMT of the phenomenon for latitudes between N 30° and N 60° is found as follows:

Take out the tabulated time and *v* corresponding to the required date. Using *v* and latitude as arguments in the table above of "Corrections to Moonrise and Moonset", extract the correction. This table is for positive *v*. If *v* is minus, reverse the sign of the correction. Apply the correction to the tabulated time.

Add a small extra correction of 1^m for every 7° of longitude if west. Subtract if east.

Convert LMT to UT by adding the longitude in time if west, or subtracting if east.

Examples of the use of these tables are given in 2.7.4

C2

2.8   CONVERSION TABLES

2.8.1   Conversion factors

To convert	Multiply by	To convert	Multiply by
Area			
sq in to sq mm	645·16	sq mm to sq in	0·00155
sq ft to sq m	0·0929	sq m to sq ft	10·76
Length (See 2.8.2 below for ft-m-ft)			
in to mm	25·40	mm to in	0·0394
yds to m	0·914	m to yds	1·094
fathoms to m	1·8288	m to fathoms	0·5468
nautical miles (M) to kilometres	1·852	kilometres to nautical miles	0·539957
nautical miles to statute miles	1·1515	statute miles to nautical miles	0·8684
Note: 1 cable equals 1/10 M, approx 185m.			
Velocity (See also Ch 5, 5.1.2 for knots to m/sec)			
ft/sec to m/sec	0·3048	m/sec to ft/sec	3·281
ft/sec to miles/hr	0·682	miles/hr to ft/sec	1·467
ft/min to m/sec	0·0051	m/sec to ft/min	196·8
knots to miles/hr	1·1515	miles/hr to knots	0·868
knots to km/hr	1·8520	km/hr to knots	0·5400
Mass			
lb to kg	0·4536	kg to lb	2·205
tons to tonnes (1000 kg)	1·016	tonnes to tons (2240 lb)	0·9842
Pressure (See also Ch 5, 5.1.3; inc °C to °F to °C)			
inches of mercury to millibars	33·86	millibars to inches of mercury	0·0295
lb/sq in to kg/sq cm	0·0703	kg/sq cm to lb/sq in	14·22
lb/sq in to atmospheres	0·0680	atmospheres to lb/sq in	14·7
Volume			
cu ft to galls	6·25	galls to cu ft	0·16
cu ft to litres	28·33	litres to cu ft	0·035
Capacity			
pints to litres	0·568	litres to pints	1·76
galls to litres	4·546	litres to galls	0·22
Imp galls to US galls	1·2	US galls to Imp galls	0·833

2.8.2   Feet to metres, metres to feet

Explanation: The central columns of figures in **bold** type can be referenced to the left to convert metres into feet, or to the right to convert feet into metres. For example, five lines down: 5 metres = 16·40 feet, or 5 feet = 1·52 metres. Alternatively multiply feet by 0.3048 for metres, or multiply metres by 3.2808 for feet.

Feet		Metres	Feet		Metres	Feet		Metres	Feet		Metres
3·28	**1**	0·30	45·93	**14**	4·27	88·58	**27**	8·23	131·23	**40**	12·19
6·56	**2**	0·61	49·21	**15**	4·57	91·86	**28**	8·53	134·51	**41**	12·50
9·84	**3**	0·91	52·49	**16**	4·88	95·14	**29**	8·84	137·80	**42**	12·80
13·12	**4**	1·22	55·77	**17**	5·18	98·43	**30**	9·14	141·08	**43**	13·11
16·40	**5**	1·52	59·06	**18**	5·49	101·71	**31**	9·45	144·36	**44**	13·41
19·69	**6**	1·83	62·34	**19**	5·79	104·99	**32**	9·75	147·64	**45**	13·72
22·97	**7**	2·13	65·62	**20**	6·10	108·27	**33**	10·06	150·92	**46**	14·02
26·25	**8**	2·44	68·90	**21**	6·40	111·55	**34**	10·36	154·20	**47**	14·33
29·53	**9**	2·74	72·18	**22**	6·71	114·83	**35**	10·67	157·48	**48**	14·63
32·81	**10**	3·05	75·46	**23**	7·01	118·11	**36**	10·97	160·76	**49**	14·94
36·09	**11**	3·35	78·74	**24**	7·32	121·39	**37**	11·28	164·04	**50**	15·24
39·37	**12**	3·66	82·02	**25**	7·62	124·67	**38**	11·58			
42·65	**13**	3·96	85·30	**26**	7·92	127·95	**39**	11·89			

Chapter 3

Radio Navigational Aids

Contents

3.1 INTRODUCTION Page 48
3.1.1 Position fixing systems

3.2 SATELLITE SYSTEMS 48
3.2.1 Global Positioning System (GPS)
3.2.2 Dilution of precision
3.2.3 Datum
3.2.4 Integrity monitoring
3.2.5 Differential GPS (DGPS)
3.2.5.1 DGPS beacons in NW Europe

3.3 HYPERBOLIC SYSTEMS 50
3.3.1 Decca
3.3.2 Loran-C

3.4 WAYPOINTS 52
3.4.1 Waypoint navigation
3.4.2 Navigational displays
3.4.3 Loading waypoints

3.5 RDF BEACONS 53
3.5.1 Operation
3.5.2 Types of emission
3.5.3 Errors in radio bearings
3.5.4 Calibration
3.5.5 Distance finding
Table 3(1) RDF beacons – UK/Eire   55
Table 3(2) RDF beacons – Continent   58

3.6 RADAR 60
3.6.1 Radar in yachts
3.6.2 Collision avoidance
3.6.3 Navigational aid

3.7 RACONS 60
3.7.1 Description
3.7.2 Characteristics
Table 3(3)   Racons – Europe   61

C3

Summary

This Chapter provides basic information on position fixing systems, ie GPS, Decca and Loran-C, and the navigational use of waypoints, together with details of individual RDF & DGPS beacons and Racons.

Further information on procedures and possible errors, together with the subjects listed below, is given in Chapter 4 of *The Macmillan & Silk Cut Yachtsman's Handbook*:

Aids to navigation; developments; navigational aids and position fixing systems; satellite position fixing system; Global Positioning System (GPS); differential GPS; hyperbolic position fixing systems; Decca; Loran-C; radar in yachts; how radar works; radar for collision avoidance; radar as a navigational aid; radar beacons (Racons); marine and aeronautical RDF beacons; DF receiving sets; directional radio beacons; beacons incorporating distance finding; aero RDF beacons operating procedures; errors in radio bearings; calibration; radio direction finding; half convergency; VHF emergency direction finding; QTG service from coast radio stations.

3.1   INTRODUCTION

3.1.1   Position fixing systems

Three radio position fixing systems are available to yachtsmen. Satellite navigation is provided by the Global Positioning System (GPS) with a world-wide fixing accuracy of approximately 100m in any weather. Decca and Loran-C are hyperbolic area navigation systems which provide continuous fixing within coverage areas, albeit with less accuracy and reliability. Radio Direction Finding (RDF) is obsolescent and being phased out.

The choice of navigation aids for a yacht largely depends on the boat's intended usage, the particular waters to be sailed, and the owner's requirements, interests and the depth of his pocket.

3.2   SATELLITE SYSTEMS

3.2.1   Global Positioning System (GPS)

GPS provides highly accurate, worldwide, continuous three-dimensional position fixing (latitude, longitude and altitude), together with velocity and time data in all weathers.

The GPS constellation, shown in Fig 3(1), consists of 24 operational satellites configured in six orbital planes. Satellites orbit the earth in approximately 12 hours at a height of about 10,900M. Three of the satellites operate as active spares.

GPS provides two levels of service. These are:

(1)   **Standard Positioning Service (SPS)**
(2)   **Precise Positioning Service (PPS)**

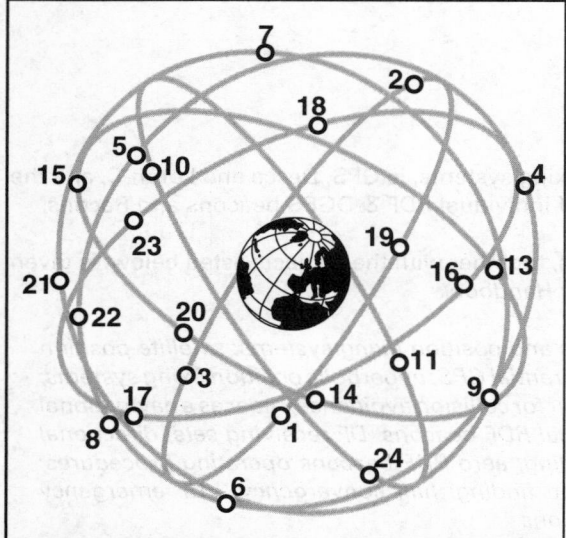

Fig 3(1)   The GPS constellation contains 21 operational satellites and three active spares at orbital heights of 10,900M arranged in six orbital planes inclined to the equator at 55°. The satellite spacing is arranged to ensure at least four satellites are in view from anywhere on earth.

SPS is available to all civil users at no cost and is of interest to yachtsmen. PPS provides greater accuracy but, at present, is reserved solely for military purposes and is only made available to selected civil users when specially authorised.

The principle on which GPS works is the accurate measurement of the distance between the receiver and the satellites which transmit precisely timed signals, together with information on their accurate position in space. In very simplistic terms each satellite transmits a PPS and SPS code saying 'this is my position and this is the time'.

By knowing the exact times of transmission and reception of the signal the transit time can be established. Multiply the transit time by the speed of light (161,829 miles per second) to get the range to the satellite. If similar measurements are made on three satellites, three intersecting range circles, each centred on the satellite's position at the time of transmission, are obtained. Barring other errors, the intersection of the three range circles represents the yacht's position

GPS basic system errors are relatively small, of the order of 19-20m using SPS. Current US plans for the use of SPS are based on a denial of full system accuracy by the use of cryptology. This is called Selective Availability (SA). The imposition of SA means there is no guarantee that a standard GPS yacht receiver will give a horizontal fix of better than ±100m, 140m vertically, and time to 340 nanoseconds for 95% of the time. Accuracy will be ±300m for 99·99% of the time. As fix accuracy continually varies when SA is switched on, no assumptions can be made about fix accuracy at any given time. SPS accuracy can be much improved by the use of differential GPS (DGPS); see 3.2.3.

GPS receivers vary from single-channel to multi-channel receivers. Better fixing is obtained by tracking more than the minimum three satellites required to produce a two-dimensional fix (latitude and longitude). A receiver with at least six dedicated channels is the most suitable for a yacht.

3.2.2   Dilution of precision

In conventional coastal navigation it is generally recommended to avoid using any visual position lines whose angle of cut is less than 30°. The accuracy of GPS fixes equally depends on the angle of cut of its position lines, but it is the receiver, rather than the navigator, which selects those satellites offering the best fix geometry.

The efficiency of the satellite geometry is indicated by Dilution of Precision (DOP), a value computed from the angular separation between various satellites. The larger the separation the better the fix geometry is, and the lower the DOP value.

Efficiency is most likely to be degraded when there are less than 5 satellites visible, or when DOP is greater than 5. Since high DOP is caused by poor satellite geometry, these events usually coincide.

The potential inaccuracy of a 2D GPS fix resulting from poor geometry is expressed as Horizontal Dilution of Precision (HDOP). The accuracy of a GPS fix varies with the capability of the receiver and receiver-to-satellite geometry. Receivers are programmed to select satellites which give the lowest HDOP value. If the HDOP value exceeds a certain figure, usually 4 or 5, the receiver gives a warning, or stops computing fixes until satellite geometry improves.

3.2.3   Datum
GPS satellites are referenced to the World Geodetic System 84 (WGS 84) datum. This means that satellite fixes cannot accurately be plotted on Admiralty charts, which are referenced to a local datum, until suitable corrections have been applied.

UK Admiralty charts are based on the Ordnance Survey of Great Britain 1936 (OSGB 36) datum. Admiralty charts of the NW European coast are based on the European 1950 Datum (ED 50). Admiralty charts always state which datum is used in a note on 'Satellite-Derived Positions' printed under the main title. The note also indicates the amount of correction required between satellite and chart positions.

The approximate difference between WGS 84, OSGB 36 and ED 50 datums in the Dover Strait are shown in Fig 3(2). The size of the error will vary at each location and can be substantial in some parts of the world such as the Pacific.

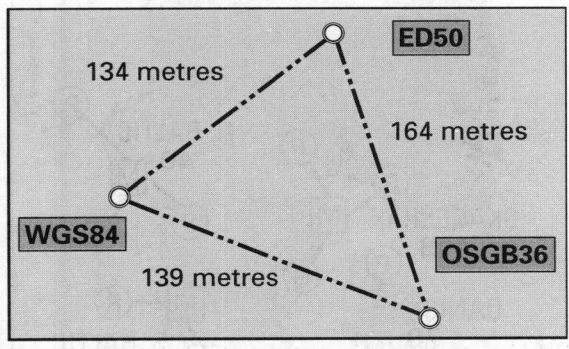

Fig 3(2)   Chart datum differences in the Dover Strait

Good GPS receivers offer a choice of many different chart datums; always ensure that the chart datum set on the receiver is the same datum as the chart in use.

3.2.4   Integrity monitoring
Urgent information on GPS is given in navigational broadcasts by BT CRS on VHF or MF, and by any Navtex station under message category J.

Information is also available from the US CG GPS Information Centre (GPSIC) on ☎ 00 1 703 313 5907 in a pre-recorded daily status message. GPSIC duty personnel can be contacted on ☎ 00 1 703 313 5900.

3.2.5   Differential GPS
The primary purpose of Differential GPS (DGPS) is to monitor the integrity of GPS. Greater navigational accuracy is a secondary feature. DGPS requires additional equipment onboard and may only appeal to those who need the highest accuracy.

The modus operandi, in the simplest possible terms, is as follows: A DGPS shore station 'knows' precisely where it is. It also 'knows' where the GPS satellites think it is. The difference (differential) between these two positions is transmitted by the DGPS station to any GPS receiver within range which is equipped to receive DGPS information. To transmit the information it uses a number of strategically located RDF MF beacons around the British Isles and NW Europe. The differential information is processed by the GPS receiver onboard and restores the accuracy of GPS to about 10 metres, ie what it would have been if Selective Availability had not been imposed.

Since August 1998 a free, unencrypted public DGPS service for vessels navigating around the coasts of the UK and Eire has been on trial; see below. The 6 UK Trinity House beacons with ranges of 100M have been on trial since 25 May 1998. The 3 UK Northern Lights beacons with 150M ranges have been on trial since July 1998. Other lighthouse authorities are expected to upgrade their beacons in similar degree.

3.2.5.1 DGPS beacons in NW Europe
* Planned; ‡ On trial; Frequencies in kHz; Range in M.

United Kingdom	Freq	M
Lizard lt 49°57'·57N 05°12'·07W	284·00‡	100
St Catherine's Pt 50°34'·50N 01°17'·80W	293·50‡	100
North Foreland lt 51°22'·50N 01°26'·83E	310·50‡	100
Flamborough Hd 54°06'·97N 00°04'·86W	302·50‡	100
Girdle Ness 57°08'·32N 02°02'·83W	311·00‡	150
Sumburgh Hd 59°51'·30N 01°16'·37W	304·00‡	150
Butt of Lewis 58°30'·93N 06°15'·72W	294·00‡	150
Point Lynas lt 53°24'·98N 04°17'·30W	305·00‡	100
Nash Point lt 51°24'·03N 03°33'·06W	299·00‡	100
Eire		
Mizen Head lt 51°27'·05N 09°48'·80W	300·50*	100
Loop Head lt 52°33'·65N 09°55'·90W	312·00*	100
Tory Island lt 55°16'·35N 08°14'·72W	313·50*	150
West France		
Pte St Mathieu 48°19'·85N 04°46'·17W	291·50*	40
Les Baleines lt 46°14'·70N 01°33'·60W	299·50‡	40
Pte de la Coubre 45°41'·87N 01°13'·93W		
1655, 3328·8 (specialised equipment needed)		330
Cap Ferret lt 44°38'·77N 01°14'·81W	287·00*	40
North France		
Pte de Barfleur 49°41'·87N 01°15'·87W	297·50‡	
Belgium		
Oostende 51°14'·36N 02°55'·94E	311·50‡	38
Netherlands		
Hoek van Holland 51°58'·90N 04°06'·83E	287·50	40
Ameland lt 53°27'·02N 05°37'·60E	299·50	40
Germany		
Düne (Helgoland) 54°11'·20N 07°54'·38E	313·00‡	70

3.3   HYPERBOLIC SYSTEMS

3.3.1   Decca

The Decca Navigator System is an old, but accurate short-to-medium range hyperbolic fixing system well suited to coastal and landfall navigation. Good coverage is available over the UK and NW Europe to a range of approximately 400M by day, and 250M by night, from transmitters.

The six UK Decca Chains will cease to operate at the end of March 2000. Decca Chains still available in the UK and NW Europe are shown below.

The principle on which Decca works is the accurate measurement of the time difference taken by radio waves travelling between at least two transmitters. This is achieved by measuring the phase differences.

Radio waves are affected by weather, season, radio noise, time of day and night, terrain over which the radio waves pass, and range from transmitters. Decca errors are mostly quite small, but can have navigational significance.

Abnormal radio propagation may occur whenever atmospheric pressure is about 10 Millibars (Mbs) or more above the average. Average MSL pressure in July is approximately 1017 Mbs in the English Channel and 1012 Mbs in Scotland.

There are two main types of error:

(1) **Fixed errors:** resulting from variations in the velocity of radio waves over different types of terrain, or the presence of land between transmitter and receiver. The effect of fixed errors can be very pronounced when close to the coast. Fixed errors are constant at any given location. Racal-Decca publishes data sheets giving fixed error corrections for each Decca Chain but unfortunately these are in a form which can only be applied to large ship receivers using Decca co-ordinates, rather than latitude/longitude. It is not possible to apply fixed error corrections to yacht receivers which only give a latitude/longitude read-out.

(2) **Variable errors:** are due to the effect of skywave/groundwave interference and to the other factors mentioned above. Generally speaking, conditions are worse on winter nights than in summer and errors are bigger at the extremities of the coverage area than in the centre.

For practical navigation purposes it is unwise to assume an accuracy of better than 0·25M at ranges of 50-100M from transmitters, and up to 1·5M or more at the limits of coverage, especially when abnormal propagation conditions are present.

Fig 3(3)   DECCA CHAINS – NORTH-WEST EUROPE

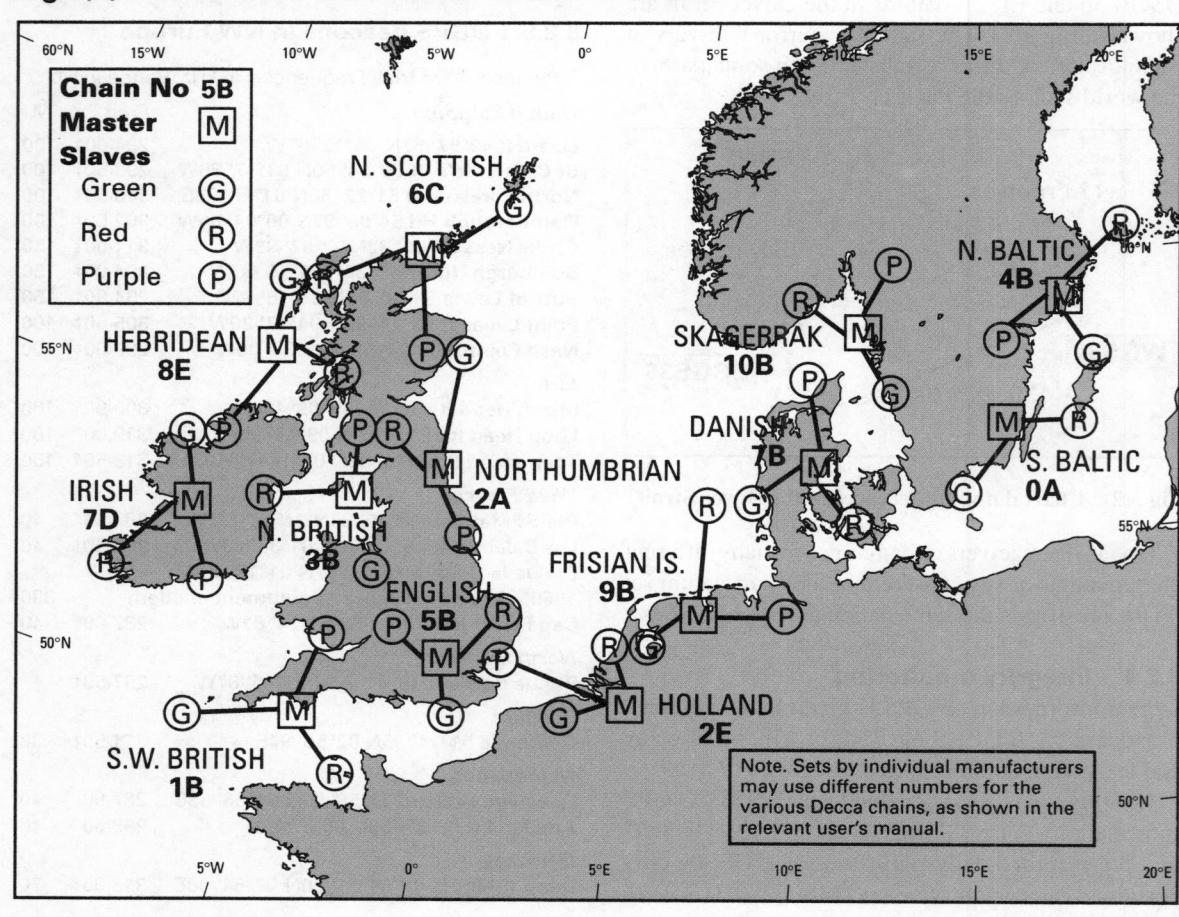

Fig 3(4)   LORAN-C CHAINS – NORTH-WEST EUROPE

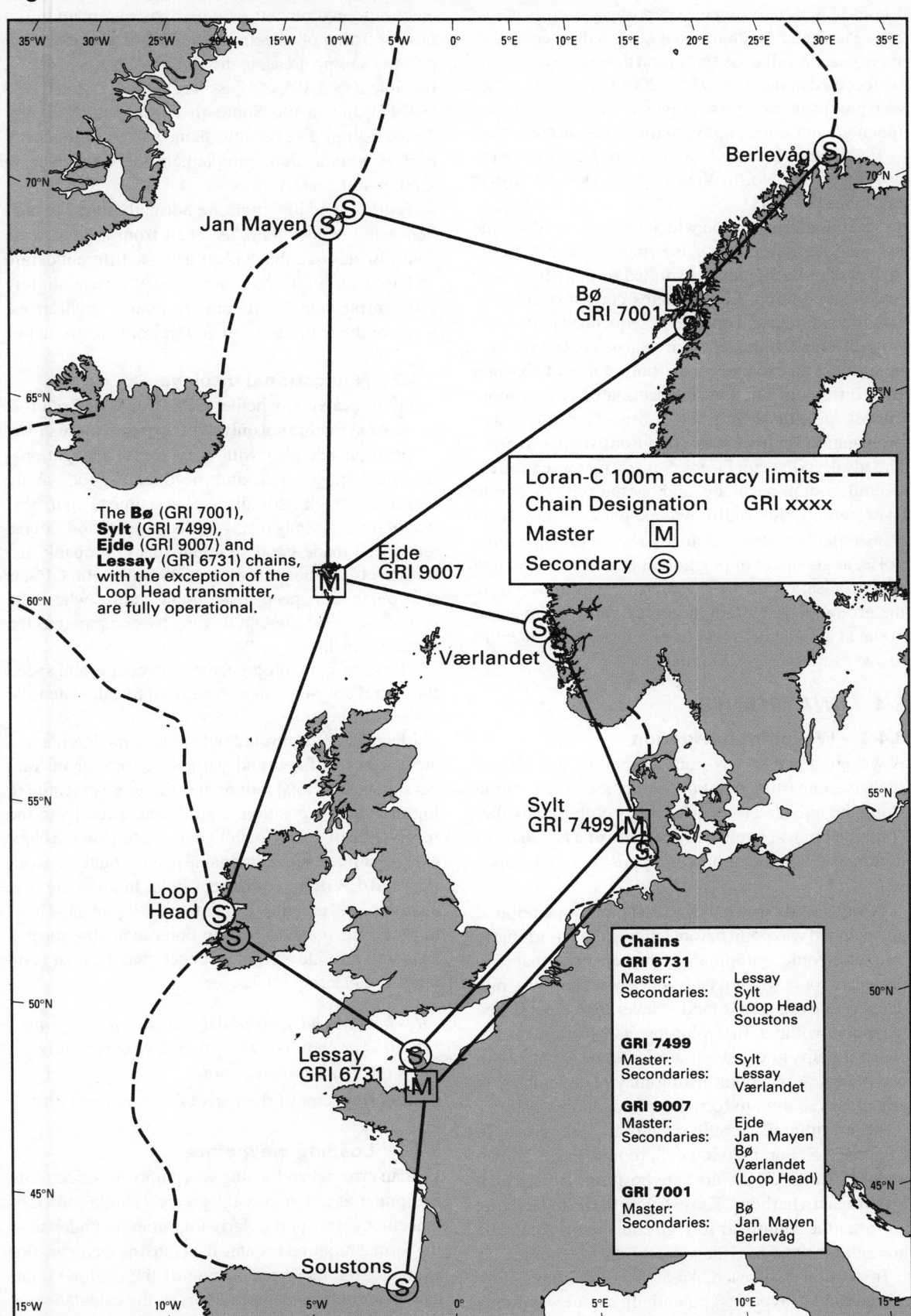

C3

3.3.2 Loran-C

Loran-C is a long-range hyperbolic system suitable for coastal and offshore navigation within coverage. It provides continuous fixing and the groundwave can be received at ranges of 800-1200M. Loran-C pulses also propagate as skywaves which may be received at much greater range, but with much less accuracy.

Four new Loran-C chains provide extensive coverage over North-West Europe, and the British Isles. See Fig 3(4).

The basic principle on which Loran-C works is the accurate measurement of the time difference in the arrival of pulse signals transmitted from a Master and Secondary station. Loran chains consist of three to five transmitters and operate in sequenced pairs. The time difference obtained from each pair of transmitters determines an exclusive hyperbolic curve of constant time difference and the intersection of two or more curves produces the fix. Loran-C radio wave propagation is affected by conditions similar to those already described for Decca. Several factors can affect overall system accuracy such as the type of terrain over which the radio waves pass, range from transmitters, system geometry, weather, electronic noise, angle of cut of position lines and gradient, and synchronisation errors between transmitters. Using the groundwave system, accuracy varies from about 100m at a range of 200M from transmitters, to 250m to 1M or more at 500M range.

3.4   WAYPOINTS

3.4.1   Waypoint navigation

A waypoint can be any point chosen by a navigator such as a departure point or destination, any position along the intended route where it is proposed to alter course, a point at a selected distance off a headland or lighthouse, a buoy, or any other position in the open sea.

Always study the chart first and plot the position of any planned waypoint before loading the co-ordinates into electronic equipment. This ensures that any projected route will not take you across shallows, into danger, or even across land. Never load a published waypoint without first plotting its position on the chart. It helps to tag either a number or a name onto waypoints. A waypoint listing may be assembled in any order required to form a route or sailing plan.

Approximately 3,600 waypoints are given in Chapter 8. For individual harbours those shown under NAVIGATION are safe positions from which to approach a harbour. Those below the harbour name and after the county (or foreign equivalent) locate the hbr entrance and provide a good final waypoint.

In section 4 of each Area (Coastal Lights, Fog Signals and Waypoints) potentially useful waypoints are underlined.

For convenience when loading waypoints into electronic equipment, or when passage planning, a tabular listing of selected waypoints is also given for popular sailing areas, ie the English Channel (8.1.7), the Solent (8.2.19), off East Anglia (8.4.7), the Clyde (8.9.17) and in the Southern North Sea (8.20.38). These listings give only the name and co-ordinates of each waypoint; they complement the data given in section 4 of each Area.

Latitude and longitude are normally stated to one-hundredth of a minute, as taken from a large-scale chart. Be advised that a chart using a different datum or based on a different survey may give a slightly different position. Charts may also contain small errors, just like the read-out from an electronic instrument.

3.4.2   Navigational displays

Modern receivers, whether GPS, Decca or Loran-C, present navigators not only with a continuous read-out of position but also with very useful navigational information, eg course and speed made good, along and across-track error, distance and time to go to next waypoint, etc. Many receivers display position, course and speed made good simultaneously. Probably the most useful of these displays, especially with GPS, is the course and speed made good facility where the continuous read-out can be directly compared to the required track.

The same data, if compared with course and speed through the water, can also be used to calculate tidal set and drift quickly.

Electronic systems are only aids to navigation and are subject to fixed and variable errors, or on rare occasions even total failure. It is therefore essential to log the yacht's position, course and speed from the receiver display and to plot your position on the chart at regular intervals. This enables you quickly to work up a DR/EP if the equipment fails. In any case it is always sound practice to maintain a DR plot, or at least to plot your position by any other available means. This will provide a separate check that the boat is on track and clearing all dangers.

It is better to have absolutely no idea of where one is – and to know it – than to believe confidently that one is where one is not.
Cassini (Director of the Paris Observatoire, 1770)

3.4.3   Loading waypoints

Human error when loading waypoints into electronic equipment is potentially the greatest single source of inaccuracy. It is particularly important to understand the format required to enter data into the receiver. For example, the incorrect placing of the decimal point can result in considerable errors in the calculation of bearing and distance.

Following the precautions listed below can help to prevent errors being made when loading waypoints:

(1)   Check the intended route between waypoints for navigational safety.

(2)   Never use a published waypoint without first plotting its position on the chart.

(3)   Check that any latitude/longitude coordinates that you have taken off the chart are correct.

(4)   Check whether East or West longitude is the default setting in your receiver; if necessary change.

(5)   Double-check that waypoints have been keyed into the receiver correctly.

(6)   Get an independent check if possible.

(7)   Measure the tracks and distances on the chart and cross-check them against those computed in the receiver's passage plan.

3.5   RDF BEACONS

3.5.1   Operation

Radio Direction Finding (RDF) is a simple, but often inaccurate, method whereby yachtsmen can establish an approximate position using a radio receiver with a directional antenna to obtain bearings from marine or aeronautical RDF beacons. With the increasing use of GPS, Decca and Loran, RDF is rapidly becoming obsolescent. Some strategically placed marine RDF beacons are used solely to provide a Differential GPS service (DGPS); see 3.2.5.

Marine and Aeronautical RDF beacons transmit continuously (except in Portugal) on MF and are non-directional, ie they can be received and interpreted throughout 360°, as opposed to radiating along a particular bearing aligned with a chan or harbour ent.

The navigator tunes to the listed frequency, identifies the beacon by its Morse ident (13 secs), which is followed by a long dash (47 secs), during which time the DF antenna is rotated until a minimum (or null) signal is obtained. In this antenna position, the bearing from the yacht to the beacon is either read directly off the associated compass, or from a digital read-out.

Note: MF DF should not be confused with VHF DF, and vice versa. The latter enables a suitably equipped shore station to give a vessel in emergency her true bearing from the station; see 6.9.3 for details.

3.5.2   Types of emission

All marine RDF beacons transmit an A1A emission. These transmissions are unmodulated and need a DF receiver with a Beat Frequency Oscillator (BFO) to be switched ON so as to receive the A1A transmissions and identify the beacon.

Aeronautical RDF beacons mostly use Non-A2A emissions which require the BFO to be switched ON for DF use, and OFF to identify the station. Individual RDF receivers vary, so consult the manufacturer's handbook for precise instructions on the use of the BFO switch.

3.5.3   Errors in radio bearings

The various errors to which radio bearings are subject fall into two categories:

a.   signal errors (caused by distance from the beacon, night or skywave effect particularly near sunset and sunrise, land effect or coastal refraction where the beam passes over high ground or along the coast, and synchronised transmissions of two beacons); and

b.   errors on board the boat (caused by quadrantal error due to magnetic objects re-radiating the incoming signal, compass error, the possibility of inadvertently taking a reciprocal bearing, and operating error due to inexperience or bad weather). Do not rely on radio bearings exclusively, unless three or more give an acceptable cocked hat.

3.5.4   Calibration

A DF set can be calibrated for quadrantal error by taking simultaneous radio and visual bearings of a beacon on different headings. Alternatively, radio bearings may be taken from a known position, and the bearing of the beacon taken from the chart. There are also a few dedicated calibration stations in the UK and other countries, but these are mainly intended for use by commercial shipping.

3.5.5   Distance finding

The RDF beacons at Castle Breakwater, St Peter Port, Guernsey and La Corbière light, Jersey, allow radio and sound (fog) signals to be synchronised so as to find a reasonably accurate distance from the beacon. La Corbière also transmits coded wind information. See 8.14.12 and 8.14.14, for details.

C3

Fig 3(5)   RDF AND DGPS BEACONS – NW EUROPE

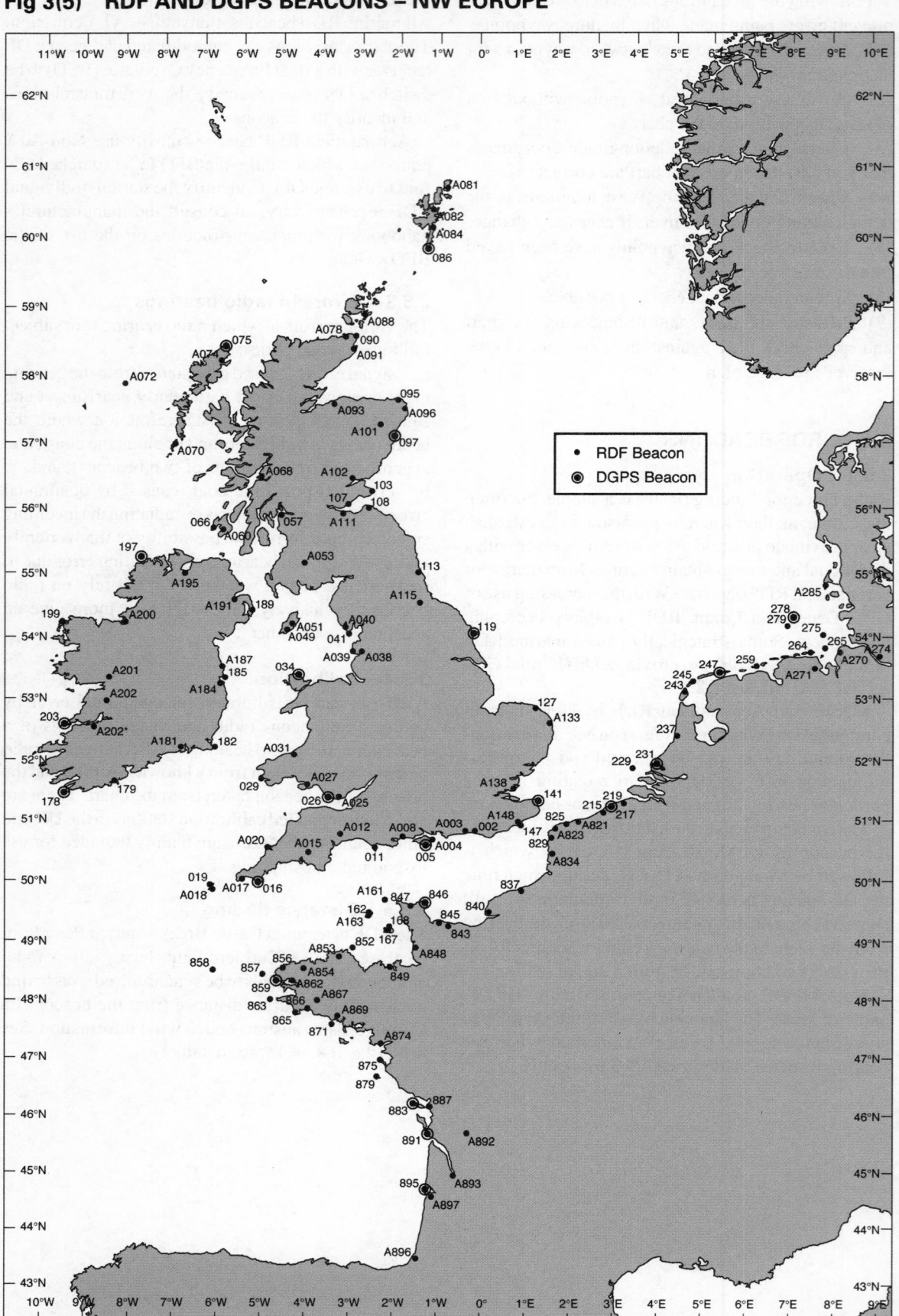

TABLE 3(1)   MARINE AND AERONAUTICAL RDF BEACONS – UK and EIRE

See map at Fig 3(5). Note: Beacon Nos are the last 3 digits of Nos published in ALRS Vol 2. Those prefixed with A are Aeronautical beacons. Those suffixed with D provide DGPS; see 3.2.5.

No	Name, Latitude/Longitude	Morse Ident		Frequency	Mode	Range
	ENGLAND – SOUTH COAST (Areas 1-3)					
019	**Round Island lt**					
	49°58'·70N 06°19'·33W	**RR**	·—· ·—·	298·50	A1A	150M
A018	**St Mary's, Scilly** (HJ, Mon-Sat)					
	49°54'·82N 06°17'·43W	**STM**	··· — ——	321·00	Non A2A	15M
A017	**Penzance Heliport** (HJ, Mon-Sat)					
	50°07'·67N 05°31'·00W	**PH**	·——· ····	333·00	Non A2A	15M
016D	**Lizard lt**					
	49°57'·58N 05°12'·07W	**LZ**	·—·· ——··	284·50	A1A	70M
A015	**Plymouth**					
	50°25'·37N 04°06'·67W	**PY**	·——· —·——	396·50	Non A2A	20M
A012	**Exeter** (HJ)					
	50°45'·12N 03°17'·62W	**EX**	· —··—	337·00	Non A2A	15M
011	**Portland Bill**					
	50°30'·82N 02°27'·30W	**PB**	·——· —···	309·50	A1A	50M
A008	**Bournemouth/Hurn** (HJ)					
	50°46'·63N 01°50'·47W	**BIA**	—··· ·· ·—	339·00	Non A2A	20M
005D	**St Catherine's Pt**					
	50°34'·52N 01°17'·80W	**CP**	—·—· ·——·	293·00	A1A	50M
A004	**Bembridge**					
	50°40'·78N 01°06'·18W	**IW**	·· ·——	426·00	Non A2A	15M
A003	**Shoreham** (HJ)					
	50°49'·89N 00°17'·75W	**SHM**	··· ···· ——	332·00	Non A2A	10M
002	**Brighton Marina**					
	50°48'·67N 00°05'·95W	**BM**	—··· ——	294·50	A1A	10M
A148	**Lydd**					
	50°58'·26N 00°57'·20E	**LYX**	·—·· —·—— —··—	397·00	Non A2A	15M
147	**Dungeness lt**					
	50°54'·77N 00°58'·67E	**DU**	—·· ··—	300·50	A1A	50M
141D	**North Foreland lt**					
	51°22'·49N 01°26'·85E	**NF**	—· ··—·	311·00	A1A	50M
	CHANNEL ISLANDS (Area 14)					
A161	**Alderney**					
	49°42'·58N 02°11'·90W	**ALD**	·— ·—·· —··	383·00	Non A2A	30M
A163	**Guernsey**					
	49°26'·12N 02°38'·30W	**GRB**	——· ·—· —···	361·00	Non A2A	30M
162	**St Peter Port** (see 8.13. 12)					
	49°27'·37N 02°31'·37W	**GY**	——· —·——	304·50	A1A	10M
A168	**Jersey West**					
	49°12'·37N 02°13'·30W	**JW**	·——— ·——	329·00	Non A2A	25M
167	**La Corbière lt** (see 8.13. 14)					
	49°10'·85N 02°14'·90W	**CB**	—·—· —···	295·50	A1A	20M
	ENGLAND – EAST COAST (Areas 4 and 5)					
A138	**Southend**					
	51°34'·55N 00°42'·12E	**SND**	··· —· —··	362·50	Non A2A	20M
A133	**Great Yarmouth**					
	52°38'·10N 01°43'·73E	**ND**	—· —··	417·00	Non A2A	10M
127	**Cromer lt**					
	52°55'·45N 01°19'·10E	**CM**	—·—· ——	313·50	A1A	50M
119D	**Flamborough Head lt**					
	54°06'·95N 00°04'·87W	**FB**	··—· —···	303·00	A1A	70M
A115	**Teeside**					
	54°33'·58N 01°20'·13W	**TD**	— —··	347·50	Non A2A	25M

C3

SCOTLAND – EAST COAST (Areas 6 and 7)

No.	Name / Lat.Long.	Ident	Morse	Frequency	Emission	Range
113	**Souter Point lt** 54°58'·23N 01°21'·80W	SJ	··· ·————	292·00	A1A	50M
A111	**Edinburgh** 55°58'·72N 03°17'·03W	EDN	· —·· ——·	341·00	Non A2A	35M
107	**Inchkeith** 56°02'·02N 03°08'·08W	NK	—· —·—	286·50	A1A	10M
108	**Fidra lt** 56°04'·40N 02°47'·02W	FD	··—· —··	290·00	A1A	15M
103	**Fife Ness lt** 56°16'·73N 02°35'·10W	FP	··—· ·——·	305·00	A1A	50M
A102	**Dundee** 56°27'·30N 03°06'·83W	DND	—·· —· —··	394·00	Non A2A	25M
097D	**Girdle Ness** 57°08'·32N 02°02'·83W	GD	——· —··	311·00	A1A	50M
A101	**Aberdeen** 57°16'·13N 02°24'·18W	AOS	·— ——— ···	377·00	Non A2A	25M
A096	**Scotstown Head** 57°33'·56N 01°48'·94W	SHD	··· ···· —··	383·00	Non A2A	80M
095	**Kinnairds Head** 57°41'·87N 02°00'·13W	KD	—·— —··	301·50	A1A	50M
A093	**Kinloss** 57°39'·02N 03°35'·22W	KS	—·— ···	370·00	Non A2A	20M
A091	**Wick** 58°26'·83N 03°03'·70W	WIK	·—— ·· —·—	344·00	Non A2A	30M
090	**Duncansby Head** 58°38'·67N 03°01'·42W	DY	—·· —·——	290·50	A1A	50M
A078	**Dounreay** 58°34'·90N 03°43'·58W	DO	—·· ———	364·50	Non A2A	15M
A088	**Kirkwall** 58°57'·57N 02°54'·69W	KW	—·— ·——	395·00	Non A2A	30M
086D	**Sumburgh Head** 59°51'·30N 01°16'·37W	SB	··· —···	304·00	A1A	70M
A084	**Lerwick/Tingwall** 60°11'·30N 01°14'·78W	TL	— ·—··	376·00	Non A2A	25M
A082	**Scatsa** (HJ) 60°27'·65N 01°12'·90W	SS	··· ···	315·50	Non A2A	25M
A081	**Unst** 60°44'·33N 00°49'·17W	UT	··— —	325·00	Non A2A	20M

SCOTLAND – WEST COAST (Areas 8 and 9)

No.	Name / Lat.Long.	Ident	Morse	Frequency	Emission	Range
075D	**Butt of Lewis** 58°30'·93N 06°15'·72W	BL	—··· ·—··	289·00	A1A	70M
A074	**Stornoway** 58°12'·86N 06°19'·49W	SAY	··· ·— —·——	431·00	Non A2A	20M
A072	**St Kilda** 57°49'·00N 08°35'·00W	KL	—·— ·—··	338·00	Non A2A	30M
A070	**Barra** (Occas) 57°01'·40N 07°26'·40W	BRR	—··· ·—· ·—·	316·00	Non A2A	20M
A068	**Oban/North Connel** 56°27'·83N 05°23'·62W	CNL	—·—· —· ·—··	404·00	Non A2A	15M
066	**Rhinns of Islay** 55°40'·38N 06°30'·70W	RN	·—· —·	293·00	A1A	70M
A060	**Islay/Port Ellen** 55°40'·97N 06°14'·96W	LAY	·—·· ·— —·——	395·00	Non A2A	20M
057	**Cloch Point lt** (Calibration only, by request) 55°56'·53N 04°52'·67W	CL	—·—· ·—··	300·00	A1A	8M
A053	**New Galloway** 55°10'·65N 04°10'·11W	NGY	—· ——·· —·——	399·00	Non A2A	35M

ENGLAND (WEST COAST), ISLE OF MAN, WALES (Areas 10 and 11)

ID	Name	Coordinates	Ident	Morse	Freq	Mode	Range
A051	Carnane	54°08'·46N 04°29'·50W	CAR	−·−· ·− ·−·	366·50	Non A2A	25M
A049	Ronaldsway/IOM	54°05'·15N 04°36'·45W	RWY	·−· ·− −·−−	359·00	Non A2A	20M
041	Walney Island	54°02'·92N 03°10'·55W	FN	··−· −·	306·00	A1A	50M
A040	Barrow/Walney Island	54°07'·64N 03°15'·80W	WL	·−− ·−··	385·00	Non A2A	15M
A039	Blackpool	53°46'·36N 03°01'·59W	BPL	−···· ·−−· ·−··	420·00	Non A2A	15M
A038	Warton (HJ)	53°45'·09N 02°51'·05W	WTN	·−− − −·	337·00	Non A2A	15M
034D	Point Lynas lt	53°24'·97N 04°17'·30W	PS	·−−· ···	304·00	A1A	50M
A031	Aberporth	52°06'·92N 04°33'·57W	AP	·− ·−−·	370·50	Non A2A	20M
029	South Bishop lt	51°51'·15N 05°24'·65W	SB	··· −···	290·50	A1A	70M
A027	Swansea (HX)	51°36'·10N 04°03'·88W	SWN	··· ·−− −·	320·50	Non A2A	15M
A025	Cardiff/Rhoose	51°23'·57N 03°20'·23W	CDF	−·−· −·· ·−·	388·50	Non A2A	20M
026D	Nash Point lt	51°24'·03N 03°33'·06W	NP	−· ·−−·	299·50	A1A	50M
A020	St Mawgan	50°26'·51N 04°59'·36W	SM	··· −−	356·50	Non A2A	20M

IRELAND (Areas 12 and 13)

ID	Name	Coordinates	Ident	Morse	Freq	Mode	Range
178D	Mizen Head lt	51°27'·05N 09°48'·80W	MZ	−− −−··	300·00	A1A	100M
179	Old Head of Kinsale lt	51°36'·27N 08°31'·97W	OH	−−− ····	288·00	A1A	50M
A181	Waterford	52°11'·83N 07°05'·33W	WTD	·−− − −··	368·00	Non A2A	25M
182	Tuskar Rock lt	52°12'·15N 06°12'·38W	TR	− ·−·	286·00	A1A	50M
A184	Killiney (Dublin)	53°16'·17N 06°06'·33W	KLY	−·− ·−·· −·−−	378·00	Non A2A	50M
185	Baily	53°21'·68N 06°03'·09W	BY	−··· −·−−	289·00	A1A	50M
A187	Rush (Dublin)	53°30'·73N 06°06'·60W	RSH	·−· ··· ····	326·00	Non A2A	30M
189	South Rock lt F	54°24'·47N 05°21'·92W	SU	··· ··−	291·50	A1A	50M
A191	Belfast City	54°36'·94N 05°52'·86W	HB	···· −···	420·00	Non A2A	15M
A195	Eglinton/Londonderry	55°02'·70N 07°09'·25W	EGT	· −−· −	328·50	Non A2A	25M
197D	Tory Island lt	55°16'·35N 08°14'·72W	TY	− −·−−	313·00	A1A	100M
199	Eagle Island lt	54°16'·98N 10°05'·52W	GL	−−· ·−··	307·00	A1A	100M
A200	Sligo	54°16'·83N 08°36'·00W	SLG	··· ·−·· −−·	384·00	Non A2A	25M
A201	Galway/Carnmore	53°18'·06N 08°56'·53W	CRN	−·−· ·−· −·	321·00	Non A2A	25M
A202	Ennis	52°54'·27N 08°55'·62W	ENS	· −· ···	352·00	Non A2A	80M
A202*	Foynes	52°33'·97N 09°11'·67W	FOY	··−· −−− −·−·	395·00	Non A2A	50M
203D	Loop Head lt	52°33'·65N 09°55'·90W	LP	·−·· ·−··	311·50	A1A	50M

C3

TABLE 3(2)   MARINE AND AERONAUTICAL RDF BEACONS – CONTINENT

See map at Fig 3(5). Note: Beacon Nos are the last 3 digits of Nos published in ALRS Vol 2. Those prefixed with A are Aeronautical beacons. Those suffixed with D provide DGPS; see 3.2.5.

FRANCE – NORTH WEST COAST (Areas 15 and 16)

No.	Name / Position	Ident	Morse	Freq	Class	Range
847	Cherbourg W Fort lt 49°40'·50N 01°38'·87W	RB	·—· —···	302·00	A1A	20M
A847*	Cherbourg/Maupertus 49°38'·30N 01°22'·28W	MP	—— ·——·	373·00	A1A	
A848	Granville 48°55'·10N 01°28'·87W	GV	——· ···—	321·00	A1A	25M
849	Le Grand Jardin lt 48°40'·27N 02°04'·90W	GJ	——· ·———	306·50	A1A	10M
852	Rosédo lt, Île Bréhat 48°51'·51N 03°00'·21W	DO	—·· ———	287·50	A1A	10M
A853	Lannion 48°43'·25N 03°18'·45W	LN	·—·· —·	345·00	A1A	50M
A854	Landivisiau 48°32'·80W 04°08'·25W	LDV	·—·· —·· ···—	324·00	A1A	60M
856	Île Vierge lt 48°38'·38N 04°33'·97W	VG	···— ——·	314·00	A1A	70M
858	Ouessant SW Lanby 48°31'·20N 05°49'·10W	SW	··· ·——	305·50	A1A	10M
857	Pte de Créac'h (Île d'Ouessant) 48°27'·62N 05°07'·65W	CA	—·—· ·—	301·00	A1A	100M
859D	Pointe St Mathieu lt 48°19'·85N 04°46'·17W	SM	··· ——	291·00	A1A	50M
A862	Lanvéoc, Poulmic 48°17'·07N 04°26'·00W	BST	—··· ··· —	428·00	A1A	80M

FRANCE – WEST COAST (Areas 17 and 18)

No.	Name / Position	Ident	Morse	Freq	Class	Range
863	Île de Sein NW lt 48°02'·70N 04°51'·95W	SN	··· —·	289·50	A1A	70M
865	Eckmühl lt 47°47'·95N 04°22'·35W	ÜH	··—— ····	312·00	A1A	50M
866	Pointe de Combrit lt 47°51'·92N 04°06'·70W	CT	—·—· —	288·50	A1A	20M
A867	Quimper/Pluguffan 47°58'·08N 03°59'·82W	QR	——·— ·—·	380·00	A1A	
A869	Lorient 47°45'·75N 03°26'·43W	LOR	·—·· ——— ·—·	359·00	A1A	80M
871	Pen Men lt, Île de Groix 47°38'·97N 03°30'·36W	GX	——· —··—	298·00	A1A	50M
A874	St Nazaire/Montoir 47°20'·02N 02°02'·57W	MT	—— —	398·00	A1A	50M
875	Pointe de St Gildas 47°08'·10N 02°14'·67W	NZ	—· ——··	308·50	A1A	40M
879	Île d'Yeu Main lt 46°43'·10N 02°22'·90W	YE	—·—— ·	303·00	A1A	100M
883D	Les Baleines lt (Île de Ré) 46°14'·70N 01°33'·60W	BN	—··· —·	299·00	A1A	40M
887	La Rochelle 46°08'·97N 01°10'·27W	RE	·—· ·	295·50	A1A	40M
891D	Pointe de la Coubre 45°41'·87N 01°13'·93W	LK	·—·· —·—	292·00	A1A	100M
A892	Cognac/Châteaubernard 45°40'·13N 00°18'·53W	CGC	—·—· ——· —·—·	354·00		75M
A893	Bordeaux/Mérignac 44°55'·92N 00°33'·88W	BD	—··· —··	393·00	A1A	30M
895D	Cap Ferret lt 44°38'·77N 01°14'·81W	FT	··—· —	286·50	A1A	100M
A897	Cazaux (HJ) 44°33'·08N 01°07'·13W	CAA	—·—· ·— ·—	382·00		80M
A896	Biarritz 43°28'·25N 01°24'·18W	BZ	—··· ——··	341·00	A1A	35M

FRANCE – NORTH-EAST COAST (Area 19)

846D	**Pointe de Barfleur lt** 49°41'.87N 01°15'.87W	FG	..-. --.	297.00	A1A	70M
845	**Port en Bessin rear ldg lt** 49°20'.98N 00°45'.48W	BS	-... ...	290.00	A1A	5M
843	**Pointe de Ver lt** 49°20'.47N 00°31'.05W	ÉR	..-..-.. .-.	310.00	A1A	20M
A840	**Le Havre/Octeville** 49°35'.75N 00°11'.00E	LHO	.-.. .... ---	346.00	A2A	15M
837	**Pointe d'Ailly lt** 49°55'.00N 00°57'.55E	AL	.- .-..	305.50	A1A	50M
A834	**Le Touquet/Paris Plage** 50°32'.23N 01°35'.38E	LT	.-.. -	358.00	A2A	20M
829	**Cap d'Alprech lt** 50°41'.95N 01°33'.83E	PH	.--.	294.00	A1A	20M
825	**Calais Main lt** 50°57'.73N 01°51'.30E	CS	-.-. ...	312.50	A1A	20M
A823	**St Inglevert** 50°52'.98N 01°44'.55E	ING	.. -. --.	387.50	A1A	50M
A821	**Calais/Dunkerque** 50°59'.88N 02°03'.36E	MK	-- -.-	418.00	A1A	15M

BELGIUM (Area 20)

215	**Nieuwpoort W Pier lt** 51°09'.40N 02°43'.08E	NP	-. .--.	285.00	A1A	5M
217D	**Oostende Rear lt** 51°14'.36N 02°55'.94E	OE	--- .	312.00	A1A	40M
219	**Zeebrugge** 51°21'.66N 03°11'.33E	ZB	--.. -...	289.00	A1A	5M

NETHERLANDS (Area 20)

229	**Goeree lt** 51°55'.53N 03°40'.18E	GR	--. .-.	296.00	A1A	48M
231D	**Hoek van Holland** 51°58'.90N 04°06'.83E	HH	....	288.00	A1A	50M
237	**IJmuiden Front lt** 52°27'.75N 04°34'.55E	YM	-.-- --	288.50	A1A	20M
243	**Eierland lt** 53°10'.97N 04°51'.40E	ER	. .-.	301.00	A1A	20M
245	**Vlieland lt** 53°17'.80N 05°03'.57E	VL	...- .-..	303.50	A1A	20M
247D	**Ameland lt** 53°27'.02N 05°37'.60E	AD	.- -..	299.00	A1A	50M

GERMANY (Area 21)

259	**Borkum, Kleiner lt** 53°34'.78N 06°40'.09E	BE	-... .	302.00	A1A	20M
279	**German Bight lt V** 54°10'.80N 07°27'.60E	GB	--. -...	312.00	A1A	10M
264	**Wangerooge lt** 53°47'.45N 07°51'.52E	WE	.-- .	309.50	A1A	20M
265	**Alte Weser lt** 53°51'.85N 08°07'.72E	AR	.- .-.	309.00	A1A	20M
275	**Elbe lt F** 54°00'.00N 08°06'.58E	EL	. .-..	298.00	A1A	10M
A271	**Jever** 53°31'.18N 08°00'.92E	JEV	.--- . ...-	390.00	Non A1A	50M
A274	**Glukstadt** 53°51'.07N 09°27'.32E	GLX	--. .-.. -..-	365.00	Non A2A	30M
A270	**Nordholz** 53°47'.18N 08°48'.47E	NDO	-. -.. ---	372.00	Non A2A	30M
A285	**Westerland/Sylt** 54°51'.45N 08°24'.67E	SLT	... .-.. -	387.00	Non A2A	25M

C3

3.6   RADAR

3.6.1   Radar in yachts

Radar is useful both for navigation and for collision avoidance, but to take full advantage of it and to use it in safety demands a proper understanding of its operation and of its limitations. Read the instruction book carefully, and practise using and adjusting the set so as to get optimum performance in different conditions. It is important to learn how to interpret what is seen on the display.

Radar beams do not discriminate so well in bearing as they do in range, so an accurate fix is sometimes best obtained by a radar range and a visual bearing of the same object.

The effective range of radar is approximately line of sight, but this can be decreased or increased by abnormal conditions. Radar will not detect a low-lying coastline which is below the radar horizon.

3.6.2   Collision avoidance

Yacht radars usually have a head up display, ie the ship's head at the top of the screen; own boat is at the centre, apparently stationary. More modern radars can be linked to an electronic compass so as to provide a North-up display, ie North shown conventionally at the top of the screen.

If a target is moving in the same direction and at the same speed, it is stationary relative to own boat, and its echo should be sharp and well defined. If it is on a reciprocal course, it paints an echo with a long tail.

If an echo is on a steady bearing, and the range is decreasing, there is a risk of collision. To determine the proper action to take, plot an approaching echo three or four times, in order to determine its actual course and speed, and how close it will actually approach.

3.6.3   Navigational aid

Radar cannot see behind other objects, or round corners; it may not pick up small objects, or differentiate between two targets that are close together. As already stated, radar ranges are more accurate than radar bearings. Objects with sharp features such as buildings give a better reflection than those with curved or sloping surfaces. High cliffs make a good target, but low coastlines should be approached with extreme caution as the first thing to show on radar may be hills some distance inland.

3.7   RACONS (RADAR BEACONS)

3.7.1   Description

A Racon is a transponder beacon which, when triggered by a transmission from a vessel's radar, sends back a distinctive signal which appears on the vessel's radar display. Racons are fitted to some light-vessels, buoys and lighthouses, and are marked on charts by a magenta circle and the word Racon.

In most cases the Racon flash on the display is a line extending radially outwards from a point slightly beyond the actual position of the Racon, due to the slight delay in the response of the beacon apparatus. Thus the distance to the spot of the Racon flash is a little more than the vessel's real distance from the Racon. Some Racons give a flash composed of a Morse identification signal, often with a tail to it, the length of the tail depending on the number of Morse characters.

The typical maximum range of a Racon is about 10M, but may be as much as 25M. In practice, picking up a Racon at greater ranges depends on the power and elevation of both the Racon and the boat's radar. With abnormal radio propagation, a spurious Racon flash may be seen at much greater distances than the beacon's normal range, appearing at any random position along the correct bearing on the display. Only rely on a Racon flash if it appears to be consistent, and the boat is believed to be within its quoted range. At short range a Racon sometimes causes unwanted interference on the radar display, and this may be reduced by adjusting the rain clutter control on the set.

3.7.2   Characteristics

Details of Racons around Europe are in Table 3(3), arranged in the following columns:

(1)   Ref No: last 3 digits of number in ALRS Vol 2.

(2)   The type of Racon. The majority of Racons sweep the frequency range of marine 3cm (X-band) radar emissions. The older type of Racon (swept frequency) take 30 to 90 seconds to sweep the band.

The newer type of Racon (frequency agile) responds immediately to both 3cm and 10cm (S-band) emissions. In order that the Racon response should not obscure wanted echoes, the agile response is switched 'on' and 'off' at a predetermined rate to suit the installation.

(3)   Name of the station.

(4)   Latitude and longitude.

(5)   The sector within which signals may be received, bearings being towards the beacon, clockwise from 000° to 359°. 360° indicates all-round operation.

(6)   Approximate range, in nautical miles. This also depends on the range of the yacht's radar set.

(7)   The form of the beacon's flash on a ship's radar. Morse identification signals may be alphabetical or numerical, and are often followed by a 'tail'. Racons coded 'D' are used to mark new dangers.

Note: A Ramark is a radar beacon which transmits without having to be triggered by a ship's radar. Its flash extends from the ship's position to the edge of the display and therefore gives no indication of range.

Table 3(3) RACONS – EUROPE (For heading details see 3.7.2)

(1) No	(2) Type	(3) Name	(4) Lat	Long	(5) Sector	(6) Range	(7) Ident
UNITED KINGDOM							
South Coast, mid-Channel and Channel Islands (Areas 1-3 and 14)							
025	3 & 10 cm	Bishop Rock lt ho	49°52'·33N	06°26'·68W	245°-215°	18M	T
028	3 & 10 cm	Seven Stones lt float	50°03'·58N	06°04'·28W	360°	15M	O
022	3 & 10 cm	Wolf Rock lt ho	49°56'·67N	05°48'·48W	360°	10M	T
019	3 & 10 cm	Eddystone lt ho	50°10'·81N	04°15'·87W	360°	10M	T
284	3 & 10 cm	Channel lt float	49°54'·42N	02°53'·67W	360°	15M	O
280	3 & 10 cm	East Channel buoy	49°58'·67N	02°28'·87W	360°	10M	T
287	3 & 10 cm	Casquets lt ho	49°43'·38N	02°22'·55W	360°	25M	T
289	3 cm	Platte Fougère lt	49°30'·88N	02°29'·05W	360°		P
293	3 cm	St Helier, Demie de Pas lt	49°09'·07N	02°06'·05W	360°	10M	T
017	3 & 10cm	Bridge buoy	50°39'·59N	01°36'·80W	360°	10M	T
016	3 cm	West Bramble buoy	50°47'·17N	01°18'·57W	360°	3M	T
013	3 & 10 cm	Nab Tower lt	50°40'·05N	00°57'·07W	360°	10M	T
012	3 & 10 cm	Owers buoy	50°37'·27N	00°40'·60W	360°	10M	O
010	3 & 10 cm	English Channel buoy EC 1	50°05'·90N	01°48'·35W	360°	10M	T
007	3 & 10 cm	English Channel buoy EC 2	50°12'·10N	01°12'·40W	360°	10M	T
004	3 & 10 cm	English Channel buoy EC 3	50°18'·30N	00°36'·10W	360°	10M	T
001	3 & 10 cm	Greenwich lt vessel	50°24'·50N	00°00'·00	360°	10M	M
235	3 & 10 cm	Varne lt vessel	51°01'·26N	01°24'·01E	360°	10M	T
England East coast (Areas 4 and 5)							
230	3 & 10 cm	Sandettié lt float	51°09'·40N	01°47'·20E	360°	10M	T
226	3 & 10 cm	East Goodwin lt float	51°13'·05N	01°36'·32E	360°	10M	T
224	3 & 10 cm	Inter Bank buoy	51°16'·45N	01°52'·33E	360°	10M	M
223	3 & 10 cm	NE Goodwin buoy	51°20'·28N	01°34'·27E	360°	10M	M
216	3 & 10 cm	Dover Strait TSS, F3 lt vessel	51°23'·82N	02°00'·62E	360°	10M	T
208	3 cm	Thames Sea Reach buoy No 1	51°29'·42N	00°52'·67E	360°	10M	T
204	3 cm	Thames Sea Reach buoy No 7	51°30'·08N	00°37'·15E	360°	10M	T
212	3 & 10 cm	Outer Tongue buoy	51°30'·69N	01°26'·50E	360°	10M	T
200	3 & 10 cm	Barrow buoy No 3	51°41'·99N	01°20'·35E	360°	10M	M
196	3 & 10 cm	South Galloper buoy	51°43'·95N	01°56'·50E	360°	10M	T
193	3 & 10 cm	Sunk lt float	51°51'·00N	01°35'·00E	360°	10M	T
190	3 & 10 cm	Harwich Channel buoy No 1	51°56'·11N	01°27'·30E	360°	10M	T
186	3 & 10 cm	Outer Gabbard buoy	51°57'·80N	02°04'·30E	360°	10M	O
184	3 & 10 cm	N Shipwash buoy	52°01'·70N	01°38'·38E	360°	10M	M
182	3 & 10 cm	Orfordness lt ho	52°05'·01N	01°34'·56E	360°	18M	T
178	3 & 10 cm	Cross Sand buoy	52°37'·00N	01°59'·25E	360°	10M	T
176	3 & 10 cm	Winterton Old lt ho	52°42'·75N	01°41'·82E	360°	10M	T
172	3 & 10 cm	Smiths Knoll buoy	52°43'·50N	02°18'·00E	360°	10M	T
168	3 & 10 cm	Newarp buoy	52°48'·35N	01°55'·80E	360°	10M	O
165	3 & 10 cm	Cromer lt ho	52°55'·45N	01°19'·10E	360°	25M	O
163	3 & 10 cm	North Haisbro buoy	53°00'·20N	01°32'·40E	360°	10M	T
160	3 & 10 cm	North Well buoy	53°03'·00N	00°28'·00E	360°	10M	T
156	3 & 10 cm	Dudgeon buoy	53°16'·60N	01°17'·00E	360°	10M	O
155	3 & 10 cm	Anglia Field platform A48/19	53°22'·03N	01°39'·21E	360°	15M	Q
153	3 & 10 cm	Inner Dowsing lt vessel	53°19'·50N	00°33'·96E	360°	10M	T
149	3 & 10 cm	Dowsing platform B1D	53°33'·65N	00°52'·75E	360°	10M	T
146	3cm	Spurn lt float	53°33'·53N	00°14'·33E	360°	5M	M
144	3 & 10 cm	Humber buoy	53°36'·72N	00°21'·60E	360°	7M	T
138	3 cm	Tees fairway buoy	54°40'·93N	01°06'·37W	360°		B
Scotland East and North coasts, Orkney, Shetland and offshore (Areas 6 and 7)							
131	3 & 10 cm	St Abb's Head lt	55°54'·97N	02°08'·20W	360°	18M	T
128	3 cm	Inchkeith fairway buoy	56°03'·50N	03°00'·00W	360°	5M	T
126	3 cm	Forth North Channel buoy No 7	56°02'·80N	03°10'·87W	360°	18M	T
123	3 & 10 cm	Bell Rock lt ho	56°26'·05N	02°23'·07W	360°	18M	M
121	3 & 10 cm	Abertay buoy	56°27'·41N	02°40'·52W	360°	8M	T
118	3 & 10 cm	Scurdie Ness lt ho	56°42'·12N	02°26'·15W	360°	14-16M	T
114	3 & 10 cm	Girdle Ness lt ho	57°08'·35N	02°02'·82W	360°	25M	G
112	3 cm	Aberdeen fairway buoy	57°09'·33N	02°01'·85W	360°	7M	T
109	3 & 10 cm	Buchan Ness lt ho	57°28'·23N	01°46'·37W	360°	14-16M	O
106	3 & 10 cm	Rattray Head lt ho	57°36'·62N	01°48'·83W	360°	15M	M
104	3 & 10 cm	Kessock bridge centre mark	57°29'·99N	04°13'·71W	360°	6M	K
103	3 cm	Cromarty Firth fairway buoy	57°39'·98N	03°54'·10W	360°	5M	

C3

(1) No	(2) Type	(3) Name	(4) Lat	Long	(5) Sector	(6) Range	(7) Ident
101	3 & 10 cm	Tarbat Ness lt ho	57°51'·92N	03°46'·52W	360°	14-16M	T
100	3 & 10 cm	Platform Chevron Alba	58°03'·52N	01°04'·88E	360°		C
099	3 & 10 cm	Platform Saltire Alpha	58°25'·05N	00°19'·85E	360°		Z
098	3 & 10 cm	Platform Piper Bravo	58°27'·68N	00°15'·07E	360°		N
096	3 & 10 cm	Duncansby Head lt	58°38'·67N	03°01'·42W	360°	16M	T
094	3 & 10 cm	Lother Rock lt	58°43'·82N	02°58'·59W	360°	10M	M
091	3 & 10 cm	North Ronaldsay lt	59°23'·40N	02°22'·80W	360°	14-17M	T
089	3 & 10 cm	Rumble Rock bn	60°28'·22N	01°07'·13W	360°	8-10M	O
087	3 & 10 cm	Gruney Island lt	60°39'·20N	01°18'·03W	360°	14M	T
085	3 & 10 cm	Ve Skerries lt	60°22'·40N	01°48'·67W	360°	15M	T
083	3 & 10 cm	Petrojari Foinaven 204/24	60°18'·95N	04°16'·40W			X
081	3 & 10 cm	Sule Skerry lt	59°05'·10N	04°24'·30W	360°	20M	T

Scotland West coast (Areas 8 and 9)

No	Type	Name	Lat	Long	Sector	Range	Ident
079	3 & 10 cm	Eilean Glas lt	57°51'·43N	06°38'·45W	360°	16-18M	T
076	3 cm	Ardivachar Pt	57°22'·90N	07°25'·45W	360°	16M	T
075	3 cm	Carrach Rocks buoy	57°15'·20N	05°45'·29W	360°	5M	T
074	3 & 10cm	Hyskeir lt (Oigh Sgeir)	56°58'·15N	06°40'·80W	360°	14-17M	T
073	3 cm	Castlebay South buoy	56°56'·10N	07°27'·17W	360°	7M	T
072	3 & 10 cm	Bo Vic Chuan buoy	56°56'·17N	07°23'·25W	360°	5M	M
068	3 & 10 cm	Skerryvore lt ho	56°19'·40N	07°06'·90W	360°	18M	M
067	3 & 10 cm	Dubh Sgeir lt ho	56°14'·78N	05°40'·12W	360°	5M	M
065	3 cm	Sanda lt	55°16'·50N	05°34'·90W	360°	20M	T

England West coast and Wales (Areas 10 and 11)

No	Type	Name	Lat	Long	Sector	Range	Ident
058	3 & 10 cm	Point of Ayre lt (IoM)	54°24'·95N	04°22'·03W	360°	13-15M	M
056	3 & 10 cm	Halfway Shoal lt bn	54°01'·46N	03°11'·79W	360°	10M	B
055	3 & 10 cm	Lune Deep buoy	53°55'·80N	03°11'·00W	360°	10M	T
052	3 & 10 cm	Bar lt float	53°32'·00N	03°20'·90W	360°	10M	T
049	3 & 10 cm	The Skerries lt ho	53°25'·27N	04°36'·44W	360°	25M	T
046	3 & 10 cm	The Smalls lt ho	51°43'·23N	05°40'·10W	360°	25M	T
043	3 & 10 cm	St Gowan buoy	51°31'·90N	04°59'·70W	360°	10M	T
040	3 & 10 cm	West Helwick buoy W. HWK	51°31'·37N	04°23'·58W	360°	10M	T
037	3 & 10 cm	West Scar buoy (Swansea Bay)	51°28'·28N	03°55'·50W	360°	10M	T
036	3 & 10 cm	Cabenda buoy	51°33'·30N	03°52'·15W	360°		Q
034	3 & 10 cm	English & Welsh Grounds buoy	51°26'·90N	03°00'·10W	360°	7M	T
031	3 & 10 cm	Breaksea buoy	51°19'·85N	03°18'·98W	360°	10M	T
032		Second Severn Crossing NE	51°34'·44N	02°41'·93W			O
033		Second Severn Crossing SW	51°34'·42N	02°41'·94W			O

IRELAND

Southern half (Area 12)

No	Type	Name	Lat	Long	Sector	Range	Ident
362	3 & 10 cm	Kish Bank lt	53°18'·68N	05°55'·38W	360°	15M	T
358	3 & 10 cm	Codling Lanby	53°03'·02N	05°40'·70W	360°	10M	G
361	3 cm	Dublin Bay buoy	53°19'·90N	06°04'·58W			M
354	3 & 10 cm	Arklow buoy	52°39'·50N	05°58'·10W	360°	10M	O
351	3 & 10 cm	Tuskar Rock lt	52°12'·15N	06°12'·38W	360°	18M	T
348	3 & 10 cm	Coningbeg lt float	52°02'·38N	06°39'·45W	360°	13M	M
346	3 & 10 cm	Hook Head lt	52°07'·40N	06°55'·72W	237°-177°	10M	K
343	3 & 10 cm	Cork buoy	51°42'·90N	08°15'·50W	360°	7M	T
341	3 & 10 cm	Fastnet lt ho	51°23'·33N	09°36'·14W	360°	18M	G
338	3 & 10 cm	Bull Rock lt ho	51°35'·49N	10°18'·03W	360°	16-27M	N
380	3 & 10 cm	Inishtearaght lt	52°04'·51N	10°39'·64W	313°-221°	18M	O
378	3 & 10 cm	Ballybunnion buoy	52°32'·50N	09°46'·91W	360°	6M	M

Northern half (Area 13)

No	Type	Name	Lat	Long	Sector	Range	Ident
376	3 & 10 cm	Inisheer lt	53°02'·78N	09°31'·57 W	216°-144°	13M	K
375	3 & 10 cm	Slyne Head lt	53°23'·98N	10°14'·02W	360°	16-27M	T
373	3 & 10 cm	Rathlin O'Birne lt	54°39'·80N	08°49'·90W	284°-203°	13M	O
371	3 & 10 cm	Tory Island lt	55°16'·35N	08°14'·92W	360°	12-23M	M
370	3 & 10 cm	Inishtrahull lt	55°25'·85N	07°14'·60W	060°-310°[1]	24M	T

[1] Reduced or no signal 310°–060° (southerly sector).

No	Type	Name	Lat	Long	Sector	Range	Ident
369	3 & 10 cm	Rathlin East lt	55°18'·10N	06°10'·20W	089°-003°	15-27M	G
368	3 & 10 cm	East Maiden lt	54°55'·73N	05°43'·61W	360°	11-21M	M
367	3 & 10 cm	Mew Island lt	54°41'·91N	05°30'·75W	360°	14M	O
366	3 & 10 cm	South Rock lt V	54°24'·47N	05°21'·92W	360°	13M	T
364	3 & 10 cm	Hellyhunter buoy	54°00'·34N	06°01'·99W		5-14M	K

(1) No	(2) Type	(3) Name	(4) Lat	Long	(5) Sector	(6) Range	(7) Ident
FRANCE (Areas 15-19)							
744	3 cm	**BXA Lanby**	45°37'·60N	01°28'·60W	360°		B
740	3 cm	**St Nazaire, La Couronnée buoy**	47°07'·67N	02°20'·00W	360°	3-5M	See [1]

[1] Signals appear as a series of dots. The distance between each dot corresponds to 0·2M.

736	3 cm	**St Nazaire buoy SN 1**	47°00'·12N	02°39'·75W	360°	3-8M	Z
732	3 cm	**Chausée de Sein buoy**	48°03'·80N	05°07'·70W	360°	10M	O
728	3 cm	**Pte de Créac'h (Ouessant) lt ho**	48°27'·62N	05°07'·65W	030°-248°	20M	C
724	3 & 10 cm	**Ouessant SW Lanby**	48°31'·20N	05°49'·10W	360°	20M	M
720	3 cm	**Ouessant NE buoy**	48°45'·90N	05°11'·60W	360°	20M	B
700	3 & 10 cm	**Le Havre LHA Lanby**	49°31'·44N	00°09'·78W	360°	8-10M	See [1]

[1] Signals appear as a series of 8 dots or 8 groups of dots. The distance between each dot or group of dots corresponds to 0·3M.

696	3 cm	**Antifer approach buoy A5**	49°45'·89N	00°17'·40W	360°		K
692	3 & 10 cm	**Bassurelle buoy**	50°32'·70N	00°57'·80E	360°	5-8M	B
688	3 & 10 cm	**Vergoyer buoy N**	50°39'·70N	01°22'·30E	360°	5-8M	C
680	3 cm	**Dunkerque Lanby**	51°02'·96N	01°51'·86E	360°		See [1]

[1] Signal appears as a succession of 8 dots. The distance between each dot corresponds to 0·3M.

BELGIUM (Area 20)

No	Type	Name	Lat	Long	Sector	Range	Ident
400	3 cm	**West Hinder lt**	51°23'·36N	02°26'·35E			W
402		**Westhinder Route buoy KB**	51°20'·95N	02°43'·00E			K
405	3 & 10 cm	**Bol Van Heist lt MOW 0**	51°23'·70N	03°02'·80E	360°	10M	S
410	3 & 10 cm	**Bol Van Heist lt MOW 3**	51°23'·43N	03°11'·98E	360°	10M	H

NETHERLANDS (Area 20)

No	Type	Name	Lat	Long	Sector	Range	Ident
440	3 & 10 cm	**Keeten B buoy**	51°36'·40N	03°58'·12E	360°		K
450	3 & 10 cm	**Zuid Vlije buoy ZV11/SRK 4**	51°38'·23N	04°14'·56E	360°		K
454	3 cm	**Noord Hinder buoy NHR–SE**	51°45'·50N	02°40'·00E	360°	10M	N
458	3 cm	**Noord Hinder buoy**	52°00'·15N	02°51'·20E	360°		T
462	3 cm	**Noord Hinder N buoy**	52°10'·95N	03°04'·85E	360°	10M	K
466	3 cm	**Schouwenbank buoy**	51°45'·00N	03°14'·40E	360°	10M	O
468	3 & 10 cm	**Goeree lt**	51°55'·53N	03°40'·18E	360°	12-15M	T
472	3 & 10 cm	**Maas Centre buoy MC**	52°01'·18N	03°53'·57E	360°	10M	M
473		**Scheveningen App R&W lt buoy**	52°09'·00N	04°05'·50E	(On trial)		Z
474		**Scheveningen App Red lt buoy**	52°10'·80N	04°07'·15E	(On trial)		Q
475	3 & 10 cm	**Rijn Field platform P15–B**	52°18'·48N	03°46'·72E	030°-270°	12-15M	B
479	3 & 10 cm	**IJmuiden buoy**	52°28'·70N	04°23'·93E	360°	10M	Y
481		**Horizon P9-6 platform**	52°33'·20N	03°44'·54E			Q
483	3 & 10 cm	**Helm Veld A platform**	52°52'·39N	04°08'·58E	360°		T
487	3 & 10 cm	**Logger platform**	53°00'·90N	04°13'·05E	060°-270°	12-15M	X
485	3 cm	**Schulpengat fairway buoy SG**	52°52'·95N	04°38'·00E			Z
486		**DW Route buoy BR/S**	52°54'·95N	03°18'·15E			6
489	3 & 10 cm	**NAM Field platform K14–FA–1**	53°16'·17N	03°37'·66E	360°		7
493	3 & 10 cm	**Vlieland Lanby VL–Center**	53°27'·00N	04°40'·00E	360°	12-15M	C
496	3 & 10 cm	**Wintershall platform L8–G**	53°34'·92N	04°36'·32E	000°-340°	12-15M	G
498	3 & 10 cm	**Placid Field platform PL–K9C–PA**	53°39'·20N	03°52'·45E	360°		8
499	3 & 10 cm	**Markham Field platform J6–A**	53°49'·39N	02°56'·75E	000°-180°		M
500	3 & 10 cm	**West Friesland platform L2–FA–1**	53°57'·65N	04°29'·85E			9
505	3 cm	**DW route buoy FR/A**	54°00'·35N	04°21'·41E	360°		M
507	3 cm	**Elf Petroland platform F15-A**	54°12'·98N	04°49'·71E	360°		U
511	3 cm	**DW route buoy EF**	54°03'·30N	04°59'·80E			T
515	3 cm	**DW route buoy EF/B**	54°06'·65N	05°40'·00E			M
516	3 cm	**DW route buoy EF/C**	54°08'·30N	06°00'·00E			O
519	3 & 10 cm	**NAM Field platform F3-OLT**	54°51'·30 N	04°43'·60E	360°		D

GERMANY (North Sea Coast: Area 21)

No	Type	Name	Lat	Long	Sector	Range	Ident
540	3 cm	**Westerems buoy**	53°36'·97N	06°19'·48E	360°	8M	T
544	3 cm	**Borkumriff buoy**	53°47'·50N	06°22'·13E	360°	8M	T
548	3 cm	**GW/Ems lt float**	54°10'·00N	06°20'·80E	360°	8M	T
552	3 cm	**German Bight lt vessel**	54°10'·80N	07°27'·60E	360°	8M	T
556	3 cm	**Jade/Weser buoy**	53°58'·33N	07°38'·83E	360°	8M	T
560	3 & 10 cm	**Tonne 3/Jade 2 buoy**	53°52'·12N	07°47'·33E	360°	8M	T
564	3 cm	**Elbe lt float**	54°00'·00N	08°06'·58E	360°	8M	T

C3

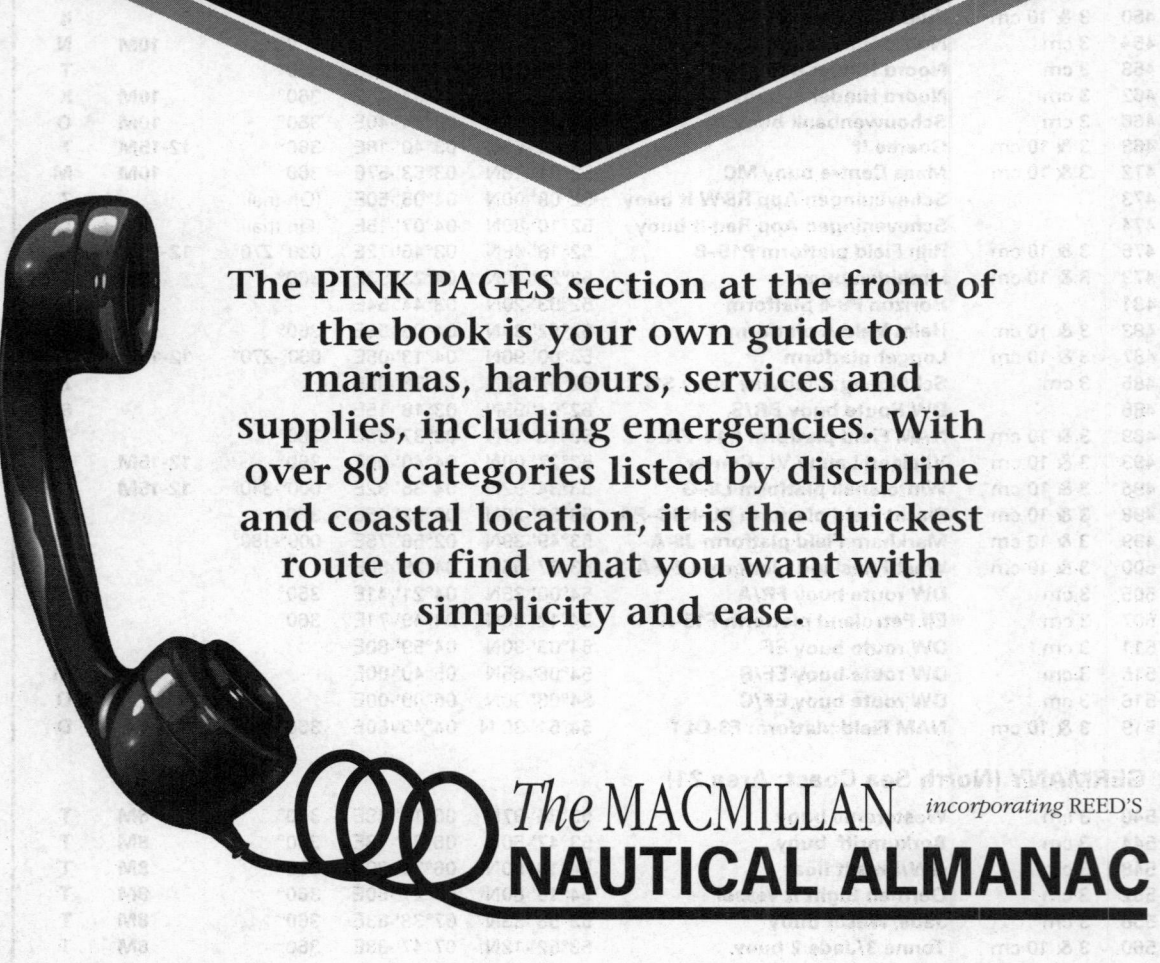

Chapter 4

Communications

Contents

4.1 INTERNATIONAL CODE   Page 66
4.1.1   Description
4.1.2   Using the International Code

4.2 RADIO COMMUNICATIONS   66
4.2.1   Radiotelephony
4.2.2   Licensing requirements
4.2.3   Radiotelephones – regulations
4.2.4   RT procedures
4.2.5   Prowords

4.3 VHF, MF AND HF RADIO   67
4.3.1   VHF radio
4.3.2   MF radio
4.3.3   HF radio

4.4 COAST RADIO STATIONS (CRS) 67
4.4.1   Introduction
4.4.2   United Kingdom

4.5 LINK CALLS   68
4.5.1   VHF calls to UK Coast Stations
4.5.2   VHF calls to foreign Coast Stations
4.5.3   MF calls to UK Coast Stations
4.5.4   HF calls – Portishead Radio
4.5.5   VHF and MF shore calls to a yacht
4.5.6   Autolink RT

4.6 SATELLITE COMMUNICATIONS 69
4.6.1   Inmarsat

4.7 PORT OPERATIONS AND VTS   69
4.7.1   Port Operations
4.7.2   Vessel traffic services

4.8 NAVIGATIONAL WARNINGS   70
4.8.1   General
4.8.2   UK
4.8.3   France
4.8.4   Belgium
4.8.5   Netherlands
4.8.6   Germany

4.9 CROSS REFERENCES   70
4.9.1   Weather information by RT
4.9.2   Safety, Medical help by RT
4.9.3   Navtex

4.10 CRS DATA & FIGURES
4.10.1   UK   71
4.10.2   Republic of Ireland   74
4.10.3   France   76
4.10.4   Belgium   78
4.10.5   Netherlands   78
4.10.6   Germany   78

4.11 INTERNET, WEB, E-MAIL   80

4.12 TIME   80
4.12.1   BBC Radio time signals
4.12.2   Standard Times

C4

Summary

Yachts often need to communicate with other vessels and with shore stations. This is commonly done by Very High Frequency (VHF) radiotelephone, so this chapter emphasises the procedures used and services available. Radio broadcasts of gale warnings and weather bulletins are described in Chapter 5, while detailed information on Distress, Urgency and Safety signals is given in Chapter 6.

A full description of the various methods of signalling and the procedures that are involved, including an explanation of the *International Code of Signals*, is given in Chapter 6 of *The Macmillan & Silk Cut Yachtsman's Handbook.*

4.1 INTERNATIONAL CODE

4.1.1 Description
Marine communication is based on the *International Code of Signals* (HMSO), which provides for safety of navigation and of persons, especially where there are language problems. The present Code came into force in 1969 and is presented in nine languages: English, French, Italian, German, Japanese, Spanish, Norwegian, Russian and Greek. Ships, aircraft and shore stations can communicate with each other in these languages without knowing a foreign tongue, provided they have a copy of the appropriate Code. The English language edition is published by HMSO.

4.1.2 Using the International Code
The Code can be used by: alphabetical flags and numeral pendants; flashing light and sound signalling in Morse; voice, using radiotelephony or loud-hailer; radiotelegraphy; or by hand flags.

Signals consist of: single-letter signals which are important or common; two-letter signals in the General Section; and three-letter signals starting with 'M' in the Medical Section.

Plates 6 and 7 on pages 20–21 show the Code flags for the alphabet and for numerals, the phonetic alphabet, the phonetic figure-spelling table, the Morse code for letters and numerals, and the meanings of important or common single-letter signals.

4.2 RADIO COMMUNICATIONS

4.2.1 Radiotelephony
Most pleasure craft communicate in plain language using a VHF radio telephone. This gives a range of up to 30-40M depending on the heights of the aerials used.

Medium Frequency (MF) sets give much greater ranges, but must be Single Sideband (SSB). Double Sideband (DSB) transmissions are prohibited except for emergency transmissions on 2182 kHz, the international MF Distress frequency.

High Frequency (HF) radio, which is more powerful and gives a much longer range than MF, is needed for ocean passages; see 4.3.2 and 4.5.4.

The various licences and operating procedures are briefly covered in 4.2.3 and 4.2.4.

4.2.2 Regulations
The regulations for using R/T communications are in the *Handbook for Marine Radio Communication* (Lloyds of London Press). They are lengthy and form part of the syllabus and examination.

Some of the more important stipulations are: operators must not divulge the contents of messages heard; Distress calls have priority; coast radio stations control communications in their areas, except distress messages; check that the channel is free before transmitting; unnecessary or superfluous messages are prohibited, as is bad language; in harbour a yacht may not use inter-ship channels except for safety; a log must be kept, recording all transmissions etc.

4.2.3 Licences
a. The **vessel** requires a Ship Radio Licence for any VHF, UHF, MF, HF, satellite or EPIRB equipment on board. It is obtained from: Wray Castle, Ship Radio Licensing, PO Box 5, Ambleside, LA22 0BF. ☎ 015394 34662. 📠 015394 34663. This allows the use of the international maritime channels; and, when afloat in the UK, of Ch M for communications between yachts, marinas and clubs, and Ch M2 for race control.
b. The **person** in charge of a set requires a combined Certificate of Competence (Pt 1) and Authority to Operate (Pt 2). For most yachtsmen this will be the Certificate of Competence, Restricted VHF Only. The RYA is responsible for the conduct of an examination. The syllabus and examination are detailed in RYA booklet G26. A new Short Range radiotelephone Certificate (SRC), incorporating GMDSS procedures, will eventually supersede the present certificate. The Radiocommunications Agency can provide details of other certificates.
c. Citizens Band and Amateur (Ham) Radio are not substitutes for proper maritime radio on VHF, MF or HF, but they can be a useful means of communication for other than safety matters. CB and Amateur Radio licences are issued by the Radio Licensing Centre at: Subscription Services Ltd, Barton House, Bond Street, Bristol BS98 1TI. Tel: 0117 921 9095.

4.2.4 RT procedures
Communications between a ship and a coast radio station are controlled by the latter, except for Distress, Urgency or Safety messages. Between two ships, the ship called ordains an agreed working channel. The name of the station called need normally only be given once, and that of the calling station twice. Once contact is made, each name need only be spoken once.

Before making a call, decide exactly what needs to be said; writing the message down may help. Speak clearly and distinctly. Names or important words can be repeated or spelt phonetically.

For a position, give latitude and longitude, or the yacht's bearing and distance from a charted object. For bearings use 360° True notation. For times use 24 hour notation, and specify UT, BST, etc.

4.2.4.1 Prowords
The following prowords should be used as they simplify and expedite communications:

ACKNOWLEDGE	'Have you received and understood?'
CONFIRM	'My version is … is that correct?'
CORRECTION	'An error has been made; the correct version is …'
I SAY AGAIN	'I repeat … (e.g. important words)'
I SPELL	'What follows is spelt phonetically'
OUT	End of work
OVER	'I have completed this part of my message, and am inviting you to reply'

RECEIVED	'Receipt acknowledged'
SAY AGAIN	'Repeat your message (or part indicated)'
STATION CALLING	Used when a station is uncertain of the identity of a station which is calling

4.3   VHF, MF and HF RADIO

4.3.1   VHF radio

VHF is used by most vessels, UK coast radio stations, harbours, CG stations and other rescue services. Its range is slightly better than the line of sight between the aerials. It pays to fit a good aerial, as high as possible. Maximum power output is 25 watts, and a lower power (usually 1 watt) is used for short ranges.

VHF sets may be: Simplex, ie transmit and receive on the same frequency, so that only one person can talk at a time; Semi-duplex, ie transmit and receive on different frequencies; or Duplex, ie simultaneous semi-duplex, so that conversation is normal.

Marine VHF frequencies are in the band 156·00 – 174·00 MHz. Frequencies are known by their international channel number (Ch). Yachts at sea are encouraged to listen on Ch 16 (156·80 MHz) which is for Distress and Safety purposes, and for calling and answering. Once contact has been made, the stations concerned **must** switch to a working channel, except for Safety matters.

Channels are designated for one or more purposes, and are listed below in order of preference.

(1) *Public correspondence* (via coast radio stations): Ch 26, 27, 25, 24, 23, 28, 04, 01, 03, 02, 07, 05, 84, 87, 86, 83, 85, 88, 61, 64, 65, 62, 66, 63, 60, 82. All can be used for duplex.

(2) *Inter-ship*: Ch 06, 08, 10, 13, 09, 72, 73, 69, 67, 77, 15, 17. These are all simplex.

(3) *Port Operations*. Simplex: Ch 12, 14, 11, 13, 09, 68, 71, 74, 10, 67, 69, 73, 17, 15.
Duplex: Ch 20, 22, 18, 19, 21, 05, 07, 02, 03, 01, 04, 78, 82, 79, 81, 80, 60, 63, 66, 62, 65, 64, 61, 84.

Ch 67 is used in the UK by CG stations as a Small Craft Safety Channel, accessed via Ch 16 (see 6.8.2).

Ch 70 is used exclusively for digital selective calling (DSC) for Distress and Safety purposes (6.6.4.1).

Ch 80 is the primary working channel between yachts and marinas; Ch M is a stand-by. Yacht clubs may apply to use Ch M2 for race control, with Ch M as stand-by.

4.3.2   MF radio

MF radiotelephones operate in the 1605–4200 kHz range. Unlike VHF and HF, MF transmissions tend to follow the curvature of the earth, which makes them suitable for direction-finding. For this reason, and because of their good range, the marine Distress R/T frequency (2182 kHz) is in the MF band.

Silent periods are observed on this frequency for 3 minutes starting at every H and H+30. During these silence periods only Distress and Urgency messages may be transmitted.

4.3.2   HF radio

HF radiotelephones use frequencies in the 4, 8, 12, 16 and 22 MHz bands (short wave) that are chosen to suit propagation conditions. HF is more expensive than MF and requires more power, but can provide world-wide coverage, although good installation and correct operation are essential for satisfactory results.

Whereas MF transmissions follow the curvature of the earth, HF waves travel upwards and bounce off the ionosphere back to earth. Reception is better at night when the ionosphere is more dense. The directional properties of HF transmissions are poor, and there is no radiotelephone HF Distress frequency.

4.4   COAST RADIO STATIONS

4.4.1   Introduction

Coast Radio Stations (CRS) control communications and link ships with the telephone network ashore. CRS operate on nominated frequencies – see 4.10.

At scheduled times they transmit traffic lists, navigation warnings, weather bulletins, and (as required) gale warnings. They still play an important role in Distress, Urgency and Safety messages.

4.4.2   United Kingdom

In the UK CRS are operated by British Telecom Maritime Services, as shown in 4.10.1. There are eight MF stations and a larger number of VHF stations, the latter providing VHF coverage for most coastal waters.

MF and VHF stations are part of one big network under centralised control. A commercial R/T (link) call received at any station within the UK will be answered by the first available Radio Officer, wherever he may be. A call to Land's End Radio might well be answered by an operator at Portpatrick Radio.

For Distress and Safety, including medical advice and assistance, and for broadcasting navigational warnings, weather forecasts, gale warnings, etc., the stations are divided into Northern and Southern Regions. The MF stations in the Southern Region comprise Land's End, Niton, and Humber Radios. The Northern Region comprises Cullercoats, Stonehaven, Wick/Norwick, Hebrides, and Portpatrick Radios. The Southern Region controlling station is Land's End, and the Northern Region station is Stonehaven. The Commercial and Broadcasting systems are separate to reduce problems in the event of equipment or line failure.

Broadcasts are on dedicated MF frequencies and on selected VHF channels (also used for link calls). The Officer in each region making the broadcast can engage and speak over the broadcast frequencies and channels of all regional stations.

Some stations keep watch on Ch 16 or 2182 kHz, although HM Coastguard is primarily responsible for monitoring Distress, Urgency and Safety calls.

Long-range service is provided by Portishead Radio on High Frequency (HF). See 4.3.2 and 4.5.4.

C4

4.5　LINK CALLS

4.5.1　VHF calls to UK coast radio stations

When within range (about 40 miles), contact a coast radio station. You can make ordinary telephone calls, reverse-charge calls, YTD calls (see below), or send telegrams.

Except in emergency, call on a working frequency as shown in 4.10.1. For a Distress or Urgency call (only) use Ch 16. Do not use a designated broadcast channel at about the time of a scheduled broadcast.

4.5.1.1　Making a call

(1) Listen for a 'clear' channel, with no transmission at all. A busy channel will have either carrier noise, speech or the engaged signal (a series of pips).

(2) The initial call must last at least 6 seconds in order to activate the coast radio station's ship-call latch equipment. For example:

Land's End Radio, Land's End Radio, this is Yacht Seabird, Seabird, Golf Oscar Romeo India, Channel 27 – Over.

(3) When the call is accepted you will hear pips, indicating that you have engaged the channel. Wait for the operator to speak. If no response, do not change channel since you may lose your turn. If you do not hear the pips you have not activated the station's transmitter or may be out of range. Try another station or call again when closer.

(4) When asked by the Radio Officer give the following: Ship's call sign (phonetics), ship's name, type of call and billing details (see below), and for a link call the telephone number required (and the name of the person in the case of a personal call).

4.5.1.2　Paying for a link call

VHF link calls through BT coast radio stations to the UK or Isle of Man can be charged to the owner's home telephone by Yacht Telephone Debit (*Yankee Tango Delta*). Be prepared to advise the operator accordingly. Payment can also be made by transfer charge or by BT Chargecard, which also applies to foreign calls. The operator makes the connection. Timing is automatic.

Note: St Peter Port and Jersey CRS are regarded as foreign stations by BT who add a handling charge of £4 – £7 on the bill. For Jersey, calls may be billed to a UK address. See page 73.

It is possible to make personal calls to certain countries and collect (reversed charge) calls to the UK. More commonly, worldwide accounting for calls is achieved by quoting an 'Accounting Authority Indicator Code' (AAIC); this must be pre-arranged with an ITU-recognised authority such as BT, who use GB14 as the AAIC .

4.5.2　VHF calls to foreign coast stations

Foreign coast radio stations are called on a working channel related to the position of the yacht. VHF calls should last several seconds and state the calling channel. A four-tone signal or pips indicate a temporary delay, but you will be answered when an operator is free.

4.5.3　MF calls to UK coast radio stations

Calls should be made on 2182 kHz. The coast station will answer on 2182 kHz, allocate a working channel, and queue you into the system.

Distress and Urgency calls should always be made on 2182 kHz, and will be answered on the same frequency. This includes medical calls which should be preceded by the Urgency signal 'PAN PAN MEDICO' (see 6.5.2). For full details of radio Distress procedures see Chapter 6.

Should a coast radio station be operating Distress traffic on 2182 kHz, call on 2191 kHz and listen for a reply on the station's broadcast frequency. You will then be allocated a channel. The Radio Officer will request the following information: Vessel's call sign, name, accounting code (AAIC – see 4.5.1.2), and category of traffic (e.g. telegram, telephone call).

4.5.4　HF calls – Portishead Radio

The long-range service in the UK is provided by Portishead Radio, operated by BT Maritime Radio. Watch is kept on the higher bands during daylight, and on the lower bands at night. A 24- hour watch is kept on the 8 MHz band.

The bands in use are announced after the Traffic Lists, broadcast every H+00, and major changes are notified during the previous week. Channels assigned to Portishead Radio are listed in 4.10.1.4. R3E (SSB reduced carrier) or J3E (SSB suppressed carrier) are the modes of transmission that are mandatory in both directions, but J3E is the preferred mode for all transmissions and should be used whenever possible.

An *Optimum Transmitting Frequency Guide* is available from Portishead Radio. It predicts the best band for contacting Portishead worldwide. It is only a guide, and bands should be monitored for the best signal. Equipment must be correctly tuned before calling, and interference not caused to calls in progress. Do not call until a channel is clear, which is announced by Portishead Radio after each period of working.

Portishead Radio offers a service to yachts which have to report regularly to a control centre, eg ARC rally, accepting reports either at fixed times or during a window; call ☎ 0800 378389 for details.

4.5.5　Calls from shore to a yacht

Telephone calls from shore to vessels at sea, via BT coast stations, are booked with Portishead Radio. The caller dials 0800 378389 for free connection to the ship's radiotelephone service. This number is used to book calls on VHF, MF or HF services. The operator will ask for the name of the vessel, station through which vessel normally communicates, voyage details, caller's name and telephone number (or number to be charged if different), person to whom you wish to speak. Portishead Radio will route the call to the appropriate coast radio station.

The CRS will call the yacht on Ch 16 or 2182 kHz to make contact. If no success, the call will be put on the Traffic List. If you are expecting a link call listen to the regular broadcasts of Traffic Lists by the nearest coast radio station (see 4.10.1).

It is also sensible to advise a CRS in advance of your route, ETA etc so that the nearest CRS will readily be able to contact you. This is known as Traffic Routing (TR); ask for a TR call.

If your yacht has a selective calling device (Selcall), you can be alerted by a coast radio station transmitting your Selcall number on Ch 16 or 2170·5 kHz. Some Selcall equipment displays the number of the station calling, but in practice when responding to a call, contact the nearest station to you.

If your vessel is subsequently contacted by other means (eg landline), a call via a coast radio station should always be cancelled.

4.5.6   Autolink RT

Autolink RT gives direct dialling from ship to shore into national and international telephone networks without going through a Coast radio station operator. It functions through an on-board unit which is easily connected to the radio, and which does not interfere with normal manual operation. This service on VHF, MF and HF gives quicker access, cheaper calls, call scrambling on some units where privacy is required, and simplified accounting. Last number redial and a ten-number memory store are available.

Do not use Autolink for Distress, Urgency and Safety (including medical) calls, but use the normal manual procedure on VHF Ch 16 or 2182 kHz.

4.6   SATELLITE COMMUNICATIONS

4.6.1   Inmarsat

The International Maritime Satellite Organisation (Inmarsat) provides satellite communication (Satcom) worldwide via satellites in geostationary orbits above the equator over the Atlantic, Pacific and Indian Oceans. Satcom is more reliable and gives better reception than HF SSB radio. The satellites are the link between Coast Earth Stations (CES) ashore, operated by organisations such as BT, and the ship-board terminals called Ship Earth Stations (SES).

For a shore-ship call, a CES connects the land-based communication network with the satellite system. The message originated on land is transmitted to a ship by one of the satellites. Conversely a ship-shore call is received, via the satellite, by the CES, which transmits it onwards over land-based networks.

Onboard ship (SES) there are several standards of terminal:

Standard 'A' terminals, with a big antenna only suitable for larger vessels, have direct dialling telephone, Telex, data and fax facilities.

Standard 'C' are smaller, and transmit/receive data or text (but not voice). Both 'A' and 'C' offer speedy connection to HM Coastguard's MRCC at Falmouth for Distress, Safety, etc.

More recently, Inmarsat 'B' was launched as an improved successor to Inmarsat 'A', while Standard 'M' now makes satellite telephone, fax and data services available to a wider range of yachts, using smaller and less expensive equipment.

4.7   PORT OPERATIONS and VTS

4.7.1   Port Operations

Most harbours and marinas use VHF R/T, while a few harbours also operate on MF (mainly for pilotage). The designated R/T channels are used solely for Port Operations or, in emergency, the safety of persons, but never for public correspondence, ie link calls and non-operational messages. Details of R/T at individual harbours are in this chapter; see also 8.0.3(k).

4.7.2   Vessel Traffic Services

An increasing number of ports are introducing Vessel Traffic Services (VTS) schemes, to improve the safety and efficiency of traffic and to protect the environment. VTS may range from the provision of information messages to the extensive management of traffic within a port or waterway, and is aimed primarily at commercial vessels which must comply with the laid down procedures.

Yachts do not normally have to comply with VTS reporting procedures, but at some ports larger yachts may come within the stipulated minimum length or tonnage.

When sailing in VTS areas valuable information about shipping movements can be obtained by listening to the VTS frequency, especially in reduced visibility. Yachts should seldom need to transmit on a VTS or port operations channel except perhaps in fog, when it may be advisable to inform port operations before crossing a busy shipping fairway. Recommended yacht tracks, if available, should be used in preference to the main fairway or deep water (DW) channel; Fig 4(1). If there is no recommended yacht track, it may be sensible to stay just outboard of the DW channel buoys.

C4

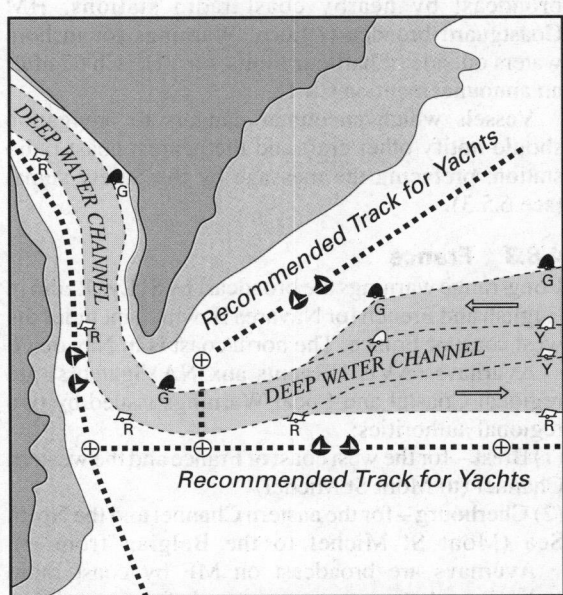

Fig 4(1) *Yachts should, whenever possible, use any recommended yachts tracks keeping well clear of the main shipping channels. If the main channels have to be crossed, do so heading at right angles. Avoid crossing ahead of oncoming commercial traffic.*

4.8   NAVIGATIONAL WARNINGS

4.8.1   General
A worldwide Navigational Warning Service covers 16 sea areas (Navareas I to XVI), each with a country nominated as Area Co-ordinator responsible for issuing long-range nav warnings. These are numbered consecutively through the year and are transmitted in English and other languages at scheduled times by RT, radiotelex and fax. Warnings cover failures or changes to navigational aids, wrecks and navigational dangers of all kinds, SAR operations, cable or pipe laying, naval exercises, etc.

Within each Navarea, Coastal Warnings and Local Warnings may also be issued. Coastal Warnings, up to 100 or 200 miles offshore, are broadcast in English and in the national language by coast radio stations. Local Warnings are issued by harbour authorities in the national language.

4.8.2   United Kingdom
The United Kingdom (together with Northern Europe and Scandinavia) is in Navarea 1. The UK is the Area Co-ordinator for long-range Navigational Warnings which are broadcast by Portishead Radio (GKA). Messages are numbered and are published in the weekly *Notices to Mariners* together with a list of warnings still in force. Warnings (see 6.6.6) are also broadcast by Navtex at Niton, Cullercoats, and Portpatrick Radio for the areas shown in Fig 5(1).

Coastal Warnings are broadcast by RT at scheduled times from coast radio stations for the Sea Regions lettered A-N in Fig 4(2). Important warnings are broadcast at any time on the Distress frequencies of 2182 kHz and VHF Ch 16

Local Warnings from harbour authorities are broadcast by nearby coast radio stations. HM Coastguard broadcasts Local Warnings for inshore waters outside of harbour limits, on VHF Ch 67 after an announcement on Ch 16.

Vessels which encounter dangers to navigation should notify other craft and the nearest coast radio station, prefacing the message by the Safety signal (see 6.5.3).

4.8.3   France
Long-range warnings are broadcast by St Lys Radio in English and French for Navarea II, which includes the west coast of France. The north coast is in Navarea I.

Avurnavs (AVis URgents aux NAVigateurs) are regional Coastal and Local Warnings issued by two regional authorities:
(1) Brest – for the west coast of France and the western Channel (to Mont St Michel)
(2) Cherbourg – for the eastern Channel and the North Sea (Mont St Michel to the Belgian frontier).

Avurnavs are broadcast on MF by coast radio stations; urgent ones on receipt and after next silence period, and at scheduled times (see 4.10.3). RT warnings are prefixed by *Sécurité Avurnav*, followed by the name of the station. Local warnings for coastal waters are broadcast in French and English by CROSS as follows:

CROSS	VHF Ch	Times (local)
Gris Nez	79	H+10
Jobourg	80	H+10 and +50
Corsen	79	H+10 and +40
Etel	80 (French only)	
Penmarc'h		0703 1903
Etel		0715 1915
St Nazaire		0733 1933
Sables d'Olonne		0745 1945
Soulac	80 (French only)	
Chassiron		0703 1903
Soulac		0715 1915
Cap Ferret		0733 1933
Contis		0745 1945
Biarritz		0803 2003

4.8.4   Belgium
Navigational Warnings are broadcast by Oostende Radio on receipt on 2761 kHz and VHF Ch 27 and at scheduled times (see 4.10.4) on 2761 kHz MF, 518 kHz (Navtex) and on Ch 27.

4.8.5   Netherlands
Navigational Warnings are no longer broadcast by Scheveningen Radio. Netherlands Coastguard broadcasts warnings on 518 kHz, IJmuiden Navtex (P), on receipt and at scheduled times (see 5.11.1).

4.8.6   Germany
Navigational Warnings (*Nautische Warnnachricht*) are no longer broadcast by Norddeich Radio. Broadcasts for the North Sea coast are contained in IJmuiden Navtex (P) transmissions. Decca Warnings for the German and Frisian Islands chains (*Decca Warnnachricht*) are included. Dangers to navigation should be reported to Seewarn Cuxhaven.

4.9   CROSS REFERENCES

4.9.1   Weather information by R/T
See Chapter 5.

4.9.2   Safety
Emergency messages (6.2), medical help by RT (6.5), GMDSS (6.6) and SAR (6.10 and 6.11) are all fully described in Chapter 6.

4.9.3   Navtex
A Navtex receiver prints, or displays electronically, navigational and meteorological warnings and other safety information. Navtex is the MSI component of GMDSS (see 6.6.6). Navtex is much used by yachtsmen for weather information; details are therefore to be found in Chapter 5, section 5.3.

Fig 4(2)   UK Coast Radio Stations

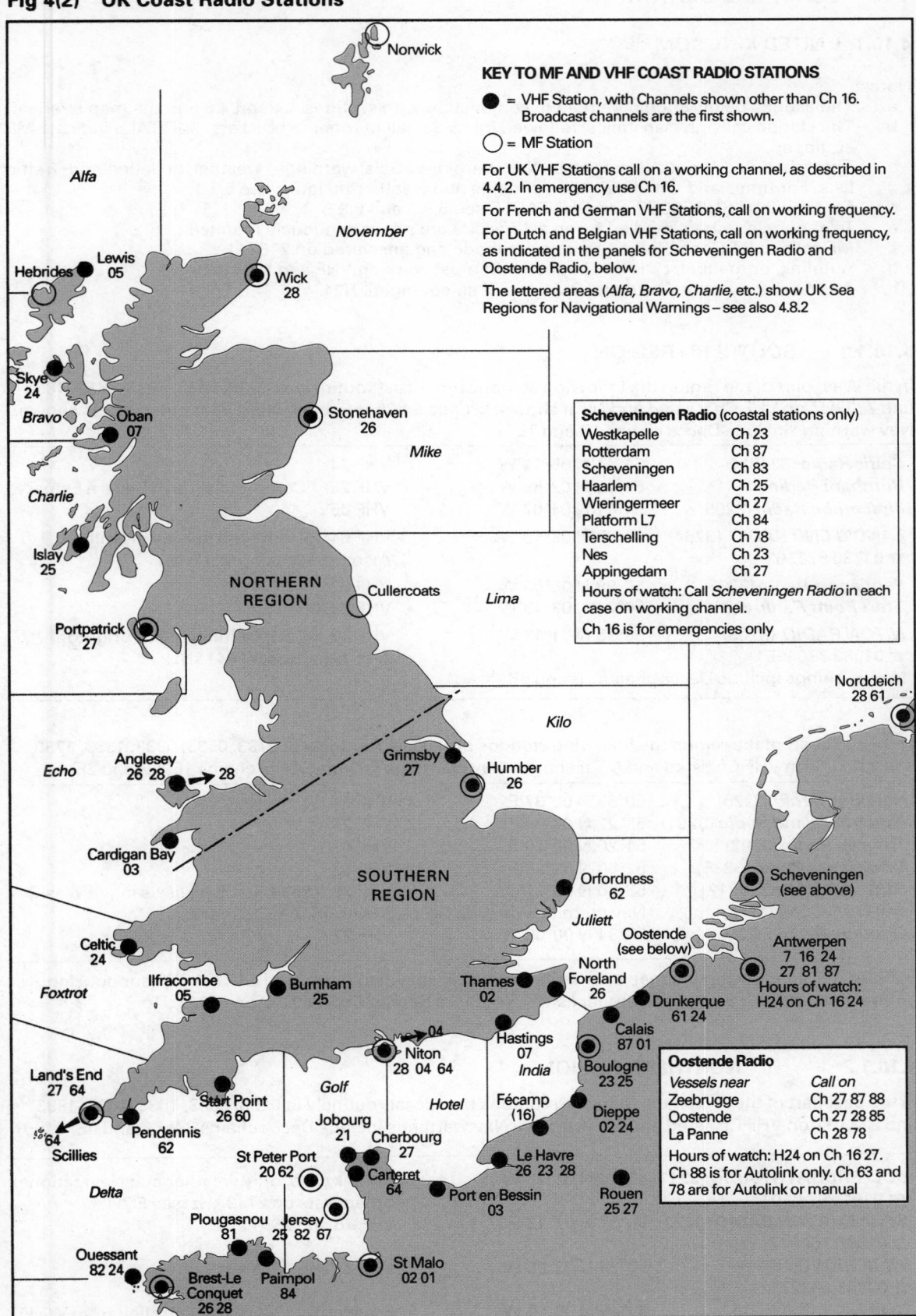

KEY TO MF AND VHF COAST RADIO STATIONS

● = VHF Station, with Channels shown other than Ch 16. Broadcast channels are the first shown.

○ = MF Station

For UK VHF Stations call on a working channel, as described in 4.4.2. In emergency use Ch 16.

For French and German VHF Stations, call on working frequency.

For Dutch and Belgian VHF Stations, call on working frequency, as indicated in the panels for Scheveningen Radio and Oostende Radio, below.

The lettered areas (*Alfa, Bravo, Charlie,* etc.) show UK Sea Regions for Navigational Warnings – see also 4.8.2

Scheveningen Radio (coastal stations only)	
Westkapelle	Ch 23
Rotterdam	Ch 87
Scheveningen	Ch 83
Haarlem	Ch 25
Wieringermeer	Ch 27
Platform L7	Ch 84
Terschelling	Ch 78
Nes	Ch 23
Appingedam	Ch 27

Hours of watch: Call *Scheveningen Radio* in each case on working channel.

Ch 16 is for emergencies only

Oostende Radio

Vessels near	*Call on*
Zeebrugge	Ch 27 87 88
Oostende	Ch 27 28 85
La Panne	Ch 28 78

Hours of watch: H24 on Ch 16 27. Ch 88 is for Autolink only. Ch 63 and 78 are for Autolink or manual

Map labels:

Norwick

Alfa

November

Hebrides
Lewis 05
Wick 28

Skye 24

Bravo
Oban 07
Stonehaven 26

Mike

Charlie

Islay 25

NORTHERN REGION

Cullercoats

Lima

Portpatrick 27

Norddeich 28 61

Kilo

Echo
Anglesey 26 28 → 28

Grimsby 27
Humber 26

Cardigan Bay 03

SOUTHERN REGION

Scheveningen (see above)

Celtic 24

Foxtrot

Ilfracombe 05
Burnham 25

Orfordness 62

Juliett

Oostende (see below)

North Foreland 26

Antwerpen 7 16 24 27 81 87
Hours of watch: H24 on Ch 16 24

Thames 02

Dunkerque 61 24

Hastings 07

Calais 87 01

Niton 28 04 64
→ 04

India

Boulogne 23 25

Land's End 27 64

Golf

Hotel

Fécamp (16)

Dieppe 02 24

Start Point 26 60

Jobourg 21

Cherbourg 27

Le Havre 26 23 28

←64
Scillies

Pendennis 62

St Peter Port 20 62

Carteret 64

Port en Bessin 03

Rouen 25 27

Delta

Plougasnou 81

Jersey 25 82 67

Ouessant 82 24

Brest-Le Conquet 26 28

Paimpol 84

St Malo 02 01

C4

4.10   COAST RADIO STATIONS

4.10.1. UNITED KINGDOM

Notes:
  a.   The listings below should be read in conjunction with sections 4.4 and 4.5 and the map overleaf.
  b.   The station callsign is in italics, followed by its Selcall number in brackets. CAPITALS indicate MF equipped.
  c.   The scheduled broadcasts contain Nav warnings, Gale warnings, weather bulletins and Traffic lists. For times and details of gale warnings and weather bulletins see 5.7.1.
  d.   For details of SUBFACTS and GUNFACTS see 6.9.2 and 6.9.3.
  e.   Telephone numbers marked by an asterisk (*) are not continuously manned.
  f.   MF calls to BT Coast Radio Stations are made and answered on 2182 kHz.
  g.   Autolink, or manual, calls can be made on most working VHF and MF channels.
  h.   All stations monitor Ch 16 and 2182 kHz, if so equipped, H24.

4.10.1.1   SOUTHERN REGION

In the West part of the region the following stations broadcast routinely at 0233, 0633, 1033, 1433, 1833 and 2233UT on VHF Ch's listed and MF if shown; broadcast Ch is in **bold** where more than one is shown. Nav warnings include Decca chains 1B and 7D.

Celtic Radio (3218)	51°41'N 05°11'W	VHF 24
Burnham Radio	51°13'N 02°59'W	VHF 25 Commercial tfc in Severn Estuary.
Ilfracombe Radio (3205)	51°11'N 04°07'W	VHF 05
LAND'S END RADIO (3204)	50°07'N 05°40'W	VHF 64; 27 (directed to Isles of Scilly)
☎ 01736 871363		Also broadcasts 2670 kHz.
Pendennis Radio (3238)	50°09'N 05°03'W	VHF 62
Start Point Radio (3224)	50°21'N 03°43'W	VHF **26**, 60
NITON RADIO (3203)	50°35'N 01°18'W	VHF **28**, 64, 85; 04 (directed to Brighton)
☎ 01983 730495*		Also broadcasts 1641 kHz.
Nav warnings include Decca chains 1B and 5B.		

In the East part of the region the following stations broadcast routinely at 0133, 0533, 0933, 1333, 1733 and 2133UT on VHF Ch listed and MF if shown. Nav warnings include Decca chains 1B, 5B and 2E.

Hastings Radio (3225)	50°52'N 00°37'E	VHF 07
North Foreland Radio (3201)	51°22'N 01°25'E	VHF 26
Thames Radio (3202)	51°20'N 00°20'E	VHF 02
Orfordness Radio (3235)	52°00'N 01°25'E	VHF 62
HUMBER RADIO (3212)	53°20'N 00°17'E	VHF 26, 1869 kHz; 85 (vessels in the Wash)
☎ 01507 473447*	Nav warnings include Decca chains 5B, 2A, 2E and 9B	
Grimsby Radio (3239)	53°34'N 00°05'W	VHF 27

SUBFACTS, announcing planned submarine activity in specified areas, and GUNFACTS announcing gunnery and missile firings, are broadcast by Southern Region CRS at 0733 and 1933UT.

4.10.1.2   NORTHERN REGION

In the East part of the region the following stations broadcast routinely at 0233, 0633, 1033, 1433, 1833 and 2233UT on VHF Ch listed and MF if shown. Nav warnings include Decca chains 2A, 6C and 0E.

CULLERCOATS RADIO (3211)	55°04'N 01°28'W	No link calls, only weather and Navigational broadcasts on 2719 kHz; see 5.7.1.
☎ 0191 297 0301*		
STONEHAVEN RADIO (3222)	56°57'N 02°13'W	VHF 26 and 2691 kHz
☎ 01569 762917		
WICK RADIO (3221)	58°26'N 03°06'W	VHF 28 and 1764 kHz
☎ 01955 602271*		
NORWICK, Shetland	60°49'N 00°49'W	Broadcasts 1770 kHz (controlled from Wick)

In the West part of the region the following stations broadcast routinely at 0203, 0603, 1003, 1403, 1803 and 2203UT on VHF Ch listed and MF if shown.

Lewis Radio (3216)	58°28'N 06°14'W	VHF 05
HEBRIDES RADIO (3234)	58°14'N 07°02'W	No VHF. Broadcasts on 1866 kHz include nav warnings on Decca chains 6C 8E
Skye Radio (3232)	57°28'N 06°41'W	VHF 24
Oban Radio (3207)	56°27'N 05°44'W	VHF 07
Islay Radio (3233)	55°46'N 06°27'W	VHF 25
PORTPATRICK RADIO (3207) ☎ 01776 810312*	54°51'N 05°07'W	VHF 27 and 1883 kHz. Broadcasts include nav warnings on Decca chains 3B, 7D and 8E.
Anglesey Radio (3206)	53°24'N 04°18'W	VHF **26**, 28
Cardigan Bay Radio (3241)	52°50'N 04°38'W	VHF 03

SUBFACTS, announcing planned submarine activity in specified areas, and GUNFACTS announcing gunnery and missile firings, are broadcast by Northern Region CRS at 0303, 0703, 1103, 1503, 1903 and 2303UT; but Wick, Cullercoats (2719kHz) and Stonehaven broadcast them only at 0703 and 1903.

4.10.1.3   CHANNEL ISLANDS

St Peter Port Radio and Jersey Radio are not operated by British Telecom, but by the States of Guernsey and of Jersey respectively.

ST PETER PORT RADIO ☎ 01481 720672	49°27'N 02°32'W	VHF **20**; 62 (link calls only); 67 (on request, for yacht safety calls); Call direct Ch 20, 62.

Broadcasts on Ch 20, 62 and 1764 kHz at 0133, 0533, 0933, 1333, 1733 and 2133UT include nav warnings and Traffic Lists. Payment for link calls must be by AAIC; YTD billing is not acceptable (see 4.5.1.2).

JERSEY RADIO ☎ 01534 41121	49°11'N 02°14'W	VHF **82**; 25 (link calls only); 67 (on request, for yacht safety calls); Call direct Ch 82, 25.

MMSI 002320060; DSC Ch 70.
Broadcasts on Ch 25, 82 and 1659 kHz at 0645†, 0745†, 1245, 1845 and 2245UT include weather messages, nav warnings and Traffic Lists. † 1 hour earlier when DST in force. Nav warnings are additionally broadcast at 0433, 0833, 1633 and 2033UT. Decca warnings for Chain 1B are broadcast on receipt and at H+03 for the next two hours. See 5.7.1 for details and times of gale warnings and weather broadcasts. Payment for link calls can be by: credit card; direct bill to UK address; to any Jersey Harbour Office account (contact Finance Dept on ☎ 01534 885511); or on arrival through a contact address.

4.10.1.4   PORTISHEAD RADIO

Located at Highbridge (Somerset), Portishead provides world-wide HF facilities for link calls by/to ships; see 4.3.2 and 4.5.4 for notes on HF radio and operating procedures. Below are listed the R/T calling channels in the 4, 8, 12, 16 and 22MHz bands. Often working will also be conducted on these channels, due to the reduction in traffic caused by the increased use of satellite communications. Portishead Radio may close in 1999. ☎ +44 (0) 1278 772200 or 0800 378389. 📠 +44 (0) 1278 792145.

	Radiotelephone HF duplex channels (carrier frequencies kHz)			
Call sign	International channel	Portishead carrier	Ship carrier	
GKT20	410	4384	4092	Main channel
GKU46	816	8764	8240	Main channel
GKV54	1224	13146	12299	Main channel
GKT62	1602	17245	16363	Main channel
GKT18	1801	19755	18780	Main channel
GKT76	2206	22711	22015	Main channel
GKU25	2502	26148	25073	Main channel

NOTE: Portishead Radio monitors H24 the above channels/frequencies, on which vessels should make their initial call. Usually higher frequencies are monitored by day and lower at night. All frequencies are J3E and R3E, power 10kW. These channels are also used for the broadcast of Distress, Urgency, Safety signals and Traffic Lists, the latter every H+00. Frequencies in use are announced after the Traffic Lists.

C4

4.10.2   IRISH COAST RADIO STATIONS

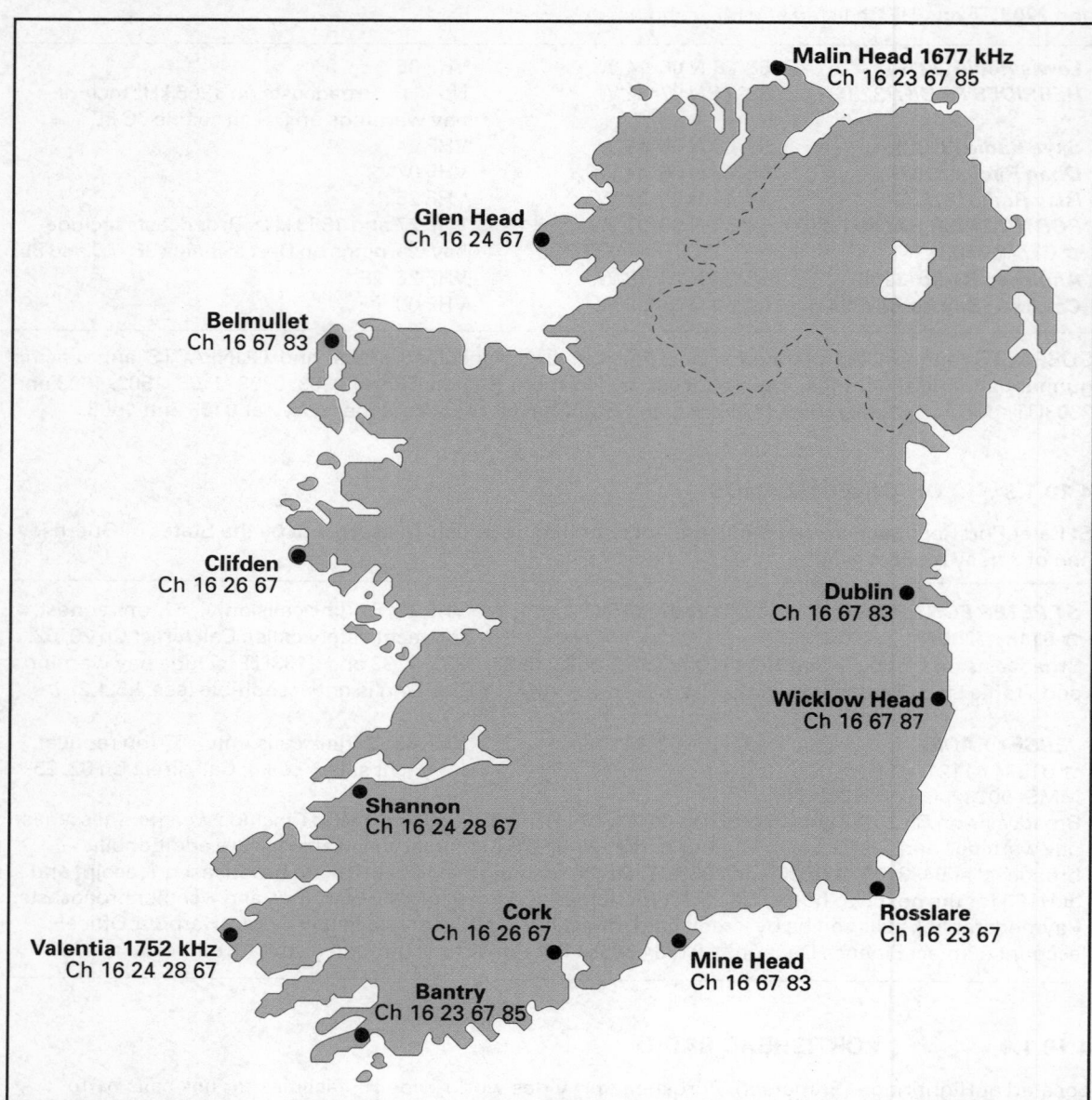

Malin Head 1677 kHz
Ch 16 23 67 85

Glen Head
Ch 16 24 67

Belmullet
Ch 16 67 83

Clifden
Ch 16 26 67

Dublin
Ch 16 67 83

Wicklow Head
Ch 16 67 87

Shannon
Ch 16 24 28 67

Cork
Ch 16 26 67

Rosslare
Ch 16 23 67

Valentia 1752 kHz
Ch 16 24 28 67

Bantry
Ch 16 23 67 85

Mine Head
Ch 16 67 83

Fig 4(3) Irish Coast Radio Stations

4.10.2.1   Irish Coast Radio Service

This service is provided by the Department of the Marine, Leeson Lane, Dublin 2. ☎ +353 (0)1 785444; ext 670 for enquiries. Traffic Lists, navigational warnings, Decca warnings, weather forecasts and gale warnings are broadcast at the scheduled times shown in the table. See 5.8.2 for times and details of Gale warnings and weather bulletins. Broadcasts are made on a working channel/frequency following a preliminary announcement on Ch 16 and 2182 kHz. Ch 67 is used for Safety messages only.

VHF calls to a coast radio station should be made on a working channel. Only use Ch 16 in case of difficulty, or in emergency. Link calls from ship-shore are available on VHF or MF.

For telephone calls from shore subscribers to ships at sea, ships should first advise Malin Head or Valentia Radio by telephone of the vessel's intended voyage or whereabouts. Ships at sea should pass a track report (TR) to the nearest coast radio station updating their voyage details. They should also listen to Traffic List broadcasts.

4.10.2.2   The following stations in North-West and South-East Ireland broadcast routinely at 0033, 0433, 0833, 1233, 1633 and 2033UT on VHF Ch's listed; broadcast Ch is in **bold** where more than one is shown. Nav warnings include Decca chains 3B, 7D and 8E. Traffic Lists: Every odd H+03 (not 0303 0703).

Clifden Radio	53°30'N 09°56'W	VHF 26
Belmullet Radio	54°16'N 10°03'W	VHF 83
Glen Head Radio	54°44'N 08°43'W	VHF 24
MALIN HEAD RADIO	55°22'N 07°21'W	VHF **23**, 85 and 1677 kHz.
☎ 353 77 70103	MMSI 002500100.	DSC: 2187·5 kHz
Dublin Radio	53°23'N 06°04'W	VHF 83
Wicklow Head Radio	52°58'N 06°00'W	VHF 87
Rosslare Radio	52°15'N 06°20'W	VHF 23
Mine Head Radio	52°00'N 07°35'W	VHF 83

4.10.2.3   The following stations in South-West Ireland broadcast routinely at 0233, 0633, 1033, 1433, 1833 and 2233UT on VHF Ch's listed; broadcast Ch is in **bold** where more than one is shown. Nav warnings include Decca chains 1B and 7D. Traffic Lists: Every odd H+33 (not 0133 0533).

Cork Radio	51°51'N 08°29'W	VHF 26
Bantry Radio	51°38'N 10°00'W	VHF **23**, 85
VALENTIA RADIO	51°56'N 10°21'W	VHF **24**, 28 and 1752 kHz.
☎ 353 667 6109	MMSI 002500200.	DSC: 2187·5 kHz
Shannon Radio	52°31'N 09°36'W	VHF 24, **28**

C4

4.10.3 FRENCH COAST RADIO STATIONS

Notes:

a)   VHF Ch 16 is monitored H24 and is reserved solely for Distress and Safety traffic.

b)   Make initial call on working channel, H24. Station callsign is in italics and Selcall number in ( ). CAPITALS indicate MF equipped; initial call should be on the foreign ship frequencies shown.

c)   VHF channels in brackets are Automatic VHF for suitably equipped ships (H24), ship-shore only.

d)   Weather bulletins are broadcast in French at 0733 & 1533 LT on italicised VHF channels. For details see 5.9.3. For details of MF weather bulletins see 5.9.4.

e)   VHF channels of coast radio stations do not broadcast Traffic Lists or Navigation Warnings. MF coast radio stations broadcast coastal and local Navigation Warnings as AVURNAVS (see 4.4.23) after announcements on 2182 kHz. All times are UT.

BELGIAN BORDER TO CAP DE LA HAGUE

Dunkerque Radio	51°02'N 02°24'E	VHF 24, *61*, (86)
Calais Radio	50°55'N 01°43'E	VHF 01, *87*, (60), (62)
BOULOGNE RADIO (1641)	50°43'N 01°37'E	VHF 23, 25, (64), (81).
☎ 03·21·33·25·26		MF: foreign ships call on 2045, 2048 kHz.

Traffic lists are broadcast on 1770 kHz every odd H+03 (UT). Nav warnings are broadcast on 1692 and 3795 kHz in French and **English** on receipt and every 4 hrs from 0133.

Dieppe Radio	49°55'N 01°03'E	VHF *02*, 24, (61)
Fécamp Radio	49°46'N 00°22'E	VHF (31), (37), (65), (78), (99). No broadcasts.
Le Havre Radio	49°31'N 00°04'E	VHF 23, *26*, 28, (62), (84)
Rouen Radio	49°27'N 01°02'E	VHF 25, 27, (01), (86). No broadcasts.
Port-en-Bessin Radio	49°20'N 00°42'W	VHF *03*, (60), (66)
Cherbourg Radio	49°38'N 01°36'W	VHF *27*, (86)
Jobourg Radio	49°43'N 01°56'W	VHF 21, (83). No broadcasts.

CAP DE LA HAGUE TO OUESSANT

Carteret Radio	49°23'N 01°47'W	VHF 64, (23), (88). No broadcasts.
Saint Malo Radio	48°38'N 02°02'W	VHF 01, *02*, (78), (85)
Paimpol Radio	48°45'N 02°59'W	VHF *84*, (87)
Plougasnou Radio	48°42'N 03°48'W	VHF *81*, (03).
BREST-LE CONQUET RADIO	48°20'N 04°44'W	VHF 26, 28, (23), (64).
☎ 02·98·89·17·89 (1643)		MF: foreign ships call on 2045, 2048 kHz.

Traffic lists are broadcast on 1635 kHz (Le Conquet) and 2691 kHz (Saint Malo) every even H+03. Nav warnings are broadcast on 1671, 1876 and 2691 kHz in French and **English** on receipt and every 4 hrs from 033; local nav warnings in French only at 0733 and 1803.

Ouessant Radio	48°27'N 05°05'W	VHF 24, *82*, (61)

OUESSANT TO SPANISH BORDER

Pont l'Abbé Radio	47°53'N 04°13'W	VHF *86*, (63), (66)
Belle Île Radio	47°21'N 03°09'W	VHF 05, *25*, (65), (87)
ST NAZAIRE RADIO	47°21'N 02°06'W	VHF 23, 24, (04), (88).
☎ 02·98·43·63·63 (1645)		MF: foreign ships call on 2045, 2048 kHz.

Traffic lists are broadcast on 1686 kHz every odd H+07. Nav warnings are broadcast on 1686, 1722 and 2740 kHz in French on receipt, after next silence period and at 0733 and 1803 for Bay of Biscay north of 46°30'N and east of 4°W.

St Herblain Radio	47°13'N 01°37'W	VHF *28*, (03)
St Hilaire de Riez Radio	46°43'N 01°57'W	VHF *27*, (62), (85)
Île de Ré Radio	46°12'N 01°22'W	VHF *21*, 26, (01), (81)
Royan Radio	45°34'N 00°58'W	VHF *23*, 25, (02), (83)
Bordeaux Radio	44°53'N 00°30'W	VHF *27*, (62), (85)
BORDEAUX-ARCACHON RADIO (1645)	44°39'N 01°10'W	VHF 28, 82, (78), (86).
		MF: foreign ships call on 2045, 2048 kHz.

Nav warnings are broadcast on 1862 kHz in French and **English** on receipt, after next silence period and every 4hrs from 0333; local nav warnings in French only at 0733 and 1803. *Gunfire Warnings:* for Landes firing range on 1635 kHz at 0733 for current day and at 1803 for next day; see also 8.18.25.

Bayonne Radio	43°16'N 01°24'W	VHF *24*, (03), (64)

Fig 4(4) French Coast Radio Stations. See also Fig 4(2)

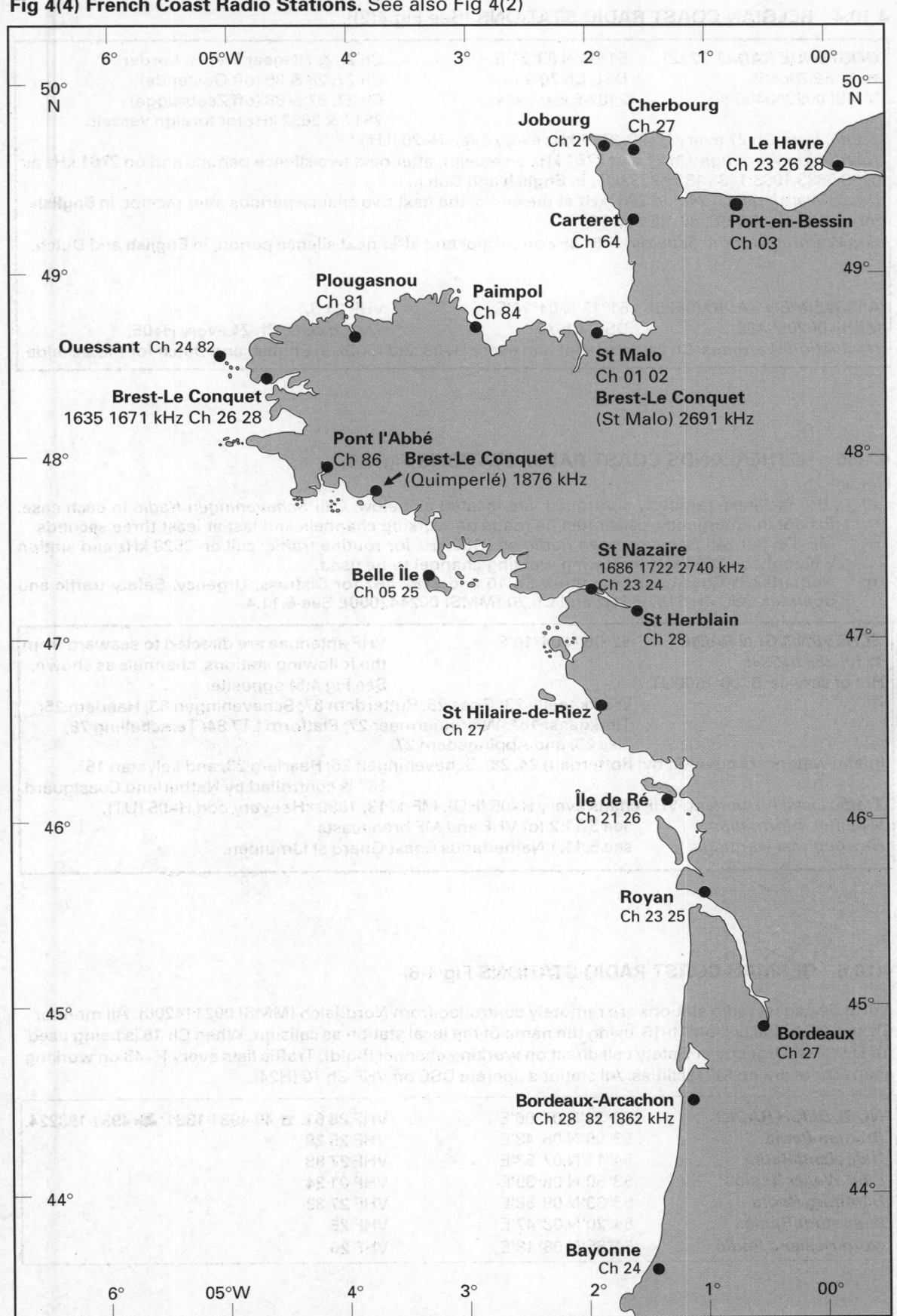

C4

4.10.4 BELGIAN COAST RADIO STATIONS (See Fig 4(2))

OOSTENDE RADIO (3222)   51°06'N 03°21'E   Ch 28 & 78 (near French border),
☎ *32 59 706565*   DSC Ch 70 and   Ch 27, 28 & 85 (off Oostende)
MMSI 002050480   2187·5 kHz (H24)   Ch 27, 87 & 88 (off Zeebrugge)
   2817 & 3632 kHz for foreign vessels.
Traffic Lists: Ch 27 every H+20. 2761 kHz every even H+20 (UT).
Navigation Warnings: Ch 27 and 2761 kHz on receipt, after next two silence periods and on 2761 kHz at:
0233 0633 1033 1433 1833 2233UT, in **English** and Dutch.
Decca Warnings: Ch 27 and 2761kHz at the end of the next two silence periods after receipt, in **English**
for chains 5B, 2A, 6C, 8E, 2E and 9B.
Fog Warnings for the Schelde: 2761 kHz on receipt and after next silence period, in **English** and Dutch.

ANTWERPEN RADIO (0485)   51°17'N 04°20'E   VHF 24 *87*
MMSI 002050485.   DSC Ch 70   *Traffic Lists:* Ch 24 every H+05.
Navigation Warnings: Ch 24 on receipt and every H+03 and H+48, in English and Dutch for the Schelde.

4.10.5 NETHERLANDS COAST RADIO STATIONS Fig 4(5)

Notes:
a)   VHF facilities, remotely controlled, are located as below. Call *Scheveningen Radio* in each case.
Except in emergency, calls must be made on working channels and last at least three seconds.
MF: Do not call *Scheveningen Radio* on 2182 kHz for routine traffic; call on 2520 kHz and station
will reply on 2824 kHz indicating working channel to be used.
b)   Netherlands Coastguard monitors Ch 16 and 2182 kHz for Distress, Urgency, Safety traffic and
operates DSC on 2187·5 kHz and Ch 70 (MMSI 002442000). See 6.11.4.

SCHEVENINGEN RADIO   52°06'N 04°16'E   VHF antennae are directed to seaward from
☎ *(0) 255 545345*   the following stations, channels as shown.
Hrs of service: 0700-1500UT.   See Fig 4(5) opposite:
   Westkapelle 23; Goes 25; Rotterdam 87; Scheveningen 83; Haarlem 25;
   Tjerkgaast 16*; Wieringermeer 27; Platform LT7 84; Terschelling 78;
   Nes 23, and Appingedam 27.
Inland waters are covered by: Rotterdam 24, **28**; Scheveningen 26; Haarlem 23, and Lelystad 16*.
   16* is controlled by Netherland Coastguard.
Traffic Lists: All working VHF chans every H+05 (HO). MF 1713, 1890 kHz every odd H+05 (UT).
Weather information: see 5.11.2 for VHF and MF broadcasts.
Navigational warnings: see 5.11.1 Netherlands Coast Guard at IJmuiden.

4.10.6 GERMAN COAST RADIO STATIONS Fig 4(6)

North Sea coast radio stations are remotely controlled from Norddeich (MMSI 002114200). All monitor
Ch 16 H24. Initial call on Ch 16 using the name of the local station as callsign. When Ch 16 is being used
for Distress, Urgency or Safety call direct on **working** channel (bold). Traffic lists every H+45 on working
chan. There are no MF facilities. All stations operate DSC on VHF Ch 70 (H24).

NORDDEICH RADIO	53°34'N 07°06'E	VHF 28 **61**. ☎ 49 4931 1831; ⌨ 4931 183224.
Bremen Radio	53°05'N 08°48'E	VHF 25 **28**
Helgoland Radio	54°11'N 07°53'E	VHF **27** 88
Elbe-Weser Radio	53°50'N 08°39'E	VHF 01 **24**
Hamburg Radio	53°33'N 09°58'E	VHF **27** 83
Eiderstedt Radio	54°20'N 08°47'E	VHF **25**
Nordfriesland Radio	54°55'N 08°18'E	VHF **26**

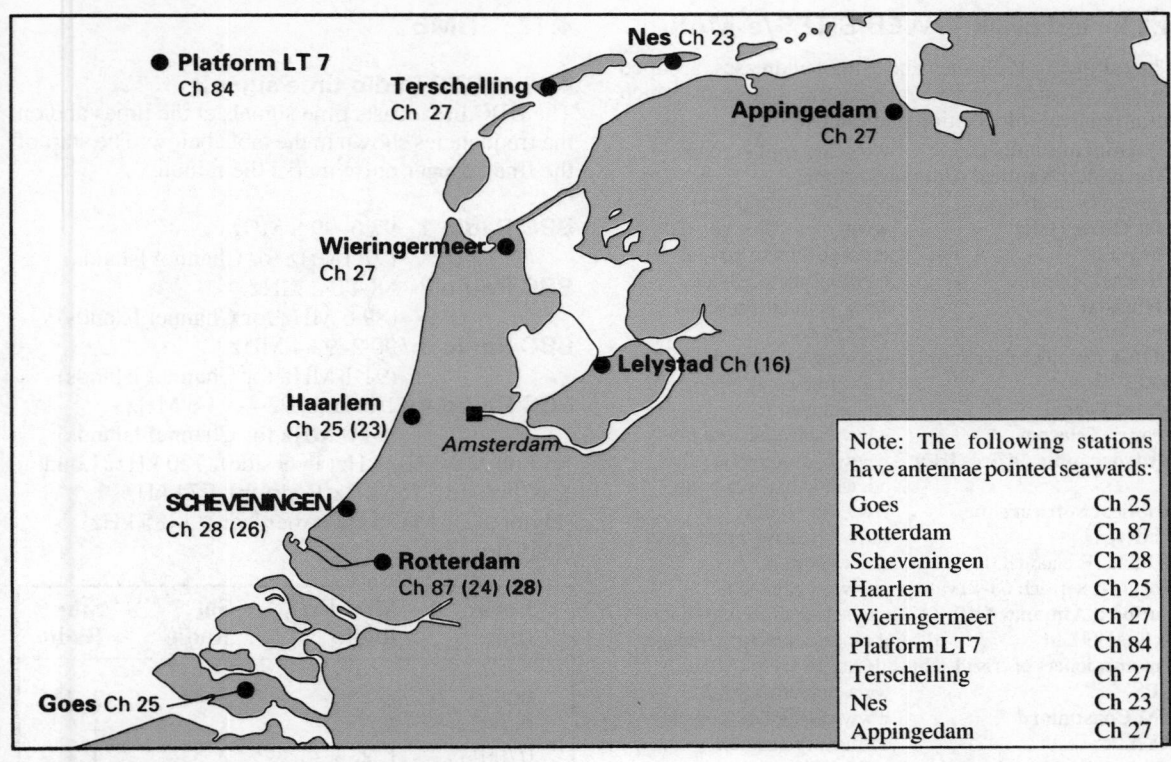

Fig 4(5) Netherlands Coast Radio Stations.
Channel numbers in brackets are for use on inland waterways.

C4

Fig 4(6) German Coast Radio Stations

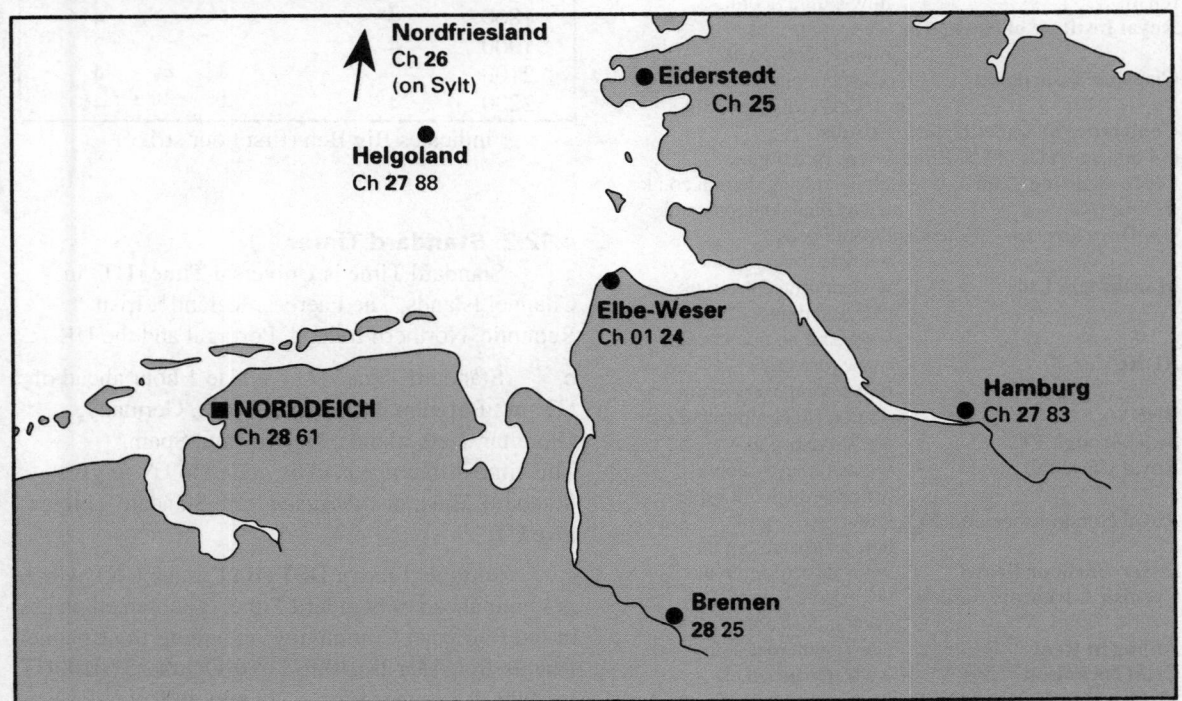

4.11   INTERNET/WEB SITES/e-MAIL

The following Web sites and e-mail addresses, grouped broadly by subject, are amongst the thousands which offer nautical information and interest:

Macmillan Publishers	www.macmillan.co.uk
Macmillan Nautical Almanac, Editor	
Neville Featherstone	MacAlman@aol.com

Met Office (UK) www.met-office.gov.uk
MetWEB metweb@meto.gov.uk
MetFAX Helpline metfax@meto.gov.uk
Meteostat www.nottingham.ac.uk/meteostat
NOAA (weather data buoys) www.nws.fsu.edu/buoy
BBC www.bbc.co.uk
Meteo France www.meteo.fr
France Telecom www.francetelecom.fr
Hydrographic Office (UK) www.hydro.gov.uk
hdc@hdc.hydro.gov.uk
Nautical Software inc www.tides.com
ColRegs www.wyenavigation.co.uk
SHOM (French HO) www.shom.fr
Royal Greenwich Observatory www.ast.cam.ac.uk
National Almanac Office nao@ast.cam.ac.uk/~nao/
Eclipse 99 Ltd ds.dial.pipex.comeclipse99page
Commissioners of Irish Lights cil@iol.ie
GPS www.navcen.uscg.mil
HM Coastguard www.coastguard.gov.uk
RYA admin@rya.org.uk
Marine Accident Investigation Board
maib.detr@gtnet.gov.uk
Sail Scotland www.sailscotland.co.uk
British Waterways www.bwscotcanals.uk.com
Caledonian MacBrayne www.calmac.co.uk
Electronic Telegraph www.telegraph.co.uk
Yachting Monthly, Yachting World, Practical Boat Owner, Motor Boat and Yachting: www.ybw.com
ybw@ipc.co.uk
Sailing Today sailingtoday@futurenet.co.uk
Imray, L, N & W Ltd www.imray.com
(charts & books) ilnw@imray.com
Royal Institute of Navigat'n www.rin.org.uk
rindir@atlas.co.uk
Cruising Association www.cruising.org.uk
office@cruising.org.uk
Conference of Yacht Cruising Clubs
(14 cruising YCs in UK/Eire) www.cycc.org.uk
Clyde Cruising Club www.clydecruising.demon.co.uk
YCs in UK www.allena.demon.co.uk
UK Hbrs directory (Solent and south coast)
www.harbours.co.uk
MarineData Ltd www.marinedata.co.uk
uk.rec.sailing
www.sailingindex.com
RORC www.rorc.org
rorc@compuserve.com
RNSA //ourworld.compuserve.com
Scarborough YC www.syc.org.uk
Royal Cork YC www.iol.ie/royalcork
office@royalcork.iol.ie
Royal Northumberland YC www.rnyc.org.uk
hon.sec@rnyc.org.uk
Dover Harbour Board www.doverport.co.uk
Cornish Adventure Sailing www.sailcas.com
cas@sailcas.com
Sailing in Kent www.btinternet.com
Crest Nicholson www.aboard.co.uk
Marina Developments Ltd www.marinas.co.uk

4.12   TIME

4.12.1 BBC Radio time signals
The BBC broadcasts time signals at the times and on the frequencies shown in the table below. The start of the final, longer pulse marks the minute.

BBC Radio 1 97·6–99·8 MHz
(97·1MHz for Channel Islands)
BBC Radio 2 88–90·2 MHz
(89·6 MHz for Channel Islands)
BBC Radio 3 90·2–92·4 MHz
(91·1 MHz for Channel Islands)
BBC Radio 4 198 kHz, 92·4–94·6 MHz
(94·8 MHz for Channel Islands)
And on MW: 603 kHz(Tyneside); 720 kHz (London & N Ireland); 756 kHz(Redruth); 774 kHz (Plymouth); 1449 kHz (Aberdeen); 1485 kHz (Carlisle).

Local time	Mon-Fri Radio	Sat Radio	Sun Radio
0000	2, 4*	2, 4*	2, 4*
0600	4	3	4
0700	1, 2, 3, 4	2, 3, 4	4
0800	1, 2, 3, 4	2, 4	2, 4
0900	4		2, 4
1000	4	4	
1100	4	4	
1200	4		
1300	2, 4	1, 4	4
1400	4	4	
1500	4		
1600	4	4	
1700	2, 4		4
1800	4*	4*	4*
1900	4		2
2100			4
2200	4	4*	4*

* indicates Big Ben (first hour strike)

4.12.2 Standard Times
a.   Standard Time is Universal Time (UT) in: Channel Islands, The Faeroes, Iceland*, Irish Republic, Northern Ireland, Portugal and the UK.

b.   Standard Time is UT + 1, ie 1 hour ahead of UT, in : Belgium, Denmark, France, Germany, Gibraltar, Netherlands, Norway and Spain.
This time difference is to be *added* to UT to give Standard Time, or *subtracted* from Standard Time to give UT.

c.   Summer time or DST (BST in the UK), which is 1 hour ahead of Standard Time, is kept in all places in the European Community, including the Channel Islands, from Mar 28 0100UT until October 31 0100UT in 1999. * Summer time is not kept in Iceland.

Chapter 5
Weather

Contents

5.1	**GENERAL WEATHER**	
	INFORMATION	**Page 82**
5.1.1	Shipping forecast: map and record	
5.1.2	Beaufort wind scale	84
5.1.3	Barometer and temperature scales	
5.1.4	Meaning of weather terms	

SOURCES OF WEATHER INFORMATION

5.2	**Radio broadcasting**	86
5.2.1	BBC Radio 4 shipping forecasts	
5.2.2	BBC inshore waters forecasts	
5.2.3	BBC land forecasts	
5.2.4	UK Local Radio Stations	

5.3	**Navtex**	86
5.3.1	Introduction	
5.3.2	Messages	
5.3.3	Message categories	
5.3.4	Stations	

5.4	**Telephone and Fax**	88
5.4.1	Recorded weather by 'phone (Marinecall)	
5.4.2	Weather by fax (MetFAX Marine)	
5.4.3	HF Radio facsimile broadcasts	

5.5	**Forecasters**	90
5.5.1	Weather Centres	
5.5.2	Forecaster access (MetCALL Direct)	

5.6	**Miscellaneous sources**	90
5.6.1	HM Coastguard	
5.6.2	Internet	
5.6.3	Press forecasts	
5.6.4	TV forecasts	
5.6.5	Volmet	
5.6.6	Met Offices and lighthouses	
5.6.7	Visual storm signals	

5.7	**UK Coast Radio Stations**	91
5.7.1	Weather messages	
Table 5(1)	Local radio stations	92
Fig 5(4)	Map of present weather stations	94

5.8	**Eire: Broadcasting and CRS**	95
5.8.1	RTE broadcasting	
5.8.2	Irish Coast Radio Stations	
Fig 5(5)	Map of Irish weather services	

5.9	**France: Broadcasting and CRS**	96
Fig 5(6)	French shipping forecast areas	

5.10	**Belgium**	98

5.11	**Netherlands**	98
Fig 5(7	N Sea shipping forecast areas	99

5.12	**Germany**	
	Broadcasting and CRS	100

C5

Summary

This chapter gives basic information on the contents of forecasts and terminology of meteorology. It also details the many sources of weather information available to yachtsmen in European waters.

Additional information on the weather and its interpretation can be found in Chapter 7 of *The Macmillan & Silk Cut Yachtsman's Handbook* where the following subjects are described in more detail:

Transfer of heat; world weather; air masses; atmospheric pressure; wind; humidity; clouds; depressions and fronts; the passage of a depression; anticyclones; fog; sea and land breezes; thunderstorms; tropical storms; glossary of meteorological terms; forecasting your own weather; bibliography.

5.1   GENERAL WEATHER INFORMATION

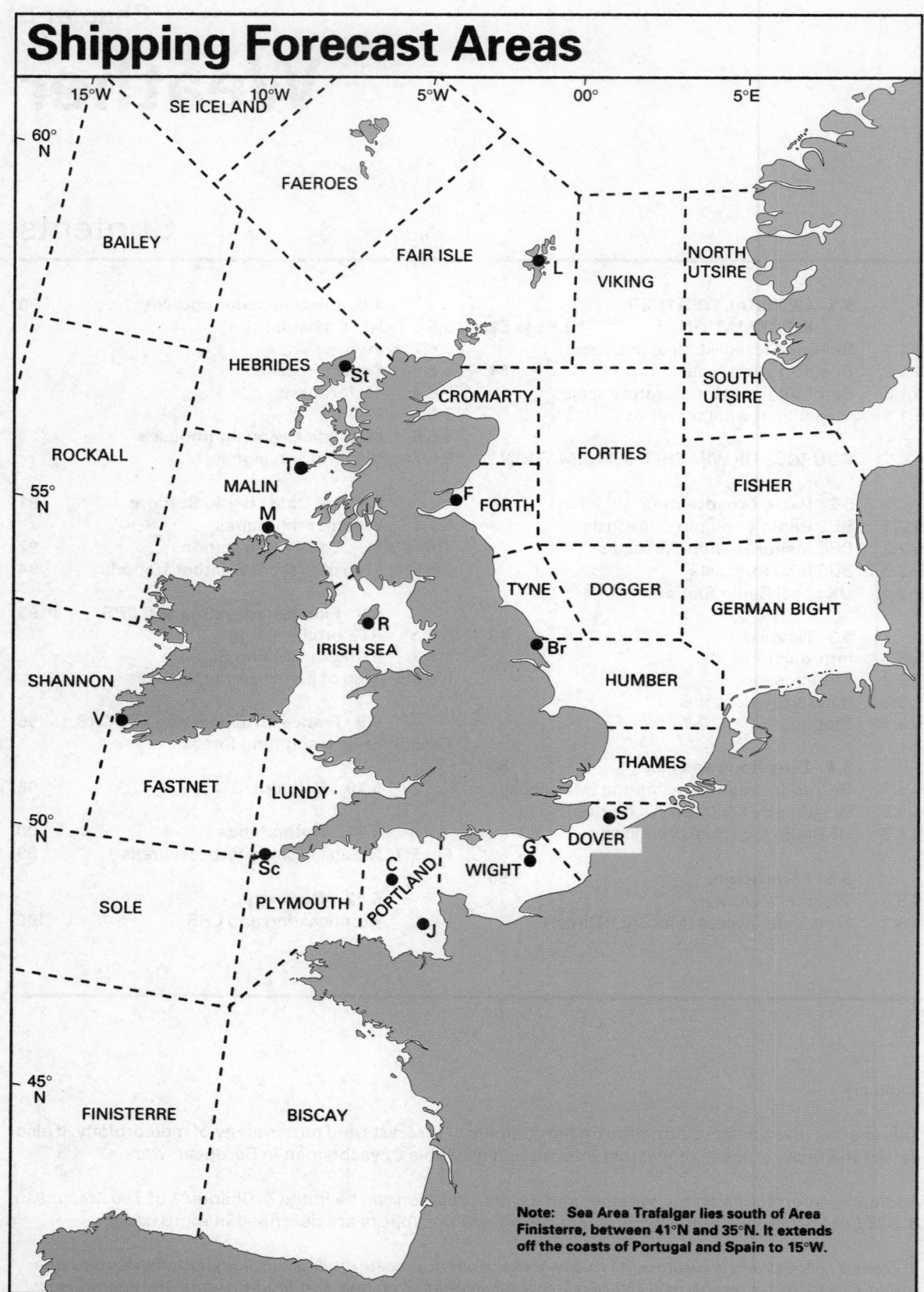

Shipping Forecast Areas

5.1.1 Map of UK shipping forecast areas

5.1.1 continued

Shipping Forecast Record   Time/Day/Date ....

GENERAL SYNOPSIS   at .... UT/BST

System	Present position	Movement	Forecast position	at

Gales	SEA AREA FORECAST	Wind (At first)	(Later)	Weather	Visibility
	VIKING				
	NORTH UTSIRE				
	SOUTH UTSIRE				
	FORTIES				
	CROMARTY				
	FORTH				
	TYNE				
	DOGGER				
	FISHER				
	GERMAN BIGHT				
	HUMBER				
	THAMES				
	DOVER				
	WIGHT				
	PORTLAND				
	PLYMOUTH				
	BISCAY				
	FINISTERRE				
	SOLE				
	LUNDY				
	FASTNET				
	IRISH SEA				
	SHANNON				
	ROCKALL				
	MALIN				
	HEBRIDES				
	BAILEY				
	FAIR ISLE				
	FAEROES				
	S E ICELAND				

COASTAL REPORTS at .... BST UT	Wind Direction	Force	Weather	Visibility	Pressure	Change
Tiree (T)						
Stornoway (St)						
Lerwick (L)						
Fife Ness (F)						
Bridlington (Br)						
Sandettié LV auto(S)						

COASTAL REPORTS	Wind Direction	Force	Weather	Visibility	Pressure	Change
Greenwich LV auto(G)						
Jersey (J)						
Channel LV auto (C)						
Scilly auto (Sc)						
Valentia (V)						
Ronaldsway (R)						
Malin Head (M)						

C5

5.1.2   Beaufort wind scale

Force	Wind speed (knots)	(km/h)	(m/sec)	Description	State of sea	Probable wave ht (m)
0	0–1	0–2	0–0·5	Calm	Like a mirror	0
1	1–3	2–6	0·5–1·5	Light air	Ripples like scales are formed	0·1
2	4–6	7–11	2–3	Light breeze	Small wavelets, still short but more pronounced, not breaking	0·2
3	7–10	13–19	4–5	Gentle breeze	Large wavelets, crests begin to break; a few white horses	0·4
4	11–16	20–30	6–8	Moderate breeze	Small waves growing longer; fairly frequent white horses	1
5	17–21	31–39	8–11	Fresh breeze	Moderate waves, taking more pronounced form; many white horses, perhaps some spray	2
6	22–27	41–50	11–14	Strong breeze	Large waves forming; white foam crests more extensive; probably some spray	3
7	28–33	52–61	14–17	Near gale	Sea heaps up; white foam from breaking waves begins to blow in streaks	4
8	34–40	63–74	17–21	Gale	Moderately high waves of greater length; edge of crests break into spindrift; foam blown in well-marked streaks	5·5
9	41–47	76–87	21–24	Severe gale	High waves with tumbling crests; dense streaks of foam; spray may affect visibility	7
10	48–55	89–102	25–28	Storm	Very high waves with long overhanging crests; dense streams of foam make surface of sea white. Heavy tumbling sea; visibility affected	9
11	56–63	104–117	29–33	Violent storm	Exceptionally high waves; sea completely covered with long white patches of foam; edges of wave crests blown into froth. Visibility affected	11
12	64 plus	118 plus	33 plus	Hurricane	Air filled with foam and spray; sea completely white with driving spray; visibility very seriously affected	14

Notes: (1) The state of sea and probable wave heights are a guide to what may be expected in the open sea, away from land. In enclosed waters, or near land with an offshore wind, wave heights will be less but the waves possibly steeper, particularly with wind against tide.

(2) The height of sea for a given wind strength depends upon the fetch and the length of time for which the wind has been blowing.

5.1.3   Barometer and temperature conversion scales

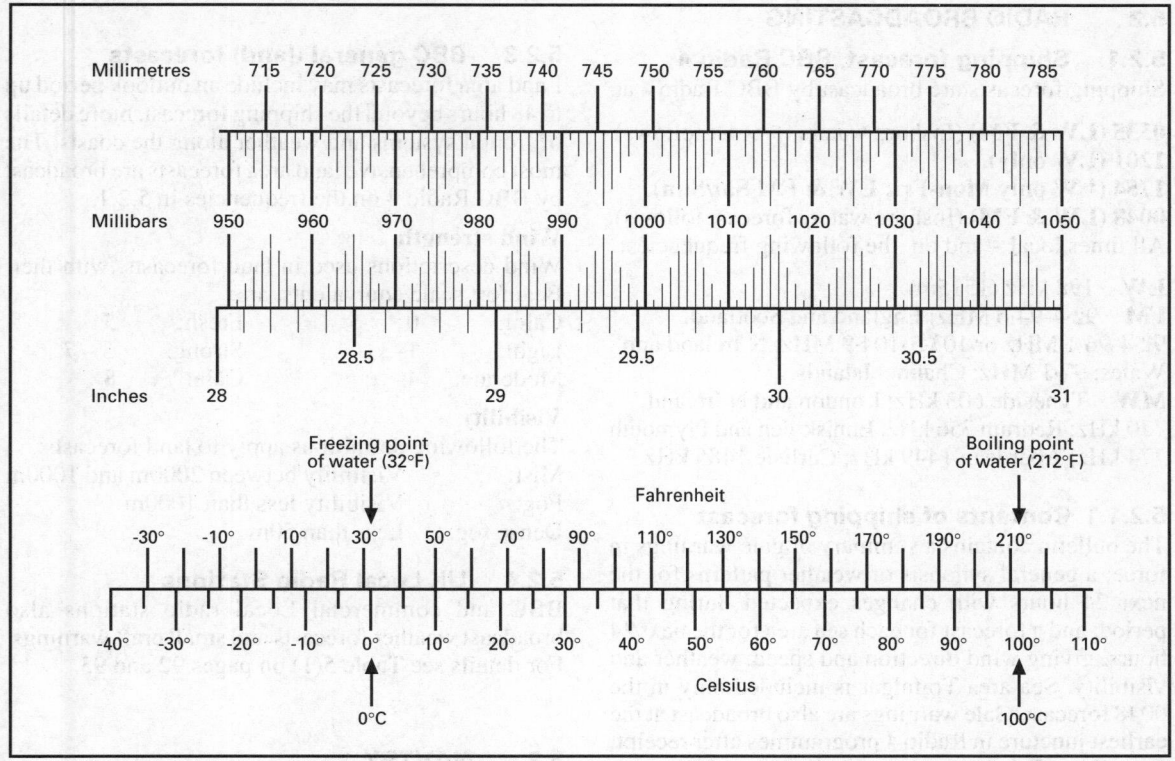

5.1.4   Meaning of terms used in weather bulletins

a.   Speed of movement of pressure systems

Slowly:	Moving at less than 15 knots
Steadily:	Moving at 15 to 25 knots
Rather quickly:	Moving at 25 to 35 knots
Rapidly:	Moving at 35 to 45 knots
Very rapidly:	Moving at more than 45 knots

b.   Visibility

Good:	More than 5 miles
Moderate:	2 – 5 miles
Poor:	1000 metres – 2 miles
Fog:	Less than 1000 metres

c.   Barometric pressure changes (tendency)

Rising or falling slowly: Pressure change of 0·1 to 1·5 millibars in the preceding 3 hours.

Rising or falling: Pressure change of 1·6 to 3·5 millibars in the preceding 3 hours.

Rising or falling quickly: Pressure change of 3·6 to 6 millibars in the preceding 3 hours.

Rising or falling very rapidly: Pressure change of more than 6 millibars in the preceding 3 hours.

Now rising (or falling): Pressure has been rising (falling) or steady in the preceding 3 hours, but at the time of observation was definitely rising (falling).

d.   Gale warnings

A **'Gale'** warning means that winds of at least force 8 (34-40 knots) or gusts reaching 43-51 knots are expected somewhere within the area, but not necessarily over the whole area. **'Severe Gale'** means winds of at least force 9 (41-47 knots) or gusts reaching 52-60 knots. **'Storm'** means winds of force 10 (48-55 knots) or gusts of 61-68 knots. **'Violent Storm'** means winds of force 11 (56-63 kn) or gusts of 69 kn or more; and **'Hurricane Force'** means winds of force 12 (64 knots or more).

Gale warnings remain in force until amended or cancelled ('gales now ceased'). If a gale persists for more than 24 hours the warning is re-issued.

e.   Timing of gale warnings

Imminent	Within 6 hrs of time of issue
Soon	Within 6 – 12 hrs of time of issue
Later	More than 12 hrs from time of issue

f.   Wind

Wind direction: Indicates the direction from which the wind is blowing.

Winds becoming cyclonic: Indicates that there will be considerable changes in wind direction across the path of a depression within the forecast area.

Veering: The changing of the wind in a clockwise direction, ie SW to W.

Backing: The changing of the wind in an anti-clockwise direction, ie W to SW.

C5

SOURCES OF WEATHER INFORMATION

5.2   RADIO BROADCASTING

5.2.1   Shipping forecast, BBC Radio 4
Shipping forecasts are broadcast by BBC Radio 4 at:

0535 (LW & FM) (Inshore waters forecast follows).
1201 (LW only).
1754 (LW only Mon-Fri; LW & FM Sat/Sun).
0048 (LW & FM) (Inshore waters forecast follows).
All times local – and on the following frequencies:

LW   198 kHz (1515m)
FM   92·4-94·6 MHz: England and Scotland;
92·4-96·1 MHz or 103·5-104·9 MHz: N Ireland and Wales; 97·1 MHz: Channel Islands.
MW   Tyneside 603 kHz; London and N Ireland 720 kHz; Redruth 756 kHz; Enniskillen and Plymouth 774 kHz; Aberdeen 1449 kHz; Carlisle 1485 kHz.

5.2.1.1   Contents of shipping forecast
The bulletin contains a summary of gale warnings in force; a general synopsis of weather patterns for the next 24 hours with changes expected during that period; and a forecast for each sea area for the next 24 hours, giving wind direction and speed, weather and visibility. Sea area Trafalgar is included only in the 0048 forecast. Gale warnings are also broadcast at the earliest juncture in Radio 4 programmes after receipt, as well as after the next news bulletin.

The forecast is followed by weather reports from coastal stations shown on page 83, as marked by their initial letters on the chart on page 82. These reports of actual weather include wind direction and Beaufort force, present weather, visibility, and (if available) sea-level pressure and tendency.

The 1201 and 1754 forecasts do not contain reports from coastal stations.

On Sundays only, at 0542, a 7 day planning outlook is broadcast which includes weather patterns likely to affect UK waters. On Saturdays only, at 0556, a three minutes "topical leisure" forecast is broadcast.

Shipping forecasts cover large sea areas, and rarely include the detailed variations that may occur near land. The Inshore waters forecast (see below) can be more helpful to yachtsmen on coastal passages.

5.2.2   Inshore waters forecast, BBC Radio 4
A forecast for inshore waters (up to 12M offshore) around the UK and N Ireland, valid until 1800, is broadcast after the 0535 and 0048 forecasts. It includes a general synopsis, forecasts of wind direction and force, visibility and weather for stretches of inshore waters referenced to well-known places and headlands, clockwise from Berwick-upon-Tweed.

Reports of actual weather at the following stations are broadcast only after the 0048 forecast: Boulmer, Bridlington, Sheerness, St Catherine's Point, Scilly auto, Milford Haven, Aberporth, Valley, Liverpool (Crosby), Ronaldsway, Machrihanish, Greenock MRCC, Stornoway, Lerwick, Wick auto, Aberdeen and Leuchars. These stations are shown on page 94.

5.2.3   BBC general (land) forecasts
Land area forecasts may include an outlook period up to 48 hours beyond the shipping forecast, more details of frontal systems and weather along the coasts. The most comprehensive land area forecasts are broadcast by BBC Radio 4 on the frequencies in 5.2.1.

Wind strength
Wind descriptions used in land forecasts, with their Beaufort scale equivalents, are:

Calm:	0	Fresh:	5
Light:	1–3	Strong:	6 – 7
Moderate:	4	Gale:	8

Visibility
The following definitions apply to land forecasts:
Mist: Visibility between 2000m and 1000m
Fog: Visibility less than 1000m
Dense fog: Less than 50m

5.2.4   UK Local Radio Stations
BBC and commercial Local radio stations also broadcast weather forecasts and small craft warnings. For details see Table 5(1) on pages 92 and 93.

5.3   NAVTEX

5.3.1   Introduction
Navtex prints or displays navigational warnings, weather forecasts and other safety information by means of a dedicated aerial and receiver with built-in printer or screen. It is a component of GMDSS.

All messages are in English on a single frequency of 518 kHz, with excellent coverage of NW Europe. A few stations, eg La Coruña (Spain), also transmit in the national language as well as English. Interference between stations is avoided by time sharing and by limiting the range of transmitters to about 300M. Thus three stations cover the UK.

The user programmes the receiver for the station(s) and message category(s) required. One or more stations may be programmed. For example, Niton (S), Corsen (A) and message categories A, E, J and L. Gale warnings (B) and SAR (D) are always printed, on receipt and on schedule.

5.3.2   Messages
Each message is prefixed by a four-character group. The first character is the code letter of the transmitting station (in the UK: S for Niton, G for Cullercoats and O for Portpatrick). The second character indicates the category of the message as in the code below. The third and fourth are message serial numbers, from 01 to 99. The serial number 00 denotes urgent messages which are always printed. Messages which are corrupt or have already been printed are rejected.

Information in a Navtex message applies only to the area for which the transmitting station is responsible, as shown in Fig 5(1).

Weather information accounts for about 75% of all messages and is particularly valuable when out of range of other sources or if there is a language problem. The sea areas covered by the 3 UK stations are:

Cullercoats   Faeroes clockwise to Wight
Niton (S)   Thames clockwise to Malin
Portpatrick   Lundy clockwise to Fair Isle

5.3.3 Message categories
A Navigational warnings
B Gale warnings
C Ice reports (unlikely to apply in UK)
D SAR information and pirate attack warnings
E Weather forecasts
F Pilot service messages
G Decca messages
H Loran-C messages
J Satnav messages
K Other electronic navaid messages
L Subfacts and Gunfacts for the UK
V Amplifying details of navigation warnings initially sent under A. The weekly oil rig list will also be transmitted using V.
Z No messages on hand at scheduled time

5.3.4 Stations
The table below shows Navtex stations in Navareas I and II with their identity codes and transmission times (UT). **Times** of weather messages are in bold.
Notes:
i.   Niton (K) transmits messages for the area bounded by the Channel median line and the French coast from Calais to Ile de Bréhat.
ii.   Oostende (M) transmits messages for the area bounded by N Foreland and Lowestoft on the UK coast, longitude 3°E and the Belgian/French coasts to Calais. Oostende (T) provides nav info for the Belgian coast and weather for sea areas Thames and Dover.

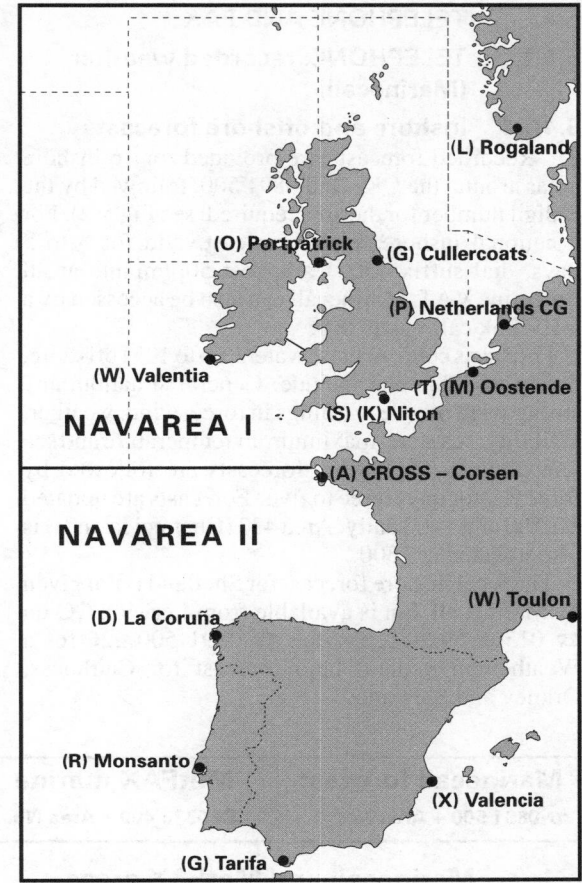

Fig 5(1) Navtex Areas – UK and NW Europe

C5

NAVAREA I (Co-ordinator = UK)

Transmission times (UT)

O –	**Portpatrick,** UK	0130	0530	**0930**	1330	1730	**2130**
G –	**Cullercoats,** UK	0048	0448	**0848**	1248	1648	**2048**
S –	**Niton,** UK	0018	0418	**0818**	1218	1618	**2018**
K –	**Niton,** UK (Note i above)	0140	0540	**0940**	1340	1740	**2140**
W –	**Valentia,** Eire (on trial 1998)	0340	0740	1140	1540	1940	2340
P –	**Netherlands CG,** IJmuiden	0348	0748	1148	1548	1948	2348
M –	**Oostende,** Belgium (Note ii)	0200	**0600**	1000	1400	**1800**	2200
T –	**Oostende,** Belgium	0248	**0648**	1048	1448	**1848**	2248
L –	**Rogaland,** Norway	**0148**	0548	**0948**	**1348**	1748	**2148**

NAVAREA II (Co-ordinator = France)

A –	**Le Stiff,** France	**0000**	0400	0800	**1200**	1600	2000
D –	**La Coruña,** Spain	0030	0430	**0830**	1230	1630	**2030**
R –	**Monsanto,** (Lisbon) Portugal	**0250**	0650	**1050**	**1450**	**1850**	**2250**
G –	**Tarifa,** Spain	0100	0500	**0900**	1300	1700	**2100**
F –	**Horta,** Azores	**0050**	**0450**	**0850**	**1250**	**1650**	2050
I –	**Las Palmas,** Islas Canarias	0100	0500	0900	1300	1700	2100

5.4   TELEPHONE AND FAX

5.4.1   TELEPHONE: recorded weather (Marinecall)

5.4.1.1   Inshore and offshore forecasts

a.   Recorded forecasts are provided for 16 inshore areas around the UK. Dial 0891 500, followed by the 3-digit number for the area required; see Fig 5(2). For a national inshore waters forecast, valid for 3 to 5 days, dial suffix 450. Calls cost 50p/minute at all times, inc VAT. Marinecall can also be accessed by a VHF link call via a CRS.

Forecasts cover inshore waters, up to 12M offshore, for up to 48hrs and include: General situation, any strong wind or gale warnings in force, wind, weather, visibility, sea state, maximum air temperature and sea temperature. The 48 hrs forecasts are followed by forecasts for days three to five. Forecasts are updated at 0700 and 1900 daily. Area 432 (Channel Islands) is also updated at 1300.

The local inshore forecast for Shetland is not given by Marinecall, but is available from Lerwick CG on ☎ 01595 692976. Or dial ☎ 0891 500 426 for a Weathercall general land forecast for Caithness, Orkney and Shetland.

b.   For 2 – 5 day planning forecasts in offshore areas (beyond 12M from the coast) dial ☎ 0891 500 and the required 3 digits below:

English Channel	992
Southern North Sea	991
Northern North Sea	985
Irish Sea	954
NW Scotland	955
Biscay	953

5.4.1.2   Coastal reports (Marinecall Select)

For latest weather reports and forecasts from 47 coastal stations dial ☎ 0891 110 010 and follow instructions, keying in the three-digit area number shown in Fig 5(2), when requested.

Each of the 16 Marinecall areas contains two to four actual weather reports, which are updated hourly.

The reports include details of wind/gusts, visibility, weather, cloud, temperature, pressure and tendency. After these reports a two day or three – five day forecast for that area is available.

Marinecall forecast	MetFAX marine
☎ 0891 500 + Area No.	📠 0336 400 + Area No.

Marinecall and MetFAX areas

Area	Area Title	Area Coverage
451	Scotland North	Cape Wrath to Rattray Head (and Orkney)
452	Scotland East	Rattray Hd to Berwick-on-Tweed
453	North-East	Berwick-on-Tweed to Whitby
454	East	Whitby to the Wash
455	Anglia	The Wash to North Foreland
456	Channel East	North Foreland to Selsey Bill
457	Mid-Channel	Selsey Bill to Lyme Regis
458	South-West	Lyme Regis to Hartland Point (including the Isles of Scilly)
459	Bristol Channel	Hartland Point to St David's Head
460	Wales	St David's Head to Colwyn Bay
461	North-West	Colwyn Bay to Mull of Galloway (also the Isle of Man)
462	Clyde	Mull of Galloway to Mull of Kintyre (also the North Channel)
463	Caledonia	Mull of Kintyre to Ardnamurchan
464	Minch	Ardnamurchan to Cape Wrath (including the Western Isles)
465	Northern Ireland	Lough Foyle to Carlingford Lough
432	Channel Islands	Marinecall
466	Channel Islands	MetFAX

Fig 5(2) Marinecall and MetFAX areas

2 to 5 day Area planning forecasts and charts; MetFAX Marine updated 0800, and charts only at 2000.

Dial ⛵: 0336 400 + 3-digit No for Area.

Area	Area coverage
468	**North West Scottish** 42/72h forecast and charts for areas Faeroes, Hebrides, Bailey, Rockall and Malin.
469	**Northern North Sea** 42/72h forecast and charts for areas Forth, Forties, Cromarty, Viking and Fair Isle.
470	**Biscay** 42/72h forecast and charts for areas East Sole, East Finisterre and Biscay.
471	**English Channel** 42/72h forecast and charts for areas Plymouth, Portland, Wight and Dover.
472	**Southern North Sea** 42/72h forecast and charts for areas Thames, Humber, German Bight, Dogger and Tyne.
473	**Irish Sea** 42/72h forecast and charts for areas Irish Sea, Lundy and Fastnet.

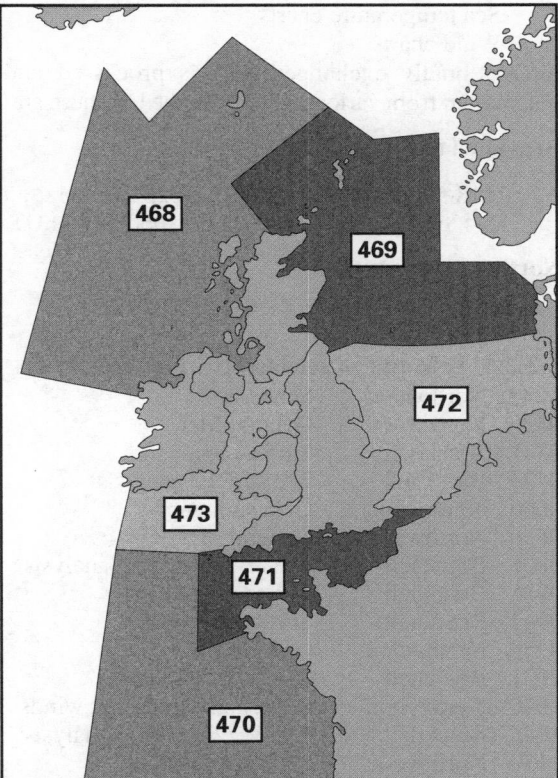

Fig 5(3) MetFAX planning forecast areas

Stations reporting current weather
(anti-clockwise from Scilly, plus Channel Islands)

458 St Mary's, Falmouth, Plymouth, Brixham
457 St Catherine's Pt, Lee-on-Solent, Thorney Is
456 Greenwich lt V, Newhaven, Dover
455 Sheerness, Walton-on-the-Naze, Weybourne
454 Easington, Holbeach, Bridlington
453 Tynemouth, Boulmer
452 Fife Ness, Aberdeen, Peterhead
451 Lossiemouth, Wick, Cape Wrath
464 Butt of Lewis, Aultbea (L Ewe), Benbecula
463 Oban, Tiree
465 Malin Head, Ballycastle, Bangor harbour
462 Machrihanish, Prestwick, Greenock
461 Walney Island, Crosby (Liverpool), Rhyll
460 Valley, Aberdaron (Bardsey Is), Aberporth
459 Milford Haven, Mumbles (Swansea), Cardiff
432 Channel lt V, Guernsey, Jersey, Ile de Bréhat

5.4.2   Weather by FAX (MetFAX Marine)
For two day forecasts and charts for inshore waters in the areas shown in Fig 5(2), dial 0336 400 plus the 3-digit number of the area required. Note: For the Channel Islands dial 0336 400 466 for ⛵, and 0891 500 432 for ☎.

For two to five day planning forecasts and 48/72h forecast charts for the Areas shown in Fig 5(3), dial 0336 400 plus the 3-digit number of the area required.

For additional fax services dial 0336 400, plus:

24h shipping forecast	441
Guide to surface charts	446
Surface analysis chart	444
24h surface forecast chart	445
Chart of latest UK weather reports	447
Index to chart of UK weather reports	448
3-5 day UK inshore forecast & charts	450
User's guide to satellite image	498
Satellite image	499
Plotted weather reports for Europe & Mediterranean	474
Marine index	401

The charge for 0336 calls is 50p per minute at all times, including VAT. For MetFAX Marine services at double speed dial 0331 100 + 3-digit area suffix; charge £1.00 at all times.

Note: METFAX and METFAX MARINE are registered trade marks of the Meteorological Office.

5.4.3   HF Radio facsimile broadcasts
Facsimile recorders that receive pictorial images such as weatherfax charts are now available for use in yachts and at marinas. The meteorological information provided is not all relevant to the average yachtsman, but among items of direct use, are:

Isobaric charts (actual and forecast)
Sea and swell charts
Satellite cloud images

C5

Sea temperature charts
Wind charts.

Internationally exchanged data is processed and transmitted from various centres. In the UK these are:

Bracknell (GFA) (Facsimile)

2618·5*, 4610, 8040, 14436, 18261** kHz; H24, except *1800-0600 and **0600-1800 UT

Northwood (Facsimile)

3652, 4307, 6452·5, 8331·5 kHz, all H24

5.3.3.1 Schedule of selected UK Fax broadcasts

0230	Northwood	Schedule
0320	Northwood	General Met
0341	Bracknell	Surface analysis
0431	Bracknell	24h surface analysis
0600	Northwood	Gale summary
0650	Northwood	General Met
0806	Bracknell	48h & 72h surface analysis
0935	Bracknell	24h sea state prog
0941	Bracknell	Surface analysis
0950	Northwood	General Met
1031	Bracknell	24h surface analysis
1040	Northwood	Routeing, significant winds
1045	Bracknell	48h & 72h surface analysis
1130	Northwood	Gale summary
1210	Northwood	General Met
1230	Northwood	Sea and swell, wave height
1500	Northwood	General Met
1530	Northwood	Schedule
1541	Bracknell	Surface analysis
1631	Bracknell	24h surface analysis
1640	Northwood	Gale summary
1730	Northwood	Sea and swell, wave height
1800	Northwood	General Met
1950	Northwood	Gale summary
2018	Bracknell	24h sea state prog
2050	Northwood	Routeing, significant winds
2120	Northwood	General Met
2141	Bracknell	Surface analysis
2222	Bracknell	48h & 72h surface analysis
2231	Bracknell	24h surface analysis
2320	Northwood	General Met
2327	Bracknell	24h surface analysis

Map areas and schedules are published in the *Admiralty List of Radio Signals, Vol 3* (NP 283).

5.5　FORECASTERS

5.5.1　Weather Centres

Forecasts for port areas can be obtained at a charge from the Weather Centres listed below:

Southampton	(01703) 228844
London	0171-696 0573 or 0171-405 4356
Birmingham	0121-717 0570
Norwich	(01603) 660779
Leeds	(0113) 2451990
Newcastle	(0191) 232 6453
Aberdeen Airport	(01224) 210574

Kirkwall Airport, Orkney	(01856) 873802
Sella Ness, Shetland	(01806) 242069
Glasgow	0141-248 3451
Manchester	0161-477 1060
Cardiff	(01222) 397020
Bristol	(0117) 927 9298
Belfast International Airport	(018494) 22339
Jersey	(01534) 46111 Ext 2229

Republic of Ireland

Central Forecast Office, Dublin (H24)	(01) 424655
Dublin Airport Met	(01) 379900 ext 4531
Cork Airport Met (0900–2000)	(021) 965974
Shannon Airport Met (H24)	(061) 61333

European continent

The ☎ Nos of forecast offices and recorded weather messages are shown under 'Telephone' for individual harbours in Areas 15–21 of Chapter 8.

5.5.2　Forecaster direct (METCALL Direct)

A Met Office forecaster can be consulted by direct telephone line H24 for detailed discussion of, for example, the synoptic situation, specific weather windows or the longer term outlook. The consultancy would normally include a briefing and answers to any questions. In the UK call ☎ 0374 555 888; from the Continent call ☎ +44 374 555 888. Payment of £15.00 is by credit card; there is no specified time limit, but 5-10 minutes is average. Helpline ☎ 01344 854435.

Note: METCALL is a trade mark of the Meteorological Office.

5.6　MISCELLANEOUS SOURCES

5.6.1　HM Coastguard

See Chap 6, Table 6(1) for routine weather broadcasts by HM CG. These include gale warnings, strong wind warnings and scheduled weather messages. The CG may also provide local weather conditions and repeat the local forecast if requested on Ch 16.

5.6.2　Internet (METWEB)

A full range of meteorological information is now available via the Internet. This includes METFAX Marine services, two day inshore forecasts, charts and satellite images. Visit the METWEB site at www.met-office.gov.uk. More information is available from the METWEB Helpline e-mail: metweb@meto.gov.uk.

Note: METWEB is a trade mark of the Meteorological Office.

5.6.3　Press forecasts

The interval between the time of issue and the time at which they are available next day makes press forecasts of only limited value to yachtsmen. However, the better papers include a synoptic chart which, in the absence of any other chart, can help to interpret the shipping forecast.

5.6.4 Television forecasts

Some TV forecasts show a synoptic chart which, with the satellite pictures, can be a useful guide to the weather situation.

In the UK Ceefax (BBC) gives the forecast for inshore waters on page 409. Teletext (ITV) gives the shipping forecast on page 107 and the inshore waters and tide times on page 108.

Antiope is the equivalent French system. In some remote areas abroad a TV forecast in a bar, cafe or even shop window may be the best or only source of weather information.

5.6.5 Volmet

Volmet is a meteorological service for airmen which reports actual weather and/or forecasts for selected airports to aircraft in flight on VHF and HF SSB. VHF reports are in the aeronautical band.

Yachtsmen may find the information of limited value, since it is in a semi-coded format and covers many airfields which are well inland. Coastal airports include St Mawgan, Leuchars, Kinloss, Prestwick and Belfast; see Fig 5(4).

The RAF continuously broadcasts actual weather reports for military and civil airports, mostly in the UK, on 5450 kHz and 11253 kHz. The reports include: airport name, wind direction and speed, cloud amount and height, temperature and dew point, sea level pressure (QNH) and any significant weather.

Shannon broadcasts on 3413 kHz (HN) and H24 on 5505 kHz, 8957 kHz and 13264 kHz. The schedule starts at H+00 and at every H+05 thereafter. Coastal airports within the coverage of this Almanac include: Shannon, Prestwick, Dublin, Amsterdam & Hamburg.

5.6.6 Reports of present weather

Reports of actual local weather can be obtained by telephone from the following Met Offices, lighthouses and other stations, as shown in Fig 5(4):

Meteorological Offices

Shoeburyness	01702 292271 ext 3476
Kinloss	01309 72161 ext 674
Kirkwall (Orkney)	01856 873802
Sella Ness (Shetland)	01806 242069
Stornoway	01851 702256 (HN 702282)
Tiree	01879 220456
Ronaldsway (IOM)	01624 823311 (HN 823313)

(0700–1700 *Mon–Fri*, except Public Holidays)

Lighthouses and other stations *Limited hours

Lizard lt ho	01326 290431
St Catherine's Pt	01983 730284
Cromer*	01263 512507
Whitby*	01947 602107
Strathy Point lt ho	01641 541210
Cape Wrath lt ho	01971 511230
Butt of Lewis lt ho	01851 81201
Rhinns of Islay lt ho	01496 860223

5.6.7 Visual storm signals

Visual storm signals used on the Continent are summarised in 8.15.8, 8.20.8 and 8.21.8.

5.7 UK COAST RADIO STATIONS

5.7.1 Weather messages

Gale warnings, a synopsis and a 24-hour forecast are broadcast at 0703 1903UT by Northern Region CRS and at 0733 1933UT by Southern Region CRS and on request.

Gale warnings are also broadcast at the end of the first silence period after receipt (i.e. at H+03 or H+33), and at 0303 0903 1503 2103UT, after an announcement on Ch 16 and 2182 kHz. They remain in force unless amended or cancelled, but are re-issued if the gale persists for more than 24 hours.

BT NORTHERN REGION Routine broadcasts at **0703 1903** UT			
Station	**Channel/Frequency**		**Sea areas**
Cullercoats	—	2719 kHz	Viking
Stonehaven	Ch 26	2691 kHz	N & S Utsire
Shetland	—	1770 kHz	Forties
Wick	Ch 28	1764 kHz	Cromarty
Lewis	Ch 05		Forth, Tyne
Hebrides	—	1866 kHz	Dogger, Fisher
Skye	Ch 24		German Bight
Oban	Ch 07		Humber
Islay	Ch 25		Thames
Portpatrick	Ch 27	1883 kHz	Lundy
Anglesey	Ch 26		Irish Sea
Cardigan Bay	Ch 03		Rockall, Malin
			Hebrides
			Bailey, Fair Isle
			Faeroes
			SE Iceland

BT SOUTHERN REGION Routine broadcasts at **0733 1933** UT			
Station	**Channel/Frequency**		**Sea areas**
Celtic	Ch 24		Tyne
Ilfracombe	Ch 05		Dogger
Land's End	Ch 27	2670 kHz	German Bight
	Ch 64 (to Scilly)		Humber
Pendennis	Ch 62		Thames
Start Point	Ch 26		Dover
Niton	Ch 28	1641 kHz	Wight
Hastings[1]	Ch 07		Portland
Thames[1]	Ch 02		Plymouth
North Foreland[1]	Ch 26		Biscay
Orfordness[1]	Ch 62		Finisterre
Humber	Ch 26	1869 kHz	Sole
Grimsby	Ch 27		Lundy
			Fastnet
			Irish Sea
			Shannon

(1) Fog warnings for River Thames broadcast when visibility falls below half a mile, at end of next silence period after receipt and repeated every two hours until amended or cancelled

JERSEY RADIO (See 4.10.1.3 for other services)

Weather messages are broadcast at 0645 0745 and 0845 (LT) and at 1245 1845 2245 (UT) and on request, after announcement on Ch 16/2182 kHz. They include near gale (F7) warnings, synopsis, 24 hr forecast, 48 hrs outlook and coastal stations reports.

Station	Channel/Frequency	Area
Jersey	Ch 25 82 1659 kHz	Channel Islands south of 50°N and east of 3°W

C5

TABLE 5(1)   UK LOCAL RADIO STATIONS – FORECASTS FOR COASTAL WATERS

The scope, details and usefulness of forecasts broadcast by local radio stations vary considerably. The times and frequencies of the broadcasts most likely to interest yachtsmen are shown below.

Small Craft Warnings (winds of Force 6+ expected within the next 12 hrs, up to 5M offshore) are broadcast at the first programme juncture or after the first news bulletin following receipt.

Station	VHF Transmitter(s)	VHF (MHz)	MF (kHz)	(m)	Coastal waters forecasts (local times) (*summer months only)	Small Craft Warnings
ENGLAND – SOUTH COAST						
BBC Radio Cornwall						
Redruth	Redruth	103·9	630	476	*Mon-Fri:* 0608 0725 0825 1225 1325 1725 1825 1925	Yes
Bodmin	Caradon Hill	95·2	657	457	*Sat:* 0725 0825 0855 1315 1325	
Scilly	Scilly	96·0			*Sun:* 0710 0825 0925 0955 1310	
BBC Radio Devon						
Exeter	Exeter	95·8	990	303	*Mon-Fri:* 0530 0605 0833 1330 1550	Yes
Plymouth	N Hessary Tor	103·4	855	351	*Sat:* 0605 0833 1305	
N Devon	Huntshaw Cross	94·8	801	375	*Sun:* 0605 0833 1307	
Torbay	N Hessary Tor	103·4	1458	206		
Wessex FM						
Lyme Bay	Bridport	96·0			Every hour 0600-2400 after news bulletin	
	Bincombe	97·2			Coastal forecast, inc sea conditions, and HW/LW times for Dorset	
BBC Solent FM					For details see 8.2.18	
Spirit FM						
	South Downs	96·6			0630 0730 0830 1630 1730 1830	Yes
	Angmering	102·3			Portsmouth to Worthing, inc Chichester Hbr and Littlehampton	
BBC Southern Counties Radio						
	Brighton/Hove	95·3	1485	202	*Mon-Fri:* 0606 0706 0823 1306 1706 1806 1906	Yes
	Heathfield	104·5	1161	258		
	Worthing	95·3			*Sat-Sun:* 0622 0652 0722 0752 0822 0852	
	Newhaven/Lewes	95·0				
BBC Radio Kent						
	Wrotham	96·7			*Mon-Fri:* 0732 0832 1310 1708 1808	Yes
	Swingate	104·2	774	388	*Sat-Sun:* 0735 0835 1310	
	Folkestone	97·6	1602	187	Forecast, synopsis and tide times, Gravesend to Dungeness	
ENGLAND – EAST COAST						
BBC Essex	Mid & N Essex	103·5	729	412	*Mon-Fri:* 0640 0740 1740 1840	
	SE Essex	95·3	1530	196	*Sat:* 0657 0757 0857 1205 1305	
	All Essex		765	392	*Sun:* 0657 0757 0857	
BBC Radio Suffolk						
	Manningtree	103·9			*Mon-Fri:* 0617 0717 0817 1330 1717 1805	Yes
	Lowestoft	95·5			*Sat-Sun:* 0705 0805 1305	
					Forecasts from Clacton-on-sea to Great Yarmouth	
BBC Radio Norfolk						
	Tacolneston	95·1	855	351	Mon-Fri: 0630-1600 at H+00 (0850 CG report)	Yes
	Great Massingham	104·4	873	344	1700* 1800* (*summer period only)	
					Sat: 0630-1300 at H+00	
					Sun: 0630-1400 at H+00	
BBC Radio Lincolnshire (Wash to the Humber)						
	Belmont	94·9	1368	219	*Mon-Fri:* 0615 0745 1145 1650 1803	Yes
					Sat: 0720 0845 1145 1445	
					Sun: 0650 0850 1145	
BBC Radio Humberside (The Humber to Bridlington)						
	High Hunsley	95·9	1485	202	*Mon-Fri:* 0632 0732 0832 1332 1632 1732 1832	Yes
					Sat-Sun: 0732 0832 1309	
BBC Radio Cleveland (Flamborough Head to Hartlepool)						
	Bilsdale	95·0			*Mon-Fri:* 0645 0745 0845 1345 1645 1715 1815	Yes
	Whitby	95·8			*Sat:* 0645 0745 0945 1245 1345	
					Sun: 0745 0845 0945	
BBC Radio Newcastle (Skelton to Berwick-upon-Tweed)						
	Pontop Pike	95·4	1458	206	*Mon-Fri:* 0655 0755 0855 1155 1255 1655 1755	Yes
	Chatton	96·0	in North		*Sat-Sun:* 0755 0855 0955	
	Newton	103·7				
Radio Borders (Holy Island to St Abbs Head)						
	Berwick-upon-Tweed	95·7			Every H+00 after news. Forecast, synopsis and storm	
	Eyemouth	103·4			warnings if in force	

Station	VHF Transmitter(s)	Frequencies VHF (MHz)	MF (kHz)	(m)	Coastal waters forecasts (local times) (*summer months only)	Small Craft Warnings
SCOTLAND – EAST COAST						
Radio Forth	Craigkelly	97·3			On receipt. Severe weather warnings for or including the	Yes
Forth AM	Colinswell		1548	194	the coastal waters of E Central Scotland and area Forth	
Radio Tay AM (Kirkcaldy to Montrose)						
	Dundee		1161	258	*Sat-Sun:* 0610 0710	Yes
	Perth		1584	189		
Moray Firth Radio (Inshore waters of Moray Firth from Fraserburgh to Caithness)						
	Mounteagle	97·4	1107		Main transmitter	
	Fraserburgh	96·7			Every H+00 (0600-1800LT) after news. Extended to 0600-1000	Yes
	Keith	102·8			if conditions deteriorate	
	Caithness	102·5			0715 Small craft forecast	
Shetland Islands Broadcasting Company (Area 150M radius from Bressay)						
	Bressay	96·2			0730 and every H+00 after news. Forecast, synopsis and outlook	
SCOTLAND – WEST COAST						
Nevis Radio (Waters around Ardnamurchan Pt, the S Minch and Hebrides)						
	Fort William	96·6			*Daily:* 0835 1750 Local shipping and inshore waters forecast	
	Mallaig, Arisaig, S Skye	102·3			*Daily:* 0710 0730 0810 0830 0910 0930, every H+06 after news	
BBC Radio Scotland						
	Burghead (Moray)		810		*Mon-Fri:* 0604 0658 0758 every H+00 1658 1758 2157 2357	
	Campbeltown	92·8				
	Lochgilphead	92·7			*Sat:* 0700 detailed forecast, synopsis for coastal and inland waters	
	Rothesay	92·9			*Sat-Sun:* 0658 every H+00 1758 2158	
Radio Clyde	Dechmont Hill		1152	261	*Daily:* H24 at H+00 (except 0300, 0800, 0900, 1100)	Yes
WEST COAST OF ENGLAND AND WALES						
BBC Radio Cumbria (Wigtown Bay to Morecambe Bay)						
N Cumbria	Sandale	95·6	756	397	*Mon-Fri:* 0632 0732 0832 1632 1732	Yes
W Cumbria	Whitehaven	104·1	1458	206	*Sat-Sun:* 0732 1132	
S Cumbria	Morecambe Bay	96·1	837	358		
Manx Radio	Snaefell	89·0			*Daily:* 0705 0805 1305 1705 2305	Yes
	Carnane	97·2				
	Jurby/Foxdale	103·7	1368	219		
BBC Radio	Allerton	95·8			*Mon-Fri:* 0705 0805 1208 1310 1605 1705 1743	Yes
Merseyside	Wallasey		1485	202	*Sat::* 0742	
BBC Radio Wales in English on MF (BBC Radio Cymru in Welsh on FM)						
	All Wales		882		*Mon-Fri:* 0658 0758 0903 1259 1734	Yes
	NE Wales		657		*Sat:* 1003 1259 1759	
	Mid Wales		1125		*Sun:* 0859 1259 1759	
Soundwave 96·4 and		96·4			*Mon-Fri:* 0725 0825 0925 and H+30	Yes
Swansea Sound 1170			1170	257	*Sat-Sun:* 0825 1003	
BBC Radio Bristol						
	Bristol	94·9	1548	194	*Mon-Fri:* 0605 0632 0659 0733 0759 0833 0859	Yes
	Bath	104·6			1259 1633 1755	
	Avon/Somerset	95·5			*Sat-Sun:* 0758 0858	
GWR & Brunel Classic Gold (Bristol Chan)			1260	238	*Daily:* Every H and H+30	Yes
NORTHERN IRELAND						
Downtown Radio						
	96·4, 96·6, 102·4MHZ		1026		*Mon-Fri:* 0705, 0805, 0905, 1005, 1320, 1403, 1503, 1710, 2315	
					Sat: 0705 0805 0905 1005 1105	Yes
					Sun: 1105 2303 (0003 Mon)	
BBC Radio Foyle (Portstewart and L Foyle to Derry)						
	Sheriff's Mountain	93·1	792		Daily: Every H+00 (0900-1600LT, except 1300), 1330, 1730LT	Yes
Q 102·9 FM (Ballycastle to Tory Island)						
	Londonderry	102·9			*Fri-Sat:* 0930. Weekend forecast, inc coastal and inshore waters	
CHANNEL ISLANDS					See 8.14.14	

C5

Fig 5(4) Reports of present weather

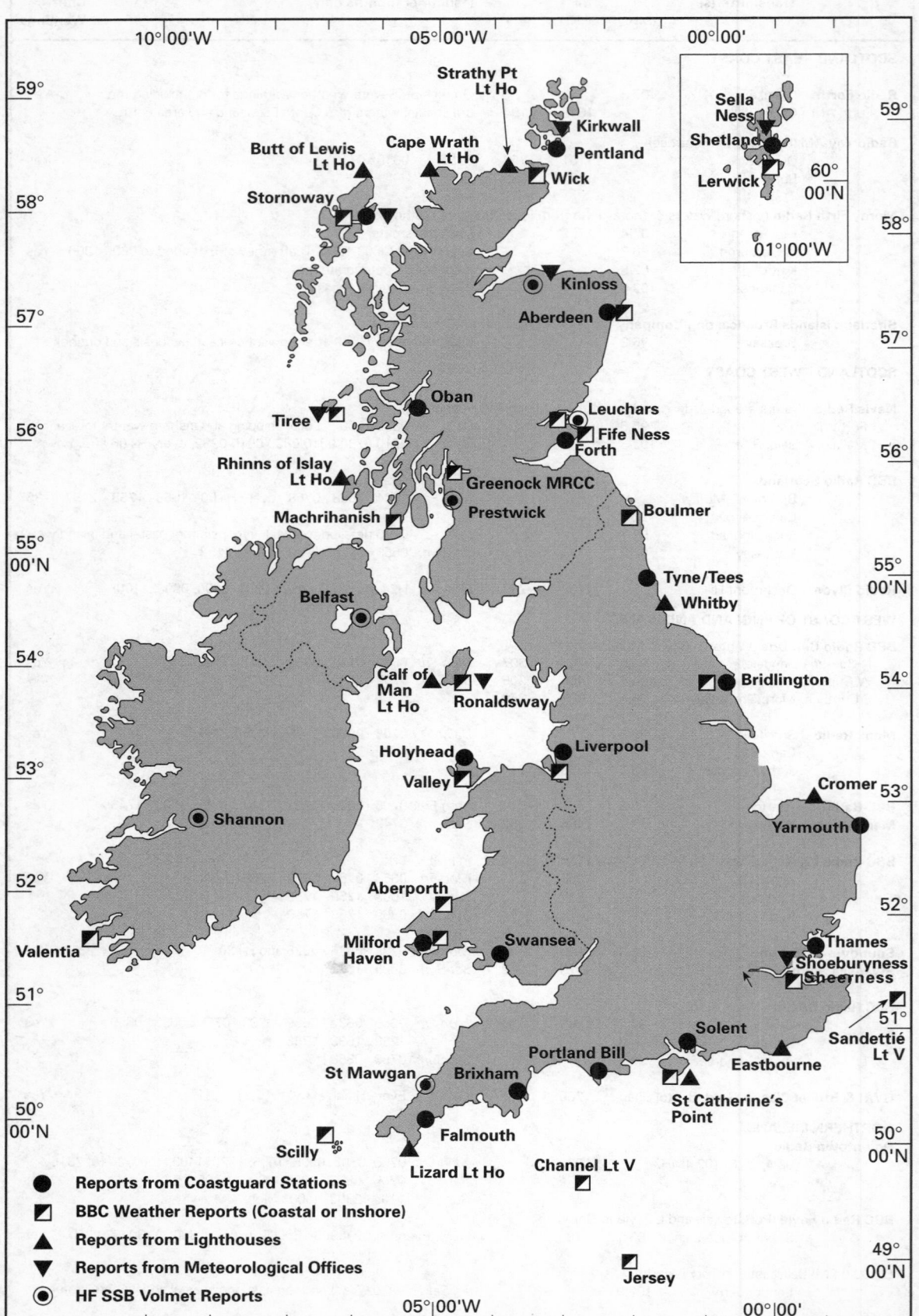

Strathy Pt Lt Ho

Kirkwall
Pentland
Wick

Butt of Lewis Lt Ho
Cape Wrath Lt Ho

Stornoway

Sella Ness
Shetland
Lerwick

Kinloss
Aberdeen

Oban

Leuchars
Fife Ness
Forth

Tiree

Rhinns of Islay Lt Ho
Machrihanish
Greenock MRCC
Prestwick

Boulmer

Tyne/Tees
Whitby

Belfast

Calf of Man Lt Ho
Ronaldsway

Bridlington

Holyhead
Valley
Liverpool

Cromer
Yarmouth

Shannon

Aberporth

Milford Haven
Swansea

Thames
Shoeburyness
Sheerness

Valentia

Solent
Eastbourne
Sandettié Lt V

St Mawgan
Brixham
Portland Bill
St Catherine's Point

Scilly
Falmouth
Lizard Lt Ho
Channel Lt V

Jersey

● **Reports from Coastguard Stations**

◢ **BBC Weather Reports (Coastal or Inshore)**

▲ **Reports from Lighthouses**

▼ **Reports from Meteorological Offices**

◉ **HF SSB Volmet Reports**

5.8　IRELAND

5.8.1　Radio Telefís Éireann (RTE): Broadcasting coastal forecasts and gale warnings

RTE Radio 1 broadcasts a synopsis, forecast and gale warnings for Irish coastal waters and the Irish Sea, a 24 hrs outlook and coastal station reports at 0602, 1253, 1834 (Sat, Sun, public hols), 1902 (Mon-Fri), 2355.
The main transmitters and frequencies are:

MW – Tullamore 567 kHz.

FM – Three Rock 88·5 MHz, Kippure 89·1 MHz, Mount Leinster 89·6 MHz, Mullaghanish 90 MHz, Maghera 88·8 MHz, Truskmore 88·2 MHz, Holywell Hill 89·2 MHz, Clermont Carn 95·2 MHz.

Gale warnings are broadcast by RTE Radio 1 at the first programme juncture after receipt and with news bulletins; also by RTE 2FM from Athlone 612 kHz, Dublin 1278 kHz and Cork 1278 kHz.

Local Radio Stations which broadcast forecasts are shown, with frequencies, in the relevant part of Areas 12 and 13.

5.8.1.1. The latest Sea area forecast and gale warnings can be obtained through Weatherdial ☎ 1550 123 855. The same info, plus isobaric, swell and wave charts are available from Weatherdial Fax on 📠 1570 131 838 (H24). RTE address is Donnybrook, Dublin 4; ☎ +353 1 2083111. Irish Central Forecast Office ☎ +353 1 8424655.

5.8.2　Coast Radio Stations (See 4.10.2 and Fig 4(3) for details of other services.)

Weather bulletins for the Irish Sea and waters up to 30M off the Irish coast are broadcast on VHF at 0103 0403 0703 1003 1303 1603 1903 2203 (LT) after announcement on Ch 16. Bulletins include gale warnings, synopsis and a 24-hour forecast. The stations and channels are: **Malin Head** 23, **Glen Head** 24, **Belmullet** 83, **Clifden** 26, **Shannon** 28, **Valentia** 24, **Bantry** 23, **Cork** 26, **Mine Head** 83, **Rosslare** 23, **Wicklow Head** 87 **and Dublin** 83.

Valentia Radio broadcasts forecasts for sea areas Shannon and Fastnet on 1752 kHz at 0833, 2033UT and on request.
Gale warnings are broadcast on above VHF chans on receipt and repeated at 0033 0633 1233 1833 (LT), after announcement on Ch 16. They are also broadcast by Valentia Radio on 1752 kHz at the end of the next silence period after receipt and at 0303 0903 1503 2103 (UT) after announcement on 2182 kHz.

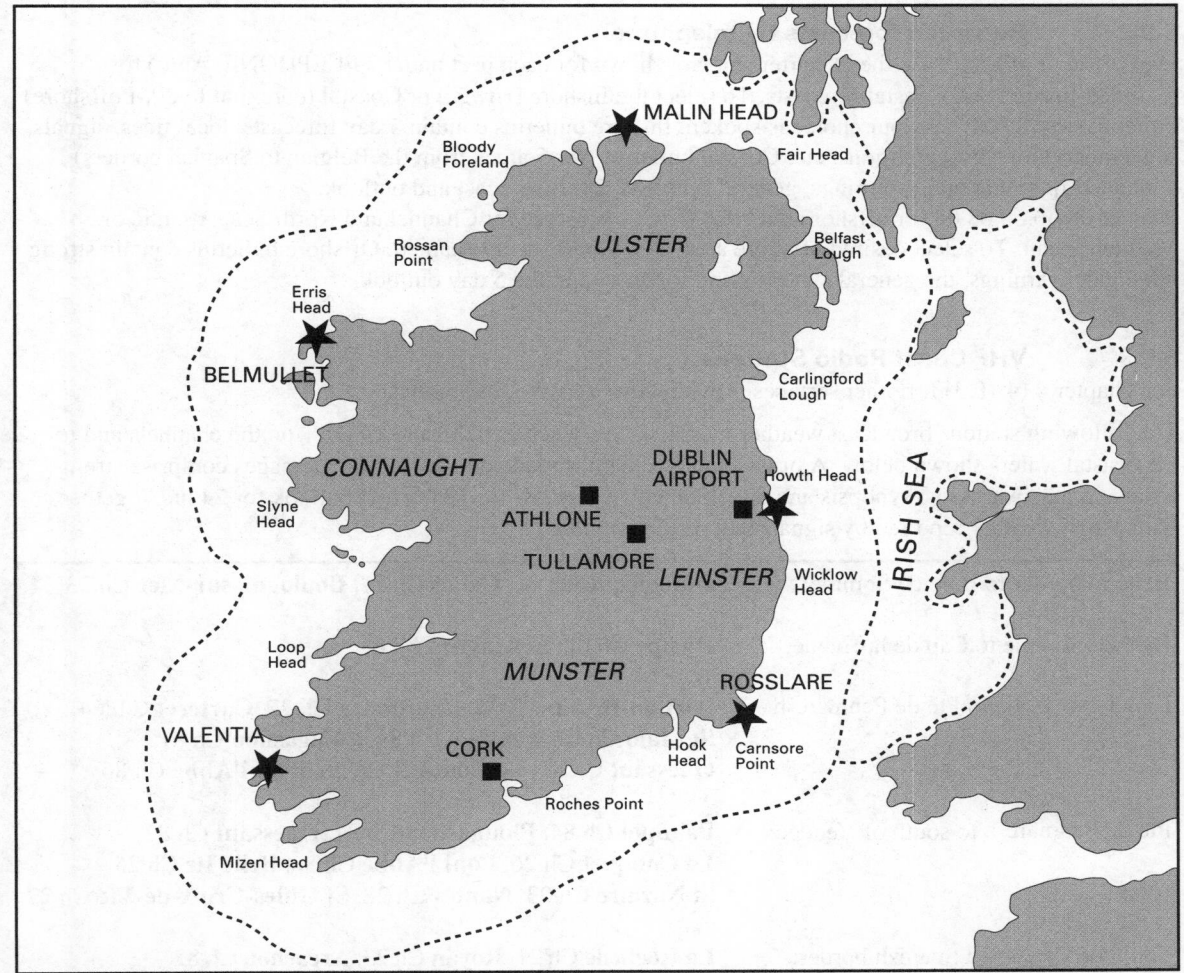

Fig 5(5) shows *PROVINCES*, coastal stations ★ and headlands referred to in forecasts; also RTE 1 or 2 transmitters ■.

5.9   FRANCE

5.9.1   Radio broadcasting

FRANCE INTER (LW)

For all areas: storm warnings, synopsis, 24h fcst and outlook, broadcast in French at 2005 daily on 162 kHz

RADIO BLEUE (MW) - essentially a music programme, but with

Forecasts in French at 0655 covering:
English Channel and North Sea	– **Paris** 864 kHz; **Lille** 1377 kHz
English Channel and East Atlantic	– **Rennes** 711 kHz; **Brest** 1404 kHz
Bay of Biscay and East Atlantic	– **Bordeaux** 1206 kHz; **Bayonne** 1494 kHz

LOCAL RADIO (FM)

Radio France Cherbourg 100·7
Coastal forecast, storm warnings, visibility, wind strength, tidal information, small craft warnings, in French, for the Cherbourg peninsula, broadcast at 0829 by:
Cherbourg 100·7 MHz; **St Vaast-la-Hougue** 85·0 MHz; **La Hague** 99·8 MHz; **Barneville Carteret** 99·9 MHz.

Radio France Armorique
Coastal forecast, storm warnings, wind strength and direction, tidal levels, advice to small craft are broadcast in French, from 18 transmitters on 101·3 MHz and 103·1 MHz, at 0829, 1229 and 1829. The area covered is the coast of N Brittany, excluding the extreme west, but including Channel Islands, Glenans and parts of S Brittany.

There are many other local radio stations broadcasting weather forecasts on FM, in French.

5.9.2   Recorded forecasts by telephone

Dial 08.36.68.08.dd (dd is the Département No, shown for each port under TELEPHONE, Auto) for recorded Inshore and Coastal forecasts. To select the Inshore (*rivage*) or Coastal (*côte;* out to 20M offshore) bulletin, say "STOP" as your choice is spoken. Inshore bulletins contain 5 day forecasts, local tides, signals, sea temperature, surf conditions, etc. Coastal bulletins (for 5 areas from the Belgian to Spanish borders) contain strong wind/gale warnings, general synopsis, 24hrs forecast and outlook.
Dial ☎ 08.36.68.08.08 for offshore bulletins (*zones du large*) for Channel and North Sea, Atlantic or Mediterranean. To select desired offshore area say "STOP" as it is named. Offshore bulletins contain strong wind/gale warnings, the general synopsis and forecast, and the 5 day outlook.

5.9.3   VHF Coast Radio Stations

See chapter 4 (4.10.3) for other services provided by Coast Radio Stations.

The following stations broadcast weather messages in French at 0733 and 1533LT on the channels and for the coastal waters shown below. A prior announcement is made on Ch 16. The messages comprise strong wind and gale warnings, synopsis and development, a forecast for 12 hrs and outlook for 24 hrs, together with actual weather reported by signal stations (*Semaphore*).

Belgian border to Baie de Somme:	**Dunkerque** Ch 61, **Calais** Ch 87, **Boulogne-sur-Mer** Ch 23
Baie de Somme to Cap de la Hague:	**Dieppe** Ch 02, **Le Havre** Ch 26
Cap de la Hague to Pte de Penmarc'h:	**Port-en-Bessin** Ch 03, **Cherbourg** Ch 27, **Carteret** C h 64, **St Malo** Ch 02, **Paimpol** Ch 84, **Plougasnou** Ch 81, **Ouessant** Ch 82, **Le Conquet** Ch 26, **Pont l'Abbé** Ch 86
Pte de Penmarc'h to south of Vendée:	**Paimpol** Ch 84, **Plougasnou** Ch 81, **Ouessant** Ch 82, **Le Conquet** Ch 26, **Pont l'Abbé** Ch 86, **Belle Île** Ch 25, **St Nazaire** Ch 23, **Nantes** Ch 28, **St Gilles-Croix-de-Vie** Ch 27
South of Vendée to Spanish border:	**La Rochelle** Ch 21, **Royan** Ch 23, **Arcachon** Ch 82, **Bayonne** Ch 24

5.9.4 MF Coast Radio Stations

Messages comprising gale warnings, synopsis & development, 24hrs forecast and outlook are broadcast, in French, by the following stations on the frequencies and at the times UT shown below, together with the sea areas covered. A prior announcement is made on 2182kHz.

Boulogne Radio broadcasts on 1692 and 3795 kHz at 0703 and 1833, for Areas 1 to 14.
Gale warnings are broadcast on receipt and at every H+03 and H+33 if gale imminent; and at every odd H+03 whilst the warning remains in force. Frequency:1770 kHz.

Le Conquet Radio broadcasts at 0733 and 1803 on the frequencies below, for Areas 14 to 24:

2691 kHz	(at St Malo)
1671, 3722 kHz	(at Le Conquet)
1876 kHz	(at Quimperlé)
1862 kHz	(at Arcachon)

Gale warnings are broadcast on receipt and at every H+03 and H+33 if gale imminent; and at every odd H+03 whilst the warning remains in force. Frequencies: 1635, 1686, 1710 and 2775 kHz.

St Nazaire Radio 1722, 2740 kHz; at 0803 1833; for Areas 14 to 24.
Gale warnings 1686 kHz at H+03 and H+33 if gale imminent, repeated at H+07 whilst warning in force.

5.9.5 Radio France Internationale (RFI)

RFI broadcasts weather messages in French on HF at 1140 UT daily. Frequencies are: 6175 kHz for North Sea, English Channel and Bay of Biscay; 11700, 15530 and 17575 kHz for the N Atlantic, E of 50°W.

Fig 5(6)
FRANCE Forecast areas
Transmissions of:
France Inter
Radio Bleue
Boulogne Radio
Le Conquet Radio
St Nazaire Radio

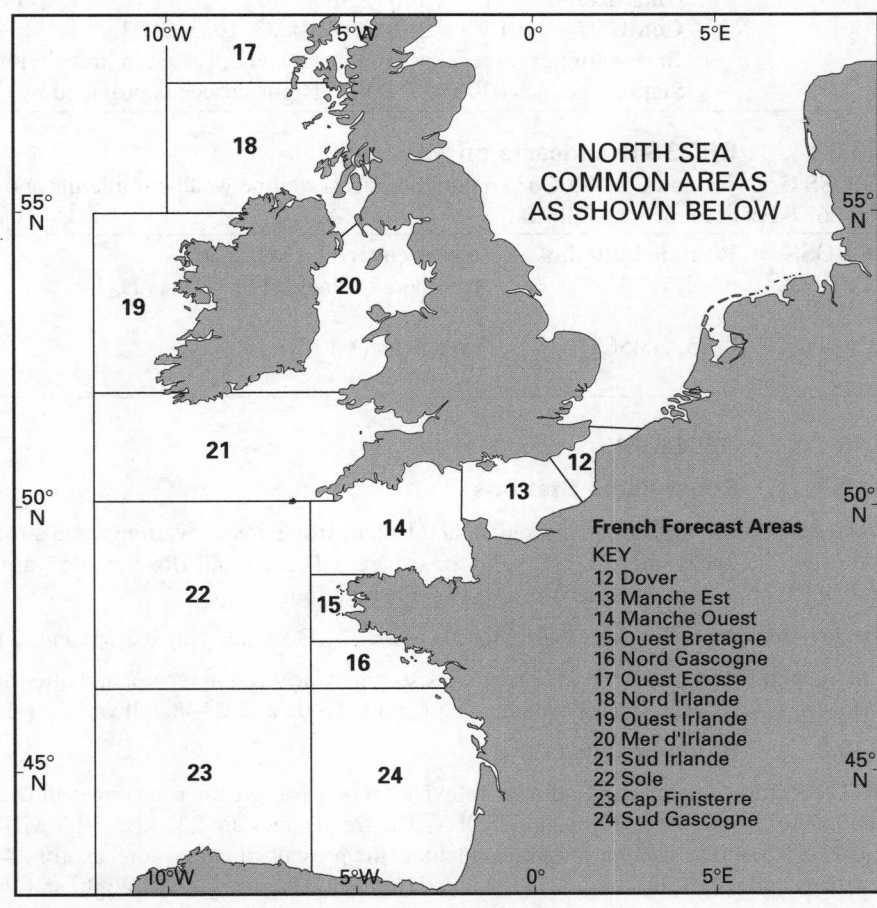

NORTH SEA COMMON AREAS AS SHOWN BELOW

French Forecast Areas
KEY
12 Dover
13 Manche Est
14 Manche Ouest
15 Ouest Bretagne
16 Nord Gascogne
17 Ouest Ecosse
18 Nord Irlande
19 Ouest Irlande
20 Mer d'Irlande
21 Sud Irlande
22 Sole
23 Cap Finisterre
24 Sud Gascogne

C5

5.9.6   CROSS Broadcasts on VHF

CROSS broadcasts in French, after an announcement on Ch 16: Gale warnings, synopsis, a 12 hrs forecast, 48 hrs outlook for coastal waters. VHF channels, coastal areas covered and local times are shown below. In the English Channel broadcasts can also be given in **English**, on request Ch 16. Gale warnings are broadcast in French and **English** by all stations on VHF channels listed below at H+03 and at other times as shown.

CROSS GRIS-NEZ Ch 79 Belgian border to Baie de Somme		
	Dunkerque 0720, 1603, 1920; **Gris-Nez** 0710, 1545, 1910; **Ailly** 0703, 1533, 1903	
	Gale warnings on receipt, on request and at H+03 and H+10, in French and **English.**	
CROSS JOBOURG Ch 80 Baie de Somme to Cap de la Hague		
	Antifer 0803, 1633, 2003; **Port-en-Bessin** 0745, 1615, 1945; **Jobourg** 0733, 1603, 1933	
	Ch 80 Cap de la Hague to Pte de Penmarc'h	
	Jobourg 0715, 1545, 1915; **Granville** 0703, 1533, 1903	
Gale warnings in French and **English** on receipt, on request and at H+03. Also by Jobourg at H+20 & +50.		
CROSS CORSEN Ch 79 Cap de la Hague to Pte de Penmarc'h		
	Times in **bold** = 1 May to 30 Sep.	
Cap Fréhel 0545, 0803, **1203**,1633, 2003; **Bodic** 0533, 0745, **1145**, 1615, 1945; **Ile de Batz** 0515, 0733, **1133**, 1603, 1933; **Le Stiff** 0503, 0715, **1115**, 1545, 1915; **Pte du Raz** 0445, 0703, **1103**, 1533, 1903.		
	Gale warnings in French and **English** on receipt, on request and at H+03.	
Le Stiff broadcasts gale warnings at H+10 and H+40; also weather bulletins in French and **English** every 3 hrs from 0150 UT. All stations broadcast fog warnings in French and **English** when visibility requires.		
CROSS ÉTEL Ch 80 Pte de Penmarc'h to L'Anse de l'Aiguillon (46°17'N 01°10'W)		
	Penmarc'h 0703, 1533, 1903; **Groix** 0715, 1545, 1915; **Belle Ile** 0733, 1603, 1933; **St Nazaire** 0745, 1615, 1945; **Ile d'Yeu** 0803, 1633, 2003; **Sables d'Olonne** 0815, 1645, 1915.	
	Gale warnings on receipt, on request and at H+03; in French, plus **English** in summer.	
Sous-CROSS SOULAC Ch 79 L'Anse de l'Aiguillon to Spanish border		
	Chassiron 0703, 1533, 1903; **Soulac** 0715, 1545, 1915; **Cap Ferret** 0733, 1603, 1933; **Contis** 0745, 1615, 1945; **Biarritz** 0803, 1633, 2003	
	Gale warnings on receipt, on request and at H+03; in French, plus **English** in summer.	
	Station operates 0700 to 2200LT. Night service is provided by CROSS Étel.	

5.9.6.1   CROSS Broadcasts on MF

CROSS Gris Nez and CROSS Corsen both broadcast routine weather bulletins and gale warnings on 1650 and 2677kHz in French, as follows:

CROSS	**Routine bulletins**	**Areas covered**; see Fig 5(6)	**Gale warnings**
Gris Nez	0833, 2033LT	Humber, Thames, French areas 12-14	On receipt, and at every odd H+03.
Corsen	0815, 2045LT	French areas 12-24	On receipt, and at every even H+03.

5.10   BELGIUM

5.10.1   Coast Radio Stations

Oostende Radio broadcasts in English and Dutch strong breeze warnings and a forecast on 2761 kHz and VHF Ch 27 at 0820 and 1720UT, valid for sea areas Thames and Dover. Gale warnings are issued in English and Dutch on receipt and after the next two silent periods.

Navtex: See section 5.3 for weather transmissions by Oostende Navtex (M) and (T).

Antwerpen Radio, on VHF Ch 24, broadcasts gale warnings on receipt and after the next two silent periods. Also strong wind warnings (F6+) on receipt and at H+03 and H+48. All valid for the Schelde estuary.

5.10.2   Radio broadcasting

BRTN Radio 1 (Belgische Radio en Televisie) broadcasts weather messages in Dutch after the news at 0600, 0700, 0800, 0900, 1700 and 2200LT. The frequencies are 927 kHz, 91·7 MHz, 94·2 MHz, 95·7 MHz and 98·5 MHz. The weather messages include the present situation, forecast for 24 hrs, outlook for the next few days and windspeed; valid for sea areas Humber, Thames, Dover, Wight and Portland.

5.11   NETHERLANDS

5.11.1   Netherlands Coast Guard (PBK)

Netherlands CG, based at IJmuiden, issues gale warnings as follows:

a.   On receipt and at the times given on page 87, via IJmuiden Navtex (P) in **English** .

b.   On receipt and every 4 hrs from 0333UT: via VHF Ch 73 broadcasts in Dutch by stations at Zoutelande, Goes, Hoek van Holland, IJmuiden, Enkhuizen, Huisduinen, Platform L4, Terschelling and Schiermonnikoog.

c.   On receipt and every 4 hrs from 0333UT, via MF 3673kHz in Dutch.
          Gale warnings are for the IJsselmeer and up to 30M off the Dutch coast; also for sea areas Viking, Forties, Fisher, Dogger, German Bight, Humber, Thames and Dover.

Navigational warnings are also issued at the same times, VHF channel/MF frequency as in (b) and (c).

5.11.2   Scheveningen Coast Radio Station (PCH)

5.11.2.1   VHF weather broadcasts

Weather messages are broadcast at 0805, 1305, 1905 and 2305LT by the stations and on the VHF channels shown below. The messages include strong breeze warnings, a synopsis, wind forecasts for up to 24 hrs. They are valid for Dutch coastal waters up to 30M offshore and the IJsselmeer. Strong breeze and gale warnings are also issued by the Netherlands Coastguard (see above).

Westkapelle Ch 23, **Rotterdam** Ch 87, **Scheveningen** Ch 83, **Haarlem** Ch 25, **Wieringermeer** Ch 27, **Platform L7** Ch 84, **Terschelling** Ch 78, **Nes** Ch 23, **Appingedam** Ch 27.

5.11.2.1   MF weather broadcasts

Scheveningen Radio broadcasts weather messages in English and Dutch daily at 0940 and 2140UT on 1713 kHz and 1890 kHz. The messages include: Near gale warnings, synopsis, 12hrs forecast, outlook for further 24hrs, and reports from coastal stations. The areas covered are the southern North Sea, Dutch coastal waters up to 30M offshore and the IJsselmeer. Gale warnings are broadcast by Netherlands Coastguard (see above).

C5

Fig 5(7)
NORTH SEA
Shipping forecast areas
As used by:
    France
    Belgium
    Netherlands
    Germany
    Norway
    United Kingdom

Notes:
(1)   Plain numbers refer to UK and French forecast areas.
(2)   Numbers in brackets with prefix N refer to German forecast areas (N1) – (N4) and (N8) – (N12); and to Norwegian areas (N1) – (N4) and (N8) – (N10).

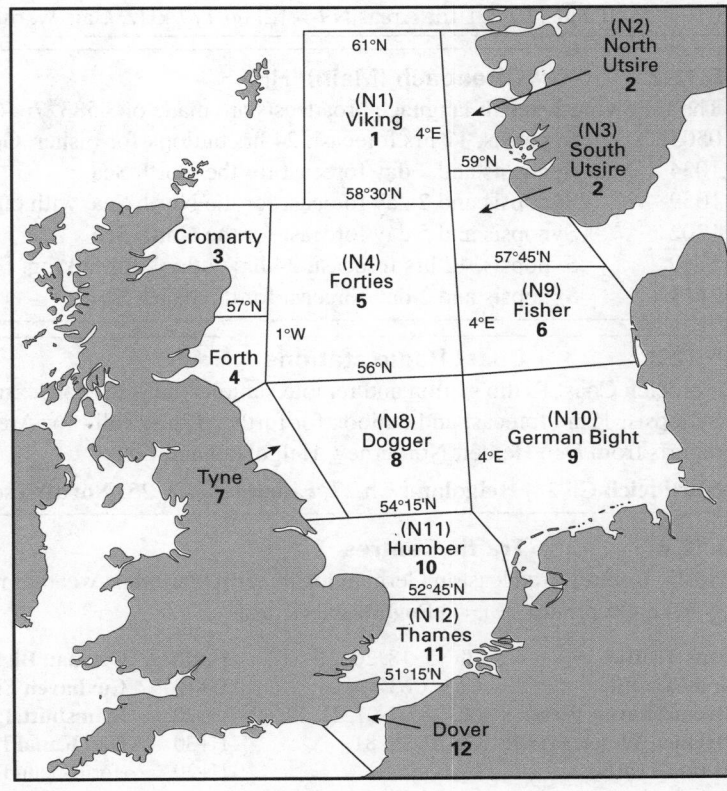

5.12   GERMANY

The German weather service (*Der Deutsche Wetterdienst*) provides weather information through a databank which is updated twice daily; more often for weather reports and textual forecasts. SEEWIS (Marine weather information system) allows data to be accessed by telephone/modem and fed into an onboard computer. The address is: German Weather Service – Shipping section, PO Box 30 11 90, 20304 Hamburg.

☎ +49 (0)40 31 90 88 14; 🖅 +49 (0)40 31 90 88 03. See also 8.21.7 for recorded telephone forecasts.

5.12.1   Radio broadcasting

5.12.1.1   Norddeutscher Rundfunk (NDR)

a.   NDR 1 Welle Nord (FM)

Weather messages in German, comprising synopsis, 12hrs forecast and 24 hrs outlook, are broadcast at 0830LT(1 May - 30 Sept) for Helgoland, Elbe and North Frisian coast, by the following stations:
Helgoland 88·9 MHz; **Hamburg** 89·5 MHz; **Flensburg** 89·6 MHz; **Heide** 90·5 MHz; **Sylt** 90·9 MHz.

b.   NDR 4 Hamburg (MW)

Weather messages in German, comprising synopsis, 12hrs forecast and 24 hrs outlook, are broadcast at 0005, 0830 and 2220LT on 702 & 972 kHz for Areas N9–N12.

5.12.1.2   Radio Bremen (RB1) (MW and FM)

Weather messages in German, comprising synopsis, 12hrs forecast and 24 hrs outlook, are broadcast at 0930 and 2305LT for Areas N9-N12, by the following stations:
Hansawelle 936, 6190 kHz; **Bremerhaven** 89·3 MHz; **Bremen** 93·8 MHz.

Also, about 0930LT, wind forecast for Weser-Ems area; and synopsis and forecast for next 12hrs in German Bight.

5.12.1.3   Deutschlandfunk (Köln) (MW)

Weather messages in German, comprising synopsis, 12hrs forecast and 24 hrs outlook, are broadcast at 0105, 0640 and 1105LT for Areas N9-N12, on 1269 kHz.

5.12.1.4   Deutschland Radio (Berlin) (LW)

Weather messages in German, comprising synopsis, 12hrs forecast and 24 hrs outlook, are broadcast at 0105, 0640 and 1105LT for Areas N9-N12, on 177 kHz. Gale warnings in German follow the news.

5.12.2   Offenbach (Main) (HF)

The following **English** language broadcasts are made on 4583, 7646 and 10100·8 kHz:

0505UT	Synopsis, 12 hrs forecast, 24 hrs outlook for Fisher, German Bight and English Channel
1034	Synopsis and 2 day forecast for the North Sea
1059	Synopsis and 2 day forecast for the North Sea, with outlook for the next few days
1202	Synopsis and 5 day forecast for the North Sea
1740	Synopsis, 12 hrs forecast, 24 hrs outlook for Viking, Forties, Dogger, Fisher and German Bight
2113	Synopsis and 2 day forecast for the North Sea

5.12.3   Coast Radio stations

Nordeich Coast Radio station and remote stations (below) broadcast in German at 0800 and 1900LT: Synopsis, 12hrs forecast and outlook for further 12hrs, valid for Areas N9-N12; followed by weather reports from Den Helder, Norderney, Helgoland and List,

Norddeich Ch 28; **Helgoland** Ch 27; **Eiderstedt** Ch 25; **Nordfrieseland** Ch 26; **Elbe-Weser** Ch 24

5.12.4   Traffic Centres

Traffic Centres broadcast in German local storm warnings, weather messages, visibility and ice reports (when appropriate). (E) = in **English** and German.

Ems Traffic	Ch 15, 18, 20, 21	H+50	**German Bight Traffic** (E)	Ch 80	H+00
Jade Traffic	Ch 20, 63	H+10	**Cuxhaven Elbe Traffic** (E)	Ch 71 (outer Elbe)	H+55
Bremerhaven Weser	02, 04, 05, 07, 21, 22, 82	H+20	**Brunsbüttel Elbe Tfc** (E)	Ch 68 (inner Elbe)	H+05
Bremen Weser Traffic	Ch 19, 78, 81	H+30	**Kiel Kanal II**	Ch 02	H+15
Hunte Traffic	Ch 63	H+30	(for E-bound vessels, in **English** on request)		and H+45

Chapter 6
Safety

Contents

6.1 SAFETY EQUIPMENT   Page 102
6.1.1 A Safety philosophy
6.1.2 Safety equipment – legal requirements
6.1.3 Safety equipment – for sea-going
       yachts 5·5 – 13·7m LOA

6.2 DEFINITIONS OF EMERGENCY 103
6.2.1 Distress
6.2.2 Urgency
6.2.3 Safety

6.3 DISTRESS SIGNALS   103
6.3.1 Authority
6.3.2 Mobile telephones
6.3.3 Visual and audible distress signals

6.4 MAYDAY CALLS   103
6.4.1 Sending a MAYDAY
6.4.2 MAYDAY acknowledgement
6.4.3 MAYDAY relay
6.4.4 Control of MAYDAY traffic

6.5 URGENCY AND SAFETY   104
6.5.1 Pan-Pan signal
6.5.2 Medical help: Pan-Pan Medico
6.5.3 Sécurité signal

6.6 GMDSS   105
6.6.1 Introduction
6.6.2 Objective
6.6.3 Distress alerting
6.6.4 Communications
6.6.5 Sea Areas
6.6.6 Maritime Safety Information (MSI)

6.7 EPIRBs   106
6.7.1 Types and installation
6.7.2 Operation
6.7.3 Registration and false alerts
6.7.4 SART

6.8 SEARCH AND RESCUE – UK 107
6.8.1 Introduction
6.8.2 Raising the alarm
6.8.3 Royal National Lifeboat Institution

6.9 HM COASTGUARD   108
6.9.1 Organisation
6.9.2 Functions
Table 6(1) HM Coastguard MRCCs/MRSCs
6.9.3 Emergency VHF DF   110
6.9.4 Yacht and Boat Safety Scheme
6.9.5 National Coastwatch Institution 112
6.9.6 Signals used in distress
6.9.7 Helicopter rescue   113
6.9.8 Abandon ship

6.10 HAZARDS   113
6.10.1 Submarines
6.10.2 Subfacts
6.10.3 Gunfacts

6.11 SAR – EIRE/CONTINENT 114
6.11.1 Ireland
6.11.2 France   114
Table 6(2) CROSS Stations
6.11.3 Belgium   116
6.11.4 Netherlands
6.11.5 Germany   116

C6

Summary

This chapter gives information about safety equipment, emergency signals, the Global Maritime Distress and Safety System (GMDSS), HM Coastguard and SAR operations in Europe.

The following subjects are described in more detail in Chapter 8 of *The Macmillan and Silk Cut Yachtsman's Handbook*: safety equipment; radar reflectors; bilge pumps; fire fighting; life jackets; safety harnesses; man overboard; life rafts; distress signals; SAR organisation; abandoning ship; helicopter rescues and first aid afloat.

6.1   SAFETY EQUIPMENT

6.1.1   A Safety philosophy

The sea demands definite qualities in the mariner – certain attitudes of mind and character: Humility, prudence and a recognition that there is no end to learning and to the acquisition of experience. Humility first because who would dare to be other than humble in the presence of the two great elements – sea and sky – and all the uncertainties which they hold for us? Prudence second – it is the ingrained characteristic of the professional seaman – the ability to distinguish between the risk which can reasonably be accepted, having regard to prevailing conditions, and the risk which must be rejected as unacceptable. Lastly learn by your own experience and by the experience of others, so that there is never an end to your learning.

The skipper is responsible for the safety of the boat and all on board. He must ensure that:
(1)   The boat is suitable in design and in construction for her intended purpose.
(2)   The boat is maintained in good condition.
(3)   The crew is competent and sufficiently strong.
(4)   The necessary safety and emergency equipment is carried, is in good condition, and the crew know how to use it.

Safety guidelines for recreational boat users can be found in a useful booklet *Safety on the Sea* published jointly by the RNLI, HM Coastguard and the RYA.

Simple precautions can eliminate accidents. Be particularly careful with bottled gas and petrol. Fit a gas detector. Turn off the gas at the bottle after use. If gas or petrol is smelt – no naked lights, and do not run electrical equipment. Test systems regularly. Carry adequate spares. Insist that crew wear life jackets and harnesses when necessary, and that they do clip on. Make sure a good lookout is maintained at all times. Listen to every forecast. Double-check all navigational calculations. Take nothing for granted.

Individual crew members are responsible for their personal gear. Nonslip shoes or boots are essential. So is foul-weather clothing with close fastenings at neck, wrists and ankles. At least two changes of sailing clothing should be carried, including warm sweaters and towelling strips as neck scarves. Other personal items include a seaman's knife and spike on a lanyard, a waterproof torch, and a supply of anti-seasick pills. Life jacket and safety harnesses are usually supplied on board, but if individuals bring their own, the skipper should make certain they are up to standard.

6.1.2   Safety equipment – legal requirements

Yachts > 45ft (13·7m) LOA are required by law to carry certain safety equipment. All yachts must carry navigation lights and sound signals which comply with the IRPCS. Racing yachts must carry the safety equipment specified for the class/event concerned.

6.1.3   Recommended Safety equipment for sea-going yachts 5·5 – 13·7m LOA

The minimum equipment which should be carried for (a) coastal and (b) offshore cruising is listed below.

Safety equipment list

	Coastal	Offshore
Personal safety		
Life jackets, BS3595, or CE equivalent per person	1	1
Harnesses, BS4224, or CE equivalent per person	1	1
Navigation		
Charts, almanac, pilot	Yes	Yes
Compass with deviation card	1	1
Hand bearing compass	1	1
Chart table instruments	Yes	Yes
Watch/clock	1	2
Echo sounder	1	1
Lead line	1	1
GPS/Loran/Decca	1	1
Radio receiver (forecasts)	1	1
Barometer	1	1
Navigation lights	Yes	Yes
Radar reflector	1	1
Foghorn	1	1
Powerful waterproof torch	1	1
Anchor with warp or chain	2	2
Towline	1	1
Man overboard		
Life buoy, with drogue and light	2	2
Buoyant heaving line	1	1
Dan buoy	–	1
Rope (or boarding) ladder	1	1
Fire		
Fire-extinguishers	2	3
Fire blanket	1	1
Flooding		
Bilge pumps	2	2
Buckets with lanyards	2	2
Leak stopping gear	Yes	Yes
Distress signals		
Hand flares, red	2	4
Hand flares, white (warning)	4	4
Red parachute rockets	2	4
Hand smoke signals	2	–
Buoyant orange smoke signals	–	–
Emergency radio transmitter	–	1
Abandon ship		
Life raft for whole crew	1	1
	or	
Dinghy with buoyancy, or inflated inflatable	1	–
Panic bag, extra water, etc.	–	1
Miscellaneous		
First-aid kit	1	1
Engine toolkit	1	1
Name/number prominently displayed	Yes	Yes
Storm canvas	Yes	Yes
Emergency steering arrangements	Yes	Yes

6.2   DEFINITIONS OF EMERGENCY

6.2.1   Distress

Distress is the most serious degree of emergency. It applies to any situation where a boat or person is threatened by grave and imminent danger and requests immediate assistance. The RT prefix associated with a Distress message is MAYDAY – see 6.4. A Distress call has priority over all other transmissions.

6.2.2   Urgency

Urgency is a lesser degree of emergency concerning the safety of a boat or person. Examples include, a vessel disabled but not sinking; medical problems (see also 6.5.2). The RT prefix associated with an Urgency message is PAN PAN – see 6.5.1.

6.2.3   Safety

Safety is the least serious degree of emergency, usually associated with a warning of hazardous navigational or meteorological circumstances. The RT prefix associated with a Safety message is SÉCURITÉ – see 6.5.3.

6.3   DISTRESS SIGNALS

6.3.1   Authority

Distress signals must only be made with the authority of the skipper, and only if the boat or a person is in grave and imminent danger, and help is urgently required; or on behalf of another vessel in distress, which for some reason is unable to make a Distress signal. When the problem is resolved, the Distress call must be cancelled by whatever means are available.

6.3.2   Mobile telephones

The use of a mobile telephone to call the Coastguard on 999 (or 112) is **NOT** considered an adequate substitute for radio communication on VHF Ch 16 or 2182 kHz, when a vessel is in a distress or other emergency situation. Mobile telephones should at best be regarded as complementary to VHF radio. They have limited coverage, even in coastal waters, and are not monitored in any way; unlike Ch 16, which at present is continuously monitored by HM CG. A mobile telephone call cannot be heard by vessels nearby which might be able to help. Mobile telephones represent another link in the chain of communication. Other vessels cannot be called by mobile telephone unless so fitted and the number is known. On-scene SAR communication may be correspondingly hampered. Mobile telephones are therefore very strongly discouraged.

6.3.3   Visual and audible distress signals

A full list of the recognised distress signals is given in Annex IV of the IRPCS. The following are those most appropriate to yachts and small craft, together with notes on their use.

(a)   Continuous sounding of any fog signalling apparatus.

In order to avoid confusion, this is best done by a succession of letters SOS in Morse (··· ——— ···).

(b)   An SOS signal made by any method.

For a yacht the most likely methods are by sound signal as in (1) above, or by flashing light.

(c)   The International Code signal 'NC'.

This can be made by flag hoist, see Plate 6.

(d)   A square flag with a ball, or anything resembling a ball, above or below it.

This is not too difficult to contrive from any square flag, and a round fender or anchor ball.

(e)   A rocket parachute flare or a hand-held flare showing a red light.

A red flare is the most effective distress signal at night. Flares serve two purposes: first to raise the alarm, and then to pinpoint the boat's position. Within about three miles from land a hand flare will do both. At greater distances a red parachute rocket (which projects a suspended flare to a height of more than 1,000ft, or 300m, and which burns for more than 40 seconds) is needed to raise the alarm, but hand flares are useful to indicate the boat's position.

Hold hand flares firmly, downwind of yourself. Rockets turn into wind; fire them vertically in normal conditions, or aim about 15° downwind in strong winds. Do not aim them into wind, or they will not gain altitude. If there is low cloud, fire rockets at 45° downwind, so that the flare burns under the cloud.

Note: White flares are not distress signals, but are used to indicate your presence to another vessel on a collision course for example. An outfit of four is suggested for boats which make night passages. Shield your eyes when using them, to protect night vision.

(f)   An orange-coloured smoke signal.

By day orange smoke signals (hand-held for short distances, or a larger buoyant type for greater ranges) are more effective than flares, although the smoke disperses quickly in a strong wind.

(g)   Slow and repeated raising/lowering of arms outstretched to each side.

The arms should be raised and lowered together, above and below the horizontal.

6.4   MAYDAY CALLS

6.4.1.   Sending a MAYDAY call

This should normally be transmitted on VHF Ch 16 or 2182 kHz, but any frequency may be used if help may thereby be obtained more quickly.

Distress, Urgency and Safety messages from vessels at sea are free of charge. A distress call has priority over all other transmissions. If heard, cease all transmissions that may interfere with the distress call or messages, and listen on the frequency concerned.

Train your crew, as necessary, so that everybody can send a distress message. It is very helpful to display the MAYDAY message format close to the radio. Before making the call, first:

C6

- Check main battery switch ON
- Switch radio ON, and select HIGH power (25 watts)
- Select VHF Ch 16 (or 2182 kHz for MF)
- Press and hold down the transmit button, and say slowly and distinctly:
- *MAYDAY MAYDAY MAYDAY*
- *THIS IS* .... (name of boat, spoken 3 times)
- *MAYDAY* ...... (name of boat spoken once)
- *MY POSITION IS* .... (latitude and longitude, or true bearing and distance from a known point)
- Nature of distress ..... (sinking, on fire, etc.)
- Aid required .... (immediate assistance)
- Number of persons on board ....
- Any other important, helpful information (eg if the yacht is drifting, whether distress rockets are being fired)
- *OVER*.

On completion of the distress message, release the transmit button and listen. The yacht's position is of vital importance, and should be repeated if time allows.

6.4.2   MAYDAY acknowledgement
In coastal waters an immediate acknowledgment should be expected, as follows:

MAYDAY .... (name of station sending the distress message, spoken three times)
THIS IS .... (name of station acknowledging, spoken three times)
RECEIVED MAYDAY.

If an acknowledgment is not received, check the set and repeat the distress call. For 2182 kHz the call should be repeated during the three-minute silence periods which commence at H+00 and H+30.

If you hear a distress message, write down the details, and if you can help you should acknowledge accordingly, but only after giving an opportunity for the nearest coast station or some larger vessel to do so.

6.4.3   MAYDAY relay
If you hear a distress message from a vessel, and it is not acknowledged, you should pass on the message as follows:

MAYDAY RELAY .... (spoken 3 times)
THIS IS .... (name of vessel re-transmitting the distress message, spoken three times)
Followed by the intercepted message.

6.4.4   Control of MAYDAY traffic
A MAYDAY call imposes general radio silence, until the vessel concerned or some other authority (e.g. the nearest Coastguard or coast radio station) cancels the distress. If necessary the station controlling distress traffic may impose radio silence as follows:

SEELONCE MAYDAY, followed by its name or other identification, on the distress frequency.

If some other station nearby believes it necessary to do likewise, it may transmit:

SEELONCE DISTRESS, followed by its name or other identification.

6.4.4.1 Relaxing radio silence
When appropriate the station controlling distress traffic may relax radio silence so that normal working is resumed with caution on the distress frequency, with subsequent communications from the casualty prefixed by the Urgency signal (below).

When complete radio silence is no longer necessary on a frequency being used for distress traffic, the controlling station may relax radio silence as follows, indicating that restricted working may be resumed:

MAYDAY
HELLO ALL STATIONS (spoken 3 times)
THIS IS .... (name or callsign)
The time ....
The name of the vessel in distress ....
PRUDONCE

If distress working continues on other frequencies these will be identified. For example, PRUDONCE on 500 kHz (WT distress frequency) and 2182 kHz, but SEELONCE on VHF Ch 16.

6.4.4.2 Cancelling radio silence
When all distress traffic has ceased, normal working is authorised as follows:

MAYDAY
HELLO ALL STATIONS (spoken 3 times)
THIS IS .... (name or callsign)
The time ....
The name of the vessel in distress
SEELONCE FEENEE.

6.5   URGENCY AND SAFETY

6.5.1   Pan-Pan – Urgency signal
The R/T Urgency signal, consisting of the words PAN-PAN spoken three times, indicates that a vessel, or station, has a very urgent message concerning the safety of a ship or person. Messages prefixed by PAN PAN take priority over all traffic except distress, and are sent on VHF Ch 16 or on 2182 kHz. The Urgency signal is appropriate when someone is lost overboard or urgent medical advice or attention is needed. It should be cancelled when the urgency is over.

Here is an example of an Urgency call and message from the yacht *Seabird,* disabled off the Needles.

PAN-PAN, PAN-PAN, PAN-PAN
Hello all stations (spoken 3 times)
This is yacht SEABIRD, SEABIRD, SEABIRD
Two nine zero degrees two miles from Needles lighthouse
Dismasted and propeller fouled
Anchor dragging and drifting east north east towards Shingles Bank
Require urgent tow
Over.

If the message itself is long or is a medical call, or communications traffic is heavy, it should be passed on a working frequencyafter an initial call on Ch 16 or 2182 kHz. Where necessary this should be indicated at the end of the initial call.

If you hear an Urgency call you should respond in the same way as for a Distress call.

If help is needed, but the boat is in no immediate danger, the proper signal is 'V' (Victor) International Code, meaning 'I require assistance'. This can be sent as a flag signal (see Plate 7), or by light or sound in Morse code ($\cdots$ —).

6.5.2   Medical help by RT
Medical advice can be obtained through any UK Coast radio station by calling on a working channel and asking for a Medico call. Medico calls are free. A Medico message should contain:
(1) Yacht's name, call sign and nationality.
(2) Yacht's position, next port of call (with ETA) and nearest harbour if required to divert.
(3) Patient's details: name, age, sex, medical history.
(4) Present symptoms and advice required.
(5) What medication is carried on board.

Urgent requests for medical advice should be made on Ch 16 (or 2182 kHz if out of VHF range) direct to HM Coastguard who will arrange with the Coast radio station for a priority, dedicated channel so that your call is connected to a doctor.

Calls for medical assistance (eg the presence of a doctor or a casualty to be off-lifted) should be made direct to HM Coastguard on Ch 16. If such a call is received by a Coast radio station it will be referred to HM Coastguard.

In emergency call PAN PAN MEDICO on Ch 16. PAN PAN Medico applies in other countries. For France call: PAN PAN Radiomédical (name of station) in French. For Belgium call: Radiomédical Oostende, in French, Dutch, English or German. For Netherlands call: PAN PAN Medico, in Dutch, English, French or German and expect response from Netherland's CG. For Germany call: PAN PAN Medico with details in German or English; this type of call is more widely used by Germans than *Funkarzt* (plus name of station).

The International Code signal 'W' (Whiskey $\cdot$ — —), means 'I require medical assistance' and can be made by a number of means; see 4.1.2.

6.5.3   Sécurité – Safety signal
This consists of the word SÉCURITÉ (pronounced SAY-CURE-E-TAY) spoken three times, and indicates that the station is about to transmit an important navigational or meteorological warning. Such messages usually originate from a coast station, and are transmitted on a working frequency after an announcement on the distress frequency.

Safety messages are usually addressed to 'All stations', and are often transmitted at the end of the first available silence period.

6.6   GMDSS

6.6.1   Introduction
The Global Maritime Distress and Safety System (GMDSS) is an improved maritime distress and safety communications system adopted by the International Maritime Organisation (IMO).

Before the advent of GMDSS, maritime distress and safety relied heavily on ships and coast radio stations keeping continuous watch on the three main international distress frequencies: 500 kHz (Morse) and R/T on 2182 kHz and VHF Ch 16. When out of range of coast radio stations, only ships in the vicinity of a distress incident could render assistance.

GMDSS was introduced in February 1992 and is scheduled to be fully implemented by February 1999. After this date the old system will operate in parallel with the new for a while. The speed with which shore stations become GMDSS-capable varies from sea area to sea area according to national policies.

Recommended reading:
ALRS, Vol 5. (UK Hydrographic Office).
GMDSS for small craft. (Clemmetsen/Fernhurst).
VHF DSC Handbook. (Fletcher/Reed's Publications).

6.6.2   Objective
The objective of GMDSS is to alert SAR authorities ashore and ships in the vicinity to a distress incident by means of satellite communications and navigation systems. As a result a coordinated SAR operation can be mounted rapidly and reliably anywhere in the world. GMDSS also provides urgency and safety communications, and promulgates Marine Safety Information (MSI); see 6.6.6.

Regardless of the sea areas in which they operate, vessels complying with GMDSS must be able to perform certain functions:
* transmit ship-to-shore distress alerts by two independent means;
* transmit ship-to-ship distress alerts;
* transmit and receive safety information eg navigation and weather warnings;
* transmit signals for locating incidents;
* receive shore-to-ship distress alerts;
* receive ship-to-ship distress alerts;
* transmit and receive communications for SAR co-ordination.

GMDSS regulations apply to all ships over 300 tons engaged in international voyages, but they affect all seagoing craft. Although not obligatory for yachts, some features of GMDSS are already of interest and, as equipment becomes more affordable, yachtsmen may decide to fit GMDSS voluntarily. This will become an increasing necessity as the present system for sending and receiving distress calls is run down.

6.6.3   Distress alerting
GMDSS requires participating ships to be able to send distress alerts by two out of three independent means. These are:

C6

1   **Digital selective calling** (DSC) using VHF Ch 70, MF 2187·5 kHz, or HF distress and alerting frequencies in the 4, 6, 8,12 and 16 MHz bands.

2   **EPIRBs** (406 MHz/121·5MHz; float-free or manually operated) using the Cospas/Sarsat satellite system; or the Inmarsat system in the 1·6 GHz band. Both types transmit distress messages which include the position and identification of the vessel in distress. See 6.v.v for further details of EPIRBs.

3   **Inmarsat**, via ship terminals.

6.6.4   Communications
GMDSS uses both terrestrial and satellite-based communications. Terrestrial communications, ie VHF, MF and HF, are employed in Digital Selective Calling (see below). Satellite communications come in the form of INMARSAT and Cospas/Sarsat (6.6.4.2/3).

6.6.4.1 Digital Selective Calling
DSC is a fundamental part of GMDSS. It is so called because information is sent by a burst of *digital* code; *selective* because it is addressed to another DSC radiotelephone. Under GMDSS, every vessel and relevant shore stations has a 9-digit identification number, known as an MMSI (Maritime Mobile Service Identity) that is used for identification in all DSC messages.

DSC is used to transmit distress alerts from ships, and to receive distress acknowledgments from ships or shore stations. DSC can also be used for relay purposes and for Urgency, Safety and routine calling and answering.

In practice, a DSC distress call sent on VHF might work roughly as follows:
Yachtsman presses the distress button; the set automatically switches to Ch 70 and transmits a coded distress message before reverting to Ch 16.

Any ship will reply directly by voice on Ch 16. But a CRS would send a distress acknowledgment on Ch 70 (automatically turning off the distress transmission), before replying on Ch 16. If a distress acknowledgment is not received from a CRS, the call will automatically be repeated about every four minutes.

6.6.4.2 Inmarsat
Inmarsat (International Maritime Satellite system), via four geostationary satellites, provides near-global communications except in the polar regions above about 70°N and 70°S.

Additionally, 1·6 GHz satellite EPIRBs, operating through Inmarsat, can also be used for alerting as an alternative to 406 MHz EPIRBs which use Cospas/Sarsat.

6.6.4.3 Cospas/Sarsat
The US/Russian Cospas/Sarsat satellites complement the various other Satcom systems. They not only detect an emergency signal transmitted by an EPIRB, but also locate it to a high degree of accuracy. There are four Cospas/Sarsat satellites operating in low polar orbits. In addition to these, 406 MHz repeater systems are operating on board five geostationary satellites.

6.6.5   Sea Areas
For the purposes of GMDSS, the world's sea area are divided into four categories in each of which ships must carry certain types of radio equipment:

A1 an area within RT coverage of at least one VHF coast radio station in which continuous alerting via DSC is available. Range: approximately 40 miles from the CRS.

A2 an area, excluding sea area Al, within RT coverage of at least one MF CRS in which continuous DSC alerting is available. Range: roughly 100-150 miles from the CRS.

A3 an area, excluding sea areas Al and A2, within coverage of an Inmarsat satellite in which continuous alerting is available.

A4 an area outside sea areas A1, A2 and A3. In practice this means the polar regions.

The UK has declared its coastal waters to be an A1 area, but intends to continue guarding Channel 16 for some time ahead. VHF DSC is operational at all UK Coastguard stations.

In 1995 France declared the English Channel to be an A1 area. As most UK yachtsmen will operate in an A1 area, a VHF radio and a Navtex receiver will initially meet GMDSS requirements. As suitable VHF DSC sets become available (and affordable) it will make sense to re-equip with DSC equipment.

6.6.6   Maritime Safety Information (MSI)
MSI refers to the vital meteorological, navigational and SAR messages which, traditionally, have been broadcast to vessels at sea by CRSs in Morse and by RT on VHF and MF.

GMDSS broadcasts MSI in English by two independent but complementary means, Navtex and SafetyNet:
Navtex on MF (518 kHz) covers coastal/offshore waters out to about 300 miles from transmitters.
SafetyNet uses the Inmarsat communications satellites to cover beyond MF range. The Enhanced Group Call (EGC) service is a part of SafetyNet which enables MSI to be sent selectively by Inmarsat-C satellites to groups of users in any of the 4 oceans.

MSI is prepared/coordinated by the nations which control the 16 Navareas used for Nav and Met warnings; see 4.8.1. The UK controls Navarea I, which covers the Atlantic between 48°27'N and 71°N, out to 40°W.

6.7   EPIRBs (Emergency Position Indicating Radio Beacons)

6.7.1   Types and installation
There are two types of approved EPIRB, those transmitting on the emergency frequencies of 121·5 MHz (civilian aeronautical distress) or 406 MHz, or both. A third type transmits on 243·0 MHz (military aeronautical distress). 121·5 MHz and 243·0 MHz are

monitored by Air Traffic Control and many aircraft; survivors should switch on an EPIRB without delay.

Dependent on type, they must be installed in a proper location so they can float free and automatically activate if the yacht sinks. Many EPIRBs have lanyards intended to secure the EPIRB to a life raft or person in the water and lanyards must not be used for securing the EPIRB to the yacht. Such action will clearly prevent a float-free type from activating and would be lost with the yacht should it sink.

6.7.2   Operation
All three frequencies can be picked up by the Cospas/Sarsat (C-S) system which uses four near-polar orbital satellites to detect and localise the signals. The processed positions are passed automatically to a Mission Control Centre (MCC) for assessment of any SAR action required; the UK MCC is co-located with RCC Plymouth.

C-S location accuracy is normally better than 5 km on 406 MHz and better than 20 km on 121·5 and 243·0 MHz. Dedicated SAR aircraft can home on 121·5 MHz and 243·0 MHz, but not on 406 MHz. Typically a helicopter at 1,000 feet can receive homing signals from about 30M range whilst a fixed-wing aircraft at higher altitudes is capable of homing from about 60M. Airliners flying on commercial air routes often receive and relay information on alerts on 121·5 MHz EPIRBs at up to 200M range. Best results are likely to be obtained from those 406 MHz EPIRBs which also transmit a 121·5 MHz signal for homing.

6.7.3   Registration and false alerts
406 MHz EPIRBs transmit data with a unique code which identifies the individual beacon. It is therefore essential that all 406 MHz EPIRBs are registered at: The EPIRB Register, HM Coastguard South Western, Pendennis Point, Castle Drive, Falmouth TR11 4WZ. Changes of ownership of a 406 MHz EPIRB, or its disposal, should also be notified.

False alerts caused by inadvertent or incorrect use of EPIRBs puts a significant burden on SAR resources. The likelihood of a false alert coinciding with a genuine distress situation is real; in consequence SAR forces could be delayed in responding to a genuine distress – with tragic results.

If an EPIRB is activated, whether accidentally or intentionally, make every reasonable effort to advise the SAR authorities.

6.7.4   SART
A SART (SAR transponder) is not an EPIRB; it is more akin to a small portable Racon. When interrogated by a search radar a SART responds with a series of easily identifiable blips visible on the radar screen. It is often carried in life rafts to assist searching ships and aircraft in finding survivors; it should be mounted at least 1m above sea level. It operates on 9GHz and has a range of about 5M from a ship's radar, and up to 40M from an aircraft.

6.8   SEARCH AND RESCUE (SAR) – UK

6.8.1   Introduction
Around the United Kingdom, the lead authority is HM Coastguard, which initiates and co-ordinates all civil maritime SAR. To assist, Coast radio stations control ship/shore communications (see 4.4.1); the RNLI provide lifeboats; the Royal Navy helps with ships; and the Royal Air Force, through military Aeronautical Rescue Co-ordination Centres (ARCC) at Kinloss and Plymouth, controls military helicopters and fixed-wing aircraft for SAR. Air Traffic Control Centres (ATCC) monitor air distress frequencies.

The ARCC at Plymouth also mans the UK Cospas/Sarsat Mission Control Centre (MCC) which receives satellite data from emergency distress beacons on 121·5 MHz, 243·0 MHz and 406 MHz (6.6.4.3).

6.8.2   Raising the alarm
If an incident afloat is seen from shore, dial 999 and ask for the Coastguard. You will be asked to report on the incident, and possibly to stay near the telephone for further communications. If at sea you receive a distress signal and you are in a position to give assistance, you are obliged to do so with all speed, unless, or until, you are specifically released.

When alerted the Coastguard summons the most appropriate help, ie they may direct vessels in the vicinity of the distress; request the launch of an RNLI lifeboat; scramble a military or Coastguard SAR helicopter; other vessels may be alerted through Coast Radio Stations or by satellite communications.

6.8.3   Royal National Lifeboat Institution (RNLI)
The RNLI is a registered charity which exists to save life at sea. It provides, on call, a 24-hour lifeboat service up to 50M out from the coasts of the UK and Irish Republic. There are 215 lifeboat stations, at which are stationed 289 lifeboats ranging from 4·9 to 17·0m in length. These consist of 123 all-weather, three intermediate and 163 inshore lifeboats. There are over 100 lifeboats in the reserve fleet.

All are capable of at least 15 knots, and new lifeboats capable of 25 knots are being introduced.

When launched on service, lifeboats over 10m keep watch on 2182 kHz and Ch 16. They can also use alternative frequencies to contact other vessels, SAR aircraft, HM Coastguard or Coast radio stations or other SAR agencies. All lifeboats are fitted with VHF and show a quick-flashing blue light.

A pamphlet *Safety on the Sea*, produced by the RNLI in co-operation with the RYA, Maritime and Coastguard Agency, BMIF and the Royal Life Saving Society, offers education and guidelines on safety related topics.

Support the RNLI by becoming a member, contact: RNLI, West Quay Road, Poole, Dorset BH15 1HZ. ☎ 01202 663000. 📠 01202 663167.

C6

6.9   HM COASTGUARD

6.9.1   Organisation

HM Coastguard combined with the Marine Safety Agency in April 1998 to form the Maritime and Coastguard Agency.

The Coastguard initiates and co-ordinates SAR around the UK and over a large part of the eastern Atlantic. Its domain is divided into five Maritime Search and Rescue Regions (SRRs), each supervised by Maritime Rescue Co-ordination Centres (MRCCs) at Falmouth, Dover, Great Yarmouth, Aberdeen, the Clyde and Swansea. Each SRR is divided into districts, each under a Maritime Rescue Sub-Centre (MRSC). Their boundaries are stated in Table 6(1) and shown in the maps at the start of Areas 1–11 in Chapter 8. The telephone number of the nearest MRCC/MRSC (or other national equivalent) is shown for each harbour.

Within each of the 21 districts thus formed there is an organisation of Auxiliary Coastguard Response Teams, grouped within sectors under the management of regular Coastguard Officers. There are about 560 regular Coastguard Officers, with more than 3,500 Auxiliaries on call for emergencies. The Coastguard also has a cliff and beach rescue role.

6.9.2   Functions

For Distress, Urgency and Safety calls covering UK waters, all MRCCs and MRSCs keep watch on VHF Ch 16, and, except Oban MRSC, on 2182 kHz. All Centres also keep watch on Ch 70 and nine on 2187·5 kHz for Digital Selective Calling (see 6.6.3). VHF Ch 10, 67, 73 are working channels; Ch 67 is the Small Craft safety channel, accessed via Ch 16.

The R/T call sign of an MRCC or MRSC is its geographical name, followed by 'Coastguard' eg, *SOLENT COASTGUARD*. Note: Coastguard Centres do not accept link calls (public correspondence).

In the Dover Strait the Channel Navigation Information Service (CNIS) provides a 24 hrs radar watch and a radio safety service for all shipping; see Table 6(1).

Local navigational warnings, which may affect craft in inshore waters but outside Port and Harbour Authority limits, are broadcast on Ch 67, after an announcement on Ch 16. There is no numerical sequence, and no specific broadcast schedule; any repetition of the broadcast is at the discretion of the originating CG.

Strong wind (F6+) and gale warnings are broadcast on Ch 67 on receipt and every 2 hours. Forecasts for local sea areas are broadcast every four hours or on request. See also 5.6.1 and Table 6(1).

TABLE 6(1)   HM Coastguard MRCCs and MRSCs

Centres below marked with * were due to have had A1 DSC operational by 1997; and those with † by 1998. All others have operational A1 DSC. All A2 DSC stations are operational, as indicated by 2187·5 kHz.

SOUTHERN REGION		
FALMOUTH COASTGUARD (MRCC). 50°09'N 05°03'W.	☎: 01326 317575.	📠: 01326 318342.
Covers Marsland Mouth to Dodman Point.	Also operates 2226 kHz.	
VHF Broadcasts every 4h from 0140 LT.	DSC MMSI 002320014 2187·5 kHz, Ch 70.	
Brixham Coastguard (MRSC). 50°24'N 03°31'W.	☎: 01803 882704.	📠: 01803 882780.
Covers Dodman Point to Straight Point.		
VHF Broadcasts every 4h from 0050 LT.	DSC MMSI 002320013, Ch 70.	
Portland Coastguard (MRSC). 50°36'N 02°27'W.	☎: 01305 760439.	📠: 01305 760452.
Covers Straight Point to Chewton Bunney.		
VHF Broadcasts every 4h from 0220 LT.	DSC MMSI 002320012, Ch 70.	
Solent Coastguard (MRSC). 50°48'N 01°12'W.	☎: 01705 552100.	📠: 01705 551763.
Covers Chewton Bunney to Beachy Head (inc IOW).		
Operates Ch 67 (H24) as calling channel for safety traffic.		
VHF Broadcasts every 4h from 0040 LT.	DSC MMSI 002320011, Ch 70.	
DOVER COASTGUARD (MRCC). 50°08'N 01°12'E.	☎: 01304 210006.	📠: 01304 202137.
Covers Beachy Head to Reculver Towers. VHF Ch 16 69 (H24) 10 11 67 73 80 (HX). 2182 kHz.		
Operates Channel Navigation Information Service (CNIS) in conjunction with Gris-Nez Traffic. Call direct on Ch 69 (primary working channel) for routine CNIS traffic. CNIS broadcasts navigational and traffic information on Ch 11 every H+40 (and at H+55 in bad visibility). Weather messages every 4h from 0040 LT on Ch 11. DSC MMSI 002320010, Ch 70.		
CHANNEL ISLANDS		
St Peter Port Radio (CRS). 49°10'·85N 02°14'30W.	☎: 01534 720672.	📠: 01534 714177
Covers the Channel Islands Northern area; Alderney Radio keeps watch Ch 16 HJ.		
Jersey Radio (CRS). 49°10'·85N 02°14'30W.	☎: 01534 41121.	📠: 01534 499089
Covers the Channel Islands Southern area.	DSC MMSI 002320060 Ch 70.	

EASTERN REGION

Thames Coastguard (MRSC). 51°51'N 01°17'E.   ☎: 01255 675516.   📠: 01255 675249.
Covers Reculver Towers to Southwold.
VHF Broadcasts every 4h from 0010 LT.   DSC MMSI 002320009, Ch 70.

*YARMOUTH COASTGUARD (MRCC). 52°37'N 01°43'E.   ☎: 01493 851336.   📠: 01493 852307.
Covers Southwold to Haile Sand Fort.
VHF Broadcasts every 4h from 0040 LT.   DSC MMSI 002320006, Ch 70.

*Humber Coastguard (MRSC). 54°06'N 00°11'W.   ☎: 01262 672317.   📠: 01262 606915.
Covers Haile Sand Fort to Port Mulgrave.
VHF Broadcasts every 4h from 0340 LT.   DSC MMSI 002320007 2187·5 kHz, Ch 70.

*Tyne Tees Coastguard (MRSC). 55°01'N 01°25'W.   ☎: 0191 2572691.   📠: 0191 2580373.
Covers Port Mulgrave to Goswick.
VHF Broadcasts every 4h from 0150 LT.   DSC MMSI 002320006 2187·5 kHz, Ch 70.

EAST AND NORTH SCOTLAND

*Forth Coastguard (MRSC). 56°17'N 02°35'W.   ☎: 01333 450666.   📠: 01333 450725.
Covers Goswick to East Haven.
VHF Broadcasts every 4h from 0205 LT.   DSC MMSI 002320005, Ch 70.

*ABERDEEN COASTGUARD (MRCC). 57°08'N 02°05'W.   ☎: 01224 592334.   📠: 01224 575920.
Covers East Haven to Ord Point. Also operates 2226 2596 kHz and VHF Ch 06.
VHF Broadcasts every 4h from 0320 LT.   DSC MMSI 00230004 2187·5 kHz, Ch 70.

†Pentland Coastguard (MRSC). 58°59'N 02°57'W.   ☎: 01856 873266.   📠: 01856 874202.
Covers Ord Point to Cape Wrath, and Orkney Islands.
VHF Broadcasts every 4h from 0135 LT.   DSC MMSI 002320002, Ch 70.

†Shetland Coastguard (MRSC). 60°09'N 01°08'W.   ☎: 01595 692976.   📠: 01595 694810.
Covers Shetland Islands.
VHF Broadcasts from 0105 LT.   DSC MMSI 002320001 2187·5 kHz, Ch 70.

WEST SCOTLAND AND NORTHERN IRELAND

†Stornoway Coastguard (MRSC). 58°12'N 06°22'W.   ☎: 01851 702013/4.   📠: 01851 704387.
Covers Cape Wrath to Applecross, Western Isles.
VHF Broadcasts every 4h from 0110 LT.   DSC MMSI 002320024 2187·5 kHz, Ch 70.

†Oban Coastguard (MRSC). 56°25'N 05°29'W.   ☎: 01631 563720.   📠: 01631 564917.
Covers Applecross to Gulf of Corryvreckan. (Does not operate 2182 kHz.)
VHF Broadcasts every 4h from 0240 LT.   DSC MMSI 002320023, Ch 70.

†CLYDE COASTGUARD (MRCC). 55°58'N 04°48'W.   ☎: 01475 729988.   📠: 01475 786955.
Covers Gulf of Corryvreckan to Mull of Galloway. Also operates 2226 kHz.
VHF Broadcasts every 4h from 0020 LT.   DSC MMSI 002320022 2187·5 kHz, Ch 70.

†Belfast Coastguard (MRSC). 54°40'N 05°40'W.   ☎: 01247 463933.   📠: 01247 465886.
Covers Northern Ireland.
VHF Broadcasts every 4h from 0305 LT.   DSC MMSI 002320021, Ch 70.

WESTERN REGION

†Liverpool Coastguard (MRSC). 53°30'N 03°03'W.   ☎: 0151 931 3341.   📠: 0151 931 3347.
Covers Mull of Galloway to Queensferry.
VHF Broadcasts every 4h from 0210 LT.   DSC MMSI 002320019 Ch 70.

†Holyhead Coastguard (MRSC). 53°19'N 04°38'W.   ☎: 01407 762051.   📠: 01407 764373.
Covers Queensferry to Friog.
VHF Broadcasts every 4h from 0235 LT.   DSC MMSI 002320016, 2187·5 kHz, Ch 70.

†Milford Haven Coastguard (MRSC). 51°41'N 05°10'W.   ☎: 01646 690909.   📠: 01646 692176.
Covers Friog to River Towy.
VHF Broadcasts every 4h from 0335 LT.   DSC MMSI 002320017 2187·5 kHz, Ch 70.

†SWANSEA COASTGUARD (MRCC). 51°34'N 03°58'W.   ☎: 01792 366534.   📠: 01792 369005.
Covers River Towy to Marsland Mouth.
VHF Broadcasts every 4h from 0005 LT.   DSC MMSI 002320016, Ch 70.

C6

Fig 6(1)   EMERGENCY VHF DF STATIONS – UK AND CONTINENT

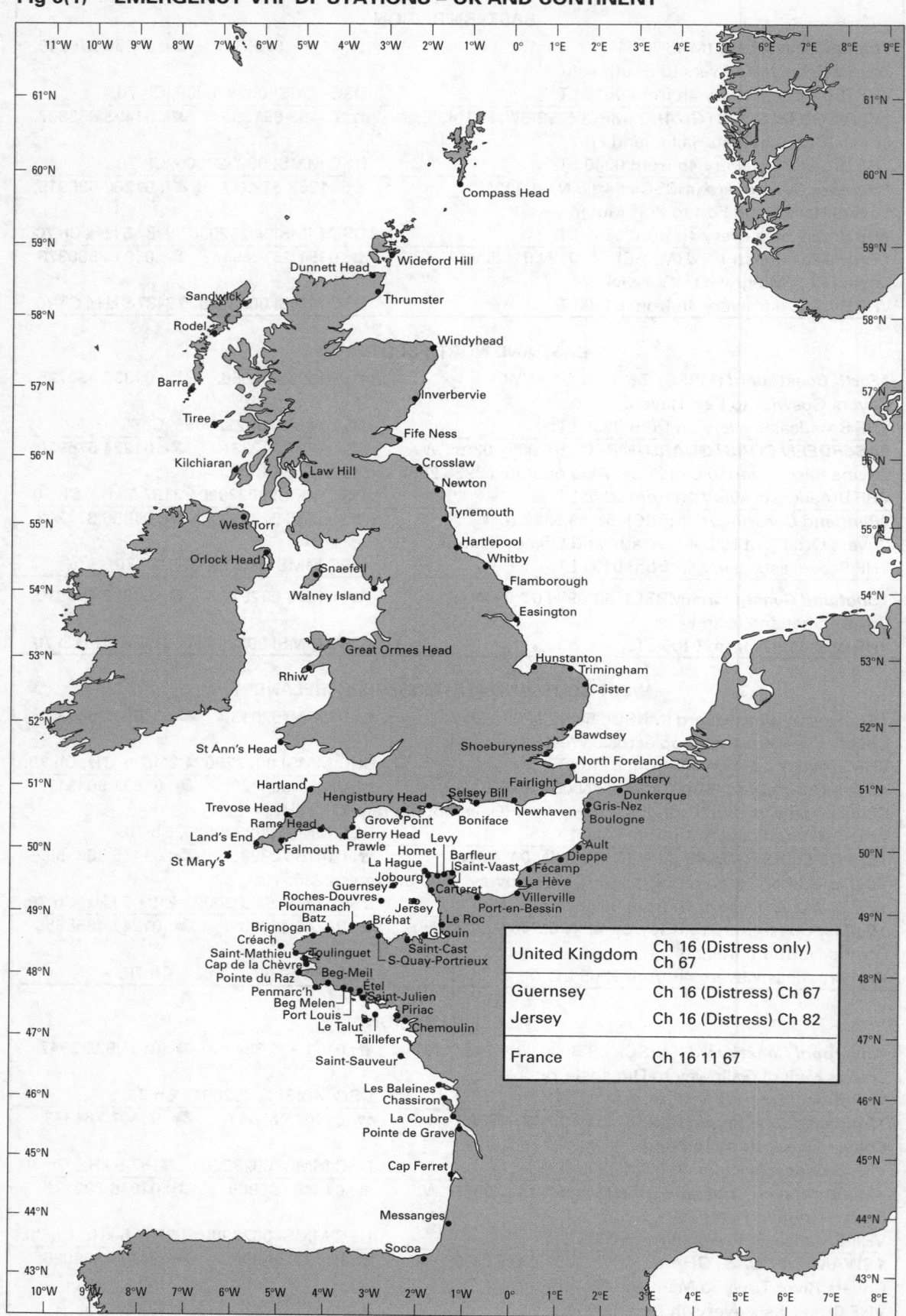

United Kingdom	Ch 16 (Distress only) Ch 67
Guernsey	Ch 16 (Distress) Ch 67
Jersey	Ch 16 (Distress) Ch 82
France	Ch 16 11 67

6.9.3   Emergency VHF DF

6.9.3.1 General
Coastguard MRCC/MRSC can provide VHF DF bearings to yachts in distress; call on Ch 16. Bearings will be passed on Ch 16 or 67 by the CG Centre as the yacht's true bearing *from the DF site*.

DF sites and their controlling CG Centres are listed below; they are shown on Admiralty charts by the symbol $\bigcirc_{RG}$.

6.9.3.2 UK VHF DF Stations

Falmouth CG	
Trevose Head	50°32'·9N 05°01'·9W
St Mary's	49°55'·7N 06°18'·2W
Land's End	50°08'·2N 05°38'·2W
Falmouth	50°08'·7N 05°02'·7W
Brixham CG	
Rame Head	50°19'·0N 04°13'·1W
Prawle	50°13'·1N 03°42'·5W
Berry Head	50°23'·9N 03°29'·0W
Portland CG	
Grove Point	50°32'·9N 02°25'·1W
Hengistbury Head	50°42'·9N 01°45'·6W
Solent CG	
Boniface	50°36'·2N 01°12'·0W
Selsey	50°43'·8N 00°48'·2W
Newhaven	50°46'·9N 00°03'·1E
Dover CG	
Fairlight	50°52'·2N 00°38'·8E
Langdon Battery	51°07'·9N 01°20'·7E
North Foreland	51°22'·5N 01°26'·8E
Thames CG	
Shoeburyness	51°31'·4N 00°46'·7E
Bawdsey	51°59'·6N 01°24'·6E
Yarmouth CG	
Trimingham	52°54'·6N 01°20'·7E
Hunstanton	52°56'·9N 00°29'·7E
Caister	52°39'·6N 01°43'·0E
Humber CG	
Easington	53°39'·1N 00°06'·0E
Flamborough	54°07'·1N 00°05'·1W
Whitby	54°29'·4N 00°36'·3W
Tyne Tees CG	
Hartlepool	54°41'·8N 01°10'·5W
Tynmouth	55°01'·1N 01°24'·9W
Newton	55°31'·0N 01°37'·1W
Forth CG	
Crosslaw	55°54'·5N 02°12'·2W
Fife Ness	56°16'·8N 02°35'·3W
Aberdeen CG	
Inverbervie	56°51'·1N 02°15'·7W
Windyhead	57°38'·9N 02°14'·5W
Shetland CG	
Compass Head	59°52'·1N 01°16'·3W
Pentland CG	
Thrumster	58°23'·6N 03°07'·3W
Dunnett Head	58°40'·3N 03°22'·5W
Wideford Hill	58°59'·3N 03°01'·4W
Stornoway CG	
Sandwick	58°12'·7N 06°21'·3W
Barra	57°00'·8N 07°30'·4W
Rodel	57°44'·9N 06°57'·4W
Oban CG	
Tiree	56°30'·6N 06°57'·7W
Clyde CG	
Kilchiaran	55°45'·9N 06°27'·2W
Law Hill	55°41'·8N 04°50'·5W
Liverpool CG	
Snaefell, IoM	54°15'·8N 04°27'·6W
Walney Island	54°06'·6N 03°15'·9W
Holyhead CG	
Great Ormes Head	53°20'·0N 03°51'·1W
Rhiw	52°50'·0N 04°37'·7W
Milford Haven CG	
St Ann's Head	51°41'·0N 05°10'·5W
Swansea CG	
Hartland	51°01'·2N 04°31'·3W
Belfast CG	
Orlock Head	54°40'·4N 05°35'·0W
West Torr	55°11'·9N 06°05'·6W
Channel Islands	
Guernsey	49°26'·3N 02°35'·8W
Jersey	49°10'·9N 02°14'·3W

In the Channel Islands a yacht should transmit on Ch 16 in distress or Ch 67 for Guernsey or Ch 82 for Jersey.

For French VHF DF services see 6.11.2.3.

6.9.4   Yacht and Boat Safety Scheme
This free scheme provides useful information about your boat and its equipment which will assist the Coastguard toward a successful SAR operation. Complete a Form CG66, obtainable from the local Coastguard station, harbour master or marina. You should inform the Coastguard if the ownership, name of the craft, or any address given on Form CG66 changes. A tear-off section can be given to a friend or relative so that they know which Coastguard station to contact if they are concerned for the boat's safety.

A CG66 is valid for three years. If it is not renewed within that time, the old CG66 will be removed from the CG records.

It is not the function of HM Coastguard to maintain watch for boats on passage, but they will record information by phone before departure or from intermediate ports, or while on passage by visual signals or VHF Ch 67 (the Small Craft Safety Channel).

When using Ch 67 for safety messages, skippers should give the name of the MRCC/MRSC holding the boat's CG66. In these circumstances the Coastguard must be told of any change to the planned movements of the boat, and it is important that they are informed of the boat's safe arrival at her ultimate destination – so as to avoid needless overdue action being taken.

C6

6.9.5   National Coastwatch Institution (NCI)

The NCI, a registered charity, was founded in 1994 to re-establish a visual watch around the UK coast.

Many former CG lookout stations are manned in daylight hours by trained volunteers. VHF Ch 16 is monitored, but NCI stations are not at present licenced to transmit on VHF. In poor visibility some stations keep a radar watch to 20M offshore. All NCI stations have telephones; see next column. They are able to report the actual local weather on request.

Any incident seen at sea, or on coastal footpaths, is passed to the nearest CG Centre for the CG to take the appropriate action. Most NCI stations can warn a yacht by light signal of an apparently dangerous course, eg 'U' ··— = *You are standing into danger.*

For further information contact:
NCI Head Office, Brea, Camborne, TR14 9DG.
☎ 01209 718894; 📠 01209 716537.

The following NCI stations were operating in 1998:

Cape Cornwall (Land's End)	01736 787890
Gwennap Head (Land's End)	01736 871351
Bass Point (Lizard)	01326 290212
Polruan (Fowey)	01726 870291
Portland Bill	01305 860178
St Alban's Head	01929 439220
Swanage	01929 422596
Felixstowe	01394 286119
Gorleston (Great Yarmouth)	01493 440384
North Denes (Great Yarmouth)	01493 332192
Mundesley (Norfolk)	01263 722399
Sheringham (Norfolk)	01263 823470
Redcar (Teesside)	01642 491606
Wylfa Head (Anglesey)	01407 711152

Stations which were due to open in 1998 included: Prawle Point, Exmouth, Needles, Dungeness, Folkestone, Lowestoft, Hartlepool and Barry.

6.9.6   Signals used in distress situations

6.9.6.1   Visual signals, shore to ships
If no radio link is possible, the following may be used to a vessel in distress or stranded off the UK coast.

(a)   Acknowledgment of distress signal.
By day: Orange smoke signal, or combined light and sound signal consisting of three signals fired at about one-minute intervals.
By night: White star rocket consisting of three single signals at about one-minute intervals.

(b)   Landing signals for small boats.
Vertical motion of a white flag or arms (white light or flare by night), or signalling K (—·—) by light or sound = *This is the best place to land.*
Direction may be given by placing a steady white light or flare at a lower level.

Horizontal motion of a white flag or arms extended horizontally (white light or flare by night), or signalling S (···) = *Landing here is highly dangerous.*
In addition, a better landing place may be signalled by carrying a white flag (flare or light), or by firing a white star signal in the direction indicated; or by signalling R (·—·) if a better landing is to the right of the direction of approach, or L (·—··) if it is to the left.

(c)   Signals for shore life-saving apparatus.
Vertical motion of a white flag or the arms (or of a white light or flare) = *Affirmative*; or specifically, *Rocket line is held; Tail block is made fast; Hawser is made fast;, Man is in breeches buoy;* or *Haul away.*

Horizontal motion of a white flag or the arms (or of a white light or flare) = *Negative;* or specifically, *Slack away* or *Avast (stop) hauling.*
NB: Rocket rescue equipment is no longer used by HM CG. Some larger vessels carry a line-throwing appliance requiring on-shore liaison before use.

(d)   Warning signal.
International Code signal U (··—) or NF = *You are running into danger.*
A white flare, white star rocket, or explosive signal may be used to draw attention to the above signals.

6.9.6.2 Signals used by SAR aircraft
A searching aircraft normally flies at about 3,000–5,000ft (900–1,500m), or below cloud, firing a green Very light every five or ten minutes and at each turning point.

On seeing a green flare, a yacht in distress should take the following action:
(1)   Wait for the green flare to die out.
(2)   Fire one red flare.
(3)   Fire another red flare after about 20 seconds. (This enables the aircraft to line up on the bearing.)
(4)   Fire a third red flare when the aircraft is overhead, or if it appears to be going badly off course.

6.9.6.3 Directing signals by aircraft
(1)   To direct a yacht towards a ship or aircraft in distress, the aircraft circles the yacht at least once. It then crosses low, ahead of the yacht, opening and closing the throttle or changing the propeller pitch. Finally it heads in the direction of the casualty.
(2)   To indicate that assistance by the yacht is no longer required, the aircraft passes low, astern of the yacht, opening and closing the throttle or changing the propeller pitch.

6.9.7   Helicopter rescue

Capability.   SAR helicopters in the UK are based at Culdrose, Portland, Lee-on-Solent, Wattisham, Leconfield, Boulmer, Lossiemouth, Sumburgh, Stornoway, Prestwick, Valley and Chivenor.

Sea King SAR helicopters can operate to a range of 300 miles and can rescue up to 18 survivors. The Sea King's automatic hover control system permits rescues at night and in fog.

Communications.   SAR helicopters are generally fitted with VHF, FM and AM, UHF and HF SSB RT and can communicate with lifeboats etc on VHF FM. Communications between ship and helicopter should normally be on VHF Ch 16 or 67; 2182 kHz SSB may also be available. If contact is difficult, communication can often be achieved through a Nimrod aircraft if on scene, or through a lifeboat, Coast radio station, or HM Coastguard.

When the helicopter is sighted by a boat in distress, a flare, an orange smoke signal, dye marker or a well-trained Aldis lamp will assist recognition (very important if there are other vessels in the vicinity). Dodgers with the boat's name or sail number are useful aids to identification.

On the yacht.   Survivors from a yacht with a mast may need to be picked up from a dinghy or life raft streamed at least 100ft (30m) away. In a small yacht with no dinghy, survivors (wearing life jackets) may need to be picked up from the water, at the end of a long warp. It is very important that no survivor boards a life raft or jumps into the sea until instructed to do so by the helicopter (either by VHF Ch 16 or 67) or by the winchman (by word of mouth). Sails should be lowered and lashed and it is helpful if the drift of the boat is reduced by a sea anchor.

If a crewman descends from the helicopter, he will take charge. Obey his instructions quickly. Never secure the winch wire to the yacht, and beware that it may carry a lethal static charge if it is not dipped (earthed) in the sea before handling.

Double lift.   Survivors may be lifted by double lift in a strop, accompanied by the crewman in a canvas seat. Or it may be necessary, with no crewman, for a survivor to position himself in the strop. Put your head and shoulders through the strop so that the padded part is in the small of the back and the toggle is in front of the face. Pull the toggle down, as close to the chest as possible. When ready, give a thumbs-up sign with an extended arm, and place both arms close down by the side of the body (resist the temptation to hang on to the strop). On reaching the helicopter, do exactly as instructed by the crew. Injured persons can be lifted strapped into a special stretcher carried in the helicopter.

Hi-line.   In some circumstances a 'Hi-line technique' may be used. This is a rope tail, attached to the helicopter winch wire by a weak link, and weighted at its lower end. When it is lowered to the yacht do not make it fast, but coil it down carefully. The helicopter pays out the winch wire and then moves to one side of the yacht and descends, while the yacht takes in the slack (keeping it outboard and clear of all obstructions) until the winch hook and strop are on board. A member of the helicopter crew may or may not be lowered with the strop. When ready to lift, the helicopter ascends and takes in the wire. Pay out the tail, keeping enough weight on it to keep it taut until the end is reached, then cast it off well clear of the yacht. But if a further lift is to be made the tail should be retained on board (not made fast) to facilitate recovery of the strop for the next lift.

When alighting from a helicopter, beware of the tail rotor which can be difficult to see. Obey all instructions given by the helicopter crew.

6.9.8   Abandon ship

Do not abandon a yacht until she is definitely sinking. A yacht is easier to find than a liferaft and provides better shelter. While she is still afloat use her resources (such as RT, for distress calls) and select extra equipment to put in the liferaft or lash into the dinghy (which should also be taken, if possible). Make all preparations.

Before entering the raft, and cutting it adrift:

(a)   Send a MAYDAY call, saying that yacht is being abandoned, with position.

(b)   Dress warmly with sweaters etc. under oilskins, and life jacket on top. Take extra clothes.

(c)   Fill any available containers with tops about ¾ full with fresh water, so that they will float.

(d)   Collect additional food, tins and tin-opener.

(e)   Collect navigational gear, torch, extra flares, bucket, length of line, First-aid kit, knife, etc.

Once in the life raft, plan for the worst. If there has not been time to collect items listed above, collect whatever flotsam is available.

(a)   Keep the inside of the raft as dry as possible. Huddle together for warmth. Close the openings as necessary, but keep a good lookout for shipping and aircraft.

(b)   Stream the drogue if necessary for stability, or so as to stay near the original position.

(c)   Ration fresh water to ¾ pint (½ litre) per person per day. Do not drink sea water or urine. Collect rain water.

(d)   Use flares sparingly, on the skipper's orders.

(e)   Take anti-seasick pills.

6.10   HAZARDS

6.10.1   Submarines

There have been incidents in which fishing vessels and occasionally yachts have been snagged or hit by submarines operating just below the surface.

The best advice available to yachts is:

C6

(a) Listen to Subfacts (6.10.2).
(b) Avoid charted submarine exercise areas.
(c) Keep clear of any vessel flying the Code Flags 'NE2' meaning that submarines are in the vicinity.
(d) Run your engine or generator even when under sail.
(e) Operate your echo sounder.
(f) At night show deck-level navigation lights, ie on pulpit and stern.

The risk is greatest in the English Channel, the Irish Sea, including the Clyde and North Channel, off W Scotland, and especially at night. Within these waters named/numbered submarine exercise areas are shown diagrammatically in 8.1.18, 8.2.34, 8.8.23 and 8.9.24.

6.10.2 Subfacts
These are broadcast warnings of planned or known submarine activity. All BT Coast radio stations in the Southern region, ie Celtic Radio anticlockwise to Grimsby Radio (see Fig 4(2)), broadcast **Subfacts – South Coast** at 0733 and 1933UT after weather forecasts. These give details of planned submarine activity in the English Channel.

All BT Coast radio stations in the Northern Region, ie Cullercoats Radio anticlockwise to Cardigan Bay Radio, broadcast Subfacts on MF and/or VHF at 0703 and 1903UT after the weather forecasts.

Subfacts – Clyde giving details of planned submarine activity off W Scotland are broadcast at 0303, 0703, 1103, 1503, 1903 and 2303UT by all BT Coast radio stations from Lewis to Cardigan Bay.

Submarine activity between Cape Wrath and 54°N is also broadcast on request by MRSCs Stornoway, Oban and Belfast on Ch 16; and by MRCC Clyde on Ch 67 at 0020, 0420, 0820, 1220, 1620 and 2020LT.

6.10.3 Gunfacts
Gunfacts are warning broadcasts informing mariners of intended naval practice firings. Such warnings do not restrict the passage of any vessel. The onus for safety lies with the naval unit concerned.

Gunfacts broadcasts will include:
(a) Local time and approximate location of intended firings, with a declared safe distance in M.
(b) Whether illuminants are to be fired.

Gunfacts include planned or known underwater explosions, gunnery and missile firings. Broadcasts for underwater explosions only will be made on Ch 16 at 1 hr, 30 mins, and immediately prior to detonation. **Gunfacts – South Coast**, issued by FOST, Plymouth for S coast exercise areas (see 8.1.18 and 8.2.34), are broadcast at 0733 and 1933 UT, following the forecast, by Southern Region Coast Radio Stations on their usual VHF channels and MF frequencies.
Gunfacts – Ship are issued by a nominated Duty Broadcast Ship and cover activity in all other UK areas excluding the English Channel exercise areas. Broadcasts will be made daily at 0800 and 1400 LT on Ch 06 or 67 after an announcement on Ch 16.

6.11   SEARCH AND RESCUE

6.11.1 IRELAND
The Irish Marine Emergency Service (IMES) is a division of the Department of Marine. IMES is the co-ordinating body responsible for all SAR operations around the coast of Ireland, and is based on MRSCs at Dublin, Malin Head and Valentia, co-located with the Coast radio stations and operated by the same staff. They are co-ordinated by the MRCC at IMES HQ, Leeson Lane, Dublin 2 (☎: (01) 6620922). Details of the MRCC/MRSCs are as follows:

DUBLIN (MRCC). 53°20'N 06°15W. ☎ 01 6620922; 📠 01 6620795. Covers Carlingford Lough to Youghal. DSC MMSI (To be notified).
†**Valentia** (MRSC). 51°56'N 10°21'W. ☎ 066 76109; 📠 066 776289. Covers Youghal to Slyne Hd. DSC A2 MMSI 0025000200 MF 2187·5 kHz. Ch 70.
†**Malin Head** (MRSC). 55°22'N' 07°21W. ☎ 077 70103; 📠 077 70221. Covers Slyne Hd to L. Foyle. DSC A2 MMSI 002500100 MF 2187·5 kHz. Ch 70.

A dedicated IMES Sikorsky S61N SAR helicopter, based at Shannon, can respond within 15 to 45 minutes and operate to a radius of 200M. It is equipped with infrared search equipment and can uplift 14 survivors. Dauphin SA 365F helicopters (based at Finner Camp in Donegal and at Baldonnel, Dublin) can operate to 150 miles by day and 70 miles at night.

IMES provides some 50 units around the coast and is on call 24 hours a day. Some of these units have a specialist cliff climbing capability.

The RNLI maintains four RNLI stations around the coast and some 26 lifeboats. Additionally, six individually community-run inshore rescue boats are available.

6.11.2 FRANCE

6.11.2.1   CROSS
France has five *Centres Régionaux Opérationnels de Surveillance et de Sauvetage* (CROSS) on the Channel and Atlantic coasts. A CROSS centre is an MRCC and a sous-CROSS centre an MRSC. They are shown on the facing page. CROSS provides a permanent, H24, all weather operational presence along the French coast and cooperates with foreign Coastguards. All centres keep watch on VHF Ch 16 and Ch 70 (DSC), and broadcast local navigational warnings, gale warnings and weather messages. Weather broadcasts are shown in 5.9.6.

The main functions of CROSS include:

(1) Co-ordinating Search and Rescue.
(2) Navigational surveillance.
(3) Broadcasting navigational warnings.
(4) Broadcasting meteorological information.
(5) Anti-pollution control.
(6) Marine and fishery surveillance.

CROSS Étel specialises in providing medical advice and responds to alerts from Cospas/Sarsat satellites.

CROSS can be contacted by R/T, by ☎, through Coast radio stations, via the National Gendarmerie or Affaires Maritimes, or via a Semaphore station. Call *Semaphore* stations on Ch 16 (working Ch 10) or by ☎ as listed on page 116.

CROSS does not handle public correspondence, ie link calls.

In addition to their safety and SAR functions, shown below, CROSS stations using, for example, the callsign *Corsen Traffic* monitor Traffic Separation Schemes in the Dover Strait, off Casquets and off Ouessant. They also broadcast navigational warnings and weather forecasts. See 5.9.6 for times and VHF channels used.

TABLE 6(2)   CROSS STATIONS

CROSS Gris-Nez   50°52'N 01°35'E   ☎ 03·21.87.21.87   📠 03·21.87.76.55   MMSI 002275100
Belgian Border to Cap d'Antifer.   SAR co-ordination VHF Ch 15 67 **68** 73. DSC Ch 70.

CROSS Jobourg   49°41'N 01°54'W   ☎ 02·33.52.72.13   📠 02·33.52.71.72   MMSI 002275200
Cap d'Antifer to Mont St Michel.   SAR co-ordination VHF Ch 15 67 **68** 73. DSC Ch 70.

CROSS Corsen   48°24'N 04°47'W   ☎ 02·96.89.31.31   📠 02·96.89.65.75   MMSI 002275300
Mont St Michel to Pointe de Penmarc'h; N to the English Channel median line; and W to 8°W.
SAR co-ordination VHF Ch 15 67 **68** 73. DSC Ch 70.

CROSS Étel   47°39'N 03°12'W   ☎ 02·97.55.35.35   📠 02·97.55.49.34   MMSI 002275000
Pointe de Penmarc'h to 46°20'N, but to Spanish border at night in lieu of sous-CROSS Soulac.
SAR co-ordination VHF Ch 15 67 **68** 73. DSC Ch 70.

sous-CROSS Soulac 45°31'N 01°07'W   ☎ 05·56.09.82.00   📠 05·56.09.79.73   MMSI 002275010
46°20'N to Spanish border 0700-2200LT; CROSS Étel covers to Spanish border at night.
SAR co-ordination VHF Ch 15 67 **68** 73. DSC Ch 70. (?13 79??)

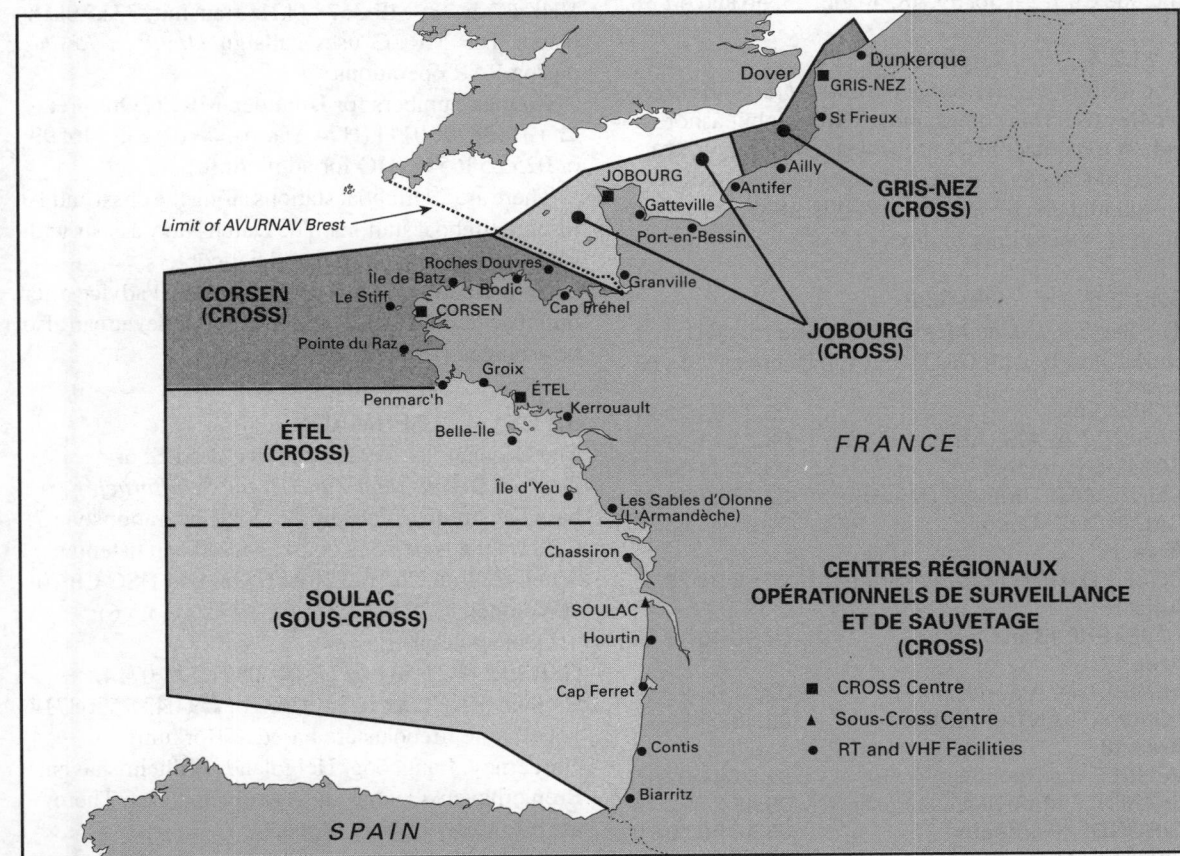

Fig 6(2)   CROSS and sous-Cross centres

6.11.2.2   Semaphore (Signal) stations

*Dunkerque	03·28·66·86·18	Ouessant Creac'h	02·96·46·80·49
Boulogne	03·21·31·32·10	*St-Mathieu	02·98·89·01·59
Ault	03·22·60·47·33	*Portzic (Ch 8)	02·98·22·90·01
Dieppe	02·35·84·23·82	Toulinguet	02·98·27·90·02
*Fécamp	02·35·28·00·91	Cap-de-la-Chèvre	02·98·27·09·55
*La Hève	02·35·46·07·81	*Pointe-du-Raz	02·98·70·66·57
*Le Havre (Ch 12)	02·35·21·74·39	*Penmarch	02·98·58·61·00
Villerville	02·31·88·11·13	Beg Meil	02·98·94·98·92
*Port-en-Bessin	02·31·21·81·51	*Port-Louis	02·97·82·52·10
St-Vaast	02·33·54·44·50	Étel	02·97·55·35·59
*Barfleur	02·33·54·04·37	Beg Melen (Groix)	02·97·86·80·13
Lévy	02·33·54·31·17	Taillefer (Belle-Ile)	02·97·31·83·18
*Le Homet	02·33·92·60·08	Talut (Belle-Ile)	02·97·31·85·07
La Hague	02·33·52·71·07	St-Julien	02·97·50·09·35
Carteret	02·33·53·85·08	Piriac-sur-Mer	02·40·23·59·87
Le Roc	02·33·50·05·85	*Chemoulin	02·40·91·99·00
Le Grouin	02·99·89·60·12	St-Sauveur (Yeu)	02·51·58·31·01
St-Cast	02·96·41·85·30	Les Baleines (Ré)	05·46·29·42·06
*StQuay-Portrieux	02·96·70·42·18	Chassiron(Oléron)	05·46·47·85·43
Bréhat	02·96·20·00·12	*La Coubre	05·46·22·41·73
*Ploumanac'h	02·96·91·46·51	Pointe-de-Grave	05·56·09·60·03
Batz	02·98·61·76·06	Cap Ferret	05·56·60·60·03
*Brignogan	02·98·83·50·84	Messanges	05·58·48·94·10
*Ouessant Stiff	02·98·48·81·50	*Socoa	05·59·47·18·54

* H24. Remainder sunrise to sunset.

6.11.2.3   Emergency VHF DF service
A yacht in emergency can call CROSS on VHF Ch 16, 11 or 67 to obtain a bearing. This will be passed as the true bearing of the yacht *from* the DF station. The semaphore stations listed above and on Fig 6(1) are also equipped with VHF DF. They keep watch on Ch 16 and other continuously scanned frequencies, which include Ch 1-29, 36, 39, 48, 50, 52, 55, 56 and 60-88.

6.11.2.4   Lifeboats
The lifeboat service *Société National de Sauvetage en Mer* (SNSM) comes under CROSS, but ashore it is best to contact local lifeboat stations direct; ☎ as listed in Chapter 8 for each harbour under SNSM. A substantial charge may be levied if a SNSM lifeboat attends a vessel not in distress.

6.11.2.5   Medical
The Service d'Aide Médicale Urgente (SAMU) works closely with CROSS; it can be contacted via:
Area 19
NORD (Lille)	03·20·54·22·22
PAS-DE-CALAIS (Arras)	03·21·71·51·51
SOMME (Amiens)	03·22·44·33·33
SEINE-MARITIME (Le Havre)	02·35·47·15·15
CALVADOS (Caen)	02·31·44·88·88

Area 15
CÔTES D'ARMOR (Saint Brieuc)	02·96·94·28·95

Area 16
FINISTERE (Brest)	02·98·46·11·33

Area 17
MORBIHAN (Vannes)	02·97·54·22·11
LOIRE-ATLANTIQUE (Nantes)	02·40·08·37·77

Area 18
VENDEE (La Roche-sur-Yon)	02·51·44·62·15
CHARENTE-MARITIME (La Rochelle)	05·46·27·32·15
GIRONDE (Bordeaux)	05·56·96·70·70
LANDES (Mont-de-Marsan)	05·58·75·44·44
PYRÉNÉES-ATLANTIQUE (Bayonne)	05·59·63·33·33

6.11.3   BELGIUM
The Belgian Pilotage Service coordinates SAR operations from Oostende MRCC. The MRCC is connected by telephone to the Oostende coast radio station (OST) which maintains listening watch H24 on Ch 16, 2182kHz and DSC Ch 70 and 2187·5kHz. MMSI 002050480. ☎ 059 706565; 📠 059 701339. Antwerpen CRS, remotely controlled by Oostende CRS, has MMSI 002050485. DSC Ch 70. See also 4.5.4.

Telephone and Fax numbers are:
MRCC Oostende ☎ 059 70 10 00; 📠 059 703605.
MRSC Nieuwpoort ☎ 058 233000.
MRSC Zeebrugge ☎ 050 545072.
RCC Brussels (Point of contact for Cospas/Sarsat): ☎ 02 720 0338; 📠 02 752 4201.

Offshore and inshore lifeboats are based at Nieuwpoort, Oostende and Zeebrugge.

The Belgian Air Force provides helicopters from Koksijde near the French border. The Belgian Navy also cooperates in SAR operations.

6.11.4   NETHERLANDS
The Netherland's Coastguard MRCC at IJmuiden coordinates SAR operations. The MRCC maintains listening watch H24 on Ch 16 and DSC Ch 70 and 2187·5kHz. MMSI 002442000. Working chans are VHF 67 & 73; MF 3673·0kHz transmit, 3315·0kHz listen. The MRCC uses callsign *IJmuiden Rescue* during SAR operations.

Contact numbers for IJmuiden MRCC Ops are:
☎ +31 (0) 900 0111 (H24 Alarm), 📠 (0) 255 546599; or 0255 546546 (HO for admin/info).

There are 24 lifeboat stations along the coast and 10 inshore lifeboat stations. The Dutch Navy assists with ships, fixed wing aircraft and helicopters.

Netherland's CG will provide medical advice after initial contact on Ch 16 or 2182kHz. Medevac can also be arranged (see 6.5.2).

6.11.5   GERMANY
The German Sea Rescue Service (GSRS, or *Deutsch Gesellschaft Zur Rettung Schiffbruchiger*) based at Bremen, coordinates SAR operations via 7 CRS on the North Sea coast. These keep listening watch H24 on Ch 16, 2182 kHz and on DSC Ch 70 at Norddeich CRS, MMSI 002114200 (4.5.6).

Contact numbers are:
GSRS ☎ 0421 537 0777; 📠 0421 537 0714.
Bremen MRCC ☎ 0421 536870; 📠 0421 5368714

Offshore lifeboats are based at Borkum, Norderney, Langeoog, Helgoland, Wilhelmshaven, Bremerhaven, Cuxhaven, Amrum and List. There are also many inshore lifeboats

The German Navy provides ships and SAR helicopters.

Chapter 7

Tides

Contents

7.1 GENERAL Page 118
7.1.1 Explanation
7.1.2 Times
7.1.3 Predicted heights of tide

7.2 DEFINITIONS 118
7.2.1 Chart datum
7.2.2 Charted depth
7.2.3 Drying height
7.2.4 Heights of lights, bridges etc
7.2.5 Height of tide
7.2.6 Rise/Fall of tide
7.2.7 Duration
7.2.8 Interval
7.2.9 Mean HW and LW Springs/Neaps
7.2.10 Mean Level
7.2.11 Range
7.2.12 Tidal coefficients

**7.3 CALCULATING TIMES AND
HEIGHTS OF HW AND LW** 119
7.3.1 Standard Ports
7.3.2 Secondary Ports: times of HW & LW
7.3.3 Secondary Ports: heights of HW & LW
7.3.4 Interpolating time and height
differences by graph

**7.4 CALCULATING INTERMEDIATE
TIMES AND HEIGHTS OF TIDE** 121
7.4.1 Standard Ports
7.4.2 Secondary Ports
7.4.3 The use of factors
7.4.4 The 'Twelfths' rule

**7.5 CALCULATING CLEARANCES
UNDER OVERHEAD OBJECTS** 122

**7.6 TIDAL PREDICTION BY
COMPUTER** 122
7.6.1. Tidecalc
7.6.2 NP 159 Harmonic Method
7.6.3 Commercial programmes

7.7 TIDAL STREAMS 123
7.7.1 Introduction
7.7.2 Tidal stream atlases
7.7.3 Tidal diamonds
7.7.4 Calculating tidal stream rates
7.7.5 Tidal streams in rivers

**7.8 METEOROLOGICAL
CONDITIONS** 124
7.8.1 Storm Tide Warning Service

7.8 STANDARD PORTS 126

Summary

This chapter explains the use of the tidal data provided in Chapter 8 and serves as an on-board reference and aide memoire on tidal calculations.

For fuller details of tides and the sea, refer also to Chapter 9 in *The Macmillan & Silk Cut Yachtsman's Handbook* where the following subjects are described in detail:

The theory of tides; definitions of terms; calculations of times and heights of HW and LW; calculations of depths of water at specific times; calculations of times at which tide reaches certain heights; 'Twelfths' rule; tidal calculations by pocket calculator; French tidal coefficients; co-tidal and co-range charts; harmonic constituents; establishment of a port; tidal stream diamonds; tidal stream information on charts and in Sailing Directions, plus: general information on the sea – how waves are formed; freak waves; wind against tide; bars; overfalls and tide races; refraction of waves; reflected waves; ocean currents, etc.

7.1   GENERAL

7.1.1   Explanation

This chapter explains how to use the tidal information contained in Chapter 8, where the daily times and heights of High Water (HW) and Low Water (LW) for Standard Ports are given, together with time and height differences for many Secondary Ports. Tidal predictions are for average meteorological conditions. In abnormal weather the times and heights of HW and LW may vary considerably. (See 7.8.)

7.1.2   Times

Tidal predictions for Standard Ports in Chapter 8 are given in the Standard, or Zone, Time shown at the top left-hand corner of each page, ie in UT (Zone 0) as kept in the UK, Channel Islands, Eire and Portugal. In France, Belgium, Netherlands, Germany and Spain Standard Time is UT+1 (Zone –1). To convert these Zone – 0100 times to UT, subtract 1 hour; see 4.12.2.

When DST (BST in UK) is in force during the summer months, as indicated by the absence of green tinting, one hour must be added to the predicted times to obtain DST (= LT).

Under each Secondary Port listed in Chapter 8 are its Zone Time, its Standard Port and the time differences required to calculate the times of HW and LW at the Secondary Port in the Zone Time of that Port. If DST is required, then one hour is added *after* the Secondary Port time difference has been applied, not before.

7.1.3   Predicted heights of tide

Predicted heights are given in metres and tenths of a metre above chart datum (CD) (see 7.2.1). Some older charts show depths in fathoms/feet. A conversion table is given in 2.8.2.

7.2   DEFINITIONS; see Fig 7(1)

7.2.1   Chart datum

Chart datum (CD) is the reference level above which heights of tide are predicted, and below which charted depths are measured. Hence the actual depth of water, or sounding, is the sum of charted depth (at that place) and the height of tide (at that time).

Tidal predictions for most British ports use as their datum Lowest Astronomical Tide (LAT), which is the lowest sea level predicted under average meteorological conditions. All Admiralty Charts of the British Isles use LAT as chart datum, but others, particularly fathom charts, do not. Where tidal predictions and charted depths are not referenced to the same datum (e.g. LAT), errors resulting in an over-estimation of depth by as much as 0·5m can occur.

7.2.2   Charted depth

Charted depth is the distance of the sea bed below chart datum, sometimes loosely and incorrectly referred to as soundings. It is shown in metres and tenths of a metre on metric charts, or in fathoms and/or feet on older charts.

7.2.3   Drying height

Drying height is the height above chart datum of the top of any feature at times covered by water. The figures are underlined on the chart, in metres and tenths of a metre on metric charts, and in fathoms and feet on older charts. The depth of water is the height of tide (at the time) minus the drying height. If the result is negative, then that feature is above water level.

7.2.4   Heights of lights, bridges etc

Charted heights of land objects such as lights, bridges are measured above the level of MHWS. See 7.5.
On French charts these charted elevations are measured above ML rather than MHWS.

7.2.5   Height of tide

The height of the tide is the vertical distance of sea level above (or very occasionally below) chart datum.

7.2.6   Rise/Fall of tide

The Rise of the tide is the amount the tide has risen since the earlier Low Water. The Fall of the tide is the amount the tide has fallen since the last High Water.

7.2.7   Duration

Duration is the time between LW and the next HW, normally slightly more than six hours, and can be used to calculate the approximate time of LW when only the time of HW is known.

7.2.8   Interval

The interval is a period of time either side of the time of HW, expressed in hours and minutes before (−) or after (+) HW. Intervals are printed in increments of one hour (−1hr and +1hr) along the bottom of tidal curves in Chapter 8.

7.2.9   Mean High Water and Low Water Springs/Neaps

Mean High Water Springs (MHWS) and Mean High Water Neaps (MHWN) are the averages of the predicted heights of the Spring or Neap tides at HW over a period of 18·6 years. Similarly, Mean Low Water Springs (MLWS) and Neaps (MLWN) are the average heights of low water for the Spring and Neap tides respectively.

7.2.10   Mean Level

Mean Level (ML) is the average of the heights of Mean High Water Springs (MHWS), Mean High Water Neaps (MHWN), Mean Low Water Springs (MLWS) and Mean Low Water Neaps (MLWN).

7.2.11   Range

The range of a tide is the difference between the heights of successive High and Low Waters. Spring range is the difference between MHWS and MLWS, and Neap range is that between MHWN and MLWN.

7.2.12   Tidal Coefficients

In France the size (range) of a tide and its proximity to Springs/Neaps is quantified by Tidal Coefficients which are listed and explained in 8.16.25.

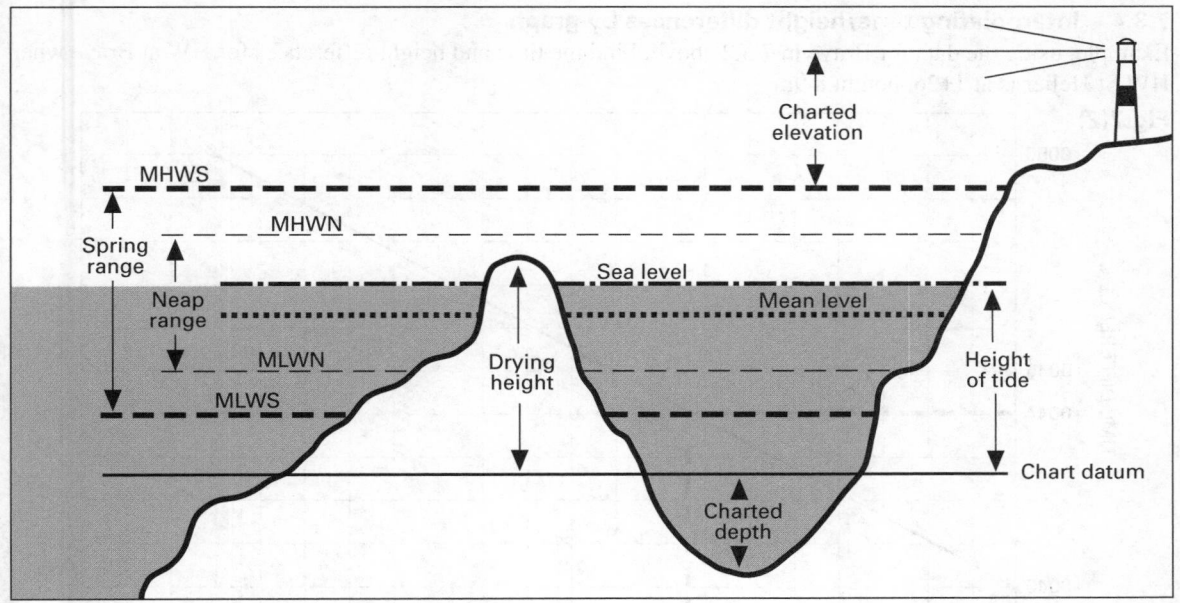

Fig 7(1)

7.3 CALCULATING TIMES AND HEIGHTS OF HW AND LW

7.3.1 Standard Ports
The predicted times and heights of HW and LW are tabulated for every Standard Port. It is stressed that these are predictions only and take no account of the effects of wind and barometric pressure; see 7.8. A list of the Standard Ports given in Chapter 8 is at 7.9.

7.3.2 Secondary Ports – times of HW and LW
Each Secondary Port in Chapter 8 has a data block for calculating times of HW and LW. The following example is for Braye (Alderney):

TIDES
– 0400 Dover; ML 3·6; Duration 0545; Zone 0 (UT).

Standard Port ST HELIER (⟶)

Times				Height (metres)			
High Water		Low Water		MHWS	MHWN	MLWN	MLWS
0300	0900	0200	0900	11·0	8·1	4·0	1·4
1500	2100	1400	2100				
Differences BRAYE							
+0050	+0040	+0025	+0105	–4·8	–3·4	–1·5	–0·5

Thus – 0400 Dover indicates that, on average, HW Braye occurs 4 hours 00 minutes before HW Dover (the times of HW Dover, in UT, can be found on the bookmark). Duration 0545 indicates that LW Braye occurs 5 hours and 45 minutes before its HW. This is a very rough and ready method.

The more accurate and usual calculation uses the Standard Port and Time Differences in the table. Thus when HW at St Helier occurs at 0300 and 1500, the Difference is + 0050, and HW at Braye then occurs at 0350 and 1550. When HW at St Helier occurs at 0900 and 2100, the Difference is + 0040, and HW at Braye occurs at 0940 and 2140.

If, as is likely, HW St Helier occurs at some other time, then the Difference for Braye must be found by interpolation: by eye, by graph (7.3.4), or by calculator. Thus, by eye, when HW St Helier occurs at 1200, the Difference is + 0045, and HW Braye occurs at 1245. The same method applies to calculating LW times.

The times thus obtained are in the Zone Time of the Secondary Port. Care must be taken where, in a very few areas, Zone Time at the Secondary Port differs from that at the Standard Port (see 7.1.2).

7.3.3 Secondary Ports – heights of HW and LW
The Secondary Port data block also contains height Differences which are applied to the heights of HW and LW at the Standard Port. Thus when the height of HW at St Helier is 11·0m (MHWS), the Difference is – 4·8m, and the height of HW at Braye is 6·2m (MHWS). When the height of HW at St Helier is 8·1m (MHWN), the Difference is – 3·4m, and the height of HW at Braye is 4·7m (MHWN).

If, as is likely, the height of tide at the Standard Port differs from the Mean Spring or Neap level, then the height Difference also must be interpolated: by eye, by graph or by calculator. Thus, by eye, if the height of HW St Helier is 9·55m (midway between MHWS and MHWN), the Difference is – 4·1m, and the height of HW at Braye is 5·45m (9·55–4·1m).

C7

7.3.4   Interpolating time/height differences by graph

Example, using the data for Braye in 7.3.2 above: Find the time and height differences for HW at Braye when HW St Helier is at 1126, height 8·9m.

Fig 7(2)

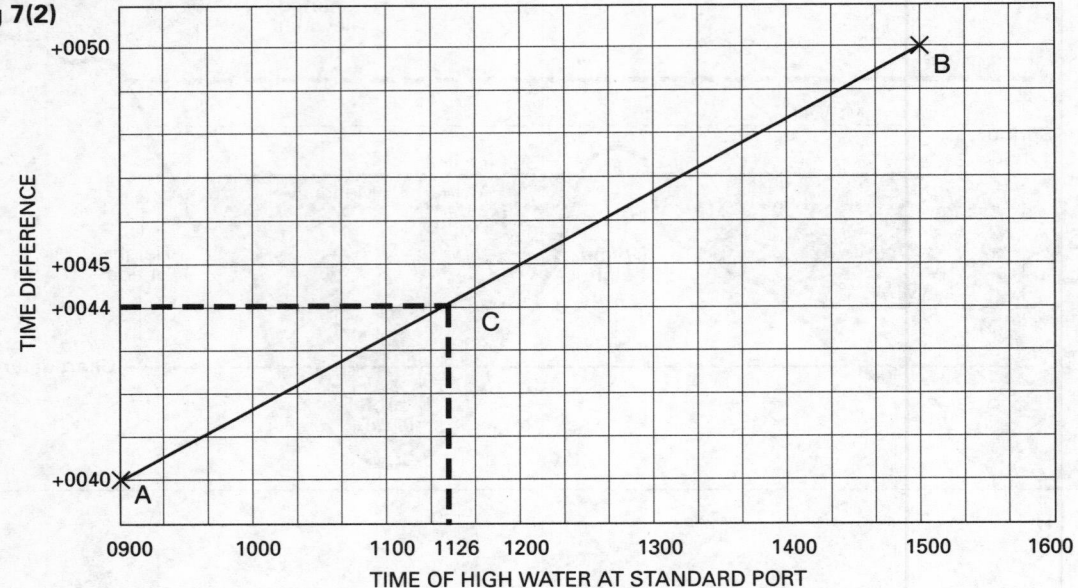

a.   Time difference; Fig 7(2)

On the horizontal axis select a scale for time at St Helier covering 0900 and 1500 (for which the relevant time differences for Braye are known). On the vertical axis, the scale must cover + 0040 to + 0050, the time differences given for 0900 and 1500.

Plot point A, the time difference (+ 0040) for HW St Helier at 0900; and point B, the time difference (+ 0050) for HW St Helier at 1500. Join AB. Enter the graph at time 1126 (HW St Helier); intersect AB at C then go horizontally to read + 0044 on the vertical axis. So that morning HW Braye is 44 minutes after HW St Helier, i.e. 1210.

Fig 7(3)

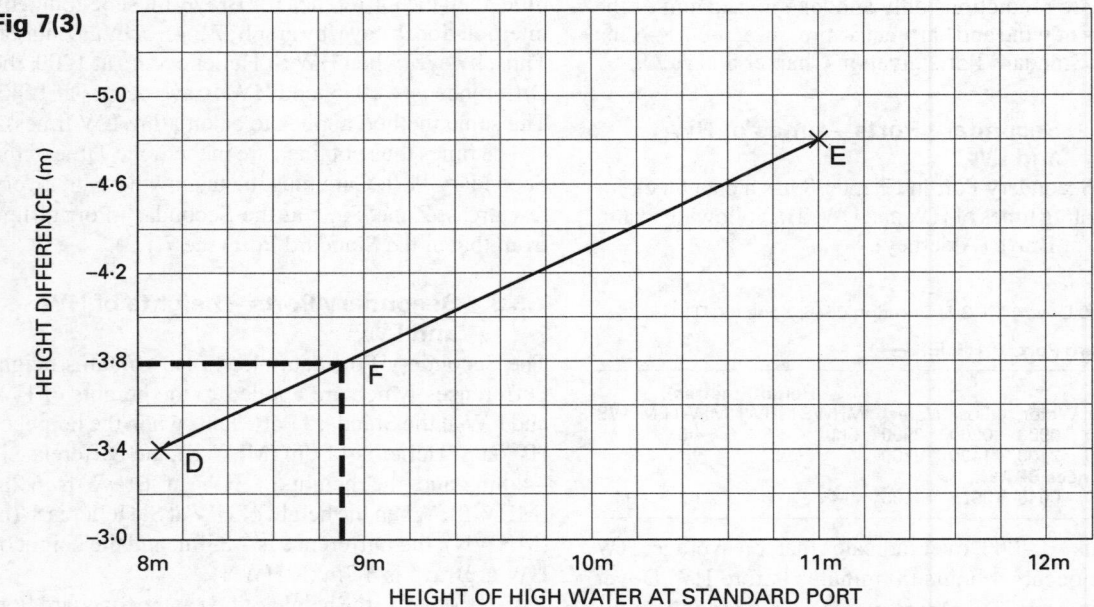

b.   Height difference; Fig 7(3)

The horizontal axis covers the height of HW at St Helier (ie 8·1 to 11·0m) and the vertical axis shows the relevant height differences (− 3·4 to − 4·8m). Plot point D, the height difference (− 3·4m) at Neaps when the height of HW St Helier is 8·1m; and E, the height

difference (− 4·8m) at Springs when the height of HW St Helier is 11·0m. Join DE. Enter the graph at 8·9m (the height of HW St Helier that morning) to intersect DE at mark F. Thence go horizontally to read off the corresponding height difference: − 3·8m. Thus the height of HW Braye that morning is 5·1m.

7.4   CALCULATING INTERMEDIATE TIMES AND HEIGHTS OF TIDE

7.4.1   Standard Ports

Intermediate times and heights of tide are best calculated from the Mean Spring and Neap curves for Standard Ports in Chapter 8. Examples below are for Leith, on a day when the predictions are:

	UT	Ht (m)
22	0202	5·3
	0752	1·0
	1417	5·4
Tu	2025	0·5

Example: Find the height of tide at Leith at 1200.
(1) On the Leith tidal diagram, Fig 7(4), plot the heights of HW and LW each side of the required time, and join them by a sloping line.
(2) Enter the HW time and other times as necessary in the boxes below the curves.
(3) From the required time, proceed vertically to the curves. The Spring curve is a solid line, and the Neap curve (where it differs) is pecked. Interpolate between the curves by comparing actual range, 4·4m in this example, with the Mean Ranges printed beside the curves; here the Spring curve applies. Never extrapolate.
(4) Proceed horizontally to the sloping line plotted in (1), and thence vertically to the height scale, to give 4·2m.

Example: To find the time at which the afternoon height of tide falls to 3·7m.

(1) On the Leith tidal diagram, Fig 7(5), plot the heights of HW and LW each side of the required event, and join them by a sloping line.
(2) Enter the HW time, and other times to cover the required event, in the boxes below the curves.
(3) From the required height, proceed vertically to the sloping line and thence horizontally to the curves. Interpolate between them as in the previous example and do not extrapolate. Here the actual range is 4·9m, and the Spring Curve applies.
(4) Proceed vertically to the time scale, and read off the time required, 1637.

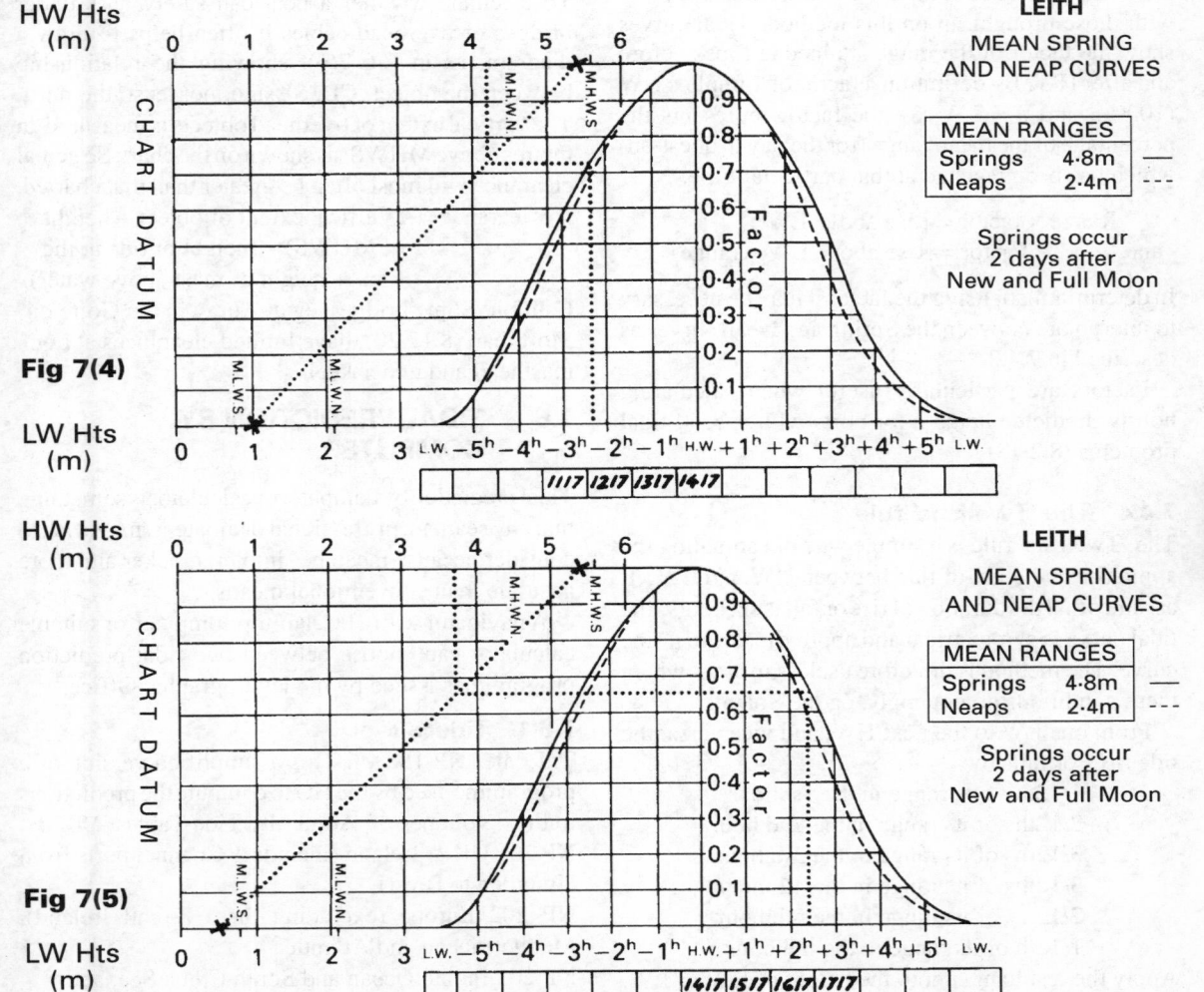

Fig 7(4)

Fig 7(5)

7.4.2   Secondary Ports

On coasts where there is little change of shape between tidal curves for adjacent Standard Ports, and where the duration of rise or fall at the Secondary Port is similar to that of the appropriate Standard Port (ie where HW and LW time differences are nearly the same), intermediate times and heights may be calculated from the Standard Port tidal curves in a similar manner to 7.4.1. The curves are entered with the times and heights of HW and LW at the Secondary Port, calculated as in 7.3.2 and 7.3.3.

Interpolation between the curves can be made by eye, using the range at the Standard Port as argument. Do not extrapolate: use the Spring Curve for Spring ranges or greater, and the Neap Curve for Neap ranges or less. With a large change in duration between Springs and Neaps the results may have a slight error, greater near LW.

Special curves for places between Swanage and Selsey (where the tide is very complex) are given in 8.2.13.

7.4.3   The use of factors

An alternative to the tidal curve method of tidal prediction is the use of factors which remains popular with those brought up on this method. Tidal curves show the factor of the range attained at times before and after HW. By definition a factor of 1 implies HW (100%), and 0 = LW. So the factor represents the percentage of the mean range (for the day in question) which has been reached at that particular time.

Range × factor = Rise above LW

and   Factor = Rise above LW ÷ range

In determining or using the factor it may be necessary to interpolate between the Spring and Neap curves as described in 7.4.2.

Factors are particularly useful when calculating hourly predicted heights for ports with special tidal problems (8.2.13).

7.4.4   The 'Twelfths' rule

The 'Twelfths' rule is a simple way of estimating the approximate height of tide between HW and LW. It assumes that the duration of rise or fall is six hours, the tidal curve is symmetrical and approximates to a sine curve. The method is therefore useless in areas where these conditions do not apply, eg the Solent.

From one LW to the next HW, and vice versa, the tide rises or falls by:

1/12th of its range in the 1st hour
2/12ths of its range in the 2nd hour
3/12ths of its range in the 3rd hour
3/12ths of its range in the 4th hour
2/12ths of its range in the 5th hour
1/12th of its range in the 6th hour

Apply the resultant sum to the height of HW or LW. Mnemonic: 1, 2, 3, 3, 2, 1.

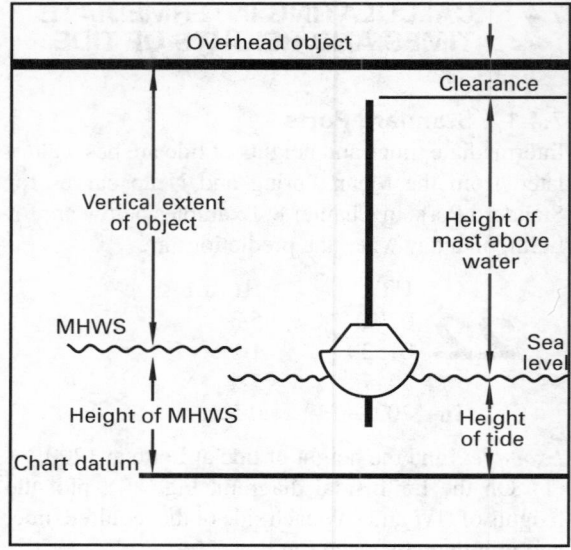

Fig 7(6)   Calculating vertical clearance

7.5   CALCULATING CLEARANCES UNDER OVERHEAD OBJECTS

To calculate whether a boat can safely pass under bridges or overhead cables it often helps to draw a diagram, as in Fig 7(6), showing the relationship between the object, CD, SL and, not least, the mast. The vertical extent of overhead objects is measured in metres above MHWS, as shown on the chart. So actual clearance will most often be greater than that charted.

Clearance = (Vertical extent of object + height
of MHWS) – (height of tide at the
time + height of mast above water).

Caution: Some bridges, eg at Auray in the Golfe du Morbihan (8.17.20), have limited clearances at both masthead and under-keel.

7.6   TIDAL PREDICTION BY COMPUTER

Tidal prediction by computer or calculator is something that any seaman, professional or amateur, may wish to consider because it can be simpler, quicker and more accurate than conventional means.

A navigator with a PC, lap-top computer or suitable calculator can choose between two tidal prediction programmes issued by the Hydrographic Office.

7.6.1   Tidecalc

Tidecalc (NP 158 v 1·1) is a simplified version of a programme used by the HO to compute the predictions in the 4 volumes of Admiralty Tide Tables(ATT):
NP 201 UK & Ireland (including Channel ports from IJmuiden to Brest);
NP 202 Europe (excluding the UK and Ireland), Mediterranean and Atlantic;
NP 203 Indian Ocean and South China Sea; and
NP 204 Pacific Ocean.

The software consists of a programme disc, and a choice of discs for 13 areas covering the world. Each area disc holds the relevant data for around 350-400 ports. Area 1 (v 4·0) covers the UK, Republic of Ireland and the Channel Islands, and Area 2 (v 4·0) covers Europe from Russia to Gibraltar excluding Iceland and Greenland, but including the Channel Islands and Mediterranean. Customised discs holding up to 400 sets of harmonic data can be supplied by the HO to meet individual user requirements.

Tidecalc includes a number of useful facilities to complement the usual presentation of times and heights of high and low water. The additional facilities include a choice of metres or feet; allowances for Daylight Saving Time; an indication of periods of daylight and twilight; the option to put in the yacht's draft, and the ability to display tabulated heights at specified times and time intervals. There is an option to display heights at intervals of 10, 20, 30, 40 or 50 minutes or one hour. Predictions can also be displayed graphically as a continuous plot of height against time.

Whichever method of tidal prediction is used, the basic accuracy depends on the accuracy of the tidal observations made, the length of time over which the observations were taken, and whether the prediction method chosen is suitable for a particular port or area.

In some geographic areas better tidal predictions may be obtained by using non-harmonic methods of prediction. Such areas include the upper reaches of many rivers like the Medway above Chatham; the Forth above Grangemouth; the Severn above Avonmouth, and the Crouch above Burnham. Other areas where non-harmonic methods result in more accurate predictions include many German ports.

Computations using Tidecalc supplement rather than replace ATT. Official tide tables remain the ultimate authority for tidal predictions.

7.6.2   NP 159 Harmonic Method

An alternative computer programme issued by the Hydrographic Office is the Simplified Harmonic Method of Tidal Prediction (NP159A) (version 2·0) available on 3.5 and 5.25 inch discs.

The programme automatically calculates the daily Tidal Angles and Factors which are found in Table VII in all volumes of ATTs. The Port Harmonic Constant, and where appropriate Shallow Water Corrections and Seasonal Changes in Mean Level, are keyed in manually from data listed in Part III of ATTs, or from NP 160 Tidal Harmonic Constants (European Waters) Edition 2 1995.

Users are required to key the relevant data into the template boxes displayed on the screen using the ENTER key to tab through the various boxes shown. A zero is entered where no value is given in ATT. For regularly used ports, up to twenty sets of Port Harmonic Constant data can be pre-stored for later use, but remember that the date is also stored and will need to be changed before using the data for any new prediction.

As changes in Port Harmonic Constants are made from time to time, for the best results it is recommended that only the constants listed in the latest edition of the ATTs are used. NP 160 (Constants for ATT Vol 1) will be updated approximately every five years.

7.6.3   Commercial programmes

A number of commercial firms offer tidal prediction programmes for use on computers or calculators. Most commercial programmes are based on the Admiralty NP 159 method of tidal prediction.

7.7   TIDAL STREAMS

7.7.1   Introduction

Tidal streams are the horizontal movement of water caused by the vertical rise and fall of the tide. They normally change direction about every six hours. They are quite different from ocean currents, such as the Gulf Stream, which run for long periods in the same direction. Tidal streams are always expressed as the direction towards which they are running.

Tidal streams are important to yachtsmen around the British Isles because they often run at about two knots, and much more strongly in a few areas, and at Spring tides. There are a few places where they can attain rates of six to eight knots.

7.7.2   Tidal stream Atlases

The strength and direction of the tidal stream in the more important areas is shown in *Admiralty Tidal Stream Atlases*, as follows:

NP	Ed'n	Date	Title
209	4	1986	Orkney and Shetland Islands
218	5	1995	North Coast of Ireland, West Coast of Scotland
219	2	1991	Portsmouth Hbr and Appr's
220	2	1991	Rosyth Hbr and Appr's
221	2	1991	Plymouth Hbr and Appr's
222	1	1992	Firth of Clyde and Appr's
233	3	1995	Dover Strait
249	2	1985	Thames Estuary, (with Co-Tidal charts)
250	4	1992	English Channel
251	3	1976	North Sea, Southern Part
252	3	1975	North Sea, North-West Part
253	1	1978	North Sea, Eastern Part
256	4	1992	Irish Sea and Bristol Channel
257	3	1973	Approaches to Portland
264	5	1993	The Channel Islands and adjacent Coasts of France
265	1	1978	France, West Coast
337	4	1993	Solent and adjacent Waters

C7

Extracts from the above (by permission of the Hydrographer and HMSO) are given in Chapter 8 for each area in the Almanac. Note: There is no official tidal stream data covering the W coast of Ireland.

The direction (set) of the streams is shown by arrows which are graded in weight and, where possible, in length to indicate the strength (rate) of the tidal stream. Thus ⟶ indicates a weak stream and ⟹ a strong stream. The figures against the arrows give the Mean Neap and Spring rates in tenths of a knot, thus 19,34 indicates a Mean Neap rate of 1·9 knots and a Mean Spring rate of 3·4 knots. The position of the comma on the Atlas represents the approximate position at which the observations were taken. Tidal stream atlases rarely show details of inshore eddies, nor the tidal inset that occurs in many bays.

7.7.3   Tidal diamonds
Tidal stream data is also given by lettered diamonds on many Admiralty charts. The diamonds refer to a table giving Set and Rates (Sp and Np) at hourly intervals before and after HW at a Standard Port. Where relevant, normal river currents are included. Information on tidal streams is also included in *Admiralty Sailing Directions*. Along open coasts the turn of the tidal stream does not necessarily occur at HW and LW. It often occurs at about half tide. The tidal stream usually turns earlier inshore than offshore.

7.7.4   Calculating tidal stream rates
Using Fig 7(7) it is possible to predict the rate of a tidal stream at intermediate times, assuming that it varies with the range of tide at Dover.

Example:
Predict the rate of the tidal stream off the northerly point of the Isle of Skye at 0420 UT on a day when the heights of tide at Dover are:

	UT	Ht(m)
LW	0328	1·4
HW	0819	6·3
LW	1602	1·1
HW	2054	6·4

The range of the tide is therefore 6·3 − 1·4 = 4·9m. Whether using either the Tidal Stream Atlas NP 218, or the Tidal Stream charts for Area 8 in Chapter 8, the appropriate chart to use is that for '4 hours before HW Dover' and this gives mean Neap and Spring rates of 09 and 17 respectively (0·9 and 1·7 kn). On Fig 7(7), Computation of Rates, on the horizontal line marked Neaps, mark the dot above 09 on the horizontal axis; likewise on the line marked Springs, mark the dot below the figure 17 on the horizontal axis. Join these two dots with a straight line. On the vertical axis, 'Mean Range Dover', find the range 4·9. From this

point go horizontally to intersect the pencil line just drawn; from this intersection go vertically to the scale of Tidal Stream Rate, either top or bottom, and read off the predicted rate. In this example it is 14 or 1·4 knots.

Perspex, clear fablon or tracing paper, can be used on top of Fig 7(7), so as to preserve it for future use.

7.7.5   Tidal streams in rivers
Tidal streams in rivers are influenced by the local topography of the river bed as well as by the phases of the Moon. At or near Springs, in a river which is obstructed, for example, by sandbanks at the entrance, the time of HW gets later going up the river; the time of LW also gets later, but more rapidly so the duration of the flood becomes shorter, and duration of ebb becomes longer. At the entrance the flood stream starts at an interval after LW which increases with the degree of obstruction of the channel; this interval between local LW and the start of the flood increases with the distance up river. The ebb begins soon after local HW along the length of the river. Hence the duration of flood is less than that of the ebb and the difference increases with distance up river.

The flood stream is normally stronger than the ebb, and runs harder during the first half of the rise of tide.

At Neaps the flood and ebb both start soon after local LW and HW respectively, and their durations and rates are roughly equal.

7.8   METEOROLOGICAL CONDITIONS
Meteorological conditions can have a significant effect on tides and tidal streams.
a.   Wind.
Broadly speaking sea level tends to rise in the direction towards which the wind is blowing and lower in the opposite direction. In practical terms there is no need to consider winds of less than Force 5.

Strong winds affect not only tide levels, but may also alter the predicted times of High or Low Water by up to one hour. This is not easy to quantify as the effect is very variable and strongly influenced by the local topography. Although exceptionally high or low tides may occur in one place, it is not always the case that the same effect will be repeated elsewhere.

A good example of how localised meteorological effects on water levels can differ from the more general rules occurs in Southampton Water where strong winds between N and NE can significantly reduce tide levels. The longer and stronger the wind blows, the greater the effect. NE winds of Force 5 can be expected to reduce predicted levels by about − 0·2m, whilst winds of Force 8 to 10 will more than double the effect to − 0·5m.

Strong winds can also be associated with high-pressure systems so the combined effects of strong wind and higher than average pressure can easily

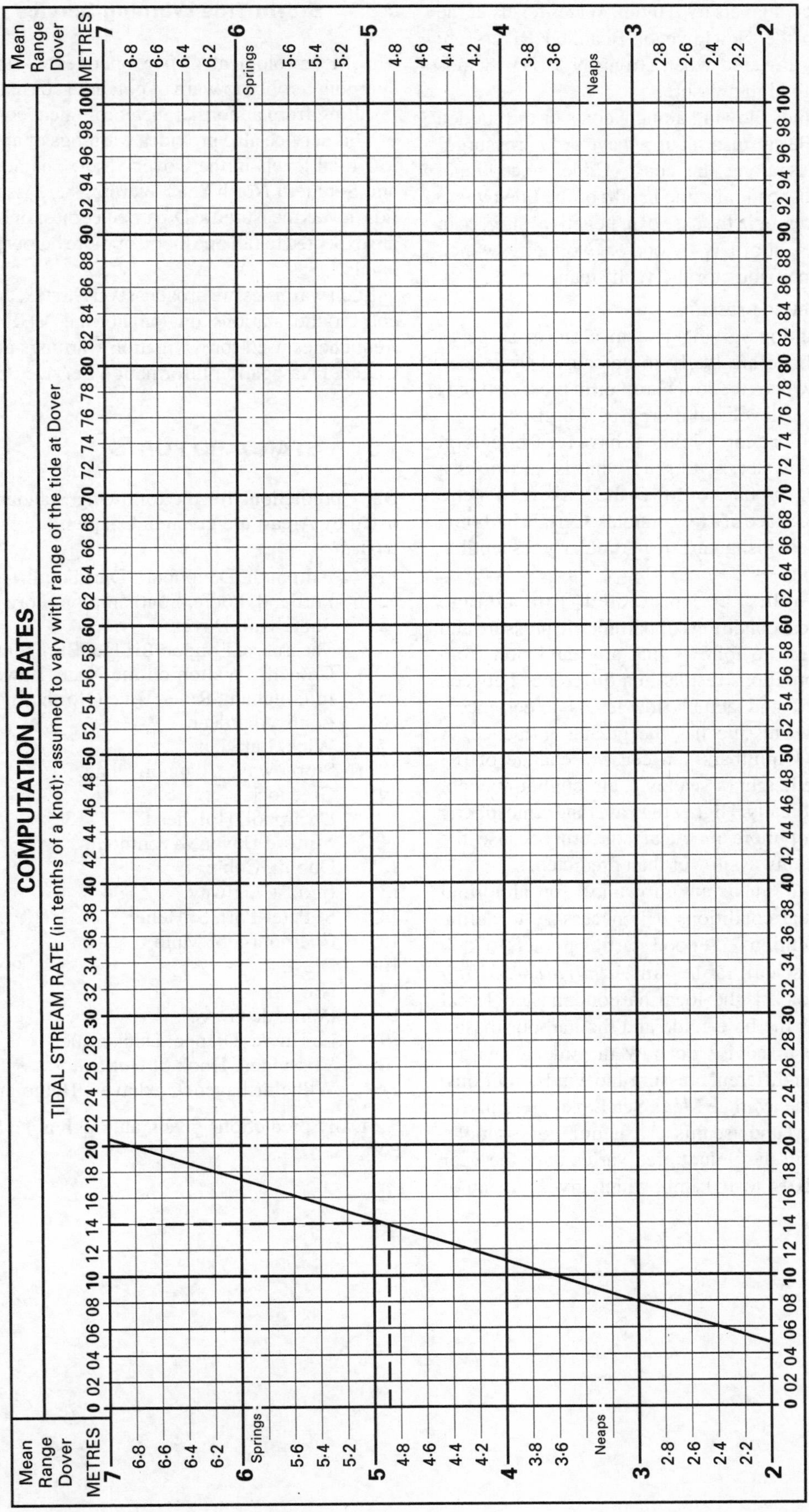

COMPUTATION OF RATES

TIDAL STREAM RATE (in tenths of a knot): assumed to vary with range of the tide at Dover

Fig 7(7) Calculating rates of tidal streams

lower predicted levels by – 0·6m. Water levels at the entrances to the Newtown or Beaulieu Rivers are significantly lowered when strong N to NW winds combine with high pressure.

Strong winds blowing along a coast or the sudden onset of a gale can also set up a wave or 'storm surge' which travels along the coast. Under exceptional conditions this can raise the height of the tide by two or three metres, or in the case of a 'negative' surge, can lower the height of LW by one or two metres which may be more serious for the yachtsman.

b.   Barometric pressure

Severe conditions giving rise to a storm surge as described above are likely to be caused by a deep depression, where the low barometric pressure tends to raise the sea level still more (see 7.8.1).

Intense minor depressions can have local effects on the height of water, setting up what is known as a *seiche* which can raise or lower the sea level a metre or more in the space of a few minutes. Certain harbours such as Wick or Fishguard are particularly susceptible to such conditions.

Tidal heights are predicted for average meteorological conditions of barometric pressure and wind. It therefore follows that any deviation from 'average' conditions results in a difference between the predicted and actual tide levels experienced. Atmospheric pressure has the greater influence. A change of 34 millibars can cause a change of 0·3 metres in the height of sea level, although it may not be felt immediately. Higher than average atmospheric pressure is of more practical concern because the water level is always lower than predicted.

In order to make an allowance for abnormal meteorological conditions it is necessary to define 'average conditions'. A good starting point is to look at the statistical tables in *Admiralty Sailing Directions*, or ask the local harbour master. Local knowledge is the best guide and the harbour master will be able to advise on how the tide levels are affected under different pressure and wind conditions.

Find out the average Mean Sea Level pressure for your local port and use this as a datum. For example, the pressure in the Solent area varies over the year from about 1014 to 1017mb, which gives a mean of 1015·5mb.

7.8.1   Storm Tide Warning Service

The Meteorological Office operates a Storm Tide Warning Service to warn of potential coastal flooding resulting from abnormal meteorological conditions.

This service also provides warnings of abnormally low tidal levels in the Dover Strait, Thames Estuary and Southern North Sea. Warnings are issued when tidal levels measured at Dover, Sheerness or Lowestoft are expected to fall one metre or more below predicted levels.

Such warnings are broadcast on Navtex, and by BT coast radio stations on the normal VHF and MF frequencies used for navigation warnings and by the Channel Navigation Information Service (CNIS).

7.9   STANDARD PORTS

Daily predictions for the following Standards Ports, listed by Areas, are given in Chapter 8:
AREA
1   Falmouth, Devonport, Dartmouth.
2   Portland, Poole, Southampton, Portsmouth.
3   Shoreham, Dover.
4   Sheerness, London Bridge, Burnham-on-Crouch*, Walton-on-the-Naze, Lowestoft.
5   Immingham, River Tyne (North Shields).
6   Leith, Aberdeen.
7   Wick, Lerwick.
8   Stornoway, Ullapool, Oban.
9   Greenock.
10   Liverpool, Holyhead.
11   Milford Haven, Avonmouth.
12   Dublin, Cobh.
13   Belfast, Galway.
14   St Peter Port, St Helier.
15   Cherbourg, St Malo.
16   Brest.
17   Nil.
18   Pointe de Grave.
19   Le Havre, Dieppe, Dunkerque.
20   Vlissingen, Hook of Holland.
21   Wilhelmshaven, Cuxhaven, Helgoland.

*   Daily predictions given, although not a Standard Port.

Chapter 8

Harbour, Coastal and Tidal Information

Contents

8.0   INTRODUCTION   Page 127
8.0.1 Map of areas   **128**
8.0.2 General information   **129**
8.0.3 Harbour information   **129**
8.0.4 Traffic Separation Schemes   **132**
8.0.5 High Speed Craft
8.0.6 UK public holidays
8.0.7 Ferry services   **133**
8.0.8 Distance Tables: Across Channel   **134**
8.0.9   Across Irish Sea **135**
8.0.10   Across N Sea   **136**

8.1   AREA 1   137
SW England. Isles of Scilly to Portland Bill

8.2   AREA 2   181
Central S England. Portland Bill to Selsey Bill

8.3   AREA 3   245
SE England. Selsey Bill to North Foreland

8.4   AREA 4   269
E England. North Foreland to Great
Yarmouth

8.5   AREA 5   323
NE England. Blakeney to Berwick-on-Tweed

8.6   AREA 6   355
SE Scotland. Eyemouth to Rattray Head

8.7   AREA 7   383
NE Scotland. Rattray Head to Cape Wrath
including Orkney and Shetland Islands

8.8   AREA 8   415
NW Scotland. Cape Wrath to Crinan Canal

8.9   AREA 9   451
SW Scotland. Crinan Canal to
Mull of Galloway

8.10   AREA 10   479
NW England, Isle of Man and N Wales.
Mull of Galloway to Bardsey Island

8.11   AREA 11   509
S Wales and Bristol Channel.
Bardsey Island to Lands End

8.12   AREA 12   545
S Ireland. Malahide clockwise to
Liscanor Bay

8.13   AREA 13   583
N Ireland. Lambay Island anti-clockwise
to Liscanor Bay

8.14   AREA 14   617
Channel Islands. Alderney to Jersey

8.15   AREA 15   643
Central N France. Pointe de Barfleur to
St Quay-Portrieux

8.16   AREA 16   675
N Brittany. Paimpol to Raz de Sein

8.17   AREA 17   707
S Brittany. Raz de Sein to River Loire

8.18   AREA 18   737
S Biscay. River Loire to Spanish border

8.19   AREA 19   769
NE France. Barfleur to Dunkerque

8.20   AREA 20   807
Belgium and the Netherlands.
Nieuwpoort to Delfzijl

8.21   AREA 21   853
Germany. Emden to Danish border

C8

8.0.1 Map of Areas

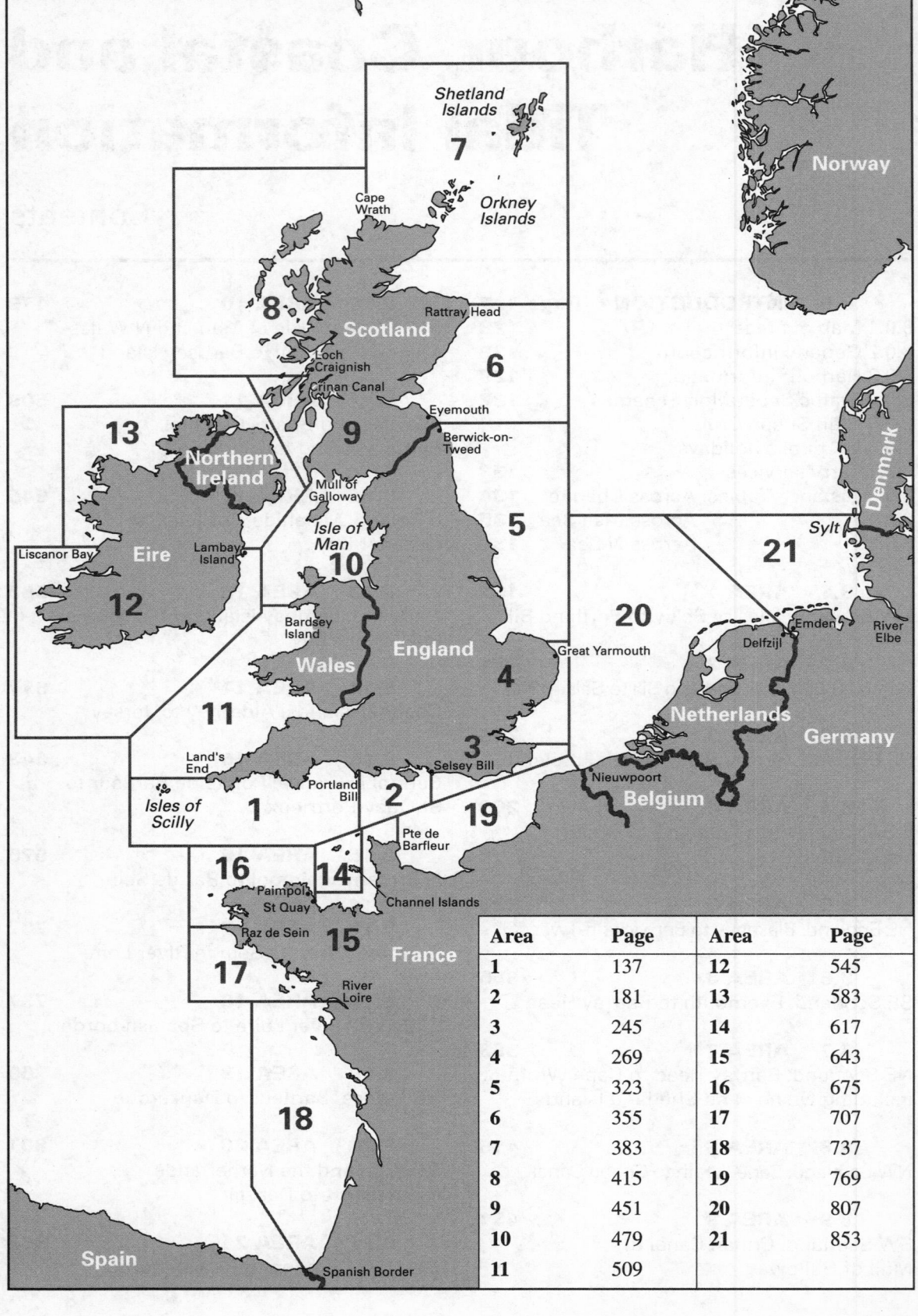

Area	Page	Area	Page
1	137	**12**	545
2	181	**13**	583
3	245	**14**	617
4	269	**15**	643
5	323	**16**	675
6	355	**17**	707
7	383	**18**	737
8	415	**19**	769
9	451	**20**	807
10	479	**21**	853
11	509		

8.0.2   General information

Harbour, coastal and tidal information is given for each of the 21 Areas shown on the map at 8.0.1, with detailed text and chartlets of 440 harbours and notes on 430 lesser harbours and anchorages. The information provided enables a skipper to assess whether he can get into a harbour (tidal height, depth, wind direction etc), and whether he wants to enter the harbour (shelter, facilities available, early closing days etc). Abbreviations and symbols are on pp 3-6. Glossaries are in Areas 15, 20 and 21.

Each Area is arranged as follows:

Index of the harbours covered in that area.

A diagram of the area showing the positions and characteristics of the harbours covered, principal lights, radiobeacons, coastal/port radio stations, weather information offices, LB stations and CG Centres with their boundaries.

Tidal stream chartlets for the area, based on Admiralty tidal stream atlases (by kind permission of the Hydrographer of the Navy and the Controller, HM Stationery Office), showing the rates and directions of tidal streams for each hour referenced to HW Dover and to HW at the relevant Standard Port. For how to use tidal stream charts see 7.7.2.

A list of principal coastal lights, fog signals and useful waypoints in the area. More powerful lights (range 15M or more) are in **bold** type; light-vessels and Lanbys are in *CAPITAL ITALICS*; fog signals are in *italics*. Latitude and longitude are shown for a selection of lights and marks, some of which are underlined as useful waypoints. Unless otherwise stated, lights are white. Elevations are in metres (m) above MHWS, and nominal ranges in nautical miles (M). Where appropriate, a brief description is given of the lighthouse or tower. Arcs of visibility, sector limits, and alignment of leading lights etc are true bearings as seen from seaward measured in a clockwise direction. Where a longitude is given (e.g. 04°12'·05W) W stands for West; W can also mean white. To avoid ambiguity, the words white or West may be written in full, except for longitude.

Passage information briefly calls attention in note form to some of the principal features of the coast, recommended routes, offlying dangers, tide races, better anchorages etc.

Table of distances in nautical miles by the most direct route, avoiding dangers, between selected places in that area and in adjacent areas. See also Tables of distances across the English Channel, Irish and North Seas in this Introduction.

Special notes in certain Areas (Ireland, Channel Is, France, Belgium, Netherlands and Germany) give information specific to that country or Area.

8.0.3   Harbour information

a.   Below the **harbour name**, the County or Unitary Council (or equivalent abroad) is given, followed by the lat/long of the hbr entrance, or equivalent. This lat/long may be used as a final waypoint after the approach WPT ⊕ given under Navigation. NB: A published waypoint should never be used without first plotting its position on the chart.

b.   A **harbour rating** is given after the lat/long. It grades a port for ease of access, facilities available and its attractiveness as a place. Although inevitably subjective, it offers a useful shorthand as to what a yachtsman may expect to find. The rating, shown below the port name as 3 figures, eg Rtg 2.3.2, is based on the following criteria:

— Ease of access (first figure):
1.   This port can be entered in *gales from any direction and at all states of tide, by day or night.*
2.   Accessible in *gales from all quarters except one; adequate depths, marks and lights.*
3.   Accessible in *strong winds from all quarters except one; possible tidal or pilotage constraints.*
4.   Only accessible in *light winds and slight swell; brief tidal window and few marks or lights.*
5.   Only accessible in *calm, settled* conditions by day with *no swell; there may be a bar and difficult pilotage.*

— Facilities available (second figure):
1.   *All possible facilities* for yacht and crew.
2.   *Many facilities available,* including all domestic needs, but with some limitations in chandlery and/or major repair work.
3.   *All domestic facilities,* but probably only a hauling-out slip and a boatyard capable of limited work; not necessarily attuned to yachting needs.
4.   *All domestic needs;* basic marine facilities.
5.   *Virtually nothing,* unless prepared to walk some distance for basic domestic needs, eg food/ water.

— Attractiveness (third figure):
1.   An attractive place; visit, if necessary *going a little out of your way* to do so.
2.   Normal for this part of the coast; *if convenient* visit the port concerned.
3.   Visit only if alternatives are unavailable. *Expect to be disappointed* and subject to inconvenience.

C8

This rating system, modified for harbours in this Almanac, was originated by the late Robin Brandon and used in successive editions of his *South Biscay Pilot,* published by Adlard Coles Nautical, to whom grateful ackowledgement is made.

c.   **Chart numbers** for Admiralty (AC), Imray Laurie Norie & Wilson (Imray), Stanfords or foreign charts are listed, largest scale first. The *numbers* of Admiralty Small Craft editions are shown in *italics*. The Ordnance Survey (OS. 1:50,000) Map numbers are given for UK and Eire.

d. **Chartlets** are based on British Admiralty, French, Dutch and German charts (as acknowledged in the Introduction).

It is emphasised that these chartlets are not designed or intended for pilotage or navigation, although every effort has been made to ensure that they accurately portray the harbour concerned. The publishers and editors disclaim any responsibility for resultant accidents or damage if they are so used. The largest scale official chart, properly corrected, should always be used.

Due to limitations of scale, chartlets do not always cover the whole area referred to in the text nor do they always contain the approach waypoint ⊕. Not every depth, mark or feature can be shown. Depths and drying heights in metres are below/ above Chart Datum; elevations are above MHWS. A light green tint shows drying areas, the darker tint indicates land.

e. **Tidal predictions** are all provided by the UK Hydrographic Office, with permissions from the French, Dutch and German Hydrographic Offices.

For each Standard Port daily predictions of times and heights of HW/LW are given. Zone times are given, but no account is taken of BST or other daylight saving times (DST). In UK and Eire times are in UT.

At the foot of each page of tidal predictions is given the height difference between Chart Datum at the port in question and Ordnance Datum (Newlyn), for UK ports. For foreign ports the height difference is referenced to the relevant national Land survey datum. This enables tidal levels along a stretch of coast to be referred to a common horizontal plane. Further notes are contained in the Admiralty Tide Tables where the height differences are also tabulated.

Time and height differences for Secondary Ports are referenced to the most suitable (not always the nearest) Standard Port. An (←) or (→) points toward the Standard Port pages. The average time difference between local HW and HW Dover is given, so that the UT (±15 minutes) of local HW can be quickly found.

Times of HW Dover are in 8.3.15 and, for quick reference, on a bookmark which also lists Range together with a visual indication of the state of the tide (Springs or Neaps). Duration (quoted for most ports), if deducted from time of HW, gives the approx time of the previous LW. Mean Level (ML) is also quoted. Given ML and the height of HW, the range and therefore height of LW can also be calculated; see also Chapter 7. It should be noted, en passant, that on French charts ML, not MHWS, is used as the reference datum for elevations of lights, bridges etc.

Tidal Coefficients are listed and explained under Brest and are applicable to all French ports on the Channel and Atlantic coasts. They also provide an immediate numerical indication of the size of a tide, without resort to calculating range.

f. **Tidal curves** are given for Standard Ports and those other ports for which full predictions are shown. Use the appropriate (np/sp) curve for tidal calculations (ie finding the height of tide at a given time, or the time for a given height). See Chapter 7 for tidal calculations.

HW −3 means 3 hrs before local HW; HW +2 means 2 hrs after. Secondary curves are given in 8.2.13 for ports between Swanage and Selsey Bill where special tidal conditions exist.

g. **Shelter** assesses the degree of shelter and advises on access, berths (for charges see under Facilities), moorings and anchorages. Access times, if quoted, are approx figures relative to mean HW. They are purely a guide for a nominal 1·5m draft, plus safety clearance, and take no account of hull form, springs/neaps, flood/ebb, swell or nature of the bottom. Their purpose is to alert a skipper to possible tidal problems. Times of lock and bridge openings etc are local (LT), unless otherwise stated.

h. **Navigation** gives the lat/long of a waypoint (⊕) suitable for starting the approach, with its bearing/ distance from/to the hbr ent or next significant feature; some ⊕s may be off the harbour chartlet. NB: A published waypoint should never be used without first plotting its position on the chart. Approach chans, buoyage, speed limits and hazards are also described.

Wrecks around the UK which are of historic or archaeological interest are protected under the Protection of Wrecks Act 1973. About 40 sites, as detailed in Annual Notice to Mariners No 16 and depicted on the larger scale Admiralty charts, are listed in this almanac under the nearest harbour or in Passage Information. Unauthorised interference, including anchoring and diving on such sites, may lead to a substantial fine.

j. **Lights and Marks** includes as much detail as space permits; some data may also be shown on the chartlet and/or in Coastal lights, fog signals and waypoints (8.AA.4) for that Area. Traffic signals for individual harbours are shown in each area. French, Belgian, Dutch and German traffic signals are in 8.15.8, 8.20.8 and 8.21.8. International Port Traffic Signals are shown at plate 9 and described on p. 23.

k. **Radio Telephone** quotes VHF Channels related to each port, marina or VTS. If not obvious, the callsign of a station is shown in *italics*. Frequencies are indicated by their International Maritime Services Channel (Ch) designator. UK Marina Channels are 80 (161·625MHz) and M (157·85MHz; also known as M1 and formerly as Ch 37). M2 (161·425MHz) is allocated to some YCs for race control. MF frequencies, if shown, are in kHz.

Ch 16, the Distress, Safety and Calling Ch, is monitored by most shore stations, and is shown after the working channels. Its Distress and Safety functions can be seriously jeopardised by excessive calling, test transmissions and illegal chatter. Initial contact can usually, and very desirably, be made on the listed working Ch, rather than on Ch 16.

Where known, preferred channels are shown in bold type, thus **14**. If there is a choice of calling channel, always indicate which channel you are using; eg, *'Dover Port Control, this is NONSUCH, NONSUCH on Channel 74, over'*. This avoids confusion if the station being called is working more than one channel.

Where local times are stated, the letters LT are added. H24 means continuous watch. Times of scheduled broadcasts are shown (for example) as H +20, ie 20 minutes past the hour.

l.   **Telephone** is followed by the dialling code in brackets, which is not repeated for individual ☎ numbers. But it may be repeated or augmented under **Facilities** if different or additional codes also apply. Eg, Portsmouth and Gosport numbers are both on (01705) as listed; but Fareham's different code (01329) is quoted separately.

In the UK the ☎s of the relevant Coastguard MRCC/MRSC (see Table 6(1)) are given under each port, but in an emergency dial 999 and ask for the Coastguard.

The procedures for international calls from/to the UK are given in 8.12.7 (Ireland), 8.15.8 (France), 8.20.8 (Belgium & The Netherlands), and 8.21.8 (Germany). These sections also give ☎s for marine emergencies abroad. All EU countries use ☎ 112 for emergency calls to Fire, Police, Ambulance, in addition to their national emergency ☎s.

m.   **Facilities** available at the harbour, marinas and yacht clubs are listed first, followed by an abbreviated summary of those marine services provided commercially (for abbreviations see the Introduction and the Dover Range card). See also the Directory of Marine Services and Supplies (pink pages at the front of the Almanac) for commercial listings.
Note: Facilities at Yacht Clubs are usually available to crews who arrive by sea (as opposed to trailing a dinghy by car) and belong to a recognised YC.

The overnight cost of a visitors alongside berth for a 30ft (9·1m) LOA boat is shown in local currency at the previous year's rates. Harbour dues, if applicable, and VAT are included; in the UK the cost of mains electricity is usually extra. Note: The cost of berthing does not influence the attractiveness of a harbour, as described under 8.0.3b.

Town facilities are also listed, and whether there is a Post Office (✉), Bank (Ⓑ), Railway Station (⇌), or commercial Airport (✈) in or near the port. Where there is not, the nearest one may be shown in ( ). Abroad, the nearest port with a UK ferry link is given (see also 8.0.7 below).

FACILITIES FOR DISABLED PEOPLE

RYA Sailability is an organisation operating in the UK under the auspices of the RYA to open up sailing and its related facilities to disabled sailors. Facilities include car parking; ramps for wheel chair access to buildings and pontoons; purpose-built toilets and showers; and at Largs (Ayrshire) a special pontoon and sailing championships. Facilities for those with sight or hearing disabilities are not widely available. Symbols used in the text of Chapter 8 are self explanatory:
♿, 👁 and 🎿, 🎿.

ENVIRONMENTAL GUIDANCE

The following notes are adapted, by kind permission of the RYA, from an RYA leaflet *Tidelines*. This leaflet offers guidance, mainly directed at newcomers to sailing, on waste disposal and the protection of the natural environment. The following points are relevant:
a.   In principle never ditch rubbish at sea.
b.   Keep it onboard and dispose of it ashore in proper receptacles. These are available in all marinas; elsewhere, eg Helford River, the 🗑 symbol is used in this almanac to indicate waste bins are provided.
c.   Readily degradable foodstuffs may be ditched at sea when more than 3M offshore (12M in the English Channel and North Sea).
d.   Foodstuffs which are not readily degradable, eg skins and peelings, should not be ditched at sea.
e.   Other rubbish, eg packaging of plastic, glass, metal, paper and cardboard; fabrics; ropelines and netting, should never be ditched at sea.
f.   Do not discharge anything except 'washing-up' water into a marina, a popular ⚓ or moorings.
g.   Oils and oily waste are particularly harmful to the water, fish and wildlife. Take old engine oil ashore in a well-sealed container or bottle. Do not pump oily bilge water overboard.
h.   Avoid fuel spillage when topping up outboards.
j.   Rowing ashore provides better exercise, less noise and no pollution compared with a 2-stroke outboard!
k.   Sewage. If possible use shoreside toilets; and only use the onboard heads in tidal waters.
l.   Consider fitting and using a holding tank. These are already compulsory in some countries. This almanac indicates where pump-out facilities, ⛽ or ♿, are known to exist. If there are none, only pump out >3M offshore.
m.   Toxic waste, eg some antifoulings, cleaning chemicals, old batteries, should be disposed of ashore at a proper facility.
n.   Wild birds, plants, fish and marine animals are usually abundant along coastlines. Respect protected sites; keep away from nesting sites and breeding colonies. Minimise noise, wash and disturbance.
o.   Go ashore at recognised landing places. Do not anchor or dry out where important and vulnerable seabed species exist, eg soft corals, eel grass.

C8

8.0.4 TRAFFIC SEPARATION SCHEMES

Traffic Separation Schemes (TSS) are essential to the safety of larger vessels and, whilst inconvenient for yachtsmen, must be accepted as another element of passage planning, or be avoided where possible. See 1.1.2 for Rule 10 of the IRPCS.

TSS are shown on most Admiralty charts. Those covered by this Almanac are depicted in the relevant geographic areas of this chapter, ie:

Area	TSS	Page
1	Off Land's End and Scilly	138
10	Off Skerries	504
11	Off Smalls	524
12	Tuskar Rock	565
	Fastnet Rock	576
13	North Channel	604
14	Casquets	618
16	Ushant	676
19	Dover Strait	800
20	West Hinder to Maas North	826
	Off Texel to Elbe approach	850/851

8.0.5 HIGH SPEED CRAFT (HSC)

HSC, aka HSS (High speed ships), may be met on many of the ferry routes around the UK, as shown in the Table below. They are defined as craft with a max speed (kn) equal to or > 7·193 x Displacement to the power of 0·1677. Thus displacement, as well as speed, is a criterion. Their speed creates for yachts a "fly-on-the-wall" situation. Admiralty SDs and charts now contain specific warnings about HSC and the need to keep a good lookout. From initial sighting at, say, 5M an HSC at 40kn can be upon you in about 7 minutes. HSC carry no special lts/signals and have no special rights or obligations under the IRPCS.

8.0.6 UK PUBLIC HOLIDAYS 1999

ENGLAND & WALES: *Jan 1*, Apr 2, Apr 5, *May 3*, May 31, Aug 30, *Dec 27, 28 and 31*.

SCOTLAND: Jan 1, *Jan 4*, Apr 2, May 3, *May 31*, Aug 2, *Dec 27, 28 and 31*.

NORTHERN IRELAND: *Jan 1*, Mar 17, Apr 2, Apr 5, *May 3*, May 31, July 12, Aug 30, *Dec 27, 28 and 31*.

Dates in italics are subject to confirmation.

8.0.7 Ferry Services

A summary is provided opposite of most of the more popular ferry routes both within UK waters and to/from the UK, together with booking/contact ☎ numbers. Ferries on the W coast of Scotland are listed in more detail at the end of Area 8.

8.0.8/9/10 Distance Tables

In addition to the Distance Tables in each of the 21 geographic Areas, there are three Distance Tables in this Introduction. These contain port-to-port distances for passages from/to the UK across the English Channel (8.0.8), Irish Sea (8.0.9) and North Sea (8.0.10). They therefore relate to several geographic areas and may be used in conjunction with the Distance Tables in these areas.

Types of HSC (Col 3)

WPC	=	Wave piercing catamaran
Mono	=	Monohull
SWATH	=	Small Water-plan Area Twin Hull
Hover	=	Hovercraft
Cat	=	Catamaran

Route	HSC name	Type	LOA (m)	Max speed (kn)	Pax/cars
Poole/Weymouth-Chan Is	Condor Express	WPC	86	40	775/185
Portsmouth-IoW	Our Lady Patricia/Pamela	Cat	30	31	440/0
Southampton-IoW	Shearwater 5/6	Hydrofoil	22	35	67/0
Southampton-IoW	Red Jet 1/2	Cat	31.5	34	138/0
Portsmouth-IoW	Double O Seven/Freedom 90	Hover	24.4	45	98/0
Newhaven-Dieppe	Stena Sealynx III	WPC	81	37	674/150
Folkestone-Boulogne	Hoverspeed G. Britain	WPC	74	35	600/90
Dover-Calais	SuperCatSea II	Mono	100	38	782/175
Dover-Calais	Stena Sealynx	WPC	74	37	450/84
Dover-Calais	Princess Margaret/Anne	Hover	56.4	50	390/55
Ramsgate/Dover-Oostende	Holyman Rapide/Diamante	WPC	78	37	674/150
Harwich-Hook of Holland	Stena Discovery	SWATH	120	40	1500/360
Stranraer-Belfast	S/C Danmark	WPC	74	35	450/80
Stranraer-Belfast	Jetliner	Mono	95	40	600/160
Stranraer-Belfast	Stena Voyager	SWATH	120	40	1500/360
Holyhead-Dun Laoghaire	Stena Explorer	SWATH	120	40	1500/360

FERRIES AROUND UK AND TO/FROM THE CONTINENT   8.0.7

This Table is a highly condensed version of many detailed schedules. It is intended to show broadly what is available and to help when cruise plans and/or crew movements are subject to change at short notice.

NOTES: 1. **Hours** = approx duration of day crossing. 2. **Frequency** = number of one-way sailings per day in summer. Specific day(s) of the week may be shown, if non-daily. 3. ☎ **Bookings** may be via a centralised number applicable to all routes.

From	To	Hours	Frequency	Company	☎ Bookings
A.	**CROSS CHANNEL** (France, Belgium; and to Spain)				
Plymouth (Mar-Nov)	Santander	23½	M, W	Brittany	0990-360360
Plymouth	Roscoff	6	1 - 3	Brittany	Ditto
Poole	Cherbourg	4¼	1 - 2	Brittany (Truckline)	Ditto
Poole	St Malo	8	F, S, Su, M	Brittany	Ditto
Portsmouth	St Malo	8¾	1	Brittany	Ditto
Portsmouth	Ouistreham (Caen)	6	3	Brittany	Ditto
Portsmouth (Jan-Mar)	Santander	31	Su	Brittany	Ditto
Portsmouth	Cherbourg	4¾	3	P & O European Ferries	0990-980555
Portsmouth	Le Havre	5¾	3	P & O European Ferries	Ditto
Portsmouth	Bilbao	33½	Su, Tu	P & O European Ferries	Ditto
Brighton	Fécamp	2 (Cat)	2 (May-Sep inc)	Brighton Ferries	01273-818333
Newhaven	Dieppe	4/2¼ (Cat)	2/4	Stena Line	0990-707070
Folkestone	Boulogne	55 mins	6	Hoverspeed (Cat)	0990-240241
Dover	Calais	35 mins	14	Hoverspeed (Hovercraft)	Ditto
Dover	Calais	1½	20	Stena Line	0990-707070
Dover	Calais	1½	14	SeaFrance	01304-204204
Dover	Calais	1¼	25	P & O European Ferries	0990-980980
Dover/Ramsgate	Ostend	4/1¾ (Cat)	4/4 - 6	Holyman Sally	0990-595522
B.	**NORTH SEA**				
Harwich	Hook of Holland	3¾ (HSS)	2	Stena Line	0990-707070
Harwich	Hamburg	18½	4 wkly	Scandinavian Seaways	0990-333000
Harwich	Esbjerg	19½	4 wkly	Scandinavian Seaways	Ditto
Harwich	Gothenburg	23½	Su, Tu	Scandinavian Seaways	Ditto
Hull	Rotterdam	12½	1	P & O N Sea Ferries	01482-377177
Hull	Zeebrugge	13¼	1	P & O N Sea Ferries	Ditto
Newcastle	IJmuiden	14	Varies; May-Sep	Scandinavian Seaways	0990-333000
Newcastle	Hamburg	23½	2 wkly	Scandinavian Seaways	Ditto
Newcastle	Gothenburg	23½	F	Scandinavian Seaways	Ditto
Newcastle	Stavanger/Bergen	18½/6	M, W, S	Color	0191-296 1313
C.	**SCOTLAND**				
Aberdeen	Lerwick+Bergen	14+12½	F	P & O Scottish Ferries	01224-572615
Scrabster	Stromness	1¾	2 - 3	P & O Scottish Ferries	01856-850655
Stromness	Lerwick	8	Su, Tu	P & O Scottish Ferries	01595-5252
Ullapool	Stornoway	3½	2	Caledonian MacBrayne	01475-650000

CalMac run ferries to 23 West Scottish islands and many mainland ports; see 8.8.21 for details, inc other companies.

From	To	Hours	Frequency	Company	☎ Bookings
D.	**IRISH SEA** (and Eire-France)				
Cork	Roscoff	14	Su, Tu	Brittany	21-378401
Cork	St Malo	18	Wed	Brittany	Ditto
Cork	Cherbourg	17½	F (Jun-Aug)	Irish Ferries	01-661 0511
Cork	Le Havre	21½	Su (Jun-Aug)	Irish Ferries	Ditto
Cork	Swansea	10	1 (not Tu)	Swansea/Cork Ferries	01792-456116
Rosslare	Cherbourg	17	S, M	Irish Ferries	01-661 0511
Rosslare	Le Havre	21	Tu, W, Th	Irish Ferries	Ditto
Rosslare	Pembroke Dock	3¾	2	Irish Ferries	0990 171717
Rosslare	Fishguard	3½/1¾ (Cat)	2/5	Stena Line	0990-707070
Dun Laoghaire	Holyhead	3¾/1¾ (HSS)	1/6	Stena Line	Ditto
Dublin	Holyhead	3¼	2	Irish Ferries	0990 171717
Belfast	Stranraer	1½ (Cat)	4 - 5	SeaCat	0345-523523
Belfast	Stranraer	3¼/1¾ (HSS)	3/5	Stena Line	0990-707070
Belfast	Liverpool	10	1	Norse Irish Ferries	01232-779090
Larne	Cairnryan	2¼	6	P & O European Ferries	0990-980666
Douglas, IOM*	Heysham	3¾	Mo, Tu, We, Th	IOM Steam Packet Co	01624-661661
Douglas, IOM	Liverpool	4¼	Fr, Sa, Su	IOM Steam Packet Co	01624-661661

*Also less frequent sailings from Douglas to Belfast (4¾), Dublin (4¾), Fleetwood (3¼) and Ardrossan (8).

From	To	Hours	Frequency	Company	☎ Bookings
E.	**CHANNEL ISLANDS**				
Jersey	Poole	3¾	2	Condor (Cat)	01305-761551
Guernsey	Poole	2½	3	Condor (Cat)	Ditto
Guernsey	Weymouth	2½	1	Condor (Cat)	Ditto. 1 May-31 Oct
Jersey	St Malo	¾	4	Condor (Cat)	Ditto
Jersey	Sark	¾	1	Condor (Cat)	Ditto
Jersey†	St Malo	2½/1¼ (Cat)	2/5	Emeraude	02.99.40.48.40

†Also Jersey (St Helier) to Guernsey, Sark, Granville; and Jersey (Gorey) to Portbail and Carteret.

C8

8.0.8   DISTANCES (M) ACROSS THE ENGLISH CHANNEL

England France/CI	Longships	Falmouth	Fowey	Plymouth bkwtr	Salcombe	Dartmouth	Torbay	Exmouth	Weymouth	Poole Hbr Ent	Needles Lt Ho	Nab Tower	Littlehampton	Shoreham	Brighton	Newhaven	Eastbourne	Rye	Folkestone	Dover
Le Conquet	112	112	123	125	125	137	144	155	172	188	194	212	230	240	245	249	261	278	295	301
L'Aberwrac'h	102	97	106	107	105	117	124	135	153	168	174	192	211	219	224	228	239	257	275	280
Roscoff	110	97	101	97	91	100	107	117	130	144	149	165	184	193	197	200	211	229	246	252
Trébeurden	120	105	106	102	94	102	109	120	129	142	147	164	181	190	194	197	208	226	244	249
Tréguier	132	112	110	101	94	98	102	112	116	128	132	147	162	170	174	177	188	206	224	229
Lézardrieux	142	121	118	107	94	100	105	114	115	126	130	140	157	165	169	172	184	201	219	224
St Quay-Portrieux	159	137	135	124	111	115	121	129	127	135	135	146	162	171	174	178	189	207	225	230
St Malo	172	149	146	133	118	120	124	132	125	130	130	143	157	166	170	173	184	202	220	225
St Helier	155	130	123	108	93	95	100	108	99	104	104	115	132	140	144	147	158	176	194	199
St Peter Port	139	113	104	89	73	70	75	81	71	79	83	97	112	120	124	127	135	156	174	179
Braye (Alderney)	146	116	106	89	72	69	71	75	54	60	62	73	91	100	103	106	114	136	153	159
Cherbourg	168	138	125	107	92	87	88	93	66	64	63	68	81	90	92	96	102	122	140	145
St Vaast-la-Hougue	194	164	150	132	116	111	112	116	83	76	72	71	80	87	88	90	96	115	132	138
Ouistreham	229	198	185	167	151	146	147	147	117	107	100	86	91	92	91	90	92	106	125	130
Deauville	236	205	192	174	158	153	154	154	122	111	104	88	89	88	87	85	87	101	120	125
Le Havre	231	200	187	169	153	148	148	148	118	105	97	82	82	83	82	79	80	94	115	120
Fécamp	242	212	197	179	163	157	157	157	120	105	96	75	71	68	65	62	62	72	90	95
Dieppe	268	237	222	204	188	180	180	180	142	125	117	91	80	75	70	64	63	60	70	75
Boulogne	290	258	242	224	208	198	195	191	153	135	127	97	81	71	66	59	47	33	28	25
Calais	305	272	257	239	223	213	210	209	168	150	141	111	96	86	81	74	62	43	26	22

NOTES

1.   This Table applies to Areas 1 – 3, 14 – 16 and 19, each of which also contains its own internal Distance Table. Approximate distances in nautical miles are by the most direct route, while avoiding dangers and allowing for Traffic Separation Schemes.

2.   For ports within the Solent, add the appropriate distances given in 8.2.6 to those shown above under either Needles light house or Nab Tower.

3.   Distances across the Irish Sea, as applicable to Areas 9 – 13, are given in 8.0.9.

4.   Distances across the North Sea, as applicable to Areas 3 – 7 and 19 – 21, are given in 8.0.10.

5.   Some aspects of planning Cross-Channel passages are covered in Passage Information, 8.3.5 final section and 8.15.5.

8.0.9   DISTANCES (M) ACROSS THE IRISH SEA

Scotland / England / Wales Ireland	Port Ellen (Islay)	Campbeltown	Troon	Portpatrick	Mull of Galloway	Kirkcudbright	Maryport	Fleetwood	Pt of Ayre (IOM)	Port St Mary (IOM)	Liverpool	Holyhead	Pwllheli	Fishguard	Milford Haven	Swansea	Avonmouth	Ilfracombe	Padstow	Longships
Tory Island	75	107	132	119	134	170	185	215	156	171	238	207	260	279	307	360	406	355	372	399
Malin Head	45	76	101	88	103	139	154	184	125	140	207	176	229	248	276	329	375	324	341	368
Lough Foyle	38	61	86	73	88	124	139	169	110	125	192	161	214	233	261	314	360	309	326	353
Portrush	31	50	76	64	80	116	131	161	102	117	184	153	206	225	253	306	352	301	318	345
Carnlough	42	35	57	32	45	81	96	126	67	78	149	115	168	187	215	268	314	363	280	307
Larne	51	39	58	24	37	72	88	118	58	70	141	106	159	178	206	259	305	254	271	298
Carrickfergus	64	48	65	26	34	69	85	115	55	66	138	101	154	173	201	254	300	249	266	293
Bangor	63	48	64	22	30	65	81	111	51	62	134	97	150	169	197	250	296	245	262	289
Strangford Lough	89	72	84	36	30	63	76	97	41	37	107	69	121	141	167	219	265	214	231	258
Carlingford Lough	117	100	112	64	60	90	103	112	70	51	118	67	111	124	149	202	248	197	214	241
Dun Laoghaire	153	136	148	100	93	119	126	120	93	69	119	56	82	94	109	162	208	157	174	201
Wicklow	170	153	165	117	108	133	140	127	108	83	123	56	67	71	90	143	189	138	155	182
Arklow	182	165	177	129	120	144	149	133	117	93	131	64	71	65	79	132	179	128	144	167
Rosslare	215	202	208	161	154	179	180	164	152	125	156	90	83	55	58	109	157	110	119	137
Tuskar Rock	216	203	209	162	155	179	182	165	152	126	152	91	82	48	51	105	150	103	112	130
Dunmore East	250	237	243	196	189	213	216	199	186	160	189	127	116	79	76	130	177	124	127	136
Youghal	281	268	274	227	220	244	247	230	217	191	220	158	147	110	103	156	200	148	139	138
Crosshaven	300	287	293	246	239	263	266	249	236	210	239	177	166	131	118	170	216	163	151	144
Baltimore	346	333	339	292	285	309	312	295	282	256	285	223	212	172	160	209	254	198	178	161
Fastnet Rock	354	341	347	300	293	317	320	303	290	264	293	231	220	181	169	216	260	207	185	170

NOTES

1. This Table applies to Areas 9 – 13, each of which also contains its own internal Distance Table. Approximate distances in nautical miles are by the most direct route, whilst avoiding dangers and Traffic Separation Schemes.

2. Some aspects of planning passages across the Irish Sea are covered in Passage Information, 8.13.5 first section.

3. Distances across the English Channel, as applicable to Areas 1 – 3, 14 – 16 and 19, are given in 8.0.8.

C8

8.0.10 DISTANCES (M) ACROSS THE NORTH SEA

UK \ Norway to France	Bergen	Stavanger	Lindesnes	Skagen	Esjberg	Sylt (List)	Brunsbüttel	Helgoland	Bremerhaven	Willhelmshaven	Delfzijl	Den Helder	IJmuiden	Scheveningen	Roompotsluis	Vlissingen	Zeebrugge	Oostende	Nieuwpoort	Dunkerque
Lerwick	210	226	288	403	428	442	517	470	510	500	493	486	497	505	551	550	552	555	562	588
Kirkwall	278	275	323	438	439	452	516	467	507	497	481	460	473	481	515	514	516	519	526	545
Wick	292	283	323	437	428	440	498	449	489	479	458	433	444	451	485	484	486	489	496	514
Inverness	356	339	381	485	461	462	529	479	519	509	487	460	471	478	513	512	514	517	524	542
Fraserburgh	288	266	296	410	383	384	451	404	444	434	412	385	396	403	430	429	431	434	441	456
Aberdeen	308	279	298	411	371	378	433	382	432	412	386	353	363	369	401	400	402	405	412	426
Dundee	362	329	339	451	394	401	448	396	436	426	395	352	359	364	390	389	385	388	395	412
Port Edgar	391	355	362	472	409	413	457	405	445	435	401	355	361	366	391	390	386	389	396	413
Berwick-on-Tweed	374	325	320	431	356	361	408	355	395	385	355	310	315	320	342	341	337	340	347	364
Hartlepool	409	353	340	440	340	331	367	312	352	342	302	241	243	247	266	265	261	264	271	288
Grimsby	463	395	362	452	324	318	342	291	332	325	288	187	182	185	199	198	190	191	201	198
Kings Lynn	485	416	379	466	330	333	343	292	344	336	283	184	183	183	197	195	187	188	198	195
Lowestoft	508	431	380	453	308	300	295	262	284	271	218	118	104	98	95	99	87	87	89	106
Harwich	540	461	410	483	330	331	320	287	309	296	243	147	126	114	94	100	84	77	80	80
Brightlingsea	558	479	428	501	348	349	338	305	327	314	261	165	144	105	108	106	92	88	86	87
Burnham-on-Crouch	567	488	437	510	357	358	347	314	336	323	270	174	151	112	109	115	99	92	93	95
London Bridge	620	543	490	560	400	408	395	361	382	374	320	222	199	149	153	149	134	125	126	114
Sheerness	580	503	450	520	360	367	353	319	340	334	280	180	157	109	113	109	94	85	86	74
Ramsgate	575	498	446	516	368	346	339	305	323	315	262	161	144	121	89	85	77	65	58	42
Dover	588	511	459	529	378	359	352	328	336	328	275	174	155	132	101	92	79	65	58	44

NOTES

1. This Table applies to Areas 3 – 7 and 19 – 21, each of which also contains its own internal Distance Table. Approximate distances in nautical miles are by the most direct route, while avoiding dangers and allowing for Traffic Separation Schemes.

2. Some aspects of planning passages across the North Sea are covered in Passage Information, 8.4.5, 8.20.5 and 8.21.5.

3. Distances across the English Channel, as applicable to Areas 1 – 3, 14 – 16 and 19, are given in 8.0.8.

VOLVO PENTA SERVICE

Sales and service centres in area 1

CORNWALL *Challenger Marine*, Freemans Wharf, Falmouth Road, Penryn TR10 8AS Tel (01326) 377222 *Marine Engineering Looe*, The Quay, East Looe PL13 1AQ Tel (01503) 262887 & 263009 **DEVON** *Darthaven Marine Ltd*, Brixham Road, Kingswear, Dartmouth TQ6 0SG Tel (01803) 752733 *Marine Engineering Looe*, Queen Anne's Marina, Queen Anne's Battery, Coxside, Plymouth PL4 0LP Tel (01752) 226143 *Starey Marine Services*, Lincombe Boatyard, Lincombe, Salcombe, TQ8 8NQ Tel (0154884) 3655 *Retreat Boatyard (Topsham) Ltd*, Retreat Boatyard, Topsham, Exeter EX3 0LS Tel (01392) 874720

VOLVO PENTA

Area 1

South-West England
Isles of Scilly to Portland Bill

8.1.1	Index	**Page 137**
8.1.2	Diagram of ports, lights, RDF bns, Coast radio and weather stns	**138**
8.1.3	Tidal stream charts	**140**
8.1.4	List of coastal lights, fog signals and waypoints	**142**
8.1.5	Passage information	**144**
8.1.6	Distance table	**146**
8.1.7	English Channel waypoints	**147**
8.1.8	Isles of Scilly	**150**
8.1.9	St Mary's (Scilly)	**151**
8.1.8	Newlyn Mousehole	**152**
8.1.11	Penzance St Michael's Mount	**152**
8.1.12	Helford River Porthleven Mullion Cove Cadgwith Coverack	**153**
8.1.13	River Fal (Tidal predictions and curves)	**154**
8.1.14	Mevagissey Porthscatho Gorran Haven Portmellon	**159**
8.1.15	Fowey Dodman Pt gunnery range Charlestown Par Polperro	**160**
8.1.16	Looe	**161**
8.1.17	Plymouth (Devonport), Standard Port, tidal curves River Tamar River Lynher	**162**
8.1.18	Submarine exercise areas	**168**
8.1.19	River Yealm River Erme River Avon Hope Cove	**169**
8.1.20	Salcombe Kingsbridge	**170**
8.1.21	Dartmouth, (Tidal predictions and curves) Dittisham Totnes	**174**
8.1.22	Brixham Paignton	**176**
8.1.23	Torquay	**176**
8.1.24	Teignmouth	**177**
8.1.25	River Exe Axmouth/Beer	**178**
8.1.26	Lyme Regis	**180**
8.1.27	Bridport	**180**

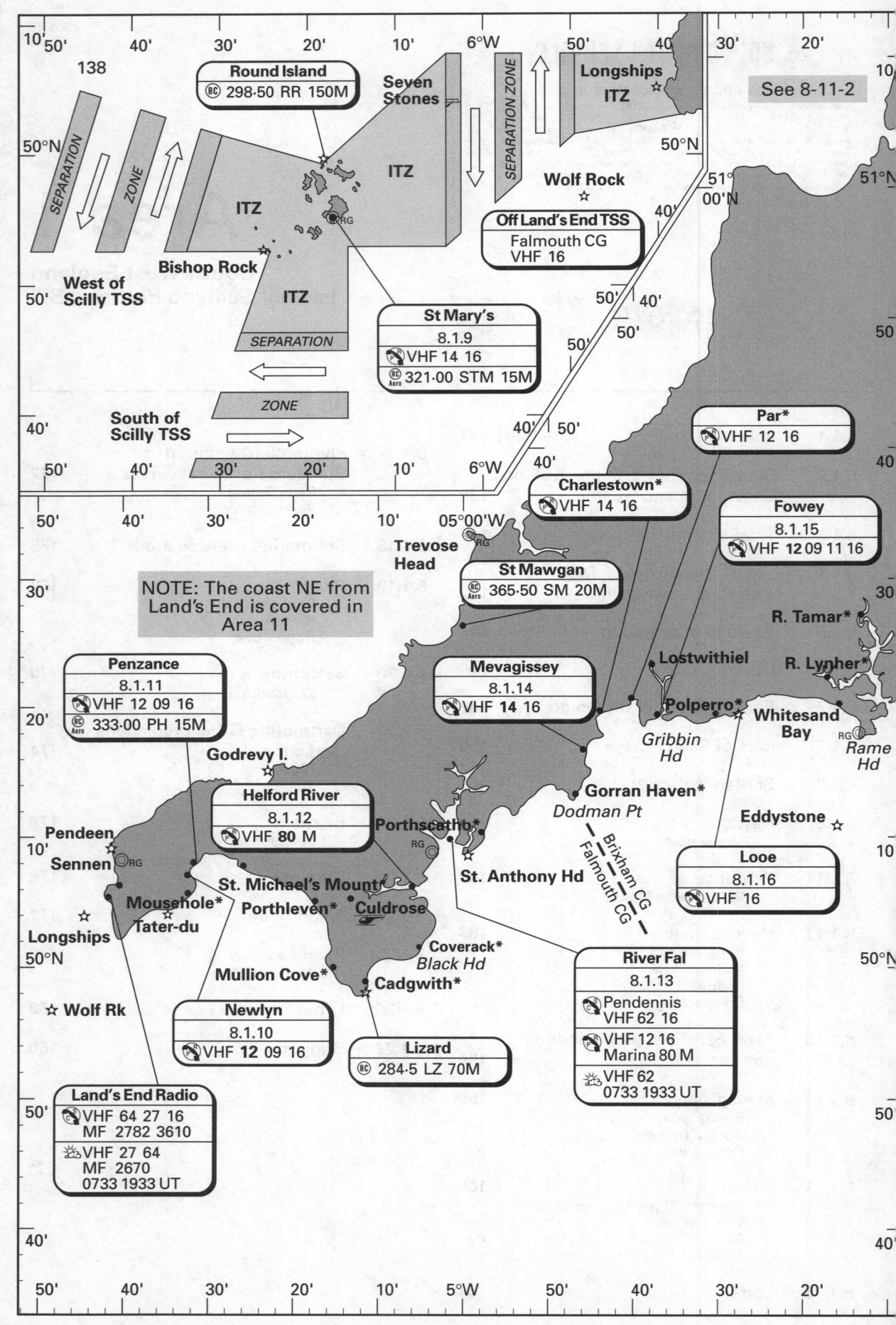

138

Round Island
RC 298·50 RR 150M

Seven Stones

Longships ITZ

See 8-11-2

SEPARATION ZONE

ITZ

SEPARATION ZONE

Wolf Rock ☆

West of Scilly TSS

ITZ

ITZ

Bishop Rock

RG

Off Land's End TSS
Falmouth CG
VHF 16

ITZ

SEPARATION

St Mary's
8.1.9
VHF 14 16
RC Aero 321·00 STM 15M

South of Scilly TSS

ZONE

Par*
VHF 12 16

Charlestown*
VHF 14 16

Fowey
8.1.15
VHF **12** 09 11 16

Trevose Head

RG

St Mawgan
RC Aero 365·50 SM 20M

R. Tamar*

Lostwithiel

R. Lynher*

NOTE: The coast NE from Land's End is covered in Area 11

Mevagissey
8.1.14
VHF **14** 16

Polperro*

Whitesand Bay

RG

Rame Hd

Penzance
8.1.11
VHF 12 09 16
RC Aero 333·00 PH 15M

Gribbin Hd

Godrevy I. ☆

Helford River
8.1.12
VHF **80** M

Porthscatho*

Gorran Haven*

Dodman Pt

Eddystone ☆

Pendeen ☆

RG

Sennen RG

Porthscatho*

RG

St. Anthony Hd

Brixham CG
Falmouth CG

Looe
8.1.16
VHF 16

Mousehole* ☆

St. Michael's Mount

Porthleven*

Culdrose

Tater-du ☆

Longships
50°N

☆ Wolf Rk

Mullion Cove*

Coverack*
Black Hd

Cadgwith*

Newlyn
8.1.10
VHF **12** 09 16

Lizard
RC 284·5 LZ 70M

River Fal
8.1.13
Pendennis
VHF 62 16
VHF 12 16
Marina 80 M
VHF 62
0733 1933 UT

Land's End Radio
VHF 64 27 16
MF 2782 3610
VHF 27 64
MF 2670
0733 1933 UT

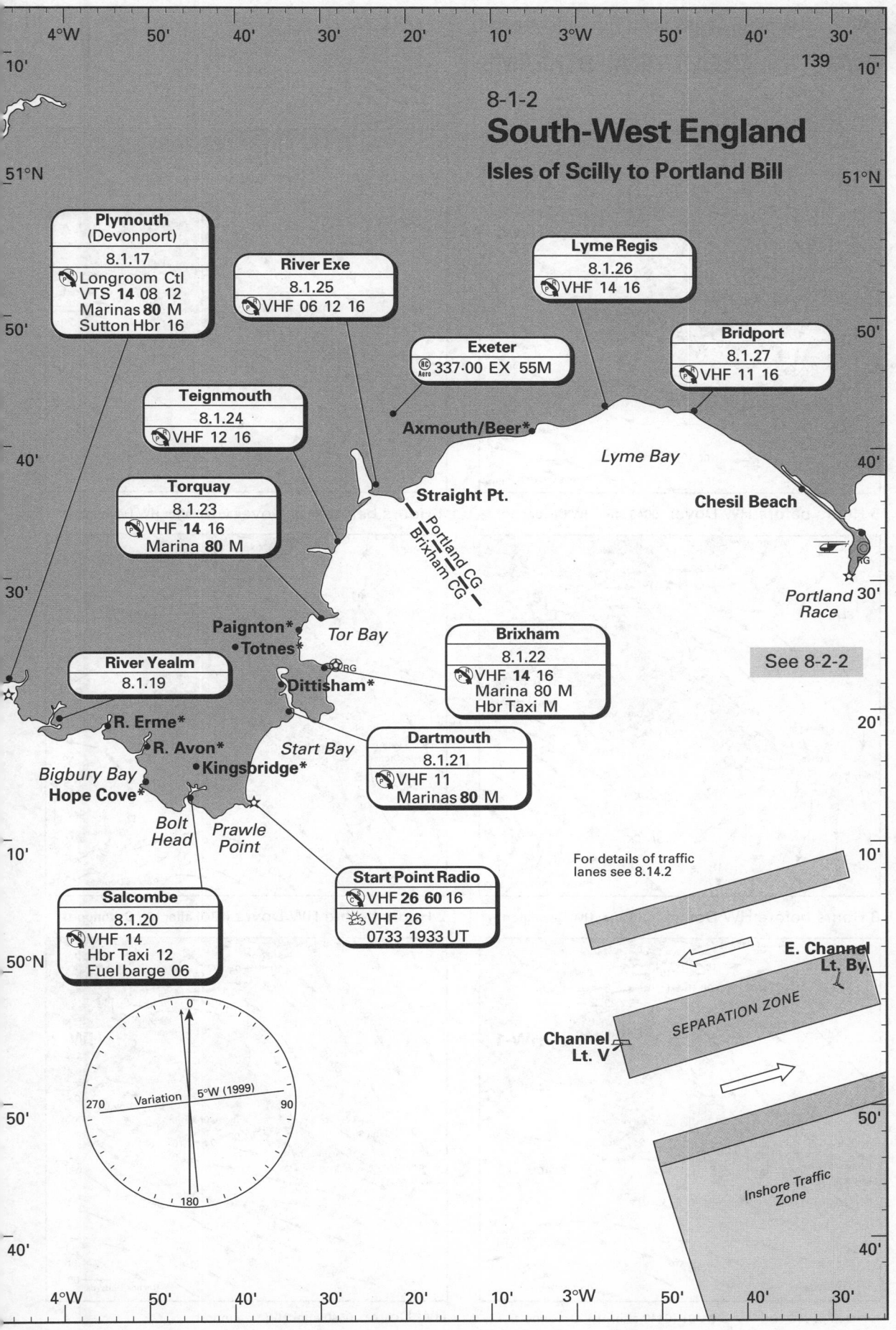

8-1-2
South-West England
Isles of Scilly to Portland Bill

Plymouth
(Devonport)
8.1.17
Longroom Ctl
VTS **14** 08 12
Marinas **80** M
Sutton Hbr 16

River Exe
8.1.25
VHF 06 12 16

Lyme Regis
8.1.26
VHF 14 16

Exeter
337·00 EX 55M

Bridport
8.1.27
VHF 11 16

Teignmouth
8.1.24
VHF 12 16

Axmouth/Beer*

Lyme Bay

Straight Pt.

Chesil Beach

Torquay
8.1.23
VHF **14** 16
Marina **80** M

Portland CG
Brixham CG

Portland Race

Paignton*
•Totnes*

Tor Bay

Brixham
8.1.22
VHF **14** 16
Marina 80 M
Hbr Taxi M

River Yealm
8.1.19

RG

•Dittisham*

See 8-2-2

•R. Erme*

Dartmouth
8.1.21
VHF 11
Marinas **80** M

• R. Avon*

Start Bay

Bigbury Bay
Hope Cove•*

•**Kingsbridge***

For details of traffic
lanes see 8.14.2

Bolt Head

Prawle Point

E. Channel
Lt. By.

Start Point Radio
VHF **26 60** 16
VHF 26
0733 1933 UT

SEPARATION ZONE

Salcombe
8.1.20
VHF 14
Hbr Taxi 12
Fuel barge 06

Channel
Lt. V

0

270   Variation   5°W (1999)   90

180

Inshore Traffic Zone

8-1-3   AREA 1 TIDAL STREAMS

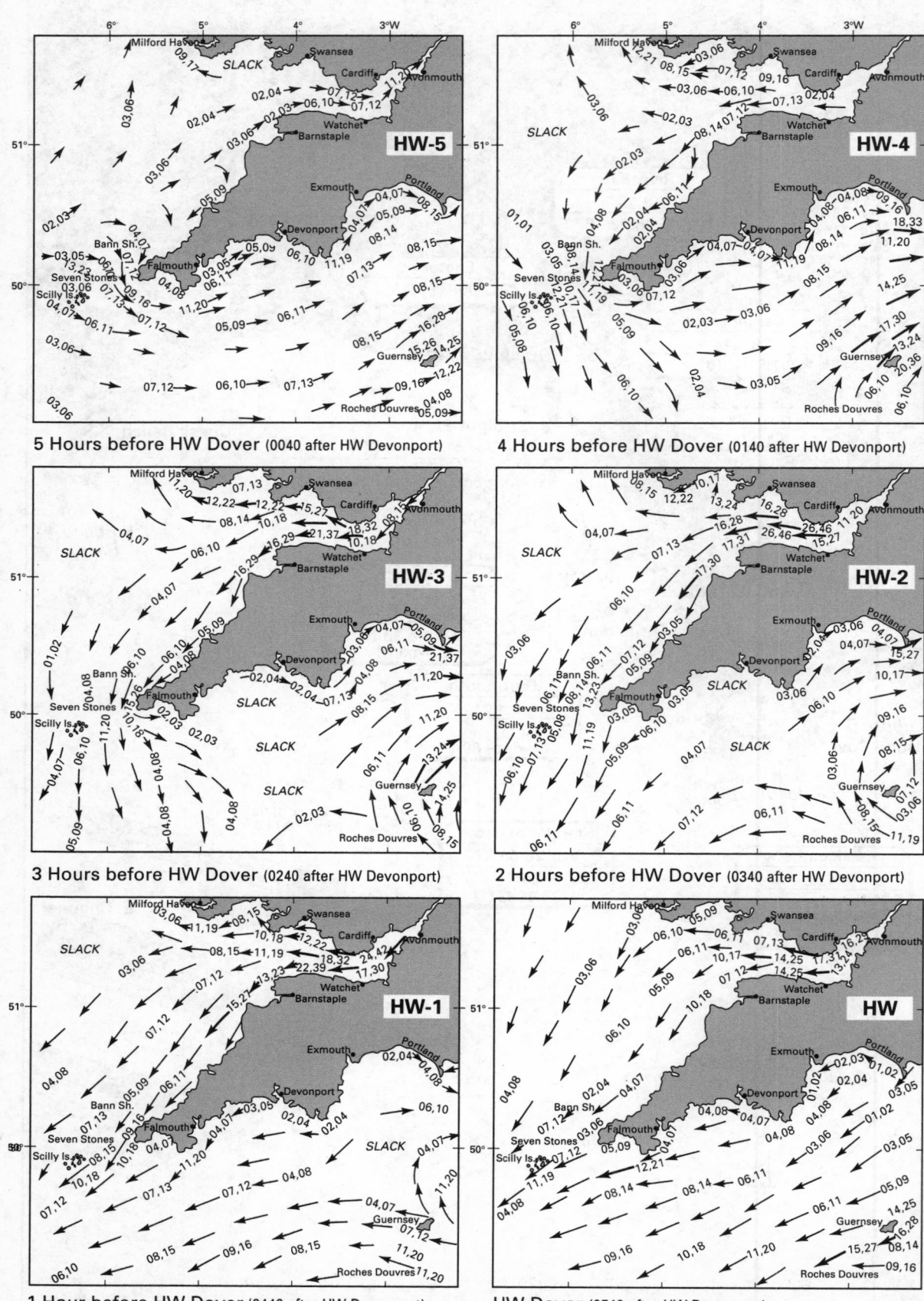

5 Hours before HW Dover (0040 after HW Devonport)

4 Hours before HW Dover (0140 after HW Devonport)

3 Hours before HW Dover (0240 after HW Devonport)

2 Hours before HW Dover (0340 after HW Devonport)

1 Hour before HW Dover (0440 after HW Devonport)

HW Dover (0540 after HW Devonport)

Eastward 8.2.3   Portland 8.2.9   Isle of Wight 8.2.24   Northward 8.11.3   Southward 8.16.3   Channel Islands 8.14.3

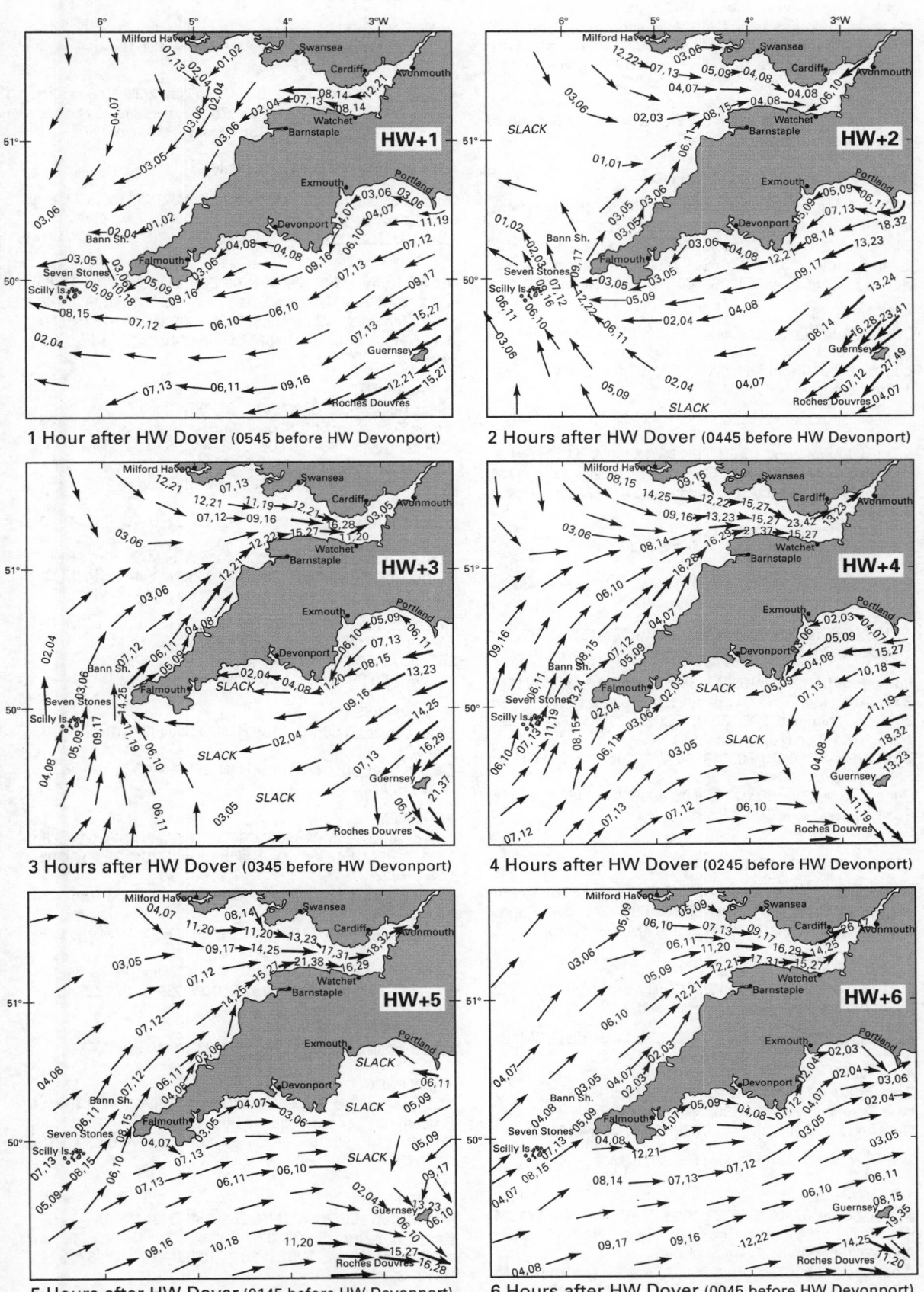

1 Hour after HW Dover (0545 before HW Devonport)

2 Hours after HW Dover (0445 before HW Devonport)

3 Hours after HW Dover (0345 before HW Devonport)

4 Hours after HW Dover (0245 before HW Devonport)

5 Hours after HW Dover (0145 before HW Devonport)

6 Hours after HW Dover (0045 before HW Devonport)

8.1.4 COASTAL LIGHTS, FOG SIGNALS AND WAYPOINTS

Lights with a nominal range of 15M or more are in **bold** print, places and features are in CAPITALS, and light-vessels, light floats and Lanbys in *CAPITAL ITALICS*. Unless otherwise stated lights are white. m = elevation in metres; M = nominal range in miles. Fog signals are in *italics*. Useful waypoints are underlined; use those on land with care. All geographical positions are referenced to the OSGB 36 datum but should be assumed to be approximate.

ISLES OF SCILLY TO LAND'S END

Bishop Rock 49°52'·33N 06°26'·68W Fl (2) 15s 44m **24M**; Gy ○ tr with helicopter platform; part obsc 204°-211°, obsc 211°-233°, 236°-259°; Racon (T); *Horn Mo (N) 90s*.
Gunner buoy 49°53'·60N 06°25'·02W; SCM.
Round Rock buoy 49°53'·06N 06°25'·13W; NCM.

- ST MARY'S
St Mary's Pool pier hd. Dir lt 115°, Fl RWG 2s 5m 4M; vis R070°-099°, W099°-129°, G129°-000°.
Ldg lts 097·3°. Front 49°55'·08N 06°18'·45W FR; W △; rear, 110m from front, FR; W X.

Bartholomew Ledges buoy 49°54'·38N 06°19'·80W; Fl R 5s; PHM.
Spanish Ledge buoy 49°53'·90N 06°18'·80W; ECM; *Bell*.
Peninnis Hd 49°54'·24N 06°18'·15W Fl 20s 36m **17M**; W○ metal tr on B frame, B cupola; vis 231°-117° but part obsc 048°-083° within 5M.
FR lts on masts to N and NE.
Hats buoy 49°56'·17N 06°17'·08W; SCM.

Round Island 49°58'·70N 06°19'·33W, Fl 10s 55m **24M**; W ○ tr; vis 021°-288°; H24; RC; *Horn (4) 60s*.

SEVEN STONES lt float 50°03'·58N 06°04'·28W, Fl (3) 30s 12m **25M**; R hull, lt tr amidships; Racon (O); *Horn (3) 60s*.

Longships 50°03'·97N 05°44'·85W, Iso WR 10s 35m **W18M, R17**/14M, H24; Gy ○ tr with helicopter platform; vis R189°-208°, R (unintens) 208°-307°, R307°-327°, W327°- 189°; *Horn 10s*. FR on radio mast 4·9M NE.
Wolf Rock 49°56'·70N 05°48'·50W, Fl 15s 34m **23M** (H24); Racon (T); *Horn 30s*.
Runnel Stone buoy 50°01'·15N 05°40'·30W, Q (6) + L Fl 15s; SCM; *Whis*.

LAND'S END TO LIZARD POINT

Tater-du 50°03'·10N 05°34'·60W Fl (3) 15s 34m **23M**; W○ tr; vis 241°-074°. Also FR 31m 13M vis 060°-074° over Runnel stone and in places 074°-077° within 4M; *Horn (2) 30s*.

- MOUSEHOLE
N pier hd 50°04'·94N 05°32'·21W 2 FG (vert) 8m 4M;   Gy mast; replaced by FR when hbr closed.

Low Lee buoy 50°05'·52N 05°31'·32W Q (3) 10s; ECM.

- NEWLYN
S pier hd 50°06'·15N 05°32'·50W Fl 5s 10m 9M; W○ tr,   R base & cupola; vis 253°-336°; *Siren 60s*.
N pier hd F WG 4m 2M; vis G238°-248°, W over hbr.

The Gear bn 50°06'·59N 05°31'·56W; IDM.

- PENZANCE
S pier hd 50°07'·03N 05°31'·63W Fl WR 5s 11m **W17M**, R12M; W ○ tr, B base; vis R (unintens) 159°-224°, R224°-268°, W268°-344·5°, R344·5°-shore.
Albert pier hd 50°07'·06N 05°31'·72W 2 FG (vert) 11m 2M.

Western Cressar bn 50°07'·21N 05°31'·07W; SCM.
Ryeman Rks bn 50°07'·22N 05°30'·27W; SCM.
Mountamopus buoy 50°04'·60N 05°26'·20W; SCM.

- PORTHLEVEN
S Pier 50°04'·87N 05°19'·03W FG 10m 4M; G metal col, lts shown when inner hbr is open.

Lizard 49°57'·58N 05°12'·07W Fl 3s 70m **25M**; W 8-sided tr; vis 250°-120°, partially vis 235°-250°; reflection may be seen inshore of these brgs; RC; Storm sigs H24; *Horn 30s*.

LIZARD POINT TO START POINT

Manacles buoy 50°02'·77N 05°01'·85W Q (3) 10s; ECM; *Bell*.
Helston buoy 50°04'·92N 05°00'·77W Fl Y 2.5s; SPM.
August Rock buoy 50°06'·07N 05°04'·88W (PA); SHM (seasonal).

St Anthony Hd 50°08'·43N 05°00'·90W Oc WR 15s 22m **W22/20M, R20M**; W 8-sided tr; vis W295°-004°, R004°-022° over Manacles, W (unintens) 022°-100°, W100°-172°; (H24); Fog Det lt L Fl 5s 18m **16M** min vis 148·75°-151·25°; *Horn 30s*.

- FALMOUTH
Black Rock bn 50°08'·68N 05°01'·95W (unlit); IDM.
Black Rock buoy 50°08'·65N 05°01'·68W Q (3) 10s; ECM.
Castle buoy 50°08'·63N 05°01'·58W Fl G 10s; SHM.
The Governor 50°09'·12N 05°02'·32W; ECM.
E bkwtr hd 50°09'·31N 05°02'·90W 2 FR (vert) 2m.
N Arm East Hd Q 19m 3M.
West Narrows buoy 50°09'·33N 05°02'·03W Fl (2) R 10s; PHM.
The Vilt buoy 50°09'·97N 05°02'·17W Fl (4) G 15s; SHM.
Northbank buoy 50°10'·32N 05°02'·12W Fl R 4s; PHM.
No 1 Port buoy 50°09'·72N 05°04'·37W QR; PHM.

Gwineas buoy 50°14'·47N 04°45'·30W Q (3) 10s; ECM; *Bell*.
'A' buoy 50°08'·50N 04°46'·30W Fl Y 10s; SPM.
'B' buoy 50°10'·90N 04°45'·50W Fl Y 5s; SPM.
'C' buoy 50°11'·05N 04°46'·40W Fl Y 2s; SPM.

- MEVAGISSEY
Victoria pier hd 50°16'·11N 04°46'·85W Fl (2) 10s 9m 12M; *Dia 30s*.
Cannis Rock buoy 50°18'·35N 04°39'·88W Q (6) + L Fl 15s; SCM; *Bell*.

- FOWEY
Fowey lt bn tr 50°19'·62N 04°38'·75W L Fl WR 5s 28m W11M, R9M; W 8-sided tr, R lantern; vis R284°-295°, W295°-028°, R028°-054°.
St Catherine's Pt 50°19'·66N 04°38'·59W FR 15m 2M; vis 150°-295°.
Lamp Rk 50°19'·67N 04°38'·31W Fl G 5s 7m 2M; vis 088°-205°.
Whitehouse Pt 50°19'·95N 04°38'·22W Iso WRG 3s 11m W11M, R8M, G8M; vis G017°-022°, W022°-032°, R032°-037°.

Udder Rock buoy 50°18'·90N 04°33'·78W; *Bell*; SCM.

- POLPERRO
Tidal basin, W pier hd 50°19'·83N 04°30·89W F or FR 4m 4M; R when hbr closed in bad weather.
Spy House Pt 50°19'·77N 04°30'·63W Iso WR 6s 30m 7M; vis W288°-060°, R060°-288°.

- LOOE
Mid Main bn 50°20'·53N 04°26'·87W Q (3) 10s 2M; ECM.
Banjo pier hd 50°21'·02N 04°27'·00W Oc WR 3s 8m **W15M**, R12M; vis W013°-207°, R207°-267°, W267°-313°, R313°-332°.

Nailzee Pt 50°20'·96N 04°27'·00W *Siren (2) 30s (occas)*.
Eddystone 50°10'·81N 04°15'·87W Fl (2) 10s 41m **20M**;
Gy tr, R lantern. FR 28m 13M (same tr) vis 112°-129° over
Hand deeps; helicopter platform, Racon (T); *Horn (3) 60s*.
Hand Deeps buoy 50°12'·65N 04°21'·04W Q (9) 15s; WCM.

• PLYMOUTH SOUND, WESTERN CHANNEL
Rame Hd, S end 50°18'·63N 04°13'·31W (unlit).
Draystone buoy 50°18'·82N 04°11'·01W Fl (2) R 5s; PHM.
Knap buoy 50°19'·52N 04°09'·94W Fl G 5s; SHM.
Plymouth bkwtr W hd 50°20'·04N 04°09'·45W Fl WR 10s
19m W12M, R9M; W○ tr; vis W262°-208°, R208°-262°.   Iso
4s (same tr) 12m 10M; vis 033°-037°; *Bell (1) 15s*.
Queens Gnd buoy 50°20'·26N 04°10'·02W Fl (2) R 10s; PHM.
New Gnd buoy 50°20'·44N 04°09'·37W Fl R 2s; PHM.
Bridge Chan SE lt bn 50°21'·00N 04°09'·47W QG; SHM.
Melampus buoy 50°21'·12N 04°08'·66W Fl R 4s; PHM.
S Winter buoy 50°21'·37N 04°08'·49W Q (6) + L Fl 15s; SCM.
S Mallard buoy 50°21'·48N 04°08'·23W VQ (6) + L Fl 10s;
SCM.

Ldg lts 349°. Front, Mallard Shoal 50°21'·58N 04°08'·26W   Q
WRG 5m W10M, R3M, G3M; W △, Or bands; vis G233°-
043°, R043°-067°, G067°-087°, W087°-099°. Ldg sector
R099°-108°; rear, 396m from front, West Hoe bn Dir WRG
9m W13M, R5M, G5M. Vis FG 309°-311° F 314°-317°, FR
320°-329°; shown H24.
Asia buoy 50°21'·53N 04°08'·81W Fl (2) R 5s; PHM.
N Drakes Is buoy 50°21'·49N 04°09'·31W Fl R 4s; PHM.
E Vanguard buoy 50°21'·43N 04°10'·63W QG; SHM.
W Vanguard buoy 50°21'46N 04°09'·92W Fl G 3s; SHM.
Devils Pt lt bn 50°21'·55N 04°09'·97W QG 5m 3M; Fl 5s in
fog.

• PLYMOUTH SOUND, EASTERN CHANNEL

Duke Rk buoy 50°20'·28N 04°08'·16W VQ (9) 10s; WCM.
Bkwtr E Hd 50°19'·98N 04°08'·18W L Fl WR 10s 9m W8M,
R6M; vis R190°-353°, W353°-001°, R001°-018°, W018°-190°.
Staddon Pt lt bn 50°20'·13N 04°07'·47W Oc WRG 10s 15m
W8M, R5M, G5M; W structure, R bands. vis G348°-038°,
G038°-050°, R050°-090°; H24.
Whidbey 50°19'·50N 04°07'·20W Oc (2) WRG 10s 29m
W8M, R6M, G6M; Or and W col; vis G000°-137·5°, W137·5°-
139·5°, R139·5°-159°; shown H24.
West Tinker buoy 50°19'·22N 04°08'·57W Q (9) 15s; WCM.
East Tinker buoy 50°19'·17N 04°08'·23W Q (3) 10s; ECM.
Bovisand Pier 50°20'·21N 04°07·65W 2 FG (vert) 4m 3M.
Wembury Pt 50°18'·97N 04°06'·55W Oc Y 10s 45m; occas.

NGS W buoy 50°11'·10N 04°00'·78W Fl Y 5s; SPM.
NGS E buoy 50°11'·20N 03°58'·95W Fl Y 10s; SPM.

• SALCOMBE
Sandhill Pt Dir lt 000° 50°13'·73N 03°46'·58W Dir Fl WRG 2s
27m W10M, R7M, G7M; R&W ◆ on W mast; vis R002·5°-
182·5°, G182·5°-357·5°, W357·5°-002·5°.
Wolf Rk buoy 50°13'·47N 03°46'·52W QG; SHM.
Blackstone Rk 50°13'·57N 03°46'·43W Q (2) G 8s 4m 2M;
G & W bn.
Starhole buoy 50°12'·50N 03°46'·80W; SPM; (Apr-Sep).
Gara buoy 50°12'·80N 03°45'·20W; SPM; (Apr-Sep).
Gammon buoy 50°12'·00N 03°45'·50W; SPM; (Apr-Sep).
Prawle buoy 50°12'·10N 03°43'·80W; SPM; (Apr-Sep).

Start Pt 50°13'·32N 03°38'·47W Fl (3) 10s 62m **25M**; W○ tr;
vis 184°-068°. FR 55m 12M (same tr) vis 210°-255° over
Skerries bank; *Horn 60s*.

START POINT TO STRAIGHT POINT

Skerries Bank buoy 50°16'·28N 03°33'·70W; PHM; *Bell*.

• DARTMOUTH
Homestone buoy 50°19'·57N 03°33'·48W; PHM.
Castle Ledge buoy 50°19'·95N 03°33'·05W Fl G 5s; SHM.
Checkstone buoy 50°20'·42N 03°33'·73W Fl (2) R 5s; PHM.
Kingswear 50°20'·78N 03°34'·02W Iso WRG 3s 9m 8M; W○
tr; vis G318°-325°, W325°-331°, R331°-340°, (TE 1989).
Bayards Cove Fl WRG 2s 5m 6M; vis G280°-289°, W289°-
297°, R297°-shore.
RDYC 1 buoy 50°18'·80N 03°35'·25W; SPM; (Apr-Oct).
RDYC 2 buoy 50°18'·68N 03°33'·29W; SPM; (Apr-Oct).
RDYC 3 buoy 50°20'·07N 03°31'·42W; SPM; (Apr-Oct).
Berry Hd 50°23'·94N 03°28'·93W Fl (2) 15s 58m 14M; W tr;
vis 100°-023°. R lts on radio mast 5·7M NW.

• BRIXHAM
Victoria bkwtr hd 50°24'·29N 03°30'·70W Oc R 15s 9m 6M.
Fairway dir lt 159° Iso WR 5s 4m 6M; vis R145°-157°, W157°-
161°, R161°-173°.
Brixham Marina SW end 2 Fl R 5s (vert) 4m 2M.

• PAIGNTON
Outfall lt bn 50°25'·92N 03°33'·09W Q (3) 10s 5m 3M.
E Quay 50°25'·92N 03°33'·29W QR 7m 3M.

• TORQUAY
Princess pier hd 50°27'·43N 03°31'·66W QR 9m 6M.
Haldon pier hd 50°27'·40N 03°31'·67W QG 9m 6M.
Marina S Pontoon E end 2 FR (vert) 2m.

• TEIGNMOUTH
The Den 50°32'·51N 03°29'·74W FR 10m 6M; Gy ○ tr; vis
225°-135°.
Powderham Terrace 50°32'·55N 03°39'·76W FR 11m 3M.
Den Point 50°32'·38N 03°29'·98W Oc G 5·5s FG (vert); △ on
G bn.
Outfall buoy 50°31'·96N 03°27'·92W Fl Y 5s; SPM.

• EXMOUTH
E Exe ECM buoy, Q (3) 10s, 50°35'·96N 03°22'·30W.
Straight Pt, Fl R 10s 34m 7M, vis 246°-071°, 50°36'·45N
03°21'·67W.
Ldg lts 305°; Front, Iso 2s 6m 7M, 50°36'·97N 03°25'·31W;
rear, Q 12m 7M, 57m from front.
DZS SPM buoy, Fl Y 3s, 50°36'·10N 03°19'·30W.
DZN SPM buoy, Fl Y 3s, 50°36'·80N 03°19'·20W.

• SIDMOUTH/AXMOUTH
Sidmouth 50°46'·46'N 03°14'·36W Fl R 5s 2M.
Axmouth pier hd 50°42'·10N 03°03'·21W Fl 5s 7m 2M.

• LYME REGIS
Ldg lts 296°. Front, Victoria pier hd 50°43'·30N 02°56'·10W
Oc WR 8s 6m W9M. R7M; Bu col; vis R296°-116°, W116°-
296°; rear, 240m from front, FG 8m 9M.

• BRIDPORT
E pier hd 50°42'·52N 02°45'·74W FG 3m 2M; (occas).
W pier hd 50°42'·52N 02°45'·77W FR 3m 2M; (occas).
W pier root 50°42'·61N 02°45'·76W Iso R 2s 9m 5M.

DZ buoy 50°36'·50N 02°42'·00W Fl Y 3s; SPM.

OFFSHORE MARKS

Channel lt F 49°54'·42N 02°53'·67W Fl 15s 12m **25M**;
Horn 20s; Racon (O).
E Channel buoy 49°58'·67N 02°28'·87W Fl Y 5s; Racon (T);
SPM.

NOTE: For English Channel Waypoints see 8.1.7.

8.1.5   PASSAGE INFORMATION

Refer to *West Country Cruising* (YM/Fishwick); *Shell Channel Pilot* (Imray/Cunliffe); *Isles of Scilly Pilot* (Imray/Brandon) and Admiralty *Channel Pilot* (NP 27). See 8.0.5 for distances across the Channel, and 8.3.5 for cross-Channel passages.

NORTH CORNWALL (charts 1149, 1156)

For the coast of North Cornwall see 8.11.5. For St Ives, Hayle, Newquay, Padstow and Bude, see 8.11.25. Certain information is repeated below for continuity and convenience.

The approaches to the Bristol Chan along N coast of Cornwall are very exposed, with little shelter in bad weather. From Land's End to St Ives the coast is rugged with high cliffs. Padstow is a refuge, except in strong NW winds. In these waters yachts need to be sturdy and well equipped, since if bad weather develops no shelter may be at hand. Streams are moderate W of Lundy, but strong around the island, and much stronger towards the Bristol Channel proper.

ISLES OF SCILLY (8.1.8 and charts *34*, *883*)

There are 50 islands, extending 21-31M WSW of Land's End, with many rky outcrops and offlying dangers. Although they are all well charted, care is needed particularly in poor vis. See 8.1.8 and .9 for details of this rewarding cruising ground.

Several approach transits are shown on chart *34*, and these should be followed, because the tidal streams around the islands are difficult to predict with accuracy. They run harder off points and over rks, where overfalls may occur. Yachts must expect to lie to their anchors. No one anch gives shelter from all winds and swell, so be ready to move at short notice.

Conspic landmarks are Bishop Rk lt ho, Round Island lt ho, the disused lt ho on St Agnes, the daymark at the E end of St Martin's, Penninis lt ho at the S end of St Mary's, and the TV mast and CG sig stn (at the old telegraph tower) both in the NW corner of St Mary's. The Decca Green slave is also here; beware inaccuracies in St Mary's Roads and Tresco channel.

ISLES OF SCILLY TO LAND'S END (chart 1148)

The Seven Stones (rks) lie 7M NE of the Isles of Scilly and 15M W of Land's End; many of them dry, with ledges in between. They are marked by lt F (fog sig) on E side. Wolf Rk (lt, fog sig) is 8M SW of Land's End, and is steep-to. The N/S lanes of Land's End TSS lie between Seven Stones and Wolf Rk. The ITZ, W of Longships, is 3M wide; see 8.1.2.

Between Scilly and Land's End (chart 1148) streams are rotatory, clockwise. Relative to HW Dover (sp rates about 1kn), they set W from HWD; N from HW + 2; NE from HW + 4; E from HW –6; SSE from HW – 4; and SW from HW – 2. For the 5-6hrs passage to Scilly leave the Runnel Stone at HWD–2; a fair W-going tide lasts for only 3hrs, with cross tides setting SW then NW to N. Consider arriving at dawn. For the return passage tidal streams are a little less critical.

LAND'S END (charts 1148, 1149, 777 and 2345)

Land's End peninsula (30M Penzance to St Ives) is often a dangerous lee shore and always a critical tidal gate. There are many inshore and offlying rks and no ports of refuge. From S to N the main features are:
Gwennap Head, with the Runnel Stone (buoyed) 1M to the S; Land's End and Longships reef 1M to the W; Cape Cornwall and The Brisons; Pendeen Head and The Wra. The coast of N Cornwall further to the E is described in 8.11.5.

The Runnel Stone (0·5m) lies 7ca S of Gwennap Hd, with rks and uncharted wrecks closer inshore. These dangers are in the R sectors of Longships and Tater-du lts. Passage between the Runnel Stone and Gwennap is not advised even in calm weather and at HW. From Gwennap Hd to Land's End, 2M NW, rks extend up to 1½ca offshore, and depths are irregular to seaward causing a bad sea in strong W winds over a W-going tide.

4 cables S of Land's End Armed Knight, a jagged 27m high rock, overlooks Longships. This is an extensive and very dangerous reef made up of Carn Brae, on which the lt ho stands, and other rky islets. About 5ca to the E and NE are Kettle's Bottom 5m and Shark's Fin 3·4m, both isolated and very dangerous drying rks. The ½M wide passage between Land's End and Kettle's Bottom is safe in calm, settled weather, but never at night. To clear Kettle's Bottom and Shark's Fin, keep the Brisons High summit just open W of Low summit brg 001°. Local streams exceed 4kn at Sp and are unpredictable. In adverse weather navigate in the ITZ, well W of Longships.

Whitesand Bay (chart 2345) is 1M NNE of Land's End. After rounding Cowloe Rks and its drying offliers, Little Bo 3·4m and Bo Cowloe 6m, the transit 150° of two bns on the cliffs E of Sennen Cove leads to a fair weather ⚓ in about 2m on the S side of the bay, only safe in offshore winds. Sennen Ch tr (110m) is conspic, almost on this transit.
Cape Cornwall (conspic ruined chy) is about 3M further N. It overlooks The Brisons, two rky islets (27 and 22m, High and Low summits) about 5ca to SW. There is no passage inside The Brisons. The Vyneck is a rk drying 1·8m 3ca NW of Cape Cornwall.

3M to NNE is Pendeen Hd (lt ho) and the Wra (or Three Stone Oar), drying rks, close N. Between C Cornwall and Pendeen overfalls and a race extend up to 1½M offshore; avoid except in calm weather and at slack water. Midway between Cape Cornwall and Pendeen a conspic TV mast is 1M inland.

Tidal Strategy

Streams run hard round Land's End, setting N/S and E/W past it. It is truly a tidal gate, and one which favours a N-bound passage – with careful timing nearly 9½ hrs of fair tide can be carried, from HWD–3 to HWD+5. Stay close inshore to use currents running counter to the tidal streams. The chartlets below, referenced to HW Dover, illustrate tidal streams and inshore currents.

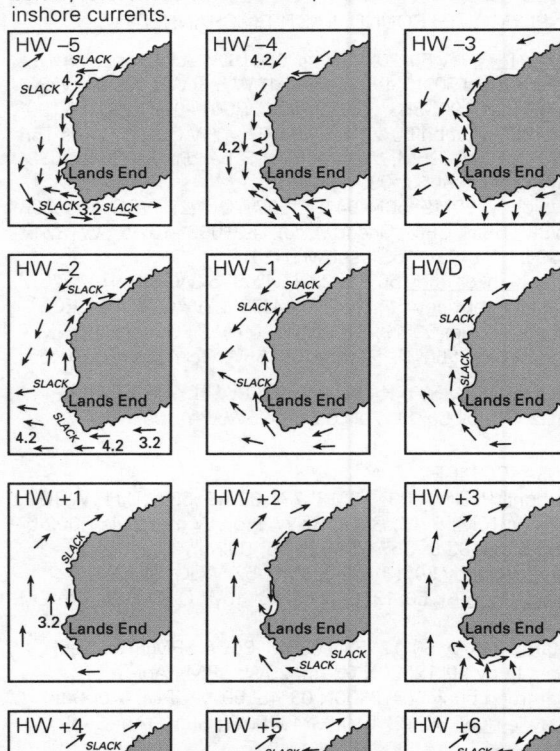

Example N-bound: At HWD+1 the N-going flood starts off Gwennap and does not turn NE along the N Cornish coast until HWD+3, but as early as HWD−3 an inshore current is beginning to run N'ly. So, N-bound, use this by arriving off Runnel Stone at HWD−2 and then keep within ¼M of the shore. If abeam Brisons at HWD, the tide and current should serve for the next 6 or 7 hrs to make good St Ives, or even Newquay and Padstow.

Example S-bound: If S-bound from St Ives to Newlyn, aim to reach the Runnel Stone by HWD+5, ie with 2 hrs of E-going tide in hand for the remaining 9M to Newlyn. This would entail leaving St Ives 5 hrs earlier, at HWD, to make the 20M passage; buck a foul tide for the first 3 hrs but use an inshore S-going current, keeping as close inshore as prudent, but having to move offshore to clear the Wra and the Brisons. This timing would suit passage from S Wales and Bristol Chan, going inshore of Longships if the weather suits.

From Ireland, ie Cork or further W, the inshore passage would not benefit. But plan to be off the Runnel Stone at HWD+5 if bound for Newlyn; or at HWD+3 if bound for Helford/Falmouth, with the W-going stream slackening and 5 hrs of fair tide to cover the remaining 20M past the Lizard.

GWENNAP HEAD TO LIZARD POINT (chart 777)

Close E of Gwennap there is no anch off Porth Curno, due to cables. Approaching Mount's Bay, the Bucks (3·3m) are 2ca ESE of Tater-du lt ho. Gull Rk (24m) is 9ca NE of Tater-du, close off the E point of Lamorna Cove. Little Heaver (dries) is 100m SW of Gull Rk, and Kemyel Rk (dries) is 1¾ca ENE. Mousehole (8.1.10) is a small drying hbr, sheltered from W and N, but exposed to E or S winds, when ent may be shut. Approach from SW side of St Clement's Is. In W winds there is good anch off the hbr.

Low Lee, a dangerous rk (1·1m) marked by ECM lt buoy, is 4ca NE of Penlee Pt. Carn Base Rk (1·8m) lies 3ca NNW of Low Lee. Newlyn (8.1.10) is only hbr in Mount's B safe to appr in strong onshore winds, but only near HW. From here to Penzance (8.1.11) beware Dog Rk and The Gear (1·9m).

From Penzance to St Michael's Mount the head of the Bay is shoal, drying 4ca off in places. Dangers include Cressar Rks, Long Rk, Hogus Rks, and Outer Penzeath Rk. Venton chy on with pierheads of St Michael's Mount at 084° leads S of these dangers. This tiny hbr dries 2·1m, but is well sheltered, with anch about 1ca W of ent, see 8.1.11.

Two dangerous rks, Guthen Rk and Maltman Rk (0·9m), lie 2ca W and S of St Michael's Mount. 1M SE is The Greeb (7m), with rks between it and shore. The Bears (dry) lie 1¾ca E of The Greeb. The Stone (dries) is 5ca S of Cudden Pt, while offshore is Mountamopus shoal marked by SCM buoy which should be passed to seaward. Welloe Rk (dries) lies 5ca SW of Trewavas Hd.

Porthleven is a small tidal hbr, entered between Great and Little Trigg Rks and pier on S side. Dry out alongside in inner hbr, closed in bad weather when appr is dangerous. In fair weather there is good anch off Porth Mellin, about 1½ca NE of Mullion Is; Porth Mellin hbr (dries) is for temp use only. 2·5M W of Lizard Pt is The Boa, a rky shoal on which sea breaks in SW gales.

The Lizard (lt, fog sig, RC) is a bold, steep headland (chart 2345). From W to E, the outer rks, all drying, are Mulvin, (2½ca SW of Lizard Pt), Taylor's Rk (2ca SSW); Clidgas Rks (5ca SW of lt ho), Men Hyr Rk (4·1m) and the Dales or Stags (5ca SSW), and Enoch Rk (3ca S). A dangerous race extends 2-3M S when stream is strong in either direction, worst in W'ly winds against W-going tide. There may be a race SE of the Lizard. Keep at least 3M to seaward if going outside the race where slack water occurs at about HW Devonport −3 and +3. Closer inshore the stream turns E at HW Devonport −5, and W at HW +2, rates up to 3kn at sp. An inshore passage is shorter, but is never free of rough water. Either side of local LW (½hr before LW Devonport = HW Dover) the drying rks above will be visible, but beware Vrogue, a dangerous sunken rk (1·8m), 1M E of the Lizard lt ho, and Craggan Rks (1·5m) 1M N of Vrogue Rk. If awaiting slack water, there are, from W to E, ⚓s at Kynance Cove, Housel Cove (NE of the lt ho and below conspic hotel), Church Cove, Cadgwith and Coverack.

LIZARD POINT TO GRIBBIN HEAD (chart 1267)

N of Black Head rks extend at least 1ca offshore; a rk drying 1·6m lies off Chynhalls Pt. Coverack gives good anch in W winds, see 8.1.12. From Dolor Pt to E of Lowland Pt are drying rks 2½ca offshore.

The Manacles (dry), 7½ca E and SE of Manacle Pt, are marked by ECM lt buoy and are in R sector of St Anthony Hd lt. Off the Manacles the stream runs NE from HW Devonport − 0345, and SW from HW+ 0200, sp rates 1·25kn. From E of the Manacles there are no offshore dangers on courses NNW to Helford River ent (8.1.12) or N to River Fal (8.1.13).

3M NNE from St Anthony Hd, Porthscatho offers safe anch in W'lies (8.1.14). Gull Rk (38m high) lies 6ca E of Nare Hd, at W side of Veryan B. The Whelps (dry) are 5ca SW of Gull Rk. There is a passage between Gull Rk and the shore. In Veryan B beware Lath Rk (2·1m) 1M SE of Portloe.

On E side of Veryan B, Dodman Pt is a 110m flat-topped cliff, with a conspic stone cross. Depths are irregular for 1M S, with heavy overfalls in strong winds over sp tide, when it is best to pass 2M off. 3 SPM lt buoys (targets) lie 2·3 to 4·8M SSE of Dodman Pt, see 8.1.15. Gorran Haven, a sandy cove with L-shaped pier which dries at sp, is a good anch in offshore winds. 2·1M NE of Dodman Pt, and 1M ENE of Gorran Haven, is Gwineas Rk (8m high) and Yaw Rk (0·9m), marked by ECM lt buoy. Passage inside Gwineas Rk is possible, but not advised in strong onshore winds or poor vis. Portmellon and Mevagissey B, (8.1.14) are good anchs in offshore winds. For Charlestown and Par, see 8.1.15. For details of naval gunnery practice between Dodman Pt and Gribbib Head, see 8.1.15.

GRIBBIN HEAD TO START POINT (charts 1267, 1613)

Gribbin Hd has a conspic daymark, a ☐ tr 25m high with R & W bands. In bad weather the sea breaks on rocks round Head. Cannis Rk (4·3m) is 2½ca SE, marked by SCM lt buoy. 3M E of Fowey (8.1.15) is Udder Rk (0·6m), 5ca offshore in E part of Lantivet Bay. Larrick Rk (4·3m) is 1½ca off Nealand Pt.

Polperro hbr dries, but the inlet gives good anch in offshore winds, see 8.1.15. Beware E Polca Rk roughly in mid-chan. E of Polperro shoals lie 2½ca off Downend Pt, (memorial). The chan between Hannafore Pt and Looe (or St George's) Island nearly dries. The Ranneys (dry) are rks extending 2½ca E and SE of the Island, see 8.1.16. There are overfalls S of Looe Island in bad weather.

Eddystone rks (chart 1613) lie 8M S of Rame Hd. Shoals extend 3ca E. Close NW of the lt ho (lt, fog sig) is the stump of old lt ho. The sea can break on Hand Deeps, sunken rks 3·5M NW of Eddystone, marked by SPM light buoy.

Rame Hd, on W side of ent to Plymouth Sound (8.1.17), is conspic cone shaped, with small chapel on top; rks extend about 1ca off and wind-over-tide overfalls may be met 1·5M to seaward. Approaching Plymouth from the W, clear Rame Hd and Penlee Point by about 8ca, then steer NNE for W end of the Breakwater. At the SE ent to Plymouth Sound, Great Mewstone (59m) is a conspic rky islet 4ca off Wembury Pt (naval gunnery range). Approaching from the E keep at least 1M offshore until clear of the drying Mewstone Ledge, 2½ca SW of Great Mewstone. The Slimers, which dry, lie 2ca E of Mewstone. E and W Ebb Rks (awash) lie 2½ca off Gara Pt (chart 30). Wembury Bay gives access to R. Yealm (8.1.19).

See 8.1.18 for submarine exercise areas from the Isles of Scilly to Start Point. These areas are also used by warships, especially near Plymouth. Yachts should try to stay clear.

Between Gara Pt and Stoke Pt, 2·5M to E, dangers extend about 4ca offshore in places. In Bigbury Bay beware Wells Rk and other dangers 5ca S of Erme Hd. From Bolt Tail to Bolt Hd keep 5ca offshore to clear Greystone Ledge, sunken rks near Ham Stone (11m), and Gregory Rks 5ca SE of Ham Stone. The Little Mew Stone and Mew Stone lie below dramatic Bolt Head. Keep approx 7½ca SE of the Mewstones before turning N for Salcombe (8.1.20).

START POINT TO STRAIGHT POINT (charts *1613, 3315*)

Start Pt (lt, horn) is 3M ENE of Prawle Pt; it is a long headland with conspic radio masts, distinctive cock's comb spine and W lt ho near end. Black Stone rk is visible (6m high) 2½ca SSE of the lt ho, with Cherrick Rks (1m) a cable further S; other drying rks lie closer inshore. The stream runs 4kn at sp, causing a race extending 1½M to the E and 1M to the S. In fair weather the overfalls can be avoided by passing close to seaward of rks; there is no clear-cut inshore passage as such. In bad weather keep at least 2M off: 1M off Start the stream sets SW from HW Devonport +4 to HW –3, and NE from HW –2 to HW +3; thus slack water is about HW –2½ and HW +3½. Inshore it turns 30 minutes earlier.

Skerries Bank, on which sea breaks in bad weather, is 6ca NNE of Start Point (chart 1634). It has least depth of 2·1m at the S end, only 9ca from Start Pt. In offshore winds there is good anch in 3m 1ca off Hallsands (1M NW of Start). Between Dartmouth (8.1.21) and Brixham (8.1.22) rks extend 5ca offshore.

Berry Head (lt) is a steep, flat-topped headland (55m). Here the stream turns N at HW Devonport – 0105, and S at HW + 0440, sp rates 1·5kn. In Torbay (chart *26*) the more obvious dangers are steep-to, but beware the Sunker 100m SW of Ore Stone, and Morris Rogue 5ca W of Thatcher Rk.

There are good anchs in Babbacombe B and in Anstey's cove in W winds; beware the Three Brothers (drying rks), S side of Anstey's cove. From Long Quarry Pt for 4M N to Teignmouth (8.1.24) there are no offlying dangers. Off Teignmouth the NNE-going stream begins at HW Devonport – 0135, and the SSW-going at HW+ 0510. In the ent the flood begins at HW Devonport – 0535, and the ebb at HW +0040. The stream runs hard off Ferry Pt; the ent is dangerous in onshore winds.

Between Teignmouth and Dawlish rks extend 1ca offshore. Beware Dawlish Rk (depth 2·1m) about 5ca off N end of town. Warren Sands and Pole Sands lie W of ent to the River Exe (8.1.25), and are liable to shift. Along the NE (Exmouth) side of the chan, towards Orcomb Pt and Straight Pt (lt), drying rks and shoals extend up to 2½ca from shore. There is a firing range off Straight Point.

LYME BAY (chart *3315*)

Start Pt is W end of Lyme B (chart *3315*), which stretches 50M ENE to Portland Bill. Tides are weak, rarely more than 0·75kn. From Start Pt to Portland Bill the tidal curve becomes progressively more distorted, especially on the rising tide. The rise is relatively fast for the 1st hr after LW; then slackens noticeably for the next 1½ hrs, before resuming the rapid rate of rise. There is often a stand at HW, not very noticeable at Start Point but lasting about 1½ hrs at Lyme Regis.

Between Torbay and Portland there is no hbr accessible in onshore winds, and yachtsmen must take care not to be caught on a lee shore. There are no dangers offshore. In offshore winds there is a good anch NE of Beer Hd, the western-most chalk cliff in England, see 8.1.25. 3·5M E of Lyme Regis (8.1.26) is Golden Cap (186m and conspic). High Ground and Pollock are rks 7ca offshore, 2M and 3M ESE of Golden Cap.

From 6M E of Bridport (8.1.27), Chesil Beach runs SE for about 8M to the N end of the Portland peninsula. From a distance The Isle of Portland does indeed look like an island, with its distinctive wedge-shaped profile sloping down from 144m at the N to the Bill at the S tip. It is mostly steep-to, but rks extend 2½ca from the Bill which is marked by a stone bn (18m) and conspic lt ho.

If heading up-Channel from Start Point, Dartmouth or Torbay time your departure to pass Portland Bill with a fair tide at all costs, especially at springs. If late, there is temp'y anchorage close inshore at Chesil Cove, abeam the highest part of Portland. See 8.2.5 for passage round the Bill either by the inshore or offshore routes.

And when they lifted up their eyes
The land appeared ahead.
They thought that it was Berry –
It was really Durlston Head.
It didn't matter in the least,
They went to Poole instead.
                  Anon

The Editor thanks most warmly the Royal Cruising Club Pilotage Foundation for their kind permission to use material written by Hugh Davies and first published in Yachting Monthly magazine. This includes the unique tidal stream chartlets on the previous page which are of major assistance in rounding Land's End.

8.1.6   DISTANCE TABLE

Approximate distances in nautical miles are by the most direct route while avoiding dangers and allowing for Traffic Separation Schemes. Places in *italics* are in adjoining areas; places in **bold** are in 8.0.8, Cross-Channel Distances.

	1	2	3	4	5	6	7	8	9	10	11	12	13	14	15	16	17	18	19	20
1. *Milford Haven*	1																			
2. *Lundy Island*	28	2																		
3. *Padstow*	67	40	3																	
4. **Longships**	100	80	47	4																
5. *St Mary's (Scilly)*	120	102	69	22	5															
6. Penzance	115	95	62	15	37	6														
7. Lizard Point	123	103	72	23	40	16	7													
8. **Falmouth**	139	119	88	39	60	32	16	8												
9. Mevagissey	152	132	99	52	69	46	28	17	9											
8. **Fowey**	157	137	106	57	76	49	34	22	7	10										
11. Looe	163	143	110	63	80	57	39	29	16	11	11									
12. **Plymouth** (bkwtr)	170	150	117	70	92	64	49	39	25	22	11	12								
13. R. Yealm (ent)	172	152	119	72	89	66	49	39	28	23	16	4	13							
14. **Salcombe**	181	161	128	81	102	74	59	50	40	36	29	22	17	14						
15. Start Point	186	166	135	86	103	80	63	55	45	40	33	24	22	7	15					
16. **Dartmouth**	195	175	142	95	116	88	72	63	54	48	42	35	31	14	9	16				
17. **Torbay**	201	181	150	101	118	96	78	70	62	55	50	39	38	24	15	11	17			
18. **Exmouth**	213	193	162	113	131	107	90	82	73	67	61	51	49	33	27	24	12	18		
19. *Lyme Regis*	226	206	173	126	144	120	104	96	86	81	74	63	62	48	41	35	30	21	19	
20. *Portland Bill*	235	215	184	135	151	128	112	104	93	89	81	73	70	55	49	45	42	36	22	20

ENGLISH CHANNEL
WAYPOINTS   8-1-7

Selected waypoints and principal lights for use in
English Channel crossings, are listed in order from
West to **East**. Further waypoints in coastal waters
are given in section 4 of each area (ie 8.1.4 to 8.3.4
on the English coast, and 8.14.4 to 8.19.4 for the
Channel Islands and the French coast). All positions
in Areas 1, 2 and 3 are referenced to the OSGB 36
datum. Areas 14, 15, 16 and 19 are referenced to the
European ED 50 datum. Offshore positions may be
referenced to either datum depending on the chart
used.

ENGLISH COAST

AREA 1

Bishop Rock lt	49°52'·33N 06°26'·68W
Bartholomew Ledge buoy	49°54'·38N 06°19'·80W
Round Is lt	49°58'·70N 06°19'·33W
Peninnis Hd lt	49°54'·24N 06°18'·15W
Seven Stones lt F	50°03'·58N 06°04'·28W
Wolf Rock lt	49°56'·70N 05°48'·50W
Longships lt	50°03'·97N 05°44'·85W
Runnel Stone buoy	50°01'·15N 05°40'·30W
Tater Du lt	50°03'·10N 05°34'·60W
Low Lee buoy	50°05'·52N 05°31'·32W
Mountamopus buoy	50°04'·60N 05°26'·20W
Lizard Pt lt	49°57'·58N 05°12'·07W
August Rk buoy (seasonal)	50°06'·07N 05°04'·88W
Manacles buoy	50°02'·77N 05°01'·85W
Black Rk buoy	50°08'·65N 05°01'·68W
Castle buoy	50°08'·63N 05°01'·58W
St Anthony Hd lt	50°08'·43N 05°00'·90W
Helston buoy	50°04'·92N 05°00'·77W
Gwineas buoy	50°14'·47N 04°45'·30W
Cannis Rk buoy	50°18'·35N 04°39'·88W
Udder Rk buoy	50°18'·90N 04°33'·78W
Hands Deep buoy	50°12'·65N 04°21'·04W
Eddystone lt	50°10'·81N 04°15'·87W
West Tinker buoy	50°19'·22N 04°08'·57W
East Tinker buoy	50°19'·17N 04°08'·23W
Start Point lt	50°13'·32N 03°38'·47W
Royal Dart YC No. 1 buoy*	50°18'·80N 03°35'·25W
Checkstone buoy	50°20'·42N 03°33'·73W
Royal Dart YC No. 2 buoy*	50°18'·68N 03°33'·29W
Castle Ledge buoy	50°19'·95N 03°33'·05W
Royal Dart YC No. 3 buoy*	50°20'·07N 03°31'·42W
Berry Head lt	50°23'·94N 03°28'·93W
East Exe buoy	50°35'·97N 03°22'·30W
Straight Point lt	50°36'·45N 03°21'·67W
DZ buoy	50°36'·50N 02°42'·00W
Portland Bill lt	50°30'·82N 02°27'·32W

AREA 2

Portland NE bkwtr lt	50°35'·12N 02°24'·99W
W Shambles buoy	50°29'·75N 02°24'·33W
E Shambles buoy	50°30'·75N 02°20'·00W
Anvil Point lt	50°35'·48N 01°57'·52W
Peverill Ledge buoy	50°36'·38N 01°56'·02W
Poole fairway buoy	50°38'·97N 01°54'·80W
Needles fairway buoy	50°38'·20N 01°38'·90W
SW Shingles buoy	50°39'·31N 01°37'·36W
Needles lt	50°39'·70N 01°35'·43W
N Head buoy	50°42'·65N 01°35'·43W
NE Shingles buoy	50°41'·93N 01°33'·32W
St Catherine's Pt lt	50°34'·52N 01°17'·80W
W Princessa buoy	50°40'·20N 01°03'·95W
Bembridge Ledge buoy	50°41'·12N 01°02'·72W
New Grounds buoy	50°41'·97N 00°58'·53W
Nab Tower lt	50°40'·05N 00°57'·07W

AREA 3

Boulder buoy	50°41'·53N 00°49'·00W
Outer Owers buoy	50°38'·75N 00°41'·30W
Owers buoy	50°37'·27N 00°40'·60W
E Borough hd buoy	50°41'·50N 00°39'·00W
Littlehampton outfall buoy	50°46'·20N 00°30'·45W
Beacham outfall buoy	50°48'·45N 00°19'·40W
Shoreham outfall buoy	50°47'·85N 00°13'·63W
Brighton marina W hd lt	50°48'·46N 00°06'·29W
Newhaven bkwtr lt	50°46'·52N 00°03'·60E
Beachy Hd lt	50°44'·00N 00°14'·60E
Sovereign Hbr buoy	50°47'·33N 00°20'·42E
Royal Sovereign lt	50°43'·42N 00°26'·18E
St Leonard's outfall buoy	50°49'·27N 00°32'·00E
Hastings W bkwtr Hd	50°51'·13N 00°35'·70E
Rye fairway buoy	50°54'·00N 00°48'·13E
Dungeness outfall buoy	50°54'·43N 00°58'·33E
Dungeness lt	50°54'·77N 00°58'·67E
Bullock Bank buoy	50°46'·90N 01°07'·70E
Folkestone bkwtr hd lt	51°04'·53N 01°11'·79E
S Varne buoy	50°55'·60N 01°17'·40E
Dover Pier extn hd	51°06'·65N 01°19'·77E
Varne Mid buoy	50°58'·90N 01°20'·00E
E Varne buoy	50°58'·20N 01°21'·00E
Varne Lanby	51°01'·25N 01°24'·00E
W Quern buoy	51°18'·95N 01°25'·00E
Ramsgate N bkwtr hd lt	51°19'·53N 01°25'·58E
Deal Bank buoy	51°12'·90N 01°25'·67E
Downs buoy	51°14'·47N 01°26'·60E
North Foreland lt	51°22'·47N 01°26'·80E
S Brake buoy	51°15'·45N 01°26'·80E
Goodwin Fork buoy	51°14'·30N 01°27'·23E
W Goodwin buoy	51°15'·28N 01°27'·32E
Brake buoy	51°16'·95N 01°28'·30E
S Goodwin lt F	51°07'·95N 01°28'·60E
NW Goodwin buoy	51°16'·54N 01°28'·67E

SW Goodwin buoy	51°08'·57N 01°28'·80E
E Brake buoy	51°19'·40N 01°29'·05E
Broadstairs Knoll buoy	51°20'·85N 01°29'·58E
Gull Stream buoy	51°18'·25N 01°29'·80E
Ramsgate (RA) buoy	51°19'·57N 01°30'·23E
N Goodwin buoy	51°17'·88N 01°30'·42E
Gull buoy	51°19'·55N 01°31'·40E
Elbow buoy	51°23'·20N 01°31'·70E
Goodwin Knoll buoy	51°19'·55N 01°32'·30E
S Goodwin buoy	51°10'·57N 01°32'·37E
NE Goodwin buoy	51°20'·28N 01°34'·27E
SE Goodwin buoy	51°12'·95N 01°34'·55E
E Goodwin buoy	51°16'·00N 01°35'·60E
E Goodwin lt F	51°13'·05N 01°36'·31E

OFFSHORE

Channel lt F	49°54'·42N 02°53'·67W
E Channel buoy	49°58'·67N 02°28'·87W
EC1 buoy	50°05'·90N 01°48'·35W
EC2 buoy	50°12'·10N 01°12'·40W
EC3 buoy	50°18'·30N 00°36'·10W
CS1 buoy	50°33'·67N 00°03'·83W
Greenwich lt V	50°24'·50N 00°00'·00
CS2 buoy	50°39'·10N 00°32'·70E
CS3 buoy	50°52'·00N 01°02'·30E
Bullock Bank buoy	50°46'·90N 01°07'·70E
N Colbart buoy	50°57'·42N 01°23'·40E
CS4 buoy	51°08'·58N 01°34'·03E
MPC buoy	51°06'·09N 01°38'·36E
S Falls buoy	51°13'·80N 01°44'·03E
F1 buoy	51°11'·20N 01°45'·03E
Mid Falls buoy	51°18'·60N 01°47'·10E
CS 5 buoy	51°23'·00N 01°50'·00E
Inter Bank buoy	51°16'·45N 01°52'·33E
F2 buoy	51°20'·38N 01°56'·30E
F3 buoy	51°23'·82N 02°00'·62E

CHANNEL ISLANDS

AREA 14

Les Hanois lt	49°26'·16N 02°42'·06W
St Martin's Point lt	49°25'·37N 02°31'·61W
Reffée buoy	49°27'·80N 02°31'·18W
Petite Canupe lt bn	49°30'·25N 02°29'·05W
Platte Fougère lt	49°30'·88N 02°29'·05W
Casquets lt	49°43'·38N 02°22'·55W
Desormes buoy	49°19'·00N 02°17'·90W
La Corbière lt	49°10'·85N 02°14'·90W
Passage Rk buoy	49°09'·59N 02°12'·18W
Alderney main lt	49°43'·81N 02°09'·77W
Diamond Rk buoy	49°10'·18N 02°08'·56W
Canger Rk buoy	49°07'·41N 02°00'·30W
Frouquier Aubert buoy	49°06'·14N 01°58'·78W
Violet buoy	49°07'·87N 01°57'·05W
NW Minquiers buoy	48°59'·70N 02°20'·50W
N Minquiers buoy	49°01'·70N 02°00'·50W
NE Minquiers buoy	49°00'·90N 01°55'·20W
SE Minquiers buoy	48°53'·50N 02°00'·00W
S Minquiers buoy	48°53'·15N 02°10'·00W
SW Minquiers buoy	48°54'·40N 02°19'·30W

FRENCH COAST

Selected waypoints in Area 15 and 16 are listed westward along the French coast from near **Cap Lévi** to **Ouessant**, and in Area 19 eastward from **Pointe de Barfleur** to **Dunkerque**. All positions are referenced to the European ED 50 datum.

AREA 15

Les Équets buoy	49°43'·68N 01°18'·28W
Basse du Rénier buoy	49°44'·90N 01°22'·10W
Cap Lévi lt	49°41'·80N 01°28'·40W
La Pierre Noire buoy	49°43'·57N 01°28'·98W
Cherbourg Fort Ouest lt	49°40'·50N 01°38'·87W
CH1 buoy	49°43'·30N 01°42'·10W
Basse Bréfort buoy	49°43'·70N 01°51'·05W
Cap de la Hague lt	49°43'·37N 01°57'·19W
Flamanville buoy	49°32'·62N 01°53'·93W
Cap de Carteret lt	49°22'·46N 01°48'·35W
Les Trois-Grunes buoy	49°21'·88N 01°55'·12W
Basses de Portbail (PB) buoy	49°18'·47N 01°44'·60W
Écrevière buoy	49°15'·33N 01°52'·08W
Basse Jourdan buoy	49°06'·90N 01°44'·07W
La Pierre-de-Herpin	48°43'·83N 01°48'·83W
La Catheue buoy	48°57'·95N 01°42'·00W
Les Ardentes buoy	48°57'·84N 01°51'·53W
Anvers buoy	48°53'·90N 01°40'·84W
Chausey, Grand Île lt	48°52'·25N 01°49'·27W
Le Videcoq buoy	48°49'·70N 01°42'·02W
Pierre d'Herpin buoy	48°43'·83N 01°48'·81W
Brunel buoy	48°40'·88N 02°05'·26W
Buharats Ouest No. 2 buoy	48°40'·30N 02°07'·48W
St Malo fairway buoy	48°41'·42N 02°07'·21W
Le Sou buoy	48°40'·15N 02°05'·24W
Bassé NE buoy	48°42'·51N 02°09'·34W
Banchenou buoy	48°40'·52N 02°11'·42W
Cap Fréhel lt	48°41'·10N 02°19'·07W
Le Rohein lt bn	48°38'·88N 02°37'·68W
Le Légué buoy	48°34'·38N 02°41'·07W
Caffa buoy	48°37'·89N 02°43'·00W
Grand Léjon lt	48°44'·95N 02°39'·90W
La Roselière buoy	48°37'·51N 02°46'·31W
Roc du Nord-Est buoy	48°39'·65N 02°44'·00W
Île Harbour	48°40'·05N 02°48'·42W

AREA 16

Roches Douvres lt	49°06'·35N 02°48'·65W
Barnouic lt	49°01'·70N 02°48'·33W
Roche Gautier buoy	49°00'·49N 02°52'·92W
L'Ost Pic	48°46'·82N 02°56'·33W
Les Echaudés buoy	48°53'·42N 02°57'·26W
Rosédo (Bréhat) lt	48°51'·51N 03°00'·21W
Les Héaux lt	48°54'·57N 03°05'·10W
La Jument des Héaux buoy	48°55'·41N 03°07'·95W
Les Sept Îles lt	48°52'·78N 03°29'·33W
Les Triagoz lt	48°52'·35N 03°38'·73W
Méloine buoy	48°45'·65N 03°50'·55W
Stolvezen buoy	48°42'·71N 03°53'·32W

Pot de Fer buoy	48°44'·29N 03°53'·93W
Bassee de Bloscon buoy	48°43'·77N 03°57'·48W
Astan buoy	48°44'·95N 03°57'·55W
Île de Batz lt	48°44'·78N 04°01'·55W
Aman-ar-Ross buoy	48°41'·94N 04°26'·96W
Lizen Van Ouest buoy	48°40'·55N 04°33'·68W
Île Vierge lt	48°38'·38N 04°33'·97W
Trépied By	48°37'·35N 04°37'·47W
Libenter buoy	48°37'·57N 04°38'·35W
Rusven Est buoy	48°36'·37N 04°38'·53W
Petite Fourche buoy	48°37'·05N 04°38'·67W
Ruzven Ouest buoy	48°36'·15N 04°39'·34W
Le Relec buoy	48°36'·05N 04°40'·76W
Grande Basse Portsall buoy	48°36'·78N 04°46'·05W
Basse Paupian buoy	48°35'·38N 04°46'·20W
Créac'h lt	48°27'·62N 05°07'·72W
Ouessant NE buoy	48°45'·90N 05°11'·60W
Ouessant SW Lanby	48°31'·20N 05°49'·10W

AREA 19

Pointe de Barfleur lt	49°41'·83N 01°15'·87W
Îles St Marcouf lt	49°29'·90N 01°08'·70W
Norfalk buoy	49°28'·83N 01°03'·40W
Est du Cardonnet buoy	49°26'·97N 01°01'·00W
Broadswood buoy	49°25'·39N 00°52'·90W
Cussy buoy	49°29'·50N 00°43'·25W
Ver-sur-Mer lt	49°20'·47N 00°31'·15W
Ouistreham buoy	49°20'·48N 00°14'·73W
Northgate buoy	49°30'·40N 00°14'·15W
LHA Lanby	49°31'·44N 00°09'·78W
A17 buoy	49°41'·60N 00°01'·75E
A18 buoy	49°42'·07N 00°02'·21E
Ratier NW buoy	49°26'·85N 00°02'·55E
Cap de la Hève lt	49°30'·79N 00°04'·24E
Cap d'Antifer lt	49°41'·07N 00°10'·00E
Pointe d'Ailly lt	49°55'·13N 00°57'·56E
Bassurelle buoy	50°32'·70N 00°57'·80E
Ecovouga Wk buoy	50°33'·70N 00°59'·20E
Vergoyer SW buoy	50°26'·90N 01°00'·10E
Daffodils buoy	50°02'·52N 01°04'·10E
Colbart SW buoy	50°48'·85N 01°16'·45E

Ridens SE buoy	50°43'·45N 01°19'·00E
ZC1 buoy	50°44'·94N 01°27'·30E
Ault lt	50°06'·32N 01°27'·31E
AT-SO buoy	50°14'·29N 01°28'·65E
Ophélie buoy	50°43'·91N 01°30'·92E
ZC2 buoy	50°53'·50N 01°31'·00E
Pointe de Haut Blanc lt	50°23'·90N 01°33'·75E
Cap d'Alprech lt	50°41'·96N 01°33'·83E
Cap Gris Nez lt	50°52'·05N 01°35'·07E
Abbeville buoy	50°56'·05N 01°37'·70E
CA3 buoy	50°56'·80N 01°41'·25E
CA4 buoy	50°58'·94N 01°45'·18E
CA6 buoy	50°58'·30N 01°45'·70E
SW Sandettié buoy	51°09'·72N 01°45'·73E
CA5 buoy	50°57'·70N 01°46'·20E
Sangatte lt	50°57'·23N 01°46'·57E
SW Ruytingen buoy	51°04'·99N 01°46'·90E
Sandettié lt F	51°09'·40N 01°47'·20E
CA8 buoy	50°58'·43N 01°48'·72E
CA2 buoy	51°00'·91N 01°48'·86E
CA10 buoy	50°58'·68N 01°50'·00E
Ruytingen W buoy	51°06'·90N 01°50'·60E
Sandettié WSW buoy	51°12'·32N 01°51'·23E
Calais lt	50°57'·73N 01°51'·28E
Calais E Hd lt	50°58'·45N 01°50'·54E
Dunkerque Lanby	51°03'·00N 01°51'·83E
RCE buoy	51°02'·40N 01°53'·20E
DKA buoy	51°02'·59N 01°57'·06E
NW Ruytingen buoy	51°09'·05N 01°57'·40E
DW5 buoy	51°02'·20N 02°01'·00E
N Sandettié buoy	51°18'·42N 02°04'·80E
Haut-fond de Gravelines	51°04'·10N 02°05'·10E
E Dyck buoy	51°05'·70N 02°05'·70E
SE Ruytingen buoy	51°09'·20N 02°09'·00E
DKB buoy	51°03'·00N 02°09'·34E
N Ruytingen buoy	51°13'·12N 02°10'·42E
Hinder 1 buoy	51°20'·90N 02°11'·06E
DW23 buoy	51°03'·60N 02°15'·25E
S Fairy buoy	51°21'·22N 02°17'·35E
Bergues buoy	51°17'·20N 02°18'·70E
S Bergues buoy	51°15'·16N 02°19'·50E
DW29 buoy	51°03'·88N 02°20'·32E
Dunkerque lt	51°02'·98N 02°21'·94E

ISLES OF SCILLY   8-1-8

The Isles of Scilly are made up of 48 islands and numerous rocky outcrops, covering an area approx 10M by 7M and lying 21 – 31M WSW of Land's End. Only six islands are inhabited: St Mary's, St Martin's, Tresco, Bryher, St Agnes and Gugh. The islands belong to the Duchy of Cornwall. Arrangements for visiting uninhabited islands are given in a booklet *Duchy of Cornwall - Information for visiting craft* obtainable from Hr Mr, Hugh Town Hbr, St Mary's. There is a LB and a HM CG Sector Base at St Mary's.
Historic Wrecks (see 8.0.3h) are at 49°52'·6N 06°26'·5N Tearing Ledge, 2ca SE of Bishop Rk Lt; and at 49°54'·26N 06°19'·83W, Bartholomew Ledges, 5ca N of Gugh.

CHARTS
AC *883, 34* (both essential); Scilly to Lands End 1148; Imray C7; Stanfords 2, 13; OS 203
TIDES
Standard Port is Devonport. Differences for St Mary's are given in 8·1·9. Tidal heights, times, directions and rates around the islands are irregular; see AC 34 for streams.
SHELTER
The Isles of Scilly are exposed to Atlantic swell and wind. Weather can be unpredictable and fast-changing. It is not a place for inexperienced navigators or poorly equipped yachts. Normal yacht ⚓s may drag on fine sand, even with plenty of scope, but holding is mostly good. That said, the islands are attractive, interesting and rewarding.

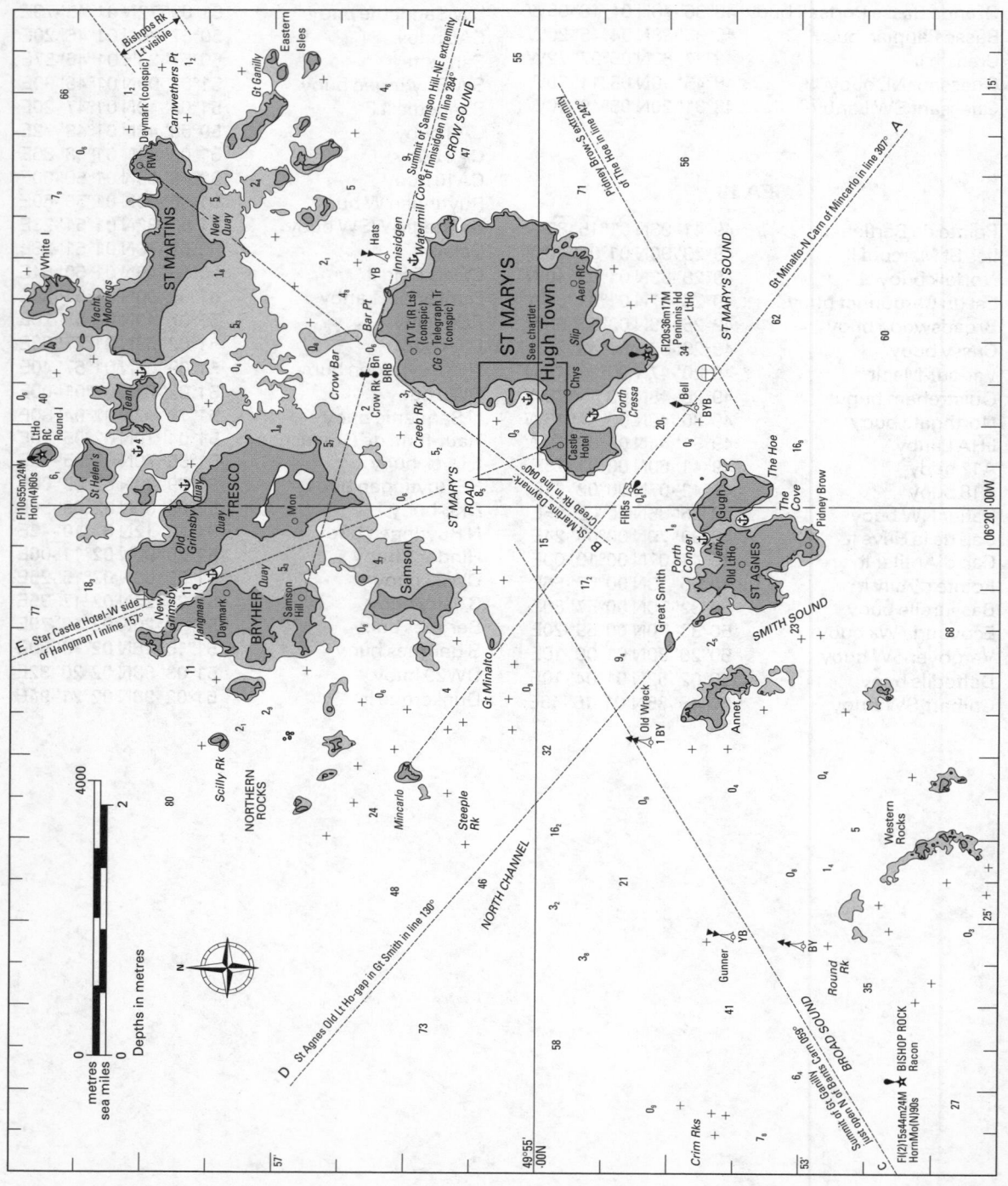

The following are some of the many ⚓s, anti-clockwise:

HUGH TOWN HBR (St Mary's). See 8·1·9 facing.

PORTH CRESSA (St Mary's, S of Hugh Town). Beware of dangers on each side of ent and submarine cables. Good ⚓ (2m) in W/NW'lies, but exposed to swell from SE to SW.

WATERMILL COVE (NE corner of St Mary's). Excellent shelter in winds S to NW. ⚓ in approx 5m.

TEAN SOUND (St Martin's, W end). Needs careful pilotage, but attractive ⚓ in better weather. More suitable for shoal draught boats which can ⚓ or take the ground out of main tidal stream in chan. St Martin's Hotel ☎ 422092, D, FW, 7 ⚓s £10 inc showers, V, R, Bar. There are several other ⚓s which can be used in settled weather.

ST HELEN'S POOL (S of St Helen's Is). Ent via St Helen's Gap to ⚓ in 1·5m - 7m. Secure, but may be swell near HW.

OLD GRIMSBY (NE side of Tresco). Green Porth & Raven's Porth, divided by a quay, form the Old Grimsby Hbr; both dry 2·3m. Beware cable in Green Porth. ⚓s 1½ca NE of quay in 2·5m; access more difficult than New Grimsby. Well sheltered in SW'lies but open to swell if wind veers N of W. Facilities: 6 ⚓s (R cans) £10, L (quay), hotel, slip.

NEW GRIMSBY (between Tresco and Bryher). Appr (line E) through New Grimsby Sound, or with adequate rise of tide across Tresco Flats. Good shelter except in NW'lies. Popular ⚓ between Hangman Is and the quay in 1·5 - 4·5m. Beware cables. 22 ⚓s £10 via Tresco Estate ☎ 22849, ☎ 22807; VHF Ch 08 for R, Bar, FW, V, ✉. Ferry to St Mary's.

THE COVE (St Agnes/Gugh). Well sheltered from W and N winds, except when the sand bar between the islands covers near HWS with a strong NW wind. Beware cables.

PORTH CONGER (St Agnes/Gugh). On the N side of the sandbar, sheltered in winds from E through S to W. May be uncomfortable when the bar is covered. Facilities: L (two quays), ferry to St Mary's; in Middle Town (¾M), St Agnes, V, ✉, R, Bar.

NAVIGATION
For TSS to the E, S and W, see 8.1.2. If unable to identify approach ldg lines/marks, then it is best to lie off. Pilotage is compulsory for all vessels, except HM Ships, trawlers <47·5m LOA and yachts <30m LOA, navigating within a radius of 6M from S tip of Samson Is excluding St Mary's Hbr. Many chans between islands have dangerous shallows, often with rky ledges. Beware lobster pots.

Line A, via St Mary's Sound, is the normal ent to St Mary's Road. Appr from the E or SE to avoid Gilstone Rk (dries 4m) 3ca E of Peninnis Hd. Spanish Ledges, off Gugh, are marked by an unlit ECM By; thence past Woolpack SCM bn and PHM By Fl R 5s (Bartholomew Ledge) to ent St Mary's Rd on 040°.

Line B, which clears Woodcock Ledge (breaks in bad wx).

Line C, from SW: Broad Sound is entered between Bishops Rk lt ho and Flemming's Ledge about 7ca to the N, then twixt Round Rk NCM and Gunner SCM buoys to Old Wreck NCM buoy; beware Jeffrey Rk, close to port. Ldg marks are more than 7M off and at first not easy to see. Smith Sound, 350° between St Agnes and Annet may also be used.

Line D, from NW: North Chan is about 7ca wide, and of easy access with good ldg marks, but beware cross tide and Steeple Rk (0·1m, 2ca to port). Intercept Line C for St Mary's Road.

Line E, from the N, leads between Bryher and Tresco, into New Grimsby Hbr (see SHELTER); thence it winds across Tresco Flats (with adequate rise of tide and good vis).

Line F, from the E & NE: Crow Sound is not difficult, with sufficient rise of tide but can be rough in strong E or S winds. From NE a yacht can pass close to Menawethan and Biggal Rk, avoiding Trinity Rk and the Ridge, which break in bad weather. Hats SCM buoy marks a shoal with an old boiler, drying 0·6m, on it. Track 254° between Bar Pt and Crow Bar (dries 0·7m), passing Crow Rk IDM bn on its N side (for best water) before altering SSW for St Mary's.

LIGHTS AND MARKS
See 8·1·4 for lts, including Seven Stones lt float, Wolf Rock lt ho and Longships lt ho. A working knowledge of the following daymarks and conspic features will greatly aid pilotage (from NE to SW):

St Martin's E end: Conical bn tr (56m) with RW bands.
Round Is: conical shaped Is with W lt ho 19/55m high.
Tresco: Abbey & FS, best seen from S. Cromwell's Castle and Hangman Is from the NW.
Bryher: Watch Hill, stone bn (43m); rounded Samson Hill.
St Mary's: TV & radio masts at N end; all with R lts. Crow Rk IDM bn, 11m on rk drying 4·6m, at N.
St Agnes: Old lt ho, ○ W tr, visible from all directions.
Bishop Rk lt ho: Grey ○ tr, 44m; helo pad above lamp.

ST MARY'S   8-1-9
Isles of Scilly 49°55'·10N 06°18'·65W   Rtg 2-3-1

CHARTS
AC 883, 34; Imray C7; Stanfords 2; OS 203

TIDES
+0607 Dover; ML 3·2; Duration 0600; Zone 0 (UT)

Standard Port DEVONPORT (→)

Times				Height (metres)			
High Water		Low Water		MHWS	MHWN	MLWN	MLWS
0000	0600	0000	0600	5·5	4·4	2·2	0·8
1200	1800	1200	1800				
Differences ST MARY'S							
−0050	−0100	−0045	−0045	+0·2	−0·1	−0·2	−0·1

SHELTER
Good in St Mary's Pool where 38 Y ⚓s lie in 5 trots close E of the LB ⌂ in at least 2m. ⚓ is prohib S of a line from the pier hd to the LB slip; to seaward of the LB ⌂; off the pier hd where the ferry turns, and in the apprs. Holding in the Pool is poor and in W/NW gales it is notorious for yachts dragging ⚓, when Porth Cressa (see 8·1·8) is safer. Hbr speed limit 3kn. NB: do not impede Scillonian III the ferry which arrives about 1200 and sails at 1630 Mon-Fri; Sat times vary with month. Also cargo ship thrice weekly.

NAVIGATION
WPT via St Mary's Sound: Spanish Ledge unlit ECM buoy, 49°53'·90N 06°18'·80W, 128°/308° from/to transit line B (040°), 1·2M. See also 8·1·4 & 8·1·8. The 097° transit leads S of Bacon Ledge (0·3m) marked by PHM buoy (Apr-Oct); the 151° transit leads into the Pool between Bacon Ledge and the Cow & Calf (drying 0·6 and 1·8m) to the E.

LIGHTS AND MARKS
Pier hd lt, Fl RWG 2s, R070°-099° (29°), W099°-129° (30°), G129°-000° (231°). 2 ldg marks, (both ☆ FR; do not confuse with aero lts) lead 097° into the Pool: front bn = W △ on pole on W pyramid; rear = black X on pole (hard to see in morning). Buzza Hill tr and power stn chy (48m) are conspic.

RADIO TELEPHONE
St Mary's Hbr VHF Ch 14 16 (0800-1700LT). Pilot Ch 69 16. Falmouth CG gives radio cover Ch 16 of the TSS/ITZ off Land's End. Do not hesitate to call the CG Ch 16 if in emergency/gales/dragging ⚓. Lands End Radio Ch 64 covers Scilly.

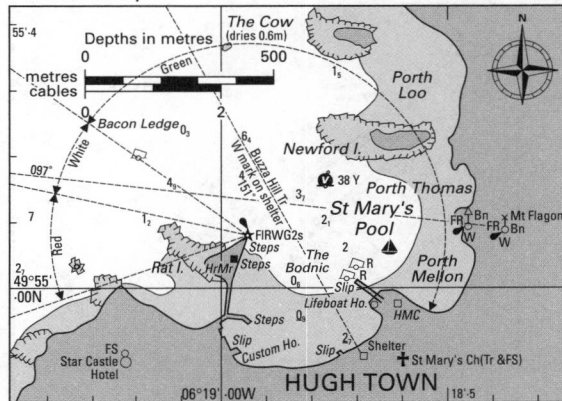

TELEPHONE (Dial code 01720)
Hr Mr 422768 (also ☎); MRCC (01326) 317575; Marinecall 0891 500458; ⌗ 0345 231110, locally 422571; ℍ 422392; Dr 422628; Police 422444; Pilot 422066; Tourist Info 422536.

FACILITIES
Hbr ⚓ dues: £10 <18m LOA, D & FW at pier outer berth 0930-1100 & 1630-1800 Mon-Fri; OT see Hr Mr for FW (nil or limited quantity in summer); for D ☎ Sibleys 422431. P (cans) via Hr Mr, Gas, Gaz, Slip. Hbr Office will hold mail for visiting yachts if addressed c/o Hr Mr, Hugh Town.
Hugh Town EC Wed; limited shopping facilities, ACA, Sh, CH, ME, El, ✉, Ⓑ, ▣. Ferry sails 0915 Mon-Fri (not Sun) from Penzance and 1630 from St Mary; (Sat varies); about 2¾hrs crossing, booking ☎ 0345-105555 (see also 8.0.4); helicopter (☎ 422646) to Penzance (➥) and fixed wing ✈ to St Just (Lands End), Exeter, Newquay, Bristol, Plymouth and Southampton, ☎ 0345 105555. There are ✉, R, V, Bar at Tresco, Bryher, St Martins and St Agnes.

NEWLYN   8-1-10

Cornwall 50°06'·15N 05°32'.52W   Rtg 3-2-2

CHARTS
AC 2345, 777; Imray C7; Stanfords 13; OS 203
TIDES
+0600 Dover; ML 3·2; Duration 0555; Zone 0 (UT)

Standard Port DEVONPORT (⟶)

Times				Height (metres)			
High Water		Low Water		MHWS	MHWN	MLWN	MLWS
0000	0600	0000	0600	5·5	4·4	2·2	0·8
1200	1800	1200	1800				
Differences NEWLYN							
−0055	−0115	−0035	−0035	+0·1	0·0	−0·2	0·0

SHELTER
Good, except in SE winds when heavy swell enters hbr; access at all tides. FVs take priority. Yachts berth on SW side of Mary Williams Pier. No ♠s, no ⚓ in hbr. Good ⚓ in Gwavas Lake in offshore winds.
NAVIGATION
WPT 50°06'·15N 05°31'·74W, 090°/270° from/to S pier, 0·5M. From NE, beware The Gear and Dog Rk 3½ca NE of hbr ent; from S beware Low Lee and Carn Base.
LIGHTS AND MARKS
S pier hd, Fl 5s 10m 9M; vis 253°-336°, W tr, R base and cupola; Siren 60s. N pier hd, F WG 4m 2M; vis G238°-248°, W over hbr. Old Quay hd, FR 3m 1M.
RADIO TELEPHONE
Call: Newlyn Hbr VHF Ch 09 12 16 (Mon-Fri 0800-1700, Sat 0800-1200LT).
TELEPHONE (Dial code 01736)
Hr Mr 362523; MRCC, ⌗, Marinecall, Police, Ⓗ, Dr: as for Penzance.
FACILITIES
Mary Williams Pier £4–£9 (every 3rd night free). **N Pier** Slip, D (cans), FW, C (6 ton); **Services:** ME, Sh, SM, Gas, El, Ⓔ, CH. **Town** EC Wed; ◎, V, R, Bar, ✉, Ⓑ (AM only), bus to Penzance for ⇌, ✈.

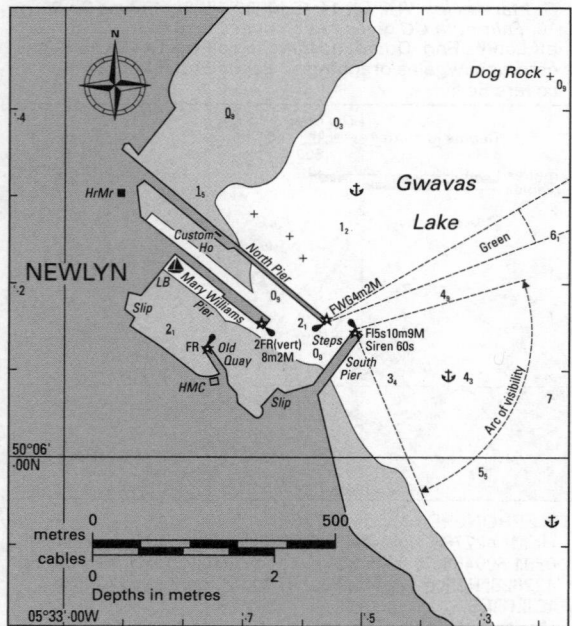

ADJACENT HARBOUR

MOUSEHOLE, Cornwall, 50°04'·93N 05°32'·20W. Rtg 4-5-1. AC 2345. HW +0550 on Dover; Tides as Newlyn; ML 3·2m; Duration 0600. Shelter good except in NE and SE winds; protected by St Clements Is from E'lies. Best appr from S, midway between St Clements Is and bkwtr. Ent 11m wide; hbr dries 1·8m, access HW±3. Ent is closed with timber baulks from Nov-Apl. Lts N pier 2 FG (vert) 8/6m 3M; 2 FR (vert) = hbr closed. Hr Mr ☎ (01736) 731511. £5. Facilities limited: FW, V, Slip. Buses to Penzance.

PENZANCE   8-1-11

Cornwall 50°07'·05N 05°31'·62W   Rtg 3-2-1

CHARTS
AC 2345, 777; Imray C7; Stanfords 13; OS 203
TIDES
−0635 Dover; ML 3·2; Duration 0550; Zone 0 (UT)

Standard Port DEVONPORT (⟶)

Times				Height (metres)			
High Water		Low Water		MHWS	MHWN	MLWN	MLWS
0000	0600	0000	0600	5·5	4·4	2·2	0·8
1200	1800	1200	1800				
Differences PENZANCE							
−0055	−0115	−0035	−0035	+0·1	0·0	−0·2	0·0
PORTHLEVEN							
−0050	−0105	−0030	−0025	0·0	−0·1	−0·2	0·0
LIZARD POINT							
−0045	−0100	−0030	−0030	−0·2	−0·2	−0·3	−0·2

SHELTER
Excellent in the wet dock (gates open HW −2 to +1), or dry out against Albert pier. 12 waiting buoys are laid E of the lt ho on S pier. Or ⚓ E of hbr, but Mounts Bay is an unsafe ⚓ in S or SE winds, which, if strong, also render the hbr ent dangerous. Hbr speed limit 5kn.
NAVIGATION
WPT 50°06'·70N 05°31'·10W, 135°/315° from/to S pier hd, 0·48M. Beware Gear Rk 0·4M S. Cressar (5ca NE of ent) and Long Rks are marked by SCM bns.
LIGHTS AND MARKS
There are no ldg lts/marks. Dock ent sigs, shown from FS at N side of Dock gate (may not be given for yachts).
2B ● (hor) (2FR (vert) by night) = Dock gates open.
2B ● (vert) (Ⓡ over Ⓖ by night) = Dock gates shut.
RADIO TELEPHONE
VHF Ch 09 12 16 (HW −2 to HW +1, and office hrs).
TELEPHONE (Dial code 01736)
Hr Mr 366113; MRCC (01326) 317575; ⌗ 0345 231110 (H24); Marinecall 0891 500458; Police 362395; Dr 363866; Ⓗ 362382.
FACILITIES
Wet Dock (50 Ⓥ) ☎ 366113, ⚓ 366114, £7.50 (every 3rd night free), M, D (cans), FW, AC, C (3 ton); **S Pier** D, FW; **Penzance YC** ☎ 364989, Bar, L, FW, R; **Services:** Slip (dry dock), ME, El, CH, SM, Sh, Gas, Gaz.
Town EC Wed (winter only); ◎, V, R, Bar, ✉, Ⓑ, ⇌, ✈.

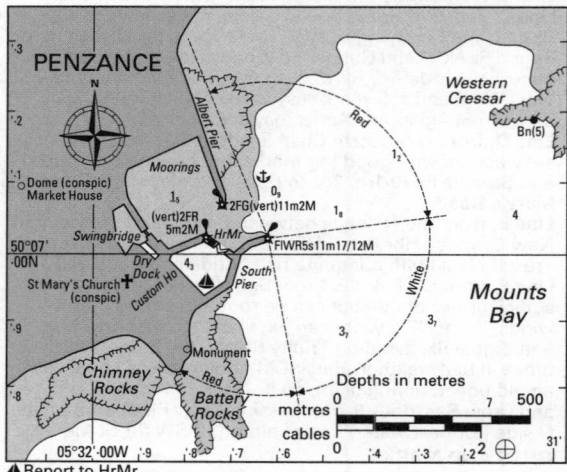

▲ Report to HrMr

ADJACENT HARBOUR

ST MICHAEL'S MOUNT, Cornwall, 50°07'·10N 05°28'·58W. AC 2345, 777. HW +0550 on Dover; Tides as Penzance; ML 3·2m; Duration 0550. Shelter good from N to SE, but only in fair wx. Hbr dries; it has approx 3·3m at MHWS and 1·4m at MHWN. Beware Hogus Rks to NW of hbr and Outer Penzeath Rk about 3ca WSW of Hogus Rks. Also beware Maltman Rk 1ca SSW of the Mount. There are no lts. Ent between piers is 30m wide. Room for 6 to ⚓ W of the pier. Call ☎ 710265 (HO). Facilities: FW, R, café; more facilities at Marazion, 5M to N. EC Wed.

ADJACENT HARBOURS ON THE LIZARD PENINSULA

PORTHLEVEN, Cornwall, 50°04´·88N 05°19´·07W. Rtg 4-4-3. AC 2345, *777*. HW +0551 on Dover; ML 3·1m; Duration 0545. See 8·1·11. Hbr dries 2m above the old LB ho but has approx 2·3m in centre of ent; access HW±3. It is open to W and SW. Beware rks round pier hd and Deazle Rks to W. Lt on S pier FG 10m 4M = inner hbr open. Inside hbr FG vis 033°-067° when required for vessels entering. Visitors go alongside the Quay on E side. Hr Mr ☎ (01326) 574270. Facilities: **Inner Hbr** AB £8, FW, L, ME, P & D (cans). **Village** EC Wed; ⊠, Ⓞ, R, Ⓑ, V, Bar.

MULLION COVE, Cornwall, 50°00´·86N, 05°15´·48W. AC 2345, *777*. Lizard HW +0552 on Dover, −0050 and −0·2m on HW Devonport; ML 3·0m; Duration 0545. Porth Mellin hbr dries 2·4m and is open to W'lies. ⚓ in Mullion Cove is safer especially in lee of Mullion Island where there is approx 3·5m, but local knowledge advised. NT owns the island and the hbr. Due to lack of space, visiting boats may only stay in hbr briefly to load/unload. No lts. There is a slip on E side of hbr. Hr Mr ☎ (01326) 240222. Only facilities at Mullion village (1M) EC Wed; Bar, V.

Historic Wrecks (see 8.0.3h) are located at:
50°03´·40N 05°17´·10W (*St Anthony*), 2M SE of Porthleven.
50°02´·33N 05°16´·40W (*Schiedam*), 1·5M N of Mullion Is.
49°58´·50N 05°14´·45W, Rill Cove, 1·4M NW of Lizard Pt.
49°57´·45N 05°12´·92W, (*Royal Anne*) The Stags, Lizard Pt.

CADGWITH, Cornwall, 49°59´·18N 05°10´·62W. AC 2345, *154, 777*. HW +0555 on Dover; −0030 on Devonport; −0·2m on Devonport; ML 3·0m. See Differences Lizard Pt under 8.1.11. Hbr dries; it is divided by a rky outcrop, The Todden. Beware the extension of this, rks called The Mare; also beware The Boa rks to ESE which cover at quarter tide. ⚓ off The Mare in about 2–3m, but not recommended in on-shore winds. There are no lts. Many local FVs operate from here and are hauled up on the shingle beach. Facilities: ⊠, Bar, R, V (1M at Ruan Minor).

COVERACK, Cornwall, 50°01´·40N 05°05´·60W. AC *154, 777*. HW +0605 on Dover; ML 3·0m; Duration 0550. See 8·1·12. Hbr dries but has 3·3m at MHWS and 2·2m at MHWN. In good weather and off-shore winds it is better to ⚓ outside. Hbr is very small and full of FVs. From the S beware the Guthens, off Chynhalls Pt; from the N, the Dava and other rks off Lowland Pt, and Manacle Rks to the NE (ECM, Q(3) 10s bell). There are no lts. Hr Mr ☎ (01326) 280583. Facilities: EC Tues; FW (hotel) D, P (cans) from garage (2M uphill), V, ⊠.

HELFORD RIVER   8-1-12

Cornwall 50°05´·75N 05·06´·00W (Ent)   Rtg 2-3-1

CHARTS
AC 147, *154*; Imray C6, Y57; Stanfords 13; OS 204
TIDES
−0613 Dover; ML 3·0; Duration 0550; Zone 0 (UT)

Reference Port FALMOUTH (⟶)

Times				Height (metres)			
High Water		Low Water		MHWS	MHWN	MLWN	MLWS
0000	0600	0000	0600	5·3	4·2	1·9	0·6
1200	1800	1200	1800				
Differences HELFORD RIVER (Ent)							
0000	−0005	−0005	0000	0·0	0·0	0·0	0·0
COVERACK							
0000	−0010	−0010	0000	0·0	0·0	0·0	0·0

SHELTER
Excellent, except in E'lies. ⚓s marked 'Visitors' on G can buoys or G pick-up buoys are administered by Moorings Officer. Ferry will collect people from yachts, if requested during normal ferry operating hrs.
⚓s at: Durgan Bay, good; off Helford, but tides strong; Navas Creek, good shelter, little room, YC wall dries 1·9m. Gillan Creek is good except in E'lies, but beware Car Croc rk in ent marked by ECM buoy in season.
Note: A local bye-law states that yachts must not ⚓ in the river and creeks W of Navas Creek due to oyster beds.

NAVIGATION
WPT 50°05´·70N 05°04´·50W, 093°/273° from/to The Voose NCM bn, 1·5M. From N beware August Rock (alias the Gedges), marked by SHM (seasonal). From SE keep well clear of Nare Pt and Dennis Hd. Speed limit 6kn in river. Keep Helford Pt open of Bosahan Pt to clear The Voose, a rky reef E of Bosahan Pt, marked by NCM (seasonal). On N side of river opposite Helford Creek avoid mud bank marked by Bar buoy SHM (seasonal). PHM & SHM buoys mark chan from Mawgan Creek to Gweek.
LIGHTS AND MARKS
Bosahan Pt on with Mawnan Shear (259°) clears August Rk (The Gedges), dangerous rks marked by unlit SHM By.
RADIO TELEPHONE
Moorings Officer VHF Ch M. Helford River SC Ch **80** M.
TELEPHONE (Dial code 01326)
Moorings Officer 221265; MRCC 317575; ⌗ 0345 231110 (H24); Marinecall 0891 500458; Police 72231; Ⓗ 572151.
FACILITIES
Moorings £5.00. Please ditch rubbish only at the Helford River SC; protect the wild life of this beautiful river.
Helford River SC ☎ 231460, Slip, FW, R, Bar, Ⓞ;
Porth Navas YC ☎ 340419/340065 (Bar), Gas, C (3 ton), M, AC, V, R, FW; **Helford Passage** Slip, L, FW, V; **Gweek Quay** ☎ 221657, ⚓ 221685, M, FW, CH, El, Sh, ME, Ⓔ, C (30 ton), BH, R; **Gillan Creek** CH, FW, M;
Services: Gas, Gaz, Slip, L, Sh, CH, Ⓞ, D (cans).
EC Wed; ⊠ (Helford, Gweek, Mawnan-Smith, Mawgan); Ⓑ Mawnan-Smith (Jan-Sept Mon, Wed, Fri AM only. Oct-May Tues, Fri AM only); ⇌ (bus to Falmouth); ✈ (Penzance or Newquay).

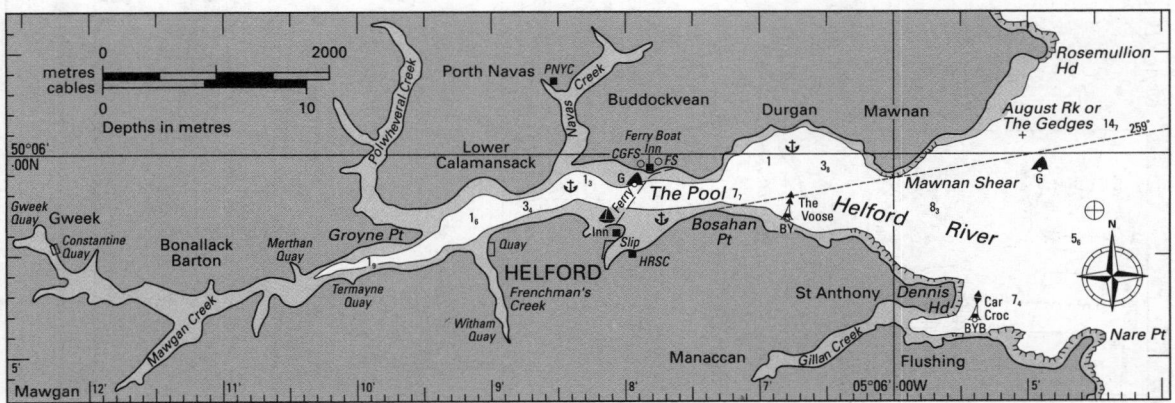

RIVER FAL   8-1-13
Cornwall 50°08'·58N 05°01'·42W (Ent)   Rtg 1-1-1

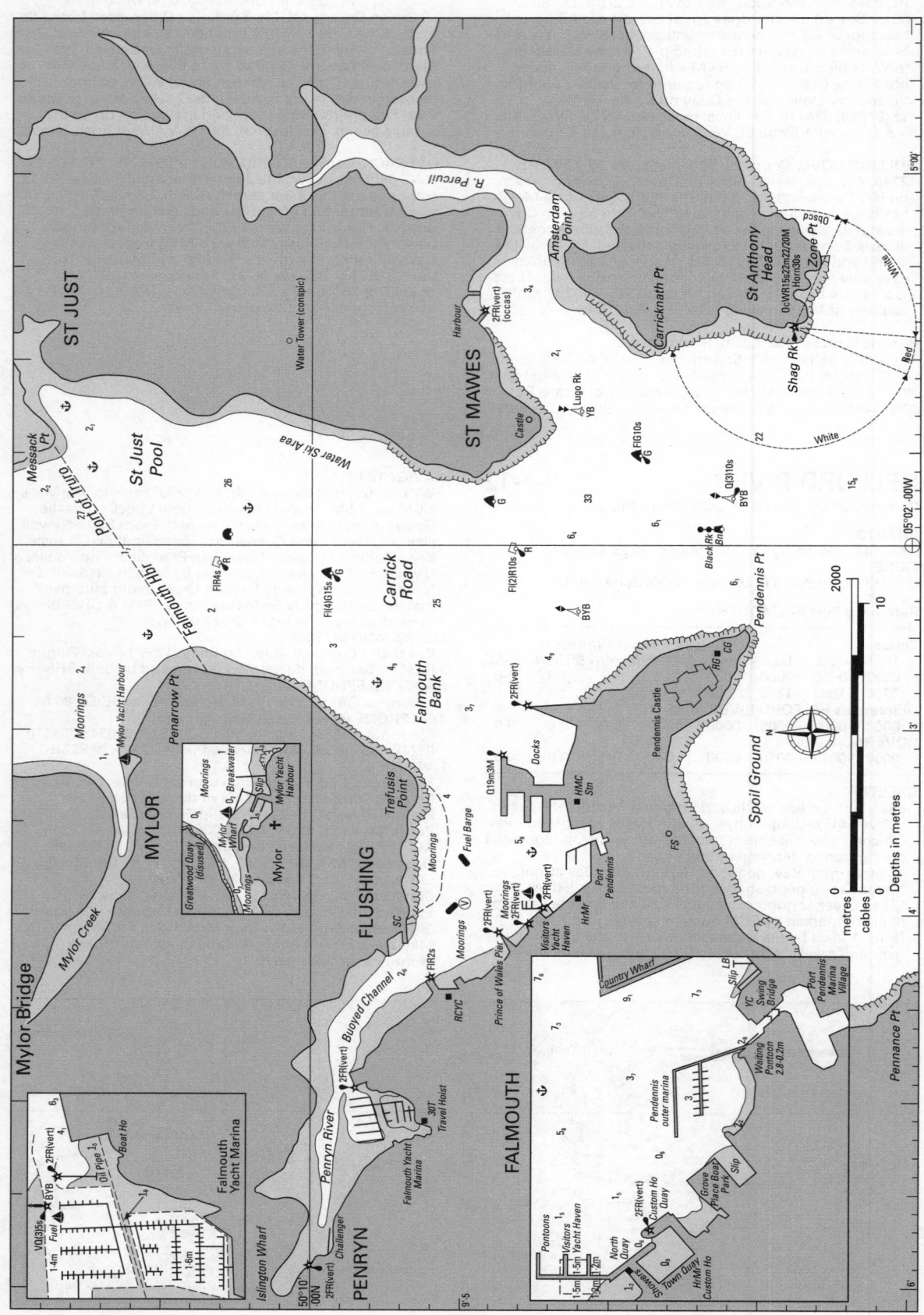

CHARTS
AC *32*, 18, *154*; Imray C6, Y58; Stanfords 13; OS 204

TIDES
−0558 Dover; ML 3·0; Duration 0550; Zone 0 (UT)
Daily Predictions and Tidal Curve are given below.
HW Truro is approx HW Falmouth +0008 and −1·8m.

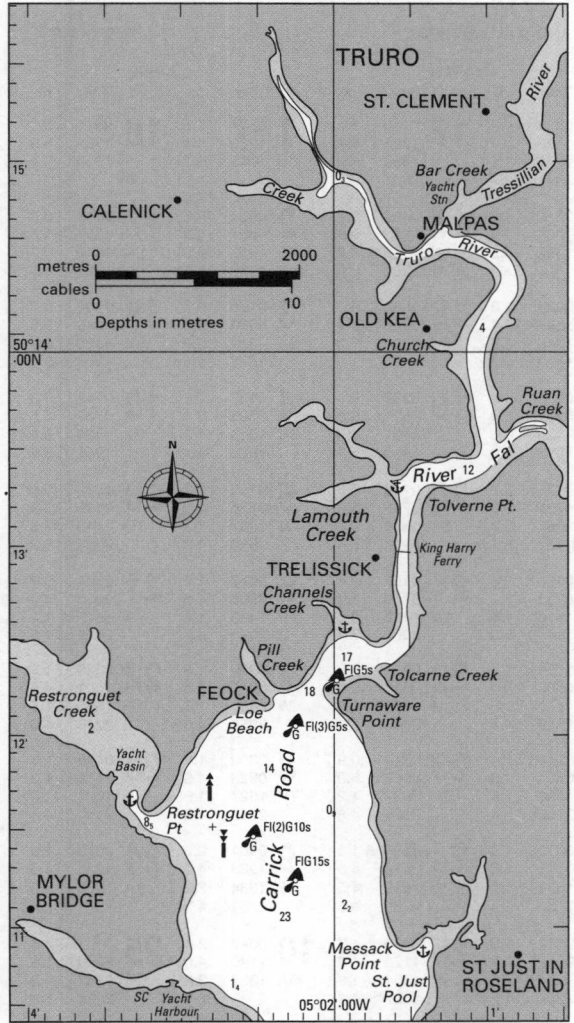

SHELTER
Excellent. There are many ⓥ berths, see below; also 18 G
⚓s clearly marked, on SW side of the fairway, owned by
Falmouth Hbr Commissioners or the Royal Cornwall YC.
The **Visitors Yacht Haven** operates Apr-Sept; pontoons
are connected to North Quay; max LOA 12m, draft 1·8m.
Port Pendennis marina, access HW±3 via lock with tfc lts.
Outer marina (73 berths) in about 3m has all tide access.
Falmouth Marina, 6ca beyond RCYC up the Penryn R, is
accessible at most tides, but at LWS beware depths of
1·4m or less due silting. On near appr pass within 20m of
outside pontoon, 2FR (vert), and leave ECM lt bn, VQ (3)
5s (hard to see), close to stbd to keep in narrow ent chan.
An unlit PHM and SHM buoy, close NE of ECM bn, mark
the Penryn R; speed limit is 8kn.
On the W bank of Carrick Road **Mylor Yacht Hbr** is
sheltered from W'lies but uncomfortable in strong E'lies.
Further up on the W bank is **Restronguet Creek**, a good ⚓
in pool (12·4m max depth), but most of the creek dries.
On E side **St Mawes Hbr** with 9 G ⚓s (contact SC) offers
excellent shelter except from SW winds, when ⚓ above
Amsterdam Pt. Off St Just is a good ⚓, but
uncomfortable in strong W/SW'lies.
Up the Fal there are pontoons & ⚓s N of Tolcarne Creek;
and good ⚓s in Tolcarne Creek, Channals Creek, Tolverne,
Ruan Creek (ⓥ pontoon) Church Creek, Mopus Reach &
Malpas (Bar Creek Yacht Stn ¼M up Tressillian R has ⚓s).
5kn speed limit in upper reaches and creeks.

NAVIGATION
WPT 50°08'·00N 05°02'·00W, 183°/003° from/to Black Rock
IDM bn, 0·68M. Ent is 1M wide and deep. Hbr accessible
in any weather or tide although fresh on-shore winds over
an ebb tide make it a bit rough. The only hazard is Black
Rk, dries 2·1m almost in the middle of the ent; pass either
side, but at night the E chan is advised keeping E of the
ECM By, Q (3) 10s. Outside the buoyed chans large areas
are quite shallow and care is needed below half tide.
Falmouth is a deep water port, taking ships up to 90,000
tons; appropriate facilities are available. Take care not to
impede shipping or ⚓ in prohib areas. Beware oyster
beds, especially in Penryn and Percuil Rivers.
Mylor Creek dries or is shoal, <1m, but Mylor Pool has
many moorings in up to 2·4m, and some pontoon berths.
A PHM and SHM buoy mark the ent to the fairway.
Restronguet Creek has a 12m deep pool at its ent, but
dries above Pandora Inn. Beware Carrick Carlys Rk 0·8m,
3ca E of ent, marked by a NCM and SCM post.
River Fal proper flows into the N end of Carrick Roads at
Turnaware Pt; beware strong tides and rips. There are ⚓s
off the various creeks. 8ca NW of Malpas a flood barrage,
lit by 2 FR/FG (vert), is usually open; 3 Fl R lts show when
it is closed. Truro dries, but can be reached on the tide.
In **St Mawes Hbr** ent keep S of the SCM buoy marking
Lugo Rk, 0·6m, which is always covered. The river dries
above Percuil.

LIGHTS AND MARKS
St Anthony Hd lt (H24), R sector covers the Manacles Rks.

RADIO TELEPHONE
Call: *Falmouth Hbr Radio*, VHF Ch 12 16 (Mon-Fri 0800-
1700LT); Hbr launch *Killigrew* Ch 12. Customs launch
Curlew Ch 12 16. Port Pendennis Marina, Royal Cornwall
YC, Falmouth Marina and Mylor Yacht Hbr: Ch 80, M (H24).
Visitors Yacht Haven Ch 12 16. Malpas Marine and St
Mawes SC: Ch M (HO). Fuel Barge Ch 16. Falmouth CG
Ch 16 67 provides radio coverage of the TSS/ITZ off Land's
End; see 8.1.2. Pendennis Radio Ch 62 (Link calls).

TELEPHONE
(Dial code Falmouth 01326; Truro 01872)
Hr Mr Falmouth 312285/314379, 🖷 211352; Hr Mr Penryn
373352; Hr Mr St Mawes 270553; MRCC 317575; ⌗ 0345
231110 (H24); Marinecall 0891 500458; Weather 42534;
Police 0990 777444; Dr 317317; Ⓗ Truro 274242.

FACILITIES
FALMOUTH
Port Pendennis Marina ☎ 311113, 🖷 313344, £18.00, AC,
FW, ⚓s, YC (R, Bar, Ⓞ, CH); outer marina, see SHELTER
Falmouth Hbr Visitors Yacht Haven (50) ☎ 312285 (Apr-
Sept inc), 🖷 211352, £11.50, P, D, FW, Access H24. About
300m E of Yacht Haven in 6m is a Visitors' ⚓age, £4.75.
Falmouth Yacht Marina (280+20 ⓥ), ☎ 316620, 🖷
313939, £18.80, AC, FW, CH, V, P (cans), D, ME, EI, Sh, Ⓞ,
BH (30 ton), C (2 ton), Gas, Gaz, SM, Bar, R; access H24,
but *least depths of 1·4m require caution at LWS*. A pipe-
line/sill drying 1·8m bisects the marina E/W.
Services: Slip, BH (60 ton), C (48 ton), ME, Sh, EI, M, SM,
Gaz, CH, ACA, FW. Fuel Barge, D only, as chartlet, Ch 16.
Town V, R, Bar, ✉, Ⓑ, ⇌, ✈ (Plymouth or Newquay).
PENRYN/FLUSHING (01326)
Challenger Marine ☎ 377222, 🖷 377800, 46 pontoon
berths, access HW±3.
Services: M, FW, P & D (cans, 500m), Slip, EI, ME, C (12
ton), Sh, SM, ACA, BY, CH.
MYLOR (01326)
Mylor Yacht Hbr (250+20 visitors) ☎ 372121, 🖷 372120,
BH (25 ton), CH, Gas, Gaz, AC, FW, Slip, C (4 ton), Sh, ME,
EI, Ⓔ, V, D, R, Bar, Ⓞ, Access HW±1.
RESTRONGUET (01326)
Restronguet Yacht Basin ☎ 373613, Slip, M, Sh; **Pandora
Inn** ☎ 372678, V, R, Bar, pontoon dries 1·9m.
Services: Ⓔ, CH, Gas, Gaz.
ST MAWES (01326)
Inner Hbr FW, Slip. **Services**: M, ⚓s (contact SC), BY, ME,
Sh, EI, SM, Gas.
MALPAS/TRURO (01872)
Bar Creek Yacht Stn ☎ 73919, M; **Malpas Marine** ☎ 71260,
M, CH, ME, EI, Sh, access H24 except LWS±1.
Services: CH, Gas. Hbr dues are levied by Truro for ⚓ing.
YACHT CLUBS
Port of Falmouth Sailing Association ☎ 211555; Royal
Cornwall YC ☎ 311105/312126 (Sec'y), M, Slip, FW, R, Bar;
Falmouth Town SC ☎ 377061; Flushing SC ☎ 374043;
Mylor YC ☎ 374391, Bar; Restronguet SC ☎ 374536; St
Mawes SC ☎ 270686.

ENGLAND – FALMOUTH

LAT 50°09′N   LONG 5°03′W

TIMES AND HEIGHTS OF HIGH AND LOW WATERS

YEAR **1999**

TIME ZONE (UT)
For Summer Time add ONE hour in non-shaded areas

JANUARY

Day	Time	m	Day	Time	m
1 F	0413 / 1057 / 1639 / 2320	5.3 / 0.9 / 5.3 / 0.8	**16** SA	0415 / 1047 / 1635 / 2306	5.0 / 1.4 / 4.9 / 1.3
2 SA O	0502 / 1148 / 1728	5.5 / 0.7 / 5.4	**17** SU ●	0456 / 1130 / 1717 / 2347	5.2 / 1.2 / 5.0 / 1.1
3 SU	0009 / 0549 / 1235 / 1818	0.7 / 5.6 / 0.6 / 5.3	**18** M	0537 / 1212 / 1800	5.3 / 1.0 / 5.1
4 M	0054 / 0636 / 1320 / 1906	0.7 / 5.6 / 0.6 / 5.3	**19** TU	0028 / 0619 / 1253 / 1842	1.0 / 5.3 / 0.9 / 5.1
5 TU	0137 / 0722 / 1402 / 1950	0.8 / 5.5 / 0.8 / 5.1	**20** W	0107 / 0659 / 1332 / 1923	1.0 / 5.3 / 0.9 / 5.1
6 W	0216 / 0800 / 1441 / 2027	1.0 / 5.3 / 1.0 / 4.9	**21** TH	0145 / 0738 / 1410 / 2002	1.0 / 5.3 / 0.9 / 5.0
7 TH	0253 / 0834 / 1517 / 2058	1.3 / 5.1 / 1.3 / 4.7	**22** F	0222 / 0818 / 1448 / 2041	1.0 / 5.2 / 1.0 / 5.0
8 F	0328 / 0907 / 1554 / 2133	1.5 / 4.9 / 1.5 / 4.5	**23** SA	0301 / 0900 / 1528 / 2127	1.2 / 5.1 / 1.2 / 4.8
9 SA	0406 / 0946 / 1635 / 2217	1.8 / 4.6 / 1.8 / 4.3	**24** SU	0344 / 0948 / 1615 / 2218	1.4 / 4.9 / 1.4 / 4.7
10 SU	0452 / 1036 / 1725 / 2318	2.0 / 4.4 / 2.0 / 4.2	**25** M	0436 / 1046 / 1713 / 2324	1.5 / 4.7 / 1.6 / 4.5
11 M	0550 / 1142 / 1827	2.2 / 4.3 / 2.1	**26** TU	0544 / 1159 / 1830	1.8 / 4.5 / 1.7
12 TU	0032 / 0659 / 1257 / 1935	4.2 / 2.2 / 4.3 / 2.1	**27** W	0040 / 0715 / 1318 / 2000	4.5 / 1.8 / 4.5 / 1.7
13 W	0146 / 0808 / 1430 / 2040	4.4 / 2.1 / 4.4 / 1.9	**28** TH	0157 / 0842 / 1430 / 2116	4.6 / 1.6 / 4.7 / 1.5
14 TH	0244 / 0910 / 1504 / 2135	4.6 / 1.8 / 4.6 / 1.6	**29** F	0303 / 0950 / 1534 / 2217	4.9 / 1.4 / 4.9 / 1.2
15 F	0332 / 1002 / 1552 / 2222	4.8 / 1.5 / 4.8 / 1.5	**30** SA	0359 / 1046 / 1627 / 2309	5.1 / 1.0 / 5.0 / 0.9
			31 SU O	0447 / 1136 / 1715 / 2356	5.3 / 0.8 / 5.2 / 0.7

FEBRUARY

Day	Time	m	Day	Time	m
1 M	0532 / 1223 / 1801	5.4 / 0.6 / 5.2	**16** TU	0516 / 1155 / 1742 ●	5.3 / 0.8 / 5.1
2 TU	0040 / 0618 / 1305 / 1846	0.6 / 5.5 / 0.6 / 5.2	**17** W	0013 / 0559 / 1238 / 1824	0.8 / 5.4 / 0.6 / 5.2
3 W	0120 / 0700 / 1344 / 1925	0.7 / 5.4 / 0.6 / 5.1	**18** TH	0055 / 0643 / 1319 / 1907	0.6 / 5.5 / 0.5 / 5.3
4 TH	0156 / 0734 / 1418 / 1955	0.8 / 5.3 / 0.8 / 5.0	**19** F	0134 / 0725 / 1358 / 1948	0.6 / 5.5 / 0.6 / 5.2
5 F	0228 / 0804 / 1449 / 2022	1.0 / 5.2 / 1.1 / 4.9	**20** SA	0211 / 0805 / 1434 / 2027	0.6 / 5.4 / 0.6 / 5.2
6 SA	0257 / 0833 / 1517 / 2053	1.3 / 5.0 / 1.4 / 4.7	**21** SU	0248 / 0847 / 1512 / 2108	0.8 / 5.2 / 0.9 / 5.0
7 SU	0326 / 0908 / 1546 / 2130	1.5 / 4.8 / 1.6 / 4.5	**22** M	0327 / 0932 / 1553 / 2155	1.1 / 5.0 / 1.2 / 4.8
8 M	0358 / 0948 / 1621 / 2216	1.8 / 4.5 / 1.9 / 4.3	**23** TU	0414 / 1025 / 1645 / 2255	1.4 / 4.7 / 1.5 / 4.5
9 TU	0444 / 1040 / 1718 / 2319	2.0 / 4.3 / 2.1 / 4.2	**24** W	0515 / 1138 / 1755	1.7 / 4.4 / 1.8
10 W	0557 / 1150 / 1835	2.2 / 4.1 / 2.2	**25** TH	0015 / 0645 / 1301 / 1939	4.4 / 1.9 / 4.3 / 1.9
11 TH	0040 / 0714 / 1319 / 1949	4.2 / 2.2 / 4.1 / 2.1	**26** F	0138 / 0830 / 1419 / 2105	4.4 / 1.7 / 4.4 / 1.6
12 F	0205 / 0825 / 1435 / 2055	4.3 / 1.9 / 4.4 / 1.8	**27** SA	0248 / 0940 / 1523 / 2206	4.7 / 1.5 / 4.7 / 1.3
13 SA	0305 / 0928 / 1530 / 2153	4.6 / 1.6 / 4.6 / 1.5	**28** SU	0345 / 1035 / 1616 / 2256	5.0 / 1.1 / 4.9 / 1.0
14 SU	0352 / 1021 / 1616 / 2243	4.9 / 1.4 / 4.8 / 1.2			
15 M	0435 / 1109 / 1659 / 2329	5.1 / 1.0 / 5.0 / 1.0			

MARCH

Day	Time	m	Day	Time	m
1 M	0432 / 1122 / 1700 / 2341	5.2 / 0.7 / 5.1 / 0.7	**16** TU	0410 / 1045 / 1636 / 2307	5.1 / 0.9 / 5.0 / 0.9
2 TU O	0514 / 1205 / 1742	5.3 / 0.6 / 5.2	**17** W ●	0452 / 1133 / 1718 / 2354	5.3 / 0.6 / 5.2 / 0.6
3 W	0022 / 0555 / 1245 / 1820	0.6 / 5.4 / 0.5 / 5.2	**18** TH	0535 / 1218 / 1801	5.5 / 0.4 / 5.3
4 TH	0059 / 0632 / 1320 / 1853	0.6 / 5.4 / 0.6 / 5.2	**19** F	0037 / 0621 / 1301 / 1845	0.4 / 5.6 / 0.3 / 5.4
5 F	0132 / 0705 / 1351 / 1922	0.7 / 5.3 / 0.7 / 5.1	**20** SA	0118 / 0706 / 1341 / 1928	0.3 / 5.6 / 0.3 / 5.4
6 SA	0200 / 0733 / 1418 / 1949	1.0 / 5.2 / 1.0 / 5.0	**21** SU	0157 / 0750 / 1419 / 2008	0.4 / 5.5 / 0.5 / 5.3
7 SU	0226 / 0803 / 1441 / 2019	1.1 / 5.0 / 1.2 / 4.8	**22** M	0234 / 0832 / 1456 / 2050	0.6 / 5.3 / 0.7 / 5.1
8 M	0248 / 0834 / 1501 / 2052	1.4 / 4.8 / 1.5 / 4.6	**23** TU	0314 / 0917 / 1537 / 2135	0.9 / 5.0 / 1.2 / 4.8
9 TU	0310 / 0911 / 1524 / 2132	1.6 / 4.5 / 1.7 / 4.4	**24** W	0359 / 1010 / 1626 / 2233	1.3 / 4.6 / 1.5 / 4.5
10 W	0342 / 0956 / 1604 / 2224	1.9 / 4.3 / 2.0 / 4.2	**25** TH	0458 / 1125 / 1734 / 2357	1.7 / 4.3 / 1.9 / 4.3
11 TH	0447 / 1058 / 1735 / 2338	2.2 / 4.1 / 2.3 / 4.1	**26** F	0629 / 1252 / 1922	1.9 / 4.2 / 2.0
12 F	0629 / 1223 / 1907	2.2 / 4.0 / 2.2	**27** SA	0122 / 0817 / 1407 / 2049	4.3 / 1.8 / 4.3 / 1.7
13 SA	0115 / 0747 / 1404 / 2020	4.2 / 2.0 / 4.2 / 1.9	**28** SU	0232 / 0924 / 1510 / 2148	4.6 / 1.5 / 4.6 / 1.4
14 SU	0232 / 0855 / 1504 / 2123	4.5 / 1.6 / 4.5 / 1.5	**29** M	0327 / 1016 / 1559 / 2236	4.9 / 1.1 / 4.8 / 1.0
15 M	0325 / 0953 / 1552 / 2218	4.8 / 1.3 / 4.8 / 1.2	**30** TU	0412 / 1107 / 1639 / 2319	5.1 / 0.8 / 5.0 / 0.8
			31 W O	0451 / 1142 / 1715 / 2358	5.2 / 0.6 / 5.1 / 0.6

APRIL

Day	Time	m	Day	Time	m
1 TH	0527 / 1220 / 1749	5.3 / 0.6 / 5.2	**16** F ●	0511 / 1154 / 1735	5.5 / 0.3 / 5.4
2 F	0034 / 0601 / 1253 / 1820	0.6 / 5.3 / 0.6 / 5.2	**17** SA	0016 / 0557 / 1240 / 1821	0.3 / 5.6 / 0.2 / 5.5
3 SA	0105 / 0633 / 1322 / 1850	0.7 / 5.2 / 0.8 / 5.1	**18** SU	0100 / 0645 / 1322 / 1907	0.2 / 5.6 / 0.2 / 5.5
4 SU	0132 / 0705 / 1346 / 1920	0.8 / 5.1 / 1.0 / 5.1	**19** M	0141 / 0732 / 1403 / 1951	0.3 / 5.5 / 0.4 / 5.4
5 M	0155 / 0735 / 1407 / 1950	1.0 / 5.0 / 1.2 / 4.9	**20** TU	0222 / 0819 / 1443 / 2033	0.5 / 5.3 / 0.8 / 5.2
6 TU	0217 / 0806 / 1426 / 2021	1.3 / 4.8 / 1.4 / 4.7	**21** W	0304 / 0906 / 1525 / 2119	0.9 / 4.9 / 1.2 / 4.9
7 W	0238 / 0840 / 1450 / 2056	1.5 / 4.5 / 1.6 / 4.5	**22** TH	0350 / 1001 / 1615 / 2216	1.3 / 4.6 / 1.5 / 4.6
8 TH	0309 / 0923 / 1527 / 2145	1.7 / 4.3 / 1.9 / 4.3	**23** F	0449 / 1116 / 1721 / 2340	1.6 / 4.3 / 1.9 / 4.4
9 F	0401 / 1023 / 1634 / 2251	2.0 / 4.1 / 2.2 / 4.2	**24** SA	0613 / 1238 / 1855	1.9 / 4.2 / 2.0
10 SA	0547 / 1140 / 1827	2.1 / 4.0 / 2.2	**25** SU	0101 / 0749 / 1347 / 2020	4.4 / 1.8 / 4.3 / 1.8
11 SU	0012 / 0711 / 1318 / 1945	4.2 / 2.0 / 4.2 / 1.9	**26** M	0207 / 0856 / 1445 / 2119	4.5 / 1.5 / 4.5 / 1.5
12 M	0147 / 0821 / 1431 / 2051	4.4 / 1.6 / 4.5 / 1.5	**27** TU	0300 / 0948 / 1531 / 2208	4.7 / 1.2 / 4.8 / 1.2
13 TU	0250 / 0922 / 1522 / 2149	4.8 / 1.3 / 4.8 / 1.2	**28** W	0345 / 1032 / 1610 / 2250	4.9 / 1.0 / 5.1 / 1.0
14 W	0340 / 1017 / 1608 / 2242	5.1 / 0.9 / 5.1 / 0.8	**29** TH	0423 / 1112 / 1645 / 2329	5.1 / 0.8 / 5.1 / 0.8
15 TH	0425 / 1107 / 1651 / 2330	5.3 / 0.5 / 5.3 / 0.5	**30** F O	0458 / 1149 / 1717	5.1 / 0.8 / 5.1

Chart Datum: 2·91 metres below Ordnance Datum (Newlyn)

ENGLAND – FALMOUTH

LAT 50°09′N   LONG   5°03′W

TIMES AND HEIGHTS OF HIGH AND LOW WATERS

YEAR **1999**

TIME ZONE (UT)
For Summer Time add ONE hour in non-shaded areas

MAY

Date	Day	Time	m	Time	m	Time	m	Time	m
1	SA	0005	0.8	0530	5.1	1223	0.8	1749	5.2
2	SU	0036	0.8	0605	5.1	1251	0.9	1822	5.1
3	M	0104	0.9	0639	5.0	1316	1.1	1854	5.1
4	TU	0129	1.1	0712	4.9	1340	1.2	1926	5.0
5	W	0154	1.3	0744	4.7	1403	1.4	1957	4.8
6	TH	0220	1.5	0819	4.5	1431	1.5	2032	4.6
7	F	0253	1.6	0901	4.3	1509	1.8	2118	4.5
8	SA	0343	1.8	0957	4.2	1609	2.0	2218	4.3
9	SU	0508	1.9	1106	4.1	1746	2.1	2333	4.3
10	M	0634	1.8	1226	4.2	1908	1.9		
11	TU	0052	4.5	0745	1.5	1346	4.5	2016	1.5
12	W	0207	4.7	0849	1.3	1447	4.8	2118	1.2
13	TH	0307	5.0	0947	0.9	1538	5.1	2214	0.9
14	F	0358	5.3	1040	0.6	1625	5.4	2306	0.6
15	SA ●	0446	5.4	1130	0.4	1711	5.5	2354	0.3
16	SU	0535	5.5	1218	0.3	1759	5.6		
17	M	0042	0.3	0626	5.5	1304	0.3	1847	5.6
18	TU	0127	0.3	0717	5.4	1348	0.5	1934	5.5
19	W	0211	0.5	0806	5.2	1432	0.8	2020	5.3
20	TH	0256	0.8	0857	4.9	1516	1.2	2107	5.0
21	F	0343	1.2	0953	4.6	1605	1.5	2201	4.7
22	SA	0438	1.5	1100	4.4	1702	1.8	2314	4.5
23	SU	0545	1.7	1211	4.2	1814	1.9		
24	M	0028	4.4	0703	1.7	1314	4.3	1932	1.9
25	TU	0132	4.4	0814	1.6	1408	4.4	2037	1.7
26	W	0224	4.6	0909	1.5	1455	4.6	2130	1.5
27	TH	0311	4.7	0956	1.3	1537	4.8	2216	1.3
28	F	0351	4.8	1038	1.1	1613	4.9	2256	1.1
29	SA	0427	4.9	1116	1.0	1647	5.0	2333	1.0
30	SU O	0503	5.0	1151	1.0	1721	5.1		
31	M	0007	1.0	0539	5.0	1222	1.1	1758	5.1

JUNE

Date	Day	Time	m	Time	m	Time	m	Time	m
1	TU	0038	1.1	0618	4.9	1251	1.1	1833	5.1
2	W	0108	1.1	0655	4.8	1320	1.2	1908	5.0
3	TH	0138	1.2	0731	4.7	1350	1.4	1941	4.9
4	F	0210	1.4	0806	4.6	1423	1.5	2017	4.8
5	SA	0247	1.5	0847	4.5	1503	1.6	2100	4.7
6	SU	0334	1.5	0937	4.4	1555	1.7	2154	4.6
7	M	0437	1.6	1038	4.3	1705	1.8	2259	4.5
8	TU	0553	1.6	1149	4.3	1826	1.8		
9	W	0011	4.5	0707	1.5	1302	4.5	1939	1.6
10	TH	0127	4.7	0815	1.3	1410	4.7	2046	1.3
11	F	0235	4.9	0918	1.0	1509	5.0	2147	1.0
12	SA	0333	5.1	1015	0.8	1601	5.2	2243	0.7
13	SU ●	0426	5.3	1109	0.6	1650	5.4	2336	0.5
14	M	0517	5.4	1200	0.5	1739	5.5		
15	TU	0026	0.4	0609	5.4	1249	0.5	1830	5.5
16	W	0114	0.4	0704	5.3	1336	0.6	1920	5.5
17	TH	0201	0.5	0755	5.1	1420	0.8	2007	5.3
18	F	0246	0.8	0845	4.9	1504	1.0	2052	5.1
19	SA	0330	1.1	0935	4.7	1548	1.4	2138	4.8
20	SU	0416	1.4	1027	4.5	1635	1.6	2228	4.6
21	M	0507	1.6	1127	4.3	1728	1.8	2334	4.4
22	TU	0606	1.7	1226	4.2	1830	1.9		
23	W	0040	4.3	0711	1.8	1322	4.3	1937	1.9
24	TH	0140	4.4	0816	1.7	1413	4.4	2041	1.7
25	F	0231	4.5	0911	1.5	1459	4.6	2134	1.5
26	SA	0317	4.6	0959	1.4	1540	4.8	2220	1.4
27	SU	0359	4.7	1041	1.3	1620	4.9	2302	1.3
28	M O	0439	4.8	1119	1.2	1659	5.0	2340	1.2
29	TU	0518	4.9	1156	1.1	1737	5.1		
30	W	0016	1.1	0600	4.9	1231	1.1	1817	5.1

JULY

Date	Day	Time	m	Time	m	Time	m	Time	m
1	TH	0052	1.1	0641	4.9	1306	1.2	1855	5.1
2	F	0127	1.1	0721	4.8	1340	1.2	1931	5.0
3	SA	0202	1.1	0757	4.7	1416	1.3	2006	5.0
4	SU	0240	1.2	0835	4.6	1454	1.4	2046	4.9
5	M	0321	1.3	0920	4.6	1538	1.5	2134	4.8
6	TU	0410	1.5	1012	4.5	1633	1.5	2231	4.7
7	W	0512	1.5	1116	4.4	1742	1.6	2340	4.6
8	TH	0626	1.5	1227	4.5	1901	1.6		
9	F	0055	4.6	0742	1.5	1339	4.6	2018	1.5
10	SA	0210	4.7	0853	1.3	1445	4.9	2126	1.2
11	SU	0315	4.9	0956	1.0	1542	5.1	2227	0.9
12	M	0411	5.1	1053	0.8	1634	5.3	2322	0.7
13	TU ●	0503	5.2	1146	0.6	1723	5.4		
14	W	0013	0.5	0555	5.3	1236	0.5	1815	5.5
15	TH	0102	0.4	0648	5.2	1322	0.6	1904	5.5
16	F	0147	0.5	0738	5.1	1405	0.7	1950	5.4
17	SA	0229	0.7	0823	5.0	1445	0.9	2028	5.2
18	SU	0308	0.9	0902	4.8	1522	1.2	2102	4.9
19	M	0346	1.2	0937	4.6	1600	1.5	2136	4.7
20	TU	0425	1.5	1013	4.4	1642	1.7	2216	4.5
21	W	0510	1.8	1103	4.2	1733	1.9	2313	4.3
22	TH	0606	1.9	1210	4.2	1835	2.1		
23	F	0029	4.2	0710	2.0	1321	4.2	1942	2.0
24	SA	0147	4.2	0817	1.9	1422	4.4	2048	1.8
25	SU	0246	4.4	0916	1.6	1512	4.6	2144	1.5
26	M	0335	4.6	1007	1.5	1557	4.9	2232	1.4
27	TU	0418	4.8	1051	1.3	1638	5.0	2315	1.2
28	W O	0500	4.9	1133	1.2	1718	5.1	2357	1.0
29	TH	0542	4.9	1214	1.1	1759	5.2		
30	F	0036	0.9	0625	5.0	1252	1.0	1840	5.2
31	SA	0114	0.9	0706	4.9	1329	1.0	1918	5.2

AUGUST

Date	Day	Time	m	Time	m	Time	m	Time	m
1	SU	0151	0.9	0744	4.9	1405	1.0	1955	5.1
2	M	0227	0.9	0822	4.9	1441	1.1	2033	5.1
3	TU	0304	1.1	0902	4.8	1520	1.2	2116	4.9
4	W	0346	1.3	0949	4.7	1607	1.5	2207	4.7
5	TH	0438	1.5	1046	4.5	1706	1.6	2313	4.5
6	F	0548	1.6	1159	4.4	1827	1.7		
7	SA	0032	4.4	0714	1.7	1317	4.5	1958	1.6
8	SU	0155	4.5	0837	1.5	1428	4.7	2114	1.4
9	M	0303	4.7	0945	1.3	1529	5.0	2217	1.1
10	TU	0400	5.0	1043	0.9	1621	5.2	2311	0.8
11	W ●	0451	5.1	1134	0.7	1710	5.4		
12	TH	0000	0.5	0539	5.2	1221	0.6	1756	5.5
13	F	0046	0.5	0628	5.2	1305	0.5	1842	5.5
14	SA	0128	0.5	0713	5.2	1344	0.6	1923	5.4
15	SU	0206	0.6	0751	5.1	1419	0.8	1956	5.2
16	M	0239	0.9	0820	4.9	1451	1.1	2023	5.0
17	TU	0310	1.2	0847	4.7	1522	1.4	2052	4.8
18	W	0340	1.5	0919	4.5	1554	1.7	2129	4.5
19	TH	0414	1.8	1001	4.3	1636	2.0	2214	4.3
20	F	0503	2.1	1057	4.2	1739	2.2	2318	4.1
21	SA	0615	2.2	1215	4.1	1854	2.2		
22	SU	0054	4.1	0729	2.1	1345	4.3	2006	2.0
23	M	0220	4.2	0838	1.9	1446	4.5	2110	1.7
24	TU	0314	4.5	0936	1.6	1534	4.8	2204	1.5
25	W	0359	4.8	1026	1.4	1617	5.1	2251	1.2
26	TH O	0441	4.9	1111	1.1	1657	5.2	2335	0.9
27	F	0521	5.1	1154	0.7	1738	5.3		
28	SA	0017	0.8	0604	5.1	1235	0.8	1819	5.4
29	SU	0057	0.7	0646	5.2	1313	0.7	1900	5.4
30	M	0134	0.6	0726	5.2	1349	0.7	1939	5.3
31	TU	0210	0.7	0804	5.1	1425	0.9	2019	5.2

Chart Datum: 2·91 metres below Ordnance Datum (Newlyn)

ENGLAND – FALMOUTH

LAT 50°09′N   LONG 5°03′W

TIMES AND HEIGHTS OF HIGH AND LOW WATERS

YEAR **1999**

TIME ZONE (UT)
For Summer Time add ONE hour in non-shaded areas

SEPTEMBER

Day	Time / m	Day	Time / m
1 W	0246 0.9 / 0844 5.0 / 1503 1.1 / 2059 5.0	16 TH	0254 1.5 / 0838 4.7 / 1506 1.6 / 2050 4.6
2 TH	0325 1.2 / 0928 4.8 / 1546 1.4 / 2148 4.7	17 F	0314 1.8 / 0916 4.5 / 1533 2.0 / 2133 4.3
3 F	0413 1.5 / 1023 4.6 / 1642 1.7 / 2253 4.5	18 SA	0345 2.1 / 1007 4.3 / 1630 2.3 / 2230 4.1
4 SA	0518 1.8 / 1137 4.4 / 1804 1.9	19 SU	0511 2.4 / 1117 4.1 / 1811 2.4 / 2355 4.0
5 SU	0021 4.3 / 0657 1.9 / 1302 4.4 / 1951 1.8	20 M	0648 2.4 / 1259 4.2 / 1930 2.2
6 M	0148 4.4 / 0831 1.7 / 1418 4.7 / 2109 1.5	21 TU	0153 4.2 / 0803 2.1 / 1418 4.5 / 2038 1.8
7 TU	0258 4.6 / 0938 1.4 / 1519 5.0 / 2208 1.2	22 W	0251 4.5 / 0906 1.7 / 1509 4.8 / 2135 1.5
8 W	0354 4.9 / 1031 1.1 / 1609 5.2 / 2258 0.8	23 TH	0337 4.8 / 0959 1.4 / 1552 5.1 / 2224 1.1
9 TH	0440 5.1 / 1119 0.8 / 1653 5.4 / ● 2343 0.6	24 F	0418 5.0 / 1046 1.1 / 1633 5.3 / 2310 0.8
10 F	0522 5.3 / 1202 0.6 / 1735 5.5	25 SA	0458 5.2 / 1131 0.8 / 1713 5.4 / ○ 2353 0.6
11 SA	0025 0.5 / 0603 5.3 / 1242 0.5 / 1815 5.5	26 SU	0538 5.3 / 1214 0.6 / 1755 5.5
12 SU	0104 0.5 / 0641 5.3 / 1318 0.6 / 1850 5.4	27 M	0035 0.5 / 0621 5.4 / 1254 0.6 / 1839 5.5
13 M	0137 0.7 / 0712 5.2 / 1350 0.8 / 1920 5.2	28 TU	0114 0.5 / 0703 5.4 / 1332 0.6 / 1921 5.5
14 TU	0207 0.9 / 0738 5.0 / 1418 1.1 / 1947 5.1	29 W	0152 0.6 / 0743 5.3 / 1410 0.8 / 2003 5.3
15 W	0232 1.2 / 0806 4.9 / 1443 1.4 / 2017 4.8	30 TH	0229 0.9 / 0825 5.2 / 1448 1.0 / 2046 5.1

OCTOBER

Day	Time / m	Day	Time / m
1 F	0308 1.2 / 0910 5.0 / 1532 1.4 / 2136 4.7	16 SA	0232 1.8 / 0841 4.6 / 1452 1.9 / 2100 4.4
2 SA	0355 1.6 / 1004 4.7 / 1628 1.7 / 2242 4.4	17 SU	0303 2.1 / 0929 4.4 / 1535 2.2 / 2156 4.1
3 SU	0501 2.0 / 1121 4.4 / 1755 2.0	18 M	0357 2.4 / 1032 4.2 / 1722 2.4 / 2311 4.0
4 M	0016 4.2 / 0648 2.1 / 1251 4.4 / 1945 1.9	19 TU	0604 2.5 / 1154 4.2 / 1852 2.3
5 TU	0144 4.4 / 0821 1.9 / 1407 4.6 / 2057 1.5	20 W	0105 4.1 / 0726 2.2 / 1334 4.5 / 2002 1.9
6 W	0250 4.7 / 0923 1.5 / 1506 5.0 / 2152 1.2	21 TH	0219 4.5 / 0832 1.8 / 1434 4.8 / 2102 1.5
7 TH	0341 4.9 / 1013 1.2 / 1553 5.2 / 2238 0.9	22 F	0308 4.8 / 0928 1.5 / 1521 5.1 / 2154 1.1
8 F	0422 5.2 / 1058 0.9 / 1634 5.4 / 2321 0.7	23 SA	0351 5.1 / 1018 1.1 / 1605 5.3 / 2242 0.8
9 SA	0500 5.3 / 1139 0.7 / 1711 5.4 / ●	24 SU	0432 5.3 / 1105 0.8 / 1647 5.4 / ○ 2328 0.6
10 SU	0000 0.6 / 0534 5.3 / 1217 0.7 / 1746 5.4	25 M	0512 5.5 / 1150 0.6 / 1730 5.6
11 M	0036 0.7 / 0607 5.3 / 1250 0.8 / 1818 5.4	26 TU	0012 0.5 / 0556 5.6 / 1234 0.5 / 1817 5.6
12 TU	0107 0.8 / 0636 5.3 / 1320 0.9 / 1846 5.2	27 W	0055 0.5 / 0641 5.6 / 1316 0.5 / 1903 5.6
13 W	0133 1.0 / 0704 5.2 / 1345 1.2 / 1915 5.1	28 TH	0135 0.6 / 0725 5.5 / 1357 0.7 / 1949 5.4
14 TH	0155 1.3 / 0733 5.0 / 1408 1.4 / 1947 4.9	29 F	0215 0.9 / 0809 5.4 / 1439 1.0 / 2035 5.1
15 F	0214 1.5 / 0805 4.8 / 1428 1.6 / 2020 4.6	30 SA	0257 1.3 / 0856 5.1 / 1525 1.4 / 2129 4.8
		31 SU	0346 1.6 / 0952 4.8 / 1622 1.7 / 2237 4.4

NOVEMBER

Day	Time / m	Day	Time / m
1 M	0451 2.0 / 1106 4.6 / 1744 2.0	16 TU	0333 2.2 / 0958 4.4 / 1630 2.2 / 2235 4.2
2 TU	0008 4.3 / 0627 2.2 / 1233 4.5 / 1922 1.9	17 W	0505 2.4 / 1107 4.4 / 1806 2.2 / 2356 4.2
3 W	0126 4.4 / 0755 2.0 / 1345 4.7 / 2032 1.6	18 TH	0640 2.2 / 1227 4.5 / 1921 1.9
4 TH	0227 4.6 / 0857 1.6 / 1442 4.9 / 2126 1.4	19 F	0126 4.4 / 0752 1.9 / 1345 4.7 / 2025 1.5
5 F	0317 4.9 / 0947 1.4 / 1529 5.1 / 2212 1.1	20 SA	0228 4.7 / 0853 1.5 / 1444 5.0 / 2122 1.2
6 SA	0358 5.1 / 1031 1.1 / 1609 5.2 / 2254 0.9	21 SU	0318 5.1 / 0949 1.2 / 1535 5.3 / 2214 0.9
7 SU	0433 5.2 / 1112 0.9 / 1644 5.3 / 2331 0.9	22 M	0404 5.3 / 1040 0.8 / 1622 5.5 / 2303 0.7
8 M	0506 5.3 / 1148 0.9 / 1716 5.3 / ●	23 TU	0448 5.5 / 1128 0.7 / 1710 5.6 / ○ 2351 0.5
9 TU	0006 0.9 / 0535 5.3 / 1222 1.0 / 1748 5.3	24 W	0533 5.6 / 1216 0.5 / 1758 5.6
10 W	0036 1.0 / 0606 5.3 / 1251 1.1 / 1820 5.2	25 TH	0037 0.5 / 0621 5.7 / 1302 0.6 / 1848 5.5
11 TH	0102 1.2 / 0638 5.2 / 1318 1.3 / 1852 5.0	26 F	0122 0.7 / 0709 5.6 / 1347 0.7 / 1938 5.4
12 F	0126 1.4 / 0709 5.1 / 1342 1.5 / 1925 4.9	27 SA	0206 0.9 / 0757 5.5 / 1433 1.0 / 2028 5.1
13 SA	0148 1.5 / 0742 5.0 / 1406 1.6 / 1959 4.7	28 SU	0251 1.2 / 0846 5.2 / 1520 1.3 / 2122 4.8
14 SU	0211 1.7 / 0818 4.8 / 1435 1.8 / 2038 4.5	29 M	0339 1.5 / 0940 5.0 / 1614 1.5 / 2211 4.5
15 M	0244 1.9 / 0901 4.6 / 1517 2.0 / 2130 4.3	30 TU	0435 1.8 / 1045 4.7 / 1718 1.8 / 2342 4.4

DECEMBER

Day	Time / m	Day	Time / m
1 W	0546 2.1 / 1202 4.6 / 1836 1.9	16 TH	0420 2.0 / 1030 4.6 / 1711 1.9 / 2311 4.3
2 TH	0051 4.4 / 0708 2.1 / 1309 4.6 / 1951 1.8	17 F	0542 2.1 / 1139 4.5 / 1831 1.9
3 F	0150 4.5 / 0818 1.9 / 1406 4.7 / 2050 1.6	18 SA	0024 4.4 / 0705 1.9 / 1251 4.6 / 1944 1.6
4 SA	0242 4.7 / 0913 1.6 / 1456 4.8 / 2139 1.5	19 SU	0139 4.6 / 0816 1.7 / 1404 4.8 / 2049 1.4
5 SU	0325 4.9 / 1000 1.4 / 1539 4.9 / 2223 1.3	20 M	0243 4.9 / 0920 1.4 / 1506 5.1 / 2148 1.1
6 M	0403 5.1 / 1042 1.3 / 1616 5.0 / 2302 1.2	21 TU	0339 5.2 / 1017 1.1 / 1601 5.3 / 2242 0.9
7 TU	0437 5.2 / 1120 1.2 / 1650 5.1 / ● 2337 1.1	22 W	0427 5.4 / 1110 0.8 / 1652 5.4 / ○ 2333 0.7
8 W	0510 5.2 / 1155 1.2 / 1724 5.1	23 TH	0515 5.6 / 1201 0.6 / 1744 5.5
9 TH	0009 1.2 / 0543 5.1 / 1227 1.2 / 1800 5.1	24 F	0023 0.6 / 0605 5.7 / 1251 0.5 / 1836 5.5
10 F	0038 1.3 / 0619 5.2 / 1257 1.3 / 1836 5.0	25 SA	0111 0.6 / 0656 5.7 / 1339 0.6 / 1929 5.4
11 SA	0105 1.4 / 0653 5.2 / 1326 1.4 / 1912 4.9	26 SU	0157 0.8 / 0747 5.6 / 1425 0.8 / 2019 5.2
12 SU	0133 1.5 / 0728 5.0 / 1356 1.5 / 1948 4.8	27 M	0241 1.0 / 0834 5.4 / 1509 1.0 / 2108 5.0
13 M	0203 1.5 / 0802 4.9 / 1428 1.6 / 2025 4.6	28 TU	0325 1.3 / 0921 5.1 / 1554 1.3 / 2159 4.7
14 TU	0237 1.7 / 0841 4.8 / 1508 1.7 / 2110 4.5	29 W	0410 1.5 / 1011 4.8 / 1642 1.6 / 2255 4.5
15 W	0321 1.9 / 0931 4.6 / 1559 1.9 / 2205 4.4	30 TH	0500 1.8 / 1110 4.6 / 1737 1.8 / 2358 4.3
		31 F	0601 2.0 / 1216 4.4 / 1844 2.0

Chart Datum: 2·91 metres below Ordnance Datum (Newlyn)

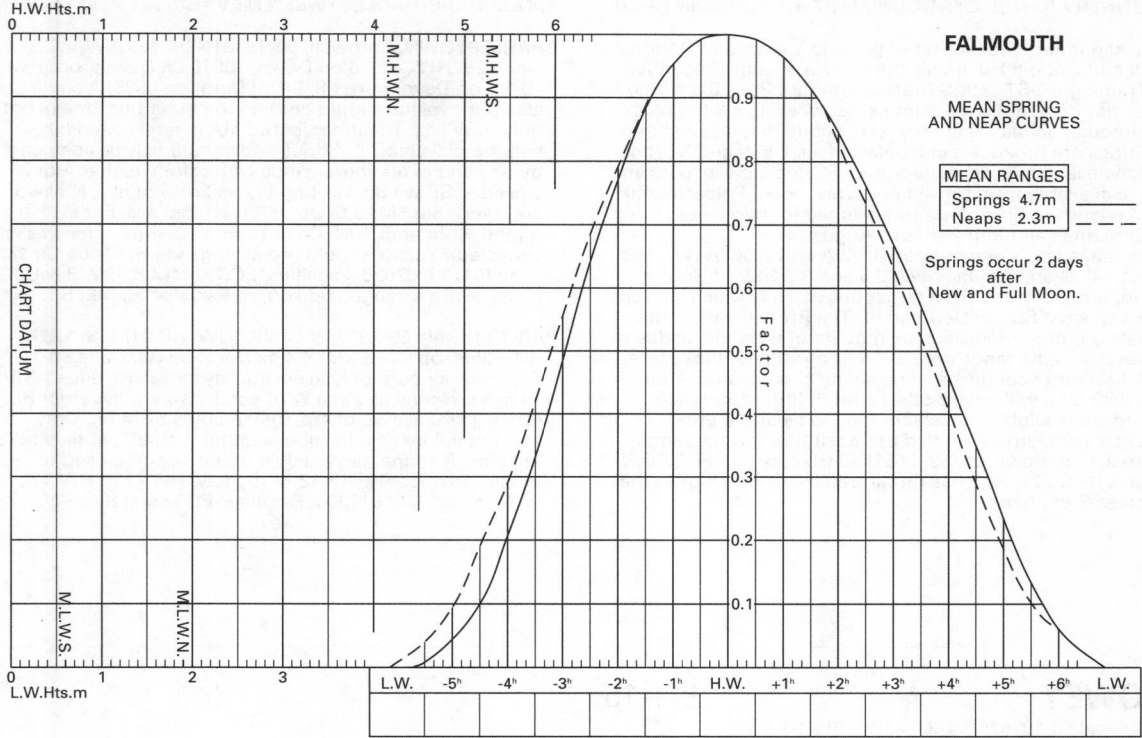

FALMOUTH

MEAN SPRING
AND NEAP CURVES

MEAN RANGES	
Springs	4.7m
Neaps	2.3m

Springs occur 2 days
after
New and Full Moon.

OTHER HARBOURS AND ANCHORAGES BETWEEN ST ANTHONY HEAD AND MEVAGISSEY

PORTSCATHO, Cornwall, 50°10´·80N 04°58´·25W. AC *154*. HW −0600 on Dover, HW −0025 and −0·2m on Devonport; ML 3·0m; Duration 0550. Small drying hbr, but in settled weather and off-shore winds ⚓ outside moorings in good holding. No Its. Hr Mr ☎ (01872) 580616. Facilities: V, FW, R, Bar, Slip, P & D (cans), Ⓑ 1000-1230 Mon, Wed, Fri, ✉.

GORRAN HAVEN, Cornwall, 50°14´·45N 04°47´·09W. AC 148, *1267*. HW −0600 on Dover, HW −0010 and −0·1m on Devonport. Shelter good with flat sand beach for drying out in off-shore wind; good ⚓ 100 to 500m E of harbour. Beware Gwineas Rk and Yaw Rk marked by ECM. Beware pot markers on appr. Not suitable ⚓ when wind is in E. Fin keelers without legs should not ⚓ closer than 300m from hbr wall where depth is 1·8m at MLWS. Facilities: ✉, V, Bar, P & D (cans, 1M), R.

PORTMELLON, Cornwall, 50°15´·70N 04°46´·91W. AC 148, *1267*. HW −0600 on Dover, HW −0010 and −0·1m on Devonport; ML 3·1m; Duration 0600. Shelter good but only suitable as a temp ⚓ in settled weather and off-shore winds. There are no Its and few facilities.

MEVAGISSEY   8-1-14

Cornwall 50°16´·12N 04°46´·86W   Rtg 3-3-1

CHARTS
AC 147, 148, *1267*; Imray C6; Stanfords 13; OS 204
TIDES
−0600 Dover; ML 3·1; Duration 0600; Zone 0 (UT)

Standard Port DEVONPORT (→)

Times				Height (metres)			
High Water		Low Water		MHWS	MHWN	MLWN	MLWS
0000	0600	0000	0600	5·5	4·4	2·2	0·8
1200	1800	1200	1800				
Differences MEVAGISSEY							
−0015	−0020	−0010	−0005	−0·1	−0·1	−0·2	−0·1

SHELTER (MEVAGISSEY continued)
Exposed to E'lies, but available at all states of the tide. Dangerous to appr in strong SE'lies. ♥ berth on S Quay in about 1·6m (D available). Bilge keelers/cats may dry out on sandy beach, SE side of W Quay. One ⚓ in Outer hbr on request to Hr Mr. ⚓ inside the hbr is prohib due to over-crowding and many FVs. ⚓ outside the S Pier is only advised in settled weather with no E in the wind. Inner hbr (dries 1·5m) is reserved for FVs, unless taking on FW.
NAVIGATION
WPT 50°16´·11N 04°46´·54W, 090°/270° from/to pier hd lt, 0·20M. Beware rky ledges off the N Quay. Hbr ent is 46m wide. Speed limit in the hbr is 3kn. Beware FVs.
LIGHTS AND MARKS
S Quay Fl (2) 10s 9m 12M, Dia 30s (fishing).
RADIO TELEPHONE
Hr Mr VHF Ch 16 14 (Summer 0900-2100LT. Winter 0900-1700LT); call on 16 for berth.
TELEPHONE (Dial code 01726)
Hr Mr 843305, (home 842496); MRSC (01803) 882704; ⌗ 0345 231110 (H24); Marinecall 0891 500458; Police 842262; Dr 843701.
FACILITIES
Outer Hbr AB (S Quay) £5, M, FW, D; **Inner Hbr** Slip, FW, C (1 ton). **Services:** BY, Sh (wood), CH, ♿. **Village** EC Thurs; V, R, ▣, Gas, Bar, Ice, ✉, Ⓑ (June-Sept 1000-1430, Oct-June 1000-1300), ⇌ (bus to St Austell), ✈ Newquay.

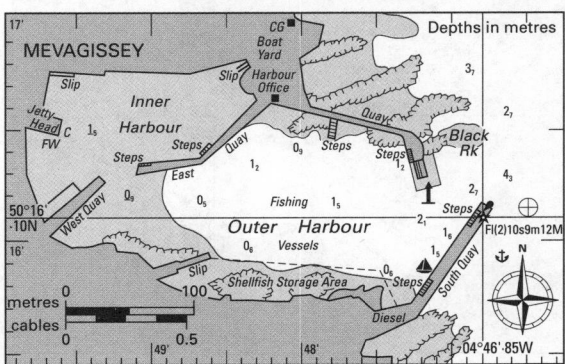

Depths in metres

GUNNERY RANGE OFF DODMAN PT AND GRIBBIN HEAD

Naval gunnery practice takes place to seaward of Dodman Pt and Gribbin Hd, under the control of Flag Officer Sea Training (FOST), HMS Drake, Plymouth PL2 2BG. Firing is by day only, approx 1-2 times per week, in a 2 hrs block, although actual firing only lasts about 15 mins. Planned firings are broadcast in Gunfacts (see 6.5.2) and Navtex. Advance details are also printed in local newspapers and are available from Hr Mrs at Fowey, Looe, Polperro and Mevagissey. Firings are not planned for two weeks over Christmas and four weeks in August.

The range is in danger areas D.006A and D.007A & B (see 8.1.18). Warships, between 2·5 and 9M SSE of Gribbin Hd, fire WSW at 3 SPM target buoys, Fl Y, which lie from 2·4 to 4·8M SSE of Dodman Pt. The RN will ensure that safety requirements can be met; if not possible, ie due to vessels in the range area, then firing will not take place. A helicopter conducts range safety surveillance. A range safety boat will advise other craft of firings and may suggest a slight course alteration to clear the area. Yachts are legally entitled to transit through the range area. For info ☎ (01752) 5557550 (H24) or call *FOST OPS* on VHF Ch 74, which is monitored by all warships in the areas S of Plymouth.

MINOR HARBOURS BETWEEN MEVAGISSEY AND FOWEY

CHARLESTOWN, Cornwall, 50°19′·81N 04°45′·28W. AC 31, 148, *1267*. HW −0555 on Dover, −0010 on Devonport; HW −0·1m on Devonport; ML 3·1m; Duration 0605. A china clay port; yachts should berth in the outer hbr (dries), but only in W'lies. The inner locked hbr is rarely used by commercial ships. Ent dries and should only be attempted by day and in off-shore winds with calm weather. Hbr is closed in SE winds. Waiting buoys 2ca S of hbr. N bkwtr 2FG (vert) 5m 1M; S bkwtr 2FR (vert) 5m 1M. Ent sig: ® (night) = hbr shut. VHF Ch14 16 (HW −2, only when vessel expected). Yachts should pre-arrange via Hr Mr on Ch 14 or ☎ (01726) 67526. Facilities: EC Thurs; AB, FW, P & D (cans or pre-arranged tanker), R, Bar, V at ✉, ME, Sh.

PAR, Cornwall, 50°20′·58N 04°42′·00W. AC 31, 148, *1267*. HW −0555 on Dover; ML 3·1m; Duration 0605. See 8.1.15. A china clay port, only in emergency for yachts; dries 1·2m. 4 chys are conspic 2½ca W of ent. Beware Killyvarder Rk (dries 2·4m) 3ca SE of ent, marked by a SHM bn. Only attempt ent by day, in calm weather with off-shore winds. Ent sigs: R shape (day) or ® lt (night) = port closed or vessel leaving. VHF Ch 12 16 (by day, HW −2 to HW +1). Hr Mr ☎ (01726) 817300. Facilities: EC Thurs; Bar, FW.

FOWEY   8-1-15

Cornwall 50°19′·62N 04°38′·47W   Rtg 1-2-1

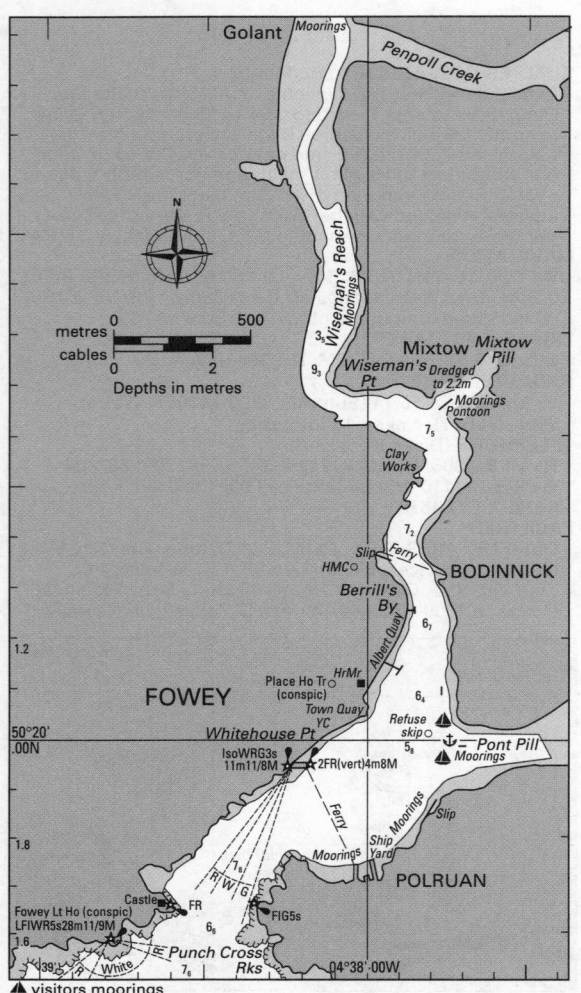

▲ visitors moorings

CHARTS
AC 31, 148, *1267*; Imray C6, Y52; Stanfords 13; OS 204

TIDES
−0540 Dover; ML 2·9; Duration 0605; Zone 0 (UT)

Standard Port DEVONPORT (→)

Times				Height (metres)			
High Water		Low Water		MHWS	MHWN	MLWN	MLWS
0000	0600	0000	0600	5·5	4·4	2·2	0·8
1200	1800	1200	1800				
Differences FOWEY							
−0010	−0015	−0010	−0005	−0·1	−0·1	−0·2	−0·2
LOSTWITHIEL							
+0005	−0010	Dries		−4·1	−4·1	Dries	
PAR							
−0005	−0015	0000	−0010	−0·4	−0·4	−0·4	−0·2

SHELTER
Good, but exposed to winds from S to SW. Gales from these directions can cause heavy swell in the lower hbr and confused seas, especially on the ebb. Entry at any tide in any conditions. Speed limit 6kn. All ⚓s are White and marked 'FHC VISITORS'. Dues £7.70 for a 30′/9m boat overnight. Pontoons are in situ May-Oct. Craft >12·5m LOA should berth/moor as directed by Hr Mr. **Pont Pill**, on the E side, offers double-berth fore and aft ⚓s and AB in 2m on a 120′ floating pontoon; there is also a refuse barge and fuel barge. Opposite Albert Quay, on the E side of the chan there is a line of single swinging ⚓s and another 120′ pontoon.

At **Albert Quay** the 'T' shaped landing pontoon is for short stay (2 hrs), plus FW. A second short stay (2 hrs) landing pontoon is 250m up-river, at Berrills BY.

At **Mixtow Pill** (5ca upriver) is a quieter 120′ pontoon in 2·2m, but only 60′ for ⚓. A ⚓ is 30m N of Wiseman's Pt.

NAVIGATION
WPT 50°19′·30N 04°38′·73W, 207°/027° from/to Whitehouse Pt lt, Iso WRG 3s, 0·72M. Appr in W sector of Fowey lt ho. W sector of Whitehouse Pt lt leads 027° through hbr ent. 3M E of ent beware Udder Rk marked by unlit SCM buoy. From SW beware Cannis Rk (4ca SE of Gribbin Hd) with SCM buoy, Q (6) + L Fl 15s. Entering hbr, keep well clear of Punch Cross Rks to stbd. Caution: Fowey is a busy commercial clay port. Unmarked chan is navigable up to Golant, but moorings restrict ⚓ space. Lerryn (1·6M) and Lostwithiel (3M) are accessible on the tide by shoal draft.

FOWEY continued

LIGHTS AND MARKS
An unlit RW tr 33m on Gribbin Hd (1·3M WSW of hbr ent) is conspic from all sea directions, as is a white house 3ca E of hbr ent. Lt ho is conspic, L Fl WR 5s 28m 11/9M, R284°-295°, W295°-028°, R028°-054°. Whitehouse Pt Iso WRG 3s 11m 11/8M, G017°-022°, W022°-032°, R032°-037°. Ent is marked by Lamp Rk SHM bn Fl G 5s 7m 2M, vis 088°-205°, and St Catherine's Pt FR 15m 2M, vis 150°-295°.

RADIO TELEPHONE
Call *Fowey Hbr Radio* Ch **12** 11 16 (HO). Hbr Patrol (0900-2000LT) Ch 12 16. *Fowey Refueller* Ch 10 16. Water taxi Ch 06. Pilots Ch 09. Tugs Ch 09.

TELEPHONE (Dial code 01726)
Hr Mr 832471, 🕾 833738; MRSC (01803) 882704; Marinecall 0891 500458; ⌗ 0345 231110 (H24); Police 72313; 🄷 832241; Dr 832451; Fowey Refueller 833055/(0836) 519341 (mobile).

FACILITIES
Albert Quay Pontoon L, FW; **Polruan Quay** Slip, P, D, L, FW, C (3 ton); **Royal Fowey YC** 🕿 832245, FW, Showers, R, Bar; **Fowey Gallants SC** 🕿 832335, Showers, Bar; **Fowey Refueller** (0900-1800LT daily; winter Mon-Fri) VHF Ch 10, 16 or 🕿 as above, D. **Services:** M, FW, Gas, Gaz, CH, ACA, Ⓔ, BY, Slip, ME, El, Sh, C (7 ton); FW, ⚓, oils disposal and ⬚ access at Berrills BY pontoon, 250m N of Albert Quay.
Town EC Wed & Sat; ✉, Ⓑ, ⇌ (bus to Par), ✈ (Newquay).

KEEPING FOWEY HARBOUR CLEAN
The Harbour Authority actively campaigns against all forms of pollution in the Harbour and estuary so as to protect and preserve the environment for both humans and wildlife. There are many species of birds, some protected, and the water supports a variety of fish and shellfish.
Yachtsmen are encouraged to use shore-side toilets and/or holding tanks and the sewage pump-out facilities at Berrill's Yard. Rubbish should be ditched in the skip on the refuse pontoon or taken ashore. Waste oils and rags must be disposed of in sealed containers.
Noise is an ever-increasing nuisance, whether caused by slapping halyards, blaring radios or noisy outboards being used in a thoughtless manner – often with the additional disturbance from wash.

MINOR HARBOUR BETWEEN FOWEY AND LOOE

POLPERRO, Cornwall, 50°19'·74N 04°30'·72W. AC 148, *1267*. HW −0554 on Dover; HW −0007 and −0·2m on Devonport; ML 3·1m; Duration 068. Shelter good, but hbr dries about 2m. There is 3·3m at MHWS and 2·5m at MHWN. The ent is 9·8m wide (closed by gate in bad weather). AB on N quay or pick up a buoy; also temp buoys outside hbr. Beware The Ranneys to W of ent, and the rks to E. Lights: Iso WR 6s 30m 7M at Spy House Pt CG Stn, vis W288°-060°, R060°-288°. Tidal Basin, W pier hd FW 4m 4M on post; shows FR when hbr closed. Dir FW (occas) shown from measured distance bns 1M and 2·2M to ENE. Hr Mr on Fish Quay, AB £11; FW on quays. EC Sat.

LOOE   8-1-16

Cornwall 50°21'·00N 04°26'·96W   Rtg 3-3-2

CHARTS
AC 147, 148, *1267*; Imray C6; Stanfords 13; OS 201

TIDES
−0538 Dover; ML 3·0; Duration 0610; Zone 0 (UT)

Standard Port DEVONPORT (→)

Times				Height (metres)			
High Water		Low Water		MHWS	MHWN	MLWN	MLWS
0000	0600	0000	0600	5·5	4·4	2·2	0·8
1200	1800	1200	1800				
Differences LOOE							
−0010	−0010	−0005	−0005	−0·1	−0·2	−0·2	−0·2
WHITSAND BAY							
0000	0000	0000	0000	0·0	+0·1	−0·1	+0·2

SHELTER
Good, but uncomfortable in strong SE winds. ⚓ in 2m E of the pier hd; access approx HW ±1½. 🅥 berth, above ferry, is marked in Y on W side of hbr which dries 2·4m to the ent. The W bank has rky outcrops to S of ferry.

NAVIGATION
WPT 50°19'·73N 04°24'·60W, 130°/310° from/to pier hd lt, 2·0M. Ent dangerous in strong SE'lies, when seas break heavily on the bar. From W, beware The Ranneys, rks 2ca SE of Looe Is. Do not attempt the rky passage between Looe Is and mainland except with local knowledge and at HW. From E, beware Longstone Rks extending 1½ca from shore NE of hbr ent. At sp, ebb tide runs up to 5kn.

LIGHTS AND MARKS
Looe Island (or St George's Is) is conspic (44m), 8ca S of the ent. Mid Main bn (off Hannafore Pt, halfway between pier hd and Looe Is) Q (3) 10s 2M; ECM. At night appr in W sector (267°-313°) of pier hd lt Oc WR 3s 8m 15/12M; vis W013°-207°, R207°-267°, W267°-313°, R313°-332°; siren (2) 30s, fishing. No lts inside hbr.

RADIO TELEPHONE
VHF Ch 16 (occas).

TELEPHONE (Dial code 01503)
Hr Mr 262839; CG 262138; MRSC (01803) 882704; Marinecall 0891 500458; ⌗ 0345 231110 (H24); Police 262233; Dr 263195.

FACILITIES
W Looe Quay AB £12.00, Slip, M, P & D (cans), L, FW, ME, El, CH; **E Looe Quay** Access HW ±3, Slip, P & D (cans), L, FW, ME, El, C (2½ ton); **Looe SC** 🕿 262559, L, R, Bar.
Services: Sh (Wood), Ⓔ, Sh, Gas.
Town EC Thurs (winter only); P, FW, V, R, Bar, 🄾, ✉, Ⓑ, ⇌, ✈ (Plymouth).

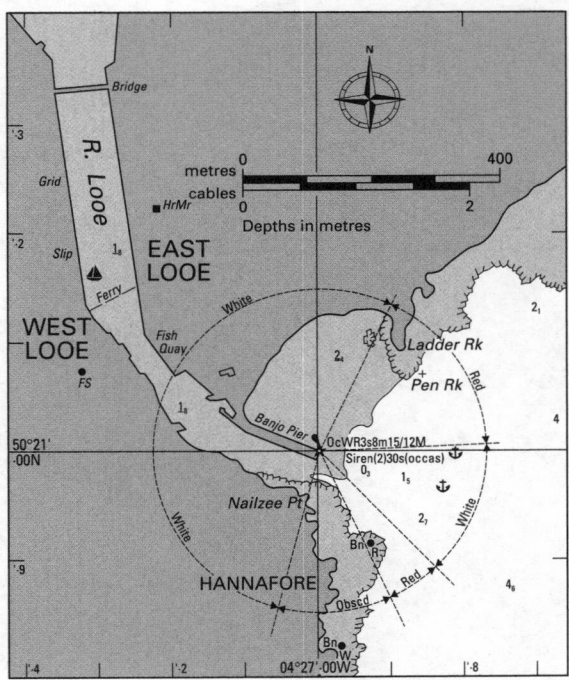

Our course down Channel had no doubt been tortuous. On June 2nd the visibility being poor, I reckoned we must be somewhere near the Manacles. But life is full of surprises. When the wind fell light we handed the mainsail in order to stitch a slender seam and while I was busy with this Noddy sighted through the haze a slender tower to the north-east – no doubt, the Eddystone. But when the sun went down and the lights came on it proved to be the Wolf Rock light. We were at least twenty miles and two points out in our reckoning. I concluded that Mischief knew the way down Channel better than her skipper.

Mostly Mischief: H.W.Tilman

With acknowledgements to the Executors of the estate of H.W.Tilman and to Hollis & Carter (Publishers 1966).

PLYMOUTH (DEVONPORT) 8-1-17

Devon   50°20'·00N 04°10'·00W (W Chan)   Rtg 1-1-1
         50°20'·00N 04°08'·00W (E Chan)

CHARTS
AC *871*, 1902, 1901, *30*, 1967, 1900, *1267, 1613*; Imray C14;
Stanfords 13; OS 201

TIDES
–0540 Dover; ML 3·3; Duration 0610; Zone 0 (UT)

Standard Port DEVONPORT (→)

Times				Height (metres)			
High Water		Low Water		MHWS	MHWN	MLWN	MLWS
0000	0600	0000	0600	5·5	4·4	2·2	0·8
1200	1800	1200	1800				
Differences BOVISAND PIER							
0000	–0020	0000	–0010	–0·2	–0·1	0·0	+0·1
TURNCHAPEL (Cattewater)							
0000	0000	+0010	–0015	0·0	+0·1	+0·2	+0·1
JUPITER POINT (R. Lynher)							
+0010	+0005	0000	–0005	0·0	0·0	+0·1	0·0
ST GERMANS (R. Lynher)							
0000	0000	+0020	+0020	–0·3	–0·1	0·0	+0·2
SALTASH (R. Tamar)							
0000	+0010	0000	–0005	+0·1	+0·1	+0·1	+0·1
CARGREEN (R. Tamar)							
0000	+0010	+0020	+0020	0·0	0·0	–0·1	0·0
COTEHELE QUAY (R. Tamar)							
0000	+0020	+0045	+0045	–0·9	–0·9	–0·8	–0·4

NOTE: Devonport is a Standard Port; predictions are given
below. Winds from SE to W increase the flood and retard
the ebb; vice versa in winds from the NW to E.

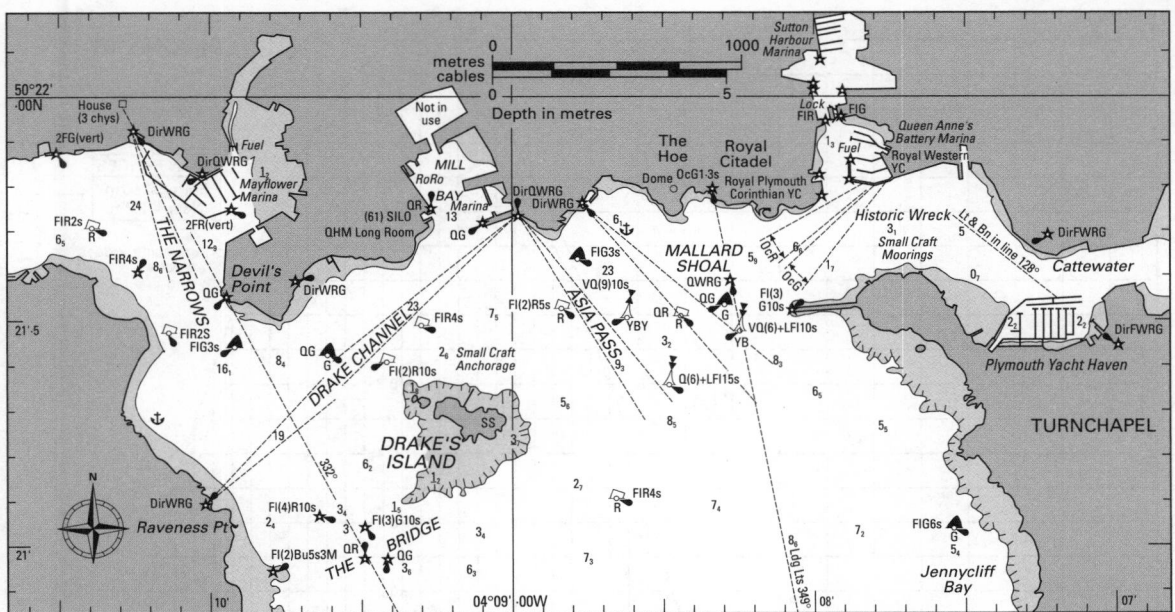

SHELTER

Excellent. Plymouth is a Naval Base, a busy commercial/ferry port principally using Mill Bay Docks, and an active fishing port based mainly on Sutton Harbour which is entered via a lock (see Facilities). There are marinas to E and W of the city centre, as well as in the Cattewater, off Torpoint and in Millbrook Lake. Around the Sound there are ⚓s, sheltered according to the wind, in Cawsand Bay, in Barn Pool (below Mt Edgcumbe), N of Drake's Island, below The Hoe and in Jennycliff Bay to the E. Also good shelter W of Cremyll and off the Hamoaze in the R Lynher and in the R Tamar/Tavy above Saltash (see overleaf).

NAVIGATION

WPT 50°19'.70N 04°09'.80W, 213°/033° from/to W bkwtr lt, 0.40M. The Sound can be entered via the W or E Chans which are well lit/buoyed with no real hazards. There are no shoal patches with less than 3.7m at MLWS. Yachts need not keep to the deep water chans.

The short cut to the Hamoaze via The Bridge (channel between Drake's Is and Mt Edgcumbe) is lit by 2 PHM and 2 SHM bns; the seaward pair show QR and QG, the inner pair Fl (4) R 10s and Fl (3) G 10s. The QR bn and the Fl (4) R 10s bn both have tide gauges calibrated to show height of tide above CD; charted depth is 2.1m. The E'ly of 3 conspic high-rise blocks brg 331° leads through The Bridge chan. Caution: a charted depth 1.8m is close SW of No 3 SHM bn, Fl (3) G 10s.

Speed limits: 10kn N of The Breakwater, 8kn in Cattewater (where outbound vessels have right of way), 4kn in Sutton Chan and 5kn in Sutton Hbr.

Historic Wrecks (see 8.0.3h) are at:
Cattewater, 50°21'.69N 04°07'.63W, 1ca N of Mount Batten. Penlee Pt, 2ca W and 7ca SW of: two sites at 50°18'.96N 04°11'.57W and 50°18'.57N 04°11'.98W.

LIGHTS AND MARKS

See 8.1.4 for complete detail. Bkwtr W hd, Fl WR 10s 19m 12/9M (vis W262°-208°, R208°-262°) and Iso 4s 12m 10M (vis 033°-037°). Bkwtr E hd, L Fl WR 10s 9m 8/6M (R190°-353°, W353°-001°, R001°-018°, W018°-190°). Mallard Shoal ldg lts 349°: Front Q WRG 10/3M (vis G233°-043°, R043°-067°, G067°-087°, W087°-099°, R099°-108°); rear 396m from front (on Hoe) Oc G 1.3s (vis 310°-040°).
There are Dir WRG lts, all lit H24 except **, at Whidbey (138.5°), Staddon Pt (044°), Withyhedge (070°), W Hoe bn (315°), Western King (271°), Mill Bay** (048.5°), Ravenness (225°), Mount Wise (343°), and Ocean Court** (085°).
In fog the following Dir W lts operate: Mallard (front) Fl 5s (vis 232°-110°); West Hoe bn F (vis 313°-317°); Eastern King Fl 5s (vis 259°-062°); Ravenness Fl (2) 15s (vis 160°-305°); Mount Wise F (vis 341°-345°); Ocean Court Fl 5s (vis 270°-100°).
Notes: Principal lts in Plymouth Sound show QY if mains power fails. N of The Bkwtr, four large mooring buoys (C, D, E & F) have Fl Y lts.

RADIO TELEPHONE

Call: *Long Room Port Control* VHF Ch 08 12 **14** 16 (H24). *Mill Bay Docks* Ch 12 14 16 (only during ferry ops). *Sutton Lock,* for lock opening and marina, Ch **12** 16 (H24). *Cattewater Hbr* Ch 14 16 (Mon-Fri, 0900-1700LT). Call Ch **80** M for Mayflower, Queen Anne's Battery, Sutton Hbr & Plymouth Yacht Haven marinas and Torpoint Yacht Hbr.

TELEPHONE (Dial code 01752)

QHM 836952; DQHM 836485; Flagstaff Port Control 552413; Longroom Control 836528; Cattewater Hr Mr 665934; ABP at Mill Bay 662191; MRSC (01803) 882704; ✉ 0345 231110 (H24); Marinecall 0891 500458; Police 701188; Dr 663138; Ⓗ 668080.

FACILITIES

Marinas (W to E)
Torpoint Yacht Hbr (60+20 Ⓥ) ☎/🛥 813658, £10, access H24, dredged 2m. FW, AC, BY, C, ME, El, Sh, Diver, SM.
Southdown Marina (35 inc Ⓥ) ☎/🛥 823084, £7.50, access HW±4; AB on pontoon (2m) or on drying quay; FW, AC, D.
Mayflower Marina (300+50 Ⓥ) ☎ 556633, 🛥 606896, £18.20 inc AC, P, D, FW, ME, El, Sh, C (2 ton); CH, Slip, Gas, Gaz, Divers, SM, BY, YC, V, R, Bar, Ⓖ.
Mill Bay Village Marina ☎ 226785, 🛥 222513, VHF Ch M. NO VISITORS. Ent lts = Oc R 4s & Oc G 4s, not on chartlet.
Queen Anne's Battery Marina (240+60 Ⓥ) ☎ 671142, 🛥 266297, £16.10, AC, P, D, ME, El, Sh, FW, BH (20 ton), C (50 ton), CH, Gas, Gaz, Ⓖ, SM, Slip, V, Bar, YC.
Sutton Hbr Marina (310) ☎ 664186, 🛥 223521, £15, P, D, FW, AC, El, ME, Sh, CH, C, BH (25 ton), Slip. Enter via lock (Barbican flood protection scheme), which maintains 3m CD in the marina. Lock (floating fenders) operates H24, free; call *Sutton Lock* VHF Ch 12 16. When tide rises to 3m above CD, gates stay open for free-flow. Tfc lts (vert): 3 Ⓡ = Stop; 3 Ⓖ = Go; 3 Fl Ⓡ = Serious hazard, wait.
Plymouth Yacht Haven (300+ Ⓥ) ☎ 404231, 🛥 484177, £14.48, dredged 2.25m, D, FW, AC, CH, BH (65 ton), ME, El, Gas, Gaz, V, Ⓖ. **Clovelly Bay Marina** (180 + Ⓥ), same ☎/🛥, integrated site, facilities as for PYH.

Clubs
Royal Western YC of England ☎ 660077, M, Bar, R; **Royal Plymouth Corinthian YC** ☎ 664327, VHF Ch M, M, R, Bar, Slip; **Plym YC** ☎ 404991; **RNSA** ☎ 557679; **Mayflower SC** ☎ 492566; **Torpoint Mosquito SC** ☎ 812508, R, Bar visitors welcome; **Saltash SC** ☎ 845988.

Services All facilities available, inc ACA; consult marina/Hr Mr for details. A *Water Sports and Events Diary* contains much useful information. **City** all facilities, ⇌, ✈.

BYE LAWS/NAVAL ACTIVITY

The whole Port is under the jurisdiction of the QHM, but certain areas are locally controlled, i.e. by Cattewater Commissioners and by ABP who operate Mill Bay Docks. Beware frequent movements of naval vessels, which have right of way in the chans. Obey MOD Police orders. Info on Naval activities may be obtained from Naval Ops.

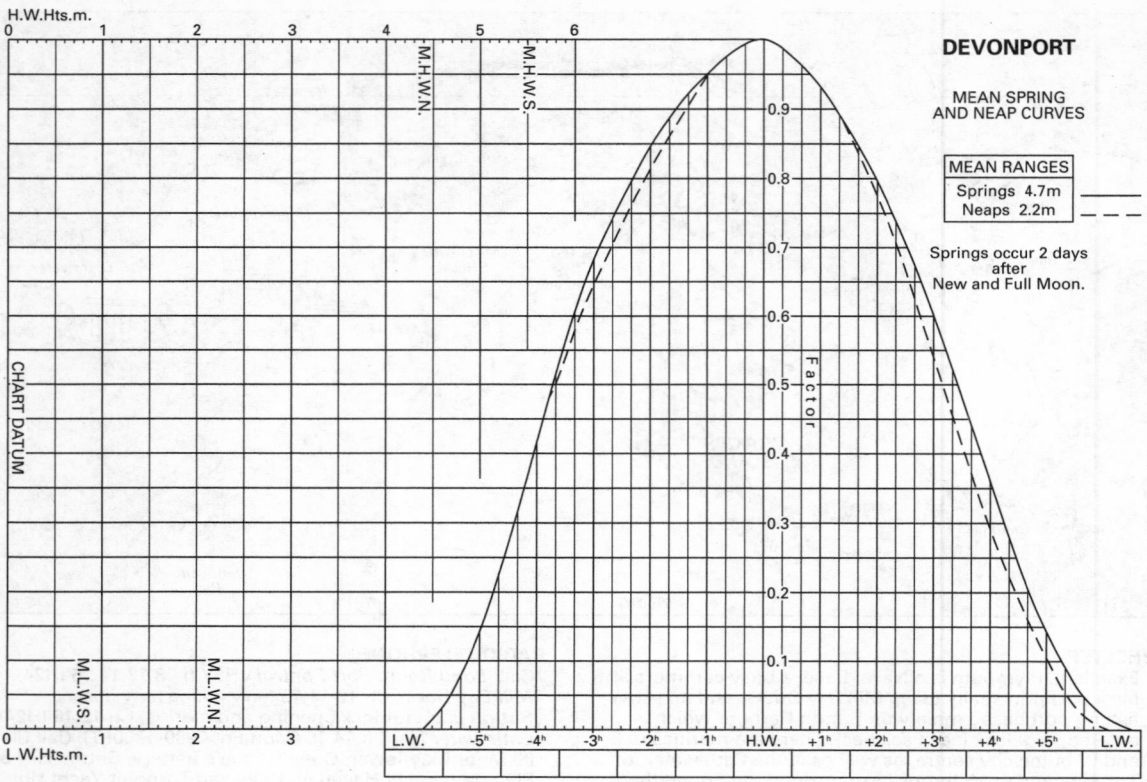

DEVONPORT

MEAN SPRING
AND NEAP CURVES

MEAN RANGES
Springs 4.7m ————
Neaps 2.2m - - - -

Springs occur 2 days
after
New and Full Moon.

☎ 501182 (H24) or Devonport Ops Room ☎ 563777 Ext 2182/3. Submarines may secure to a buoy close N of the Breakwater; they will show a Fl Y anti-collision lt. For Subfacts in the W English Channel see 8.1.18.

TRAFFIC SIGNALS

Traffic is controlled H24 by the following combinations of 3 lts WRG (vert), Fl or Oc, shown from Drake's Island and at Flagstaff Port Control Station in the Dockyard. These signals and any hoisted by HM Ships apply to the waters off the dockyard port and 125m either side of the deep water chan out to the W Ent. The Cattewater, Mill Bay Docks and Sutton Hbr are excluded.

Signal	Meaning
Unlit	No restrictions, unless passed on VHF
Ⓡ Ⓡ Ⓡ All Fl	Serious Emergency All traffic suspended
Ⓡ Ⓖ Ⓖ All Oc	Outgoing traffic only may proceed on the recommended track. Crossing traffic to seek approval from Port Control*
Ⓖ Ⓖ Ⓡ All Oc	Incoming traffic only may proceed on the recommended track. Crossing traffic to seek approval from Port Control*
Ⓖ Ⓖ Ⓦ All Oc	Vessels may proceed in either direction, but shall give a wide berth to HM Ships using the recommended track

*Call Port Control Ch 13 or 14, but craft <20m LOA may proceed in the contrary direction, with care and not impeding the passage of vessels for which the signal is intended.

Wind Strength Warning Flags and Lights
Wind flags (R & W vert stripes) are flown at Queen Anne's Battery, Mayflower Marina and The Camber (HO only) to warn of excessive winds as follows:
1 wind flag   (1 Oc Ⓦ lt)   = Rough weather, Force 5 - 6.
2 wind flags (2 Oc Ⓦ lts, vert) = Very rough weather, > F 6.

Note: These flags are supplemented by Oc Ⓦ lt(s) shown from Drake's Island, HJ when no traffic signal is in force.

Wembury Firing Range extends 16·5M offshore in an arc of 126°–244° from 50°19´.00N 04°06´.30W. Firing usually occurs Tues - Fri, 0900 – 1600 (1630 summer); occas Mon; rarely at night, weekends or public hols. No firing at Easter, Christmas and for 3 weeks in Aug. 4 large R flags are flown at Wembury Pt when range active. 4 small Y target buoys and 3 Fl Y lt buoys are aligned 300° from a point 3½ca S of Great Mewstone to a point 8ca W of the same. Other targets may be towed 1000yds astern of tug vessel. Two SPM target buoys (NGS West, Fl Y 5s, and NGS East, Fl Y 10s) are at 50°11´.1N 04°00´.8W and 50°11´.2N 03°59´.0W; do not secure to them or loiter nearby. To enter The Sound from S during firings, keep W of Eddystone lt ho. It is not advisable to pass inside the Mewstone, due to drying ledges. For info call *Wembury Range* VHF Ch 16 (working 11), advising your position; or ☎ Freephone 0800 833608 or Range Officer ☎ (01752) 862799 (HO) or 553740 ext 77412 (OT).

Diving: Keep clear of regular diving off Bovisand Pier, The Breakwater Fort and Ravenness Point. Diving signals (Flag A) are displayed.

RIVER TAMAR (and TAVY)
The Tamar is navigable on the flood for 15M to Morwhellan. R Tavy flows into the Tamar 1¼M above the bridges, but due to power lines (8m) and a bridge (7·6m) at its mouth, is only accessible to un-masted craft up to Bere Ferrers. Cargreen village is 0·7M beyond the Tavy, on the W bank, with many local moorings and ⚓ in 2m. Weir Quay on E bank has a SC, BY, M and fuel. The river S-bends, narrowing and drying, passes Cothele Quay and then turns 90° stbd to Calstock; possible AB, M, or ⚓ above the viaduct in 2m. **Tamar River SC** ☎ 362741; **Weir Quay SC** ☎ (01822) 840960, M, CH, ME; **Calstock BY** ☎ (01822) 832502, access HW ±3, M, ME, SH, C (8 ton), BH (10 ton). Facilities: P, D, V, Bar, Ⓑ (Mon a.m.), ⇌.

RIVER LYNHER (or ST GERMANS)
This river which flows into The Hamoaze about 0·8M S of the Tamar Bridge, dries extensively but is navigable on the tide for 4M up to St Germans Quay (private); but temp AB possible by prior arrangement with Quay SC. The chan, ent at Wearde Quay, is buoyed and partly lit for the first 2M. There are ⚓s, amid local moorings, at the ent to Forder Lake (N bank); SE of Ince Pt and Castle in about 3m; and at Dandy Hole, a pool with 3m, where the river bends NW and dries almost completely. Facilities: V, Bar, ✉, (½M). **Quay SC** Moorings ☎ (01503) 250370.

ENGLAND – PLYMOUTH (DEVONPORT)

LAT 50°22′N   LONG 4°11′W

TIMES AND HEIGHTS OF HIGH AND LOW WATERS

YEAR **1999**

TIME ZONE (UT)
For Summer Time add ONE hour in non-shaded areas

Chart Datum: 3·22 metres below Ordnance Datum (Newlyn)

JANUARY

Day	Time	m	Day	Time	m
1 F	0445 / 1107 / 1712 / 2330	5.4 / 0.9 / 5.4 / 0.8	**16** SA	0447 / 1057 / 1708 / 2316	5.1 / 1.4 / 5.0 / 1.3
2 SA O	0536 / 1158 / 1803	5.6 / 0.7 / 5.5	**17** SU ●	0530 / 1140 / 1752 / 2357	5.3 / 1.2 / 5.1 / 1.1
3 SU	0019 / 0623 / 1245 / 1851	0.7 / 5.7 / 0.6 / 5.4	**18** M	0612 / 1222 / 1834	5.4 / 1.0 / 5.2
4 M	0104 / 0709 / 1330 / 1937	0.7 / 5.7 / 0.6 / 5.4	**19** TU	0038 / 0652 / 1303 / 1914	1.0 / 5.4 / 0.9 / 5.2
5 TU	0147 / 0752 / 1412 / 2019	0.8 / 5.6 / 0.8 / 5.2	**20** W	0117 / 0730 / 1342 / 1953	1.0 / 5.4 / 0.9 / 5.2
6 W	0226 / 0829 / 1451 / 2055	1.0 / 5.4 / 1.0 / 5.0	**21** TH	0155 / 0808 / 1420 / 2031	1.0 / 5.4 / 0.9 / 5.1
7 TH	0303 / 0902 / 1527 / 2125	1.3 / 5.2 / 1.3 / 4.8	**22** F	0232 / 0846 / 1458 / 2109	1.0 / 5.3 / 1.0 / 5.1
8 F	0338 / 0933 / 1604 / 2158	1.6 / 5.0 / 1.6 / 4.6	**23** SA	0311 / 0927 / 1538 / 2152	1.2 / 5.2 / 1.2 / 4.9
9 SA	0416 / 1011 / 1645 / 2241	1.9 / 4.7 / 1.9 / 4.4	**24** SU	0354 / 1013 / 1625 / 2242	1.4 / 5.0 / 1.4 / 4.8
10 SU	0502 / 1059 / 1735 / 2339	2.1 / 4.5 / 2.1 / 4.3	**25** M	0446 / 1109 / 1723 / 2345	1.6 / 4.8 / 1.7 / 4.6
11 M	0600 / 1202 / 1837	2.3 / 4.4 / 2.2	**26** TU	0554 / 1220 / 1840	1.9 / 4.6 / 1.8
12 TU	0055 / 0709 / 1321 / 1945	4.3 / 2.3 / 4.4 / 2.2	**27** W	0103 / 0725 / 1342 / 2010	4.6 / 1.9 / 4.6 / 1.8
13 W	0212 / 0818 / 1435 / 2050	4.5 / 2.2 / 4.5 / 2.0	**28** TH	0223 / 0852 / 1458 / 2126	4.7 / 1.7 / 4.8 / 1.5
14 TH	0312 / 0920 / 1533 / 2145	4.7 / 1.9 / 4.7 / 1.7	**29** F	0332 / 1000 / 1604 / 2227	5.0 / 1.4 / 5.0 / 1.2
15 F	0402 / 1012 / 1623 / 2232	4.9 / 1.6 / 4.9 / 1.5	**30** SA	0430 / 1056 / 1700 / 2319	5.2 / 1.0 / 5.1 / 0.9
			31 SU O	0521 / 1146 / 1750	5.4 / 0.8 / 5.3

FEBRUARY

Day	Time	m	Day	Time	m
1 M	0006 / 0607 / 1233 / 1835	0.7 / 5.5 / 0.6 / 5.3	**16** TU ●	0551 / 1205 / 1816	5.4 / 0.8 / 5.2
2 TU	0050 / 0651 / 1315 / 1918	0.6 / 5.6 / 0.6 / 5.3	**17** W	0023 / 0633 / 1248 / 1857	0.8 / 5.5 / 0.6 / 5.3
3 W	0130 / 0731 / 1354 / 1955	0.6 / 5.5 / 0.6 / 5.2	**18** TH	0105 / 0715 / 1329 / 1938	0.6 / 5.6 / 0.5 / 5.4
4 TH	0206 / 0804 / 1428 / 2024	0.8 / 5.4 / 0.8 / 5.1	**19** F	0144 / 0755 / 1408 / 2017	0.6 / 5.6 / 0.5 / 5.3
5 F	0238 / 0833 / 1459 / 2050	1.0 / 5.3 / 1.1 / 4.8	**20** SA	0221 / 0834 / 1444 / 2055	0.6 / 5.5 / 0.6 / 5.3
6 SA	0307 / 0901 / 1527 / 2120	1.3 / 5.1 / 1.4 / 4.8	**21** SU	0258 / 0914 / 1522 / 2134	0.8 / 5.3 / 0.9 / 5.1
7 SU	0336 / 0934 / 1556 / 2155	1.6 / 4.9 / 1.7 / 4.6	**22** M	0337 / 0957 / 1603 / 2219	1.1 / 5.1 / 1.2 / 4.9
8 M	0408 / 1013 / 1631 / 2240	1.9 / 4.6 / 2.0 / 4.4	**23** TU	0424 / 1048 / 1655 / 2317	1.4 / 4.8 / 1.6 / 4.6
9 TU	0454 / 1103 / 1728 / 2340	2.1 / 4.4 / 2.2 / 4.3	**24** W	0525 / 1158 / 1805	1.8 / 4.5 / 1.9
10 W	0607 / 1210 / 1845	2.3 / 4.2 / 2.3	**25** TH	0037 / 0655 / 1325 / 1949	4.5 / 2.0 / 4.4 / 2.0
11 TH	0103 / 0724 / 1343 / 1959	4.3 / 2.3 / 4.2 / 2.2	**26** F	0203 / 0840 / 1446 / 2115	4.5 / 1.8 / 4.5 / 1.7
12 F	0232 / 0835 / 1503 / 2105	4.4 / 2.0 / 4.5 / 1.9	**27** SA	0317 / 0950 / 1553 / 2216	4.8 / 1.5 / 4.8 / 1.3
13 SA	0334 / 0938 / 1600 / 2203	4.7 / 1.7 / 4.7 / 1.6	**28** SU	0416 / 1045 / 1648 / 2306	5.1 / 1.1 / 5.0 / 1.0
14 SU	0423 / 1031 / 1648 / 2253	5.0 / 1.4 / 4.9 / 1.2			
15 M	0508 / 1119 / 1733 / 2339	5.2 / 1.0 / 5.1 / 1.0			

MARCH

Day	Time	m	Day	Time	m
1 M	0505 / 1132 / 1734 / 2351	5.3 / 0.7 / 5.2 / 0.7	**16** TU	0442 / 1055 / 1709 / 2317	5.2 / 0.9 / 5.1 / 0.9
2 TU O	0549 / 1215 / 1816	5.4 / 0.6 / 5.3	**17** W ●	0526 / 1143 / 1753	5.4 / 0.6 / 5.3
3 W	0032 / 0629 / 1255 / 1853	0.6 / 5.5 / 0.5 / 5.3	**18** TH	0004 / 0610 / 1228 / 1835	0.6 / 5.6 / 0.4 / 5.4
4 TH	0109 / 0705 / 1330 / 1925	0.6 / 5.5 / 0.6 / 5.3	**19** F	0047 / 0654 / 1311 / 1917	0.4 / 5.7 / 0.3 / 5.5
5 F	0142 / 0736 / 1401 / 1952	0.7 / 5.4 / 0.7 / 5.1	**20** SA	0128 / 0737 / 1351 / 1958	0.3 / 5.7 / 0.3 / 5.5
6 SA	0210 / 0803 / 1428 / 2018	0.8 / 5.3 / 1.0 / 5.1	**21** SU	0207 / 0819 / 1429 / 2037	0.4 / 5.6 / 0.5 / 5.4
7 SU	0236 / 0832 / 1451 / 2047	1.1 / 5.1 / 1.2 / 4.9	**22** M	0244 / 0900 / 1506 / 2117	0.6 / 5.4 / 0.8 / 5.1
8 M	0258 / 0902 / 1511 / 2119	1.4 / 4.9 / 1.5 / 4.7	**23** TU	0324 / 0943 / 1547 / 2200	0.9 / 5.1 / 1.2 / 4.9
9 TU	0320 / 0937 / 1534 / 2157	1.7 / 4.6 / 1.8 / 4.5	**24** W	0409 / 1034 / 1636 / 2256	1.3 / 4.7 / 1.6 / 4.6
10 W	0352 / 1020 / 1614 / 2247	2.0 / 4.4 / 2.1 / 4.3	**25** TH	0508 / 1146 / 1744	1.8 / 4.4 / 2.0
11 TH	0457 / 1120 / 1745 / 2358	2.3 / 4.2 / 2.4 / 4.2	**26** F	0018 / 0639 / 1315 / 1932	4.4 / 2.0 / 4.3 / 2.1
12 F	0639 / 1245 / 1917	2.3 / 4.1 / 2.3	**27** SA	0147 / 0827 / 1434 / 2059	4.4 / 1.9 / 4.4 / 1.8
13 SA	0139 / 0757 / 1430 / 2030	4.3 / 2.1 / 4.3 / 2.0	**28** SU	0300 / 0934 / 1539 / 2158	4.7 / 1.5 / 4.7 / 1.4
14 SU	0300 / 0905 / 1533 / 2133	4.6 / 1.7 / 4.6 / 1.6	**29** M	0357 / 1026 / 1630 / 2246	5.0 / 1.1 / 4.9 / 1.0
15 M	0355 / 1003 / 1623 / 2228	5.0 / 1.3 / 4.9 / 1.2	**30** TU	0444 / 1111 / 1712 / 2329	5.2 / 0.8 / 5.1 / 0.8
			31 W O	0525 / 1152 / 1750	5.3 / 0.6 / 5.2

APRIL

Day	Time	m	Day	Time	m
1 TH	0008 / 0602 / 1230 / 1823	0.6 / 5.4 / 0.6 / 5.3	**16** F ●	0545 / 1204 / 1810	5.6 / 0.3 / 5.5
2 F	0044 / 0635 / 1303 / 1853	0.6 / 5.4 / 0.6 / 5.3	**17** SA	0026 / 0631 / 1250 / 1854	0.3 / 5.7 / 0.2 / 5.6
3 SA	0115 / 0706 / 1332 / 1922	0.7 / 5.3 / 0.8 / 5.2	**18** SU	0110 / 0717 / 1332 / 1938	0.2 / 5.7 / 0.2 / 5.6
4 SU	0142 / 0736 / 1356 / 1950	0.8 / 5.2 / 1.0 / 5.2	**19** M	0151 / 0802 / 1413 / 2020	0.3 / 5.6 / 0.4 / 5.5
5 M	0205 / 0805 / 1417 / 2019	1.0 / 5.1 / 1.2 / 5.0	**20** TU	0232 / 0847 / 1453 / 2101	0.5 / 5.4 / 0.8 / 5.3
6 TU	0227 / 0835 / 1436 / 2049	1.3 / 4.9 / 1.4 / 4.8	**21** W	0314 / 0932 / 1535 / 2145	0.9 / 5.0 / 1.2 / 5.0
7 W	0248 / 0908 / 1500 / 2123	1.5 / 4.6 / 1.7 / 4.6	**22** TH	0400 / 1025 / 1625 / 2240	1.3 / 4.7 / 1.6 / 4.7
8 TH	0319 / 0949 / 1537 / 2210	1.8 / 4.4 / 2.0 / 4.4	**23** F	0459 / 1137 / 1731	1.7 / 4.4 / 2.0
9 F	0411 / 1046 / 1644 / 2313	2.1 / 4.2 / 2.3 / 4.3	**24** SA	0000 / 0623 / 1301 / 1905	4.5 / 2.0 / 4.3 / 2.1
10 SA	0557 / 1200 / 1837	2.2 / 4.1 / 2.3	**25** SU	0125 / 0759 / 1413 / 2030	4.5 / 1.9 / 4.4 / 1.9
11 SU	0034 / 0721 / 1342 / 1955	4.3 / 2.1 / 4.3 / 2.0	**26** M	0234 / 0906 / 1513 / 2129	4.6 / 1.5 / 4.6 / 1.5
12 M	0213 / 0831 / 1459 / 2101	4.5 / 1.7 / 4.6 / 1.6	**27** TU	0329 / 0958 / 1601 / 2218	4.8 / 1.2 / 4.9 / 1.2
13 TU	0319 / 0932 / 1552 / 2159	4.9 / 1.3 / 4.9 / 1.2	**28** W	0416 / 1042 / 1642 / 2300	5.0 / 1.0 / 5.0 / 1.0
14 W	0410 / 1027 / 1640 / 2252	5.2 / 0.9 / 5.2 / 0.8	**29** TH	0456 / 1122 / 1719 / 2339	5.2 / 0.8 / 5.2 / 0.8
15 TH	0458 / 1117 / 1725 / 2340	5.4 / 0.5 / 5.4 / 0.5	**30** F O	0532 / 1159 / 1752	5.2 / 0.8 / 5.2

ENGLAND – PLYMOUTH (DEVONPORT)

LAT 50°22′N   LONG 4°11′W

TIMES AND HEIGHTS OF HIGH AND LOW WATERS

YEAR **1999**

TIME ZONE (UT)
For Summer Time add ONE hour in non-shaded areas

MAY

Day	Time	m	Day	Time	m
1 SA	0015 / 0605 / 1233 / 1823	0.8 / 5.2 / 0.8 / 5.3	16 SU	0004 / 0610 / 1228 / 1833	0.3 / 5.6 / 0.3 / 5.7
2 SU	0046 / 0639 / 1301 / 1855	0.8 / 5.2 / 0.9 / 5.2	17 M	0052 / 0659 / 1314 / 1919	0.3 / 5.6 / 0.3 / 5.7
3 M	0114 / 0711 / 1326 / 1926	0.9 / 5.1 / 1.1 / 5.2	18 TU	0137 / 0748 / 1358 / 2004	0.3 / 5.5 / 0.5 / 5.6
4 TU	0139 / 0743 / 1350 / 1956	1.1 / 5.0 / 1.2 / 5.1	19 W	0221 / 0835 / 1442 / 2048	0.5 / 5.3 / 0.8 / 5.4
5 W	0204 / 0814 / 1413 / 2026	1.3 / 4.8 / 1.4 / 4.9	20 TH	0306 / 0924 / 1526 / 2133	0.8 / 5.0 / 1.2 / 5.1
6 TH	0230 / 0847 / 1441 / 2100	1.5 / 4.6 / 1.6 / 4.7	21 F	0353 / 1017 / 1615 / 2225	1.2 / 4.7 / 1.5 / 4.8
7 F	0303 / 0928 / 1519 / 2144	1.7 / 4.4 / 1.9 / 4.6	22 SA	0448 / 1122 / 1712 / 2335	1.6 / 4.5 / 1.9 / 4.6
8 SA	0353 / 1021 / 1619 / 2242	1.9 / 4.3 / 2.1 / 4.4	23 SU	0555 / 1233 / 1824	1.8 / 4.3 / 2.0
9 SU	0518 / 1128 / 1756 / 2353	2.0 / 4.2 / 2.2 / 4.4	24 M	0051 / 0713 / 1338 / 1942	4.5 / 1.8 / 4.4 / 2.0
10 M	0644 / 1248 / 1918	1.9 / 4.3 / 2.0	25 TU	0157 / 0824 / 1435 / 2047	4.5 / 1.7 / 4.5 / 1.8
11 TU	0115 / 0755 / 1412 / 2026	4.6 / 1.6 / 4.6 / 1.6	26 W	0252 / 0919 / 1524 / 2140	4.7 / 1.5 / 4.7 / 1.5
12 W	0234 / 0859 / 1515 / 2128	4.8 / 1.3 / 4.9 / 1.2	27 TH	0340 / 1025 / 1607 / 2226	4.8 / 1.3 / 4.9 / 1.3
13 TH	0336 / 0957 / 1608 / 2224	5.1 / 0.9 / 5.2 / 0.9	28 F	0422 / 1048 / 1645 / 2306	4.9 / 1.1 / 5.0 / 1.1
14 F	0429 / 1050 / 1658 / 2316	5.4 / 0.6 / 5.4 / 0.6	29 SA	0500 / 1126 / 1721 / 2343	5.0 / 1.0 / 5.1 / 1.0
15 SA	0520 / 1140 / 1746 ●	5.5 / 0.4 / 5.6	30 SU	0537 / 1201 / 1756 O	5.1 / 1.0 / 5.2
			31 M	0017 / 0614 / 1232 / 1832	1.0 / 5.1 / 1.1 / 5.2

JUNE

Day	Time	m	Day	Time	m
1 TU	0048 / 0651 / 1301 / 1906	1.1 / 5.0 / 1.1 / 5.2	16 W	0124 / 0735 / 1346 / 1950	0.4 / 5.4 / 0.6 / 5.6
2 W	0118 / 0727 / 1330 / 1939	1.1 / 4.9 / 1.2 / 5.1	17 TH	0211 / 0824 / 1430 / 2036	0.5 / 5.2 / 0.8 / 5.4
3 TH	0148 / 0801 / 1400 / 2011	1.2 / 4.8 / 1.4 / 5.0	18 F	0256 / 0912 / 1514 / 2119	0.8 / 5.0 / 1.0 / 5.2
4 F	0220 / 0835 / 1433 / 2045	1.4 / 4.7 / 1.5 / 4.9	19 SA	0340 / 1000 / 1558 / 2203	1.1 / 4.8 / 1.4 / 4.9
5 SA	0257 / 0914 / 1513 / 2127	1.5 / 4.6 / 1.7 / 4.8	20 SU	0426 / 1050 / 1645 / 2251	1.4 / 4.6 / 1.7 / 4.7
6 SU	0344 / 1002 / 1605 / 2218	1.6 / 4.5 / 1.8 / 4.7	21 M	0517 / 1148 / 1738 / 2354	1.7 / 4.4 / 1.9 / 4.6
7 M	0447 / 1101 / 1715 / 2321	1.7 / 4.4 / 1.9 / 4.6	22 TU	0616 / 1248 / 1840	1.8 / 4.3 / 2.0
8 TU	0603 / 1209 / 1836	1.7 / 4.4 / 1.9	23 W	0103 / 0721 / 1347 / 1947	4.4 / 1.9 / 4.4 / 2.0
9 W	0033 / 0717 / 1326 / 1949	4.6 / 1.6 / 4.6 / 1.7	24 TH	0205 / 0826 / 1440 / 2051	4.5 / 1.8 / 4.5 / 1.8
10 TH	0152 / 0825 / 1437 / 2056	4.8 / 1.3 / 4.8 / 1.3	25 F	0259 / 0921 / 1528 / 2144	4.6 / 1.6 / 4.7 / 1.6
11 F	0303 / 0928 / 1538 / 2157	5.0 / 1.0 / 5.1 / 1.0	26 SA	0347 / 1009 / 1611 / 2230	4.7 / 1.4 / 4.9 / 1.4
12 SA	0403 / 1025 / 1633 / 2253	5.2 / 0.8 / 5.3 / 0.7	27 SU	0430 / 1051 / 1653 / 2312	4.8 / 1.2 / 5.0 / 1.3
13 SU	0459 / 1119 / 1724 / ● 2346	5.4 / 0.6 / 5.5 / 0.6	28 M	0512 / 1129 / 1733 / O 2350	4.9 / 1.2 / 5.1 / 1.2
14 M	0552 / 1210 / 1814	5.5 / 0.5 / 5.6	29 TU	0553 / 1206 / 1812	5.0 / 1.1 / 5.2
15 TU	0036 / 0643 / 1259 / 1903	0.4 / 5.5 / 0.5 / 5.6	30 W	0026 / 0634 / 1241 / 1850	1.1 / 5.0 / 1.1 / 5.2

JULY

Day	Time	m	Day	Time	m
1 TH	0102 / 0713 / 1316 / 1927	1.1 / 5.0 / 1.2 / 5.2	16 F	0157 / 0808 / 1415 / 2019	0.5 / 5.2 / 0.7 / 5.5
2 F	0137 / 0751 / 1350 / 2001	1.1 / 4.9 / 1.2 / 5.1	17 SA	0239 / 0851 / 1455 / 2056	0.7 / 5.1 / 0.9 / 5.3
3 SA	0212 / 0826 / 1426 / 2035	1.1 / 4.8 / 1.3 / 5.1	18 SU	0318 / 0929 / 1532 / 2129	0.9 / 4.9 / 1.2 / 5.0
4 SU	0250 / 0903 / 1504 / 2113	1.2 / 4.7 / 1.4 / 5.0	19 M	0356 / 1002 / 1610 / 2201	1.2 / 4.7 / 1.4 / 4.8
5 M	0331 / 0946 / 1548 / 2159	1.3 / 4.7 / 1.5 / 4.9	20 TU	0435 / 1037 / 1652 / 2240	1.6 / 4.5 / 1.8 / 4.4
6 TU	0420 / 1036 / 1643 / 2254	1.5 / 4.6 / 1.6 / 4.6	21 W	0520 / 1125 / 1743 / 2334	1.9 / 4.3 / 2.0 / 4.4
7 W	0522 / 1137 / 1752	1.6 / 4.5 / 1.7	22 TH	0616 / 1232 / 1845	2.0 / 4.3 / 2.2
8 TH	0000 / 0636 / 1249 / 1911	4.7 / 1.6 / 4.6 / 1.7	23 F	0052 / 0720 / 1346 / 1952	4.3 / 2.1 / 4.3 / 2.1
9 F	0119 / 0752 / 1404 / 2028	4.7 / 1.5 / 4.7 / 1.5	24 SA	0213 / 0827 / 1449 / 2058	4.3 / 2.0 / 4.5 / 1.9
10 SA	0237 / 0903 / 1513 / 2136	4.8 / 1.3 / 5.0 / 1.2	25 SU	0314 / 0926 / 1541 / 2154	4.5 / 1.7 / 4.7 / 1.6
11 SU	0344 / 1006 / 1613 / 2237	5.0 / 1.1 / 5.2 / 0.7	26 M	0405 / 1017 / 1628 / 2242	4.7 / 1.5 / 5.0 / 1.4
12 M	0443 / 1103 / 1707 / 2332	5.2 / 0.8 / 5.4 / 0.7	27 TU	0451 / 1101 / 1711 / 2325	4.9 / 1.3 / 5.1 / 1.2
13 TU	0537 / 1156 / 1758 ●	5.3 / 0.6 / 5.5	28 W	0534 / 1143 / 1753 O	5.0 / 1.2 / 5.2
14 W	0023 / 0629 / 1246 / 1848	0.5 / 5.4 / 0.5 / 5.6	29 TH	0007 / 0616 / 1224 / 1833	1.0 / 5.0 / 1.1 / 5.3
15 TH	0112 / 0720 / 1332 / 1935	0.4 / 5.3 / 0.6 / 5.6	30 F	0046 / 0658 / 1302 / 1912	0.9 / 5.1 / 1.0 / 5.3
			31 SA	0124 / 0737 / 1339 / 1949	0.9 / 5.0 / 1.0 / 5.3

AUGUST

Day	Time	m	Day	Time	m
1 SU	0201 / 0814 / 1415 / 2024	0.9 / 5.0 / 1.0 / 5.2	16 M	0249 / 0848 / 1501 / 2051	0.9 / 5.0 / 1.1 / 5.0
2 M	0237 / 0850 / 1451 / 2101	0.9 / 5.0 / 1.1 / 5.2	17 TU	0320 / 0914 / 1532 / 2119	1.2 / 4.8 / 1.4 / 4.9
3 TU	0314 / 0929 / 1530 / 2142	1.1 / 4.9 / 1.2 / 5.0	18 W	0350 / 0945 / 1604 / 2154	1.5 / 4.6 / 1.8 / 4.6
4 W	0356 / 1014 / 1617 / 2231	1.3 / 4.8 / 1.5 / 4.8	19 TH	0424 / 1025 / 1646 / 2238	1.9 / 4.4 / 2.1 / 4.4
5 TH	0448 / 1109 / 1716 / 2334	1.5 / 4.6 / 1.7 / 4.6	20 F	0513 / 1119 / 1749 / 2339	2.2 / 4.3 / 2.3 / 4.2
6 F	0558 / 1220 / 1837	1.7 / 4.5 / 1.8	21 SA	0625 / 1237 / 1904	2.3 / 4.2 / 2.3
7 SA	0055 / 0724 / 1341 / 2008	4.5 / 1.8 / 4.6 / 1.7	22 SU	0118 / 0739 / 1411 / 2016	4.2 / 2.2 / 4.4 / 2.1
8 SU	0221 / 0847 / 1456 / 2124	4.6 / 1.6 / 4.8 / 1.4	23 M	0247 / 0848 / 1514 / 2120	4.3 / 2.0 / 4.6 / 1.8
9 M	0332 / 0955 / 1559 / 2227	4.8 / 1.3 / 5.1 / 1.1	24 TU	0343 / 0946 / 1604 / 2214	4.6 / 1.7 / 4.9 / 1.5
10 TU	0432 / 1053 / 1654 / 2321	5.1 / 1.0 / 5.3 / 0.8	25 W	0430 / 1036 / 1649 / 2301	4.9 / 1.4 / 5.2 / 1.2
11 W	0525 / 1144 / 1744 ●	5.2 / 0.7 / 5.5	26 TH	0514 / 1121 / 1731 / O 2345	5.0 / 1.1 / 5.3 / 0.9
12 TH	0010 / 0614 / 1231 / 1830	0.5 / 5.3 / 0.6 / 5.6	27 F	0556 / 1204 / 1813	5.2 / 0.9 / 5.4
13 F	0056 / 0701 / 1315 / 1914	0.4 / 5.3 / 0.5 / 5.6	28 SA	0027 / 0638 / 1245 / 1852	0.8 / 5.2 / 0.8 / 5.5
14 SA	0138 / 0744 / 1354 / 1953	0.5 / 5.3 / 0.6 / 5.5	29 SU	0107 / 0718 / 1323 / 1931	0.7 / 5.3 / 0.7 / 5.5
15 SU	0216 / 0820 / 1429 / 2025	0.6 / 5.2 / 0.8 / 5.3	30 M	0144 / 0756 / 1359 / 2009	0.6 / 5.3 / 0.7 / 5.4
			31 TU	0220 / 0833 / 1435 / 2047	0.7 / 5.2 / 0.9 / 5.3

Chart Datum: 3·22 metres below Ordnance Datum (Newlyn)

ENGLAND – PLYMOUTH (DEVONPORT)

LAT 50°22′N   LONG 4°11′W

TIMES AND HEIGHTS OF HIGH AND LOW WATERS

YEAR **1999**

SEPTEMBER

	Time	m		Time	m
1 W	0256 0911 1513 2126	0.9 5.1 1.1 5.1	**16** TH	0304 0906 1516 2117	1.6 4.8 1.7 4.7
2 TH	0335 0953 1556 2213	1.2 4.9 1.4 4.8	**17** F	0324 0942 1543 2158	1.9 4.6 2.1 4.4
3 F	0423 1046 1652 2315	1.6 4.7 1.8 4.6	**18** SA	0355 1031 1640 2253	2.2 4.4 2.4 4.2
4 SA	0528 1157 1814	1.9 4.5 2.0	**19** SU	0521 1138 1821	2.5 4.2 2.5
5 SU	0043 0707 1326 2001	4.4 2.0 4.5 1.9	**20** M	0016 0658 1323 1940	4.1 2.5 4.3 2.3
6 M	0214 0841 1445 2119	4.5 1.8 4.8 1.6	**21** TU	0219 0813 1445 2048	4.3 2.2 4.6 1.9
7 TU	0327 0948 1549 2218	4.7 1.4 5.1 1.2	**22** W	0320 0916 1538 2145	4.6 1.8 4.9 1.5
8 W	0425 1041 1641 2308	5.0 1.1 5.3 0.8	**23** TH	0407 1009 1623 2234	4.9 1.4 5.2 1.1
9 TH ●	0513 1129 1727 2353	5.2 0.8 5.5 0.6	**24** F	0451 1056 1706 2320	5.1 1.1 5.4 0.8
10 F	0557 1212 1810	5.4 0.6 5.6	**25** SA ○	0532 1141 1748	5.3 0.8 5.5
11 SA	0035 0637 1252 1848	0.5 5.4 0.5 5.6	**26** SU	0003 0613 1224 1829	0.6 5.4 0.6 5.6
12 SU	0114 0713 1328 1922	0.5 5.4 0.6 5.5	**27** M	0045 0653 1304 1911	0.5 5.5 0.6 5.6
13 M	0147 0743 1400 1950	0.7 5.3 0.8 5.3	**28** TU	0124 0734 1342 1951	0.5 5.5 0.6 5.4
14 TU	0217 0808 1428 2016	0.9 5.1 1.1 5.2	**29** W	0202 0813 1420 2032	0.6 5.4 0.8 5.4
15 W	0242 0835 1453 2045	1.2 5.0 1.4 4.9	**30** TH	0239 0853 1458 2113	0.9 5.3 1.0 5.2

OCTOBER

	Time	m		Time	m
1 F	0318 0936 1542 2201	1.2 5.1 1.4 4.8	**16** SA	0242 0909 1502 2127	1.9 4.7 2.0 4.5
2 SA	0405 1028 1638 2305	1.7 4.8 1.8 4.5	**17** SU	0313 0954 1545 2220	2.2 4.5 2.3 4.2
3 SU	0511 1142 1805	2.1 4.5 2.1	**18** M	0407 1055 1732 2332	2.5 4.3 2.5 4.1
4 M	0038 0658 1314 1955	4.3 2.2 4.5 2.0	**19** TU	0614 1215 1902	2.6 4.3 2.4
5 TU	0209 0831 1434 2107	4.5 2.0 4.8 1.6	**20** W	0129 0736 1359 2012	4.2 2.3 4.6 2.0
6 W	0319 0933 1535 2202	4.8 1.5 5.1 1.2	**21** TH	0246 0842 1502 2112	4.6 1.9 4.9 1.5
7 TH	0412 1023 1624 2248	5.0 1.2 5.3 0.9	**22** F	0337 0938 1551 2204	4.9 1.5 5.2 1.1
8 F	0455 1108 1707 2331	5.3 0.9 5.5 0.7	**23** SA	0422 1024 1637 2252	5.2 1.1 5.4 0.8
9 SA ●	0534 1149 1745	5.4 0.7 5.5	**24** SU ○	0505 1115 1721 2338	5.4 0.8 5.6 0.6
10 SU	0010 0609 1227 1820	0.6 5.4 0.7 5.5	**25** M	0547 1200 1805	5.6 0.6 5.7
11 M	0046 0641 1300 1851	0.7 5.4 0.8 5.5	**26** TU	0022 0630 1244 1850	0.5 5.7 0.5 5.7
12 TU	0117 0709 1330 1918	0.8 5.4 0.9 5.3	**27** W	0105 0713 1326 1934	0.5 5.7 0.6 5.7
13 W	0143 0735 1355 1946	1.0 5.3 1.2 5.2	**28** TH	0145 0755 1407 2018	0.6 5.6 0.7 5.5
14 TH	0205 0803 1418 2016	1.3 5.1 1.4 5.0	**29** F	0225 0838 1449 2103	0.9 5.5 1.0 5.2
15 F	0224 0834 1438 2048	1.6 4.9 1.7 4.7	**30** SA	0307 0923 1535 2154	1.3 5.2 1.4 4.9
			31 SU	0356 1016 1632 2300	1.7 4.9 1.8 4.5

NOVEMBER

	Time	m		Time	m
1 M	0501 1128 1754	2.1 4.7 2.1	**16** TU	0343 1022 1640 2258	2.3 4.5 2.3 4.3
2 TU	0029 0637 1256 1932	4.4 2.3 4.6 2.0	**17** W	0515 1129 1816	2.5 4.5 2.3
3 W	0151 0805 1411 2042	4.5 2.1 4.8 1.7	**18** TH	0017 0650 1249 1931	4.3 2.3 4.6 2.0
4 TH	0255 0907 1510 2136	4.7 1.7 5.0 1.4	**19** F	0151 0802 1410 2035	4.5 2.0 4.8 1.6
5 F	0347 0957 1559 2222	5.0 1.4 5.2 1.1	**20** SA	0256 0903 1513 2132	4.8 1.6 5.1 1.2
6 SA	0429 1041 1641 2304	5.2 1.1 5.3 0.9	**21** SU	0348 0959 1605 2224	5.2 1.2 5.4 0.9
7 SU	0506 1122 1718 2341	5.3 0.9 5.4 0.9	**22** M	0436 1050 1655 2313	5.4 0.9 5.6 0.7
8 M ●	0540 1158 1751	5.4 0.9 5.4	**23** TU ○	0522 1138 1744	5.6 0.7 5.7
9 TU	0016 0610 1232 1822	0.9 5.4 1.0 5.4	**24** W	0001 0608 1226 1832	0.5 5.7 0.5 5.7
10 W	0046 0640 1301 1853	1.0 5.4 1.1 5.3	**25** TH	0047 0654 1312 1920	0.5 5.8 0.6 5.6
11 TH	0112 0710 1328 1924	1.2 5.3 1.3 5.1	**26** F	0132 0740 1357 2008	0.7 5.7 0.7 5.5
12 F	0136 0740 1352 1955	1.4 5.2 1.5 5.0	**27** SA	0216 0826 1443 2056	0.9 5.6 1.0 5.2
13 SA	0158 0812 1416 2028	1.6 5.1 1.7 4.8	**28** SU	0301 0913 1530 2148	1.2 5.3 1.3 4.9
14 SU	0221 0846 1445 2106	1.8 4.9 1.9 4.6	**29** M	0349 1005 1624 2248	1.6 5.1 1.6 4.7
15 M	0254 0928 1527 2155	2.0 4.7 2.1 4.4	**30** TU	0445 1108 1728	1.9 4.8 1.9

DECEMBER

	Time	m		Time	m
1 W	0002 0556 1223 1846	4.5 2.2 4.7 2.0	**16** TH	0430 1053 1721 2332	2.1 4.7 2.0 4.4
2 TH	0114 0718 1333 2001	4.5 2.2 4.7 1.9	**17** F	0552 1159 1841	2.2 4.6 2.0
3 F	0216 0828 1433 2100	4.6 2.0 4.8 1.7	**18** SA	0046 0715 1314 1954	4.5 2.0 4.7 1.7
4 SA	0310 0923 1525 2149	4.8 1.7 4.9 1.5	**19** SU	0204 0826 1430 2059	4.7 1.8 4.9 1.4
5 SU	0355 1010 1609 2233	5.0 1.5 5.0 1.3	**20** M	0311 0930 1535 2158	5.0 1.4 5.2 1.1
6 M	0435 1052 1648 2312	5.2 1.3 5.1 1.2	**21** TU	0409 1027 1633 2252	5.3 1.1 5.4 0.9
7 TU ●	0510 1130 1724 2347	5.3 1.2 5.2 1.1	**22** W ○	0500 1120 1726 2343	5.5 0.8 5.5 0.7
8 W	0544 1205 1759	5.3 1.2 5.3	**23** TH	0550 1211 1818	5.7 0.6 5.6
9 TH	0019 0617 1237 1834	1.2 5.4 1.2 5.2	**24** F	0033 0639 1301 1909	0.6 5.8 0.6 5.6
10 F	0048 0652 1307 1909	1.3 5.3 1.3 5.1	**25** SA	0121 0728 1349 1959	0.6 5.8 0.6 5.5
11 SA	0115 0725 1336 1943	1.4 5.3 1.4 5.0	**26** SU	0207 0816 1435 2047	0.8 5.7 0.8 5.3
12 SU	0143 0758 1406 2017	1.5 5.1 1.5 4.9	**27** M	0251 0902 1519 2134	1.0 5.5 1.0 5.1
13 M	0213 0831 1438 2053	1.6 5.0 1.7 4.7	**28** TU	0335 0947 1604 2223	1.3 5.2 1.3 4.8
14 TU	0247 0909 1518 2136	1.8 4.9 1.8 4.6	**29** W	0420 1035 1652 2317	1.6 4.9 1.7 4.6
15 W	0331 0956 1609 2229	2.0 4.7 2.0 4.5	**30** TH	0510 1131 1747	1.9 4.7 1.9
			31 F	0019 0611 1238 1854	4.4 2.1 4.5 2.1

Chart Datum: 3·22 metres below Ordnance Datum (Newlyn)

NAVAL EXERCISE AREAS (SUBFACTS & GUNFACTS)   8-1-18

Submarines and warships use the areas below and others E'ward to Nab Twr (8.2.34). Areas where submarines are planned to operate during all or part of the ensuing 24 hrs are broadcast daily on VHF at 0733 and 1933UT by the 4 Coast Radio Stations as shown below and by other CRS as shown in 4.10.1.1 and 6.9.2. Subfacts and Gunfacts are mentioned on Navtex by Niton at 0818 and 2018UT daily (see 5.3.3). Further info may be obtained from Naval Ops, Plymouth ☎ (01752) 501182. See 6.9.1 for general advice on submarine activity which also occurs in other sea areas. Submarines on the surface and at periscope depth will keep constant watch on VHF Ch 16. The former will comply strictly with IRPCS; the latter will not close to within 1500 yards of a FV without express permission from the FV.

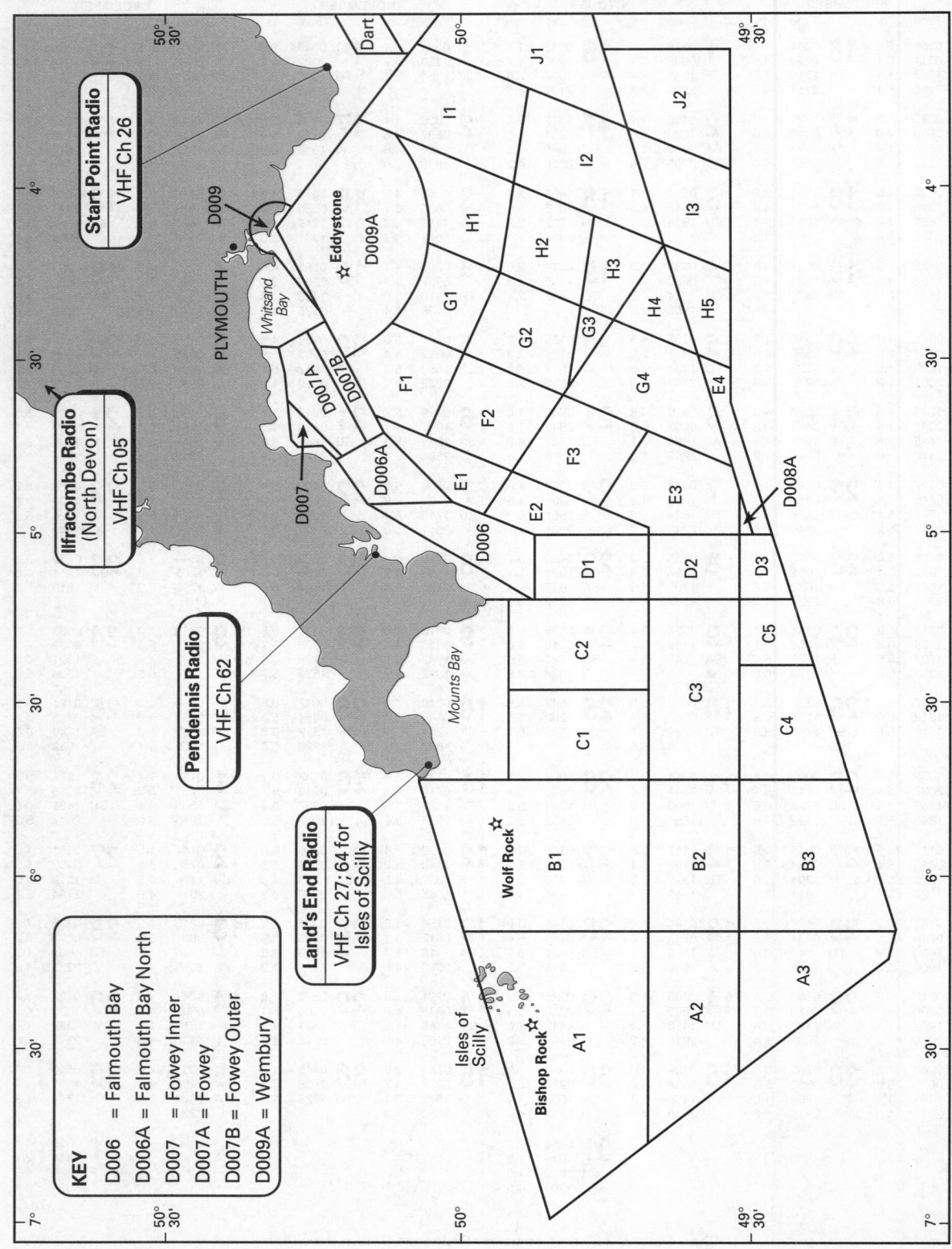

KEY

D006 = Falmouth Bay
D006A = Falmouth Bay North
D007 = Fowey Inner
D007A = Fowey
D007B = Fowey Outer
D009A = Wembury

Start Point Radio — VHF Ch 26

Ilfracombe Radio (North Devon) — VHF Ch 05

Pendennis Radio — VHF Ch 62

Land's End Radio — VHF Ch 27; 64 for Isles of Scilly

RIVER YEALM Devon 50°18'·55N 04°04'·06W (Ent)   Rtg 3-4-1

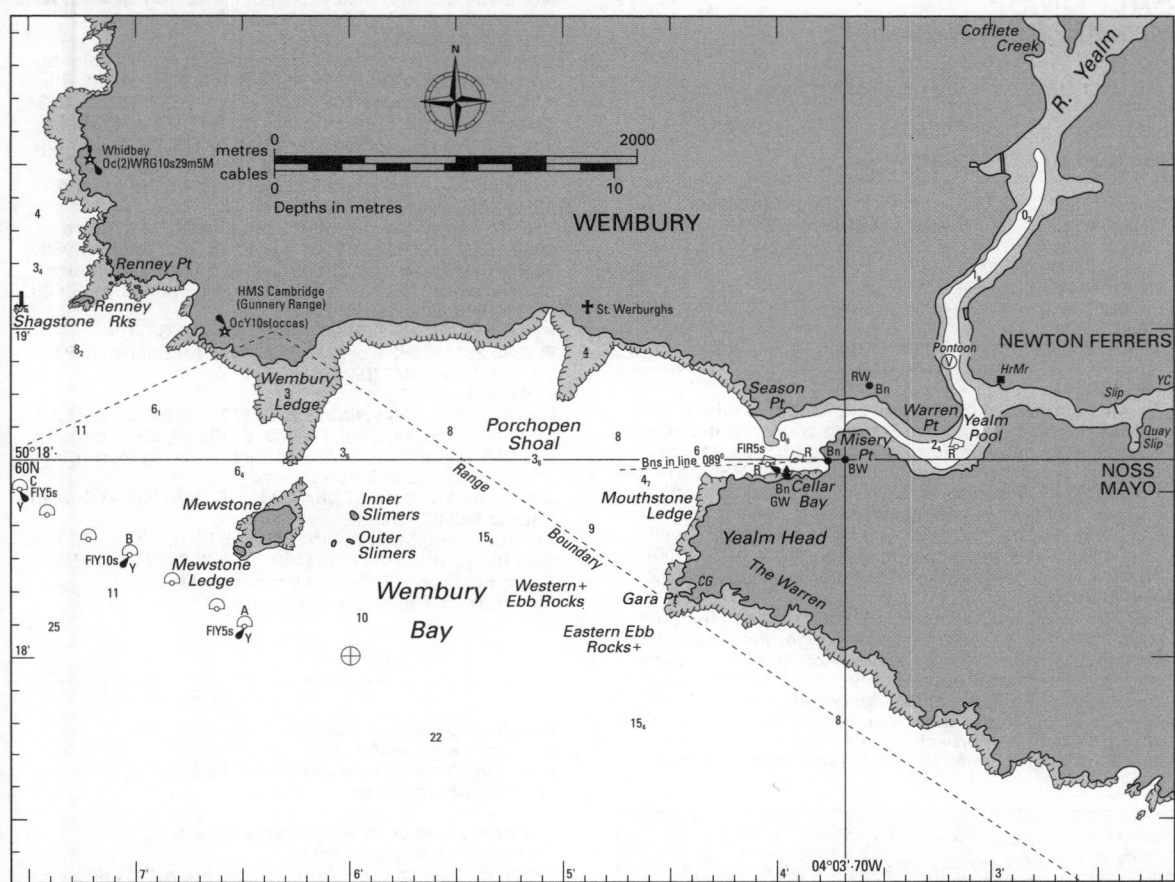

CHARTS
AC 30,1900,1613; Imray C6, C14; Stanfords 13; OS 201
TIDES
−0522 Dover; ML 3·2; Duration 0615; Zone 0 (UT)

Standard Port DEVONPORT (←—)

Times				Height (metres)			
High Water		Low Water		MHWS	MHWN	MLWN	MLWS
0000	0600	0000	0600	5·5	4·4	2·2	0·8
1200	1800	1200	1800				

Differences RIVER YEALM ENTRANCE
+0006 +0006 +0002 +0002   −0·1   −0·1   −0·1   −0·1
Note: Strong SW winds hold up the ebb and raise levels, as does the river if in spate.

SHELTER
Very good. Ent easy except in strong onshore winds. ⚓ in Cellar Bay is open to NW winds. ♥ pontoons in The Pool and up-river. No ⚓ in river due to lack of space.
NAVIGATION
WPT 50°18'·00N 04°06'·00W, 240°/060° from/to Season Pt, 1·4M. For details of **Wembury firing range** and target buoys, see 8.1.17. The SE edge of the range lies across the ent to the Yealm. The W & E Ebb rks and the Inner & Outer Slimers are dangerous, lying awash on E and W sides of Wembury Bay.
Ldg bns (W △, B stripe) in line at 089° clear Mouthstone Ledge, but **not** the sand bar. Two PHM buoys (Apr-Oct) mark end of sand bar and **must** be left to port on entry; the seaward buoy is Fl R 5s. When abeam, **but not before**, bn (G ▲ on W □) on S shore, turn NE toward bn (W □, R stripe) on N shore. From sand bar to Misery Pt, river carries only 1·2m at MLWS. Leave Spit PHM buoy off Warren Pt to port. It is impossible to beat in against an ebb tide. Speed limit 6kn.
LIGHTS AND MARKS
Great Mewstone (57m) is conspic 1·5M to W of river ent. Bns as above. Only light is outer PHM buoy Fl R 5s at ent.

TELEPHONE (Dial code 01752)
Hr Mr 872533; MRSC (01803) 882704; ⌗ 0345 231110 (H24); Marinecall 0891 500458; Police 701188; Dr 880392.
RADIO TELEPHONE None.
FACILITIES
Yealm Pool M, pontoon £9, L, FW; **Yealm YC** ☎ 872291, FW, Bar; **Newton Ferrers** L, Slip, FW, V, Gas, Gaz, R, Bar, ✉; **Services:** Sh, SM. **Bridgend** L, Slip (HW±2½), FW; **Noss Mayo** L, Slip, FW, V, R, Bar; Nearest fuel 3M at Yealmpton. ≈ ✈ (Plymouth).

ADJACENT ANCHORAGES IN BIGBURY BAY

RIVER ERME, Devon, 50°18'·12N 03°57'·60W. AC 1613. HW − 0525 on Dover; +0015 and −0·6m on HW Devonport. Temp day ⚓ in 3m at mouth of drying river, open to SW. Access near HW, but only in offshore winds and settled wx. Beware Wells Rk (1·2m) 1M SE of ent. Appr from SW, clear of Edwards Rk. Ent between Battisborough Is and W. Mary's Rk (dries 1·1m) keeping to the W. No facilities. Two Historic Wrecks are at 50°18'·15N 03°57'·41W and 50°18'·41N 03°57'·19W on W side of the ent; see 8.0.3h.

RIVER AVON, Devon, 50°16'·61N 03°53'·60W. AC 1613. Tides as R Erme, above. Enter drying river HW −1, only in offshore winds and settled wx. Appr close E of conspic Burgh Is & Murray's Rks, marked by bn. Narrow chan hugs cliffy NW shore, then turns SE and N off Bantham. A recce at LW or local knowledge would assist. Streams run hard, but able to dry out in good shelter clear of moorings. V, ✉, Bar at Bantham. Aveton Gifford accessible by dinghy, 2·5M.

HOPE COVE, Devon, 50°14'·62N 03°51'·75W. AC 1613. Tides as R Erme, above; ML 2·6m; Duration 0615. Popular day ⚓ in centre of cove, but poor holding ground and only safe in offshore winds. Appr with old LB ho brg 110° and ⚓ SW of pier hd. Beware rk, drying 2·5m, ½ca offshore and 3ca E of Bolt Tail. No lts. Facilities: very limited in village, EC Thurs; but good at Kingsbridge (6M bus), or Salcombe, (4M bus).

SALCOMBE   8-1-20

Devon 50°13'·55N 03°46'·60W. Rtg 3-2-1

CHARTS
AC *28, 1634, 1613*; Imray C6, Y48; Stanfords 13; OS 202

TIDES
–0523 Dover; ML 3·1; Duration 0615; Zone 0 (UT)

Standard Port DEVONPORT (←)

Times				Height (metres)			
High Water		Low Water		MHWS	MHWN	MLWN	MLWS
0100	0600	0100	0600	5·5	4·4	2·2	0·8
1300	1800	1300	1800				
Differences SALCOMBE							
0000	+0010	+0005	–0005	–0·2	–0·3	–0·1	–0·1
START POINT							
+0005	+0030	–0005	+0005	–0·2	–0·4	–0·1	–0·1

SHELTER
Perfectly protected hbr but ent exposed to S winds. The estuary is 4M long and has 8 drying creeks off it. Limited ‡ on SE side between ferry and ‡ prohib area. Plenty of deep water ⌀s. (Hr Mr's launch will contact VHF Ch14, on duty 0600-2100 in season; 0600-2200 in peak season). S'ly winds can cause an uncomfortable swell in the ‡ off the town. Visitors' pontoon and ⌀s in the Bag are well sheltered. Short stay pontoon (1 hour max, 0700-1900) by Hr Mr's office has 1m. Water taxi via Hr Mr, VHF Ch 12.

NAVIGATION
WPT 50°12'·40N 03°46'·60W, 180°/000° from/to Sandhill Pt lt, 1·3M. The bar (0·7m) can be dangerous at sp ebb tides with strong on-shore winds. Access HW±4½, but at springs this window applies only if swell height does not exceed 1m. The Bar is not as dangerous as rumour may have it, except in the above conditions; if in doubt, call Hr Mr Ch 14 before approaching. Rickham Rk, E of the Bar, has 3·1m depth. Speed limit 8kn; radar checks in force.

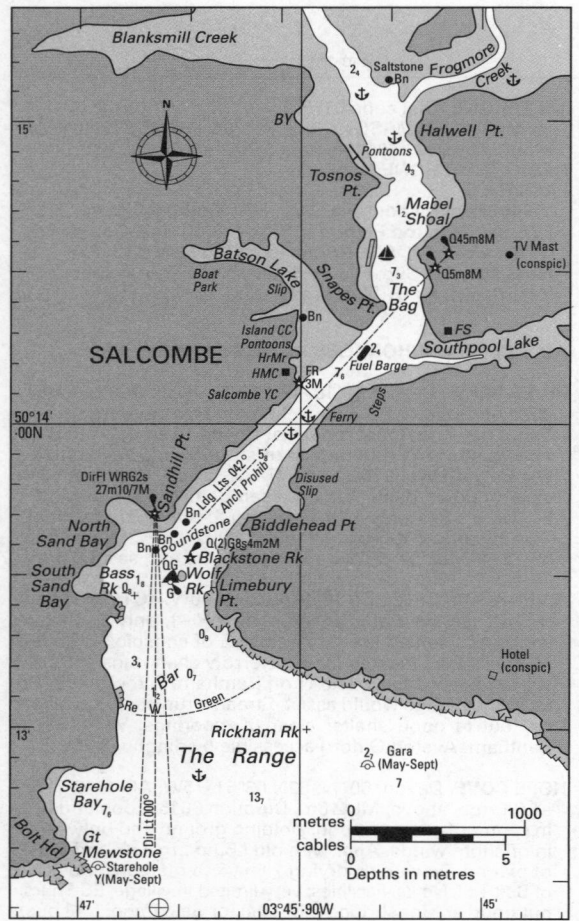

Note: The site of a Historic Wreck (50°12'·70N 03°44'·33W) is at Moor Sand, 1M WNW of Prawle Pt; see 8.0.3h.

LIGHTS AND MARKS
Outer ldg marks: Sandhill Pt bn on with Poundstone bn 000°. Sandhill Pt Dir lt 000°, Fl WRG 2s 27m 10/7M; R and W ♦ on W mast: vis R002°-182°, G182°-357°, W357°-002°. Beware unmarked Bass Rk (dries 0·8m) close W of ldg line and Wolf Rk, marked by SHM By QG, close E of ldg line. After passing Wolf Rk, pick up Inner ldg lts, Q Fl 042°, leaving Blackstone Rk Q (2) G 8s 4m 2M to stbd.

RADIO TELEPHONE
VHF Ch 14 call *Salcombe Hbr* or *Launch* (Mon-Thurs 0900-1645, Fri 0900-1615); 14 May-14 Sept Sat/Sun 0900-1615). Call *Water taxi* Ch 12. Call: *ICC Base* (clubhouse) and *Egremont* (ICC floating HQ) Ch M. *Fuel Barge* Ch 06.

TELEPHONE (Dial code 01548)
Hr Mr 843791, 🚲 842033; MRSC (01803) 882704; ⌗ 0345 231110 (H24) or (01752) 234600; Marinecall 0891 500458; Police 842107; Dr 842284.

FACILITIES
Harbour (300+150 visitors) ☎ 843791, £9.60 for ⌀ or AB on Ⓥ pontoon. M, Slip, Ⓔ, P, D, L, ME, EI, C (15 ton), Sh, CH, SM, Water Taxi; FW at visitors' pontoon by Hr Mr's Office. Public ⌙ at Batson Creek.
Salcombe YC ☎ 842872/842593, L, R, Bar; **Island Cruising Club** ☎ 843483, Bar, Ⓡ.
Services: Slip, M, P, D, FW, ME, CH, EI, Sh, ACA, Ⓔ, SM;
Fuel Barge ☎ (0836) 775644 or (01752) 223434, D, P.
Town EC Thurs; Ⓡ, ✉, Ⓑ, all facilities, ⇌ (bus to Plymouth or Totnes), ✈ (Plymouth).

Sunset and evening star,
And one clear call for me!
And may there be no moaning of the bar,
When I put out to sea,

But such a tide as moving seems asleep,
Too full for sound and foam,
When that which drew from out the boundless deep
Turns again home.

Twilight and evening bell,
And after that the dark!
And may there be no sadness of farewell,
When I embark;

For though from out our bourne of Time and Place
The flood may bear me far,
I hope to see my Pilot face to face
When I have crost the bar.

Crossing the Bar: Alfred Lord Tennyson (1809-1892)

Tennyson's famous poem written whilst on board a yacht at Salcombe. The description of putting out to sea on a calm evening is actually used as a metaphor for death.

ADJACENT HARBOUR UP-RIVER

KINGSBRIDGE, Devon, 50°16'·85N 03°46'·45W. AC *28*. HW = HW Salcombe +0005. Access HW±2½ for <2m draft/bilge keelers, max LOA 11m. Berth on visitors' pontoon E side or wall on W side of basin, drying 3·4m to soft mud. Best to pre-check berth availability with Hr Mr Salcombe. The 3M chan to Kingsbridge is marked beyond Salt Stone SHM perch by R/W PHM poles with R can topmarks. 6ca N of Salt Stone a secondary chan marked by PHM buoys diverges slowly E into Balcombe Creek. There is a private ferry pontoon at New Quay, 3ca before the visitors' pontoon. Facilities: Slip, SM.
Town EC Thurs; V, R, Bar, ✉, Ⓑ, Ⓡ.

ENGLAND – DARTMOUTH

LAT 50°21′N   LONG 3°34′W

TIMES AND HEIGHTS OF HIGH AND LOW WATERS

YEAR **1999**

TIME ZONE (UT)
For Summer Time add ONE hour in non-shaded areas

JANUARY

Day	Time	m	Day	Time	m
1 F	0508 / 1106 / 1735 / 2329	4.8 / 0.7 / 4.8 / 0.6	**16** SA	0510 / 1056 / 1731 / 2315	4.5 / 1.2 / 4.4 / 1.1
2 SA O	0600 / 1157 / 1828	5.0 / 0.5 / 4.9	**17** SU ●	0554 / 1139 / 1817 / 2356	4.7 / 1.0 / 4.5 / 0.9
3 SU	0018 / 0648 / 1245 / 1915	0.5 / 5.1 / 0.4 / 4.8	**18** M	0637 / 1221 / 1858	4.8 / 0.8 / 4.6
4 M	0104 / 0733 / 1330 / 2000	0.5 / 5.0 / 0.4 / 4.8	**19** TU	0038 / 0716 / 1303 / 1938	0.8 / 4.8 / 0.7 / 4.6
5 TU	0146 / 0814 / 1411 / 2041	0.6 / 5.0 / 0.5 / 4.6	**20** W	0117 / 0753 / 1341 / 2015	0.8 / 4.8 / 0.7 / 4.6
6 W	0225 / 0851 / 1449 / 2116	0.8 / 4.8 / 0.8 / 4.4	**21** TH	0154 / 0830 / 1419 / 2052	0.8 / 4.8 / 0.7 / 4.5
7 TH	0301 / 0923 / 1525 / 2145	1.1 / 4.6 / 1.1 / 4.2	**22** F	0230 / 0907 / 1456 / 2130	0.8 / 4.7 / 0.8 / 4.5
8 F	0335 / 0953 / 1601 / 2217	1.4 / 4.4 / 1.4 / 4.0	**23** SA	0309 / 0947 / 1535 / 2211	1.0 / 4.6 / 1.0 / 4.3
9 SA	0413 / 1030 / 1641 / 2259	1.7 / 4.1 / 1.7 / 3.8	**24** SU	0351 / 1032 / 1622 / 2300	1.2 / 4.4 / 1.2 / 4.2
10 SU	0458 / 1117 / 1730 / 2356	1.9 / 3.9 / 1.9 / 3.7	**25** M	0442 / 1127 / 1719	1.4 / 4.2 / 1.5
11 M	0555 / 1218 / 1833	2.1 / 3.8 / 2.0	**26** TU	0002 / 0549 / 1236 / 1836	4.0 / 1.7 / 4.0 / 1.6
12 TU	0110 / 0705 / 1337 / 1941	3.7 / 2.2 / 3.8 / 2.0	**27** W	0118 / 0721 / 1358 / 2006	4.0 / 1.7 / 4.0 / 1.6
13 W	0229 / 0814 / 1453 / 2047	3.9 / 2.0 / 3.9 / 1.8	**28** TH	0241 / 0849 / 1517 / 2123	4.1 / 1.5 / 4.2 / 1.3
14 TH	0331 / 0917 / 1553 / 2143	4.1 / 1.7 / 4.1 / 1.5	**29** F	0352 / 0958 / 1625 / 2225	4.4 / 1.2 / 4.4 / 1.0
15 F	0423 / 1010 / 1645 / 2231	4.3 / 1.4 / 4.3 / 1.3	**30** SA	0452 / 1055 / 1723 / 2318	4.6 / 0.8 / 4.5 / 0.7
			31 SU O	0545 / 1145 / 1815	4.8 / 0.6 / 4.7

FEBRUARY

Day	Time	m	Day	Time	m
1 M	0005 / 0632 / 1233 / 1859	0.5 / 4.9 / 0.4 / 4.7	**16** TU ●	0616 / 1204 / 1841	4.8 / 0.6 / 4.6
2 TU	0050 / 0715 / 1315 / 1941	0.4 / 5.0 / 0.4 / 4.7	**17** W	0022 / 0657 / 1248 / 1921	0.6 / 4.9 / 0.4 / 4.7
3 W	0130 / 0754 / 1353 / 2017	0.4 / 4.9 / 0.4 / 4.6	**18** TH	0105 / 0739 / 1329 / 2001	0.4 / 5.0 / 0.3 / 4.8
4 TH	0205 / 0826 / 1427 / 2046	0.6 / 4.8 / 0.6 / 4.5	**19** F	0143 / 0817 / 1407 / 2039	0.4 / 5.0 / 0.3 / 4.7
5 F	0236 / 0854 / 1457 / 2111	0.8 / 4.7 / 0.9 / 4.4	**20** SA	0220 / 0855 / 1442 / 2116	0.4 / 4.9 / 0.4 / 4.7
6 SA	0305 / 0922 / 1525 / 2140	1.1 / 4.5 / 1.2 / 4.2	**21** SU	0256 / 0935 / 1520 / 2154	0.6 / 4.7 / 0.7 / 4.5
7 SU	0333 / 0954 / 1553 / 2214	1.4 / 4.3 / 1.5 / 4.0	**22** M	0334 / 1016 / 1600 / 2238	0.9 / 4.5 / 1.0 / 4.3
8 M	0405 / 1032 / 1627 / 2258	1.7 / 4.0 / 1.8 / 3.8	**23** TU	0421 / 1106 / 1651 / 2334	1.2 / 4.2 / 1.4 / 4.0
9 TU	0450 / 1121 / 1724 / 2357	1.9 / 3.8 / 2.0 / 3.7	**24** W	0521 / 1214 / 1800	1.6 / 3.9 / 1.7
10 W	0602 / 1226 / 1841	2.1 / 3.6 / 2.1	**25** TH	0052 / 0651 / 1341 / 1945	3.9 / 1.8 / 3.8 / 1.8
11 TH	0118 / 0720 / 1359 / 1955	3.7 / 2.1 / 3.6 / 2.0	**26** F	0220 / 0837 / 1505 / 2112	3.9 / 1.6 / 3.9 / 1.5
12 F	0250 / 0832 / 1522 / 2102	3.8 / 1.8 / 3.9 / 1.7	**27** SA	0337 / 0948 / 1614 / 2214	4.2 / 1.3 / 4.2 / 1.1
13 SA	0354 / 0936 / 1621 / 2201	4.1 / 1.5 / 4.1 / 1.4	**28** SU	0438 / 1044 / 1711 / 2305	4.5 / 0.9 / 4.4 / 0.8
14 SU	0445 / 1030 / 1711 / 2252	4.4 / 1.2 / 4.3 / 1.0			
15 M	0531 / 1118 / 1757 / 2338	4.6 / 0.8 / 4.5 / 0.8			

MARCH

Day	Time	m	Day	Time	m
1 M	0528 / 1131 / 1758 / 2350	4.7 / 0.5 / 4.6 / 0.5	**16** TU	0504 / 1054 / 1732 / 2316	4.6 / 0.7 / 4.5 / 0.7
2 TU O	0614 / 1214 / 1841	4.8 / 0.4 / 4.7	**17** W ●	0550 / 1142 / 1818	4.8 / 0.4 / 4.7
3 W	0032 / 0654 / 1255 / 1917	0.4 / 4.9 / 0.3 / 4.7	**18** TH	0003 / 0635 / 1227 / 1859	0.4 / 5.0 / 0.2 / 4.8
4 TH	0109 / 0729 / 1330 / 1948	0.4 / 4.9 / 0.4 / 4.7	**19** F	0047 / 0718 / 1311 / 1940	0.2 / 5.1 / 0.1 / 4.9
5 F	0141 / 0759 / 1400 / 2014	0.5 / 4.8 / 0.5 / 4.6	**20** SA	0128 / 0800 / 1350 / 2020	0.1 / 5.1 / 0.1 / 4.9
6 SA	0209 / 0825 / 1427 / 2040	0.6 / 4.7 / 0.8 / 4.5	**21** SU	0206 / 0841 / 1428 / 2058	0.2 / 5.0 / 0.3 / 4.8
7 SU	0234 / 0853 / 1449 / 2108	0.9 / 4.5 / 1.0 / 4.3	**22** M	0242 / 0921 / 1504 / 2137	0.4 / 4.8 / 0.6 / 4.6
8 M	0256 / 0923 / 1509 / 2139	1.2 / 4.3 / 1.3 / 4.1	**23** TU	0322 / 1003 / 1544 / 2219	0.7 / 4.5 / 1.0 / 4.3
9 TU	0318 / 0957 / 1531 / 2216	1.5 / 4.0 / 1.6 / 3.9	**24** W	0406 / 1052 / 1632 / 2314	1.1 / 4.1 / 1.4 / 4.0
10 W	0349 / 1039 / 1611 / 2305	1.8 / 3.8 / 1.9 / 3.7	**25** TH	0504 / 1202 / 1739	1.6 / 3.8 / 1.8
11 TH	0453 / 1137 / 1740	2.1 / 3.6 / 2.2	**26** F	0034 / 0635 / 1331 / 1928	3.8 / 1.8 / 3.7 / 1.9
12 F	0014 / 0635 / 1300 / 1913	3.6 / 2.1 / 3.5 / 2.1	**27** SA	0204 / 0823 / 1452 / 2056	3.8 / 1.7 / 3.8 / 1.6
13 SA	0155 / 0753 / 1448 / 2027	3.7 / 1.9 / 3.7 / 1.8	**28** SU	0319 / 0932 / 1559 / 2156	4.1 / 1.3 / 4.1 / 1.2
14 SU	0319 / 0902 / 1553 / 2131	4.0 / 1.5 / 4.0 / 1.4	**29** M	0418 / 1024 / 1652 / 2245	4.4 / 0.9 / 4.3 / 0.8
15 M	0416 / 1001 / 1645 / 2226	4.3 / 1.1 / 4.3 / 1.0	**30** TU	0506 / 1110 / 1735 / 2328	4.6 / 0.6 / 4.5 / 0.6
			31 W O	0549 / 1151 / 1815	4.7 / 0.4 / 4.6

APRIL

Day	Time	m	Day	Time	m
1 TH	0007 / 0627 / 1230 / 1848	0.4 / 4.8 / 0.4 / 4.7	**16** F ●	0610 / 1203 / 1835	5.0 / 0.1 / 4.9
2 F	0044 / 0659 / 1303 / 1917	0.4 / 4.8 / 0.4 / 4.7	**17** SA	0025 / 0655 / 1250 / 1918	0.1 / 5.1 / 0.0 / 5.0
3 SA	0115 / 0730 / 1331 / 1945	0.5 / 4.7 / 0.6 / 4.6	**18** SU	0110 / 0740 / 1331 / 2001	0.0 / 5.1 / 0.0 / 5.0
4 SU	0141 / 0759 / 1355 / 2012	0.6 / 4.6 / 0.8 / 4.6	**19** M	0150 / 0824 / 1412 / 2042	0.1 / 5.0 / 0.2 / 4.9
5 M	0204 / 0827 / 1416 / 2041	0.8 / 4.5 / 1.0 / 4.4	**20** TU	0230 / 0908 / 1451 / 2122	0.3 / 4.8 / 0.6 / 4.7
6 TU	0226 / 0856 / 1434 / 2110	1.1 / 4.3 / 1.2 / 4.2	**21** W	0312 / 0952 / 1532 / 2205	0.7 / 4.4 / 1.0 / 4.4
7 W	0246 / 0929 / 1458 / 2143	1.3 / 4.0 / 1.5 / 4.0	**22** TH	0357 / 1044 / 1622 / 2258	1.1 / 4.1 / 1.4 / 4.1
8 TH	0317 / 1008 / 1534 / 2229	1.6 / 3.8 / 1.8 / 3.8	**23** F	0455 / 1154 / 1726	1.5 / 3.8 / 1.8
9 F	0408 / 1104 / 1640 / 2331	1.9 / 3.6 / 2.1 / 3.7	**24** SA	0016 / 0618 / 1316 / 1901	3.9 / 1.8 / 3.7 / 1.9
10 SA	0552 / 1216 / 1833	2.0 / 3.5 / 2.1	**25** SU	0141 / 0755 / 1430 / 2027	3.9 / 1.7 / 3.8 / 1.7
11 SU	0049 / 0717 / 1358 / 1951	3.7 / 1.9 / 3.7 / 1.8	**26** M	0252 / 0903 / 1532 / 2126	4.0 / 1.3 / 4.0 / 1.3
12 M	0230 / 0828 / 1518 / 2058	3.9 / 1.5 / 4.0 / 1.4	**27** TU	0349 / 0956 / 1622 / 2216	4.2 / 1.0 / 4.3 / 1.0
13 TU	0339 / 0930 / 1613 / 2157	4.3 / 1.1 / 4.3 / 1.0	**28** W	0438 / 1041 / 1704 / 2259	4.4 / 0.8 / 4.4 / 0.8
14 W	0431 / 1025 / 1702 / 2251	4.6 / 0.7 / 4.6 / 0.8	**29** TH	0519 / 1121 / 1743 / 2338	4.6 / 0.6 / 4.6 / 0.6
15 TH	0521 / 1116 / 1749 / 2339	4.8 / 0.3 / 4.8 / 0.3	**30** F O	0556 / 1158 / 1817	4.6 / 0.6 / 4.6

Chart Datum: 2·62 metres below Ordnance Datum (Newlyn)

TIME ZONE (UT)
For Summer Time add ONE hour in non-shaded areas

ENGLAND – DARTMOUTH

LAT 50°21′N   LONG 3°34′W

TIMES AND HEIGHTS OF HIGH AND LOW WATERS

YEAR **1999**

MAY

	Time	m		Time	m
1 SA	0014 / 0630 / 1233 / 1848	0.6 / 4.6 / 0.6 / 4.7	**16** SU	0003 / 0635 / 1227 / 1857	0.1 / 5.0 / 0.1 / 5.1
2 SU	0046 / 0703 / 1301 / 1919	0.6 / 4.6 / 0.7 / 4.6	**17** M	0052 / 0723 / 1314 / 1942	0.1 / 5.0 / 0.1 / 5.1
3 M	0114 / 0735 / 1326 / 1949	0.7 / 4.5 / 0.9 / 4.6	**18** TU	0136 / 0810 / 1357 / 2026	0.1 / 4.9 / 0.3 / 5.0
4 TU	0138 / 0806 / 1349 / 2018	0.9 / 4.4 / 1.0 / 4.5	**19** W	0220 / 0856 / 1440 / 2109	0.3 / 4.7 / 0.6 / 4.8
5 W	0203 / 0836 / 1412 / 2048	1.1 / 4.2 / 1.2 / 4.3	**20** TH	0304 / 0944 / 1524 / 2153	0.6 / 4.4 / 1.0 / 4.5
6 TH	0229 / 0908 / 1439 / 2121	1.3 / 4.0 / 1.4 / 4.1	**21** F	0350 / 1036 / 1612 / 2244	1.0 / 4.1 / 1.3 / 4.2
7 F	0301 / 0948 / 1517 / 2204	1.5 / 3.8 / 1.7 / 4.0	**22** SA	0444 / 1139 / 1708 / 2352	1.4 / 3.9 / 1.7 / 4.0
8 SA	0350 / 1040 / 1616 / 2300	1.7 / 3.8 / 1.9 / 3.8	**23** SU	0550 / 1248 / 1819	1.6 / 3.7 / 1.8
9 SU	0514 / 1145 / 1751	1.8 / 3.6 / 2.0	**24** M	0106 / 0709 / 1354 / 1938	3.9 / 1.6 / 3.8 / 1.8
10 M	0009 / 0640 / 1303 / 1914	3.8 / 1.7 / 3.7 / 1.8	**25** TU	0214 / 0820 / 1453 / 2044	3.9 / 1.5 / 3.9 / 1.6
11 TU	0131 / 0751 / 1429 / 2022	4.0 / 1.4 / 4.0 / 1.4	**26** W	0311 / 0916 / 1544 / 2138	4.1 / 1.3 / 4.1 / 1.3
12 W	0252 / 0856 / 1535 / 2125	4.2 / 1.1 / 4.3 / 1.0	**27** TH	0400 / 1023 / 1628 / 2224	4.2 / 1.1 / 4.3 / 1.1
13 TH	0356 / 0955 / 1629 / 2222	4.5 / 0.7 / 4.6 / 0.7	**28** F	0444 / 1047 / 1708 / 2305	4.3 / 0.9 / 4.4 / 0.9
14 F	0451 / 1049 / 1721 / 2315	4.8 / 0.4 / 4.8 / 0.4	**29** SA	0523 / 1125 / 1745 / 2342	4.4 / 0.8 / 4.5 / 0.8
15 SA ●	0544 / 1139 / 1811	4.9 / 0.2 / 5.0	**30** SU ○	0601 / 1200 / 1821	4.5 / 0.8 / 4.6
			31 M	0016 / 0639 / 1232 / 1856	0.8 / 4.5 / 0.9 / 4.6

JUNE

	Time	m		Time	m
1 TU	0048 / 0715 / 1301 / 1930	0.9 / 4.4 / 0.9 / 4.6	**16** W	0124 / 0758 / 1345 / 2012	0.2 / 4.8 / 0.4 / 5.0
2 W	0118 / 0750 / 1330 / 2002	0.9 / 4.3 / 1.0 / 4.5	**17** TH	0210 / 0846 / 1429 / 2057	0.3 / 4.6 / 0.6 / 4.8
3 TH	0147 / 0823 / 1359 / 2033	1.0 / 4.2 / 1.2 / 4.4	**18** F	0254 / 0933 / 1512 / 2139	0.6 / 4.4 / 0.8 / 4.6
4 F	0219 / 0856 / 1431 / 2106	1.2 / 4.1 / 1.3 / 4.3	**19** SA	0337 / 1019 / 1555 / 2222	0.9 / 4.2 / 1.2 / 4.3
5 SA	0255 / 0935 / 1511 / 2147	1.3 / 4.0 / 1.5 / 4.2	**20** SU	0423 / 1108 / 1641 / 2309	1.2 / 4.0 / 1.5 / 4.1
6 SU	0341 / 1021 / 1602 / 2237	1.4 / 3.9 / 1.6 / 4.1	**21** M	0513 / 1204 / 1733	1.5 / 3.8 / 1.7
7 M	0443 / 1119 / 1711 / 2338	1.4 / 3.8 / 1.7 / 4.0	**22** TU	0010 / 0611 / 1303 / 1836	3.9 / 1.6 / 3.7 / 1.8
8 TU	0558 / 1225 / 1832	1.5 / 3.8 / 1.7	**23** W	0118 / 0717 / 1404 / 1943	3.8 / 1.7 / 3.8 / 1.8
9 W	0048 / 0713 / 1342 / 1945	4.0 / 1.4 / 4.0 / 1.5	**24** TH	0222 / 0822 / 1458 / 2048	3.9 / 1.6 / 3.9 / 1.6
10 TH	0209 / 0821 / 1455 / 2053	4.2 / 1.1 / 4.2 / 1.1	**25** F	0318 / 0918 / 1548 / 2142	4.0 / 1.4 / 4.1 / 1.4
11 F	0322 / 0925 / 1558 / 2155	4.4 / 0.8 / 4.5 / 0.8	**26** SA	0408 / 1007 / 1632 / 2229	4.1 / 1.2 / 4.3 / 1.2
12 SA	0424 / 1023 / 1655 / 2252	4.6 / 0.6 / 4.7 / 0.5	**27** SU	0452 / 1050 / 1716 / 2311	4.2 / 1.1 / 4.4 / 1.1
13 SU ●	0522 / 1118 / 1748 / 2345	4.8 / 0.4 / 4.9 / 0.3	**28** M ○	0535 / 1128 / 1748 / 2349	4.3 / 1.0 / 4.5 / 1.0
14 M	0617 / 1209 / 1839	4.9 / 0.3 / 5.0	**29** TU	0618 / 1205 / 1837	4.4 / 0.9 / 4.6
15 TU	0036 / 0707 / 1259 / 1927	0.2 / 4.9 / 0.3 / 5.0	**30** W	0025 / 0658 / 1241 / 1914	0.9 / 4.4 / 0.9 / 4.6

JULY

	Time	m		Time	m
1 TH	0102 / 0737 / 1316 / 1950	0.9 / 4.4 / 1.0 / 4.6	**16** F	0156 / 0830 / 1414 / 2041	0.3 / 4.6 / 0.5 / 4.9
2 F	0136 / 0813 / 1349 / 2023	0.9 / 4.3 / 1.0 / 4.5	**17** SA	0237 / 0912 / 1453 / 2117	0.5 / 4.5 / 0.7 / 4.7
3 SA	0211 / 0848 / 1425 / 2056	0.9 / 4.2 / 1.1 / 4.5	**18** SU	0316 / 0949 / 1529 / 2149	0.7 / 4.3 / 1.0 / 4.4
4 SU	0248 / 0924 / 1502 / 2134	1.0 / 4.1 / 1.2 / 4.4	**19** M	0353 / 1021 / 1607 / 2220	1.0 / 4.1 / 1.3 / 4.2
5 M	0328 / 1005 / 1545 / 2218	1.1 / 4.1 / 1.3 / 4.3	**20** TU	0431 / 1055 / 1648 / 2258	1.4 / 3.9 / 1.6 / 4.0
6 TU	0417 / 1054 / 1639 / 2312	1.3 / 4.0 / 1.4 / 4.2	**21** W	0516 / 1142 / 1738 / 2351	1.7 / 3.7 / 1.8 / 3.8
7 W	0518 / 1154 / 1747	1.4 / 3.9 / 1.5	**22** TH	0611 / 1247 / 1841	1.8 / 3.7 / 2.0
8 TH	0016 / 0632 / 1304 / 1907	4.1 / 1.4 / 4.0 / 1.5	**23** F	0107 / 0716 / 1403 / 1948	3.7 / 1.9 / 3.7 / 1.9
9 F	0135 / 0748 / 1421 / 2024	4.1 / 1.3 / 4.1 / 1.3	**24** SA	0230 / 0823 / 1508 / 2055	3.7 / 1.8 / 3.9 / 1.7
10 SA	0255 / 0900 / 1532 / 2134	4.2 / 1.1 / 4.4 / 1.0	**25** SU	0333 / 0923 / 1601 / 2152	3.9 / 1.5 / 4.1 / 1.4
11 SU	0404 / 1004 / 1634 / 2236	4.4 / 0.8 / 4.6 / 0.7	**26** M	0426 / 1015 / 1650 / 2241	4.1 / 1.3 / 4.4 / 1.2
12 M	0505 / 1102 / 1730 / 2331	4.6 / 0.6 / 4.8 / 0.5	**27** TU	0514 / 1100 / 1734 / 2324	4.3 / 1.1 / 4.5 / 1.0
13 TU ●	0601 / 1155 / 1823	4.7 / 0.4 / 4.9	**28** W ○	0558 / 1142 / 1818	4.4 / 1.0 / 4.6
14 W	0022 / 0654 / 1246 / 1912	0.3 / 4.8 / 0.3 / 5.0	**29** TH	0006 / 0641 / 1223 / 1857	0.8 / 4.4 / 0.9 / 4.7
15 TH	0112 / 0743 / 1331 / 1958	0.3 / 4.7 / 0.4 / 5.0	**30** F	0046 / 0722 / 1302 / 1936	0.7 / 4.5 / 0.8 / 4.7
			31 SA	0124 / 0800 / 1338 / 2011	0.7 / 4.4 / 0.8 / 4.7

AUGUST

	Time	m		Time	m
1 SU	0200 / 0836 / 1414 / 2046	0.7 / 4.4 / 0.8 / 4.6	**16** M	0247 / 0909 / 1459 / 2112	0.7 / 4.4 / 0.9 / 4.5
2 M	0235 / 0911 / 1449 / 2122	0.7 / 4.4 / 0.9 / 4.6	**17** TU	0318 / 0935 / 1529 / 2139	1.0 / 4.2 / 1.2 / 4.3
3 TU	0312 / 0949 / 1528 / 2202	0.9 / 4.3 / 1.0 / 4.4	**18** W	0347 / 1005 / 1601 / 2213	1.3 / 4.0 / 1.6 / 4.0
4 W	0353 / 1033 / 1614 / 2249	1.1 / 4.2 / 1.3 / 4.2	**19** TH	0421 / 1044 / 1642 / 2256	1.7 / 3.8 / 1.9 / 3.8
5 TH	0444 / 1127 / 1712 / 2351	1.3 / 4.0 / 1.5 / 4.0	**20** F	0509 / 1136 / 1744 / 2356	2.0 / 3.7 / 2.1 / 3.6
6 F	0553 / 1236 / 1833	1.5 / 3.9 / 1.6	**21** SA	0620 / 1252 / 1900	2.1 / 3.6 / 2.1
7 SA	0110 / 0720 / 1357 / 2004	3.9 / 1.6 / 4.0 / 1.5	**22** SU	0134 / 0735 / 1428 / 2012	3.6 / 2.0 / 3.8 / 1.9
8 SU	0239 / 0844 / 1515 / 2121	4.0 / 1.4 / 4.2 / 1.2	**23** M	0306 / 0845 / 1533 / 2117	3.7 / 1.8 / 4.0 / 1.6
9 M	0352 / 0953 / 1620 / 2225	4.2 / 1.1 / 4.5 / 0.9	**24** TU	0403 / 0944 / 1625 / 2212	4.0 / 1.5 / 4.3 / 1.3
10 TU	0454 / 1052 / 1717 / 2320	4.5 / 0.8 / 4.7 / 0.6	**25** W	0452 / 1035 / 1712 / 2300	4.3 / 1.2 / 4.6 / 1.0
11 W ●	0549 / 1143 / 1808 / 2344	4.6 / 0.5 / 4.9 / 0.7	**26** TH ○	0537 / 1120 / 1755 / 2344	4.4 / 0.9 / 4.7 / 0.7
12 TH	0009 / 0639 / 1231 / 1855	0.3 / 4.7 / 0.4 / 5.0	**27** F	0621 / 1203 / 1838	4.6 / 0.7 / 4.7
13 F	0056 / 0725 / 1315 / 1938	0.2 / 4.7 / 0.3 / 5.0	**28** SA	0026 / 0702 / 1245 / 1916	0.6 / 4.6 / 0.6 / 4.9
14 SA	0137 / 0807 / 1353 / 2015	0.3 / 4.7 / 0.4 / 4.9	**29** SU	0107 / 0741 / 1323 / 1954	0.5 / 4.7 / 0.5 / 4.9
15 SU	0215 / 0842 / 1428 / 2047	0.4 / 4.6 / 0.6 / 4.7	**30** M	0143 / 0818 / 1358 / 2031	0.4 / 4.7 / 0.5 / 4.8
			31 TU	0219 / 0854 / 1433 / 2108	0.5 / 4.6 / 0.7 / 4.7

Chart Datum: 2·62 metres below Ordnance Datum (Newlyn)

ENGLAND – DARTMOUTH

LAT 50°21′N   LONG 3°34′W

TIMES AND HEIGHTS OF HIGH AND LOW WATERS

YEAR 1999

TIME ZONE (UT)
For Summer Time add ONE hour in non-shaded areas

SEPTEMBER

Day	Time	m	Day	Time	m
1 W	0254 / 0932 / 1511 / 2146	0.7 / 4.5 / 0.9 / 4.5	**16** TH	0302 / 0927 / 1514 / 2137	1.4 / 4.2 / 1.5 / 4.1
2 TH	0332 / 1012 / 1553 / 2232	1.0 / 4.3 / 1.2 / 4.2	**17** F	0322 / 1002 / 1540 / 2217	1.7 / 4.0 / 1.9 / 3.8
3 F	0420 / 1104 / 1648 / 2333	1.4 / 4.1 / 1.6 / 4.0	**18** SA	0352 / 1049 / 1636 / 2311	2.0 / 3.8 / 2.2 / 3.6
4 SA	0524 / 1213 / 1809	1.7 / 3.9 / 1.8	**19** SU	0517 / 1155 / 1816	2.3 / 3.6 / 2.3
5 SU	0058 / 0703 / 1342 / 1957	3.8 / 1.8 / 3.9 / 1.7	**20** M	0032 / 0654 / 1339 / 1936	3.5 / 2.3 / 3.7 / 2.1
6 M	0231 / 0838 / 1504 / 2116	3.9 / 1.6 / 4.2 / 1.4	**21** TU	0237 / 0809 / 1504 / 2045	3.7 / 2.0 / 4.0 / 1.7
7 TU	0347 / 0946 / 1610 / 2216	4.1 / 1.2 / 4.5 / 1.0	**22** W	0340 / 0913 / 1558 / 2143	4.0 / 1.6 / 4.3 / 1.3
8 W	0447 / 1040 / 1703 / 2307	4.4 / 0.9 / 4.7 / 0.6	**23** TH	0428 / 1007 / 1645 / 2233	4.3 / 1.2 / 4.6 / 0.9
9 TH ●	0536 / 1128 / 1751 / 2352	4.6 / 0.6 / 4.9 / 0.4	**24** F	0514 / 1055 / 1729 / 2319	4.5 / 0.9 / 4.8 / 0.6
10 F	0622 / 1211 / 1835	4.8 / 0.4 / 5.0	**25** SA O	0556 / 1140 / 1813	4.7 / 0.6 / 4.9
11 SA	0035 / 0701 / 1252 / 1912	0.3 / 4.8 / 0.3 / 5.0	**26** SU	0002 / 0638 / 1223 / 1854	0.4 / 4.8 / 0.4 / 5.0
12 SU	0114 / 0737 / 1328 / 1945	0.4 / 4.8 / 0.4 / 4.9	**27** M	0045 / 0718 / 1304 / 1935	0.3 / 4.9 / 0.4 / 5.0
13 M	0146 / 0806 / 1359 / 2012	0.5 / 4.7 / 0.6 / 4.7	**28** TU	0124 / 0757 / 1341 / 2013	0.3 / 4.9 / 0.4 / 5.0
14 TU	0216 / 0830 / 1427 / 2038	0.7 / 4.5 / 0.9 / 4.6	**29** W	0201 / 0835 / 1419 / 2053	0.4 / 4.8 / 0.6 / 4.8
15 W	0240 / 0856 / 1451 / 2106	1.0 / 4.4 / 1.2 / 4.3	**30** TH	0237 / 0914 / 1456 / 2134	0.7 / 4.7 / 0.8 / 4.6

OCTOBER

Day	Time	m	Day	Time	m
1 F	0316 / 0956 / 1539 / 2220	1.0 / 4.5 / 1.2 / 4.2	**16** SA	0240 / 0930 / 1500 / 2147	1.7 / 4.1 / 1.8 / 3.9
2 SA	0402 / 1047 / 1634 / 2323	1.5 / 4.2 / 1.6 / 3.9	**17** SU	0311 / 1013 / 1542 / 2239	2.0 / 3.9 / 2.1 / 3.6
3 SU	0507 / 1159 / 1800	1.9 / 3.9 / 1.9	**18** M	0404 / 1113 / 1727 / 2349	2.3 / 3.7 / 2.3 / 3.5
4 M	0053 / 0654 / 1329 / 1951	3.7 / 2.0 / 3.9 / 1.8	**19** TU	0609 / 1231 / 1858	2.4 / 3.7 / 2.2
5 TU	0226 / 0828 / 1452 / 2104	3.9 / 1.8 / 4.2 / 1.4	**20** W	0145 / 0732 / 1416 / 2008	3.6 / 2.1 / 4.0 / 1.8
6 W	0339 / 0931 / 1555 / 2200	4.2 / 1.3 / 4.5 / 1.0	**21** TH	0305 / 0839 / 1521 / 2109	4.0 / 1.7 / 4.3 / 1.3
7 TH	0433 / 1021 / 1646 / 2247	4.4 / 1.0 / 4.7 / 0.7	**22** F	0357 / 0936 / 1612 / 2202	4.3 / 1.3 / 4.6 / 0.9
8 F	0518 / 1107 / 1730 / 2330	4.7 / 0.7 / 4.9 / 0.5	**23** SA	0444 / 1026 / 1659 / 2251	4.6 / 0.9 / 4.8 / 0.6
9 SA ●	0558 / 1148 / 1810	4.8 / 0.5 / 4.9	**24** SU O	0528 / 1114 / 1745 / 2337	4.8 / 0.6 / 5.0 / 0.4
10 SU	0009 / 0634 / 1226 / 1845	0.4 / 4.8 / 0.5 / 4.9	**25** M	0612 / 1159 / 1830	5.0 / 0.4 / 5.1
11 M	0046 / 0705 / 1300 / 1915	0.4 / 4.8 / 0.6 / 4.9	**26** TU	0021 / 0655 / 1244 / 1914	0.3 / 5.1 / 0.3 / 5.1
12 TU	0117 / 0733 / 1330 / 1941	0.6 / 4.8 / 0.7 / 4.7	**27** W	0105 / 0737 / 1326 / 1957	0.3 / 5.1 / 0.4 / 5.1
13 W	0142 / 0758 / 1354 / 2008	0.8 / 4.7 / 1.0 / 4.6	**28** TH	0144 / 0817 / 1406 / 2040	0.4 / 5.0 / 0.5 / 4.9
14 TH	0204 / 0825 / 1417 / 2038	1.1 / 4.5 / 1.2 / 4.4	**29** F	0224 / 0859 / 1447 / 2124	0.7 / 4.9 / 0.8 / 4.6
15 F	0223 / 0855 / 1436 / 2109	1.4 / 4.3 / 1.5 / 4.1	**30** SA	0305 / 0943 / 1532 / 2213	1.1 / 4.6 / 1.2 / 4.3
			31 SU	0353 / 1035 / 1628 / 2318	1.5 / 4.3 / 1.6 / 3.9

NOVEMBER

Day	Time	m	Day	Time	m
1 M	0457 / 1145 / 1749	1.9 / 4.1 / 1.9	**16** TU	0340 / 1041 / 1636 / 2316	2.1 / 3.9 / 2.1 / 3.7
2 TU	0045 / 0633 / 1311 / 1928	3.8 / 2.1 / 4.0 / 1.8	**17** W	0511 / 1146 / 1811	2.3 / 3.9 / 2.1
3 W	0208 / 0801 / 1428 / 2039	3.9 / 1.9 / 4.2 / 1.5	**18** TH	0033 / 0646 / 1304 / 1927	3.7 / 2.1 / 4.0 / 1.8
4 TH	0314 / 0904 / 1529 / 2134	4.1 / 1.5 / 4.4 / 1.2	**19** F	0208 / 0758 / 1427 / 2032	3.9 / 1.8 / 4.2 / 1.4
5 F	0408 / 0955 / 1620 / 2220	4.4 / 1.2 / 4.6 / 0.9	**20** SA	0315 / 0900 / 1531 / 2130	4.2 / 1.4 / 4.5 / 1.0
6 SA	0451 / 1040 / 1703 / 2303	4.6 / 0.9 / 4.7 / 0.7	**21** SU	0409 / 0957 / 1626 / 2222	4.6 / 1.0 / 4.8 / 0.7
7 SU	0529 / 1121 / 1742 / 2340	4.7 / 0.7 / 4.8 / 0.7	**22** M	0458 / 1049 / 1718 / 2312	4.8 / 0.7 / 5.0 / 0.5
8 M ●	0604 / 1157 / 1816	4.7 / 0.7 / 4.8	**23** TU O	0546 / 1137 / 1808	5.0 / 0.5 / 5.1
9 TU	0015 / 0635 / 1232 / 1847	0.7 / 4.8 / 0.8 / 4.8	**24** W	0000 / 0633 / 1225 / 1856	0.3 / 5.1 / 0.5 / 5.1
10 W	0046 / 0704 / 1301 / 1917	0.8 / 4.8 / 0.9 / 4.7	**25** TH	0047 / 0718 / 1312 / 1943	0.3 / 5.2 / 0.4 / 5.0
11 TH	0112 / 0734 / 1328 / 1947	1.0 / 4.7 / 1.1 / 4.5	**26** F	0131 / 0803 / 1356 / 2030	0.5 / 5.1 / 0.5 / 4.9
12 F	0135 / 0803 / 1351 / 2017	1.2 / 4.6 / 1.3 / 4.4	**27** SA	0215 / 0848 / 1441 / 2117	0.7 / 5.0 / 0.8 / 4.6
13 SA	0157 / 0834 / 1415 / 2050	1.4 / 4.5 / 1.5 / 4.2	**28** SU	0259 / 0852 / 1528 / 2207	1.0 / 4.7 / 1.1 / 4.3
14 SU	0220 / 0907 / 1443 / 2127	1.6 / 4.2 / 1.7 / 4.0	**29** M	0346 / 1024 / 1621 / 2306	1.4 / 4.5 / 1.4 / 4.1
15 M	0252 / 0948 / 1525 / 2214	1.8 / 4.1 / 1.9 / 3.8	**30** TU	0441 / 1126 / 1724	1.7 / 4.2 / 1.7

DECEMBER

Day	Time	m	Day	Time	m
1 W	0018 / 0551 / 1239 / 1842	3.9 / 2.0 / 4.1 / 1.8	**16** TH	0427 / 1111 / 1717 / 2349	1.9 / 4.1 / 1.8 / 3.8
2 TH	0129 / 0714 / 1349 / 1957	3.9 / 2.0 / 4.1 / 1.7	**17** F	0547 / 1215 / 1837	2.0 / 4.0 / 1.8
3 F	0234 / 0824 / 1451 / 2057	4.0 / 1.8 / 4.2 / 1.5	**18** SA	0101 / 0711 / 1329 / 1950	3.9 / 1.8 / 4.1 / 1.5
4 SA	0329 / 0920 / 1545 / 2147	4.2 / 1.5 / 4.3 / 1.3	**19** SU	0221 / 0822 / 1448 / 2056	4.1 / 1.6 / 4.3 / 1.2
5 SU	0416 / 1008 / 1630 / 2232	4.4 / 1.3 / 4.4 / 1.1	**20** M	0330 / 0928 / 1555 / 2156	4.4 / 1.2 / 4.5 / 0.9
6 M	0457 / 1051 / 1711 / 2311	4.6 / 1.1 / 4.5 / 1.0	**21** TU	0430 / 1025 / 1655 / 2251	4.7 / 0.9 / 4.8 / 0.7
7 TU ●	0533 / 1129 / 1748 / 2346	4.7 / 1.0 / 4.6 / 0.9	**22** W O	0523 / 1119 / 1750 / 2342	4.9 / 0.6 / 4.9 / 0.5
8 W	0608 / 1204 / 1824	4.7 / 1.0 / 4.6	**23** TH	0615 / 1210 / 1843	5.1 / 0.4 / 5.0
9 TH	0018 / 0642 / 1237 / 1858	1.0 / 4.8 / 1.0 / 4.6	**24** F	0033 / 0703 / 1301 / 1933	0.4 / 5.2 / 0.4 / 5.0
10 F	0048 / 0716 / 1307 / 1933	1.1 / 4.7 / 1.1 / 4.5	**25** SA	0121 / 0751 / 1348 / 2021	0.4 / 5.2 / 0.4 / 4.9
11 SA	0115 / 0748 / 1335 / 2006	1.2 / 4.7 / 1.2 / 4.4	**26** SU	0206 / 0838 / 1433 / 2108	0.6 / 5.1 / 0.6 / 4.7
12 SU	0142 / 0820 / 1405 / 2039	1.3 / 4.5 / 1.3 / 4.3	**27** M	0249 / 0923 / 1517 / 2154	0.8 / 4.9 / 0.8 / 4.5
13 M	0212 / 0852 / 1436 / 2114	1.4 / 4.4 / 1.5 / 4.1	**28** TU	0332 / 1006 / 1601 / 2242	1.1 / 4.6 / 1.1 / 4.2
14 TU	0245 / 0930 / 1516 / 2156	1.6 / 4.3 / 1.6 / 4.0	**29** W	0417 / 1053 / 1648 / 2334	1.4 / 4.3 / 1.5 / 4.0
15 W	0328 / 1015 / 1606 / 2248	1.8 / 4.1 / 1.8 / 3.9	**30** TH	0506 / 1148 / 1742	1.7 / 4.1 / 1.7
			31 F	0035 / 0606 / 1253 / 1850	3.8 / 1.9 / 3.9 / 1.9

Chart Datum: 2·62 metres below Ordnance Datum (Newlyn)

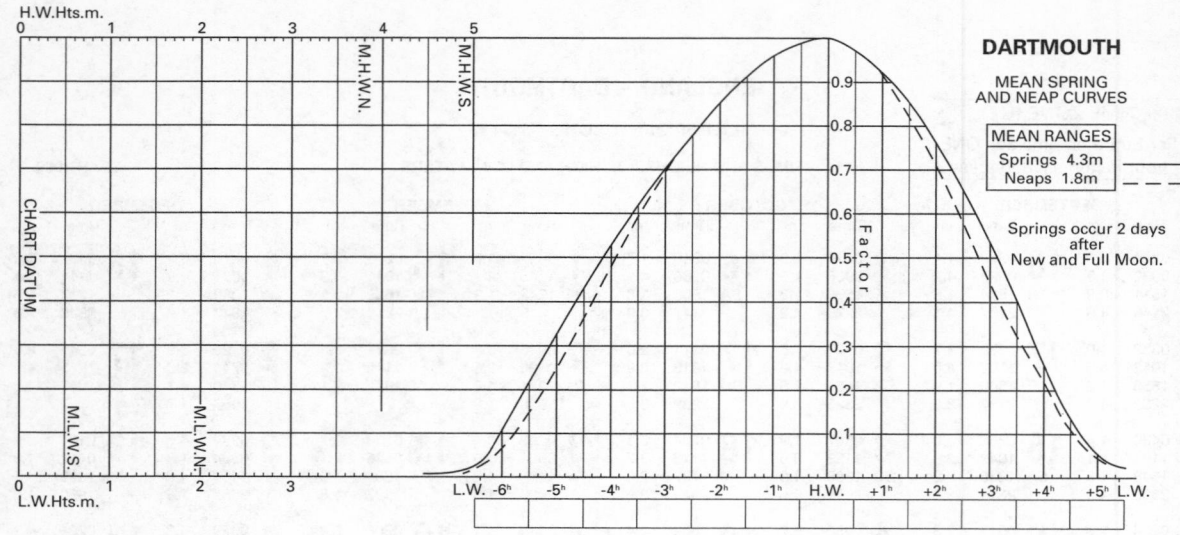

DARTMOUTH

MEAN SPRING
AND NEAP CURVES

MEAN RANGES
Springs 4.3m
Neaps 1.8m

Springs occur 2 days
after
New and Full Moon.

DARTMOUTH   8-1-21

Devon 50°20′·63N 03°33′·88W   Rtg 1-1-1

CHARTS
AC *2253, 1634, 1613*; Imray C5, Y47, Y43; Stanfords 12, 13;
OS 202

TIDES
−0510 Dover; ML 2·8; Duration 0630; Zone 0 (UT)

DARTMOUTH (←—)

Times				Height (metres)			
High Water		Low Water		MHWS	MHWN	MLWN	MLWS
0100	0600	0100	0600	4·9	3·8	2·0	0·6
1300	1800	1300	1800				

Differences GREENWAY QUAY (DITTISHAM)

+0015	+0020	+0025	+0010	0·0	0·0	0·0	0·0

TOTNES

+0015	+0015	+0115	+0035	−1·4	−1·5	Dries	Dries

NOTE: Dartmouth tidal predictions for each day of the year
are given above.

SHELTER
Excellent inside hbr, but ent can be difficult in strong SE
to SW winds. In mid-stream there are 8 big unlit mooring
buoys for commercial vessels/FVs; do not ⚓ over their
ground chains, as shown on AC 2253. Only space to ⚓ is
E of fairway, from abeam Nos 3 to 5 buoys.
The 3 marinas (Darthaven, Dart and Noss-on-Dart) have
Ⓥ berths. Apart from the pontoons off the Royal Dart YC,
the extensive pontoons and mooring trots elsewhere in
the hbr are run by the Hr Mr, who should be contacted by
VHF/☎. The most likely Ⓥ berths/⚓s from S to N are:
W bank: pontoon off Dartmouth YC (May-Sep); Town
jetty (W side only) near Boat Camber; N end of pontoon
just S of Dart marina (26′/8m max LOA).
E of fairway: (NB six pontoons N of Darthaven marina
are for locals only). Some ⚓s are in the mooring trots
from abeam No 5A buoy to the cable ferry. The 2
pontoons N of Fuel barge are for visitors.

NAVIGATION
WPT 50°19′·50N 03°32′·80W, 148°/328° from/to Kingswear
lt, Iso WRG, 1·5M. To the E of ent, on Inner Froward Pt
(153m) is a conspic daymark, obelisk (24·5m). There is no
bar and the hbr is always accessible. Speed limit 6kn.

LIGHTS AND MARKS
Kingswear Main lt 328°, Iso WRG 3s 9m 8M, W 325°-331°.
Bayard's Cove lt 293°, Fl WRG 2s 5m 6M, W 289°-297°.
Entry buoys as on chartlet. Within hbr, all jetty/ pontoon
lts to the W are 2FR (vert); and 2FG (vert) to the E.

RADIO TELEPHONE
Hr Mr call *Dartnav* VHF Ch 11 16 (Mon-Fri 0830-1800; Sat
0900-1200). Darthaven marina, Ch **80 M**; Dart marina,
Noss-on-Dart marina and Dart Sailing Centre, Ch 80. Fuel
barge Ch 06. Water taxi: call Ch 16, work Ch 08 06 M.

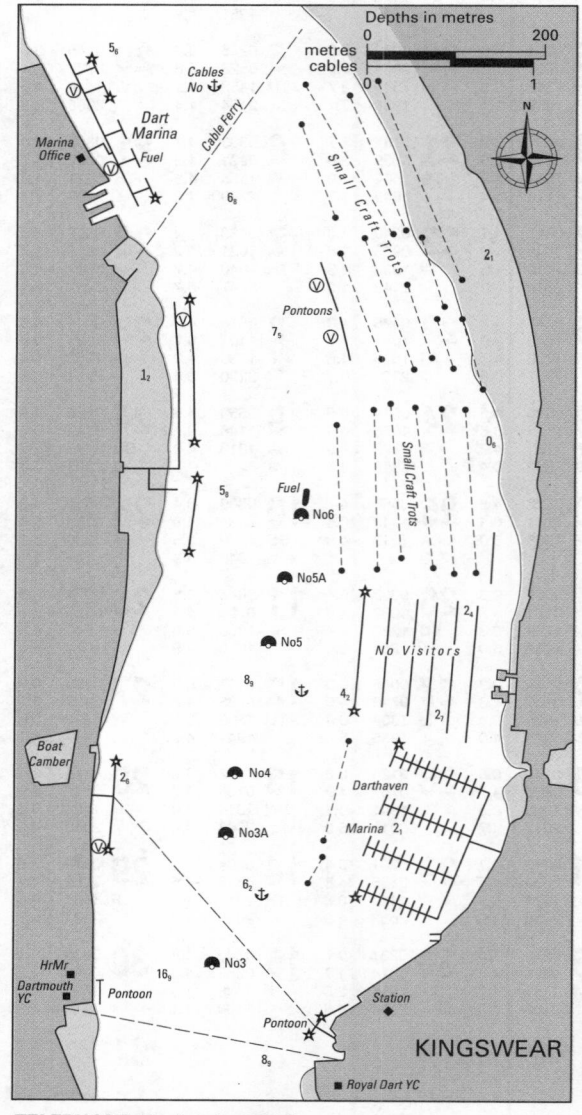

TELEPHONE (Dial code 01803)
Hr Mr 832337; MRSC 882704; ▥ 0345 231110 (H24); Police
832288; Marinecall 0891 500458; Dr 832212; Ⓗ 832255.

FACILITIES
Harbour/Marinas
Hbr Authority (450+90 Ⓥ), ☎ 832337, 🚤 833631; £12.13 - £13.53 (W bank pontoons), M, FW, Slip, V, R, ♿.

Darthaven Marina (230+12 Ⓥ) ☎ 752242, 🚤 752722, £16.47 inc £4.20 hbr dues, FW, ME, El, Gas, Gaz, 🅾, Sh, CH, Bar, R, BH (30 ton), AC, Ⓔ;

Dart Marina (110, inc up to 30 Ⓥs) ☎ 835570 Ext 241, 🚤 832307, £26.42 inc £4.20 hbr dues, D, FW, AC, ME, El, Sh, C (9 ton), 2 Slips, ⚓ at fuel berth, Gas, Gaz, CH, Bar, R, 🅾;

Noss-on-Dart Marina (150) ☎ 835570 Ext 248, 🚤 832307, £16.75 inc £4.20 hbr dues, FW, AC, ME, El, Sh, C (18 ton), CH, Gas, Gaz, 🅾;

Dart Sailing Centre ☎ 752702, AB, AC, Bar, R;

Creekside BY (Old Mill Creek) ☎ 832649, Slip, dry dock, M, ME, Sh, El, C (1 ton), CH, AB.

Clubs
Royal Dart YC ☎ 752272, M, L, FW, Bar; **Dartmouth YC** ☎ 832305, L, FW, Bar, R. Royal Regatta, last week August.

Services
M, ME, El, Sh, BH, CH, SM, rigging, masts, Ⓔ; **Water Taxi** ☎ 833727, (VHF Ch 16 06 08); **Fuel Barge** ☎ (0836) 775643 or 834136 out of hrs, VHF Ch 06, D; next to No 6 buoy. Galmpton Creek: CH, D, FW, L, M, C (6 ton), ME, Sh, SM, BY, Slip, AC, BH (53, 16 ton), El, Ⓔ; Slip at Higher Ferry.

Town EC Wed; ♿ WC/showers, V, P (cans), R, Bar, 🅾 (0800-2000 daily), ✉, Ⓑ, 🚉 ☎ 555872 (steam train in season to Paignton, or bus to Totnes/Paignton), ✈ (Plymouth/ Exeter).

UP RIVER TO DITTISHAM AND TOTNES
The R Dart is navigable on the flood to Totnes bridge, about 5·5M above Dittisham. HW Totnes = HW Dartmouth +0015. Speed limit 6kn to S end of Home Reach (1M from Totnes); then Dead Slow. No lights above The Noss.
Directions: Use AC 2253. Leave Anchor Stone (2½ca below Dittisham) to port. No ⚓ off Dittisham, but there are several ⚓s. From Dittisham brgs of 020° and 310° on successive Boat Houses lead between Lower Back and Flat Owers banks; or keep E of the latter. Thereafter 8 PHM and 3 SHM buoys, unlit and numbered in sequence (rather than evens to port/odds to stbd), plus some perches, mark the bends up to Home Reach; the channel favours the outside of bends. Unmasted boats can go beyond the bridge to the weir.
Berthing: Baltic Wharf BY ☎ 01803-865505, W bank just below Totnes, has drying AB (30), AC, FW, BH (16 ton), C (35 ton), ME, visitors welcomed. Steamer Quay is for ferries (leisure developments planned). Limited, drying AB on soft mud in the W Arm near the Steam Packet Inn, ☎ 863880, AC, FW, R, Bar, 🅾.
Totnes: EC Thurs; usual amenities; mainline 🚉.

BRIXHAM   8-1-22

Devon 50°24'·28N 03°30'·79W   Rtg 2-2-2

CHARTS
AC *26, 1613, 1634, 3315*; Imray C5, Y43; Stanfords 12; OS 202

TIDES
–0505 Dover; ML 2·9; Duration 0635; Zone 0 (UT)

Standard Port DEVONPORT (←)

Differences BRIXHAM are the same as TORQUAY (→)

SHELTER
Very good in marina; also at YC pontoon in SW corner of hbr, but outer hbr is dangerous in NW winds. ⚓s (W) to E of main fairway. Inner hbr dries. To W of hbr are ⚓s in Fishcombe Cove and Elberry Cove (beware water skiers).

NAVIGATION
WPT 50°24'·70N 03°30'·00W, 050°/230° from/to Victoria bkwtr lt, 0·60M. No dangers; easy access. Note: Around Torbay are controlled areas, close inshore and marked by Y SPM buoys, mainly for swimmers; boats may enter with caution, speed limit 5kn.

LIGHTS AND MARKS
Berry Hd lt, Fl (2) 15s 58m 15M, is 1·2M ESE of ent. Bkwtr hd Oc R 15s 9m 6M, W tr. 3 R ● or 3 Ⓡ lts (vert) at ent = hbr closed. At SE end of hbr a Dir lt Iso WR 5s 4m 6M, vis R145°-157°, W157°-161°, R161°-173° leads 159° into the fairway, marked by two pairs of lateral lt buoys.

RADIO TELEPHONE
Marina: Ch 80. YC and Water Taxi: *Shuttle* Ch M. Hr Mr Ch 14 16 (May-Sept 0800-1800LT; Oct-Apr 0900-1700, Mon-Fri). Brixham CG: Ch 16 10 67 73.

TELEPHONE (Dial code 01803)
Marina 882929; Hr Mr 853321; Pilot 882214; MRSC 882704; ⌨ 0345 231110 (H24); Marinecall 0891 500458; Police 882231; Dr 882731; Ⓗ 882153.

FACILITIES
Marina (480 inc Ⓥ) ☎ 882929, ⚓ 882737, £13.75, Access H24, AC, FW, D (0900-2000, Apr-Sep inc), R, Bar, ☑; **Hbr Office** (New Fish Quay) Slip, M, L, FW, C (2 ton), AB, D; **Brixham YC** ☎ 853332, Ⓥ pontoon, M, L, Slip, FW, R, Bar; **Services:** CH, ACA, ME, (H24), P (cans), El, Ⓔ. **Town** EC Wed; R, Bar, ☑, ✉, Ⓑ, ⇌ (bus to Paignton), ✈ (Exeter).

ADJACENT HARBOUR

PAIGNTON, Devon, 50°25'·93N 03°33'·29W. AC *26, 1613*. HW –0500 on Dover, +0035 on Devonport; HW –0·6m on Devonport; ML 2·9m; Duration 0640. Hbr dries 1·3m and is only suitable for max LOA 27'/8·2m. E winds cause a heavy swell in hbr. Rks extend 180m E from E wall. Black Rk has ECM tr, Q (3) 10s 5m 3M. QR 7m 3M lt on E arm of ent. Hr Mr (summer only) ☎ (01803) 557812. **Paignton SC** ☎ 525817; Facilities: EC Wed, M, ME, Sh, Gas, CH, ACA.

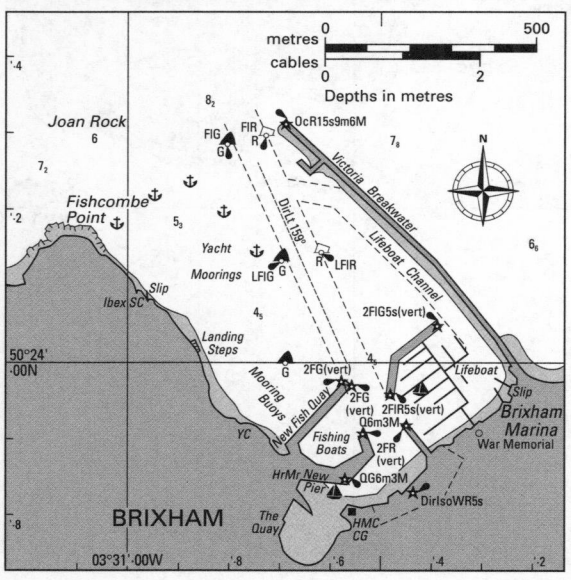

TORQUAY   8-1-23

Devon 50°27'·42N 03°31'·66W   Rtg 2-2-2

CHARTS
AC *26, 1613, 3315*; Imray C5, Y43; Stanfords 12; OS 202

TIDES
–0500 Dover; ML 2·9; Duration 0640; Zone 0 (UT)

Standard Port DEVONPORT (←)

Times				Height (metres)			
High Water		Low Water		MHWS	MHWN	MLWN	MLWS
0100	0600	0100	0600	5·5	4·4	2·2	0·8
1300	1800	1300	1800				

Differences TORQUAY
| +0025 | +0045 | +0010 | 0000 | –0·6 | –0·7 | –0·2 | –0·1 |

Note: There is often a stand of about 1 hour at HW

SHELTER
Good, but some swell in hbr with strong SE winds, which may make the narrow ent difficult due to backwash. No ⚓ within hbr. NW of Hope's Nose there are ⚓s at Hope Cove, Anstey's Cove and Babbacombe Bay, sheltered in W'lies.

NAVIGATION
WPT 50°27'·00N 03°31'·50W, 165°/345° from/to Haldon pier lt, 0·40M. Access at all tides. Inner (Old) hbr dries completely. Speed limit 5kn. 3 R ● or 3 R lts = hbr closed.

LIGHTS AND MARKS
No ldg marks/lts. Princess Pier head QR 9m 6M. Haldon pier hd QG 9m 6M. S pier hd 2FG (vert) 5M. All lts may be difficult to discern against town lts.

RADIO TELEPHONE
Port VHF Ch 14 16 (May-Sept 0800-1800LT; Oct-Apr 0900-1700, Mon-Fri). Marina Ch 80 (H24), M. *Torquay Fuel* Ch M.

TELEPHONE (Dial code 01803)
Hr Mr 292429; MRSC 882704; ⌨ 0345 231110 (H24); Police 0990 777444; Marinecall 0891 500458; Dr 212429; Ⓗ 614567.

FACILITIES
Marina (440+60 Ⓥ) ☎ 214624, ⚓ 291634, £19.00, FW, ME, Gas, Gaz, ♿, ☑, AC, SM, Ⓔ, El, Sh, CH, V, R, Bar, ACA. **S Pier** FW, C (6 ton), P & D: Torquay Fuel ☎ 294509/mobile 0385 226839 & VHF Ch M (Apr-Sept, 0830-1900 Mon-Sat, 1000-1900 Sun); **Haldon Pier** FW, AB; **Princess Pier** L; **Royal Torbay YC** ☎ 292006, R, Bar.

Town V, R, ☑, Bar, ✉, Ⓑ, ⇌, ✈ (Exeter or Plymouth).

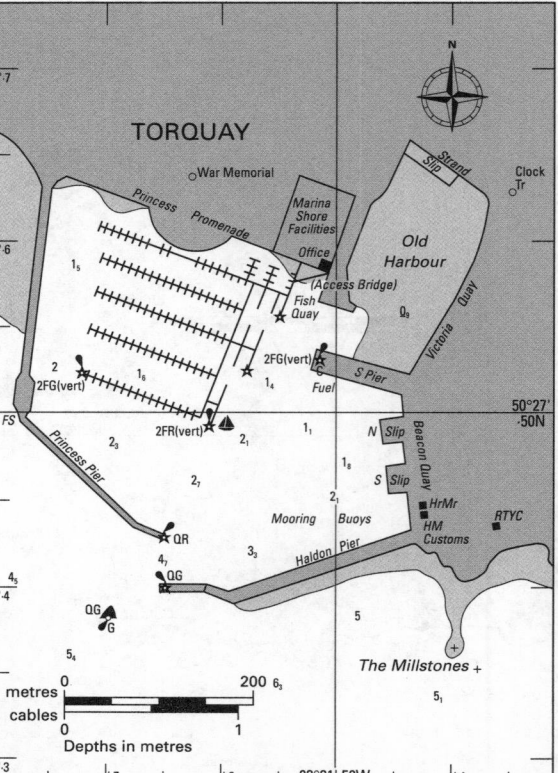

TEIGNMOUTH 8-1-24
Devon 50°32'·36N 03°30'·00W (Abeam The Point)   Rtg 3-3-2

CHARTS
AC *26, 3315*; Imray C5, Y43; Stanfords 12; OS 192

TIDES
−0450 Dover; ML 2·7; Duration 0625; Zone 0 (UT)

Standard Port DEVONPORT (◄──)

Times				Height (metres)			
High Water		Low Water		MHWS	MHWN	MLWN	MLWS
0100	0600	0100	0600	5·5	4·4	2·2	0·8
1300	1800	1300	1800				
Differences TEIGNMOUTH (Approaches)							
+0025	+0040	0000	0000	−0·7	−0·8	−0·3	−0·2
SHALDON BRIDGE							
+0035	+0050	+0020	+0020	−0·9	−0·9	−0·2	0·0

SHELTER
Hbr completely sheltered, but difficult to enter especially with strong winds from NE to S when surf forms on the bar. Access HW±3. Appr chan is not buoyed so local advice is recommended. No AB, but two ⚓s just N of SHM lt buoy, Fl G 5s. Speed limit is 8kn.

NAVIGATION
WPT 50°32'·40N 03°29'·20W, 076°/256° from/to training wall lt, 0·43M. Bar shifts very frequently. Beware rks off the Ness; and variable extent of Salty flats. Clearance under Shaldon bridge is 4·2m at MHWS (AC 26), but it is reported locally to be at most 2·9m at MHWS and approx 5·8m at MLWS. Avoid a Historic wreck site (50°32'·92N 03°29'·17W; just off chartlet), close inshore by Church Rks to ENE of Ch Tr (see 8.0.3h).

LIGHTS AND MARKS
The Ness, high red sandstone headland, and church tower are both conspic from afar; close NE of the latter, just off N edge of chartlet, Teign Corinthian YC bldg (cream colour) is also conspic. At seaward end of outfall, 105° The Ness 1·25M, is a Y buoy, Fl Y 5s, at 50°31'·93N 03°27'·81W. Y buoy, Fl Y 2s, marks S edge of Spratt Sand. Once round The Point, Oc G 5·5s and FG (vert), two F Bu lts on quay align 022°, but are not official ldg lts.

RADIO TELEPHONE
VHF Ch 12 16 (Mon-Fri: 0800-1700; Sat 0900-1200 LT).
TELEPHONE (Dial code 01626)
Hr Mr 773165; MRSC (01803) 882704; ⌗ 0345 231110 (H24); Marinecall 0891 500458; Police 772433; Dr 774355; Ⓗ 772161.
FACILITIES
E Quay Polly Steps Slip (up to 10m); **Teign Corinthian YC** ☎ 772734, ⚓ £8.00, M, FW, Bar; **Services:** ME, CH, El, Slip, BY, Sh, D, C (8 ton), Gas, Gaz, FW, CH, Ⓔ.
Town EC Thurs; P & D (cans, 1M), L, FW, V, R, Ⓞ, Bar, ✉, Ⓑ, ⇌, ✈ (Exeter).

AGENTS WANTED
If you are interested in becoming our agent for any of the following ports, please write to: The Editor, Edington House, Trent, Sherborne, Dorset DT9 4SR, England – and get your free copy of the Almanac annually. You do not have to live in a port to be the agent, but should at least be a fairly regular visitor.

Plymouth	Port Haliguen
Walton-on-the-Naze	La Trinité-sur-Mer
Hopeman	Piriac
Burghead	St Nazaire/Loire
Findhorn	Pornic
Nairn	St Gilles-Croix-de-Vie
Inverness	Les Sables d'Olonne
Loch Aline	River Seudre
Craobh	Port Bloc/Gironde
Workington	Anglet/Bayonne
Lough Swilly	St Jean-de-Luz
Portbail	Hendaye
St Malo/Dinard	Grandcamp-Maisy
Le Légué/St Brieuc	Port-en-Bessin
Lampaul	Ouistreham/Caen
L'Aberildut	Dives
Douarnenez	St Valéry-en-Caux
Lorient	Dunkerque
River Étel	Emden
Le Palais (Belle Ile)	Langeoog

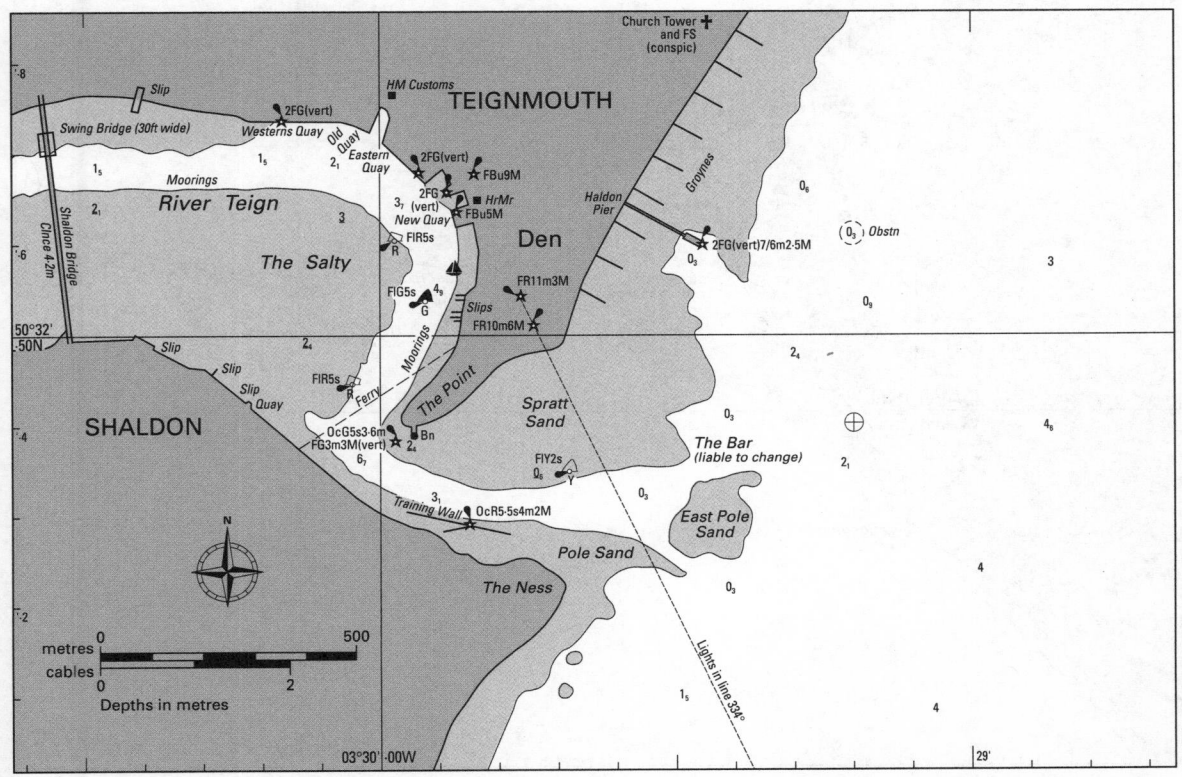

RIVER EXE   8-1-25

Devon 50°36'·91N 03°25'·33W (Abeam Exmouth)   Rtg 3-2-2

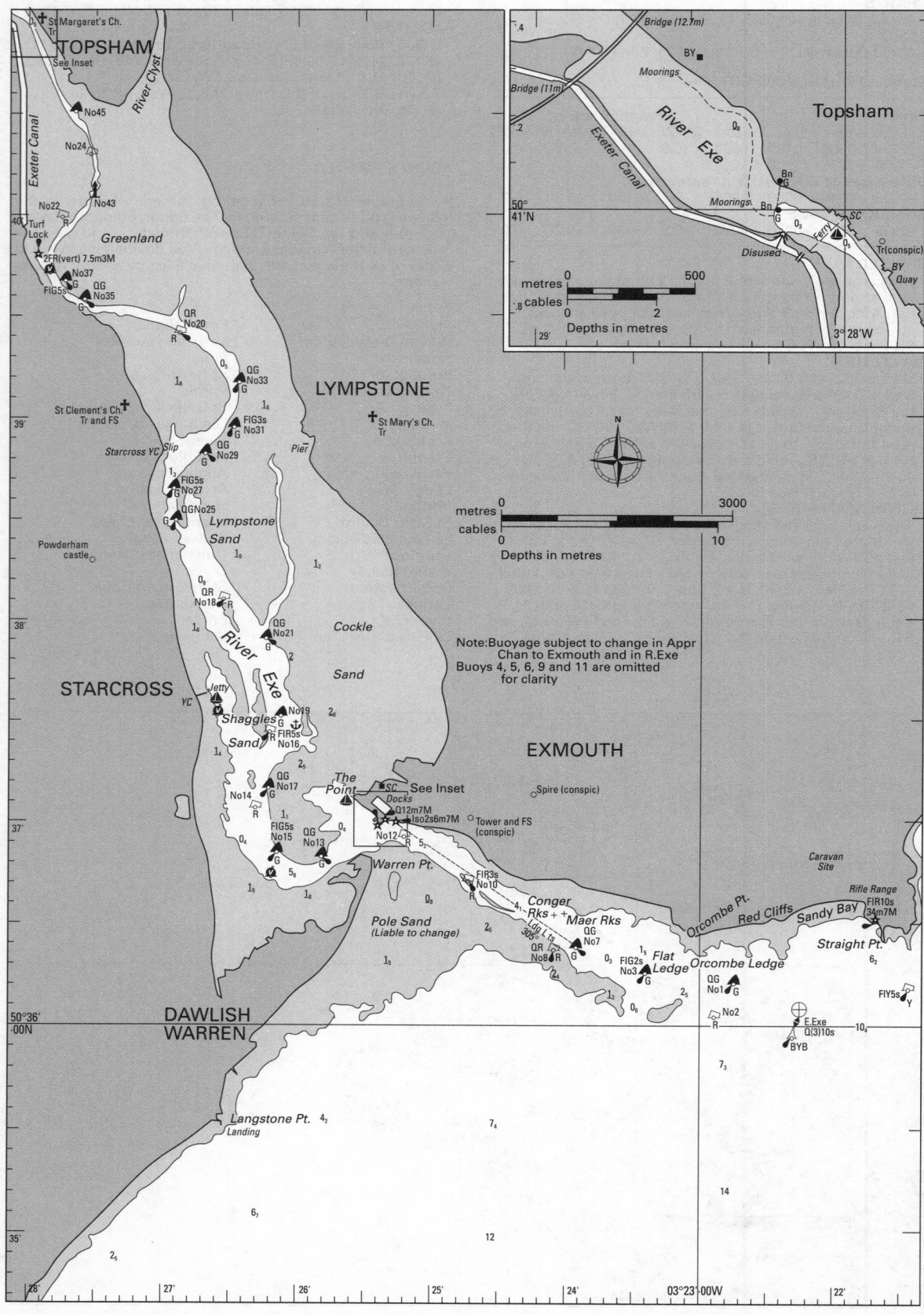

CHARTS
AC 2290, *3315*; Imray C5, Y43; Stanfords 12; OS 192

TIDES
–0445 Dover; ML 2·1; Duration 0625; Zone 0 (UT)

Standard Port DEVONPORT (◄──)

Times				Height (metres)			
High Water		Low Water		MHWS	MHWN	MLWN	MLWS
0100	0600	0100	0600	5·5	4·4	2·2	0·8
1300	1800	1300	1800				
Differences EXMOUTH (Approaches)							
+0030	+0050	+0015	+0005	–0·9	–1·0	–0·5	–0·3
EXMOUTH DOCK							
+0035	+0055	+0050	+0020	–1·5	–1·6	–0·9	–0·6
STARCROSS							
+0040	+0110	+0055	+0025	–1·4	–1·5	–0·8	–0·1
TOPSHAM							
+0045	+0105	No data		–1·5	–1·6	No data	

SHELTER
Good inside R Exe, but ent difficult in fresh winds from E and S. Caution: strong tidal streams, see below.
Exmouth Dock is a yacht basin, 2m depth, usually full of local boats. Call Dock Mr VHF Ch 14 for possible berth. In dock ent the pontoon is much used by local ferries/water taxi. Swing bridge opens on request; stays open HN.
Estuary. ⚓s are in The Bight (2ca SW of No 13 SHM lt buoy, near large ship's mooring buoy), off Starcross, Turf Lock and Topsham SC; water taxi will advise. ⚓ may be found E of Starcross clear of chan, ie 1ca SSE of No 19 buoy in 2·1m.
At **Topsham** the river carries about 0·4m. Options: ⚓ in appr's, dry out at the Quay, find a mooring or berth at BY pontoon.

NAVIGATION
WPT East Exe ECM buoy Q (3)10s, 50°35'·97N 03°22'·30W, 111°/291° from/to No 7 SHM buoy, QG, 1·03M.
Caution: Royal Marine firing range at Straight Pt, just E of Exe buoy, has a danger area to SE, marked by 2 DZ SPM lt buoys. R flags are flown when the range is in use (likely times 0800-1600, Mon-Fri); call *Straight Pt Range* VHF Ch 08 16. From the E, check also with safety launch.
Approach is best started at approx LW+2 when hazards can be seen and some shelter obtained. In the appr chan tide runs up to 3·3kn on sp ebb; with wind against tide a confused, breaking sea quickly builds. In the narrows off Warren Pt the flood stream runs at 3-4kn and the ebb can exceed 4½kn when the banks uncover.
Ent chan is well marked/lit, but night entry is not advised. There are drying rky ledges to the N of chan; to the south Pole Sands dry up to 2·8m. Least depths of 0·5m & 1·0m occur in the chan between Nos 3 and 7 buoys, best water to stbd. The chan narrows to about 100m between Nos 11 and 10 buoys. After No 10 buoy it is important not to cut the corner round Warren Pt; stand on for 0·5M toward Exmouth Dock and well past No 12 PHM buoy, before altering to the SW. Up-to-date AC 2290 is essential.
The estuary bottom is sand/mud, free of rocks. Follow the curve of the chan, rather than a straight line between buoys. Some bends are marked on the outside only. The estuary is an international conservation area. 10kn speed limit is in force.
Exeter Ship Canal (3·0m depth). Contact Hr Mr ☎ (01392) 274306 or Ch 12 for non-tidal berth in Turf Basin for visitors and lay-ups; the latter also in Exeter Basin.

LIGHTS AND MARKS
Straight Pt has conspic caravan site close W and red cliffs to W and NNE. Exmouth ✠ tr and FS are conspic, about 2M WNW of the East Exe buoy. Ldg lts 305° at Exmouth: front Iso 2s 6m 7M; rear Q 12m 7M; do not use seaward of No 8 PHM buoy. Note: Approach buoys 4, 5, 6, 9 & 11 (all unlit), plus some others up-river, are not shown on chartlet due to small scale.

RADIO TELEPHONE
Exmouth Dock Mr VHF Ch 14 16; Water Taxi at Exmouth, call *Conveyance* Ch M 16. Port of Exeter Ch 12 16 (Mon-Fri: 0730-1730LT); Hbr Patrol 12 16 in summer.

TELEPHONE (Dial code Exmouth 01395)
Exmouth Dock Co 274767; Dock Mr 269314; Exeter Hr Mr 274306; MRSC (01803) 882704; ⌗ 0345 231110 (H24); Marinecall 0891 500458; Police 264651; Dr 273001; Ⓗ 279684.

FACILITIES
EXMOUTH (01395)
Yacht Basin, ☎ 269314, £17, FW, D, No Ⓥ berths as such; showers/WC to be provided, or use **Exe SC** ☎ 264607.
Town EC Wed; P, Sh, CH, El, Ⓔ, ACA, SM, Gas, Gaz, V, R, ⊚, Bar, ✉, Ⓑ, ⇌.
STARCROSS (01626)
Starcross Fishing & Cruising Club ☎ 890582; **Starcross YC** ☎ 890470; **Starcross Garage** ☎ 890225, P & D (cans), ME, Gas. **Village** V, Bar, ✉, Ⓑ, ⇌.
TOPSHAM (01392)
Topsham SC ☎ 877524, Slip, L, FW, Bar;
Trouts BY ☎ 873044, AB, M, D, Gas, Gaz, C, FW, Sh.
Retreat BY ☎ 874270, (access HW±2), M, D, FW, ME, C, CH, Sh.
Town P, CH, SM, ACA, R, V, ⊚, Bar, ✉, Ⓑ, ⇌.
EXETER (01392)
Hr Mr, River & Canal Office, Haven Rd, Exeter EX2 8DU, ☎ 274306: canal berths, £8.50 for 2 days minimum, and laying up.
City all amenities; CH, ME, ACA, ⇌, ✈.

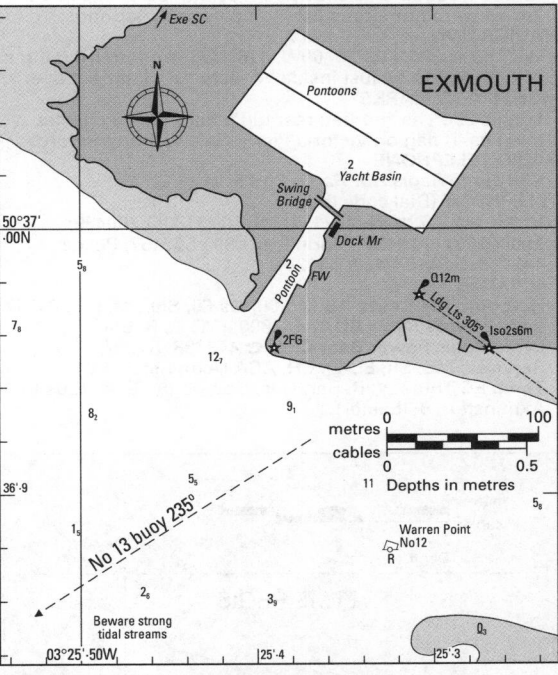

EXMOUTH DOCK 50°37'·00N 03°25'·37W

HARBOUR WEST OF LYME REGIS

AXMOUTH/BEER, Devon, 50°42'·10N 03°03'·20W. AC 3315. HW –0455 on Dover, +0045 and –1·1m on Devonport; ML 2·3m; Duration 0640. MHWS 4·1m, MHWN 3·1m. A small drying hbr on R Axe for boats max draught 1·2m, LOA 8·5m, able to take the ground. Appr chan to bar (dries 0·5m) is unmarked and often shifts; prior knowledge from YC is essential. Enter, in settled weather only, at HW via 7m wide ent with SHM bn; turn hard port inside. A bridge (2m clearance) crosses the river 2ca from ent. Facilities:
Axe YC ☎ (01297) 20043, Slip, pontoon, M, BH, Bar;
Services: ME, CH, D (cans), CH.
Beer Roads, 1M WSW, is ⚓ sheltered from prevailing W'ly, but open to S/SE winds. Landing on open beach.
Beer & Seaton: EC Thurs; R, V, P & D (cans), Bar, Gas, ✉.

LYME REGIS   8-1-26

Dorset 50°43'·17N 02°56'·10W   Rtg 3-3-2

CHARTS
AC *3315*; Imray C5; Stanfords 12; OS 193

TIDES
−0455 Dover; ML 2·4; Duration 0700; Zone 0 (UT)

Standard Port DEVONPORT (←)

Times				Height (metres)			
High Water		Low Water		MHWS	MHWN	MLWN	MLWS
0100	0600	0100	0600	5·5	4·4	2·2	0·8
1300	1800	1300	1800				
Differences LYME REGIS							
+0040	+0100	+0005	−0005	−1·2	−1·3	−0·5	−0·2

NOTE: Rise is relatively fast for the 1st hour after LW, but slackens for the next 1½ hrs, after which the rapid rate is resumed. There is often a stand of about 1½ hours at HW.

SHELTER
Good in the hbr (dries up to 2·1m), except in strong E or SE winds when swell enters and it may be best to dry inside the North Wall. A stone pier, The Cobb, protects the W and S sides of the hbr; a rocky extension to E end of this pier covers at half tide and is marked by unlit PHM bn. Access about HW±2½. Max LOA 9m in hbr. Dry out on clean, hard sand against Victoria Pier (0·3 – 1·3m) or in settled weather ⚓ as shown. 8 R cylindrical ⚓s lie in 1·5-2m. Beware numerous fishing floats and moorings.

NAVIGATION
WPT 50°43'·00N 02°55'·60W, 116°/296° from/to front ldg lt 0·35M; best to be just inside W sector until hbr ent opens.

LIGHTS AND MARKS
Ldg lts 296°, as chartlet; rear ldg lt hard to see against town lts. R flag on Victoria Pier = Gale warning in force.

RADIO TELEPHONE
Call *Lyme Regis Hbr Radio* Ch 16; work Ch 14.

TELEPHONE (Dial code 01297)
Hr Mr 442137 ☎/📠 442137; MRSC (01305) 760439; ⌗ 0345 231110 (H24); Marinecall 0891 500457; Police 442603; Dr 445777; Ⓗ 442254.

FACILITIES
Harbour (The Cobb) AB £10.00, ⚓s £5, Slip, M, FW, P & D (cans); **Lyme Regis SC** ☎ 442800, FW, ⚒, R, Bar; **Lyme Regis Power Boat Club** ☎ 443788, R, Bar; **Services:** ME, Sh, El, Ⓔ, CH, ACA (Axminster, 5M). **Town** EC Thurs; V, R, Bar, Gas, Gaz, ✉, Ⓑ, ▣, ⇌ (bus to Axminster), ✈ (Exeter).

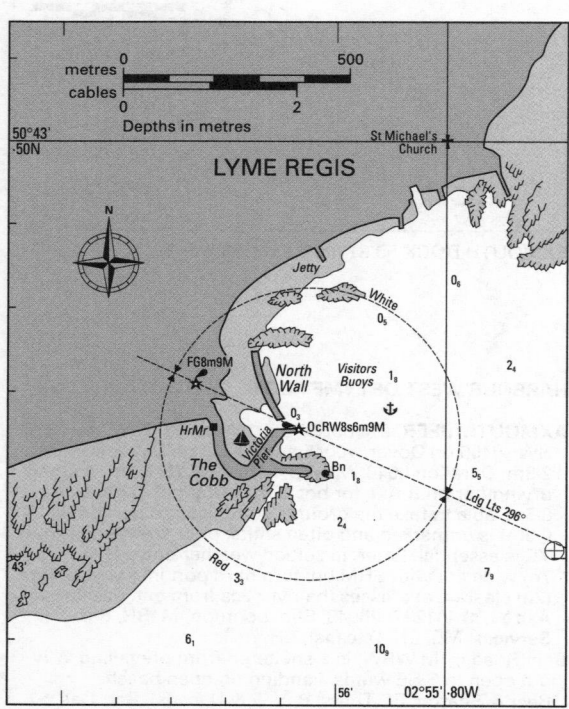

BRIDPORT   8-1-27

Dorset 50°42'·52N 02°45'·77W   Rtg 5-3-1

CHARTS
AC *3315*; Imray C5; Stanfords 12; OS 193

TIDES
−0500 Dover; ML 2·3; Duration 0650; Zone 0 (UT)

Standard Port DEVONPORT (←)

Times				Height (metres)			
High Water		Low Water		MHWS	MHWN	MLWN	MLWS
0100	0600	0100	0600	5·5	4·4	2·2	0·8
1300	1800	1300	1800				
Differences BRIDPORT (West Bay)							
+0025	+0040	0000	0000	−1·4	−1·4	−0·6	−0·2
CHESIL BEACH							
+0040	+0055	−0005	+0010	−1·6	−1·5	−0·5	0·0
CHESIL COVE							
+0035	+0050	−0010	+0005	−1·5	−1·6	−0·5	−0·2

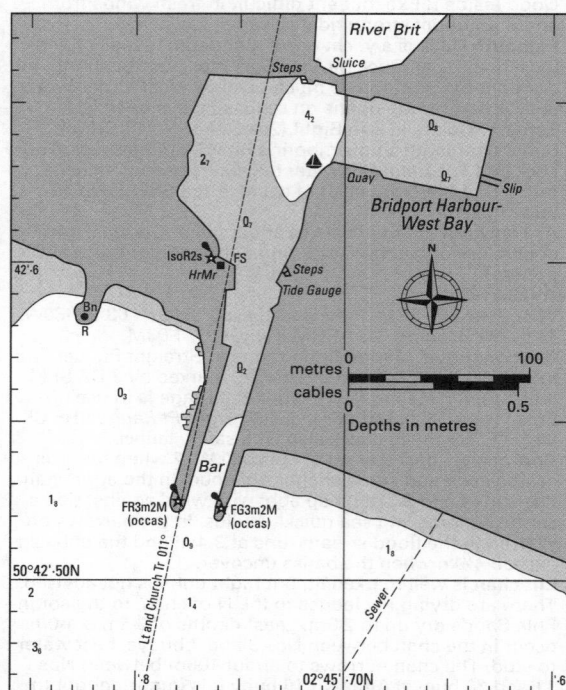

NOTE: Rise is relatively fast for first hr after LW, thence a slackening for the next 1½ hrs, after which the rapid rise is resumed. There is often a stand of about 1½ hrs at HW.

SHELTER
Good in hbr, but the narrow (12m), 180m long drying ent, is dangerous in even moderate on-shore winds; access HW±2, in favourable weather. Do not attempt entry in >F4/5 S'lies. Hbr dries apart from pool and former coaster berths scoured 2·1m by sluice water. There is little space; call Hr Mr Ch 11 for berth or dry out at E end of Quay.

NAVIGATION
WPT 50°41'·55N 02°46'·00W, 191°/011° from/to ent, 0·75M. No offshore dangers. SPM buoy, Fl, Y 5s, marks sewer outfall 5ca SSW of ent.

LIGHTS AND MARKS
Ldg marks 011°, church tr on with W pier hd. At night Iso R 2s 9m 5M on Hr Mr's office in line 011° with FR 3m 2M on W pier. Entry sig: B ● = hbr closed.

RADIO TELEPHONE
Call: *Bridport Radio* VHF Ch 11 16.

TELEPHONE (Dial code 01308)
Hr Mr ☎ & 📠 423222; MRSC (01305) 760439; ⌗ 0345 231110 (H24); Marinecall 0891 500457; Police 422266; Dr 421109.

FACILITIES
Quay AB £10, M, FW, Slip, P & D (cans), ▣, Sh, ME, V, R. **Town** CH, V, R, Bar, ✉, Ⓑ, ⇌ (bus to Axminster), ✈ (Exeter). Bridport town is 1½M N of hbr, known locally as West Bay.

Area 2

Central Southern England
Portland Bill to Selsey Bill

8.2.1	Index	**Page 181**
8.2.2	Diagram of ports, lights, RDF bns, Coast radio and weather stns	**182**
8.2.3	Tidal stream charts	**184**
8.2.4	List of coastal lights, fog signals and waypoints	**186**
8.2.5	Passage information	**189**
8.2.6	Distance table	**190**
8.2.7	English Channel waypoints	**See 8.1.7**
8.2.8	Portland, Standard Port, tidal curves	**191**
8.2.9	Portland: Tidal stream charts	**192**
8.2.10	Weymouth	**197**
8.2.11	Lulworth ranges Church Ope Cove Ringstead Bay Durdle Door Lulworth Cove Worbarrow Bay Chapman's Pool	**198**
8.2.12	Swanage	**199**
8.2.13	Special tidal problems between Swanage and Selsey Bill: Tidal curves	**200**
8.2.14	Poole Harbour: Times and heights of LW; heights of HW Studland Bay Wareham	**208**
8.2.15	Christchurch	**212**
8.2.16	Keyhaven	**212**
8.2.17	Needles Channel Alum Bay Totland Bay Freshwater Bay	**213**
8.2.18	The Solent area	**214**
8.2.19	Solent waypoints	**216**
8.2.20	Yarmouth (I o W)	**218**
8.2.21	Lymington	**219**
8.2.22	Newtown River (I o W)	**220**
8.2.23	Beaulieu River	**221**
8.2.24	Cowes (I o W) and R Medina Folly Reach Newport	**222**
8.2.25	IoW: Tidal stream charts	**224**
8.2.26	Southampton, Standard Port, tidal curves	**226**
8.2.27	River Hamble Hill Head Ashlett Creek	**228**
8.2.28	Wootton Creek (I o W)	**233**
8.2.29	Ryde (I o W)	**233**
8.2.30	Bembridge (I o W)	**234**
8.2.31	Portsmouth, Standard Port, tidal curves	**238**
8.2.32	Langstone Harbour	**241**
8.2.33	Chichester Harbour	**242**
8.2.34	Subfacts diagram	**244**

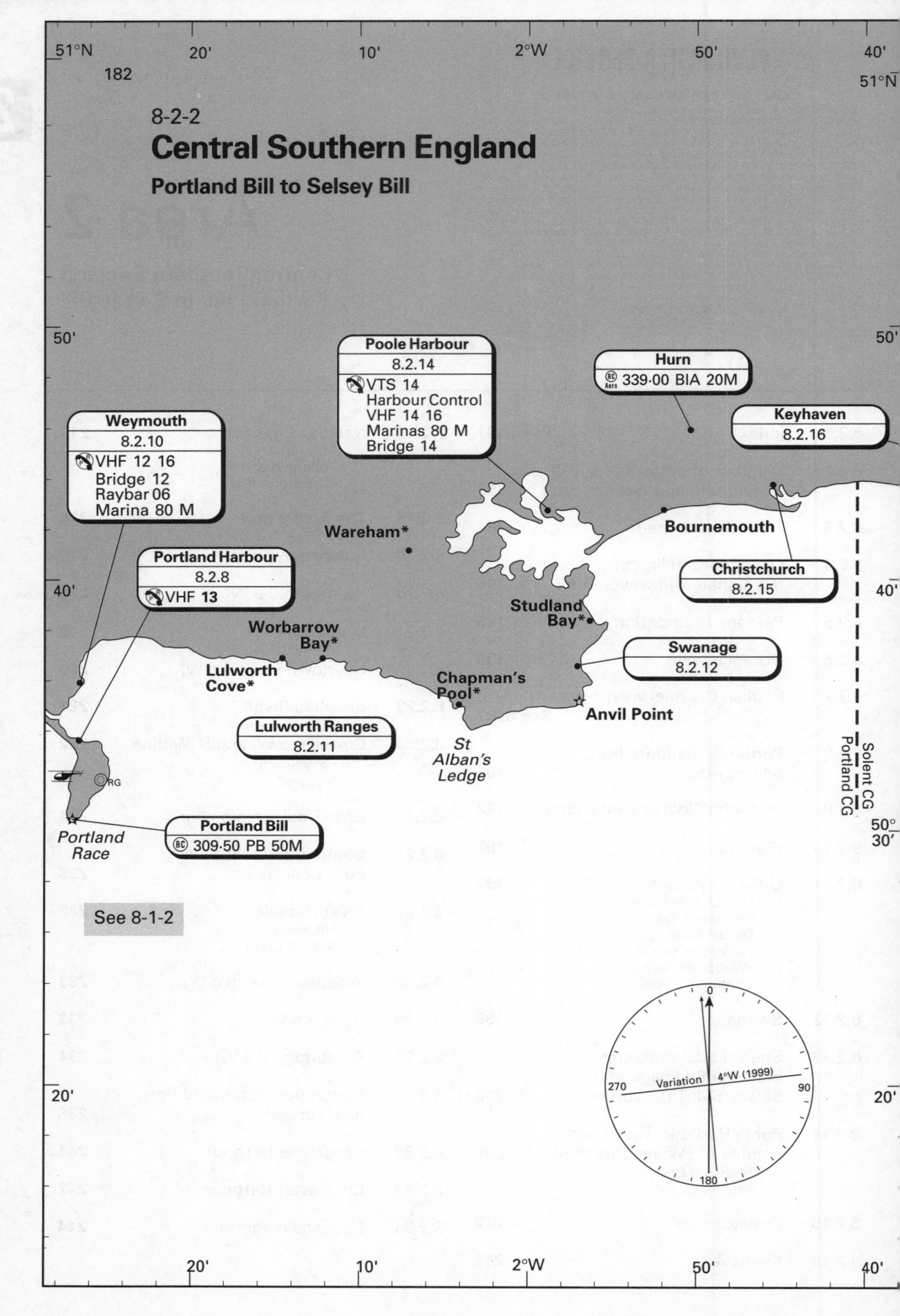

8-2-2
Central Southern England
Portland Bill to Selsey Bill

Poole Harbour
8.2.14
VTS 14
Harbour Control
VHF 14 16
Marinas 80 M
Bridge 14

Hurn
339·00 BIA 20M

Keyhaven
8.2.16

Weymouth
8.2.10
VHF 12 16
Bridge 12
Raybar 06
Marina 80 M

Wareham*

Bournemouth

Portland Harbour
8.2.8
VHF 13

Christchurch
8.2.15

Worbarrow
Bay*

Studland
Bay*

Lulworth
Cove*

Chapman's
Pool*

Swanage
8.2.12

Lulworth Ranges
8.2.11

St
Alban's
Ledge

Anvil Point

RG

See 8-1-2

*Portland
Race*

Portland Bill
309·50 PB 50M

Solent CG
Portland CG

270 Variation 4°W (1999) 90

180

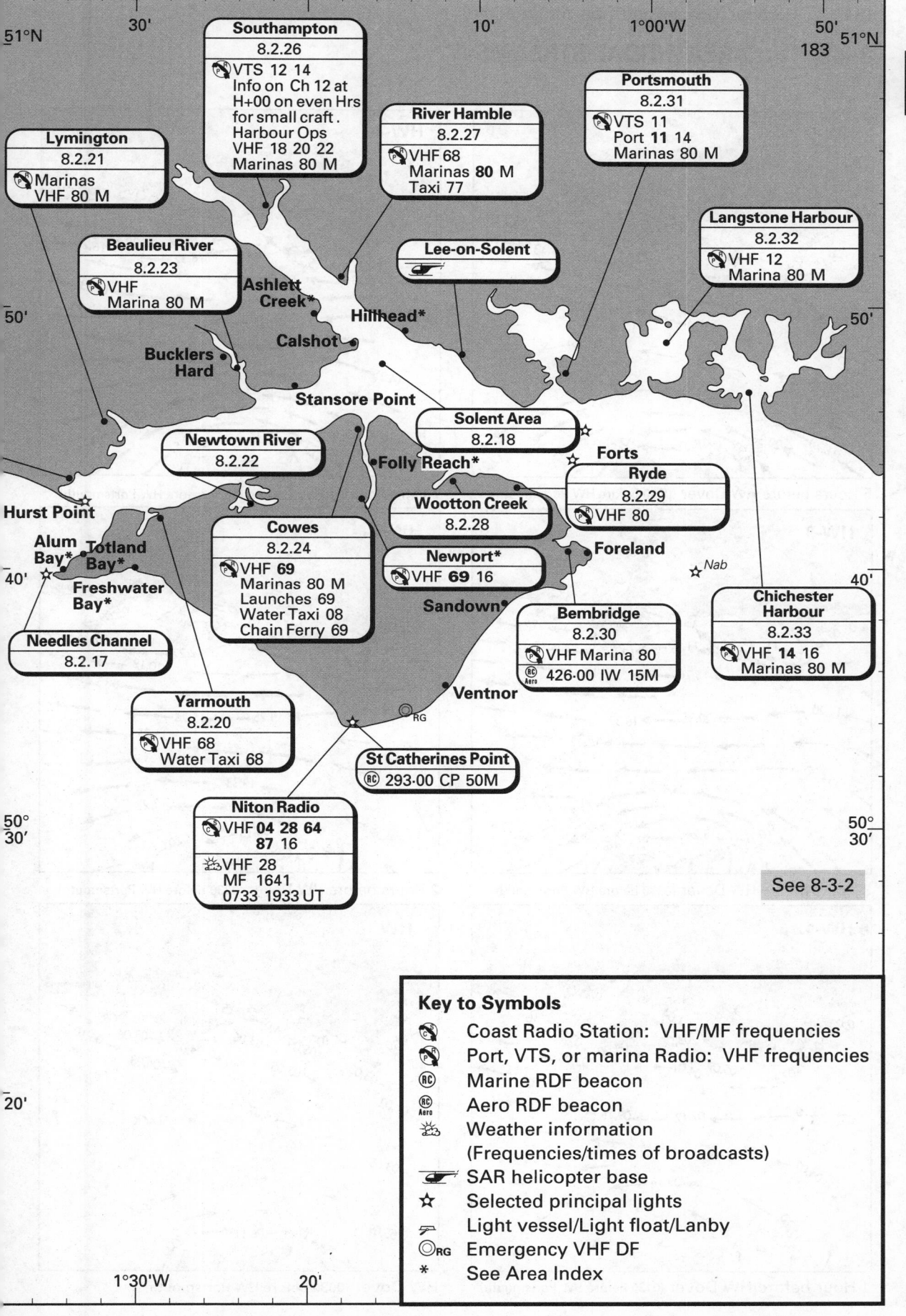

2

183

Southampton
8.2.26
VTS 12 14
Info on Ch 12 at
H+00 on even Hrs
for small craft .
Harbour Ops
VHF 18 20 22
Marinas 80 M

Lymington
8.2.21
Marinas
VHF 80 M

River Hamble
8.2.27
VHF 68
Marinas **80** M
Taxi 77

Portsmouth
8.2.31
VTS 11
Port **11** 14
Marinas 80 M

Beaulieu River
8.2.23
VHF
Marina 80 M

Lee-on-Solent

Langstone Harbour
8.2.32
VHF 12
Marina 80 M

Ashlett
Creek*

Hillhead*

Calshot

Bucklers
Hard

Stansore Point

Solent Area
8.2.18

Forts

Newtown River
8.2.22

Folly Reach*

Ryde
8.2.29
VHF 80

Hurst Point

Wootton Creek
8.2.28

Foreland

Alum
Bay* Totland
Bay*

Freshwater
Bay*

Cowes
8.2.24
VHF **69**
Marinas 80 M
Launches 69
Water Taxi 08
Chain Ferry 69

Newport*
VHF **69** 16

Sandown

Nab

**Chichester
Harbour**
8.2.33
VHF **14** 16
Marinas 80 M

Needles Channel
8.2.17

Bembridge
8.2.30
VHF Marina 80
426·00 IW 15M

Ventnor

Yarmouth
8.2.20
VHF 68
Water Taxi 68

RG

St Catherines Point
293·00 CP 50M

Niton Radio
VHF **04 28 64**
      87 16
VHF 28
MF 1641
0733 1933 UT

See 8-3-2

Key to Symbols

Coast Radio Station: VHF/MF frequencies

Port, VTS, or marina Radio: VHF frequencies

Marine RDF beacon

Aero RDF beacon

Weather information
(Frequencies/times of broadcasts)

SAR helicopter base

☆ Selected principal lights

Light vessel/Light float/Lanby

RG Emergency VHF DF

* See Area Index

51°N   30'   10'   1°00'W   50'   51°N

50'   50'

40'   40'

50°
30'   50°
30'

20'

1°30'W   20'

8-2-3   AREA 2 TIDAL STREAMS

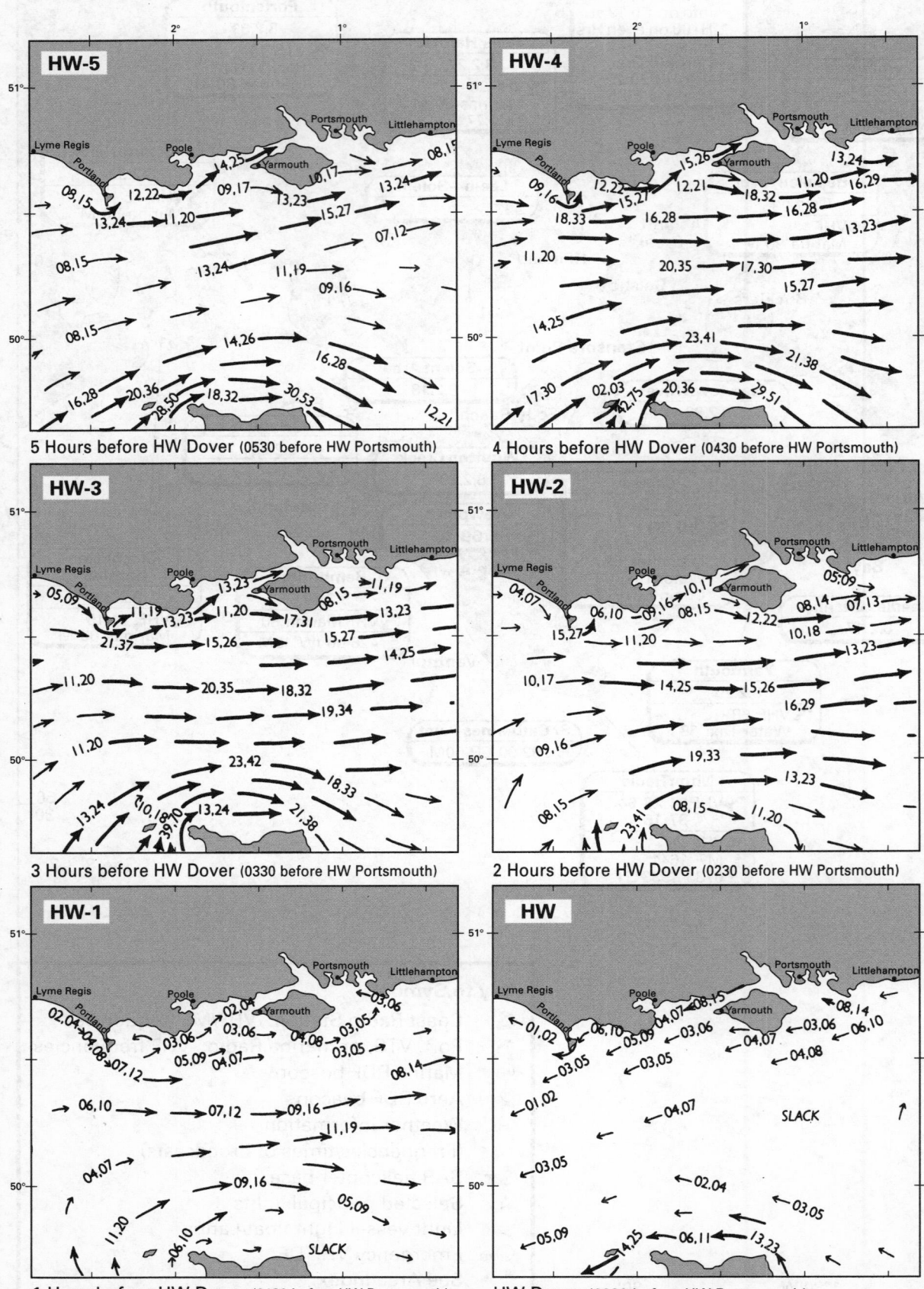

5 Hours before HW Dover (0530 before HW Portsmouth)

4 Hours before HW Dover (0430 before HW Portsmouth)

3 Hours before HW Dover (0330 before HW Portsmouth)

2 Hours before HW Dover (0230 before HW Portsmouth)

1 Hour before HW Dover (0130 before HW Portsmouth)

HW Dover (0030 before HW Portsmouth)

Westward 8.1.3   Portland 8.2.9   Isle of Wight 8.2.25   Eastward 8.3.3   Southward 8.15.3   Channel Islands 8.14.3

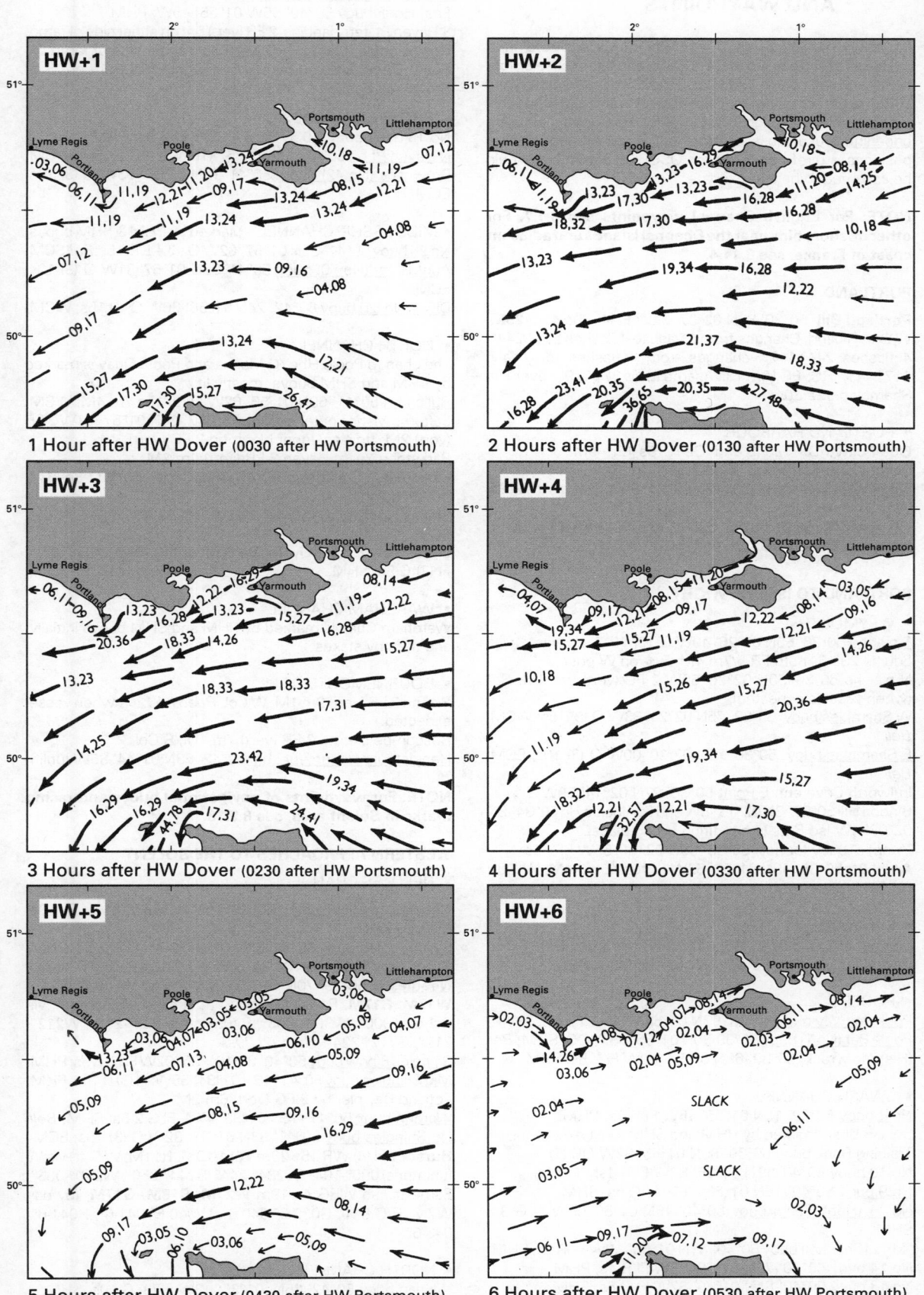

1 Hour after HW Dover (0030 after HW Portsmouth)

2 Hours after HW Dover (0130 after HW Portsmouth)

3 Hours after HW Dover (0230 after HW Portsmouth)

4 Hours after HW Dover (0330 after HW Portsmouth)

5 Hours after HW Dover (0430 after HW Portsmouth)

6 Hours after HW Dover (0530 after HW Portsmouth)

8.2.4   COASTAL LIGHTS, FOG SIGNALS AND WAYPOINTS

Lights with a nominal range of 15M or more are in **bold** print, places and features are in CAPITALS, and light-vessels, light floats and Lanbys in *CAPITAL ITALICS*. Unless otherwise stated lights are white. m = elevation in metres; M = nominal range in miles. Fog signals are in *italics*. Useful waypoints are underlined; use those on land with care. All geographical positions are referenced to the OSGB 36 datum but should be assumed to be approximate.

NOTE: For English Channel waypoints see 8.1.7. For other offshore aids near the Channel Islands and adjacent coast of France, see 8.14.4.

PORTLAND

Portland Bill 50°30'·82N 02°27'·32W Fl (4) 20s 43m **25M**; W ○ tr, R band. Changes from 1 flash to 4 flashes 221°-244°, 4 flashes 244°-117°, changes from 4 flashes to 1 flash 117°-141°; RC; FR 19m 13M (same tr) vis 271°-291° over The Shambles. *Dia 30s.*

- PORTLAND HARBOUR
Outer bkwtr D Head (S end) Oc R 15s 12m 5M.
Outer bkwtr Fort Head (N end) QR 14m 5M; vis 013°-268°.
NE bkwtr (A Head) 50°35'·12N 02°24'·99W Fl 10s 22m **20M**; W tr.
NE bkwtr (B Head) 50°35'·62N 02°25'·80W FR 11m 5M.
Northern Arm C Head (SE end) FG 11m 5M.

PORTLAND TO ISLE OF WIGHT

- WEYMOUTH
S pier hd 50°36'·50N 02°26'·40W Q 10m 9M; tfc sigs.
Ldg lts 239·6° both FR 5/7m 4M; R ♦ on W post.
N pier hd 50°36'·50N 02°26'·60W 2 FG (vert) 9m 6M. *Bell* (when vessels expected).
W Shambles buoy 50°29'·75N 02°24'·33W Q (9) 15s; WCM; *Bell.*
E Shambles buoy 50°30'·75N 02°20'·00W Q (3) 10s; ECM; *Bell.*
Lulworth Cove ent, E Point 50°36'·97N 02°14'·69W.
Bindon Hill 50°37'·3N 02°13'·6W and St Alban's Hd 50°34'·8N 02°03'·4W Iso R 2s (when firing taking place).
"Atomic" buoy (outfall) 50°35'·00N 02°11'·55W Fl Y 5s.
Anvil Pt 50°35'·48N 01°57'·52W Fl 10s 45m **24M**; W ○ tr; vis 237°-076°; (H24).

- SWANAGE
Pier hd 50°36'·52N 01°56'·88W 2 FR (vert) 6m 3M.
Peveril Ledge buoy 50°36'·38N 01°56'·02W; PHM.

- POOLE
Poole fairway buoy 50°38'·97N 01°54'·80W L Fl 10s; SWM.
Poole Bar (No 1) buoy 50°39'·30N 01°55'·08W QG; SHM; *Bell.*
(Historic wreck) 50°39'·68N 01°54'·80W Fl Y 5s; SPM.

- SWASH CHANNEL
No 2 buoy 50°39'·19N 01°55'·16W Fl R 2s; PHM.
Swash Chan marked by PHM and SHM, unlit except for:
Training Bank buoy 50°39'·80N 01°55'·82W QR (T).
No 10 buoy 50°40'·11N 01°55'·82W Fl R 4s; PHM.
No 9 buoy 50°40'·16N 01°55'·70W Fl G 5s; SHM.
No 11 (Hook Sand) buoy 50°40'·46N 01°56'·05W Fl G 3s; SHM.
No 12 (Channel) buoy 50°40'·41N 01°56'·18W Fl R 2s; PHM.
No 14 buoy 50°40'·76N 01°56'·73W Fl R 4s; PHM.
No 13 buoy 50°40'·84N 01°56'·62W Fl G 5s; SHM.

- EAST LOOE CHANNEL
E Looe No 16A PHM buoy, QR, 50°41'·14N 01°55'·85W.
East Hook buoy 50°40'·55W 01°55'·15W; PHM.
S Haven Pt, ferry landing 2 FR (vert) 5m on either side of ramp.
Ferry landing, E side 2 FG (vert) 3m, either side of ramp.
South Deep: Marked by lt bns and unlit bns from ent S of Brownsea Castle to Furzey Is.

- BROWNSEA ROADS
No 18 buoy 50°41'·02N 01°57'·32W Fl R 5s; PHM.
N Haven Pt bn 50°41'·12N 01°57'·10W Q (9) 15s 5m; WCM.
Brownsea (No 42) buoy 50°41'·13N 01°57'·33W Q (3) 10s; ECM.

- MIDDLE SHIP CHANNEL – Marked by PHM & SHM buoys.
No 20 buoy 50°41'·35N 01°57'·02W Q (6) + L Fl 15s; *Bell* SCM.
Aunt Betty (No 50) buoy 50°41'·93N 01°57'·31W Q (3) 10s; ECM.
Diver (No 51) buoy 50°42'·24N 01°58'·26W Q (9) 15s; WCM.

- NORTH CHANNEL
The chan to Poole Hbr YC Marina and Poole Quay is marked by PHM and SHM buoys, mostly lit.
Bullpit bn 50°41'·69N 01°56'·62W Q (9) 15s 7m 4M; WCM.
Salterns Marina outer bkwtr hd 50°42'·20N 01°57'·01W 2 FR (vert) 2M; tfc sigs. Inner bkwtr hd 2 FG (vert) 3M.
Parkstone Yacht Haven 2 FR (vert) 4m 2M.
Parkstone YC platform 50°42'·33N 01°58'·00W Q 8m 1M; hut on dolphin.
Stakes No 55 buoy 50°42'·39N 01°58'·93W Q (6) + L Fl 15s; SCM.
Little Chan, E side, Oyster Bank bn 50°42'·59N 01°59'·05W Fl (2) G 5s; SHM.

- WAREHAM CHANNEL
Wareham Chan is marked by PHM and SHM buoys initially, and then by stakes.

- BOURNEMOUTH
Pier hd 2 FR (vert) 9m 1M; W Col. *Reed (2) 120s* when vessel expected.
Boscombe pier hd 2 FR (vert) 7m 1M; R Col.
Hengistbury Hd, groyne, bn 50°42'·63N 01°44'·85W (unlit).

NOTE: For waypoints of navigational buoys and racing marks in Solent area, see 8.2.18.

WESTERN APPROACHES TO THE SOLENT

- NEEDLES CHANNEL

Needles fairway buoy 50°38'·20N 01°38'·90W L Fl 10s; SWM; *Whis.*
SW Shingles buoy 50°39'·31N 01°37'·36W Fl R 2·5s; PHM.
Bridge buoy 50°39'·59N 01°36'·80W VQ (9) 10s; Racon (T); WCM.
Needles lt 50°39'·70N 01°35'·43W Oc (2) WRG 20s 24m **W17M**, **R17M**, R14M G14M; ○ tr, R band and lantern; vis Rshore -300°, W300°-083°; R (unintens) 083°-212°, W212°-217°, G217°-224°. *Horn (2) 30s.*
Shingles Elbow buoy 50°40'·31N 01°35'·92W Fl (2) R 5s; PHM.
Mid Shingles buoy 50°41'·18N 01°34'·58W; Fl (3) R 10s; PHM.
Totland Bay pier hd 2 FG (vert) 6m 2M.
Warden buoy 50°41'·45N 01°33'·47W Fl G 2·5s; SHM; *Bell.*
NE Shingles buoy 50°41'·93N 01°33'·32W Q (3) 10s; ECM.
Hurst Pt Fl (4) WR 15s 23m W14/13M, R11M; W ○ tr; vis W (unintens) 080°-104°, W234°-244°, R244°-250°, W250°-053°.
Same tr, Iso WRG 4s 19m **W21M, R18M, G17M**, (by day W7M, R/G 5M), G038·6°-040·6°, W040·6°-041·6°, R041·6°-043·6°.

- NORTH CHANNEL
N Head buoy 50°42'·65N 01°35'·43W Fl (3) G 10s; SHM.

THE WEST SOLENT

Sconce buoy 50°42'·50N 01°31'·35W Q; NCM; *Bell*.
Black Rock buoy 50°42'·55N 01°30'·55W, Fl G 5s, SHM.
Fort Victoria pier hd 50°42'·42N 01°31'·08W 2 FG (vert) 4M.

• YARMOUTH
YMS 2, 50°42'·86N 01°29'·40W Fl Y 2·5s; SPM.
Pier hd, centre, 50°42'·48N 01°29'·88W 2 FR (vert) 2M;
G col. High intensity FW (occas).

• LYMINGTON
Jack in the Basket 50°44'·25N 01°30'·50W Fl R 2s 9m.
Ldg lts 319·5°. Front, 50°45'·16N 01°31'·57W FR 12m 8M;
vis 309·5°-329·5°; rear, 363m from front, FR 17m 8M.
Cross Boom No 2 50°44'·33N 01°30'·50W Fl R 2s 4m 3M; R
□ on pile.
No 1 50°44'·38N 01°30'·39W Fl G 2s 2m 3M; G △ on pile.

• SOLENT MARKS
Durn's Pt obstn, S end, 50°45'·37N 01°26'·95W QR; dolphin.
Hamstead Ledge buoy 50°43'·83N 01°26'10W Fl (2) G 5s; SHM.
W Lepe buoy 50°45'·20N 01°24'·00W Fl R 5s; PHM.
Salt Mead buoy 50°44'·48N 01°22'·95W Fl (3) G 10s; SHM.
Gurnard Ledge buoy 50°45'·48N 01°20'·50W Fl G 4s; SHM.
E Lepe buoy 50°46'·08N 01°20'·82W Fl (2) R 5s; PHM; *Bell*.
Gurnard buoy 50°46'·18N 01°18'·75W Q; NCM.

• BEAULIEU RIVER
Beaulieu Spit, E end 50°46'·83N 01°21'·67W Fl R 5s 3M;
R dolphin; vis 277°-037°.
No 2 bn 50°46'·89N 01°21·69W; PHM.
Ent chan bns Nos. 5, 9, 19, 21 Fl G 4s; bns Nos 12, 20 Fl R 4s.

• SOLENT MARKS
NE Gurnard buoy 50°47'·03N 01°19'·33W Fl (3) R 10s; PHM.
W Bramble buoy 50°47'·17N 01°18'·57W VQ (9) 10s; WCM;
Bell 15s; Racon (T).
Thorn Knoll buoy 50°47'·47N 01°18'·35W Fl G 5s; SHM.
Bourne Gap buoy 50°47'·79N 01°18'·26W Fl R 3s; PHM.
N Thorn buoy 50°47'·88N 01°17'·75W QG; SHM.
W Knoll buoy 50°47'·52N 01°17'·68W; SHM.
Outfall 50°48'·25N 01°18'·73W Iso R 10s 6m 5M; col on ■
structure; Ra refl; FR lt on each corner; *Horn 20s*.

• SOUTHAMPTON WATER
CALSHOT SPIT lt F 50°48'·32N 01°17'·55W Fl 5s 12m 11M;
R hull, lt tr amidships; *Horn (2) 60s*.
E Knoll buoy 50°47'·93N 01°16'·74W; SHM.
Castle Pt buoy 50°48'·68N 01°17'·58W IQR 10s; PHM.
Reach buoy 50°49'·02N 01°17'·56W Fl (3) G 10s; SHM.
Coronation buoy 50°49'·51N 01°17'·53W Fl Y 5s; SPM.
Hook buoy 50°49'·49N 01°18'·21W QG 15s; SHM; *Horn*.
Fawley Chan No 2 lt bn 50°49'·45N 01°18'·75W Fl R 3s; PHM.
Bald Head buoy 50°49'·88N 01°18'·15W; SHM.

• RIVER HAMBLE
Hamble Pt buoy 50°50'·12N 01°18'·57W Q (6) + L Fl 15s; SCM.
Ldg lts 345·5°. Front, No 6 pile 50°50'·58N 01°18'·74W   Oc
(2) R 12s 4m 2M; rear, 820m from front, QR 12m; W mast;
vis 341·5°-349·5°.
No 1 pile 50°50'·31N 01°18'·57W Fl G 3s 3M; SHM.
No 2 pile 50°50'·36N 01°18'·68W Q (3) 10s 3M; ECM.
Ldg lts 026·1°, Warsash Shore. Front, 50°50'·98N 01°18'·32W
QG; vis 010°-040°; rear, Sailing Club, Iso G 6s; vis 022°-030°.
Pile, Fl (2+1) R 10s, 50°51'·01N 01°18'·44W (oil spill boom).

Esso Marine terminal, SE end 50°50'·05N 01°19'·33W 2 FR
(vert) 9m 10M.
BP Hamble jetty 50°50'·90N 01°19'·50W 2 FG (vert) 5/3m 2M
(on each side of the 4 dolphins).
Greenland buoy 50°51'·07N 01°20'·29W IQ G 10s; SHM.

Cadland buoy 50°50'·99N 01°20'·45W Fl R 3s; PHM.
Lains Lake buoy 50°51'·55N 01°21'·57W Fl (2) R 4s; PHM.
Hound buoy 50°51'·65N 01°21'·43W Fl (3) G 10s; SHM.
Netley buoy 50°51'·99N 01°21'·72W Fl G 3s; SHM.
NW Netley buoy 50°52'·28N 01°22'·65W Fl G 7s; SHM.
Deans Elbow buoy 50°52'·12N 01°22'·67W Oc R 4s; PHM.
Weston Shelf buoy 50°52'·68N 01°23'·17W Fl (3) G 15s; SHM.

• HYTHE
Hythe Knock buoy 50°52'·79N 01°23'·73W Fl R 3s; PHM.
Hythe pier hd 50°52'·45N 01°23'·52W 2 FR (vert) 12/5m 5M.
Marina village lt bn 50°52'·23N 01°23'·48W Q (3) 10s; ECM.
Lock 50°52'·52N 01°23'·89W 2 FG (vert), G △; 2 FR (vert), R □.

• SOUTHAMPTON/RIVER ITCHEN
Swinging Ground No 1 buoy 50°52'·97N 01°23'·35W Oc G
4s; SHM.
E side. No 1 dolphin 50°53'·12N 01°23'·32W QG; SHM.
No 2 dn 50°53'·27N 01°23'·28W Fl G 5s 2M; SHM.
No 3 dn 50°53'·45N 01°23'·18W Fl G 7s; SHM.
No 4 pile 50°53'·58N 01°23'·07W QG 4m 2M; SHM.
Itchen bridge. FW on bridge span each side marks main chan.
2 FG (vert) 2M each side on E pier. 2 FR (vert) 2M each side
on W pier.
Crosshouse lt bn 50°54'·01N 01°23'·11W Oc R 5s 5m 2M;
PHM.
Chapel lt bn 50°54'·11N 01°23'·13W Fl G 3s 5m 3M; SHM.
Shamrock Quay SW end 50°54'·46N 01°22'·84W 2 FR (vert)
4m, and NE end 2 FR (vert) 4m.
No 5 lt bn 50°54'·46N 01°22'·67W Fl G 3s.
No 6 lt bn 50°54'·55N 01°22'·54W Fl R 3s.
No 7 lt bn 50°54'·56N 01°22'·40W Fl (2) G 5s.
No 9 lt bn 50°54'·70N 01°22'·39W Fl (4) G 10s.
Kemps Marina jetty hd 50°54'·79N 01°22'·57W 2 FG (vert)
5m 1M.

• SOUTHAMPTON/RIVER TEST
Town Quay marina ent 50°53'·65N 01°24'·23W 2 FG (vert).
Gymp buoy 50°53'·14N 01°24'·21W QR; PHM.
Queen Elizabeth II terminal, S end 50°52'·97N 01°23'·64W
4 FG (vert) 16m 3M.
Lower Foul Gd lt bn 50°53'·23N 01°24'·46W Fl (2) R 10s; PHM.
Upper Foul Gd lt bn 50°53'·50N 01°24'·80W Fl (2) R 10s; PHM.
Town Quay ldg lts 329°, both FY 12/22m 3/2M (occas).
Gymp Elbow buoy 50°53'·48N 01°24'·53W Oc R 4s; PHM.
Pier hd buoy 50°53'·64N 01°24'·57W QG; SHM.
Dibden Bay buoy 50°53'·66N 01°24'·84W Q; NCM.
Swinging Ground No 2 buoy 50°53'·78N 01°25'·03W Fl (2) R
10s; PHM.
Cracknore buoy 50°53'·91N 01°25'·12W Oc R 8s; PHM.
Millbrook buoy 50°54'·08N 01°26'·73W QR; PHM.
Bury buoy 50°54'·10N 01°27'·04W Fl R 5s; PHM.
Eling buoy 50°54'·45N 01°27'·75W Fl R 5s; PHM.

THE EAST SOLENT

• NORTH CHANNEL/HILLHEAD
Calshot buoy 50°48'·40N 01°16'·95W VQ; NCM; *Bell 30s*.
Hillhead buoy 50°48'·04N 01°15'·92W Fl R 2·5s; PHM.
E Bramble buoy 50°47'·20N 01°13'·56W VQ (3) 5s; ECM; *Bell*.
Hillhead bn 50°49'·03N 01°14'·69W; Or bn.

• COWES
No 4 buoy 50°46'·04N 01°17'·78W QR; PHM.
No 3 buoy 50°46'·04N 01°17'·93W QG; SHM.
Ldg lts 164°. Front, 50°45'·87N 01°17'·76W Iso 2s 3m 6M;
rear, 290m from front, Iso R 2s 5m 3M; vis 120°-240°.
E bkwtr hd 50°45'·84N 01°17'·43W Fl R 3s 3M.
Cowes Yacht Haven N end 50°45'·69N 01°17'·62W 2 FG (vert).
E Cowes Marina N end 50°45'·15N 01°17'·44W 2 FR (vert).

- SOLENT MARKS

Prince Consort buoy 50°46'·38N 01°17'·47W VQ; NCM.
W Ryde Mid buoy 50°46'·45N 01°15'·70W Q (9) 15s; WCM.
Norris buoy 50°45'·92N 01°15'·40W Fl (3) R 10s; PHM.
N Ryde Mid buoy 50°46'·58N 01°14'·30W Fl (4) R 20s; PHM.
S Ryde Mid buoy 50°46'·10N 01°14'·08W Fl G 5s; SHM.
Peel Bank buoy 50°45'·57N 01°13'·25W Fl (2) R 5s; PHM.
SE Ryde Mid buoy 50°45'·90N 01°12'·00W VQ (6)+
L Fl 10s; SCM.
NE Ryde Mid buoy 50°46'·18N 01°11'·80W Fl (2) R 10s; PHM.

- WOOTTON

Wootton NCM bn, Q 1M, 50°44'·53N 01°12'·02W.
No 1 SHM bn, Fl (2) G 5s, 50°44'·37N 01°12'·26W.
No 2 PHM bn, Fl R 5s, 50°44'·22N 01°12'·38W.

- SOLENT MARKS

Mother Bank buoy 50°45'·45N 01°11'·13W Fl R 3s; PHM.
Browndown buoy 50°46'·54N 01°10'·87W Fl (2) G 10s; SHM.
Stokes Bay wk buoy 50°46'·67N 01°10'·58W; SHM.

- RYDE

Pier, NW corner, N and E corner marked by 2 FR (vert). In fog
FY from N corner, vis 045°-165°, 200°-320°.
Marina E side, 2 FR (vert) 7m 1M, 50°43'·95N 01°09'·20W.
W side, Fl G 3s 7m 1M, 50°43'·93N 01°09'·23W.

- SOLENT MARKS

Ft Gilkicker 50°46'·40N 01°08'·38W Oc G 10s 7M.
N Sturbridge buoy 50°45'·31N 01°08'·15W VQ; NCM.
NE Mining Gnd buoy 50°44'·71N 01°06'·30W Fl Y 10s; SPM.

- PORTSMOUTH APPROACHES

Horse Sand Ft 50°44'·97N 01°04'·25W Iso G 2s 21m 8M;
large ○ stone structure.
Saddle 50°45'·17N 01°04'·78W VQ (3) G 10s; SHM.
Horse Sand buoy 50°45'·48N 01°05'·17W Fl G 2·5s; SHM.
Outer Spit buoy 50°45'·55N 01°05'·41W Q (6) + L Fl 15s; SCM.
Boyne buoy 50°46'·12N 01°05'·17W Fl G 5s; SHM.
Spit Refuge buoy 50°46'·02N 01°05'·37W Fl R 5s; PHM.
Spit Sand Ft, N side 50°46'·20N 01°05'·80W Fl R 5s 18m 7M;
large ○ stone structure.
Castle buoy 50°46'·43N 01°05'·30W Fl (2) G 6s; SHM.
Southsea Castle N corner 50°46'·66N 01°05'·25W Iso 2s
16m 11M, W stone tr, B band; vis 337°-071°.
Dir lt001·5° Dir WRG 11m W13M, R5M, G5M; same structure
FG 351·5°-357·5°, Al WG 357·5°-000° (W phase incr with
brg), FW 000°-003°, AlWR 003°-005·5° (R phase incr with
brg), FR 005·5°-011·5°.
Ridge buoy 50°46'·42N 01°05'·57W Fl (2) R 6s; PHM.
No 1 Bar buoy 50°46'·73N 01°05'·72W Fl (3) G 10s; SHM.
No 2 buoy 50°46'·66N 01°05'·58W Fl (3) R 10s; PHM.
No 3 buoy 50°47'·04N 01°06'·17W QG; SHM.
No 4 buoy 50°46'·98N 01°06'·27W QR; PHM.

- PORTSMOUTH HARBOUR

Ft Blockhouse 50°47'·34N 01°06'·65W Dir lt 320°; Dir WRG
6m W13M, R5M, G5M; Oc G 310°-316°, Al WG 316°-318·5°
(W phase incr with brg), Oc 318·5°-321·5°, AlWR 321·5°-324°
(R phase incr with brg), OcR 324°-330°. 2 FR (vert) 20m E.
Victoria pile 50°47'·31N 01°06'·40W Oc G 15s 1M; SHM.
Dolphin, close E of C & N Marina, 50°47'·82N 01°06'·89W,
Hbr ent dir lt (Fuel Jetty) WRG 2m 1M; vis Iso G 2s 322·5°-
330°, Al WG 330°-332·5°, Iso 2s 332·5°-335° (main chan), Al
WR 335°-337·5°, Iso R 2s 337.5°-345° (Small Boat Chan).
Ballast buoy 50°47'·63N 01°06'·73W Fl R 2·5s; PHM.
The Point 50°47'·54N 01°06'·48W QG 2M; SHM.
No 98 SCM bn, Q (6) + L Fl 15s, 50°48'·58N 01°06'·69W.
No 57 PHM bn, FL (3) R 5s, 50°48'·84N 01°07'·23W.
Port Solent lock ent 50°50'·58N 01°06'·25W Fl (4) G 10s.

EASTERN APPROACHES TO THE SOLENT

No Man's Land Ft 50°44'·37N 01°05'·60W Iso R 2s 21m 8M;
large ○ stone structure.
Horse Elbow wk buoy 50°44'·40N 01°03'·35W; SHM.
Horse Elbow buoy 50°44'·23N 01°03'·80W QG; SHM.
Warner buoy 50°43'·84N 01°03'·93W QR; PHM; *Whis*.
Dean Elbow buoy 50°43'·66N 01°01'·78W Fl (3) G 15s; SHM.
St Helens buoy 50°40'·32N 01°02'·32W Fl (3) R 15s; PHM.
Horse Tail buoy 50°43'·20N 01°00'·14W Fl (2) G 10s; SHM.
Nab East buoy 50°42'·82N 01°00'·70W Fl (2) R 10s; PHM.
Dean Tail South buoy 50°43'·10N 00°59'·49W Q (6) + L Fl 10s;
SCM.
Nab End buoy 50°42'·60N 00°59'·38W Fl R 5s; PHM.
New Grounds buoy 50°41'·97N 00°58'·53W VQ (3) 5s; ECM.

- BEMBRIDGE

St Helen's Ft (IOW) 50°42'·30N 01°05'·00W Fl (3) 10s 16m
8M; large ○ stone structure.
Bembridge tide gauge 50°42'·45N 01°04'·95W Fl Y 2s 1M;
SPM.

- LANGSTONE HARBOUR AND APPROACHES

Winner buoy 50°45'·07N 01°00'·01W; SCM.
Roway wk bn 50°46'·08N 01°02'·20W Fl (2) 5s; IDM.
Langstone fairway buoy 50°46'·28N 01°01'·27W L Fl 10s;
SWM.
Eastney Pt lt bn 50°47'·20N 01°01'·58W QR 2m 2M.
S Lake 50°49'·45N 00°59'·80W Fl G 3s 3m 2M; SHM.
Binness 50°49'·60N 00°59'·85W Fl R 3s 3m 2M; PHM.

- CHICHESTER ENTRANCE

Bar lt bn 50°45'·88N 00°56'·38W Fl WR 5s 14m W7M, R5M;
vis W322°-080°, R080°-322°; tide gauge. Same structure,   Fl
(2) R 10s 7m 2M; vis 020°-080°.
Eastoke lt bn 50°46'·62N 00°56'·08W QR 2m 3M; R□ on pile.
W Winner lt bn 50°46'·85N 00°55'·88W QG; G △ on pile.

- EMSWORTH CHANNEL

Verner lt bn 50°48'·27N 00°56'·57W Fl R 10s; PHM.
Marker Pt 50°48'·87N 00°56'·65W Fl (2) G 10s 8m; SHM.
NE Hayling lt bn 50°49'·60N 00°56'·77W Fl (2) R 10s 8m;
PHM.
Emsworth lt bn 50°49'·63N 00°56'·70W Q (6) + L Fl 15s;
SCM, tide gauge.

- CHICHESTER CHANNEL

East Hd lt bn 50°47'·32N 00°54'·67W Fl (4) G 10s; G △ on pile;
SHM; tide gauge.
Camber lt bn 50°47'·83N 00°53'·93W Q (6) + L Fl 15s; SCM.
Chalkdock lt bn 50°48'·46N 00°53'·27W Fl (2) G 10s; G △ on
pile; SHM.
Itchenor jetty   50°48'·43N 00°51'·90W 2 FG (vert); tide
gauge.
Birdham lt bn 50°48'·33N 00°50'·18W Fl (4) G 10s; pile, SHM;
depth gauge.
Chichester Yacht Basin lt bn 50°48'·42N 00°49'·87W Fl G 5s
6m; SHM; tide gauge.

- SOUTH EAST COAST OF THE ISLE OF WIGHT

St Catherine's Pt 50°34'·52N 01°17'·80W Fl 5s 41m **26M**;
vis 257°-117°; H24. RC. FR 35m 13M (same tr) vis 099°-116°.
Ventnor pier 50°35'·45N 01°12'·25W 2 FR (vert) 10m 3M.
Sandown pier hd 50°39'·02N 01°09'·09W 2 FR (vert) 7m 2M.
W Princessa buoy 50°40'·20N 01°03'·95W Q (9) 15s; WCM.
Bembridge Ledge buoy 50°41'·12N 01°02'·72W Q (3) 10s;
ECM.

Nab Tower. 50°40'·05N 00°57'·07W Fl 10s 27m **16M**;
Horn (2) 30s; Racon (T); vis 300°-120°.

8.2.5 PASSAGE INFORMATION

Reference books include: Admiralty *Channel Pilot*; *South Coast Cruising* (YM/Fishwick); *Shell Channel Pilot* (Imray/Cunliffe); *The Solent* (Imray/Bowskill); and *Creeks and Harbours of the Solent* (Adlard Coles). See 8.0.5 for distances across the Channel, and 8.3.5 and 8.15.5 for notes on cross-Channel passages.

THE PORTLAND RACE (chart 2255)

South of the Bill lies Portland Race in which severe and very dangerous sea states occur. Even in settled weather it should be carefully avoided by small craft, although at neaps it may be barely perceptible.

The Race occurs at the confluence of two strong S-going tidal streams which run down each side of Portland for almost 10 hours out of 12 at springs. These streams meet the main E-W stream of the Channel, producing large eddies on either side of Portland and a highly confused sea state with heavy overfalls in the Race. The irregular contours of the sea-bed, which shoals abruptly from depths of over 100m some 2M out S of the Bill to as little as 9m on Portland Ledge 1M further N, greatly contribute to the violence of the Race. Portland Ledge strongly deflects the flow of water upwards, so that on the flood the Race lies SE of the Bill and vice versa on the ebb. Conditions deteriorate with wind-against-tide, especially at springs; in an E'ly gale against the flood stream the Race may spread eastward to The Shambles bank. The Race normally extends about 2M S of the Bill, but further S in bad weather.

The Tidal Stream chartlets at 8.2.9 show the approx hourly positions of the Race. They are referenced to HW Portland, for the convenience of those leaving or making for Portland/Weymouth; and to HW Dover for those on passage S of the Bill. The smaller scale chartlets at 8.2.3 show the English Chan streams referenced to HW at Dover and Portsmouth.

Small craft may avoid the Race either by passing clear to seaward of it, between 3 and 5M S of the Bill; or by using the inshore passage if conditions suit. This passage is a stretch of relatively smooth water between 1ca and 3ca off the Bill (depending on wind), which should not however be used at springs nor at night; beware lobster pots. Timing is important to catch "slackish" water around the Bill, i.e:

> **Westbound** = from HW Dover – 1 to HW + 2
> (HW Portland + 4 to HW – 6).
> **Eastbound** = from HW Dover + 5 to HW – 4
> (HW Portland – 3 to HW + 1).

From either direction, close Portland at least 2M N of the Bill to utilise the S-going stream; once round the Bill, the N-going stream will set a yacht away from the Race area.

PORTLAND TO CHRISTCHURCH BAY (chart 2615)

The Shambles bank is about 3M E of Portland Bill, and should be avoided at all times. In bad weather the sea breaks heavily on it. It is marked by buoys on its E side and at SW end. E of Weymouth are rky ledges extending 3ca offshore as far as Lulworth Cove, which provides a reasonable anch in fine, settled weather and offshore winds; as do Worbarrow Bay and Chapman's Pool (8.2.11).

A firing range extends 5M offshore between Lulworth and St Alban's Hd. Yachts must pass through this area as quickly as possible, when the range is in use, see 8.2.11. Beware Kimmeridge Ledges, which extend over 5ca seaward.

St Alban's Head (107m and conspic) is steep-to and has a dangerous race off it which may extend 3M seaward. The race lies to the E on the flood and to the W on the ebb; the latter is the more dangerous. A narrow passage, at most 5ca wide and very close inshore, avoids the worst of the overfalls. There is an eddy on W side of St Alban's Head, where the

stream runs almost continuously SE. 1M S of St Alban's Head the ESE stream begins at HW Portsmouth + 0520, and the WNW stream at HW –0030, with sp rates of 4·75kn.

There is deep water quite close inshore between St Alban's Hd and Anvil Pt (lt). 1M NE of Durlston Hd, Peveril Ledge runs 2½ca seaward, causing quite a bad race which extends nearly 1M eastwards, particularly on W-going stream against a SW wind. Proceeding towards the excellent shelter of Poole Harbour (8.2.14), overfalls may be met off Ballard Pt and Old Harry on the W-going stream. Studland Bay (8.2.14 and chart 2172) is a good anch except in NE to SE winds. Anch about 4ca WNW of Handfast Pt. Avoid foul areas on chart.

Poole Bay offers good sailing in waters sheltered from W and N winds, with no dangers to worry the average yacht. Tidal streams are weak N of a line between Handfast Pt and Hengistbury Hd and within Christchurch Bay. Hengistbury Hd is a dark headland, S of Christchurch hbr (8.2.15), with a groyne extending 1ca S and Beerpan Rks a further 100m offshore. Beware lobster pots in this area. Christchurch Ledge extends 2·75M SE from Hengistbury Hd. The tide runs hard over the ledge at sp, and there may be overfalls.

WESTERN APPROACHES TO SOLENT (charts 2219, 2050)

The Needles (see 8.2.17) are distinctive rks at the W end of the Isle of Wight. The adjacent chalk cliffs of High Down are conspic from afar, but the lt may not be seen by day until relatively close. Goose Rk, dries, is about 50m WNW of the lt ho, 100-150m WSW of which is a drying wreck. The NW side of Needles Chan is defined by the Shingles bank, parts of which dry and on which the sea breaks violently in the least swell. The SE side of the bank is fairly steep-to, the NW side shelves more gradually. On the ebb the stream sets very strongly (3·4kn) WSW across the Shingles. The Needles Channel is well lit and buoyed and in fair weather presents no significant problems. But even a SW F4 over the ebb will cause breaking seas near Bridge and SW Shingles buoys.

In bad weather broken water and overfalls extend along The Bridge, a reef which runs 8ca W of the lt ho with extremity marked by WCM lt buoy. S to W gales against the ebb raise very dangerous breaking seas in the Needles Chan, here only 250m wide. The sea state can be at its worst shortly after LW when the flood has just begun. There is then no wind-over-tide situation, but a substantial swell is raised as a result of the recently turned stream. In such conditions use the E route to the Solent, S of the IOW and via Nab Tower; or find shelter at Poole or Studland.

In strong winds the North Channel, N of the Shingles, is preferable to the Needles Channel. The two join S of Hurst Pt, where overfalls and tide rips may be met. Beware The Trap, a shoal spit 150m SE of Hurst Castle.

In E winds Alum B, close NE of the Needles, is an attractive daytime anch with its coloured cliffs, but beware Long Rk (dries) in middle of B, and Five Fingers Rk 1½ca SW of Hatherwood Pt on N side. Totland Bay is good anch in settled weather, but avoid Warden Ledge.

THE SOLENT (charts 2040, 394)

Within the Solent there are few dangers in mid-chan. The most significant is Bramble bank (dries) between Cowes and Calshot. The main shipping chan (buoyed) passes S and W of the Brambles, but yachts can use the North Chan to the NE of the Brambles at any state of tide. Tidal streams are strong at sp, but principally follow the direction of the main chan. An Area of Concern between Cowes and Calshot provides added safety for larger ships; see 8.2.18 for details.

Several inshore spits, banks, rocks and ledges, which a yachtsman should know, include: Pennington and Lymington Spits on the N shore; Black Rk 4ca W of entrance to Yarmouth

(8.2.20); Hamstead Ledge 8ca W of entrance to Newtown River (8.2.22) and Saltmead Ledge 1·5M to E; Gurnard Ledge 1·5M W of Cowes; Lepe, Middle and Beaulieu Spit, S and W of the ent to Beaulieu R. (8.2.23); the shoals off Stone Pt, where three bns mark cable area; Shrape Mud, which extends N from the breakwater of Cowes hbr (8.2.24) and along to Old Castle Pt; the shoals and isolated rks which fringe the island shore from Old Castle Pt to Ryde (8.2.29), including either side of the ent to Wootton Creek (8.2.28); and Calshot Spit which extends almost to the lt F which marks the turn of chan into Southampton Water.

Southampton Water is a busy commercial waterway with large tankers, containerships, lesser craft and ferries. Yachts should monitor VHF Ch 12 to ascertain shipping movements. Between the Esso jetty off Fawley and the BP jetty on the E side the channel is narrow for large vessels; yachts can easily stay clear by seeking shoal water. N of this area there is adequate water for yachts close outboard of the main buoyed channel; the banks are of gently shelving soft mud, apart from foul ground between Hythe and Marchwood. Unlit marks and large mooring buoys may however be hard to see against the many shore lights. Except in strong N'lies, Southampton Water and the R Test and Itchen provide sheltered sailing. The River Hamble is convenient, but somewhat crowded.

Depending on the wind direction, there are many good anchs: For example, in W winds there is anch on E side of Hurst, as close inshore as depth permits, NE of High lt. In S winds, or in good weather, anch W of Yarmouth hbr ent, as near shore as possible; reasonably close to town, see 8.2.20.

In winds between W and N there is good anch in Stanswood Bay, about 1M NE of Stansore Pt. Just N of Calshot Spit there is shelter from SW and W. Osborne Bay, 2M E of Cowes, is sheltered from winds between S and W. In E winds Gurnard Bay, the other side of Cowes is preferable. In N winds anch in Stokes Bay. At E end of IOW there is good anch off Bembridge in winds from S, SW or W; but clear out if wind goes into E. There are also places which a shoal-draught boat can explore at the top of the tide, such as Ashlett Creek (8.2.27) between Fawley and Calshot, Eling up the R Test, and the upper reaches of the R Medina (8.2.24).

ISLE OF WIGHT – SOUTH COAST (chart *2045*)

From the Needles eastward to Freshwater Bay the cliffs can be approached to within 1ca, but beyond the E end of chalk cliffs there are ledges off Brook and Atherfield which require at least 5ca offing. The E-going stream sets towards these dangers. 4M SSW of the Needles the stream turns E x N at

HW Portsmouth + 0530, and W at HW – 0030, sp rate 2kn. St Catherine's lt ho (lt, RC) is conspic. It is safe to pass 2ca off, but a race occurs off the Point and can be very dangerous at or near sp with a strong opposing wind; particularly SE of the Pt on a W-going stream in a W gale, when St Catherine's should be given a berth of at least 2M. 1·25M SE of the Pt the stream turns E x N at HW Portsmouth + 0520, and W x S at HW – 0055, sp rate 3·75kn.

Rocks extend about 2½ca either side of Dunnose where a race occurs. In Sandown Bay anch off Shanklin or Sandown where the streams are weak inshore. Off the centre of the Bay they turn NE x E at HW Portsmouth + 0500, and SW x W at HW – 0100, sp rates 2 kn. The Yarborough Monument is conspic above Culver Cliff. Whitecliff Bay provides an anch in winds between W and N. From here to Foreland (Bembridge Pt) the coast is fringed by a ledge of rks (dry) extending up to 3ca offshore, and it is advisable to keep to seaward (E) of Bembridge Ledge ECM lt buoy.

EASTERN APPROACHES TO SOLENT (charts 2050, *2045*)

4·5M E of Foreland is Nab Tr (lt, fog sig), a conspic steel and concrete structure (28m), marking Nab Shoal for larger vessels and of no direct significance to yachtsmen. NW of Nab Tr, the E approach to the Solent via Spithead, presents few problems and is far safer in SW/W gales than the Needles Channel.

The main chan is well buoyed and easy to follow, but there is plenty of water for the normal yacht to the S of it when approaching No Man's Land Fort and Horse Sand Fort, between which craft must pass. Submerged barriers lie SW of the former and N of the latter. Ryde Sand dries extensively and is a trap for the unwary; so too is Hamilton Bank on the W side of the chan to Portsmouth (8.2.31).

Nab Tr is also a most useful landmark when approaching the E end of Isle of Wight, or when making for the hbrs of Langstone (8.2.32) or Chichester (8.2.33). Both these hbrs, with offlying sands, are on a dangerous lee shore in strong S'ly winds. East and West Winner flank the ent to Langstone Hbr. Similarly, E and W Pole Sands, drying 1m, lie either side of the ent chan from Chichester Bar bn. SE from Chichester Bar the whole of Bracklesham Bay is shallow, with a pronounced inshore set at certain states of the tide; yachts should keep at least 2M offshore. Further along a low-lying coast, is Selsey Bill with extensive offshore rocks and shoals. Pass these to seaward of the Owers SCM lt buoy, or via the Looe Chan (see 8.3.5) in suitable conditions. Boulder SHM lt buoy is at the W ent to this chan, about 6M SE of Chichester Bar bn. Medmery Bank, 3·7m, is 1M WNW of Boulder.

8.2.6   DISTANCE TABLE

Approximate distances in nautical miles are by the most direct route, whilst avoiding dangers and allowing for Traffic Separation Schemes. Places in *italics* are in adjoining areas; places in **bold** are also in 8.0.8, Cross-Channel Distances.

	1	2	3	4	5	6	7	8	9	10	11	12	13	14	15	16	17	18	19	20
1. *Exmouth*	1																			
2. *Lyme Regis*	21	2																		
3. **Portland Bill**	36	22	3																	
4. **Weymouth**	46	32	8	4																
5. Swanage	58	44	22	22	5															
6. **Poole Hbr ent**	65	51	28	26	6	6														
7. **Needles Lt Ho**	73	58	35	34	14	14	7													
8. Lymington	79	64	42	40	20	24	6	8												
9. Yarmouth (IOW)	77	63	40	39	18	22	4	2	9											
8. Beaulieu R. ent	84	69	46	45	25	29	11	7	7	10										
11. Cowes	86	71	49	46	28	27	14	10	9	2	11									
12. Southampton	93	78	55	54	34	34	20	16	16	9	9	12								
13. R. Hamble (ent)	90	75	53	51	32	34	18	12	13	6	6	5	13							
14. Portsmouth	96	81	58	57	37	35	23	19	19	12	10	18	13	14						
15. Langstone Hbr	98	84	61	59	39	39	25	21	21	14	12	21	18	5	15					
16. Chichester Bar	101	86	63	62	42	42	28	23	24	17	15	23	18	8	5	16				
17. Bembridge	97	81	59	58	38	39	24	18	19	13	10	18	15	5	6	8	17			
18. **Nab Tower**	102	86	64	63	43	44	29	23	24	18	15	24	19	10	7	6	6	18		
19. St Catherine's Pt	82	68	45	44	25	25	12	19	21	27	15	36	29	20	20	19	17	15	19	
20. *Littlehampton*	117	102	79	79	60	61	46	44	45	38	36	45	42	31	28	25	28	22	35	20

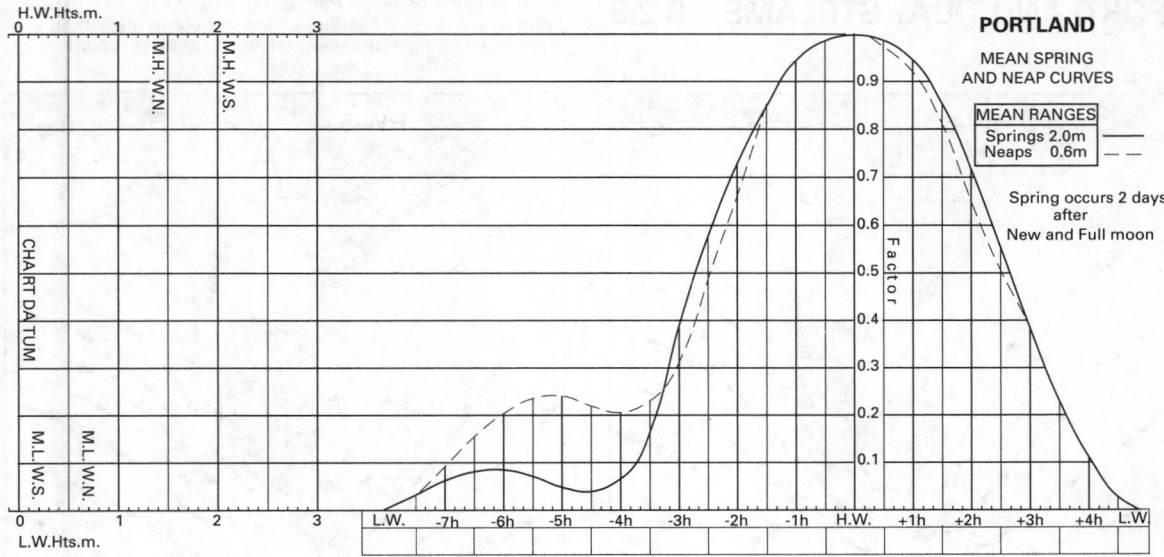

PORTLAND

MEAN SPRING
AND NEAP CURVES

MEAN RANGES
Springs 2.0m ⎯⎯⎯
Neaps   0.6m - - -

Spring occurs 2 days
after
New and Full moon

PORTLAND HARBOUR   8-2-8

Dorset 50°35'·11N 02°24'·90W (E Ship Chan)   Rtg 2-4-3

CHARTS
AC 2268, 2255, *2610*; Imray C4, C5; Stanfords 12; OS 194

TIDES
–0430 Dover; ML 1·0; Zone 0 (UT)

Standard Port PORTLAND (→)

Times				Height (metres)			
High Water		Low Water		MHWS	MHWN	MLWN	MLWS
0100	0700	0100	0700	2·1	1·4	0·8	0·1
1300	1900	1300	1900				

LULWORTH COVE and MUPE BAY (Worbarrow Bay)

+0005	+0015	–0005	0000	+0·1	+0·1	+0·2	+0·1

NOTE: Portland is a Standard Port; daily predictions are
given below. Double LWs occur. Predictions are for the
first LW. The second LW occurs from 3 to 4 hrs later and
may, at Springs, occasionally be lower than the first.

SHELTER
Poor, due to lack of wind breaks. ⚓ on W side of hbr in
about 3m between ☆ Fl (4) 10s and ☆ L Fl 10s. E Fleet is
only suitable for small craft with lowering masts. Better
options for yachts are Weymouth old hbr or new marina.
Note: Helicopters often fly at low altitudes for long spells,
H24, over S part of the hbr.
Portland Harbour is owned by Portland Port Ltd, the
statutory Hbr Authority. The port is being re-developed
for commercial operations. Cable & Wireless have moved
their maritime commercial operations to inner Coaling
Pier. Outer Coaling pier is operating as a cargo terminal.
Future plans include a Ro-Ro ferry terminal, cruise ship
stopovers and a "One Stop Shop". Plans for a fishing hbr
and a marina are shelved for the immediate future.

NAVIGATION
WPT 50°35'·07N 02°24'·00W, 090°/270° from/to E Ship
Chan, Fort Hd, 0·50M. The S Chan is permanently closed.
Speed limit in the hbr is 12kn. Beware rky reef extending
1ca off Sandsfoot Cas, shoals E of Small Mouth and fast
catamarans ex-Weymouth. 4 mooring buoys lie between
Coaling and Queens Piers; 4 noise range lt buoys are 7ca
SE of D Head and 3 degaussing buoys (1 lit) are 400m SE
of Weymouth S Pier head. Portland Race (see 8.2.5 and
8.2.9) is extremely dangerous. Avoid the Shambles bank.

LIGHTS AND MARKS
Bill of Portland (S end) Fl (4) 20s 43m 25M; W tr, R band.
The number of flashes changes in arcs 221°-244° and
117°-141°; see 8.2.4 for details. FR 19m 13M, same tr, vis
271°-291° (20°) over The Shambles, Dia 30s. Other lts as
on chartlet.

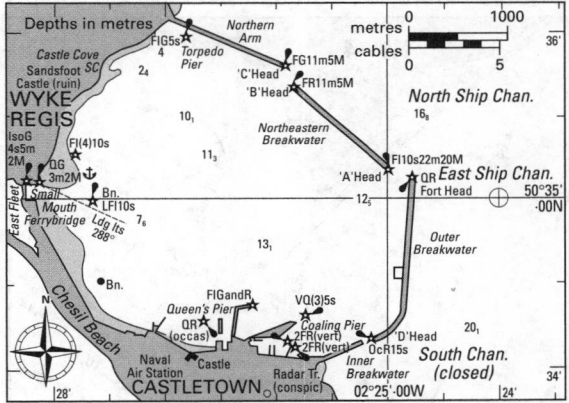

RADIO TELEPHONE
Yachts must call *Portland Harbour Radio* VHF Ch 13, H24,
for entry/dep at Points PN and PE (respectively 0·5M to
seaward of A and C Heads). Port Ops Ch 14, 20, 28, 71, 74.
Note: Portland CG offers radio coverage of the Casquets
TSS on Ch 69 16.

TELEPHONE (Dial code 01305)
Port Control 824044, Ⓗ 824055; ⌗ 0345 231110 (H24);
MRSC 760439; Marinecall 0891 500457; Police 821205; Dr
(GP) 820422; Ⓗ (Emergency) 820341.

FACILITIES
Hbr dues apply to yachts: £3.00 daily for 6 – 9.15m LOA.
Castle Cove SC ☎ 783708, M, L, FW; **Services:** Slip, M, L,
FW, ME, Sh, C, CH, El (mobile workshop).
Town ⊠, Ⓑ, ⇌ (bus to Weymouth), ✈ (Bournemouth).

*There is no set of the sea in Portland Race: no run and
sway: no regular assault. It is a chaos of pyramidical
waters leaping up suddenly without calculation, or rule
of advance. It is not a charge, but a scrimmage; a
wrestling bout; but a wrestling bout of a thousand
against one. It purposely raises a clamour to shake its
adversary's soul, wherein it most resembles a gigantic
pack of fighting dogs, for it snarls, howls, yells, and all
this most terrifically. Its purpose is to kill, and to kill with
a savage pride.
And all these things you find out if you get mixed up in it
on a very small boat.*

The Cruise of the Nona: Hilaire Belloc. Pimlico (Publishers).
Reprinted by permission of the Peters Fraser & Dunlop Group Ltd.

PORTLAND TIDAL STREAMS 8-2-9

Tidal Streams between Portland Bill and St Alban's Head by Peter Bruce (Boldre Marine) offers complementary tidal stream data based on recent research for oil companies.

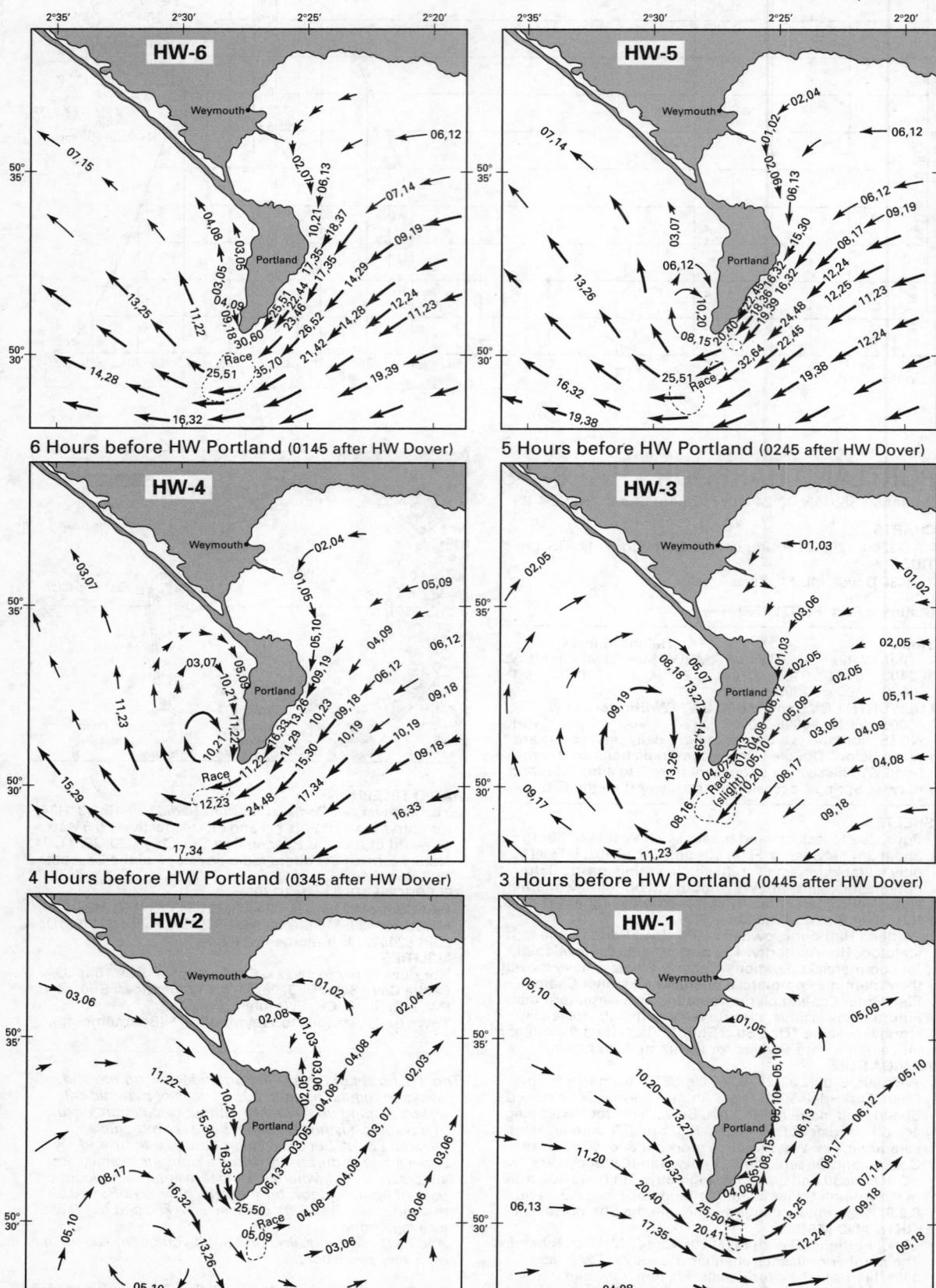

6 Hours before HW Portland (0145 after HW Dover)

5 Hours before HW Portland (0245 after HW Dover)

4 Hours before HW Portland (0345 after HW Dover)

3 Hours before HW Portland (0445 after HW Dover)

2 Hours before HW Portland (0545 after HW Dover)

1 Hour before HW Portland (0540 before HW Dover)

General Area 2   8.2.3

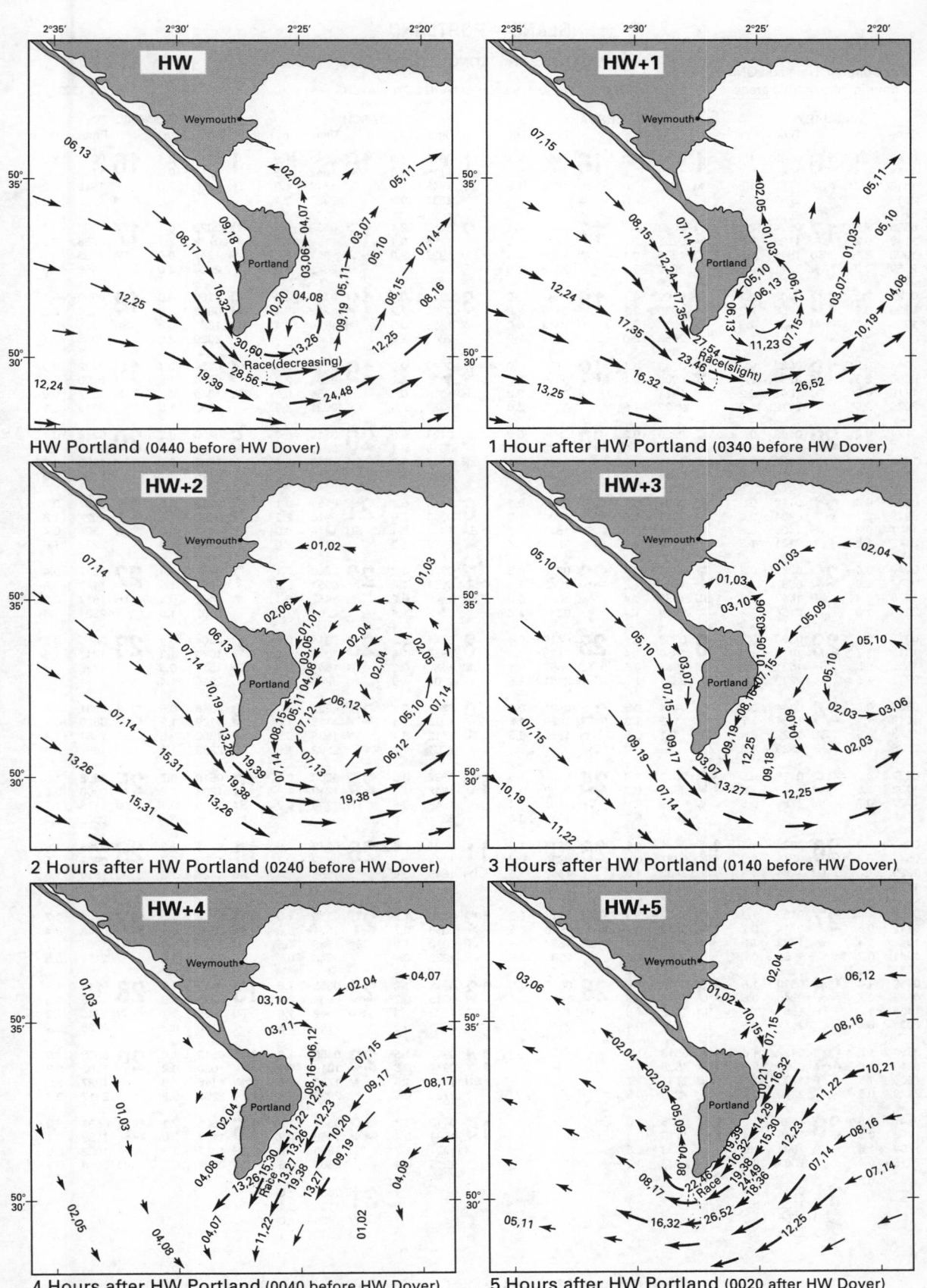

HW Portland (0440 before HW Dover)

1 Hour after HW Portland (0340 before HW Dover)

2 Hours after HW Portland (0240 before HW Dover)

3 Hours after HW Portland (0140 before HW Dover)

4 Hours after HW Portland (0040 before HW Dover)

5 Hours after HW Portland (0020 after HW Dover)

ENGLAND – PORTLAND

LAT 50°34′N   LONG 2°26′W

TIMES AND HEIGHTS OF HIGH AND LOW WATERS

YEAR **1999**

TIME ZONE (UT)
For Summer Time add ONE hour in non-shaded areas

JANUARY

Day	Time	m	Time	m	Time	m	Time	m
1 F	0542	2.1	1051	0.4	1813	2.0	2312	0.2
16 SA	0536	1.9	1048	0.4	1757	1.8	2259	0.3
2 SA O	0635	2.2	1140	0.3	1905	2.1	2359	0.2
17 SU ●	0624	2.0	1129	0.3	1846	1.8	2341	0.3
3 SU	0723	2.3	1226	0.2	1953	2.1		
18 M	0708	2.1	1208	0.3	1932	1.9		
4 M	0043	0.2	0806	2.3	1310	0.2	2036	2.0
19 TU	0022	0.2	0750	2.1	1248	0.2	2012	1.9
5 TU	0124	0.2	0845	2.2	1351	0.2	2114	1.9
20 W	0103	0.2	0829	2.1	1327	0.2	2048	1.8
6 W	0203	0.3	0919	2.1	1431	0.3	2147	1.8
21 TH	0142	0.2	0904	2.0	1406	0.2	2121	1.8
7 TH	0240	0.4	0947	1.9	1510	0.4	2216	1.6
22 F	0221	0.2	0937	1.9	1447	0.2	2154	1.8
8 F	0317	0.5	1015	1.7	1550	0.5	2247	1.5
23 SA	0300	0.3	1013	1.8	1531	0.3	2233	1.7
9 SA	0353	0.6	1049	1.6	1633	0.6	2328	1.4
24 SU	0344	0.4	1054	1.7	1622	0.4	2320	1.6
10 SU	0437	0.7	1132	1.5	1727	0.7		
25 M	0438	0.5	1146	1.6	1726	0.5		
11 M	0022	1.3	0547	0.8	1229	1.4	1834	0.7
26 TU	0020	1.5	0549	0.6	1254	1.5	1840	0.6
12 TU	0133	1.4	0712	0.8	1341	1.4	1941	0.7
27 W	0139	1.5	0714	0.7	1423	1.5	1959	0.6
13 W	0250	1.4	0822	0.7	1458	1.4	2038	0.6
28 TH	0310	1.6	0840	0.6	1551	1.6	2111	0.5
14 TH	0354	1.6	0918	0.6	1606	1.5	2129	0.5
29 F	0427	1.8	0950	0.5	1703	1.7	2212	0.4
15 F	0447	1.8	1006	0.5	1704	1.6	2215	0.4
30 SA	0529	1.9	1045	0.4	1804	1.9	2303	0.3
31 SU O	0624	2.1	1132	0.3	1856	2.0	2348	0.2

FEBRUARY

Day	Time	m	Time	m	Time	m	Time	m
1 M	0712	2.2	1215	0.2	1942	2.0		
16 TU ●	0654	2.1	1151	0.1	1920	1.9		
2 TU	0029	0.1	0753	2.2	1256	0.1	2022	2.0
17 W	0006	0.1	0738	2.2	1233	0.1	2002	2.0
3 W	0109	0.1	0830	2.2	1334	0.1	2056	2.0
18 TH	0049	0.0	0819	2.2	1313	0.0	2039	2.0
4 TH	0146	0.1	0900	2.1	1411	0.1	2123	1.8
19 F	0129	0.0	0856	2.2	1354	0.0	2112	2.0
5 F	0220	0.2	0924	1.9	1445	0.2	2146	1.7
20 SA	0208	0.0	0930	2.1	1434	0.1	2144	1.9
6 SA	0251	0.3	0949	1.8	1514	0.3	2212	1.6
21 SU	0247	0.1	1004	1.9	1515	0.2	2219	1.8
7 SU	0316	0.4	1018	1.6	1535	0.4	2243	1.4
22 M	0328	0.3	1042	1.7	1601	0.3	2259	1.6
8 M	0338	0.5	1050	1.4	1558	0.5	2321	1.3
23 TU	0416	0.4	1128	1.6	1657	0.5	2351	1.5
9 TU	0414	0.6	1132	1.3	1641	0.6		
24 W	0521	0.6	1229	1.5	1811	0.6		
10 W	0019	1.3	0520	0.7	1239	1.2	1800	0.7
25 TH	0104	1.5	0652	0.7	1401	1.4	1941	0.6
11 TH	0141	1.3	0727	0.8	1407	1.3	1947	0.6
26 F	0246	1.6	0836	0.7	1542	1.5	2102	0.6
12 F	0307	1.4	0849	0.7	1533	1.4	2057	0.6
27 SA	0413	1.6	0946	0.5	1657	1.6	2201	0.5
13 SA	0416	1.6	0943	0.5	1642	1.5	2151	0.4
28 SU	0517	1.8	1036	0.4	1754	1.8	2249	0.3
14 SU	0513	1.8	1028	0.4	1741	1.7	2239	0.3
15 M	0605	2.0	1110	0.3	1833	1.8	2323	0.2

MARCH

Day	Time	m	Time	m	Time	m	Time	m
1 M	0610	2.0	1118	0.2	1843	1.9	2331	0.2
16 TU	0542	1.9	1047	0.2	1814	1.9	2302	0.1
2 TU O	0656	2.1	1158	0.1	1925	2.0		
17 W ●	0633	2.1	1130	0.0	1901	2.0	2346	0.0
3 W	0010	0.1	0735	2.2	1236	0.0	2001	2.0
18 TH	0719	2.2	1212	-0.1	1944	2.1		
4 TH	0049	0.0	0809	2.2	1313	0.0	2032	2.0
19 F	0029	-0.1	0801	2.3	1254	-0.1	2021	2.2
5 F	0124	0.0	0836	2.1	1347	0.0	2057	1.9
20 SA	0110	-0.1	0839	2.3	1335	-0.1	2056	2.1
6 SA	0158	0.1	0900	2.0	1418	0.1	2119	1.8
21 SU	0151	-0.1	0916	2.2	1416	0.0	2130	2.0
7 SU	0225	0.2	0924	1.8	1440	0.2	2142	1.6
22 M	0230	0.1	0951	2.0	1457	0.1	2204	1.9
8 M	0245	0.3	0950	1.6	1452	0.3	2206	1.5
23 TU	0311	0.2	1030	1.8	1541	0.3	2243	1.7
9 TU	0302	0.4	1016	1.6	1512	0.4	2231	1.4
24 W	0359	0.4	1115	1.6	1635	0.5	2332	1.6
10 W	0332	0.5	1048	1.3	1546	0.5	2311	1.3
25 TH	0503	0.6	1219	1.4	1748	0.7		
11 TH	0421	0.6	1141	1.2	1645	0.6		
26 F	0043	1.5	0639	0.7	1358	1.4	1924	0.7
12 F	0025	1.3	0556	0.7	1316	1.2	1838	0.7
27 SA	0230	1.5	0831	0.6	1535	1.5	2048	0.7
13 SA	0213	1.3	0815	0.7	1502	1.3	2025	0.6
28 SU	0355	1.6	0934	0.5	1642	1.6	2144	0.5
14 SU	0341	1.5	0917	0.5	1621	1.5	2127	0.5
29 M	0456	1.8	1018	0.4	1735	1.8	2228	0.4
15 M	0446	1.7	1004	0.4	1721	1.7	2216	0.3
30 TU	0547	1.9	1056	0.2	1820	1.9	2307	0.3
31 W O	0631	2.0	1133	0.1	1900	2.0	2346	0.1

APRIL

Day	Time	m	Time	m	Time	m	Time	m
1 TH	0710	2.1	1210	0.0	1935	2.0		
16 F	0654	2.2	1149	-0.1	1919	2.2		
2 F	0023	0.1	0742	2.1	1247	0.0	2004	2.0
17 SA ●	0006	-0.1	0738	2.3	1233	-0.1	1959	2.3
3 SA	0100	0.0	0809	2.0	1321	0.0	2029	2.0
18 SU	0050	-0.1	0820	2.3	1315	-0.1	2038	2.2
4 SU	0134	0.1	0834	1.9	1350	0.1	2052	1.9
19 M	0132	0.0	0900	2.2	1357	0.0	2115	2.1
5 M	0200	0.2	0900	1.8	1409	0.2	2115	1.7
20 TU	0213	0.1	0939	2.0	1439	0.2	2152	2.0
6 TU	0219	0.3	0926	1.6	1422	0.3	2137	1.6
21 W	0257	0.2	1021	1.8	1524	0.4	2232	1.8
7 W	0237	0.4	0951	1.5	1441	0.4	2157	1.5
22 TH	0347	0.4	1110	1.6	1617	0.6	2321	1.6
8 TH	0304	0.4	1020	1.3	1511	0.5	2230	1.4
23 F	0450	0.6	1217	1.5	1726	0.7		
9 F	0348	0.6	1109	1.2	1602	0.6	2329	1.3
24 SA	0031	1.5	0620	0.7	1351	1.4	1857	0.7
10 SA	0510	0.7	1233	1.2	1750	0.7		
25 SU	0208	1.5	0808	0.6	1513	1.5	2022	0.7
11 SU	0110	1.3	0723	0.7	1427	1.3	1949	0.7
26 M	0326	1.6	0907	0.5	1614	1.6	2116	0.6
12 M	0258	1.5	0841	0.5	1551	1.5	2057	0.5
27 TU	0424	1.7	0948	0.4	1704	1.7	2159	0.5
13 TU	0412	1.7	0933	0.3	1653	1.7	2150	0.3
28 W	0514	1.8	1025	0.3	1748	1.9	2238	0.3
14 W	0512	1.9	1020	0.2	1746	1.9	2237	0.2
29 TH	0558	1.9	1102	0.2	1827	2.0	2317	0.3
15 TH	0605	2.1	1104	0.0	1834	2.1	2322	0.0
30 F O	0637	2.0	1139	0.1	1902	2.0	2356	0.2

Chart Datum: 0·93 metres below Ordnance Datum (Newlyn)

ENGLAND – PORTLAND

LAT 50°34′N   LONG 2°26′W

TIMES AND HEIGHTS OF HIGH AND LOW WATERS

YEAR **1999**

TIME ZONE (UT)
For Summer Time add ONE hour in non-shaded areas

MAY

Day	Time	m	Time	m	Time	m	Time	m
1 SA	0711	2.0	1217	0.1	1933	2.0		
2 SU	0034	0.1	0741	2.0	1253	0.1	2000	2.0
3 M	0109	0.2	0810	1.9	1322	0.2	2027	1.9
4 TU	0137	0.2	0838	1.8	1343	0.3	2053	1.8
5 W	0158	0.3	0906	1.7	1401	0.4	2115	1.7
6 TH	0219	0.4	0933	1.5	1423	0.4	2137	1.6
7 F	0249	0.4	1005	1.4	1455	0.5	2209	1.5
8 SA	0332	0.5	1052	1.3	1544	0.6	2300	1.4
9 SU	0444	0.6	1205	1.3	1718	0.7		
10 M	0023	1.4	0628	0.6	1345	1.3	1907	0.7
11 TU	0209	1.5	0755	0.5	1511	1.5	2022	0.6
12 W	0331	1.7	0857	0.4	1617	1.7	2119	0.4
13 TH	0437	1.9	0949	0.2	1713	1.9	2210	0.3
14 F	0534	2.0	1038	0.1	1805	2.1	2258	0.1
15 SA	0627	2.2	1125	0.0	1853	2.2	●2345	0.0
16 SU	0717	2.3	1211	0.0	1938	2.3		
17 M	0030	0.0	0802	2.3	1257	0.0	2020	2.3
18 TU	0115	0.0	0847	2.2	1341	0.1	2101	2.2
19 W	0200	0.1	0930	2.0	1425	0.2	2142	2.0
20 TH	0245	0.3	1015	1.8	1510	0.4	2224	1.9
21 F	0335	0.4	1105	1.7	1600	0.6	2311	1.7
22 SA	0433	0.6	1207	1.5	1700	0.7		
23 SU	0010	1.6	0544	0.6	1323	1.5	1813	0.8
24 M	0128	1.5	0710	0.6	1436	1.5	1932	0.8
25 TU	0241	1.5	0819	0.6	1535	1.6	2034	0.7
26 W	0341	1.6	0906	0.5	1625	1.7	2122	0.6
27 TH	0432	1.7	0947	0.4	1709	1.8	2205	0.5
28 F	0517	1.7	1027	0.3	1749	1.9	2247	0.4
29 SA	0558	1.8	1107	0.3	1826	1.9	2328	0.3
30 SU	0637	1.9	1147	0.2	1901	2.0	O	
31 M	0008	0.3	0713	1.9	1225	0.2	1935	2.0

JUNE

Day	Time	m	Time	m	Time	m	Time	m
1 TU	0045	0.3	0748	1.9	1258	0.3	2007	2.0
2 W	0116	0.3	0822	1.8	1326	0.3	2037	1.9
3 TH	0143	0.3	0853	1.7	1352	0.4	2104	1.8
4 F	0210	0.4	0923	1.6	1420	0.5	2130	1.7
5 SA	0244	0.4	0956	1.5	1455	0.5	2202	1.6
6 SU	0327	0.5	1040	1.4	1543	0.6	2248	1.5
7 M	0427	0.5	1140	1.4	1655	0.7	2354	1.5
8 TU	0546	0.5	1259	1.4	1823	0.7		
9 W	0121	1.5	0707	0.5	1425	1.4	1941	0.6
10 TH	0248	1.6	0818	0.4	1537	1.7	2047	0.5
11 F	0401	1.8	0919	0.3	1640	1.9	2144	0.4
12 SA	0505	1.9	1014	0.2	1737	2.1	2238	0.3
13 SU	0604	2.1	1106	0.1	1834	2.2	●2328	0.2
14 M	0658	2.1	1155	0.1	1920	2.3		
15 TU	0017	0.1	0749	2.2	1243	0.1	2007	2.3
16 W	0104	0.1	0836	2.1	1328	0.1	2051	2.2
17 TH	0149	0.2	0922	2.0	1412	0.2	2133	2.1
18 F	0234	0.2	1006	1.9	1455	0.4	2213	2.0
19 SA	0320	0.4	1050	1.7	1539	0.5	2252	1.8
20 SU	0409	0.5	1136	1.6	1628	0.6	2333	1.6
21 M	0504	0.6	1230	1.5	1726	0.7		
22 TU	0021	1.5	0606	0.6	1335	1.4	1833	0.8
23 W	0122	1.4	0713	0.6	1441	1.4	1941	0.8
24 TH	0231	1.4	0814	0.6	1537	1.5	2041	0.7
25 F	0335	1.5	0906	0.5	1625	1.6	2132	0.6
26 SA	0429	1.6	0952	0.4	1709	1.8	2218	0.5
27 SU	0519	1.7	1037	0.4	1752	1.9	2302	0.3
28 M	0606	1.7	1119	0.3	1834	1.9	O2344	0.4
29 TU	0651	1.8	1200	0.3	1914	2.0		
30 W	0022	0.1	0732	1.8	1238	0.3	1952	2.0

JULY

Day	Time	m	Time	m	Time	m	Time	m
1 TH	0058	0.3	0811	1.8	1312	0.3	2028	2.0
2 F	0131	0.3	0846	1.8	1346	0.3	2100	1.9
3 SA	0204	0.3	0918	1.7	1420	0.4	2130	1.8
4 SU	0240	0.3	0950	1.6	1456	0.4	2202	1.7
5 M	0321	0.4	1028	1.6	1539	0.5	2242	1.6
6 TU	0411	0.4	1117	1.5	1634	0.6	2334	1.6
7 W	0514	0.5	1219	1.5	1744	0.6		
8 TH	0041	1.5	0628	0.5	1336	1.5	1901	0.6
9 F	0206	1.6	0744	0.5	1459	1.6	2017	0.6
10 SA	0330	1.6	0855	0.4	1612	1.8	2125	0.5
11 SU	0443	1.8	0958	0.3	1717	1.9	2225	0.4
12 M	0548	1.9	1054	0.2	1815	2.1	2319	0.3
13 TU	0646	2.0	1144	0.2	1908	2.2	●	
14 W	0008	0.2	0738	2.1	1232	0.1	1955	2.3
15 TH	0055	0.1	0826	2.1	1316	0.1	2039	2.3
16 F	0138	0.1	0909	2.0	1357	0.2	2119	2.2
17 SA	0220	0.2	0947	1.9	1436	0.3	2153	2.0
18 SU	0300	0.3	1022	1.8	1515	0.4	2223	1.8
19 M	0340	0.4	1053	1.6	1555	0.5	2251	1.6
20 TU	0422	0.5	1127	1.5	1639	0.6	2326	1.5
21 W	0509	0.6	1211	1.4	1734	0.7		
22 TH	0012	1.4	0608	0.7	1312	1.3	1845	0.8
23 F	0114	1.3	0718	0.7	1428	1.4	1959	0.8
24 SA	0229	1.3	0824	0.6	1538	1.5	2101	0.7
25 SU	0344	1.4	0920	0.5	1633	1.6	2153	0.6
26 M	0446	1.5	1009	0.5	1723	1.8	2239	0.5
27 TU	0541	1.7	1054	0.4	1811	1.9	2321	0.4
28 W	0632	1.8	1137	0.3	1857	2.0	O	
29 TH	0001	0.3	0718	1.9	1218	0.2	1939	2.1
30 F	0039	0.2	0800	1.9	1256	0.2	2018	2.1
31 SA	0116	0.2	0837	1.9	1333	0.2	2054	2.0

AUGUST

Day	Time	m	Time	m	Time	m	Time	m
1 SU	0153	0.2	0910	1.9	1410	0.2	2126	1.9
2 M	0230	0.2	0940	1.8	1447	0.3	2157	1.8
3 TU	0310	0.3	1014	1.7	1526	0.4	2232	1.7
4 W	0354	0.3	1055	1.6	1612	0.5	2315	1.6
5 TH	0449	0.4	1147	1.5	1713	0.6		
6 F	0013	1.5	0558	0.5	1257	1.5	1832	0.7
7 SA	0133	1.5	0720	0.6	1427	1.5	2000	0.7
8 SU	0310	1.5	0843	0.5	1554	1.7	2119	0.6
9 M	0433	1.7	0950	0.4	1704	1.9	2220	0.4
10 TU	0540	1.8	1045	0.3	1804	2.1	2311	0.3
11 W	0637	2.1	1133	0.2	1856	2.2	●2357	0.2
12 TH	0726	2.1	1217	0.1	1942	2.3		
13 F	0040	0.1	0810	2.1	1258	0.1	2022	2.3
14 SA	0121	0.1	0848	2.1	1337	0.1	2057	2.2
15 SU	0159	0.1	0921	2.0	1413	0.2	2126	2.1
16 M	0235	0.2	0947	1.8	1448	0.3	2149	1.9
17 TU	0308	0.3	1010	1.7	1520	0.4	2213	1.7
18 W	0337	0.4	1037	1.5	1548	0.6	2242	1.5
19 TH	0400	0.6	1112	1.4	1619	0.7	2318	1.4
20 F	0429	0.7	1202	1.3	1720	0.8		
21 SA	0012	1.3	0537	0.7	1316	1.3	1916	0.8
22 SU	0136	1.2	0738	0.7	1447	1.4	2036	0.7
23 M	0310	1.3	0851	0.6	1600	1.6	2131	0.6
24 TU	0423	1.5	0944	0.5	1657	1.7	2216	0.5
25 W	0522	1.6	1030	0.4	1748	1.9	2257	0.4
26 TH	0614	1.8	1112	0.3	1836	2.1	O2337	0.2
27 F	0701	1.9	1154	0.2	1921	2.2		
28 SA	0016	0.1	0743	2.0	1235	0.1	2002	2.2
29 SU	0056	0.1	0821	2.0	1314	0.1	2039	2.2
30 M	0135	0.1	0854	2.0	1352	0.1	2112	2.1
31 TU	0213	0.1	0924	1.9	1430	0.2	2144	2.0

Chart Datum: 0·93 metres below Ordnance Datum (Newlyn)

TIME ZONE (UT)
For Summer Time add ONE hour in non-shaded areas

ENGLAND – PORTLAND

LAT 50°34′N   LONG 2°26′W

TIMES AND HEIGHTS OF HIGH AND LOW WATERS   YEAR **1999**

SEPTEMBER

Day	Time	m		Day	Time	m
1 W	0252 / 0956 / 1509 / 2218	0.2 / 1.8 / 0.3 / 1.8		16 TH	0249 / 0954 / 1502 / 2203	0.4 / 1.6 / 0.5 / 1.5
2 TH	0335 / 1034 / 1553 / 2259	0.3 / 1.7 / 0.5 / 1.7		17 F	0300 / 1019 / 1522 / 2230	0.5 / 1.5 / 0.6 / 1.4
3 F	0426 / 1122 / 1653 / 2354	0.5 / 1.6 / 0.6 / 1.5		18 SA	0324 / 1053 / 1604 / 2314	0.6 / 1.4 / 0.8 / 1.2
4 SA	0536 / 1228 / 1818	0.6 / 1.5 / 0.7		19 SU	0411 / 1200 / 1808	0.8 / 1.3 / 0.9
5 SU	0118 / 0709 / 1409 / 2000	1.4 / 0.7 / 1.5 / 0.7		20 M	0044 / 0617 / 1349 / 2009	1.2 / 0.8 / 1.4 / 0.8
6 M	0310 / 0839 / 1545 / 2118	1.5 / 0.7 / 1.7 / 0.6		21 TU	0241 / 0821 / 1522 / 2105	1.3 / 0.8 / 1.5 / 0.6
7 TU	0431 / 0943 / 1654 / 2213	1.6 / 0.7 / 1.9 / 0.5		22 W	0403 / 0917 / 1626 / 2148	1.5 / 0.6 / 1.7 / 0.5
8 W	0531 / 1032 / 1749 / 2258	1.8 / 0.4 / 2.0 / 0.3		23 TH	0500 / 1003 / 1720 / 2229	1.7 / 0.5 / 1.9 / 0.3
9 TH ●	0622 / 1116 / 1837 / 2339	2.0 / 0.3 / 2.2 / 0.2		24 F	0550 / 1046 / 1810 / 2309	1.9 / 0.3 / 2.1 / 0.2
10 F	0707 / 1156 / 1920	2.1 / 0.2 / 2.3		25 SA O	0636 / 1128 / 1856 / 2350	2.1 / 0.2 / 2.2 / 0.1
11 SA	0018 / 0746 / 1235 / 1957	0.1 / 2.1 / 0.1 / 2.3		26 SU	0719 / 1209 / 1938	2.2 / 0.1 / 2.3
12 SU	0056 / 0820 / 1312 / 2028	0.1 / 2.1 / 0.1 / 2.2		27 M	0030 / 0757 / 1250 / 2016	0.0 / 2.2 / 0.1 / 2.3
13 M	0132 / 0848 / 1347 / 2053	0.1 / 2.0 / 0.2 / 2.0		28 TU	0111 / 0832 / 1330 / 2052	0.0 / 2.2 / 0.1 / 2.2
14 TU	0205 / 0910 / 1419 / 2114	0.2 / 1.9 / 0.3 / 1.9		29 W	0151 / 0904 / 1409 / 2127	0.1 / 2.1 / 0.2 / 2.0
15 W	0232 / 0931 / 1445 / 2138	0.3 / 1.7 / 0.4 / 1.7		30 TH	0231 / 0938 / 1450 / 2203	0.2 / 2.0 / 0.3 / 1.9

OCTOBER

Day	Time	m		Day	Time	m
1 F	0313 / 1015 / 1537 / 2246	0.4 / 1.8 / 0.5 / 1.7		16 SA	0220 / 0937 / 1447 / 2157	0.5 / 1.6 / 0.6 / 1.4
2 SA	0405 / 1102 / 1641 / 2346	0.6 / 1.7 / 0.7 / 1.5		17 SU	0242 / 1005 / 1524 / 2239	0.6 / 1.5 / 0.7 / 1.3
3 SU	0518 / 1210 / 1814	0.8 / 1.6 / 0.8		18 M	0320 / 1057 / 1649 / 2359	0.8 / 1.4 / 0.8 / 1.2
4 M	0127 / 0659 / 1402 / 2001	1.4 / 0.8 / 1.6 / 0.7		19 TU	0458 / 1237 / 1927	0.9 / 1.4 / 0.8
5 TU	0314 / 0830 / 1532 / 2109	1.5 / 0.8 / 1.7 / 0.6		20 W	0207 / 0740 / 1435 / 2028	1.3 / 0.9 / 1.5 / 0.7
6 W	0422 / 0928 / 1634 / 2155	1.7 / 0.7 / 1.9 / 0.5		21 TH	0334 / 0845 / 1549 / 2114	1.5 / 0.7 / 1.7 / 0.5
7 TH	0513 / 1013 / 1725 / 2235	1.9 / 0.5 / 2.0 / 0.3		22 F	0431 / 0933 / 1646 / 2156	1.7 / 0.5 / 1.9 / 0.3
8 F	0558 / 1052 / 1810 / 2312	2.0 / 0.4 / 2.1 / 0.2		23 SA	0520 / 1017 / 1738 / 2239	2.0 / 0.4 / 2.1 / 0.2
9 SA	0639 / 1130 / 1851 / 2349	2.1 / 0.3 / 2.2 / 0.1		24 SU O	0606 / 1100 / 1826 / 2321	2.1 / 0.2 / 2.2 / 0.1
10 SU	0716 / 1208 / 1926	2.2 / 0.2 / 2.2		25 M	0650 / 1142 / 1911	2.3 / 0.1 / 2.3
11 M	0025 / 0747 / 1244 / 1955	0.1 / 2.2 / 0.2 / 2.1		26 TU	0004 / 0730 / 1225 / 1952	0.0 / 2.3 / 0.1 / 2.3
12 TU	0101 / 0813 / 1319 / 2019	0.1 / 2.1 / 0.2 / 2.0		27 W	0046 / 0808 / 1307 / 2032	0.0 / 2.3 / 0.1 / 2.2
13 W	0132 / 0834 / 1350 / 2042	0.2 / 2.0 / 0.3 / 1.9		28 TH	0128 / 0845 / 1349 / 2111	0.1 / 2.2 / 0.2 / 2.1
14 TH	0156 / 0856 / 1413 / 2107	0.3 / 1.9 / 0.4 / 1.7		29 F	0210 / 0922 / 1433 / 2152	0.3 / 2.1 / 0.4 / 1.9
15 F	0207 / 0918 / 1426 / 2131	0.5 / 1.7 / 0.5 / 1.5		30 SA	0254 / 1002 / 1524 / 2240	0.5 / 2.0 / 0.5 / 1.7
				31 SU	0346 / 1050 / 1630 / 2346	0.7 / 1.8 / 0.7 / 1.5

NOVEMBER

Day	Time	m		Day	Time	m
1 M	0457 / 1159 / 1800	0.9 / 1.6 / 0.8		16 TU	0300 / 1027 / 1612 / 2327	0.8 / 1.5 / 0.8 / 1.3
2 TU	0127 / 0632 / 1344 / 1941	1.5 / 0.9 / 1.6 / 0.7		17 W	0415 / 1142 / 1808	0.9 / 1.5 / 0.8
3 W	0256 / 0806 / 1505 / 2043	1.6 / 0.9 / 1.7 / 0.6		18 TH	0114 / 0635 / 1335 / 1934	1.3 / 0.9 / 1.5 / 0.7
4 TH	0356 / 0903 / 1604 / 2126	1.7 / 0.8 / 1.8 / 0.5		19 F	0249 / 0800 / 1504 / 2031	1.5 / 0.8 / 1.7 / 0.5
5 F	0444 / 0946 / 1652 / 2203	1.9 / 0.6 / 1.9 / 0.4		20 SA	0353 / 0856 / 1608 / 2121	1.7 / 0.6 / 1.8 / 0.3
6 SA	0526 / 1023 / 1736 / 2239	2.0 / 0.5 / 2.0 / 0.3		21 SU	0446 / 0945 / 1704 / 2207	1.9 / 0.5 / 2.0 / 0.2
7 SU	0606 / 1101 / 1816 / 2316	2.1 / 0.4 / 2.0 / 0.3		22 M	0535 / 1032 / 1756 / 2254	2.1 / 0.3 / 2.1 / 0.1
8 M ●	0641 / 1138 / 1851 / 2353	2.1 / 0.3 / 2.0 / 0.2		23 TU O	0622 / 1117 / 1846 / 2339	2.3 / 0.2 / 2.2 / 0.1
9 TU	0712 / 1216 / 1920	2.1 / 0.3 / 2.0		24 W	0706 / 1203 / 1933	2.4 / 0.2 / 2.2
10 W	0029 / 0738 / 1252 / 1948	0.2 / 2.1 / 0.3 / 1.9		25 TH	0024 / 0749 / 1249 / 2017	0.2 / 2.4 / 0.2 / 2.2
11 TH	0101 / 0804 / 1324 / 2016	0.3 / 2.0 / 0.4 / 1.8		26 F	0109 / 0831 / 1334 / 2101	0.2 / 2.3 / 0.3 / 2.1
12 F	0125 / 0830 / 1347 / 2044	0.4 / 1.9 / 0.4 / 1.7		27 SA	0154 / 0912 / 1421 / 2147	0.3 / 2.2 / 0.4 / 1.9
13 SA	0140 / 0853 / 1404 / 2110	0.5 / 1.8 / 0.5 / 1.6		28 SU	0240 / 0955 / 1513 / 2236	0.5 / 2.0 / 0.5 / 1.7
14 SU	0158 / 0914 / 1428 / 2139	0.6 / 1.7 / 0.6 / 1.5		29 M	0330 / 1042 / 1612 / 2337	0.7 / 1.8 / 0.6 / 1.6
15 M	0222 / 0942 / 1505 / 2220	0.6 / 1.6 / 0.7 / 1.4		30 TU	0429 / 1141 / 1724	0.8 / 1.7 / 0.7

DECEMBER

Day	Time	m		Day	Time	m
1 W	0054 / 0543 / 1301 / 1845	1.5 / 0.9 / 1.6 / 0.7		16 TH	0358 / 1113 / 1707	0.7 / 1.5 / 0.6
2 TH	0214 / 0709 / 1419 / 1955	1.5 / 0.9 / 1.6 / 0.7		17 F	0015 / 0529 / 1235 / 1831	1.4 / 0.8 / 1.5 / 0.6
3 F	0317 / 0820 / 1521 / 2044	1.6 / 0.8 / 1.7 / 0.6		18 SA	0146 / 0702 / 1409 / 1943	1.5 / 0.8 / 1.6 / 0.5
4 SA	0407 / 0908 / 1612 / 2124	1.7 / 0.7 / 1.7 / 0.5		19 SU	0306 / 0814 / 1528 / 2044	1.6 / 0.7 / 1.7 / 0.4
5 SU	0450 / 0950 / 1657 / 2204	1.8 / 0.6 / 1.8 / 0.4		20 M	0409 / 0914 / 1633 / 2140	1.8 / 0.5 / 1.9 / 0.3
6 M	0529 / 1030 / 1737 / 2244	1.9 / 0.5 / 1.8 / 0.4		21 TU	0506 / 1008 / 1731 / 2232	2.0 / 0.4 / 2.0 / 0.2
7 TU ●	0605 / 1110 / 1815 / 2323	2.0 / 0.4 / 1.9 / 0.3		22 W O	0558 / 1059 / 1827 / 2323	2.2 / 0.3 / 2.1 / 0.2
8 W	0639 / 1150 / 1850	2.1 / 0.4 / 1.9		23 TH	0649 / 1149 / 1919	2.3 / 0.2 / 2.2
9 TH	0001 / 0711 / 1229 / 1925	0.3 / 2.1 / 0.4 / 1.9		24 F	0011 / 0736 / 1238 / 2008	0.1 / 2.3 / 0.2 / 2.1
10 F	0036 / 0743 / 1303 / 1959	0.3 / 2.1 / 0.4 / 1.8		25 SA	0058 / 0822 / 1325 / 2055	0.2 / 2.3 / 0.2 / 2.1
11 SA	0105 / 0814 / 1330 / 2031	0.4 / 2.0 / 0.4 / 1.7		26 SU	0143 / 0906 / 1412 / 2139	0.2 / 2.2 / 0.3 / 2.0
12 SU	0130 / 0842 / 1354 / 2101	0.5 / 1.9 / 0.5 / 1.6		27 M	0227 / 0948 / 1459 / 2223	0.4 / 2.1 / 0.4 / 1.8
13 M	0155 / 0908 / 1422 / 2131	0.5 / 1.8 / 0.5 / 1.6		28 TU	0312 / 1029 / 1548 / 2308	0.5 / 1.9 / 0.5 / 1.6
14 TU	0223 / 0937 / 1459 / 2209	0.6 / 1.7 / 0.6 / 1.5		29 W	0359 / 1110 / 1641 / 2359	0.6 / 1.7 / 0.6 / 1.5
15 W	0301 / 1016 / 1550 / 2301	0.7 / 1.6 / 0.6 / 1.4		30 TH	0454 / 1157 / 1742	0.8 / 1.6 / 0.6
				31 F	0100 / 0559 / 1254 / 1846	1.4 / 0.8 / 1.5 / 0.7

Chart Datum: 0·93 metres below Ordnance Datum (Newlyn)

WEYMOUTH   8-2-10

Dorset 50°36'·54N 02°26'·50W   Rtg 2-2-1

CHARTS
AC 2172, 2268, 2255, 2610; Imray C4, C5; Stanfords 12; OS 194

TIDES
–0438 Dover; ML 1·1; Zone 0 (UT)

Standard Port PORTLAND (←)

Predictions for Weymouth are as for Portland. Mean ranges are small: 0·6m at np and 2·0m at sp.
NOTE: Double LWs occur; predictions are for first LW. A LW stand lasts about 4 hrs at sp and 1 hr at nps.
Due to an eddy, the tidal stream in Weymouth Roads is W-going at all times except HW –0510 to HW –038.

SHELTER
Good, but swell enters outer hbr and The Cove in strong E winds. Berthing options from seaward:
In The Cove on pontoon S side or on the N side (Custom House Quay) off RDYC. Pontoons also line part of the N side; fender boards are available elsewhere. In season rafting-up is the rule. (The quays between The Cove and the lifting bridge are reserved for FVs).
The municipal pontoons just beyond the lifting bridge (see NAVIGATION) are for residents only; no visitors. N of these Weymouth Marina, dredged 2·5m, has 300 berths in complete shelter.
It is feasible to ‡ in Weymouth Bay, NE of hbr ent in about 3m, but necessarily some way offshore due to the drying sands and buoyed watersport areas inshore. See also 8.2.8 for possible ‡ in Portland Harbour.

NAVIGATION
WPT 50°36'·68N, 02°26'·10W 060°/240° from/to front ldg lt, 0·50M. The hbr ent lies deep in the NW corner of Weymouth Bay; it could in some conditions be confused with the N ent to Portland Hbr. Hbr speed limit is 'Dead Slow'. Comply with IPTS.
The **bridge** lifts (LT) 0800, 1000, 1200, 1400, 1600, 1800 on request throughout the year. Later lifts are at 1930 Apr & Sept; 2030 May & Aug; 2000 and 2130 Jun & Jul. Oct to Mar, 1 hr's notice by telephone is required for all lifts.
Five mins before lift times, craft should be visible to, and in contact VHF Ch 12 with, the bridge. 3FR or 3FG (vert) on both sides of the bridge are tfc lts, not navigational lts; outbound vessels take priority. Waiting pontoons are close E of bridge on S side and also on the marina side.
Clearances when the bridge is down are approx 2·7m MHWS, 3·8m MHWN, 4·6m MLWN, 5·2m MLWS.

In winter many fishing factory ships are often at ‡ in the NE part of Weymouth Bay.
NOTE: If heading E, check Lulworth firing programme; see overleaf and the Supplements for current dates.

LIGHTS AND MARKS
Conspic ch spire, 6ca NNW of hbr ent, is a useful day mark to help find the ent when approaching from SE past the Portland bkwtrs or from the E. Note: On the E side of Portland Hbr (see 8.2.8), approx 7ca ESE of 'D' Head lt, are 4 SPM lt buoys (marking a Noise range).
Portland 'A' Head lt ho, Fl 10s 22m 20M, is 1·7M SE of hbr ent and provides the best initial guidance at night; it is also a conspic W tr.
Caution: About 500m SE of Weymouth S Pier there are 3 SPM buoys (one Fl Y 2s) marking DG Range. Pierhead lts may be hard to see against shore lts.
Ldg lts 240°, 2 FR (H24), are 500m inside the pierhds; daymarks (same position) are R open ◇s on W poles; they are not visible until the hbr ent is opened.
IPTS must be obeyed. They are shown from a RW mast near the root of the S pier. There is one additional signal:
    2 Ⓡ over 1 Ⓖ = Ent and dep prohib (ent obstructed).
If no sigs are shown, vessels are clear to enter or leave with caution.

RADIO TELEPHONE
Weymouth Harbour VHF Ch 12 16 (0800-2000 in summer and when vessel due); *Weymouth Town Bridge* also on 12. *Weymouth Marina* Ch 80. Ch 06 *Raybar* for diesel.

TELEPHONE (Dial code 01305)
Hr Mr 206278/206423, ☎ 206422; Bridge 206423/789357; Marina 767576; MRSC 760439; Marinecall 0891 500457; ⌗ 0345 231110 (H24); Police 251212; Ⓗ 772211.

FACILITIES
Marina (300) ☎ 767576, ⚓ 767575; (237 inc Ⓥ) £17.18 (£5 for <5 hrs, 1000-1600), FW, AC;
Outer Hbr and The Cove AB £11.50 (£4 for <4 hrs), FW, M, Slip near WSC;
Custom House Quay FW, AB, AC (not on S side), showers (free);
Royal Dorset YC ☎ 786258, M, Bar; **Weymouth SC** ☎ 785481, M, Bar;
Services: CH, Sh, ACA, Gaz, Rigging, Slip, ME, Ⓔ, EI, CH. D (Wyatt's Wharf pontoon on S bank, close W of LB; ☎ 787039, mobile 0378 570228); also D from road tanker on N side, daily 0700-1900, min quantity 25ltrs: ☎ 775465 or mobile 0860 912401 or call *Raybar* VHF Ch 06.
Town EC Wed; P & D (cans), FW, ◙, V, R, Bar, ✉, Ⓑ, ⇌, ✈ (Bournemouth).

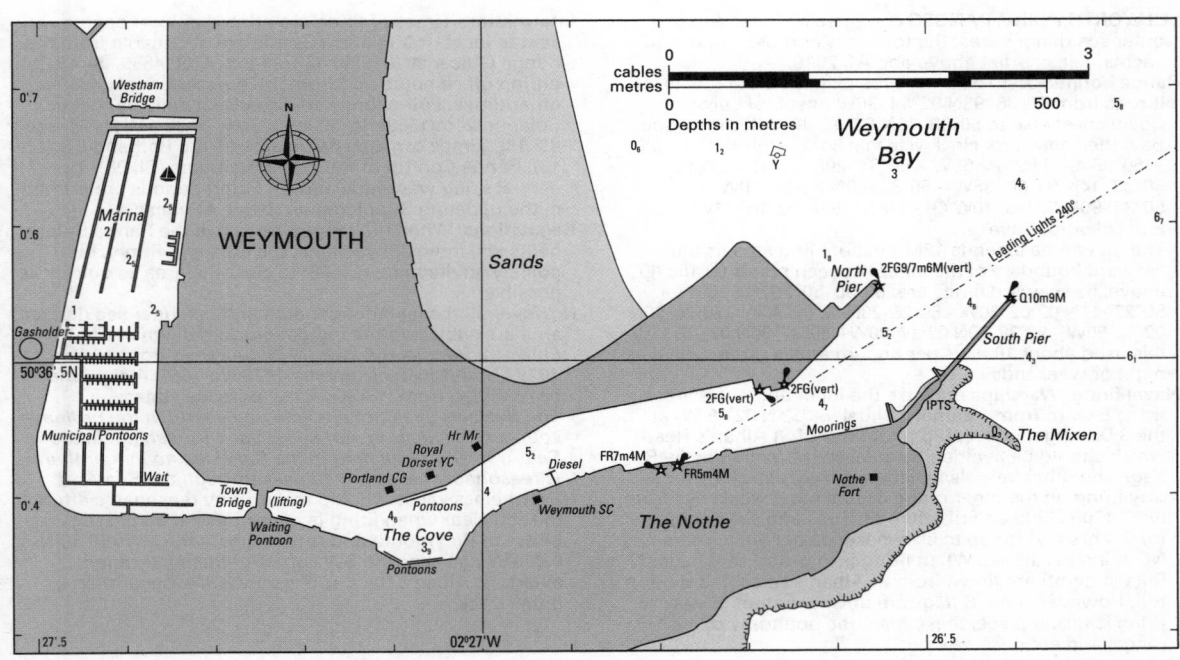

LULWORTH FIRING RANGES

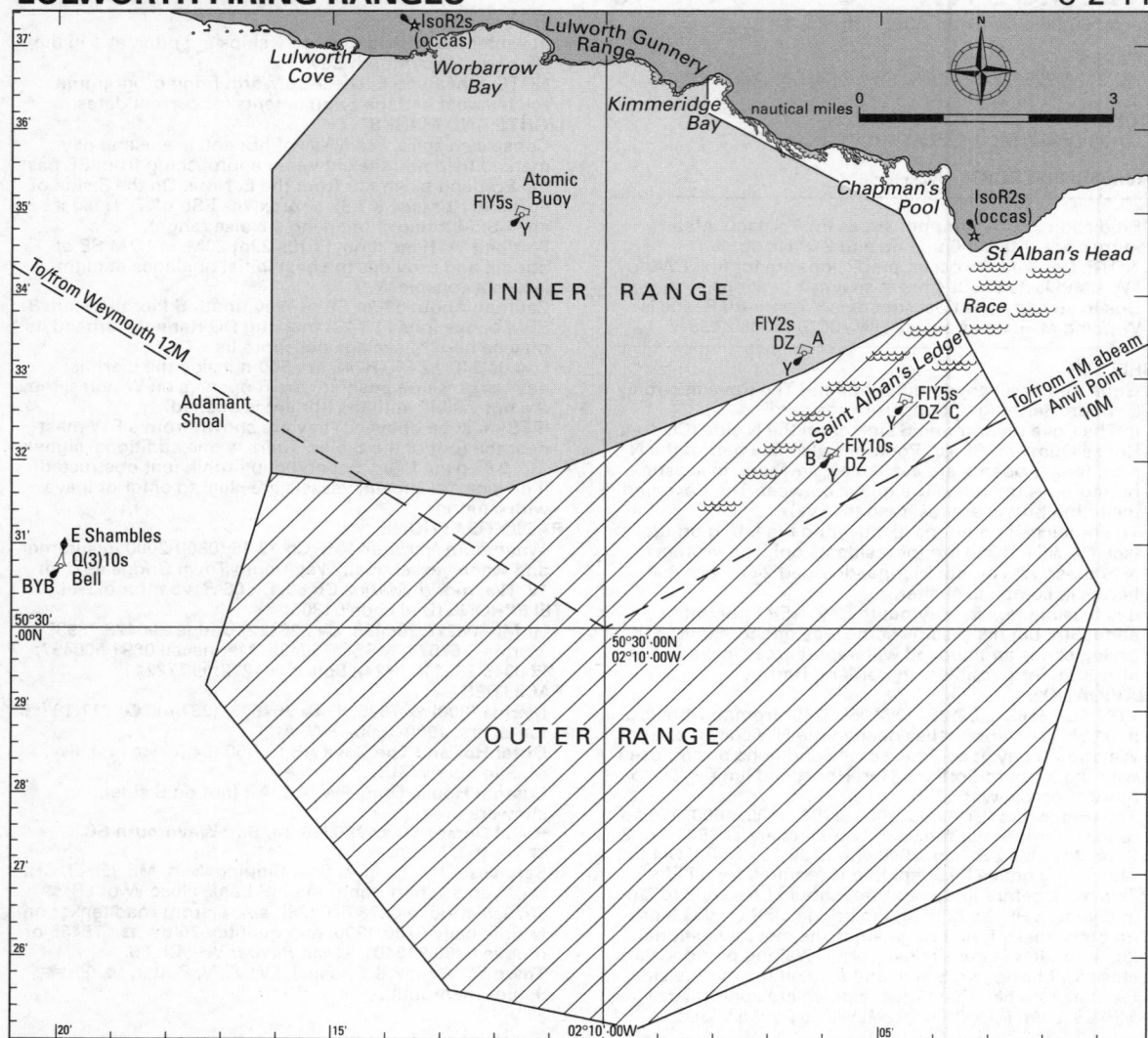

LULWORTH FIRING RANGES comprise an inner and an outer sea danger area; the former is of most concern to yachts. See chartlet above and AC 2610.

Range boundaries: The inner area extends 5·5M offshore. It runs from 50°36′·93N 02°14′·36W (just E of Lulworth Cove) coastwise to 50°36′·70N 02°08′·15W (Kimmeridge Bay) then seaward, clockwise via: 50°36′·26N 02°08′·15W – 50°35′·00N 02°04′·60W – 50°34′·20N 02°03′·15W Ⓐ – 50°33′·14N 02°06′·35W – 50°31′·60N 02°12′·20W – 50°31′·90N 02°16′·10W Ⓑ – 50°35′·56N 02°16′·11W – just E of Lulworth Cove.

The outer area extends 12M offshore and adjoins the seaward boundary of the inner between points Ⓐ and Ⓑ above. Its seaward limits are: 50°30′·50N 02°01′·00W – 50°27′·11N 02°02′·60W – 50°25′·20N 02°09′·40W – 50°25′·60N 02°12′·80W – 50°29′·30N 02°17′·30W – 50°31′·90N 02°16′·11W. It is used about 10 days per annum and is rarely active at night or weekends.

Naval firing: Warships may use the inner and outer areas, firing E'ward from Adamant Shoal (50°33′N 02°19′W) at the 3 DZ target buoys, (up to 3M SW of St Alban's Head) which should be avoided by at least 1M. Warships fly R flags and other vessels/helicopters may patrol the area.

Army firing on the inner range occurs most weekdays from 0930-1700 (1200 on Fri), often on Tues and Thurs nights for 3-4 hrs and for up to six weekends per year. There is NO firing in August. When firing is in progress R flags (Fl R lts at night) are flown from St Alban's Head and Bindon Hill. However some R flags are flown whether or not firing is taking place; these mark the boundary of the range land area.

Information: Times of firing are printed in local papers, sent to local Hr Mrs and YCs and are obtainable from the Range Officer ☎ (01929) 462721 ext. 4700/4859, ☎ 4912, during office hours and from the guardroom ext 4819 at other times. Firing times are broadcast daily by Radio Solent (221m/1359kHz, 300m/999kHz or 96·1MHz FM (see 8.2.18). Times can also be obtained from Portland CG (Ch 16), Range Control or Range Safety Boats (Ch 08). The annual firing weekends and No Firing periods are printed in the updating Supplements to this Almanac.

Regulations: When the ranges are active the Range Safety boats will intercept yachts in the area and firmly, but politely, invite them (Ch 08) to clear the area as quickly as possible.

However all the land danger area and the inner sea danger area are subject to the regulations laid down in *The Lulworth Ranges Byelaws 1978 operative from 10 Nov 1978 - Statutory Instruments 1978 No 1663.* A copy may be obtained from HMSO. A key passage states:
The Byelaws shall not apply to any vessel in the ordinary course of navigation, not being used for fishing, in the Sea Area and remaining in the Sea Area no longer than is reasonably necessary to pass through the Sea Area.

Nevertheless yachts should make every reasonable effort to keep clear when firing is in progress. If on passage between Weymouth and Anvil Point, a track via 50°30′N 02°10′W just clips the SW corner of the inner range, avoids St Alban's Race and is only 3·3M longer than a direct track.

ANCHORAGES BETWEEN PORTLAND AND SWANAGE
Essential to read *Inshore along the Dorset Coast* (P. Bruce).

CHURCH OPE COVE, Dorset, 50°32´·23N 02°25´·56W. AC
2268, 2255. Tidal data as for Portland. A small cove on
the E side of the Isle of Portland, about midway between
the Bill and Portland Hbr. It is completely open to the E,
but could serve as a tempy ⚓ in about 3m off the shingle
beach, to await a fair tide around the Bill.

RINGSTEAD BAY, Dorset, 50°37´·80N 02°20´·40W. AC 2610.
Tides as for Weymouth, 4M to WSW. Tempy ⚓ in 3-5m
toward the E end of the bay. Ringstead Ledges, drying,
define the W end of the bay. Rks on the E side restrict the
effective width to about 3ca; easiest appr is from SE.

DURDLE DOOR, Dorset, 50°37´·24N 02°16´·50W. AC 2610.
Tides as for Lulworth Cove (see 8.2.8), 1M E. Durdle Door
is a conspic rock archway. Close E of it Man o' War Cove
offers ⚓ for shoal draft in settled weather. To the W, ⚓
may be found, with caution, inside The Bull, Blind Cow,
The Cow and The Calf which form part of a rocky reef.

LULWORTH COVE, Dorset, 50°36´·97N 02°14´·74W. AC
2172. HW –0449 on Dover, see 8.2.8 Tides; ML 1·2m. Good
shelter in fair weather and offshore winds, but heavy swell
enters the cove in S and SW winds; if strong the ⚓ becomes
untenable. Enter the cove slightly E of centre. A Y mooring
buoy for the range safety launch is in the middle in about
4m. ⚓ in NE part in 2·5m. Holding is poor. 8kn speed limit.
Local moorings, village and slip are on W side. Facilities:
EC Wed/Sat; FW at tap in car park, Bar, ✉, R, Slip.

WORBARROW BAY, Dorset, 50°37´·00N 02°12´·00W. AC
2172. Tides as Lulworth Cove/Mupe Bay, see 8.2.8.
Worbarrow is a 1½M wide bay, close E of Lulworth Cove.
It is easily identified from seaward by the V-shaped gap
in the hills at Arish Mell, centre of bay just E of Bindon
Hill. Bindon Hill also has a conspic white chalk scar due
to cliff falls. Caution: Mupe Rks at W end and other rks
1ca off NW side. ⚓s in about 3m sheltered from W or E
winds at appropriate end. The bay lies within Lulworth
Ranges (see above); landing prohib at Arish Mell. No
lights/facilities.

CHAPMAN'S POOL, Dorset, 50°35´·50N 02°03´·85W. AC
2172. Tidal data: interpolate between Mupe Bay (8.2.8)
and Swanage (8. 2.12). Chapman's Pool, like Worbarrow
Bay, Brandy Bay and Kimmeridge Bay, is picturesque
and convenient when the wind is off-shore. ⚓ in depths
of about 3m in centre of bay to avoid tidal swirl, but
beware large unlit B buoy (for Range Safety boat). From
here to St Alban's Hd the stream runs SSE almost
continuously due to a back eddy. No lights or facilities.

AGENTS WANTED

SWANAGE 8-2-12
Dorset 50°36´·42N 01°56´·97W   Rtg 2-4-2

CHARTS
AC *5600.1, 2172, 2610*, 2175; Imray C4; Stanfords 12, 15;
OS 195

TIDES
HW Sp–0235 & +0125, Np –0515 & +0120 on Dover; ML 1·5

Standard Port PORTSMOUTH (⟶)

Times				Height (metres)			
High Water		Low Water		MHWS	MHWN	MLWN	MLWS
0000	0600	0500	1100	4·7	3·8	1·9	0·8
1200	1800	1700	2300				

Differences SWANAGE

–0250	+0105	–0105	–0105	–2·7	–2·2	–0·7	–0·3

NOTE: Double HWs occur except at nps and predictions are for
the higher HW. Near nps there is a stand, and the predictions
shown are for the middle of the stand. See 8.2.13.

SHELTER
Good ⚓ in winds from SW to N, but bad in E/SE winds
>F4 due to swell which may persist for 6 hrs after a blow.
>F6 holding gets very difficult; Poole is nearest refuge.
AB on pier (open Apr-Oct) subject to wind & sea state.

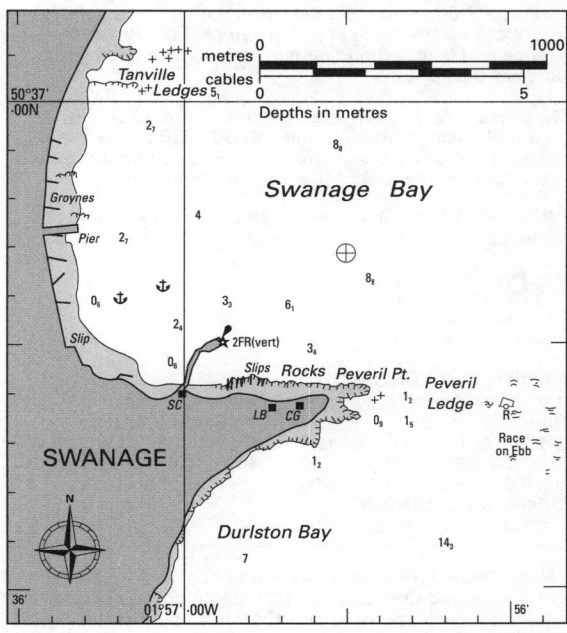

NAVIGATION
WPT 50°36´·70N 01°56´·50W, 054°/234° from/to pier hd,
0·30M. Coming from S beware Peveril Ledge and its Race
which can be vicious with a SW wind against the main
ebb. It is best to keep 1M seaward of Durlston Head and
Peveril Point. On the W side of Swanage B, keep clear of
Tanville and Phippards Ledges, approx 300m offshore.
To the S of the pier are the ruins of an old pier.

LIGHTS AND MARKS
The only lts are 2 FR (vert) on the pier; difficult to see due
to confusing street lts. Peveril Ledge PHM buoy is unlit
and hard to pick out at night due to Anvil Pt lt; keep 0·5M
clear of it to the E.

RADIO TELEPHONE
None.

TELEPHONE (Dial code 01929)
MRSC (01305) 760439; ⌗ 0345 231110 (H24) or (01202)
685157; Marinecall 0891 500457; Police 422004; Dr 422231;
Ⓗ 422282.

FACILITIES
Pier, L*, FW, AB* £8, £3 for <3hrs; after 2100 gain access
to pier from ashore via **Swanage SC** ☎ 422987, Slip, L,
FW, Bar; **Boat Park** (Peveril Pt), Slip, FW, L;
Services: Diving. **Town** P & D (cans, 1½M), FW, V, R, Bar,
✉, Ⓑ, ⇌ (mainline connection in season), ✈ (Hurn).

SPECIAL TIDAL PROBLEMS BETWEEN SWANAGE AND SELSEY   8-2-13

Due to the complex tidal variations between Swanage and Selsey/Nab Twr, applying the usual secondary port time & height differences gives only approximate predictions. More accurate values are obtained by using the individual curves discussed below.

Individual curves, as shown on the following two pages, are given for each port to cater for the rapidly changing tidal characteristics and distorted tidal curves in this area. Because their low water (LW) points are more sharply defined than high water (HW), the times on these curves are referenced to LW, but in all other respects they are used as described in Chapter 7.

Critical curve. Since the curves at ports between Swanage and Yarmouth, IOW differ considerably in shape and duration between Springs and Neaps, the tide cannot adequately be defined by only Sp and Np curves. A third, "critical", curve is therefore shown for that Portsmouth range (as indicated in the lower right of the graph) at which the heights of the two HWs are equal for the port concerned. Interpolation should be between this critical curve and either the Sp or Np curve, as appropriate. **Note** that whilst the critical curve extends throughout the tidal cycle, the spring and neap curves stop at the higher HW. Thus, for example, at 7hrs after LW Lymington, with a Portsmouth range of 3·8m (near Sp), the factor should be referenced to the next LW; whereas if the Portsmouth range had been 2·0m (near Np), it should be referenced to the previous LW.

The procedure is shown step-by-step in the following example using the **Differences SWANAGE** below and the special curves for Swanage, Poole (Ent) and Bournemouth re-printed at the foot of this page for convenience.

Example: To find the height of tide at Swanage at 0200 on a day when the tidal predictions for Portsmouth are:

19 0100   4·6
M 0613   1·1
    1314   4·5
    1833   0·8

Standard Port PORTSMOUTH (→)

Times				Height (metres)			
High Water		Low Water		MHWS	MHWN	MLWN	MLWS
0000	0600	0500	1100	4·7	3·8	1·9	0·8
1200	1800	1700	2300				
Differences SWANAGE							
−0250	+0105	−0105	−0105	−2·7	−2·2	−0·7	−0·3

Note: Double HWs occur, except at nps, at ports between Swanage and Christchurch. HW height differences, as given for each secondary port, always apply to the higher HW (that which reaches a factor of 1·0 on the curves). This higher HW should be used to obtain the range at the Secondary Port. HW time differences, which are not needed for this example, also refer to the higher HW.

(1) Complete the upper part of the tidal prediction form (next Col), omitting the HW time column (boxes 1, 5 & 9).
(2) On the left of the Swanage tidal curve diagram, plot the Secondary Port HW and LW heights (1·9m and 0·7m from (1) above), and join these points with a sloping line.

TIDAL PREDICTION FORM   Time or height required *0200*

		TIME		HEIGHT	
		HW	LW	HW	LW
Standard Port *Portsmouth*	1	2 *0613*	3 *4.6*	4 *1.1*	
Differences	5	6 *-0105*	7 *-2.7*	8 *-0.4*	
Secondary Port *Swanage*	9	10 *0508*	11 *1.9*	12 *0.7*	
Duration (or time from HW to LW)	13	9-10 or 10-9	Range Stand. Port	14 *3.5*	3-4
			Range Secdy. Port	15 *1.2*	11-12

*Springs/Neaps/Interpolate

Start: height at given time ↓ 10	Time reqd.	16 *0200*	17+18
17-16	Time of LW	17 *0508*	10
	Interval	18 *-0308*	Date *19th Nov*
	Factor	19 *0.84*	Time Zone *O(GMT)*
19 x 15	Rise above LW	20 *1.0*	22-21
12	Height of LW	21 *0.7*	12 Start: time for given height ↑
20 + 21	Height reqd.	22 *1.7*	

*Delete as necessary

(3) The time required (0200) is 3hr 8min before the time of LW at the Secondary Port, so from this point draw a line vertically up towards the curves.
(4) It is necessary to interpolate for the day's range at Portsmouth (3·5m), which is about mid-way between the spring curve (3·9m) and the critical curve (2·8m). (This incidentally gives a point level with a factor of 0·84).
(5) From this point draw a horizontal line to intersect the sloping line constructed in (2) above.
(6) From the intersection of the horizontal line and the sloping line, proceed vertically to the height scale at the top, and read off the height required, 1·7m.

The Factor method of doing the calculation, instead of the graphical method just described, is shown in the lower part of the completed tidal prediction form above. The procedure follows that given in 7·4·3. Note that box 17 is amended to read 'Time of LW'.

The Table (Intermediate heights of tide: Swanage to Nab Tower) at the end of this section offers a less accurate but quicker method of finding intermediate heights of tide for certain places between Swanage and Nab Tower. It is reproduced from earlier Admiralty Tide Tables.
Note 1: The green tinted area represents the period when the tide stands or in which a second HW may occur.
2. The upper of the three HW and LW height figures given is for mean spring tides, the middle for average tides and the lower for mean neap tides.
To use this table, determine whether the time required is nearer to HW or LW at Portsmouth; work out the interval (between time required and the nearest HW or LW at Portsmouth). Extract the height of the relevant predicted HW or LW. By interpolation between the heights of HW (left hand column) or LW (right hand column), read off the height of tide under the appropriate column (hours before/after HW or hours before/after LW).

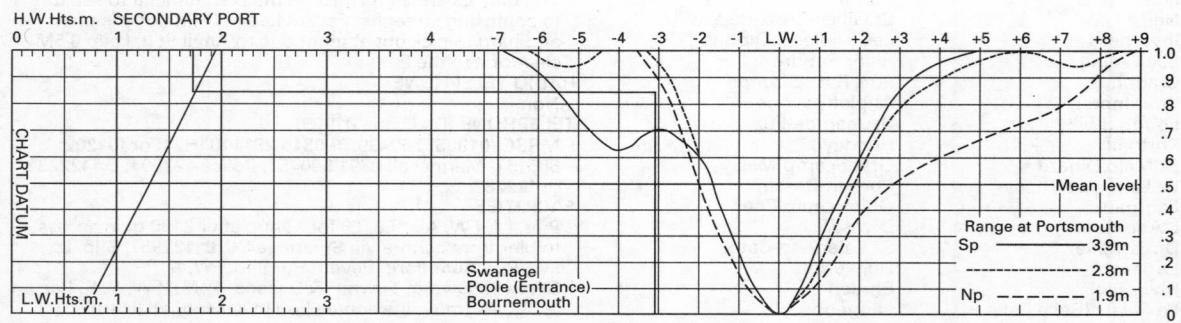

TIDAL CURVES – SWANAGE TO SELSEY

Individual tidal curves for places between Swanage and Selsey are given below, and their use is explained above. In this area the times of LW are defined much more sharply than the times of HW, and the curves are therefore drawn with their times related to LW instead of HW. Apart from referencing the times to LW, the procedure for obtaining intermediate times and heights of tide with these curves is the same as for normal Secondary Ports (see 7·4·2). For places between Swanage and Yarmouth IOW a third curve is shown, for the range at Portsmouth at which the two HWs are equal at the port concerned; for interpolation between the curves see the previous page.

Note 1.* Due to the constriction of the R Medina, Newport requires special treatment since the hbr dries 1·4m. The calculation should be made using the LW time and height differences for Cowes, and the HW height differences for Newport. Any calculated heights which fall below 1·4m should be treated as 1·4m.

Note 2.*** Wareham and Tuckton LWs do not fall below 0·7m except under very low river flow conditions.

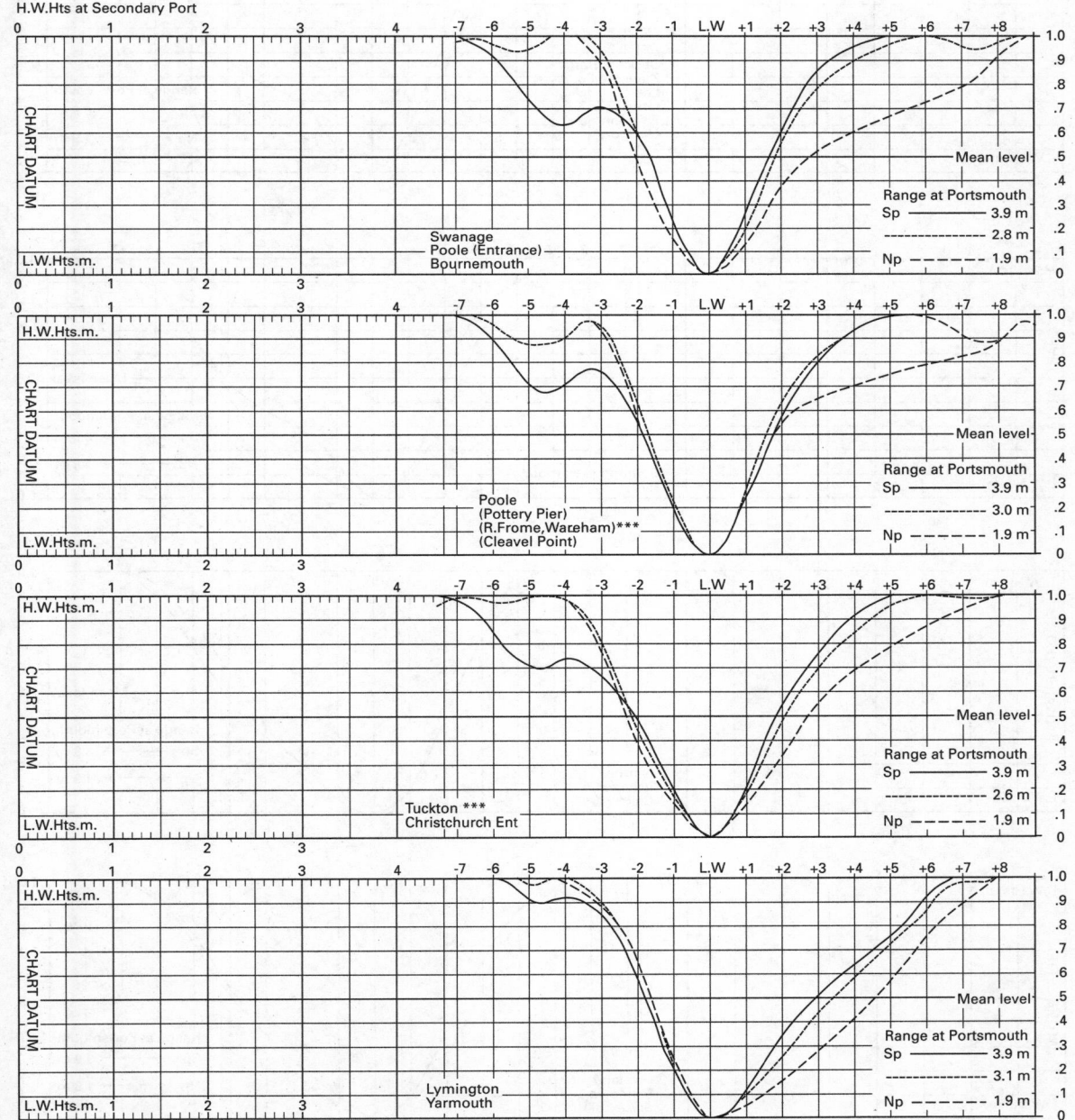

TIDAL CURVES *continued*

H.W.Hts at Secondary Ports

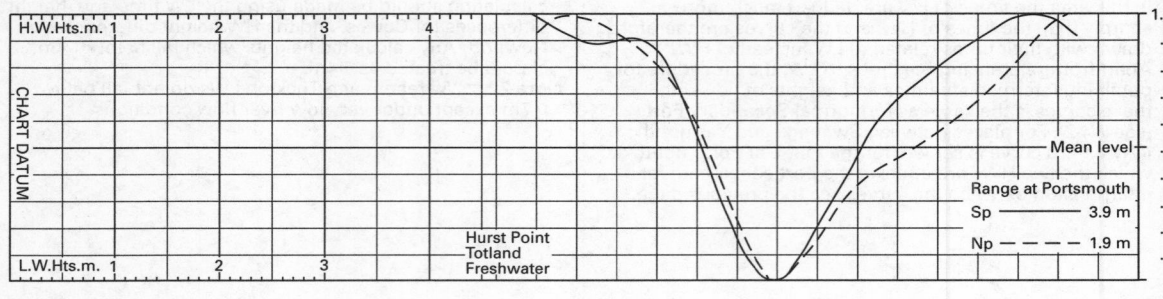

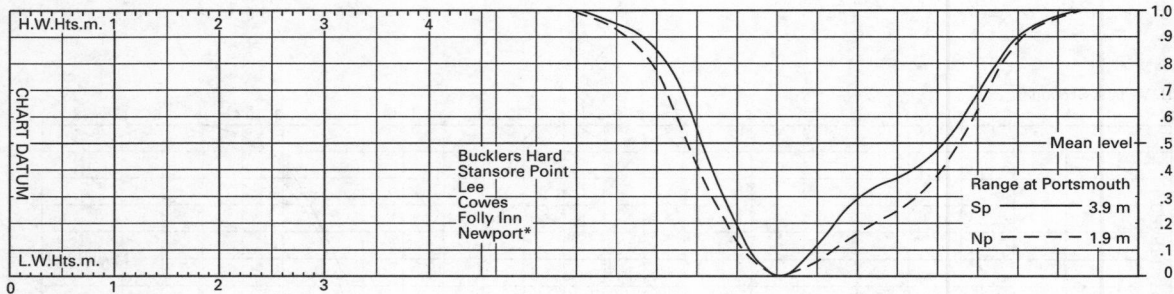

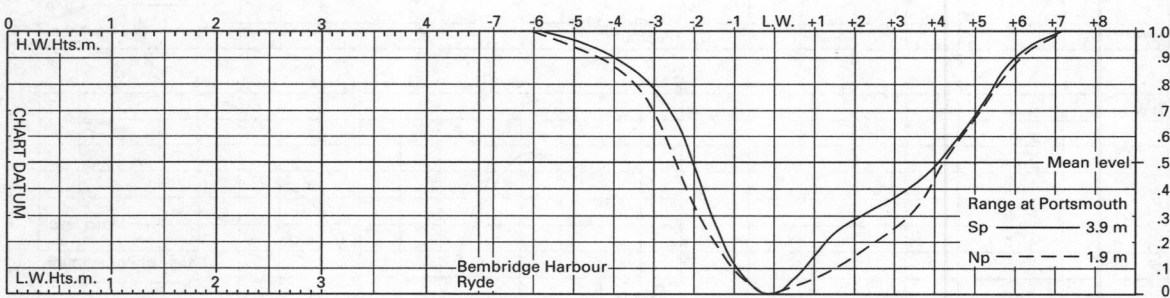

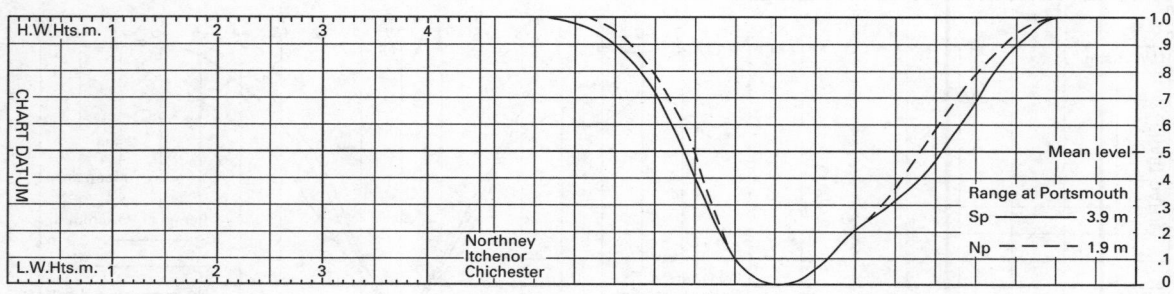

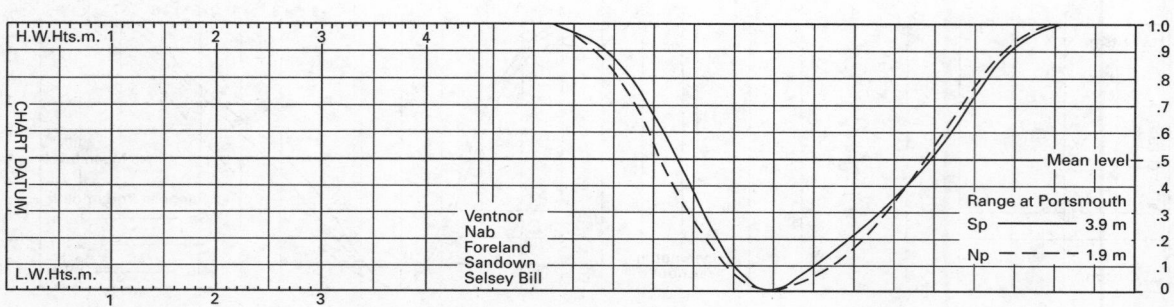

INTERMEDIATE HEIGHTS OF TIDE: SWANAGE TO NAB TOWER

(To be used for finding intermediate heights in metres for places named; see page 200)

Place	Height of H.W. at Portsmouth	HOURLY HEIGHTS ABOVE CHART DATUM AT THE PLACE													Height of L.W. at Portsmouth
		Hours before or after HIGH WATER AT PORTSMOUTH							Hours before or after LOW WATER AT PORTSMOUTH						
		−3	−2	−1	HW	+1	+2	+3	−2	−1	LW	+1	+2	+3	
	m.	m.	m.	m.	m.	m.	m.	m.	m.	m.	m.	m.	m.	m.	m.
SWANAGE	4·7	1·9	1·8	1·5	1·3	1·4	1·2	0·8	0·6	0·3	0·8	1·3	1·7	1·8	0·6
	4·3	1·6	1·6	1·5	1·5	1·2	1·4	1·1	0·9	0·8	1·0	1·3	1·5	1·6	1·2
	3·8	1·5	1·5	1·5	1·5	1·6	1·5	1·3	1·2	1·1	1·2	1·3	1·4	1·4	1·8
POOLE ENTRANCE	4·7	2·0	1·9	1·6	1·4	1·5	1·4	0·9	0·7	0·3	0·8	1·3	1·6	1·9	0·6
	4·3	1·6	1·6	1·5	1·5	1·5	1·5	1·1	1·0	0·8	0·9	1·2	1·5	1·6	1·2
	3·8	1·4	1·5	1·5	1·5	1·6	1·5	1·3	1·2	1·1	1·1	1·2	1·3	1·4	1·8
POOLE BRIDGE	4·7	2·2	2·2	1·9	1·6	1·6	1·7	1·3	1·1	0·6	0·5	1·0	1·6	1·9	0·6
	4·3	1·8	1·7	1·6	1·7	1·8	1·8	1·5	1·4	1·0	0·8	1·1	1·5	1·7	1·2
	3·8	1·5	1·5	1·6	1·7	1·8	1·8	1·5	1·5	1·3	1·2	1·3	1·5	1·5	1·8
BOURNE-MOUTH	4·7	2·1	2·0	1·7	1·5	1·5	1·5	0·9	0·7	0·3	0·6	1·2	1·7	1·9	0·6
	4·3	1·6	1·7	1·6	1·6	1·6	1·5	1·2	1·0	0·8	0·8	1·2	1·4	1·5	1·2
	3·8	1·5	1·5	1·5	1·5	1·6	1·5	1·4	1·3	1·1	1·1	1·2	1·3	1·4	1·8
CHRIST-CHURCH HARBOUR †	4·7	1·8	1·8	1·5	1·3	1·5	1·1	0·7	0·7	0·5	0·4	0·9	1·3	1·6	0·6
	4·3	1·5	1·5	1·4	1·5	1·5	1·2	0·9	0·8	0·6	0·6	1·0	1·2	1·4	1·2
	3·8	1·2	1·2	1·3	1·4	1·4	1·1	0·9	0·8	0·6	0·7	0·9	1·0	1·1	1·8
FRESHWATER BAY	4·7	2·4	2·5	2·4	2·2	2·2	1·9	1·1	0·9	0·5	0·8	1·5	2·0	2·2	0·6
	4·3	2·2	2·3	2·2	2·2	2·2	1·9	1·4	1·2	0·9	1·1	1·5	1·8	2·0	1·2
	3·8	1·9	2·0	2·2	2·2	2·2	2·0	1·6	1·6	1·3	1·3	1·6	1·7	1·8	1·8
TOTLAND BAY	4·7	2·3	2·5	2·4	2·3	2·3	2·1	1·4	1·1	0·5	0·8	1·4	1·8	2·1	0·6
	4·3	2·1	2·3	2·3	2·3	2·2	2·1	1·6	1·4	0·9	1·1	1·4	1·7	1·9	1·2
	3·8	2·0	2·1	2·3	2·3	2·2	2·1	1·8	1·7	1·4	1·4	1·6	1·8	1·8	1·8
HURST POINT	4·7	2·3	2·6	2·7	2·5	2·5	2·3	1·6	1·2	0·5	0·7	1·3	1·7	2·0	0·6
	4·3	2·0	2·3	2·5	2·5	2·4	2·3	1·7	1·5	1·1	1·0	1·4	1·7	1·9	1·2
	3·8	1·9	2·1	2·3	2·3	2·3	2·2	1·8	1·7	1·4	1·3	1·5	1·7	1·9	1·8
YARMOUTH I.O.W	4·7	2·4	2·8	3·0	2·8	2·8	2·7	1·8	1·5	0·7	0·8	1·4	1·8	1·8	0·6
	4·3	2·2	2·5	2·7	2·7	2·7	2·6	1·9	1·6	1·1	1·2	1·6	1·8	2·0	1·2
	3·8	2·0	2·3	2·5	2·5	2·5	2·3	1·9	1·7	1·5	1·5	1·6	1·7	1·8	1·8
LYMINGTON	4·7	2·2	2·6	3·0	2·8	2·9	2·8	2·1	1·7	0·7	0·5	1·1	1·6	1·9	0·6
	4·3	2·0	2·3	2·7	2·7	2·7	2·6	2·1	1·8	1·1	1·0	1·3	1·6	1·7	1·2
	3·8	1·9	2·2	2·4	2·5	2·5	2·4	2·0	1·8	1·5	1·4	1·5	1·6	1·7	1·8
SOLENT BANKS	4·7	2·4	2·9	3·4	3·3	3·2	3·0	2·2	1·8	0·7	0·6	1·2	1·8	2·0	0·6
	4·3	2·2	2·6	3·0	3·1	3·0	2·9	2·2	1·9	1·2	1·1	1·4	1·6	1·9	1·2
	3·8	2·1	2·3	2·6	2·7	2·7	2·6	2·2	2·0	1·6	1·5	1·7	1·9	2·0	1·6
COWES ROAD	4·7	2·5	3·4	4·1	4·2	4·1	3·8	3·0	2·5	1·1	0·6	1·2	1·8	2·1	0·6
	4·3	2·4	3·1	3·7	3·8	3·7	3·5	2·8	2·6	1·5	1·2	1·5	1·8	2·1	1·2
	3·8	2·5	3·0	3·3	3·4	3·4	3·2	2·7	2·5	2·0	1·7	1·9	2·0	2·2	1·8
CALSHOT CASTLE	4·7	2·6	3·6	4·3	4·4	4·3	4·1	3·2	2·6	1·2	0·7	1·3	1·9	2·2	0·6
	4·3	2·6	3·3	3·8	4·0	4·0	3·7	3·0	2·6	1·6	1·2	1·6	2·0	2·2	1·2
	3·8	2·7	3·2	3·5	3·6	3·6	3·4	2·8	2·6	2·0	1·9	2·0	2·2	2·3	1·8
LEE-ON-SOLENT	4·7	2·7	3·6	4·4	4·5	4·4	4·2	3·1	2·5	1·1	0·6	1·2	1·8	2·1	0·6
	4·3	2·7	3·4	3·9	4·1	4·0	3·7	2·9	2·5	1·4	1·2	1·6	2·0	2·2	1·2
	3·8	2·7	3·2	3·6	3·7	3·6	3·3	2·8	2·6	2·1	1·9	2·0	2·2	2·4	1·8
RYDE	4·7	2·7	3·7	4·3	4·5	4·3	4·0	2·9	2·4	1·1	0·7	1·2	1·8	2·1	0·6
	4·3	2·7	3·4	4·0	4·1	4·0	3·7	2·9	2·6	1·6	1·3	1·6	1·9	2·2	1·2
	3·8	2·7	3·2	3·6	3·7	3·6	3·4	2·9	2·7	2·1	1·9	2·0	2·2	2·4	1·8
NAB TOWER	4·7	2·9	3·8	4·4	4·5	4·3	3·6	2·4	2·0	0·9	0·6	1·0	1·5	2·1	0·6
	4·3	2·9	3·6	4·1	4·2	4·0	3·4	2·5	2·2	1·4	1·2	1·4	1·8	2·2	1·2
	3·8	2·9	3·3	3·7	3·7	3·6	3·1	2·6	2·3	1·9	1·7	1·8	2·1	2·4	1·8
SANDOWN	4·7	2·6	3·3	3·8	4·0	3·8	3·3	2·1	1·7	0·8	0·6	1·0	1·5	1·9	0·6
	4·3	2·6	3·0	3·5	3·6	3·5	3·1	2·2	1·9	1·3	1·1	1·4	1·7	2·0	1·2
	3·8	2·6	2·9	3·2	3·3	3·1	2·8	2·3	2·1	1·8	1·6	1·7	1·9	2·2	1·8
VENTNOR	4·7	2·8	3·3	3·7	3·8	3·5	2·9	2·0	1·7	1·0	0·9	1·3	1·7	2·1	0·6
	4·3	2·6	3·1	3·4	3·4	3·2	2·8	2·1	1·9	1·4	1·3	1·6	1·9	2·2	1·2
	3·8	2·5	2·8	3·1	3·1	3·0	2·8	2·3	2·2	1·8	1·7	1·9	2·1	2·3	1·8

Note—The green tinted area represents the period during which the tide stands, or during which a second high water may occur.
† Heights at Christchurch are for inside the bar; outside the bar, L.W. falls about 0·6 mteres lower at Springs.

HEIGHTS OF TIDE AT POOLE (TOWN QUAY)

The four curves below are an alternative to those shown in 8.2.13. They derive from Reeds Nautical Almanac where they found favour, but their accuracy (as with many things tidal) should be treated as approximate. They enable a speedy estimate to be made of the Height of Tide at hourly intervals after the time of the preceding LW at Poole (Town Quay). The curves are drawn for LW heights of 0·3, 0·6 (MLWS), 0·9 and 1·2 metres (MLWN) above Chart Datum. The small range of tide (neaps 0·4m; springs 1·5m) is immediately apparent, as are the HW stand at neaps and the double HWs at springs.

Note: All references are to LW because at Poole (and at other ports between Swanage and Selsey; see 8.2.13) the times and heights of LW are more sharply defined than those of HW. HW times & heights are complicated by a stand of tide at HW at neaps and by double HWs at springs. The times of 1st and 2nd HWs cannot therefore be readily predicted with any accuracy.

Procedure:
1. Extract time and height of the preceding LW from the Poole tidal predictions (→).
2. Using the tidal curve graph whose LW height is closest to the predicted height of LW, enter at the time required, ie corresponding to the appropriate number of hours after last LW.
3. Extract the estimated height of tide (above CD).
3a. For a more exact estimate, repeat the process using the next nearest curve, then interpolate.

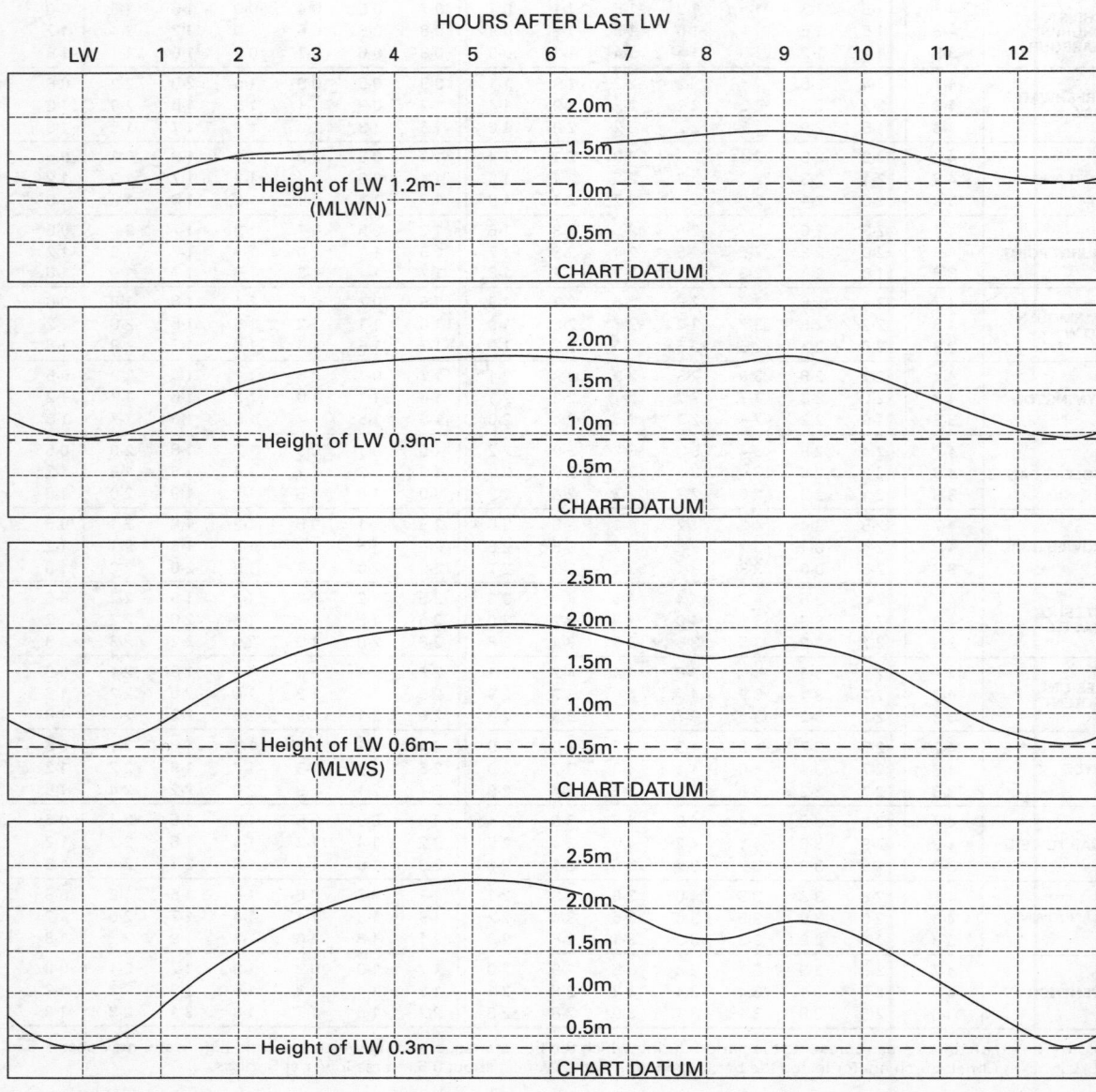

ENGLAND – POOLE HARBOUR

LAT 50°42′N   LONG 1°59′W

TIMES AND HEIGHTS OF HIGH AND LOW WATERS

YEAR **1999**

TIME ZONE (UT)
For Summer Time add ONE hour in non-shaded areas

JANUARY

Day	Time	m	Day	Time	m
1 F	0317 / 1547	0.7 / 2.3 / 0.6 / 2.2	16 SA	0322 / 1545	0.9 / 2.1 / 0.8 / 2.0
2 SA O	0406 / 1635	0.6 / 2.3 / 0.5 / 2.3	17 SU ●	0402 / 1624	0.8 / 2.1 / 0.7 / 2.1
3 SU	0453 / 1722	0.6 / 2.3 / 0.5	18 M	0438 / 1702	0.8 / 2.1 / 0.7
4 M	0540 / 1807	2.3 / 0.6 / 2.3 / 0.5	19 TU	0517 / 1740	2.1 / 0.7 / 2.1 / 0.6
5 TU	0624 / 1849	2.3 / 0.7 / 2.2 / 0.6	20 W	0556 / 1820	2.1 / 0.7 / 2.1 / 0.5
6 W	0706 / 1929	2.2 / 0.8 / 2.1 / 0.7	21 TH	0637 / 1900	2.2 / 0.7 / 2.1 / 0.6
7 TH	0748 / 2010	2.1 / 0.9 / 2.0 / 0.8	22 F	0720 / 1944	2.1 / 0.7 / 2.1 / 0.6
8 F	0832 / 2053	2.0 / 1.0 / 1.9 / 0.9	23 SA	0808 / 2032	2.1 / 0.8 / 2.0 / 0.7
9 SA	0921 / 2142	1.9 / 1.1 / 1.8 / 1.1	24 SU	0901 / 2128	2.1 / 0.9 / 2.0 / 0.8
10 SU	1021 / 2244	1.9 / 1.3 / 1.7 / 1.2	25 M	1004 / 2234	2.0 / 1.0 / 1.9 / 0.9
11 M	1133 / 2354	1.8 / 1.3 / 1.6 / 1.3	26 TU	1120 / 2350	1.9 / 1.0 / 1.8 / 1.0
12 TU	1242	1.8 / 1.3 / 1.6	27 W	1238	1.9 / 1.0 / 1.8
13 W	0101 / 1337	1.2 / 1.8 / 1.1 / 1.8	28 TH	0107 / 1349	1.0 / 2.0 / 0.9 / 1.9
14 TH	0155 / 1424	1.1 / 1.9 / 1.0 / 1.9	29 F	0213 / 1447	0.9 / 2.1 / 0.8 / 2.0
15 F	0240 / 1506	1.0 / 2.0 / 0.9 / 2.0	30 SA	0310 / 1539	0.8 / 2.2 / 0.7 / 2.1
			31 SU O	0359 / 1625	0.7 / 2.2 / 0.5 / 2.2

FEBRUARY

Day	Time	m	Day	Time	m
1 M	0443 / 1709	0.6 / 2.3 / 0.5 / 2.2	16 TU ●	0421 / 1642	0.7 / 2.1 / 0.5 / 2.2
2 TU	0525 / 1750	2.3 / 0.6 / 2.2 / 0.5	17 W	0501 / 1724	0.6 / 2.1 / 0.5
3 W	0605 / 1828	2.2 / 0.6 / 2.2 / 0.5	18 TH	0542 / 1804	2.2 / 0.5 / 2.2 / 0.4
4 TH	0642 / 1902	2.2 / 0.7 / 2.1 / 0.6	19 F	0623 / 1845	2.3 / 0.5 / 2.2 / 0.4
5 F	0717 / 1936	2.1 / 0.8 / 2.0 / 0.7	20 SA	0705 / 1928	2.3 / 0.5 / 2.2 / 0.5
6 SA	0752 / 2010	2.1 / 0.9 / 1.9 / 0.8	21 SU	0750 / 2014	2.2 / 0.6 / 2.1 / 0.6
7 SU	0828 / 2048	2.0 / 1.0 / 1.9 / 0.8	22 M	0840 / 2106	2.1 / 0.7 / 2.0 / 0.8
8 M	0911 / 2135	1.9 / 1.1 / 1.8 / 1.1	23 TU	0938 / 2211	2.0 / 0.9 / 1.9 / 0.9
9 TU	1011 / 2244	1.8 / 1.3 / 1.6 / 1.3	24 W	1055 / 2333	1.9 / 1.0 / 1.8 / 1.1
10 W	1139	1.7 / 1.3 / 1.6	25 TH	1221	1.8 / 1.0 / 1.8
11 TH	0013 / 1259	1.3 / 1.7 / 1.3 / 1.6	26 F	0057 / 1337	1.0 / 1.9 / 1.0 / 1.9
12 F	0124 / 1356	1.2 / 1.8 / 1.1 / 1.8	27 SA	0207 / 1438	0.9 / 2.0 / 0.8 / 2.0
13 SA	0217 / 1441	1.1 / 1.9 / 0.9 / 1.9	28 SU	0303 / 1527	0.8 / 2.1 / 0.7 / 2.1
14 SU	0301 / 1523	0.9 / 2.0 / 0.8 / 2.0			
15 M	0342 / 1603	0.8 / 2.1 / 0.7 / 2.1			

MARCH

Day	Time	m	Day	Time	m
1 M	0349 / 1611	0.7 / 2.1 / 0.5 / 2.2	16 TU	0319 / 1540	0.8 / 2.0 / 0.6 / 2.1
2 TU O	0430 / 1650	0.6 / 2.1 / 0.5 / 2.2	17 W ●	0400 / 1620	0.6 / 2.1 / 0.5 / 2.2
3 W	0509 / 1728	0.5 / 2.1 / 0.5	18 TH	0440 / 1702	0.5 / 2.2 / 0.4
4 TH	0545 / 1803	2.2 / 0.5 / 2.1 / 0.5	19 F	0522 / 1745	2.3 / 0.4 / 2.3 / 0.4
5 F	0618 / 1835	2.1 / 0.6 / 2.1 / 0.5	20 SA	0604 / 1827	2.3 / 0.4 / 2.3 / 0.4
6 SA	0647 / 1904	2.1 / 0.7 / 2.1 / 0.7	21 SU	0647 / 1911	2.3 / 0.4 / 2.3 / 0.4
7 SU	0716 / 1932	2.1 / 0.7 / 2.0 / 0.8	22 M	0732 / 1957	2.1 / 0.5 / 2.1 / 0.6
8 M	0746 / 2004	2.0 / 0.9 / 1.9 / 0.9	23 TU	0821 / 2050	2.1 / 0.7 / 2.0 / 0.8
9 TU	0821 / 2045	1.9 / 1.0 / 1.8 / 1.1	24 W	0919 / 2155	2.0 / 0.8 / 1.9 / 1.0
10 W	0907 / 2142	1.8 / 1.1 / 1.7 / 1.3	25 TH	1035 / 2318	1.8 / 1.0 / 1.8 / 1.1
11 TH	1019 / 2316	1.6 / 1.3 / 1.6 / 1.4	26 F	1203	1.7 / 1.0 / 1.8
12 F	1211	1.6 / 1.3 / 1.6	27 SA	0044 / 1323	1.1 / 1.8 / 1.0 / 1.9
13 SA	0052 / 1325	1.3 / 1.7 / 1.1 / 1.8	28 SU	0156 / 1422	1.0 / 1.9 / 0.9 / 2.0
14 SU	0152 / 1415	1.1 / 1.8 / 1.0 / 1.9	29 M	0249 / 1510	0.8 / 2.0 / 0.7 / 2.1
15 M	0237 / 1458	0.9 / 1.9 / 0.8 / 2.0	30 TU	0332 / 1550	0.7 / 2.1 / 0.6 / 2.1
			31 W O	0410 / 1627	0.6 / 2.1 / 0.5 / 2.1

APRIL

Day	Time	m	Day	Time	m
1 TH	0445 / 1703	0.5 / 2.1 / 0.5	16 F ●	0416 / 1637	0.4 / 2.3 / 0.4 / 2.3
2 F	0519 / 1736	2.1 / 0.5 / 2.1 / 0.5	17 SA	0501 / 1722	0.3 / 2.3 / 0.3
3 SA	0551 / 1806	2.1 / 0.5 / 2.1 / 0.6	18 SU	0545 / 1807	2.4 / 0.3 / 2.3 / 0.4
4 SU	0620 / 1835	2.1 / 0.6 / 2.1 / 0.7	19 M	0631 / 1853	2.3 / 0.4 / 2.3 / 0.4
5 M	0646 / 1901	2.1 / 0.7 / 2.0 / 0.8	20 TU	0717 / 1942	2.3 / 0.4 / 2.2 / 0.6
6 TU	0714 / 1932	2.0 / 0.8 / 1.9 / 0.9	21 W	0808 / 2035	2.1 / 0.6 / 2.1 / 0.6
7 W	0747 / 2011	1.9 / 0.9 / 1.8 / 1.0	22 TH	0905 / 2140	2.0 / 0.8 / 1.9 / 1.0
8 TH	0829 / 2102	1.8 / 1.0 / 1.8 / 1.2	23 F	1017 / 2259	1.8 / 1.0 / 1.8 / 1.1
9 F	0931 / 2223	1.7 / 1.2 / 1.6 / 1.3	24 SA	1139	1.7 / 1.0 / 1.8
10 SA	1109	1.6 / 1.3 / 1.6	25 SU	0021 / 1256	1.1 / 1.8 / 1.0 / 1.9
11 SU	0008 / 1243	1.3 / 1.6 / 1.1 / 1.8	26 M	0131 / 1356	1.0 / 1.8 / 0.9 / 2.0
12 M	0117 / 1341	1.1 / 1.8 / 1.0 / 1.9	27 TU	0223 / 1441	0.9 / 1.9 / 0.8 / 2.1
13 TU	0207 / 1428	0.9 / 1.9 / 0.9 / 2.0	28 W	0306 / 1521	0.8 / 2.0 / 0.7 / 2.1
14 W	0251 / 1511	0.7 / 2.0 / 0.6 / 2.2	29 TH	0343 / 1558	0.7 / 2.0 / 0.6 / 2.1
15 TH	0334 / 1554	0.5 / 2.1 / 0.4 / 2.3	30 F O	0418 / 1632	0.6 / 2.0 / 0.6 / 2.1

Chart Datum: 1·40 metres below Ordnance Datum (Newlyn)

TIME ZONE (UT)
For Summer Time add ONE hour in non-shaded areas

ENGLAND – POOLE HARBOUR

LAT 50°42'N   LONG 1°59'W

TIMES AND HEIGHTS OF HIGH AND LOW WATERS

YEAR **1999**

MAY

Day	Time / m	Day	Time / m
1 SA	0451 0.6 / 2.0 / 1707 0.6	16 SU	0439 0.4 / 2.3 / 1701 0.4
2 SU	0524 2.1 0.6 / 1739 2.0 0.7	17 M	0527 2.4 0.4 / 1749 2.3 0.4
3 M	0554 2.1 0.7 / 1808 2.0 0.7	18 TU	0616 2.3 0.4 / 1838 2.3 0.5
4 TU	0621 2.1 0.7 / 1837 2.0 0.8	19 W	0705 2.3 0.5 / 1927 2.2 0.6
5 W	0649 2.0 0.8 / 1908 0.9	20 TH	0755 2.1 0.6 / 2021 2.1 0.8
6 TH	0722 1.9 0.9 / 1947 1.0	21 F	0851 2.0 0.8 / 2120 2.0 0.9
7 F	0806 1.9 1.0 / 2037 1.8 1.1	22 SA	0953 1.9 0.9 / 2229 1.9 1.0
8 SA	0902 1.8 1.1 / 2146 1.8 1.3	23 SU	1105 1.8 1.0 / 2342 1.9 1.1
9 SU	1021 1.7 1.1 / 2313 1.8 1.3	24 M	1215 1.7 1.0 / 1.9
10 M	1148 1.7 1.1 / 1.8	25 TU	0051 1.1 / 1316 1.8 1.0 / 1.9
11 TU	0030 1.1 / 1258 1.8 0.9 / 1.9	26 W	0146 1.0 / 1405 1.8 0.9 / 2.0
12 W	0130 0.9 / 1351 1.9 0.8 / 2.1	27 TH	0231 0.9 / 1446 1.9 0.9 / 2.0
13 TH	0219 0.8 / 1439 2.1 0.6 / 2.2	28 F	0311 0.8 / 1525 1.9 0.8 / 2.0
14 F	0306 0.6 / 1526 2.1 0.5 / 2.3	29 SA	0348 0.7 / 1602 2.0 0.7 / 2.0
15 SA ●	0353 0.4 / 1613 2.3 0.4 / 2.4	30 SU O	0424 0.7 / 1638 2.0 0.7 / 2.1
		31 M	0458 0.7 / 1714 2.0 0.7

JUNE

Day	Time / m	Day	Time / m
1 TU	0530 2.1 0.7 / 1746 0.8	16 W	0603 2.3 0.4 / 1824 2.3 0.5
2 W	0601 2.0 0.7 / 1818 2.0 0.8	17 TH	0652 2.3 0.5 / 1913 2.3 0.7
3 TH	0632 2.0 0.8 / 1851 2.0 0.9	18 F	0741 2.1 0.6 / 2002 2.1 0.8
4 F	0708 2.0 0.8 / 1930 0.9	19 SA	0829 2.0 0.7 / 2054 2.1 0.9
5 SA	0750 1.9 0.9 / 2019 1.9 1.0	20 SU	0921 1.9 0.9 / 2151 2.0 1.0
6 SU	0843 1.9 0.9 / 2118 1.9 1.1	21 M	1020 1.8 1.0 / 2255 1.9 1.1
7 M	0948 1.8 0.9 / 2229 1.9 1.1	22 TU	1123 1.7 1.0 / 1.9
8 TU	1102 1.8 0.9 / 2342 1.9 1.0	23 W	0000 1.1 / 1225 1.7 1.1 / 1.8
9 W	1212 1.8 0.9	24 TH	0102 1.1 / 1322 1.7 1.0 / 1.9
10 TH	0050 0.9 / 1315 1.9 0.8 / 2.1	25 F	0153 1.0 / 1410 1.8 1.0 / 1.9
11 F	0149 0.8 / 1411 2.0 0.7 / 2.2	26 SA	0236 0.9 / 1453 1.9 0.9 / 2.0
12 SA	0241 0.7 / 1503 2.1 0.6 / 2.3	27 SU	0318 0.8 / 1534 1.9 0.9 / 2.0
13 SU ●	0333 0.5 / 1555 2.2 0.5 / 2.3	28 M O	0357 0.8 / 1613 2.0 0.8 / 2.0
14 M	0423 0.4 / 1644 2.3 0.5 / 2.3	29 TU	0433 0.7 / 1650 2.0 0.8 / 2.0
15 TU	0514 0.4 / 1736 2.3 0.5	30 W	0510 0.7 / 1726 2.0 0.8

JULY

Day	Time / m	Day	Time / m
1 TH	0545 2.0 0.7 / 1801 2.1 0.8	16 F	0636 2.2 0.5 / 1854 2.3 0.7
2 F	0619 2.0 0.7 / 1838 2.1 0.8	17 SA	0719 2.1 0.5 / 1938 2.2 0.7
3 SA	0655 2.0 0.7 / 1918 2.0 0.8	18 SU	0800 2.0 0.7 / 2021 2.1 0.8
4 SU	0738 2.0 0.8 / 2003 2.0 0.9	19 M	0844 2.0 0.8 / 2107 2.0 1.0
5 M	0825 1.9 0.8 / 2056 2.0 0.9	20 TU	0930 1.9 1.0 / 2200 1.9 1.1
6 TU	0920 1.9 0.9 / 2156 2.0 1.0	21 W	1025 1.8 1.1 / 2304 1.8 1.1
7 W	1025 1.9 0.9 / 2307 1.9 1.0	22 TH	1131 1.6 1.2 / 1.8
8 TH	1136 1.9 0.9 / 2.0	23 F	0012 1.2 / 1238 1.6 1.2 / 1.8
9 F	0018 0.9 / 1247 1.9 0.9 / 2.0	24 SA	0115 1.1 / 1336 1.7 1.1 / 1.8
10 SA	0126 0.9 / 1351 2.0 0.8 / 2.1	25 SU	0206 1.0 / 1426 1.8 1.0 / 1.9
11 SU	0226 0.7 / 1448 2.1 0.7 / 2.2	26 M	0251 0.9 / 1510 1.9 0.9 / 2.0
12 M	0320 0.6 / 1542 2.1 0.7 / 2.3	27 TU	0332 0.8 / 1551 2.0 0.9 / 2.0
13 TU ●	0412 0.5 / 1632 2.3 0.6 / 2.3	28 W O	0411 0.7 / 1630 2.0 0.8 / 2.0
14 W	0502 0.4 / 1722 2.3 0.5	29 TH	0449 0.7 / 1707 2.1 0.7
15 TH	0550 2.3 0.4 / 1809 2.3 0.6	30 F	0526 2.1 0.6 / 1745 2.1 0.7
		31 SA	0604 2.1 0.6 / 1823 2.1 0.7

AUGUST

Day	Time / m	Day	Time / m
1 SU	0641 2.1 0.6 / 1901 2.1 0.7	16 M	0727 2.1 0.7 / 1945 2.1 0.8
2 M	0722 2.1 0.7 / 1945 2.1 0.7	17 TU	0801 2.0 0.8 / 2022 2.0 0.9
3 TU	0806 2.0 0.7 / 2033 2.1 0.8	18 W	0840 1.9 0.9 / 2103 1.9 1.0
4 W	0857 2.0 0.8 / 2129 2.0 0.9	19 TH	0925 1.8 1.1 / 2158 1.8 1.2
5 TH	0957 1.9 0.9 / 2237 2.0 1.0	20 F	1030 1.7 1.3 / 2317 1.8 1.3
6 F	1110 1.8 1.0 / 2355 1.9 1.0	21 SA	1155 1.6 1.3 / 1.7
7 SA	1229 1.8 0.9 / 1.9	22 SU	0038 1.3 / 1308 1.6 1.3 / 1.8
8 SU	0112 0.9 / 1341 1.9 1.0 / 2.0	23 M	0140 1.1 / 1403 1.8 1.1 / 1.9
9 M	0217 0.8 / 1441 2.0 0.8 / 2.1	24 TU	0228 1.0 / 1447 1.9 1.0 / 2.0
10 TU	0313 0.7 / 1535 2.1 0.7 / 2.2	25 W	0310 0.8 / 1528 2.0 0.9 / 2.0
11 W ●	0402 0.5 / 1623 2.2 0.7 / 2.3	26 TH O	0349 0.7 / 1607 2.1 0.8 / 2.1
12 TH	0448 0.5 / 1708 2.3 0.6	27 F	0427 0.6 / 1644 2.1 0.7 / 2.1
13 F	0533 2.3 0.4 / 1751 2.3 0.6	28 SA	0506 0.5 / 1723 2.2 0.6
14 SA	0613 2.2 0.5 / 1831 2.3 0.6	29 SU	0544 2.1 0.5 / 1802 2.2 0.5
15 SU	0651 2.1 0.5 / 1909 2.2 0.7	30 M	0623 2.1 0.5 / 1842 2.2 0.5
		31 TU	0702 2.1 0.5 / 1924 2.2 0.6

Chart Datum: 1.40 metres below Ordnance Datum (Newlyn)

ENGLAND – POOLE HARBOUR

LAT 50°42′N   LONG 1°59′W

TIMES AND HEIGHTS OF HIGH AND LOW WATERS   YEAR 1999

TIME ZONE (UT) — For Summer Time add ONE hour in non-shaded areas

Heights below are given as "m / m" for each listed time (tide at the given time / following opposite tide). ● = new moon, O = full moon.

SEPTEMBER

Day	Time	m	Time	m
1 W	0746	2.1 / 0.7	2012	2.1 / 0.7
2 TH	0835	2.0 / 0.8	2106	2.0 / 0.9
3 F	0936	1.9 / 1.0	2216	1.9 / 1.0
4 SA	1056	1.8 / 1.1	2341	1.9 / 1.1
5 SU	1222	1.8 / 1.1	—	1.9
6 M	0105	1.0 / 1.9	1336	1.0 / 2.0
7 TU	0210	0.9 / 2.0	1435	0.9 / 2.1
8 W	0304	0.7 / 2.1	1525	0.8 / 2.2
9 TH ●	0350	0.6 / 2.3	1609	0.7 / 2.2
10 F	0431	0.5 / 2.3	1649	0.6 / 2.2
11 SA	0511	0.5 / 2.3	1728	0.5 / 2.3
12 SU	0547	2.2 / 0.5	1803	2.3 / 0.6
13 M	0621	2.1 / 0.5	1836	2.2 / 0.7
14 TU	0652	2.1 / 0.7	1908	2.1 / 0.8
15 W	0723	2.0 / 0.8	1939	2.0 / 0.9

Day	Time	m	Time	m
16 TH	0755	1.9 / 0.9	2014	1.9 / 1.0
17 F	0833	1.8 / 1.1	2059	1.8 / 1.2
18 SA	0930	1.7 / 1.3	2209	1.7 / 1.3
19 SU	1109	1.6 / 1.4	2358	1.6 / 1.4
20 M	1240	1.6 / 1.4	—	1.7
21 TU	0112	1.2 / 1.8	1338	1.2 / 1.8
22 W	0203	1.0 / 1.9	1423	1.0 / 2.0
23 TH	0244	0.9 / 2.0	1503	0.9 / 2.0
24 F	0323	0.7 / 2.1	1541	0.7 / 2.1
25 SA O	0402	0.6 / 2.2	1619	0.6 / 2.2
26 SU	0439	0.5 / 2.3	1658	0.5 / 2.3
27 M	0520	0.4 / 2.3	1740	0.5
28 TU	0600	2.3 / 0.4	1821	2.3 / 0.5
29 W	0642	2.3 / 0.5	1905	2.3 / 0.5
30 TH	0727	2.2 / 0.7	1952	2.1 / 0.7

OCTOBER

Day	Time	m	Time	m
1 F	0818	2.1 / 0.8	2048	2.0 / 0.9
2 SA	0923	2.0 / 1.0	2159	1.9 / 1.0
3 SU	1045	1.8 / 1.1	2328	1.8 / 1.1
4 M	1212	1.8 / 1.1	—	1.8
5 TU	0052	1.0 / 1.9	1327	1.1 / 1.9
6 W	0158	0.9 / 2.1	1423	0.9 / 2.1
7 TH	0247	0.8 / 2.2	1509	0.8 / 2.1
8 F	0330	0.7 / 2.3	1549	0.7 / 2.2
9 SA ●	0408	0.5 / 2.3	1626	0.6 / 2.2
10 SU	0443	0.5 / 2.3	1701	0.6 / 2.3
11 M	0518	2.2 / 0.5	1735	2.2 / 0.6
12 TU	0551	2.1 / 0.6	1805	2.1 / 0.7
13 W	0621	2.1 / 0.7	1835	2.1 / 0.8
14 TH	0649	2.1 / 0.8	1904	2.0 / 0.9
15 F	0719	2.0 / 1.0	1936	2.0 / 1.0

Day	Time	m	Time	m
16 SA	0755	1.9 / 1.1	2016	1.9 / 1.1
17 SU	0844	1.8 / 1.3	2113	1.8 / 1.3
18 M	1006	1.8 / 1.4	2256	1.6 / 1.4
19 TU	1157	1.7	—	1.7
20 W	0030	1.3 / 1.8	1304	1.3 / 1.8
21 TH	0128	1.1 / 1.9	1351	1.1 / 1.9
22 F	0212	0.9 / 2.1	1432	0.9 / 2.1
23 SA	0252	0.7 / 2.2	1512	0.7 / 2.2
24 SU O	0331	0.6 / 2.3	1552	0.6 / 2.3
25 M	0412	0.5 / 2.3	1632	0.5 / 2.3
26 TU	0453	0.5 / 2.4	1716	0.4 / 0.6
27 W	0538	2.3 / 0.5	1801	2.4 / 0.5
28 TH	0624	2.3 / 0.5	1848	2.3 / 0.5
29 F	0712	2.3 / 0.7	1938	2.2 / 0.7
30 SA	0806	2.1 / 0.8	2035	2.0 / 0.9
31 SU	0909	2.0 / 1.0	2144	1.9 / 1.0

NOVEMBER

Day	Time	m	Time	m
1 M	1028	1.9 / 1.1	2307	1.8 / 1.1
2 TU	1151	1.9 / 1.2	—	1.8
3 W	0026	1.1 / 2.0	1305	1.1 / 1.9
4 TH	0132	1.0 / 2.1	1400	1.0 / 2.0
5 F	0222	0.9 / 2.1	1444	0.8 / 2.1
6 SA	0303	0.8 / 2.2	1523	0.8 / 2.1
7 SU	0340	0.7 / 2.2	1600	0.7 / 2.1
8 M ●	0415	0.7 / 2.2	1633	0.7 / 2.1
9 TU	0449	0.7 / 2.2	1707	0.7
10 W	0522	2.1 / 0.7	1739	2.1 / 0.7
11 TH	0553	2.1 / 0.8	1808	2.1 / 0.8
12 F	0622	2.1 / 0.9	1837	2.1 / 0.9
13 SA	0652	2.0 / 1.0	1908	2.0 / 1.0
14 SU	0727	2.0 / 1.1	1947	1.9 / 1.1
15 M	0813	1.9 / 1.3	2039	1.8 / 1.2

Day	Time	m	Time	m
16 TU	0917	1.8 / 1.4	2151	1.7 / 1.3
17 W	1049	1.8 / 1.4	2323	1.7 / 1.3
18 TH	1211	1.8 / 1.3	—	1.8
19 F	0036	1.1 / 1.9	1309	1.1 / 1.9
20 SA	0131	0.9 / 2.1	1357	0.9 / 2.0
21 SU	0216	0.8 / 2.2	1441	0.7 / 2.1
22 M	0301	0.7 / 2.3	1525	0.6 / 2.3
23 TU O	0346	0.5 / 2.4	1611	0.5 / 2.3
24 W	0431	0.5 / 2.4	1657	0.5 / 2.4
25 TH	0519	2.4 / 0.5	1747	2.4 / 0.5
26 F	0608	2.4 / 0.5	1836	2.3 / 0.5
27 SA	0658	2.3 / 0.7	1927	2.2 / 0.7
28 SU	0752	2.2 / 0.8	2022	2.0 / 0.8
29 M	0853	2.1 / 1.0	2124	2.0 / 0.9
30 TU	1001	2.0 / 1.1	2232	1.9 / 1.0

DECEMBER

Day	Time	m	Time	m
1 W	1116	1.9 / 1.1	2344	1.8 / 1.1
2 TH	1227	1.9 / 1.1	—	1.8
3 F	0051	1.0 / 2.0	1327	1.0 / 1.9
4 SA	0146	1.0 / 2.0	1414	1.0 / 1.9
5 SU	0230	0.9 / 2.1	1455	0.9 / 2.0
6 M	0310	0.8 / 2.1	1532	0.8 / 2.0
7 TU ●	0347	0.8 / 2.1	1608	0.8 / 2.1
8 W	0423	0.8 / 2.1	1643	0.7 / 2.1
9 TH	0457	0.8 / 2.1	1717	0.7
10 F	0530	2.1 / 0.8	1749	2.1 / 0.8
11 SA	0602	2.1 / 0.9	1819	2.1 / 0.8
12 SU	0633	2.0 / 0.9	1851	2.0 / 0.9
13 M	0709	2.0 / 1.0	1928	2.0 / 0.9
14 TU	0751	2.0 / 1.1	2015	1.9 / 1.0
15 W	0845	1.9 / 1.2	2111	1.8 / 1.1

Day	Time	m	Time	m
16 TH	0951	1.9 / 1.3	2222	1.8 / 1.1
17 F	1109	1.9 / 1.2	2337	1.8 / 1.1
18 SA	1221	1.9 / 1.1	—	1.9
19 SU	0044	1.0 / 2.0	1322	1.0 / 2.0
20 M	0142	0.9 / 2.2	1415	0.8 / 2.1
21 TU	0235	0.7 / 2.3	1506	0.7 / 2.2
22 W O	0326	0.7 / 2.4	1556	0.5 / 2.3
23 TH	0416	0.5 / 2.4	1645	0.5 / 2.3
24 F	0506	0.5 / 2.4	1737	0.4 / 2.3
25 SA	0556	2.3 / 0.6	1826	2.3 / 0.5
26 SU	0646	2.3 / 0.7	1915	2.3 / 0.5
27 M	0737	2.3 / 0.8	2003	2.1 / 0.7
28 TU	0829	2.1 / 0.9	2055	2.0 / 0.8
29 W	0926	2.1 / 1.0	2150	1.9 / 0.9
30 TH	1029	2.0 / 1.1	2253	1.8 / 1.0
31 F	1138	1.9 / 1.2	2354	1.7 / 1.1

Chart Datum: 1·40 metres below Ordnance Datum (Newlyn)

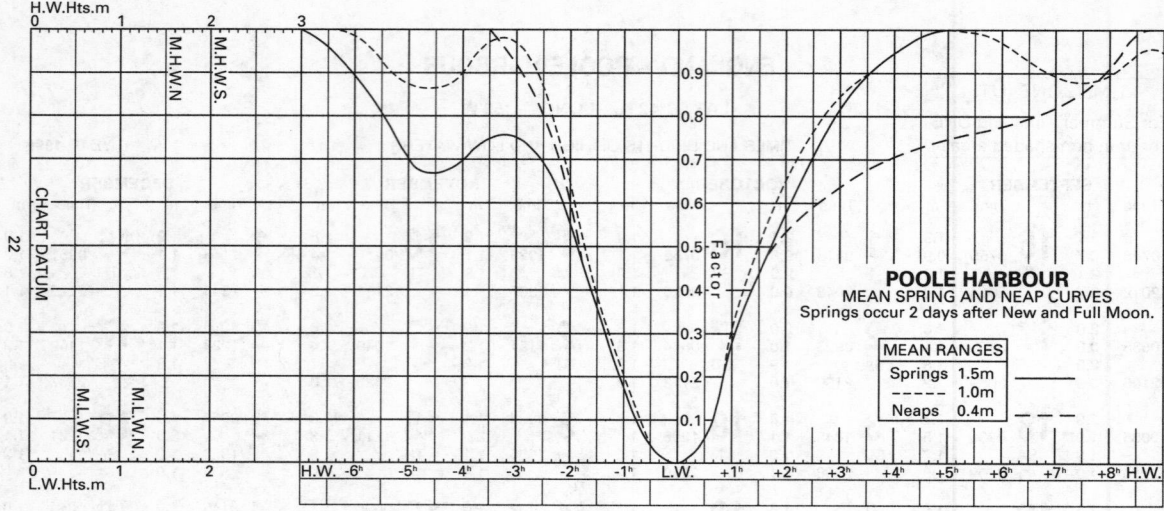

POOLE HARBOUR
MEAN SPRING AND NEAP CURVES
Springs occur 2 days after New and Full Moon.

MEAN RANGES		
Springs	1.5m	————
	1.0m	‑ ‑ ‑ ‑
Neaps	0.4m	‑ ‑ ‑ ‑

POOLE HARBOUR   8-2-14

Dorset 50°40'.90N 01°56'.88W (Ent)   Rtg 2-1-1

CHARTS
AC 2611, 2175; Imray C4, Y23; Stanfords 12, 15, 7; OS 195

TIDES
Town Quay –0141, +0114 Dover; ML 1·5; Zone 0 (UT)
Daily predictions of the times and hts of LW, but only the
hts of HW, are on the preceding pages for the Standard
Port of **POOLE HARBOUR** (near the Ro-Ro terminal); sp
and neap curves are above. (The 4 curves before these
predictions simplify intermediate calculations.)
The Secondary Port differences below should be used in
conjunction with 8.2.13.

Standard Port PORTSMOUTH (→)

Times				Height (metres)			
High Water		Low Water		MHWS	MHWN	MLWN	MLWS
0000	0600	0500	1100	4·7	3·8	1·9	0·8
1200	1800	1700	2300				
Differences POOLE HARBOUR ENTRANCE							
–0230	+0115	–0045	–0020	–2·5	–2·1	–0·6	–0·2
POTTERY PIER							
–0150	+0200	–0010	0000	–2·7	–2·1	–0·6	0·0
CLEAVEL POINT							
–0220	+0130	–0025	–0015	–2·6	–2·3	–0·7	–0·3
WAREHAM (River Frome)							
–0140	+0205	+0110	+0035	–2·5	–2·1	–0·7	+0·1

Double HWs occur, except at nps. The ht of the 2nd HW is
always about 1·8m; only the ht of the 1st HW varies from
sp to nps. The tide is above Mean Level (1·5m) from
about LW+2 to next LW–2. Strong and continuous winds
from E to SW may raise sea levels by as much as 0·2m;
W to NE winds may lower levels by 0·1m. Barometric
pressure effects can also be apppreciable, see Chapter 7.

SHELTER
An excellent hbr with narrow ent; access in all conditions
except very strong E/SE winds. ⚓s wherever sheltered
from the wind and clear of chans, moorings and shellfish
beds; especially in South Deep, off W end of Brownsea Is
and off Shipstal Pt. The S half of the hbr is designated as
a Quiet Area (see chartlet) with speed limit of 6kn. A 6kn
limit also covers from Stakes SCM By, past Poole Quay
and Poole Bridge up to Cobbs Quay in Holes Bay.
A 10kn speed limit applies to the rest of the hbr, ie West
from the seaward app chans (defined by an arc of radius
1400m centred on S Haven Pt, 50°40'·78N 01°56'·91W) to
the junction of R Frome with R Trent at 02°04'·60W (see
chartlet). Note: From 1 Oct to 31 Mar the 10kn limit does
not apply in the North, Middle Ship and Wareham Chans.
Fines of up to £1000 ca be imposed for speeding.

NAVIGATION
WPT Poole Bar (No 1 SHM) By, QG, 50°39'·32N 01°55'·10W,
148°/328° from/to Haven Hotel, 1·95M. In strong SE-S winds

the Bar is dangerous especially on the ebb. In Studland
Bay and close to training bank beware lobster pots. From
Poole Bar to Shell Bay a recreational **Boat Chan**, suitable
for craft < 3m draught, parallels the W side of the Swash
Channel, close to the E of the Training Bank.
East Looe Chan (buoyed) is liable to shift and may have
less water than charted; only 1m was reported 1ca ENE
of East Looe No 16a PHM buoy. 5 groynes to the N are
marked by SHM bns, the two most W'ly are lit, 2 FG (vert).
Within the hbr the two chans (Middle Ship and North) up
to Poole are clearly marked by lateral buoys, mostly lit,
with cardinal buoys at divisions. Outside the chans there
are extensive shoal or drying areas.
Middle Ship Chan is dredged 6·0m for ferries to/from the
Hamworthy terminal; it is mostly only 80m wide. Leisure
craft should keep out of Middle Ship Chan, by using a
Boat Chan which parallels S of the dredged chan between
the PHM buoys and, further outboard, stakes with PHM
topmarks marking the edge of the bank. Depth is 2·0m in
this chan, but 1·5m closer to the stakes. Caution: When
large ferries pass, a temporary, but significant reduction
in depth may be remedied by closing the PHM buoys.
North Channel, the other option, is now dredged 4m and
widened to 80m for ships. It remains suitable for yachts/
leisure craft; best water is on the outside of chan bends.
Yachts cruising to the W should check Lulworth gunnery
range (see 8.2.11). Info is shown in the Hr Mr's office and
printed in the Supplements to this Almanac.

LIGHTS AND MARKS
See chartlet and 8.2.4 for main buoys, beacons and lts.
Sandbanks Chain Ferry shows a Fl W lt (rotating) and a B
● above the leading Control cabin by D/N to indicate
which way it is going. In fog it sounds 1 long and 2 short
blasts every 2 mins. When stationary at night it shows a
FW lt; in fog it rings a bell for 5 sec every minute.
Poole Bridge (Lights shown from bridge tr)
Ⓡ   = Do not approach bridge;
Fl Ⓖ = Bridge lifting, proceed with caution; Ⓖ= Proceed.
Bridge lifts routinely for small craft at: Mon-Fri 0930,
1030, 1230, 1430, 1630, 1830, 2130; Sat, Sun & Bank hols
= as Mon-Fri, plus 0730; at 2345 daily bridge will also lift
if any vessels are waiting. Each lift only permits one cycle
of traffic in each direction. Pleasure craft may pass when
the bridge lifts on request for a commercial vessel;
monitor Ch 14. Bridge will not usually lift during weekday
road traffic Rush Hours 0730-0930 and 1630-1830.

RADIO TELEPHONE
Call: Poole Hbr Control VHF Ch 14 16 (H24). Salterns
Marina Ch M 80; Parkstone Haven Ch M; Poole YC Haven,
call Pike Ch M; Poole Bridge, call PB Ch 14. Cobbs Quay,
call CQ Base Ch 80.

TELEPHONE (Dial code 01202)
Hr Mr 440233, 🚢 440231; Pilots 666401; Bridge 674115;
MRSC (01305) 760439; ⌗ 0345 231110 (H24); Met (01703)
228844; Marinecall 0891 500457; Police 552099;
Ⓗ 675100.

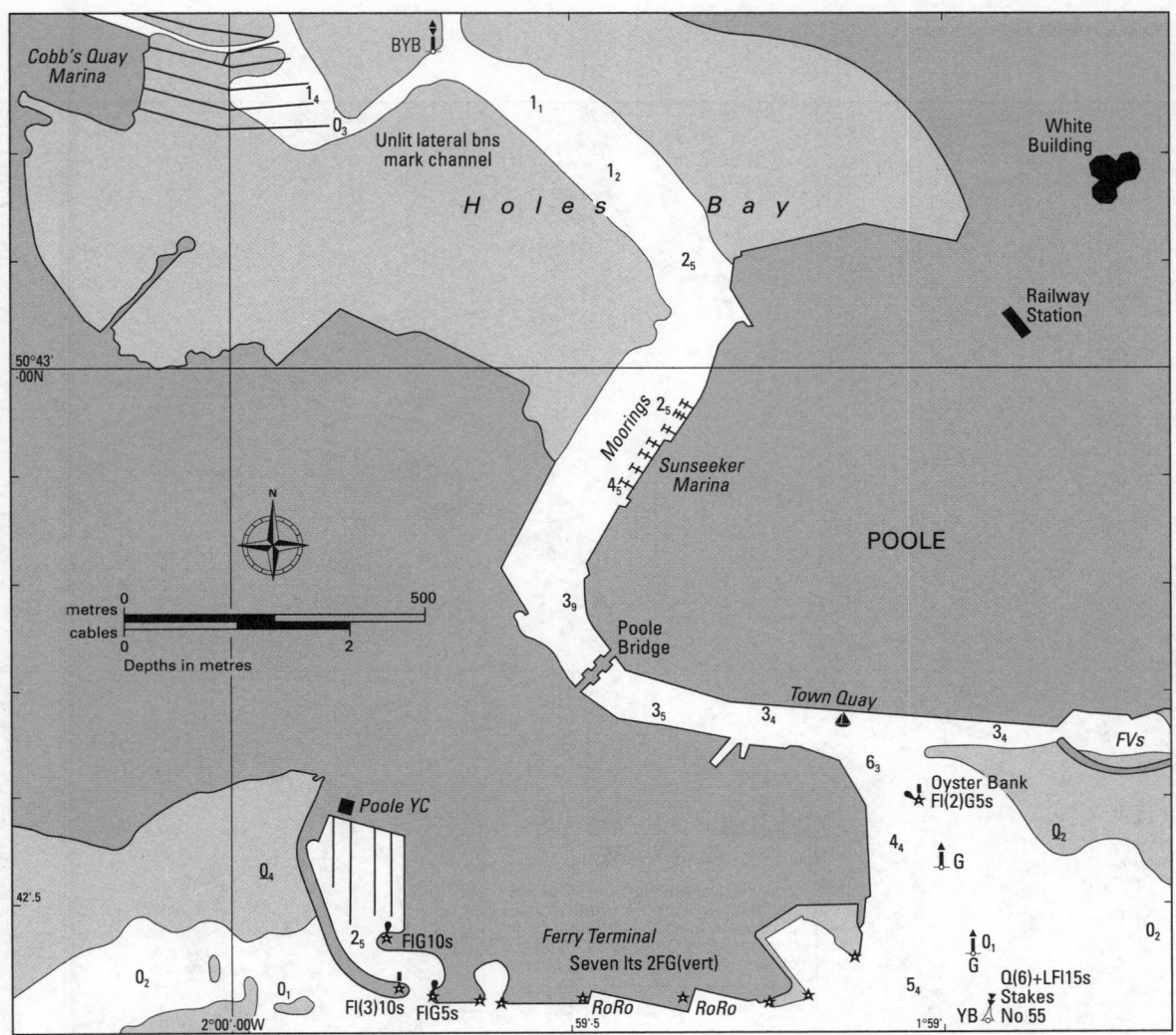

FACILITIES The following are some of the many facilities:
Marinas (from seaward)
   Salterns Marina (300, few visitors) ☎ 709971, 📠 700398, £26, max draft 2·5m, AC, FW, P, D, ME, EI, Ⓔ, Sh, CH, Gas, Gaz, C (5 ton), BH (45 ton), Bar, R, Ⓘ. Appr from No 31 SHM buoy, Fl G 5s.
   Parkstone Haven, (Parkstone YC ☎ 743610), some Ⓥ berths, £16; dredged 2m. Access from North Chan near No 35 SHM buoy, Fl G 5s. Appr chan, dredged 2·5m, is marked by SHM buoy (Fl G 3s), 2 PHM and 3 SHM unlit buoys. Ldg daymarks 006°, both Y ◇s; ldg lts, front Iso Y 4s, rear FY. 2 FG and 2FR (vert) on bkwtr hds.
   Poole Quay (AB £9.03, Sh, FW) is close to town facilities. Berthing Office on the quay is open 0800-2200, Apr-Sept. Hbr Office is at 20, New Quay Rd, Poole BH15 4AF.
   Lake Yard (56 AB + 6 Ⓥ; 90M + 6🛥) ☎ 674531, 📠 677518, £14.75, P, D, AC, FW, CH, Slip, Gas/Gaz, ME, EI, Sh, C (5 ton), BH (50 ton), Bar; ent marked by 2FR (vert) and two 2FG (vert).
Beyond Poole Bridge:
   Sunseeker International Marina (50) ☎ 685335, AC, Sh, D, BH (30 ton), FW, ME, EI, CH, V, R, Bar;
   Cobbs Quay Marina (850, some visitors) ☎ 674299, 📠 665217, £18, Slip, P, D, Gas, Ⓘ, SM, FW, AC, ME, EI, Ⓔ, Sh, C (10 ton), CH, R, Bar;
Public Landing Places: On Poole Quay, in Holes Bay and by ferry hards at Sandbanks.
Fuel Poole Bay Fuels barge (May-Sep 0900-1800; moored near Aunt Betty buoy, No 50) P, D, Gas, Gaz, V, Off licence.
Corrals (S side of Poole Quay adjacent bridge) P & D; **Salterns marina** P & D.
Yacht Clubs: Royal Motor YC ☎ 707227, M, Bar, R; **Poole Bay YC; Parkstone YC** ☎ 743610 (Parkstone Haven); **Poole YC** ☎ 672687.

Services
A complete range of marine services is available; consult marina/Hr Mr for exact locations. **Town** EC Wed; ✉, Ⓑ, ⇌, ✈. Ferry to Cherbourg and Channel Islands (all year).
PERSONAL WATER CRAFT (PWC) may only be used in an area N of Brownsea Island where there is an exemption from the hbr speed limit of 10kn. PWCs are not allowed in the Quiet Area in the S of the hbr, nor must they linger in the hbr ent. Permits can be obtained from the Hr Mr.

ADJACENT HARBOUR AND ANCHORAGE

WAREHAM, Dorset, 50°41'·00N 02°06'·48W. AC 2611. HW –0030 (Np), +0320 (Sp) on Dover (see 8.2.12 & ·13). Shelter very good, appr narrow and winding up R Frome but well marked by buoys and posts at ent. Beware prohib ⚓s (salmon holes) marked on the chart; also many moored boats. Passage is unlit; keep to the outside of all bends. Max draft 1·2m to Wareham Quay.
Facilities: **Ridge Wharf Yacht Centre** (180+6 visitors) (½M upstream of R Frome ent) ☎ (01929) 552650, £14, Access HW±2 approx AB, M, FW, P, D, ME, EI, Gas, AC, BH (20 ton), Slip, Sh, CH; **Redclyffe YC** ☎ 551227 (½M below bridge); **Wareham Quay** AB, FW, R. **Town** EC Wed, P & D (cans), V, Gas, R, Bar, ✉, Ⓑ, ⇌, Dr ☎ 3444.

STUDLAND BAY, Dorset, 50°38'·70N 01°55'·82W. AC 2172, 2175. Tides approx as for Swanage (8.2.11). Shelter is good except in N/ E winds. Beware Redend Rks off S shore. Best ⚓ in about 3m, 3ca NW of The Yards (three strange projections on the chalk cliffs near Handfast Pt). **Village**: EC Thurs; FW, V, R, ✉, hotel, P & D (cans), No marine facilities. A Historic Wreck (see 8.0.3h) is at 50°39'·67N 01°54'·79W, 4½ca NNE of Poole Bar buoy.

POOLE HARBOUR continued

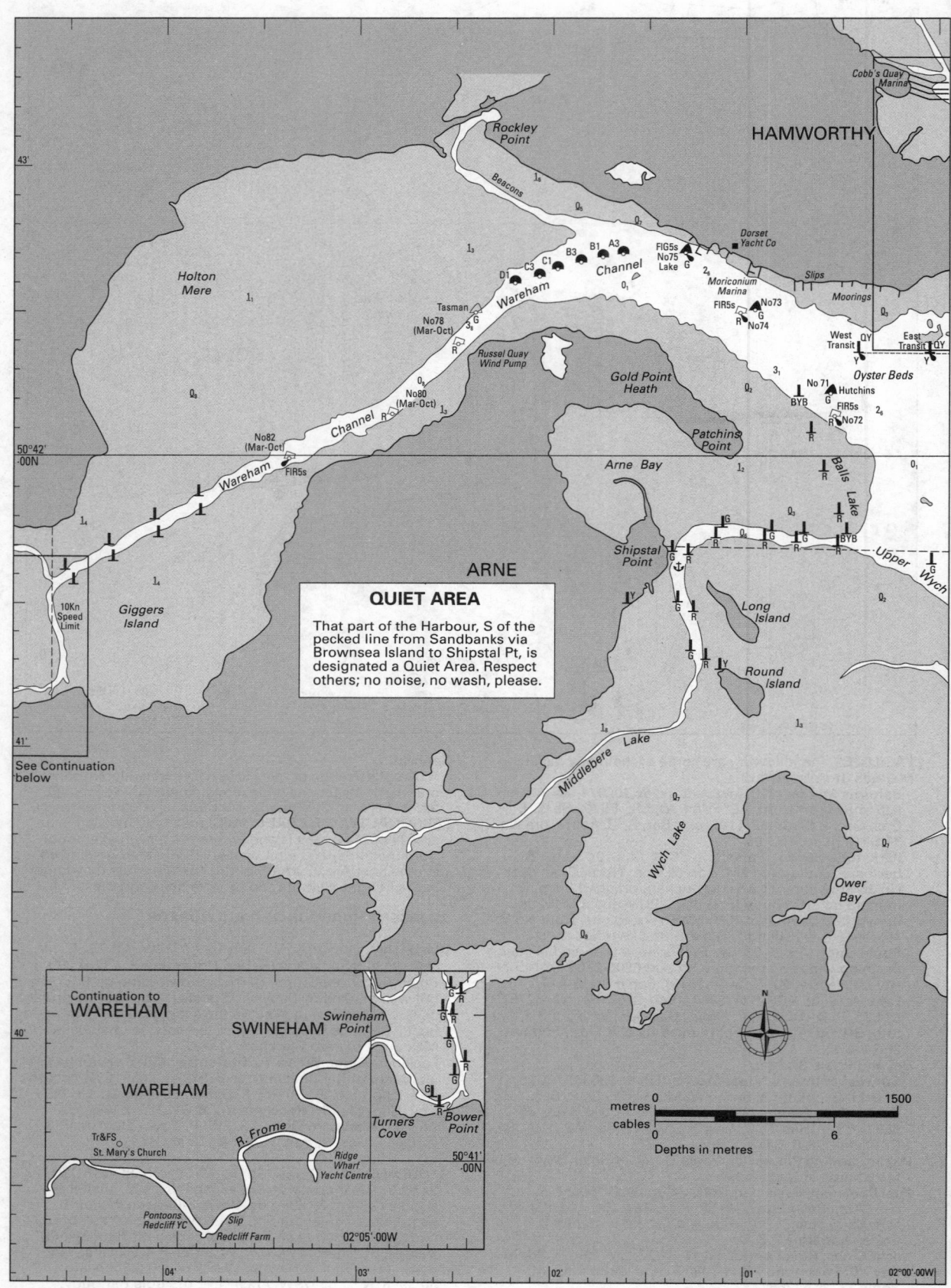

QUIET AREA

That part of the Harbour, S of the
pecked line from Sandbanks via
Brownsea Island to Shipstal Pt, is
designated a Quiet Area. Respect
others; no noise, no wash, please.

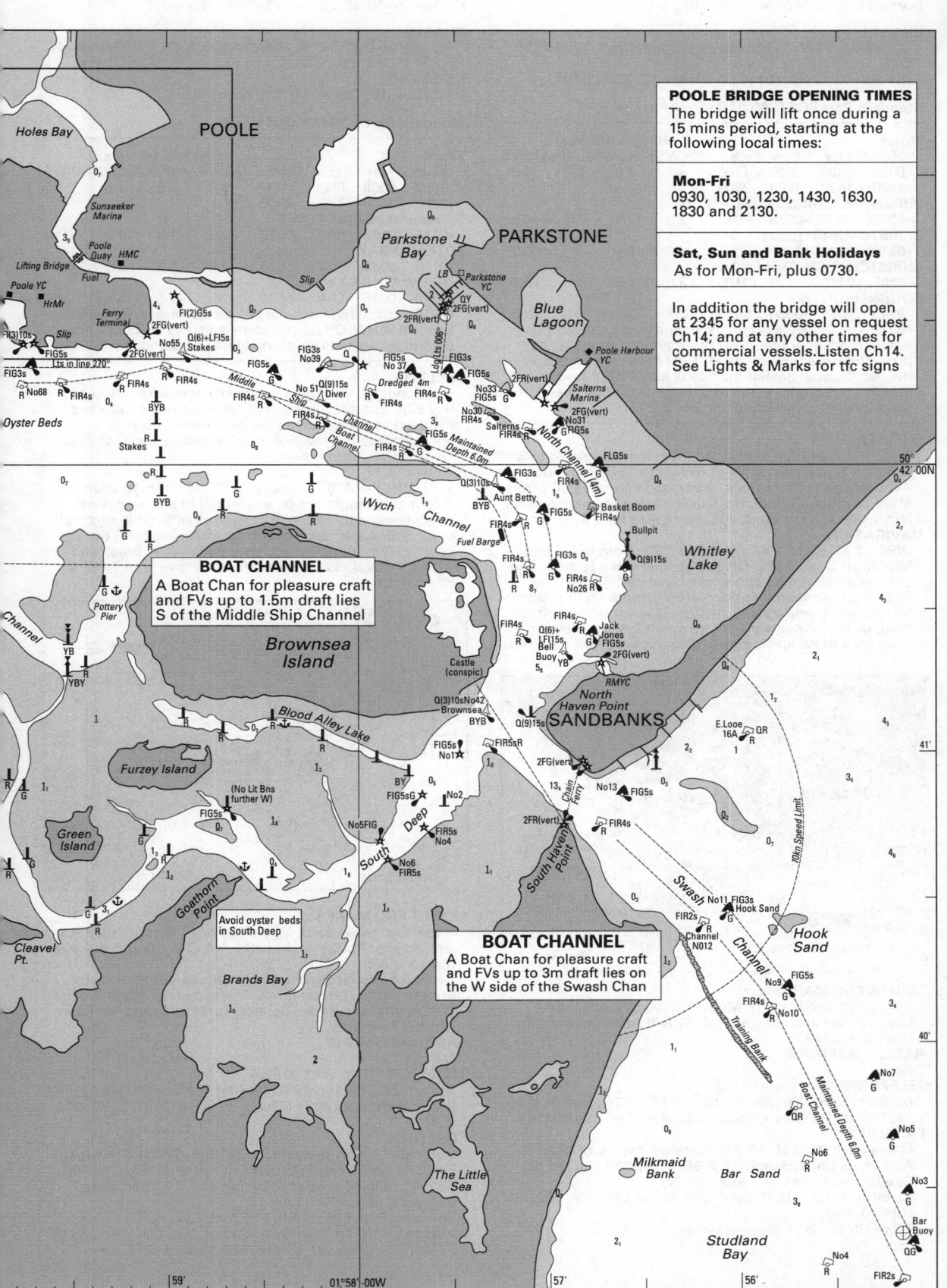

POOLE BRIDGE OPENING TIMES

The bridge will lift once during a 15 mins period, starting at the following local times:

Mon-Fri
0930, 1030, 1230, 1430, 1630, 1830 and 2130.

Sat, Sun and Bank Holidays
As for Mon-Fri, plus 0730.

In addition the bridge will open at 2345 for any vessel on request Ch14; and at any other times for commercial vessels.Listen Ch14. See Lights & Marks for tfc signs

BOAT CHANNEL
A Boat Chan for pleasure craft and FVs up to 1.5m draft lies S of the Middle Ship Channel

BOAT CHANNEL
A Boat Chan for pleasure craft and FVs up to 3m draft lies on the W side of the Swash Chan

Avoid oyster beds in South Deep

CHRISTCHURCH   8-2-15

Dorset 50°43'.50N 01°44'.25W   Rtg 4-1-1

CHARTS
AC 5600.1, 2172, 2219; Imray C4; Stanfords 7, 12; OS 195

TIDES
HW Sp −0210, Np, −0140 Dover; ML 1·2; Zone 0 (UT)

Standard Port PORTSMOUTH (⟶)

Times				Height (metres)			
High Water		Low Water		MHWS	MHWN	MLWN	MLWS
0000	0600	0500	1100	4·7	3·8	1·9	0·8
1200	1800	1700	2300				
Differences CHRISTCHURCH (Ent)							
−0230	+0030	−0035	−0035	−2·9	−2·4	−1·2	−0·2
CHRISTCHURCH (Quay)							
−0210	+0100	+0105	+0055	−2·9	−2·4	−1·0	0·0
CHRISTCHURCH (Tuckton)							
−0205	+0110	+0110	+0105	−3·0	−2·5	−1·0	+0·1
BOURNEMOUTH							
−0240	+0055	−0050	−0030	−2·7	−2·2	−0·8	−0·3

NOTE: Double HWs occur, except near nps; predictions are for the higher HW. Near nps there is a stand, when predictions are for mid-stand. Tidal levels are for inside the bar. Outside the bar the tide is about 0·6m lower at sp. Floods (or drought) in the two rivers cause considerable variations from predicted hts. See 8.2.13.

SHELTER
Good in lee of Hengistbury Hd, elsewhere exposed to SW winds. R Stour, navigable at HW up to Tuckton, and the R Avon up to the first bridge, give good shelter in all winds. Most ⚓s in the hbr dry. No ⚓ in chan. No berthing at ferry jetty by Mudeford sandbank. Hbr speed limit 4kn.

NAVIGATION
WPT 50°43'.50N 01°43'.50W, 090°/270° from/to NE end of Mudeford Quay 0·5M. The bar/chan is liable to shift. The ent is difficult on the ebb which reaches 4-5kn in 'The Run'. Recommended ent/dep at HW/stand. Chan inside hbr is narrow and mostly shallow (approx 0·3m) soft mud; mean ranges are 1·2m sp and 0·7m nps. Beware groynes S of Hengistbury Hd, Beerpan and Yarranton Rks.

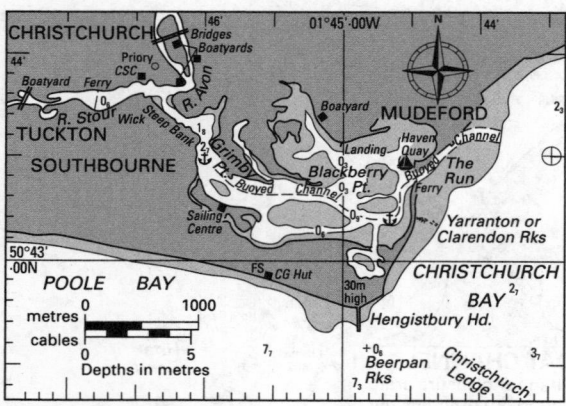

LIGHTS AND MARKS
2 FG (vert) at NE end of Mudeford Quay. Unlit chan buoys in hbr and apps are locally laid April-Oct inc; info from ☎ 483250.

RADIO TELEPHONE
None.

TELEPHONE (Dial code 01202)
MRSC (01305) 760439; ⌗ 0345 231110 (H24); Marinecall 0891 500457; Police 486333; Ⓗ 303626; Casualty 704167.

FACILITIES
Elkins BY ☎ 483141, AB £12; Rossiter Yachts ☎ 483250, AB £11.50; Christchurch SC (CSC) ☎ 483150, limited AB £8.50, monohulls only, max LOA 9m.
Services: M*, L*, D, P (cans), FW, El, Sh, CH, ACA, Gas, C (10 ton), Slip.
Town ✉, Ⓑ, ⇌, ✈ (Bournemouth).

KEYHAVEN   8-2-16

Hampshire 50°42'.82N 01·33'·18W   Rtg 4-3-1

CHARTS
AC 5600.4, 2021, 2219, 2040; Imray C4, C3, Y20; Stanfords 7, 11, 12; OS 196

TIDES
−0020, +0105 Dover; ML 2·0; Zone 0 (UT)

Standard Port PORTSMOUTH (⟶)

Times				Height (metres)			
High Water		Low Water		MHWS	MHWN	MLWN	MLWS
0000	0600	0500	1100	4·7	3·8	1·9	0·8
1200	1800	1700	2300				
Differences HURST POINT							
−0115	−0005	−0030	−0025	−2·0	−1·5	−0·5	−0·1
TOTLAND BAY							
−0130	−0045	−0040	−0040	−2·0	−1·5	−0·5	−0·1
FRESHWATER BAY							
−0210	+0025	−0040	−0020	−2·1	−1·5	−0·4	0·0

NOTE: Double HWs occur at or near sp, when predictions are for the first HW. Off springs there is a stand of about 2 hrs; predictions are then for the middle of the stand. See 8.2.13.

SHELTER
Good, but the river gets extremely congested. Access HW ±4½. Ent difficult on ebb. All moorings and ⚓s are exposed to winds across the marshland. River is administered by New Forest DC aided by the Keyhaven Consultative Committee.

NAVIGATION
WPT 50°42'.70N 01°32'.50W, 115°/295° from/to chan ent, 0·40M. Ent should not be attempted in strong E winds. Bar is constantly changing. Leave chan SHM buoys well to stbd. Beware lobster pots. Approaching from the W, beware The Shingles bank over which seas break and which partly dries. At Hurst Narrows give 'The Trap' a wide berth.

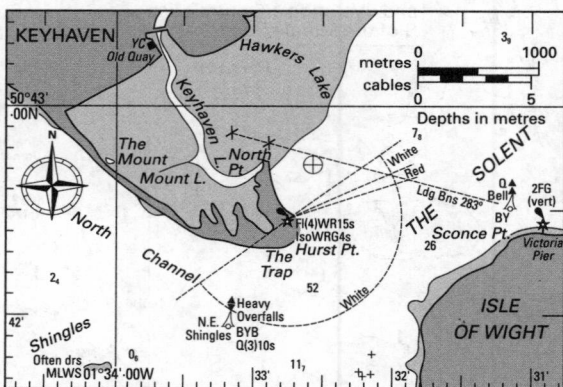

LIGHTS AND MARKS
When E of Hurst Point lt, two ldg bns ('X' topmarks) lead 283° to ent of buoyed chan; the R & G ent buoys are the more visible.
See 8.2.4 and facing chartlet for all the visibility sectors of both lights at Hurst Point. The sectors of Hurst Pt Iso WRG 4s have been deliberately omitted from the above chartlet for clarity.

RADIO TELEPHONE
None.

TELEPHONE (Dial code 01590)
R. Warden 645695; MRSC (01705) 552100; ⌗ 0345 231110 (H24); Marinecall 0891 500457; Police 615101; Dr 643022; Ⓗ 677011.

FACILITIES
Quay Slip, L; Keyhaven YC ☎ 642165, C, M, L (on beach), FW, Bar; New Forest District Council ☎ (01703) 285000, Slip, M; Milford-on-Sea P, D, FW, CH, V, R, Bar; Hurst Castle SC M, L, FW;
Services: Slip, ME, El, Sh, C (9 ton), CH.
Village EC (Milford-on-Sea) Wed; R, Bar, CH, V, ✉ and Ⓑ (Milford-on-Sea), ⇌ (bus to New Milton), ✈ (Hurn).

NEEDLES CHANNEL   8-2-17

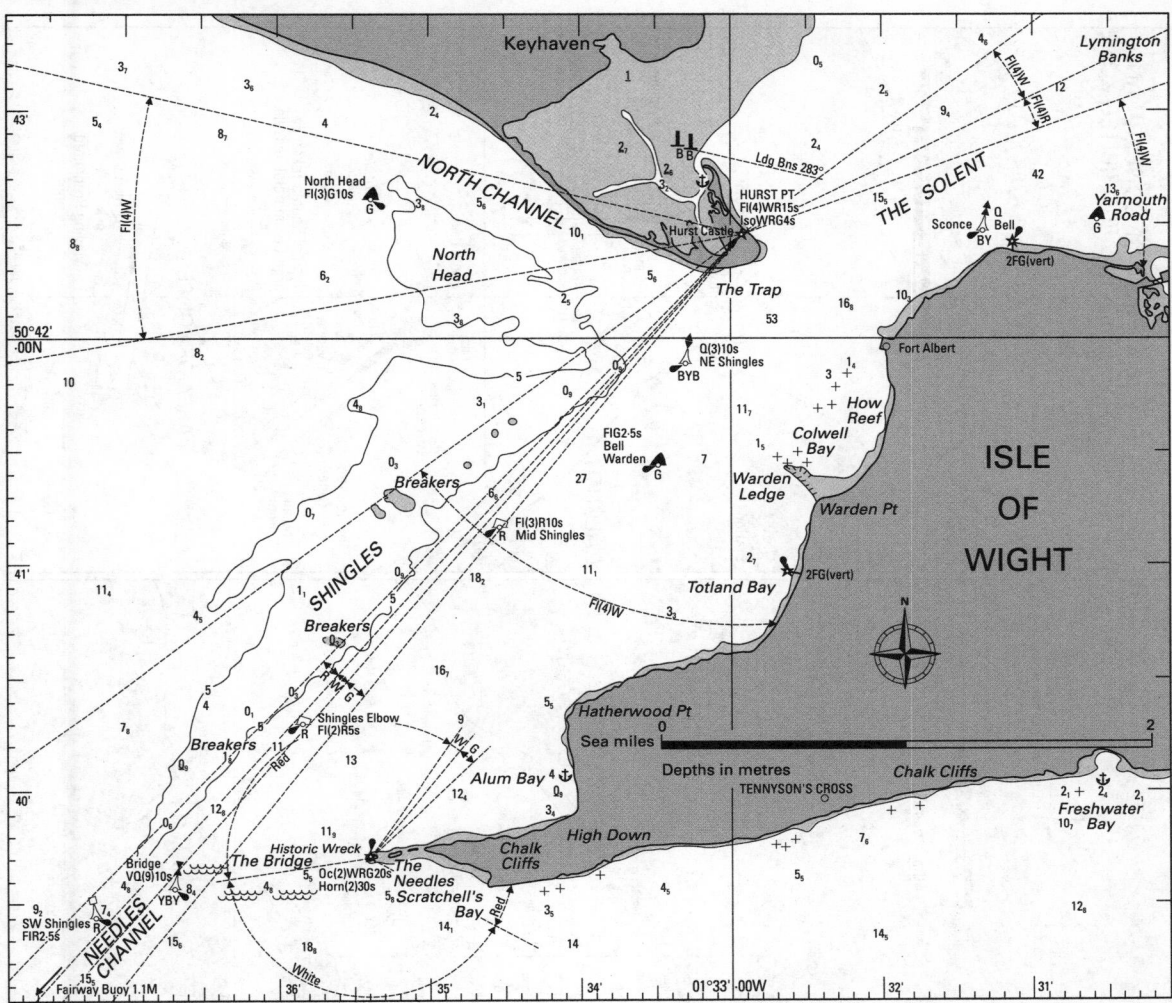

The Needles are distinctive rocks at the W end of the Isle of Wight (see AC 2219, *5600.4)*. The adjacent chalk cliffs of High Down are conspic from afar; the light ho may not be seen by day until relatively close. Goose Rk, dries, is about 50m WNW of the light ho, 100-150m WSW of which is a drying wreck. The NW side of the Needles Chan is defined by the Shingles bank, parts of which dry and on which the sea breaks violently in the least swell. The SE side of the bank is fairly steep-to, the NW side shelves more gently. Dredgers frequently work on the Shingles.
On the ebb the stream sets very strongly (3·4kn) WSW across the Shingles. The Needles Chan is well lit/buoyed and in fair weather presents no significant problems. But even a SW Force 4 against the ebb will raise breaking seas near Bridge and SW Shingles buoys.

In bad weather broken water and overfalls extend along The Bridge, a reef which runs 8ca W of the lt ho with its W extremity marked by Bridge WCM lt buoy. S to W gales against the ebb raise very dangerous breaking seas in the Needles Chan, here only 250m wide. The sea state can be at its worst shortly after LW when the flood has just begun. There is then no wind-over-tide situation, but a substantial swell is raised as a result of the recently turned stream. In such conditions use the E route to the Solent, S of the IOW and via Nab Tower; or find shelter at Poole or Studland.

In strong winds the North Channel, N of the Shingles, is preferable to the Needles Channel. The two join S of Hurst Point where overfalls and tide rips may be met. Beware The Trap, a shoal spit extending 150m SE of Hurst Castle.

ANCHORAGES BETWEEN THE NEEDLES AND YARMOUTH

ALUM BAY, 50°40'·07N 01°34'·25W. *AC 5600.4, 2021*. Tides as for Totland B. Very good shelter in E and S winds, but squally in gales. Distinctive white cliffs to S and multi-coloured cliffs and chairlift to E. Appr from due W of chairlift to clear Five Fingers Rk, dries 0·6m, to the N and Long Rk, a reef drying 0·9m at its E end, to the S. ‡ in about 4m off the new pier. A Historic Wreck (see 8.0.3h) is at 50°39'·7N 01°35'·45W.

TOTLAND BAY, 50°40'·95N 01°32'·78W. *AC 5600.4, 2219*. Tides, see 8.2.16 and 8.2.13; ML 1·9m. Good shelter in E'lies in wide shelving bay between Warden Ledge (rks 4ca offshore) to the N and Hatherwood Pt to the SW. Appr W of Warden SHM buoy Fl G 2·5s to ‡ out of the tide in 2m between pier (2FG vert) and old LB house; good holding. Colwell Bay, to the N between Warden Pt and Fort Albert, is generally rky and shallow.

ANCHORAGE EAST OF THE NEEDLES, SOUTH IOW

FRESHWATER BAY, 50°40'·04N 01°30'·53W. AC *5600.4, 2021*. Tides see 8.2.16 and 8.2.13; ML 1·6m. Good shelter from the N, open to the S. The bay is 3·2M E of Needles lt ho and 1·2M E of Tennyson's Cross. Conspic marks: on W side Redoubt Fort; a hotel on N side; Stag, Arch and Mermaid Rks to the E. The bay is shallow, with rky drying ledges ¾ca either side and a rk (0·1m) almost in the centre. Best to ‡ in about 2m just outside. V, R, Bar, ⊠.

SOLENT AREA   8-2-18

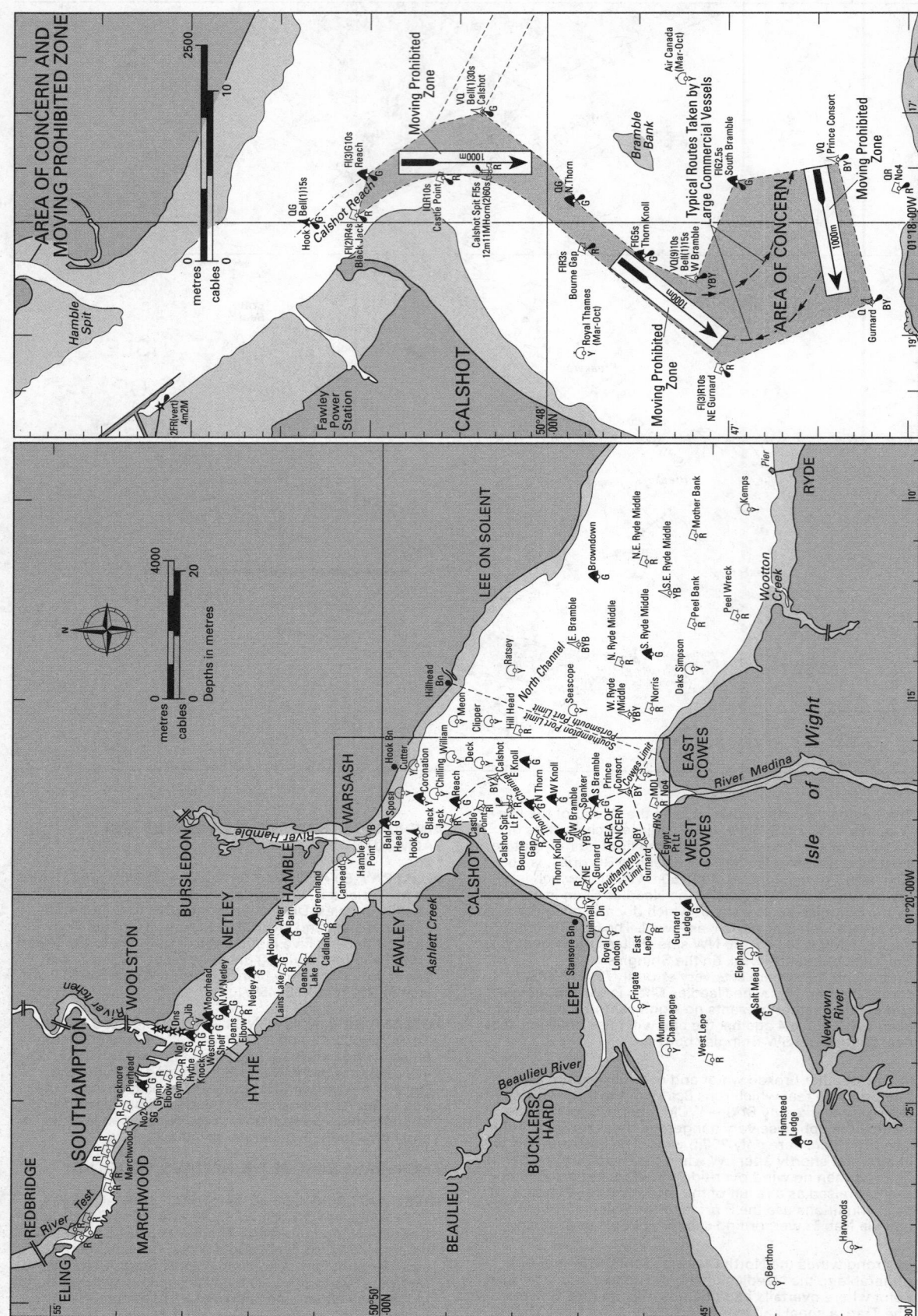

Charts

In addition to normal ACs, the Solent and approaches are covered by AC 5600, intended for yachtsmen. This is a folio of 10 A2 size charts in a clear plastic wallet, price £31.95. 5600.1 covers from Anvil Pt to Selsey Bill at 1:150,000 scale. 5600.2 and .3 cover the W and E Solent at 1:75,000. Other charts (1:25,000) are listed under the hbrs which they cover.

Vessel Traffic Service (VTS)

A VTS, operated by Southampton on VHF Ch 12 14, controls shipping in the Solent between the Needles and Nab Tower including Southampton Water. Portsmouth Hbr and its appr's N of a line from Gilkicker Pt to Outer Spit buoy are controlled on Ch 11 by QHM Portsmouth.

The VTS is primarily intended to monitor and co-ordinate the safe passage of commercial ships which must report at designated points. It includes compulsory pilotage, a radar service on request, berthing instructions and tug assistance.

Pleasure craft, particularly at night or in poor visibility, can be forewarned of ship movements (and likely avoiding action), simply by listening on VHF Ch 12, or Ch 11 for QHM Portsmouth. Traffic information is routinely broadcast by Southampton VTS on VHF Ch 12 every H, 0600 to 2200LT, Fri-Sun and Bank Hols from Easter to last weekend in Oct. From 1 June to 30 Sept broadcasts are daily at the same times.

Pleasure Craft and Commercial Shipping

In the interests of safety it is important that good co-operation between pleasure craft and commercial shipping be maintained. Yachtsmen should always bear in mind the restricted field of vision from large ships at close quarters, their limited ability to manoeuvre at slow speeds, and the constraints imposed by narrow and shallow channels.

An **Area of Concern** (AOC) covers one of the busiest parts of the Solent to improve safety for large vessels. The AOC (see chartlet opposite) covers the Western Approach and Thorn Channels. It is delineated by the following lt buoys, clockwise fom Prince Consort NCM: Gurnard NCM, NE Gurnard PHM, Bourne Gap PHM, Calshot lt Float, Castle Pt PHM, Black Jack PHM, Reach PHM, Calshot NCM, N Thorn SHM, Thorn Knoll SHM, W Bramble WCM and S Bramble SHM.

The AOC, which is criss-crossed by many pleasure craft, is also negotiated by large ships bound to/from Southampton normally via the E Solent. Inbound ships usually pass Prince Consort NCM and turn first to the southward toward Gurnard NCM, before starting their critical stbd turn into the Thorn Chan. They turn port around Calshot to clear the AOC. Typical tracks are depicted opposite.

To minimise the risk of collision with small craft, any large vessel >150m LOA, on entering the AOC, is enclosed by a **Moving Prohibited Zone** (MPZ) which extends 1000m ahead of the vessel and 100m on either beam.
Small craft <20m LOA must remain outside this MPZ, using seamanlike anticipation of likely turns.

The large vessel, displaying a B cylinder by day or 3 all-round Ⓡ lts (vert) by night, will normally be preceded by a Hbr patrol launch showing a Fl Bu lt and working Ch 12 (callsign *SP*).

The VTS will identify large ships and approx timings of MPZ as part of the hourly broadcasts (see above). All pleasure craft in the vicinity are strongly advised to monitor Ch 12 in order to create a mental picture. Be particularly alert when in, or approaching, the triangle defined by East Lepe, Hook and West Ryde Middle buoys.

VHF Radio Telephone

The proliferation of VHF radios in yachts and, it must be said, often poor R/T procedures cause problems for legitimate users and can seriously hamper emergency situations. Yachtsmen are reminded that Ch 16 is a DISTRESS, SAFETY and CALLING Ch. If another calling Ch is available use it in preference to Ch 16; otherwise, use Ch 16 as briefly as possible to make contact before shifting to a working Ch. Note also that initial contact with Solent CG should be on Ch 67, NOT Ch 16 (see next column). For ship-to-ship messages the recognised VHF channels include 06, 08, 72 and 77.
Yachts in the Solent should listen on Ch 12 and on Ch 11 for Portsmouth. Other Ch's are listed under each port entry.

Local Signals

Outward bound vessels normally hoist the following flag signals during daylight hours.

Signal	Meaning
International 'E' Flag over Answering Pendant	} I am bound East (Nab Tower)
Answering Pendant Over International 'W' Flag	} I am bound West (The Needles)

Southampton patrol launches have HARBOUR MASTER painted on their after cabin in B lettering on Y background. At night a Fl Bu all-round lt is shown above the W masthead lt.

Reference

Much useful information is given in the *Solent Year Book,* published by the Solent Cruising and Racing Association (SCRA); also in a free booklet *The Yachtsman's Guide to Southampton Water* and a leaflet *Enjoy the Solent.*
Solent Hazards by Peter Bruce, published by Boldre Marine, goes closer inshore than other Pilot books.

Weather and Navigation Broadcasts

Sailing info from BBC Radio Solent: 96·1 MHz VHF and 999 kHz (300m); 103·8 MHz and 1359 kHz (221m) in West Dorset.
A   Local weather forecast.
B   Forecast, Coastal stn reports, CG reports, Shipping movements, Tidal details and Gunnery firing times.
C   Live forecast from Southampton Weather Centre.

Daily Broadcasts (LT)

0500	A (Mon-Fri)	1325	C (Mon-Fri)
0530	B (Mon-Fri)	1400	A
0600	A	1500	A (Mon-Sat)
0630	A	1505	C (Sun only)
0635	B (Mon-Fri)	1525	C (Mon-Fri)
0700	A	1600	A
0735	C	1625	C (Mon-Fri)
0745	B (Mon-Sat)	1700	A
0800	A	1735	C (Mon-Fri)
0830	A (Sun only)	1759	C (Sat only)
0835	C (Mon-Sat)	1800	A (Mon-Fri, Sun)
0850	B (Mon-Fri)	1835	C (Mon-Fri)
0900	A (Mon-Sat)	1900	A (Mon-Fri)
0905	C (Sun only)	2000	A (Mon-Fri)
1000	A	2100	A (Mon-Fri)
1100	A	2205	A (Mon-Fri)
1200	A	2305	C (Mon-Fri)
1300	A (Mon-Fri)		
1305	A (Sun only)		
1310	C (Sat only)		

Dial ☎ 0891 500 457 for Marinecall forecasts for this area, or for Marine MetFax dial 0336 400 457. Southampton Weather Centre is ☎ (01703) 228844. Solent CG broadcasts on Ch 67 local strong wind warnings on receipt; and local forecasts every 4 hrs from 0400LT, but every 2 hrs if strong wind warnings are in force.

Solent Coastguard

The Maritime Rescue Sub Centre (MRSC) at Lee-on-Solent ☎ (01705) 552100 coordinates all SAR activities in Solent District, which is bounded by a line from Highcliffe south to the EC1 buoy; E to the Greenwich Lt V; thence N to Beachy Head. It is the busiest CG District in the UK, because of the huge concentration of pleasure craft within its bounds.

It is manned H24, year round by at least 3 CG Officers who can call on the RNLI, Solent Safety rescue boats and the CG Rescue helicopter based at Lee. Sector and Auxiliary CGs are based on the IOW, Calshot, Eastney, Hayling, Littlehampton, Shoreham, Newhaven and elsewhere.

Solent CG keeps watch on VHF Ch 67 and 16. Uniquely, the initial call to *Solent Coastguard* should be made on Ch 67, the working channel; this is because Ch 16 is often very busy especially in the summer. Ch 67 is also heavily loaded and is only for essential traffic. Listen out before transmitting; be brief, to the point and use correct R/T procedures.

Save valuable R/T time by telephoning Solent CG before sailing; they will be glad to advise you. In general terms, they will always stress: Up-to-date forecasts; awareness of tidal streams; sound knowledge of "Rule of the Road" and local Notices to Mariners; adequate fuel, plus reserves, for your passage, and a sharp lookout at all times. Bon voyage!

SOLENT AREA WAYPOINTS

8.2.18

Waypoints marked with an asterisk (*) are special (yellow) racing marks, which may be removed in winter. Racing buoys marked with a bullet (•) against the longitude are only laid during Cowes week. Other waypoints are navigational buoys, unless otherwise stated. All positions are referenced to the OSGB 36 datum.

After Barn	50°51'·50N 01°20'·73W
*Air Canada	50°47'·30N 01°16'·73W
*Alpha (Cowes)	50°46'·24N 01°18'·11W•
*Alpha (Portsmouth)	50°46'·58N 01°07'·50W
*Ashlett	50°49'·95N 01°19'·67W
*Autohelm	50°46'·55N 01°21'·37W
Bald Head	50°49'·88N 01°18'·15W
Bank lt bn	50°53'·58N 01°23'·23W
*Bay	50°46'·02N 00°57'·81W
Bembridge Ledge	50°41'·12N 01°02'·72W
Bembridge tide gauge	50°42'·43N 01°04'·93W
*Berthon	50°44'·18N 01°29'·13W
*Beta (Cowes)	50°46'·25N 01°17'·53W•
*Beta (Portsmouth)	50°46'·57N 01°06'·25W
Black Jack	50°49'·10N 01°18'·00W
Black Rock	50°42'·55N 01°30'·55W
*Bob Kemp	50°45'·15N 01°09'·55W
Boulder (Looe Chan)	50°41'·53N 00°49'·00W
*Bouldnor	52°42'·70N 01°28'·90W
Bourne Gap	50°47'·79N 01°18'·26W
*Bowring	50°47'·28N 01°12'·00W
Boyne	50°46'·12N 01°05'·17W
Bramble bn	50°47'·38N 01°17'·06W
Bridge	50°39'·59N 01°36'·80W
*Brookes & Gatehouse (ex Alpha)	50°46'·40N 01°07'·80W
Browndown	50°46'·54N 01°10'·87W
*Brunswick Gate (ex Echo)	50°46'·05N 01°05'·56W
Bury	50°54'·10N 01°27'·04W
Cadland	50°50'·99N 01°20'·45W
Calshot	50°48'·40N 01°16'·95W
Calshot Spit lt F	50°48'·32N 01°17'·55W
*Camper & Nicholsons	50°47'·05N 01°06'·68W
Castle (NB)	50°46'·43N 01°05'·30W
Castle Point	50°48'·68N 01°17'·58W
*Cathead	50°50'·58N 01°19'·15W
*Champagne Mumm	50°45'·60N 01°23'·03W
Chi	50°45'·48N 00°56'·91W
Chichester Bar Bn	50°45'·88N 00°56'·38W
*Chilling	50°49'·18N 01°17'·37W
Chi Spit	50°45'·68N 00°56'·48W
*Clipper	50°48'·43N 01°15'·63W
*Colten ('C')	50°43'·84N 01°31'·13W
Coronation	50°49'·51N 01°17'·53W
Cowes breakwater lt	50°45'·84N 01°17'·43W
Cowes No 3	50°46'·04N 01°17'·95W
Cowes No 4	50°46'·04N 01°17'·78W
Cracknore	50°53'·91N 01°25'·12W
Crosshouse lt bn	50°54'·01N 01°23'·11W
*Cutter	50°49'·42N 01°16'·82W

*Daks-Simpson	50°45'·50N 01°14'·30W
*DB Marine	50°46'·13N 01°13'·00W
Dean Elbow	50°43'·66N 01°01'·78W
Deans Elbow	50°52'·12N 01°22'·67W
Deans Lake	50°51'·35N 01°21'·53W
Dean Tail South	50°43'·10N 00°59'·49W
*Deck	50°48'·60N 01°16'·57W
*Delta (Portsmouth)	50°46'·01N 01°06'·20W
Dibden Bay	50°53'·66N 01°24'·84W
*Dunford ('B')	50°43'·38N 01°31'·54W
*Durns	50°45'·40N 01°25'·80W•
Durns Pt obstn (S end)	50°45'·37N 01°26'·95W
East Bramble	50°47'·20N 01°13'·56W
East Knoll	50°47'·93N 01°16'·74W
East Lepe	50°46'·09N 01°20'·81W
*Echo (Portsmouth)	50°46'·09N 01°05'·7W
*Elephant	50°44'·60N 01°21'·80W
Eling	50°54'·45N 01°27'·75W
Fairway (Needles)	50°38'·20N 01°38'·90W
*Gamma (Portsmouth)	50°46'·34N 01°06'·00W
Greenland	50°51'·07N 01°20'·29W
Gurnard	50°46'·18N 01°18'·76W
Gurnard Ledge	50°45'·48N 01°20'·50W
Gymp	50°53'·14N 01°24'·21W
Gymp Elbow	50°53'·49N 01°24'·53W
Hamble Point	50°50'·12N 01°18'·57W
Hamstead Ledge	50°43'·83N 01°26'·10W
*Hard	50°44'·92N 00°57'·81W
*Harwoods	50°42'·81N 01°28'·75W
Hillhead	50°48'·00N 01°15'·92W
Hook	50°49'·49N 01°18'·21W
Horse Elbow	50°44'·23N 01°03'·80W
Horse Sand	50°45'·48N 01°05'·17W
Horse Sand Fort lt	50°44'·97N 01°04'·25W
Horse Tail	50°43'·20N 01°00'·14W
Hound	50°51'·65N 01°21'·43W
*Hurst ('A')	50°42'·87N 01°32'·46W
Hythe Knock	50°52'·79N 01°23'·73W
Jack in Basket	50°44'·25N 01°30'·50W
*Jackson ('H')	50°44'·30N 01°28'·16W
*Jardines	50°48'·10N 01°14'·55W
*Jib	50°52'·93N 01°22'·97W
*Kelvin Hughes	50°47'·30N 01°14'·50W•
Lains Lake	50°51'·55N 01°21'·56W
*Lambeth	50°41'·50N 01°41'·60W
Langstone Fairway	50°46'·28N 01°01'·27W
Lee Pt Bn	50°47'·40N 01°11'·85W
*Lucas	50°46'·24N 01°08'·67W

Main Passage	50°45'·98N 01°04'·02W
Marchwood	50°53'·95N 01°25'·48W
*Marina Developments	50°46'·12N 01°16'·55W
*Mark	50°49'·53N 01°18'·85W
*Meon	50°49'·15N 01°15'·62W
Mid Shingles	50°41'·18N 01°34'·58W
Milbrook	50°54'·08N 01°26'·73W
Mixon Bn	50°42'·35N 00°46'·21W
Moorhead	50°52'·52N 01°22'·81W
*Moreton	50°42'·02N 01°03'·14W
*Morse (ex Delta)	50°46'·12N 01°06'·33W
Mother Bank	50°45'·45N 01°11'·13W
Nab 1	50°41'·23N 00°56'·43W
Nab 2	50°41'·70N 00°56'·71W
Nab 3	50°42'·17N 00°57'·05W
Nab East	50°42'·82N 01°00'·70W
Nab End	50°42'·60N 00°59'·38W
Nab Tower	50°40'·05N 00°57'·07W
NE Gurnard	50°47'·03N 01°19'·33W
NE Mining Ground	50°44'·71N 01°06'·30W
NE Ryde Middle	50°46'·18N 01°11'·80W
NE Shingles	50°41'·93N 01°33'·32W
Needles Fairway	50°38'·20N 01°38'·90W
Netley	50°51'·99N 01°21'·72W
New Grounds	50°41'·97N 00°58'·53W
*Newtown	50°44'·15N 01°23'·70W•
Newtown G By	50°43'·57N 01°24'·70W
No Mans Land Fort lt	50°44'·37N 01°05'·60W
Norris	50°45'·92N 01°15'·40W
North Head	50°42'·65N 01°35'·43W
North Ryde Middle	50°46'·58N 01°14'·28W
North Sturbridge	50°45'·31N 01°08'·15W
North Thorn	50°47'·88N 01°17'·75W
NW Netley	50°52'·28N 01°22'·65W
*Ocean Safety (ex Beken)	50°45'·75N 01°19'·67W
*ODM ('D') (Lymington)	50°44'·18N 01°30'·10W
Outer Nab	50°41'·00N 00°56'·65W
Outer Spit	50°45'·55N 01°05'·41W
Peel Bank	50°45'·57N 01°13'·25W
Peel Wreck	50°44'·85N 01°13'·30W
Pier Head	50°53'·64N 01°24'·57W
Poole Fairway	50°38'·97N 01°54'·80W
Portsmouth No 3 Bar	50°47'·04N 01°06'·17W
Portsmouth No 4	50°46'·98N 01°06'·27W
Prince Consort	50°46'·38N 01°17'·47W
*Pylewell ('E')	50°44'·58N 01°29'·43W
*Quinnell	50°47'·03N 01°19'·80W
*Ratsey	50°47'·63N 01°13'·56W
Reach	50°49'·02N 01°17'·56W
Ridge	50°46'·42N 01°05'·57W
*Rocwel	50°43'·02N 01°27'·04W
Roway Wk	50°46'·08N 01°02'·20W

*Royal Albert	50°46'·48N 01°05'·87W
*Royal Southern	50°48'·85N 01°15'·48W
*Royal Thames	50°47'·78N 01°19'·17W
*Ruthven	50°42'·67N 01°03'·45W
Ryde Pier Hd	50°44'·35N 01°09'·51W
*RYS flagstaff	50°45'·97N 01°17'·97W
Saddle	50°45'·17N 01°04'·78W
Salt Mead	50°44'·48N 01°22'·95W
Sconce	50°42'·50N 01°31'·35W
*Seafile	50°46'·55N 01°21'·37W
*Seascope	50°47'·38N 01°15'·82W
SE Ryde Middle	50°45'·90N 01°12'·00W
Shingles Elbow	50°40'·31N 01°35'·92W
*S.M. (Special Mark)	50°46'·12N 01°16'·76W
*Snowden (ex Trap)	50°46'·17N 01°17'·51W
South Bramble	50°46'·95N 01°17'·65W
South Ryde Middle	50°46'·10N 01°14'·08W
*Spanker	50°47'·08N 01°17'·98W
Spit Refuge	50°46'·12N 01°05'·37W
Spit Sand Fort Lt	50°46'·20N 01°05'·85W
*Sposa	50°49'·63N 01°17'·50W
St Helens	50°43'·33N 01°02'·32W
Stokes Bay Wreck	50°46'·67N 01°10'·58W
Street	50°41'·65N 00°48'·80W
*Sunsail	50°46'·40N 01°15'·00W
Swinging Ground No 1	50°52'·97N 01°23'·35W
Swinging Ground No 2	50°53'·79N 01°25'·03W
SW Mining Ground	50°44'·63N 01°07'·95W
SW Shingles	50°39'·31N 01°37'·36W
*Tanners ('G')	50°44'·80N 01°28'·47W
Thorn Knoll	50°47'·47N 01°18'·35W
Trinity House (Cowes)	50°46'·10N 01°17'·15W
*Vail Williams (ex Beta Portsmouth)	50°46'·80N 01°07'·25W
Warden	50°41'·45N 01°33'·47W
Warner	50°43'·84N 01°03'·93W
West Bramble	50°47'·17N 01°18'·57W
*W – E	50°45'·48N 00°58'·70W
West Knoll	50°47'·52N 01°17'·68W
West Lepe	50°45'·20N 01°24'·00W
Weston Shelf	50°52'·68N 01°23'·17W
West Princessa	50°40'·20N 01°03'·95W
West Ryde Middle	50°46'·45N 01°15'·70W
William	50°49'·00N 01°16'·40W
Winner	50°45'·07N 01°00'·01W
*Woolwich	50°43'·00N 01°38'·00W
Wootton Bn	50°44'·50N 01°12'·10W
*Yachthaven ('D')	50°44'·18N 01°30'·10W
*Yachting World	50°45'·08N 01°27'·25W
*YMS 2	50°42'·86N 01°29'·40W
*Yarmouth No 4	50°46'·82N 01°28'·42W

YARMOUTH   8-2-20

Isle of Wight 50°42'·39N 01°29'·97W   Rtg 1-2-1

CHARTS
AC *5600.5, 2021, 2040*; Imray C3, Y20; Stanfords 11, 18; OS 196

TIDES
Sp –0050, +0150, Np +0020 Dover; ML 2·0; Zone 0 (UT)

Standard Port PORTSMOUTH (→)

Times				Height (metres)			
High Water		Low Water		MHWS	MHWN	MLWN	MLWS
0000	0600	0500	1100	4·7	3·8	1·9	0·8
1200	1800	1700	2300				
Differences YARMOUTH							
–0105	+0005	–0025	–0030	–1·6	–1·3	–0·4	0·0

NOTE: Double HWs occur at or near sp; at other times there is a stand lasting about two hrs. Predictions refer to the first HW when there are two; otherwise to the middle of the stand. See 8.2.13.

SHELTER
Good from all directions of wind and sea, but swell enters if wind strong from N/NE. Hbr dredged 2m from ent to bridge; access H24. Moor fore-and-aft on piles in 5 rows, A to E; on the Town Quay, or on pontoon if <9m LOA. Boats over 15m LOA, 4m beam or 2·4m draft should give notice of arrival. Berthing on S Quay is normally only for fuel, C, FW, or to load people/cargo. Hbr gets very full in season and may be closed to visitors. 31 Y ⚓s outside hbr (see chartlet) and ⚓ further to the N or S.

NAVIGATION
WPT 50°42'·55N 01°29'·93W, 008°/188° from/to abeam car ferry terminal, 2ca. Dangers on appr are Black Rock (SHM buoy Fl G 5s) and shoal water to the N of the E/W bkwtr. Beware ferries. Caution: strong ebb in the ent at sp. Speed limit 4kn in hbr apprs from abeam pierhead, in the hbr and up-river.

⚓ prohib in hbr and beyond R Yar road bridge. This swing bridge opens for access to the moorings and BYs up-river at Saltern Quay: (May-Sept) 0800, 0900, 1000, 1200, 1400, 1600, 1730, 1830, 2000LT; and on request (Oct-May). The river is navigable by dinghy at HW almost up to Freshwater.
A **Historic Wreck** (see 8.0.3h) is at 50°42'·52N 01°29'·59W, 2ca ExN from end of pier; marked by Y SPM buoy.

LIGHTS AND MARKS
Ldg bns (2 W ◊ on B/W masts) and Idg Its (FG 5/9m 2M), on quay, 188°. When hbr is closed to visitors (eg when full in summer or at week-ends) a R flag is flown at the pier head and an illuminated board 'Harbour Full' is displayed at the ent, plus an extra Ⓡ. In fog a high intensity Ⓦ It is shown from the pier hd and from the inner E pier, together with a Ⓨ.

RADIO TELEPHONE
Hr Mr VHF Ch 68. Water Taxi Ch 15.

TELEPHONE (Dial code 01983 = code for whole of IOW)
Hr Mr 760321, ☎ 761192; MRSC (01705) 552100; ⌗ 0345 231110 (H24); Marinecall 0891 500457; Police 52800; Dr 760434.

FACILITIES
Hbr £8 on piles, Town Quay, pontoon or ⚓; Slip, P, D, L, M, Gaz, FW, C (5 ton), Ice, ▢, &;
Yarmouth SC ☎ 760270, Bar, L;
Royal Solent YC ☎ 760256, Bar, R, L, Slip;
Services Note: Most marine services/BYs are located near Salterns Quay, 500m up-river above the bridge, or ½M by road. BY, Slip, M, ME, EI, Sh, CH, Gas, Gaz, SM, C, Divers.
Town EC Wed; V, R, Bar, ✉, Ⓑ (May-Sept 1000-1445, Sept-May a.m. only), ⇌ (Lymington), ✈ (Bournemouth/ Southampton).

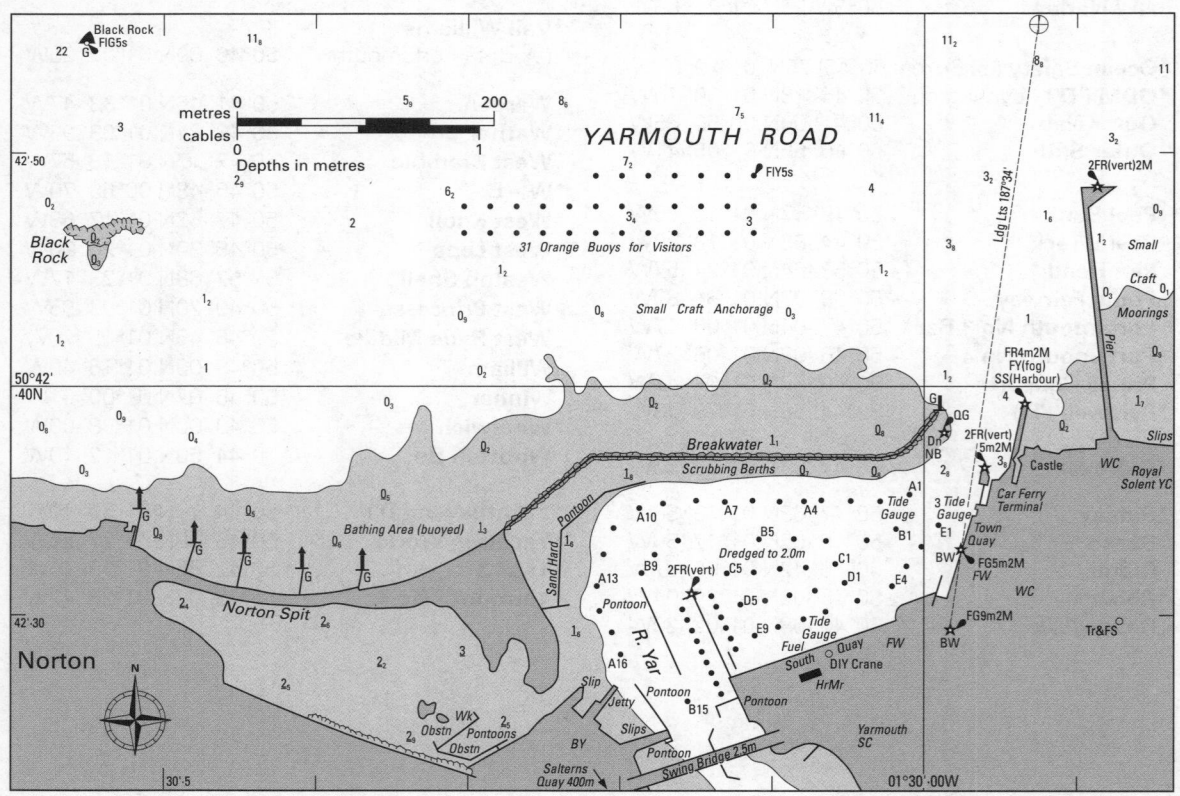

LYMINGTON   8-2-21

Hampshire 50°45'·10N 01·31'·32W   Rtg 1-1-1

CHARTS
AC *5600.5, 2021, 2040, 2045*; Imray C3, Y20, Y30;
Stanfords 11, 18; OS 196

TIDES
Sp −0040, +0100, Np +0020 Dover; ML 2·0; Zone 0 (UT)

Standard Port PORTSMOUTH (→)

Times				Height (metres)			
High Water		Low Water		MHWS	MHWN	MLWN	MLWS
0000	0600	0500	1100	4·7	3·8	1·9	0·8
1200	1800	1700	2300				

Differences LYMINGTON

−0110	+0005	−0020	−0020	−1·7	−1·2	−0·5	−0·1

NOTE: Double HWs occur at or near sp and on other
occasions there is a stand lasting about 2hrs. Predictions
refer to the first HW when there are two. At other times
they refer to the middle of the stand. See 8.2.13.

RADIO TELEPHONE
Marinas VHF Ch **80** M (office hrs).

TELEPHONE (Dial code 01590)
Hr Mr 672014; MRSC (01705) 552100; ☎ 0345 231110 (H24);
Marinecall 0891 500457; Police 675411; Dr 672953; Ⓗ
677011.

FACILITIES
Marinas:
Lymington Yacht Haven (475+100 visitors), 2m depth, all
tides access, ☎ 677071, ⚓ 678186, £16.60, P, D, AC, FW,
BY, ME, EI, Sh, C (10 ton), BH (40 ton), CH, Gas, Gaz, Ⓞ, &;
Lymington Marina (300+100 visitors), ☎ 673312, ⚓
676353, £14.10, Slip, P, AC, D, FW, ME, EI, Sh, CH, BH (100
ton), C, (37, 80 ton), Gas, Gaz, Ⓞ;
Town Quay AB £7.00, M, FW, Slip (see Hr Mr); **Bath Road**
public pontoon, FW.

Clubs: Royal Lymington YC ☎ 672677, R, Bar, &; **Lymington
Town SC** ☎ 674514, AB, R, Bar.

Services: M, FW, ME, EI, Sh, C (16 ton), CH, Ⓔ, SM, ACA.

Town EC Wed; every facility including ✉, Ⓑ, ≈, ✈
(Bournemouth or Southampton).

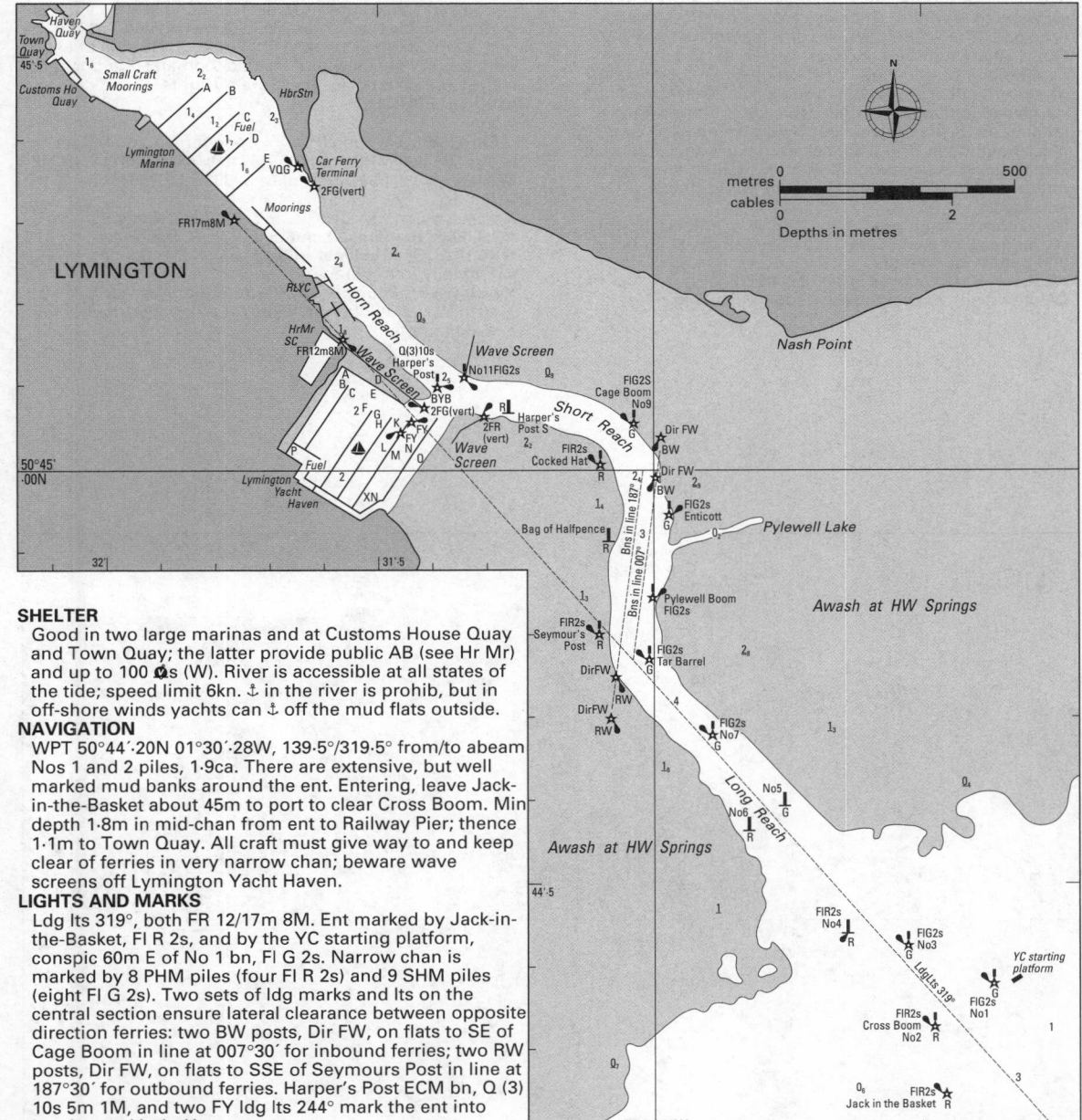

SHELTER
Good in two large marinas and at Customs House Quay
and Town Quay; the latter provide public AB (see Hr Mr)
and up to 100 ⚓s (W). River is accessible at all states of
the tide; speed limit 6kn. ⚓ in the river is prohib, but in
off-shore winds yachts can ⚓ off the mud flats outside.

NAVIGATION
WPT 50°44'·20N 01°30'·28W, 139·5°/319·5° from/to abeam
Nos 1 and 2 piles, 1·9ca. There are extensive, but well
marked mud banks around the ent. Entering, leave Jack-
in-the-Basket about 45m to port to clear Cross Boom. Min
depth 1·8m in mid-chan from ent to Railway Pier; thence
1·1m to Town Quay. All craft must give way to and keep
clear of ferries in very narrow chan; beware wave
screens off Lymington Yacht Haven.

LIGHTS AND MARKS
Ldg lts 319°, both FR 12/17m 8M. Ent marked by Jack-in-
the-Basket, Fl R 2s, and by the YC starting platform,
conspic 60m E of No 1 bn, Fl G 2s. Narrow chan is
marked by 8 PHM piles (four Fl R 2s) and 9 SHM piles
(eight Fl G 2s). Two sets of ldg marks and lts on the
central section ensure lateral clearance between opposite
direction ferries: two BW posts, Dir FW, on flats to SE of
Cage Boom in line at 007°30' for inbound ferries; two RW
posts, Dir FW, on flats to SSE of Seymours Post in line at
187°30' for outbound ferries. Harper's Post ECM bn, Q (3)
10s 5m 1M, and two FY ldg lts 244° mark the ent into
Lymington Yacht Haven.

NEWTOWN RIVER   8-2-22

Isle of Wight 50°43'·42N 01°24'·58W   Rtg 3-4-1

CHARTS
AC *5600.5, 2021, 2040, 1905*; Imray C3, Y20; Stanfords 11, 18; OS 196

TIDES
Sp –0108, Np +0058, Dover; ML 2·3; Zone 0 (UT)

Standard Port PORTSMOUTH (→)

Times				Height (metres)			
High Water		Low Water		MHWS	MHWN	MLWN	MLWS
0000	0600	0500	1100	4·7	3·8	1·9	0·8
1200	1800	1700	2300				

Differences SOLENT BANK (Data approximate)

–0100	0000	–0015	–0020	–1·3	–1·0	–0·3	–0·1

NOTE: Double HWs occur at or near springs; at other times there is a stand which lasts about 2hrs. Predictions refer to the first HW when there are two. At other times they refer to the middle of the stand. See 8·2·13.

SHELTER
3½M E of Yarmouth, Newtown gives good shelter, but is exposed to N winds. There are 6 ⚓s (R/W) in Clamerkin Lake and 18 (R/W) in the main arm leading to Shalfleet Quay, all are numbered; check with Hr Mr. Do not ⚓ beyond boards showing "Anchorage Limit" on account of oyster beds. Fin keel boats can stay afloat from ent to Hamstead landing or to Clamerkin Limit Boards. Public landing on E side of river N of Newtown quay by conspic black boathouse. The whole eastern peninsula ending in Fishhouse Pt is a nature reserve; yachtsmen are asked not to land there. 5kn speed limit in hbr is strictly enforced.
If no room in river, good ⚓ in 3-5m W of ent, but beware rky ledges E of Hamstead Ledge SHM buoy, Fl (2) G 5s, and piles with dolphin.
At Solent Bank (approx 50°44'·5N 01°25'·5W), 1M NW of Newtown ent, expect to see dredgers working.

NAVIGATION
WPT 50°43'·80N 01°25'·10W, 310°/130° from/to ldg bn, 0·46M. From W, make good Hamstead Ledge SHM buoy, thence E to pick up ldg marks.
From E, keep N of Newtown gravel banks where W/SW winds over a sp ebb can raise steep breaking seas; leave R spherical bar buoy to port.
Best ent is from about HW –4, on the flood but while the mud flats are still visible. Ent lies between two shingle spits and can be rough in N winds especially near HW. There is only about 0·9m over the bar.
Inside the ent so many perches mark the mud banks that confusion may result. Near junction to Causeway Lake depth is only 0·9m and beyond this water quickly shoals. At ent to Clamerkin Lake (1·2 - 1·8m) keep to SE to avoid gravel spit off W shore, marked by two PHM perches; the rest of chan is marked by occas perches. Beware many oyster beds in Western Haven and Clamerkin Lake. There is a rifle range at top of Clamerkin Lake and in Spur Lake; R flags flown during firing. High voltage power line across Clamerkin at 50°42'·78N 01°22'·58W has clearance of only 9m and no shore markings.

LIGHTS AND MARKS
Conspic TV mast (152m) bearing about 150° (3·3M from hbr ent) provides initial approach track. In season a forest of masts inside the hbr are likely to be evident. The ldg bns, 130°, are off Fishhouse Pt in mud on NE side of ent: front bn, RW bands with Y-shaped topmark; rear bn, W with W disc in B circle. There are no lights.

RADIO TELEPHONE
None.

TELEPHONE (Dial code 01983 = code for whole of IOW)
Hr Mr 531424; MRSC (01705) 552100; ⌗ 0345 231110 (H24); Marinecall 0891 500457; Police 528000; Dr 760434.

FACILITIES
Newtown Quay M £8.50, L, FW; **Shalfleet Quay** Slip, M, L, AB; **Lower Hamstead Landing** L, FW; **R. Seabroke** ☎ 531213, Sh; **Shalfleet Village** V, Bar, P & D (cans; in emergency from garage).
Newtown EC Thurs; ✉, Ⓑ (Yarmouth or Newport), ⇌ (bus to Yarmouth, ferry to Lymington), ✈ (Bournemouth or Southampton).

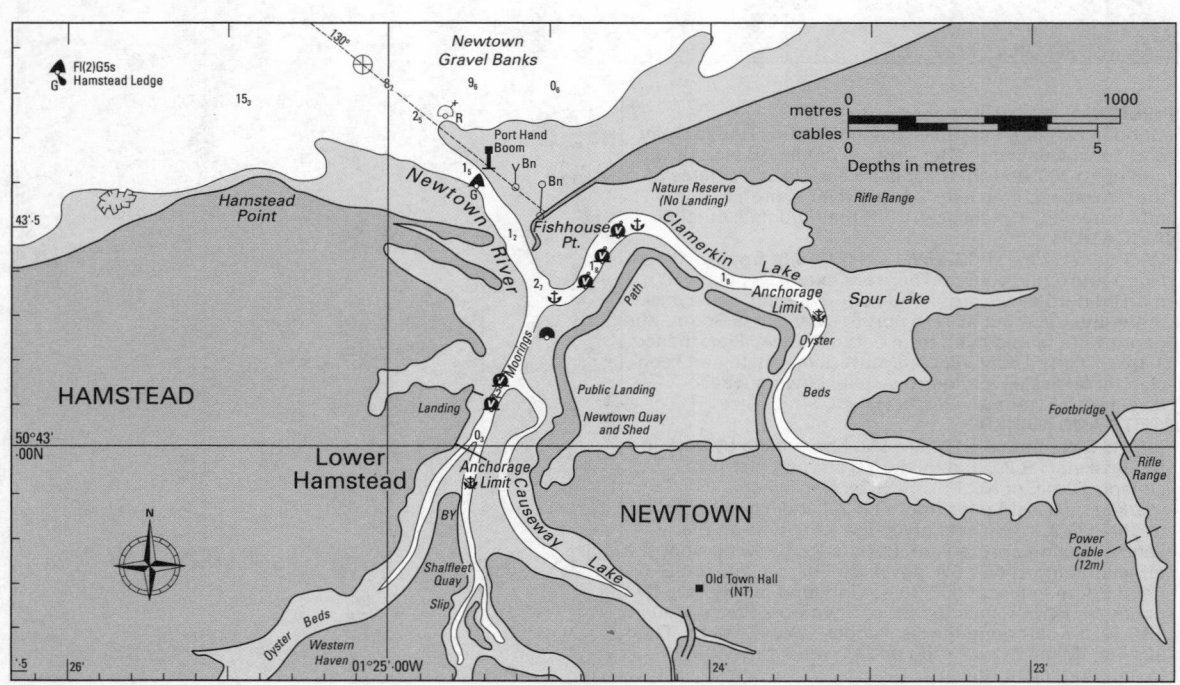

BEAULIEU RIVER   8-2-23
Hampshire 50°47'·00N 01°21'·76W (Ent)   Rtg 3-2-1

CHARTS
AC *5600.5, 2021, 2040, 1905*; Imray C3; Y20; Stanfords 11, 18; OS 196

TIDES
–0100 and +0140 Dover; ML 2·4; Zone 0 (UT)

Standard Port PORTSMOUTH (→)

Times				Height (metres)			
High Water		Low Water		MHWS	MHWN	MLWN	MLWS
0000	0600	0500	1100	4·7	3·8	1·9	0·8
1200	1800	1700	2300				

BUCKLER'S HARD

–0040	–0010	+0010	–0010	–1·0	–0·8	–0·2	–0·3

STANSORE POINT

–0050	–0010	–0005	–0010	–0·9	–0·6	–0·2	0·0

NOTE: Double HWs occur at or near springs; the 2nd HW is approx 1¾ hrs after the 1st. On other occasions there is a stand which lasts about two hrs. The predictions refer to the first HW when there are two, or to the middle of the stand. See 8.2.13.

SHELTER
Very good in all winds. ⚓ possible in reach between Lepe Ho and Beaulieu River SC, but preferable to proceed to Buckler's Hard Yacht Hbr (AB and **V** pile moorings). Many of the landing stages/slips shown on the chartlet (and AC 2021) are privately owned and should not be used. The uppermost reaches of the river are best explored first by dinghy due to the lack of channel markers and the short duration of the HW stand.
Rabies: Craft with animals from abroad are prohibited in the river.

NAVIGATION
WPT 50°46'·50N 01°21'·25W, 144°/324° from/to abeam Beaulieu Spit dolphin (Fl R 5s), 4ca. There are patches drying 0·3m approx 100m S of Beaulieu Spit. 1ca further SSE, close W of the ldg line, are shoal depths 0·1m. Ent dangerous LW±2. The swatchway off Beaulieu River SC is closed. A speed limit of 5kn applies to the whole river.

LIGHTS AND MARKS
Ldg marks at ent 324° must be aligned exactly due to shoal water either side of ldg line. The front is No 2 bn, R with Or dayglow topmark, △ shape above □; the rear is Lepe Ho. Beaulieu Spit, R dolphin with W band, Fl R 5s 3M vis 277°-037°; ra refl, should be left approx 40m to port. The old CG cottages and Boat House are conspic, approx 320m E of Lepe Ho. The river is clearly marked by R and G bns and perches. SHM bns 5, 9, 19 and 21 are all Fl G 4s; PHM bns 12 and 20 are Fl R 4s. Marina pontoons A, C and E have 2FR (vert).

RADIO TELEPHONE
None.

TELEPHONE (Dial code 01590)
Hr Mr 616200/616234, 🛥 616211, Mobile (0860) 919196; MRSC (01705) 552100; ▦ 0345 231110 (H24); Marinecall 0891 500457; Police (01703) 845511; Dr 612451 or (01703) 845955; Ⓗ 77011.

FACILITIES
Buckler's Hard Yacht Hbr £21.50 (110+20 **V**) ☎ 616200, 🛥 616211, Slip, M (£9 on piles), P, D, AC, FW, ME, El, Sh, C (1 ton), BH (26 ton), SM, Gas, Gaz, CH, ▣, V, R, Bar.
Village V (Stores ☎ 616293), R, Bar, ✉ (Beaulieu), Ⓑ (Mon, Wed, Fri AM or Hythe), ⇌ (bus to Brockenhurst), ✈ (Bournemouth or Southampton).

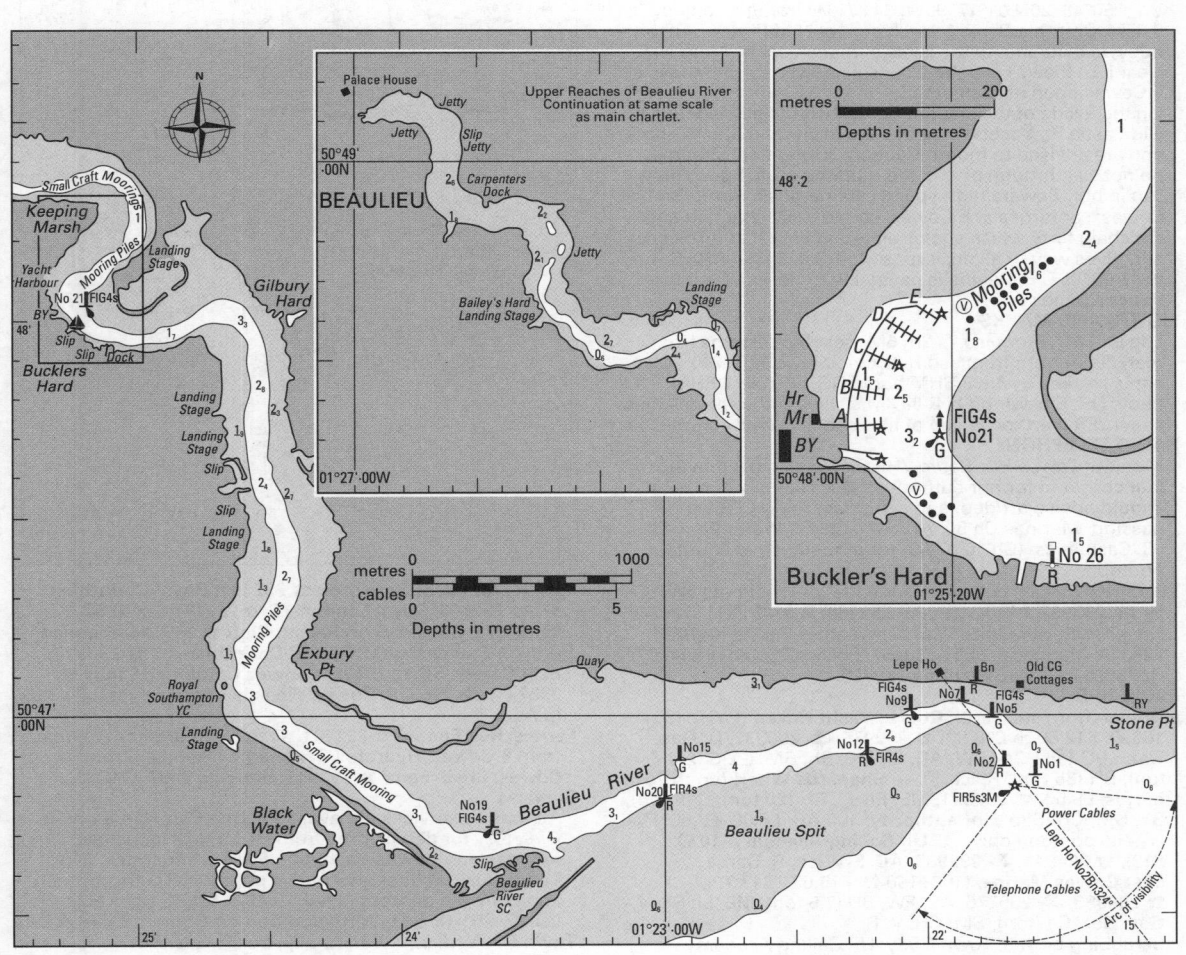

COWES/RIVER MEDINA   8-2-24

Isle of Wight 50°45'·86N 01°17'·72W   Rtg 1-1-1

CHARTS

AC *5600.6, 2793, 2040, 394*; Imray C3, Y20; Stanfords 11, 18; OS 196

TIDES

+0029 Dover; ML 2·7; Zone 0 (UT)

Standard Port PORTSMOUTH (→)

Times				Height (metres)			
High Water		Low Water		MHWS	MHWN	MLWN	MLWS
0000	0600	0500	1100	4·7	3·8	1·9	0·8
1200	1800	1700	2300				
Differences COWES							
−0015	+0015	0000	−0020	−0·5	−0·3	−0·1	0·0
FOLLY INN							
−0015	+0015	0000	−0020	−0·6	−0·4	−0·1	+0·2
NEWPORT							
No data		No data		−0·6	−0·4	+0·1	+0·8

NOTE: Double HWs occur at or near sp. On other occasions a stand occurs lasting up to 2hrs; times given represent the middle of the stand. See 8·2·13, especially for Newport.

SHELTER

Good at Cowes Yacht Haven and above the chain ferry, but outer hbr exposed to N and NE winds. ⚓ prohib in hbr. Visitors may pick up/secure to any mooring/piles/pontoon so labelled, ie: 12 large ⚓s off The Green and N of front ldg lt (off The Parade); piles S of Cowes Yacht Haven; Thetis Pontoon (short stay/overnight only, dredged 2·5m); pontoons S of the chain ferry (W Cowes); 'E' Pontoon off E Cowes SC. See opposite for pontoons in Folly Reach; Island Harbour marina on E bank beyond Folly Inn and in Newport (dries). Good ⚓ in Osborne Bay, 2M E, sheltered from SE to W; no landing.

NAVIGATION

WPT 50°46'·20N 01°17'·90W, 344°/164° from/to front ldg lt, 0·35M. Bramble Bank, 1·1m, lying 1M N of Prince Consort buoy, is a magnet to the keels of many yachts. From N, to clear it to the W keep the 2 conspic power stn chimneys at E Cowes open of each other.
On the E side of the ent, the Shrape (mud flats) extends to Old Castle Pt. Yachts must use the main chan near W shore and are advised to motor. Caution: strong tidal streams; do not sail through or ⚓ in the mooring area. Speed limit 6kn in hbr. Beware high-speed catamarans/hydrofoils at W Cowes; car ferries at E Cowes, commercial shipping and the chain ferry which shows all round Fl W lt at fore-end, and gives way to all tfc; it runs Mon-Sat: 0435-0030, Sun 0635-0010LT. R Medina is navigable to Newport, but the upper reaches dry.

LIGHTS AND MARKS

Ldg lts 164°: Front Iso 2s 3m 6M, post by Customs Ho; rear, 290m from front, Iso R 2s 5m 3M, vis 120°-240°. Chan ent is marked by No 3 SHM buoy, QG, and No 4 PHM buoy, QR. E bkwtr hd Fl R 3s 3M. Jetties and some dolphins show 2FR (vert) on E side of hbr, and 2FG (vert) on W side.

RADIO TELEPHONE

Monitor *Cowes Hbr Radio* VHF Ch **69**; also used by hbr launches and for hbr authority's ⚓s. Yachts >30m LOA should advise arr/dep, and call *Chain Ferry* Ch 69 if passing. Marinas Ch 80. *Hbr Taxi* Ch 77. *Water Taxi* Ch 08. Casualties: (Ch 16/67/69) for ambulance at Fountain pontoon.

TELEPHONE (Dial code 01983 = code for whole of IOW)

Hr Mr 293952; MRSC (01705) 552100; ⌗ 0345 231110 (H24); Folly Reach Hbr Office 295722; Weather Centre (01703) 228844; Marinecall 0891 500457; Police 528000; Ⓗ 524081; Dr 295251; Cowes Yachting 280770.

FACILITIES

Marinas (from seaward): **Cowes Yacht Haven** (CYH), (35+ 165 Ⓥ, £12.80 to £18.80) ☎ 299975, ⚓ 200332, D, Gas, Gaz, LPG (all H24), FW, AC, El, ME, Sh, SM, Ⓔ, C (2·5 ton), BH (35 ton), R, Ice, ⬚, ♿. **Shepards Wharf** (up to 75 berths, £8.50) ☎ 297821, ME, El, Ⓔ, BH (20 ton), C (6 ton), BY, SM, CH, Slip. **Hbr authority**: 100 AB, £6.00 -£8.50; FW (Thetis pontoon only), ♿. **UK Sailing Academy** (10 Ⓥ, £12), ☎ 294941, ⚓ 295938, AC, FW, Ice, R, Bar, ♿. **East Cowes Marina**, (150+150 Ⓥ, £15.03 - £17.72), ☎ 293983, ⚓ 299276, AC, FW, BH (7.5 ton), ME, El, Sh, V, Gas, Gaz, C (7ton), SM, CH, V, R.
Scrubbing berths: Town Quay, UK Sailing Academy.

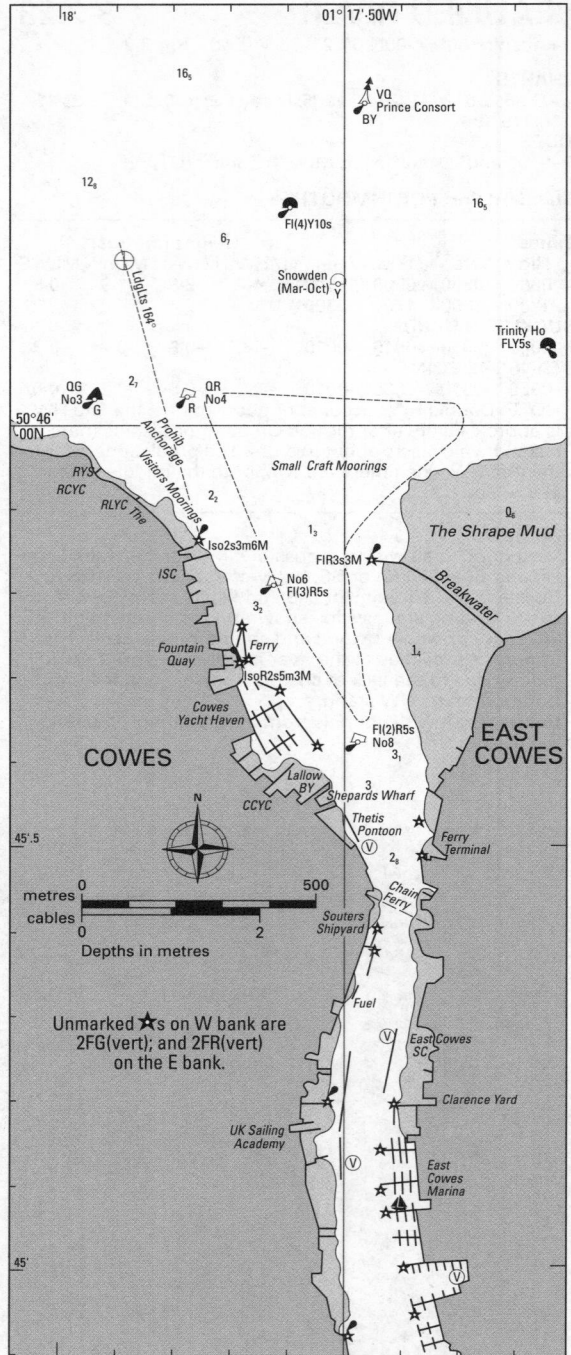

YCs: Royal Yacht Squadron ☎ 292191; **Royal Corinthian YC** ☎ 292608; **Royal London YC** ☎ 299727; **Island SC** ☎ 296621; **Royal Ocean Racing Club** ☎ 295144 (manned only in Cowes Week); **Cowes Corinthian YC** ☎ 296333; **East Cowes SC** ☎ 294394; **Cowes Combined Clubs** ☎ 295744, ⚓ 295329. Cowes Week is normally 1st full week in Aug.
Ferries: Red Funnel ☎ 292101, all to Southampton: Car/pax from E Cowes; Hydrofoil/Catamaran (foot pax) from W Cowes; **Chain Ferry** ☎ 293041; **Hbr Taxi** 0467 494262.
Services
All marine services are available. See *Port Handbook & Directory* for details (free from Hr Mr, hbr launches, marinas and Cowes Yachting). **FW** from marinas, Old Town Quay, Whitegates public pontoon, Thetis pontoon and Folly Inn pontoon. **Fuel:** CYH, D & LPG only, H24, ; Lallows BY (P & D); MST pontoon off Souters BY (P & D).
Town EC Wed; P, D, Bar, ⬚, Slip, ✉, Ⓑ, Gas, Gaz.

RIVER MEDINA, FOLLY REACH TO NEWPORT

FOLLY REACH, 50°44'·00N 01°16'·90W. Above Medham
ECM bn, VQ (3) 5s, there are depths of 1m to S Folly bn,
QG. There are Ⓥ pontoons along W bank, S of residents'
ones. Hr Mr ☎ 295722 and Ch 69 *Folly Launch*. **Folly Inn** ⌖,
☎ 297171, AB (pontoon) £8.50, M, Slip, scrubbing berth.
Island Harbour Marina (5ca S of Folly Inn), (150 + 100 Ⓥ),
£11.70 to £12.60; 2·1m), ☎ 822999, ⛽ 526020, AC, BH (25
ton), D (HO), Gas, Gaz, ⌖, ME, CH, BY, Slip, Bar, R. VHF
Ch 80. Excellent shelter; appr via marked, dredged chan
with waiting pontoon to stbd, withies to port. Access HW
±4 to lock (HO; H24 by arrangement) with R/G tfc lts.
Ryde Queen paddle steamer is conspic.

NEWPORT, 50°42'·18N 01°17'·35W. Tides see 8·2·13 and
facing page. Above Island Hbr marina the 1·2M long chan
to Newport dries, but from HW Portsmouth –1½ to HW +2
it carries 2m or more. S from Folly Inn, the hbr authority
is IoW Council. Speed limit 6kn up to Seaclose, S of
Newport Rowing Club (NRC); thence 4kn to Newport. The
chan, which is buoyed and partially lit, favours the W
bank; night appr not recommended. Power lines have
33m clearance. Ldg marks/lts are 192°, W ◇ bns 7/11m, on
the E bank, both lit 2FR (hor).
In Newport, Ⓥs' pontoons on the E/SE sides of the basin
have 1·4m HW ±2. Bilge keelers lie alongside pontoons
on soft mud; fin keelers against quay wall on firm, level
bottom. Fender boards can be supplied.
Newport Yacht Hbr (40 Ⓥs, £9), ⌖, Hr Mr ☎ 525994, ⛽
823333, VHF Ch 69 (HO or as arranged), AC, FW, BY, C (10
ton), R; Classic Boat Centre.
Town EC Thurs; P & D (cans), El, Sh, Slip, Gaz, Gas, Ⓑ,
Bar, Dr, Ⓗ , ✉, ⌖, R, V.

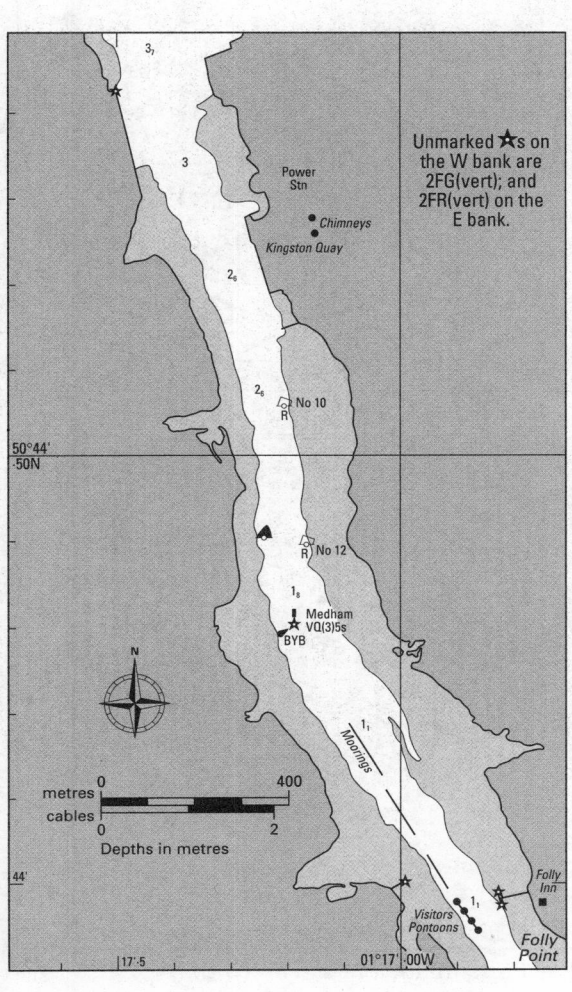

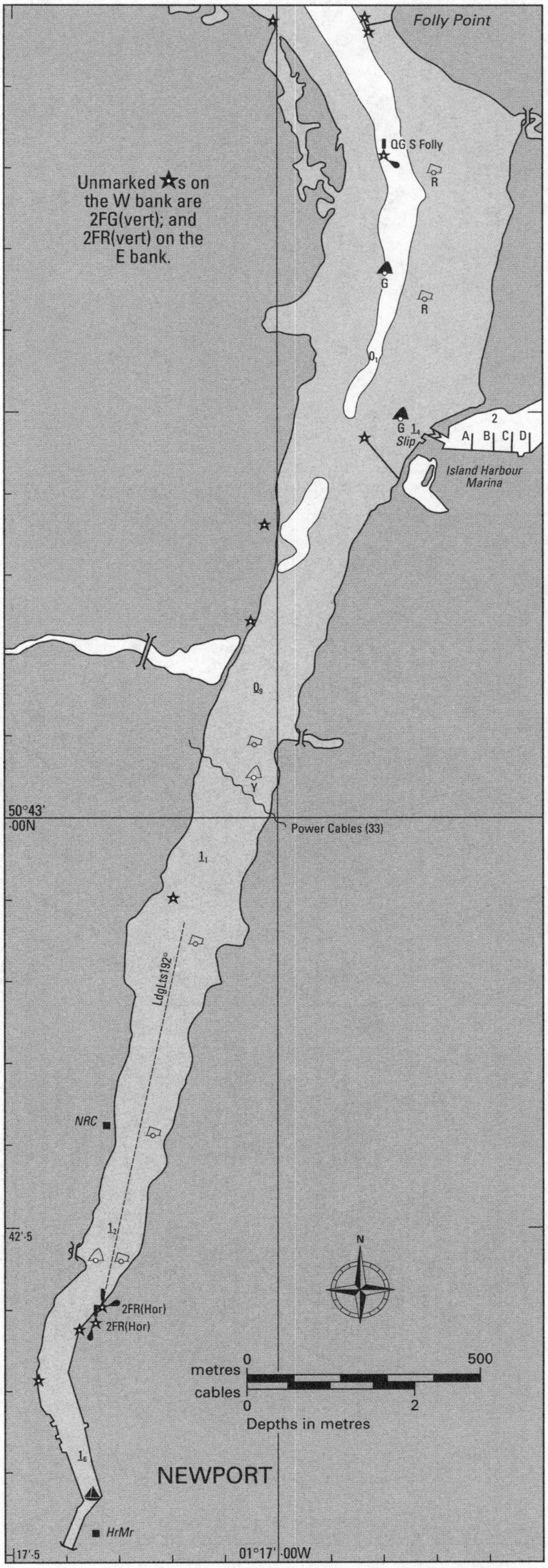

Unmarked ☆s on
the W bank are
2FG(vert); and
2FR(vert) on the
E bank.

Depths in metres

Unmarked ☆s on
the W bank are
2FG(vert); and
2FR(vert) on the
E bank.

NEWPORT

Depths in metres

8-2-24 ISLE OF WIGHT TIDAL STREAMS

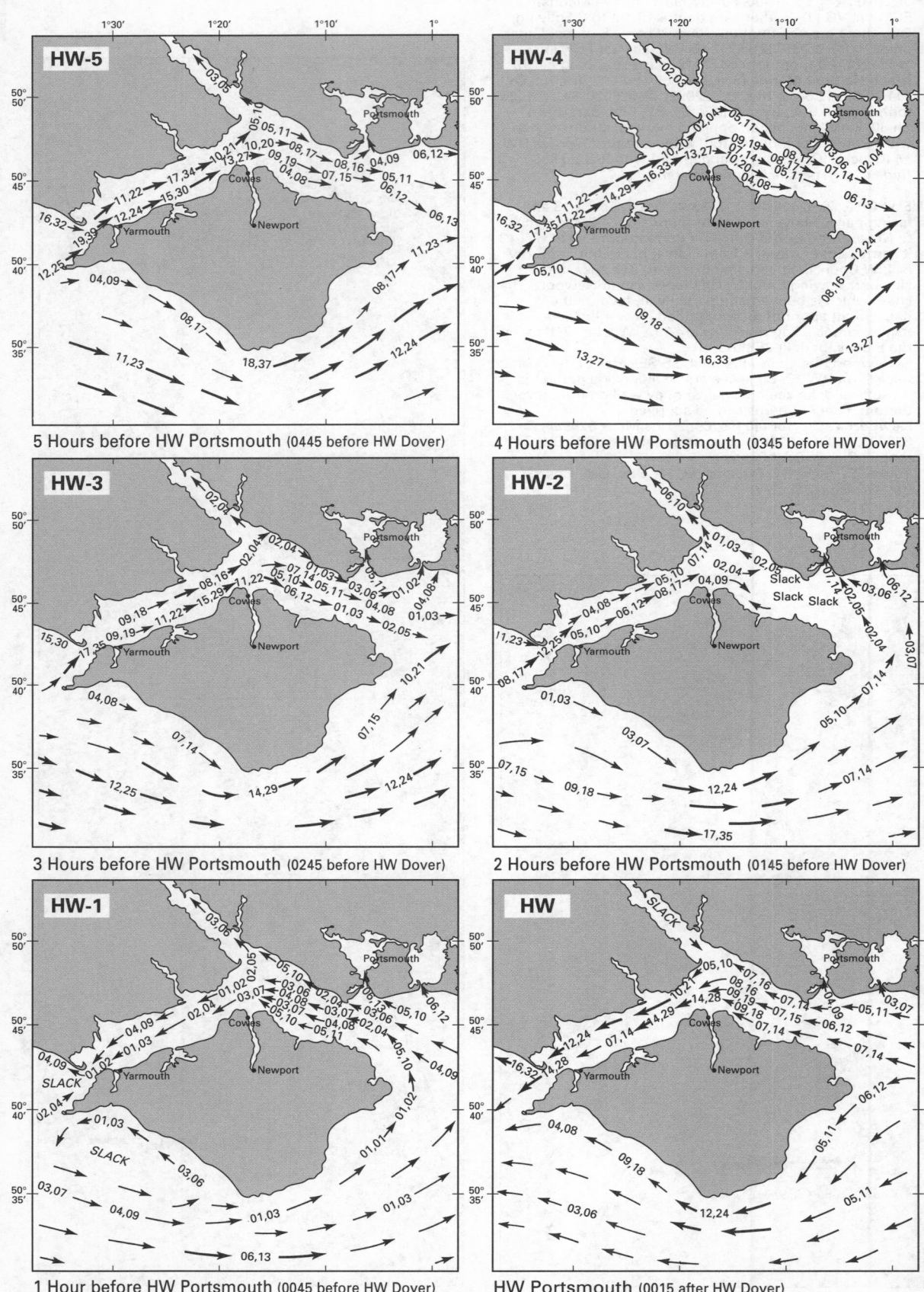

5 Hours before HW Portsmouth (0445 before HW Dover)

4 Hours before HW Portsmouth (0345 before HW Dover)

3 Hours before HW Portsmouth (0245 before HW Dover)

2 Hours before HW Portsmouth (0145 before HW Dover)

1 Hour before HW Portsmouth (0045 before HW Dover)

HW Portsmouth (0015 after HW Dover)

General Area 2: 8.2.3

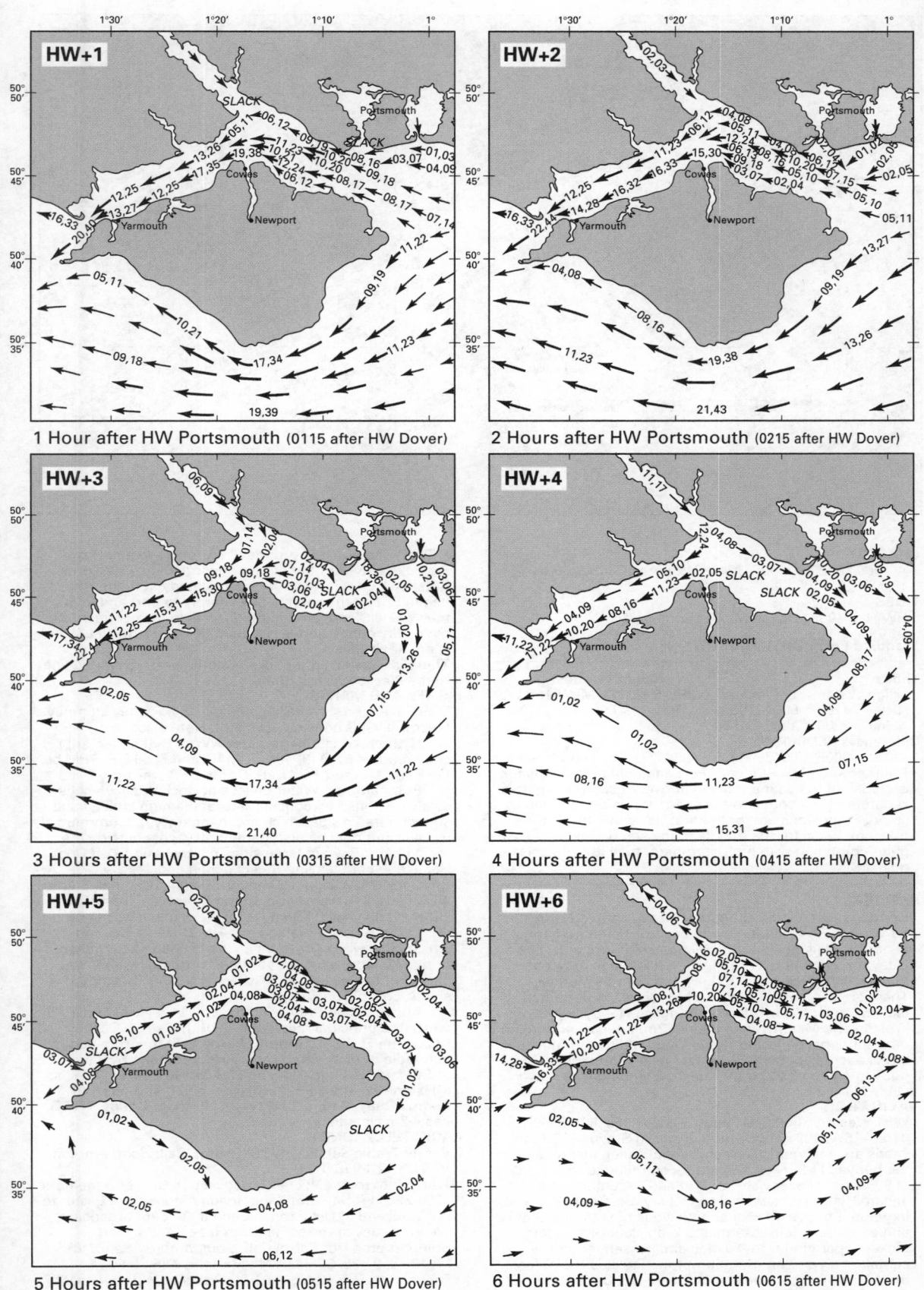

1 Hour after HW Portsmouth (0115 after HW Dover)

2 Hours after HW Portsmouth (0215 after HW Dover)

3 Hours after HW Portsmouth (0315 after HW Dover)

4 Hours after HW Portsmouth (0415 after HW Dover)

5 Hours after HW Portsmouth (0515 after HW Dover)

6 Hours after HW Portsmouth (0615 after HW Dover)

SOUTHAMPTON   8-2-26

Hampshire 50°52'·90N 01°23'·40W   Rtg 1-1-2

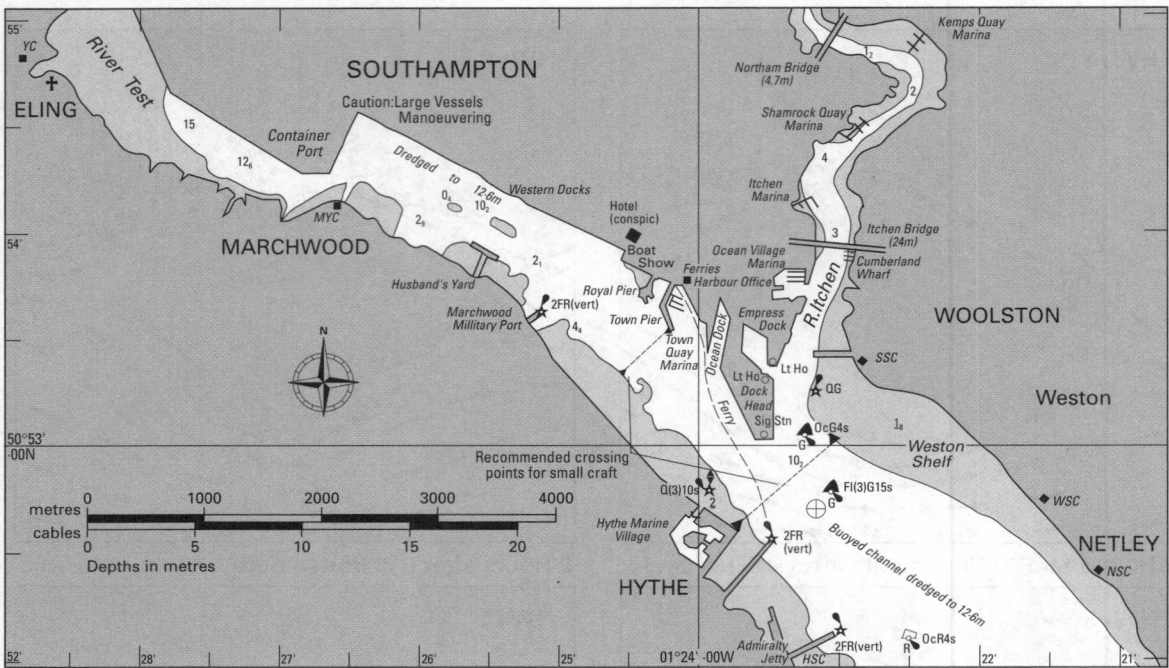

CHARTS
AC *5600.8, 2041, 1905, 394, 2045*; Imray C3; Stanfords 11, 18; OS 196

TIDES
HW (1st) −0001 Dover; ML 2·9; Zone 0 (UT)

Standard Port SOUTHAMPTON (→)

Times				Height (metres)			
High Water		Low Water		MHWS	MHWN	MLWN	MLWS
0400	1100	0000	0600	4·5	3·7	1·8	0·5
1600	2300	1200	1800				

Differences REDBRIDGE

−0020	+0005	0000	−0005	−0·1	−0·1	−0·1	−0·1

Southampton is a Standard Port and tidal predictions for each day of the year are given above. At sp there are two separate HWs about two hrs apart; at nps there is a long stand. Predictions are for the first HW when there are two, otherwise for the middle of the stand. See 8.2.13. NE gales combined with high barometer may lower sea level by 0·6m.

SHELTER
Good in most winds, although a heavy chop develops in SE winds >F4, when it may be best to shelter in marinas. ☉ berths available in Hythe Marina (with lock ent), Town Quay marina, (ent to R Test), and on R Itchen at Ocean Village, Itchen, Shamrock Quay and Kemp's Marinas. There are no specific yacht ⚓s but temp ⚓ is permitted (subject to Hr Mr) off club moorings at Netley, Hythe, Weston and Marchwood in about 2m. Keep clear of main or secondary chans and Hythe Pier. Public moorings for larger yachts opposite Royal Pier near Gymp Elbow PHM buoy in 4m (contact Hr Mr); nearest landing is at Town Quay Marina.

NAVIGATION
WPT Weston Shelf SHM buoy, Fl (3) G 15s, 50°52'·68N 01°23'·16W, 138°/318° from/to Port Sig Stn, 0·40M. Main chans are well marked. Yachts should keep just outside the buoyed lit fairway and are recommended to cross it at 90° abeam Fawley chy, at Cadland/Greenland buoys, abeam Hythe and abeam Town Quay. Caution: several large unlit buoys off Hythe, both sides of the main chan, and elsewhere. It is essential to keep clear of very large tankers operating from Fawley and passenger and container ships from Southampton. See also 8·2·20 for the Area of Concern between Cowes and Calshot. .

R Test   There is foul ground at Marchwood and Royal Pier; extensive container port beyond. Eling Chan dries.
R Itchen   Care is necessary, particularly at night. Above Itchen Bridge the chan bends sharply to port and favours the W side. There are unlit moorings in the centre of the river. Navigation above Northam Bridge (4·7m clearance) is not advisable.
There is a speed limit of 6kn in both rivers above the line Hythe Pier to Weston Shelf.

LIGHTS AND MARKS
Main lts are on the chartlet and in 8.2.4. Fawley chimney (198m, R lts) is conspic day/night. Note also:
(1) Hythe Marina Village, close NW of Hythe Pier: appr chan marked by Q (3) 10s, ECM bn and Fl (2) R 5s PHM bn. Lock ent, N side 2 FG (vert); S side 2 FR (vert).
(2) Southampton Water divides at Dock Head which is easily identified by conspic silos and a high lattice mast showing traffic sigs which are mandatory for commercial vessels, but may be disregarded by yachts outside the main chans. Beware large ships manoeuvering off Dock Head, and craft leaving Rivers Itchen and Test.
(3) Dock Hd, W side (Queen Elizabeth II Terminal, S end) 4 FG (vert) 3M; framework tr; marks ent to R Test. Town Quay Marina has 2 FR and 2 FG (vert) on wavebreaks.
(4) Ent to R Itchen marked by SHM Oc G 4s, beyond which piles with G lts mark E side of chan ldg to Itchen bridge (24·4m); a FW lt at bridge centre marks the main chan. Ent to Ocean Village is facing Vosper Thorneycroft sheds, conspic on E bank.
(5) Above Itchen Bridge, marked by 2 FR (vert) and 2 FG (vert), the principal marks are: Crosshouse bn Oc R 5s; Chapel bn Fl G 3s. **Caution**: 8 large unlit mooring buoys in middle of river. Shamrock Quay pontoons 2 FR (vert) at SW and NE ends; No 5 bn Fl G 3s; No 7 bn Fl (2) G 5s; Millstone Pt jetty 2 FR (vert); No 9 bn Fl (4) G 10s and Kemps Quay Marina 2 FG (vert). Northam Bridge, FR/FG, has 4·7m clearance.

RADIO TELEPHONE
Vessel Traffic Services (VTS) Centre. Call: *Southampton VTS* Ch **12** 14 16 (H24).
Traffic info for small craft broadcast on Ch 12 on the hour 0600-2200 Fri-Sun and Bank Holiday Mons from Easter to last weekend in Oct. From 1 June to 30 Sept broadcasts are every day at the same times (see 8.2.20).
Southampton Hbr Patrol Call: *Southampton Patrol* VHF Ch **12** 16, 01-28, 60-88 (H24). Marinas VHF Ch **80** M.
Fuel barges in R Itchen, call *Mr Diesel* or *Wyefuel* Ch 08.

2

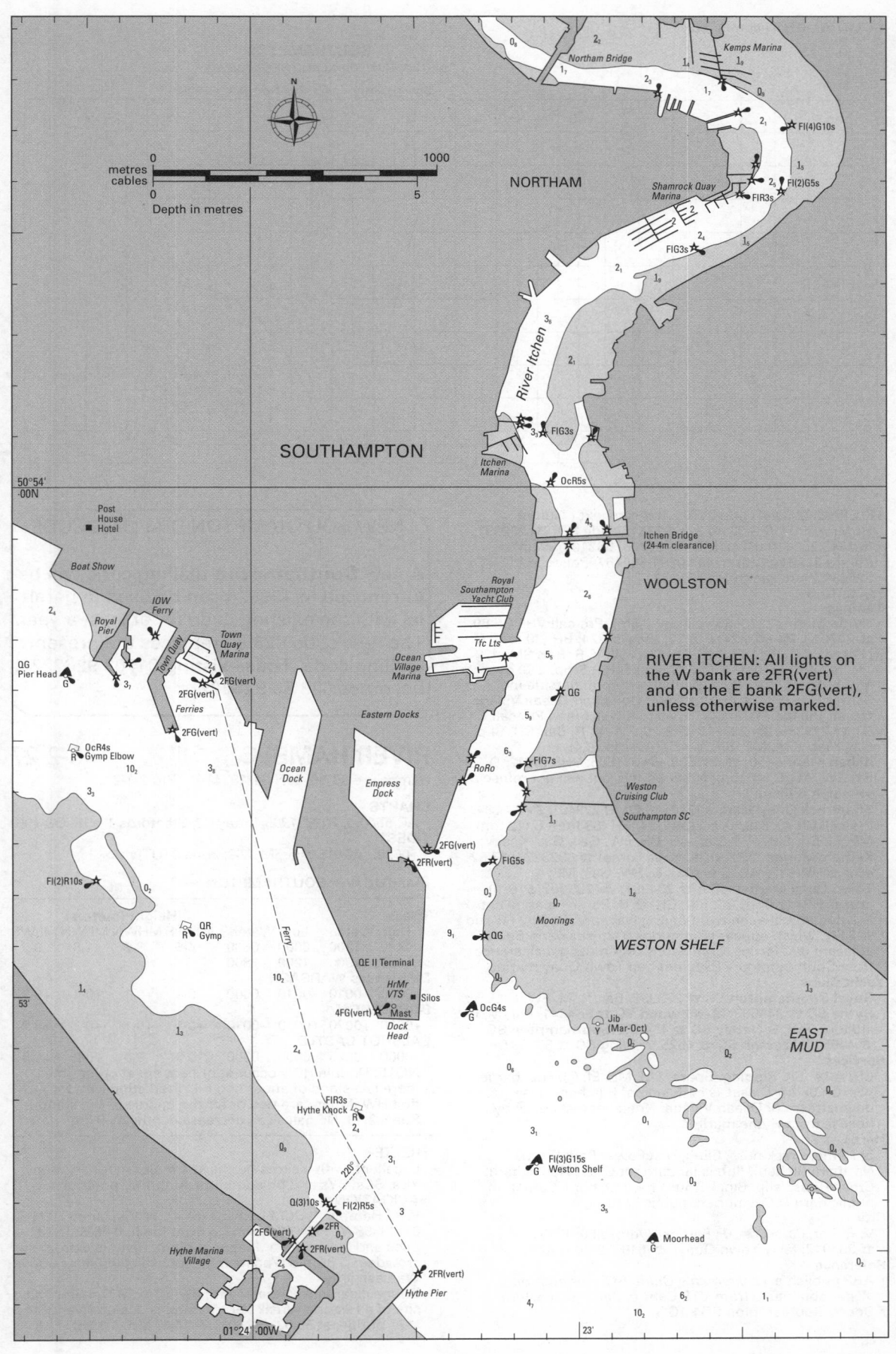

NORTHAM

Kemps Marina

Northam Bridge

Shamrock Quay Marina

Fl(4)G10s

Fl(2)G5s

FlR3s

FlG3s

River Itchen

SOUTHAMPTON

FlG3s

OcR5s

Itchen Marina

Itchen Bridge (24·4m clearance)

WOOLSTON

Royal Southampton Yacht Club

Post House Hotel

Boat Show

RIVER ITCHEN: All lights on the W bank are 2FR(vert) and on the E bank 2FG(vert), unless otherwise marked.

IOW Ferry

Royal Pier

Town Quay

Town Quay Marina

QG Pier Head

2FG(vert)

2FG(vert)

Ferries

2FG(vert)

Ocean Village Marina

Tfc Lts

QG

OcR4s
Gymp Elbow

Ocean Dock

Eastern Docks

RoRo

FlG7s

Empress Dock

Weston Cruising Club

Southampton SC

Fl(2)R10s

2FG(vert)

2FR(vert)

FlG5s

QR
Gymp

Moorings

WESTON SHELF

QG

Ferry

QE II Terminal

HrMr VTS   Silos

4FG(vert)   Mast

Dock Head

OcG4s

Jib (Mar–Oct)

EAST MUD

FlR3s
Hythe Knock

220°

Q(3)10s

Fl(2)R5s

Fl(3)G15s
Weston Shelf

2FG(vert)

2FR(vert)

Hythe Marina Village

Moorhead

2FR(vert)

Hythe Pier

metres
cables
0   1000
0   5
Depth in metres

50°54'·00N

53'

01°24'·00W

23'

SOUTHAMPTON continued

SOUTHAMPTON
MEAN SPRING AND NEAP CURVES
Springs occur 2 days after New and Full Moon

MEAN RANGES
Springs 4.0m
Neaps   1.9m

TELEPHONE (Dial code 01703, but see next column)
Hr Mr ABP & VTS 330022, 339733 outside HO; ⛴ 232991; ⌗ 0345 231110 (H24); MRSC (01705) 552100; Weather Centre 228844; Marinecall 0891 500457; Police 581111; Dr 226631 (Port Health); Ⓗ 777222.

FACILITIES
Marinas
Hythe Marina (220+50 visitors; 2·5m). Pre-call VHF Ch 80. ☎ 207073, ⛴ 842424, £18.20, access H24; BH (30 ton), C (12 ton), AC, P, D, EI, ME, Sh, CH, FW, V, R, Bar, SM, ⚓, Ⓖ. Tfc lts (vert) at lock: 3 Ⓡ = Wait; 3 Fl R = Stop; 2 Ⓖ over Ⓦ = proceed, free-flow. Waiting pontoon outside lock. Ferries from Hythe pier to Town Quay and Ocean Village.
Ocean Village Marina (450; visitors welcome). Pre-call Ch 80, ☎ 229385, ⛴ 233515, £18.20, FW, V, R, Bar, CH, Slip, Gas, Gaz, Kos, ME, Sh, Ⓞ, AC, (Access H24), Ⓖ.
Itchen Marina (50) ☎ 631500, ⛴ 335606; VHF Ch 12. D, BY, FW, AC, C (40 ton); No Ⓥ berths, but will not refuse a vessel in difficulty.
Shamrock Quay Marina (220+40 Ⓥ). ☎ 229461, ⛴ 333384. Pre-call Ch 80. £18.20, access H24, BH (63 ton), C (12 ton), ME, EI, Sh, SM, Ⓞ, R, Bar, AC, CH, FW, Gas, Gaz, Kos, V;
Kemp's Marina (220; visitors welcome) ☎ 632323, £17.62, access HW±3½, AC, C (5 ton), D, FW, Gas, ME;
Town Quay Marina (136) ☎ 234397, ⛴ 235302, £16.10, access H24 (2·6m), AC, FW, CH, Ⓞ, R, Bar, Ⓖ; marina ent is a dogleg between two floating wavebreaks (☆ 2 FR and ☆ 2 FG) which appear continuous from seaward. Beware adjacent fast ferries. Craft >20m LOA must get clearance from Southampton VTS to ent/dep Town Quay marina.
Yacht Clubs
Royal Southampton YC ☎ 223352, Bar, R, M, FW, L, Ⓞ, Ⓖ; **Hythe SC** ☎ 846563; **Marchwood YC** ☎ 864641, Bar, M, C (10 ton), FW, L; **Netley SC** ☎ 454272; **Southampton SC** ☎ 446575; **Weston SC** ☎ 452527; **Eling SC** ☎ 863987.
Services
CH, ACA, Sh, Rigging, Spars, SM, ME, EI, Ⓔ. Fuel barge, VHF Ch 08 *Mr Diesel*, is on E side of R Itchen, close downstream of Ocean Village. Note: nearest petrol by hose is from Hythe marina.
Hards
at Hythe, Crackmore, Eling, Mayflower Park (Test), Northam (Itchen). Public landings at Cross House hard, Cross House slip, Block House hard (Itchen), Carnation public hard & Cowporters public hard.
City
V, R, Bar, Ⓑ, ✉, ⇌, ✈, Ferries/Hydrofoil to IOW, ☎ 333042; ferry Town Quay, ☎ 840722, to Hythe.
Reference
ABP publish a *Yachtsman's Guide to Southampton Water* obtainable from VTS Centre, Berth 37, Eastern Docks, Southampton SO1 1GG.

NEW SOUTHAMPTON DIALLING CODE

A new **Southampton** dialling code will be introduced in 1999. It can be used in parallel with the existing code for at least a year. The new code 023 80 replaces the present dialling code. Thus existing 01703 926222 becomes 023 80 926222.

RIVER HAMBLE   8-2-27
Hampshire 50°50'·90N 01°18'·41W   Rtg 2-1-2

CHARTS
AC *5600.8, 2022, 1905*; Imray C3; Stanfords 11, 18; OS 196
TIDES
+0020, −0010 Dover; ML 2·9; Zone 0 (UT)

Standard Port SOUTHAMPTON (⟶)

Times				Height (metres)			
High Water		Low Water		MHWS	MHWN	MLWN	MLWS
0400	1100	0000	0600	4.5	3.7	1.8	0.5
1600	2300	1200	1800				
Differences WARSASH							
+0020	+0010	+0010	0000	0·0	+0·1	+0·1	+0·3
BURSLEDON							
+0020	+0020	+0010	+0010	+0·1	+0·1	+0·2	+0·2
CALSHOT CASTLE							
0000	+0025	0000	0000	0·0	0·0	+0·2	+0·3

NOTE: Double HWs occur at or near sp; at other times there is a stand of about two hrs. Predictions are for the first HW if there are two or for the middle of the stand. See 8.2.13. NE gales can decrease depths by 0·6m.

SHELTER
Excellent, with visitors berths at 4 major marinas, many YCs, SCs, BYs and on some Hbr Authority pontoons.
NAVIGATION
WPT Hamble Pt SCM buoy, Q (6) + L Fl 15s, 50°50'·12N 01°18'·58W, 166°/346° from/to front ldg lt, 0·48M. Unlit piles and buoys are a danger at night. River is extremely crowded; ⚓ prohib. Yachts may not use spinnakers above Warsash jetty.
Bridge clearances: Road 4·0m; Rly 6·0m; M27 4·3m. The site of a Historic Wreck (*Grace Dieu*) is 3ca up-river of the M27 bridge, at 50°53'·51N 01°17'·24W, (see 8.0.3h).

RIVER HAMBLE *continued*

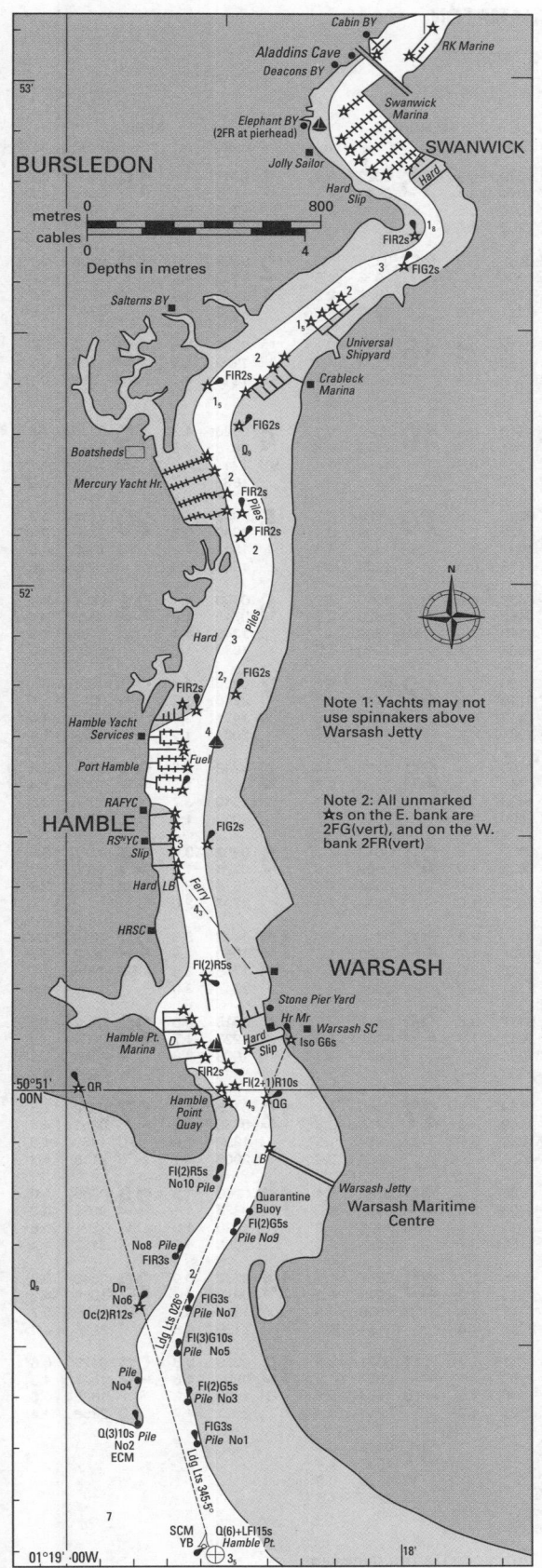

LIGHTS AND MARKS
Ldg Its 345°: Front Oc (2) R 12s 4m 2M, No 6 pile bn; rear, 820m from front, QR 12m, W mast on shore; vis 341°-349°. No 1 pile Fl G 3s 3M, SHM. No 2 pile Q (3) 10s 3M, ECM. No 3 pile Fl (2) G 5s, SHM. No 5 pile Fl (3) G 10s, SHM. Ldg Its 026° on E shore: front QG, pile bn; rear Iso G 6s. No 7 pile Fl G 3s, SHM. No 8 pile Fl R 3s, PHM. No 9 pile Fl (2) G 5s, SHM. No 10 pile Fl (2) R 5s, PHM. In mid-stream between Warsash and Hamble Pt Marina there is a clearly marked visitors' pontoon, between other private pontoons. Above Warsash, jetties and pontoons on the E side are marked by 2FG (vert) Its, and those on the W side by 2FR (vert) Its. Lateral piles are Fl G 2s or Fl R 2s (see chartlet).

RADIO TELEPHONE
Call: *Hamble Hbr Radio* Ch **68** 16 (April-Oct: Daily 0830-1930. Nov-Mar: Mon-Fri 0830-1700; Sat 0830-1300). Marinas Ch **80** M. Water Taxi Ch 77. See also 8.2.25 for VTS and info broadcasts.
TELEPHONE (Dial code 01703) on Hamble side. Note: On E side of river, dial code is 01489 (Locks Heath) and all ☎ numbers begin 57, 58 or 88.
Hr Mr 576387; MRSC (01705) 552100; ⌗ 0345 231110 (H24); Southampton Weather Centre 228844; Marinecall 0891 500457; Police 581111; Dr 57318.

FACILITIES
Marinas:
Hamble Pt Marina (220+10 Ⓥ) ☎ 452464, ⏚ 456440; pre-call Ch 80. Access H24; £14.81, AC, CH, D, BH (65 ton), C (7 ton), Ⓔ, El, FW, Gas, Gaz, ME, Sh, V, YC, Bar;
Port Hamble Marina (340+ Ⓥ) ☎ 452741, ⏚ 455206; pre-call Ch 80. Access H24; £13.74, AC, ▢, Bar, BH (100 ton), C (7 ton), CH, D, P, Ⓔ, FW, Gas, Gaz, ME, Sh, El, SM, Slip;
Mercury Yacht Hbr (346+ Ⓥ) ☎ 455994, ⏚ 457369; pre-call Ch 80. Access H24; £8.58, AC, Bar, BH (20 ton), El, Slip, CH, D, Ⓔ, FW, Gas, Gaz, ME, P, Sh, SM, V, ▢;
Swanwick Marina (380+ Ⓥ) ☎ 885000 (after 1700, 885262), ⏚ 885509, £12, AC, BH (60 ton), C (12 ton), CH, D, Ⓔ, FW, Gas, Gaz, ⌗, ▢, ME, P, ✉, Sh, SM, V, (Access H24).
The Hbr Authority jetty in front of the conspic B/W Hr Mr's Office at Warsash has limited AB (£15 for 24hrs); also Ⓥ pontoons in mid-stream. A public jetty is on the W bank near the Bugle carpark. Ⓥ pile moorings are opposite Port Hamble marina.
Yacht Clubs:
Hamble River SC ☎ 452070; **RAFYC** ☎ 452208, Bar, R, L; **Royal Southern YC** ☎ 453271; **Warsash SC** ☎ 583575.
Services:
A very wide range of marine services is available; consult marina/Hr Mr for locations. CH, Ⓔ, BY, AB, C (12 ton), Ⓔ, FW, Gas, Gaz, M, ME, R, Sh, Slip, SM; Riggers, BH (25 ton), ACA, Divers. **Piper Marine Services** ☎ 454563, (or call *Piper Fuel* Ch M), D, P.
Hards. At Warsash, Hamble and Swanwick.
Slips at Warsash, Hamble, Bursledon & Lower Swanwick.
Scrubbing piles at Warsash by Hr Mr's slipway; on W bank upriver of public jetty near Bugle; between Port Hamble and Mercury marinas; by slip opposite Swanwick marina. ✉ (Hamble, Bursledon, Warsash and Lower Swanwick); Ⓑ (Hamble, Bursledon, Sarisbury Green, Swanwick, Warsash); ⇌ (Hamble and Bursledon); ✈ (Southampton). *Hamble River Guide* available from Hr Mr.

ADJACENT HARBOURS

ASHLETT CREEK, Hants, 50°49'·98N 01°19'·40W. AC *5600.8, 2022, 1905.* Tides approx as Calshot Castle (opposite). Small drying (2·1m) inlet across from R Hamble; best for shoal-draft vessels. Appr at HW close to Esso Marine Terminal. Unlit chan, marked by 3 PHM buoys, 1 SHM buoy and 2 PHM bns, has four 90° bends. Ldg bns are hard to find; local knowledge desirable. Berth at drying quay. Facilities: AB, M, FW, Slip, Hard, Pub. **Esso SC.**

HILL HEAD, Hants, 50°49'·05N 01°14'·45W. AC *5600.8, 2022, 1905.* HW +0030 on Dover; see 8.2.30 LEE-ON-SOLENT diffs. Short term ⚓ for small craft at mouth of R Meon. Bar dries ¼M offshore. Ent dries 1·2m at MLWS. Appr on 030° towards Hill Head SC ho (W, conspic); bns mark chan, ● topmarks to port, ▲ ones to stbd. Small hbr to W inside ent where yachts can lie in soft mud alongside bank. Facilities: **Hill Head SC** ☎ (01329) 664843. **Hill Head village** EC Thurs; ✉, CH, V, P & D (cans).

ENGLAND – SOUTHAMPTON

LAT 50°54′N   LONG 1°24′W

TIMES AND HEIGHTS OF HIGH AND LOW WATERS   YEAR 1999

TIME ZONE (UT)
For Summer Time add ONE hour in non-shaded areas

JANUARY

Day	Time	m	Time	m	Time	m	Time	m
1 F	0319	0.8	0946	4.7	1551	0.6	2213	4.6
16 SA	0327	1.2	0954	4.3	1551	0.9	2219	4.3
2 SA ○	0411	0.6	1035	4.8	1641	0.5	2302	4.6
17 SU ●	0408	1.0	1030	4.4	1630	0.8	2255	4.4
3 SU	0500	0.6	1121	4.8	1727	0.4	2348	4.7
18 M	0447	0.9	1106	4.5	1708	0.6	2331	4.5
4 M	0546	0.6	1205	4.7	1811	0.4		
19 TU	0525	0.8	1143	4.5	1745	0.6		
5 TU	0032	4.6	0628	0.6	1249	4.6	1851	0.6
20 W	0008	4.5	0603	0.7	1222	4.5	1822	0.6
6 W	0116	4.5	0710	0.9	1331	4.5	1930	0.8
21 TH	0048	4.5	0641	0.8	1303	4.5	1901	0.6
7 TH	0158	4.4	0749	1.1	1412	4.3	2007	1.0
22 F	0129	4.5	0722	0.8	1345	4.4	1942	0.8
8 F	0241	4.2	0830	1.3	1456	4.1	2047	1.3
23 SA	0214	4.4	0806	1.0	1432	4.3	2028	1.0
9 SA	0327	4.0	0915	1.6	1543	3.9	2134	1.6
24 SU	0304	4.3	0857	1.2	1524	4.1	2122	1.2
10 SU	0419	3.9	1011	1.8	1640	3.7	2234	1.8
25 M	0401	4.2	0957	1.3	1627	4.0	2227	1.4
11 M	0521	3.8	1120	1.9	1751	3.7	2346	1.9
26 TU	0508	4.1	1110	1.5	1741	3.9	2344	1.5
12 TU	0631	3.8	1231	1.9	1908	3.7		
27 W	0623	4.0	1229	1.4	1901	3.9		
13 W	0056	1.8	0737	3.9	1334	1.7	2012	3.8
28 TH	0101	1.4	0737	4.1	1342	1.3	2013	4.1
14 TH	0155	1.7	0831	4.0	1425	1.4	2101	4.0
29 F	0210	1.2	0842	4.3	1446	1.0	2114	4.3
15 F	0244	1.4	0915	4.2	1510	1.2	2142	4.2
30 SA	0309	1.0	0937	4.5	1540	0.7	2206	4.4
31 SU ○	0401	0.7	1025	4.6	1629	0.5	2252	4.5

FEBRUARY

Day	Time	m	Time	m	Time	m	Time	m
1 M	0448	0.6	1109	4.6	1713	0.4	2335	4.6
16 TU ●	0428	0.7	1047	4.5	1650	0.5	2311	4.5
2 TU	0531	0.5	1149	4.6	1754	0.3		
17 W	0508	0.5	1125	4.6	1729	0.3	2349	4.6
3 W	0014	4.6	0611	0.5	1228	4.6	1831	0.4
18 TH	0548	0.5	1204	4.6	1808	0.3		
4 TH	0052	4.5	0647	0.6	1305	4.4	1905	0.6
19 F	0029	4.6	0627	0.5	1245	4.6	1847	0.3
5 F	0129	4.4	0721	0.8	1341	4.3	1936	0.8
20 SA	0110	4.6	0706	0.5	1327	4.5	1927	0.5
6 SA	0205	4.3	0753	1.1	1418	4.1	2007	1.1
21 SU	0153	4.5	0748	0.6	1411	4.4	2009	0.7
7 SU	0242	4.1	0827	1.3	1456	3.9	2042	1.4
22 M	0240	4.4	0834	0.9	1501	4.2	2058	1.0
8 M	0323	3.9	0908	1.6	1541	3.7	2127	1.7
23 TU	0333	4.1	0930	1.2	1601	4.0	2200	1.3
9 TU	0413	3.7	1004	1.9	1641	3.5	2233	2.0
24 W	0439	3.9	1041	1.5	1717	3.8	2321	1.6
10 W	0520	3.6	1123	2.0	1803	3.5		
25 TH	0601	3.8	1209	1.5	1848	3.8		
11 TH	0001	2.0	0641	3.6	1248	1.9	1930	3.6
26 F	0048	1.6	0726	3.9	1331	1.4	2008	3.9
12 F	0119	1.9	0754	3.8	1352	1.6	2032	3.8
27 SA	0203	1.4	0836	4.1	1436	1.1	2109	4.2
13 SA	0216	1.6	0848	4.0	1443	1.3	2119	4.1
28 SU	0301	1.1	0929	4.3	1528	0.8	2157	4.4
14 SU	0304	1.3	0931	4.2	1528	1.0	2158	4.3
15 M	0347	1.0	1009	4.4	1609	0.7	2234	4.4

MARCH

Day	Time	m	Time	m	Time	m	Time	m
1 M	0349	0.8	1014	4.4	1614	0.5	2239	4.5
16 TU	0322	0.9	0943	4.4	1545	0.6	2209	4.5
2 TU ○	0432	0.6	1054	4.5	1655	0.5	2317	4.5
17 W ●	0405	0.6	1023	4.5	1627	0.3	2247	4.6
3 W	0512	0.5	1130	4.5	1732	0.3	2351	4.5
18 TH	0448	0.3	1103	4.7	1709	0.1	2327	4.7
4 TH	0549	0.4	1204	4.5	1807	0.3		
19 F	0529	0.2	1144	4.8	1750	0.1		
5 F	0025	4.5	0622	0.5	1237	4.4	1838	0.5
20 SA	0008	4.8	0609	0.1	1226	4.8	1829	0.1
6 SA	0057	4.4	0652	0.6	1310	4.3	1905	0.7
21 SU	0050	4.7	0650	0.2	1309	4.7	1910	0.3
7 SU	0130	4.3	0719	0.8	1343	4.2	1931	1.0
22 M	0133	4.6	0731	0.4	1354	4.5	1952	0.6
8 M	0203	4.1	0747	1.1	1418	4.0	2000	1.3
23 TU	0220	4.4	0816	0.7	1444	4.3	2040	1.0
9 TU	0239	3.9	0820	1.4	1456	3.8	2037	1.6
24 W	0312	4.1	0909	1.1	1544	4.0	2142	1.4
10 W	0320	3.8	0904	1.7	1546	3.6	2131	1.9
25 TH	0418	3.9	1020	1.5	1703	3.7	2306	1.7
11 TH	0417	3.6	1012	1.9	1700	3.5	2257	2.1
26 F	0545	3.7	1152	1.6	1839	3.7		
12 F	0539	3.5	1149	2.0	1837	3.5		
27 SA	0039	1.7	0715	3.8	1317	1.5	1958	3.9
13 SA	0036	2.0	0708	3.6	1313	1.7	1954	3.7
28 SU	0152	1.4	0824	4.0	1420	1.2	2056	4.2
14 SU	0145	1.7	0813	3.9	1412	1.4	2047	4.0
29 M	0247	1.1	0915	4.2	1509	0.9	2141	4.3
15 M	0237	1.3	0902	4.1	1500	1.0	2129	4.3
30 TU	0331	0.8	0957	4.3	1551	0.6	2219	4.4
31 W ○	0411	0.6	1033	4.4	1630	0.5	2253	4.5

APRIL

Day	Time	m	Time	m	Time	m	Time	m
1 TH	0448	0.5	1106	4.4	1706	0.4	2325	4.4
16 F ●	0424	0.3	1040	4.7	1645	0.1	2304	4.9
2 F	0523	0.4	1138	4.4	1739	0.4	2355	4.4
17 SA	0508	0.1	1123	4.8	1729	0.0	2347	4.9
3 SA	0555	0.5	1209	4.4	1810	0.5		
18 SU	0551	0.1	1207	4.8	1811	0.1		
4 SU	0026	4.3	0623	0.6	1241	4.3	1836	0.7
19 M	0030	4.8	0633	0.1	1253	4.7	1853	0.3
5 M	0058	4.3	0649	0.8	1314	4.2	1901	0.9
20 TU	0116	4.7	0716	0.4	1340	4.5	1938	0.6
6 TU	0130	4.1	0715	1.0	1348	4.1	1929	1.2
21 W	0204	4.4	0802	0.7	1432	4.3	2027	1.0
7 W	0203	4.0	0746	1.2	1424	3.9	2004	1.5
22 TH	0258	4.1	0855	1.1	1534	4.0	2129	1.4
8 TH	0242	3.8	0827	1.5	1510	3.7	2052	1.8
23 F	0404	3.8	1003	1.4	1653	3.8	2251	1.7
9 F	0332	3.6	0924	1.8	1616	3.6	2207	2.0
24 SA	0527	3.7	1128	1.6	1821	3.8		
10 SA	0446	3.5	1050	1.9	1745	3.6	2347	2.0
25 SU	0019	1.7	0652	3.7	1309	1.5	1935	4.0
11 SU	0615	3.6	1223	1.7	1908	3.8		
26 M	0129	1.5	0800	3.9	1351	1.3	2031	4.2
12 M	0105	1.7	0730	3.8	1332	1.4	2008	4.1
27 TU	0222	1.3	0851	4.1	1439	1.0	2115	4.3
13 TU	0203	1.3	0826	4.1	1426	1.0	2056	4.3
28 W	0305	1.0	0932	4.2	1521	0.8	2152	4.4
14 W	0252	0.9	0913	4.3	1514	0.6	2139	4.6
29 TH	0343	0.8	1008	4.2	1559	0.7	2225	4.4
15 TH	0339	0.6	0957	4.6	1600	0.3	2221	4.7
30 F ○	0420	0.6	1041	4.3	1636	0.6	2256	4.4

Chart Datum: 2·74 metres below Ordnance Datum (Newlyn)

ENGLAND – SOUTHAMPTON

LAT 50°54'N   LONG 1°24'W

TIMES AND HEIGHTS OF HIGH AND LOW WATERS

YEAR 1999

TIME ZONE (UT)
For Summer Time add ONE hour in non-shaded areas

MAY

Day	Time	m	Time	m	Time	m	Time	m
1 SA	0455	0.5	1112	4.3	1710	0.6	2326	4.3
2 SU	0527	0.5	1143	4.3	1742	0.7	2357	4.3
3 M	0557	0.6	1216	4.2	1811	0.8		
4 TU	0029	4.2	0624	0.8	1250	4.2	1837	1.0
5 W	0103	4.2	0651	0.9	1325	4.2	1907	1.2
6 TH	0138	4.0	0723	1.1	1403	4.0	1943	1.5
7 F	0217	3.9	0803	1.4	1448	3.9	2030	1.7
8 SA	0305	3.8	0856	1.6	1548	3.8	2136	1.9
9 SU	0410	3.7	1008	1.7	1704	3.8	2301	1.9
10 M	0529	3.7	1132	1.6	1821	3.9		
11 TU	0020	1.7	0644	3.8	1247	1.4	1926	4.1
12 W	0124	1.3	0747	4.1	1348	1.0	2020	4.4
13 TH	0219	1.0	0841	4.3	1442	0.7	2109	4.6
14 F	0311	0.6	0930	4.5	1532	0.4	2156	4.8
15 SA ●	0400	0.3	1018	4.7	1621	0.2	2242	4.9
16 SU	0447	0.2	1105	4.8	1708	0.2	2328	4.9
17 M	0534	0.1	1152	4.8	1754	0.2		
18 TU	0014	4.8	0618	0.2	1240	4.7	1839	0.4
19 W	0102	4.6	0704	0.4	1330	4.5	1926	0.7
20 TH	0151	4.4	0750	0.7	1423	4.3	2017	1.1
21 F	0245	4.2	0842	1.0	1523	4.1	2116	1.4
22 SA	0346	3.9	0942	1.3	1632	4.0	2226	1.7
23 SU	0458	3.8	1053	1.5	1748	3.9	2343	1.7
24 M	0614	3.7	1206	1.6	1858	4.0		
25 TU	0050	1.6	0721	3.8	1309	1.5	1954	4.1
26 W	0145	1.4	0816	3.9	1401	1.3	2041	4.2
27 TH	0231	1.2	0902	4.0	1445	1.1	2121	4.3
28 F	0311	1.0	0941	4.1	1526	1.0	2156	4.3
29 SA	0350	0.8	1016	4.2	1605	0.9	2228	4.3
30 SU O	0427	0.7	1049	4.2	1642	0.8	2301	4.3
31 M	0502	0.7	1121	4.2	1717	0.9	2333	4.3

JUNE

Day	Time	m	Time	m	Time	m	Time	m
1 TU	0534	0.7	1155	4.2	1750	1.0		
2 W	0007	4.2	0604	0.8	1231	4.2	1820	1.1
3 TH	0043	4.2	0635	0.9	1308	4.2	1853	1.2
4 F	0120	4.1	0709	1.1	1347	4.1	1930	1.4
5 SA	0200	4.0	0749	1.2	1432	4.0	2016	1.5
6 SU	0247	3.9	0838	1.4	1526	4.0	2114	1.7
7 M	0345	3.8	0939	1.5	1630	4.0	2224	1.7
8 TU	0452	3.8	1051	1.5	1740	4.0	2338	1.6
9 W	0604	3.9	1203	1.4	1847	4.0		
10 TH	0045	1.3	0711	4.1	1310	1.1	1947	4.4
11 F	0147	1.1	0811	4.2	1411	0.9	2042	4.6
12 SA	0244	0.8	0907	4.4	1507	0.7	2133	4.7
13 SU ●	0338	0.5	0959	4.6	1600	0.5	2223	4.8
14 M	0430	0.3	1050	4.6	1651	0.4	2312	4.8
15 TU	0519	0.3	1140	4.7	1741	0.4		
16 W	0001	4.7	0606	0.3	1230	4.6	1828	0.6
17 TH	0050	4.6	0653	0.4	1319	4.5	1916	0.8
18 F	0138	4.5	0738	0.6	1410	4.4	2004	1.0
19 SA	0228	4.2	0825	0.9	1503	4.2	2054	1.3
20 SU	0321	4.0	0914	1.2	1600	4.1	2151	1.6
21 M	0418	3.8	1010	1.5	1701	4.0	2254	1.7
22 TU	0522	3.7	1113	1.6	1806	3.9	2359	1.7
23 W	0630	3.7	1218	1.7	1908	3.9		
24 TH	0100	1.7	0733	3.7	1317	1.6	2002	4.0
25 F	0153	1.5	0828	3.8	1409	1.5	2048	4.1
26 SA	0239	1.3	0913	4.0	1455	1.3	2128	4.2
27 SU	0321	1.1	0953	4.1	1538	1.2	2205	4.3
28 M O	0401	0.9	1029	4.1	1618	1.0	2240	4.3
29 TU	0439	0.8	1103	4.2	1656	1.0	2314	4.3
30 W	0515	0.8	1138	4.2	1732	1.0	2349	4.3

JULY

Day	Time	m	Time	m	Time	m	Time	m
1 TH	0549	0.8	1213	4.3	1807	1.0		
2 F	0026	4.3	0622	0.9	1251	4.3	1842	1.1
3 SA	0104	4.3	0658	0.9	1331	4.2	1919	1.2
4 SU	0145	4.2	0737	1.0	1414	4.2	2002	1.3
5 M	0230	4.1	0822	1.1	1503	4.2	2053	1.4
6 TU	0321	4.0	0915	1.3	1559	4.1	2152	1.5
7 W	0421	4.0	1017	1.4	1703	4.1	2300	1.5
8 TH	0529	4.0	1127	1.4	1812	4.2		
9 F	0012	1.4	0639	4.0	1240	1.3	1919	4.3
10 SA	0121	1.2	0748	4.1	1347	1.1	2021	4.4
11 SU	0224	1.0	0850	4.3	1449	0.9	2118	4.6
12 M	0323	0.7	0947	4.4	1546	0.7	2211	4.7
13 TU ●	0417	0.5	1039	4.6	1640	0.6	2301	4.7
14 W	0508	0.4	1129	4.6	1730	0.6	2349	4.7
15 TH	0555	0.4	1217	4.6	1817	0.6		
16 F	0035	4.6	0640	0.4	1304	4.6	1901	0.7
17 SA	0120	4.5	0721	0.6	1349	4.5	1943	0.9
18 SU	0204	4.3	0801	0.8	1433	4.3	2025	1.2
19 M	0248	4.1	0841	1.1	1519	4.1	2108	1.4
20 TU	0334	3.9	0923	1.4	1608	4.0	2158	1.7
21 W	0426	3.7	1015	1.7	1704	3.8	2258	1.8
22 TH	0529	3.6	1119	1.8	1810	3.8		
23 F	0007	1.9	0642	3.6	1231	1.9	1918	3.8
24 SA	0113	1.8	0752	3.7	1335	1.8	2016	3.9
25 SU	0208	1.6	0847	3.9	1429	1.6	2104	4.1
26 M	0255	1.3	0931	4.0	1515	1.4	2144	4.2
27 TU	0337	1.1	1009	4.2	1557	1.2	2220	4.3
28 W O	0417	0.9	1044	4.3	1637	1.0	2256	4.3
29 TH	0456	0.8	1119	4.3	1715	0.9	2331	4.4
30 F	0533	0.8	1154	4.4	1752	0.9		
31 SA	0008	4.4	0609	0.7	1232	4.4	1828	0.9

AUGUST

Day	Time	m	Time	m	Time	m	Time	m
1 SU	0046	4.4	0645	0.7	1311	4.4	1905	0.9
2 M	0126	4.4	0723	0.8	1353	4.4	1946	1.0
3 TU	0209	4.3	0804	0.9	1438	4.3	2031	1.1
4 W	0257	4.2	0852	1.1	1530	4.2	2124	1.3
5 TH	0353	4.1	0949	1.3	1632	4.1	2230	1.5
6 F	0500	4.0	1100	1.5	1743	4.1	2347	1.5
7 SA	0617	3.9	1220	1.5	1900	4.1		
8 SU	0104	1.4	0735	4.0	1336	1.4	2010	4.3
9 M	0214	1.2	0843	4.2	1441	1.1	2111	4.4
10 TU	0314	0.9	0941	4.4	1539	0.9	2203	4.6
11 W ●	0407	0.6	1031	4.5	1630	0.7	2250	4.6
12 TH	0455	0.5	1117	4.6	1717	0.6	2334	4.7
13 F	0540	0.4	1200	4.6	1800	0.6		
14 SA	0015	4.6	0620	0.4	1241	4.6	1840	0.6
15 SU	0055	4.5	0658	0.5	1320	4.5	1916	0.8
16 M	0133	4.4	0731	0.8	1357	4.3	1950	1.0
17 TU	0210	4.2	0803	1.0	1435	4.2	2024	1.3
18 W	0249	4.0	0837	1.4	1515	4.0	2102	1.6
19 TH	0333	3.8	0917	1.7	1603	3.8	2152	1.9
20 F	0428	3.6	1015	2.0	1705	3.7	2305	2.1
21 SA	0544	3.5	1139	2.1	1826	3.7		
22 SU	0029	2.0	0712	3.6	1302	2.1	1941	3.8
23 M	0138	1.8	0819	3.8	1404	1.8	2037	4.0
24 TU	0229	1.5	0907	4.0	1452	1.5	2120	4.2
25 W	0314	1.2	0945	4.2	1535	1.2	2158	4.3
26 TH O	0355	0.9	1021	4.4	1615	1.0	2233	4.4
27 F	0434	0.7	1055	4.5	1654	0.8	2309	4.5
28 SA	0513	0.6	1131	4.5	1733	0.7	2346	4.6
29 SU	0551	0.5	1209	4.6	1810	0.6		
30 M	0024	4.6	0628	0.5	1249	4.6	1847	0.6
31 TU	0105	4.6	0706	0.6	1330	4.5	1927	0.8

Chart Datum: 2·74 metres below Ordnance Datum (Newlyn)

ENGLAND – SOUTHAMPTON

LAT 50°54′N   LONG 1°24′W

TIMES AND HEIGHTS OF HIGH AND LOW WATERS

YEAR **1999**

TIME ZONE (UT)
For Summer Time add ONE hour in non-shaded areas

SEPTEMBER

Day	Time	m	Day	Time	m
1 W	0148 / 0746 / 1415 / 2010	4.5 / 0.8 / 4.4 / 1.0	**16** TH	0208 / 0814 / 1429 / 2013	4.1 / 1.4 / 4.0 / 1.5
2 TH	0235 / 0831 / 1505 / 2101	4.3 / 1.1 / 4.3 / 1.2	**17** F	0247 / 0828 / 1510 / 2055	3.9 / 1.7 / 3.9 / 1.8
3 F	0331 / 0927 / 1607 / 2207	4.1 / 1.4 / 4.1 / 1.5	**18** SA	0335 / 0917 / 1605 / 2159	3.7 / 2.0 / 3.7 / 2.1
4 SA	0441 / 1042 / 1724 / 2331	3.9 / 1.6 / 4.0 / 1.7	**19** SU	0447 / 1040 / 1726 / 2336	3.5 / 2.3 / 3.6 / 2.2
5 SU	0607 / 1211 / 1851	3.9 / 1.7 / 4.0	**20** M	0623 / 1222 / 1857	3.6 / 2.2 / 3.7
6 M	0058 / 0733 / 1333 / 2006	1.6 / 4.0 / 1.5 / 4.2	**21** TU	0100 / 0741 / 1333 / 2002	2.0 / 3.8 / 2.0 / 3.9
7 TU	0209 / 0840 / 1437 / 2105	1.3 / 4.2 / 1.3 / 4.4	**22** W	0159 / 0834 / 1424 / 2049	1.6 / 4.1 / 1.6 / 4.2
8 W	0305 / 0934 / 1530 / 2153	1.0 / 4.4 / 1.0 / 4.6	**23** TH	0245 / 0915 / 1508 / 2129	1.3 / 4.3 / 1.3 / 4.4
9 TH	0354 / 1019 / 1616 / ●2236	0.7 / 4.6 / 0.7 / 4.6	**24** F	0328 / 0952 / 1549 / 2206	0.9 / 4.5 / 0.9 / 4.6
10 F	0437 / 1100 / 1658 / 2314	0.5 / 4.6 / 0.6 / 4.6	**25** SA	0409 / 1028 / 1630 / O2244	0.6 / 4.6 / 0.7 / 4.7
11 SA	0518 / 1137 / 1737 / 2350	0.4 / 4.6 / 0.5 / 4.6	**26** SU	0449 / 1106 / 1710 / 2322	0.4 / 4.7 / 0.5 / 4.8
12 SU	0555 / 1212 / 1813	0.4 / 4.6 / 0.6	**27** M	0529 / 1145 / 1749	0.3 / 4.8 / 0.4
13 M	0025 / 0628 / 1246 / 1845	4.5 / 0.6 / 4.5 / 0.7	**28** TU	0002 / 0607 / 1226 / 1828	4.8 / 0.4 / 4.8 / 0.5
14 TU	0059 / 0658 / 1320 / 1914	4.4 / 0.8 / 4.4 / 1.0	**29** W	0044 / 0647 / 1309 / 1909	4.7 / 0.5 / 4.7 / 0.6
15 W	0133 / 0725 / 1353 / 1942	4.2 / 1.0 / 4.2 / 1.2	**30** TH	0129 / 0728 / 1354 / 1952	4.6 / 0.7 / 4.5 / 0.9

OCTOBER

Day	Time	m	Day	Time	m
1 F	0217 / 0814 / 1445 / 2044	4.4 / 1.1 / 4.3 / 1.2	**16** SA	0212 / 0752 / 1430 / 2015	4.0 / 1.7 / 3.9 / 1.7
2 SA	0315 / 0912 / 1549 / 2151	4.1 / 1.5 / 4.1 / 1.6	**17** SU	0257 / 0837 / 1520 / 2109	3.8 / 2.0 / 3.8 / 2.0
3 SU	0430 / 1031 / 1712 / 2320	3.9 / 1.8 / 3.9 / 1.7	**18** M	0401 / 0947 / 1632 / 2235	3.7 / 2.2 / 3.7 / 2.1
4 M	0603 / 1206 / 1844	3.9 / 1.8 / 3.9	**19** TU	0528 / 1129 / 1801	3.7 / 2.3 / 3.7
5 TU	0049 / 0728 / 1326 / 1957	1.6 / 4.0 / 1.6 / 4.2	**20** W	0010 / 0652 / 1251 / 1916	2.0 / 3.8 / 2.0 / 3.9
6 W	0157 / 0830 / 1425 / 2052	1.4 / 4.3 / 1.3 / 4.4	**21** TH	0118 / 0752 / 1347 / 2011	1.7 / 4.1 / 1.7 / 4.2
7 TH	0248 / 0919 / 1513 / 2137	1.1 / 4.5 / 1.0 / 4.5	**22** F	0209 / 0839 / 1435 / 2056	1.3 / 4.4 / 1.3 / 4.4
8 F	0332 / 1000 / 1554 / 2215	0.8 / 4.6 / 0.8 / 4.6	**23** SA	0255 / 0920 / 1519 / 2137	0.9 / 4.6 / 0.9 / 4.6
9 SA	0412 / 1036 / 1633 / ●2250	0.6 / 4.6 / 0.7 / 4.6	**24** SU	0339 / 1000 / 1602 / O2218	0.6 / 4.8 / 0.6 / 4.8
10 SU	0450 / 1109 / 1709 / 2323	0.5 / 4.6 / 0.6 / 4.6	**25** M	0422 / 1041 / 1645 / 2259	0.4 / 4.9 / 0.4 / 4.9
11 M	0525 / 1141 / 1743 / 2354	0.5 / 4.5 / 0.6 / 4.5	**26** TU	0504 / 1122 / 1728 / 2342	0.3 / 4.9 / 0.3 / 4.9
12 TU	0557 / 1212 / 1814	0.7 / 4.5 / 0.8	**27** W	0547 / 1205 / 1810	0.5 / 4.8 / 0.4
13 W	0027 / 0625 / 1245 / 1841	4.4 / 0.9 / 4.4 / 0.9	**28** TH	0026 / 0628 / 1250 / 1852	4.8 / 0.5 / 4.8 / 0.6
14 TH	0100 / 0652 / 1317 / 1907	4.3 / 1.1 / 4.3 / 1.2	**29** F	0113 / 0713 / 1338 / 1938	4.7 / 0.8 / 4.6 / 0.8
15 F	0134 / 0719 / 1352 / 1937	4.2 / 1.4 / 4.1 / 1.4	**30** SA	0205 / 0801 / 1431 / 2031	4.4 / 1.1 / 4.3 / 1.2
			31 SU	0305 / 0901 / 1535 / 2137	4.2 / 1.5 / 4.1 / 1.5

NOVEMBER

Day	Time	m	Day	Time	m
1 M	0420 / 1018 / 1656 / 2301	4.0 / 1.8 / 3.9 / 1.7	**16** TU	0328 / 0912 / 1551 / 2146	3.8 / 2.1 / 3.8 / 1.9
2 TU	0549 / 1147 / 1824	3.9 / 1.9 / 3.9	**17** W	0440 / 1033 / 1707 / 2311	3.8 / 2.1 / 3.8 / 1.9
3 W	0025 / 0707 / 1304 / 1935	1.7 / 4.1 / 1.7 / 4.1	**18** TH	0558 / 1157 / 1824	3.9 / 2.0 / 3.9
4 TH	0130 / 0807 / 1401 / 2029	1.5 / 4.3 / 1.4 / 4.3	**19** F	0026 / 0704 / 1303 / 1927	1.7 / 4.1 / 1.7 / 4.1
5 F	0221 / 0854 / 1446 / 2113	1.2 / 4.4 / 1.2 / 4.4	**20** SA	0127 / 0759 / 1357 / 2021	1.4 / 4.4 / 1.3 / 4.3
6 SA	0303 / 0934 / 1527 / 2151	1.0 / 4.5 / 1.0 / 4.4	**21** SU	0219 / 0847 / 1447 / 2108	1.0 / 4.6 / 0.9 / 4.6
7 SU	0342 / 1009 / 1604 / 2225	0.7 / 4.6 / 0.8 / 4.5	**22** M	0308 / 0933 / 1535 / 2154	0.7 / 4.8 / 0.6 / 4.7
8 M	0419 / 1041 / 1640 / ●2256	0.7 / 4.5 / 0.7 / 4.4	**23** TU	0355 / 1017 / 1622 / O2240	0.5 / 4.9 / 0.4 / 4.8
9 TU	0454 / 1112 / 1714 / 2328	0.7 / 4.5 / 0.7 / 4.4	**24** W	0442 / 1102 / 1708 / 2326	0.4 / 5.0 / 0.3 / 4.9
10 W	0527 / 1143 / 1745	0.8 / 4.5 / 0.8	**25** TH	0528 / 1148 / 1754	0.4 / 4.9 / 0.4
11 TH	0000 / 0557 / 1216 / 1813	4.4 / 0.9 / 4.4 / 0.9	**26** F	0013 / 0613 / 1236 / 1840	4.8 / 0.5 / 4.8 / 0.5
12 F	0035 / 0625 / 1250 / 1841	4.3 / 1.1 / 4.3 / 1.1	**27** SA	0103 / 0700 / 1325 / 1927	4.7 / 0.8 / 4.6 / 0.7
13 SA	0110 / 0654 / 1325 / 1911	4.2 / 1.3 / 4.2 / 1.3	**28** SU	0155 / 0750 / 1418 / 2018	4.5 / 1.1 / 4.4 / 1.1
14 SU	0148 / 0728 / 1404 / 1949	4.1 / 1.6 / 4.1 / 1.6	**29** M	0253 / 0847 / 1518 / 2118	4.3 / 1.4 / 4.2 / 1.4
15 M	0232 / 0812 / 1450 / 2038	4.0 / 1.8 / 3.9 / 1.8	**30** TU	0400 / 0955 / 1628 / 2228	4.1 / 1.7 / 4.0 / 1.6

DECEMBER

Day	Time	m	Day	Time	m
1 W	0515 / 1111 / 1744 / 2342	4.0 / 1.8 / 3.9 / 1.7	**16** TH	0358 / 0948 / 1621 / 2218	4.0 / 1.8 / 3.9 / 1.7
2 TH	0629 / 1223 / 1856	4.1 / 1.7 / 3.9	**17** F	0506 / 1102 / 1732 / 2333	4.0 / 1.8 / 3.9 / 1.6
3 F	0048 / 0731 / 1324 / 1955	1.6 / 4.2 / 1.6 / 4.1	**18** SA	0615 / 1214 / 1843	4.1 / 1.6 / 4.0
4 SA	0143 / 0821 / 1413 / 2044	1.4 / 4.3 / 1.4 / 4.2	**19** SU	0042 / 0719 / 1319 / 1946	1.4 / 4.3 / 1.3 / 4.2
5 SU	0229 / 0904 / 1456 / 2125	1.3 / 4.4 / 1.2 / 4.2	**20** M	0144 / 0816 / 1417 / 2043	1.2 / 4.5 / 1.0 / 4.4
6 M	0311 / 0941 / 1535 / 2201	1.1 / 4.4 / 1.0 / 4.4	**21** TU	0240 / 0908 / 1512 / 2135	0.9 / 4.7 / 0.7 / 4.6
7 TU	0350 / 1015 / 1612 / ●2235	1.0 / 4.4 / 0.9 / 4.3	**22** W	0333 / 0958 / 1604 / O2225	0.7 / 4.8 / 0.5 / 4.7
8 W	0427 / 1048 / 1648 / 2308	0.9 / 4.4 / 0.8 / 4.4	**23** TH	0424 / 1047 / 1654 / 2314	0.5 / 4.9 / 0.4 / 4.8
9 TH	0503 / 1122 / 1722 / 2341	0.9 / 4.4 / 0.8 / 4.4	**24** F	0514 / 1135 / 1742	0.5 / 4.9 / 0.3
10 F	0536 / 1154 / 1753	1.0 / 4.4 / 0.9	**25** SA	0003 / 0602 / 1224 / 1829	4.8 / 0.5 / 4.8 / 0.4
11 SA	0016 / 0607 / 1229 / 1823	4.3 / 1.1 / 4.3 / 1.0	**26** SU	0053 / 0650 / 1312 / 1915	4.7 / 0.7 / 4.7 / 0.6
12 SU	0052 / 0638 / 1306 / 1855	4.3 / 1.2 / 4.3 / 1.2	**27** M	0143 / 0737 / 1401 / 2002	4.6 / 0.9 / 4.5 / 0.8
13 M	0130 / 0713 / 1344 / 1931	4.2 / 1.4 / 4.2 / 1.3	**28** TU	0234 / 0827 / 1453 / 2051	4.4 / 1.2 / 4.3 / 1.1
14 TU	0212 / 0753 / 1427 / 2015	4.1 / 1.6 / 4.0 / 1.5	**29** W	0329 / 0921 / 1548 / 2145	4.2 / 1.4 / 4.0 / 1.4
15 W	0300 / 0844 / 1518 / 2109	4.0 / 1.7 / 3.9 / 1.6	**30** TH	0428 / 1021 / 1651 / 2247	4.0 / 1.7 / 3.8 / 1.6
			31 F	0533 / 1129 / 1801 / 2354	3.9 / 1.8 / 3.8 / 1.7

Chart Datum: 2·74 metres below Ordnance Datum (Newlyn)

WOOTTON CREEK   8-2-28

Isle of Wight 50°44'·06N 01°12'·68W   Rtg 1-5-1

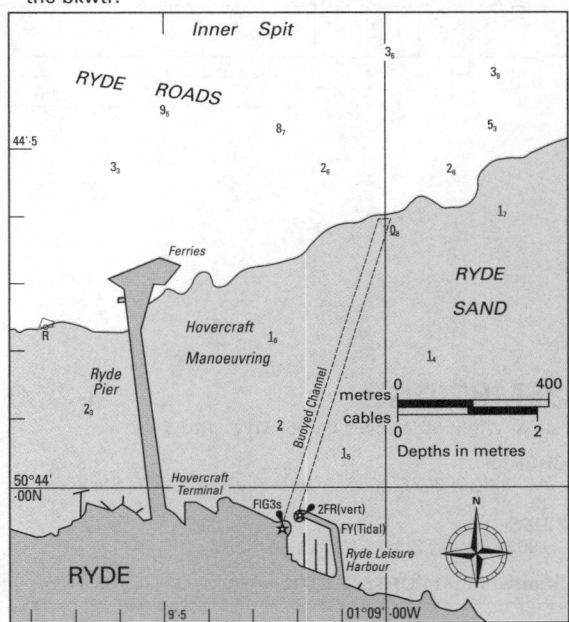

CHARTS
AC *5600.6, 2022, 394*; Imray C3, Y20; Stanfords 11, 18; OS 196

TIDES
+0023 Dover; ML 2·8; Zone 0 (UT). Use RYDE differences 8.2.28; see also 8.2.13.

SHELTER
Good except in stormy N or E winds. Above the ferry, the creek dries. Moor to piles or ⚓s off RVYC; no AB. No ⚓ in the fairway. Speed limit 5kn.

NAVIGATION
WPT Wootton NCM Bn, Q, 50°44'·51N 01°12'·04W, 044°/ 224° from/to ferry slip, 0·64M. Beware large ferries, leaving astern and turning at Wootton Bn. It is difficult to beat in on the ebb.

LIGHTS AND MARKS
Ent to creek due S of SE Ryde Middle SCM and 1·75M W of Ryde Pier. The unlit PHM bn marking Wootton Rks (W of chan ent) is prone to disappear due to stress of weather. Visitors from/to the W should round No 1 bn.
The chan is marked by four SHM bns and two PHMs, all lit. Keep in W sector of Dir lt, Oc WRG 10s, G221°-224°, W224°-225½°, R225½°-230½°. By ferry terminal, turn onto ldg marks on W shore △ ▽, which form a ◇ when in transit 270°.

RADIO TELEPHONE
None.

TELEPHONE (Dial code 01983)
Royal Victoria YC 882325; MRSC (01705) 552100; ⌖ 0345 231110 (H24); Marinecall 0891 500457; Police 528000; Dr 882424.

FACILITIES
Royal Victoria YC ☎ 882325, Slip, Piles, ⚓s, FW, R, Bar; **Village** EC = Thurs, Wootton Bridge = Wed; ✉ (Wootton Bridge, Ryde), Ⓑ (Ryde), ⇌ (ferry to Portsmouth), ✈ (Southampton).

RYDE   8-2-29

Isle of Wight 50°43'·95N 01°09'·22W   Rtg 3-4-2

CHARTS
AC *5600.7, 394, 2045*; Imray C3, C15; Stanfords 11, 18; OS 196

TIDES
+0022 Dover; ML 2·8m; Zone 0 (UT). See 8.2.13

Standard Port PORTSMOUTH (→)

Times				Height (metres)			
High Water		Low Water		MHWS	MHWN	MLWN	MLWS
0000	0600	0500	1100	4·7	3·8	1·9	0·8
1200	1800	1700	2300				
Differences RYDE							
–0010	+0010	–0005	–0010	–0·2	–0·1	0·0	+0·1

SHELTER
Small hbr 300m E of Ryde Pier; dries approx 2·3m. Access for shoal draft approx HW–2½ to +2. Berth on E'ly of three pontoons; long and fin keel yachts should dry out against the bkwtr.

NAVIGATION
WPT 50°44'·32N 01°09'·15W, No 1 SHM buoy, 017°/197° from/to hbr ent, 6ca. From the E, best to stay North of No Man's Land Fort and SW Mining Ground Y buoy to clear Ryde Sands. Drying channel 197° across Ryde Sands (1·5m - 1·7m) is marked by 3 SHM and 3 PHM unlit buoys. Beware hovercraft manoeuvering between Ryde pier and marina; and ferries from/to pierhead.

LIGHTS AND MARKS
Ryde Ch spire (Holy Trinity) brg 200° gives initial appr. Hbr ent lts are 2 FR and Fl G 3s 7m 1M. Hbr has W flood-lights inside ent. Ryde pier is lit by 3 sets of 2FR (vert) and a FY fog lt.

RADIO TELEPHONE
Ryde Harbour VHF Ch 80.

TELEPHONE (Dial code 01983)
Hr Mr 613879; MRSC (01705) 552100; ⌖ 0345 231110 (H24); Marinecall 0891 500457; Police 528000; Ⓗ 524081.

FACILITIES
Marina (100+70 Ⓥ) ☎/📠 613879, £8.00, FW, Slip, ▣, ♿. **Services:** P & D (cans) from garage, Gas, V, R, Bar, **Town** EC Thurs; all domestic facilities nearby. Hovercraft from Ryde Pier to Southsea for mainland ⇌; ✈ Southampton.

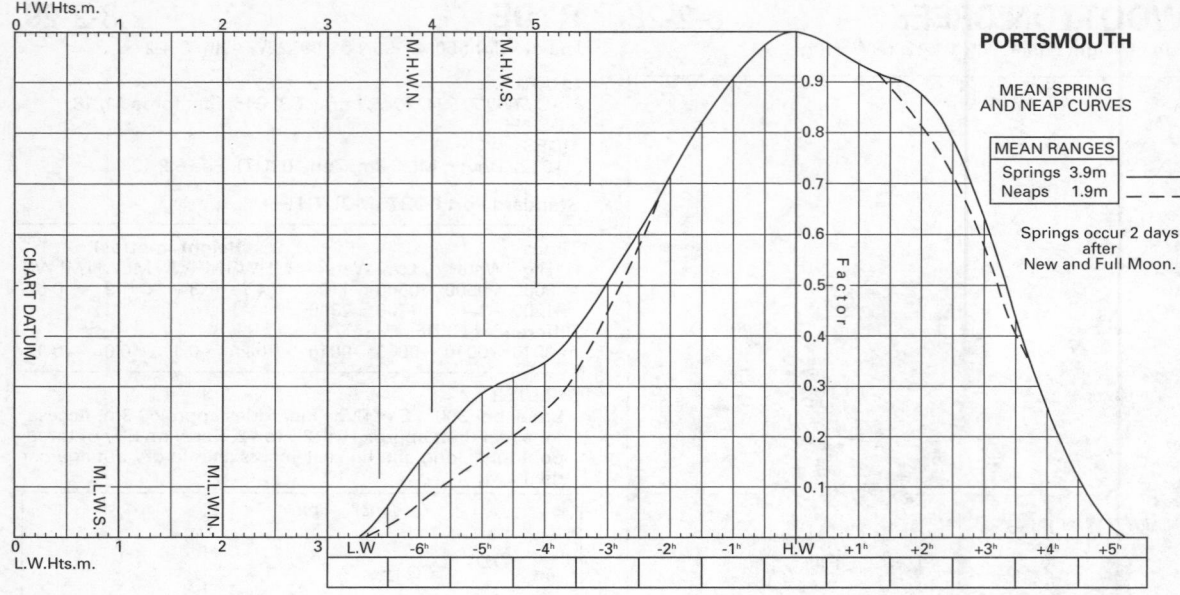

PORTSMOUTH

MEAN SPRING
AND NEAP CURVES

MEAN RANGES	
Springs	3.9m
Neaps	1.9m

Springs occur 2 days
after
New and Full Moon.

BEMBRIDGE   8-2-30

Isle of Wight 50°41'·59N 01°06'·31W   Rtg 3-2-2

CHARTS
AC *5600.3, 2022, 2050, 2045*; Imray C15, C3, C9; Stanfords
18; OS 196

TIDES
+0020 Dover; Zone 0 (UT). See 8.2.13

Standard Port PORTSMOUTH (→)

Times				Height (metres)			
High Water		Low Water		MHWS	MHWN	MLWN	MLWS
0000	0600	0500	1100	4·7	3·8	1·9	0·8
1200	1800	1700	2300				
Differences BEMBRIDGE HARBOUR							
−0010	+0005	+0020	0000	−1·6	−1·5	−1·4	−0·6
FORELAND (LB Slip)							
−0005	0000	+0005	+0010	−0·1	−0·1	0·0	+0·1
VENTNOR							
−0025	−0030	−0025	−0030	−0·8	−0·6	−0·2	+0·2
SANDOWN							
0000	+0005	+0010	+0025	−0·6	−0·5	−0·2	0·0

SHELTER
Good, but difficult ent in NNE gales. No access LW ±2½
for 1·5m draft; carefully check tide gauge which indicates
depth over the bar. Speed limit 6kn. Visitors' berths at
marina, Fisherman's Wharf and afloat on pontoon
between Nos 15 & 17 SHM buoys. No ⚓ in chan and hbr,
but Priory Bay is sheltered ⚓ in winds from S to WNW.

NAVIGATION
WPT tide gauge, Fl Y 2s, 50°42'·43N 01°04'·93W, approx
2ca E of ent to well-buoyed, but unlit chan. The bar,
between Nos 6 and 10 buoys, almost dries. Avoid the
gravel banks between St Helen's Fort, Nodes Pt and N to
Seaview, by keeping to ent times above.

LIGHTS AND MARKS
St Helens Fort Fl (3) 10s 16m 8M; no ⚓ within 1ca radius
of Fort. Conspic W seamark on shore where chan turns S.
Caution: there are numerous unlit Y racing marks off
Bembridge and Seaview (Apr-Oct).

RADIO TELEPHONE
Call *Bembridge Marina* VHF Ch **80**; *Hbr Launch* Ch M.

TELEPHONE (Dial code 01983)
Hr Mr 872828; MRSC (01705) 552100; ⌗ 0345 231110
(H24); Marinecall 0891 500457; Police 528000; Dr 872614.

FACILITIES
Marina (40+100 visitors) ☎ 872828, ⚓ 872922, £12.75, ♿,
FW, ME, EI, AC, ⊡, V, R, Bar; **St Helen's Quay** FW, CH;
Brading Haven YC ☎ 872289, Bar, R, FW; **Bembridge SC**
☎ 872686;
Services: M, Slip, BY, P & D (cans), ME, EI, Sh, Gas.
Town EC Thurs; V, R, Bar, ✉, Ⓑ, ➤ (Ryde), ✈ (So'ton).

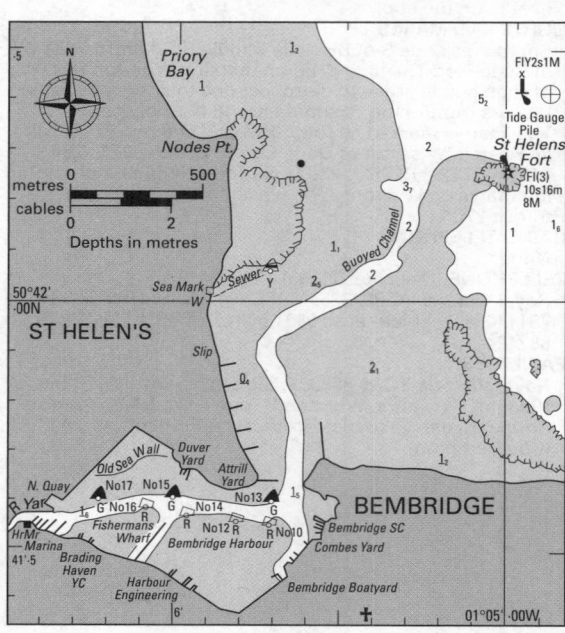

ENGLAND – PORTSMOUTH

LAT 50°48′N   LONG 1°07′W

TIMES AND HEIGHTS OF HIGH AND LOW WATERS   YEAR 1999

TIME ZONE (UT)
For Summer Time add ONE hour in non-shaded areas

JANUARY

Day	Time	m	Day	Time	m
1 F	0329 / 1020 / 1600 / 2250	1.0 / 4.9 / 0.8 / 4.7	16 SA	0335 / 1021 / 1558 / 2249	1.3 / 4.5 / 1.1 / 4.4
2 SA O	0420 / 1110 / 1650 / 2341	0.8 / 4.9 / 0.8 / 4.8	17 SU ●	0415 / 1100 / 1638 / 2327	1.2 / 4.5 / 1.0 / 4.5
3 SU	0508 / 1157 / 1736	0.8 / 4.9 / 0.6	18 M	0453 / 1138 / 1716	1.1 / 4.6 / 0.9
4 M	0028 / 0553 / 1243 / 1820	4.8 / 0.8 / 4.8 / 0.7	19 TU	0006 / 0531 / 1217 / 1753	4.6 / 1.0 / 4.6 / 0.8
5 TU	0114 / 0636 / 1326 / 1901	4.8 / 0.8 / 4.7 / 0.8	20 W	0046 / 0609 / 1256 / 1832	4.6 / 0.9 / 4.6 / 0.7
6 W	0158 / 0717 / 1408 / 1940	4.7 / 1.1 / 4.5 / 0.9	21 TH	0126 / 0649 / 1337 / 1912	4.7 / 0.9 / 4.6 / 0.8
7 TH	0240 / 0758 / 1448 / 2019	4.6 / 1.3 / 4.3 / 1.2	22 F	0208 / 0731 / 1420 / 1954	4.6 / 1.0 / 4.5 / 0.8
8 F	0321 / 0841 / 1530 / 2101	4.4 / 1.5 / 4.1 / 1.4	23 SA	0252 / 0817 / 1506 / 2041	4.6 / 1.1 / 4.4 / 1.0
9 SA	0404 / 0929 / 1614 / 2149	4.2 / 1.8 / 3.9 / 1.7	24 SU	0341 / 0909 / 1557 / 2135	4.5 / 1.3 / 4.3 / 1.2
10 SU	0452 / 1027 / 1706 / 2249	4.1 / 2.0 / 3.8 / 1.9	25 M	0436 / 1011 / 1657 / 2240	4.3 / 1.5 / 4.1 / 1.4
11 M	0549 / 1139 / 1811	4.0 / 2.0 / 3.7	26 TU	0542 / 1126 / 1810 / 2357	4.2 / 1.6 / 4.0 / 1.5
12 TU	0001 / 0655 / 1250 / 1925	2.0 / 4.0 / 2.0 / 3.7	27 W	0657 / 1246 / 1933	4.2 / 1.6 / 4.0
13 W	0109 / 0800 / 1347 / 2032	1.9 / 4.0 / 1.8 / 3.9	28 TH	0116 / 0811 / 1359 / 2047	1.5 / 4.3 / 1.4 / 4.2
14 TH	0205 / 0854 / 1435 / 2124	1.7 / 4.2 / 1.6 / 4.1	29 F	0224 / 0915 / 1459 / 2150	1.3 / 4.5 / 1.1 / 4.4
15 F	0252 / 0940 / 1518 / 2208	1.5 / 4.3 / 1.3 / 4.3	30 SA	0322 / 1010 / 1552 / 2243	1.1 / 4.7 / 0.9 / 4.6
			31 SU O	0412 / 1059 / 1639 / 2331	0.9 / 4.7 / 0.7 / 4.7

FEBRUARY

Day	Time	m	Day	Time	m
1 M	0458 / 1144 / 1723	0.8 / 4.8 / 0.6	16 TU ●	0435 / 1119 / 1657 / 2347	0.9 / 4.6 / 0.7 / 4.7
2 TU	0015 / 0539 / 1227 / 1803	4.8 / 0.8 / 4.7 / 0.6	17 W	0515 / 1200 / 1738	0.8 / 4.6 / 0.6
3 W	0056 / 0618 / 1306 / 1840	4.7 / 0.8 / 4.7 / 0.7	18 TH	0027 / 0555 / 1242 / 1817	4.7 / 0.6 / 4.7 / 0.5
4 TH	0133 / 0654 / 1343 / 1914	4.7 / 0.9 / 4.5 / 0.8	19 F	0108 / 0635 / 1324 / 1857	4.8 / 0.6 / 4.7 / 0.5
5 F	0208 / 0728 / 1419 / 1946	4.6 / 1.1 / 4.4 / 1.0	20 SA	0150 / 0716 / 1407 / 1939	4.8 / 0.6 / 4.7 / 0.6
6 SA	0243 / 0802 / 1455 / 2019	4.5 / 1.3 / 4.2 / 1.2	21 SU	0233 / 0800 / 1452 / 2023	4.7 / 0.8 / 4.5 / 0.8
7 SU	0319 / 0837 / 1533 / 2056	4.3 / 1.5 / 4.1 / 1.5	22 M	0318 / 0848 / 1541 / 2114	4.5 / 1.0 / 4.3 / 1.1
8 M	0359 / 0919 / 1617 / 2142	4.1 / 1.8 / 3.9 / 1.8	23 TU	0409 / 0945 / 1638 / 2217	4.3 / 1.3 / 4.1 / 1.4
9 TU	0446 / 1017 / 1712 / 2249	3.9 / 2.0 / 3.7 / 2.0	24 W	0512 / 1100 / 1750 / 2339	4.1 / 1.6 / 3.9 / 1.7
10 W	0549 / 1145 / 1826	3.8 / 2.1 / 3.6	25 TH	0632 / 1228 / 1921	4.0 / 1.6 / 3.9
11 TH	0020 / 0705 / 1307 / 1949	2.1 / 3.8 / 2.0 / 3.7	26 F	0105 / 0757 / 1347 / 2042	1.6 / 4.1 / 1.5 / 4.1
12 F	0133 / 0816 / 1406 / 2054	1.9 / 4.0 / 1.7 / 4.0	27 SA	0218 / 0907 / 1450 / 2144	1.4 / 4.3 / 1.2 / 4.4
13 SA	0228 / 0912 / 1453 / 2144	1.7 / 4.2 / 1.4 / 4.2	28 SU	0315 / 1002 / 1540 / 2234	1.2 / 4.5 / 0.9 / 4.6
14 SU	0313 / 0957 / 1536 / 2227	1.4 / 4.3 / 1.1 / 4.4			
15 M	0355 / 1039 / 1617 / 2307	1.1 / 4.5 / 0.9 / 4.5			

MARCH

Day	Time	m	Day	Time	m
1 M	0402 / 1049 / 1625 / 2318	1.0 / 4.6 / 0.7 / 4.7	16 TU	0332 / 1015 / 1553 / 2243	1.1 / 4.4 / 0.8 / 4.6
2 TU O	0444 / 1131 / 1705 / 2357	0.8 / 4.6 / 0.6 / 4.7	17 W ●	0413 / 1058 / 1634 / 2324	0.8 / 4.6 / 0.6 / 4.7
3 W	0523 / 1209 / 1742	0.7 / 4.6 / 0.6	18 TH	0455 / 1141 / 1716	0.6 / 4.7 / 0.4
4 TH	0033 / 0558 / 1244 / 1816	4.7 / 0.7 / 4.6 / 0.4	19 F	0006 / 0536 / 1225 / 1758	4.8 / 0.4 / 4.8 / 0.4
5 F	0105 / 0630 / 1318 / 1847	4.6 / 0.8 / 4.5 / 0.7	20 SA	0048 / 0617 / 1309 / 1839	4.9 / 0.4 / 4.8 / 0.4
6 SA	0136 / 0659 / 1350 / 1915	4.6 / 0.9 / 4.5 / 0.9	21 SU	0131 / 0659 / 1353 / 1922	4.9 / 0.4 / 4.6 / 0.5
7 SU	0207 / 0727 / 1424 / 1943	4.5 / 1.0 / 4.3 / 1.1	22 M	0214 / 0743 / 1439 / 2007	4.8 / 0.6 / 4.6 / 0.8
8 M	0240 / 0756 / 1459 / 2014	4.3 / 1.3 / 4.2 / 1.4	23 TU	0259 / 0830 / 1528 / 2058	4.6 / 0.9 / 4.4 / 1.1
9 TU	0314 / 0830 / 1538 / 2053	4.2 / 1.5 / 4.0 / 1.7	24 W	0349 / 0927 / 1626 / 2202	4.3 / 1.2 / 4.1 / 1.5
10 W	0355 / 0915 / 1627 / 2149	3.9 / 1.8 / 3.8 / 2.0	25 TH	0451 / 1041 / 1739 / 2324	4.0 / 1.5 / 3.9 / 1.7
11 TH	0451 / 1025 / 1737 / 2322	3.7 / 2.0 / 3.6 / 2.2	26 F	0613 / 1210 / 1912	3.8 / 1.6 / 3.9
12 F	0610 / 1218 / 1905	3.7 / 2.0 / 3.7	27 SA	0052 / 0745 / 1332 / 2031	1.7 / 3.9 / 1.5 / 4.1
13 SA	0100 / 0735 / 1334 / 2021	2.0 / 3.8 / 1.8 / 3.9	28 SU	0206 / 0855 / 1433 / 2130	1.5 / 4.1 / 1.3 / 4.4
14 SU	0202 / 0840 / 1426 / 2116	1.7 / 4.0 / 1.5 / 4.2	29 M	0301 / 0948 / 1522 / 2217	1.2 / 4.3 / 1.0 / 4.5
15 M	0249 / 0931 / 1510 / 2201	1.4 / 4.2 / 1.1 / 4.4	30 TU	0345 / 1032 / 1603 / 2258	1.0 / 4.5 / 0.8 / 4.6
			31 W O	0424 / 1112 / 1641 / 2334	0.8 / 4.5 / 0.7 / 4.6

APRIL

Day	Time	m	Day	Time	m
1 TH	0500 / 1147 / 1717	0.7 / 4.5 / 0.6	16 F ●	0430 / 1118 / 1652 / 2342	0.5 / 4.8 / 0.4 / 4.9
2 F	0006 / 0533 / 1220 / 1749	4.6 / 0.7 / 4.5 / 0.7	17 SA	0515 / 1205 / 1736	0.3 / 4.9 / 0.3
3 SA	0036 / 0604 / 1252 / 1819	4.6 / 0.7 / 4.5 / 0.8	18 SU	0027 / 0558 / 1252 / 1820	5.0 / 0.3 / 4.9 / 0.4
4 SU	0105 / 0632 / 1324 / 1847	4.5 / 0.8 / 4.5 / 0.9	19 M	0112 / 0643 / 1339 / 1905	4.9 / 0.4 / 4.8 / 0.5
5 M	0135 / 0658 / 1357 / 1913	4.5 / 1.0 / 4.4 / 1.1	20 TU	0157 / 0728 / 1427 / 1952	4.8 / 0.5 / 4.7 / 0.8
6 TU	0206 / 0725 / 1431 / 1943	4.4 / 1.1 / 4.2 / 1.3	21 W	0244 / 0817 / 1519 / 2044	4.6 / 0.8 / 4.5 / 1.1
7 W	0238 / 0757 / 1507 / 2020	4.2 / 1.4 / 4.0 / 1.6	22 TH	0335 / 0913 / 1617 / 2147	4.3 / 1.2 / 4.2 / 1.5
8 TH	0315 / 0838 / 1553 / 2110	4.0 / 1.6 / 3.9 / 1.9	23 F	0436 / 1023 / 1729 / 2304	4.0 / 1.5 / 4.0 / 1.7
9 F	0406 / 0938 / 1657 / 2229	3.8 / 1.9 / 3.7 / 2.1	24 SA	0556 / 1145 / 1854	3.8 / 1.6 / 4.0
10 SA	0518 / 1114 / 1820	3.6 / 2.0 / 3.7	25 SU	0028 / 0723 / 1304 / 2007	1.7 / 3.9 / 1.5 / 4.2
11 SU	0015 / 0645 / 1251 / 1941	2.1 / 3.7 / 1.8 / 3.9	26 M	0140 / 0831 / 1406 / 2104	1.6 / 4.0 / 1.3 / 4.3
12 M	0126 / 0800 / 1351 / 2041	1.8 / 3.9 / 1.5 / 4.2	27 TU	0234 / 0924 / 1453 / 2151	1.3 / 4.2 / 1.1 / 4.5
13 TU	0218 / 0857 / 1439 / 2129	1.4 / 4.2 / 1.1 / 4.4	28 W	0318 / 1008 / 1534 / 2231	1.1 / 4.3 / 1.0 / 4.5
14 W	0303 / 0945 / 1523 / 2214	1.0 / 4.4 / 0.8 / 4.7	29 TH	0356 / 1046 / 1611 / 2306	0.9 / 4.4 / 0.8 / 4.5
15 TH	0347 / 1031 / 1607 / 2258	0.7 / 4.6 / 0.5 / 4.8	30 F O	0432 / 1121 / 1647 / 2337	0.8 / 4.4 / 0.8 / 4.5

Chart Datum: 2·73 metres below Ordnance Datum (Newlyn)

ENGLAND – PORTSMOUTH

LAT 50°48′N   LONG 1°07′W

TIMES AND HEIGHTS OF HIGH AND LOW WATERS

YEAR **1999**

TIME ZONE (UT)
For Summer Time add ONE hour in non-shaded areas

MAY

Day	Time	m	Time	m	Day	Time	m	Time	m
1 SA	0506	0.8	1153	4.4	16 SU	0454	0.4	1146	4.9
	1721	0.8				1715	0.4		
2 SU	0006	4.5	0538	0.8	17 M	0007	5.0	0541	0.4
	1226	4.4	1752	0.9		1236	4.9	1802	0.5
3 M	0036	4.5	0607	0.9	18 TU	0055	4.9	0629	0.4
	1259	4.4	1821	1.0		1326	4.9	1850	0.6
4 TU	0107	4.5	0633	1.0	19 W	0142	4.8	0716	0.6
	1332	4.4	1849	1.1		1416	4.7	1938	0.8
5 W	0139	4.4	0701	1.1	20 TH	0231	4.6	0805	0.8
	1407	4.3	1919	1.3		1509	4.6	2030	1.1
6 TH	0211	4.2	0733	1.3	21 F	0323	4.4	0859	1.1
	1445	4.1	1957	1.5		1606	4.4	2128	1.4
7 F	0249	4.1	0815	1.5	22 SA	0420	4.1	1000	1.4
	1530	4.0	2045	1.8		1709	4.2	2235	1.6
8 SA	0337	3.9	0910	1.7	23 SU	0528	3.9	1110	1.5
	1628	3.9	2153	2.0		1821	4.1	2349	1.7
9 SU	0441	3.8	1027	1.8	24 M	0645	3.8	1222	1.6
	1739	3.9	2319	2.0		1929	4.1		
10 M	0558	3.8	1155	1.7	25 TU	0059	1.7	0754	3.9
	1856	4.0				1325	1.5	2027	4.2
11 TU	0038	1.7	0714	3.9	26 W	0156	1.5	0850	4.0
	1306	1.4	2001	4.2		1415	1.4	2116	4.3
12 W	0139	1.4	0818	4.2	27 TH	0242	1.3	0936	4.1
	1401	1.1	2055	4.5		1458	1.2	2157	4.4
13 TH	0230	1.1	0913	4.4	28 F	0323	1.1	1016	4.2
	1451	0.8	2144	4.7		1538	1.1	2233	4.4
14 F	0318	0.8	1005	4.6	29 SA	0401	1.0	1052	4.3
	1539	0.6	2232	4.9		1616	1.0	2305	4.4
15 SA ●	0406	0.5	1056	4.8	30 SU O	0438	0.9	1127	4.4
	1627	0.5	2320	5.0		1653	1.0	2337	4.5
					31 M	0513	0.9	1201	4.4
						1728	1.0		

JUNE

Day	Time	m	Time	m	Day	Time	m	Time	m
1 TU	0009	4.5	0544	0.9	16 W	0039	4.9	0616	0.5
	1236	4.4	1759	1.1		1314	4.8	1836	0.7
2 W	0043	4.4	0614	1.0	17 TH	0128	4.8	0704	0.6
	1311	4.4	1830	1.2		1404	4.8	1924	0.9
3 TH	0117	4.4	0644	1.1	18 F	0217	4.6	0751	0.8
	1348	4.4	1903	1.3		1454	4.6	2012	1.1
4 F	0152	4.4	0719	1.2	19 SA	0305	4.4	0838	1.0
	1427	4.3	1941	1.4		1545	4.5	2102	1.3
5 SA	0231	4.2	0800	1.3	20 SU	0356	4.2	0929	1.3
	1511	4.2	2028	1.6		1637	4.3	2158	1.6
6 SU	0318	4.1	0851	1.4	21 M	0449	4.0	1026	1.5
	1603	4.1	2126	1.7		1733	4.1	2300	1.7
7 M	0414	4.0	0955	1.5	22 TU	0550	3.8	1129	1.6
	1704	4.1	2235	1.7		1835	4.1		
8 TU	0520	4.0	1107	1.5	23 W	0007	1.8	0658	3.8
	1813	4.1	2349	1.6		1233	1.7	1936	4.0
9 W	0633	4.0	1219	1.4	24 TH	0110	1.7	0803	3.8
	1921	4.3				1331	1.6	2031	4.1
10 TH	0058	1.4	0742	4.2	25 F	0203	1.5	0858	4.0
	1324	1.2	2022	4.5		1421	1.5	2118	4.2
11 F	0159	1.1	0845	4.4	26 SA	0248	1.4	0944	4.1
	1422	1.0	2117	4.7		1505	1.4	2158	4.3
12 SA	0253	0.9	0942	4.6	27 SU	0330	1.2	1024	4.2
	1515	0.8	2210	4.8		1547	1.3	2235	4.4
13 SU ●	0346	0.7	1037	4.7	28 M O	0410	1.1	1102	4.3
	1608	0.7	2300	4.9		1627	1.2	2311	4.4
14 M	0437	0.5	1130	4.8	29 TU	0448	1.0	1138	4.4
	1659	0.6	2350	4.9		1705	1.1	2346	4.4
15 TU	0528	0.5	1222	4.9	30 W	0524	1.0	1215	4.4
	1749	0.6				1740	1.1		

JULY

Day	Time	m	Time	m	Day	Time	m	Time	m
1 TH	0022	4.4	0558	1.0	16 F	0112	4.7	0648	0.6
	1253	4.5	1814	1.1		1347	4.8	1906	0.9
2 F	0058	4.4	0631	1.0	17 SA	0157	4.6	0730	0.7
	1331	4.5	1850	1.1		1431	4.7	1948	1.0
3 SA	0136	4.4	0707	1.0	18 SU	0240	4.4	0810	0.9
	1410	4.4	1929	1.2		1514	4.5	2030	1.2
4 SU	0216	4.3	0748	1.1	19 M	0322	4.3	0852	1.2
	1453	4.4	2013	1.3		1555	4.4	2115	1.5
5 M	0300	4.2	0834	1.2	20 TU	0406	4.1	0937	1.5
	1540	4.3	2104	1.4		1639	4.2	2207	1.7
6 TU	0351	4.2	0928	1.3	21 W	0454	3.9	1031	1.7
	1633	4.3	2203	1.5		1728	4.0	2309	1.8
7 W	0450	4.1	1031	1.4	22 TH	0552	3.7	1137	1.9
	1735	4.2	2312	1.5		1829	3.9		
8 TH	0559	4.1	1142	1.4	23 F	0019	1.9	0704	3.7
	1845	4.3				1246	1.9	1936	3.9
9 F	0025	1.4	0713	4.1	24 SA	0124	1.8	0816	3.8
	1255	1.4	1953	4.4		1346	1.8	2036	4.0
10 SA	0135	1.3	0823	4.3	25 SU	0217	1.6	0912	4.0
	1401	1.2	2055	4.6		1437	1.6	2126	4.2
11 SU	0237	1.0	0927	4.5	26 M	0303	1.4	0958	4.2
	1500	1.0	2152	4.7		1522	1.4	2208	4.3
12 M	0333	0.8	1025	4.6	27 TU	0345	1.2	1039	4.3
	1555	0.9	2245	4.8		1604	1.3	2247	4.4
13 TU ●	0426	0.6	1119	4.8	28 W O	0425	1.0	1117	4.4
	1647	0.8	2336	4.8		1644	1.1	2325	4.4
14 W	0516	0.5	1210	4.8	29 TH	0504	0.9	1155	4.5
	1736	0.7				1721	1.0		
15 TH	0024	4.8	0603	0.5	30 F	0002	4.5	0540	0.8
	1300	4.8	1822	0.8		1234	4.6	1758	1.0
					31 SA	0040	4.5	0617	0.8
						1312	4.6	1835	1.0

AUGUST

Day	Time	m	Time	m	Day	Time	m	Time	m
1 SU	0119	4.5	0653	0.8	16 M	0208	4.5	0738	0.9
	1351	4.6	1913	1.0		1436	4.6	1955	1.1
2 M	0200	4.5	0733	0.9	17 TU	0245	4.3	0811	1.2
	1432	4.6	1955	1.0		1511	4.4	2031	1.4
3 TU	0243	4.4	0815	1.0	18 W	0323	4.1	0848	1.4
	1516	4.5	2042	1.1		1548	4.2	2111	1.6
4 W	0330	4.3	0905	1.2	19 TH	0406	3.9	0932	1.7
	1605	4.4	2136	1.3		1632	4.0	2205	1.9
5 TH	0426	4.2	1004	1.4	20 F	0459	3.8	1036	2.0
	1703	4.3	2243	1.5		1727	3.9	2323	2.0
6 F	0533	4.0	1116	1.6	21 SA	0609	3.7	1202	2.1
	1813	4.2				1840	3.8		
7 SA	0002	1.5	0652	4.0	22 SU	0046	2.0	0734	3.7
	1237	1.6	1931	4.2		1317	2.0	1957	3.9
8 SU	0121	1.4	0812	4.2	23 M	0150	1.8	0844	4.0
	1351	1.5	2041	4.4		1413	1.8	2057	4.1
9 M	0228	1.2	0920	4.4	24 TU	0239	1.5	0934	4.2
	1453	1.2	2141	4.6		1459	1.5	2143	4.3
10 TU	0325	0.9	1018	4.6	25 W	0322	1.2	1015	4.4
	1548	1.0	2234	4.7		1548	1.3	2224	4.4
11 W	0416	0.7	1109	4.7	26 TH O	0402	1.0	1054	4.5
	1637	0.9	2323	4.8 ●		1621	1.1	2302	4.5
12 TH	0503	0.6	1157	4.8	27 F	0441	0.8	1132	4.6
	1722	0.8				1659	0.9	2341	4.6
13 F	0008	4.8	0546	0.5	28 SA	0520	0.7	1210	4.7
	1242	4.8	1804	0.8		1737	0.8		
14 SA	0051	4.7	0626	0.6	29 SU	0020	4.6	0557	0.6
	1323	4.8	1843	0.8		1249	4.7	1815	0.8
15 SU	0131	4.6	0703	0.7	30 M	0100	4.6	0635	0.6
	1401	4.7	1920	0.9		1329	4.7	1854	0.7
					31 TU	0141	4.6	0714	0.7
						1409	4.7	1935	0.8

Chart Datum: 2·73 metres below Ordnance Datum (Newlyn)

2

ENGLAND – PORTSMOUTH

LAT 50°48′N   LONG 1°07′W

TIMES AND HEIGHTS OF HIGH AND LOW WATERS

YEAR **1999**

TIME ZONE (UT)
For Summer Time add ONE hour in non-shaded areas

Chart Datum: 2·73 metres below Ordnance Datum (Newlyn)

SEPTEMBER

Time	m		Time	m
1 W 0224 / 0756 / 1452 / 2021	4.6 / 0.9 / 4.6 / 1.0	**16** TH	0245 / 0805 / 1504 / 2023	4.2 / 1.4 / 4.2 / 1.6
2 TH 0311 / 0844 / 1540 / 2114	4.4 / 1.1 / 4.4 / 1.3	**17** F	0324 / 0842 / 1543 / 2107	4.0 / 1.8 / 4.0 / 1.9
3 F 0406 / 0943 / 1637 / 2222	4.2 / 1.5 / 4.2 / 1.5	**18** SA	0413 / 0937 / 1635 / 2215	3.8 / 2.1 / 3.8 / 2.1
4 SA 0515 / 1101 / 1751 / 2348	4.0 / 1.7 / 4.1 / 1.7	**19** SU	0522 / 1114 / 1748	3.7 / 2.3 / 3.7
5 SU 0642 / 1229 / 1918	4.0 / 1.8 / 4.1	**20** M	0005 / 0651 / 1248 / 1916	2.2 / 3.7 / 2.2 / 3.8
6 M 0113 / 0808 / 1346 / 2035	1.6 / 4.1 / 1.6 / 4.3	**21** TU	0121 / 0811 / 1348 / 2026	1.9 / 3.9 / 1.9 / 4.0
7 TU 0221 / 0916 / 1447 / 2134	1.3 / 4.4 / 1.3 / 4.5	**22** W	0213 / 0904 / 1434 / 2115	1.6 / 4.2 / 1.6 / 4.3
8 W 0316 / 1009 / 1538 / 2224	1.0 / 4.6 / 1.1 / 4.7	**23** TH	0256 / 0947 / 1515 / 2157	1.3 / 4.4 / 1.3 / 4.4
9 TH 0403 / 1056 / 1623 / ● 2308	0.8 / 4.8 / 0.9 / 4.7	**24** F	0336 / 1026 / 1554 / 2236	1.0 / 4.6 / 1.0 / 4.6
10 F 0445 / 1138 / 1704 / 2349	0.6 / 4.8 / 0.7 / 4.7	**25** SA	0415 / 1105 / 1633 / O 2316	0.8 / 4.7 / 0.8 / 4.7
11 SA 0525 / 1217 / 1742	0.6 / 4.8 / 0.7	**26** SU	0454 / 1144 / 1713 / 2357	0.6 / 4.8 / 0.7 / 4.8
12 SU 0026 / 0600 / 1253 / 1816	4.7 / 0.6 / 4.8 / 0.8	**27** M	0534 / 1224 / 1753	0.5 / 4.9 / 0.6
13 M 0102 / 0633 / 1326 / 1848	4.6 / 0.7 / 4.7 / 0.9	**28** TU	0039 / 0613 / 1306 / 1833	4.8 / 0.5 / 4.8 / 0.6
14 TU 0135 / 0704 / 1357 / 1919	4.5 / 0.9 / 4.6 / 1.1	**29** W	0123 / 0654 / 1348 / 1916	4.8 / 0.7 / 4.8 / 0.7
15 W 0209 / 0734 / 1429 / 1949	4.6 / 1.2 / 4.4 / 1.3	**30** TH	0208 / 0738 / 1432 / 2002	4.7 / 0.9 / 4.6 / 1.0

OCTOBER

Time	m		Time	m
1 F 0256 / 0827 / 1521 / 2056	4.5 / 1.2 / 4.4 / 1.3	**16** SA	0249 / 0805 / 1502 / 2025	4.1 / 1.8 / 4.1 / 1.8
2 SA 0353 / 0930 / 1619 / 2206	4.3 / 1.5 / 4.2 / 1.6	**17** SU	0335 / 0852 / 1550 / 2121	3.9 / 2.1 / 3.9 / 2.1
3 SU 0504 / 1050 / 1736 / 2334	4.0 / 1.8 / 4.0 / 1.7	**18** M	0438 / 1013 / 1657 / 2301	3.8 / 2.3 / 3.7 / 2.2
4 M 0635 / 1219 / 1910	4.0 / 1.8 / 4.0	**19** TU	0602 / 1204 / 1824	3.8 / 2.3 / 3.8
5 TU 0100 / 0801 / 1336 / 2026	1.6 / 4.2 / 1.7 / 4.2	**20** W	0038 / 0726 / 1312 / 1942	2.0 / 3.9 / 2.0 / 4.0
6 W 0208 / 0903 / 1434 / 2122	1.4 / 4.5 / 1.4 / 4.5	**21** TH	0137 / 0825 / 1401 / 2038	1.7 / 4.2 / 1.7 / 4.2
7 TH 0259 / 0953 / 1521 / 2208	1.1 / 4.7 / 1.1 / 4.6	**22** F	0223 / 0912 / 1443 / 2124	1.4 / 4.5 / 1.3 / 4.5
8 F 0343 / 1036 / 1602 / 2249	0.9 / 4.8 / 0.9 / 4.7	**23** SA	0304 / 0954 / 1524 / 2207	1.0 / 4.7 / 1.0 / 4.7
9 SA 0422 / 1115 / 1640 / ● 2326	0.7 / 4.8 / 0.8 / 4.7	**24** SU	0344 / 1035 / 1605 / O 2250	0.8 / 4.8 / 0.8 / 4.8
10 SU 0458 / 1150 / 1715	0.7 / 4.8 / 0.8	**25** M	0426 / 1117 / 1647 / 2335	0.6 / 4.9 / 0.6 / 4.9
11 M 0000 / 0532 / 1222 / 1748	4.7 / 0.7 / 4.7 / 0.8	**26** TU	0508 / 1200 / 1730	0.5 / 5.0 / 0.5
12 TU 0033 / 0604 / 1252 / 1818	4.6 / 0.8 / 4.6 / 0.9	**27** W	0020 / 0551 / 1244 / 1814	4.9 / 0.6 / 5.0 / 0.6
13 W 0105 / 0633 / 1322 / 1847	4.6 / 1.0 / 4.6 / 1.1	**28** TH	0107 / 0636 / 1329 / 1900	4.9 / 0.7 / 4.9 / 0.7
14 TH 0138 / 0701 / 1353 / 1915	4.5 / 1.2 / 4.4 / 1.3	**29** F	0154 / 0723 / 1416 / 1948	4.8 / 0.9 / 4.7 / 0.9
15 F 0212 / 0730 / 1425 / 1946	4.5 / 1.5 / 4.3 / 1.5	**30** SA	0246 / 0815 / 1507 / 2044	4.6 / 1.2 / 4.4 / 1.3
		31 SU	0344 / 0917 / 1607 / 2151	4.4 / 1.6 / 4.2 / 1.6

NOVEMBER

Time	m		Time	m
1 M 0455 / 1034 / 1722 / 2312	4.2 / 1.8 / 4.0 / 1.7	**16** TU	0403 / 0925 / 1614 / 2158	4.0 / 2.2 / 3.8 / 2.0
2 TU 0620 / 1158 / 1851	4.1 / 1.9 / 4.0	**17** W	0514 / 1054 / 1728 / 2329	3.9 / 2.2 / 3.8 / 2.0
3 W 0034 / 0738 / 1313 / 2004	1.7 / 4.3 / 1.7 / 4.2	**18** TH	0633 / 1218 / 1847	1.9 / 4.0 / 3.9
4 TH 0141 / 0839 / 1410 / 2100	1.5 / 4.5 / 1.5 / 4.3	**19** F	0044 / 0739 / 1318 / 1954	1.8 / 4.2 / 1.7 / 4.2
5 F 0233 / 0928 / 1456 / 2146	1.3 / 4.6 / 1.2 / 4.5	**20** SA	0140 / 0833 / 1407 / 2048	1.4 / 4.5 / 1.4 / 4.4
6 SA 0315 / 1010 / 1536 / 2226	1.1 / 4.7 / 1.1 / 4.6	**21** SU	0227 / 0921 / 1453 / 2138	1.1 / 4.7 / 1.0 / 4.6
7 SU 0353 / 1047 / 1613 / 2302	0.9 / 4.7 / 1.0 / 4.6	**22** M	0313 / 1006 / 1538 / 2227	0.9 / 4.9 / 0.8 / 4.8
8 M 0429 / 1120 / 1648 / ● 2335	0.9 / 4.7 / 0.9 / 4.6	**23** TU	0359 / 1052 / 1625 / O 2315	0.7 / 5.0 / 0.6 / 4.9
9 TU 0504 / 1150 / 1721	0.9 / 4.7 / 0.9	**24** W	0446 / 1139 / 1712	0.6 / 5.0 / 0.5
10 W 0006 / 0536 / 1220 / 1752	4.6 / 1.0 / 4.6 / 1.0	**25** TH	0004 / 0533 / 1226 / 1800	5.0 / 0.6 / 5.0 / 0.6
11 TH 0038 / 0606 / 1251 / 1821	4.6 / 1.1 / 4.5 / 1.1	**26** F	0054 / 0621 / 1314 / 1848	5.0 / 0.7 / 4.9 / 0.7
12 F 0112 / 0634 / 1323 / 1849	4.5 / 1.3 / 4.5 / 1.3	**27** SA	0144 / 0710 / 1403 / 1938	4.9 / 0.9 / 4.7 / 0.9
13 SA 0146 / 0704 / 1355 / 1919	4.4 / 1.5 / 4.3 / 1.5	**28** SU	0237 / 0802 / 1455 / 2031	4.7 / 1.2 / 4.5 / 1.1
14 SU 0224 / 0738 / 1431 / 1957	4.3 / 1.7 / 4.2 / 1.7	**29** M	0334 / 0901 / 1552 / 2131	4.5 / 1.5 / 4.3 / 1.4
15 M 0307 / 0822 / 1515 / 2047	4.1 / 2.0 / 4.0 / 1.9	**30** TU	0438 / 1008 / 1658 / 2238	4.3 / 1.7 / 4.1 / 1.6

DECEMBER

Time	m		Time	m
1 W 0550 / 1122 / 1814 / 2351	4.2 / 1.8 / 4.0 / 1.7	**16** TH	0432 / 0958 / 1643 / 2228	4.1 / 2.0 / 4.0 / 1.7
2 TH 0701 / 1235 / 1927	4.2 / 1.8 / 4.0	**17** F	0540 / 1114 / 1754 / 2343	4.1 / 1.9 / 4.0 / 1.7
3 F 0059 / 0803 / 1336 / 2027	1.6 / 4.3 / 1.6 / 4.1	**18** SA	0651 / 1228 / 1908	4.2 / 1.7 / 4.1
4 SA 0156 / 0855 / 1425 / 2117	1.5 / 4.4 / 1.5 / 4.2	**19** SU	0052 / 0754 / 1331 / 2014	1.5 / 4.4 / 1.5 / 4.3
5 SU 0241 / 0939 / 1507 / 2200	1.4 / 4.5 / 1.3 / 4.3	**20** M	0152 / 0850 / 1426 / 2113	1.3 / 4.7 / 1.2 / 4.5
6 M 0322 / 1017 / 1545 / 2237	1.2 / 4.6 / 1.2 / 4.4	**21** TU	0247 / 0942 / 1518 / 2208	1.0 / 4.8 / 0.9 / 4.7
7 TU 0400 / 1050 / 1622 / ● 2311	1.1 / 4.6 / 1.1 / 4.5	**22** W	0339 / 1032 / 1609 / O 2301	0.9 / 5.0 / 0.7 / 4.9
8 W 0437 / 1122 / 1658 / 2343	1.1 / 4.6 / 1.0 / 4.5	**23** TH	0430 / 1122 / 1700 / 2352	0.7 / 5.0 / 0.6 / 4.9
9 TH 0512 / 1153 / 1731	1.1 / 4.6 / 1.0	**24** F	0520 / 1211 / 1750	0.7 / 5.0 / 0.5
10 F 0016 / 0544 / 1226 / 1802	4.5 / 1.2 / 4.5 / 1.1	**25** SA	0043 / 0609 / 1301 / 1838	4.9 / 0.8 / 4.9 / 0.6
11 SA 0051 / 0615 / 1259 / 1831	4.5 / 1.3 / 4.5 / 1.2	**26** SU	0135 / 0658 / 1350 / 1926	4.9 / 0.9 / 4.8 / 0.7
12 SU 0127 / 0645 / 1334 / 1903	4.5 / 1.4 / 4.4 / 1.3	**27** M	0225 / 0747 / 1440 / 2013	4.8 / 1.1 / 4.6 / 0.9
13 M 0205 / 0720 / 1410 / 1939	4.4 / 1.6 / 4.3 / 1.4	**28** TU	0317 / 0838 / 1530 / 2103	4.6 / 1.3 / 4.4 / 1.2
14 TU 0246 / 0801 / 1451 / 2024	4.3 / 1.7 / 4.1 / 1.5	**29** W	0409 / 0933 / 1623 / 2157	4.5 / 1.5 / 4.1 / 1.4
15 W 0334 / 0853 / 1542 / 2119	4.2 / 1.9 / 4.0 / 1.7	**30** TH	0505 / 1035 / 1721 / 2258	4.3 / 1.7 / 3.9 / 1.6
		31 F	0607 / 1144 / 1829	4.2 / 1.9 / 3.8

PORTSMOUTH   8-2-31

Hampshire 50°47'·35N 01°06'·58W (Entrance)   Rtg 2-1-2

CHARTS
AC *5600.7 & .9*, 2628, 2629, 2625, *2631, 394, 2050, 2045*; Imray C3, C9; Stanfords 11, 18; OS 197

TIDES
+0029 Dover; ML 2·8; Zone 0 (UT)

Standard Port PORTSMOUTH (←)

High Water		Low Water		Height (metres)			
				MHWS	MHWN	MLWN	MLWS
0500	1000	0000	0600	4·7	3·8	1·9	0·8
1700	2200	1200	1800				

Differences LEE-ON-SOLENT

−0005	+0005	−0015	−0010	−0·2	−0·1	+0·1	+0·2

Portsmouth is a Standard Port; daily predictions are given above. See also 8·2·13. Strong winds from NE to SE, coupled with a high barometer, may lower levels by 1m and delay times of HW and LW by 1hr; the opposite may occur in strong W'lies with low pressure.

SHELTER
Excellent. This very large hbr affords shelter in some area for any wind. There are two marinas on the Gosport side, two at Fareham and one at the N end of Portchester Lake, plus several yacht pontoons/jetties and many moorings (see Facilities). Good shelter in The Camber, but this is a busy little commercial dock and often full; beware the Isle of Wight car ferry docking near the ent. Portsmouth is a major naval base and Dockyard Port; all vessels come under the QHM's authority. If > 20m LOA, ask QHM's permission (VHF Ch 11) to enter, leave or move in hbr, especially in fog. Fishing and ‡ in chans are prohib.

NAVIGATION
WPT No 4 Bar buoy, QR, 50°46'·98N 01°06'·27W, 150°/330° from/to hbr ent (W side), 4½ca. Beware very strong tides in hbr ent, commercial shipping and ferries, Gosport ferry and HM Ships.
Speed limit is 10kn within hbr and within 1000 yds of the shore in any part of the Dockyard Port; speed = speed through the water. Outside the hbr ent, the Dockyard Port limits embrace the Solent from Hillhead and Old Castle Pt (close NE of Cowes) eastward to Eastney and Shanklin (IOW), thence almost out to Nab Tr (see AC 394 & 2050).
Historic Wrecks (see 8.0.3h) are at: 50°45'·8N 01°06'·2W (site of *Mary Rose*), marked by SPM buoys; 5ca SSW of Spit Sand Ft. *Invincible* lies at 50°44'·34N 01°02'·23W, 117° Horse Sand Fort 1·45M, marked by SPM buoy.
Approaches: From the W, yachts can use the Swashway Chan (to NW of Spit Sand Fort) which carries about 2m; keep War Memorial and RH edge of block of flats on at 049°. The Inner Swashway Chan (Round Tr on 029°. NB: rear transit, diving tank, has been demolished) carries only 0·1m; local knowledge required.
Approaching inshore from E, the submerged barrier, which extends from Southsea to Horse Sand Fort, should only be crossed via the unlit Inshore Boat passage (0·9m) 1ca off the beach, marked by R & G piles; or via the Main Passage (min depth 1·2m) 7ca further S, marked by G pile and dolphin, QR.
A Small Boat Channel for craft < 20m LOA lies at the hbr ent, parallel to and outboard of the W edge of the main dredged chan. It runs from abeam No 4 Bar buoy, QR (off Clarence Pier) to Ballast buoy, Fl R 2·5s, and extends about 50m off Fort Blockhouse. A depth gauge is on pile BC4. Yachts should enter by the Small Boat Chan; they may also enter on the E side of the main chan, but clear of it and close inshore. All yachts must leave via the Small Boat Chan. Yachts may only cross the main chan N of Ballast buoy or S of No 4 Bar buoy. Yachts must motor (if so fitted) between No 4 Bar and Ballast buoys; winds at the ent may be fickle or gusty and tides run hard. At night the Small Boat Chan is covered by the Oc R sector (324°-330°) of the Dir WRG lt on Fort Blockhouse (W side of hbr ent), until close to the hbr ent. Thereafter the Iso R 2s sector (337·5°-345°) of the Dir WRG lt 2m 1M (dolphin E of Gosport Marina) leads 341° through the ent and close abeam Ballast Bank PHM buoy, Fl R 2·5s.

LIGHTS AND MARKS
From E of the IOW, Nab Tower, Fl 10s 27m 16M, is conspic about 10M SE of the hbr ent. In the inner appr's there are 3 conspic forts: Horse Sand Fort, Iso G 2s; No Man's Land Fort, Iso R 2s, and Spit Sand Fort, Fl R 5s.
Ldg marks/lts: St Jude's ✠ spire and Southsea Castle lt ho in transit 003° lead between Outer Spit SCM buoy, Q (6) + L Fl 15s, and Horse Sand SHM buoy, Fl G 2·5s. At night keep in the W sector (000°-003°) between the Al WG and Al WR sectors of the Dir lt (H24) on Southsea Castle, which also shows a lt Iso 2s 16m 11M, vis 337°-071° (94°).

FIRING RANGE
Tipner Rifle Range as shown on chartlet. The danger area extends 2,500 metres from firing range. When firing is in progress, R flag or ⓡ lt on Tipner Range FS indicates yachts should clear the range danger area or transit it as quickly as possible.

RADIO TELEPHONE
Yachts should monitor Ch **11** (H24) for traffic/nav info. For the Camber call *Portsmouth Hbr Radio* (Commercial Port) Ch 11 14 (H24).
Haslar Marina and *Port Solent* Ch **80** M (H24). *Gosport Marina* call Ch **80** M (HO). Fareham Marina Ch M (summer 0900-1730). Wicor Marina Ch 80 (0900-1730, Mon-Sat). Naval activities to the S/SE of Portsmouth and IOW may be advised by Solent CG Ch 67 or ☎ (01705) 552100; or Naval Ops ☎ 722008. Naval vessels use Ch 13. The positions and times of naval firings and underwater explosions are broadcast daily at 0800 and 1400LT Ch 06; preceded by a Securité call on Ch 16. Warnings of underwater explosions will also be broadcast on Ch 16 at 1 hour, at 30 mins and just before the detonation.
TELEPHONE (Portsmouth/Gosport 01705; Fareham 01329) QHM 723124; DQHM 723794/☎ 722831; Hbr Control (H24) 723694; Commercial Docks 297395; Camber Berthing Offices ☎ 297395 Ext 310; ⌗ 0345 231110 (H24); MRSC 552100; Marinecall 0891 500457; Weather Centre (01703) 228844; Police 321111; Dr (Gosport) 80922; Fareham Health Centre (01329) 282911; Ⓗ 822331.

FACILITIES
Marinas (from seaward)
Haslar Marina, ☎ 601201, ☎ 602201, £16.10, (550+ 50 Ⓥ); Access H24; Ⓥ at L pontoon, near conspic former lt ship, Bar & R (☎ 219847); FW, AC, Gas, Gaz, CH, ME, Ⓔ, ⊘, Slip (upstream of Haslar bridge). RNSA berths at S end.
Gosport Marina (350, some visitors) ☎ 524811, ☎ 589541, £13.47, P, D, FW, ME, El, Sh, BH (150, 40 ton), CH, V, R, AC, Bar, Gas, Gaz, SM, ⊘. Note: There are RNSA pontoons at the N end of Cold Hbr, inside the Fuel Jetty. Also 150 pile moorings (some dry); contact Haslar Marina.
   Services: CH, P, D, ACA, El, Ⓔ, ME, Sh, BY, SM, Slip, C.
Gosport EC Wed; ⊠, Ⓑ, ⇌ (Portsmouth), ✈ (Southampton).
   Services SM, ACA; **Hbr** Moorings ☎ 832484.
City of Portsmouth (3M) EC Wed (Southsea Sat); ⊠, Ⓑ, ⇌, Ferries to Caen (Ouistreham), Cherbourg, Le Havre, St Malo, Bilbao, Santander (winter) and IoW (see 8.0.4); ✈ (Southampton).
Port Solent Marina, see page 240 for chartlet and text.
FAREHAM (01329)
   Fareham Marina ☎ 822445, M, Slip, D, FW, ME, El, Ⓔ, Sh, V, Bar, CH; (Access HW±3); **Fareham Yacht Hbr; Wicor Marine** (200) ☎ 237112, ☎ 825660, Slip, M, D, ME, Sh, CH, AC, BH (10 ton), C (7 ton), FW, El, Ⓔ, Gas, Gaz. Fareham Lake is well marked, but only partially lit up to Bedenham Pier and unlit thereafter. Chan dries 0·9m in final 5ca to Town Quay.
Services: M, Sh, CH, ME, Slip, El, Ⓔ, D, FW, Gas, AC, SM.
Town EC Wed; ⊠, Ⓑ, ⇌, ✈ (Southampton).
Clubs
   Royal Naval Sailing Association ☎ 823524, ☎ 870654; **Royal Naval & Royal Albert YC** ☎ 825924, M, Bar; **Portsmouth SC** ☎ 820596; **Portchester SC** ☎ 376375; **Hardway SC** ☎ 581875, Slip, M, L, FW, C (mast stepping only), AB; **Gosport CC** ☎ (01329) 47014 or (0860) 966390; **Fareham Sailing & Motor Boat Club** ☎ (01329) 280738.

continued

PORTSMOUTH *continued*

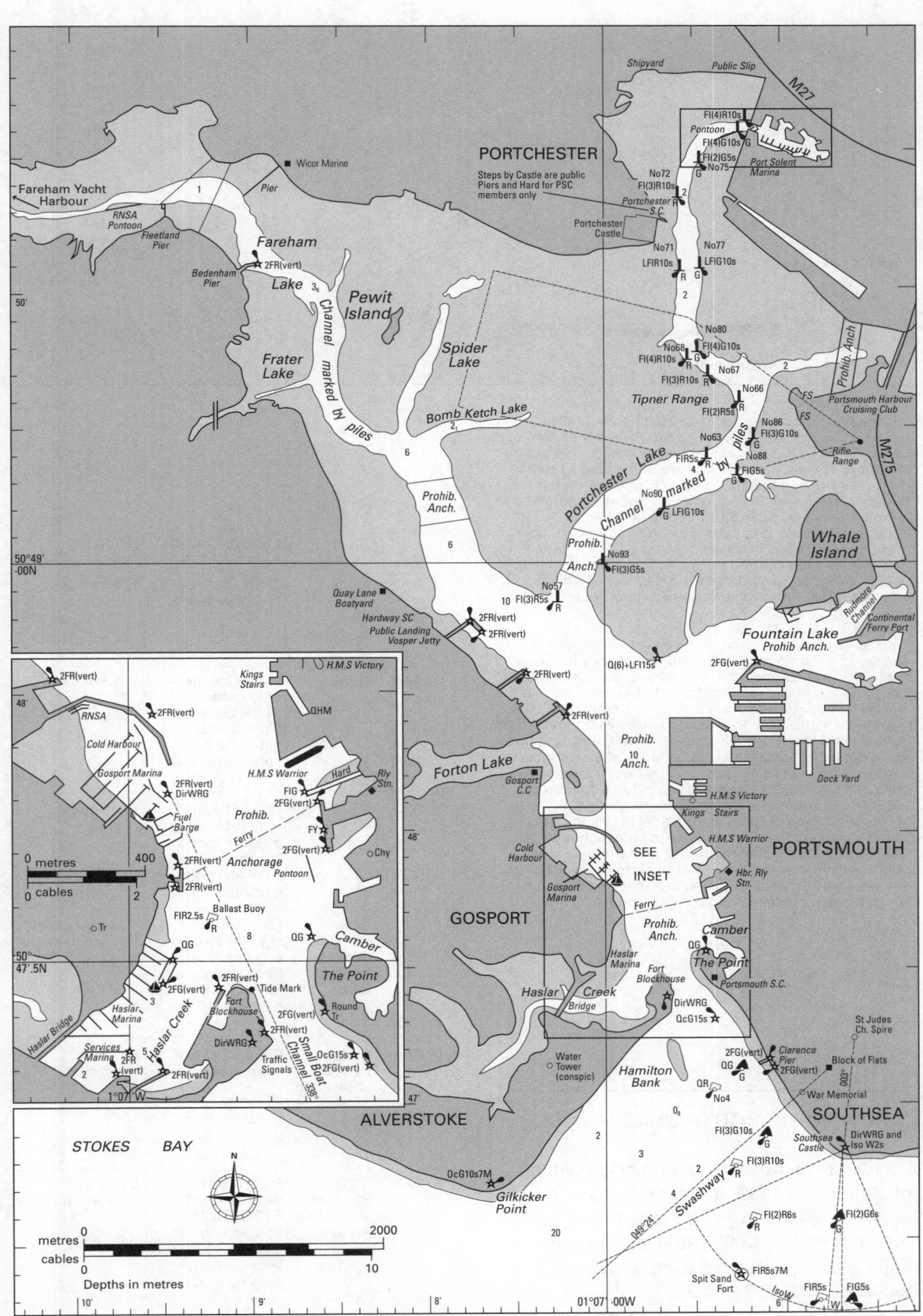

Shipyard   Public Slip

PORTCHESTER

M27

Fl(4)R10s
Pontoon
Fl(4)G10s/G
Fl(2)G5s
G   No75
No72
Fl(3)R10s
R   2
Port Solent
Marina

Steps by Castle are public
Piers and Hard for PSC
members only

Portchester
S.C.

Portchester Castle

No71   No77
LFlR10s   LFlG10s
R   2   G

Wicor Marine

Fareham Yacht Harbour
RNSA Pontoon
Fleetland Pier
Bedenham Pier
2FR(vert)
Fareham
Lake   3₈
Pewit Island
Frater Lake
Spider Lake
Channel marked by piles
6
Bomb Ketch Lake   2₄
Prohib. Anch.
6

No80
No68   Fl(4)G10s
Fl(4)R10s   G
R   No67
No66
Fl(3)R10s
R
Fl(2)R5s
No63   No86
G   Fl(3)G10s
FlR5s G No88
4   G FlG5s
Tipner Range
Portchester Lake   Channel marked by piles
No90 LFlG10s
G

FS
FS
Portsmouth Harbour Cruising Club
Rifle Range

Prohib. Anch.

M275

Whale Island

50' ─────

50°49'·00N ─────

Prohib. Anch.
6
Prohib.
Anch.
No93
Fl(3)G5s

Rudmore Channel
Continental Ferry Port

Quay Lane Boatyard
Hardway SC
Public Landing
Vosper Jetty
10   Fl(3)R5s
No57
R
2FR(vert)
2FR(vert)

Fountain Lake
Prohib Anch.

Q(6)+LFl15s
2FG(vert)

H.M.S Victory
Kings Stairs
QHM

2FR(vert)
2FR(vert)

Prohib.
10
Anch.

H.M.S Victory
Kings Stairs

H.M.S Warrior

Dock Yard

PORTSMOUTH

H.M.S Warrior   Hard   Rly Stn.
FlG
2FG(vert)
FY
2FG(vert)
Ferry
Anchorage Pontoon
Chy
2FR(vert)
2FR(vert)
FlR2.5s
R
Ballast Buoy
QG   8   QG
Camber
2FG(vert)
2FR(vert)   Tide Mark
Fort Blockhouse
DirWRG
2FR(vert)
Round Tr
OcG15s
2FG(vert)
Traffic Signals
Small Boat Channel 338°
5   Haslar Creek
2FR (vert)   2FR(vert)

Forton Lake
Gosport C.C.

Cold Harbour
Gosport Marina
Haslar Marina
Fort Blockhouse
Haslar Creek
Bridge

GOSPORT

SEE
INSET
Ferry
Prohib.
Anch.
Camber
The Point
Hbr. Rly Stn.
DirWRG
QcG15s
Portsmouth S.C.

St Judes Ch. Spire
2FG(vert)   Clarence Pier
QG   G   2FG(vert)
300°
Block of Flats
QR   No4   War Memorial
0₈
DirWRG and Iso W2s
Southsea Castle

SOUTHSEA

Hamilton Bank
Water Tower (conspic)

2
3
Fl(3)G10s
2   Fl(3)R10s
R
4   Swashway
046°24'
Fl(2)R6s
R
Fl(2)G6s
G

Spit Sand Fort
FlR5s7M
FlR5s   FlG5s
IsoW
6   W

STOKES   BAY
N
metres 0 ─────── 2000
cables 0 ─────── 10
Depths in metres

OcG10s7M
Gilkicker Point
20

INSET:
2FR(vert)
RNSA
2FR(vert)
Cold Harbour
Gosport Marina
2FR(vert)
DirWRG
Fuel Barge
Prohib.
Anchorage   Pontoon
metres 0 ──── 400
cables 0 ──── 2
2FR(vert)
Tr
FlR2.5s
R
QG
8
Haslar Bridge
2FG(vert)
3   Haslar Creek
Haslar Marina
Fort Blockhouse
Services Marina
2FR (vert)
5
2FR(vert)
2FR(vert)
DirWRG
1°07'W

ALVERSTOKE

48'
50°
47'·5N
47'

10'   9'   8'   01°07'·00W

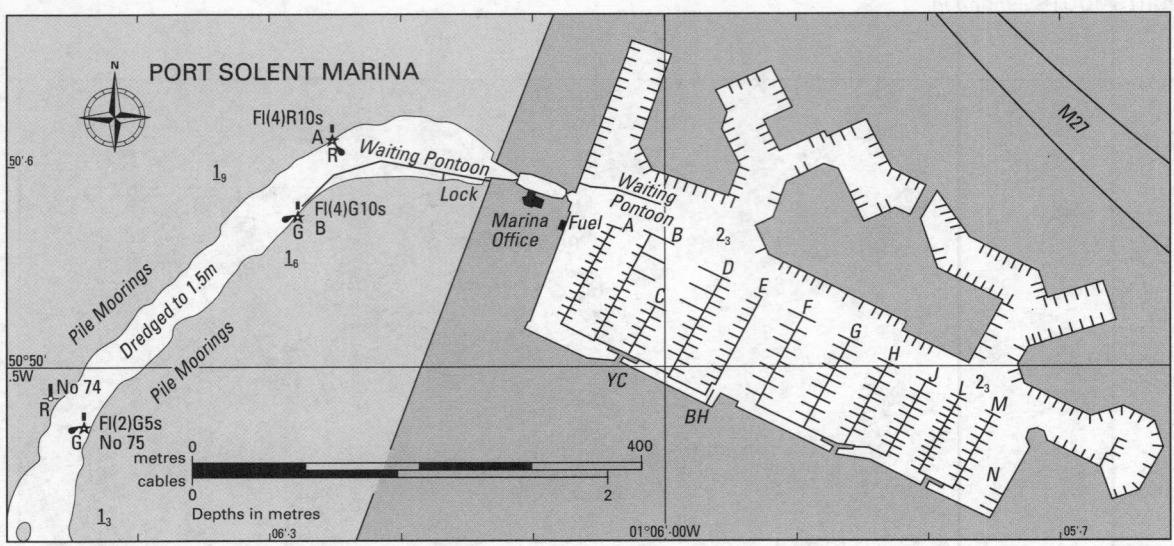

Port Solent, Portchester, (900) ☎ 210765, 🛥 324241,
£18.71, P, D, FW, AC, ME, EI, Ⓔ, Sh, BH (40 ton), CH, V, R,
Bar, Gas, Gaz, LPG, 🗵, 🅖. Portchester Lake is marked by
lit/unlit piles; unusually, PHMs are numbered 57 to 74
(from seaward), and SHMs 95 to 75. Beware unlit naval
buoys at the S end. Do not delay crossing Tipner Range,
S limit marked by piles 63/87 and N by 70/78.
Portchester Castle is conspic 5ca SSW of marina. Call
marina Ch 80 when inbound passing pile 78. Pile B, Fl (4)
G 10s, marks the waiting pontoon. See chartlet above.
Access H24 via chan dredged 1·5m to lock (43m x 9·1m);
enter on 3 Ⓖ (vert) or on loudspeaker instructions.

LOCAL VISUAL SIGNALS
   The traffic signals, shown in the next column, are
displayed at Fort Blockhouse and sometimes in the
vessel concerned and must be obeyed; except that craft
<20m LOA may use the Small Boat Chan H24 despite the
displayed tfc sigs. Monitor Ch 11. The Channel (or main
channel) is defined as the main navigable channels of the
harbour and the approach channel from Outer Spit buoy.
Fog Routine is broadcast on Ch 11 and 13, when it comes into
force, ie when the QHM considers that visibility is so low
that normal shipping movements would be dangerous.
Yachts may continue at the skipper's discretion, but with
great caution and keeping well clear of the main chan. They
should be aware that the presence of radar echoes from
small vessels within the main channel can cause much
doubt and difficulty to the Master of a large vessel. For their
own safety and that of major vessels they are strongly
advised not to proceed. Monitor VHF Ch 11 at all times.

		SIGNAL	MEANING AND APPLICATION	HOISTED/ DISPLAYED BY
1.	DAY	None.	Clear Channel – both directions.	Blockhouse.
	NIGHT	Ⓡ Ⓖ Ⓖ		
2.	DAY	None.	Clear Channel – only outgoing traffic allowed. No vessel shall enter the main or approach channel from seaward.	Blockhouse.
	NIGHT	Ⓦ Ⓖ		
3.	DAY	None.	Clear Channel – only incoming traffic allowed. No other vessel shall leave the harbour.	Blockhouse.
	NIGHT	Ⓖ Ⓦ		
4.	DAY	Code Pennant above Pennant Zero.	Clear Channel – signal flown by privileged vessel. Such vessels are to be given a clear passage.	Vessels & tugs in whose favour signal is in force
	NIGHT	None		
5.	DAY	Code Pennant above flag Alpha.	Diving – vessel conducting diving.	By vessel concerned.
	NIGHT	Ⓡ Ⓦ Ⓡ		
6.	DAY	Code Pennant above flag Romeo above flag Yankee.	POTENTIALLY HAZARDOUS OPERATIONS. You should proceed at slow speed when passing me.	By vessel concerned.
	NIGHT	None		

NEW PORTSMOUTH DIALLING CODE

A new **Portsmouth** dialling code will be
introduced in 1999. It can be used in parallel with the existing code for at least a year.
The new code 023 92 replaces the present
dialling code. Thus existing 01705 926222
becomes 023 92 926222.

2

LANGSTONE HARBOUR   8-2-32
Hampshire 50°47'·20N 01°01'·45W (Ent)   Rtg 3-2-2

CHARTS
AC *5600.9, 3418, 2045*; Imray C3, Y33; Stanfords 10, 11; OS 196, 197

TIDES
+0022 Dover; Zone 0 (UT)

Standard Port PORTSMOUTH (←)

Times				Height (metres)			
High Water		Low Water		MHWS	MHWN	MLWN	MLWS
0500	1000	0000	0600	4·7	3·8	1·9	0·8
1700	2200	1200	1800				
Differences LANGSTONE							
0000	0000	+0010	+0010	+0·1	+0·1	0·0	0·0
NAB TOWER							
+0015	0000	+0015	+0015	−0·2	0·0	+0·2	0·0

SHELTER
Very good in marina (2·4m) to W inside ent, access HW±3 over tidal flap 1·6m CD; waiting pontoon. Ent is 7m wide. 6 Y ⚓s at W side of hbr ent, 6 more on E side; max LOA 9m. Or ⚓ out of the fairway in Russell's Lake or Langstone Chan (water ski area); or see Hr Mr (E side of ent). Hbr speed limit 10kn.

NAVIGATION
WPT 50°46'·28N 01°01'·27W, Langstone Fairway SWM buoy, L Fl 10s, 168°/348° from/to QR lt at ent, 0·94M. Bar has about 1·8m. Ent chan lies between East and West Winner drying banks, which afford some protection. Appr is easy in most weather, best from HW −3 to +1, but avoid entry against the ebb, esp at sp and in strong onshore winds. In strong S/SE winds do not attempt entry.

LIGHTS AND MARKS
Ldg marks (concrete dolphins), or Fairway buoy on with conspic chy, lead 344° just clear of East Winner. The ent itself deepens and favours the W side. The narrow appr chan to Southsea Marina is marked by 7 SHM piles, only the first of which is lit, Fl G. There are 9 PHM piles; the 4th, 6th and 9th are Fl R. The lock has R/G ent sigs, as it is too narrow for 2 boats to pass; vessels going with the tide have priority.

RADIO TELEPHONE
Harbour VHF Ch 12 16 (Summer 0830-1700 daily. Winter: Mon-Fri 0830-1700; Sat-Sun 0830-1300). Marina Ch 80 M (0800-1800 daily).

TELEPHONE (Dial code 01705)
Hr Mr 463419; MRSC 552100; ⌗ 0345 231110 (H24); Marinecall 0891 500457; Police 321111; Dr 465721.

FACILITIES
Southsea Marina (300) ☎ 822719, ☎ 822220, £10.80, AC, FW, D, Access HW±3, CH, BH (20 ton), Gaz, C (6 ton);
Hayling Pontoon (E side of ent), AB, P, D, FW, L, Slip;
Langstone SC ☎ 484577, Slip, M, L, FW, Bar;
Eastney Cruising Ass'n (ECA) ☎ 734103, 6 ⚓s; **Hayling Ferry SC**; **Locks SC** ☎ 829833; **Tudor SC** (Hilsea) ☎ 662002, Slip, M, FW, Bar.
Towns: EC Havant Wed; ✉ (Eastney, Hayling), ⒷB (Havant, Hayling, Emsworth), ⇌ (bus to Havant), ✈ (Southampton).

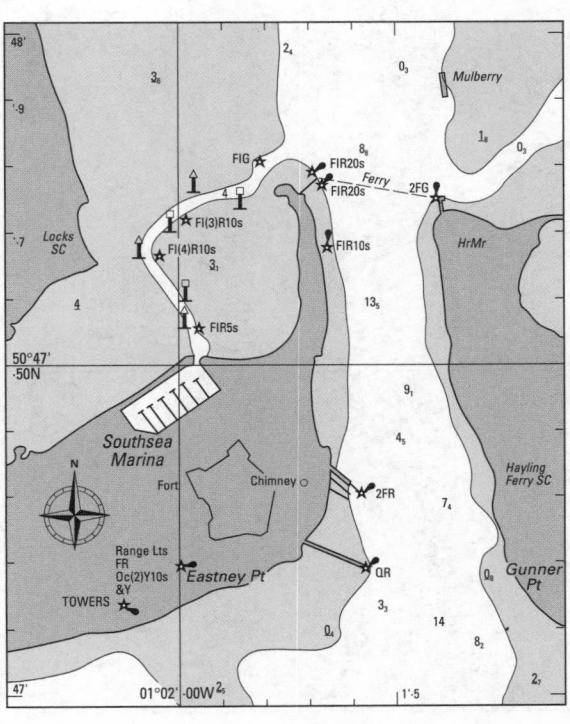

CHICHESTER HARBOUR   8-2-33
W. Sussex 50°46'·83N 00°55'·97W   Rtg 3-1-1

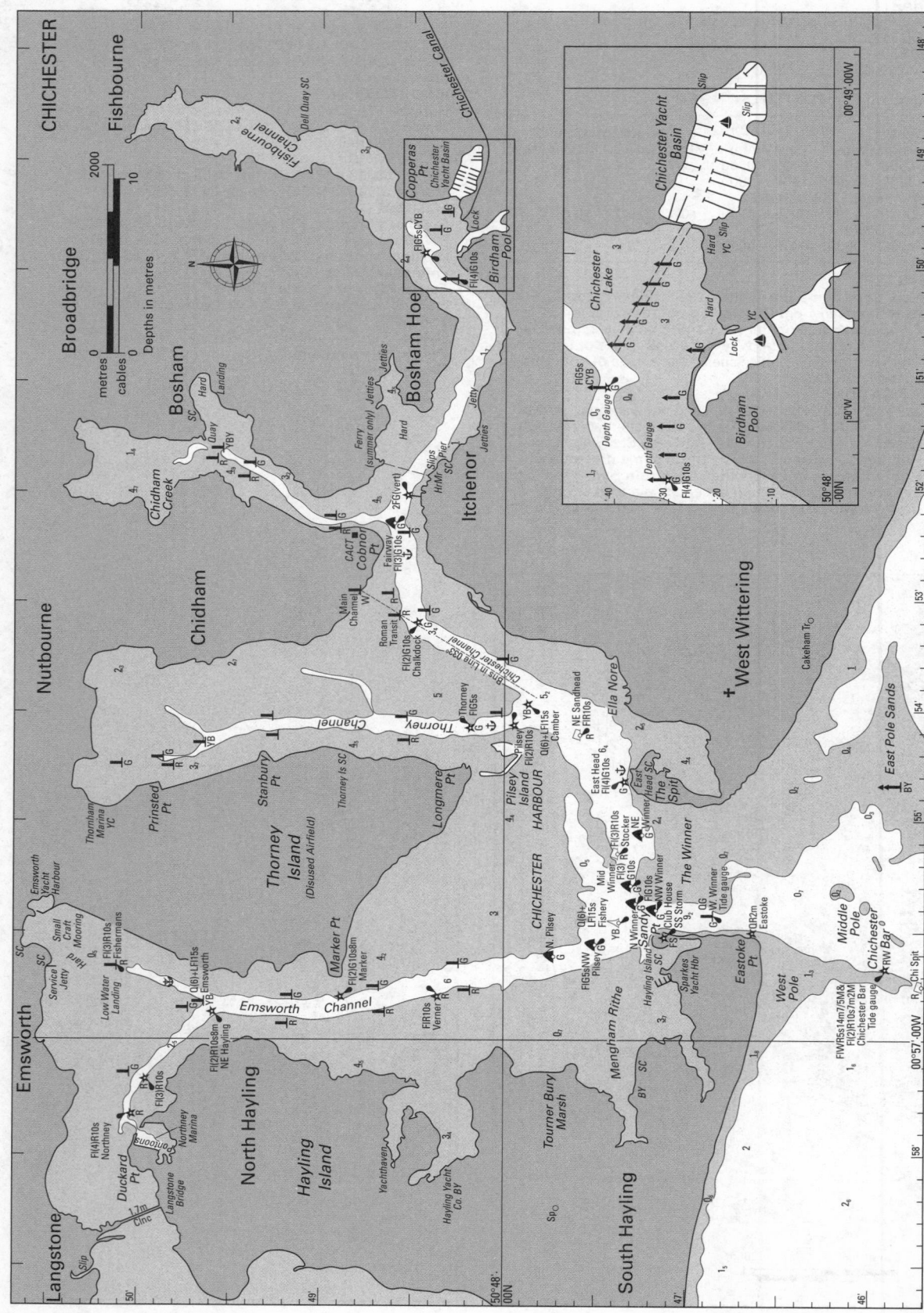

CHARTS
AC *3418, 2045*; Imray C4, C9, Y33; Stanfords 10, 11; OS 197
TIDES
+0027 Dover; ML 2·8; Zone 0 (UT); see curves on 8·2·13

Standard Port PORTSMOUTH (←—)

Times				Height (metres)			
High Water		Low Water		MHWS	MHWN	MLWN	MLWS
0500	1000	0000	0600	4·7	3·8	1·9	0·8
1700	2200	1200	1800				
Differences HARBOUR ENTRANCE							
–0010	+0005	+0015	+0020	+0·2	+0·2	0·0	+0·1
NORTHNEY							
+0010	+0015	+0015	+0025	+0·2	0·0	–0·2	–0·3
ITCHENOR							
–0005	+0005	+0005	+0025	+0·1	0·0	–0·2	–0·2
BOSHAM							
0000	+0010	No data		+0·2	+0·1	No data	
DELL QUAY							
+0005	+0015	No data		+0·2	+0·1	No data	
SELSEY BILL							
–0005	–0005	+0035	+0035	+0·6	+0·6	0·0	0·0

SHELTER
Excellent in all five main chans, ie: Emsworth, Thorney, Chichester, Bosham, Itchenor Reach and Fishbourne. There are six yacht hbrs and marinas (see FACILITIES); also about 50 🛟s at Emsworth and Itchenor. Recognised ⚓s in Thorney Chan off Pilsey Is; off E Head (uncomfortable in NE winds); and in Chichester Chan off Chalkdock Point. Hbr speed limit of 8kn is rigidly enforced; max fine £2500.
NAVIGATION
WPT 50°45'·50N 00°56'·50W, 193°/013° from/to Bar Bn, 0·4M. Best entry is HW –3 to +1, to avoid confused seas on the ebb, esp in onshore winds >F 5. Do not attempt entry in S'ly gales. Bar is dredged 1·5m, but after gales depths may vary ±0·75m. Leave Bar Bn (tide gauge) close to port; the chan N'ward is effectively only about 200m wide.

APPROACHES: **From the W**, the astern transit 255° of No Man's Land Fort and Ryde ⌖ spire (hard to see) leads to the Bar Bn. Closer in, transit 064° of Target NCM Bn with Cakeham Tr leads 6ca S of Bar Bn; thence alter 013° as Eastoke Pt opens to E of Bar Bn. CHI SPIT unlit PHM buoy (approx 2ca SxW of Bar Bn, Apr-Nov) must be rounded to clear W Pole spit, dries 0·2m. This spit lies within the 020°-080° sector of the ☆ Fl (2) R 10s, below the main Bar bn 0·4M. **From the E/SE** (Looe Chan) keep W for 2M, then NW; pick up an astern brg 184° of Nab Tr, toward the Bar Bn, so as to clear the shoals of Bracklesham Bay. The former Owers LANBY is now a SCM buoy, Q (6) + L Fl 15s, Whis, Racon. Note: An Historic Wreck (*Hazardous*) lies at 50°45'·10N 00°51'·47W, brg 105°/3·2M from Bar Bn; see 8.0.3h.

ENTRANCE: Pass between Eastoke bn QR and W Winner bn QG (tide gauge). Three SHM lt buoys mark the edge of The Winner shoal, dries, to stbd of the ent. At Fishery SCM buoy, Q (6) + L Fl 15s, chan divides: N to Emsworth and ENE toward Chichester. Stocker's Sand, dries 2·4m, is marked by 3 PHM lt buoys. East Head bn, Fl (4) G 10s, (tide gauge) marks start of anchorage.

EMSWORTH CHANNEL: Chan is straight, broad, deep and well marked/lit in the 2·5M reach to Emsworth SCM bn, Q (6) + L Fl 15s, where Sweare Deep forks NW to Northney. Good ⚓s especially N of Sandy Pt near ent to chan. Here an unlit ECM bn marks chan to Sparkes Yacht Hbr.

THORNEY CHANNEL: Strangers should go up at half-flood. Ent is at Camber SCM bn, Q (6) + L Fl 15s; pass between Pilsey and Thorney Lt bns, thereafter chan is marked by perches. Above Stanbury Pt chan splits, Prinsted Chan to port (full of moorings) and Nutbourne Chan to stbd; both dry at N ends. There is plenty of room to ⚓ in Thorney Chan, well protected from E and SE winds.

CHICHESTER CHANNEL: This runs up to Itchenor Reach and Bosham Chan. From NE Sandhead PHM by, Fl R 10s, transit 033° of Roman Transit bn on with Main Chan Bn and distant clump of trees leads to Chalkdock Bn, Fl (2) G 10s. Here alter 082° to Fairway buoy, Fl (3) G 10s; on this reach a measured half-mile is marked by Y perches. At Deep End SCM bn turn N into Bosham Chan, or ESE into Itchenor Reach, for Birdham Pool and Chichester Marina. ⚓ prohib in Itchenor Reach and Bosham Chan.

LIGHTS AND MARKS
Bar Bn, R/W wooden twr + R can topmark, Fl WR 5s 14m 7/5M, vis W 322°-080°, R080°-322°; and same tr, Fl (2) R 10s 7m 2M, 020°-080°; also tide gauge. 3 SHM Bys: NW Winner Fl G 10s; N Winner Fl (2) G10s; Mid Winner Fl (3) G 10s. Fishery SCM Q (6)+L Fl 15s. All chans well marked.
RADIO TELEPHONE
Hr Mr, call *Chichester* VHF Ch **14** 16 (Patrol craft *Aella* on Ch14). (Apl-Sept: 0900-1300, 1400-1730. Oct-Mar: Mon-Fri 0900-1300, 1400-1730. Sat 0900-1300). Tarquin Yacht Hbr and Northney Marina Ch **80** M. Chichester Marina Ch M.
TELEPHONE (Dial code 01243)
Chichester Hbr Conservancy Office 512301, 📠 513026; ⌗ 0345 231110 (H24); MRSC (01705) 552100; Weather info (01705) 8091; Marinecall 0891 500457; Police 536733; Ⓗ 787970.
FACILITIES
EMSWORTH CHANNEL
Emsworth Yacht Harbour (200+20 Ⓥ) ☎ 377727, 📠 378498, £10; access HW±2 over 2·4m sill which maintains 1·5m inside, Slip, Gas, ME, EI, AC, Sh, P, D, FW, BH (60 ton), C (20 ton). **Service jetty** (E of Emsworth SC) 50m long, ☆ 2FR (vert); access HW±4. Free for max 2 hrs stay, FW.
Slips at South St, Kings St, and Slipper Mill; contact the Warden ☎ 376422.
Services: ME, Sh, CH, EI, ACA; Emsworth EC Wed.
HAYLING ISLAND (01705)
Sparkes Yacht Hbr (150 + 30 Ⓥ) ☎ 463572, mobile 0370-365610, 📠 465741, £36.00, access all tides via chan dredged 2m; pontoons have 1·6m. Slip, ME, EI, FW, P, D, AC, M, Gas, Gaz, Ⓞ, Sh, C (25 ton), CH. From close N of Sandy Pt, appr on transit 277° of two x bns; thence alter S, past 3 PHM bns to marina.
Northney Marina (260+27 visitors) ☎ 466321, 📠 461467; pre-call Ch 80. Access all tides via chan 1m; £8.93, D, Bar, FW, AC, EI, Sh, BH (35 ton), R, CH, ME;
Services: ME, EI, Slip, BH (8 ton), P, FW, Sh, CH. EC Wed.
THORNEY CHANNEL
Thornham Marina (77+6 visitors), ☎ 375335, 📠 371522, £7.00, appr via drying chan, P & D (cans), FW, Sh, ME, C (10 ton), BH (12 ton), Slip, R, Bar. **Services**: CH, BY.
CHICHESTER CHANNEL/ITCHENOR REACH
Hard available at all stages of the tide. There are 6 🛟s off Itchenor jetty and a 90ft pontoon. For moorings apply Hr Mr. **Services**: Slip, P & D (cans), CH, Sh, FW, M, EI, Ⓔ, ME. Itchenor EC Thurs.
BOSHAM CHANNEL
For moorings (200+) contact the Quaymaster ☎ 573336. ⚓ prohib in chan which mostly dries, access HW±2.
Bosham Quay Hard, L, FW, AB; **Services**: SM. EC Wed.
CHICHESTER LAKE
Birdham Pool: (230+10 visitors) ☎ 512310, £12, enter chan at Birdham SHM bn, Fl (4) G 10s, with depth gauge; access HW ±3 via lock. **Services**: Slip, P, D, FW, EI, Ⓔ, AC, Sh, CH, Gas, ME, SM, C (3 ton).
Chichester Marina: (1000+50 visitors) ☎ 512731, 📠 513472, £16.04, enter chan at CYB SHM pile, Fl G 5s, with depth gauge; 6kn speed limit. The well marked chan has approx 0·5m below CD; no access LW ±1½; a waiting pontoon is outside the lock.
Traffic sigs:
    Q Ⓡ (S of tr) = <1m water in chan.
    Q Ⓨ (top of tr) = both gates open (free flow).
Lock sigs: Ⓡ = Wait; Ⓖ = Enter.
Yachts lock out in numerical sequence, as assigned by lock-keeper on Ch 80, except during free-flow. From Easter to 30 Sep, the lock is manned Mon-Thur 0700-2100; Fri 0700 -2359; Sat, Sun, Bank Hols 0600-2359; all LT. 1 Oct to Easter: Contact ☎ 512731 or call VHF Ch M, 80.
Services: Slip, P, D, FW, ME, EI, Sh, AC, Gas, Gaz, CH, BY, BH (20 ton), V, R, Bar, Ⓞ, ACA, SM, Ⓖ.
FISHBOURNE CHANNEL
Dell Quay: Possible drying berth against the Quay, apply to Hbr Office, public slip. **Services**: Sh, Slip, BH, M, L.
Clubs
Bosham SC ☎ 572341; **Chichester YC** ☎ 512918, R, Bar, Ⓞ; **Chichester Cruiser and Racing Club** ☎ 371731; **Dell Quay SC** ☎ 785080; **Emsworth SC** ☎ 373065; **Emsworth Slipper SC** ☎ 372523; **Hayling Island SC** ☎ (01705) 463768; **Itchenor SC** ☎ 512400; **Mengham Rithe SC** ☎ (01705) 463337; **Thorney Island SC**; **W Wittering SC**.
Cobnor Activities Centre Trust (at Cobnor Pt) gets many young people, inc disabled ♿, afloat. ☎ 01243 572791.

NAVAL EXERCISE AREAS (SUBFACTS & GUNFACTS)

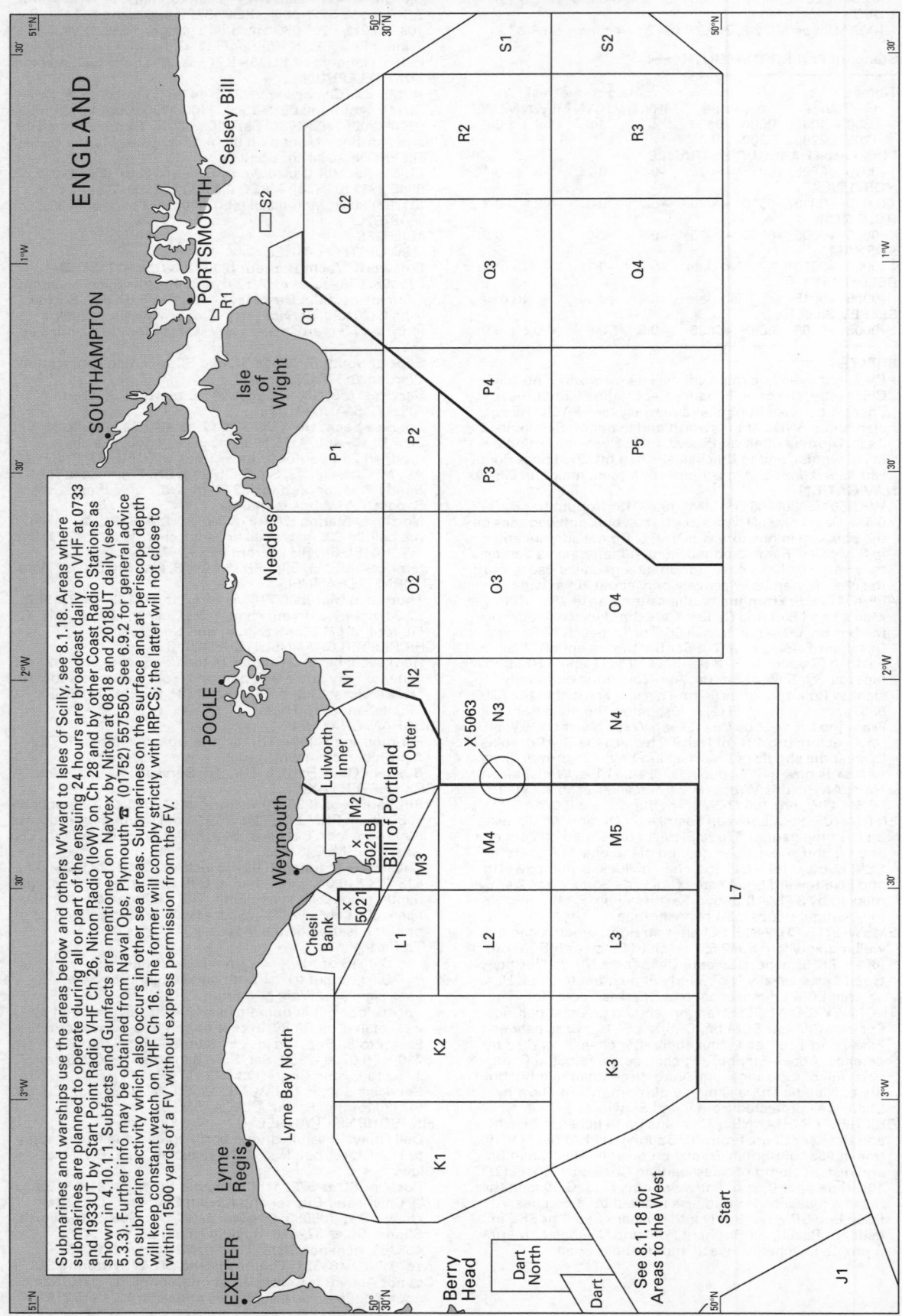

Submarines and warships use the areas below and others W'ward to Isles of Scilly, see 8.1.18. Areas where submarines are planned to operate during all or part of the ensuing 24 hours are broadcast daily on VHF at 0733 and 1933UT by Start Point Radio VHF Ch 26, Niton Radio (IoW) on Ch 28 and by other Coast Radio Stations as shown in 4.10.1.1. Subfacts and Gunfacts are mentioned on Navtex by Niton at 0818 and 2018UT daily (see 5.3.3). Further info may be obtained from Naval Ops, Plymouth ☎ (01752) 557550. See 6.9.2 for general advice on submarine activity which also occurs in other sea areas. Submarines on the surface and at periscope depth will keep constant watch on VHF Ch 16. The former will comply strictly with IRPCS; the latter will not close to within 1500 yards of a FV without express permission from the FV.

VOLVO PENTA SERVICE

Sales and service centres in area 3

SUSSEX *Felton Marine Engineering,* Brighton Marina, Brighton BN2 5UF Tel (01273) 601779 **LONDON** *John A. Sparks & Co. Ltd,* Ardwell Road, Streatham Hill SW2 4RT Tel 0181- 674 3434

3

Area 3

South-East England
Selsey Bill to North Foreland

VOLVO PENTA

8.3.1	Index	**Page 245**
8.3.2	Diagram of ports, lights, RDF bns, Coast radio and weather Stns	**246**
8.3.3	Tidal stream charts	**248**
8.3.4	List of coastal lLights, fog signals and waypoints	**250**
8.3.5	Passage information	**252**
8.3.6	Distance table	**253**
8.3.7	English Channel waypoints	**See 8.1.7**
8.3.8	Littlehampton	**254**
8.3.9	Shoreham, Standard Port, tidal curves	**255**
8.3.10	Brighton	**259**
8.3.11	Newhaven	**260**
8.3.12	Eastbourne	**260**
8.3.13	Rye Hastings	**261**
8.3.14	Folkestone	**262**
8.3.15	Dover, Standard Port, tidal curves	**262**
8.3.16	Dover Strait	**267**
8.3.17	Ramsgate Sandwich	**268**

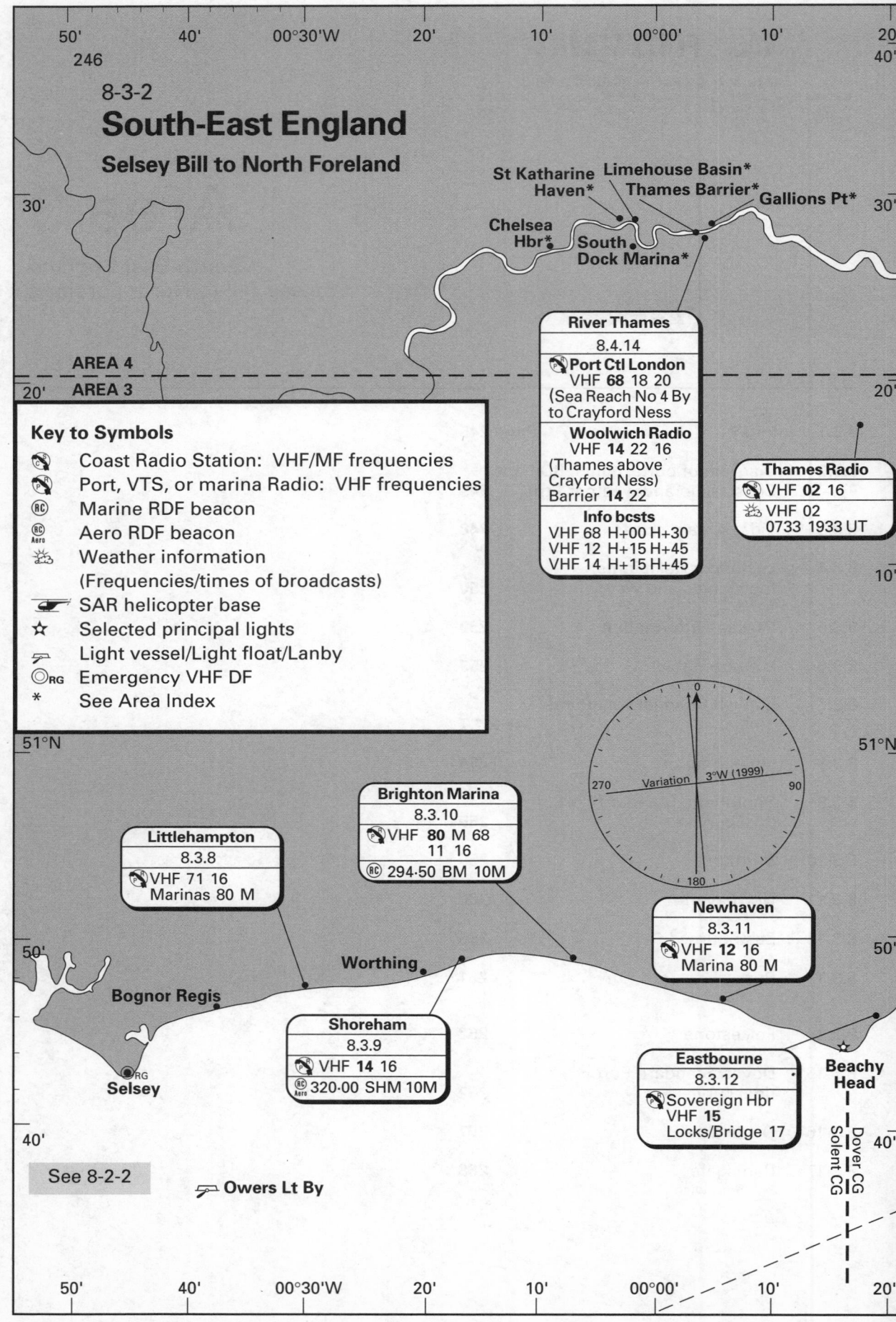

8-3-2

South-East England

Selsey Bill to North Foreland

50' 40' 00°30'W 20' 10' 00°00' 10' 20

30' 30' 30'

St Katharine Limehouse Basin*
Haven* Thames Barrier* Gallions Pt*
Chelsea
Hbr* South
Dock Marina*

River Thames

8.4.14

🕭 **Port Ctl London**
VHF **68** 18 20
(Sea Reach No 4 By
to Crayford Ness

Woolwich Radio
VHF **14** 22 16
(Thames above
Crayford Ness)
Barrier **14** 22

Info bcsts
VHF 68 H+00 H+30
VHF 12 H+15 H+45
VHF 14 H+15 H+45

Thames Radio

🕭 VHF **02** 16
🌦 VHF 02
0733 1933 UT

AREA 4

AREA 3 20' 20'

Key to Symbols

🕭 Coast Radio Station: VHF/MF frequencies
🕭ᴿ Port, VTS, or marina Radio: VHF frequencies
Ⓡⓒ Marine RDF beacon
Ⓡⓒ Aero Aero RDF beacon
🌦 Weather information
  (Frequencies/times of broadcasts)
🚁 SAR helicopter base
☆ Selected principal lights
🚤 Light vessel/Light float/Lanby
⒪ʀɢ Emergency VHF DF
* See Area Index

10'

51°N 51°N

0

270 Variation 3°W (1999) 90

180

Brighton Marina

8.3.10

🕭 VHF **80** M 68
11 16
Ⓡⓒ 294·50 BM 10M

Newhaven

8.3.11

🕭 VHF **12** 16
Marina 80 M

Littlehampton

8.3.8

🕭ᴿ VHF 71 16
Marinas 80 M

50' 50'

Worthing

Bognor Regis

Shoreham

8.3.9

🕭 VHF **14** 16
Ⓡⓒ Aero 320·00 SHM 10M

Eastbourne

8.3.12

🕭 Sovereign Hbr
VHF **15**
Locks/Bridge 17

**Beachy
Head**

⒪ʀɢ
Selsey

40' 40'

See 8-2-2

🚤 Owers Lt By

Dover CG
Solent CG

50' 40' 00°30'W 20' 10' 00°00' 10' 20'

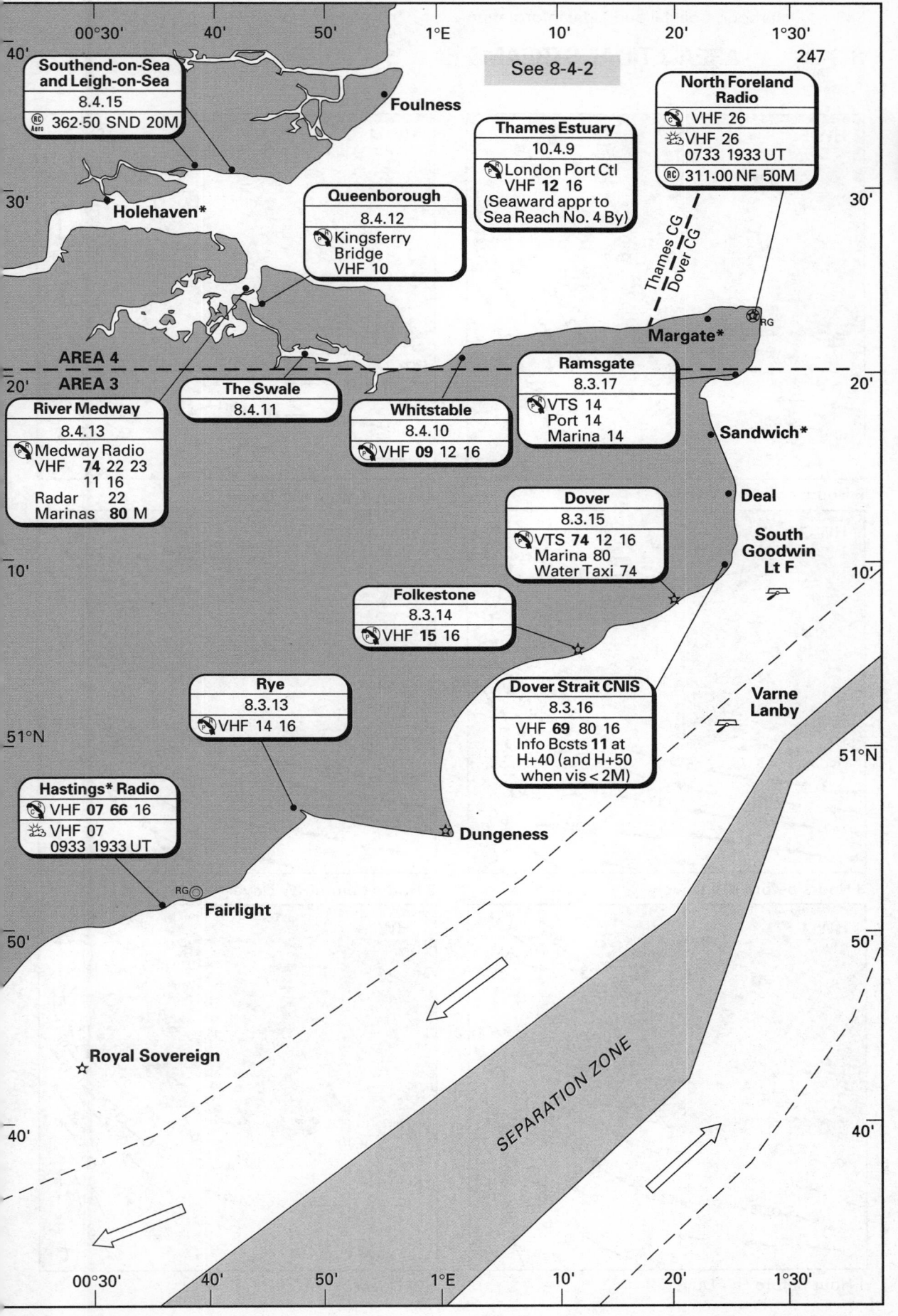

3

See 8-4-2

Foulness

Southend-on-Sea and Leigh-on-Sea
8.4.15
362·50 SND 20M

Holehaven*

Queenborough
8.4.12
Kingsferry Bridge
VHF 10

Thames Estuary
10.4.9
London Port Ctl
VHF 12 16
(Seaward appr to Sea Reach No. 4 By)

North Foreland Radio
VHF 26
VHF 26
0733 1933 UT
311·00 NF 50M

Thames CG
Dover CG

Margate* RG

AREA 4

AREA 3

The Swale
8.4.11

River Medway
8.4.13
Medway Radio
VHF 74 22 23
11 16
Radar 22
Marinas 80 M

Whitstable
8.4.10
VHF 09 12 16

Ramsgate
8.3.17
VTS 14
Port 14
Marina 14

Sandwich*

Deal

Dover
8.3.15
VTS 74 12 16
Marina 80
Water Taxi 74

South Goodwin Lt F

Folkestone
8.3.14
VHF 15 16

Rye
8.3.13
VHF 14 16

Dover Strait CNIS
8.3.16
VHF 69 80 16
Info Bcsts 11 at
H+40 (and H+50
when vis < 2M)

Varne Lanby

Hastings* Radio
VHF 07 66 16
VHF 07
0933 1933 UT

Dungeness

RG **Fairlight**

Royal Sovereign

SEPARATION ZONE

8-3-3   AREA 3 TIDAL STREAMS

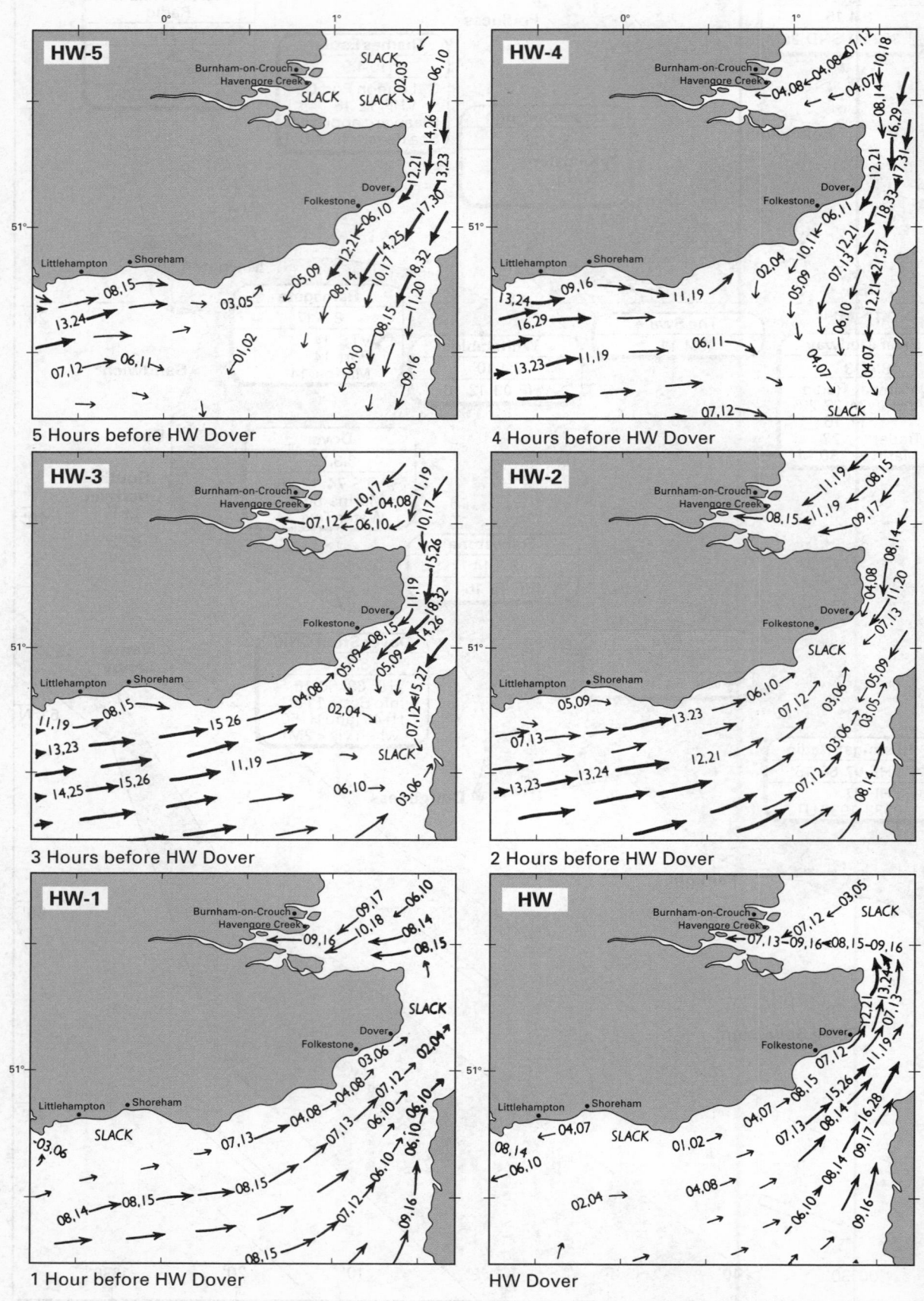

5 Hours before HW Dover

4 Hours before HW Dover

3 Hours before HW Dover

2 Hours before HW Dover

1 Hour before HW Dover

HW Dover

Westward 8.2.3   Southward 8.19.3   Northward 8.4.3   Thames Estuary 8.4.8   Eastward 8.20.3

3

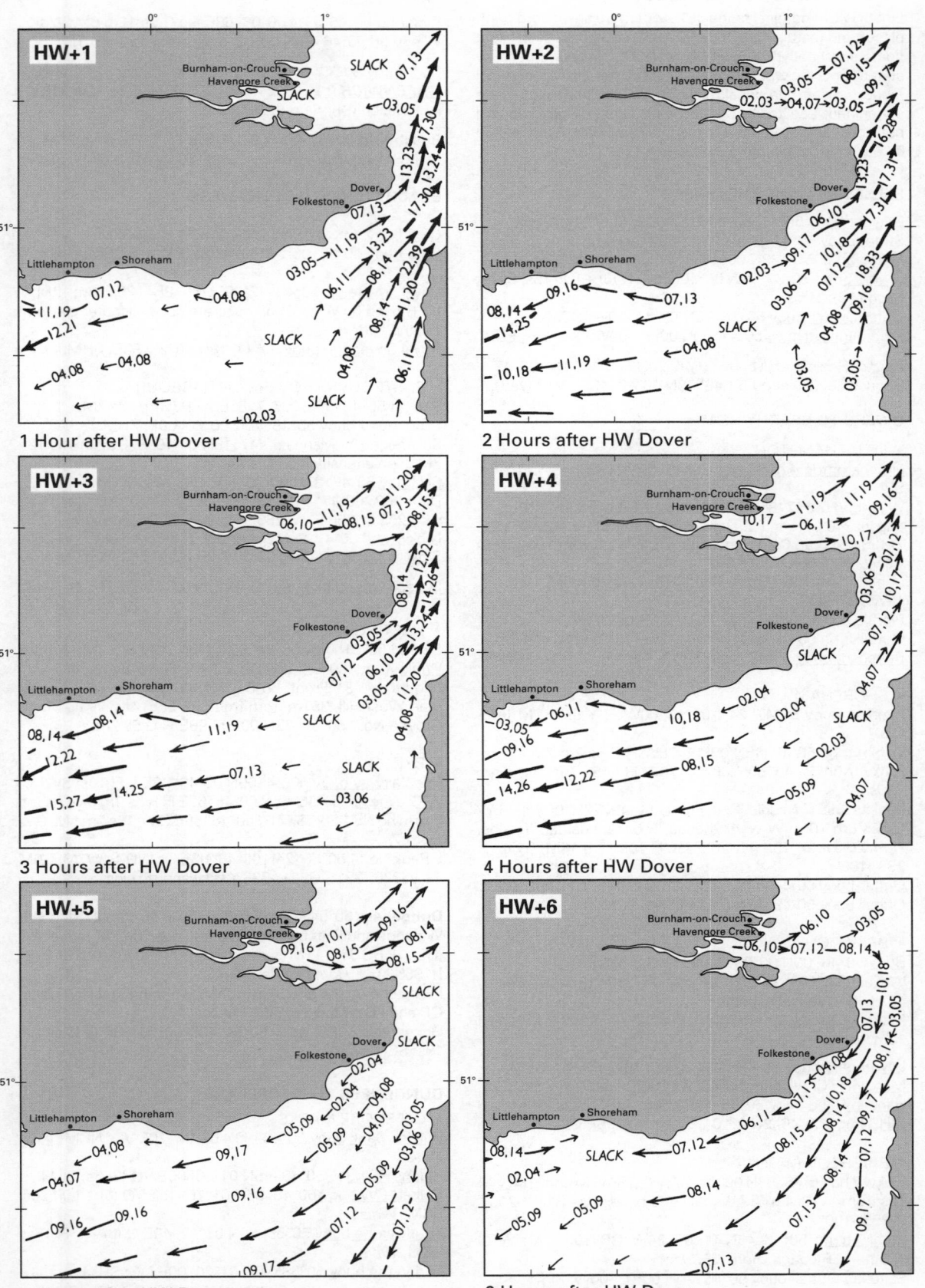

1 Hour after HW Dover

2 Hours after HW Dover

3 Hours after HW Dover

4 Hours after HW Dover

5 Hours after HW Dover

6 Hours after HW Dover

8.3.4   COASTAL LIGHTS, FOG SIGNALS AND WAYPOINTS

Lights with a nominal range of 15M or more are in **bold** print, places and features are in CAPITALS, and light-vessels, light floats and Lanbys in *CAPITAL ITALICS*. Unless otherwise stated lights are white. m = elevation in metres; M = nominal range in miles. Fog signals are in *italics*. Useful waypoints are underlined; use those on land with care. All geographical positions are referenced to the OSGB 36 datum but should be assumed to be approximate.

SELSEY BILL AND THE OWERS

Boulder buoy 50°41'·53N 00°49'·00W Fl G 2·5s; SHM.
Street buoy 50°41'·65N 00°48'·80W; PHM.
Mixon bn 50°42'·33N 00°46'·21W (unlit); PHM.
Owers buoy 50°37'·27N 00°40'·60W Q (6) + L Fl 15s; SCM; Racon (O); *Whis*.
Outer Owers buoy 50°38'·75N 00°41'·30W; SCM.
E Borough Hd buoy 50°41'·50N 00°39'·00W Q (3) 10s; ECM.

Bognor Regis outfall buoy 50°45'·20N 00°41'·50W; SPM.
Bognor Regis pier hd 50°46'·70N 00°40'·42W 2 FR (vert).

OWERS TO BEACHY HEAD

• LITTLEHAMPTON
Littlehampton outfall buoy 50°46'·20N 00°30'·45W Fl Y 5s; SPM.
W pier hd 50°47'·85N 00°32'·37W 2 FR (vert) 7m 6M.
Ldg lts 346°. Front, E pier hd 50°48'·06N 00°32'·42W FG 6m 7M; B col; rear, 64m from front, Oc WY 7·5s 9m 10M; W tr; vis W290°-356°, Y356°-042°.
Lt bn 50°46'·16N 00°29'·44W Fl (5) Y 20s 9m 5M.
• WORTHING
Pier hd 50°48'·38N 00°22'·02W 2 FR (vert) 6m 1M.
Outfall lt bn 50°48'·35N 00°20'·22W Fl R 2·5s 3m; PHM.
Beecham buoy 50°48'·45N 00°19'·40W Fl (2) R 10s; PHM.

• SHOREHAM
Express buoy 50°47'·24N 00°17'·00W Fl Y 5s; SPM (Apr-Oct).
W bkwtr hd 50°49'·45N 00°14'·78W Fl R 5s 7m 7M.
E bkwtr hd 50°49'·50N 00°14'·70W Fl G 5s 7m 8M; *Siren 120s*.
Ldg lts 355°. Middle Pier Front, 50°49'·72N 00°14'·78W Oc 5s 8m 10M; W watch-house, R base; tidal lts, tfc sigs; *Horn 20s*; **rear**, 192m from front, Fl 10s 13m **15M**; Gy tr vis 283°-103°.
Outfall buoy 50°47'·84N 00°13'·63W Q (6) + L Fl 15s; SCM.
Outfall buoy 50°49'·43N 00°14'·29W; SCM.

• BRIGHTON
Buoy 50°46'·00N 00°08'·30W Fl Y 3s; SPM.
W pier hd 50°49'·12N 00°09'·00W Fl R 10s 13m 2M; *Bell (1) 13s* (when vessel expected).
Marine Palace pier hd 50°48'·88N 00°08'·12W 2 FR (vert) 10m 2M.

Lowenbrau buoy 50°48'·40N 00°06'·40W Fl Y 4s; SPM.
Mercantile Credit buoy 50°48'·90N 00°08'·40W Fl Y 6s; SPM.
Hand in Hand buoy 50°46'·1N 00°08'·1W Fl Y 3s; SPM.
MHB buoy 50°46'·2N 00°04'·5W Fl Y 2s; SPM.

• BRIGHTON MARINA
E bkwtr hd 50°48'·53N 00°06'·27W QG 8m 7M and Fl (4) WR 20s 16m W10M, R8M; W pillar, G bands; vis R260°-295°, W295°-100°.
W bkwtr hd 50°48'·45N 00°06'·29W QR 10m 7M; W ○ structure, R bands; *Horn (2) 30s*.
Saltdean Outfall buoy 50°46'·70N 00°02'·00W; SPM.

• NEWHAVEN
Bkwtr hd 50°46'·52N 00°03'·60E Oc (2) 10s 17m 12M; *Horn 30s*.
E pier hd 50°46'·77N 00°03'·68E Iso G 5s 12m 6M; W tr.
W pier hd 50°46'·88N 00°03'·53E 2 FR (vert); SS Tfc.

CS 1 buoy 50°33'·67N 00°03'·83W Fl Y 2·5s; SPM; *Whis*.
GREENWICH lt V 50°24'·50N 00°00'·00 Fl 5s 12m **21M**; R hull; Racon (M); Ra refl; *Horn 30s*.

Beachy Hd 50°44'·00N 00°14'·60E Fl (2) 20s 31m **25M**; W ○ tr, R band and lantern; vis 248°-101°; (H24); *Horn 30s*.

BEACHY HEAD TO DUNGENESS

CS 2 buoy 50°39'·10N 00°32'·70E Fl Y 5s; SPM.
CS 3 buoy 50°52'·00N 01°02'·30E Fl Y 10s; SPM; *Bell*.

Royal Sovereign 50°43'·42N 00°26'·18E Fl 20s 28m 12M; W tr, R band on W cabin on concrete col; helicopter platform; *Horn (2) 30s*.
Royal Sovereign buoy 50°44'·18N 00°25'·93E; PHM.

• EASTBOURNE/SOVEREIGN HARBOUR
Pier hd 50°45'·88N 00°17'·85E 2 FR (vert) 8m 2M.
Langney Pt buoy 50°46'·70N 00°20'·00E; PHM.
Sovereign Hbr Marina 50°47'·18N 00°19'·87E Fl (3) 15s 12m 7M; high intensity lt on Martello tr.
SH buoy 50°47'·37N 00°20'·80E L Fl 10s; SWM.
Dir lt 258° 50°47'·24N 00°19'·82E Dir Fl WRG 5s 4m 1M; vis G252·5°-256·5°, W256·5°-259·5°, R259·5°-262·5°.
N bkwtr hd 50°47'·29N 00°20'·06E Fl G 5s 3m 6M.
S bkwtr hd 50°47'·26N 00°20'·12E Fl (4) R 12s 3m 6M

St Leonard's outfall buoy 50°49'·27N 00°32'·00E Fl Y 5s; SPM.

• HASTINGS
Pier hd 50°51'·03N 00°34'·50E 2 FR (vert) 8m 5M; W hut.
W bkwtr hd 50°51'·13N 00°35'·70E Fl R 2·5s 5m 4M.
Ldg lts 356·3°. Front, 50°51'·24N 00°35'·45E FR 14m 4M; rear, West Hill, 357m from front, FR 55m 4M; W tr.
Groyne No 3 50°51'·23N 00°35'·90E Fl G 5s 2m.

• RYE
Rye Fairway buoy 50°54'·00N 00°48'·13E L Fl 10s; SWM.
W Groyne hd 50°55'·55N 00°46'·65E Fl R 5s 7m 6M; Ra refl.
E Arm hd No 1 50°55'·71N 00°46'·56E Q (9) 15s 7m 5M; G △; *Horn 7s*.
E Bank No 11 50°56'·24N 00°46'·03E Oc WG 4s W7M, G6M; vis W326°-331°, G331°-326°; Tidal and tfc sigs.

Dungeness 50°54'·77N 00°58'·67E Fl 10s 40m **27M**; B ● tr, W bands and lantern, floodlit; partly obsc'd 078°-shore; RC; (H24). F RG 37m 11M (same tr); vis R057°-073°, G073°-078°, R196°-216°; *Horn (3) 60s*.
FR lts shown 2·4 and 5·2M WNW when firing taking place.
QR and FR on radio mast 1·2M NW.
Dungeness outfall buoy 50°54'·43N 00°58'·33E Q (6) + L Fl 15s; SCM.

DUNGENESS TO N FORELAND

• OFFSHORE MARKS
Bullock Bank buoy 50°46'·90N 01°07'·70E VQ; NCM; *Whis*.
Ridens SE buoy 50°43'·45N 01°19'·00E VQ (3) 5s; ECM.
Colbart SW buoy 50°48'·85N 01°16'·45E VQ (6) + L Fl 10s; SCM; *Whis*.
South Varne buoy 50°55'·60N 01°17'·40E Q (6) + L Fl 15s; SCM; *Whis*.
Mid Varne buoy 50°58'·90N 01°20'·00E QG; SHM.
East Varne buoy 50°58'·20N 01°21'·00E Fl R 2·5s; PHM.

Colbart N buoy 50°57'·42N 01°23'·40E VQ; NCM.

VARNE Lanby 51°01'·25N 01°24'·00E Fl R 20s12m**19M**; Racon (T); *Horn 30s.*
CS 4 buoy 51°08'·58N 01°34'·03E Fl (4) Y 15s; SPM; *Whis.*
CS 5 buoy 51°23'·00N 01°50'·00E Fl (4) Y 15s; SPM.
MPC buoy 51°06'·09N 01°38'·36E Fl Y 2·5s; SPM.

• FOLKESTONE
Hythe Flats outfall buoy 51°02'·50N 01°05'·43E Fl Y 5s; SPM.
Bkwtr hd   51°04'·53N 01°11'·79E Fl (2) 10s 14m **22M**; *Dia (4) 60s.* In fog Fl 2s; vis 246°-306°, intens 271·5°-280·5°.
Outer Hbr E pier hd 51°04'·73N 01°11'·48E QG 16m 1M.

Shakespeare Cliff W end 51°06'·05N 01°16'·12E Fl R 5s.
Shakespeare Cliff E end 51°06'·28N 01°16'·95E Fl R 5s.

• DOVER
Admiralty Pier extension hd   51°06'·65N 01°19'·77E Fl 7·5s 21m **20M**; W tr; vis 096°-090°, obsc in The Downs by S Foreland inshore of 226°; *Horn 10s*; IPTS.
S bkwtr W hd 51°06'·75N 01°19'·90E Oc R 30s 21m **18M**; W tr.
Knuckle 51°07'·02N 01°20'·59E Fl (4) WR 10s 15m **W15M**, R13M; W tr; vis R059°-239°, W239°-059°.
N head 51°07'·17N 01°20'·71E Fl R 2·5s 11m 5M.
E Arm hd 51°07'·27N 01°20'·70E Port Control sig stn; Fl G 5s 12m 5M; *Horn (2) 30s.*

• GOODWIN SANDS
S GOODWIN lt F, Fl (2) 20s 12m **15M**; R hull with lt tr amidships; *Horn (2) 60s;* 51°07'·95N 01°28'·60E.
SW Goodwin SCM buoy, Q (6) + L Fl 15s; 51°08'·57N 01°28'·80E.
S Goodwin PHM buoy, Fl (4) R 15s; 51°10'·57N 01°32'·37E.
SE Goodwin PHM buoy, Fl (3) R 10s, 51°12'·95N 01°34'·55E.
E GOODWIN lt F, Fl 15s 12m **21M**; R hull with lt tr amidships; Racon (T); *Horn 30s;* 51°13'·20N 01°36'·50E.
E Goodwin ECM buoy, Q (3) 10s, 51°16'·00N 01°35'·60E.
NE Goodwin ECM buoy, Q (3) 10s; Racon (M); 51°20'·28N 01°34'·27E.

• DEAL
Pier hd 51°13'·40N 01°24'·65E 2 FR (vert) 7m 5M.
Sandown outfall dn 51°14'·45N 01°24'·56E Fl R 2·5s; Ra refl.

• THE DOWNS
Deal Bank buoy 51°12'·90N 01°25'·67E; QR; PHM.
Goodwin Fork buoy 51°14'·30N 01°27'·23E Q (6) + L Fl 15s; SCM; *Bell.*
Downs buoy 51°14'·47N 01°26'·60E Fl (2) R 5s; PHM.

• GULL STREAM
W Goodwin buoy 51°15'·28N 01°27'·32E Fl G 5s; SHM.
S Brake buoy 51°15'·45N 01°26'·80E Fl (3) R 10s; PHM.
NW Goodwin buoy 51°16'·54N 01°28'·67E Q (9) 15s; WCM; *Bell.*
Brake buoy 51°16'·95N 01°28'·30E Fl (4) R 15s; PHM; *Bell.*
N Goodwin buoy 51°17'·88N 01°30'·42E Fl G 2·5s; SHM.
Gull Stream buoy 51°18'·25N 01°29'·80E QR; PHM.
Gull buoy 51°19'·55N 01°31'·40E VQ (3) 5s; ECM.
Goodwin Knoll buoy 51°19'·55N 01°32'·30E Fl (2) G 5s; SHM.

• RAMSGATE CHANNEL
B2 buoy 51°18'·03N 01°24'·20E; SHM.
W Quern buoy 51°18'·95N 01°25'·50E Q (9) 15s; WCM.

• RIVER STOUR/SANDWICH
Chan marked by PHM and SHM buoys and bns.
Pegwell Bay, Sandwich app 51°18'·72N 01°23'·05E Fl R 10s 3m 4M; framework tr; moved to meet changes in chan.

• RAMSGATE
RA buoy 51°19'·57N 01°30'·23E Q(6) + L Fl 15s; SCM.
E Brake buoy 51°19'·40N 01°29'·05E Fl R 5s; PHM.
No 1 buoy 51°19'·53N 01°27'·40E QG; SHM.
No 2 buoy 51°19'·66N 01°27'·24E Fl (4) R 10s; PHM.
No 3 buoy 51°19'·32N 01°26'·42E Fl G 2·5s; SHM.
No 4 buoy 51°19'·26N 01°26'·67E QR; PHM.
No 5 buoy 51°19'·52N 01°26'·42E Q(6) + L Fl 15s; SCM.
No 6 buoy 51°19'·43N 01°26'·42E Fl (2) R 5s; PHM.
N Quern buoy 51°19'·38N 01°26'·25E Q; NCM.
S bkwtr hd 51°19'·43N 01°25'·52E VQ R 10m 5M; W pillar, R bands.
N bkwtr hd 51°19'·53N 01°25'·58E Q G 10m 5M; W pillar, G bands.

W Marine terminal Dir lt 270°, Dir Oc WRG 10s 10m 5M; B △, Or stripe; vis G259°-269°, W269°-271°, R271°-281°; rear 493m from front Oc 5s 17m 5M; B ▽, Or stripe; vis 263°-278°.

• BROADSTAIRS
Broadstairs Knoll buoy 51°20'·85N 01°29'·58E Fl R 2·5s; PHM.
Pier SE end 51°21'·46N 01°26'·83E 2 FR (vert) 7m 4M.

N Foreland   51°22'·47N 01°26'·80E Fl (5) WR 20s 57m **W19M, R16M, R15M**; W 8-sided tr; vis W shore-150°, R(16M)150°-181°,R(15M) 181°-200°, W200°-011°; RC.

• OFFSHORE MARKS
South Falls buoy 51°13'·80N 01°44'·03E Q (6) + L Fl 15s; SCM.
F1 buoy 51°11'·20N 01°45'·03E; Fl (4) Y 15s; SPM.
Inter Bank buoy 51°16'·45N 01°52'·33E Fl Y 5s; Racon (M); SPM.
Mid Falls buoy 51°18'·60N 01°47'·10E Fl (3) R 10s; PHM; *Bell.*
F2 buoy 51°20'·38N 01°56'·30E Fl (4) Y 15s; SPM; *Bell.*

3

AGENTS WANTED

If you are interested in becoming our agent for any of the following ports, please write to: The Editor, Edington House, Trent, Sherborne, Dorset DT9 4SR, England – and get your free copy of the Almanac annually. You do not have to live in a port to be the agent, but should at least be a fairly regular visitor.

Plymouth	Port Haliguen
Walton-on-the-Naze	La Trinité-sur-Mer
Hopeman	Piriac
Burghead	St Nazaire/Loire
Findhorn	Pornic
Nairn	St Gilles-Croix-de-Vie
Inverness	Les Sables d'Olonne
Loch Aline	River Seudre
Craobh	Port Bloc/Gironde
Workington	Anglet/Bayonne
Lough Swilly	St Jean-de-Luz
Portbail	Hendaye
St Malo/Dinard	Grandcamp-Maisy
Le Légué/St Brieuc	Port-en-Bessin
Lampaul	Ouistreham/Caen
L'Aberildut	Dives
Douarnenez	St Valéry-en-Caux
Lorient	Dunkerque
River Étel	Emden
Le Palais (Belle Ile)	Langeoog

8.3.5 PASSAGE INFORMATION

Reference books include: Admiralty *Channel Pilot*; *Shell Channel Pilot* (Imray/Cunliffe); and *South Coast Cruising* (YM/Fishwick). See 8.0.5 for cross-Channel distances.

THE EASTERN CHANNEL

This area embraces the greatest concentration of commercial shipping in the world. In such waters the greatest danger to a small yacht is being run down by a larger vessel, especially in poor visibility. In addition to the many ships plying up and down the traffic lanes, there are fast ferries, hovercraft and hydrofoils passing to and fro between English and Continental harbours; warships and submarines on exercises; fishing vessels operating both inshore and offshore; many other yachts; and static dangers such as lobster pots and fishing nets which are concentrated in certain places.

Even for coastal cruising it is essential to know about the TSS and ITZ, see 8.19.28; eg, note that the SW-bound TSS lane from the Dover Strait passes only 4M off Dungeness. Radar surveillance of the Dover Strait (8.3.16) is maintained at all times by the Channel Navigation Information Service (CNIS).

In this area the weather has a big effect on tidal streams, and on the range of tides. The rates of tidal streams vary with the locality, and are greatest in the narrower parts of the Channel and off major headlands. In the Dover Strait sp rates can reach 4kn, but elsewhere in open water they seldom exceed 2kn. Also N winds, which give smooth water and pleasant sailing off the shores of England, can cause rough seas on the French coast; and vice versa. With strong S'lies the English coast between Isle of Wight and Dover is very exposed, and shelter is hard to find. The Dover Strait has a funnelling effect and in strong winds can become very rough.

SELSEY BILL AND THE OWERS (chart *1652*)

Selsey Bill is a low headland, off which lie the Owers, groups of rks and shoals extending 3M to the S, and 5M to the SE. Just W and SW of the Bill, The Streets (awash) extend 1·25M seaward. 1·25M SSW of the Bill are The Grounds (or Malt Owers) and The Dries (dry). 1M E of The Dries, and about 1·25M S of the lifeboat house on E side of Selsey Bill is The Mixon a group of rks marked by bn at E end.

Immediately S of the above dangers is the Looe Chan, which runs E/W about 7½ca S of Mixon bn. It is marked by buoys at W end, where it is narrowest between Brake (or Cross) Ledge on N side and Boulder Bank to the S. In daylight, good visibility and moderate weather, the Looe Chan is an easy and useful short cut. The E-going stream begins at HW Portsmouth + 0430, and the W-going at HW Portsmouth – 0135, sp rates 2·5 kn. Beware lobster pots in this area.

In poor visibility or in bad weather (and always in darkness) keep S of the Owers SCM lt buoy, 7M SE of Selsey Bill, marking SE end of Owers. Over much of the Owers there is less than 3m, and large parts virtually dry; so a combination of tidal stream and strong wind produces heavy breaking seas and overfalls over a large area.

OWERS TO BEACHY HEAD (charts *1652, 536*)

The coast from Selsey Bill to Brighton is low, faced by a shingle beach, and with few offlying dangers, Bognor Rks (dry in places) extend 1·75M E from a point 1M W of the pier, and Bognor Spit extends E and S from the end of them. Middleton ledge are rks running 8ca offshore, about 1·5M E of Bognor pier, with depths of less than 1m. Shelley Rks lie 5ca S of Middleton ledge, with depths of less than 1m.

Winter Knoll, about 2·5M SSW of Littlehampton (8.3.8) has depths of 2·1m. Kingston Rks, depth 2m, lie about 3·25M ESE of Littlehampton. An unlit outfall bn is 3ca off Goring -on-sea (2M W of Worthing pier). Grass Banks, an extensive shoal with 2m depth at W end, lie about 1M S of Worthing pier. Elbow shoal, with depth of 3·1m, lies E of Grass Banks.

Off Shoreham (8.3.9) Church Rks, with depth of 0·3m, lie 1·5M W of the hbr ent and 2½ca offshore. Jenny Rks, with depth 0·9m, are 1·25M E of the ent, 3ca offshore.

At Brighton (8.3.10) the S Downs form the coastline, and high chalk cliffs are conspic from here to Beachy Head. There are no dangers more than 3ca offshore, until Birling Gap, where a rky ledge begins, on which is built Beachy Head lt ho (fog sig). Head Ledge (dries) extends about 4ca S. 2M S of Beachy Hd the W-going stream begins at HW Dover + 0030, and the E-going at HW Dover – 0520, sp rates 2·25kn. In bad weather there are overfalls off the Head, which should then be given a berth of 2M.

BEACHY HEAD TO DUNGENESS

Royal Sovereign lt tr (fog sig) is 7·4M E of Beachy Head. The extensive Royal Sovereign shoals lie from 3M NW of the tr to 1·5M N of it, and have a minimum depth of 3·5m. There are strong eddies over the shoals at sp, and the sea breaks on them in bad weather.

On the direct course from Royal Sovereign lt tr to clear Dungeness there are no dangers. Along the coast in Pevensey B and Rye B there are drying rky ledges or shoals extending 5ca offshore in places. These include Boulder Bank near Wish tr, S of Eastbourne (8.3.12); Oyster Reef off Cooden; Bexhill Reef off Bexhill-on-Sea; Bopeep Rks off St Leonards; and the shoals at the mouth of R Rother, at entrance to Rye (8.3.13). There are also banks 2-3M offshore, on which the sea builds in bad weather. Avoid the firing range danger area between Rye and Dungeness (lt, fog sig, RC). The nuclear power station is conspic at SE extremity of the low-lying spit. The Pt is steep-to on SE side. Good anch close NE of Dungeness.

DUNGENESS TO NORTH FORELAND (charts *1892, 1828*)

From Dungeness to Folkestone (8.3.14) the coast forms a bay. Beware Roar bank, depth 2·7m, E of New Romney: otherwise there are no offlying dangers, apart from Hythe firing range. Good anch off Sandgate in offshore winds. Off Folkestone the E-going stream starts at HW Dover – 0155, sp rate 2kn; the W-going at HW Dover + 0320, sp rate 1·5kn.

Passing Dover (8.3.15) and S Foreland keep 1M offshore. Do not pass too close to Dover, because ferries/jetfoils leave at speed, and there can be considerable backwash and lumpy seas off the breakwaters. 8M S of Dover in the TSS is the Varne, a shoal 7M long with least depth 3·3m and heavy seas in bad weather, marked by Lanby and 3 buoys. Between S and N Foreland the N-going stream begins at about HW Dover – 0150, and the S-going at about HW Dover + 0415.

The Goodwin Sands are drying, shifting shoals, extending about 10M from S to N, and 5M from W to E at their widest part. The E side is relatively steep-to; large areas dry up to 2·7m. The sands are well marked by lt Fs and buoys. Kellett Gut is an unmarked chan about 5ca wide, running SW/NE through the middle of the sands, but it is not regularly surveyed and is liable to change. The Gull Stream (buoyed) leads from The Downs, inside Goodwin Sands and outside Brake Sands to the S of Ramsgate (8.3.17). The Ramsgate chan leads inside the Brake Sands and Cross Ledge.

CROSS-CHANNEL PASSAGES

This section applies broadly to any crossing, ranging from the short (4-5hrs) Dover Strait route, through the much used, medium length Solent-Cherbourg route (13hrs; see 8.15.5), to the longer passages (20+hrs) from SW England to North Brittany. Distances are tabulated at 8.0.8. Whatever the length of passage, **thorough planning** is the key to a safe and efficient crossing. Maximum experience of crossing the Channel as crew/navigator is also invaluable, before the psychological hurdle of first skippering a boat across.

A **Planning check-list** must oblige a skipper/navigator to:

a.   Study the meteorological situation several days before departure, so that windows of opportunity, eg high pressure, may be predicted and bad weather avoided.

b.   Consider the forecast wind direction and likely shifts, so that the probability of obtaining a good slant can be improved. Prevailing winds are SW/W, except in the spring when NE/ E winds are equally likely. The advantages of getting well to windward cannot be over-emphasised. If heading for St Malo from Brighton, for example, it might pay to make westing along the coast (working the tides to advantage) so as to depart from St Catherine's Point, the Needles, Anvil Point or even Portland Bill when crossing towards Barfleur, Cherbourg, Cap de la Hague or Alderney.

c.   Choose the route, departure points and landfalls so that time on passage and out of sight of identifiable marks is minimised. This can much reduce anxiety and fatigue (which may soon become apparent in a family crew). The risk of navigational errors, particularly those due to leeway and tidal streams, is also reduced. It is sound practice to take back bearings on the departure mark.

d.   Take account of tidal constraints at the point of departure and destination; and en route tidal gates, eg Hurst Narrows.

e.   Work out the hourly direction and rate of tidal streams expected during (and after) the crossing; so as to lay off the total drift angle required to make good the desired track. Only rarely do 6 hours of E-going tide cancel out 6 hours of W-going (or vice versa); streams off the French coast are usually stronger. Try to arrive up-tide of destination. Note the times and areas of races and overfalls and keep well clear.

f.   Consider actions to be taken in poor visibility/fog when the range at which marks may be seen is much reduced (and risk of collision with other vessels equally increased). Statistically fog is unlikely in summer (except in certain notorious areas, eg off Ushant) and visibility is often greater than 6M. A landfall at night or dawn/dusk is frequently easier due to the additional range provided by lights.

g.   Observe the legal requirement to head at 90° across any TSS (1.1.2); consider motoring to expedite such crossing.

h.   Make use of additional navigational info such as soundings, for example when crossing the distinctive contours of the Hurd Deep; the rising or dipping ranges of major lights; fixing on clearly identifiable radar targets, if so equipped; and the sighting of TSS buoys and light floats. Note: The charted 2M exclusion circles around EC1, EC2 and EC3 buoys apply only to IMO-Convention vessels, ie not yachts.

j.   Keep a harbour of refuge in mind if caught out by fog, gales or gear failure. For example, if unable to make Cherbourg in a strong SSW'ly and E-going tide, it may be better to bear away and run for St Vaast in the lee of the peninsular. Or heave to and stay at sea.

k.   Finally, even if using electronic navigation, write up the ship's log and maintain a DR plot. This is both a safeguard, and a source of pride (when proven accurate); it also ensures the highest degree of navigational awareness.

Routes from ports within Area 3

Passages from Brighton, Newhaven or Eastbourne to Dieppe or adjacent French ports are relatively short and direct. The route crosses the Dover Strait TSS whose SW-bound lane lies only 7M S of Beachy Head. A departure from close W of CS2 buoy will satisfy the 90° crossing rule and minimise the time spent in the TSS. During the 19M crossing of the TSS, it is worth listening to the VHF broadcasts of navigational and traffic information made by CNIS. These include details of vessels which appear to be contravening Rule 10.

Dover to Calais or Boulogne is only about 25M (see 8.3.16) but the route crosses the congested Dover Strait TSS. Keep a very sharp lookout for ships in the traffic lanes and ferries crossing them. Do not attempt to cross in fog or poor visibility. Listen to CNIS and to the relevant hbr VHF channel. From Ramsgate to/from Dutch/Belgian ports, see 8.20.6.

> The sea is calm to-night.
> The tide is full, the moon lies fair
> Upon the straits; – on the French coast the light
> Gleams and is gone; the cliffs of England stand,
> Glimmering and vast, out in the tranquil bay.

> Dover Beach. Matthew Arnold (1822-1888)

8.3.6   DISTANCE TABLE

Approximate distances in nautical miles are by the most direct route, whilst avoiding dangers and allowing for Traffic Separation Schemes. Places in *italics* are in adjoining areas; places in **bold** are in 8.0.8, Cross-Channel Distances; places underlined are in 8.0.10, Distances across the North Sea.

	1	2	3	4	5	6	7	8	9	10	11	12	13	14	15	16	17	18	19	20
1. *Portland Bill Lt*	1																			
2. **Nab Tower**	60	2																		
3. **Boulder Lt Buoy**	65	5	3																	
4. **Owers Lt Buoy**	69	11	8	4																
5. **Littlehampton**	78	19	13	12	5															
6. **Shoreham**	90	32	24	21	13	6														
7. **Brighton**	93	35	28	24	17	5	7													
8. **Newhaven**	97	40	34	29	24	12	7	8												
9. **Beachy Head Lt**	104	46	41	36	30	20	14	8	9											
8. **Eastbourne**	111	51	45	40	34	24	19	12	7	10										
11. **Rye**	129	72	67	62	56	46	41	34	25	23	11									
12. Dungeness Lt	134	76	71	66	60	50	44	38	30	26	9	12								
13. **Folkestone**	152	92	84	81	76	65	60	53	43	40	23	13	13							
14. **Dover**	157	97	89	86	81	70	65	58	48	45	28	18	5	14						
15. Ramsgate	172	112	104	101	96	85	80	73	63	60	43	33	20	15	15					
16. N Foreland Lt	175	115	107	104	99	88	83	76	66	63	46	36	23	18	3	16				
17. *Sheerness*	206	146	139	135	132	119	114	107	97	96	79	67	54	49	34	31	17			
18. *London Bridge*	248	188	184	177	177	161	156	149	139	141	124	109	96	91	76	73	45	18		
19. *Burnham-on-Crouch*	216	156	148	145	140	129	124	117	107	104	87	75	64	59	44	41	34	76	19	
20. *Harwich*	212	152	144	141	136	125	120	113	103	100	83	73	60	55	40	37	50	83	31	20

LITTLEHAMPTON   8-3-8

W. Sussex 50°47'·84N 00°32'·33W   Rtg 3-3-2

CHARTS
AC *1991, 1652*; Imray C9; Stanfords 9; OS 197

TIDES
+0015 Dover; ML 2·8; Zone 0 (UT)

Standard Port SHOREHAM (→)

Times				Height (metres)			
High Water		Low Water		MHWS	MHWN	MLWN	MLWS
0500	1000	0000	0600	6·3	4·8	1·9	0·6
1700	2200	1200	1800				
Differences LITTLEHAMPTON (ENT)							
+0010	0000	−0005	−0010	−0·4	−0·4	−0·2	−0·2
LITTLEHAMPTON (NORFOLK WHARF)							
+0015	+0005	0000	+0045	−0·7	−0·7	−0·3	+0·2
ARUNDEL							
No data	+0120	No data		−3·1	−2·8	No data	
PAGHAM							
+0015	0000	−0015	−0025	−0·7	−0·5	−0·1	−0·1
BOGNOR REGIS							
+0010	−0005	−0005	−0020	−0·6	−0·5	−0·2	−0·1

NOTE: Tidal hts in hbr are affected by flow down R Arun.
Tide seldom falls lower than 0·9m above CD.

SHELTER
Good. Ent dangerous in strong SE winds which cause
swell up the hbr. The bar (0·7 to 0·9m) is rough in SW'lies.
Visitors berth initially at Town Quay and contact Hr Mr.

NAVIGATION
WPT 50°47'·50N 00°32'·20W, 166°/346° from/to front ldg lt,
0·60M. Bar ½M offshore. Hbr accessible from HW−3 to
HW+2½ for approx 1·5m draft. The ebb runs so fast (4 – 6
kn) at sp that yachts may have difficulty entering. From
HW−1 to HW+4 a strong W-going tidal stream sets across
the ent; keep to E side. Speed limit 6½kn.
On E side of ent chan a training wall which covers at half-
tide is marked by 7 poles and unlit bn at S end. The W pier
is a long, prominent structure of wood piles; beware shoal
ground within its arm. A tide gauge on end shows height
of tide above CD. To obtain depth on the bar subtract
0·7m from indicated depth.

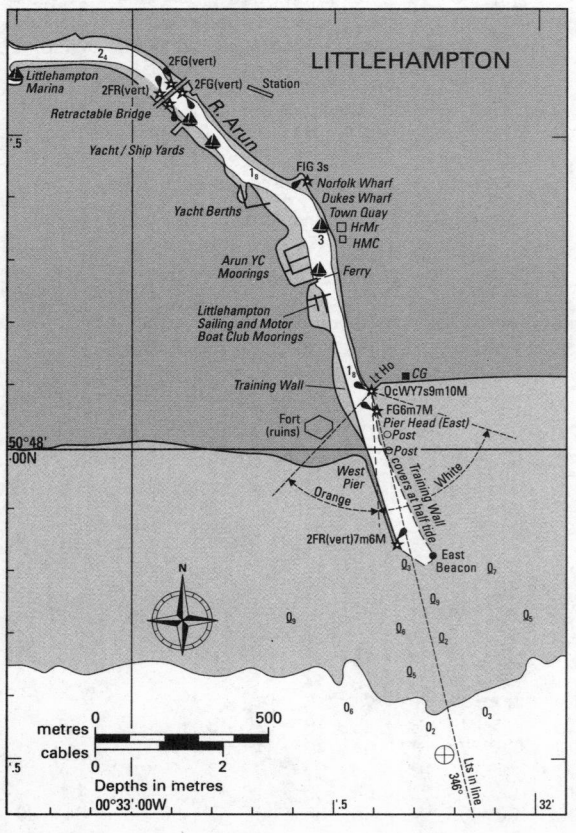

LITTLEHAMPTON

River Arun.
A retractable footbridge (3·6m clearance
MHWS; 9·4m above CD) 3ca above Town Quay gives
access for masted craft to Littlehampton marina. It is
opened by request to Hr Mr before 1630 previous day. The
River Arun is navigable on the tide by small, unmasted
craft for 24M via Ford, Arundel and beyond; consult Hr Mr.

LIGHTS AND MARKS
High-rise bldg (38m) is conspic 0·4M NNE of hbr ent. A
pile with small platform and ☆, Fl Y (5) 20s 5M, is 2·5M
SE of hbr ent at 50°46'·1N 00°29'·5W.
Ldg lts 346°: Front FG on B column; Rear, lt ho Oc WY 7·5s
at root of E bkwtr, W 290°-356°, Y 356°-042°. The Fl G 3s lt
at Norfolk Wharf leads craft upstream, once inside hbr ent.
When Pilot boat with P1 at the bow displays the Pilot flag
'H' (WR vert halves) or Ⓦ over Ⓡ lts, all boats keep clear
of ent; large ship moving.
Footbridge sigs, from high mast to port:
Fl G lt = open; Fl R = closed.
Bridge's retractable centre section (22m wide) has 2 FR
(vert) to port and 2 FG (vert) to stbd at both upstream and
downstream ends.

RADIO TELEPHONE
Hr Mr VHF Ch 71 16 (0900-1700LT); Pilots Ch 71 16 when
vessel due. Bridge Ch 71. Marinas Ch **80** M (office hrs).

TELEPHONE (Dial code 01903)
Hr Mr 721215; MRSC (01705) 552100; ⌗ 0345 231110
(H24); Marinecall 0891 500456; Police 731733; Dr 714113.

FACILITIES
Town Quay AB £10, FW, C (5 ton), ME, Sh;
Services: BY, M, Sh (Wood), ACA.
Littlehampton Sailing & Motor Club ☎ 715859, M, FW, Bar;
Arun YC (90+10 visitors), £7.50, ☎ 714533/716016, (dries;
access HW±3), M, AC, FW, Bar, Slip, R, Showers, &;
Littlehampton Marina (120 + 30 Ⓥ), £17.62, ☎ 713553,
🕿 732264, Slip, BH (12 ton), CH, P, D, V, R, Bar, FW, AC,
Sh, ME, &;
Ship and Anchor Marina, about 2M up-river at Ford, (50+,
some visitors) ☎ (01243) 551262, (access HW±4), Slip,
FW, ME, Sh, CH, V, R, Bar.
Town EC Wed; P, D, V, R, Bar, ✉, Ⓑ, ⇌, ✈ (Shoreham).

3

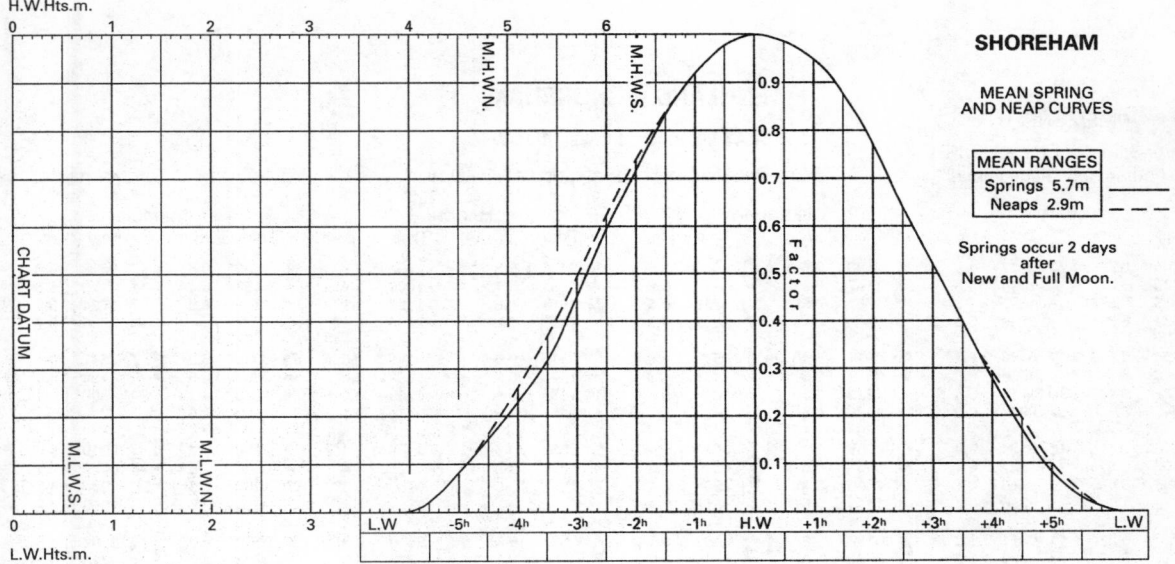

H.W.Hts.m.

SHOREHAM

MEAN SPRING
AND NEAP CURVES

MEAN RANGES
Springs 5.7m
Neaps 2.9m

Springs occur 2 days
after
New and Full Moon.

CHART DATUM

M.H.W.N. M.H.W.S.

M.L.W.S. M.L.W.N.

Factor

L.W -5h -4h -3h -2h -1h H.W +1h +2h +3h +4h +5h L.W

L.W.Hts.m.

SHOREHAM 8-3-9

W. Sussex 50°49′.50N 00°14′.76W   Rtg 3-3-2

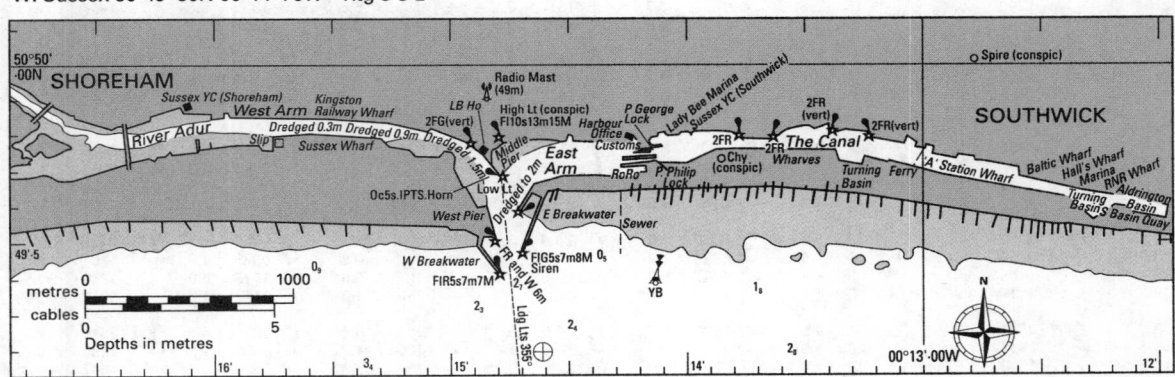

CHARTS
AC 2044, *1652*; Imray C9; Stanfords 9; OS 197/8
TIDES
+0009 Dover; ML 3·3; Duration 0605; Zone 0 (UT)

Standard Port SHOREHAM (→)

Times				Height (metres)			
High Water		Low Water		MHWS	MHWN	MLWN	MLWS
0500	1000	0000	0600	6·3	4·8	1·9	0·6
1700	2200	1200	1800				

Differences WORTHING

+0010	0000	–0005	–0010	–0·1	–0·2	0·0	0·0

NOTE: Shoreham is a Standard Port and tidal predictions
for the year are given below.

SHELTER
Excellent, once through the lock and into The Canal. The
shallow water (dredged 1·9m) at the ent can be very rough
in strong on-shore winds and dangerous in onshore gales.
Lady Bee and Aldrington (E end of The Canal) marinas,
least depth 2m, both welcome visitors; they are managed
by the Hbr Authority. Visitors are advised not to use the
drying Western Arm if possible. Hbr speed limit = 4kn.
NAVIGATION
WPT 50°49′.20N 00°14′.72W, 175°/355° from/to front ldg
lt, 0·52M. From E, beware Jenny Rks (0·9m) and from the
W, Church Rks (0·3m). The Eastern Arm leads to Prince
George Lock, the N'ly of two locks, which opens H24 @
H+30 for arrivals and H for departures; also, if not busy,
at other times on request VHF Ch 14. Lock ent is 6m wide,
pontoon inside on S wall; sill is 0·26m below CD, denying
access only at about LWS±1. Lock will advise exact depth

on Ch 14. Waiting space on S side of central lead-in pier.
Commercial ships use Prince Philip lock; yachts to keep
clear. A Ro-Ro ramp and terminal are on S side of lock.
LIGHTS AND MARKS
Conspic, light-coloured chy (109m), 0.6M ENE of hbr ent,
is visible from 20M offshore. Radio mast is conspic 170m
N of High lt. A SCM buoy, Q(6) + L Fl 15s, marking outfall
diffusers, bears 157°/1·8M from hbr ent.
Ldg lts 355°: front Oc 5s 8m 10M; rear High lt, Fl 10s 13m 15M.
Traffic Sigs IPTS (Sigs 2 and 5, Oc) are shown from
Middle Pier. Note : Ⓨ Fl lt exempts small craft.
Oc R 3s (from LB ho, directed at E or W Arms) = No exit.
Lock Sigs (Comply strictly to avoid turbulence):
3 Ⓡ (vert)   = do not approach lock.
ⒼⓌ Ⓖ (vert) = clear to approach lock.
RADIO TELEPHONE
Call *Shoreham Hbr Radio* VHF Ch **14** 16 (H24) Hr Mr and
lock. Lock will advise Lady Bee marina of arrivals, 0830-
1800 M-Sat; 1000-1400 Sun.
TELEPHONE (Dial code 01273)
Hr Mr 592613, ☎ 592492; Locks 592366; MRSC (01705)
552100; ⌗ 0345 231110 (H24); Marinecall 0891 500456;
Police 454521; Ⓗ 455622; Dr 461101 (Health Centre).
FACILITIES
Lady Bee Marina (110+10 Ⓥ) ☎ 596680, ☎ 870349, (best
to pre-arrange), £16.00 inc lock fee, £11 for subsequent
nights; Access as lock times, AB, P & D (cans), FW, AC,
CH, ME, El, Sh, SM, R, V, Slip;
Sussex YC ☎/☎ 464868, welcomes visitors, but has only
one AB in The Canal, so prior notice advised; also a drying
½ tide pontoon in the Western Arm(limited Ⓥ), R, Bar, Ⓖ.
Services: P & D also on N side of W Arm HW±3; ACA.
Town EC Wed; ⊙, ⊠, Ⓑ, ⇌, ✈.

ENGLAND – SHOREHAM

LAT 50°50′N   LONG 0°15′W

TIMES AND HEIGHTS OF HIGH AND LOW WATERS

YEAR **1999**

> **TIME ZONE (UT)**
> For Summer Time add ONE hour in non-shaded areas

JANUARY

Date	Time	m		Date	Time	m
1 F	0404	0.7		**16** SA	0417	1.2
	1020	6.3			1014	5.8
	1633	0.5			1640	1.0
	2251	6.3			2239	5.8
2 SA O	0454	0.6		**17** SU ●	0456	1.1
	1110	6.5			1053	6.0
	1722	0.4			1718	0.8
	2340	6.4			2318	6.0
3 SU	0542	0.6		**18** M	0534	0.9
	1157	6.5			1131	6.1
	1808	0.4			1756	0.7
					2356	6.1
4 M	0027	6.5		**19** TU	0611	0.9
	0628	0.6			1209	6.2
	1243	6.4			1833	0.7
	1853	0.5				
5 TU	0111	6.4		**20** W	0034	6.2
	0712	0.7			0647	0.8
	1325	6.2			1248	6.2
	1936	0.6			1909	0.6
6 W	0153	6.2		**21** TH	0112	6.2
	0754	0.9			0725	0.8
	1406	6.0			1328	6.1
	2017	0.8			1948	0.7
7 TH	0234	6.0		**22** F	0152	6.2
	0835	1.1			0807	0.8
	1446	5.7			1409	6.0
	2057	1.1			2030	0.7
8 F	0315	5.7		**23** SA	0236	6.0
	0918	1.4			0853	1.0
	1528	5.4			1455	5.8
	2139	1.3			2117	0.9
9 SA	0359	5.4		**24** SU	0324	5.8
	1005	1.6			0947	1.2
	1616	5.1			1548	5.6
	2226	1.6			2211	1.1
10 SU	0450	5.1		**25** M	0421	5.6
	1057	1.9			1050	1.4
	1712	4.8			1650	5.3
	2320	1.9			2317	1.4
11 M	0548	4.9		**26** TU	0529	5.4
	1158	2.0			1204	1.5
	1814	4.7			1807	5.1
12 TU	0026	2.0		**27** W	0038	1.5
	0649	4.9			0649	5.3
	1317	2.0			1324	1.5
	1918	4.7			1934	5.2
13 W	0145	1.9		**28** TH	0156	1.4
	0750	5.0			0810	5.5
	1428	1.7			1433	1.2
	2020	5.0			2049	5.5
14 TH	0248	1.7		**29** F	0300	1.2
	0846	5.3			0916	5.8
	1518	1.5			1531	0.9
	2113	5.3			2150	5.8
15 F	0336	1.5		**30** SA	0355	0.9
	0932	5.6			1012	6.0
	1600	1.2			1622	0.7
	2158	5.6			2243	6.1
				31 SU O	0444	0.7
					1101	6.2
					1710	0.5
					2330	6.3

FEBRUARY

Date	Time	m		Date	Time	m
1 M	0530	0.6		**16** TU ●	0513	0.8
	1147	6.3			1113	6.2
	1754	0.5			1735	0.6
					2338	6.3
2 TU	0014	6.4		**17** W	0552	0.6
	0613	0.6			1153	6.3
	1229	6.3			1814	0.5
	1836	0.5				
3 W	0055	6.4		**18** TH	0017	6.4
	0653	0.6			0630	0.5
	1308	6.2			1234	6.4
	1915	0.5			1852	0.4
4 TH	0132	6.3		**19** F	0057	6.5
	0731	0.8			0710	0.5
	1343	6.1			1314	6.4
	1950	0.7			1932	0.4
5 F	0206	6.1		**20** SA	0136	6.4
	0806	0.9			0752	0.5
	1415	5.8			1355	6.3
	2025	0.9			2014	0.5
6 SA	0237	5.8		**21** SU	0218	6.3
	0842	1.1			0837	0.7
	1446	5.6			1438	6.1
	2101	1.1			2059	0.7
7 SU	0307	5.5		**22** M	0303	6.0
	0921	1.4			0926	0.9
	1519	5.3			1548	5.8
	2141	1.4			2150	1.0
8 M	0342	5.2		**23** TU	0356	5.6
	1006	1.6			1025	1.2
	1603	4.9			1627	5.3
	2228	1.7			2252	1.4
9 TU	0434	4.9		**24** W	0502	5.3
	1100	1.9			1138	1.5
	1713	4.6			1742	5.0
	2327	2.0				
10 W	0555	4.7		**25** TH	0016	1.7
	1206	2.1			0623	5.0
	1832	4.6			1307	1.6
					1919	5.0
11 TH	0040	2.1		**26** F	0143	1.6
	0706	4.7			0758	5.1
	1327	2.0			1421	1.4
	1940	4.7			2042	5.2
12 F	0204	2.0		**27** SA	0249	1.4
	0809	5.0			0910	5.5
	1444	1.7			1519	1.1
	2041	5.0			2143	5.6
13 SA	0308	1.7		**28** SU	0344	1.0
	0903	5.3			1004	5.8
	1534	1.3			1609	0.8
	2132	5.4			2232	6.0
14 SU	0354	1.3				
	0950	5.7				
	1616	1.0				
	2216	5.8				
15 M	0434	1.0				
	1032	6.0				
	1656	0.8				
	2258	6.1				

MARCH

Date	Time	m		Date	Time	m
1 M	0431	0.8		**16** TU	0408	0.9
	1051	6.1			1009	5.9
	1654	0.6			1628	0.7
	2317	6.2			2234	6.1
2 TU O	0515	0.6		**17** W ●	0448	0.6
	1133	6.2			1052	6.2
	1736	0.5			1709	0.5
	2357	6.3			2316	6.4
3 W	0555	0.6		**18** TH	0529	0.4
	1212	6.2			1135	6.4
	1815	0.5			1750	0.3
					2357	6.6
4 TH	0033	6.3		**19** F	0610	0.3
	0631	0.6			1217	6.5
	1247	6.2			1831	0.2
	1850	0.5				
5 F	0107	6.2		**20** SA	0038	6.6
	0705	0.6			0652	0.2
	1317	6.1			1259	6.6
	1922	0.6			1913	0.2
6 SA	0135	6.1		**21** SU	0119	6.6
	0736	0.7			0735	0.3
	1343	5.9			1340	6.4
	1954	0.8			1956	0.3
7 SU	0157	5.9		**22** M	0200	6.4
	0808	0.9			0820	0.5
	1407	5.7			1424	6.2
	2026	1.0			2042	0.6
8 M	0219	5.7		**23** TU	0245	6.1
	0842	1.1			0909	0.8
	1436	5.5			1513	5.8
	2101	1.3			2133	1.0
9 TU	0250	5.4		**24** W	0338	5.6
	0920	1.4			1006	1.2
	1512	5.1			1613	5.3
	2140	1.6			2235	1.4
10 W	0330	5.0		**25** TH	0443	5.1
	1007	1.7			1119	1.5
	1600	4.8			1728	5.0
	2233	1.9				
11 TH	0427	4.6		**26** F	0000	1.7
	1112	2.0			0604	4.8
	1734	4.5			1252	1.7
	2350	2.2			1905	4.9
12 F	0621	4.5		**27** SA	0129	1.7
	1233	2.1			0747	4.9
	1903	4.6			1405	1.5
					2030	5.2
13 SA	0117	2.1		**28** SU	0235	1.4
	0734	4.7			0858	5.3
	1401	1.8			1502	1.2
	2009	4.9			2128	5.6
14 SU	0234	1.7		**29** M	0328	1.1
	0834	5.1			0943	5.6
	1502	1.4			1551	0.9
	2104	5.4			2215	5.9
15 M	0326	1.3		**30** TU	0413	0.8
	0924	5.6			1034	5.9
	1547	1.0			1633	0.7
	2151	5.8			2256	6.1
				31 W O	0454	0.6
					1114	6.1
					1713	0.6
					2334	6.2

APRIL

Date	Time	m		Date	Time	m
1 TH	0532	0.6		**16** F ●	0503	0.3
	1150	6.1			1115	6.5
	1749	0.5			1724	0.2
					2336	6.7
2 F	0008	6.2		**17** SA	0547	0.1
	0606	0.6			1159	6.6
	1223	6.1			1809	0.1
	1822	0.6				
3 SA	0038	6.1		**18** SU	0019	6.7
	0638	0.6			0632	0.1
	1250	6.0			1244	6.6
	1854	0.6			1853	0.2
4 SU	0102	6.0		**19** M	0102	6.6
	0708	0.7			0718	0.2
	1314	5.9			1328	6.5
	1925	0.8			1939	0.3
5 M	0122	5.9		**20** TU	0146	6.4
	0738	0.8			0805	0.4
	1338	5.8			1414	6.2
	1955	0.9			2027	0.6
6 TU	0146	5.7		**21** W	0232	6.0
	0809	1.0			0855	0.7
	1406	5.6			1505	5.8
	2026	1.2			2119	1.0
7 W	0217	5.4		**22** TH	0326	5.6
	0843	1.3			0951	1.1
	1440	5.3			1604	5.4
	2103	1.5			2221	1.4
8 TH	0255	5.1		**23** F	0429	5.1
	0925	1.6			1101	1.5
	1525	5.0			1713	5.1
	2152	1.8			2342	1.7
9 F	0346	4.7		**24** SA	0544	4.8
	1025	1.8			1230	1.6
	1630	4.6			1841	4.9
	2304	2.1				
10 SA	0514	4.5		**25** SU	0107	1.7
	1144	2.0			0723	4.8
	1823	4.6			1341	1.5
					2004	5.2
11 SU	0031	2.0		**26** M	0213	1.4
	0657	4.6			0834	5.1
	1312	1.8			1438	1.2
	1934	4.9			2102	5.5
12 M	0152	1.7		**27** TU	0305	1.2
	0802	5.0			0926	5.4
	1422	1.4			1525	1.0
	2032	5.4			2149	5.8
13 TU	0250	1.3		**28** W	0349	0.9
	0855	5.5			1010	5.7
	1513	1.0			1607	0.8
	2122	5.8			2230	5.9
14 W	0336	0.9		**29** TH	0428	0.8
	0943	5.9			1049	5.8
	1557	0.7			1646	0.7
	2207	6.2			2306	6.0
15 TH	0419	0.5		**30** F O	0505	0.7
	1029	6.2			1124	5.9
	1640	0.4			1722	0.7
	2252	6.5			2339	6.0

Chart Datum: 3·27 metres below Ordnance Datum (Newlyn)

ENGLAND – SHOREHAM

LAT 50°50′N   LONG 0°15′W

TIMES AND HEIGHTS OF HIGH AND LOW WATERS

YEAR 1999

TIME ZONE (UT)
For Summer Time add ONE hour in non-shaded areas

Chart Datum: 3·27 metres below Ordnance Datum (Newlyn)

MAY

Day		Time	m	Time	m	Time	m	Time	m
1	SA	0539	0.7	1154	5.9	1756	0.7		
2	SU	0006	6.0	0612	0.7	1222	5.9	1828	0.7
3	M	0031	5.9	0643	0.7	1249	5.8	1859	0.8
4	TU	0056	5.8	0713	0.8	1316	5.7	1929	1.0
5	W	0123	5.7	0744	1.0	1345	5.6	2001	1.1
6	TH	0154	5.5	0817	1.1	1420	5.4	2038	1.4
7	F	0232	5.2	0900	1.4	1504	5.1	2126	1.6
8	SA	0322	4.9	0955	1.6	1602	4.9	2230	1.8
9	SU	0431	4.7	1104	1.7	1730	4.8	2348	1.8
10	M	0612	4.7	1223	1.7	1854	5.0		
11	TU	0105	1.6	0724	5.0	1337	1.4	1956	5.4
12	W	0210	1.2	0823	5.4	1436	1.0	2050	5.8
13	TH	0303	0.8	0916	5.8	1525	0.7	2140	6.2
14	F	0351	0.5	1005	6.2	1613	0.4	2227	6.5
15 ●	SA	0438	0.3	1054	6.4	1700	0.3	2315	6.6
16	SU	0526	0.1	1143	6.5	1748	0.2		
17	M	0002	6.7	0613	0.1	1231	6.6	1836	0.3
18	TU	0048	6.6	0701	0.2	1319	6.5	1924	0.4
19	W	0135	6.3	0750	0.4	1407	6.2	2013	0.6
20	TH	0223	6.0	0841	0.7	1457	5.9	2105	1.0
21	F	0314	5.6	0936	1.0	1552	5.6	2203	1.3
22	SA	0412	5.2	1032	1.3	1652	5.3	2314	1.6
23	SU	0516	4.9	1156	1.5	1800	5.1		
24	M	0034	1.7	0635	4.8	1307	1.5	1920	5.1
25	TU	0141	1.5	0756	4.9	1405	1.4	2025	5.3
26	W	0234	1.3	0853	5.1	1454	1.2	2115	5.5
27	TH	0320	1.1	0938	5.4	1524	1.1	2156	5.7
28	F	0400	1.0	1018	5.5	1617	1.0	2233	5.8
29	SA	0438	0.9	1052	5.7	1654	0.9	2305	5.8
30 O	SU	0513	0.8	1124	5.8	1730	0.9	2335	5.9
31	M	0548	0.8	1155	5.8	1805	0.9		

JUNE

Day		Time	m	Time	m	Time	m	Time	m
1	TU	0004	5.8	0621	0.8	1227	5.8	1837	0.9
2	W	0034	5.8	0653	0.8	1258	5.7	1909	1.0
3	TH	0105	5.7	0725	0.9	1331	5.7	1942	1.1
4	F	0139	5.6	0800	1.0	1407	5.6	2020	1.2
5	SA	0218	5.4	0842	1.2	1450	5.4	2106	1.4
6	SU	0306	5.2	0932	1.3	1542	5.2	2203	1.5
7	M	0405	5.0	1032	1.5	1647	5.1	2310	1.6
8	TU	0519	4.9	1141	1.5	1804	5.2		
9	W	0023	1.5	0640	5.1	1255	1.3	1916	5.4
10	TH	0133	1.2	0748	5.4	1402	1.1	2017	5.8
11	F	0233	0.9	0848	5.7	1459	0.8	2113	6.1
12	SA	0327	0.6	0943	6.0	1551	0.6	2206	6.3
13 ●	SU	0418	0.4	1037	6.3	1642	0.4	2257	6.5
14	M	0509	0.3	1128	6.4	1732	0.4	2347	6.5
15	TU	0558	0.2	1219	6.5	1822	0.4		
16	W	0036	6.5	0647	0.3	1308	6.4	1910	0.5
17	TH	0124	6.3	0736	0.4	1356	6.3	1958	0.7
18	F	0211	6.0	0825	0.6	1444	6.1	2047	0.9
19	SA	0259	5.7	0915	0.9	1532	5.8	2139	1.2
20	SU	0348	5.4	1007	1.2	1622	5.5	2234	1.5
21	M	0442	5.1	1105	1.5	1716	5.2	2338	1.7
22	TU	0539	4.8	1213	1.6	1815	5.1		
23	W	0053	1.7	0644	4.8	1321	1.7	1920	5.1
24	TH	0155	1.6	0758	4.9	1418	1.6	2023	5.2
25	F	0247	1.4	0855	5.1	1506	1.4	2113	5.4
26	SA	0331	1.2	0940	5.3	1549	1.3	2154	5.5
27	SU	0411	1.1	1018	5.5	1629	1.1	2231	5.7
28 O	M	0449	0.9	1055	5.6	1707	1.0	2307	5.8
29	TU	0526	0.9	1131	5.8	1744	1.0	2341	5.8
30	W	0602	0.8	1207	5.8	1819	1.0		

JULY

Day		Time	m	Time	m	Time	m	Time	m
1	TH	0015	5.8	0637	0.8	1242	5.8	1853	1.0
2	F	0050	5.8	0711	0.8	1316	5.8	1927	1.0
3	SA	0126	5.7	0746	0.9	1353	5.8	2004	1.0
4	SU	0206	5.7	0825	1.0	1435	5.7	2048	1.1
5	M	0250	5.5	0911	1.1	1522	5.6	2139	1.2
6	TU	0342	5.4	1005	1.2	1616	5.5	2238	1.3
7	W	0443	5.2	1107	1.3	1721	5.4	2347	1.4
8	TH	0556	5.2	1220	1.4	1835	5.4		
9	F	0101	1.3	0715	5.3	1335	1.3	1947	5.6
10	SA	0210	1.1	0826	5.5	1440	1.1	2052	5.8
11	SU	0311	0.8	0928	5.8	1537	0.8	2150	6.1
12	M	0405	0.6	1025	6.1	1630	0.6	2244	6.3
13 ●	TU	0456	0.4	1118	6.3	1720	0.5	2336	6.4
14	W	0546	0.3	1208	6.4	1809	0.5		
15	TH	0024	6.4	0633	0.3	1256	6.5	1855	0.6
16	F	0111	6.3	0719	0.4	1341	6.4	1940	0.7
17	SA	0154	6.1	0804	0.6	1424	6.2	2024	0.9
18	SU	0236	5.8	0846	0.8	1505	5.9	2107	1.1
19	M	0318	5.5	0929	1.1	1548	5.6	2150	1.3
20	TU	0403	5.2	1013	1.4	1633	5.3	2237	1.6
21	W	0454	4.9	1103	1.7	1725	5.1	2332	1.8
22	TH	0551	4.7	1203	1.9	1823	4.9		
23	F	0043	1.9	0654	4.7	1324	1.9	1924	4.9
24	SA	0207	1.8	0801	4.8	1433	1.8	2025	5.1
25	SU	0302	1.6	0900	5.1	1523	1.5	2117	5.3
26	M	0346	1.3	0948	5.4	1606	1.3	2202	5.6
27	TU	0426	1.0	1030	5.6	1645	1.1	2242	5.8
28 O	W	0504	0.9	1109	5.8	1724	1.0	2320	5.9
29	TH	0542	0.8	1146	5.9	1800	0.9	2357	6.0
30	F	0618	0.7	1223	6.0	1836	0.9		
31	SA	0033	6.0	0653	0.7	1259	6.1	1911	0.8

AUGUST

Day		Time	m	Time	m	Time	m	Time	m
1	SU	0111	6.0	0729	0.7	1336	6.1	1948	0.8
2	M	0150	6.0	0807	0.7	1416	6.0	2029	0.9
3	TU	0232	5.8	0850	0.9	1500	5.9	2116	1.0
4	W	0319	5.6	0940	1.1	1550	5.7	2211	1.2
5	TH	0415	5.4	1039	1.3	1650	5.4	2318	1.4
6	F	0525	5.2	1153	1.5	1804	5.3		
7	SA	0037	1.5	0651	5.1	1317	1.5	1926	5.3
8	SU	0157	1.3	0814	5.3	1429	1.3	2041	5.6
9	M	0301	1.0	0921	5.7	1528	1.0	2143	5.9
10	TU	0355	0.8	1017	6.1	1620	0.8	2237	6.1
11 ●	W	0445	0.5	1108	6.3	1709	0.6	2326	6.3
12	TH	0532	0.4	1155	6.4	1754	0.6		
13	F	0011	6.3	0616	0.5	1240	6.5	1837	0.6
14	SA	0054	6.3	0658	0.5	1320	6.4	1918	0.7
15	SU	0133	6.1	0737	0.6	1358	6.2	1955	0.8
16	M	0208	5.9	0813	0.8	1433	6.0	2031	1.0
17	TU	0242	5.7	0849	1.1	1507	5.7	2108	1.2
18	W	0317	5.3	0928	1.4	1543	5.4	2150	1.5
19	TH	0400	5.0	1013	1.7	1631	5.0	2239	1.8
20	F	0502	4.7	1109	2.0	1735	4.7	2341	2.0
21	SA	0612	4.6	1219	2.2	1843	4.7		
22	SU	0100	2.0	0722	4.7	1352	2.1	1949	4.9
23	M	0230	1.8	0826	5.0	1457	1.8	2047	5.2
24	TU	0320	1.4	0920	5.3	1543	1.4	2136	5.5
25	W	0401	1.1	1004	5.7	1622	1.2	2218	5.8
26 O	TH	0440	0.9	1045	6.0	1700	1.0	2257	6.0
27	F	0518	0.7	1123	6.1	1738	0.8	2336	6.1
28	SA	0555	0.6	1201	6.3	1814	0.7		
29	SU	0014	6.2	0631	0.5	1238	6.3	1851	0.6
30	M	0053	6.3	0708	0.5	1316	6.3	1929	0.6
31	TU	0131	6.2	0748	0.6	1355	6.3	2010	0.7

ENGLAND – SHOREHAM

LAT 50°50′N   LONG   0°15′W

TIMES AND HEIGHTS OF HIGH AND LOW WATERS

YEAR **1999**

TIME ZONE (UT)
For Summer Time add ONE hour in non-shaded areas

Chart Datum: 3.27 metres below Ordnance Datum (Newlyn)

SEPTEMBER

#	Time	m	Time	m
1 W	0212 / 0830 / 1438 / 2056	6.1 / 0.8 / 6.1 / 0.9	**16** TH	0228 / 0848 / 1444 / 2107	5.5 / 1.3 / 5.4 / 1.5
2 TH	0258 / 0919 / 1527 / 2149	5.8 / 1.0 / 5.7 / 1.2	**17** F	0301 / 0929 / 1520 / 2153	5.1 / 1.7 / 5.0 / 1.8
3 F	0354 / 1018 / 1627 / 2256	5.4 / 1.4 / 5.4 / 1.5	**18** SA	0349 / 1023 / 1619 / 2254	4.8 / 2.0 / 4.7 / 2.1
4 SA	0506 / 1136 / 1745	5.1 / 1.7 / 5.1	**19** SU	0528 / 1135 / 1804	4.5 / 2.3 / 4.5
5 SU	0022 / 0639 / 1307 / 1916	1.7 / 5.0 / 1.7 / 5.1	**20** M	0011 / 0647 / 1303 / 1916	2.2 / 4.6 / 2.2 / 4.7
6 M	0148 / 0810 / 1421 / 2038	1.5 / 5.2 / 1.5 / 5.4	**21** TU	0145 / 0754 / 1425 / 2018	2.0 / 4.9 / 1.9 / 5.0
7 TU	0252 / 0916 / 1519 / 2138	1.2 / 5.6 / 1.1 / 5.8	**22** W	0249 / 0850 / 1514 / 2108	1.6 / 5.3 / 1.5 / 5.5
8 W	0344 / 1009 / 1609 / 2228	0.9 / 6.0 / 0.8 / 6.1	**23** TH	0333 / 0936 / 1555 / 2152	1.2 / 5.8 / 1.1 / 5.8
9 TH ●	0431 / 1055 / 1654 / 2312	0.6 / 6.3 / 0.6 / 6.3	**24** F	0412 / 1017 / 1633 / 2233	0.9 / 6.1 / 0.8 / 6.1
10 F	0514 / 1138 / 1736 / 2354	0.5 / 6.5 / 0.6 / 6.3	**25** SA O	0449 / 1057 / 1710 / 2313	0.6 / 6.3 / 0.6 / 6.3
11 SA	0555 / 1218 / 1815	0.5 / 6.5 / 0.6	**26** SU	0527 / 1136 / 1749 / 2353	0.5 / 6.5 / 0.5 / 6.4
12 SU	0032 / 0632 / 1255 / 1850	6.3 / 0.5 / 6.4 / 0.7	**27** M	0606 / 1215 / 1828	0.4 / 6.5 / 0.5
13 M	0107 / 0707 / 1328 / 1924	6.2 / 0.7 / 6.2 / 0.8	**28** TU	0033 / 0646 / 1255 / 1909	6.5 / 0.4 / 6.5 / 0.5
14 TU	0136 / 0739 / 1356 / 1956	6.0 / 0.8 / 6.0 / 0.9	**29** W	0113 / 0728 / 1335 / 1952	6.4 / 0.5 / 6.4 / 0.6
15 W	0202 / 0812 / 1418 / 2029	5.7 / 1.0 / 5.7 / 1.2	**30** TH	0155 / 0813 / 1418 / 2040	6.2 / 0.7 / 6.1 / 0.9

OCTOBER

#	Time	m	Time	m
1 F	0242 / 0903 / 1509 / 2134	5.9 / 1.1 / 5.7 / 1.2	**16** SA	0225 / 0851 / 1440 / 2114	5.3 / 1.6 / 5.1 / 1.7
2 SA	0340 / 1004 / 1612 / 2241	5.4 / 1.5 / 5.3 / 1.6	**17** SU	0306 / 0941 / 1529 / 2211	5.0 / 2.0 / 4.8 / 2.0
3 SU	0456 / 1124 / 1732	5.1 / 1.8 / 5.0	**18** M	0412 / 1053 / 1708 / 2326	4.6 / 2.2 / 4.5 / 2.2
4 M	0010 / 0631 / 1257 / 1911	1.8 / 5.0 / 1.8 / 5.0	**19** TU	0608 / 1217 / 1840	4.6 / 2.2 / 4.6
5 TU	0135 / 0801 / 1409 / 2030	1.6 / 5.2 / 1.5 / 5.3	**20** W	0052 / 0718 / 1339 / 1944	2.0 / 4.9 / 2.0 / 5.0
6 W	0238 / 0903 / 1505 / 2125	1.3 / 5.7 / 1.2 / 5.7	**21** TH	0206 / 0815 / 1437 / 2037	1.7 / 5.3 / 1.5 / 5.4
7 TH	0328 / 0952 / 1552 / 2212	1.0 / 6.0 / 0.9 / 6.0	**22** F	0256 / 0904 / 1521 / 2123	1.3 / 5.8 / 1.1 / 5.9
8 F	0412 / 1036 / 1634 / 2254	0.7 / 6.3 / 0.7 / 6.2	**23** SA	0338 / 0947 / 1601 / 2207	0.9 / 6.2 / 0.8 / 6.2
9 SA	0452 / 1115 / 1713 / 2332	0.6 / 6.4 / 0.6 / 6.3	**24** SU O	0418 / 1029 / 1641 / 2249	0.6 / 6.5 / 0.5 / 6.4
10 SU	0530 / 1152 / 1749	0.5 / 6.4 / 0.6	**25** M	0459 / 1110 / 1723 / 2332	0.5 / 6.6 / 0.4 / 6.6
11 M	0007 / 0605 / 1226 / 1823	6.2 / 0.6 / 6.3 / 0.7	**26** TU	0541 / 1152 / 1806	0.4 / 6.7 / 0.3
12 TU	0038 / 0637 / 1254 / 1854	6.1 / 0.7 / 6.1 / 0.8	**27** W	0015 / 0625 / 1235 / 1850	6.6 / 0.4 / 6.6 / 0.4
13 W	0103 / 0708 / 1317 / 1925	6.0 / 0.9 / 5.9 / 0.9	**28** TH	0058 / 0710 / 1318 / 1937	6.5 / 0.5 / 6.5 / 0.5
14 TH	0127 / 0740 / 1338 / 1957	5.8 / 1.1 / 5.7 / 1.1	**29** F	0143 / 0758 / 1404 / 2026	6.3 / 0.7 / 6.1 / 0.8
15 F	0153 / 0813 / 1405 / 2032	5.6 / 1.3 / 5.5 / 1.4	**30** SA	0233 / 0851 / 1457 / 2122	5.9 / 1.1 / 5.7 / 1.2
31 SU	0333 / 0953 / 1601 / 2227	5.5 / 1.5 / 5.3 / 1.5		

NOVEMBER

#	Time	m	Time	m
1 M	0446 / 1110 / 1717 / 2352	5.2 / 1.8 / 5.0 / 1.7	**16** TU	0336 / 1012 / 1604 / 2241	4.9 / 2.0 / 4.7 / 2.0
2 TU	0613 / 1237 / 1851	5.1 / 1.8 / 5.0	**17** W	0504 / 1128 / 1748 / 2357	4.8 / 2.1 / 4.7 / 1.9
3 W	0112 / 0737 / 1348 / 2008	1.6 / 5.3 / 1.6 / 5.2	**18** TH	0633 / 1245 / 1902	4.9 / 1.9 / 4.9
4 TH	0214 / 0839 / 1443 / 2103	1.4 / 5.6 / 1.3 / 5.5	**19** F	0112 / 0735 / 1350 / 2001	1.7 / 5.3 / 1.6 / 5.3
5 F	0305 / 0928 / 1529 / 2149	1.1 / 5.9 / 1.0 / 5.8	**20** SA	0213 / 0828 / 1442 / 2052	1.4 / 5.7 / 1.2 / 5.8
6 SA	0348 / 1010 / 1610 / 2230	0.9 / 6.1 / 0.8 / 6.0	**21** SU	0303 / 0916 / 1529 / 2140	1.0 / 6.1 / 0.8 / 6.1
7 SU	0427 / 1049 / 1648 / 2307	0.8 / 6.2 / 0.8 / 6.1	**22** M	0348 / 1002 / 1614 / 2226	0.7 / 6.4 / 0.5 / 6.4
8 M ●	0504 / 1124 / 1724 / 2340	0.8 / 6.2 / 0.7 / 6.1	**23** TU O	0434 / 1047 / 1700 / 2313	0.5 / 6.6 / 0.4 / 6.6
9 TU	0539 / 1154 / 1757	0.8 / 6.2 / 0.8	**24** W	0520 / 1133 / 1748	0.4 / 6.7 / 0.3
10 W	0008 / 0611 / 1221 / 1829	6.0 / 0.9 / 6.0 / 0.8	**25** TH	0000 / 0607 / 1219 / 1835	6.6 / 0.4 / 6.7 / 0.3
11 TH	0035 / 0643 / 1245 / 1900	6.0 / 1.0 / 5.9 / 0.9	**26** F	0048 / 0656 / 1306 / 1924	6.5 / 0.5 / 6.5 / 0.5
12 F	0102 / 0714 / 1311 / 1932	5.8 / 1.1 / 5.7 / 1.1	**27** SA	0136 / 0746 / 1355 / 2014	6.4 / 0.7 / 6.2 / 0.7
13 SA	0130 / 0747 / 1340 / 2006	5.7 / 1.3 / 5.5 / 1.3	**28** SU	0228 / 0839 / 1448 / 2108	6.1 / 1.0 / 5.8 / 1.0
14 SU	0202 / 0823 / 1415 / 2045	5.5 / 1.6 / 5.3 / 1.6	**29** M	0324 / 0938 / 1546 / 2209	5.8 / 1.3 / 5.5 / 1.3
15 M	0242 / 0909 / 1501 / 2136	5.2 / 1.8 / 5.0 / 1.8	**30** TU	0426 / 1047 / 1651 / 2321	5.4 / 1.6 / 5.1 / 1.6

DECEMBER

#	Time	m	Time	m
1 W	0537 / 1205 / 1808	5.2 / 1.7 / 5.0	**16** TH	0410 / 1041 / 1640 / 2306	5.1 / 1.8 / 4.9 / 1.7
2 TH	0036 / 0655 / 1315 / 1929	1.6 / 5.2 / 1.7 / 5.0	**17** F	0526 / 1152 / 1802	5.1 / 1.8 / 5.0
3 F	0140 / 0802 / 1413 / 2031	1.6 / 5.4 / 1.5 / 5.2	**18** SA	0018 / 0645 / 1303 / 1917	1.6 / 5.3 / 1.6 / 5.2
4 SA	0234 / 0856 / 1501 / 2120	1.4 / 5.6 / 1.3 / 5.5	**19** SU	0129 / 0750 / 1406 / 2019	1.4 / 5.6 / 1.3 / 5.6
5 SU	0320 / 0940 / 1544 / 2203	1.2 / 5.8 / 1.1 / 5.7	**20** M	0230 / 0846 / 1502 / 2115	1.2 / 6.0 / 0.9 / 5.9
6 M	0402 / 1019 / 1624 / 2240	1.1 / 5.9 / 1.0 / 5.8	**21** TU	0324 / 0938 / 1554 / 2208	0.9 / 6.3 / 0.6 / 6.2
7 TU	0440 / 1053 / 1701 / 2312	1.0 / 6.0 / 0.9 / 5.9	**22** W O	0415 / 1029 / 1644 / 2259	0.7 / 6.5 / 0.4 / 6.4
8 W	0516 / 1124 / 1736 / 2342	1.0 / 6.0 / 0.9 / 5.9	**23** TH	0505 / 1118 / 1734 / 2350	0.5 / 6.6 / 0.3 / 6.5
9 TH	0550 / 1153 / 1810	1.0 / 6.0 / 0.9	**24** F	0555 / 1208 / 1823	0.5 / 6.6 / 0.3
10 F	0013 / 0623 / 1222 / 1842	5.9 / 1.0 / 5.9 / 0.9	**25** SA	0039 / 0644 / 1257 / 1912	6.6 / 0.5 / 6.5 / 0.4
11 SA	0044 / 0655 / 1252 / 1915	5.9 / 1.1 / 5.8 / 1.0	**26** SU	0129 / 0733 / 1345 / 2001	6.5 / 0.7 / 6.3 / 0.6
12 SU	0114 / 0728 / 1323 / 1948	5.8 / 1.2 / 5.7 / 1.2	**27** M	0217 / 0824 / 1434 / 2051	6.3 / 0.9 / 6.0 / 0.8
13 M	0147 / 0802 / 1359 / 2024	5.6 / 1.4 / 5.5 / 1.3	**28** TU	0307 / 0917 / 1524 / 2142	6.0 / 1.1 / 5.7 / 1.1
14 TU	0225 / 0844 / 1441 / 2109	5.5 / 1.6 / 5.3 / 1.5	**29** W	0358 / 1012 / 1617 / 2237	5.7 / 1.4 / 5.3 / 1.4
15 W	0312 / 0936 / 1534 / 2203	5.3 / 1.7 / 5.1 / 1.6	**30** TH	0452 / 1115 / 1714 / 2341	5.4 / 1.7 / 5.0 / 1.6
31 F	0552 / 1227 / 1819	5.2 / 1.8 / 4.9		

Chart Datum: 3.27 metres below Ordnance Datum (Newlyn)

BRIGHTON   8-3-10

E. Sussex 50°48'·50N 00°06'·28W   Rtg 2-1-1

3

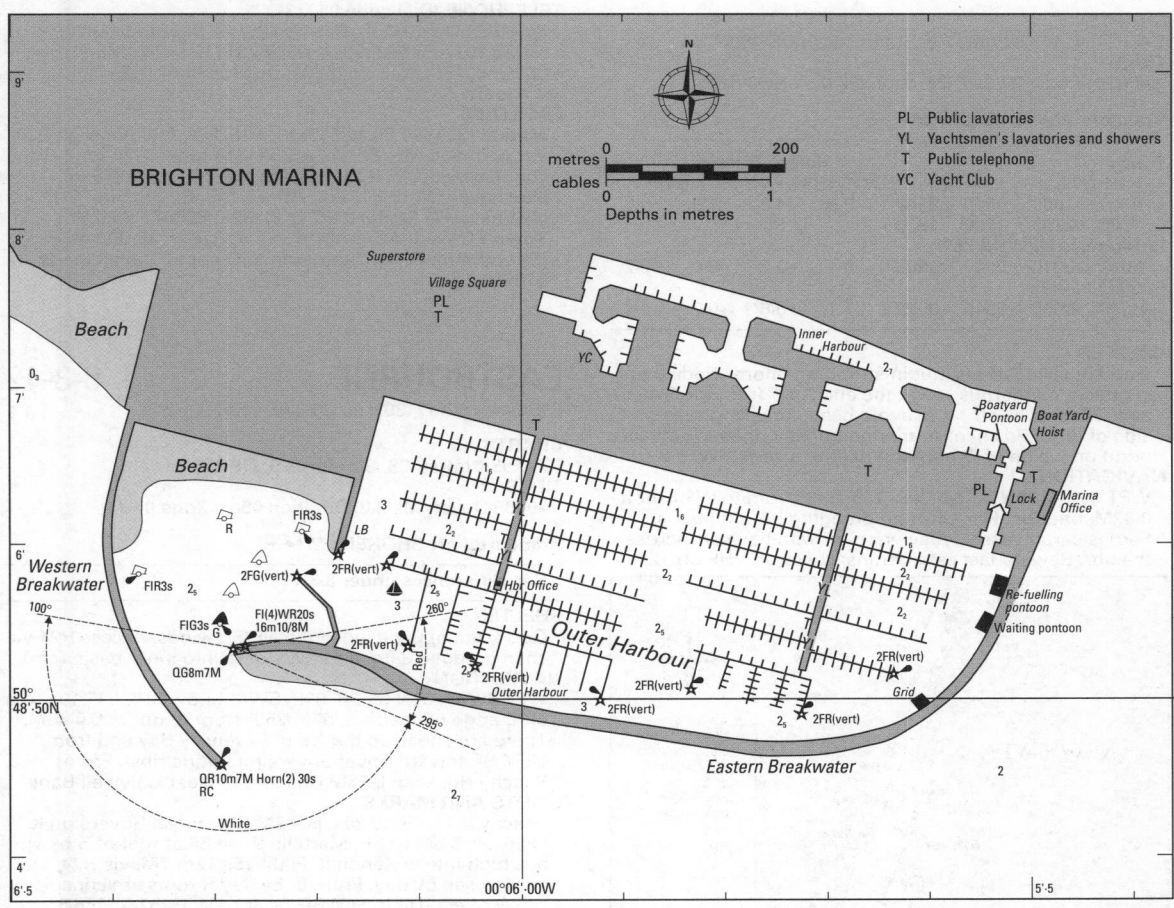

PL   Public lavatories
YL   Yachtsmen's lavatories and showers
T   Public telephone
YC   Yacht Club

Depths in metres

CHARTS

AC *1991, 1652*; Imray C9; Stanfords 9; OS 198

TIDES

+0004 Dover; ML 3·5; Duration 0605; Zone 0 (UT)

Standard Port SHOREHAM (←)

Times				Height (metres)			
High Water		Low Water		MHWS	MHWN	MLWN	MLWS
0500	1000	0000	0600	6·3	4·8	1·9	0·6
1700	2200	1200	1800				
Differences BRIGHTON							
–0010	–0005	–0005	–0005	+0·3	+0·1	0·0	–0·1

SHELTER

Good in the marina under all conditions, but in strong
S'ly winds confused seas can make the final appr very
rough. Speed limit 5kn.

NAVIGATION

WPT 50°48'·20N 00°06'·29W, 180°/000° from/to W bkwtr
lt, 0·26M. Ent chan dredged 2·5m, but after gales silting
may occur especially on E side. In heavy weather, best
appr is from SSE to avoid worst of the backlash from
bkwtrs; beware shallow water E of ent in R sector of lt Fl
(4) WR 20s. A Historic Wreck (see 8.0.3h) is at 50°48'·6N
00°06'·49W, immediately W of the marina's W bkwtr.

LIGHTS AND MARKS

The marina is at the E end of the town, where white cliffs
extend eastward. Daymark: conspic white hospital block,
brg 334° leads to ent. Y spar buoy, Fl Y 4s, is 2ca S of W
bkwtr.
Navigational lts may be hard to see against shore glare:
E bkwtr Fl (4) WR 20s (intens) 16m 10/8M; vis R260°-295°,
W295°-100°. E bkwtr hd QG 8m 7M. W bkwtr hd, tr R/W
bands, QR 10m 7M; Horn (2) 30s. RC = BM 294·5 kHz, 10M.
Inner Hbr lock controlled by normal R/G lts, 0800-2000LT.

RADIO TELEPHONE

Call: *Brighton Control* VHF Ch **M** 80 16 (H24); 68 11.

TELEPHONE (Dial code 01273)

. Hr Mr 819919; BY 609235; MRSC (01705) 552100;
▓ 0345 231110 (H24); Marinecall 0891 500456; Police
606744; Ⓗ 696955; Dr 686863.

FACILITIES

Marina (1600+200 visitors) ☎ 819919, ⚓ 675082, £15.68,
▓, FW, P, D, AC, Gas, Gaz, ⊚, R, Bar, BY, BH (60 ton), C
(35 ton), ⟨⊟, ⟨⟨; **Brighton Marina YC** ☎ 818711, Bar, R.
Services El, Ⓔ, ME, Sh, SM, CH, ACA, Divers, Riggers,
Superstore.
Hbr Guides available from Hbr Office or by post.
Bus service from marina; timetable info ☎ 674881.
Electric railway runs from marina to Palace Pier, Mar-Oct.
Town V, R, Bar, ✉, Ⓑ, ⇌, ✈ (Shoreham).

NEWHAVEN   8-3-11

E. Sussex 50°46'·80N 00°03'·63E   Rtg 2-2-2

CHARTS
AC 2154, *1652*; Imray C9; Stanfords 9; OS 198
TIDES
+0004 Dover; ML 3·6; Duration 0550; Zone 0 (UT)

Standard Port SHOREHAM (←)

Times				Height (metres)			
High Water		Low Water		MHWS	MHWN	MLWN	MLWS
0500	1000	0000	0600	6·3	4·8	1·9	0·6
1700	2200	1200	1800				
Differences NEWHAVEN							
–0015	–0010	0000	0000	+0·4	+0·2	0·0	–0·2
EASTBOURNE							
–0010	–0005	+0015	+0020	+1·1	+0·6	+0·2	+0·1

SHELTER
Good in all weathers, but in strong on-shore winds there is often a dangerous sea at the ent. Appr from the SW, to pass 50m off bkwtr hd to avoid heavy breaking seas on E side of dredged chan. At marina (mostly dries to soft silt), berth on inside of Ⓥ pontoon (0.0m), access HW±3½.
NAVIGATION
WPT 50°46'·20N 00°03'·70E, 168°/348° from/to W bkwtr lt, 0·32M. Caution: Hbr silts and dredging is continuous. Ferries/cargo vessels may warp off with hawsers across the hbr. Beware fast catamarans; check on VHF Ch 12.

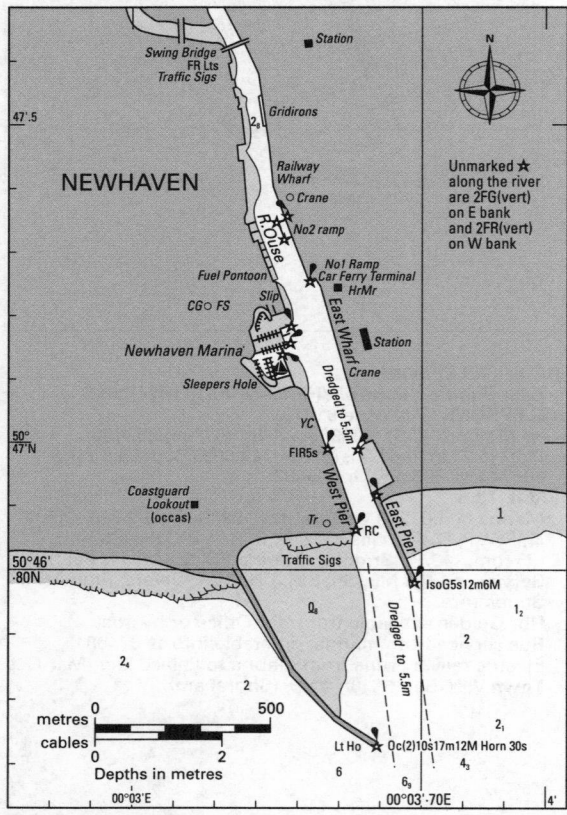

LIGHTS AND MARKS
Lt Ho on W bkwtr is conspic, as is an orange container crane opposite the marina.
Traffic sigs, displayed from tr on W side of river:

▼ over ●, or Ⓖ	= Only ent permitted.
● over ▼, or Ⓡ	= Only departure permitted.
● ▼ ● (vert) or	
ⓇⒼⓇ (vert)	= No ent or departure.
● or ⒼⓇ (vert)	= Entry and dep permitted with care for vessels under 15m LOA.

Swing bridge sigs:

Fl Ⓖ	= Bridge opening or closing.
Ⓡ	= Vessels may pass N to S.
Ⓖ	= Vessels may pass S to N.

RADIO TELEPHONE
Port VHF Ch 12 16 (H24). Swingbridge opening Ch 12. Marina Ch **80** M (0800-1700).
TELEPHONE (Dial code 01273)
Hr Mr 514131 (H24), ☎ 517342; Hbr Sig Stn 517922; MRSC (01705) 552100; ∰ 0345 231110 (H24); Marinecall 0891 500456; Police 515801; Dr 515076; Ⓗ 609411 (Casualty 696955).
FACILITIES
Marina (300+50 Ⓥ) ☎ 513881, £16, FW, fuel pontoon 200 yds N of ent, ME, El, Sh, AC, BH (18 ton), C (10 ton), CH, Gas, Gaz, Slip, V, R, Bar, Ⓞ; **Marina YC** ☎ 513976; **Newhaven YC** ☎ 513770, AB, M, ME, El, Sh, Slip, CH; **Newhaven & Seaford SC** ☎ (01323) 890077, M, FW. **Town** EC Wed; ACA, SM, P, Ⓔ, V, R, Bar, ✉, Ⓑ, ⇌, ✈ (Shoreham). Ferry/catamaran to Dieppe; Stena Line ☎ 516699.

EASTBOURNE   8-3-12

E. Sussex 50°47'·30N 00°20'·00E   Rtg 2-1-2

CHARTS
AC *536*; Imray C8; Stanfords 9; OS 199
TIDES
–0005 Dover; ML 3·8; Duration 0540; Zone 0 (UT)

Standard Port SHOREHAM (←)

See Differences under 8.3.11

SHELTER
Good, but apprs exposed to NE/SE winds. Access H24 via chan dredged 2·0m and twin locks into inner basin (4m).
NAVIGATION
WPT 50°47'·37N 00°20'·81E, SWM buoy 'SH', L Fl 10s (4ca off E edge of chartlet), 079°/259° from/to hbr ent, 0·45M. There are shoals to the NE in Pevensey Bay and from 2·5M SE toward Royal Sovereign lt (tide rips). From Beachy Hd, keep 0·75M offshore to clear Holywell Bank.
LIGHTS AND MARKS
Beachy Hd lt, Fl (2) 20s, is 4·7M SW; Royal Sovereign lt, Fl 20s, is 5·5M to SE. Martello tr No 66 at root of S bkwtr has high intens Xenon lt, Fl (3) 15s 12m 7M, vis H24; but hard to see by day. From E, by day R roofs are conspic WSW of ent. Dir lt, Fl WRG 5s 4m 1M, G252·5°-256·5°, W256·5°-259·5°, R259·5°-262·5°, leads 258° into channel marked by 5 SHM buoys, Fl G 3s, and 3 PHM buoys, Fl R 3s. N and S bkwtr hds, both painted white, are Fl G 5s 3m 6M and Fl (4) R 12s 3m 6M. Eastbourne pier, 2 FR, is 2M S of hbr ent; an unlit PHM buoy is approx 5ca S.
RADIO TELEPHONE
Call *Sovereign Harbour* VHF Ch **17**, 15 (H24) for nav info and for locks/berthing. IPTS (Sigs 2, 3 and 5) for each lock indicate lock availability; gates close every H and H+30.

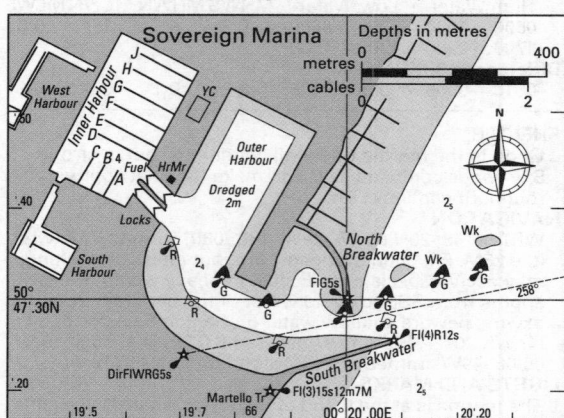

TELEPHONE (Dial code 01323)
Hr Mr 470099; MRSC (01304) 210008; ∰ 0345 231110 (H24); Marinecall 0891 500456; Police 722522; Dr 720555; Ⓗ 417400.
FACILITIES
Sovereign Marina (418 berths), ☎ 470099, ☎ 470077, £15.53, FW, AC, D & P (H24), BH (50 tons), ME, Sh, CH, Ⓞ, YC, supermarket. **Town** (2½M) all needs, ⇌, ✈ (Gatwick).

RYE   8-3-13

E. Sussex 50°55'.57N 00°46'.69E   Rtg 3-4-1

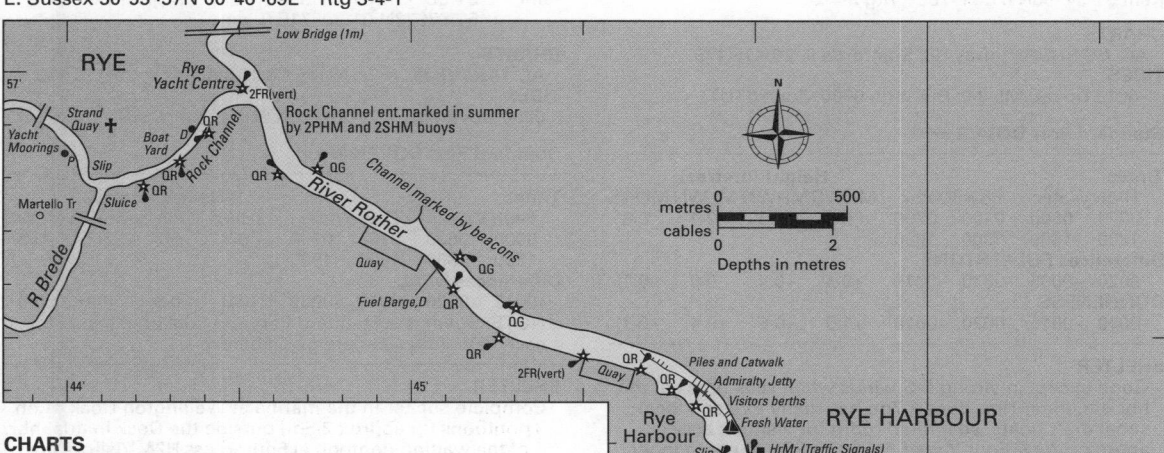

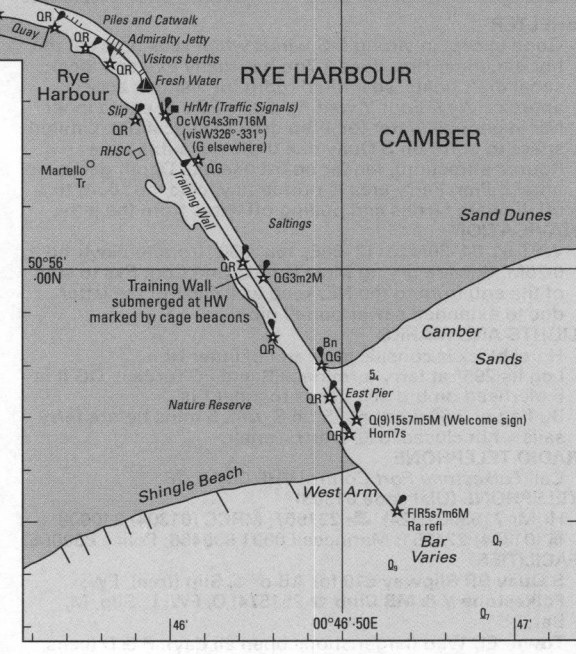

CHARTS
AC *1991, 536*; Imray C8; Stanfords 9; OS 189
TIDES
ML 2·0; Zone 0 (UT); Duration 3·25hrs sp, 5hrs nps

Standard Port DOVER (→)

Times				Height (metres)			
High Water		Low Water		MHWS	MHWN	MLWN	MLWS
0000	0600	0100	0700	6·8	5·3	2·1	0·8
1200	1800	1300	1900				
Differences RYE (Approaches)							
+0005	−0010	No data		+1·0	+0·7	No data	
RYE HARBOUR							
+0005	−0010	Dries		−1·4	−1·7	Dries	
HASTINGS							
0000	−0010	−0030	−0030	+0·8	+0·5	+0·1	−0·1

SHELTER
Very good in R Rother, but appr is exposed to prevailing SW winds with little shelter in Rye Bay. There are good ⚓s in lee of Dungeness (6M to E) or in N'lies ⚓ 5ca N of the Rye Fairway buoy. Rye Harbour is a small village, ¾M inside on W bank, used by commercial shipping. Hbr dries completely to soft mud. Berth initially on Admiralty Jetty and see Hr Mr for AB or M; ⚓ prohib. Speed limit 6kn. Rye Town (a Cinque Port) is 2M up river; ent via Rock Chan, visitors' AB on NE side of Strand Quay.
NAVIGATION
WPT Rye Fairway SWM By, L Fl 10s, 50°54'.00N 00°48'.13E, 150°/330° from/to W Arm tripod lt, 1·81M. Bar dries 2·75m about 2ca offshore and needs care when wind >F6 from SE to SW. Enter HW −2 to HW +3. Beware: Bar and shoals E and W of ent with ground swell or surf; narrow ent (42m) and chan (30m); flood runs 4·5kn (max HW −3 to HW −1).
Depth of water over the bar can be judged by day from how many horizontal timbers can be seen on West Arm tripod structure (approx 2ca N of the bar): 3, 2 or 1 timbers indicate water depths over the bar of about 0·5m, 2·0m or 3·5m (1·6ft, 6·5ft or 11·5ft) respectively.
LIGHTS AND MARKS
Dir Oc WG 4s lt on Hr Mr's office has W sector (326°-331°) covering ent/river. W Arm lt Fl R 5s 7m 6M, wooden tripod, radar reflector. E Arm hd, Q (9) 15s 7m 5M; Horn 7s, G △. On E Pier a floodlit "Welcome to Rye" sign is considered too bright by some, but helpful by others. Rock Chan ent marked by a QR and QG lt buoy in season.
IPTS (Sigs 2 & 5 only) are shown to seaward (3M) from Hr Mr's office and up-river (1M) from Admiralty Jetty.
RADIO TELEPHONE
VHF Ch 14 16 (0900-1700LT, HW±2 or when vessel due). To avoid commercial ships monitor Ch 14 before arr/dep.
TELEPHONE (Dial code 01797)
Hr Mr 225225, 🕾 227429; MRCC (01304) 210008; ⌗ (01304) 224251; Marinecall 0891 500456; Police 222112; Dr 222031; Ⓗ 222109.
FACILITIES
Admiralty Jetty £9.50, Slip, M, L, FW; **Strand Quay** AB, M, P & D (50m, cans), FW, Shwrs, Ⓖ; **Hbr** ME, El, BY, Sh, CH, C (15 ton), C (3 ton), Slip (26 ton), Ⓔ, ACA; **Rye Hbr SC** (Sec'y) 🕾 344645. **Town** EC Tues; ⊠, Ⓑ, ≷, ✈ (Lydd).

Note: A Historic Wreck (*Anne*; see 8.0.3h) is about 4M WSW of Rye, close inshore at 50°53'.42N 00°41'.91E.

ARMY FIRING RANGES off Lydd, centred on 50°54'N 00°53'E: a Sea Danger Area extends 3M offshore and stretches E from Rye Fairway buoy to a N/S line approx 1·5M W of Dungeness lt ho. When firing takes place, about 300 days p.a. 0830–1630LT (often to 2300), R flags/R lts are displayed ashore and a Range Safety Craft may be on station. Call *Lydd Ranges* Ch 73 13 or 🕾 01303 225518/225519. Radar fixes may also be obtained by VHF. Vessels may legally transit through the Sea Danger Area, but should not enter or remain in it for other purposes. If possible vessels should transit S of Stephenson Shoal. See also 8.3.14 for Hythe ranges.

ADJACENT ANCHORAGE

HASTINGS, E Sussex, 50°50'.84N 00°35'.60E. AC *536*. Tides, s ee 10-3-13; ML 3·8m; Duration 0530. Strictly a settled weather ⚓ or emergency shelter; landing places on pier. The stone bkwtr is in disrepair and serves only to protect FVs. Beware dangerous wreck 3ca SE of pier head. Ldg lts 356°, both FR 14/55m 4M: front on W metal column; rear 357m from front, on 5-sided W tr on West Hill. Pier hd 2 FR (vert) 8m 5M from white hut; W bkwtr hd Fl R 2·5s 5m 4M; Fl G 5s 2m, 30m from head of No3 Groyne (E bkwtr). A Historic Wreck (*Amsterdam*; see 8.0.3h) is about 2M W of pier, close inshore at 50°50'.7N 00°31'.65E. Facilities: EC Wed; ⌗ (01304) 224251. ACA (St Leonard's). Few marine services, but all shore needs at Hastings and St Leonard's. YC 🕾 (01424) 420656.

FOLKESTONE   8-3-14

Kent 51°04'·56N 01°11'·78E   Rtg 3-4-2

CHARTS
AC *1991, 1892*; Imray C8; Stanfords 9, 20; OS 179
TIDES
−0010 Dover; ML 3·9; Duration 0500; Zone 0 (UT)

Standard Port DOVER (⟶)

Times				Height (metres)			
High Water		Low Water		MHWS	MHWN	MLWN	MLWS
0000	0600	0100	0700	6·8	5·3	2·1	0·8
1200	1800	1300	1900				
Differences FOLKESTONE							
−0020	−0005	−0010	−0010	+0·4	+0·4	0·0	−0·1
DUNGENESS							
−0010	−0015	−0020	−0010	+1·0	+0·6	+0·4	+0·1

SHELTER
Good except in strong E-S winds when seas break at the hbr ent. Inner Hbr, dries 1·7m, has many FVs and local shoal draft boats, so limited room for visitors; access approx HW±2. Four Y waiting ⚓s lie ESE of ent to inner hbr in enough water for 1·5m draft to stay afloat. Limited space to berth on S Quay due to Soviet submarine (tourist attraction); fender board needed. Depth gauge on hd of E Pier. Ferry area is prohib to yachts; no room to ⚓ off. Beware ferries and pulling off wires from the jetty.
NAVIGATION
WPT 51°04'·30N 01°12'·00E, 150°/330° from/to bkwtr hd lt, 0·26M. Beware drying Mole Hd Rks and Copt Rks to stbd of the ent; from/to the NE, keep well clear of the latter due to extended sewer outfall pipe.
LIGHTS AND MARKS
Hotel block is conspic at W end of Inner Hbr.
Ldg lts 295° at ferry terminal, FR and FG (occas). QG lt at E pierhead on brg 305° leads to inner hbr.
Bu flag or 3 Ⓡ (vert) at FS on S arm, 5 mins before ferry sails = hbr closed. 3 Ⓖ (vert) = enter.
RADIO TELEPHONE
Call *Folkestone Port Control* VHF Ch 15, 16.
TELEPHONE (Dial code 01303)
Hr Mr 715300 (H24), ☎ 221567; MRCC (01304) 210008; ☏ (01304) 224251; Marinecall 0891 500456; Police 850055.
FACILITIES
S Quay BR Slipway £10 for AB or ⚓, Slip (free), FW; **Folkestone Y & MB Club** ☎ 251574, D, FW, L, Slip, M, Bar, ♿.
Town EC Wed (larger shops open all day); P & D (cans, 100 yds), V, R, Bar, ✉, Ⓑ, ⇌, ✈ (Lydd). Freight ferries and Hoverspeed (Seacat) to Boulogne.

ARMY FIRING RANGES (centred on 51°02'N 01°03'E) have a Sea Danger Area extending 2M offshore, from Hythe to Dymchurch (approx 5M and 8M WSW of Folkestone hbr). Vessels may legally transit through the Sea Danger Area, but should not enter or remain in it for other purposes. When firing takes place, about 300 days p.a. 0830–1630LT (often to 2300), R flags/R lts are displayed ashore and a Range Safety Craft may be on station. Radar fixes may also be obtained by VHF. Call *Hythe Ranges* Ch 73 13 or ☎ 01303 249541 Ext 8179/8133, ☏ Ext 8138. See 8.3.13.

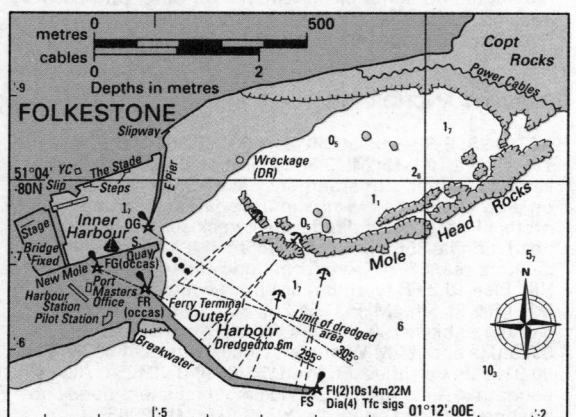

DOVER   8-3-15

Kent   51°06'·71N 01°19'·83E (W ent)   Rtg 1-1-2
        51°07'·22N 01°20'·71E (E ent)

CHARTS
AC *1698, 1828, 1892*; Imray C8; Stanfords 9, 20; OS 179
TIDES
0000 Dover; ML 3·7; Duration 0505; Zone 0 (UT)

Standard Port DOVER (⟶)

Times				Height (metres)			
High Water		Low Water		MHWS	MHWN	MLWN	MLWS
0000	0600	0100	0700	6·8	5·3	2·1	0·8
1200	1800	1300	1900				
Differences DEAL							
+0010	+0020	+0010	+0005	−0·6	−0·3	0·0	0·0

NOTE: Dover is a Standard Port and tidal predictions for each day of the year are given below.

SHELTER
Complete shelter in the marina at Wellington Dock or on 3 pontoons (in approx 2·5m) outside the Dock in tidal hbr, E of the waiting pontoon (1·5m); access H24. Visitors are welcomed and usually escorted by hbr launch to the marina. Dock gates, and swing bridge, open HW ±1½ nps and approx HW−1½ to HW+3 sp, depending on range. In the Outer Hbr the small craft moorings (33 W ⚓s) and ⚓ are tenable in offshore winds, but exposed to winds from NE through S to SW; in gales a heavy sea builds up. Small craft may not be left unattended at ⚓ in Outer Hbr.
NAVIGATION
WPT from SW, 51°06'·15N 01°19'·77E, 180°/000° from/to Admiralty Pier lt ho, 0·5M.
WPT from NE, 51°07'·27N 01°21'·51E, 090°/270° from/to S end Eastern Arm, 0·5M.
Beware lumpy seas/overfalls outside the bkwtrs and the frequent ferries, hovercraft and catamarans using both ents. Strong tides across ents and high walls make ent under sail slow and difficult; use of engine very strongly recommended. Near the W ent do not sail between NCM buoy, Q, (marking wreck) and the S bkwtr.
Specific permission to ent/leave the hbr via E or W ent must first be obtained from Port Control on VHF Ch 74. Comply with IPTS and any VHF instructions from Port Control or hbr patrol launch. Clearance for small/slow craft is not normally given until within 200m of ent; advise if you have no engine.
If no VHF, use following Aldis Lamp sigs:
SV (··· ·−−) = I wish to enter port
SW (··· ·−−) = I wish to leave port
Port Control will reply OK (−−− −·−) or
                  Wait (·−− ·− ·· −).
A Q Ⓦ lt from Port Control tr or patrol launch = keep clear of ent you are approaching. Beware fast hovercraft/catamarans on rounding Prince of Wales pier.
Marina sigs: In the final appr, especially near LW, stay in deep water as defined by the W sector (324°-333°) of the F WR lt, 3 unlit SHM poles and an unlit SHM buoy. IPTS are shown, plus a small Fl Ⓨ lt 5 min before bridge is swung.
Note: A Historic Wreck (see 8.0.3h) is adjacent to the Eastern Arm bkwtr at 51°07'·6N 01°20'·8E (see chartlet). There are 4 more Historic Wrecks on the Goodwin Sands.
LIGHTS AND MARKS
Lts as on chartlet & 8.3.4. Port Control tr (conspic) is at S end of E Arm and shows IPTS for the E ent on panels; for W ent, IPTS are on panels near Admiralty Pier sig stn.
RADIO TELEPHONE
Call: *Dover Port Control* VHF Ch **74** 12 16. Hbr launch and Water Taxi Ch 74. *Dover Marina* Ch 80, only within tidal hbr/marina. Chan Nav Info Service (CNIS) broadcasts tfc/nav/wx/tidal info Ch 11 at H+40; also, if vis < 2M, at H+55. *Dover Coastguard* Ch **69** 16 80, gives TSS surveillance.
TELEPHONE (Dial code 01304)
Hr Mr 240400 Ext 4540; Marina 241663; MRCC 210008; ☏ 224251; Marinecall 0891 500456; Police 240055; Ⓗ 201624.
FACILITIES
Marina (240+150 visitors) ☎ 241663, ☏ 242549, £12.18 in marina, £13.50 in tidal hbr (both inc AC), FW, C, Slip, D; *Dover Yachtsman's Manual* is obtainable from marina.
Royal Cinque Ports YC ☎ 206262, L, M, C, FW, Bar, R;
Services: D, ME, El, Sh, SM, ACA, CH, Ⓔ (H24 service).
Town EC Wed; P (cans), V, R, Bar, ✉, Ⓑ, ⇌, ✈ (Lydd).

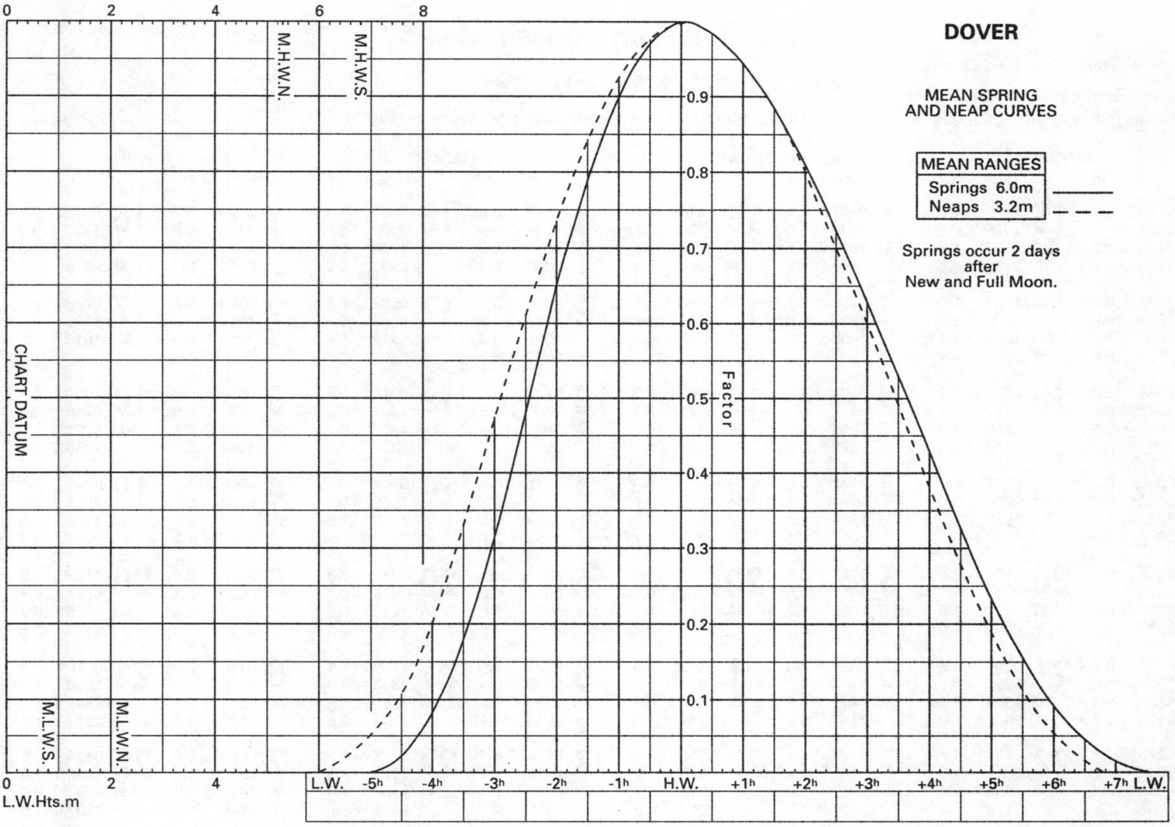

DOVER

MEAN SPRING AND NEAP CURVES

MEAN RANGES	
Springs 6.0m	—
Neaps 3.2m	- - -

Springs occur 2 days after
New and Full Moon.

H.W.Hts.m

CHART DATUM

M.H.W.N.   M.H.W.S.

Factor

0.9
0.8
0.7
0.6
0.5
0.4
0.3
0.2
0.1

M.L.W.S.   M.L.W.N.

L.W.Hts.m

L.W. -5h -4h -3h -2h -1h H.W. +1h +2h +3h +4h +5h +6h +7h L.W.

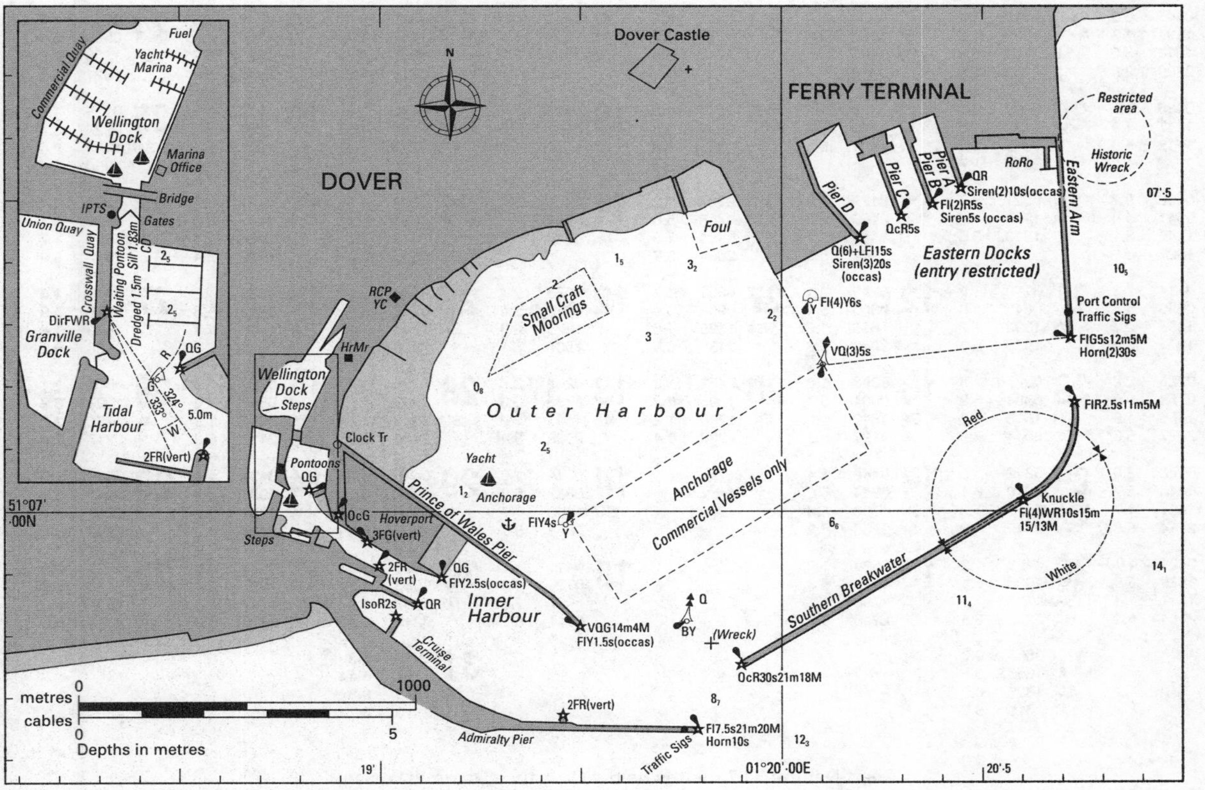

Dover Castle

FERRY TERMINAL

Restricted area
Historic Wreck
07'·5

DOVER

Commercial Quay
Fuel
Yacht Marina
Wellington Dock
Marina Office
Bridge
Gates
IPTS
Union Quay
Waiting Pontoon Sill 1.83m
CD Dredged 1.5m Sill 1.5m
Crosswall Quay
DirFWR
Granville Dock
QG
334°
333° W
5.0m
2FR(vert)
Tidal Harbour

RCP YC
HrMr
Wellington Dock Steps
Clock Tr
Pontoons QG
OcG Hoverport
3FG(vert)
Steps
2FR (vert)
QG
FIY2.5s(occas)
IsoR2s QR
Inner Harbour
Cruise Terminal
VQG14m4M
FIY1.5s(occas)

Small Craft Moorings

Outer Harbour

Yacht Anchorage
FIY4s

Anchorage
Commercial Vessels only

Foul

Pier D
Pier C
Pier B
Pier A
QR RoRo
Siren(2)10s(occas)
FI(2)R5s
Siren5s (occas)
QcR5s

Q(6)+LFI15s
Siren(3)20s (occas)

FI(4)Y6s

VQ(3)5s

Eastern Docks (entry restricted)

Eastern Arm

Port Control Traffic Sigs
FIG5s12m5M
Horn(2)30s

Red
FIR2.5s11m5M

Knuckle
FI(4)WR10s15m 15/13M
White

14,1

11,4

6,6

Southern Breakwater

Q
BY
(Wreck)
OcR30s21m18M

8,7

Prince of Wales Pier

2FR(vert)
Admiralty Pier
Traffic Sigs
FI7.5s21m20M
Horn10s
12,3

51°07' ·00N

metres 0   1000
cables 0   5
Depths in metres

19'   01°20'·00E   20'·5

10,5

ENGLAND – DOVER

LAT 51°07′N   LONG 1°19′E

TIMES AND HEIGHTS OF HIGH AND LOW WATERS   YEAR 1999

TIME ZONE (UT)
For Summer Time add ONE hour in non-shaded areas

JANUARY

Day	Time	m	Time	m	Time	m	Time	m
1 F	0504	1.1	1008	6.7	1741	0.9	2236	6.7
2 SA O	0603	0.9	1057	6.8	1835	0.8	2322	6.8
3 SU	0654	0.8	1143	6.8	1923	0.8		
4 M	0005	6.8	0742	0.8	1228	6.7	2006	0.9
5 TU	0049	6.8	0826	0.8	1311	6.6	2046	1.0
6 W	0131	6.7	0907	1.0	1354	6.4	2122	1.2
7 TH	0214	6.5	0946	1.2	1438	6.1	2157	1.5
8 F	0258	6.2	1022	1.4	1526	5.8	2230	1.7
9 SA	0346	6.0	1101	1.7	1618	5.6	2309	2.0
10 SU	0439	5.7	1147	1.9	1719	5.3		
11 M	0002	2.2	0541	5.5	1247	2.1	1825	5.2
12 TU	0114	2.3	0650	5.4	1352	2.1	1931	5.3
13 W	0226	2.2	0754	5.5	1455	1.9	2027	5.5
14 TH	0328	2.0	0846	5.7	1551	1.7	2114	5.8
15 F	0421	1.7	0929	5.9	1641	1.4	2154	6.1
16 SA	0507	1.4	1008	6.1	1726	1.3	2232	6.3
17 SU	0550	1.2	1046	6.3	1808	1.1	●2308	6.4
18 M	0631	1.1	1123	6.4	1850	1.0	2344	6.6
19 TU	0712	1.0	1200	6.5	1929	1.0		
20 W	0020	6.6	0752	1.0	1237	6.5	2008	1.0
21 TH	0057	6.7	0832	0.9	1315	6.5	2045	1.0
22 F	0137	6.7	0911	1.0	1356	6.4	2124	1.1
23 SA	0221	6.6	0952	1.1	1443	6.3	2206	1.2
24 SU	0310	6.4	1037	1.2	1537	6.0	2255	1.5
25 M	0409	6.1	1132	1.5	1646	5.7	2356	1.7
26 TU	0521	5.9	1239	1.7	1813	5.6		
27 W	0110	1.9	0645	5.8	1353	1.7	1935	5.6
28 TH	0227	1.8	0808	5.9	1508	1.6	2044	5.9
29 F	0342	1.5	0910	6.1	1627	1.3	2142	6.2
30 SA	0455	1.2	1006	6.4	1735	1.1	2232	6.5
31 SU O	0556	0.9	1055	6.5	1828	0.9	●2315	6.7

FEBRUARY

Day	Time	m	Time	m	Time	m	Time	m
1 M	0647	0.8	1138	6.6	1914	0.8	2355	6.8
2 TU	0732	0.7	1217	6.6	1953	0.8		
3 W	0034	6.8	0811	0.7	1254	6.6	2027	0.9
4 TH	0112	6.8	0846	0.8	1331	6.4	2057	1.1
5 F	0149	6.6	0917	1.0	1407	6.2	2122	1.2
6 SA	0224	6.4	0944	1.2	1444	6.0	2146	1.5
7 SU	0259	6.1	1011	1.4	1523	5.7	2218	1.7
8 M	0338	5.8	1046	1.7	1613	5.4	2259	2.0
9 TU	0433	5.4	1135	2.0	1725	5.1	2358	2.3
10 W	0550	5.2	1249	2.2	1841	5.1		
11 TH	0127	2.4	0706	5.2	1410	2.1	1947	5.3
12 F	0246	2.1	0809	5.4	1516	1.9	2042	5.6
13 SA	0348	1.8	0901	5.7	1612	1.6	2127	5.9
14 SU	0440	1.4	0944	6.0	1703	1.3	2208	6.2
15 M	0528	1.2	1025	6.3	1750	1.1	2246	6.5
16 TU	0614	0.9	1104	6.5	1834	0.9	●2324	6.7
17 W	0658	0.8	1142	6.6	1917	0.8		
18 TH	0002	6.8	0741	0.7	1220	6.7	1956	0.7
19 F	0041	6.9	0821	0.6	1259	6.7	2034	0.7
20 SA	0121	6.9	0859	0.6	1340	6.7	2111	0.8
21 SU	0203	6.8	0937	0.8	1424	6.5	2151	1.0
22 M	0250	6.6	1019	1.0	1516	6.1	2236	1.3
23 TU	0345	6.2	1109	1.4	1621	5.8	2332	1.6
24 W	0455	5.8	1213	1.7	1745	5.5		
25 TH	0045	1.9	0624	5.5	1331	1.9	1916	5.4
26 F	0207	1.9	0755	5.6	1454	1.8	2034	5.7
27 SA	0332	1.7	0909	5.9	1625	1.5	2135	6.0
28 SU	0451	1.3	1005	6.2	1729	1.2	2223	6.4

MARCH

Day	Time	m	Time	m	Time	m	Time	m
1 M	0549	0.9	1049	6.4	1818	0.9	2303	6.6
2 TU O	0637	0.7	1127	6.5	1859	0.8	2339	6.7
3 W	0717	0.7	1200	6.6	1934	0.8		
4 TH	0015	6.8	0750	0.7	1234	6.5	2002	0.9
5 F	0050	6.7	0819	0.8	1306	6.5	2026	1.0
6 SA	0122	6.6	0843	0.9	1337	6.3	2046	1.1
7 SU	0150	6.4	0905	1.1	1403	6.2	2110	1.3
8 M	0214	6.2	0930	1.3	1429	5.9	2141	1.5
9 TU	0242	5.9	1004	1.6	1501	5.6	2219	1.8
10 W	0323	5.6	1046	1.9	1552	5.3	2308	2.1
11 TH	0435	5.2	1145	2.2	1748	5.0		
12 F	0025	2.4	0622	5.0	1325	2.3	1907	5.1
13 SA	0205	2.3	0735	5.3	1443	2.0	2009	5.4
14 SU	0314	1.9	0833	5.6	1543	1.7	2058	5.8
15 M	0411	1.4	0920	6.0	1637	1.3	2141	6.2
16 TU	0503	1.1	1002	6.3	1726	1.0	2222	6.6
17 W	0552	0.8	1042	6.6	1814	0.8	●2301	6.8
18 TH	0640	0.6	1121	6.8	1858	0.7	2341	7.0
19 F	0724	0.5	1200	6.8	1939	0.5		
20 SA	0021	7.1	0804	0.4	1240	6.9	2017	0.5
21 SU	0102	7.1	0843	0.4	1322	6.8	2055	0.6
22 M	0145	6.9	0921	0.6	1408	6.6	2136	0.8
23 TU	0233	6.6	1002	1.0	1500	6.3	2221	1.2
24 W	0329	6.2	1051	1.4	1605	5.8	2316	1.6
25 TH	0440	5.7	1155	1.8	1723	5.5		
26 F	0029	1.9	0607	5.4	1316	2.0	1853	5.4
27 SA	0154	2.0	0747	5.4	1444	1.9	2019	5.6
28 SU	0324	1.7	0852	5.7	1613	1.6	2120	6.0
29 M	0440	1.3	0954	6.1	1712	1.2	2205	6.3
30 TU	0533	1.0	1033	6.3	1757	1.0	2243	6.5
31 W O	0617	0.8	1107	6.4	1836	0.9	●2319	6.7

APRIL

Day	Time	m	Time	m	Time	m	Time	m
1 TH	0653	0.7	1138	6.5	1907	0.9	2353	6.7
2 F	0723	0.8	1210	6.5	1933	0.9		
3 SA	0026	6.7	0747	0.9	1241	6.5	1953	1.0
4 SU	0055	6.8	0808	0.9	1308	6.4	2015	1.1
5 M	0118	6.4	0831	1.1	1329	6.3	2041	1.2
6 TU	0138	6.2	0859	1.2	1351	6.1	2112	1.4
7 W	0205	6.0	0932	1.5	1423	5.9	2149	1.7
8 TH	0244	5.7	1012	1.8	1508	5.5	2234	2.0
9 F	0339	5.3	1103	2.1	1625	5.2	2337	2.3
10 SA	0540	5.1	1228	2.3	1824	5.1		
11 SU	0121	2.2	0701	5.2	1406	2.1	1932	5.4
12 M	0238	1.9	0802	5.6	1510	1.7	2026	5.8
13 TU	0337	1.4	0852	6.0	1605	1.3	2112	6.3
14 W	0431	1.1	0935	6.4	1657	1.0	2154	6.6
15 TH	0524	0.8	1017	6.7	1747	0.8	2236	6.9
16 F	0615	0.5	1057	6.9	1834	0.6	●2318	7.1
17 SA	0703	0.4	1138	7.0	1918	0.5		
18 SU	0000	7.1	0746	0.4	1221	7.0	1959	0.5
19 M	0044	7.1	0826	0.4	1306	6.9	2041	0.5
20 TU	0130	6.9	0907	0.7	1355	6.7	2123	0.8
21 W	0220	6.6	0950	1.0	1449	6.3	2211	1.1
22 TH	0319	6.2	1040	1.4	1551	6.0	2307	1.6
23 F	0427	5.7	1144	1.8	1701	5.6		
24 SA	0018	1.8	0546	5.4	1300	2.0	1821	5.5
25 SU	0138	1.9	0726	5.4	1422	2.0	1950	5.6
26 M	0259	1.7	0839	5.7	1539	1.7	2052	5.9
27 TU	0410	1.3	0928	5.9	1639	1.4	2138	6.2
28 W	0504	1.1	1007	6.2	1725	1.2	2217	6.4
29 TH	0547	1.0	1040	6.3	1803	1.1	2253	6.5
30 F O	0622	0.9	1112	6.4	1835	1.0	●2328	6.5

Chart Datum: 3·67 metres below Ordnance Datum (Newlyn)

ENGLAND – DOVER

LAT 51°07′N   LONG   1°19′E

TIMES AND HEIGHTS OF HIGH AND LOW WATERS

YEAR **1999**

3

MAY

Day	Time	m	Day	Time	m
1 SA	0650 / 1144 / 1900	1.0 / 6.5 / 1.0	**16** SU	0641 / 1119 / 1858 / 2342	0.5 / 6.9 / 0.5 / 7.1
2 SU	0000 / 0713 / 1215 / 1923	6.5 / 1.0 / 6.4 / 1.1	**17** M	0729 / 1205 / 1945	0.4 / 7.0 / 0.5
3 M	0029 / 0737 / 1243 / 1948	6.4 / 1.0 / 6.4 / 1.1	**18** TU	0029 / 0813 / 1254 / 2030	7.0 / 0.5 / 6.9 / 0.6
4 TU	0051 / 0804 / 1305 / 2018	6.3 / 1.1 / 6.3 / 1.2	**19** W	0118 / 0858 / 1344 / 2116	6.8 / 0.7 / 6.7 / 0.8
5 W	0112 / 0835 / 1328 / 2051	6.2 / 1.3 / 6.2 / 1.4	**20** TH	0211 / 0943 / 1437 / 2205	6.5 / 1.0 / 6.4 / 1.1
6 TH	0141 / 0909 / 1401 / 2128	6.1 / 1.5 / 6.0 / 1.6	**21** F	0308 / 1033 / 1534 / 2300	6.2 / 1.4 / 6.1 / 1.4
7 F	0220 / 0948 / 1446 / 2211	5.8 / 1.7 / 5.8 / 1.8	**22** SA	0409 / 1130 / 1635	5.8 / 1.7 / 5.8
8 SA	0312 / 1036 / 1550 / 2308	5.5 / 2.0 / 5.5 / 2.0	**23** SU	0002 / 0517 / 1236 / 1742	1.7 / 5.5 / 1.9 / 5.6
9 SU	0443 / 1142 / 1729	5.3 / 2.2 / 5.3	**24** M	0109 / 0641 / 1344 / 1902	1.8 / 5.4 / 2.0 / 5.6
10 M	0034 / 0620 / 1320 / 1848	2.1 / 5.3 / 2.2 / 5.5	**25** TU	0218 / 0757 / 1451 / 2011	1.7 / 5.5 / 1.8 / 5.8
11 TU	0157 / 0726 / 1431 / 1948	1.8 / 5.6 / 1.8 / 5.9	**26** W	0323 / 0850 / 1552 / 2103	1.5 / 5.7 / 1.6 / 6.1
12 W	0300 / 0820 / 1529 / 2039	1.4 / 6.0 / 1.4 / 6.3	**27** TH	0419 / 0932 / 1643 / 2146	1.4 / 5.9 / 1.4 / 6.2
13 TH	0356 / 0907 / 1623 / 2126	1.1 / 6.4 / 1.1 / 6.6	**28** F	0505 / 1009 / 1725 / 2225	1.2 / 6.1 / 1.3 / 6.3
14 F	0453 / 0951 / 1717 / 2211	0.8 / 6.6 / 0.8 / 6.9	**29** SA	0542 / 1043 / 1800 / 2300	1.2 / 6.3 / 1.2 / 6.3
15 SA ●	0548 / 1035 / 1809 / 2256	0.6 / 6.8 / 0.6 / 7.0	**30** SU O	0614 / 1117 / 1829 / 2333	1.1 / 6.3 / 1.2 / 6.3
			31 M	0643 / 1150 / 1858	1.1 / 6.4 / 1.1

JUNE

Day	Time	m	Day	Time	m
1 TU	0003 / 0712 / 1221 / 1928	6.3 / 1.1 / 6.3 / 1.1	**16** W	0020 / 0804 / 1244 / 2022	6.8 / 0.6 / 6.8 / 0.6
2 W	0031 / 0744 / 1247 / 2002	6.2 / 1.2 / 6.3 / 1.2	**17** TH	0110 / 0851 / 1332 / 2110	6.7 / 0.8 / 6.7 / 0.8
3 TH	0057 / 0818 / 1315 / 2037	6.2 / 1.3 / 6.3 / 1.3	**18** F	0159 / 0935 / 1421 / 2157	6.5 / 1.0 / 6.6 / 1.0
4 F	0127 / 0853 / 1349 / 2114	6.1 / 1.4 / 6.2 / 1.4	**19** SA	0251 / 1020 / 1512 / 2244	6.2 / 1.3 / 6.3 / 1.2
5 SA	0206 / 0932 / 1433 / 2157	6.0 / 1.6 / 6.0 / 1.6	**20** SU	0344 / 1106 / 1605 / 2334	5.9 / 1.6 / 6.0 / 1.5
6 SU	0256 / 1017 / 1529 / 2249	5.8 / 1.7 / 5.8 / 1.7	**21** M	0442 / 1158 / 1702	5.6 / 1.8 / 5.8
7 M	0401 / 1114 / 1639 / 2356	5.6 / 1.9 / 5.7 / 1.8	**22** TU	0029 / 0545 / 1256 / 1807	1.7 / 5.4 / 2.0 / 5.6
8 TU	0527 / 1229 / 1757	5.5 / 1.9 / 5.7	**23** W	0128 / 0656 / 1357 / 1918	1.8 / 5.4 / 2.0 / 5.6
9 W	0113 / 0644 / 1347 / 1907	1.7 / 5.7 / 1.8 / 5.9	**24** TH	0227 / 0800 / 1459 / 2021	1.8 / 5.5 / 1.9 / 5.7
10 TH	0221 / 0747 / 1451 / 2007	1.4 / 5.9 / 1.5 / 6.2	**25** F	0325 / 0852 / 1555 / 2112	1.7 / 5.7 / 1.7 / 5.9
11 F	0322 / 0840 / 1551 / 2100	1.2 / 6.2 / 1.2 / 6.5	**26** SA	0417 / 0935 / 1644 / 2154	1.5 / 5.9 / 1.5 / 6.1
12 SA	0423 / 0930 / 1651 / 2151	0.9 / 6.5 / 0.9 / 6.7	**27** SU	0501 / 1014 / 1725 / 2232	1.4 / 6.1 / 1.4 / 6.1
13 SU ●	0525 / 1019 / 1748 / 2241	0.7 / 6.7 / 0.6 / 6.9	**28** M O	0540 / 1051 / 1801 / 2307	1.3 / 6.2 / 1.2 / 6.2
14 M	0623 / 1107 / 1843 / 2330	0.6 / 6.8 / 0.6 / 6.9	**29** TU	0617 / 1126 / 1836 / 2340	1.2 / 6.3 / 1.2 / 6.2
15 TU	0716 / 1156 / 1934	0.6 / 6.9 / 0.6	**30** W	0653 / 1159 / 1913	1.2 / 6.3 / 1.1

JULY

Day	Time	m	Day	Time	m
1 TH	0012 / 0729 / 1231 / 1949	6.2 / 1.2 / 6.4 / 1.1	**16** F	0059 / 0839 / 1318 / 2058	6.6 / 0.8 / 6.8 / 0.7
2 F	0044 / 0806 / 1303 / 2027	6.2 / 1.2 / 6.4 / 1.2	**17** SA	0143 / 0919 / 1401 / 2139	6.5 / 1.0 / 6.7 / 0.8
3 SA	0117 / 0843 / 1339 / 2105	6.2 / 1.3 / 6.4 / 1.2	**18** SU	0227 / 0956 / 1445 / 2217	6.3 / 1.2 / 6.5 / 1.1
4 SU	0154 / 0921 / 1419 / 2146	6.2 / 1.3 / 6.3 / 1.3	**19** M	0312 / 1032 / 1531 / 2256	6.0 / 1.4 / 6.2 / 1.4
5 M	0238 / 1002 / 1508 / 2231	6.1 / 1.5 / 6.2 / 1.4	**20** TU	0401 / 1109 / 1620 / 2338	5.7 / 1.7 / 5.9 / 1.7
6 TU	0332 / 1050 / 1605 / 2326	5.9 / 1.6 / 6.0 / 1.5	**21** W	0457 / 1154 / 1717	5.5 / 2.0 / 5.6
7 W	0438 / 1151 / 1713	5.7 / 1.7 / 5.9	**22** TH	0030 / 0559 / 1256 / 1822	1.9 / 5.3 / 2.2 / 5.4
8 TH	0033 / 0558 / 1305 / 1828	1.6 / 5.7 / 1.8 / 5.9	**23** F	0132 / 0707 / 1405 / 1931	2.0 / 5.3 / 2.2 / 5.4
9 F	0145 / 0716 / 1417 / 1940	1.5 / 5.8 / 1.6 / 6.0	**24** SA	0236 / 0810 / 1510 / 2034	2.0 / 5.5 / 2.0 / 5.6
10 SA	0254 / 0821 / 1525 / 2044	1.4 / 6.0 / 1.4 / 6.3	**25** SU	0334 / 0903 / 1607 / 2123	1.8 / 5.7 / 1.7 / 5.8
11 SU	0401 / 0919 / 1631 / 2142	1.0 / 6.3 / 1.1 / 6.5	**26** M	0426 / 0947 / 1654 / 2204	1.6 / 6.0 / 1.5 / 6.0
12 M	0509 / 1012 / 1734 / 2236	1.0 / 6.5 / 0.9 / 6.7	**27** TU	0512 / 1025 / 1737 / 2241	1.4 / 6.2 / 1.3 / 6.2
13 TU ●	0612 / 1102 / 1833 / 2327	0.8 / 6.7 / 0.7 / 6.7	**28** W O	0554 / 1101 / 1817 / 2317	1.2 / 6.3 / 1.1 / 6.3
14 W	0707 / 1149 / 1926	0.7 / 6.8 / 0.6	**29** TH	0635 / 1137 / 1857 / 2352	1.1 / 6.4 / 1.1 / 6.2
15 TH	0014 / 0755 / 1234 / 2014	6.7 / 0.7 / 6.8 / 0.6	**30** F	0715 / 1211 / 1937	1.1 / 6.5 / 1.0
			31 SA	0026 / 0753 / 1246 / 2016	6.4 / 1.1 / 6.6 / 1.0

AUGUST

Day	Time	m	Day	Time	m
1 SU	0101 / 0831 / 1322 / 2054	6.4 / 1.1 / 6.6 / 1.1	**16** M	0158 / 0922 / 1415 / 2141	6.4 / 1.2 / 6.5 / 1.1
2 M	0137 / 0907 / 1401 / 2131	6.4 / 1.1 / 6.6 / 1.0	**17** TU	0236 / 0948 / 1454 / 2209	6.1 / 1.4 / 6.3 / 1.4
3 TU	0218 / 0945 / 1446 / 2212	6.3 / 1.2 / 6.5 / 1.2	**18** W	0317 / 1013 / 1535 / 2238	5.9 / 1.7 / 5.9 / 1.7
4 W	0307 / 1029 / 1537 / 2259	6.1 / 1.4 / 6.3 / 1.4	**19** TH	0406 / 1048 / 1626 / 2320	5.5 / 2.0 / 5.6 / 2.0
5 TH	0406 / 1122 / 1641	5.9 / 1.6 / 6.0	**20** F	0510 / 1140 / 1733	5.3 / 2.3 / 5.3
6 F	0000 / 0525 / 1232 / 1800	1.6 / 5.6 / 1.8 / 5.8	**21** SA	0028 / 0621 / 1307 / 1846	2.3 / 5.2 / 2.4 / 5.2
7 SA	0116 / 0656 / 1351 / 1925	1.8 / 5.6 / 1.8 / 5.8	**22** SU	0152 / 0731 / 1430 / 1956	2.3 / 5.3 / 2.3 / 5.4
8 SU	0233 / 0811 / 1507 / 2039	1.7 / 5.8 / 1.6 / 6.0	**23** M	0300 / 0831 / 1534 / 2053	2.0 / 5.6 / 1.9 / 5.7
9 M	0350 / 0915 / 1621 / 2142	1.4 / 6.1 / 1.3 / 6.3	**24** TU	0357 / 0918 / 1626 / 2137	1.7 / 5.9 / 1.6 / 6.0
10 TU	0504 / 1009 / 1728 / 2236	1.2 / 6.4 / 1.0 / 6.5	**25** W	0447 / 0958 / 1712 / 2215	1.4 / 6.2 / 1.3 / 6.2
11 W ●	0605 / 1056 / 1826 / 2323	0.9 / 6.7 / 0.8 / 6.6	**26** TH O	0532 / 1035 / 1756 / 2252	1.2 / 6.4 / 1.1 / 6.4
12 TH	0657 / 1138 / 1916	0.8 / 6.8 / 0.6	**27** F	0615 / 1111 / 1839 / 2328	1.1 / 6.6 / 0.9 / 6.5
13 F	0004 / 0741 / 1219 / 1959	6.7 / 0.8 / 6.8 / 0.6	**28** SA	0657 / 1147 / 1920	1.0 / 6.7 / 0.8
14 SA	0043 / 0820 / 1258 / 2038	6.6 / 0.8 / 6.8 / 0.7	**29** SU	0004 / 0736 / 1224 / 1959	6.6 / 0.9 / 6.8 / 0.8
15 SU	0120 / 0853 / 1337 / 2111	6.7 / 1.0 / 6.7 / 0.8	**30** M	0040 / 0813 / 1301 / 2036	6.7 / 0.9 / 6.9 / 0.8
			31 TU	0117 / 0849 / 1340 / 2113	6.6 / 0.9 / 6.8 / 0.9

Chart Datum: 3·67 metres below Ordnance Datum (Newlyn)

ENGLAND – DOVER

LAT 51°07′N   LONG 1°19′E

TIMES AND HEIGHTS OF HIGH AND LOW WATERS   YEAR **1999**

TIME ZONE (UT)
For Summer Time add ONE hour in non-shaded areas

SEPTEMBER

Date	Time	m	Date	Time	m
1 W	0158 / 0926 / 1424 / 2151	6.5 / 1.0 / 6.6 / 1.1	16 TH	0228 / 0929 / 1443 / 2149	6.0 / 1.6 / 6.0 / 1.7
2 TH	0245 / 1008 / 1515 / 2237	6.3 / 1.3 / 6.3 / 1.4	17 F	0302 / 1004 / 1524 / 2227	5.7 / 1.9 / 5.6 / 2.0
3 F	0344 / 1059 / 1620 / 2335	5.9 / 1.6 / 5.9 / 1.8	18 SA	0403 / 1049 / 1643 / 2321	5.3 / 2.2 / 5.2 / 2.3
4 SA	0506 / 1208 / 1746	5.6 / 2.0 / 5.6	19 SU	0537 / 1159 / 1808	5.1 / 2.5 / 5.1
5 SU	0054 / 0641 / 1333 / 1918	2.0 / 5.5 / 2.0 / 5.6	20 M	0101 / 0652 / 1348 / 1921	2.5 / 5.2 / 2.4 / 5.2
6 M	0222 / 0803 / 1458 / 2039	2.0 / 5.7 / 1.8 / 5.9	21 TU	0227 / 0756 / 1500 / 2021	2.3 / 5.5 / 2.1 / 5.6
7 TU	0350 / 0909 / 1620 / 2142	1.6 / 6.0 / 1.4 / 6.2	22 W	0328 / 0846 / 1555 / 2107	1.9 / 5.9 / 1.6 / 6.0
8 W	0501 / 1001 / 1723 / 2231	1.3 / 6.4 / 1.0 / 6.5	23 TH	0420 / 0928 / 1644 / 2147	1.5 / 6.2 / 1.3 / 6.3
9 TH	0555 / 1043 / 1815 / ● 2312	1.0 / 6.7 / 0.8 / 6.6	24 F	0506 / 1005 / 1730 / 2225	1.2 / 6.5 / 1.0 / 6.6
10 F	0641 / 1122 / 1859 / 2347	0.9 / 6.8 / 0.7 / 6.7	25 SA	0551 / 1043 / 1815 / ○ 2302	1.0 / 6.8 / 0.8 / 6.7
11 SA	0720 / 1158 / 1937	0.8 / 6.9 / 0.7	26 SU	0633 / 1120 / 1858 / 2338	0.9 / 6.9 / 0.7 / 6.8
12 SU	0020 / 0752 / 1235 / 2009	6.7 / 0.9 / 6.9 / 0.8	27 M	0713 / 1158 / 1938	0.8 / 7.0 / 0.7
13 M	0054 / 0820 / 1310 / 2036	6.6 / 1.0 / 6.8 / 0.9	28 TU	0016 / 0751 / 1238 / 2015	6.9 / 0.8 / 7.1 / 0.7
14 TU	0127 / 0842 / 1343 / 2058	6.4 / 1.2 / 6.6 / 1.2	29 W	0055 / 0829 / 1319 / 2052	6.9 / 0.8 / 7.0 / 0.8
15 W	0158 / 0902 / 1413 / 2120	6.3 / 1.4 / 6.3 / 1.4	30 TH	0139 / 0908 / 1405 / 2132	6.7 / 1.0 / 6.7 / 1.1

OCTOBER

Date	Time	m	Date	Time	m
1 F	0228 / 0952 / 1459 / 2218	6.4 / 1.3 / 6.3 / 1.5	16 SA	0212 / 0932 / 1432 / 2152	5.9 / 1.8 / 5.7 / 2.0
2 SA	0331 / 1044 / 1609 / 2318	6.0 / 1.7 / 5.9 / 1.9	17 SU	0252 / 1015 / 1528 / 2240	5.6 / 2.2 / 5.3 / 2.3
3 SU	0453 / 1154 / 1736	5.6 / 2.0 / 5.6	18 M	0433 / 1113 / 1729 / 2354	5.2 / 2.4 / 5.1 / 2.6
4 M	0041 / 0622 / 1322 / 1911	2.2 / 5.5 / 2.1 / 5.5	19 TU	0609 / 1256 / 1845	5.2 / 2.5 / 5.2
5 TU	0215 / 0749 / 1454 / 2034	2.1 / 5.7 / 1.8 / 5.8	20 W	0144 / 0716 / 1420 / 1946	2.4 / 5.4 / 2.2 / 5.6
6 W	0344 / 0855 / 1612 / 2132	1.7 / 6.0 / 1.4 / 6.2	21 TH	0252 / 0809 / 1519 / 2035	2.0 / 5.8 / 1.7 / 6.0
7 TH	0447 / 0943 / 1709 / 2215	1.4 / 6.4 / 1.0 / 6.4	22 F	0346 / 0854 / 1611 / 2117	1.6 / 6.3 / 1.3 / 6.4
8 F	0535 / 1023 / 1756 / 2251	1.1 / 6.7 / 0.8 / 6.6	23 SA	0435 / 0934 / 1659 / 2156	1.3 / 6.6 / 1.0 / 6.7
9 SA	0616 / 1059 / 1835 / ● 2323	1.0 / 6.8 / 0.8 / 6.7	24 SU	0521 / 1013 / 1747 / ○ 2234	1.0 / 6.9 / 0.8 / 6.9
10 SU	0651 / 1135 / 1908 / 2354	1.0 / 6.9 / 0.8 / 7.0	25 M	0606 / 1053 / 1832 / 2313	0.9 / 7.1 / 0.7 / 7.0
11 M	0720 / 1209 / 1935	1.0 / 6.8 / 1.0	26 TU	0649 / 1133 / 1915 / 2353	0.8 / 7.2 / 0.6 / 7.0
12 TU	0026 / 0743 / 1242 / 1957	6.6 / 1.1 / 6.7 / 1.1	27 W	0730 / 1215 / 1956	0.7 / 7.1 / 0.7
13 W	0057 / 0803 / 1311 / 2017	6.5 / 1.2 / 6.5 / 1.2	28 TH	0036 / 0811 / 1301 / 2036	7.0 / 0.8 / 7.0 / 0.9
14 TH	0123 / 0826 / 1334 / 2042	6.4 / 1.4 / 6.3 / 1.4	29 F	0123 / 0854 / 1350 / 2118	6.8 / 1.0 / 6.7 / 1.4
15 F	0145 / 0856 / 1358 / 2114	6.2 / 1.6 / 6.0 / 1.7	30 SA	0217 / 0941 / 1449 / 2207	6.5 / 1.3 / 6.3 / 1.6
			31 SU	0321 / 1036 / 1600 / 2308	6.1 / 1.6 / 5.9 / 2.0

NOVEMBER

Date	Time	m	Date	Time	m
1 M	0434 / 1146 / 1720	5.8 / 2.0 / 5.6	16 TU	0322 / 1044 / 1623 / 2311	5.5 / 2.2 / 5.2 / 2.4
2 TU	0027 / 0554 / 1308 / 1851	2.2 / 5.6 / 2.0 / 5.5	17 W	0506 / 1159 / 1800	5.3 / 2.3 / 5.3
3 W	0155 / 0721 / 1433 / 2012	2.1 / 5.7 / 1.8 / 5.7	18 TH	0043 / 0626 / 1330 / 1905	2.4 / 5.5 / 2.1 / 5.5
4 TH	0316 / 0828 / 1546 / 2107	1.8 / 6.0 / 1.5 / 6.0	19 F	0206 / 0727 / 1436 / 1959	2.1 / 5.8 / 1.8 / 5.9
5 F	0417 / 0917 / 1642 / 2149	1.5 / 6.3 / 1.2 / 6.3	20 SA	0306 / 0817 / 1533 / 2045	1.7 / 6.2 / 1.4 / 6.3
6 SA	0505 / 0957 / 1727 / 2224	1.3 / 6.5 / 1.0 / 6.4	21 SU	0359 / 0901 / 1626 / 2127	1.4 / 6.6 / 1.1 / 6.6
7 SU	0545 / 1034 / 1804 / 2256	1.2 / 6.7 / 1.0 / 6.6	22 M	0450 / 0944 / 1717 / 2208	1.1 / 6.9 / 0.8 / 6.8
8 M	0619 / 1109 / 1835 / ● 2327	1.1 / 6.7 / 1.0 / 6.6	23 TU	0539 / 1027 / 1808 / ○ 2251	0.9 / 7.1 / 0.7 / 7.0
9 TU	0647 / 1143 / 1900	1.2 / 6.7 / 1.1	24 W	0627 / 1112 / 1855 / 2336	0.7 / 7.1 / 0.7 / 7.0
10 W	0000 / 0710 / 1215 / 1922	6.6 / 1.2 / 6.6 / 1.2	25 TH	0714 / 1158 / 1941	0.7 / 7.1 / 0.7
11 TH	0031 / 0733 / 1243 / 1946	6.5 / 1.3 / 6.4 / 1.3	26 F	0023 / 0800 / 1247 / 2026	7.0 / 0.8 / 6.9 / 0.9
12 F	0056 / 0801 / 1306 / 2016	6.4 / 1.4 / 6.3 / 1.4	27 SA	0113 / 0847 / 1340 / 2112	6.8 / 0.9 / 6.7 / 1.1
13 SA	0118 / 0833 / 1330 / 2049	6.3 / 1.5 / 6.1 / 1.6	28 SU	0207 / 0937 / 1439 / 2202	6.6 / 1.2 / 6.3 / 1.5
14 SU	0146 / 0909 / 1404 / 2127	6.1 / 1.7 / 5.8 / 1.9	29 M	0306 / 1032 / 1543 / 2258	6.3 / 1.4 / 6.0 / 1.8
15 M	0225 / 0951 / 1451 / 2213	6.0 / 2.0 / 5.5 / 2.1	30 TU	0408 / 1133 / 1652	6.0 / 1.7 / 5.7

DECEMBER

Date	Time	m	Date	Time	m
1 W	0003 / 0516 / 1241 / 1810	2.0 / 5.8 / 1.8 / 5.5	16 TH	0358 / 1119 / 1642 / 2345	5.7 / 2.0 / 5.4 / 2.1
2 TH	0114 / 0633 / 1351 / 1929	2.1 / 5.7 / 1.8 / 5.6	17 F	0518 / 1233 / 1812	5.6 / 2.0 / 5.5
3 F	0225 / 0746 / 1500 / 2028	2.0 / 5.8 / 1.7 / 5.8	18 SA	0106 / 0635 / 1348 / 1918	2.1 / 5.8 / 1.8 / 5.8
4 SA	0331 / 0841 / 1600 / 2114	1.8 / 6.0 / 1.5 / 6.0	19 SU	0220 / 0738 / 1453 / 2013	1.8 / 6.1 / 1.5 / 6.1
5 SU	0425 / 0927 / 1649 / 2153	1.6 / 6.2 / 1.3 / 6.2	20 M	0322 / 0831 / 1553 / 2103	1.5 / 6.4 / 1.2 / 6.4
6 M	0509 / 1007 / 1728 / 2228	1.4 / 6.4 / 1.3 / 6.3	21 TU	0421 / 0922 / 1652 / 2150	1.2 / 6.7 / 1.0 / 6.6
7 TU	0545 / 1043 / 1800 / 2303	1.3 / 6.5 / 1.2 / 6.4	22 W	0517 / 1011 / 1749 / ○ 2238	1.0 / 6.9 / 0.8 / 6.8
8 W	0616 / 1118 / 1828 / 2337	1.3 / 6.5 / 1.2 / 6.5	23 TH	0611 / 1100 / 1843 / 2327	0.8 / 7.0 / 0.7 / 6.9
9 TH	0644 / 1151 / 1856	1.3 / 6.4 / 1.2	24 F	0704 / 1149 / 1934	0.7 / 6.9 / 0.7
10 F	0009 / 0713 / 1221 / 1926	6.5 / 1.3 / 6.3 / 1.3	25 SA	0015 / 0755 / 1240 / 2022	6.9 / 0.8 / 6.8 / 0.8
11 SA	0038 / 0744 / 1248 / 1959	6.4 / 1.3 / 6.2 / 1.4	26 SU	0104 / 0844 / 1331 / 2108	6.9 / 0.8 / 6.6 / 1.0
12 SU	0103 / 0819 / 1315 / 2033	6.3 / 1.4 / 6.1 / 1.5	27 M	0154 / 0933 / 1423 / 2153	6.7 / 0.9 / 6.4 / 1.2
13 M	0131 / 0855 / 1347 / 2111	6.2 / 1.6 / 6.0 / 1.6	28 TU	0245 / 1020 / 1518 / 2239	6.5 / 1.1 / 6.1 / 1.5
14 TU	0209 / 0935 / 1429 / 2152	6.1 / 1.7 / 5.8 / 1.8	29 W	0338 / 1109 / 1615 / 2328	6.2 / 1.4 / 5.8 / 1.8
15 W	0256 / 1022 / 1524 / 2242	5.9 / 1.9 / 5.6 / 2.0	30 TH	0436 / 1201 / 1718	5.9 / 1.7 / 5.5
			31 F	0023 / 0539 / 1259 / 1827	2.0 / 5.7 / 1.8 / 5.4

Chart Datum: 3·67 metres below Ordnance Datum (Newlyn)

DOVER STRAIT
8-3-16

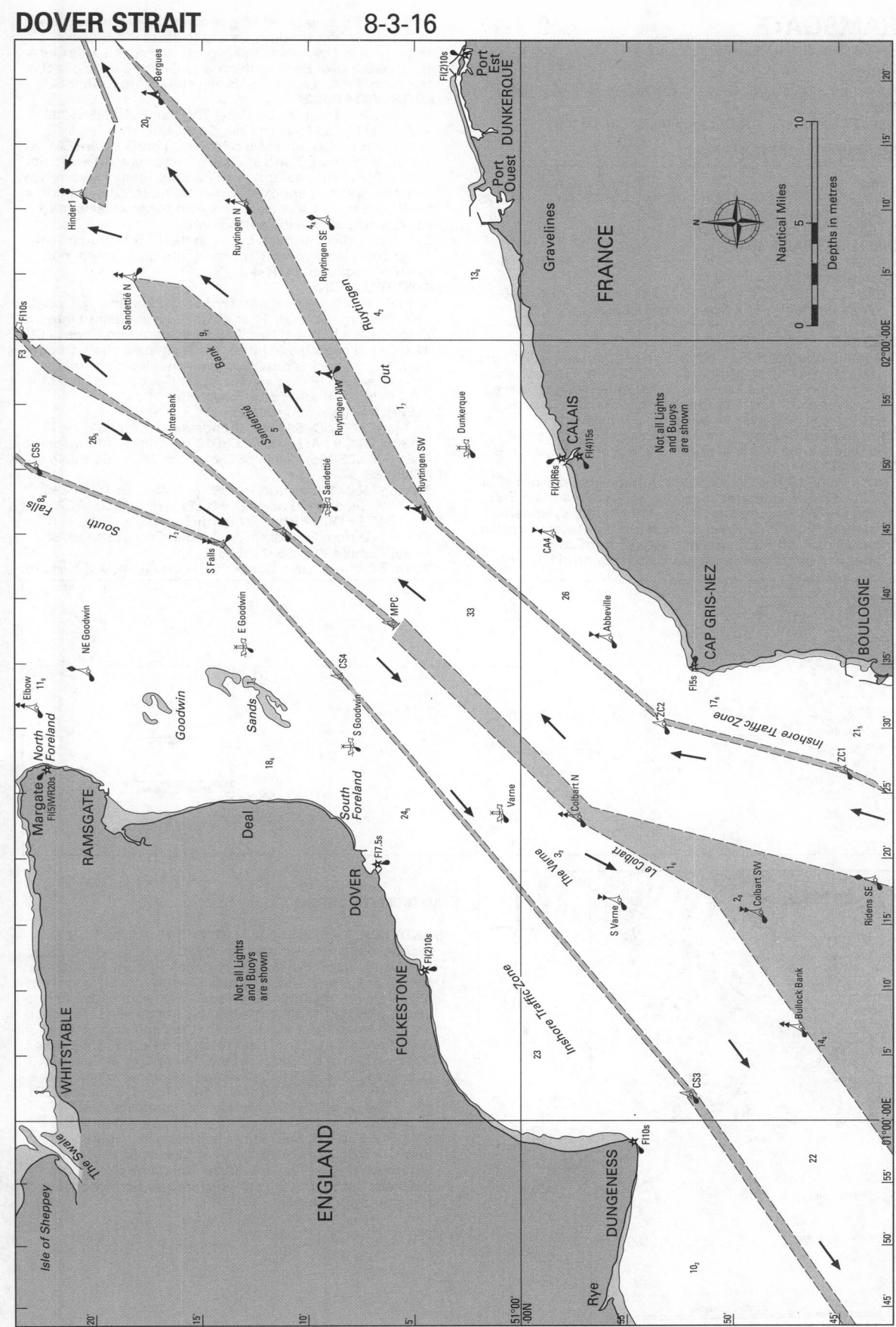

RAMSGATE   8-3-17

Kent 51°19'·48N 01°25'·60E   Rtg 1-2-1

CHARTS
AC 1827, *1828, 323*; Imray C1, C8; Stanfords 5, 9, 20; OS 179
TIDES
+0030 Dover; ML 2·7; Duration 0530; Zone 0 (UT)

Standard Port DOVER (←—)

Times				Height (metres)			
High Water		Low Water		MHWS	MHWN	MLWN	MLWS
0000	0600	0100	0700	6·8	5·3	2·1	0·8
1200	1800	1300	1900				
Differences RAMSGATE							
+0030	+0030	+0017	+0007	−1·6	−1·3	−0·7	−0·4
RICHBOROUGH							
+0015	+0015	+0030	+0030	−3·4	−2·6	−1·7	−0·7

HW Broadstairs = HW Dover +0037 approx.

SHELTER
Good in marina, min depth 3m. Access approx HW ±2 via
flap gate and lifting bridge. Close ESE of the marina ent,
107 pontoon berths in 2m are accessible H24, protected
by wavebreaks. Extra berths may be available in West
Gully; larger vessels can berth on S Breakwater.
Anti-Rabies Byelaw: Animals, inc dogs/cats, are totally
banned ashore or afloat within the Royal Harbour limits.
NAVIGATION
WPT 51°19'·40N 01°27'·80E, 090°/270° from/to S bkwtr, 1·45M.
Many ferries/catamarans use the well-marked main E-W
chan (3·3M long, dredged 7·5m, 110m wide; as upper
chartlet). For ent/dep yachts must use the Recommended
Yacht Track on the S side of the main buoyed chan.
Enter/dep under power, or advise Port Control if unable

to motor. Ent/dep Royal Hbr directly; do not manoeuvre
in the outer hbr. Holding area to the S of the S bkwtr
must be used by yachts to keep the hbr ent clear for ferry
tfc. Beware Dike Bank to the N and Quern Bank close S of
the chan. Cross Ledge and Brake shoals are further S.
LIGHTS AND MARKS
Ldg lts 270°: front Dir Oc WRG 10s 10m 5M, G259°-269°,
W269°-271°, R271°-281°; rear, Oc 5s 17m 5M.
N bkwtr hd = QG 10m 5M; S bkwtr hd = VQ R 10m 5M. At
E Pier, **IPTS** (Sigs 2 and 3) visible from seaward and from
within Royal Hbr, control appr into hbr limits (abeam Nos
1 & 2 buoys) and ent/exit to/from Royal Hbr. In addition a
Fl Orange lt = ferry is under way; **no other vessels may
move without specific permission**.
Ent to marina controlled by separate IPTS to stbd of ent.
Siren sounded approx 10 mins before gate closes; non-
opening indicated by R ● or Ⓡ.
RADIO TELEPHONE
A VTS operates, mainly for ferries/catamarans, but small
craft must monitor Ch 14 at all times until cleared into, or
before leaving, Royal Hbr. Call *Ramsgate Port Control* Ch
14 (H24) to enter/leave hbr or to cross main chan. Due to
frequent tfc, yachts **mus**t comply with all orders, which
can supersede IPTS. Call *Ramsgate Dock Office* Ch 80 for
a berth in the marina or in Royal Hbr.
TELEPHONE (Dial code 01843)
Hr Mr 592277, 🛳 590941; Broadstairs Hr Mr 861879; ⌗
(01304) 224251 (H24); MRCC (01304) 210008; Marinecall
0891 500 455/456; Police 581724; Dr 852853; Ⓗ 225544.
FACILITIES
Marina (400+100 visitors) ☎ 592277, 🛳 590941, £12.60,
AC, FW, Slips, C (10 ton), Ⓔ, ME, El, Sh, BH, CH, ACA,
Gaz, SM, Ⓞ; **Outer Hbr** (107 berths), 2m, access H24, AC,
FW. P & D from Fuel Barge, *Foy Boat* Ch 14 or ☎ 592662.
Royal Temple YC ☎ 591766, Bar.
Town EC Thurs; Gas, Gaz, V, R, Bar, ✉, Ⓑ, ⇌, ✈ (Manston).

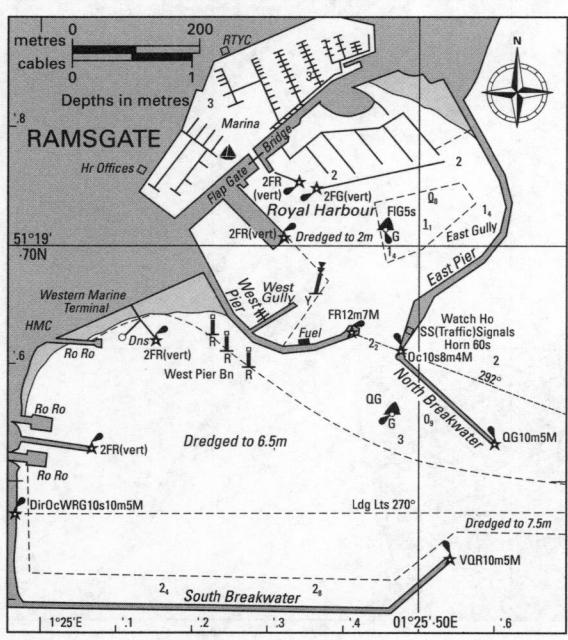

ADJACENT HARBOUR

SANDWICH, Kent, 51°16'·80N 01°21'·30E. AC 1827 *1828*.
Richborough differences above; ML 1·4m; Duration 0520.
HW Sandwich Town quay is HW Richborough +1. Access
HW ±1 at sp for draft 2m to reach Sandwich; arrive off ent
at HW Dover. Visitors should seek local knowledge before
arriving by day; night ent definitely not advised. The chan
to Shell Ness is marked by bn Fl R 10s and small lateral
buoys and beacons, all with rotating reflective topmarks.
Visitors' berths on S bank of the River Stour at Town
Quay ☎ (01304) 613283. Limited turning room before the
swing bridge, 1·7m clearance when closed. Facilities: EC
Wed; Slip, ⌗ ☎ 224251; **Marina** (50+some visitors)
☎ 613783 (max LOA 18m, 2·1m draft), BH (15 ton), Sh,
Slip, FW, SM, ME, CH, Gas; D & P (cans from garage);
Sandwich Sailing and Motorboat Club ☎ 611116 and
Sandwich Bay Sailing and Water Ski Clubs offer some
facilities. Both ports are administered by Sandwich Port &
Haven Commissioners.

VOLVO PENTA SERVICE

Sales and service centres in area 4

KENT *Ensign Marine Services Ltd.* Wellington Dock, Union Street, Dover CT17 9BY Tel (01304) 240004 *John Hawkins Marine*, Ships Stores, Medway Bridge Marina, Manor Lane, Borstal, Rochester ME1 3HS Tel (01634) 840812 **ESSEX** *Volspec Ltd*, Woodrolfe Road, Tollesbury, Maldon CM9 8SE Tel (01621) 869756 *French Marine Motors Ltd*, 61/63 Waterside, Brightlingsea CO7 0AX Tel (01206) 302133 **NORFOLK** *Marinepower Engineering*, The Mill, (off Station Road), Wood Green, Salhouse, Norwich NR13 6NS Tel (01603) 720001 **NORTHAMPTONSHIRE** *CVS Pentapower*, St. Andrews Road, Northampton NN1 2LF Tel (01604) 638537/638409/636173 **SUFFOLK** *Northgate Marine*, 27 Acorn Units, Ellough Industrial Estate, Beccles, Suffolk NR34 7TD Tel (01502) 716657 *French Marine Motors Ltd*, Suffolk Yacht Harbour, Levington, Ipswich IP10 0LN Tel (01473) 659882 *Volspec Ltd*, Woolverstone Marina, Woolverstone, Ipswich IP9 1AS Tel (01473) 780144

VOLVO PENTA

Area 4 4

East England
North Foreland to Great Yarmouth

8.4.1 Index **Page 269**

8.4.2 Diagram of ports, lights, RDF bns, Coast radio and weather stns **270**

8.4.3 Tidal stream charts **272**

8.4.4 List of coastal lights, fog signals and waypoints **274**

8.4.5 Passage information **278**

8.4.6 Distance table **279**

8.4.7 East Anglian waypoints **280**

8.4.8 Thames Estuary tidal stream charts **282**

8.4.9 Thames Estuary **284**

8.4.10 Whitstable **285**
  Margate
  Herne Bay

8.4.11 The Swale **286**

8.4.12 Queenborough **287**

8.4.13 River Medway (Sheerness, Standard Port, tidal curves) **288**

8.4.14 River Thames (London Bridge, Standard Port, tidal curves) **293**
  Holehaven
  Gravesend
  Thames tidal barrier
  Gallions Point marina
  South Dock marina
  Limehouse Basin marina
  St Katherine Haven
  Chelsea Harbour

8.4.15 Southend-on-Sea, Leigh-on-Sea **302**

8.4.16 River Roach/Havengore **303**

8.4.17 Burnham-on-Crouch (inc tidal predictions) **304**

8.4.18 River Blackwater **308**

8.4.19 River Colne **309**

8.4.20 Walton Backwaters Standard Port, tidal curves **310**

8.4.21 River Stour **314**

8.4.22 River Orwell **314**

8.4.23 River Deben **316**

8.4.24 River Ore/Alde **316**

8.4.25 Southwold **317**

8.4.26 Lowestoft, Standard Port, tidal curves **318**

8.4.27 Great Yarmouth **322**
  Norfolk Broads

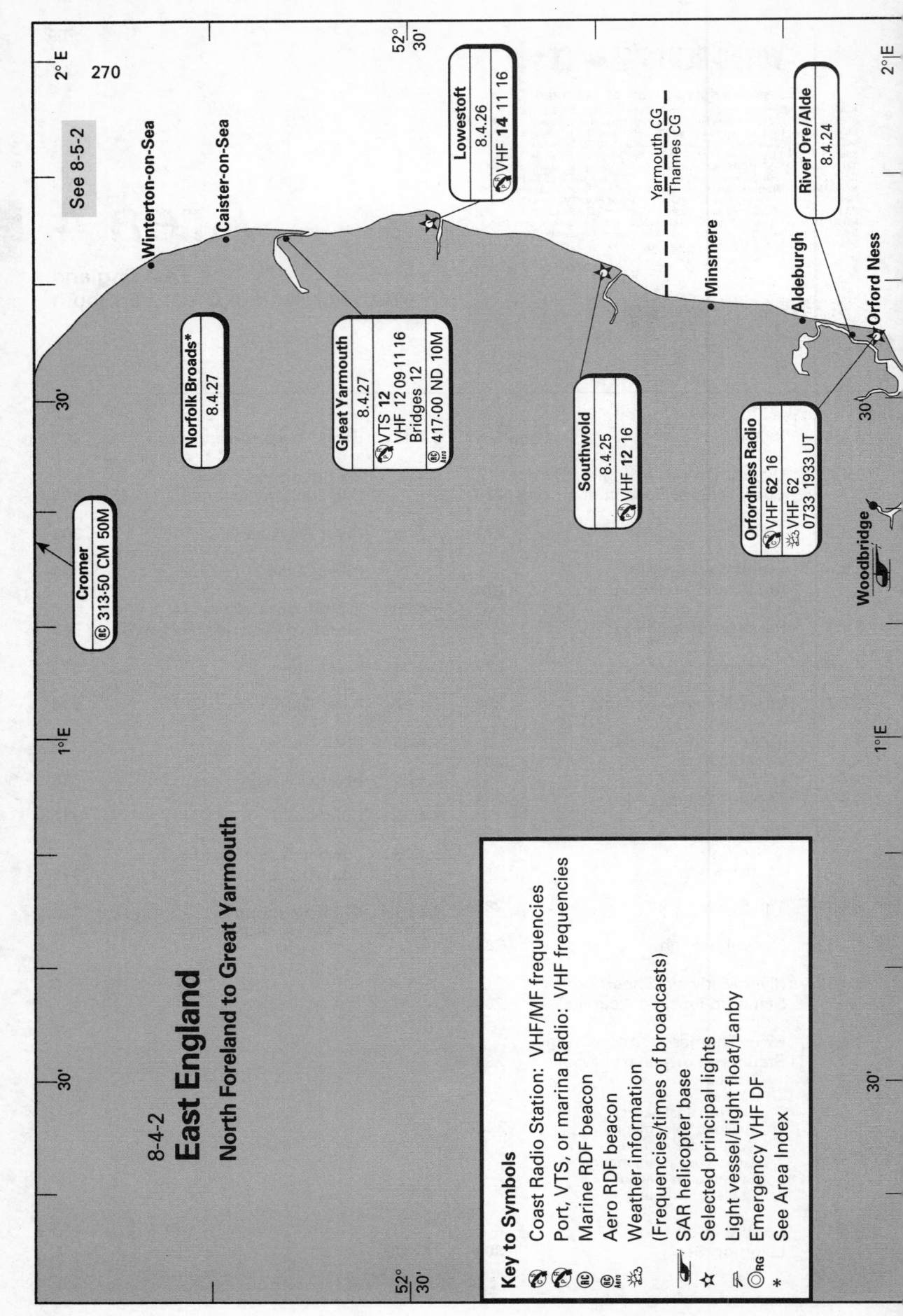

See 8-5-2

8-4-2
East England
North Foreland to Great Yarmouth

Cromer
313·50 CM 50M

Norfolk Broads*
8.4.27

Great Yarmouth
8.4.27
VTS 12
VHF 12 09 11 16
Bridges 12
417·00 ND 10M

Lowestoft
8.4.26
VHF **14** 11 16

Winterton-on-Sea

Caister-on-Sea

Yarmouth CG
Thames CG

Minsmere

Southwold
8.4.25
VHF 12 16

Aldeburgh

Orford Ness

River Ore/Alde
8.4.24

Orfordness Radio
VHF 62 16
VHF 62
0733 1933 UT

Woodbridge

Key to Symbols

Coast Radio Station: VHF/MF frequencies
Port, VTS, or marina Radio: VHF frequencies
Marine RDF beacon
Aero RDF beacon
Weather information
(Frequencies/times of broadcasts)
SAR helicopter base
Selected principal lights
Light vessel/Light float/Lanby
Emergency VHF DF
See Area Index

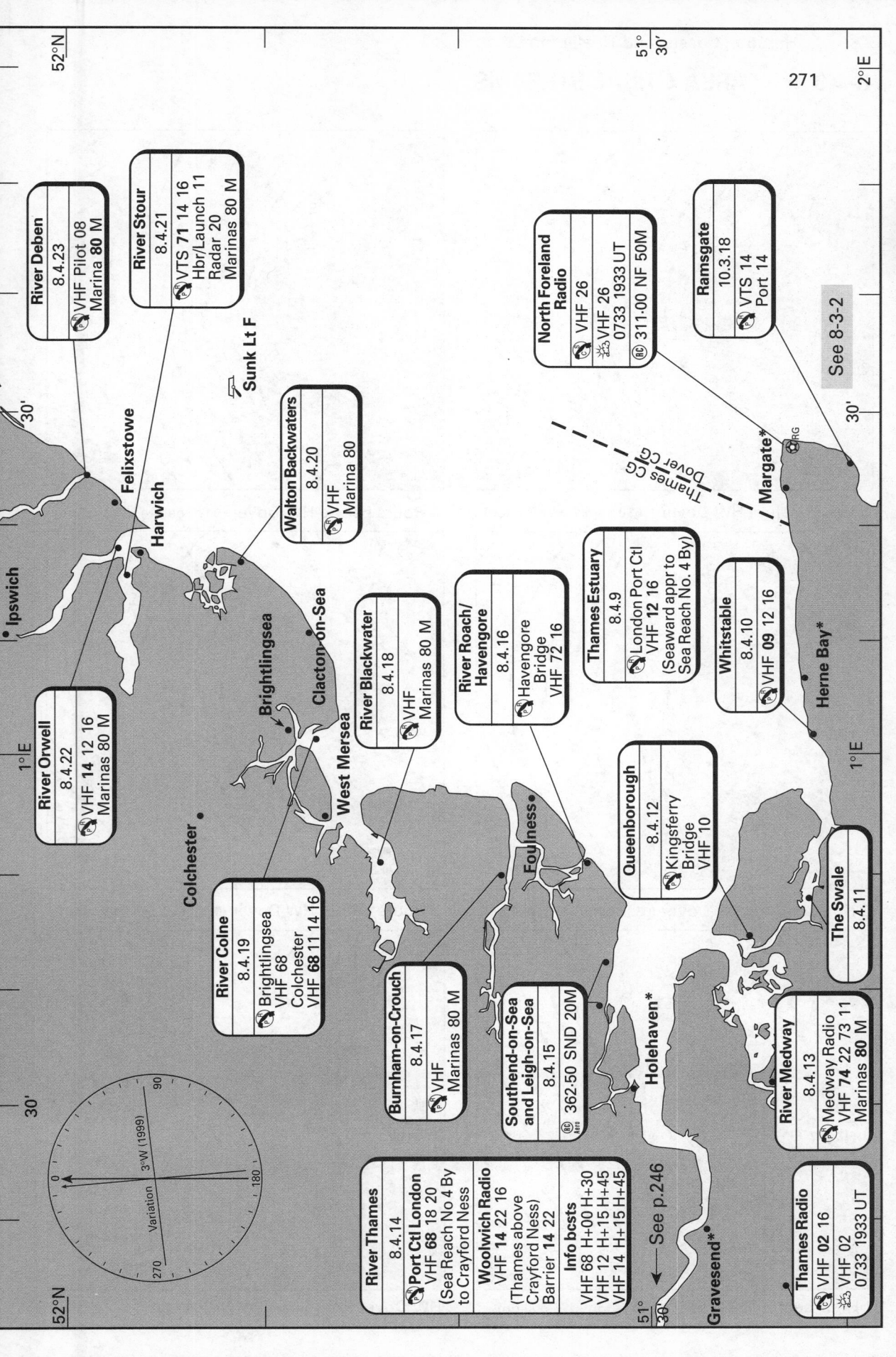

271

4

River Deben
8.4.23
VHF Pilot 08 Marina **80 M**

River Stour
8.4.21
VTS **71** 14 16
Hbr/Launch 20 Radar 11
Marinas **80 M**

North Foreland Radio
VHF 26
VHF 26 0733 1933 UT
311·00 NF 50M

Ramsgate
10.3.18
VTS 14
Port 14

See 8-3-2

Sunk Lt F

Felixstowe

Harwich

Ipswich

Walton Backwaters
8.4.20
VHF Marina 80

Thames CG
Dover CG

Margate*

River Orwell
8.4.22
VHF **14** 12 16
Marinas 80 M

Brightlingsea

Clacton-on-Sea

River Blackwater
8.4.18
VHF Marinas 80 M

River Roach/ Havengore
8.4.16
Havengore Bridge
VHF 72 16

Thames Estuary
8.4.9
London Port Ctl VHF **12** 16
(Seaward appr to Sea Reach No. 4 By)

Whitstable
8.4.10
VHF **09** 12 16

Herne Bay*

Colchester

West Mersea

River Colne
8.4.19
Brightlingsea VHF 68
Colchester VHF **68** 11 14 16

Foulness

Queenborough
8.4.12
Kingsferry Bridge VHF 10

The Swale
8.4.11

Burnham-on-Crouch
8.4.17
VHF Marinas 80 M

Southend-on-Sea and Leigh-on-Sea
8.4.15
362·50 SND 20M

Holehaven*

River Medway
8.4.13
Medway Radio VHF **74** 22 73 11
Marinas **80 M**

Variation 3°W (1999)

River Thames
8.4.14
Port Ctl London VHF **68** 18 20
(Sea Reach No 4 By to Crayford Ness)
Woolwich Radio VHF **14** 22 16
(Thames above Crayford Ness)
Barrier **14** 22
Info bcsts
VHF 68 H+00 H+30
VHF 12 H+15 H+45
VHF 14 H+15 H+45

See p.246

Gravesend*

Thames Radio
VHF 02 16
VHF 02 0733 1933 UT

8-4-3   AREA 4 TIDAL STREAMS

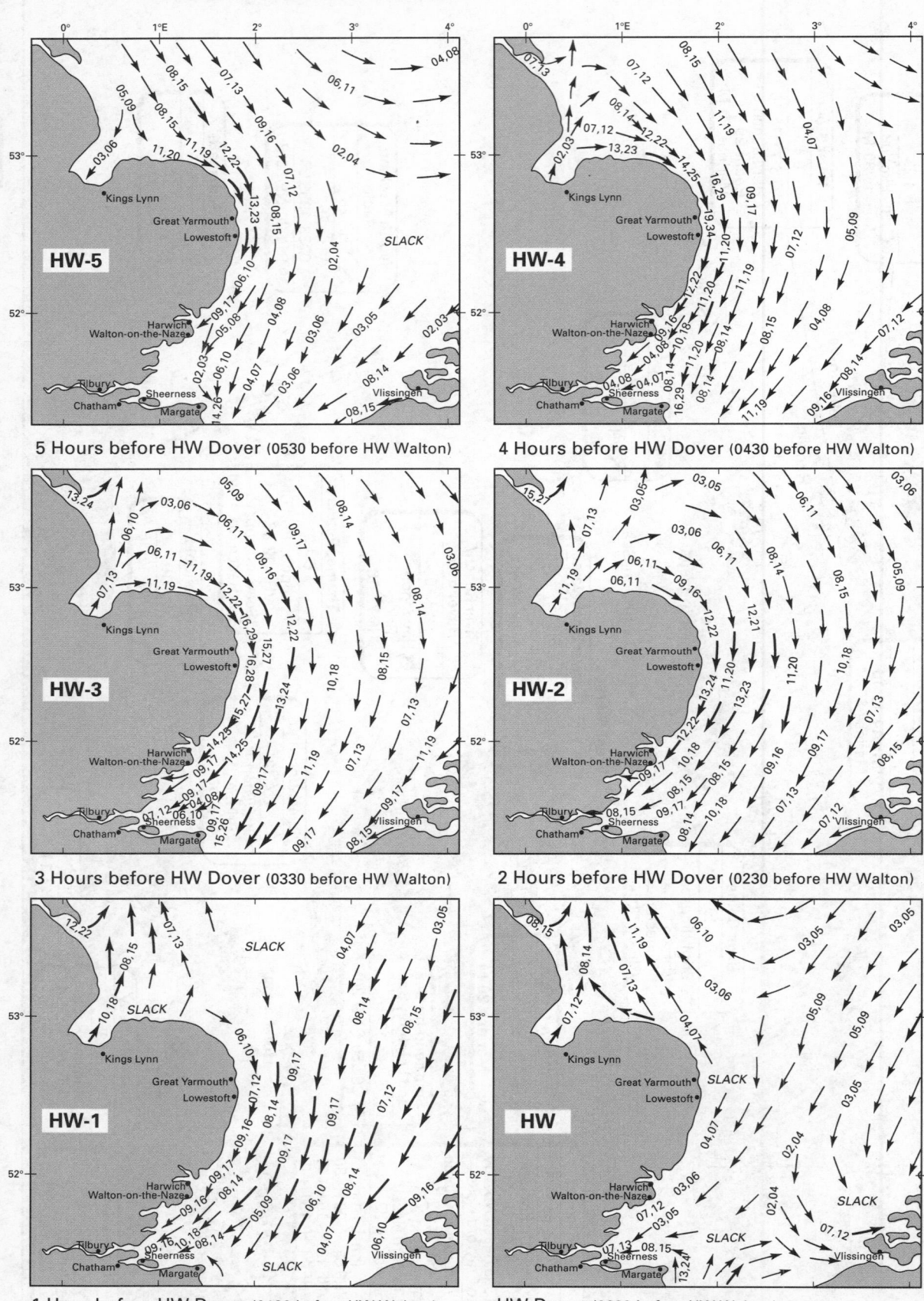

5 Hours before HW Dover (0530 before HW Walton)

4 Hours before HW Dover (0430 before HW Walton)

3 Hours before HW Dover (0330 before HW Walton)

2 Hours before HW Dover (0230 before HW Walton)

1 Hour before HW Dover (0130 before HW Walton)

HW Dover (0030 before HW Walton)

Southward 8.3.3   Thames Estuary 8.4.8   Northward 8.5.3   Eastward 8.20.3

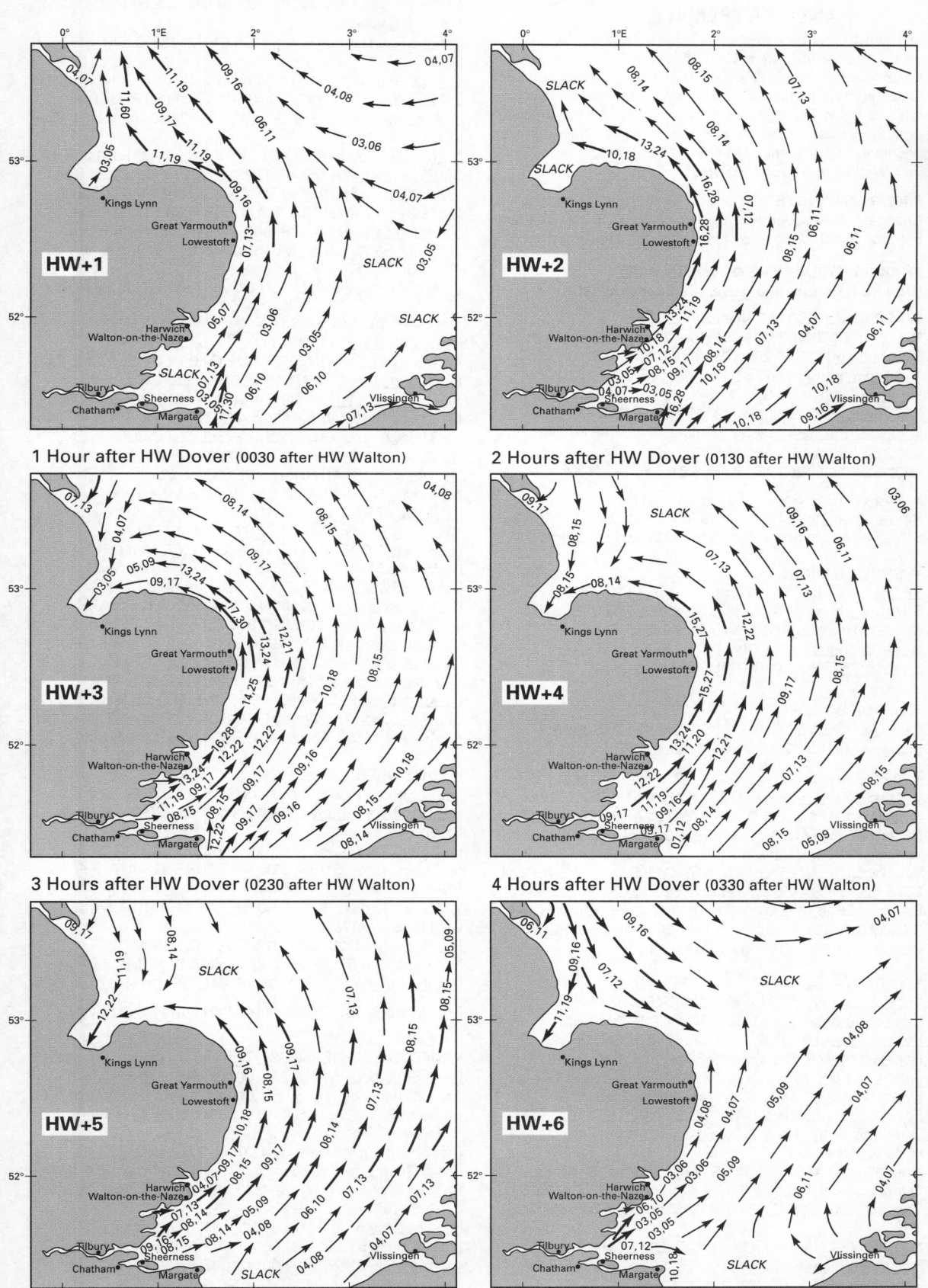

1 Hour after HW Dover (0030 after HW Walton)

2 Hours after HW Dover (0130 after HW Walton)

3 Hours after HW Dover (0230 after HW Walton)

4 Hours after HW Dover (0330 after HW Walton)

5 Hours after HW Dover (0430 after HW Walton)

6 Hours after HW Dover (0530 after HW Walton)

8.4.4 COASTAL LIGHTS, FOG SIGNALS AND WAYPOINTS

Lights with a nominal range of 15M or more are in **bold** print, places and features are in CAPITALS, and light-vessels, light floats and Lanbys in *CAPITAL ITALICS*. Unless otherwise stated lights are white. m = elevation in metres; M = nominal range in miles. Fog signals are in *italics*. Useful waypoints are underlined; use those on land with care. All geographical positions are referenced to the OSGB 36 datum but should be assumed to be approximate.

IMPORTANT NOTE

Changes are frequently made to buoyage in the Thames Estuary. Check *Notices to Mariners* for the latest information.

THAMES ESTUARY – SOUTHERN PART
(Direction of buoyage generally East to West)

- APPROACHES TO THAMES ESTUARY
F3 Lt F 51°23'·82N 02°00'·62E Fl 10s 12m **22M**; Racon; *Horn 10s*.
Falls hd buoy 51°28'·20N 01°50'·00E Q; NCM.
Drill Stone buoy 51°25'·80N 01°43'·00E Q (3) 10s; NCM.
NE Spit buoy 51°27'·90N 01°30'·00E VQ (3) 5s; ECM.
Elbow buoy 51°23'·20N 01°31'·70E Q; NCM.
Foreness Pt outfall buoy 51°24'·60N 01°26'·10E Fl Y 5s; SPM.
Longnose buoy 51°24'·12N 01°26'·18E; PHM.
Longnose Spit buoy 51°23'·90N 01°25'·85E; NCM.

- MARGATE
Promenade Pier N hd 51°23'·64N 01°22'·90E Fl R 5s.
Stone Pier hd FR 18m 4M. (QW marks tide gauge 385m NNW.)

- GORE CHANNEL
SE Margate buoy 51°24'·10N 01°20'·50E Q (3) 10s; ECM.
S Margate buoy 51°23'·88N 01°16'·75E Fl G 2·5s; SHM.
Margate Hook bn 51°24'·14N 01°14'·39E; SCM.
Hook Spit buoy 51°24'·05N 01°12'·65E; SHM.
E Last buoy 51°24'·00N 01°12'·28E QR; PHM.

- HERNE BAY
Pier hd 51°22'·90N 01°07'·00E Q 8m 4M, (isolated).
Pier, near root 51°22'·36N 01°07'·30E 2 FR (vert).

- WHITSTABLE
Whitstable Street buoy 51°23'·83N 01°01'·70E Q; NCM.
Oyster buoy 51°22'·12N 01°01'·27E Fl (2) R 10s; PHM.
NE Arm F 15m 8M; W mast; FR 10m 5M (same structure) shown when ent/dep prohib.
W Quay dn 51°21'·82N 01°01'·55E Fl WRG 5s 2m W5M, R3M, G3M; vis W118°-156°, G156°-178°, R178°-201°.
E Quay, N End 51°21'·80N 01°01'·65E 2 FR (vert) 4m 1M.
S Quay dir lt 122·5° 51°21'·73N 01°01'·80E Oc WRG 5s 7m vis: G110°-121°, W121°-124°, R124°-134°.

- THE SWALE
Columbine buoy 51°24'·23N 01°01'·45E; SHM.
Columbine Spit buoy 51°23'·83N 01°00'·13E; SHM.
Pollard Spit buoy 51°22'·95N 00° 58'·67E QR; PHM.
Ham Gat buoy 51°23'·05N 00°58'·42E; SHM.
Sand End buoy 51°21'·40N 00°56'·00E Fl G 5s; SHM.
Faversham Spit buoy 51°20'·74N 00°54'·31E; NCM.
Fowley Spit buoy 51°21'·46N 00°51'·57E Q (3) 10s; ECM.
Queenborough Hard S1 buoy 51°24'·96N 00°44'·28E Fl R 3s; PHM.
Queenborough Pt lt (S) 51°25'·31N 00°44'·13E Fl R 4s.
Queenborough Pt Lt (N) 51°25'·42N 00°44'·11E QR 3m 2M.
Queenborough Spit buoy 51°25'·78N 00°44'·03E Q (3) 10s; ECM.

- QUEENS CHANNEL/FOUR FATHOMS CHANNEL
E Margate buoy 51°27'·00N 01°26'·50E Fl R 2·5s; PHM.
Spaniard buoy 51°26'·20N 01°04'·10E Q (3) 10s; ECM.
Spile buoy 51°26'·40N 00°55'·80E Fl G 2·5s; SHM.

- PRINCES CHANNEL
Outer Tongue buoy 51°30'·70N 01°26'·50E L Fl 10s; SWM; Racon (T); *Whis*.
Tongue Sand S buoy 51°29'·40N 01°22'·15E Q (6) + L Fl 15s; SCM.
Tongue Sand N buoy 51°29'·65N 01°22'·13E Q; NCM.
E Tongue buoy 51°28'·72N 01°18'·72E Fl (2) R 5s; PHM.
S Shingles buoy 51°29'·20N 01°16'·12E Q (6) + L Fl 15s; SCM; *Bell*.
N Tongue buoy 51°28'·78N 01°13'·18E Fl (3) R 10s; PHM.
SE Girdler buoy 51°29'·47N 01°10'·00E Fl (3) G 10s; SHM.
W Girdler buoy 51°29'·58N 01°06'·82E Q (9)15s; WCM; *Bell*.
Girdler buoy 51°29'·15N 01°06'·50E Fl (4) R 15s; PHM.
Shivering Sand Trs 51°29'·90N 01°04'·90E. Tide gauge.
Shivering Sand Tr N buoy 51°29'·75N 01°04'·90E Q (6) + L Fl 15s; SCM; *Bell*.
E Redsand buoy 51°29'·38N 01°04'·15E Fl (2) R 5s; PHM.

- NORTH EDINBURGH CHANNEL/KNOB CHANNEL
Edinburgh buoy 51°31'·42N 01°21'·53E QR; PHM.
No 1 buoy 51°31'·55N 01°21'·92E Q (6) + L Fl 15s; SCM; *Bell*.
Patch buoy 51°32'·24N 01°20'·91E Fl (2) R 10s; PHM.
SE Longsand buoy 51°32'·24N 01°21'·22E QG; SHM.
No 2 buoy 51°32'·88N 01°20'·24E Fl (3) R 10s; PHM.
No 3 buoy 51°32'·98N 01°20'·46E Q (9) 15s; WCM.
No 4 buoy 51°33'·22N 01°19'·41E Fl R 2·5s; PHM; *Bell*.
No 5 buoy 51°33'·42N 01°19'·43E Fl G 2·5s; SHM.
No 6 buoy 51°33'·36N 01°18'·19E Fl R 2·5s; PHM.
No 7 buoy 51°33'·58N 01°18'·24E Fl G 2·5s; SHM.
NW Long Sand bn 51°34'·72N 01°18'·16E; SHM.
No 8 buoy 51°33'·19N 01°16'·65E Fl (3) R 10s; PHM.
No 9 buoy 51°33'·46N 01°16'·70E Fl (3) G 10s; SHM; *Bell*.
Shingles Patch buoy 51°32'·98N 01°15'·47E Q; NCM.
N Shingles buoy 51°32'·66N 01°14'·35E Fl R 2·5s; PHM.
Tizard buoy 51°32'·90N 01°13'·00E Q (6) + L Fl 15s; SCM.
Mid Shingles buoy 51°31'·93N 01°12'·08E Fl (2) R 5s; PHM.
NE Knob buoy 51°32'·00N 01°10'·10E QG; SHM.
NW Shingles buoy 51°31'·23N 01°09'·83E VQ; NCM.
SE Knob buoy 51°30'·86N 01°06'·51E Fl G 5s; SHM.
Shivering Sand Trs N buoy 51°29'·96N 01°04'·88E Q; NCM.
Knob buoy 51°30'·66N 01°04'·38E Iso 5s; SWM; *Bell*.

- OAZE DEEP
S Oaze buoy 51°30'·00N 01°00'·80E Fl (2) G 5s; SHM.
Red Sand Trs N buoy 51°28'·70N 00°59'·42E Fl (3) R 10s; PHM; *Bell*.
Red Sand Trs E buoy 51°28'·57N 00°59'·78E QG; SHM.
SW Oaze buoy 51°29'·03N 00°57'·03E Q (6) + L Fl 15s; SCM.
W Oaze buoy 51°29'·03N 00°55'·53E Q (9) 10s; WCM.
Cant bn 51°27'·73N 00°55'·45E (unlit).
E Cant buoy 51°28'·50N 00°55'·70E QR; PHM.
Mid Cant lt bn 51°26'·85N 00°49'·90E Q; NCM.
W Cant buoy 51°27'·19N 00°45'·61E QR; PHM.

Medway buoy 51°28'·80N 00°52'·92E Mo (A) 6s; SWM.

- MEDWAY, SHEERNESS
Grain Edge buoy 51°27'·58N 00°45'·57E; SHM.
Jacobs Bank obstn buoy 51°26'·94N 00°45'·29E VQ; NCM.
Garrison Pt Ro-Ro 51°26'·91N 00°44'·92E 2 FR (vert); dn; *Horn (3) 30s*.
Grain Hard buoy 51°26'·94N 00°44'·27E Fl G 5s; SHM.
Isle of Grain 51°26'·6N 00°43'·5E Q WRG 20m W13M, R7M, G8M; R & W ◇ on R Tr; vis R220°-234°, G234°-241°, W241°-013°; Ra refl.
N. Kent buoy 51°26'·10N 00°43'·57E QG; SHM.
S. Kent buoy 51°25'·95N 00°43'·77E Fl R 5s; PHM.
Victoria buoy 51°25'·93N 00°42'·94E Fl (3) G 10s; SHM.
Stoke No 13 buoy 51°25'·73N 00°39'·91E Fl G 5s; SHM.
No 15 buoy 51°24'·72N 00°38'·53E Fl G 10s; SHM.

Darnett No 23 buoy 51°24'·57N 00°35'·72E QG; SHM.
Folly No 25 buoy 51°24'·07N 00°35'·33E Fl (3) G 10s; SHM.
Gillingham Reach No 27 buoy 51°23'·88N 00°34'·82E Fl G 10s; SHM.

RIVER THAMES

• SEA REACH, NORE AND YANTLET
No 1 buoy 51°29'·42N 00°52'·67E Fl Y 2·5s; SPM; Racon.
No 2 buoy 51°29'·37N 00°49'·85E Iso 5s; SWM.
No 3 buoy 51°29'·30N 00°46'·63E L Fl 10s; SWM.
No 4 buoy 51°29'·58N 00°44'·28E Fl Y 2·5s; SPM.
No 5 buoy 51°29'·92N 00°41'·55E Iso 5s; SWM.
No 6 buoy 51°30'·00N 00°39'·95E Iso 2s; SWM.
No 7 buoy 51°30'·07N 00°37'·15E Fl Y 2·5s; SPM; Racon.
Nore Swatch buoy 51°28'·26N 00°45'·65E Fl (4) R 15s; PHM.
Mid Swatch buoy 51°28'·65N 00°44'·27E Fl G 5s; SHM.
W Nore Sand buoy 51°29'·39N 00°40'·97E Fl (3) R 10s; PHM.
East Blyth buoy 51°29'·68N 00°37'·90E Fl (2) R 10s; PHM.
West Lee Middle buoy 51°30'·45N 00°38'·93E QG; SHM.
Chapman buoy 51°30'·40N 00°37'·03E Fl (3) G 10s; SHM; *Bell.*
Mid Blyth buoy 51°30'·05N 00°32'·50E Q; NCM.

• LEIGH-ON-SEA/SOUTHEND-ON-SEA
South Shoebury buoy 51°30'·40N 00°52'·50E Fl G 5s; SHM.
Shoebury lt bn 51°30'·28N 00°49'·38E Fl (3) G 10s 5m 5M.
Inner Shoebury bn 51°30'·15N 00°49'·05E Fl Y 2·5s.
SE Leigh buoy 51°29'·40N 00°47'·17E Q (6) + L Fl 15s; SCM.
West Shoebury buoy 51°30'·20N 00°45'·83E Fl G 2·5s; SHM.
Southend Pier E end 51°30'·84N 00°43'·51E 2 FG (vert) 7m; *Horn Mo (N) 30s.*
Pier W hd 2 FG (vert) 13m 8M.
Leigh buoy 51°31'·04N 00°42'·67E; SHM.

• CANVEY ISLAND/HOLEHAVEN
Canvey jetty hd E end 51°30'·36N 00°34'·25E 2 FG (vert); *Bell (1) 10s.*
W hd 2 FG (vert) 13m 8M.
Lts 2 FR (vert) to port, and 2 FG (vert) to stbd, are shown from wharves etc. up-river of this point.
Shornmead 51°26'·97N 00°26'·63E Fl (2) WRG 10s 12m **W17M**, R13M, G13M; vis G054°-081·5°, R081·5°-086·2°, W086·2°-088·7°, G088·7°-141°, W141°-205°, R205°-213°.

• GRAVESEND
Thames Navigation Service pier 51°26'·68N 00°22'·57E FR.
Northfleet Lower 51°26'·9N 00°20'·4E Oc WR 5s 15m **W17M**, R14M; vis W164°-271°, R271°-S shore.
Northfleet Upper 51°26'·90N 00°20'·17E Oc WRG 10s 30m **W16M**, R12M, G12M; vis R126°-149°, W149°-159°, G159°-268°, W268°-279°.
Broadness 51°28'·0N 00°18'·7E Oc R 5s 12m 12M; R metal tr.
Queen Elizabeth II bridge NE 51°27'·95N 00°15'·72E Fl G 5s.
Crayford Ness Fl 5s 19m 14M, radar tr, 51°28'·90N 00°12'·80E; and FW 17m 3M, same tr.
Cross Ness, Fl 5s 11m 8M, R tr, 51°30'·80N 00°07'·80E.

• THAMES TIDAL BARRIER
Span G, up-river for small craft, 51°29'·88N 00°02'·31E.
Span B, down-river for small craft, 51°29'·70N 00°02'·33E.

• SOUTH DOCK MARINA
Greenland Pier S hd 51°29'·64N 00°01'·80W 2 FR (vert).

• LIMEHOUSE BASIN MARINA/REGENT'S CANAL
Lock ent 51°30'·52N 00°02'·14W 2 FG (vert).

• ST KATHERINE HAVEN
Harrison's Wharf 51°30'·33N 00°04'·23W 2 FG (vert).

• CHELSEA HARBOUR MARINA
Pier, N head 51°28'·43N 00°10'·73W 2 FG (vert).

THAMES ESTUARY – NORTHERN PART

• KENTISH KNOCK
Kentish Knock buoy 51°38'·50N 01°40·50E Q (3) 10s; ECM; *Whis.*
S Knock buoy 51°34'·73N 01°36'·10E Q (6) + L Fl 15s; SCM; *Bell.*

• KNOCK JOHN CHANNEL
No 7 buoy 51°32'·00N 01°06'·50E Fl (4) G 15s; SHM.
No 5 buoy 51°32'·75N 01°08'·68E Fl (3) G 10s; SHM.
No 4 buoy 51°32'·60N 01°08'·82E L Fl R 10s; PHM.
No 2 buoy 51°33'·08N 01°09'·95E Fl (3) R 10s; PHM.
No 3 buoy 51°33'·20N 01°09'·80E Q (6) + L Fl 15s; SCM.
No 1 buoy 51°33'·72N 01°10'·82E Fl G 5s; SHM.
Knock John buoy 51°33'·50N 01°11'·08E Fl (2) R 5s; PHM.

• BLACK DEEP
No 12 buoy 51°33'·80N 01°13'·60E Fl (4) R 15s; PHM.
No 11 buoy 51°34'·30N 01°13'·50E Fl (3) G 10s; SHM.
No 10 buoy 51°34'·70N 01°15'·70E QR; PHM.
No 9 buoy 51°35'·10N 01°15'·20E Q (6) + L Fl 15s; SCM.
No 8 buoy 51°36'·20N 01°20'·00E Q; NCM.
No 7 buoy 51°37'·05N 01°17'·80E QG; SHM.
No 6 buoy 51°38'·49N 01°24'·51E Fl R 2·5s; PHM.
No 5 buoy 51°39'·50N 01°23'·10E VQ (3) 5s; ECM; *Bell.*
No 4 buoy 51°41'·39N 01°28'·59E Fl (2) R 5s; PHM.
Long Sand bn 51°41'·44N 01°29'·56E; SHM.
No 3 buoy 51°41'·95N 01°26'·07E Fl (3) G 15s; SHM.
No 1 buoy 51°44'·00N 01°28'·20E Fl G 5s; SHM.
Sunk Head Tr buoy 51°46'·60N 01°30'·60E Q; NCM; *Whis.*
No 2 buoy 51°45'·60N 01°32'·30E Fl (4) R 15s; WCM.
Black Deep buoy 51°46'·60N 01°34'·05E QR; PHM.
Trinity buoy 51°49'·00N 01°36'·50E Q (6) + L Fl 15s; SCM; *Whis.*
Long Sand hd buoy 51°47'·87N 01°39'·53E VQ; NCM; *Bell.*

• BARROW DEEP (selected buoys)
SW Barrow buoy 51°31'·80N 01°00'·53E Q (6) + L Fl 15s; SCM; *Bell.*
Barrow No.11 buoy 51°33'·73N 01°05'·85E Fl G 2·5s; SHM.
Barrow No 9 buoy 51°35'·31N 01°10'·40E VQ (3) 5s; ECM.
SW Sunk bn 51°36'·50N 01°14'·85E; SHM.
Barrow No 6 buoy 51°37'·27N 01°14'·79E Fl (4) R 15s; PHM.
Barrow No 4 buoy 51°39'·85N 01°17'·60E VQ (9) 10s; WCM.
Barrow No 3 buoy 51°41'·99N 01°20'·35E Q (3) 10s; ECM; Racon (M).
Barrow No 2 buoy 51°41'·95N 01°23'·00E Fl (2) R 5s; PHM.
Little Sunk bn 51°41'·89N 01°24'·85E; SHM.

• WEST SWIN AND MIDDLE DEEP
Blacktail (W) lt bn 51°31'·43N 00°55'·30E Iso G 10s 10m 6M.
Blacktail (E) lt bn 51°31'·75N 00°56'·60E Iso G 5s 10m 6M.
Blacktail Spit buoy 51°31'·45N 00°56'·85E Fl (3) G 10s; SHM.
SW Swin buoy 51°32'·68N 01°00'·79E Fl (2) R 5s; PHM.
W Swin buoy 51°33'·82N 01°03'·30E; PHM.
Maplin buoy 51°34'·00N 01°02'·40E Q (3) 10s; ECM; *Bell.*
Maplin Edge buoy 51°35'·30N 01°03'·75E; SHM.
Maplin Bank buoy 51°35'·47N 01°04'·80E Fl (3) R 10s; PHM.

• EAST SWIN (KING'S) CHANNEL
NE Maplin buoy 51°37'·43N 01°04'·90E Fl G 5s; SHM; *Bell.*
W Hook Middle buoy 51°39'·15N 01°08'·07E; PHM.
S Whitaker buoy 51°40'·20N 01°09'·15E Fl (2) G 10s; SHM.
N Middle buoy 51°41'·00N 01°12'·00E; NCM.
W Sunk buoy 51°44'·30N 01°25'·90E Q (9) 15s; WCM.
Gunfleet Spit buoy 51°45'·30N 01°21'·80E Q (6) + L Fl 15s; SCM; *Bell.*
Gunfleet Old lt ho 51°46'·08N 01°20'·52E.

• WHITAKER CHANNEL AND RIVER CROUCH
Whitaker buoy 51°41'·40N 01°10'·61E Q (3) 10s; ECM; *Bell.*
Whitaker No 6 buoy 51°40'·66N 01°08'·17E Q; NCM.

Swin Spitway buoy 51°41'·92N 01°08'·45E Iso 10s; SWM; *Bell*.
Whitaker bn 51°39'·62N 01°06'·30E; IDM.
Swallow Tail buoy 51°40'·44N 01°04'·81E; SHM.
Ridge buoy 51°40'·10N 01°04'·99E FI R 10s; PHM.
S Buxey buoy 51°39'·82N 01°02'·60E FI (3) G 15s; SHM.
Sunken Buxey buoy 51°39'·50N 01°00'·60E Q; NCM.
Buxey No 1 buoy 51°39'·02N 01°00'·86E VQ (6) + L FI 10s; SCM.
Buxey No 2 buoy 51°38'·94N 01°00'·26E Q; NCM.
Outer Crouch buoy 51°38'·35N 00°58'·61E Q (6) + L FI 15s; SCM.
Crouch buoy 51°37'·60N 00°56'·49E FI R 10s; PHM.
Inner Crouch buoy 51°37'·19N 00°55'·22E L FI 10s; SWM.
Horse Shoal buoy 51°37'·08N 00°51'·62E Q; NCM.

• RIVER ROACH/HAVENGORE
Branklet buoy 51°36'·95N 00°52'·24E; SPM.

• BURNHAM-ON-CROUCH
Fairway No 1 buoy 51°37'·07N 00°51'·10E QG; SHM.
Fairway No 5 buoy 51°37'·20N 00°49'·67E QG; SHM.
Fairway No 9 buoy 51°37'·32N 00°48'·87E QG; SHM.
Fairway No 11 buoy 51°37'·43N 00°48'·40E QG; SHM.
Burnham Yacht Hbr buoy 51°37'·48N 00°48'·31E FI Y 5s; SPM.

• RAY SAND CHANNEL
Buxey bn 51°41'·13N 01°01'·38E (unlit); NCM.

• GOLDMER GAT/WALLET
NE Gunfleet buoy 51°49'·90N 01°27'·90E Q (3) 10s; ECM.
Wallet No 2 buoy 51°48'·85N 01°23'·10E FI R 5s; PHM.
Wallet No 4 buoy 51°46'·50N 01°17'·33E FI (4) R 10s; PHM.
Walton Pier hd 51°50'·58N 01°16'·90E 2 FG (vert) 5m 2M.
Wallet Spitway buoy 51°42'·83N 01°07'·42E L FI 10s; SWM; *Bell*.
Knoll buoy 51°43'·85N 01°05'·17E Q; NCM.
Eagle buoy 51°44'·10N 01°03'·92E QG; SHM.
NW Knoll buoy 51°44'·32N 01°02'·27E FI (2) R 5s; PHM.
Colne Bar buoy 51°44'·58N 01°02'·67E FI (2) G 5s; SHM.
Bench Head buoy 51°44'·66N 01°01'·20E; SHM.

• RIVER BLACKWATER
The Nass lt bn 51°45'·75N 00°54'·88E VQ (3) 5s 6m 2M; ECM.
Thirslet buoy 51°43'·71N 00°50'·49E FI (3) G 10s; SHM.
No 1 buoy 51°43'·41N 00°48'·13E; SHM.
No 2 buoy 51°42'·78N 00°46'·58E FI R 3s; PHM.
Osea Island pier hd 51°43'·05N 00°46'·59E 2 FG (vert).
No 3 buoy 51°42'·88N 00°46'·16E; SHM.
N Double No 7 buoy 51°43'·22N 00°44'·87E FI G 3s; SHM.
No 8 buoy 51°43'·91N 00°43'·35E; PHM.

• RIVER COLNE/BRIGHTLINGSEA
Inner Bench hd No 2 buoy 51°45'·93N 01°01'·86E FI (2) R 5s; PHM.
No 9 buoy 51°47'·33N 01°01'·17E FI G 3s; SHM.
No 13 buoy 51°47'·72N 01°00'·91E FI G; SHM.
Brightlingsea Spit buoy 51°48'·05N 01°00'·80E Q (6) + L FI 15s; SCM.
Brightlingsea buoy 51°48'·19N 01°01'·18E FI (3) G 5s; SHM.
Ldg lts 041°. Front, 51°48'·4N 01°01'·3E FR 7m 4M; W □, R stripe on post; vis 020°-080°; rear, 50m from front, FR 10m 4M; W ■, R stripe on post. FR lts are shown on 7 masts between 1·5M and 3M NW when firing occurs.
Hardway hd 51°48'·2N 01°01'·5E 2 FR (vert) 2m.
Batemans Tr 51°48'·3N 01°00'·8E FY 12m.
Fingringhoe Wick pier hd 2 FR (vert) 6m (occas).
No 23 51°50'·60N 00°59'·00E FI G 5s 5m.
Rowhedge Wharf FY 11m.
• CLACTON-ON-SEA
Berthing arm 51°47'·00N 01°09'·60E 2 FG (vert) 5m 4M; *Reed (2) 120s* (occas).

• WALTON BACKWATERS
Naze Tr 51°51'·85N 01°17'·40E.
Pye End buoy 51°55'·00N 01°18'·00E L FI 10s; SWM.
No 2 buoy 51°54'·54N 01°16'·90E; PHM; Ra refl.
No 3 Crab Knoll buoy 51°54'·36N 01°16'·49E; SHM; Ra refl.
No 4 High Hill buoy 51°54'·02N 01°16'·07E FI R 10s; PHM.
No 5 buoy 51°54'·25N 01°16'·33E; SHM.
No 6 buoy 51°53'·76N 01°15'·80E; PHM.
No 7 buoy 51°53'·78N 01°15'·65E; SHM.
No 8 buoy 51°53'·39N 01°15'·53E; PHM.
Island Point buoy 51°53'·27N 01°15'·44E; NCM.
No 10 Mussel Bank buoy 51°53'·31N 01°15'·49E; PHM.
No 12 buoy 51°53'·26N 01°15'·51E; PHM.
No 14 Frank Bloom buoy 51°53'·21N 01°15'·61E; PHM.
East Coast Sails buoy 51°53'·14N 01°15'·66E; SHM.
Plumtrees Stone Pt buoy 51°53'·01N 01°15'·73E; PHM.

HARWICH APPROACHES/ R STOUR AND ORWELL (Direction of buoyage North to South)

• MEDUSA CHANNEL
Medusa buoy 51°51'·20N 01°20'·46E FI G 5s; SHM.
Stone Banks buoy 51°53'·16N 01°19'·33E; PHM.

• CORK SAND /ROUGH SHOALS
S Cork buoy 51°51'·30N 01°24'·20E; SCM.
Roughs Tr SE buoy 51°53'·61N 01°29'·05E Q (3) 10s; ECM.
Roughs Tr NW buoy 51°53'·78N 01°28'·88E Q (9) 15s; WCM.
Rough buoy 51°55'·16N 01°31'·11E VQ; NCM.
Cork Sand lt bn 51°55'·19N 01°25'·31E Q; NCM.

• HARWICH CHANNEL
SUNK Lt F 51°51'·00N 01°35'·00E FI (2) 20s 12m **24M**; R hull with lt tr; Racon (T); *Horn (2) 60s*.
S Threshold buoy 51°52'·44N 01°33'·29E Q (6) + L FI 15s.
S Shipwash buoy 51°52'·68N 01°34'·16E Q (6) + L FI 15s; SCM.
E Fort Massac buoy 51°53'·33N 01°32'·90E VQ (3) 5s; ECM.
Shiphead buoy 51°53'·76N 01°34'·01E FI R 5s; PHM.
N Threshold buoy 51°54'·46N 01°33'·58E FI Y 5s; SPM.
SW Shipwash buoy 51°54'·72N 01°34'·32E Q (9)15s; WCM.
Haven buoy 51°55'·73N 01°32'·67E Mo (A) 5s; SWM.
Shipway buoy 51°56'·73N 01°30'·77E Iso 5s; SWM; *Whis*.
Cross buoy 51°56'·20N 01°30'·59E FI (3) Y 10s; SPM.
Harwich Chan No 1 buoy 51°56'·11N 01°27'·30E FI Y 2·5s; SPM; Racon (T).
Washington buoy 51°56'·49N 01°26'·70E QG; SHM.
Felixstowe Ledge buoy 51°56'·30N 01°24'·53E FI (3) G 10s; SHM.
Wadgate Ledge buoy 51°56'·08N 01°22'·20E FI (4) G 15s; SHM.
Platters buoy 51°55'·61N 01°21'·07E; Q (6) + L FI 15s; SCM.
Rolling Ground buoy 51°55'·52N 01°19'·86E QG; SHM.
Beach End buoy 51°55'·59N 01°19'·31E FI (2) G 5s; SHM.
NW Beach buoy 51°55'·87N 01°18'·98E FI (3) G 10s; SHM; *Bell*.
Fort buoy 51°56'·18N 01°18'·98E FI (4) G 15s; SHM.

• EDGE OF RECOMMENDED YACHT TRACK
Cork Sand buoy 51°55'·43N 01°25'·95E FI (3) R 10s; PHM.
Pitching Ground buoy 51°55'·39N 01°21'·16E FI (4) R 15s; PHM.
Inner Ridge buoy 51°55'·31N 01°19'·68E QR; PHM.
Landguard buoy 51°55'·35N 01°18'·98E Q; NCM.
Cliff Foot buoy 51°55'·69N 01°18'·64E FI R 5s; PHM.
S Shelf buoy 51°56'·17N 01°18'·67E FI (2) R 5s; PHM.
N Shelf buoy 51°56'·65N 01°18'·70E QR; PHM.
Grisle buoy 51°56'·86N 01°18'·43E FI R 2·5s; PHM.
Guard buoy 51°57'·03N 01°17'·88E FI R 5s; PHM; *Bell*.
• RIVER STOUR/HARWICH
Wharves, jetties and piers show 2 FR (vert).
Shotley Spit buoy 51°57'·26N 01°17'·67E Q (6) + L FI 15s; SCM.

Shotley Marina lock E side dir lt 339·5° 51°57'·43N 01°16'·71E 3m 1M (uses Moiré pattern); Or structure.
Shotley Marina ent E side 51°57'·23N 01°16'·84E Fl (4) G 15s; G △ on pile.
Shotley Marina 51°57'·24N 01°16'·82E VQ (3) 5s; ECM.
Shotley Ganges per E hd 51°57'·18N 01°16'·34E 2 FG (vert) 4m 1M; G post.
Parkeston buoy 51°57'·06N 01°15'·44E Fl (3) G 10s; SHM.
Erwarton Ness lt bn 51°57'·10N 01°13'·35E Q (6) + L Fl 15s 4M; SCM Bn.
Holbrook lt bn 51°57'·19N 01°10'·46E VQ (6) + L Fl 10s 4M; SCM bn.
Mistley, Baltic Wharf 51°56'·69N 01°05'·31E 2 FR (vert).

• RIVER ORWELL/IPSWICH
College buoy 51°57'·52N 01°17'·44E Fl (2) R 10s; PHM.
Pepys buoy 51°57'·71N 01°17'·00E Fl (4) R 15s; PHM.
Fagbury buoy 51°57'·94N 01°16'·91E Fl G 2·5s; SHM.
Orwell buoy 51°58'·14N 01°16'·65E Fl R 2·5s; PHM.
No 1 buoy 51°58'·26N 01°16'·78E Fl G 5s; SHM.
Suffolk Yacht Harbour. Ldg lts 51°59'·77N 01°16'·22E. Front Iso Y 1M, Rear Oc Y 4s 1M.
Butt PHM buoy, 51°59'·90N 01°13'·47E.
'O' PHM buoy, Fl R 2·5s, 51°59'·94N 01°13'·08E.
Woolverstone Marina 52°00'·4N 01°11'·8E 2 FR (vert).
Orwell Bridge FY 39m 3M at centre; 2 FR (vert) on Pier 9 and 2 FG (vert) on Pier 10.
No 12 PHM buoy (off Fox's Marina), Fl R 12s, 52°02'·08N 01°09'·45E.
Ipswich lock SS (Tfc) 52°02'·77N 01°09'·85E.

HARWICH TO ORFORDNESS

• FELIXSTOWE/RIVER DEBEN/WOODBRIDGE HAVEN
Felixstowe Town pier hd 51°57'·37N 01°21'·02E 2 FG (vert) 7m.
Woodbridge Haven SWM buoy 51°58'·15N 01°23'·90E.
Ldg lts Fl or Fl Y moved as required (on request). Front W △ on R I. Rear; R line on I.
Felixstowe Ferry, E side 51°59'·40N 01°23'·72E 2 FG (vert). W side 2 FR (vert).

• RIVER ORE/RIVER ALDE
Orford Haven SWM buoy 52°01'·44N 01°27'·60E.

• OFFSHORE MARKS
S Galloper buoy 51°43'·95N 01°56'·50E Q (6) L Fl 15s; SCM; Racon (T); Whis.
N Galloper buoy 51°50'·00N 01°59'·50E Q; NCM.
S Inner Gabbard buoy 51°51'·20N 01°52'·40E Q (6) + L Fl 15s; SCM.
N Inner Gabbard buoy 51°59'·10N 01°56'·10E Q; NCM.
Outer Gabbard buoy 51°57'·80N 02°04'·30E Q (3) 10s; ECM; Racon (O); Whis.
NHR-SE buoy 51°45'·50N 02°40'·00E Fl G 5s; SHM; Racon (N).
NHR-S buoy 51°51'·40N 02°28'·79E Fl Y 10s; SPM; Bell.

• SHIPWASH/BAWDSEY BANK
E Shipwash buoy 51°57'·05N 01°38'·00E VQ (3) 5s; ECM.
NW Shipwash buoy 51°58'·33N 01°36'·33E Fl R 5s; PHM.
N Shipwash buoy 52°01'·70N 01°38'·38E Q 7M; NCM; Racon (M); Bell.
S Bawdsey buoy 51°57'·20N 01°30'·32E Q (6) + L Fl 15s; SCM; Whis.
Mid Bawdsey buoy 51°58'·85N 01°33'·70E Fl (3) G 10s; SHM.
NE Bawdsey buoy 52°01'·70N 01°36'·20E Fl G 10s; SHM.

• CUTLER/WHITING BANKS
Cutler buoy 51°58'·50N 01°27'·60E; SHM.
SW Whiting buoy 52°01'·10N 01°30'·90E; SCM.
Whiting Hook buoy 52°02'·95N 01°31'·93E; PHM.
NE Whiting buoy 52°03'·77N 01°33'·88E; ECM.

ORFORDNESS TO WINTERTON
(Direction of buoyage South to North)

Orford Ness 52°05'·00N 01°34'·60E Fl 5s 28m **25M**; W ○ tr, R bands. F RG 14m R14M, **G15M** (same tr); vis R shore-210°, R038°-047°, G047°-shore; Racon (T).

Aldeburgh Ridge buoy 52°06'·82N 01°37'·60E; PHM.
Sizewell Power station, pipeline hds 52°12'·70N 01°37'·90E 2 FR (vert) 12/10m. Sizewell cooling water intake and outfall 52°12'·90N 01°38'·15E each Fl R 5s.

SOUTHWOLD
Southwold lt ho 52°19'·60N 01°41'·00E Fl (4) WR 20s 37m **W17M**, **R15M**, R14M; W ○ tr; vis R (intens) 204°-220°, W220°-001°, R001°-032·3°.
N Pier hd 52°18'·77N 01°40'·63E Fl G 1·5s 4m 4M.
S Pier hd QR 4m 2M.

• LOWESTOFT APPROACHES VIA STANFORD CHANNEL
E Barnard buoy 52°25'·11N 01°46'·50E Q (3) 10s; ECM.
Newcome Sand buoy 52°26'·40N 01°47'·15E QR; PHM.
S Holm buoy 52°27'·22N 01°47'·32E VQ (6) + L Fl 10s; SCM.
Stanford buoy 52°27'·33N 01°46'·78E Fl R 2·5s; PHM.
N Newcome buoy 52°28'·29N 01°46'·43E Fl (4) R 15s; PHM.
SW Holm buoy 52°28'·10N 01°47'·16E Fl (2) G 5s; SHM.
Lowestoft 52°29'·18N 01°45'·46E Fl 15s 37m **28M**; W tr; part obscd 347°-shore.
Outer Hbr S Pier hd Oc R 5s 12m 6M; Horn (4) 60s; tfc sigs.
N Pier hd 52°28'·29N 01°45'·50E Oc G 5s 12m 8M.
Claremont pier 52°27'·86N 01°44'·98E 2 FR (vert) 5/4m 4M.

LOWESTOFT NORTH ROAD AND CORTON ROAD
Lowestoft Ness buoy 52°28'·82N 01°46'·38E Q (6) + L Fl 15s; SCM; Bell.
Lowestoft Ness 52°28'·87N 01°46'·35E VQ (3) 5s; ECM; Bell.
W Holm buoy 52°29'·80N 01°47'·20E Fl (3) G 10s; SHM.
NW Holm buoy 52°31'·90N 01°46'·80E Fl (4) G 15s; SHM.

• GREAT YARMOUTH APPROACHES VIA HOLM CHAN
E Newcome buoy 52°28'·48N 01°49'·32E Fl (2) R 5s; PHM.
Corton buoy 52°31'·10N 01°51'·50E Q (3) 10s; ECM; Whis.
E. Holm buoy 52°31'·06N 01°49'·42E Fl (3) R 10s; PHM.
S Corton buoy 52°32'·15N 01°50'·12E Q (6) + L Fl 15s; SCM.
NE Holm buoy 52°32'·27N 01°48'·31E Fl R 2·5s; PHM.
Holm buoy 52°33'·50N 01°48'·08E Fl G 2·5s; SHM.
Holm Sand buoy 52°33'·65N 01°47'·08E Q; NCM.
W Corton buoy 52°34'·46N 01°46'·42E Q (9) 15s; WCM.

• GREAT YARMOUTH/GORLESTON
Gorleston S Pier hd Fl R 3s 11m 11M; vis 235°-340°; Horn (3) 60s.
Ldg lts 264°. Front, 52°34'·30N 01°44'·07E Oc 3s 6m 10M. Rear, Brush Oc 6s 7m 10M, also FR 20m 6M; R ○ Tr.
N Pier hd 52°34'·36N 01°44'·49E QG 8m 6M; vis 176°-078°.
South Denes outfall 52°35'·10N 01°44'·50E QR 5m 2M; R △.
Wellington Pier hd 52°35'·92N 01°44'·42E 2 FR (vert) 8m 3M.
Jetty hd 52°36'·10N 01°44'·48E 2 FR (vert) 7m 2M.
Britannia Pier hd 52°36'·47N 01°44'·57E 2 FR (vert) 11m 4M.

• CAISTER ROADS/COCKLE GATWAY
SW Scroby buoy 52°35'·80N 01°46'·37E Fl G 2·5s; SHM.
Scroby Elbow buoy 52°37'·32N 01°46'·50E Fl (2) G 5s; SHM.
Mid Caister buoy 52°38'·96N 01°45'·77E Fl (2) R 5s; PHM; Bell.
N Scroby platform, 52°40'·10N 01°47'·20E Fl (5) Y 20s 10m 5M on N and S sides; same platform, mast Fl R 3s 50m 3M.
NW Scroby buoy 52°40'·35N 01°46'·44E Fl (3) G 10s; SHM.
N Caister buoy 52°40'·40N 01°45'·66E Fl (3) R 10s; PHM.
Hemsby buoy 52°42'·00N 01°44'·95E Fl R 2·5s; PHM.
N Scroby buoy 52°42'·49N 01°44'·80E VQ; NCM; Whis.
Cockle buoy 52°44'·00N 01°43'·70E VQ (3) 5s; ECM; Bell.
Winterton lt ho (disused) 52°42'·75N 01°41'·80E Racon (T).

8.4.5　PASSAGE INFORMATION

Reference books include: *East Coast Rivers* (YM/Coote) from the Swale to Southwold. The Admiralty *Dover Strait Pilot* also goes to Southwold. *North Sea Passage Pilot* (Imray/Navin) and *The East Coast* (Imray/Bowskill) cover the whole Area.

THE THAMES ESTUARY (chart *1183*, *1975*)

To appreciate the geography of the Thames Estuary there is a well-known analogy between its major sandbanks and the fingers and thumb of the left hand, outstretched palm-down: With the thumb lying E over Margate Sand, the index finger covers Long Sand; the middle finger represents Sunk Sand and the third finger delineates West and East Barrow; the little finger points NE along Buxey and Gunfleet Sands.

The intervening channels are often intricate, but the main ones, in sequence from south to north, are:
a. between the Kent coast and thumb – Four Fathoms, Horse, Gore and South Chans; sometimes known as the overland route due to relatively shallow water.
b. between thumb and index finger – Queens and Princes Chans leading seaward to Knock Deep.
c. between index and middle fingers – Knob Chan leading to Knock Deep via the Edinburgh Chans across Long Sand and the Shingles. Knock John Chan and Black Deep, the main shipping channels.
d. between middle and third fingers – Barrow Deep.
e. between third and little fingers – W and E Swin, Middle Deep and Whitaker Chan leading seaward to King's Chan.
f. between little finger and the Essex coast – The Wallet and Goldmer Gat.

The sandbanks shift constantly in the Thames Estuary. Up-to-date charts showing the latest buoyage changes are essential, but it is unwise to put too much faith in charted depths over the banks; a reliable echosounder is vital. The main chans carry much commercial shipping and are well buoyed and lit, but this is not so in lesser chans and swatchways which are convenient for yachtsmen, particularly when crossing the estuary from N to S, or vice versa. Unlit, unmarked minor chans (eg Fisherman's Gat or S Edinburgh Chan; in the latter there is a Historic Wreck (see 8.0.3h) at 51°31'·7N 01°14'·9E) should be used with great caution, which could indeed be the hallmark of all passage-making in the Thames Estuary. Good vis is needed to pick out buoys/marks, and to avoid shipping.

CROSSING THE THAMES ESTUARY (See 8.4.9)

Study the tides carefully and understand them, so as to work the streams to best advantage and to ensure sufficient depth at the times and places where you expect to be, or might be later (see 8.4.3 and 8.4.8). In principle it is best to make most of the crossing on a rising tide, ie departing N Foreland or the vicinity of the Whitaker buoy at around LW. The stream runs 3kn at sp in places, mostly along the chans but sometimes across the intervening banks. With wind against tide a short, steep sea is raised, particularly in E or NE winds.

Making N from N Foreland to Orford Ness or beyond (or vice versa) it may be preferable to keep to seaward of the main banks, via Kentish Knock and Long Sand Head buoys, thence to N Shipwash lt buoy 14M further N.

Bound NW from N Foreland it is approximately 26M to the Rivers Crouch, Blackwater or Colne. A safe route is through either the Princes or the North Edinburgh Channels, thence S of the Tizard, Knob and West Barrow banks to the West Swin, before turning NE into Middle Deep and the East Swin. This is just one of many routes which could be followed, depending on wind direction, tidal conditions and confidence in electronic aids in the absence of marks.

A similar, well-used route in reverse, ie to the SE, lies via the Wallet Spitway, to the Whitaker lt buoy, through Barrow Swatchway to SW Sunk bn; thence via the N Edinburgh Chan, toward the E Margate lt buoy keeping E of Tongue Sand tr. Beware shoal waters off Barrow and Sunk Sands.

Port Control London can give navigational help to yachts on VHF Ch 12; Thames CG at Walton-on-the-Naze can also assist. The Thames Navigation Service has radar coverage between the Naze and Margate, eastward to near the Dutch coast.

NORTH FORELAND TO LONDON BRIDGE

N Foreland has a conspic lt ho, RC (chart *1828*), with buoys offshore. From HW Dover – 0120 to + 0045 the stream runs N from The Downs and W into Thames Estuary. From HWD + 0045 to + 0440 the N-going stream from The Downs meets the E-going stream from Thames Estuary, which in strong winds causes a bad sea. From HWD – 0450 to – 0120 the streams turn W into Thames Estuary and S towards The Downs. If bound for London, round N Foreland against the late ebb in order to carry a fair tide from Sheerness onward.

For vessels drawing less than 2m the most direct route from North Foreland to the Thames and Medway is via South Chan, Gore Chan, Horse Chan, Kentish Flats, Four Fathom Chan and Cant; but it is not well marked particularly over the Kentish Flats. An alternative, deeper route is East of Margate Sand and the Tongue, to set course through Princes Channel to Oaze Deep; larger vessels proceed via the North Edinburgh Channel. W-going streams begin at approx HW Sheerness – 0600 and E-going at HW Sheerness + 0030.

Margate or Whitstable (8.4.10) afford little shelter for yachts. The Swale (8.4.11) provides an interesting inside route S of the Isle of Sheppey with access to Sheerness and the R Medway (8.4.13). If sailing from N Foreland to the Thames, Queenborough (8.4.12) offers the first easily accessible, all-tide, deep-water shelter. The Medway Chan is the main appr to Sheerness from the Warp and the Medway Fairway buoy.

Close N is Sea Reach No 1 buoy and the start of Yanlet Chan and the Thames river which is buoyed up to Gravesend. See 8.4.14 for the Thames Barrier and for yacht facilities in London and some PLA regulations on this busy river. Yachts should beware the large amount of floating debris, general turbulence and absence of bolt-holes other than listed marinas. Off Shoeburyness, Leigh Channel diverges to Southend, Leigh-on-sea (8.4.15) and Canvey Island/Benfleet.

SHOEBURYNESS TO RIVER COLNE (charts *1185*, *1975*)

Maplin and Foulness Sands extend nearly 6M NE from Foulness Pt, the extremity being marked by Whitaker bn. On N side of Whitaker chan leading to R. Crouch (8.4.17) and R. Roach (8.4.16) lies Buxey Sand, inshore of which is the Ray Sand chan (dries), a convenient short cut between R. Crouch and R. Blackwater with sufficient rise of tide.

To seaward of Buxey Sand and the Spitway, Gunfleet Sand extends 10M NE, marked by buoys and drying in places. A conspic disused lt tr stands on SE side of Gunfleet Sand, about 6M SSE of the Naze tr, and here the SW-going (flood) stream begins about HW Sheerness + 0600, and the NE-going stream at about HW Sheerness – 0030, sp rates 2kn.

The Rivers Blackwater (8.4.18) and Colne (8.4.19) share a common estuary which is approached from the NE via NE Gunfleet lt buoy; thence along Goldmer Gat and the Wallet towards Knoll and Eagle lt buoys. For the Colne turn NNW via Colne Bar buoy towards Inner Bench Hd buoy keeping in mid-chan. For R. Blackwater, head WNW for NW Knoll and Bench Hd buoys. From the S or SE, make for the Whitaker ECM buoy, thence through the Spitway, via Swin Spitway and Wallet Spitway buoys to reach Knoll buoy and deeper water.

RIVER COLNE TO HARWICH (chart *1975*, 1593)

4M SW of the Naze tr at Hollands Haven a conspic radar tr (67m, unlit) is an excellent daymark. From the S, approach Walton and Harwich via the Medusa chan about 1M E of Naze tr. At N end of this chan, 1M off Dovercourt, Pye End buoy marks chan SSW to Walton Backwaters (8.4.20). Harwich and Landguard Point are close to the N. Making Harwich from the SE beware the drying Cork Sand, which lies N/S.

Sunk It Float (Fog sig, RC), 11M E of The Naze, marks the outer apprs to Harwich (8.4.21), an extensive and well sheltered hbr accessible at all times (chart *2693*). The Harwich DW channel begins 1·5M NNW of Sunk It Float and runs N between Rough and Shipwash shoals, then W past the Cork Sand PHM It buoy. It is in constant use by commercial shipping, so yachts should approach via the Recommended Track for yachts. Approaching from NE and 2M off the ent to R. Deben (8.4.23), beware Cutler shoal, with least depth of 1·2m, marked by SHM buoy on E side; Wadgate Ledge and the Platters are about 1·5M ENE of Landguard Point. S of Landguard Point the W-going (flood) stream begins at HW Harwich + 0600, and the E-going stream at HW Harwich, sp rates about 1·5kn. Note: HW Harwich is never more than 7 mins after HW Walton; LW times are about 10 mins earlier.

HARWICH TO ORFORD NESS (chart *2052*)

Shipwash shoal, buoyed and with least depth 0·5m near its S end, runs NNE from 9M E of Felixstowe to 4M SSE of Orford Ness. Inshore of this is Shipway Chan, then Bawdsey Bank, buoyed with depths of 2m, on which the sea breaks in E'ly swell. The Sledway Chan lies between Bawdsey Bank and Whiting Bank (buoyed) which is close SW of Orford Ness, and has least depth of 1m. Hollesley Chan, about 1M wide, runs inshore W and N of this bank. In the SW part of Hollesley B is the ent to Orford Haven and the R Ore/Alde (8.4.24).

There are overfalls S of Orford Ness on both the ebb and flood streams. 2M E of Orford Ness the SW-going stream begins at HW Harwich + 0605, sp rate 2·5kn; the NE-going stream begins at HW Harwich – 0010, sp rate 3kn.

Note: The direction of local buoyage becomes S to N off Orford Ness (52°05'N).

ORFORDNESS TO GREAT YARMOUTH (chart 1543)

N of Orford Ness seas break on Aldeburgh Ridge (1.3m), but the coast is clear of offlying dangers past Aldeburgh and Southwold (8.4.25), as far as Benacre Ness, 5M S of Lowestoft. Sizewell power stn is a conspic □ bldg 1·5M N of Thorpe Ness. Keep 1·5M offshore to avoid fishing floats.

Lowestoft (8.4.26) is best approached from both S and E by the buoyed/lit Stanford chan, passing E of Newcome Sand and SW of Holm Sand; beware possible strong set across hbr ent. From the N, approach through Cockle Gatway, Caister Road, Yarmouth Road, passing Great Yarmouth; then proceed S through Gorleston, Corton and Lowestoft North Roads (buoyed). 1M E of hbr ent, the S-going stream begins at HW Dover –0600, and the N-going at HW Dover, sp rates 2·6kn.

In the approaches to Great Yarmouth (8.4.27) from seaward the banks are continually changing; use the buoyed chans which, from N and S, are those described in the preceding paragraph. But from the E the shortest approach is via Corton ECM It buoy and the Holm Channel leading into Gorleston Road. The sea often breaks on North Scroby, Middle Scroby and Caister Shoal (all of which dry), and there are heavy tide rips over parts of Corton and South Scroby Sands, Middle and South Cross Sands, and Winterton Overfalls.

1M NE of ent to Gt Yarmouth the S-going stream begins at HW Dover –0600, and the N-going at HW Dover – 0015, sp rates 2·3kn. Breydon Water (tidal) affects streams in the Haven; after heavy rain the out-going stream at Brush Quay may exceed 5kn. For Norfolk Broads, see 8.4.27. About 12M NE of Great Yarmouth lie Newarp Banks, on which the sea breaks in bad weather.

CROSSING FROM THAMES ESTUARY TO BELGIUM OR THE NETHERLANDS (charts 1610, 1872, 3371, *1406*, 1408)

Important factors in choosing a route include the need to head at 90° across the various TSSs; to avoid areas where traffic converges; to make full use of available ITZs and to keep well clear of offshore oil/gas activities (see 8.5.5). It is best to avoid the areas westward of W Hinder It, around Nord Hinder It buoy and the Maas routes W of the Hook of Holland. For Distances across N Sea, see 8.0.10 and for further notes on North Sea crossings, see 8.20.5.

8.20.36 illustrates the strategy of crossing the N Hinder South TSS and then either crossing the W Hinder TSS eastward of W Hinder It before proceeding to Belgian ports; or proceeding on a more direct route for ports between Zeebrugge and Hook of Holland.

From Rivers Crouch, Blackwater, Colne or from Harwich take departure from Long Sand Hd It buoy to S Galloper It buoy, thence to W Hinder It (see 8.20.5), crossing the TSS at right angles near Garden City It buoy; see 8.20.36. Care must be taken throughout with tidal streams, which may be setting across the yacht's track. The area is relatively shallow, and in bad weather seas are steep and short.

For ports between Hook of Holland and Texel it may be best to diverge to the NE so as to cross the several Deep Water (DW) routes, and their extensions, as quickly as possible, to the N of Nord Hinder It buoy and the Maas TSS. If bound for ports NE of Texel keep well S of the TX1 It buoy and then inshore of the Off Texel-Vlieland-Terschelling-German Bight TSS, 8.20.37, which is well buoyed on its S side.

8.4.6   DISTANCE TABLE

Approximate distances in nautical miles are by the most direct route, whilst avoiding dangers and allowing for Traffic Separation Schemes. Places in *italics* are in adjoining areas; places in **bold** are in 8.0.10, Distances across the North Sea.

		1	2	3	4	5	6	7	8	9	10	11	12	13	14	15	16	17	18	19	20
1.	*Ramsgate*	**1**																			
2.	Whitstable	22	**2**																		
3.	**Sheerness**	34	14	**3**																	
4.	Gravesend	56	36	22	**4**																
5.	**London Bridge**	76	55	45	23	**5**															
6.	Southend-on-Sea	35	17	6	20	43	**6**														
7.	Havengore	33	15	12	32	55	12	**7**													
8.	**Burnham-on-Crouch**	44	36	34	53	76	33	30	**8**												
9.	West Mersea	43	38	29	49	72	30	29	22	**9**											
8.	**Brightlingsea**	41	36	28	47	71	28	26	22	8	**10**										
11.	Walton-on-the-Naze	40	40	46	59	82	39	37	25	23	23	**11**									
12.	**Harwich**	40	40	50	65	83	40	41	31	24	24	6	**12**								
13.	Ipswich	49	49	59	74	92	49	50	40	33	33	15	9	**13**							
14.	River Deben (ent)	45	45	55	71	89	46	46	35	38	38	10	6	15	**14**						
15.	River Ore (ent)	47	47	60	75	93	50	51	38	43	43	14	10	19	4	**15**					
16.	Southwold	62	67	80	95	113	70	71	58	63	63	33	30	39	23	20	**16**				
17.	**Lowestoft**	72	77	90	105	123	80	81	68	73	73	43	40	49	33	30	10	**17**			
18.	Great Yarmouth	79	84	97	112	130	87	88	76	81	80	51	52	61	41	38	18	7	**18**		
19.	*Blakeney*	123	128	141	156	174	131	132	120	125	124	95	96	105	85	82	62	51	44	**19**	
20.	*Bridlington*	207	198	224	226	244	201	215	204	205	204	181	175	184	169	165	145	135	114	79	**20**

EAST ANGLIAN WAYPOINTS   8-4-7

Selected waypoints and major lights for use between the Thames Estuary and the Wash are listed below. Further waypoints in adjacent waters are given in 8.3.4, 8.4.4 and 8.5.4 for the English Coast, and 8.19.4, 8.20.4 and 8.21.4 for the coasts of NE France, Belgium, the Netherlands and Germany. Positions are referenced to OSGB 36 datum.

Aldeburgh Ridge By	52°06'·82N 01°37'·60E
Barnard E Lt By	52°25'·11N 01°46'·50E
Barrow No 3 Lt By	51°41'·99N 01°20'·35E
Barrow No 6 Lt By	51°37'·27N 01°14'·79E
Barrow No 9 Lt By	51°35'·31N 01°10'·40E
Barrow No 11 Lt By	51°33'·73N 01°05'·85E
Barrow SW Lt By	51°31'·80N 01°00'·53E
Bawdsey NE Lt By	52°01'·70N 01°36'·20E
Bawdsey S Lt By	51°57'·20N 01°30'·32E
Bawdsey Mid Lt By	51°58'·85N 01°33'·70E
Bench Head Lt By	
Black Deep Lt By	51°46'·60N 01°34'·05E
Black Deep No 1 Lt By	51°44'·00N 01°28'·20E
Black Deep No 3 Lt By	51°41'·95N 01°26'·07E
Black Deep No 5 Lt By	51°39'·50N 01°23'·10E
Black Deep No 7 Lt By	51°37'·05N 01°17'·80E
Black Deep No 11 Lt By	51°34'·30N 01°13'·50E
Blacktail E Lt Bn	51°31'·75N 00°56'·60E
Blacktail W Lt Bn	51°31'·43N 00°55'·30E
Blacktail Spit Lt By	51°31'·45N 00°56'·85E
Blakeney Overfalls Lt By	53°03'·00N 01°01'·50E
Blyth E Lt By	51°29'·68N 00°37'·90E
Blyth Mid Lt By	51°30'·05N 00°32'·50E
Boston No 1 Lt By	52°57'·87N 00°15'·22E
Boston Roads Lt By	52°57'·67N 00°16'·23E
Burnham Flats Lt By	53°07'·50N 00°35'·00E
Buxey Bn	51°41'·13N 01°01'·38E
Buxey No 1 Lt By	51°39'·02N 01°00'·86E
Buxey No 2 Lt By	51°38'·94N 01°00'·26E
Buxey S Lt By	51°39'·82N 01°02'·60E
Caister Mid Lt By	52°38'·96N 01°45'·77E
Cant Bn	51°27'·73N 00°55'·45E
Cant E Lt By	51°28'·50N 00°55'·70E
Cant Mid Lt Bn	51°26'·85N 00°49'·90E
Chapman Lt By	51°30'·40N 00°37'·03E
Cliff Foot Lt By	51°55'·69N 01°18'·64E
Cockle Lt By	52°44'·00N 01°43'·70E
Colne Bar Lt By	51°44'·58N 01°02'·67E
Columbine By	51°24'·23N 01°01'·45E
Columbine Spit By	51°23'·83N 01°00'·13E
Cork S By	51°51'·30N 01°24'·20E
Cork Sand Lt Bn	51°55'·19N 01°25'·31E
Cork Sand Lt By	51°55'·43N 01°25'·95E
Corton Lt By	52°31'·10N 01°51'·50E
Corton S Lt By	52°32'·15N 01°50'·12E
Corton W Lt By	52°34'·46N 01°46'·42E
Cromer Lt	52°55'·45N 01°19'·10E
Cross Sand Lt By	52°37'·00N 01°59'·25E
Cross Sand NE Lt By	52°43'·00N 01°53'·80E
Cross Sand E Lt By	52°40'·00N 01°53'·80E
Crouch Lt By	51°37'·60N 00°56'·49E
Crouch Fairway No 1 Lt By	51°37'·08N 00°51'·11E
Crouch Inner Lt By	51°37'·19N 00°55'·22E
CS 5 Lt By	51°23'·00N 01°50'·00E
Cutler Lt By	51°58'·50N 01°27'·60E
Docking N Lt By	53°14'·80N 00°41'·60E
Docking E Lt By	53°09'·80N 00°50'·50E
Drill Stone Lt By	51°25'·80N 01°43'·00E
Eagle Lt By	51°44'·10N 01°03'·92E
East Last Lt By	51°24'·00N 01°12'·28E
Edinburgh Lt By	51°31'·42N 01°21'·53E
Elbow Lt By	51°23'·20N 01°31'·70E
F3 Lt Float	51°23'·82N 02°00'·62E
Falls Hd Lt By	51°28'·20N 01°50'·00E
Faversham Spit By	51°20'·74N 00°54'·31E
Felixstowe Ledge Lt By	51°56'·30N 01°24'·53E
Foulness Lt By	51°39'·82N 01°03'·92E
Gabbard N Inner Lt By	51°59'·10N 01°56'·10E
Gabbard S Inner Lt By	51°51'·20N 01°52'·40E
Galloper N Lt By	51°50'·00N 01°59'·50E
Galloper S Lt By	51°43'·95N 01°56'·50E
Girdler Lt By	51°29'·15N 01°06'·50E
Girdler SE Lt By	51°29'·47N 01°10'·00E
Girdler W Lt By	51°29'·58N 01°06'·82E
Grain Hard Lt By	51°26'·94N 00°44'·27E
Guard Lt By	51°57'·03N 01°17'·88E
Gunfleet NE Lt By	51°49'·90N 01°27'·90E
Gunfleet Old Lt Ho	51°46'·08N 01°20'·52E
Gunfleet Spit Lt By	51°45'·30N 01°21'·80E
Haisbro N Lt By	53°00'·20N 01°32'·40E
Haisbro Mid Lt By	52°54'·20N 01°41'·70E
Haisbro S Lt By	52°50'·80N 01°48'·40E
Hammond Knoll E Lt By	52°52'·30N 01°58'·75E
Harwich Chan No 1	51°56'·11N 01°27'·30E
Haven Lt By	51°55'·73N 01°32'·67E
Hemsby Lt By	52°41'·84N 01°45'·00E
Holm Lt By	52°33'·50N 01°48'·08E
Holm E Lt By	52°31'·06N 01°49'·42E
Holm S Lt By	52°27'·33N 01°47'·32E
Holm SW Lt By	52°28'·36N 01°47'·28E
Holm W Lt By	52°29'·80N 01°47'·20E
Holm NW Lt By	52°31'·90N 01°46'·80E
Hook Middle W By	51°39'·15N 01°08'·07E
Hook Spit By	51°24'·05N 01°12'·65E
Horse Shoal Lt By	51°37'·07N 00°51'·62E
Kentish Knock Lt By	51°38'·50N 01°40'·50E
Knob Lt By	51°30'·66N 01°04'·38E
Knob NE Lt By	51°32'·00N 01°10'·10E
Knob SE Lt By	51°30'·86N 01°06'·51E
Knock S Lt By	51°34'·73N 01°36'·10E
Knock John Lt By	51°33'·46N 01°11'·08E
Knoll Lt By	51°43'·85N 01°05'·17E
Knoll NW Lt By	51°44'·32N 01°02'·27E
Landguard Lt By	51°55'·35N 01°18'·98E
Lee W Mid Lt By	51°30'·45N 00°38'·93E
Leigh By	51°31'·04N 00°42'·67E
Leigh SE Lt By	51°29'·40N 00°47'·17E
Little Sunk Bn	51°41'·89N 01°24'·85E
Long Sand Bn	51°41'·44N 01°29'·56E
Long Sand Hd Lt By	51°47'·87N 01°39'·53E
Long Sand SE Lt By	51°32'·24N 01°21'·22E
Long Sand NW Bn	51°34'·72N 01°18'·16E
Lowestoft Lt Ho	52°29'·18N 01°45'·46E
Lynn Knock Lt By	53°04'·40N 00°27'·31E
Maplin Lt By	51°34'·00N 01°02'·40E

Maplin NE Lt By	51°37'·43N 01°04'·90E	Shingles NW Lt By	51°31'·23N 01°09'·83E
Maplin Bank Lt By	51°35'·47N 01°04'·80E	Shingles Patch Lt By	51°32'·98N 01°15'·47E
Margate E Lt By	51°27'·00N 01°26'·50E	Shingles S Lt By	51°29'·20N 01°16'·12E
Margate SE Lt By	51°24'·10N 01°20'·50E	Shiphead Lt By	51°53'·76N 01°34'·01E
Margate S Lt By	51°23'·88N 01°16'·75E	Shipwash N Lt By	52°01'·70N 01°38'·38E
Margate Hook Bn	51°24'·14N 01°14'·39E	Shipwash E Lt By	51°57'·05N 01°38'·00E
Margate Outfall Lt By	51°24'·59N 01°26'·10E	Shipwash S Lt By	51°52'·68N 01°34'·16E
Medusa Lt By	51°51'·20N 01°20'·46E	Shipwash SW Lt By	51°54'·72N 01°34'·32E
Medway Lt By	51°28'·80N 00°52'·92E	Shipwash NW Lt By	51°58'·33N 01°36'·33E
		Shivering Sand Trs N Lt By	51°29'·98N 01°04'·86E
Nass Lt Bn	51°45'·75N 00°54'·88E	Shivering Sand Trs S Lt By	51°29'·75N 01°04'·93E
Naze Tr	51°51'·85N 01°17'·40E	Shoebury Inner Bn	51°30'·15N 00°49'·05E
Newarp Lt F	52°48'·35N 01°55'·80E	Shoebury Lt Bn	51°30'·28N 00°49'·38E
Newcome N Lt By	52°28'·29N 01°46'·43E	Shoebury S Lt By	51°30'·40N 00°52'·50E
Newcome E Lt By	52°28'·48N 01°49'·32E	Shoebury W Lt By	51°30'·20N 00°45'·83E
Newcome Sand Lt By	52°26'·40N 01°47'·16E	Smiths Knoll Lt By	52°43'·50N 02°18'·00E
NHR-S Lt By	51°51'·40N 02°28'·79E	Southwold Lt Ho	52°19'·60N 01°41'·00E
NHR-SE Lt By	51°45'·50N 02°40'·00E	Spaniard Lt By	51°26'·20N 01°04'·10E
Nore Sand W Lt By	51°29'·25N 00°41'·80E	Spile Lt By	51°26'·40N 00°55'·80E
Nore Swatch Lt By	51°28'·26N 00°45'·65E	Spit NE Lt By	51°27'·90N 01°30'·00E
North Foreland Lt	51°22'·47N 01°26'·80E	Stanford Lt By	52°27'·33N 01°46'·78E
		Stone Banks By	51°53'·16N 01°19'·33E
Oaze S Lt By	51°30'·00N 01°00'·80E	Sunk Lt F	51°51'·00N 01°35'·00E
Oaze SW Lt By	51°29'·03N 00°57'·03E	Sunk Lt By (Wash- Cork Hole)	52°56'·27N 00°23'·50E
Oaze W Lt By	51°29'·03N 00°55'·53E	Sunk SW Bn	51°36'·50N 01°14'·85E
Orford Haven By	52°01'·63N 01°27'·67E	Sunk W Lt By	51°44'·30N 01°25'·90E
Orford Ness Lt Ho	52°05'·00N 01°34'·60E	Sunk Head Tr Lt By	51°46'·60N 01°30'·60E
Outer Crouch Lt By	51°38'·35N 00°58'·61E	Sunken Buxey Lt By	51°39'·50N 01°00'·70E
Outer Gabbard Lt By	51°57'·80N 02°04'·30E	Swallow Tail By	51°40'·44N 01°04'·81E
Outer Tongue Lt By	51°30'·70N 01°26'·50E	Swatch Mid Lt By	51°28'·65N 00°44'·27E
Oyster Lt By	51°22'·12N 01°01'·27E	Swin Spitway Lt By	51°41'·92N 01°08'·45E
		Swin SW Lt By	51°32'·68N 01°00'·79E
Patch Lt By	51°32'·24N 01°20'·91E	Swin W By	51°33'·82N 01°03'·30E
Pitching Ground Lt By	51°55'·39N 01°21'·16E		
Pollard Spit Lt By	51°22'·95N 00°58'·67E	Tizard Lt By	51°32'·90N 01°13'·00E
Pye End Lt By	51°55'·00N 01°18'·00E	Tongue E Lt By	51°28'·72N 01°18'·72E
		Tongue N Lt By	51°28'·78N 01°13'·18E
Race S Lt By	53°08'·18N 00°56'·81E	Tongue Sand Tr N Lt By	51°29'·65N 01°22'·13E
Redsand E Lt By	51°29'·38N 01°04'·15E	Tongue Sand Tr S Lt By	51°29'·40N 01°22'·15E
Red Sand Trs E Lt By	51°28'·57N 00°59'·78E	Trinity Lt By	51°49'·00N 01°36'·50E
Red Sand Trs N Lt By	51°28'·70N 00°59'·42E		
Ridge Inner Lt By	51°55'·31N 01°19'·68E	Wallet No.2 Lt By	51°48'·85N 01°23'·10E
Ridge Lt By	51°40'·10N 01°05'·00E	Wallet No.4 Lt By	51°46'·50N 01°17'·33E
Rough Lt By	51°55'·16N 01°31'·11E	Wallet Spitway Lt By	51°42'·83N 01°07'·42E
Roughs Tr NW Lt By	51°53'·78N 01°28'·88E	Washington Lt By	51°56'·49N 01°26'·70E
Roughs Tr SE Lt By	51°53'·61N 01°29'·05E	Well N Lt By	53°03'·00N 00°28'·00E
		Wells Fairway Lt By	52°59'·85N 00°49'·71E
Scott Patch Lt By	53°11'·10N 00°36'·50E	Whitaker Bn	51°39'·62N 01°06'·30E
Scroby Elbow Lt By	52°37'·32N 01°46'·50E	Whitaker Lt By	51°41'·40N 01°10'·61E
Scroby N Lt By	52°42'·49N 01°44'·80E	Whiting Hook By	52°02'·95N 01°31'·93E
Scroby NW Lt By	52°40'·35N 01°46'·44E	Whiting NE Lt By	52°03'·77N 01°33'·88E
Scroby SW Lt By	52°35'·80N 01°46'·37E	Whiting SW Lt By	52°01'·10N 01°30'·90E
Shelf N Lt By	51°56'·65N 01°18'·70E	Whitstable Street Lt By	51°23'·83N 01°01'·70E
Sheringham E Lt By	53°02'·20N 01°15'·00E	Winterton Ridge S Lt By	52°47'·20N 02°03'·60E
Sheringham W Lt By	53°02'·93N 01°06'·87E	Woodbridge Haven By	51°58'·15N 01°23'·90E
Shingles Mid Lt By	51°31'·93N 01°12'·08E	Woolpack Lt By	53°02'·65N 00°31'·55E
Shingles N Lt By	51°32'·66N 01°14'·35E		

4

8-4-8   THAMES ESTUARY TIDAL STREAMS

Due to very strong rates of tidal streams in some areas, eddies may occur. Where possible, some indication of these is shown, but in many areas there is insufficient information or eddies are unstable.

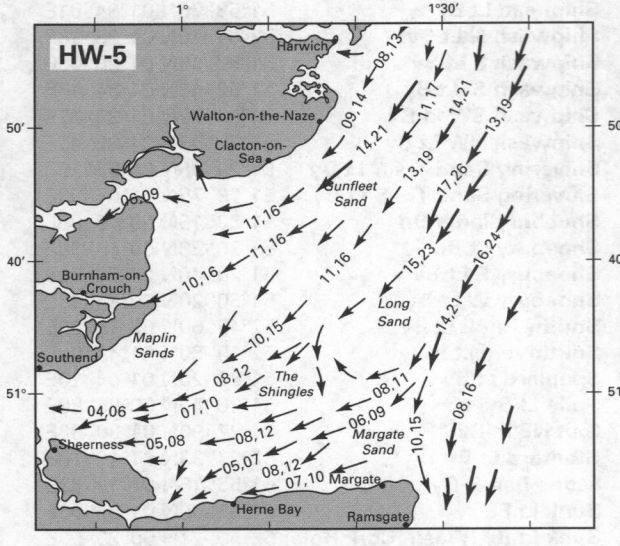

5 Hours before HW Sheerness (0335 before HW Dover)

4 Hours before HW Sheerness (0235 before HW Dover)

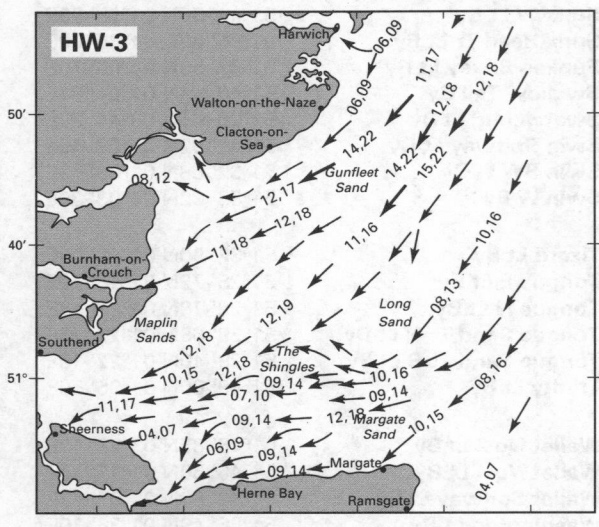

3 Hours before HW Sheerness (0135 before HW Dover)

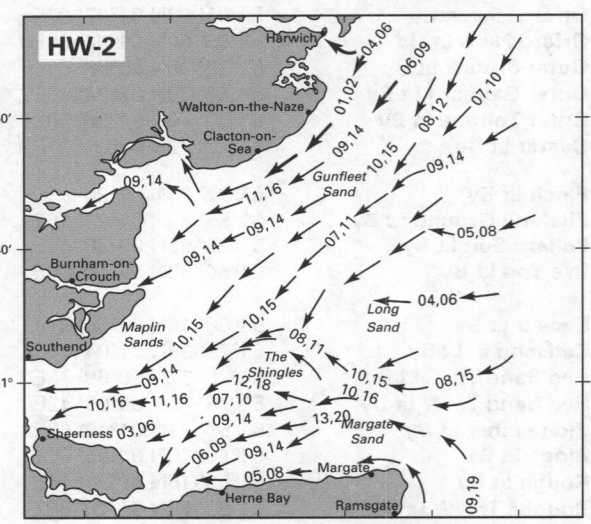

2 Hours before HW Sheerness (0035 before HW Dover)

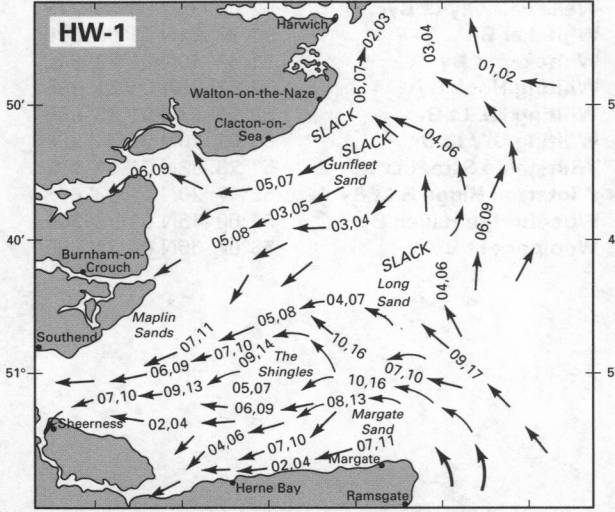

1 Hour before HW Sheerness (0025 after HW Dover)

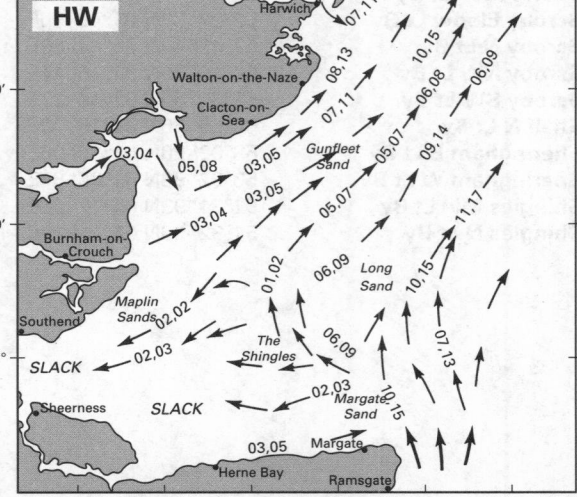

HW Sheerness (0125 after HW Dover)

4

Due to very strong rates of tidal streams in some areas, eddies may occur. Where possible, some indication of these is shown, but in many areas there is insufficient information or eddies are unstable.

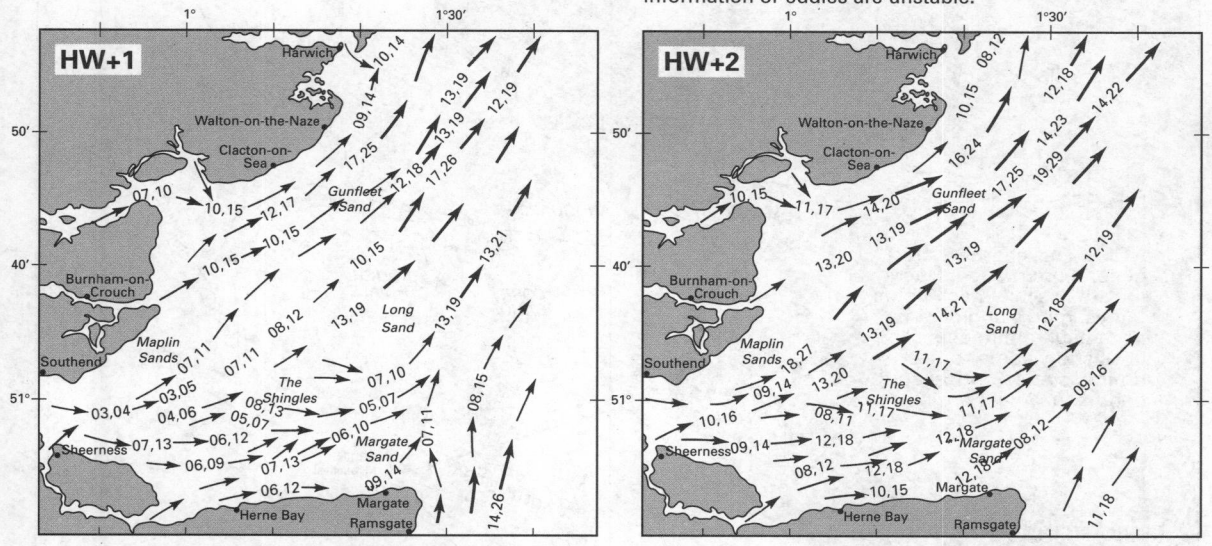

1 Hour after HW Sheerness (0225 after HW Dover)

2 Hours after HW Sheerness (0325 after HW Dover)

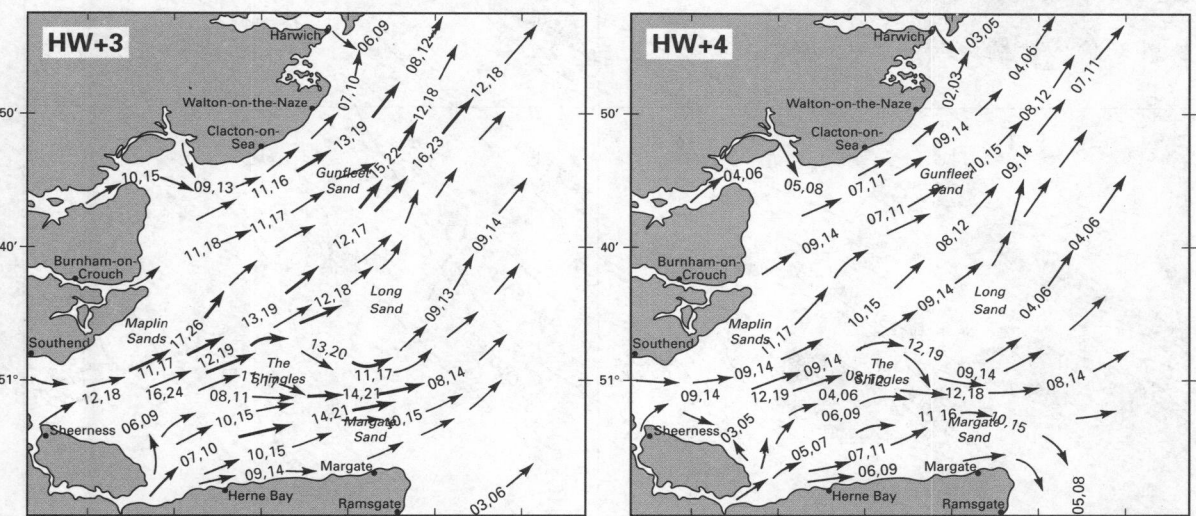

3 Hours after HW Sheerness (0425 after HW Dover)

4 Hours after HW Sheerness (0525 after HW Dover)

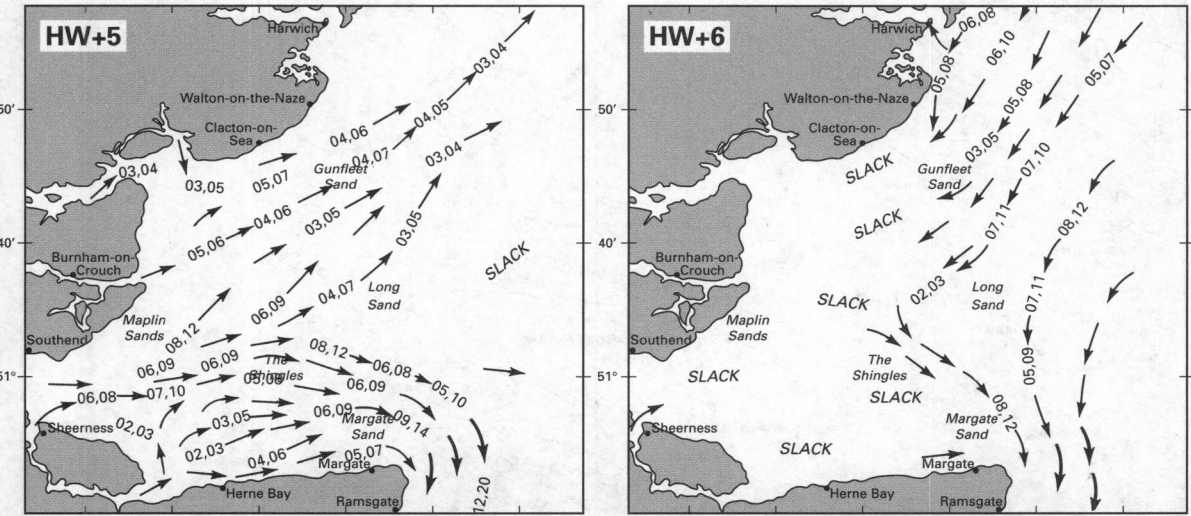

5 Hours after HW Sheerness (0600 before HW Dover)

6 Hours after HW Sheerness (0500 before HW Dover)

THAMES ESTUARY   8-4-9

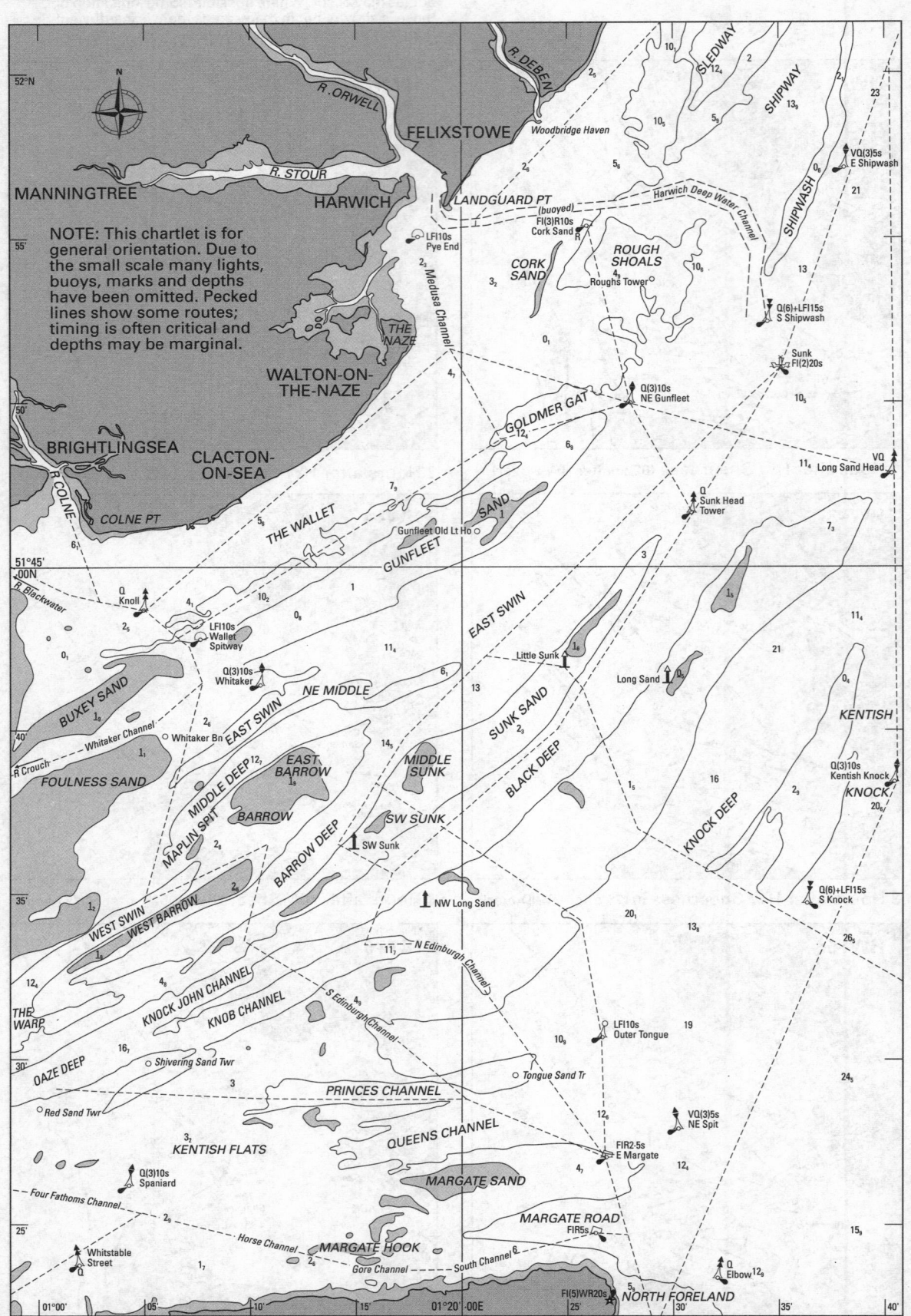

WHITSTABLE   8-4-10

Kent 51°21'·83N 01°01'·56E   Rtg 3-4-2

CHARTS
AC 2571, *1607*; Imray Y14; Stanfords 5; OS 179
TIDES
+0135 Dover; ML 3·0; Duration 0605; Zone 0 (UT)

Standard Port SHEERNESS (→)

Times				Height (metres)			
High Water		Low Water		MHWS	MHWN	MLWN	MLWS
0200	0800	0200	0700	5·8	4·7	1·5	0·6
1400	2000	1400	1900				
Differences WHITSTABLE							
−0008	−0011	+0005	0000	−0·3	−0·3	0·0	−0·1
MARGATE							
−0050	−0040	−0020	−0050	−0·9	−0·9	−0·1	0·0
HERNE BAY							
−0025	−0015	0000	−0025	−0·5	−0·5	−0·1	−0·1

SHELTER
Good, except in strong winds from NNW to NE. Hbr dries up to 1·7m; access HW±1 for strangers. Yacht berths are limited to genuine refuge seekers since priority is given to commercial shipping. Fender board needed against piled quays or seek a mooring to NW of hbr, (controlled by YC).
NAVIGATION
WPT 51°22'·62N 01°01'·20E, 165°/345° from/to W Quay dolphin, 0·83M. From E keep well seaward of Whitstable Street, a hard drying sandspit, which extends 1M N from the coast; shoals a further 1M to seaward are marked by Whitstable Street NCM lt buoy. From W avoid Columbine and Pollard Spits. Appr (not before half flood) direct in the G sector or via Whitstable Oyster PHM lt buoy in W sector of dolphin lt. Beware many oyster beds and banks near approaches, which are very shallow.
LIGHTS AND MARKS
Off head of W Quay on a dolphin, ☆ Fl WRG 5s 2m 5/3M, covers the approaches, vis W118°-156°, G156°-178°, R178°-201°. At the head of the hbr a Dir lt, Oc WRG 5s, leads 122½° into hbr ent, vis G110°-121°, W121°-124°(3°), R124°-134°. Tfc sigs at NE arm: FW 15m 8M = hbr open; FR 10m 5M = hbr closed.
RADIO TELEPHONE
Call *Whitstable Harbour Radio* VHF Ch **09** 12 16 (Mon-Fri: 0800-1700LT). Other times: HW −3 to HW+1). Tidal info is available on request.

TELEPHONE (Dial code 01227)
Hr Mr 274086, ☎ 265441; MRSC (01255) 675518; ⌗ (01304) 224251 (H24); Marinecall 0891 500455; Police 770055; Dr 59440.
FACILITIES
Hbr ☎ 274086, AB £11.00, FW, D, C (10 ton);
Whitstable YC ☎ 272942, M, R, Slip, L, FW, Bar.
Services: ME, C, CH, ACA, SM, Gas, Ⓔ.
Town EC Wed; Ⓞ, P, V, R, Bar, ✉, Ⓑ, ⇌, → Lydd/Manston.

MINOR HARBOURS WEST OF NORTH FORELAND

MARGATE, Kent, 51°23'·40N 01°22'·75E. AC 1827, 1828, 323; Imray Y7, C1; Stanfords 5; OS 179. HW+0045 on Dover; ML 2·6; Duration 0610; see 8.4.10. Small hbr drying <u>3</u>m, inside bkwtr (Stone Pier) FR 18m 4M; exposed to NW'lies. Appr's: from E, via Longnose NCM buoy, keeping about 5ca offshore; from N, via Margate PHM buoy Fl R 2·5s; from W via Gore Chan and S Chan to SE Margate ECM buoy, Q (3) 10s. Beware ruins of old pier, known as the Iron Jetty, Fl R 5s, extending 2½ca N from root of Stone Pier. VHF none. Facilities: **Margate YC** ☎ (01843) 292602, R, Bar. **Town** EC Thurs; D & P (cans from garage), R, V, Bar, ✉, Ⓑ, ⇌, → Manston.

HERNE BAY, Kent, 51°22'·37N 01°07'·32E. AC 1607. Tides see 8.4.10. Close E of pier, a 400m long bkwtr gives drying shelter for dayboats/dinghies. Lts: QW 8m 4M is 6ca offshore (former pier hd); bkwtr hd 2FR (vert); pier hd 2FG (vert); R bn on B dolphin, Fl Y 5s, is approx 1M ENE of bkwtr hd. Reculvers twrs are conspic 3M to the E. Slip. **Town** EC Thurs; P, Ⓔ, R, V, Bar, ✉, Ⓑ, Ⓞ.

WHITSTABLE

THE SWALE   8-4-11

Kent   Rtg 3-2-2

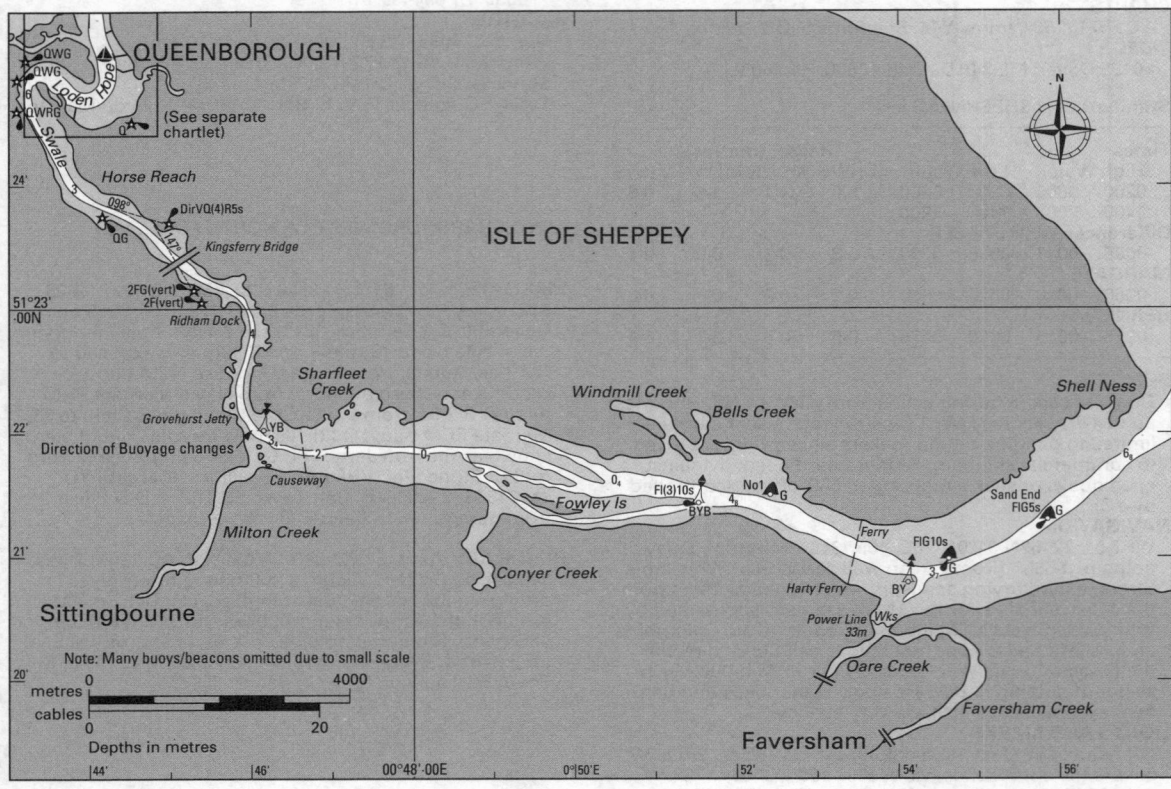

CHARTS
AC 2571, *2482, 2572, 1834*, 3683; Imray Y18, Y14;
Stanfords 5, 8; OS 178

TIDES
Queenborough +0130 Dover; Harty Ferry +0120 Dover; ML
(Harty Ferry) 3·0; Duration 0610; Zone 0 (UT). Faversham
HW differences are –0·2m on Sheerness; no other data.

Standard Port SHEERNESS (→)

Times				Height (metres)			
High Water		Low Water		MHWS	MHWN	MLWN	MLWS
0200	0800	0200	0700	5·8	4·7	1·5	0·6
1400	2000	1400	1900				

Differences R. SWALE (Grovehurst Jetty)

–0007	0000	0000	+0016	0·0	0·0	0·0	–0·1

Grovehurst Jetty is close N of the ent to Milton Creek.

SHELTER
Excellent in the Swale, the 14M chan between the Isle of
Sheppey and the N Kent coast, from Shell Ness in the E
to Queenborough in the W. Yachts can enter the drying
creeks of Faversham, Oare, Conyer, and Milton. Beware
wrecks at ent to Faversham Creek. Many moorings line
the chan from Faversham to Conyer Creeks. See 8.4.12
for Queenborough, all-tide access.

NAVIGATION
E ent WPT: Columbine Spit SHM, 51°23′·84N 01°00′·13E,
050°/230° from/to ent to buoyed chan 1·3M. The first chan
buoys are Pollard Spit PHM QR and Ham Gat SHM unlit;
buoys are moved to suit the shifting chan. Speed limit 8kn.
The chan is well marked from Faversham to Milton
Creek. The middle section from 1·5M E of Conyer Creek
to 0·5M E of Milton Creek is narrowed by drying
mudbanks and carries least depths of 0·4m. Direction of
buoyage changes at Milton Creek. There are numerous
oyster beds in the area. Kingsferry Bridge (see below)
normally opens H and H+30 for masted craft on request,
but subject to railway trains; temp anchs off SW bank.
The **W ent** is marked by Queenborough Spit ECM buoy,
Q (3) 10s, 1M S of Garrison Pt, at 51°25′·78N 00°44′·03E.

LIGHTS AND MARKS
No fixed lts at E ent. In W Swale the following lights are
intended for large coasters using the narrow chan:
(1) Dir ent lt Q 16m 5M; vis 163°-168°.
(2) Round Loden Hope bend: two Q WG and one Q WRG
    on bns; keep in G sectors. See 8.4.13 chartlet.
(3) Horse Reach ldg lts 113°: front QG 7m 5M; rear Fl G 3s
    10m 6M. Dir lt 098°, VQ (4) R 5s 6m 5M.
(4) Kingsferry Bridge ldg lts 147°: front 2FG(vert) 9m 7M;
    rear 2 FW (vert) 11m 10M. Lts on bridge: two x 2 FG
    (vert) on SW buttresses; two x 2 FR (vert) on NE.

Kingsferry Bridge traffic sigs:

No lts	= Bridge down (3·35m MHWS).
Al Q Ⓡ/Ⓖ	= Centre span lifting.
F Ⓖ	= Bridge open (29m MHWS).
Q Ⓡ	= Centre span lowering. Keep clear.
Q Ⓨ	= Bridge out of action.

Best to request bridge opening on VHF Ch 10; normally
opens H and H+30.

RADIO TELEPHONE
Call: *Medway Radio* VHF Ch **74** 16 22 (H24); Kingsferry
Bridge Ch 10 (H24).

TELEPHONE (Dial code 01795)
Hr Mr (Medway Ports Ltd) 580003; MRSC (01255) 675518;
⌗ (01474) 537115 (H24); Marinecall 0891 500455; Police
536639; Dr or Ⓗ via Medway Navigation Service 663025.

FACILITIES
FAVERSHAM: **Services:** BY, AB £5, M, AC, FW, Ⓔ, ME, EI,
Sh, C (40 ton), SM, D, C (25 ton).
   Town EC Thurs; V, R, Bar, Gas, ✉, Ⓑ, ⇌, ✈ Gatwick.
OARE CREEK: **Services:** AB £5, M, C (8 ton), ME, EI, Sh, CH;
   Hollow Shore Cruising Club ☎ 533254, Bar.
CONYER CREEK: **Swale Marina** ☎ 521562, ⌁ 520788, £5,
BH (15 ton), ME, Sh, C (3 ton), Slip; **Conyer Marina** ☎
521711 AB £5 (50 berth marina planned); **Conyer CC**.
   Services: CH, SM, Rigging, BY, ME, Sh, EI, Ⓔ, Slip, D.
MILTON CREEK (Sittingbourne): **Crown Quay** M, FW.
   Town EC Wed; V, R, Bar, ✉, Ⓑ, ⇌, ✈ (Gatwick); also the
Dolphin Yard Sailing Barge Museum.
QUEENBOROUGH: See 8.4.12.

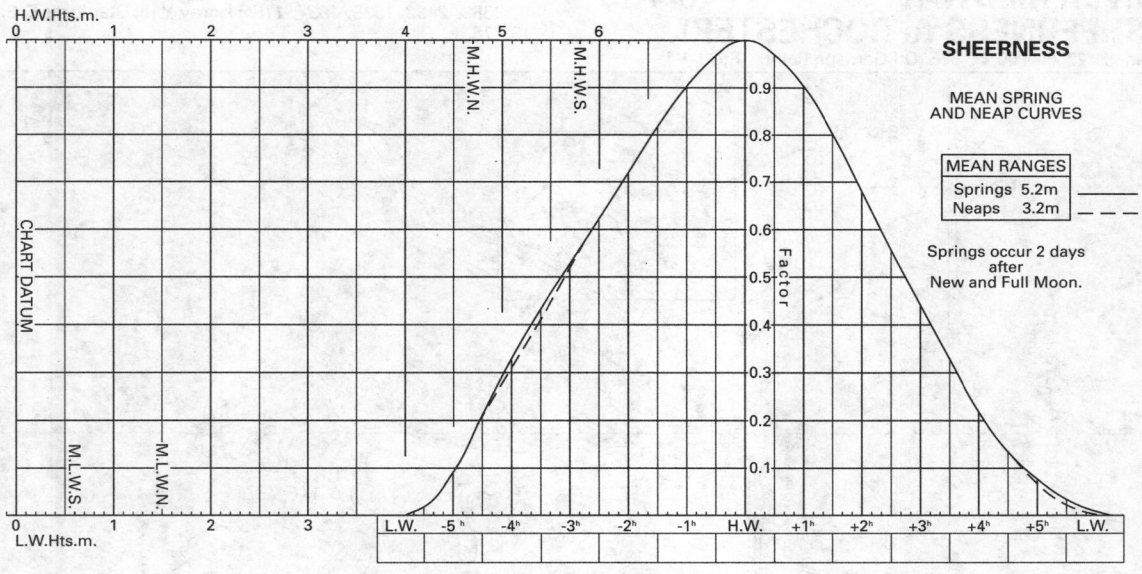

SHEERNESS

MEAN SPRING
AND NEAP CURVES

MEAN RANGES	
Springs	5.2m
Neaps	3.2m

Springs occur 2 days
after
New and Full Moon.

4

QUEENBOROUGH   8-4-12

Kent (Isle of Sheppey) 51°25'·01N 00°44'·29E   Rtg 1·2·2

CHARTS
AC *1834,* 3683, 2572; Imray Y14/18, C1; Stanford 8; OS 178

TIDES
Use 8.4.13 Sheerness, 2M to the N. +0130 Dover; ML 3·0;
Duration 0610; Zone 0 (UT).

SHELTER
Good, except near HW in strong N'ly winds. The first
deep-water refuge W of N Foreland, accessible at all tides
from Garrison Pt (8.4.13); or from the Swale (8.4.11) on
the tide. An all-tide pontoon/jetty (5m depth at end) on E
bank is for landing/short stay only; both sides of the jetty
are foul. 10 ⚓s on E side, N of all-tide landing; 4 Ⓥ berths
on concrete lighter on W side or at 2 Y ⚓s (4 boats on
each) close S of The Hard, a drying causeway. Speed
limit 8kn.

NAVIGATION
WPT: see 8.4.13 for appr via Garrison Pt. Enter the river
at Queenborough Spit ECM buoy, Q (3) 10s, 51°25'·78N
00°44'·03E. The chan narrows between drying banks and
moorings. See 8.4.11 if approaching from the Swale.

LIGHTS AND MARKS
Lights as chartlet. Note: Q 16m 5M lt, vis 163°-168°, on
river bend covers the appr chan. All-tide landing 2 FR
(vert). Concrete lighter Fl G 3s.

RADIO TELEPHONE
Monitor *Medway Radio* VHF Ch **74** for tfc info. Call Ch 08
Sheppey One (Q'boro Hr Mr) for berths, also water taxi at
weekends only. For QYC call *Queen Base* Ch M, 80, M2.

TELEPHONE (Dial code 01795)
Hr Mr 662051; MRSC (01255) 675518; ⌗ (01474) 537115
(H24); Marinecall 0891 500455; Police 580055; Dr 583828;
Ⓗ (01634) 830000 (Gillingham).

FACILITIES
Hbr Controller (AB/🅟 £5.00) ☎/📠 662051, AC, FW on all-
tide Landing. **Queenborough YC** ☎ 663955, M, R, Bar, ♿,
📠, ♨; **The Creek** (dries) Slip, Scrubbing berth (FW, AC).
Services: BY, ME, El, Sh, CH, C (10 ton); Gas;
Town EC Wed; P & D (cans), V, R, Bar, ✉, ⇌, ✈ (Gatwick).

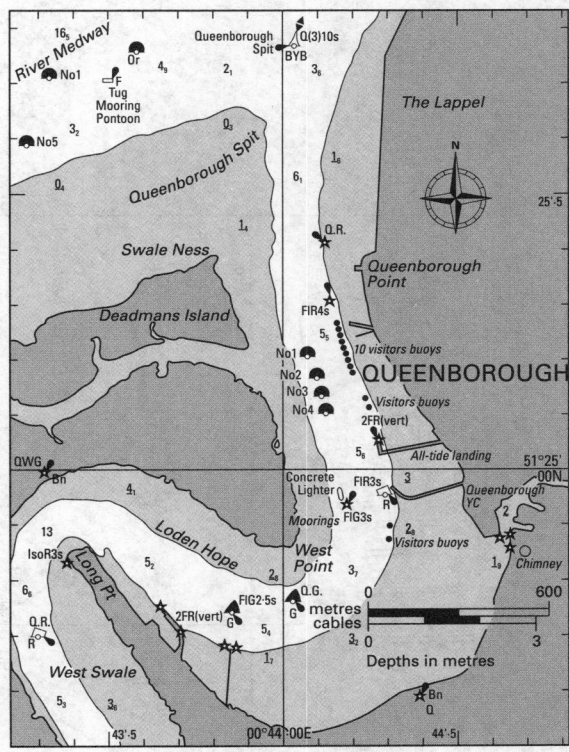

RIVER MEDWAY
(SHEERNESS to ROCHESTER)   8-4-13

Kent 51°27'·00N 00°44'·60E (Off Garrison Point)   Rtg 1-1-1

CHARTS
AC 3683, *2482*, 1835, *1834*, *1185*; Imray Y18; Stanfords 5, 8; OS 178

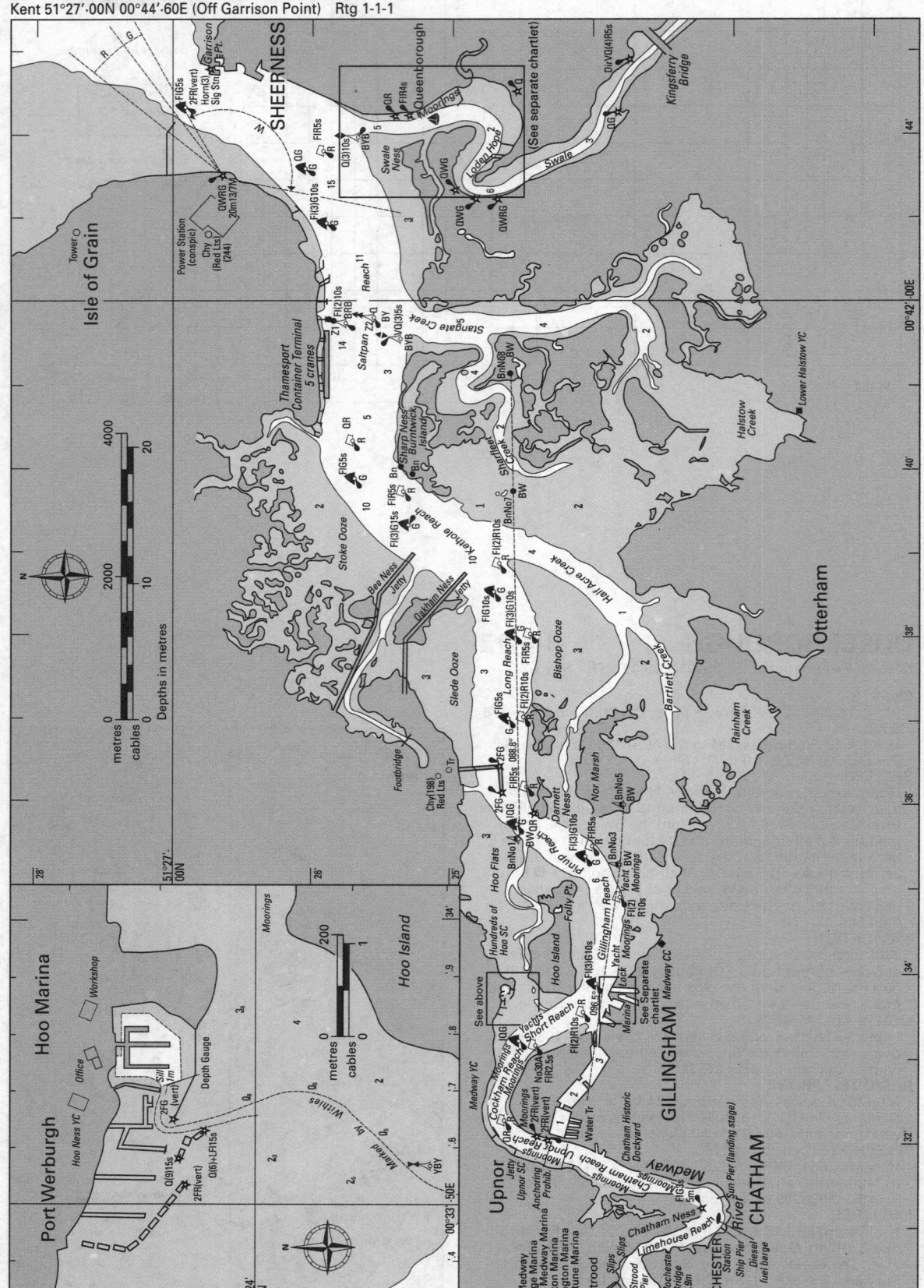

TIDES
+0130 Dover; ML 3·1; Duration 0610; Zone 0 (UT)

Standard Port SHEERNESS (→)

Times				Height (metres)			
High Water		Low Water		MHWS	MHWN	MLWN	MLWS
0200	0800	0200	0700	5·8	4·7	1·5	0·6
1400	2000	1400	1900				
Differences BEE NESS							
+0002	+0002	0000	+0005	+0·2	+0·1	0·0	0·0
BARTLETT CREEK							
+0016	+0008	No data		+0·1	0·0	No data	
DARNETT NESS							
+0004	+0004	0000	+0010	+0·2	+0·1	0·0	−0·1
CHATHAM (Lock Approaches)							
+0010	+0012	+0012	+0018	+0·3	+0·1	−0·1	−0·2
UPNOR							
+0015	+0015	+0015	+0025	+0·2	+0·2	−0·1	−0·1
ROCHESTER (STROOD PIER)							
+0018	+0018	+0018	+0028	+0·2	+0·2	−0·2	−0·3
WOULDHAM							
+0030	+0025	+0035	+0120	−0·2	−0·3	−1·0	−0·3
NEW HYTHE							
+0035	+0035	+0220	+0240	−1·6	−1·7	−1·2	−0·3
ALLINGTON LOCK							
+0050	+0035	No data		−2·1	−2·2	−1·3	−0·4

NOTE: Sheerness tidal predictions are given below.

SHELTER
There are 3 marinas downriver of Rochester Bridge and 4 above. Sheerness is solely a commercial hbr. See 8.4.12 for Queenborough and access to/from The Swale. Lower reaches of the Medway are exposed to strong NE winds, but Stangate and Half Acre Creeks are secure in all winds and give access to lesser creeks. There are good ⚓s in Sharfleet Creek; from about HW−4 it is possible to go via the "back-door" into Half Acre Creek. Speed limit is 6kn W of Folly Pt (Hoo Island).

NAVIGATION
WPT Medway SWM buoy, Mo(A) 6s, 51°28'·80N 00°52'·92E, 069°/249° from/to Garrison Pt, 5·5M. The wreck of the 'Richard Montgomery' is visible 2M NE of river ent. The estuary offers a huge area to explore, although much of it dries out to mud. Some minor creeks are buoyed. The river is well buoyed/marked up to Rochester and tidal up to Allington Lock (21·6M). The Leisure Sailing Guide and Medway Ports River Byelaws 1991 are obtainable from Port of Sheerness Ltd, Sheerness Docks, Kent ME12 1RX.

Bridge Clearances (MHWS):
Rochester	5·9m
Medway (M2)	29·6m
New Hythe (footbridge)	11·3m
Aylesford (pedestrian)	2·87m
Aylesford (Road)	3·26m
Maidstone Bypass (M20)	9·45m

LIGHTS AND MARKS
See 8.4.4 and chartlet for details of most lts. NB: not all buoys are shown due to small scale. Isle of Grain lt Q WRG 20m 13/7/8M R220°-234°, G234°-241°, W241°-013°. Power stn chy (242m) Oc and FR lts. Tfc Sigs: Powerful lt, Fl 7s, at Garrison Pt means large vessel under way: if shown up river = inbound; if to seaward = outbound.

RADIO TELEPHONE
Call: Medway Radio VHF Ch **74** 16 (H24). Monitor Ch 74 underway and Ch 16 at ⚓. Radar assistance is available on request Ch 22. Ch **80** M for marinas: Gillingham, Hoo (H24), Medway Bridge (0900-1700LT) and Port Medway (0800-2000LT). Link calls via Thames Radio Ch 02, 83.

TELEPHONE (Dial codes 01795 Sheerness; 01634 Medway)
Hr Mr (01795) 561234, 🕿 660072; MRSC (01255) 675518; ⌗ (01474) 537115 (H24); Marinecall 0891-500455; Police (01634) 811281, (01795) 661451; Dr via Medway Navigation Service (01795) 663025.

FACILITIES (all 01634 dial code, unless otherwise stated)
Marinas (from seaward up to Rochester Bridge)
Gillingham Marina (250+12 **V**s) 🕿 280022, 🕿 280164, £15.03 E basin (access via lock HW±4½), W basin HW±2, P, D, AC, FW, ME, El, Ⓔ, Sh, Gas, Gaz, CH, BH (20 ton), C (1 ton), Slip, V, Bar. Note: the effects of cross-tide, especially the ebb, off the lock ent are reduced by a timber baffle at 90° to the stream (close W of the lock). An angled pontoon deflects the stream and is also the fuel berth; the outboard end is lit by 2FR (vert).

Medway Pier Marine 🕿 851113, D, FW, Slip, C (6 ton), BY, Ⓔ;
Hoo Marina (220) £10, 🕿 250311, 🕿 251761, FW, Sh, ME, SM, AC, CH, El, Ⓔ, D (cans), C (20 ton), Gas, Gaz; access to W basin HW±1½; HW±3 to E basin (via sill 1m above CD); an unlit WCM buoy marks chan ent; waiting buoys in river.
Port Werburgh (W of Hoo marina; see chartlet inset).
Chatham Maritime. Under development, call 🕿 890331 for use of lock and possible AB in Basins 1 and 2. Basin 3 is for commercial vessels.
Marinas (between Rochester Bridge and Allington Lock)
Medway Bridge Marina (160+15 visitors) 🕿 843576, 🕿 843820, £11.75, Slip, D, P, FW, ME, El, Ⓔ, Sh, C (3 ton), BH (10 ton), Gas, Gaz, SM, AC, CH, V, R, Bar;
Port Medway Marina (50) 🕿 720033, 🕿 720315, FW, AC, BH (16 ton), C;
Cuxton Marina (150+some visitors) 🕿 721941, 🕿 290853, Slip, FW, ME, El, Ⓔ, Sh, BH (12 ton), AC, CH;
Elmhaven Marina (60) 🕿 240489, Slip, FW, ME, El, Sh, C, AC;
Allington Lock operates HW−3 to +2, 🕿 (01622) 752450.
Allington Marina (120) 🕿 (01622) 752057, above the lock; CH, ME, El, Sh, P, D, Slip, C (10 ton), FW, Gas, Gaz;
Notes: All moorings are administered by YCs or marinas. ACA (Sheerness). Fuel Barge at Ship Pier, Rochester, 🕿 813773. Landing (only) at Gillingham Pier, Gillingham Dock steps, Sun Pier (Chatham), Ship Pier, Town Quay (Rochester) and Strood Pier. Slips at Commodores Hard, and Gillingham.

Clubs
Sheppey YC (Sheerness) 🕿 663052; **Lower Halstow YC** 🕿 (01227) 458554; **Medway Cruising Club** (Gillingham) 🕿 856489, Bar, M, L, FW; **Hoo Ness YC** 🕿 250052, Bar, R, M, L, FW; **Hundred of Hoo SC** 🕿 250102; **Medway Motor Cruising Club** 🕿 827194; **Medway Motor YC** 🕿 389856; **Medway YC** (Upnor) 🕿 718399; **Upnor SC** 🕿 718043; **Royal Engineers YC** 🕿 844555; **RNSA** (Medway) 🕿 744565; **Rochester CC** 🕿 841350, Bar, R, M, FW, L, 🔲; **Strood YC** 🕿 718261, Bar, M, C (1·5 ton), FW, L, Slip.
Towns: EC Wed; all facilities R, V, 🔲, ✉, ⇌, ✈ (Gatwick).

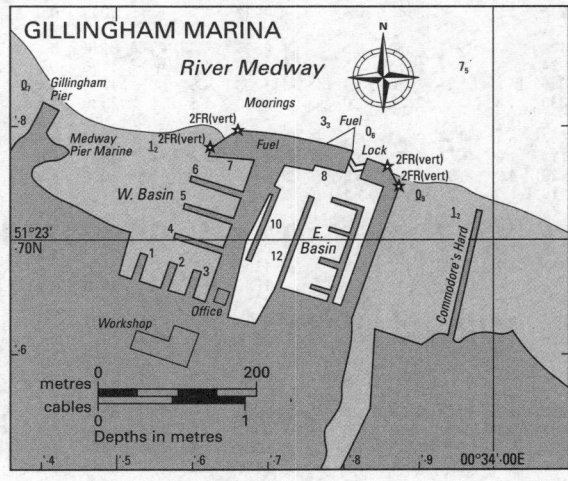

GILLINGHAM MARINA

ENGLAND – SHEERNESS

LAT 51°27′N   LONG 0°45′E

TIMES AND HEIGHTS OF HIGH AND LOW WATERS

YEAR **1999**

> **TIME ZONE (UT)**
> For Summer Time add ONE hour in non-shaded areas

JANUARY

Day	Time	m		Day	Time	m
1 F	0525 / 1137 / 1758	0.8 / 5.7 / 0.6		**16** SA	0531 / 1148 / 1752	1.0 / 5.3 / 0.9
2 SA O	0004 / 0622 / 1230 / 1847	5.7 / 0.6 / 5.8 / 0.5		**17** SU ●	0004 / 0612 / 1229 / 1831	5.6 / 0.9 / 5.5 / 0.8
3 SU	0052 / 0713 / 1319 / 1932	5.8 / 0.5 / 5.9 / 0.5		**18** M	0045 / 0653 / 1308 / 1910	5.7 / 0.7 / 5.6 / 0.7
4 M	0137 / 0801 / 1405 / 2015	5.8 / 0.4 / 5.9 / 0.6		**19** TU	0124 / 0734 / 1347 / 1949	5.7 / 0.6 / 5.7 / 0.7
5 TU	0221 / 0845 / 1449 / 2054	5.8 / 0.4 / 5.8 / 0.8		**20** W	0202 / 0816 / 1425 / 2028	5.7 / 0.5 / 5.7 / 0.7
6 W	0302 / 0925 / 1531 / 2130	5.7 / 0.6 / 5.6 / 1.0		**21** TH	0240 / 0858 / 1504 / 2106	5.7 / 0.4 / 5.7 / 0.7
7 TH	0343 / 1001 / 1613 / 2203	5.5 / 0.7 / 5.4 / 1.2		**22** F	0318 / 0937 / 1545 / 2142	5.6 / 0.5 / 5.6 / 0.8
8 F	0424 / 1034 / 1655 / 2236	5.3 / 0.9 / 5.2 / 1.3		**23** SA	0358 / 1016 / 1630 / 2220	5.5 / 0.5 / 5.4 / 1.0
9 SA	0507 / 1110 / 1739 / 2318	5.1 / 1.0 / 4.9 / 1.5		**24** SU	0443 / 1058 / 1719 / 2305	5.4 / 0.7 / 5.3 / 1.1
10 SU	0556 / 1159 / 1831	4.9 / 1.2 / 4.7		**25** M	0536 / 1150 / 1818	5.2 / 0.8 / 5.1
11 M	0014 / 0655 / 1306 / 1931	1.7 / 4.7 / 1.3 / 4.6		**26** TU	0004 / 0641 / 1258 / 1927	1.2 / 5.1 / 0.9 / 5.0
12 TU	0130 / 0804 / 1421 / 2038	1.7 / 4.6 / 1.3 / 4.7		**27** W	0120 / 0758 / 1419 / 2041	1.3 / 5.0 / 1.0 / 5.0
13 W	0249 / 0913 / 1527 / 2141	1.7 / 4.7 / 1.2 / 4.9		**28** TH	0245 / 0916 / 1538 / 2154	1.2 / 5.1 / 1.0 / 5.2
14 TH	0353 / 1014 / 1622 / 2235	1.5 / 4.9 / 1.1 / 5.1		**29** F	0407 / 1028 / 1647 / 2258	1.1 / 5.3 / 0.8 / 5.4
15 F	0445 / 1104 / 1710 / 2322	1.2 / 5.2 / 1.0 / 5.4		**30** SA	0518 / 1130 / 1746 / 2353	1.1 / 5.5 / 0.7 / 5.6
				31 SU O	0617 / 1223 / 1835	0.6 / 5.7 / 0.6

FEBRUARY

Day	Time	m		Day	Time	m
1 M	0041 / 0706 / 1310 / 1918	5.7 / 0.5 / 5.8 / 0.6		**16** TU ●	0025 / 0637 / 1250 / 1854	5.7 / 0.6 / 5.7 / 0.7
2 TU	0125 / 0749 / 1352 / 1958	5.8 / 0.4 / 5.8 / 0.6		**17** W	0106 / 0721 / 1329 / 1935	5.8 / 0.4 / 5.8 / 0.6
3 W	0205 / 0829 / 1431 / 2035	5.8 / 0.4 / 5.8 / 0.7		**18** TH	0145 / 0804 / 1408 / 2015	5.9 / 0.3 / 5.8 / 0.5
4 TH	0243 / 0905 / 1508 / 2107	5.7 / 0.4 / 5.7 / 0.8		**19** F	0223 / 0846 / 1448 / 2052	5.9 / 0.2 / 5.9 / 0.5
5 F	0318 / 0935 / 1542 / 2135	5.6 / 0.6 / 5.5 / 1.0		**20** SA	0301 / 0925 / 1527 / 2127	5.9 / 0.2 / 5.8 / 0.6
6 SA	0353 / 1001 / 1616 / 2159	5.4 / 0.7 / 5.3 / 1.1		**21** SU	0341 / 1002 / 1610 / 2202	5.8 / 0.4 / 5.6 / 0.7
7 SU	0427 / 1029 / 1652 / 2228	5.2 / 0.9 / 5.1 / 1.3		**22** M	0424 / 1040 / 1656 / 2243	5.6 / 0.5 / 5.4 / 0.9
8 M	0506 / 1106 / 1733 / 2310	5.0 / 1.0 / 4.8 / 1.5		**23** TU	0515 / 1126 / 1752 / 2338	5.4 / 0.8 / 5.1 / 1.1
9 TU	0553 / 1156 / 1825	4.7 / 1.3 / 4.6		**24** W	0620 / 1231 / 1900	5.1 / 1.0 / 4.9
10 W	0007 / 0656 / 1309 / 1931	1.7 / 4.5 / 1.5 / 4.5		**25** TH	0054 / 0739 / 1358 / 2019	1.2 / 4.9 / 1.2 / 4.9
11 TH	0133 / 0814 / 1437 / 2047	1.7 / 4.4 / 1.5 / 4.6		**26** F	0231 / 0905 / 1524 / 2138	1.3 / 5.0 / 1.2 / 5.0
12 F	0306 / 0931 / 1547 / 2156	1.6 / 4.6 / 1.3 / 4.9		**27** SA	0402 / 1022 / 1638 / 2246	1.1 / 5.2 / 1.0 / 5.3
13 SA	0412 / 1034 / 1643 / 2253	1.3 / 4.9 / 1.1 / 5.2		**28** SU	0515 / 1123 / 1736 / 2342	0.8 / 5.5 / 0.8 / 5.5
14 SU	0506 / 1124 / 1730 / 2341	1.0 / 5.3 / 0.9 / 5.5				
15 M	0553 / 1208 / 1813	0.8 / 5.5 / 0.8				

MARCH

Day	Time	m		Day	Time	m
1 M	0609 / 1213 / 1822	0.6 / 5.7 / 0.7		**16** TU	0529 / 1142 / 1751	0.7 / 5.6 / 0.8
2 TU O	0027 / 0653 / 1256 / 1901	5.7 / 0.5 / 5.8 / 0.7		**17** W ●	0000 / 0616 / 1226 / 1834	5.7 / 0.5 / 5.8 / 0.6
3 W	0108 / 0731 / 1333 / 1938	5.7 / 0.4 / 5.8 / 0.6		**18** TH	0042 / 0702 / 1307 / 1916	5.9 / 0.3 / 5.8 / 0.5
4 TH	0145 / 0805 / 1408 / 2011	5.8 / 0.4 / 5.8 / 0.6		**19** F	0123 / 0746 / 1347 / 1957	6.0 / 0.1 / 5.8 / 0.4
5 F	0219 / 0837 / 1440 / 2042	5.8 / 0.4 / 5.7 / 0.7		**20** SA	0202 / 0828 / 1427 / 2036	6.0 / 0.1 / 6.0 / 0.4
6 SA	0251 / 0905 / 1510 / 2106	5.7 / 0.5 / 5.6 / 0.8		**21** SU	0242 / 0907 / 1507 / 2112	6.1 / 0.1 / 5.9 / 0.5
7 SU	0322 / 0930 / 1540 / 2128	5.5 / 0.6 / 5.4 / 1.0		**22** M	0323 / 0944 / 1549 / 2148	5.9 / 0.3 / 5.7 / 0.6
8 M	0353 / 0955 / 1611 / 2153	5.3 / 0.8 / 5.2 / 1.1		**23** TU	0408 / 1022 / 1636 / 2229	5.7 / 0.6 / 5.5 / 0.8
9 TU	0426 / 1026 / 1647 / 2226	5.1 / 1.0 / 5.0 / 1.2		**24** W	0501 / 1109 / 1730 / 2323	5.4 / 0.9 / 5.2 / 1.0
10 W	0507 / 1108 / 1732 / 2313	4.8 / 1.3 / 4.8 / 1.4		**25** TH	0606 / 1213 / 1839	5.1 / 1.2 / 4.9
11 TH	0600 / 1206 / 1833	4.5 / 1.5 / 4.5		**26** F	0041 / 0726 / 1340 / 1959	1.4 / 4.9 / 1.4 / 4.8
12 F	0022 / 0715 / 1338 / 1953	1.6 / 4.4 / 1.7 / 4.5		**27** SA	0223 / 0853 / 1509 / 2121	1.2 / 5.0 / 1.3 / 5.0
13 SA	0208 / 0844 / 1508 / 2115	1.6 / 4.5 / 1.5 / 4.7		**28** SU	0354 / 1009 / 1623 / 2230	1.0 / 5.3 / 1.1 / 5.2
14 SU	0333 / 0958 / 1612 / 2221	1.3 / 4.8 / 1.2 / 5.1		**29** M	0502 / 1108 / 1719 / 2323	0.7 / 5.6 / 0.9 / 5.5
15 M	0435 / 1054 / 1704 / 2313	1.0 / 5.2 / 1.0 / 5.4		**30** TU	0552 / 1155 / 1802	0.5 / 5.7 / 0.8
				31 W O	0007 / 0630 / 1235 / 1838	5.6 / 0.5 / 5.7 / 0.7

APRIL

Day	Time	m		Day	Time	m
1 TH	0046 / 0704 / 1309 / 1912	5.7 / 0.5 / 5.8 / 0.6		**16** F ●	0015 / 0638 / 1242 / 1853	5.9 / 0.2 / 6.0 / 0.5
2 F	0120 / 0735 / 1340 / 1944	5.7 / 0.4 / 5.8 / 0.6		**17** SA	0058 / 0724 / 1324 / 1937	6.0 / 0.1 / 6.1 / 0.4
3 SA	0153 / 0805 / 1410 / 2014	5.7 / 0.4 / 5.7 / 0.7		**18** SU	0141 / 0807 / 1406 / 2019	6.1 / 0.1 / 6.1 / 0.4
4 SU	0224 / 0834 / 1438 / 2040	5.7 / 0.5 / 5.7 / 0.8		**19** M	0223 / 0848 / 1448 / 2059	6.1 / 0.2 / 6.0 / 0.4
5 M	0254 / 0901 / 1507 / 2103	5.6 / 0.6 / 5.5 / 0.9		**20** TU	0308 / 0927 / 1531 / 2139	6.0 / 0.4 / 5.8 / 0.5
6 TU	0324 / 0927 / 1538 / 2127	5.4 / 0.8 / 5.4 / 1.0		**21** W	0356 / 1008 / 1619 / 2223	5.8 / 0.7 / 5.5 / 0.7
7 W	0357 / 0957 / 1613 / 2158	5.2 / 1.0 / 5.2 / 1.1		**22** TH	0450 / 1055 / 1713 / 2318	5.5 / 1.0 / 5.2 / 0.9
8 TH	0434 / 1033 / 1654 / 2241	4.9 / 1.3 / 4.9 / 1.2		**23** F	0555 / 1158 / 1820	5.2 / 1.3 / 5.0
9 F	0523 / 1124 / 1749 / 2342	4.7 / 1.5 / 4.7 / 1.4		**24** SA	0034 / 0710 / 1320 / 1937	1.0 / 5.0 / 1.4 / 4.9
10 SA	0630 / 1242 / 1905	4.5 / 1.7 / 4.5		**25** SU	0208 / 0830 / 1443 / 2055	1.0 / 5.1 / 1.4 / 5.0
11 SU	0113 / 0755 / 1420 / 2031	1.5 / 4.6 / 1.6 / 4.7		**26** M	0330 / 0944 / 1555 / 2203	0.9 / 5.3 / 1.2 / 5.2
12 M	0249 / 0916 / 1532 / 2143	1.2 / 4.9 / 1.3 / 5.0		**27** TU	0434 / 1042 / 1651 / 2257	0.7 / 5.5 / 1.0 / 5.4
13 TU	0358 / 1019 / 1630 / 2240	0.9 / 5.3 / 1.0 / 5.4		**28** W	0522 / 1128 / 1734 / 2341	0.6 / 5.6 / 0.9 / 5.5
14 W	0457 / 1112 / 1721 / 2330	0.6 / 5.6 / 0.8 / 5.7		**29** TH	0559 / 1207 / 1810	0.6 / 5.7 / 0.8
15 TH	0550 / 1158 / 1809	0.4 / 5.9 / 0.6		**30** F O	0019 / 0631 / 1241 / 1843	5.6 / 0.5 / 5.7 / 0.7

Chart Datum: 2·90 metres below Ordnance Datum (Newlyn)

ENGLAND – SHEERNESS

LAT 51°27′N   LONG   0°45′E

TIMES AND HEIGHTS OF HIGH AND LOW WATERS

YEAR **1999**

4

TIME ZONE (UT)
For Summer Time add ONE hour in non-shaded areas

MAY

Day	Time	m	Time	m	Time	m	Time	m
1 SA	0054	5.7	0702	0.5	1311	5.7	1916	0.7
2 SU	0126	5.7	0733	0.5	1340	5.7	1946	0.7
3 M	0158	5.6	0804	0.6	1410	5.7	2015	0.7
4 TU	0229	5.5	0834	0.7	1441	5.6	2043	0.8
5 W	0301	5.4	0904	0.8	1513	5.4	2112	0.9
6 TH	0335	5.2	0935	1.0	1548	5.2	2144	1.0
7 F	0413	5.1	1011	1.2	1629	5.0	2225	1.1
8 SA	0500	4.9	1057	1.4	1720	4.8	2322	1.2
9 SU	0600	4.7	1204	1.6	1828	4.7		
10 M	0038	1.2	0715	4.8	1330	1.5	1947	4.8
11 TU	0206	1.1	0833	5.0	1446	1.3	2101	5.1
12 W	0319	0.8	0941	5.4	1549	1.1	2204	5.4
13 TH	0422	0.6	1039	5.6	1646	0.8	2258	5.7
14 F	0520	0.4	1130	5.9	1740	0.7	2348	5.9
15 SA ●	0613	0.3	1217	6.0	1830	0.5		
16 SU	0035	6.0	0701	0.2	1302	6.1	1918	0.4
17 M	0122	6.1	0746	0.2	1347	6.0	2004	0.3
18 TU	0208	6.1	0830	0.3	1431	5.9	2049	0.3
19 W	0256	6.0	0913	0.5	1517	5.8	2134	0.4
20 TH	0346	5.8	0956	0.7	1605	5.6	2220	0.6
21 F	0440	5.5	1042	1.0	1658	5.3	2313	0.8
22 SA	0539	5.2	1139	1.3	1759	5.1		
23 SU	0020	0.9	0645	5.1	1249	1.4	1907	4.9
24 M	0137	1.0	0756	5.1	1404	1.4	2020	5.0
25 TU	0249	0.9	0906	5.1	1513	1.3	2127	5.1
26 W	0351	0.8	1006	5.3	1611	1.2	2224	5.3
27 TH	0440	0.8	1055	5.5	1658	1.0	2311	5.4
28 F	0521	0.8	1135	5.5	1738	0.9	2351	5.5
29 SA	0556	0.7	1210	5.6	1814	0.8		
30 SU O	0027	5.5	0630	0.7	1243	5.6	1848	0.7
31 M	0102	5.6	0704	0.6	1315	5.7	1921	0.7

JUNE

Day	Time	m	Time	m	Time	m	Time	m
1 TU	0136	5.6	0738	0.7	1347	5.7	1954	0.7
2 W	0209	5.5	0812	0.7	1421	5.6	2028	0.7
3 TH	0243	5.4	0846	0.8	1455	5.5	2102	0.8
4 F	0319	5.3	0920	1.0	1531	5.3	2138	0.8
5 SA	0358	5.2	0957	1.1	1612	5.2	2219	0.9
6 SU	0444	5.1	1040	1.3	1700	5.0	2310	1.0
7 M	0538	5.0	1135	1.4	1759	4.9		
8 TU	0013	1.0	0642	5.0	1246	1.4	1908	4.9
9 W	0128	0.9	0754	5.1	1400	1.3	2021	5.1
10 TH	0241	0.8	0904	5.3	1509	1.1	2128	5.3
11 F	0349	0.6	1007	5.5	1613	0.9	2229	5.6
12 SA	0452	0.5	1103	5.7	1713	0.7	2324	5.8
13 SU ●	0549	0.4	1155	5.9	1810	0.6		
14 M	0017	5.9	0641	0.3	1244	5.9	1903	0.4
15 TU	0108	6.0	0729	0.3	1331	6.0	1953	0.3
16 W	0157	6.0	0815	0.4	1417	5.9	2042	0.3
17 TH	0246	5.9	0900	0.6	1504	5.8	2129	0.4
18 F	0335	5.8	0943	0.7	1550	5.6	2214	0.5
19 SA	0424	5.6	1026	1.0	1639	5.4	2300	0.7
20 SU	0515	5.3	1112	1.2	1731	5.2	2351	0.8
21 M	0610	5.1	1206	1.4	1830	5.0		
22 TU	0050	1.0	0710	5.0	1312	1.5	1934	4.9
23 W	0155	1.0	0815	4.9	1420	1.5	2041	4.9
24 TH	0258	1.0	0919	5.0	1523	1.4	2144	5.0
25 F	0353	1.0	1013	5.1	1618	1.2	2237	5.2
26 SA	0441	0.9	1059	5.3	1705	1.1	2322	5.3
27 SU	0524	0.8	1139	5.4	1747	0.9		
28 M O	0003	5.4	0603	0.8	1217	5.6	1824	0.8
29 TU	0041	5.5	0640	0.7	1253	5.6	1901	0.7
30 W	0117	5.7	0717	0.7	1329	5.7	1938	0.7

JULY

Day	Time	m	Time	m	Time	m	Time	m
1 TH	0153	5.5	0754	0.7	1405	5.6	2016	0.6
2 F	0229	5.5	0831	0.8	1442	5.6	2055	0.6
3 SA	0306	5.5	0908	0.9	1518	5.5	2134	0.7
4 SU	0345	5.4	0945	1.0	1557	5.3	2214	0.7
5 M	0428	5.3	1024	1.1	1641	5.2	2257	0.8
6 TU	0516	5.2	1109	1.2	1732	5.1	2349	0.8
7 W	0614	5.1	1207	1.3	1834	5.1		
8 TH	0052	0.9	0720	5.1	1317	1.3	1945	5.1
9 F	0207	0.8	0831	5.2	1433	1.2	2058	5.2
10 SA	0321	0.7	0939	5.4	1546	1.0	2206	5.4
11 SU	0429	0.6	1042	5.6	1655	0.8	2309	5.6
12 M	0531	0.6	1139	5.7	1758	0.6		
13 TU ●	0006	5.8	0626	0.5	1231	5.8	1854	0.4
14 W	0059	5.9	0715	0.5	1319	5.9	1946	0.3
15 TH	0148	6.0	0802	0.7	1405	5.9	2033	0.3
16 F	0234	5.9	0845	0.6	1449	5.8	2117	0.3
17 SA	0318	5.8	0925	0.8	1532	5.7	2158	0.4
18 SU	0401	5.6	1003	1.0	1614	5.5	2235	0.6
19 M	0444	5.4	1038	1.2	1657	5.3	2311	0.8
20 TU	0528	5.1	1116	1.4	1744	5.1	2354	1.0
21 W	0617	4.9	1205	1.5	1839	4.8		
22 TH	0050	1.2	0713	4.8	1312	1.6	1944	4.7
23 F	0159	1.3	0818	4.7	1429	1.6	2055	4.7
24 SA	0306	1.2	0923	4.9	1537	1.4	2200	4.9
25 SU	0405	1.1	1021	5.1	1634	1.2	2254	5.1
26 M	0456	0.9	1110	5.3	1722	1.0	2339	5.3
27 TU	0540	0.9	1153	5.5	1804	0.9		
28 W O	0020	5.4	0620	0.8	1234	5.6	1843	0.7
29 TH	0059	5.6	0659	0.8	1312	5.7	1923	0.6
30 F	0136	5.7	0737	0.7	1350	5.7	2004	0.5
31 SA	0213	5.7	0816	0.7	1427	5.7	2045	0.5

AUGUST

Day	Time	m	Time	m	Time	m	Time	m
1 SU	0250	5.7	0854	0.8	1503	5.7	2125	0.5
2 M	0328	5.6	0930	0.9	1540	5.6	2202	0.5
3 TU	0409	5.5	1005	1.0	1621	5.4	2240	0.7
4 W	0454	5.4	1044	1.1	1707	5.3	2324	0.8
5 TH	0546	5.2	1134	1.2	1805	5.2		
6 F	0022	0.9	0649	5.1	1241	1.3	1917	5.1
7 SA	0139	1.0	0802	5.1	1406	1.3	2037	5.1
8 SU	0301	1.0	0917	5.2	1531	1.1	2154	5.3
9 M	0416	0.9	1027	5.4	1648	0.8	2302	5.5
10 TU	0520	0.7	1128	5.6	1753	0.7	2356	5.5
11 W ●	0615	0.7	1220	5.8	1847	0.5		
12 TH	0051	5.9	0709	0.6	1307	5.9	1935	0.3
13 F	0135	5.9	0746	0.6	1349	5.9	2017	0.3
14 SA	0217	5.9	0825	0.7	1429	5.9	2056	0.3
15 SU	0256	5.8	0902	0.8	1507	5.8	2131	0.5
16 M	0332	5.6	0933	1.0	1544	5.6	2201	0.5
17 TU	0408	5.4	1000	1.2	1619	5.4	2228	0.8
18 W	0443	5.2	1026	1.3	1657	5.1	2300	1.0
19 TH	0522	5.0	1102	1.5	1743	4.9	2345	1.3
20 F	0611	4.8	1155	1.7	1842	4.6		
21 SA	0051	1.5	0713	4.6	1316	1.8	1958	4.5
22 SU	0218	1.6	0828	4.6	1451	1.7	2118	4.6
23 M	0331	1.4	0940	4.9	1601	1.4	2222	4.9
24 TU	0429	1.2	1039	5.2	1655	1.1	2313	5.3
25 W	0517	1.0	1127	5.5	1741	0.9	2356	5.5
26 TH O	0600	0.9	1210	5.7	1824	0.7		
27 F	0036	5.7	0639	0.8	1251	5.8	1905	0.5
28 SA	0114	5.8	0718	0.7	1329	5.9	1947	0.4
29 SU	0152	5.9	0758	0.7	1406	5.9	2028	0.4
30 M	0230	5.9	0835	0.7	1443	5.9	2107	0.4
31 TU	0307	5.8	0911	0.8	1520	5.8	2144	0.5

Chart Datum: 2·90 metres below Ordnance Datum (Newlyn)

TIME ZONE (UT)
For Summer Time add ONE hour in non-shaded areas

ENGLAND – SHEERNESS

LAT 51°27′N   LONG 0°45′E

TIMES AND HEIGHTS OF HIGH AND LOW WATERS   YEAR 1999

SEPTEMBER

Day	Time	m	Time	m		Day	Time	m	Time	m
1 W	0347	5.7	0944	0.9		**16** TH	0401	5.3	0945	1.2
	1600	5.6	2219	0.6			1617	5.2	2216	1.1
2 TH	0430	5.5	1021	1.0		**17** F	0435	5.1	1015	1.4
	1647	5.4	2301	0.9			1656	4.9	2255	1.4
3 F	0521	5.3	1109	1.2		**18** SA	0518	4.9	1100	1.6
	1744	5.2	2358	1.1			1747	4.6	2350	1.6
4 SA	0624	5.0	1217	1.3		**19** SU	0615	4.6	1205	1.8
	1900	5.0					1858	4.4		
5 SU	0119	1.3	0740	4.9		**20** M	0117	1.8	0732	4.5
	1352	1.4	2025	5.0			1351	1.8	2027	4.5
6 M	0249	1.3	0902	5.0		**21** TU	0251	1.7	0856	4.7
	1527	1.2	2148	5.2			1521	1.5	2143	4.8
7 TU	0407	1.1	1016	5.3		**22** W	0356	1.4	1003	5.1
	1646	0.9	2257	5.5			1621	1.1	2239	5.2
8 W	0511	0.9	1117	5.6		**23** TH	0448	1.1	1056	5.6
	1747	0.6	2351	5.8			1712	0.9	2326	5.6
9 TH	0603	0.8	1206	5.7		**24** F	0533	1.0	1142	5.7
●	1835	0.5					1758	0.6		
10 F	0036	5.9	0645	0.8		**25** SA	0008	5.8	0614	0.8
	1250	5.9	1916	0.4		O	1224	5.9	1841	0.5
11 SA	0117	5.9	0724	0.7		**26** SU	0048	5.8	0655	0.7
	1328	5.9	1952	0.4			1303	6.0	1924	0.4
12 SU	0153	5.9	0759	0.7		**27** M	0127	6.0	0735	0.7
	1405	5.9	2026	0.4			1342	6.0	2006	0.3
13 M	0227	5.8	0832	0.8		**28** TU	0206	6.0	0814	0.7
	1439	5.8	2057	0.5			1420	6.0	2045	0.3
14 TU	0259	5.7	0901	1.0		**29** W	0245	6.0	0850	0.7
	1511	5.6	2124	0.7			1500	5.9	2122	0.5
15 W	0330	5.5	0923	1.1		**30** TH	0325	5.8	0926	0.8
	1543	5.4	2148	0.9			1543	5.8	2200	0.7

OCTOBER

Day	Time	m	Time	m		Day	Time	m	Time	m
1 F	0409	5.6	1005	0.9		**16** SA	0358	5.2	0943	1.3
	1632	5.5	2243	1.0			1621	5.0	2217	1.4
2 SA	0500	5.3	1055	1.1		**17** SU	0438	5.0	1024	1.4
	1732	5.2	2341	1.3			1707	4.8	2305	1.7
3 SU	0605	5.0	1206	1.3		**18** M	0530	4.7	1122	1.6
	1849	5.0					1809	4.6		
4 M	0104	1.5	0723	4.9		**19** TU	0017	1.9	0640	4.6
	1347	1.3	2015	5.0			1248	1.7	1931	4.5
5 TU	0235	1.4	0846	5.0		**20** W	0155	1.8	0806	4.7
	1521	1.1	2137	5.3			1429	1.5	2054	4.8
6 W	0353	1.2	1000	5.3		**21** TH	0311	1.6	0921	5.0
	1635	0.8	2242	5.6			1539	1.1	2158	5.2
7 TH	0455	1.0	1059	5.6		**22** F	0408	1.3	1019	5.4
	1731	0.6	2333	5.8			1635	0.8	2250	5.6
8 F	0543	0.9	1147	5.7		**23** SA	0458	1.0	1108	5.7
	1813	0.6					1726	0.6	2337	5.9
9 SA	0016	5.9	0621	0.9		**24** SU	0544	0.9	1153	5.9
	1227	5.8	1849	0.6 ●		O	1813	0.5		
10 SU	0053	5.8	0656	0.8		**25** M	0020	6.0	0627	0.7
	1304	5.9	1921	0.6			1236	6.1	1858	0.4
11 M	0125	5.8	0729	0.8		**26** TU	0102	6.1	0710	0.7
	1337	5.9	1952	0.6			1317	6.1	1941	0.4
12 TU	0156	5.8	0800	0.8		**27** W	0142	6.1	0752	0.6
	1410	5.8	2021	0.6			1359	6.1	2023	0.4
13 W	0226	5.7	0828	0.9		**28** TH	0223	6.0	0833	0.6
	1441	5.7	2048	0.8			1442	6.0	2103	0.5
14 TH	0255	5.6	0851	1.0		**29** F	0306	5.8	0914	0.7
	1512	5.5	2114	0.9			1529	5.8	2143	0.8
15 F	0325	5.4	0914	1.1		**30** SA	0352	5.6	0957	0.8
	1544	5.3	2142	1.2			1621	5.6	2229	1.1
						31 SU	0445	5.3	1050	1.0
							1723	5.3	2327	1.4

NOVEMBER

Day	Time	m	Time	m		Day	Time	m	Time	m
1 M	0549	5.1	1202	1.2		**16** TU	0457	4.9	1057	1.4
	1836	5.1					1735	4.8	2333	1.7
2 TU	0045	1.6	0704	4.9		**17** W	0559	4.7	1207	1.4
	1335	1.2	1956	5.1			1845	4.7		
3 W	0211	1.5	0823	5.0		**18** TH	0052	1.8	0715	4.7
	1500	1.0	2113	5.3			1334	1.3	2002	4.8
4 TH	0326	1.4	0935	5.3		**19** F	0215	1.6	0832	5.0
	1609	0.8	2216	5.5			1451	1.1	2112	5.2
5 F	0427	1.2	1033	5.5		**20** SA	0321	1.3	0937	5.3
	1702	0.7	2307	5.7			1555	0.8	2212	5.5
6 SA	0514	1.1	1121	5.6		**21** SU	0418	1.1	1032	5.6
	1742	0.7	2349	5.7			1652	0.6	2304	5.8
7 SU	0552	1.0	1201	5.7		**22** M	0510	0.9	1122	5.9
	1816	0.7					1744	0.5	2352	6.0
8 M	0024	5.7	0626	0.9		**23** TU	0600	0.8	1210	6.0
●	1237	5.7	1846	0.7		O	1833	0.4		
9 TU	0056	5.7	0658	0.8		**24** W	0037	6.0	0648	0.6
	1311	5.8	1917	0.7			1256	6.1	1919	0.4
10 W	0126	5.8	0730	0.8		**25** TH	0122	6.0	0735	0.5
	1343	5.7	1948	0.7			1342	6.1	2004	0.4
11 TH	0156	5.7	0759	0.9		**26** F	0206	5.8	0822	0.5
	1415	5.6	2018	0.8			1430	6.0	2047	0.6
12 F	0226	5.6	0826	1.0		**27** SA	0251	5.8	0908	0.6
	1447	5.5	2047	1.0			1520	5.9	2131	0.8
13 SA	0258	5.5	0854	1.0		**28** SU	0339	5.6	0955	0.7
	1520	5.3	2117	1.1			1612	5.6	2217	1.1
14 SU	0331	5.3	0926	1.1		**29** M	0431	5.4	1048	0.8
	1557	5.1	2151	1.3			1710	5.4	2310	1.3
15 M	0410	5.1	1005	1.2		**30** TU	0530	5.2	1151	1.0
	1640	4.9	2234	1.5			1814	5.2		

DECEMBER

Day	Time	m	Time	m		Day	Time	m	Time	m
1 W	0016	1.5	0637	5.0		**16** TH	0525	4.9	1136	1.2
	1306	1.1	1924	5.1			1807	4.9		
2 TH	0131	1.6	0748	5.0		**17** F	0000	1.6	0629	4.9
	1420	1.0	2035	5.1			1245	1.1	1915	4.9
3 F	0242	1.5	0859	5.1		**18** SA	0114	1.5	0742	5.0
	1527	1.0	2140	5.2			1402	1.0	2028	5.1
4 SA	0346	1.4	1000	5.3		**19** SU	0229	1.4	0854	5.2
	1621	0.9	2233	5.4			1514	0.9	2134	5.3
5 SU	0438	1.2	1051	5.4		**20** M	0337	1.2	0958	5.4
	1704	0.9	2317	5.5			1619	0.7	2233	5.6
6 M	0520	1.1	1134	5.5		**21** TU	0439	1.0	1056	5.7
	1740	0.8	2355	5.5			1718	0.5	2327	5.7
7 TU	0557	1.0	1212	5.6		**22** W	0538	0.8	1149	5.8
●	1814	0.8				O	1812	0.5		
8 W	0028	5.6	0631	0.9		**23** TH	0018	5.9	0633	0.6
	1248	5.6	1847	0.7			1241	6.0	1902	0.4
9 TH	0101	5.7	0705	0.8		**24** F	0106	5.9	0725	0.5
	1322	5.6	1921	0.7			1331	6.0	1949	0.5
10 F	0133	5.7	0737	0.8		**25** SA	0153	5.9	0816	0.4
	1355	5.6	1954	0.8			1421	6.0	2035	0.6
11 SA	0205	5.6	0809	0.8		**26** SU	0240	5.8	0904	0.4
	1428	5.5	2026	0.9			1510	5.9	2119	0.8
12 SU	0239	5.5	0842	0.9		**27** M	0327	5.7	0951	0.5
	1503	5.4	2059	1.0			1559	5.7	2202	1.0
13 M	0313	5.4	0917	0.9		**28** TU	0415	5.5	1038	0.6
	1540	5.2	2134	1.2			1650	5.5	2247	1.2
14 TU	0351	5.2	0956	1.0		**29** W	0506	5.3	1126	0.8
	1621	5.1	2212	1.3			1743	5.2	2336	1.4
15 W	0434	5.1	1041	1.1		**30** TH	0601	5.1	1221	1.0
	1709	5.0	2259	1.5			1841	5.0		
						31 F	0036	1.5	0704	5.0
							1325	1.1	1945	4.9

Chart Datum: 2·90 metres below Ordnance Datum (Newlyn)

RIVER THAMES   8-4-14

London: from Canvey Island to Teddington lock
Ratings: 1-2 (marinas), 5 (tideway)-1 (London), 2 (tideway)-1

SEQUENCE

Information is arranged as far as possible from seaward, starting abeam Canvey Island and continuing up-river to the head of the tidal Thames at Teddington. See 8.4.15 for Southend-on-Sea and Leigh-on-Sea.

CHARTS

AC 3319, *2484*, 3337, 2151, 1186, *1185*; Imray C2, C1; Stanfords 5; OS 176, 177, 178.
Books include: *Nicholsons Guide to the Thames*; *River Thames Book* (Imray). The Port of London Authority (PLA), Devon House, 58-60 St Katharine's Way, London E1 9LB; ☎ (0171) 265 2656, 📠 0171 265 2699, issues free: *Yachtsman's Guide*; *Pleasure Users Guide*; *Leisure Guide*. *Port of London River Byelaws* & *Tide Tables* are for sale.

4

CANVEY ISLAND TO CRAYFORDNESS

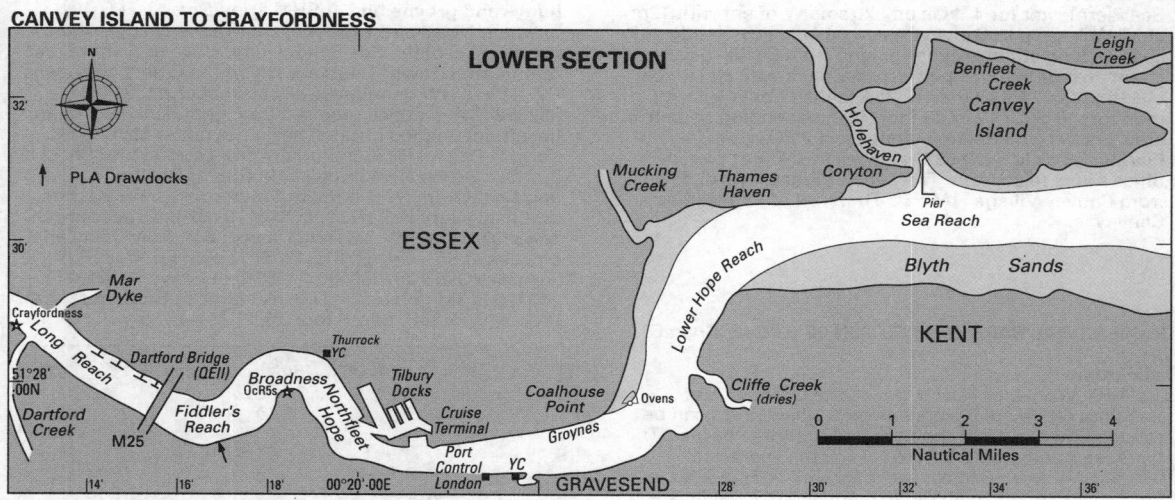

CRAYFORDNESS TO TOWER BRIDGE

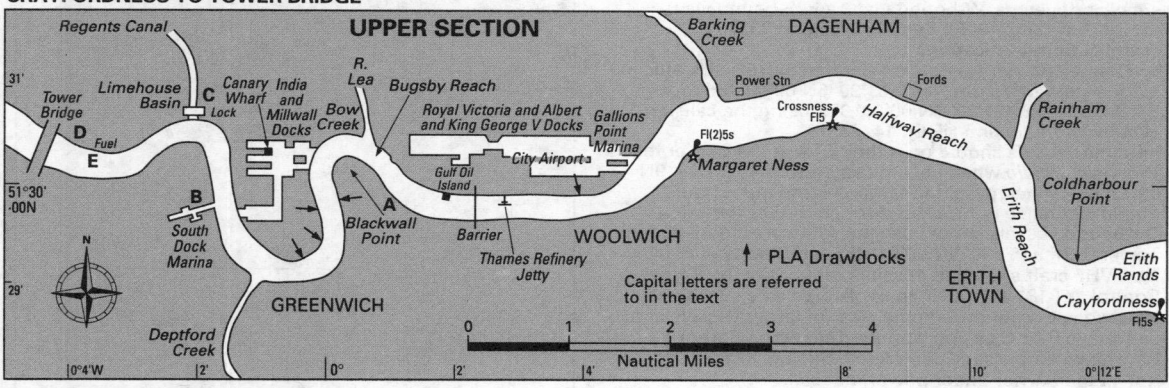

TOWER BRIDGE TO TEDDINGTON

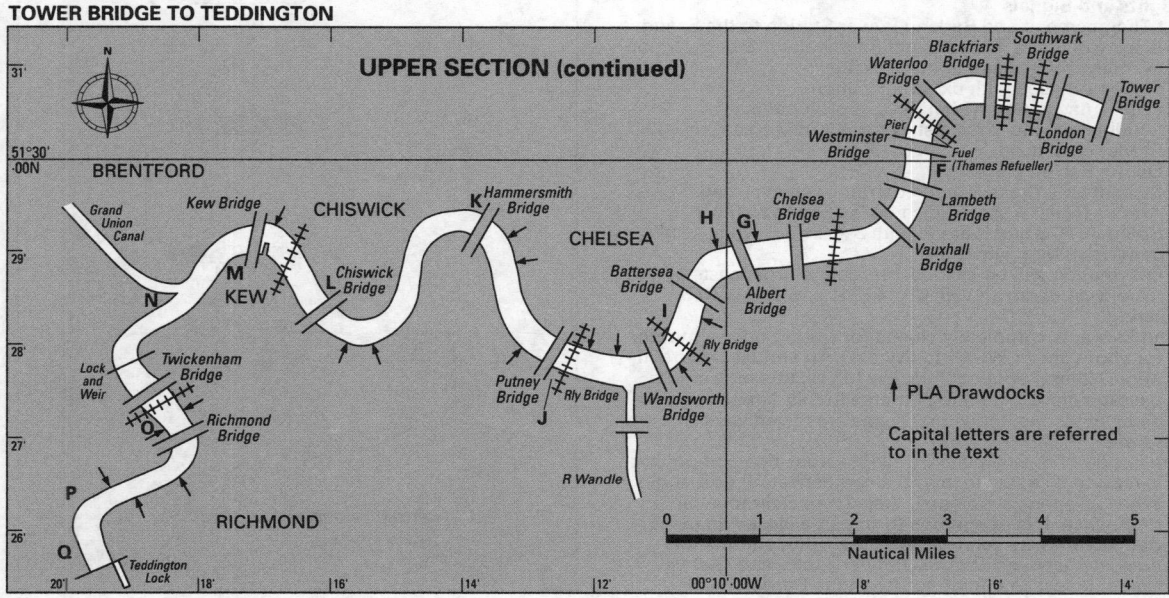

RIVER THAMES *continued*

HARBOURS IN LOWER REACHES OF RIVER THAMES

HOLEHAVEN, Essex, 51°30′·55N 00°33′·50E. AC 2484, 1186. HW +0140 on Dover; use differences for CORYTON, see 8·4·15; ML 3·0m; Duration 068. Shelter is good, but beware swell from passing traffic. Note: There is an 8kn speed limit in the river off Coryton and Shellhaven; keep at least 60m clear of berthed tankers and refinery jetties. See Piermaster for 4 Y ⚓s on extreme W of ent with 12m at MLWS. Keep to Canvey Is side on ent. ⚓ on W edge of chan as long stone groynes extend from E side. 0·5M N of ent an overhead oil pipe crosses chan with clearance of 11m, plus 2 FY lts (horiz). PLA launch *Canvey Patrol* monitors VHF Ch 12 or 68 (not H24), depending on patrol area. Lts Coryton Refinery Jetty No 4 2 FG (vert).
Piermaster ☎ (01268) 683041; Facilities: FW at pier in office hours (also from 'The Lobster Smack' yard); P & D from Canvey Village (1M); EC Thurs; all other facilities on Canvey Is.

THAMES TIDAL BARRIER 51°29′·88N 00°02′·31E (Span G)

Description
Located at Woolwich Reach, it protects London from flooding. There are 9 piers between which gates can be rotated upwards from the river bed to form a barrier. The piers are numbered 1-9 from N to S; the spans are lettered A-K from S to N (see diagram). A, H, J & K are not navigable. C-F, with depth 5·8m and 61m wide, are for larger vessels. Spans B and G, with 1·25m, are for small craft/yachts, W-bound via G and E-bound via B (51°29′·70N 00°02′·33E). See AC 2484 and 3337.

Control & Communications
The Thames Barrier Navigation Centre controls all traffic in a Zone from Margaret Ness (51°30′·5N 00°05′·6E) to Blackwall Point (51°30′·3N 00°00′·3E), using the callsign *Woolwich Radio* on VHF Ch **14**, 22, 16.
Inbound vessels should pass their ETA at the Barrier to *Woolwich Radio* when abeam Crayford Ness (51°28′·9N 00°12′·8E). When passing Margaret Ness they should obtain clearance to proceed through the Barrier.
Outbound vessels should use the same procedure abeam Tower Bridge (51°30′·3N 00°04′·4E) and Blackwall Point.
Non-VHF craft should, if possible, pre-notify the Barrier Control ☎ 0181-855 0315; then observe all visual signals, proceed with caution keeping clear of larger vessels and use spans B or G as appropriate. Telephone Barrier Control when passage completed. Sailing vessels should transit the Barrier under power, not sail.

Lights and Signals
At Thamesmead and Barking Power Station to the E, and Blackwall Stairs (N bank) and Blackwall Pt (S bank) to the W, noticeboards and lights indicate:
Fl Ⓨ = proceed with extreme caution.
Fl Ⓡ = navigation within Zone is prohibited.
Loudhailers may pass instructions and Morse K (—·—) = Barrier closed.
On the Barrier piers:
St Andrew's Cross (R lts) = barrier or span closed.
Arrows (G lts) = span indicated is open to traffic.
Spans A, H, J and K are lit with 3 Ⓡ in ▽ = No passage.

Spans open for navigation
Information will be included in routine broadcasts by *Woolwich Radio* on VHF Ch 14 at H + 15 and H + 45.

Testing
The Barrier is completely closed for testing once a month, for about 3hrs, LW –1½ to LW +1½. An annual closure in Sept/Oct lasts about 10 hrs, LW to LW; this may affect passage plans. The Supplements to this Almanac give dates of testing. Individual spans are tested weekly.

Beware
On N side of river (Spans E and F) a cross-tide component is reported; expect to lay-off a compensating drift angle. When all spans are closed, keep 200m clear to avoid turbulence. **It is dangerous to transit a closed span, as the gate may be semi-raised.** Small craft should not navigate between Thames Refinery Jetty and Gulf Oil Island, unless intending to transit the Barrier.

GRAVESEND, Kent, 51°26′·58N 00°23′·00E (lock into Canal basin). AC 1186, 2151. HW +0150 on Dover; ML 3·3m; Duration 0610. Use Tilbury diffs overleaf. Caution: Off the N bank, from Coalhouse Pt to 7ca E of Gravesend, 6 groynes (tops dry 1·0m) project approx 400m almost into the fairway; their outer ends are marked by SHM bns, Fl G 2·5s. 5 Y buoys downstream of No 6 groyne (the most E'ly) indicate that **no passage exists inshore of the Y buoys and groyne bns**. A SHM buoy *Diver*, L Fl G 10s, between Nos 3 and 2 groynes, marks the N edge of the fairway. ⚓ E of the Sea School jetty, close to S shore, but remote from town. There are ⚓s off the Club. Lock opens HW –1½ to HW on request to lock-keeper, ☎ (01474) 352392 (24hrs notice required for night tides). Boats can be left unattended in canal basin but not at ⚓s. Royal Terrace Pier hd FR. Call *Port Control London* VHF Ch 12 if E of Sea Reach No 4 buoy (1.4M SSE of Southend pier); and Ch 68 from No 4 buoy to Crayfordness. Broadcasts on Ch 68 every H & H+30. ⌗ 537115 (H24); **Gravesend SC** ☎ 533974, Bar, FW, M, P & D (cans); **Services:** C (at canal ent, ask at SC), CH, Ⓔ, ME, El, Sh. **Town** EC Wed, R, V.
Thurrock YC (51°28′·30N 00°19′·57E) at Grays, ☎ (01375) 373720 is 3M upriver on N bank opposite Broadness. 1 ⚓, D on site, P (2M), Bar, R (occas).

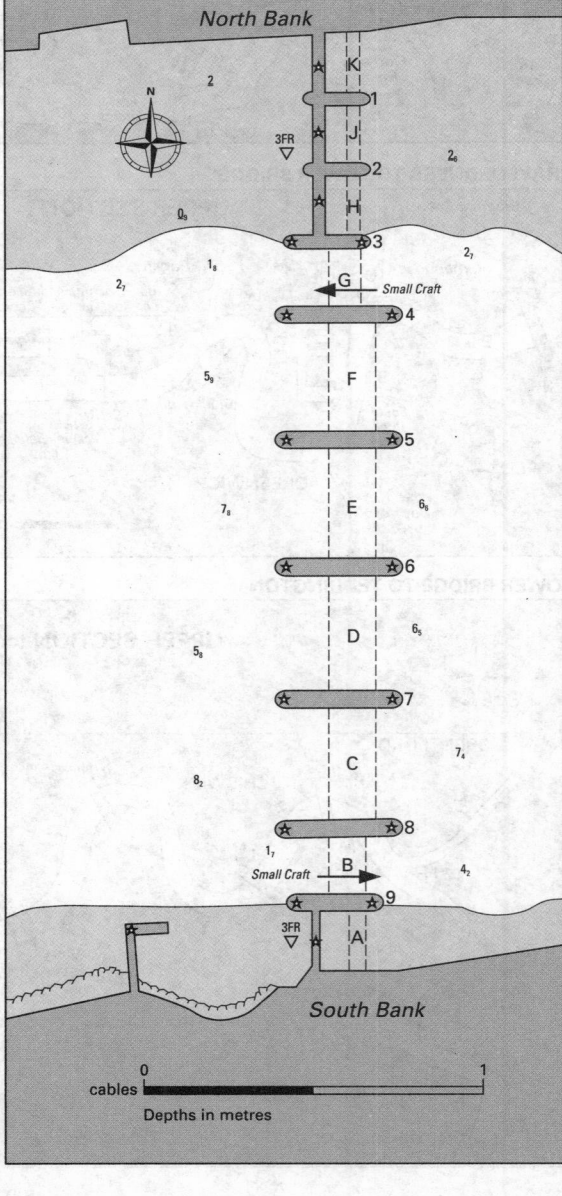

TIDES

+0252 Dover; ML 3·6; Duration 0555; Zone 0 (UT)

Standard Port LONDON BRIDGE (→)

Times				Height (metres)			
High Water		Low Water		MHWS	MHWN	MLWN	MLWS
0300	0900	0400	1100	7·1	5·9	1·3	0·5
1500	2100	1600	2300				

Differences TILBURY

−0055	−0040	−0050	−0115	−0·7	−0·5	+0·1	0·0

WOOLWICH (GALLIONS POINT)

−0020	−0020	−0035	−0045	−0·1	0·0	+0·2	0·0

ALBERT BRIDGE

+0025	+0020	+0105	+0110	−0·9	−0·8	−0·7	−0·4

HAMMERSMITH BRIDGE

+0040	+0035	+0205	+0155	−1·4	−1·3	−1·0	−0·5

KEW BRIDGE

+0055	+0050	+0255	+0235	−1·8	−1·8	−1·2	−0·5

RICHMOND LOCK

+0105	+0055	+0325	+0305	−2·2	−2·2	−1·3	−0·5

London Bridge is a Standard Port; daily predictions are below. The river is tidal up to Richmond Footbridge where there is a half-tide lock and a weir with overhead sluice gates. When down, ie closed, these gates maintain at least 1·72m between Richmond and Teddington bridges; the half-tide lock, on the Surrey bank, must then be used. At other times (approx HW ±2) pass through the 3 central arches. Above Putney the ht of LW may be below CD if the water flow over Teddington Weir is reduced; warnings are broadcast by Woolwich Radio qv. If the Thames Barrier (previous page) is closed, water levels will vary greatly from predictions.

TIDES – TIME DIFFERENCES ON LONDON BRIDGE

Place	MHWS	MHWN	MLWN	MLWS
Gravesend Town Pier	−0059	−0044	−0106	−0125
Broadness Lt Ho	−0052	−0040	−0101	−0119
Stoneness Lt Ho	−0048	−0037	−0059	−0114
Coldharbour Point	−0037	−0030	−0053	−0103
Royal Albert Dock Ent	−0029	−0024	−0043	−0050
Woolwich Ferry	−0028	−0024	−0042	−0047
Royal Victoria Dock Ent	−0021	−0018	−0031	−0025
India & Millwall Dock Ent	−0018	−0015	−0026	−0029
Greenwich Pier	−0014	−0012	−0020	−0023
Deptford Creek	−0012	−0011	−0018	−0021
Millwall Dock Ent	−0010	−0008	−0014	−0016
Surrey Dock Greenland Ent	−0010	−0008	−0013	−0015
London Bridge	0000	0000	0000	0000
Westminster Bridge	+0012	+0011	+0031	+0035
Battersea Bridge	+0023	+0020	+0109	+0110
Putney Bridge	+0032	+0030	+0138	+0137
Chiswick Bridge	+0049	+0044	+0235	+0224
Teddington Lock	+0106	+0056	—	—

NAVIGATION

The tidal Thames is divided by the PLA into a lower section = from sea to Crayfordness; and an upper section = Crayfordness to Teddington.

Some general points: Going up or down river, keep as far to stbd as is safe and seamanlike. Boats approaching a bridge against the tide give way to those approaching with the tide; but pleasure craft should always keep clear of commercial vessels, especially tug/barge tows. Above Cherry Garden Pier (Wapping), vessels over 40m always have priority. Speed should be such as to minimise wash, but an 8kn speed limit applies inshore off Southend, off Shellhaven and Coryton, and above Wandsworth Bridge. Some of the potential hazards are outlined below:

Lower section. In Sea Reach, keep well S of the main chan to clear tankers turning abeam Canvey Is and Shellhaven. In Lower Hope hold the NW bank until Ovens SHM buoy; long groynes extend from the N bank for the next 2M. The Tilbury landing stage is used by the Gravesend ferry and cruise liners. In Northfleet Hope beware ships/tugs turning into Tilbury Docks; container berths and a grain terminal are close up-river. Long Reach has Ro-Ro berths on both banks up/down stream of QE II bridge. Tankers berth at Purfleet (N bank).

Upper section. Avoid unhandy tug/lighter tows en route to Erith. Thames Police and PLA launches are very helpful to yachts. In emergency call *Thames Patrol* Ch 12, 68 or 14, giving position relative to landmarks, rather than by lat/long. Expect frequent passenger launches from/to Greenwich, The Tower and Westminster. Passage by night is not advised. See below for bridge warning lights.

BRIDGES

Name of Bridge	Distance from London Bridge Nautical Miles	Clearance below centre span MHWS (m)
Dartford (QEII)	17·68 below	54·1
Tower	0·49 below	8·6
London Bridge	0.00	8·9
Cannon St. Railway	0·16	7·1
Southwark	0·24	7·4
Blackfriars Railway	0·62	7·0
Blackfriars	0·63	7·1
Waterloo	1·12	8·5
Charing Cross Railway	1·32	7·0
Westminster	1·64	5·4
Lambeth	2·02	6·5
Vauxhall	2·46	5·6
Victoria Railway	3·31	6·0
Chelsea	3·40	6·6
Albert	4·04	4·9
Battersea	4·27	5·5
Battersea Railway	4·83	6·1
Wandsworth	5·46	5·8
Fulham Railway	6·31	6·9
Putney	6·45	5·5
Hammersmith	7·97	3·7
Barnes Railway	9·55	5·4
Chiswick	8·22	6·9
Kew Railway	8·98	5·6
Kew	11·33	5·3
Richmond Footbridge	13·49	5·5
Twickenham	13·64	5·9
Richmond Railway	13·67	5·3
Richmond	13·97	5·3

Tower Bridge sounds horn for 10s, every 20s when bascules are open for shipping.

Iso W 2s lts each side of 17 bridges (Tower to Wandsworth) warn of an approaching large vessel/tug (which has switched on the lts electronically); other craft keep clear. A ▽ of R discs (® lts) below a bridge span = this arch closed.

PIERS WHERE LANDING CAN BE MADE BY ARRANGEMENT

Piers with *, contact PLA Central booking Service ☎ 0171 265 2666, ☎ 0171 265 2617.

Greenwich Pier*, Tower Pier*	
London Bridge City Pier	0171 403 5939
Charing Cross Pier*, Westminster Pier*	
Lambeth Pier	0171 839 2164
Festival Pier*	
Cadogan Pier	0171 349 8585
Putney Pier	0171 378 1211
Kew Pier)	0171 930 2062
Richmond Landing Stage)	
Hampton Court Pier	0181 781 9758

LIGHTS AND MARKS

Glare from the many shore lts makes navigation by night difficult or even risky. Margaret Ness Fl (2) 5s 11m 8M.

RADIO TELEPHONE

Pleasure craft are encouraged to monitor:

Port Control London Ch 12 Sea to Sea Reach No 4 buoy;
                       Ch 68 No 4 buoy to Crayfordness.
Woolwich Radio   Ch 14 Up-river from Crayfordness.

Sea Reach No 4 buoy is 1.35M SSE of Southend pierhead at 51°29'·58N 00°44'·28E. Craft >20m LOA must have VHF radio. Smaller craft with no VHF should call ☎ 0181-855 0315 before & after transiting the Thames Barrier. Routine traffic, weather, tidal and nav info is broadcast by *Port Control London* on Ch 12 at H +15 and H +45 and on Ch 68 at H and H +30; also by *Woolwich Radio* on Ch 14 at H +15 and H +45. The latter will warn if ht of LW upstream of Putney falls below CD. For marina VHF see next page.

TELEPHONE (Dial code 0171 Central London; 0181 Outer; but see new codes/numbers on page 298)

PLA: **Operational enquiries 01474 560311**; General non-operational enquiries, below Crayfordness: (01474) 562200, ☎ 562281; above Crayfordness: 0171 265 2656, ☎ 265 2699; Duty Port Controller Gravesend (01474) 560311; Duty Officer Woolwich 0181 855 0315; Port Health Authority (Tilbury 01375) 842663 (H24); Thames MRSC (01255) 675518; River Police HQ (Wapping) 0171 275 4421; London Weather Centre 0171 831 5968; Tower Bridge 0171 407 0922; ⌗ (01474) 537115 (H24); Richmond Lock 0181 940 0634; **Marinecall** 0891 500 455; ⊞ 0171 987 7011.

SHELTER

Very good in Marinas, see below; also at the following:
Bow Creek (Bugsby's Reach), Deptford Creek (HW±2);
Upstream of fixed bridges: at places shown under
FACILITIES below and at Chas Newens (BY, Putney), Alan
See (Hammersmith), Auto Marine Services (Chiswick),
Howlett's BY (Twickenham) & Tough's BY (Swan Island).
PLA Draw Docks, arrowed on chartlets, are former barge
inlets which dry to chalk/gravel; in emergency they may
offer refuge but are open to wash. See also previous
page for Piers where temp'y berth may be pre-arranged .

FACILITIES (Bold letters in brackets appear on chartlets)
GREENWICH (0181)

Greenwich YC (A) ☎ 8587339; VHF Ch M. FW, 1 ⚓, ME.
LIMEHOUSE REACH (0171)

See below for **S Dock Marina (B)** & **Limehouse Basin (C)**.
POOL OF LONDON (0171)

St Katharine Haven (D): see below and for Fuel barge **(E)**.
NB: ALL BRIDGES BEYOND TOWER BRIDGE ARE FIXED.
WESTMINSTER BRIDGE (S side)

Westminster Petroleum Ltd (F) (Fuel barge). Call *Thames
Refueller* VHF Ch 14, ☎ 0831 110681, Gas, CH, D, L.
CHELSEA (0171)

Cadogan Pier (G) ☎ 352 4604, M, L; **Chelsea Yacht & Boat
Co (H)** ☎ 352 1427, M, Gas; **Chelsea Hbr (I)** (see over).
WANDSWORTH & HAMMERSMITH (0181)

Hurlingham YC (J) ☎ 788 5547, M, CH, ME, FW, El, Sh; **Dove
Marina (K)** ☎ 748 9474, AB, M, FW.

CHISWICK (0181)

Chiswick Pier Trust, ☎ 0181 742 2713, £10. At 51°28'·90N
00°14'·95W there is a 50m long pontoon, 2FG (vert). All
tide access, max draft 1·4m. FW, AC, ⚓. Visitors welcome.
Chiswick Quay Marina (L) (50) ☎ 994 8743, Access HW±2
via lock, M, FW, BY, M, ME, El, Sh.
KEW (0181)

Kew Marina (M) ☎ 940 8364, M, CH, D, P, Gas, SM;
BRENTFORD (0181)

Ent to Grand Union Canal, M, AB. **Brentford Dock Marina
(N)** (80+10 visitors) ☎ 568 0287 (VHF Ch M), AC, Bar, CH,
El, FW, ME, R, V, Sh, Access HW±2½;
RICHMOND (0181)

(O), Richmond Slipway BY, CH, D, Gas, M, FW, ME, El, Sh.
TWICKENHAM & TEDDINGTON (0181)

(P) Eel Pie Island BY, CH, AC, ME, M, Gas, C (6 ton), Sh,
El, FW; **(Q) Swan Island Hbr**, D, M, ME, El, Sh, FW, Gas,
Slip, AB, C (30 ton), CH.

ADMIRALTY CHART AGENTS (Central London)

Brown & Perring, 36/44 Tabernacle St	☎ 0171-253 4517
Kelvin Hughes, 145 Minories	709 9076
London Yacht Centre, 13 Artillery Lane	247 0521
Ocean Leisure, 13/14 Northumberland Ave	930 5050
Stanfords, 12/14 Long Acre	836 1321
Telesonic Marine, 60/62 Brunswick Centre	837 4106
Capt. O.M.Watts, 7 Dover St	493 4633

MARINAS ON THE TIDAL THAMES (From seaward: Woolwich to Chelsea)

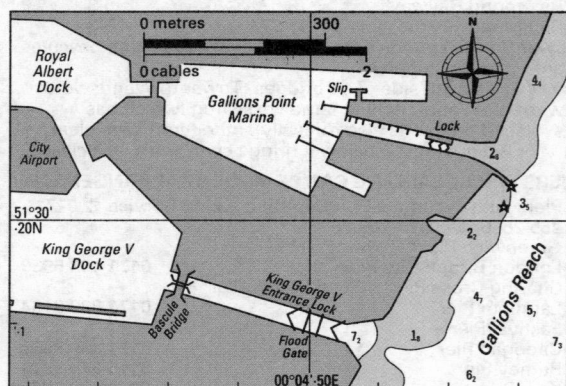

GALLIONS POINT MARINA, London, 51°30'·27N 00°04'·76E
in original entry basin for Royal Albert Dock. AC 2151,
2484. Tides as for Gallions Pt (8.4.14). Marina ☎ 0171-476
7054 (H24). VHF Ch M, when vessel expected. The fuel
barge LENNARD is conspic, berthed outside the lock; D,
Gas on sale. Access via lock HW±5; 8m depth in basin.
AB approx £9.40. Two ☆s 2FG (vert) on river pier. Usual
facilities inc security H24. DLR to central London, until
0030. Woolwich ferry & foot tunnel 15 mins walk. ✈
London City airport is adjacent.

SOUTH DOCK MARINA, London, 51°29'·62N 00°01'·87W.
AC 3337, *2484*. Tides as for Surrey Dock Greenland Ent
(8.4.14). 1·1M above Greenwich, 2·5M below Tower
Bridge. Baltic Quay building at SW end of marina is
conspic with five arched rooftops. Waiting pontoon at
Greenland Pier. Approx access via lock HW±2 for 2m
draft; HW±4 for 1m draft. **Marina** ☎ 0171-252 2244, 🖶
237 3806, (372 + ❷ £12). VHF Ch **M** 80. **Facilities:** AC, ME,
Sh, El, FW, CH, C (20 ton), Bar, R, V, 🖾, ♿, SDYC; Dr ☎
237 1078; Ⓗ ☎ 955 5000; Police ☎ 252 2836. 🚋, Surrey
Quays Tube stn, ✈ City Airport.

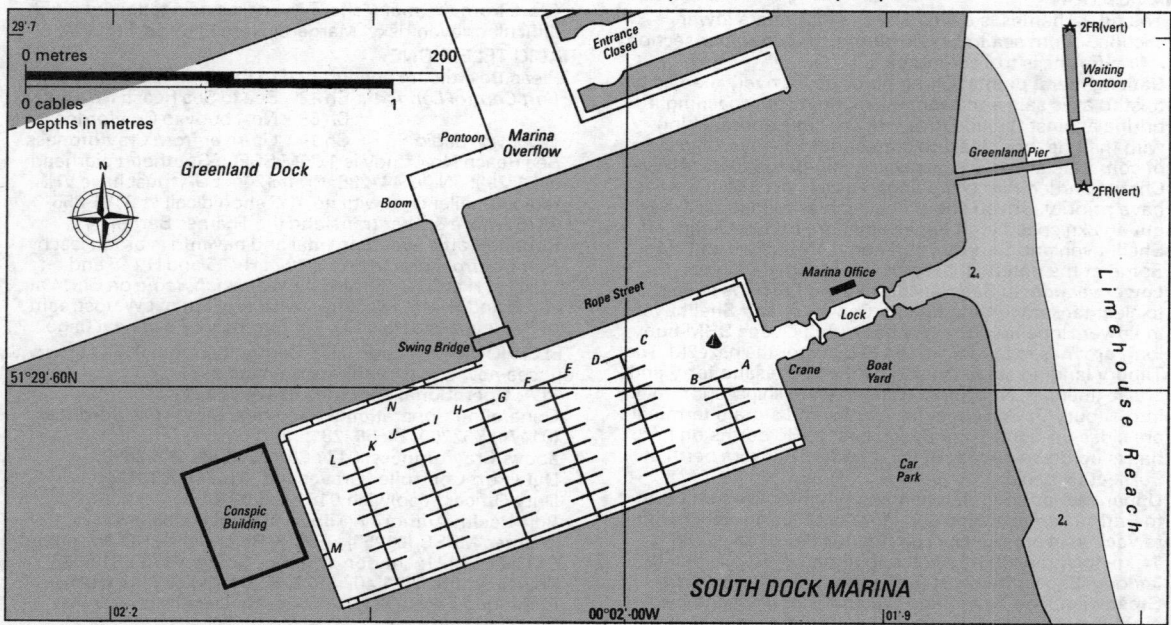

SOUTH DOCK MARINA

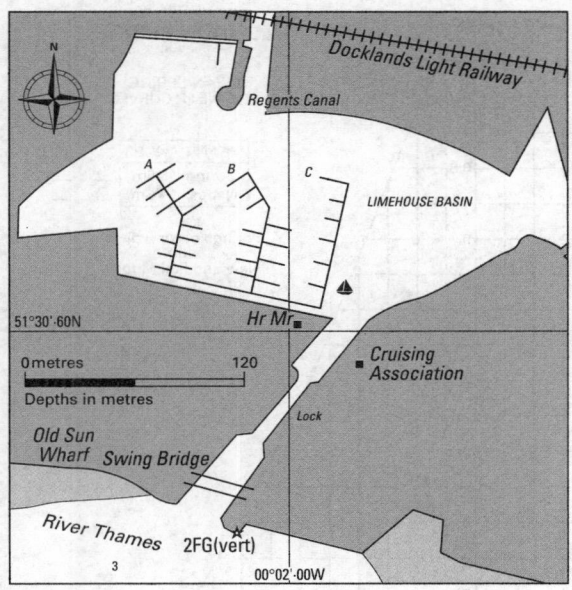

LIMEHOUSE BASIN, London, 51°30'·54N 00°02'·17W. Entry HW±3 via swing bridge/lock, 0800-1800LT daily Apr-Oct; 0800-1630 Nov-Mar; other times by prior arrangement to Hr Mr & BWB lock, ☎ 0171-308 9930. Waiting pontoon in lock entrance is accessible outside LW±1½. Call VHF Ch 80 *Limehouse Marina*. Facilities: (90 berths £10.00) FW, AC, H24 security, ▣, ⇌, DLR; also entry to Regents Canal and R Lea. Marina is managed by Cruising Association at: 1 Northey St, Limehouse Basin, E14 8BT, ☎ 0171-537 2828, ☏ 537 2266; temporary membership, open: 1130-1500 & 1700-2300 Mon-Fri, 1130-2300 Sat, 1200-1500 & 1900-2230 Sun; Bar, R, ♿▣.

4

ST KATHARINE HAVEN, London, 51°30'·33N 00°04'·25W. AC 3337, 3319. HW +0245 on Dover. Tides as London Bridge (8·4·14). Be aware of cross tide at mid-flood/ebb. Good shelter under all conditions. Tower Bridge and the Tower of London are uniquely conspic, close up-river. A waiting pontoon is close downstream of ent in 0.1 - 1.9m; or berth on inshore side of St Katharine Pier, 30m upriver of ent; limited berthing/shore access, only suitable for shoal draft. Pleasure launches berth on S side of pier.

St Katharine Haven Call *St Katharines* VHF Ch 80 M. Lock (41m x 12·5m with 2 small lifting bridges), access HW –2 to HW +1½, season 0600-2030, winter 0800-1800LT; other times by prior arrangement. R/G tfc lts at ent. Lock is shut Tues and Wed, Nov to Feb.
Facilities (100 + 50 Ⓥ, usually in Centre Basin or East Dock; pre-booking advised in season) ☎ 0171-481 8350 (H24)/ 488 0555, ☏ 702 2252, £14.20, FW, AC, CH, ME, El, Sh, Gas, Sewage pump-out, YC, Bar, R, V, ⌗, ▣.
Fuel Barge is 400m downstream of lock ent. ☎ 0171-481 1774; VHF Ch 14 *Burgan*. D & Gas, 0900-1600 Mon-Fri; 0900-1300 Sun.

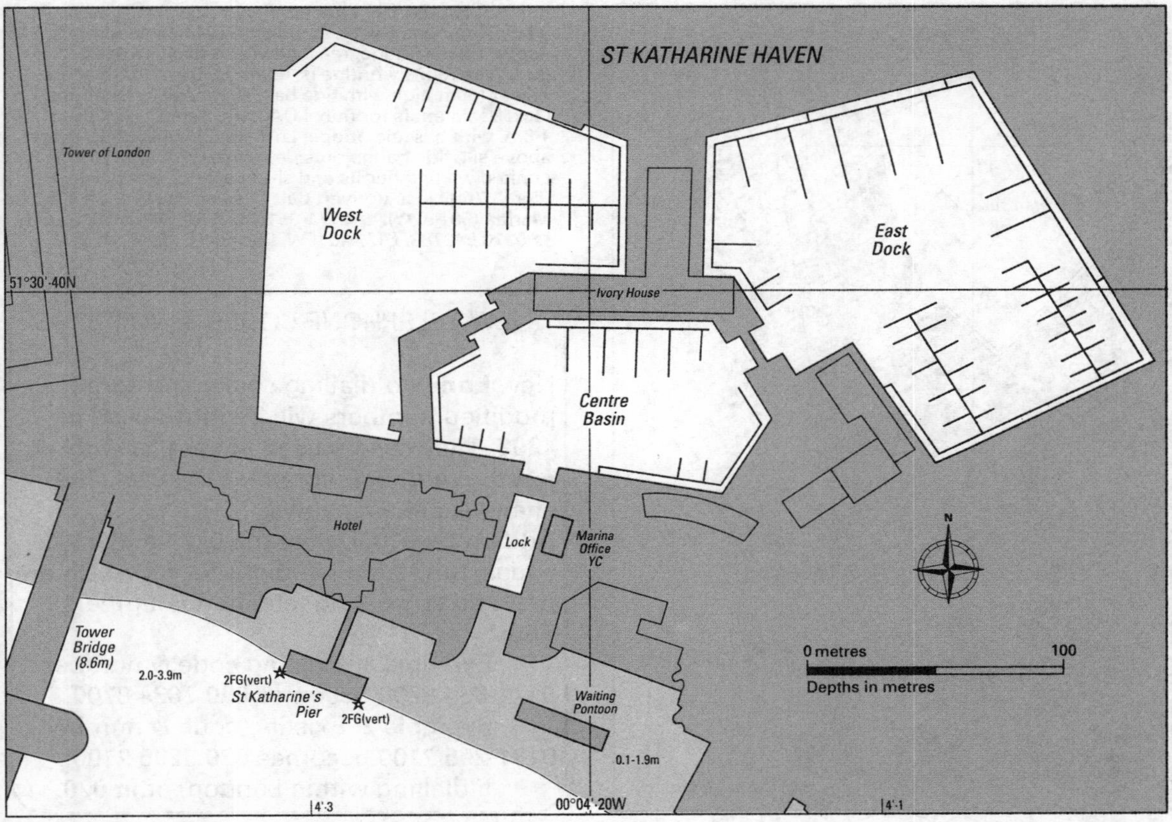

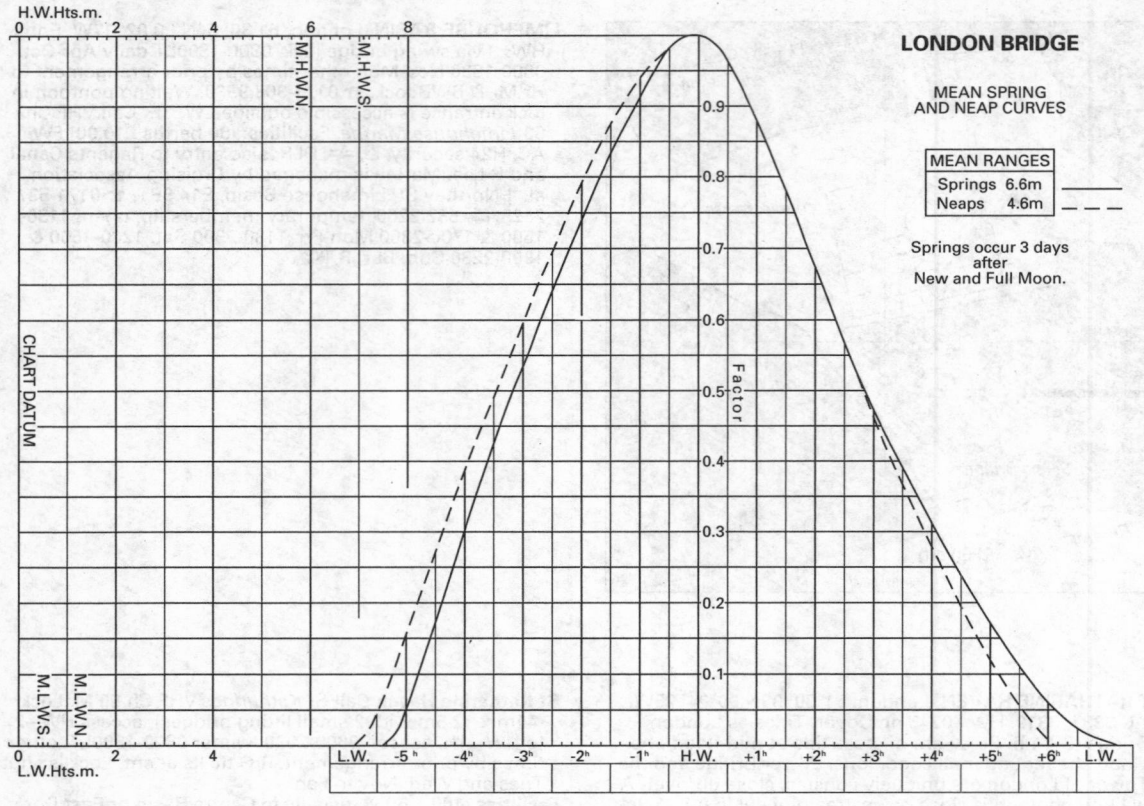

LONDON BRIDGE

MEAN SPRING
AND NEAP CURVES

MEAN RANGES	
Springs 6.6m	———
Neaps 4.6m	– – –

Springs occur 3 days
after
New and Full Moon.

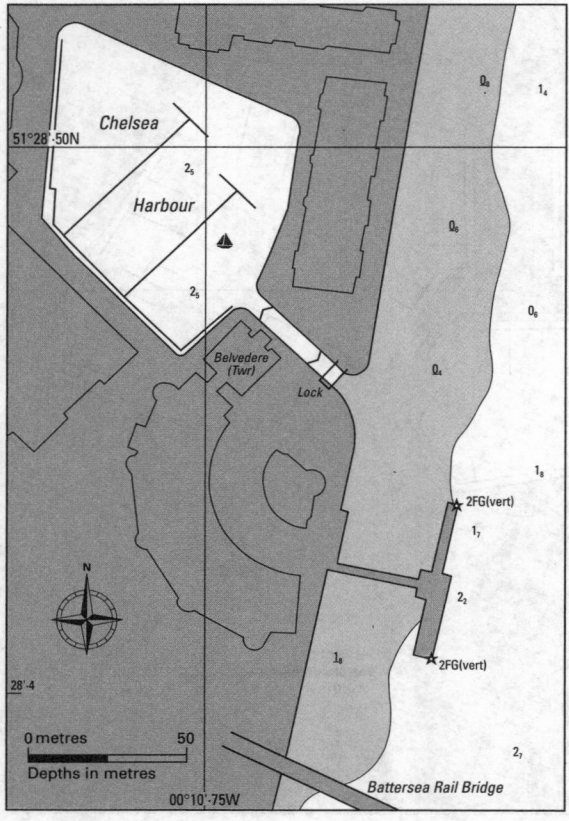

CHELSEA HARBOUR, London, 51°28'·45N 00°10'·72W. AC 3319. Tides: see 8·4·14. Good shelter in all conditions, 5M above Tower Bridge, reached via 14 fixed bridges. Battersea railway bridge is 120m upstream. Belvedere Tower (80m high with tide ball) is conspic, next to the lock. Basin ent is for max LOA 24m, beam 5·5m, draft 1·8m, with bascule bridge. Lock opens when 2·5m water above sill; tide gauge outside, access HW ±1½, R/G tfc lts. Limited waiting berths and shore access on Chelsea Hbr Pier (1·7m) close upriver. Call *Chelsea Hbr* VHF Ch 80. **Marina** (50+10 Ⓥ). ☎ 0171-351 4433, 📠 352 7868, mobile ☎ 0370 542783, £12, AC, FW, Bar, R, YC, Ⓑ, Ⓚ, ⚓, V.

NEW TELEPHONE CODES & NUMBERS

New **London** dialling codes and some modified numbers will be introduced in 1999. They can be used in parallel with existing numbers for at least a year. The changes are as follows:
Add prefix 020. Delete the 0171 and 0181 codes, but retain the digits 7 or 8 which are prefixed to existing telephone numbers. Thus:

Example 1: Existing code & number 0171-634 8700 becomes 020 7634 8700.

Example 2: Existing code & number 0181-295 2100 becomes 020 8295 2100.

If dialling within London, omit 020.

ENGLAND – LONDON BRIDGE

LAT 51°30′N   LONG   0°05′W

TIMES AND HEIGHTS OF HIGH AND LOW WATERS

YEAR **1999**

4

TIME ZONE (UT)
For Summer Time add ONE hour in non-shaded areas

JANUARY

Day	Time	m	Time	m	Time	m	Time	m
1 F	0029	6.9	0712	0.7	1251	7.0	1939	0.5
16 SA	0037	6.5	0649	1.0	1306	6.5	1919	0.9
2 SA O	0121	7.1	0808	0.4	1343	7.3	2030	0.4
17 SU ●	0122	6.7	0745	0.8	1349	6.7	2006	0.8
3 SU	0210	7.2	0900	0.2	1433	7.4	2116	0.5
18 M	0203	6.8	0835	0.7	1429	6.8	2049	0.8
4 M	0255	7.2	0948	0.2	1521	7.4	2159	0.6
19 TU	0242	6.9	0921	0.7	1509	6.9	2129	0.8
5 TU	0339	7.1	1031	0.2	1606	7.3	2236	0.7
20 W	0319	6.9	1003	0.7	1548	7.0	2207	0.8
6 W	0419	6.9	1110	0.4	1649	7.1	2309	0.8
21 TH	0356	6.9	1040	0.6	1629	7.0	2243	0.8
7 TH	0456	6.7	1143	0.6	1730	6.8	2337	1.1
22 F	0435	6.8	1115	0.6	1711	6.9	2319	0.8
8 F	0532	6.5	1215	0.8	1810	6.5		
23 SA	0516	6.8	1150	0.7	1756	6.8	2358	0.9
9 SA	0006	1.2	0611	6.3	1250	1.0	1852	6.2
24 SU	0601	6.7	1229	0.8	1845	6.5		
10 SU	0043	1.4	0657	6.0	1334	1.2	1942	5.9
25 M	0043	1.0	0652	6.4	1318	1.0	1941	6.3
11 M	0132	1.6	0757	5.7	1427	1.3	2042	5.8
26 TU	0138	1.2	0754	6.2	1419	1.2	2049	6.1
12 TU	0235	1.7	0911	5.6	1526	1.4	2149	5.8
27 W	0249	1.4	0911	6.1	1541	1.3	2203	6.1
13 W	0341	1.6	1024	5.7	1627	1.3	2251	6.0
28 TH	0418	1.4	1029	6.2	1717	1.2	2311	6.3
14 TH	0445	1.5	1125	6.0	1729	1.2	2347	6.3
29 F	0552	1.2	1138	6.5	1826	1.0		
15 F	0548	1.3	1219	6.3	1828	1.0		
30 SA	0012	6.6	0659	0.8	1239	6.8	1922	0.7
31 SU O	0106	6.9	0756	0.4	1332	7.1	2013	0.5

FEBRUARY

Day	Time	m	Time	m	Time	m	Time	m
1 M	0155	7.1	0847	0.2	1421	7.3	2100	0.5
16 TU ●	0143	6.8	0822	0.6	1410	7.0	2036	0.7
2 TU	0240	7.1	0934	0.1	1507	7.3	2143	0.5
17 W	0225	6.9	0912	0.5	1452	7.1	2121	0.7
3 W	0322	7.0	1016	0.1	1548	7.2	2222	0.7
18 TH	0304	7.0	0956	0.4	1532	7.2	2202	0.6
4 TH	0358	6.9	1052	0.3	1626	7.0	2253	0.8
19 F	0342	7.1	1034	0.4	1612	7.2	2238	0.6
5 F	0431	6.8	1122	0.5	1659	6.8	2316	1.0
20 SA	0420	7.1	1107	0.4	1659	7.1	2312	0.6
6 SA	0503	6.7	1147	0.7	1733	6.7	2333	1.0
21 SU	0500	7.1	1137	0.5	1736	6.9	2345	0.7
7 SU	0538	6.5	1209	0.8	1809	6.5	2359	1.1
22 M	0543	6.9	1209	0.6	1821	6.6		
8 M	0619	6.3	1240	1.0	1851	6.2		
23 TU	0023	0.8	0631	6.6	1250	0.9	1912	6.2
9 TU	0038	1.2	0706	6.0	1325	1.2	1940	6.0
24 W	0111	1.1	0729	6.2	1345	1.3	2019	5.9
10 W	0131	1.4	0803	5.7	1429	1.4	2039	5.8
25 TH	0217	1.4	0850	5.9	1503	1.6	2142	5.8
11 TH	0246	1.6	0913	5.6	1540	1.5	2151	5.8
26 F	0349	1.6	1018	6.0	1657	1.5	2255	6.0
12 F	0400	1.5	1035	5.7	1647	1.4	2305	6.0
27 SA	0542	1.2	1207	6.1	1809	1.1	2357	6.4
13 SA	0508	1.3	1144	6.0	1752	1.1		
28 SU	0646	0.7	1227	6.8	1905	0.8		
14 SU	0006	6.3	0616	1.1	1240	6.4	1852	0.9
15 M	0058	6.6	0724	0.8	1327	6.7	1946	0.8

MARCH

Day	Time	m	Time	m	Time	m	Time	m
1 M	0051	6.8	0739	0.3	1320	7.1	1955	0.5
16 TU	0029	6.5	0702	0.8	1301	6.8	1925	0.8
2 TU O	0140	7.0	0828	0.1	1407	7.3	2041	0.4
17 W ●	0118	6.8	0802	0.5	1347	7.1	2017	0.6
3 W	0224	7.1	0913	0.0	1449	7.2	2124	0.4
18 TH	0201	7.0	0853	0.3	1430	7.3	2105	0.5
4 TH	0302	7.0	0954	0.1	1527	7.1	2202	0.6
19 F	0242	7.2	0938	0.2	1511	7.4	2148	0.4
5 F	0336	6.9	1029	0.3	1559	6.9	2234	0.7
20 SA	0322	7.3	1017	0.2	1552	7.4	2226	0.3
6 SA	0405	6.8	1057	0.5	1628	6.8	2253	0.9
21 SU	0403	7.4	1051	0.2	1634	7.3	2301	0.4
7 SU	0435	6.7	1115	0.7	1659	6.7	2302	0.9
22 M	0445	7.3	1120	0.4	1715	7.0	2333	0.5
8 M	0509	6.6	1128	0.8	1734	6.6	2326	0.8
23 TU	0528	7.1	1150	0.6	1759	6.7		
9 TU	0548	6.5	1153	0.8	1813	6.4		
24 W	0008	0.7	0616	6.7	1229	0.9	1848	6.2
10 W	0000	0.9	0631	6.2	1231	1.0	1858	6.1
25 TH	0054	1.0	0715	6.2	1321	1.4	1955	5.8
11 TH	0044	1.1	0722	5.9	1324	1.4	1952	5.8
26 F	0158	1.4	0840	5.9	1438	1.7	2125	5.7
12 F	0147	1.4	0824	5.6	1450	1.6	2058	5.7
27 SA	0333	1.5	1007	6.0	1633	1.7	2237	5.9
13 SA	0321	1.6	0940	5.6	1611	1.5	2219	5.8
28 SU	0525	1.1	1113	6.4	1747	1.2	2337	6.4
14 SU	0437	1.4	1106	5.9	1721	1.3	2332	6.1
29 M	0625	0.6	1210	6.8	1842	0.8		
15 M	0550	1.1	1210	6.3	1826	1.0		
30 TU	0031	6.7	0716	0.2	1301	7.1	1931	0.5
31 W O	0119	7.0	0802	0.0	1347	7.2	2017	0.4

APRIL

Day	Time	m	Time	m	Time	m	Time	m
1 TH	0202	7.0	0846	0.0	1427	7.2	2100	0.4
16 F ●	0133	7.1	0827	0.2	1405	7.4	2043	0.3
2 F	0240	7.0	0926	0.2	1501	7.0	2138	0.5
17 SA	0218	7.3	0913	0.1	1448	7.5	2129	0.2
3 SA	0312	6.8	1000	0.4	1530	6.8	2210	0.7
18 SU	0302	7.5	0955	0.1	1531	7.5	2210	0.1
4 SU	0340	6.7	1027	0.6	1557	6.8	2228	0.8
19 M	0346	7.5	1031	0.2	1614	7.3	2248	0.2
5 M	0410	6.7	1042	0.8	1628	6.8	2236	0.8
20 TU	0431	7.4	1104	0.3	1657	7.1	2324	0.3
6 TU	0443	6.6	1053	0.8	1702	6.7	2259	0.7
21 W	0517	7.2	1136	0.6	1741	6.7		
7 W	0521	6.5	1120	0.8	1741	6.5	2332	0.7
22 TH	0001	0.5	0607	6.8	1215	0.9	1830	6.3
8 TH	0604	6.3	1156	1.0	1825	6.3		
23 F	0046	0.9	0708	6.3	1306	1.4	1938	5.9
9 F	0013	0.9	0653	6.0	1243	1.3	1916	6.0
24 SA	0148	1.2	0830	6.0	1417	1.7	2103	5.8
10 SA	0107	1.3	0752	5.8	1353	1.6	2018	5.8
25 SU	0315	1.3	0947	6.1	1554	1.7	2212	6.0
11 SU	0241	1.5	0902	5.7	1534	1.6	2134	5.8
26 M	0453	1.0	1049	6.5	1714	1.3	2311	6.3
12 M	0407	1.3	1024	6.0	1649	1.4	2251	6.1
27 TU	0554	0.6	1145	6.8	1812	0.9		
13 TU	0522	1.0	1134	6.4	1756	1.1	2353	6.4
28 W	0004	6.7	0644	0.3	1235	7.0	1902	0.6
14 W	0634	0.7	1230	6.8	1858	0.8		
29 TH	0053	6.9	0730	0.2	1320	7.1	1949	0.4
15 TH	0046	6.8	0734	0.4	1319	7.1	1953	0.5
30 F O	0137	6.9	0814	0.2	1400	7.1	2032	0.4

Chart Datum: 3·20 metres below Ordnance Datum (Newlyn)

ENGLAND – LONDON BRIDGE

LAT 51°30′N   LONG   0°05′W

TIMES AND HEIGHTS OF HIGH AND LOW WATERS   YEAR **1999**

TIME ZONE (UT)
For Summer Time add ONE hour in non-shaded areas

MAY

Day	Time	m	Time	m	Time	m	Time	m
1 SA	0215	6.9	0853	0.3	1434	6.9	2111	0.5
2 SU	0248	6.7	0928	0.5	1502	6.8	2142	0.7
3 M	0318	6.6	0956	0.7	1530	6.7	2203	0.8
4 TU	0348	6.6	1011	0.8	1601	6.7	2215	0.8
5 W	0422	6.6	1028	0.8	1636	6.7	2240	0.7
6 TH	0500	6.5	1058	0.8	1715	6.6	2314	0.7
7 F	0543	6.4	1135	0.9	1758	6.3	2355	0.9
8 SA	0632	6.2	1221	1.2	1849	6.1		
9 SU	0047	1.1	0728	6.0	1322	1.5	1948	5.9
10 M	0207	1.2	0835	6.0	1452	1.4	2058	5.9
11 TU	0336	1.1	0948	6.1	1614	1.4	2211	6.1
12 W	0451	0.9	1058	6.5	1723	1.1	2316	6.5
13 TH	0602	0.6	1157	6.8	1827	0.8		
14 F	0013	6.8	0704	0.4	1250	7.1	1925	0.5
15 SA ●	0105	7.1	0758	0.2	1339	7.4	2019	0.3
16 SU	0155	7.4	0847	0.1	1426	7.4	2109	0.1
17 M	0243	7.5	0932	0.1	1512	7.4	2154	0.0
18 TU	0330	7.6	1013	0.2	1556	7.3	2237	0.1
19 W	0418	7.5	1050	0.3	1641	7.1	2316	0.2
20 TH	0507	7.3	1125	0.6	1727	6.8	2356	0.4
21 F	0559	6.9	1204	0.9	1816	6.4		
22 SA	0040	0.7	0657	6.5	1252	1.3	1918	6.1
23 SU	0135	0.9	0808	6.3	1352	1.6	2032	5.9
24 M	0243	1.1	0917	6.2	1506	1.7	2138	6.0
25 TU	0401	1.0	1017	6.4	1623	1.5	2237	6.2
26 W	0510	0.8	1112	6.6	1731	1.2	2331	6.4
27 TH	0605	0.6	1203	6.8	1827	0.9		
28 F	0022	6.6	0653	0.5	1249	6.9	1916	0.7
29 SA	0108	6.7	0738	0.4	1330	6.9	2000	0.6
30 SU ○	0148	6.7	0818	0.5	1405	6.8	2040	0.6
31 M	0224	6.7	0855	0.6	1437	6.8	2113	0.7

JUNE

Day	Time	m	Time	m	Time	m	Time	m
1 TU	0257	6.6	0924	0.8	1508	6.7	2139	0.8
2 W	0330	6.6	0947	0.8	1540	6.7	2202	0.8
3 TH	0405	6.6	1012	0.9	1616	6.7	2230	0.8
4 F	0444	6.5	1044	0.9	1654	6.6	2306	0.7
5 SA	0526	6.5	1123	0.9	1737	6.4	2347	0.8
6 SU	0614	6.4	1208	1.1	1826	6.3		
7 M	0037	0.9	0708	6.2	1303	1.3	1922	6.1
8 TU	0143	1.0	0810	6.2	1415	1.4	2027	6.1
9 W	0300	1.0	0917	6.3	1535	1.3	2136	6.2
10 TH	0416	0.9	1025	6.5	1648	1.1	2242	6.5
11 F	0530	0.7	1127	6.8	1757	0.9	2343	6.8
12 SA	0636	0.5	1224	7.0	1901	0.6		
13 SU ●	0041	7.0	0733	0.3	1317	7.2	1958	0.4
14 M	0135	7.3	0825	0.2	1406	7.3	2051	0.2
15 TU	0226	7.4	0913	0.2	1454	7.4	2141	0.0
16 W	0316	7.5	0957	0.2	1540	7.3	2226	0.0
17 TH	0406	7.5	1038	0.4	1626	7.1	2309	0.1
18 F	0454	7.3	1115	0.6	1711	6.9	2349	0.3
19 SA	0544	7.0	1153	0.8	1757	6.6		
20 SU	0029	0.5	0635	6.7	1234	1.1	1847	6.3
21 M	0113	0.7	0733	6.4	1321	1.4	1948	6.1
22 TU	0204	0.9	0836	6.2	1417	1.6	2054	6.0
23 W	0302	1.1	0936	6.1	1519	1.6	2156	6.0
24 TH	0404	1.1	1032	6.2	1624	1.5	2253	6.1
25 F	0508	1.0	1124	6.4	1732	1.3	2347	6.3
26 SA	0607	0.8	1213	6.6	1833	1.0		
27 SU	0036	6.7	0657	0.7	1258	6.7	1923	0.9
28 M ○	0121	6.6	0741	0.6	1338	6.8	2007	0.8
29 TU	0202	6.6	0822	0.7	1415	6.8	2046	0.7
30 W	0239	6.7	0858	0.7	1450	6.8	2122	0.7

JULY

Day	Time	m	Time	m	Time	m	Time	m
1 TH	0315	6.6	0930	0.8	1525	6.7	2155	0.8
2 F	0351	6.6	1002	0.8	1601	6.7	2228	0.7
3 SA	0430	6.7	1037	0.9	1638	6.6	2303	0.7
4 SU	0511	6.6	1115	0.9	1719	6.6	2341	0.7
5 M	0557	6.6	1157	1.0	1804	6.5		
6 TU	0025	0.8	0647	6.4	1246	1.1	1856	6.4
7 W	0118	0.9	0744	6.3	1344	1.2	1956	6.3
8 TH	0222	1.0	0848	6.2	1456	1.3	2104	6.2
9 F	0338	1.0	0956	6.3	1613	1.3	2213	6.3
10 SA	0501	0.9	1101	6.5	1732	1.1	2320	6.6
11 SU	0612	0.8	1202	6.8	1842	0.8		
12 M	0022	6.9	0712	0.5	1258	7.0	1943	0.4
13 TU ●	0120	7.1	0806	0.3	1350	7.2	2038	0.2
14 W	0213	7.4	0856	0.3	1438	7.3	2129	0.0
15 TH	0303	7.4	0943	0.3	1525	7.2	2216	0.0
16 F	0351	7.4	1025	0.4	1609	7.2	2258	0.0
17 SA	0437	7.3	1103	0.6	1650	7.0	2335	0.2
18 SU	0521	7.1	1137	0.8	1730	6.8		
19 M	0009	0.4	0603	6.7	1210	1.0	1810	6.5
20 TU	0043	0.7	0647	6.4	1245	1.2	1854	6.2
21 W	0122	0.9	0736	6.1	1329	1.4	1948	6.0
22 TH	0211	1.1	0834	5.9	1424	1.6	2055	5.8
23 F	0307	1.2	0937	5.8	1525	1.6	2205	5.8
24 SA	0409	1.2	1039	6.0	1628	1.5	2309	5.9
25 SU	0512	1.1	1135	6.2	1733	1.3		
26 M	0005	6.2	0613	0.9	1227	6.5	1839	1.0
27 TU	0055	6.5	0706	0.7	1313	6.7	1936	0.8
28 W ○	0139	6.7	0754	0.7	1355	6.7	2025	0.7
29 TH	0220	6.8	0838	0.7	1434	6.8	2110	0.6
30 F	0259	6.8	0919	0.7	1511	6.8	2150	0.6
31 SA	0336	6.8	0956	0.8	1546	6.8	2227	0.6

AUGUST

Day	Time	m	Time	m	Time	m	Time	m
1 SU	0414	6.8	1032	0.8	1622	6.6	2259	0.6
2 M	0454	6.8	1107	0.8	1700	6.8	2331	0.6
3 TU	0536	6.7	1144	0.8	1742	6.7		
4 W	0007	0.7	0622	6.5	1226	1.0	1829	6.5
5 TH	0050	0.8	0714	6.3	1315	1.2	1925	6.3
6 F	0144	1.1	0817	6.1	1420	1.4	2033	6.1
7 SA	0258	1.3	0929	6.0	1542	1.4	2151	6.1
8 SU	0436	1.3	1041	6.2	1715	1.3	2305	6.3
9 M	0556	1.0	1146	6.5	1831	0.8		
10 TU	0011	6.7	0657	0.7	1243	6.8	1931	0.4
11 W ●	0109	7.1	0750	0.4	1335	7.1	2025	0.1
12 TH	0201	7.3	0840	0.3	1423	7.2	2114	-0.1
13 F	0249	7.4	0926	0.3	1507	7.2	2159	-0.1
14 SA	0333	7.4	1009	0.4	1547	7.1	2239	0.2
15 SU	0414	7.2	1046	0.5	1624	7.0	2314	0.2
16 M	0452	7.0	1118	0.7	1658	6.8	2342	0.5
17 TU	0526	6.7	1143	0.9	1732	6.6		
18 W	0007	0.7	0600	6.5	1206	1.1	1809	6.4
19 TH	0035	0.9	0639	6.2	1238	1.2	1853	6.1
20 F	0115	1.2	0725	5.9	1327	1.5	1948	5.7
21 SA	0213	1.4	0824	5.7	1435	1.6	2058	5.5
22 SU	0322	1.5	0940	5.7	1545	1.6	2223	5.6
23 M	0429	1.4	1055	5.9	1652	1.4	2333	6.0
24 TU	0535	1.1	1155	6.3	1801	1.1		
25 W	0028	6.4	0636	0.9	1247	6.6	1909	0.8
26 TH ○	0115	6.7	0730	0.7	1332	6.8	2005	0.6
27 F	0158	6.9	0820	0.6	1413	6.9	2054	0.5
28 SA	0238	7.0	0905	0.6	1451	6.9	2138	0.5
29 SU	0316	7.1	0946	0.7	1526	7.0	2216	0.5
30 M	0354	7.1	1023	0.7	1602	7.0	2248	0.5
31 TU	0432	7.0	1057	0.7	1639	7.0	2315	0.6

Chart Datum: 3·20 metres below Ordnance Datum (Newlyn)

ENGLAND – LONDON BRIDGE

LAT 51°30′N   LONG 0°05′W

TIMES AND HEIGHTS OF HIGH AND LOW WATERS

YEAR **1999**

TIME ZONE (UT)
For Summer Time add ONE hour in non-shaded areas

4

SEPTEMBER

Day	Time	m	Day	Time	m
1 W	0513 / 1130 / 1720 / 2345	6.9 / 0.7 / 6.9 / 0.7	**16** TH	0519 / 1126 / 1734 / 2343	6.6 / 1.0 / 6.5 / 0.9
2 TH	0556 / 1206 / 1806	6.6 / 0.9 / 6.7	**17** F	0555 / 1153 / 1815	6.4 / 1.1 / 6.2
3 F	0021 / 0644 / 1250 / 1859	0.9 / 6.3 / 1.1 / 6.3	**18** SA	0014 / 0638 / 1233 / 1903	1.1 / 6.1 / 1.3 / 5.8
4 SA	0111 / 0745 / 1351 / 2009	1.2 / 5.9 / 1.4 / 5.9	**19** SU	0103 / 0729 / 1338 / 2004	1.5 / 5.8 / 1.6 / 5.5
5 SU	0223 / 0907 / 1521 / 2138	1.6 / 5.7 / 1.6 / 5.9	**20** M	0229 / 0836 / 1508 / 2123	1.7 / 5.6 / 1.7 / 5.5
6 M	0419 / 1027 / 1708 / 2257	1.6 / 5.9 / 1.3 / 6.2	**21** TU	0351 / 1007 / 1620 / 2254	1.7 / 5.7 / 1.5 / 5.8
7 TU	0541 / 1132 / 1819	1.2 / 6.3 / 0.8	**22** W	0501 / 1120 / 1730 / 2356	1.4 / 6.0 / 1.1 / 6.3
8 W	0001 / 0640 / 1229 / 1915	6.7 / 0.8 / 6.8 / 0.3	**23** TH	0605 / 1215 / 1841	1.1 / 6.5 / 0.8
9 TH ●	0057 / 0732 / 1319 / 2006	7.1 / 0.4 / 7.1 / 0.0	**24** F	0045 / 0703 / 1303 / 1940	6.7 / 0.8 / 6.8 / 0.6
10 F	0146 / 0820 / 1404 / 2053	7.4 / 0.3 / 7.2 / -0.2	**25** SA O	0130 / 0755 / 1345 / 2030	7.0 / 0.7 / 7.0 / 0.4
11 SA	0231 / 0906 / 1446 / 2136	7.4 / 0.2 / 7.2 / -0.1	**26** SU	0211 / 0843 / 1424 / 2115	7.2 / 0.6 / 7.1 / 0.4
12 SU	0311 / 0947 / 1523 / 2214	7.3 / 0.3 / 7.1 / 0.1	**27** M	0251 / 0927 / 1502 / 2155	7.2 / 0.5 / 7.2 / 0.4
13 M	0347 / 1024 / 1556 / 2247	7.1 / 0.5 / 6.9 / 0.4	**28** TU	0330 / 1007 / 1541 / 2229	7.2 / 0.5 / 7.2 / 0.4
14 TU	0418 / 1054 / 1626 / 2312	6.9 / 0.8 / 6.8 / 0.6	**29** W	0410 / 1043 / 1621 / 2257	7.2 / 0.5 / 7.2 / 0.6
15 W	0447 / 1112 / 1658 / 2327	6.7 / 0.9 / 6.7 / 0.8	**30** TH	0450 / 1116 / 1703 / 2325	7.0 / 0.6 / 7.1 / 0.7

OCTOBER

Day	Time	m	Day	Time	m
1 F	0532 / 1150 / 1749	6.7 / 0.8 / 6.7	**16** SA	0519 / 1119 / 1745 / 2334	6.5 / 1.0 / 6.3 / 1.1
2 SA	0000 / 0618 / 1234 / 1843	1.0 / 6.2 / 1.1 / 6.3	**17** SU	0601 / 1156 / 1831	6.2 / 1.2 / 6.0
3 SU	0048 / 0718 / 1335 / 1958	1.4 / 5.8 / 1.4 / 5.9	**18** M	0016 / 0649 / 1248 / 1927	1.4 / 5.9 / 1.5 / 5.7
4 M	0159 / 0851 / 1511 / 2132	1.8 / 5.6 / 1.6 / 5.9	**19** TU	0119 / 0749 / 1424 / 2035	1.7 / 5.7 / 1.7 / 5.6
5 TU	0359 / 1011 / 1655 / 2244	1.8 / 5.9 / 1.2 / 6.3	**20** W	0306 / 0908 / 1547 / 2201	1.8 / 5.6 / 1.5 / 5.8
6 W	0519 / 1113 / 1759 / 2344	1.4 / 6.3 / 0.6 / 6.8	**21** TH	0423 / 1033 / 1657 / 2313	1.6 / 5.9 / 1.2 / 6.1
7 TH	0617 / 1208 / 1852	0.9 / 6.8 / 0.2	**22** F	0529 / 1135 / 1805	1.2 / 6.3 / 0.8
8 F	0037 / 0708 / 1258 / 1940	7.2 / 0.5 / 7.1 / 0.0	**23** SA	0009 / 0629 / 1226 / 1906	6.7 / 0.9 / 6.7 / 0.6
9 SA ●	0125 / 0756 / 1342 / 2025	7.4 / 0.3 / 7.2 / -0.1	**24** SU O	0057 / 0725 / 1312 / 2000	7.0 / 0.7 / 7.0 / 0.4
10 SU	0208 / 0840 / 1422 / 2107	7.4 / 0.3 / 7.2 / 0.0	**25** M	0142 / 0817 / 1355 / 2047	7.2 / 0.5 / 7.2 / 0.3
11 M	0246 / 0922 / 1458 / 2145	7.2 / 0.4 / 7.0 / 0.3	**26** TU	0224 / 0904 / 1438 / 2130	7.3 / 0.4 / 7.4 / 0.3
12 TU	0317 / 0959 / 1528 / 2216	7.0 / 0.6 / 6.8 / 0.6	**27** W	0306 / 0948 / 1521 / 2207	7.3 / 0.4 / 7.4 / 0.4
13 W	0344 / 1027 / 1557 / 2237	6.8 / 0.8 / 6.7 / 0.8	**28** TH	0348 / 1028 / 1605 / 2240	7.3 / 0.4 / 7.4 / 0.5
14 TH	0411 / 1040 / 1628 / 2244	6.7 / 1.0 / 6.6 / 0.9	**29** F	0431 / 1105 / 1651 / 2311	7.1 / 0.5 / 7.2 / 0.7
15 F	0443 / 1051 / 1704 / 2303	6.7 / 1.0 / 6.5 / 0.9	**30** SA	0514 / 1143 / 1739 / 2347	6.7 / 0.7 / 6.9 / 1.0
			31 SU	0601 / 1227 / 1836	6.3 / 1.0 / 6.4

NOVEMBER

Day	Time	m	Day	Time	m
1 M	0034 / 0700 / 1329 / 1951	1.4 / 5.9 / 1.3 / 6.0	**16** TU	0618 / 1223 / 1900	6.1 / 1.3 / 6.0
2 TU	0142 / 0832 / 1456 / 2114	1.8 / 5.7 / 1.4 / 6.1	**17** W	0046 / 0714 / 1336 / 2002	1.5 / 5.9 / 1.5 / 5.9
3 W	0322 / 0947 / 1627 / 2221	1.8 / 5.9 / 1.1 / 6.4	**18** TH	0206 / 0822 / 1506 / 2114	1.7 / 5.8 / 1.4 / 6.0
4 TH	0447 / 1047 / 1730 / 2319	1.5 / 6.3 / 0.7 / 6.7	**19** F	0338 / 0940 / 1618 / 2226	1.6 / 5.9 / 1.2 / 6.3
5 F	0547 / 1141 / 1822	1.1 / 6.7 / 0.4	**20** SA	0448 / 1048 / 1726 / 2329	1.3 / 6.3 / 0.9 / 6.6
6 SA	0011 / 0639 / 1232 / 1910	7.0 / 0.7 / 7.0 / 0.2	**21** SU	0553 / 1147 / 1831	1.0 / 6.6 / 0.7
7 SU	0059 / 0728 / 1317 / 1954	7.2 / 0.5 / 7.1 / 0.2	**22** M	0023 / 0653 / 1240 / 1928	7.0 / 0.8 / 7.0 / 0.5
8 M ●	0141 / 0813 / 1357 / 2035	7.2 / 0.4 / 7.0 / 0.3	**23** TU O	0113 / 0750 / 1329 / 2019	7.2 / 0.6 / 7.2 / 0.4
9 TU	0218 / 0854 / 1433 / 2113	7.0 / 0.5 / 6.9 / 0.5	**24** W	0200 / 0842 / 1417 / 2106	7.3 / 0.4 / 7.4 / 0.4
10 W	0248 / 0931 / 1504 / 2143	6.9 / 0.7 / 6.7 / 0.8	**25** TH	0245 / 0930 / 1504 / 2148	7.1 / 0.3 / 7.5 / 0.5
11 TH	0314 / 0958 / 1533 / 2202	6.8 / 0.9 / 6.6 / 1.0	**26** F	0330 / 1015 / 1552 / 2227	7.3 / 0.3 / 7.5 / 0.5
12 F	0342 / 1010 / 1605 / 2212	6.7 / 1.0 / 6.4 / 1.0	**27** SA	0415 / 1058 / 1641 / 2303	7.1 / 0.4 / 7.3 / 0.7
13 SA	0414 / 1027 / 1641 / 2236	6.7 / 1.0 / 6.5 / 1.0	**28** SU	0500 / 1139 / 1731 / 2340	6.8 / 0.5 / 7.0 / 1.0
14 SU	0450 / 1057 / 1721 / 2311	6.6 / 1.0 / 6.4 / 1.0	**29** M	0547 / 1224 / 1827	6.5 / 0.8 / 6.7
15 M	0531 / 1135 / 1807 / 2353	6.4 / 1.1 / 6.2 / 1.2	**30** TU	0024 / 0644 / 1317 / 1932	1.3 / 6.1 / 1.0 / 6.3

DECEMBER

Day	Time	m	Day	Time	m
1 W	0122 / 0801 / 1424 / 2045	1.6 / 5.9 / 1.2 / 6.2	**16** TH	0027 / 0645 / 1305 / 1933	1.3 / 6.1 / 1.2 / 6.2
2 TH	0234 / 0913 / 1540 / 2149	1.8 / 6.0 / 1.1 / 6.3	**17** F	0127 / 0746 / 1417 / 2037	1.4 / 6.0 / 1.2 / 6.2
3 F	0354 / 1014 / 1648 / 2246	1.7 / 6.2 / 1.0 / 6.5	**18** SA	0244 / 0855 / 1532 / 2145	1.5 / 6.1 / 1.1 / 6.3
4 SA	0506 / 1110 / 1744 / 2339	1.4 / 6.4 / 0.8 / 6.7	**19** SU	0403 / 1005 / 1646 / 2252	1.4 / 6.3 / 1.0 / 6.5
5 SU	0605 / 1201 / 1834	1.1 / 6.7 / 0.6	**20** M	0516 / 1111 / 1758 / 2352	1.2 / 6.5 / 0.8 / 6.8
6 M	0028 / 0656 / 1249 / 1919	6.8 / 0.8 / 6.8 / 0.5	**21** TU	0625 / 1211 / 1901	0.9 / 6.8 / 0.7
7 TU ●	0111 / 0742 / 1332 / 2001	6.9 / 0.6 / 6.8 / 0.6	**22** W O	0047 / 0727 / 1307 / 1956	7.0 / 0.7 / 7.1 / 0.5
8 W	0149 / 0824 / 1410 / 2039	6.9 / 0.7 / 6.8 / 0.7	**23** TH	0138 / 0824 / 1400 / 2047	7.2 / 0.4 / 7.4 / 0.4
9 TH	0221 / 0901 / 1443 / 2111	6.8 / 0.8 / 6.7 / 0.9	**24** F	0227 / 0917 / 1450 / 2134	7.3 / 0.3 / 7.5 / 0.5
10 F	0250 / 0930 / 1515 / 2132	6.8 / 0.9 / 6.6 / 1.0	**25** SA	0314 / 1006 / 1540 / 2217	7.3 / 0.2 / 7.5 / 0.5
11 SA	0320 / 0950 / 1547 / 2151	6.7 / 1.0 / 6.6 / 1.0	**26** SU	0400 / 1051 / 1629 / 2256	7.2 / 0.2 / 7.4 / 0.7
12 SU	0352 / 1013 / 1621 / 2221	6.6 / 1.0 / 6.6 / 1.0	**27** M	0445 / 1133 / 1718 / 2333	7.0 / 0.3 / 7.2 / 0.9
13 M	0429 / 1045 / 1703 / 2257	6.6 / 1.0 / 6.5 / 1.0	**28** TU	0531 / 1214 / 1808	6.7 / 0.5 / 6.9
14 TU	0509 / 1124 / 1747 / 2338	6.5 / 1.0 / 6.4 / 1.1	**29** W	0011 / 0618 / 1256 / 1901	1.1 / 6.4 / 0.7 / 6.5
15 W	0554 / 1209 / 1837	6.3 / 1.1 / 6.3	**30** TH	0055 / 0715 / 1343 / 2002	1.3 / 6.1 / 1.0 / 6.2
			31 F	0147 / 0824 / 1437 / 2106	1.6 / 5.9 / 1.1 / 6.1

Chart Datum: 3·20 metres below Ordnance Datum (Newlyn)

SOUTHEND-ON-SEA/
LEIGH-ON-SEA   8-4-15

Essex (Lat/Long as for Waypoint) Rtg 3-5-2

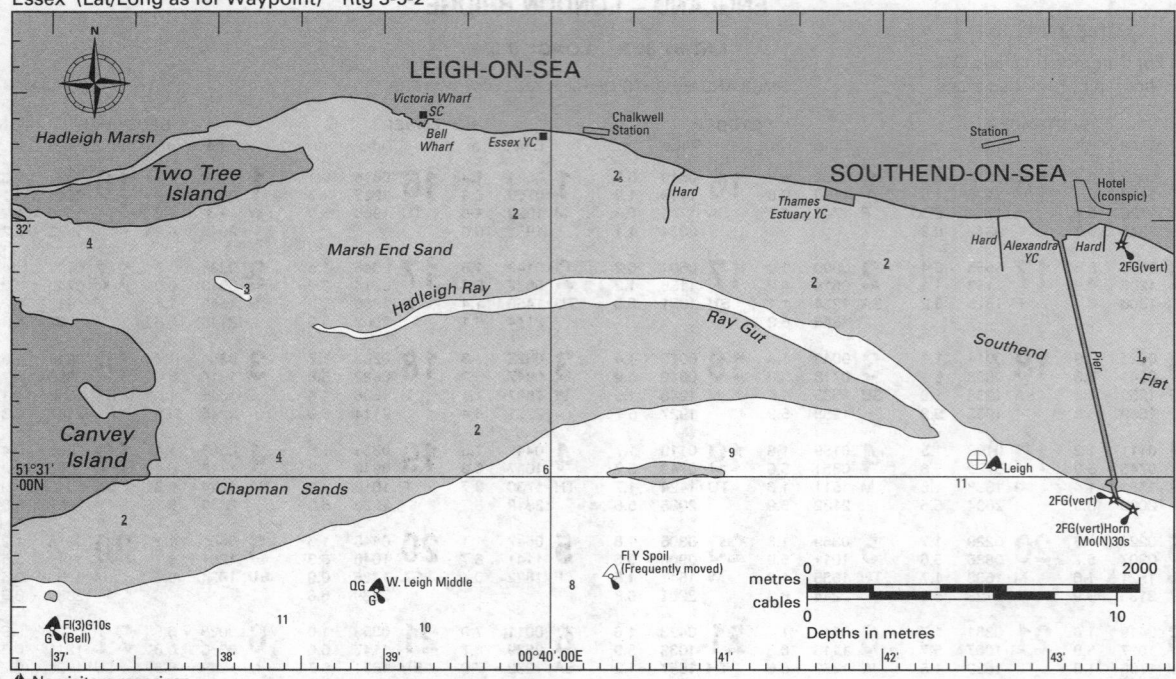

⚠ No visitors moorings

CHARTS
AC *1185, 1183*; Imray C2, Y6; Stanfords 5, 8; OS 178

TIDES
+0125 Dover; ML 3·0; Duration 0610; Zone 0 (UT)

Standard Port SHEERNESS (⟵)

Times				Height (metres)			
High Water		Low Water		MHWS	MHWN	MLWN	MLWS
0200	0800	0200	0700	5·8	4·7	1·5	0·6
1400	2000	1400	1900				
Differences SOUTHEND-ON-SEA							
−0005	−0005	−0005	−0005	0·0	0·0	−0·1	−0·1
CORYTON							
+0010	+0010	0000	+0010	+0·5	+0·4	−0·1	−0·1

SHELTER
The whole area dries soon after half ebb, except Ray Gut
(0·4 - 4·8m) which leads to Leigh Creek and Hadleigh Ray,
either side of Two Tree Island, thence to Benfleet Creek; all
are buoyed, but echo-sounder is essential. At Leigh-on-Sea
some drying moorings are available; or yachts can take the
ground alongside Bell Wharf or Victoria Wharf. It is also
possible to secure at the end of Southend Pier to collect
stores, FW. NOTE: Southend-on-Sea and Leigh-on-Sea are
both part of the lower PLA Area and an 8kn speed limit is
enforced in inshore areas. Southend BC launches *Alec
White II* , *Sidney Bates II* or *Low Way* patrol area (VHF Ch
68 16), Apr-Oct.

NAVIGATION
WPT Leigh SHM buoy, 51°31'·04N 00°42'·67E, at ent to
Ray Gut; this SHM buoy can be left close to port on
entering Ray Gut, since there is now more water NE of it
than to the SW. Appr from Shoeburyness, keep outside
the W Shoebury SHM buoy, Fl G 2·5s. Beware some 3000
small boat moorings 1M either side of Southend Pier.
Speed limit in Canvey Island/Hadleigh Ray areas is 8kn.

LIGHTS AND MARKS
Pier lts as on chartlet.

RADIO TELEPHONE
Thames Navigation Service: *Port Control London* VHF Ch 68.

TELEPHONE (Dial code 01702)
Hr Mr 611889, ☎ 355110; Hr Mr Leigh-on-Sea 710561;
MRSC (01255) 675518; Essex Police Marine Section
(01268) 775533; ✠ (01473) 235704 (H24); Marinecall 0891
500455; Police 341212; Dr 49451; Ⓗ 348911.

FACILITIES
SOUTHEND-ON-SEA: **Southend Pier** ☎ 215620, AB £6.20,
M, L, FW, Bar; **Alexandra YC** ☎ 340363, Bar, FW; **Thorpe
Bay YC** ☎ 587563, Bar, L, Slip, R, FW; **Thames Estuary YC**
☎ 345967; **Halfway YC** ☎ 582025, pre-book 1 ⚓, FW;
Town EC Wed. CH, ACA, Ⓔ, V, R, Bar, ✉, Ⓑ, ⇌, ✈.
LEIGH-ON-SEA: **Essex YC** ☎ 78404, FW, Bar; **Leigh on Sea
SC** ☎ 76788, FW, Bar; **Bell Wharf**, AB (1st 24hrs free, then
£4.25 for subsequent 24 hrs); **Victoria Wharf** AB, SM, Slip;
Town: EC Wed, P &D (cans), ME, El, Sh, C, CH, SM.
CANVEY ISLAND: **Services:** Slip, M, D, FW, ME, El, Sh, C,
Gas, CH, Access HW±2; **Island YC** ☎ 683729.
BENFLEET: **Benfleet YC** ☎ (01268) 792278, Access HW±2½,
M, Slip, FW, D (by day), CH, ME, El, Sh, C, Bar, V, ▣.

AGENTS WANTED

If you are interested in becoming our agent for any of the
following ports, please write to: The Editor, Edington House,
Trent, Sherborne, Dorset DT9 4SR, England – and get your
free copy of the Almanac annually. You do not have to live in
a port to be the agent, but should at least be a fairly regular
visitor.

Plymouth	Port Haliguen
Walton-on-the-Naze	La Trinité-sur-Mer
Hopeman	Piriac
Burghead	St Nazaire/Loire
Findhorn	Pornic
Nairn	St Gilles-Croix-de-Vie
Inverness	Les Sables d'Olonne
Loch Aline	River Seudre
Craobh	Port Bloc/Gironde
Workington	Anglet/Bayonne
Lough Swilly	St Jean-de-Luz
Portbail	Hendaye
St Malo/Dinard	Grandcamp-Maisy
Le Légué/St Brieuc	Port-en-Bessin
Lampaul	Ouistreham/Caen
L'Aberildut	Dives
Douarnenez	St Valéry-en-Caux
Lorient	Dunkerque
River Étel	Emden
Le Palais (Belle Ile)	Langeoog

RIVER ROACH/HAVENGORE

8-4-16

Essex 51°36'·95N 00°52'·24E (Branklet SPM buoy), R Roach Rtg 1-5-1. 51°33'·59N 00°50'·62E, Havengore Bridge, Rtg 5-5-3

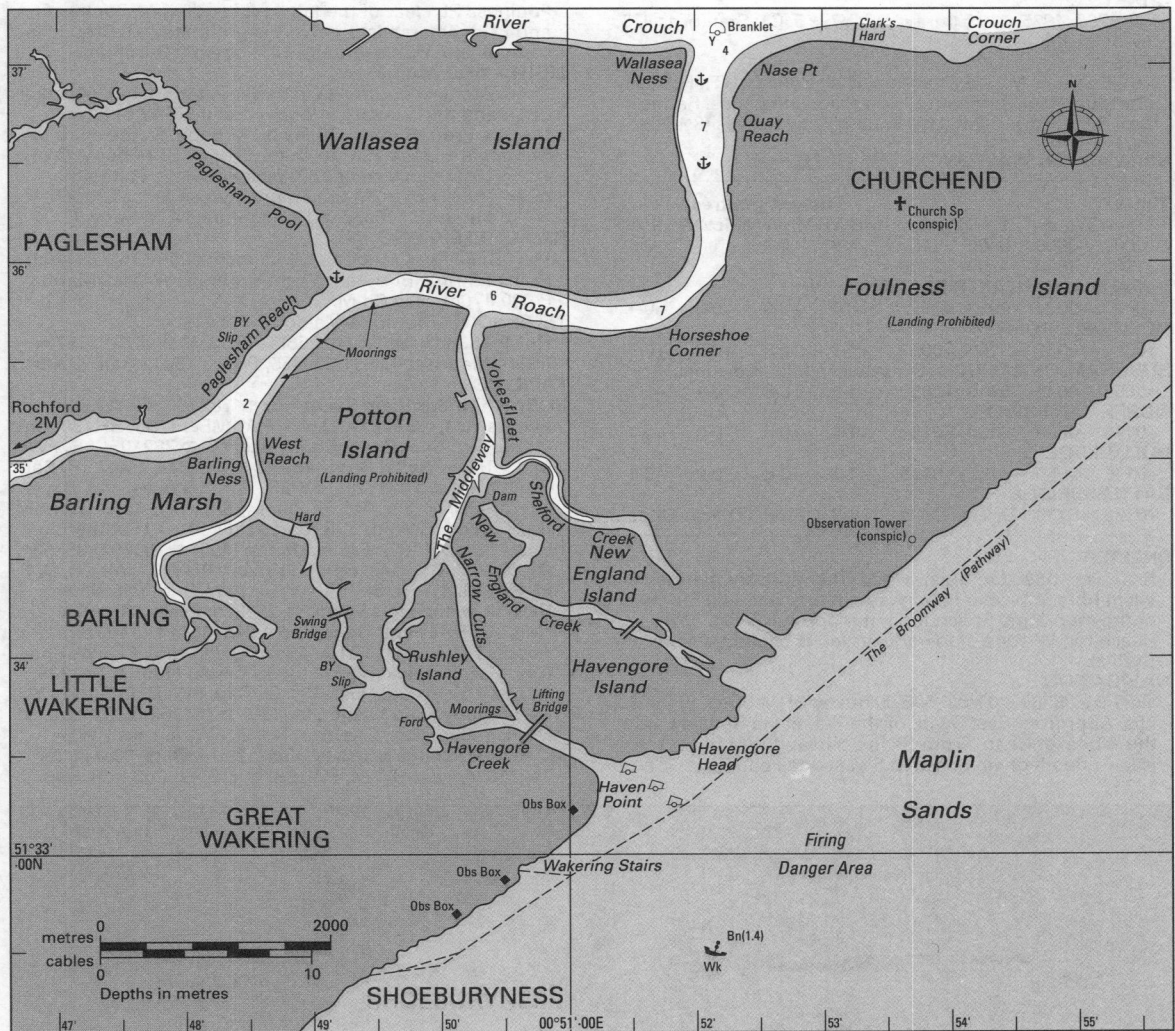

CHARTS
AC *3750, 1185*; Imray C1, Y17; Stanfords 4, 5; OS 178
TIDES
+0110 Dover; ML 2·7; Duration 0615; Zone 0 (UT)

Standard Port WALTON-ON-THE-NAZE (→)

Times				Height (metres)			
High Water		Low Water		MHWS	MHWN	MLWN	MLWS
0000	0600	0500	1100	4·2	3·4	1·1	0·4
1200	1800	1700	2300				
Differences ROCHFORD							
+0050	+0040	Dries		−0·8	−1·1	Dries	

SHELTER
Good. The Roach gives sheltered sailing and access to a network of secluded creeks, including Havengore (the "backdoor" from the Crouch to the Thames Estuary). ⚓s behind sea-walls can be found for all winds at: Quay Reach (often more protected than the Crouch), Paglesham Reach (possible moorings from BY at East End), West Reach, Barling Reach and Yokes Fleet. An ⚓ light is essential due to freighters H24. Speed limit 8kn. Crouch Hbr Authority controls R Roach and Crouch, out to Foulness Pt.
NAVIGATION
Normal access H24 to the Roach is from R Crouch (see 8.4.17 for WPT from seaward); the ent between Branklet SPM buoy and Nase Pt is narrowed by mudbanks. Unlit buoys up-river to Barling Ness, above which few boats go.

To exit at Havengore Creek, appr via Middleway and Narrow Cuts to reach the bridge before HW.
Entry via **Havengore Creek** is possible in good weather, with great care and adequate rise of tide (max draft 1·5m at HW sp). Shoeburyness Range is usually active Mon-Fri 0600-1700LT; give 24hrs notice to Range Officer by ☎. Subsequent clearance on VHF by Havengore lifting bridge (☎ HW±2, HJ); no passage unless bridge raised. Least water is over the shifting bar, just inside creek ent. From the S, cross Maplin Sands at HW −1 from S Shoebury SHM buoy, Fl G 5s (51°30'·40N 00°52'·50E), leaving Pisces wreck (conspic, 1M from ent) to port.
LIGHTS AND MARKS
Unlit, but night entry to R Roach may be possible.
RADIO TELEPHONE
VHF Ch 72 16 is worked by Range Officer (*Shoe Base*) (HO); Radar Control (*Shoe Radar*) (HO); & Bridge keeper (*Shoe Bridge*) (HW±2 by day). Radar guidance may be available.
TELEPHONE (Dial code 01702= Southend)
Crouch Hbr Mr (01621) 783602; Range Officer 292271 Ext 3211; Havengore Bridge Ext 3436; Marinecall 0891 500455; ⌗ (01473) 235704 (H24); MRSC (01255) 675518; Dr 218678.
FACILITIES
Paglesham (East End) M £5, FW, D, slip, EI, ME (from BY), Sh, Bar; **Gt Wakering**: Slip, P, D, FW, ME, EI, Sh, C, CH (from BY); @ Rochford **Wakering YC** ☎ 530926, M, L, Bar. **Towns** EC Wed Gt Wakering & Rochford; V, R, Bar, ✉ (Great Wakering and Barling); most facilities, Ⓑ and ⇌ in Rochford and Shoeburyness, ✈ (Southend).

BURNHAM-ON-CROUCH   8-4-17

Essex 51°37'·47N 00°48'·33E (Yacht Hbr)   Rtg 1-1-2

CHARTS
AC *3750, 1975, 1183*; Imray Y17, Y7, Y6, C1; Stanfords 4, 5, 19, 1; OS168

TIDES
+0115 Dover; ML 2·5; Duration 0610; Zone 0 (UT). Full daily predictions for Burnham are on following pages. Ranges: Sp = 5·0m; Np = 3·2m. Use Walton Tidal Curves (8.4.20)

Standard Port WALTON-ON-THE-NAZE (→)

Times				Height (metres)			
High Water		Low Water		MHWS	MHWN	MLWN	MLWS
0000	0600	0500	1100	4·2	3·4	1·1	0·4
1200	1800	1700	2300				

Differences WHITAKER BEACON
| +0022 | +0024 | +0033 | +0027 | +0·6 | +0·5 | +0·2 | +0·1 |

HOLLIWELL POINT
| +0034 | +0037 | +0100 | +0037 | +1·1 | +0·9 | +0·3 | +0·1 |

BURNHAM-ON-CROUCH (but see also full predictions)
| +0050 | +0035 | +0115 | +0050 | +1·0 | +0·8 | −0·1 | −0·2 |

NORTH FAMBRIDGE
| +0115 | +0050 | +0130 | +0100 | +1·1 | +0·8 | 0·0 | −0·1 |

HULLBRIDGE
| +0115 | +0050 | +0135 | +0105 | +1·1 | +0·8 | 0·0 | −0·1 |

BATTLESBRIDGE
| +0120 | +0110 | Dries | Dries | −1·8 | −2·0 | Dries | Dries |

SHELTER
River is exposed to most winds. There are six marinas or yacht hbrs. ⚓ prohib in fairway but possible just E or W of the moorings. Speed limit in moorings is 8kn. Cliff Reach (off W edge of lower chartlet) is sheltered from SW'lies.

NAVIGATION
WPT 51°39'·82N 01°02'·60E, S Buxey SHM buoy, Fl (3) G 15s. Appr from East Swin, or the Wallet via Spitway, into the Whitaker Chan. From Swin Spitway SWM buoy, there is least depth of 4m between Swallowtail and Buxey Sand.

Near Sunken Buxey seas can be hazardous with strong wind over tide. Ray Sand Chan (dries 1·7m) is usable on the tide by shoal draft boats as a short cut from/to the Blackwater. Shoeburyness Artillery ranges lie E and S of Foulness Pt, clear of the fairway. Landing on Foulness and Bridgemarsh Is (up river) is prohibited. R. Crouch is navigable to Battlesbridge, 10M beyond Burnham.

LIGHTS AND MARKS
There are few landmarks to assist entering, but Whitaker Chan and the river are lit/buoyed to 0·5M W of Essex Marina. From Sunken Buxey NCM buoy, Q, the spire of St Mary's ⚑ leads 233° to Outer Crouch SCM buoy, Q (6) + L Fl 15s; thence steer 240° past Foulness Pt into the river. There is a 2·2M unlit gap between Inner Crouch SWM buoy, L Fl 10s, and Horse Shoal NCM buoy, Q.

RADIO TELEPHONE
VHF Ch 80 for: Crouch Hr Mr Launch (0900-1700LT, w/e); Essex Marina; Burnham Yacht Harbour; W Wick Marina (1000-1700), also Ch M.

TELEPHONE (Dial code Maldon = 01621)
Hr Mr 783602; MRSC (01255) 675518; ⌗ (01473) 235704 (H24); Marinecall 0891 500455; Police 782121; Dr 782054.

FACILITIES
BURNHAM: **Burnham Yacht Hbr** ☎ 782150, 🖅 785848, Access H24, (350) £10, D, AC, FW, ME, El, Sh, BH (30 ton), CH, 🅟, Bar, Slip; **Royal Corinthian YC** ☎ 782105, AB, FW, M, L, R, Bar; **Royal Burnham YC** ☎ 782044, FW, L, R, Bar; **Crouch YC** ☎ 782252, L, FW, R, Bar; **Services:** AB, BY, C (15 ton), D, P, FW, ME, El, Sh, M, Slip, CH, ACA, Gas, SM, Gaz. **Town** EC Wed; V, R, Bar, ✉, Ⓑ, ≥, ✈ (Southend).
WALLASEA (01702): **Essex Marina** (400) ☎ (01702) 258531, 🖅 258227, BY, Gas, Bar, C (13 ton), BH (40 ton), CH, D, P, El, FW, M, ME, R, Sh, Slip, V; Ferry to Burnham Town Hard at w/ends in season, ☎ 258870; **Essex YC**; ACA.
FAMBRIDGE: **N Fambridge Yacht Stn** (150) ☎ 740370, Access HW±5, M, CH, Sh, ME, BY, C (5 ton), El, FW, Slip, Gas, Gaz; **W Wick Marina** (Stow Creek) (180) ☎ 741268, Access HW±5, Gas, Gaz, CH, El, Slip, FW, D, C (5 ton), YC, Bar; **Brandy Hole Yacht Stn** (120) ☎ (01702) 230248, L, M, ME, Sh, Slip, Gas, Gaz, Bar, BY, D, FW, Access HW±4.
ALTHORNE: **Bridge Marsh Marina** (125 + 6 Ⓥ) ☎ 740414, 🖅 742216, Access HW±4, FW, Sh, 🅟, ME, El, C (8 ton), Slip.

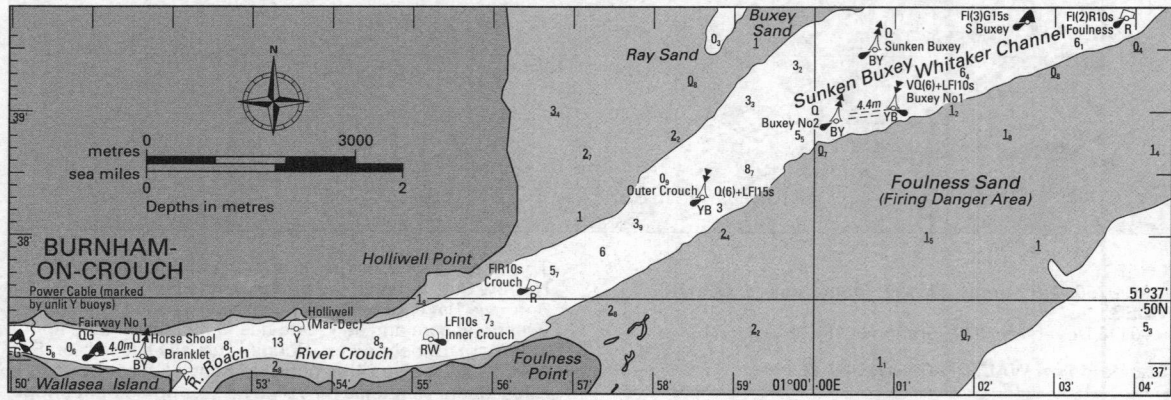

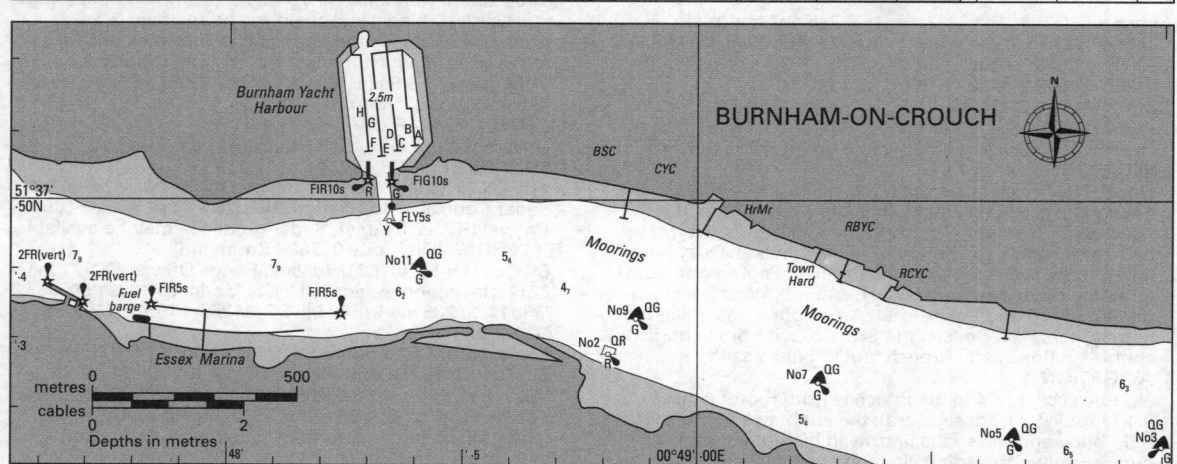

ENGLAND – BURNHAM–ON–CROUCH

LAT 51°37′N   LONG 0°48′E

TIMES AND HEIGHTS OF HIGH AND LOW WATERS

YEAR **1999**

TIME ZONE (UT)
For Summer Time add ONE hour in non-shaded areas

4

JANUARY

Day	Time	m	Day	Time	m
1 F	0540 / 1124 / 1811 / 2356	0.4 / 5.1 / 5.1 / 5.1	**16** SA	0554 / 1141 / 1810 / 2358	0.7 / 4.8 / 0.7 / 5.0
2 SA O	0635 / 1219 / 1855	0.2 / 5.2 / 0.3	**17** SU ●	0635 / 1223 / 1847	0.5 / 5.0 / 0.5
3 SU	0047 / 0722 / 1309 / 1937	5.2 / 0.1 / 5.3 / 0.3	**18** M	0038 / 0712 / 1303 / 1922	5.0 / 0.4 / 5.1 / 0.5
4 M	0132 / 0807 / 1356 / 2015	5.2 / 0.1 / 5.3 / 0.4	**19** TU	0114 / 0747 / 1339 / 1956	5.0 / 0.3 / 5.1 / 0.5
5 TU	0214 / 0850 / 1437 / 2053	5.2 / 0.1 / 5.2 / 0.5	**20** W	0151 / 0824 / 1416 / 2029	5.1 / 0.3 / 5.1 / 0.5
6 W	0253 / 0931 / 1519 / 2129	5.1 / 0.1 / 5.1 / 0.7	**21** TH	0226 / 0900 / 1454 / 2104	5.1 / 0.2 / 5.1 / 0.5
7 TH	0330 / 1012 / 1558 / 2205	5.0 / 0.2 / 4.8 / 0.8	**22** F	0302 / 0937 / 1535 / 2142	5.0 / 0.2 / 5.1 / 0.5
8 F	0407 / 1052 / 1638 / 2243	4.7 / 0.4 / 4.7 / 1.0	**23** SA	0343 / 1019 / 1619 / 2225	5.0 / 0.2 / 5.0 / 0.5
9 SA	0448 / 1134 / 1722 / 2327	4.6 / 0.5 / 4.5 / 1.1	**24** SU	0428 / 1104 / 1709 / 2314	4.8 / 0.3 / 4.7 / 0.7
10 SU	0536 / 1226 / 1812	4.3 / 0.8 / 4.2	**25** M	0521 / 1200 / 1807	4.7 / 0.4 / 4.5
11 M	0027 / 0636 / 1327 / 1918	1.2 / 4.2 / 0.9 / 4.1	**26** TU	0016 / 0624 / 1315 / 1915	0.9 / 4.5 / 0.5 / 4.3
12 TU	0141 / 0751 / 1432 / 2031	1.2 / 4.2 / 0.9 / 4.2	**27** W	0137 / 0742 / 1440 / 2031	0.9 / 4.5 / 0.7 / 4.3
13 W	0259 / 0902 / 1536 / 2135	1.1 / 4.3 / 0.9 / 4.5	**28** TH	0305 / 0900 / 1557 / 2143	0.8 / 4.6 / 0.5 / 4.6
14 TH	0408 / 1002 / 1634 / 2227	1.0 / 4.5 / 0.8 / 4.6	**29** F	0425 / 1011 / 1702 / 2247	0.7 / 4.7 / 0.5 / 4.7
15 F	0505 / 1053 / 1724 / 2315	0.8 / 4.7 / 0.7 / 4.8	**30** SA	0532 / 1114 / 1758 / 2344	0.4 / 5.0 / 0.4 / 5.0
			31 SU O	0628 / 1211 / 1843	0.2 / 5.1 / 0.4

FEBRUARY

Day	Time	m	Day	Time	m
1 M	0035 / 0714 / 1300 / 1923	5.1 / 0.1 / 5.2 / 0.4	**16** TU ●	0018 / 0655 / 1245 / 1904	5.0 / 0.3 / 5.1 / 0.4
2 TU	0119 / 0755 / 1343 / 2000	5.1 / 0.0 / 5.2 / 0.4	**17** W	0058 / 0732 / 1323 / 1939	5.1 / 0.2 / 5.2 / 0.4
3 W	0158 / 0834 / 1421 / 2034	5.1 / 0.1 / 5.2 / 0.4	**18** TH	0134 / 0808 / 1400 / 2013	5.2 / 0.1 / 5.3 / 0.3
4 TH	0233 / 0909 / 1456 / 2105	5.1 / 0.0 / 5.1 / 0.5	**19** F	0211 / 0844 / 1438 / 2049	5.2 / 0.0 / 5.3 / 0.3
5 F	0304 / 0942 / 1529 / 2135	5.0 / 0.2 / 5.0 / 0.7	**20** SA	0248 / 0920 / 1518 / 2126	5.2 / 0.1 / 5.2 / 0.3
6 SA	0336 / 1014 / 1601 / 2205	5.0 / 0.3 / 4.7 / 0.7	**21** SU	0328 / 0958 / 1600 / 2207	5.2 / 0.1 / 5.1 / 0.3
7 SU	0411 / 1048 / 1635 / 2242	4.7 / 0.4 / 4.6 / 0.8	**22** M	0411 / 1041 / 1647 / 2253	5.1 / 0.2 / 4.8 / 0.5
8 M	0450 / 1129 / 1717 / 2328	4.6 / 0.7 / 4.3 / 1.0	**23** TU	0500 / 1132 / 1741 / 2349	4.8 / 0.4 / 4.5 / 0.7
9 TU	0539 / 1225 / 1807	4.3 / 0.9 / 4.2	**24** W	0602 / 1245 / 1847	4.5 / 0.7 / 4.2
10 W	0033 / 0641 / 1333 / 1914	1.1 / 4.1 / 1.0 / 4.1	**25** TH	0111 / 0722 / 1418 / 2008	0.9 / 4.3 / 0.8 / 4.2
11 TH	0151 / 0804 / 1445 / 2035	1.1 / 4.1 / 1.0 / 4.1	**26** F	0252 / 0849 / 1543 / 2128	0.8 / 4.3 / 0.8 / 4.3
12 F	0313 / 0922 / 1554 / 2148	1.1 / 4.2 / 0.9 / 4.3	**27** SA	0419 / 1006 / 1650 / 2235	0.7 / 4.6 / 0.7 / 4.6
13 SA	0428 / 1024 / 1655 / 2245	0.9 / 4.5 / 0.8 / 4.6	**28** SU	0525 / 1108 / 1744 / 2331	0.3 / 5.0 / 0.5 / 4.8
14 SU	0527 / 1117 / 1745 / 2334	0.7 / 4.7 / 0.7 / 4.8			
15 M	0616 / 1202 / 1828	0.4 / 5.0 / 0.5			

MARCH

Day	Time	m	Day	Time	m
1 M	0618 / 1201 / 1828	0.2 / 5.1 / 0.4	**16** TU	0548 / 1138 / 1803 / 2352	0.3 / 5.0 / 0.5 / 5.0
2 TU O	0021 / 0700 / 1248 / 1905	5.1 / 0.1 / 5.2 / 0.4	**17** W ●	0632 / 1222 / 1842	0.2 / 5.2 / 0.3
3 W	0104 / 0737 / 1328 / 1940	5.1 / 0.1 / 5.2 / 0.4	**18** TH	0035 / 0711 / 1303 / 1919	5.1 / 0.0 / 5.3 / 0.4
4 TH	0140 / 0811 / 1401 / 2012	5.1 / 0.1 / 5.1 / 0.4	**19** F	0115 / 0747 / 1342 / 1956	5.3 / -0.1 / 5.5 / 0.1
5 F	0212 / 0842 / 1431 / 2040	5.1 / 0.1 / 5.0 / 0.4	**20** SA	0154 / 0824 / 1420 / 2033	5.3 / -0.1 / 5.5 / 0.1
6 SA	0239 / 0909 / 1459 / 2107	5.0 / 0.2 / 4.8 / 0.4	**21** SU	0232 / 0900 / 1500 / 2111	5.5 / -0.1 / 5.3 / 0.1
7 SU	0307 / 0937 / 1527 / 2136	5.0 / 0.3 / 4.8 / 0.4	**22** M	0313 / 0939 / 1543 / 2152	5.3 / 0.0 / 5.1 / 0.2
8 M	0340 / 1007 / 1559 / 2209	4.8 / 0.4 / 4.7 / 0.5	**23** TU	0357 / 1021 / 1629 / 2239	5.2 / 0.2 / 4.8 / 0.3
9 TU	0416 / 1045 / 1637 / 2250	4.7 / 0.7 / 4.6 / 0.8	**24** W	0447 / 1113 / 1722 / 2335	4.8 / 0.5 / 4.5 / 0.5
10 W	0500 / 1133 / 1724 / 2343	4.5 / 0.8 / 4.3 / 0.9	**25** TH	0549 / 1223 / 1826	4.5 / 0.8 / 4.1
11 TH	0555 / 1242 / 1821	4.2 / 1.0 / 4.1	**26** F	0059 / 0711 / 1400 / 1949	0.8 / 4.3 / 1.0 / 4.1
12 F	0100 / 0708 / 1400 / 1938	1.1 / 4.0 / 1.1 / 4.0	**27** SA	0245 / 0840 / 1527 / 2110	0.8 / 4.3 / 0.9 / 4.2
13 SA	0226 / 0837 / 1516 / 2103	1.0 / 4.2 / 1.0 / 4.2	**28** SU	0407 / 0954 / 1632 / 2217	0.5 / 4.6 / 0.8 / 4.6
14 SU	0349 / 0952 / 1623 / 2211	0.9 / 4.3 / 0.9 / 4.5	**29** M	0509 / 1053 / 1724 / 2312	0.3 / 5.0 / 0.7 / 4.8
15 M	0455 / 1049 / 1716 / 2305	0.7 / 4.7 / 0.7 / 4.7	**30** TU	0559 / 1144 / 1809	0.1 / 5.1 / 0.5
			31 W O	0000 / 0639 / 1227 / 1845	5.0 / 0.1 / 5.1 / 0.4

APRIL

Day	Time	m	Day	Time	m
1 TH	0043 / 0713 / 1305 / 1918	5.1 / 0.1 / 5.1 / 0.4	**16** F ●	0008 / 0647 / 1240 / 1858	5.2 / 0.0 / 5.5 / 0.2
2 F	0118 / 0744 / 1338 / 1948	5.0 / 0.2 / 5.0 / 0.4	**17** SA	0052 / 0725 / 1322 / 1938	5.3 / -0.1 / 5.5 / 0.1
3 SA	0148 / 0812 / 1405 / 2016	5.0 / 0.2 / 4.8 / 0.4	**18** SU	0134 / 0804 / 1403 / 2018	5.5 / -0.1 / 5.5 / 0.0
4 SU	0215 / 0838 / 1429 / 2042	5.0 / 0.3 / 4.8 / 0.3	**19** M	0217 / 0843 / 1444 / 2058	5.5 / -0.1 / 5.3 / 0.0
5 M	0242 / 0905 / 1457 / 2110	5.0 / 0.3 / 4.8 / 0.3	**20** TU	0300 / 0923 / 1528 / 2142	5.5 / 0.1 / 5.1 / 0.1
6 TU	0314 / 0934 / 1529 / 2144	4.8 / 0.4 / 4.8 / 0.4	**21** W	0347 / 1006 / 1614 / 2231	5.2 / 0.3 / 4.8 / 0.2
7 W	0351 / 1008 / 1607 / 2223	4.7 / 0.7 / 4.7 / 0.5	**22** TH	0438 / 1057 / 1707 / 2329	5.0 / 0.7 / 4.6 / 0.4
8 TH	0432 / 1052 / 1653 / 2313	4.6 / 0.9 / 4.5 / 0.8	**23** F	0541 / 1204 / 1810	4.6 / 1.0 / 4.2
9 F	0524 / 1152 / 1748	4.2 / 1.0 / 4.2	**24** SA	0052 / 0657 / 1336 / 1928	0.7 / 4.3 / 1.1 / 4.2
10 SA	0020 / 0628 / 1315 / 1857	0.9 / 4.1 / 1.2 / 4.1	**25** SU	0226 / 0819 / 1459 / 2043	0.7 / 4.5 / 1.1 / 4.3
11 SU	0144 / 0752 / 1436 / 2018	1.0 / 4.1 / 1.1 / 4.1	**26** M	0343 / 0930 / 1605 / 2149	0.4 / 4.6 / 0.9 / 4.6
12 M	0307 / 0914 / 1545 / 2131	0.8 / 4.3 / 0.9 / 4.3	**27** TU	0442 / 1027 / 1657 / 2244	0.3 / 4.8 / 0.8 / 4.7
13 TU	0419 / 1016 / 1642 / 2230	0.5 / 4.7 / 0.7 / 4.7	**28** W	0531 / 1117 / 1743 / 2332	0.2 / 5.0 / 0.5 / 5.0
14 W	0515 / 1107 / 1732 / 2320	0.3 / 5.1 / 0.5 / 5.0	**29** TH	0613 / 1200 / 1822	0.2 / 5.1 / 0.5
15 TH	0604 / 1154 / 1818	0.2 / 5.2 / 0.3	**30** F O	0014 / 0646 / 1239 / 1856	5.0 / 0.2 / 5.0 / 0.4

Chart Datum: 2·35 metres below Ordnance Datum (Newlyn)

ENGLAND – BURNHAM–ON–CROUCH

LAT 51°37'N   LONG   0°48'E

TIMES AND HEIGHTS OF HIGH AND LOW WATERS

YEAR **1999**

TIME ZONE (UT)
For Summer Time add ONE hour in non-shaded areas

Chart Datum: 2·35 metres below Ordnance Datum (Newlyn)

MAY

Day	Time	m	Time	m		Day	Time	m	Time	m
1 SA	0051 / 1311	5.0 / 5.0	0715 / 1926	0.3 / 0.4		16 SU	0028 / 1301	5.3 / 5.5	0705 / 1922	-0.1 / 0.1
2 SU	0123 / 1338	4.8 / 4.8	0743 / 1953	0.3 / 0.4		17 M	0116 / 1346	5.5 / 5.3	0746 / 2006	0.0 / 0.0
3 M	0151 / 1404	4.8 / 4.8	0810 / 2021	0.4 / 0.4		18 TU	0202 / 1429	5.5 / 5.3	0827 / 2049	0.0 / 0.0
4 TU	0220 / 1432	4.8 / 4.8	0838 / 2051	0.4 / 0.4		19 W	0248 / 1514	5.5 / 5.1	0923 / 2136	0.2 / 0.0
5 W	0254 / 1505	4.8 / 4.8	0908 / 2125	0.5 / 0.4		20 TH	0337 / 1601	5.2 / 5.0	0953 / 2226	0.4 / 0.3
6 TH	0330 / 1544	4.7 / 4.7	0942 / 2205	0.7 / 0.5		21 F	0429 / 1652	5.0 / 4.7	1043 / 2322	0.8 / 0.3
7 F	0412 / 1629	4.6 / 4.5	1022 / 2250	0.9 / 0.7		22 SA	0526 / 1749	4.7 / 4.5	1141	1.0
8 SA	0501 / 1722	4.3 / 4.2	1115 / 2348	1.0 / 0.8		23 SU	0033 / 1258	0.5 / 1.2	0631 / 1855	4.5 / 4.3
9 SU	0602 / 1825	4.2 / 4.1	1229	1.1		24 M	0153 / 1418	0.5 / 1.2	0745 / 2005	4.5 / 4.3
10 M	0107 / 1352	0.8 / 1.1	0714 / 1938	4.2 / 4.2		25 TU	0305 / 1528	0.5 / 1.0	0853 / 2109	4.6 / 4.5
11 TU	0228 / 1503	0.7 / 1.0	0832 / 2048	4.5 / 4.3		26 W	0406 / 1625	0.4 / 0.9	0952 / 2207	4.7 / 4.6
12 W	0339 / 1605	0.4 / 0.8	0938 / 2150	4.7 / 4.7		27 TH	0455 / 1713	0.4 / 0.7	1042 / 2257	4.8 / 4.8
13 TH	0440 / 1659	0.2 / 0.5	1034 / 2246	5.0 / 5.0		28 F	0538 / 1757	0.3 / 0.5	1127 / 2342	5.0 / 4.8
14 F	0534 / 1752	0.1 / 0.3	1125 / 2339	5.2 / 5.2		29 SA	0616 / 1834	0.4 / 0.5	1208	5.0
15 SA ●	0623 / 1838	0.0 / 0.2	1214	5.3		30 SU O	0022 / 1244	4.8 / 5.0	0648 / 1905	0.4 / 0.4
						31 M	0058 / 1315	4.8 / 4.8	0718 / 1934	0.4 / 0.4

JUNE

Day	Time	m	Time	m		Day	Time	m	Time	m
1 TU	0131 / 1343	4.8 / 4.8	0747 / 2005	0.5 / 0.4		16 W	0150 / 1416	5.5 / 5.2	0814 / 2043	0.2 / 0.0
2 W	0202 / 1414	4.8 / 4.8	0818 / 2037	0.5 / 0.4		17 TH	0236 / 1500	5.5 / 5.2	0856 / 2129	0.3 / 0.0
3 TH	0236 / 1448	4.8 / 4.8	0849 / 2111	0.5 / 0.4		18 F	0325 / 1546	5.2 / 5.1	0938 / 2217	0.5 / 0.1
4 F	0314 / 1527	4.7 / 4.7	0923 / 2151	0.7 / 0.4		19 SA	0412 / 1631	5.1 / 4.8	1023 / 2305	0.8 / 0.2
5 SA	0355 / 1609	4.7 / 4.6	1002 / 2233	0.8 / 0.5		20 SU	0503 / 1721	4.8 / 4.6	1112	1.0
6 SU	0442 / 1658	4.6 / 4.5	1049 / 2325	0.9 / 0.5		21 M	0000 / 1210	0.4 / 1.1	0558 / 1816	4.6 / 4.5
7 M	0537 / 1756	4.5 / 4.3	1147	1.0		22 TU	0104 / 1324	0.5 / 1.2	0659 / 1918	4.3 / 4.3
8 TU	0031 / 1303	0.7 / 1.1	0639 / 1900	4.5 / 4.3		23 W	0212 / 1437	0.7 / 1.2	0806 / 2023	4.3 / 4.3
9 W	0146 / 1418	0.5 / 1.0	0751 / 2008	4.5 / 4.3		24 TH	0315 / 1543	0.7 / 1.0	0907 / 2125	4.5 / 4.5
10 TH	0301 / 1527	0.4 / 0.8	0859 / 2114	4.7 / 4.7		25 F	0411 / 1640	0.7 / 0.9	1003 / 2219	4.6 / 4.6
11 F	0408 / 1629	0.3 / 0.5	1001 / 2214	5.0 / 5.0		26 SA	0459 / 1729	0.5 / 0.8	1052 / 2309	4.8 / 4.7
12 SA	0507 / 1728	0.1 / 0.4	1057 / 2311	5.1 / 5.1		27 SU	0543 / 1813	0.5 / 0.7	1136 / 2354	4.8 / 4.8
13 SU ●	0601 / 1822	0.1 / 0.2	1151	5.2		28 M O	0622 / 1848	0.5 / 0.5	1217	5.0
14 M	0008 / 1243	5.3 / 5.3	0649 / 1911	0.2 / 0.1		29 TU	0036 / 1254	4.8 / 5.0	0656 / 1920	0.5 / 0.4
15 TU	0101 / 1331	5.3 / 5.3	0732 / 1957	0.1 / 0.0		30 W	0112 / 1327	4.8 / 4.8	0729 / 1952	0.5 / 0.4

JULY

Day	Time	m	Time	m		Day	Time	m	Time	m
1 TH	0147 / 1359	4.8 / 4.8	0801 / 2025	0.5 / 0.4		16 F	0224 / 1444	5.3 / 5.2	0840 / 2116	0.4 / 0.0
2 F	0221 / 1434	4.8 / 4.8	0834 / 2100	0.7 / 0.4		17 SA	0308 / 1526	5.2 / 5.1	0920 / 2157	0.5 / 0.1
3 SA	0258 / 1510	4.8 / 4.8	0908 / 2137	0.7 / 0.3		18 SU	0351 / 1605	5.1 / 5.0	0959 / 2238	0.7 / 0.2
4 SU	0338 / 1550	4.8 / 4.7	0945 / 2217	0.7 / 0.4		19 M	0432 / 1646	4.8 / 4.8	1039 / 2319	0.9 / 0.4
5 M	0422 / 1634	4.7 / 4.6	1027 / 2301	0.8 / 0.4		20 TU	0517 / 1730	4.6 / 4.6	1123	1.0
6 TU	0512 / 1725	4.6 / 4.5	1117 / 2354	0.9 / 0.4		21 W	0007 / 1219	0.7 / 1.2	0606 / 1823	4.3 / 4.3
7 W	0608 / 1824	4.6 / 4.5	1220	1.0		22 TH	0106 / 1330	0.8 / 1.2	0704 / 1929	4.2 / 4.2
8 TH	0106 / 1337	0.5 / 1.0	0714 / 1932	4.5 / 4.5		23 F	0211 / 1447	0.9 / 1.2	0813 / 2038	4.2 / 4.2
9 F	0225 / 1453	0.5 / 0.9	0823 / 2041	4.6 / 4.6		24 SA	0317 / 1559	0.9 / 1.0	0919 / 2143	4.3 / 4.3
10 SA	0339 / 1606	0.4 / 0.7	0931 / 2149	4.7 / 4.8		25 SU	0418 / 1658	0.8 / 0.7	1016 / 2240	4.6 / 4.6
11 SU	0445 / 1712	0.3 / 0.4	1034 / 2253	5.0 / 5.0		26 M	0510 / 1748	0.7 / 0.7	1107 / 2330	4.8 / 4.7
12 M	0544 / 1813	0.2 / 0.3	1133 / 2354	5.1 / 5.2		27 TU	0557 / 1830	0.7 / 0.5	1152	5.0
13 TU O	0635 / 1903	0.2 / 0.1	1227 / 1905	5.2 / 0.4		28 W	0015 / 1233	4.8 / 5.0	0636 / 1905	0.5 / 0.4
14 W	0050 / 1317	5.3 / 5.2	0718 / 1949	0.2 / 0.0		29 TH	0055 / 1310	5.0 / 5.0	0711 / 1938	0.5 / 0.4
15 TH	0139 / 1402	5.3 / 5.3	0800 / 2034	0.3 / 0.0		30 F	0131 / 1344	5.0 / 5.0	0745 / 2012	0.5 / 0.3
						31 SA	0205 / 1417	5.0 / 5.0	0818 / 2046	0.5 / 0.3

AUGUST

Day	Time	m	Time	m		Day	Time	m	Time	m
1 SU	0240 / 1452	5.1 / 5.0	0840 / 2120	0.5 / 0.2		16 M	0323 / 1534	5.1 / 5.1	0931 / 2204	0.7 / 0.2
2 M	0319 / 1529	5.0 / 5.0	0927 / 2156	0.5 / 0.2		17 TU	0356 / 1607	4.8 / 4.8	1005 / 2237	0.8 / 0.4
3 TU	0400 / 1610	5.0 / 4.8	1007 / 2236	0.7 / 0.3		18 W	0431 / 1644	4.7 / 4.7	1040 / 2315	0.9 / 0.7
4 W	0446 / 1657	4.8 / 4.7	1052 / 2324	0.8 / 0.4		19 TH	0509 / 1729	4.5 / 4.5	1124	1.0
5 TH	0540 / 1753	4.6 / 4.6	1146	0.9		20 F	0004 / 1225	0.9 / 1.2	0557 / 1826	4.2 / 4.2
6 F	0028 / 1301	0.5 / 1.0	0641 / 1901	4.5 / 4.5		21 SA	0110 / 1343	1.0 / 1.2	0700 / 1945	4.1 / 4.1
7 SA	0152 / 1428	0.7 / 0.9	0755 / 2019	4.5 / 4.5		22 SU	0223 / 1507	1.1 / 1.1	0825 / 2106	4.2 / 4.2
8 SU	0316 / 1552	0.7 / 0.8	0909 / 2136	4.6 / 4.6		23 M	0335 / 1623	1.0 / 1.0	0939 / 2212	4.5 / 4.5
9 M	0430 / 1705	0.5 / 0.5	1019 / 2245	4.7 / 4.8		24 TU	0438 / 1721	0.9 / 0.8	1036 / 2305	4.7 / 4.7
10 TU	0530 / 1805	0.4 / 0.3	1121 / 2347	5.0 / 5.1		25 W	0530 / 1806	0.8 / 0.5	1125 / 2352	4.8 / 5.0
11 W ●	0622 / 1855	0.4 / 0.1	1216	5.2		26 TH O	0614 / 1844	0.7 / 0.4	1209	5.1
12 TH	0041 / 1304	5.3 / 5.3	0704 / 1938	0.3 / 0.0		27 F	0033 / 1248	5.1 / 5.1	0650 / 1918	0.5 / 0.3
13 F	0127 / 1347	5.3 / 5.3	0744 / 2018	0.4 / 0.0		28 SA	0110 / 1323	5.2 / 5.1	0724 / 1952	0.5 / 0.2
14 SA	0209 / 1425	5.3 / 5.2	0821 / 2056	0.4 / 0.0		29 SU	0145 / 1358	5.2 / 5.2	0759 / 2025	0.4 / 0.2
15 SU	0247 / 1500	5.2 / 5.2	0857 / 2130	0.5 / 0.1		30 M	0220 / 1432	5.2 / 5.2	0833 / 2058	0.4 / 0.1
						31 TU	0258 / 1508	5.2 / 5.2	0909 / 2134	0.4 / 0.2

ENGLAND – BURNHAM–ON–CROUCH

LAT 51°37′N   LONG 0°48′E

TIMES AND HEIGHTS OF HIGH AND LOW WATERS   YEAR **1999**

TIME ZONE (UT)
For Summer Time add ONE hour in non-shaded areas

4

SEPTEMBER

Day	Time	m	Time	m	Time	m	Time	m
1 W	0338	5.1	0949	0.5	1549	5.1	2212	0.3
16 TH	0348	4.8	1005	0.8	1606	4.7	2229	0.7
2 TH	0423	5.0	1033	0.7	1634	4.8	2258	0.4
17 F	0423	4.6	1045	0.9	1647	4.5	2312	0.9
3 F	0514	4.7	1126	0.8	1731	4.6	2357	0.8
18 SA	0506	4.4	1137	1.1	1739	4.2		
4 SA	0615	4.5	1239	0.9	1842	4.5		
19 SU	0015	1.1	0603	4.2	1252	1.2	1849	4.0
5 SU	0127	0.9	0734	4.3	1416	1.0	2010	4.3
20 M	0133	1.2	0721	4.1	1417	1.2	2022	4.1
6 M	0302	0.9	0856	4.5	1546	0.8	2133	4.6
21 TU	0252	1.2	0853	4.2	1539	1.0	2140	4.3
7 TU	0418	0.8	1008	4.7	1657	0.4	2241	4.8
22 W	0403	1.1	1000	4.6	1643	0.8	2236	4.7
8 W	0516	0.7	1108	5.0	1755	0.2	2339	5.2
23 TH	0457	0.9	1051	4.8	1732	0.5	2323	5.0
9 TH ●	0606	0.5	1200	5.2	1841	0.1		
24 F	0544	0.7	1138	5.1	1817	0.3		
10 F	0028	5.3	0647	0.4	1247	5.3	1920	0.1
25 SA O	0006	5.2	0625	0.5	1218	5.2	1853	0.2
11 SA	0111	5.3	0724	0.4	1328	5.3	1956	0.1
26 SU	0045	5.3	0701	0.4	1258	5.2	1928	0.1
12 SU	0149	5.2	0759	0.5	1402	5.2	2028	0.2
27 M	0122	5.3	0737	0.4	1334	5.3	2002	0.1
13 M	0222	5.1	0832	0.5	1433	5.1	2058	0.2
28 TU	0159	5.5	0814	0.3	1412	5.3	2037	0.1
14 TU	0251	5.0	0902	0.5	1501	5.0	2126	0.3
29 W	0237	5.3	0852	0.3	1450	5.3	2113	0.2
15 W	0319	4.8	0932	0.7	1531	5.0	2155	0.5
30 TH	0318	5.2	0933	0.4	1532	5.2	2152	0.3

OCTOBER

Day	Time	m	Time	m	Time	m	Time	m
1 F	0402	5.0	1019	0.5	1620	5.0	2238	0.7
16 SA	0347	4.7	1015	0.8	1615	4.6	2229	1.0
2 SA	0453	4.7	1114	0.7	1719	4.6	2337	0.9
17 SU	0430	4.6	1104	1.0	1703	4.3	2324	1.2
3 SU	0556	4.3	1231	0.9	1833	4.3		
18 M	0523	4.3	1210	1.1	1806	4.1		
4 M	0109	1.1	0718	4.2	1411	0.9	2005	4.3
19 TU	0044	1.3	0631	4.1	1332	1.1	1931	4.1
5 TU	0247	1.1	0842	4.5	1536	0.7	2125	4.6
20 W	0208	1.3	0800	4.2	1451	1.0	2056	4.3
6 W	0401	1.0	0952	4.7	1642	0.4	2228	4.8
21 TH	0319	1.2	0915	4.5	1559	0.8	2157	4.7
7 TH	0457	0.8	1049	4.9	1736	0.2	2322	5.2
22 F	0419	1.0	1011	4.7	1654	0.5	2247	5.1
8 F	0545	0.7	1140	5.0	1821	0.1		
23 SA	0509	0.8	1140	5.0	1742	0.3	2332	5.2
9 SA ●	0008	5.3	0626	0.5	1224	5.2	1857	0.2
24 SU O	0555	0.5	1146	5.2	1825	0.2		
10 SU	0049	5.2	0702	0.5	1303	5.2	1929	0.2
25 M	0016	5.5	0636	0.4	1229	5.3	1904	0.1
11 M	0124	5.1	0735	0.5	1336	5.1	1959	0.4
26 TU	0058	5.5	0716	0.3	1311	5.5	1941	0.1
12 TU	0154	5.0	0806	0.5	1404	5.1	2025	0.4
27 W	0137	5.5	0757	0.2	1353	5.5	2018	0.1
13 W	0218	5.0	0835	0.5	1432	5.0	2051	0.5
28 TH	0218	5.3	0837	0.2	1435	5.5	2056	0.3
14 TH	0243	5.0	0903	0.7	1501	4.8	2119	0.5
29 F	0300	5.2	0922	0.3	1520	5.2	2137	0.4
15 F	0312	4.8	0936	0.7	1536	4.7	2151	0.8
30 SA	0346	5.0	1010	0.4	1611	5.0	2224	0.8
31 SU	0436	4.7	1108	0.5	1710	4.7	2323	1.1

NOVEMBER

Day	Time	m	Time	m	Time	m	Time	m
1 M	0541	4.5	1224	0.8	1824	4.5		
16 TU	0452	4.3	1136	1.0	1733	4.3	2350	1.3
2 TU	0049	1.3	0658	4.3	1354	0.8	1947	4.5
17 W	0554	4.2	1249	1.0	1841	4.2		
3 W	0220	1.2	0817	4.5	1513	0.5	2102	4.6
18 TH	0114	1.3	0709	4.2	1404	0.9	2002	4.3
4 TH	0333	1.1	0925	4.7	1617	0.4	2203	5.0
19 F	0230	1.2	0823	4.3	1513	0.8	2110	4.6
5 F	0432	0.9	1021	5.1	1709	0.3	2254	5.1
20 SA	0335	1.0	0926	4.7	1613	0.5	2208	5.0
6 SA	0520	0.7	1111	5.1	1753	0.3	2340	5.2
21 SU	0432	0.8	1021	5.0	1707	0.3	2258	5.2
7 SU	0602	0.7	1155	5.1	1830	0.3		
22 M	0524	0.5	1112	5.1	1757	0.2	2346	5.3
8 M ●	0020	5.1	0639	0.5	1235	5.1	1901	0.4
23 TU O	0614	0.4	1201	5.3	1841	0.1		
9 TU	0055	5.1	0712	0.5	1308	5.0	1929	0.5
24 W	0033	5.5	0659	0.2	1250	5.5	1922	0.2
10 W	0124	5.0	0743	0.5	1338	5.0	1957	0.5
25 TH	0117	5.5	0743	0.1	1336	5.6	2003	0.2
11 TH	0149	5.0	0812	0.5	1407	5.0	2023	0.5
26 F	0201	5.3	0827	0.1	1422	5.5	2044	0.3
12 F	0215	5.0	0841	0.5	1437	4.8	2051	0.7
27 SA	0245	5.2	0914	0.2	1510	5.3	2126	0.5
13 SA	0244	4.8	0914	0.7	1512	4.8	2123	0.8
28 SU	0331	5.0	1005	0.3	1601	5.1	2212	0.8
14 SU	0320	4.8	0952	0.8	1552	4.7	2159	1.0
29 M	0421	4.8	1101	0.4	1656	4.8	2306	1.1
15 M	0401	4.6	1039	0.9	1637	4.5	2247	1.1
30 TU	0520	4.6	1206	0.5	1801	4.6		

DECEMBER

Day	Time	m	Time	m	Time	m	Time	m
1 W	0015	1.2	0626	4.3	1323	0.7	1913	4.5
16 TH	0519	4.3	1203	0.8	1803	4.3		
2 TH	0138	1.3	0739	4.3	1436	0.7	2025	4.5
17 F	0017	1.2	0622	4.3	1314	0.8	1911	4.3
3 F	0255	1.2	0846	4.6	1540	0.5	2126	4.7
18 SA	0135	1.1	0734	4.3	1426	0.7	2021	4.6
4 SA	0357	1.0	0946	4.8	1634	0.5	2219	4.8
19 SU	0247	1.0	0842	4.6	1533	0.5	2127	4.7
5 SU	0450	0.9	1037	5.0	1718	0.5	2306	5.0
20 M	0354	0.8	0945	4.8	1636	0.4	2225	5.0
6 M	0537	0.7	1124	5.0	1759	0.5	2348	5.0
21 TU	0455	0.5	1043	5.1	1732	0.3	2320	5.1
7 TU ●	0619	0.7	1206	5.0	1834	0.5		
22 W O	0554	0.4	1139	5.2	1824	0.2		
8 W	0025	5.0	0652	0.5	1243	5.0	1904	0.7
23 TH	0012	5.2	0646	0.2	1232	5.5	1908	0.2
9 TH	0058	5.0	0724	0.5	1316	5.0	1932	0.7
24 F	0101	5.3	0733	0.1	1324	5.5	1951	0.3
10 F	0126	5.0	0754	0.5	1348	4.8	2001	0.7
25 SA	0147	5.3	0821	0.0	1411	5.5	2033	0.4
11 SA	0154	5.0	0824	0.5	1419	4.8	2032	0.7
26 SU	0232	5.2	0908	0.0	1459	5.3	2114	0.5
12 SU	0225	4.8	0858	0.5	1454	4.8	2103	0.8
27 M	0316	5.1	0955	0.1	1546	5.2	2157	0.7
13 M	0300	4.8	0936	0.5	1532	4.7	2139	0.9
28 TU	0402	5.0	1045	0.2	1635	5.0	2243	0.9
14 TU	0340	4.7	1018	0.7	1615	4.6	2221	1.0
29 W	0451	4.7	1136	0.4	1728	4.7	2334	1.1
15 W	0425	4.6	1105	0.7	1705	4.5	2312	1.1
30 TH	0546	4.5	1237	0.5	1826	4.5		
31 F	0040	1.2	0649	4.3	1343	0.7	1934	4.3

Chart Datum: 2·35 metres below Ordnance Datum (Newlyn)

RIVER BLACKWATER   8-4-18

Essex 51°45'·30N 00°55'·00E (5ca S of Nass bn)
Rtgs: Maldon 3-4-2; Heybridge Basin 3-5-2

CHARTS
AC *3741, 1975, 1183*; Imray, Y17; OS 168

TIDES
Maldon +0130 Dover; ML 2·8; Duration 0620; Zone 0 (UT)

Standard Port WALTON-ON-THE-NAZE (→)

Times				Height (metres)			
High Water		Low Water		MHWS	MHWN	MLWN	MLWS
0000	0600	0500	1100	4·2	3·4	1·1	0·4
1200	1800	1700	2300				
Differences SUNK HEAD							
0000	+0002	−0002	+0002	−0·3	−0·3	−0·1	−0·1
CLACTON-ON-SEA							
+0012	+0010	+0025	+0008	+0·3	+0·1	0·0	0·0
WEST MERSEA							
+0035	+0015	+0055	+0010	+0·9	+0·4	+0·1	+0·1
BRADWELL							
+0035	+0023	+0047	+0004	+1·1	+0·8	+0·2	+0·1
OSEA ISLAND							
+0057	+0045	+0050	+0007	+1·1	+0·9	+0·1	0·0
MALDON							
+0107	+0055	No data		−1·3	−1·1		No data

SHELTER
Good, as appropriate to wind. Marinas at Tollesbury, Bradwell and Maylandsea. ⚓ restricted by oyster beds and many moorings. At W Mersea there is a pontoon for landing (limited waiting); also pile moorings in Ray Chan or ⚓ in Mersea Quarters, access approx HW±1½. Berths at Heybridge Basin, access via lock approx HW −1 to HW; a SHM buoy opposite the lock marks the deep water ent. Access to Chelmer & Blackwater Canal (not navigable).

NAVIGATION
WPT Knoll NCM, Q, 51°43'·85N 01°05'·17E, 107°/287° from/to Nass bn, ECM VQ (3) 5s, 6·7M. Speed limit 8kn W of Osea Is.
WEST MERSEA: Avoid oyster beds between Cobmarsh and Packing Marsh Is and in Salcott Chan. ⚓ in Mersea Quarters.
BRADWELL: No dangers, but only suitable for small craft and area gets very crowded; see below under Lts & Marks.
TOLLESBURY FLEET: Proceeding via S Chan up Woodrolfe Creek, a tide gauge shows depth over marina ent sill (approx 3m at MHWS and 2m at MHWN). Speed limits: Woodrolfe Creek 4kn upper reaches; Tollesbury Fleet S Chan 8kn.

LIGHTS AND MARKS
Bradwell Creek ent has bn QR with tide gauge showing depth in ft in Creek; this bn must be left to STBD on entry. 4 PHM buoys, 3 SHM withies and 2 B/W △ ldg bns mark the chan which doglegs past a SHM buoy to marina ent. Power stn is conspic 7ca NNE.
MALDON: From S of Osea Is, 'The Doctor', No 3 SHM buoy on with Blackwater SC lt, Iso G 5s, lead 300° approx up the chan; or No 3 and No 8 buoys in line at 305°. Beyond No 8 buoy, the chan which shifts and carries 0·2m, is buoyed up to Maldon. Access near HW; pontoons dry to soft mud.

RADIO TELEPHONE
Bradwell and Tollesbury Marinas VHF Ch 80 M (HO).
Blackwater Marina VHF Ch M, 0900-2300.

TELEPHONE (Dial code 01621 Maldon; 01206 Colchester/ West Mersea)
Hr Mr 856726; R. Bailiff (Maldon Quay) 856487, Office 875837, Mobile 0860 456802; Canal lockmaster 853506; MRSC (01255) 675518; ☎ (01473) 235704 (H24); Marinecall 0891 500455; Police (Colchester) 762212, (W Mersea) 382930; Dr 854118, or W Mersea 382015.

FACILITIES
WEST MERSEA (01206)
   Town EC Wed; P, D, FW, ME, El, CH, V, R, Bar, ✉, Ⓑ, ⇌ (bus to Colchester, Ⓗ ☎ 01206-853535), ✈ (Southend/ Stansted).
TOLLESBURY (01621)
   Tollesbury Marina (240+20 visitors) ☎ 868471, ⚓ 868489, Slip, D, AC, BH (10 ton), Gas, Gaz, FW, ME, El, Sh, C (5 ton), CH, V, R, Bar, Ⓞ, Access HW±1½;
   Tollesbury Cruising Club ☎ 869561, Bar, R, M, C (20 ton), D, CH, FW, L, Slip, AC, ME, El, Sh;
   Services: Slip access HW±2 , FW, ME, El, Sh, CH.
   Village EC Wed; P, V, R, Bar, ✉, Ⓑ (Tues, Thurs 1000-1430), ⇌ (bus to Witham), ✈ (Southend or Cambridge).
BRADWELL (01621)
   Bradwell Marina (280, some Ⓥ) ☎ 776235, ⚓ 776393, £9.75, Slip, AC, Gas, Gaz, D, P, FW, ME, El, Sh, BH (16 ton), CH, R, Bar, Access HW±4½, approx 2m; **Bradwell Quay YC** ☎ 776539, M, FW, Bar, L, Slip. **Town** ✉, ⇌ (bus/ taxi to Southminster), ✈ (Southend).
MAYLANDSEA (01621)
   Blackwater Marina (230) ☎ 740264, ⚓ 742122, £7, Slip, D, Sh, CH, R, Bar; Access HW±2. 150 moorings in chan. Taxi to Southminster ⇌.
MALDON (01621)
   Maldon Quay Hr Mr/River bailiff ☎ 856487, Mobile ☎ 0860 456802, VHF Ch 16 *Highspirits* (work boat); M, P, D, FW, AB, Slip; **Maldon Little Ship Club** ☎ 854139, Bar;
   Services: Slip, D, Sh, CH, M, ACA, SM, ME, El, Ⓔ.
   Town EC Wed; ✉, Ⓑ, ⇌ (bus to Chelmsford, Ⓗ ☎ (01245) 440761), ✈ (Southend, Cambridge or Stansted).
HEYBRIDGE BASIN (01621)
   Lockmaster ☎ 853506 **Blackwater SC** ☎ 853923, L, FW;
   Services: Slip, D, L, M, FW, ME, El, SH, C. Bus to Heybridge/Maldon.

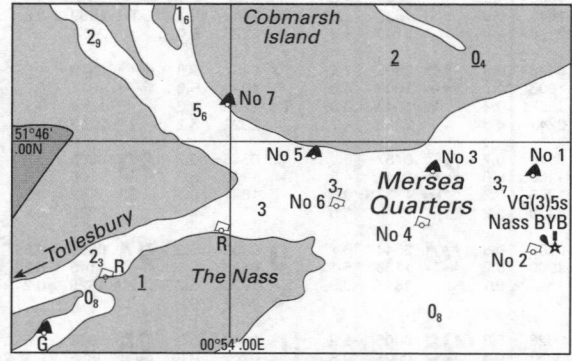

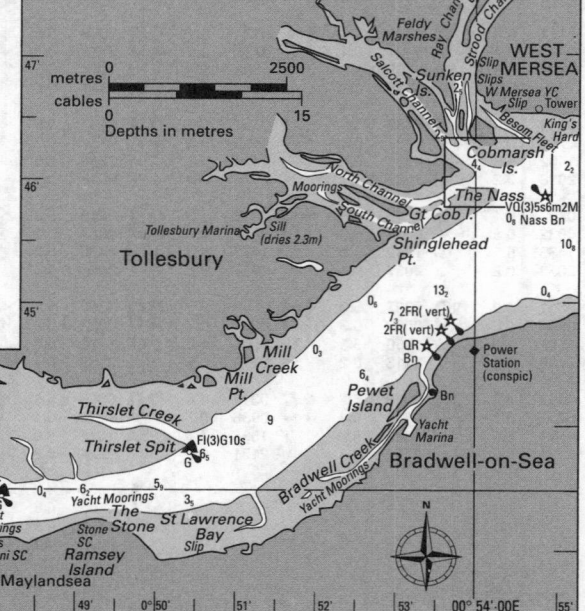

RIVER COLNE   8-4-19

Essex 51°47'·95N 01°00'·70E (Brightlingsea)   Rtg 3-2-2

CHARTS
AC *3741, 1975, 1183*; Imray, Y17; Stanfords 4, 5; OS 168
TIDES
+0050 Dover; ML 2·5; Duration 0615; Zone 0 (UT)

Standard Port WALTON-ON-THE-NAZE (→)

Times				Height (metres)			
High Water		Low Water		MHWS	MHWN	MLWN	MLWS
0000	0600	0500	1100	4·2	3·4	1·1	0·4
1200	1800	1700	2300				
Differences BRIGHTLINGSEA							
+0025	+0021	+0046	+0004	+0·8	+0·4	+0·1	0·0
COLCHESTER							
+0035	+0025	Dries out		0·0	−0·3	Dries out	

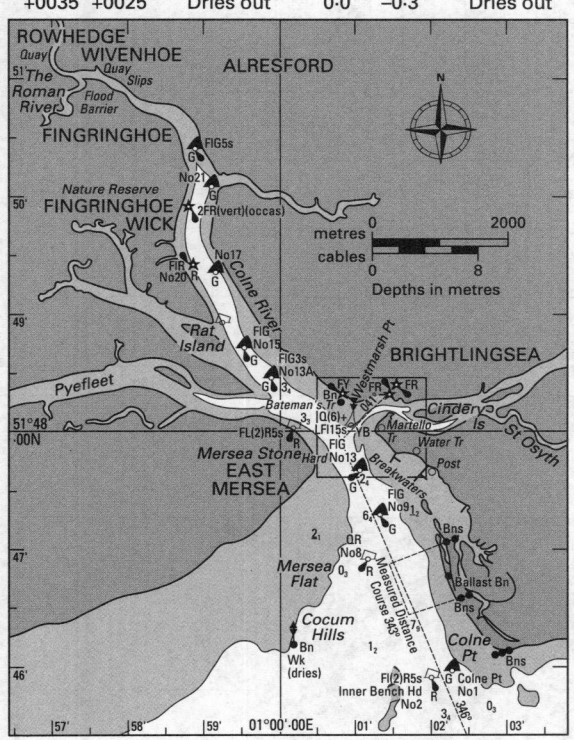

LIGHTS AND MARKS
Well buoyed/lit up to Wivenhoe. Ldg lts/marks 041° for Brightlingsea: both FR 7/10m 4M; dayglo W □, orange stripe on posts; adjusted to suit the chan. Then Spit SCM buoy, Q (6) + L Fl 15s, and chan buoys Fl (3) G 5s and Fl R 5s, plus NCM bn Q where chan is divided by Cindery Is. Bateman's Tr (conspic) by Westmarsh Pt has a FY sodium lt 12m. Pyefleet Chan and other creeks are unlit.
The flood barrier is marked by 2FR/FG (vert) on both sides and there are bns, QR/QG, up/downstream on the river banks. To facilitate the passage of large vessels, Dir lts above and below the barrier are as follows: for up-stream tfc 305°, Oc WRG 5s 5/3M, vis G300°-304·7°, W304·7°-305·3°, R305·3°-310°; and for down-stream tfc 125°, Oc WRG 5s 5/3M, vis G120°-124.8, W°124.8°-125.2°, R125.2°-130°. Daymarks are W ▽ with Or vert stripe.
RADIO TELEPHONE
Brightlingsea Port Radio VHF Ch 68. Colchester Ch **68** 11 14 16 (Office hrs and HW–2 to HW+1).
TELEPHONE (Dial code 01206 Brightlingsea & Colchester)
Hr Mr (Brightlingsea) 302200; Hr Mr (Colchester) 827316; MRSC (01255) 675518; ☷ (01473) 235704 (H24); Marinecall 0891 500455; Police (01255) 221312; Dr 303875.

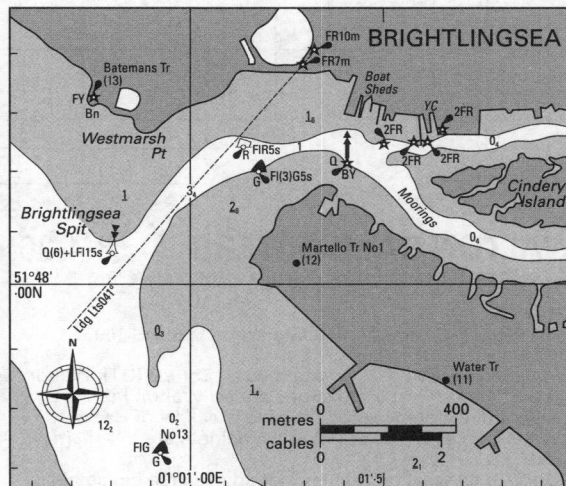

SHELTER
Suitable shelter can be found from most winds, but outer hbr is exposed to W'lies. In the creek S of Cindery Island are pile moorings (as shown) and long pontoons in about 1m, with possible AB for **Ø**s. ‡ prohib in Brightlingsea Hbr, but there are ‡s to the NW of Mersea Stone Pt and in Pyefleet Chan, E of Pewit Island.
R Colne is navigable for 4·5m draft to Wivenhoe, where the river dries; and to The Hythe, Colchester (3m draft).
NAVIGATION
WPT Colne Bar By, SHM Fl (2) G 5s, 51°44'·58N 01°02'·66E, 160°/340° from/to Mersea Stone, 3·6M. See also 8·4·18.
Extensive mud and sand banks flank the ent chan. Much traffic in the Colne; large coasters use the Brightlingsea chans. The ent to Brightlingsea Creek is very narrow at LW and carries about 1m.
A flood barrier 2ca below Wivenhoe church is normally open (30m wide) allowing unrestricted passage; keep to stbd, max speed 5kn. Tfc lts on N pier are 3FR (vert), vis up/downstream. When lit, they indicate either the barrier gates are shut or a large vessel is passing through; other traffic must keep clear. (See LIGHTS AND MARKS).
Speed limits in the approaches and up-river:
No 13 buoy to Fingringhoe (No 24 buoy) = 8kn; but Nos 12 to 16 buoys = 5kn;
No 24 buoy to Colchester = 4kn;
Brightlingsea Harbour = 4kn.

FACILITIES
BRIGHTLINGSEA
Town Hard ☎ 303535, L, FW, Pile moorings £5; **Colne YC** ☎ 302594, L, FW, R, Bar; **Brightlingsea SC** Slip, Bar; **Services**: M, L, FW, ME, El, Ⓔ, Sh, CH, ACA, P & D (cans), Gas, SM, BY, C, Slip.
Town P & D (cans), FW, ME, El, Sh, C (mobile), CH, V, R, Bar, ✉, Ⓑ, ⇌ (bus to Wivenhoe or Colchester), ✈ (Southend or Stansted).
WIVENHOE: **Wivenhoe SC.**
Village P, V, Bar, ✉, Ⓑ (AM only), ⇌.

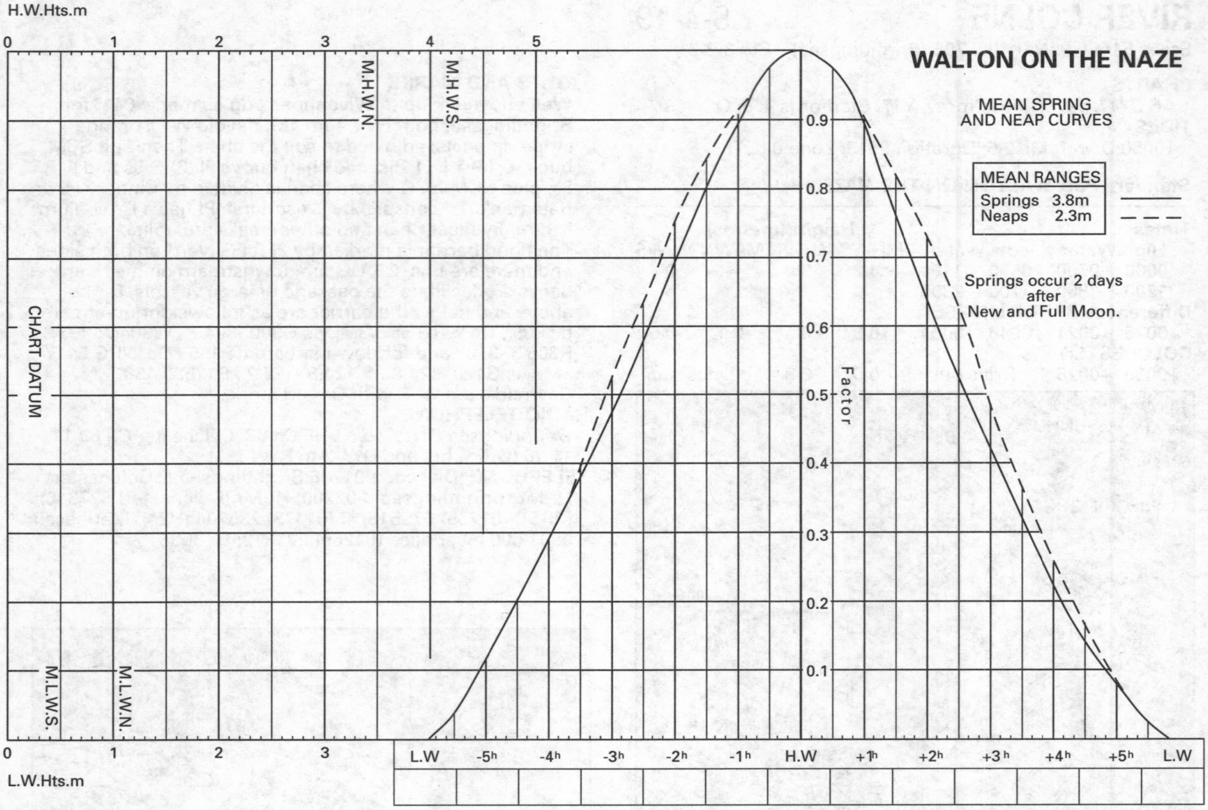

H.W.Hts.m

WALTON ON THE NAZE

MEAN SPRING
AND NEAP CURVES

MEAN RANGES	
Springs	3.8m
Neaps	2.3m

Springs occur 2 days
after
New and Full Moon.

CHART DATUM

M.H.W.N. M.H.W.S.

Factor

0.9
0.8
0.7
0.6
0.5
0.4
0.3
0.2
0.1

M.L.W.S. M.L.W.N.

L.W. -5h -4h -3h -2h -1h H.W. +1h +2h +3h +4h +5h L.W.

L.W.Hts.m

WALTON BACKWATERS   8-4-20
Essex 51°54'·54N 01°16'·90E (No 2 PHM buoy)   Rtg 3-1-2

CHARTS
AC *2695, 2052*; Imray, Y16; Stanfords 5, 6; OS 169

TIDES
+0030 Dover; ML 2·2; Duration 0615; Zone 0 (UT). Walton
is a Standard Port. Predictions are for Walton Pier, ie to
seaward. Differences for Bramble Creek (N of Hamford
Water) are +10, −7, −5, +10 mins; heights are all +0·3m.

SHELTER
Good in all weather, but ent not advised if a big sea is
running from the NE. Berth HW±5 in Titchmarsh Marina,
ent dredged 1·3m; or on adjacent pontoons in the Twizzle.
Good ⚓s in Hamford Water (keep clear of Oakley Creek)
and in N end of Walton Chan, 2ca S of Stone Pt on E side.
Walton Yacht Basin more suited for long stay; appr dries.

NAVIGATION
WPT Pye End SWM buoy, L Fl 10s, 51°55'·00N 01°18'·00E,
054°/234° from/to buoyed chan ent, 1·0M. NB this stretch
carries only 0·9m. From S, appr via Medusa Chan; from N
and E via the Harwich recomended yacht track. At narrow
ent to Walton Chan leave NCM buoy to stbd, and 3 PHM
buoys close to port; after a fourth PHM off Stone Pt stay
mid-chan. Beware lobster pots off the Naze and Pye
Sands and oyster beds in the Backwaters.

LIGHTS AND MARKS
Naze Tr (49m) is conspic 3M S of Pye End buoy. 2M NNE
at Felixstowe, cranes and Y flood lts are conspic D/N. SW
of Pye End buoy Nos 4 and 7 are the only lit chan buoys.

RADIO TELEPHONE
Titchmarsh marina Ch 80, 0800-2000 in season.

TELEPHONE (Dial code 01255)
Hr Mr 851887; MRSC 675518; ⌗ (01473) 235704 (H24);
Marinecall 0891 500455; Police 241312; ⊞ 502446.

FACILITIES
Titchmarsh Marina (450+visitors), ☎ 672185, ⚓ 851901,
£9, Access HW±5 over sill 1·3m, D, FW, AC, Gas, Gaz, ME,
CH, El, BH (10 ton), TraveLift (35 ton), Slip, R, Bar;
Walton Yacht Basin/Walton & Frinton YC (60) ☎ 675526,
AB (long stay), FW, AC, R, Bar;
Services: Slip, M, D, C (½ ton), El. **Town** EC Wed; P, SM,
V, R, Bar, ⌷, Ⓑ, ⇌, ✈ (Southend/Cambridge).

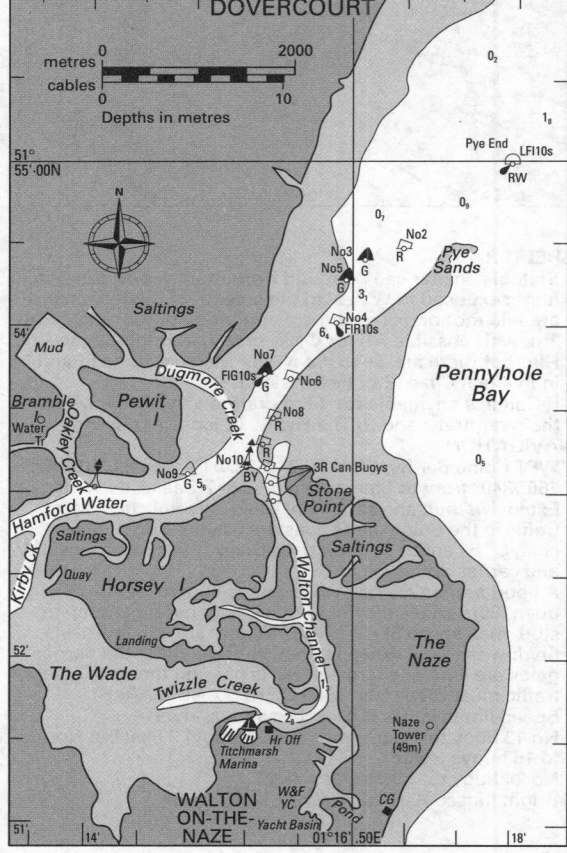

ENGLAND – WALTON–ON–THE–NAZE

LAT 51°51'N   LONG 1°16'E

TIMES AND HEIGHTS OF HIGH AND LOW WATERS

YEAR **1999**

4

TIME ZONE (UT)
For Summer Time add ONE hour in non-shaded areas

JANUARY

Day	Time	m	Day	Time	m
1 F	0427 / 1037 / 1656 / 2308	0.6 / 4.1 / 0.5 / 4.1	**16** SA	0440 / 1053 / 1655 / 2310	0.8 / 3.9 / 0.8 / 4.0
2 SA O	0521 / 1130 / 1743 / 2357	0.4 / 4.2 / 0.5 / 4.2	**17** SU	0521 / 1134 / 1734 / ●2348	0.7 / 4.0 / 0.7 / —
3 SU	0612 / 1220 / 1828	0.3 / 4.3 / 0.5	**18** M	0601 / 1213 / 1812	0.6 / 4.1 / 0.7
4 M	0043 / 0700 / 1308 / 1909	4.2 / 0.3 / 4.3 / 0.6	**19** TU	0025 / 0639 / 1251 / 1848	4.0 / 0.5 / 4.1 / 0.7
5 TU	0127 / 0747 / 1352 / 1950	4.2 / 0.3 / 4.2 / 0.7	**20** W	0103 / 0718 / 1329 / 1924	4.1 / 0.5 / 4.1 / 0.7
6 W	0208 / 0831 / 1435 / 2029	4.1 / 0.3 / 4.0 / 0.8	**21** TH	0140 / 0758 / 1409 / 2002	4.1 / 0.4 / 4.1 / 0.7
7 TH	0247 / 0915 / 1516 / 2107	4.0 / 0.4 / 3.9 / 0.9	**22** F	0218 / 0838 / 1452 / 2043	4.0 / 0.4 / 4.1 / 0.7
8 F	0325 / 0958 / 1558 / 2148	3.8 / 0.6 / 3.8 / 1.1	**23** SA	0300 / 0922 / 1538 / 2129	4.0 / 0.4 / 4.0 / 0.7
9 SA	0408 / 1043 / 1643 / 2235	3.7 / 0.7 / 3.6 / 1.2	**24** SU	0347 / 1011 / 1630 / 2221	3.9 / 0.5 / 3.8 / 0.8
10 SU	0458 / 1134 / 1736 / 2335	3.5 / 0.9 / 3.4 / 1.3	**25** M	0442 / 1109 / 1726 / 2324	3.8 / 0.6 / 3.6 / 1.0
11 M	0601 / 1231 / 1841	3.4 / 1.0 / 3.3	**26** TU	0548 / 1220 / 1838	3.6 / 0.7 / 3.5
12 TU	0044 / 0713 / 1332 / 1951	1.3 / 3.4 / 1.0 / 3.4	**27** W	0040 / 0704 / 1339 / 1951	0.8 / 3.6 / 0.8 / 3.5
13 W	0157 / 0821 / 1431 / 2052	1.2 / 3.5 / 1.0 / 3.6	**28** TH	0203 / 0847 / 1451 / 2100	0.9 / 3.7 / 0.7 / 3.7
14 TH	0301 / 0918 / 1525 / 2143	1.1 / 3.6 / 0.9 / 3.7	**29** F	0317 / 0927 / 1552 / 2202	0.8 / 3.8 / 0.7 / 3.8
15 F	0354 / 1008 / 1612 / 2229	0.9 / 3.8 / 0.8 / 3.9	**30** SA	0420 / 1028 / 1644 / 2256	0.6 / 4.0 / 0.6 / 4.0
			31 SU O	0514 / 1122 / 1730 / 2345	0.4 / 4.1 / 0.6 / 4.1

FEBRUARY

Day	Time	m	Day	Time	m
1 M	0603 / 1210 / 1813	0.3 / 4.2 / 0.6	**16** TU	0543 / 1155 / 1753 ●	0.5 / 4.1 / 0.6
2 TU	0030 / 0647 / 1255 / 1852	4.1 / 0.2 / 4.2 / 0.6	**17** W	0008 / 0622 / 1234 / 1830	4.1 / 0.4 / 4.2 / 0.6
3 W	0111 / 0729 / 1335 / 1929	4.1 / 0.3 / 4.2 / 0.6	**18** TH	0046 / 0701 / 1313 / 1907	4.2 / 0.3 / 4.3 / 0.5
4 TH	0147 / 0807 / 1411 / 2003	4.1 / 0.3 / 4.1 / 0.7	**19** F	0124 / 0740 / 1353 / 1946	4.2 / 0.2 / 4.3 / 0.5
5 F	0220 / 0843 / 1445 / 2035	4.0 / 0.4 / 4.0 / 0.8	**20** SA	0203 / 0819 / 1434 / 2026	4.2 / 0.2 / 4.2 / 0.5
6 SA	0253 / 0917 / 1519 / 2108	4.0 / 0.5 / 3.8 / 0.9	**21** SU	0244 / 0900 / 1518 / 2110	4.2 / 0.3 / 4.1 / 0.6
7 SU	0329 / 0954 / 1555 / 2147	3.8 / 0.6 / 3.7 / 0.9	**22** M	0329 / 0946 / 1607 / 2159	4.1 / 0.4 / 3.9 / 0.7
8 M	0410 / 1038 / 1638 / 2236	3.7 / 0.8 / 3.5 / 1.1	**23** TU	0421 / 1041 / 1703 / 2259	3.9 / 0.6 / 3.6 / 0.8
9 TU	0501 / 1133 / 1730 / 2340	3.5 / 1.0 / 3.4 / 1.2	**24** W	0525 / 1152 / 1811	3.6 / 0.8 / 3.4
10 W	0606 / 1237 / 1837	3.3 / 1.1 / 3.3	**25** TH	0016 / 0645 / 1319 / 1929	1.0 / 3.5 / 0.9 / 3.4
11 TH	0053 / 0725 / 1344 / 1955	1.2 / 3.3 / 1.1 / 3.3	**26** F	0151 / 0809 / 1438 / 2046	0.9 / 3.5 / 0.9 / 3.5
12 F	0210 / 0840 / 1448 / 2105	1.2 / 3.4 / 1.0 / 3.5	**27** SA	0311 / 0922 / 1540 / 2150	0.8 / 3.7 / 0.8 / 3.7
13 SA	0320 / 0940 / 1545 / 2200	1.0 / 3.6 / 0.9 / 3.7	**28** SU	0413 / 1022 / 1631 / 2244	0.5 / 4.0 / 0.7 / 3.9
14 SU	0415 / 1030 / 1632 / 2247	0.8 / 3.8 / 0.8 / 3.9			
15 M	0501 / 1114 / 1714 / 2329	0.6 / 4.0 / 0.7 / 4.0			

MARCH

Day	Time	m	Day	Time	m
1 M	0503 / 1113 / 1714 / 2332	0.4 / 4.1 / 0.6 / 4.1	**16** TU	0435 / 1050 / 1649 / 2304	0.5 / 4.0 / 0.7 / 4.0
2 TU O	0548 / 1158 / 1754	0.3 / 4.2 / 0.6	**17** W	0518 / 1133 / 1729 / ●2345	0.4 / 4.2 / 0.5 / 4.1
3 W	0014 / 0628 / 1239 / 1831	4.1 / 0.3 / 4.2 / 0.6	**18** TH	0600 / 1213 / 1809	0.2 / 4.3 / 0.4
4 TH	0052 / 0704 / 1314 / 1905	4.1 / 0.3 / 4.1 / 0.6	**19** F	0026 / 0639 / 1254 / 1848	4.3 / 0.1 / 4.4 / 0.3
5 F	0125 / 0738 / 1345 / 1936	4.1 / 0.3 / 4.0 / 0.6	**20** SA	0106 / 0718 / 1334 / 1928	4.3 / 0.1 / 4.3 / 0.3
6 SA	0154 / 0808 / 1414 / 2005	4.0 / 0.4 / 3.9 / 0.6	**21** SU	0146 / 0758 / 1416 / 2010	4.4 / 0.1 / 4.3 / 0.3
7 SU	0223 / 0838 / 1443 / 2036	4.0 / 0.5 / 3.9 / 0.6	**22** M	0229 / 0840 / 1500 / 2054	4.3 / 0.2 / 4.1 / 0.4
8 M	0257 / 0910 / 1517 / 2112	3.9 / 0.6 / 3.8 / 0.7	**23** TU	0315 / 0925 / 1548 / 2144	4.2 / 0.4 / 3.9 / 0.5
9 TU	0335 / 0950 / 1557 / 2156	3.8 / 0.8 / 3.7 / 0.9	**24** W	0407 / 1020 / 1643 / 2244	3.9 / 0.7 / 3.6 / 0.7
10 W	0421 / 1042 / 1645 / 2253	3.6 / 0.9 / 3.5 / 1.0	**25** TH	0512 / 1131 / 1751	3.6 / 1.0 / 3.4
11 TH	0518 / 1149 / 1745	3.4 / 1.1 / 3.3	**26** F	0005 / 0634 / 1302 / 1911	0.9 / 3.5 / 1.1 / 3.3
12 F	0006 / 0631 / 1302 / 1900	1.2 / 3.2 / 1.2 / 3.2	**27** SA	0144 / 0800 / 1423 / 2029	0.9 / 3.5 / 1.0 / 3.4
13 SA	0126 / 0757 / 1413 / 2022	1.1 / 3.3 / 1.1 / 3.4	**28** SU	0300 / 0911 / 1523 / 2133	0.7 / 3.7 / 0.9 / 3.7
14 SU	0243 / 0909 / 1515 / 2127	1.0 / 3.5 / 1.0 / 3.6	**29** M	0358 / 1008 / 1612 / 2226	0.5 / 4.0 / 0.8 / 3.9
15 M	0345 / 1004 / 1605 / 2219	0.7 / 3.8 / 0.8 / 3.8	**30** TU	0445 / 1056 / 1654 / 2312	0.3 / 4.1 / 0.7 / 4.0
			31 W O	0526 / 1138 / 1732 / 2353	0.3 / 4.1 / 0.6 / 4.1

APRIL

Day	Time	m	Day	Time	m
1 TH	0602 / 1216 / 1808	0.3 / 4.1 / 0.6	**16** F	0534 / 1150 / 1746 ●	0.2 / 4.4 / 0.4
2 F	0029 / 0635 / 1250 / 1840	4.0 / 0.4 / 4.0 / 0.6	**17** SA	0002 / 0615 / 1233 / 1829	4.3 / 0.1 / 4.4 / 0.3
3 SA	0100 / 0705 / 1318 / 1910	4.0 / 0.4 / 3.9 / 0.6	**18** SU	0046 / 0657 / 1316 / 1912	4.4 / 0.1 / 4.4 / 0.2
4 SU	0128 / 0734 / 1343 / 1938	4.0 / 0.5 / 3.9 / 0.5	**19** M	0130 / 0739 / 1359 / 1956	4.4 / 0.1 / 4.3 / 0.2
5 M	0157 / 0803 / 1412 / 2009	4.0 / 0.5 / 3.9 / 0.5	**20** TU	0216 / 0822 / 1444 / 2043	4.4 / 0.3 / 4.1 / 0.3
6 TU	0230 / 0834 / 1446 / 2045	3.9 / 0.6 / 3.9 / 0.6	**21** W	0304 / 0909 / 1533 / 2135	4.2 / 0.5 / 3.9 / 0.4
7 W	0308 / 0911 / 1525 / 2127	3.8 / 0.8 / 3.8 / 0.7	**22** TH	0358 / 1003 / 1628 / 2237	4.0 / 0.8 / 3.7 / 0.6
8 TH	0352 / 0958 / 1613 / 2220	3.7 / 1.0 / 3.6 / 0.9	**23** F	0503 / 1113 / 1734 / 2358	3.7 / 1.1 / 3.4 / 0.8
9 F	0445 / 1102 / 1710 / 2328	3.4 / 1.1 / 3.4 / 1.0	**24** SA	0621 / 1239 / 1850	3.5 / 1.2 / 3.4
10 SA	0553 / 1220 / 1821	3.3 / 1.3 / 3.2	**25** SU	0126 / 0740 / 1357 / 2003	0.8 / 3.6 / 1.2 / 3.5
11 SU	0047 / 0714 / 1336 / 1939	1.1 / 3.3 / 1.2 / 3.3	**26** M	0238 / 0848 / 1458 / 2106	0.6 / 3.7 / 1.0 / 3.7
12 M	0205 / 0832 / 1440 / 2049	0.9 / 3.5 / 1.0 / 3.5	**27** TU	0333 / 0943 / 1547 / 2159	0.5 / 3.9 / 0.9 / 3.8
13 TU	0311 / 0932 / 1533 / 2145	0.7 / 3.8 / 0.8 / 3.8	**28** W	0419 / 1030 / 1630 / 2245	0.4 / 4.0 / 0.7 / 4.0
14 W	0404 / 1021 / 1620 / 2233	0.5 / 4.1 / 0.7 / 4.0	**29** TH	0458 / 1112 / 1708 / 2325	0.4 / 4.1 / 0.7 / 4.0
15 TH	0450 / 1106 / 1703 / 2319	0.3 / 4.2 / 0.5 / 4.2	**30** F O	0533 / 1149 / 1744	0.4 / 4.0 / 0.6

Chart Datum: 2·16 metres below Ordnance Datum (Newlyn)

ENGLAND – WALTON–ON–THE–NAZE

LAT 51°51′N   LONG 1°16′E

TIMES AND HEIGHTS OF HIGH AND LOW WATERS

YEAR **1999**

TIME ZONE (UT)
For Summer Time add ONE hour in non-shaded areas

MAY

Day	Time	m	Day	Time	m
1 SA	0001	4.0	16 SU	0554	0.1
	0604	0.5		1211	4.4
	1222	4.0		1812	0.3
	1816	0.6			
2 SU	0034	3.9	17 M	0027	4.4
	0634	0.5		0638	0.2
	1250	3.9		1258	4.3
	1845	0.6		1859	0.2
3 M	0103	3.9	18 TU	0115	4.4
	0703	0.6		0722	0.2
	1317	3.9		1343	4.3
	1915	0.6		1946	0.2
4 TU	0134	3.9	19 W	0203	4.4
	0734	0.6		0807	0.4
	1346	3.9		1430	4.1
	1948	0.6		2036	0.2
5 W	0209	3.9	20 TH	0254	4.2
	0806	0.7		0855	0.6
	1421	3.9		1519	4.0
	2025	0.6		2130	0.4
6 TH	0247	3.8	21 F	0348	4.0
	0843	0.8		0948	0.9
	1501	3.8		1612	3.8
	2107	0.7		2230	0.5
7 F	0330	3.7	22 SA	0448	3.8
	0926	1.0		1050	1.1
	1548	3.6		1712	3.6
	2156	0.8		2340	0.7
8 SA	0422	3.5	23 SU	0556	3.6
	1023	1.1		1204	1.3
	1643	3.4		1819	3.5
	2258	0.9			
9 SU	0525	3.4	24 M	0055	0.7
	1137	1.2		0707	3.6
	1749	3.3		1319	1.3
				1926	3.5
10 M	0012	0.9	25 TU	0203	0.7
	0637	3.4		0812	3.7
	1254	1.2		1424	1.1
	1900	3.4		2028	3.6
11 TU	0128	0.8	26 W	0259	0.6
	0752	3.6		0909	3.8
	1401	1.1		1517	1.0
	2008	3.5		2123	3.7
12 W	0234	0.6	27 TH	0345	0.6
	0855	3.8		0957	3.9
	1458	0.9		1602	0.7
	2107	3.8		2211	3.9
13 TH	0331	0.4	28 F	0425	0.5
	0949	4.0		1040	4.0
	1549	0.7		1643	0.7
	2201	4.0		2254	3.9
14 F	0422	0.3	29 SA	0501	0.6
	1038	4.2		1119	4.0
	1638	0.5		1720	0.7
	2251	4.2		2333	3.9
15 SA	0509	0.3	30 SU	0535	0.6
	1125	4.3		1154	4.0
	1725	0.4	O	1754	0.6
●	2339	4.3			
31 M	0008	3.9			
	0607	0.6			
	1226	3.9			
	1825	0.6			

JUNE

Day	Time	m	Day	Time	m
1 TU	0042	3.9	16 W	0102	4.4
	0639	0.7		0708	0.4
	1255	3.9		1329	4.2
	1858	0.6		1939	0.2
2 W	0115	3.9	17 TH	0151	4.4
	0712	0.7		0753	0.5
	1327	3.9		1416	4.2
	1933	0.6		2029	0.2
3 TH	0151	3.9	18 F	0241	4.2
	0746	0.7		0839	0.7
	1403	3.9		1503	4.1
	2010	0.6		2120	0.3
4 F	0230	3.8	19 SA	0331	4.1
	0822	0.8		0927	0.9
	1443	3.9		1551	3.9
	2052	0.6		2212	0.4
5 SA	0313	3.8	20 SU	0424	3.9
	0904	0.9		1019	1.1
	1527	3.7		1642	3.7
	2138	0.7		2309	0.6
6 SU	0402	3.7	21 M	0521	3.7
	0955	1.0		1119	1.2
	1619	3.6		1740	3.6
	2233	0.7			
7 M	0459	3.6	22 TU	0009	0.7
	1057	1.1		0623	3.5
	1719	3.5		1228	1.3
	2338	0.8		1841	3.5
8 TU	0604	3.5	23 W	0113	0.8
	1208	1.2		0727	3.5
	1824	3.5		1337	1.3
				1944	3.5
9 W	0049	0.7	24 TH	0212	0.8
	0713	3.6		0826	3.6
	1319	1.1		1438	1.1
	1929	3.6		2043	3.6
10 TH	0159	0.6	25 F	0304	0.8
	0818	3.8		0919	3.7
	1423	0.9		1531	1.0
	2032	3.8		2135	3.7
11 F	0301	0.5	26 SA	0349	0.7
	0917	4.0		1007	3.9
	1521	0.7		1617	0.9
	2130	4.0		2223	3.9
12 SA	0356	0.3	27 SU	0430	0.7
	1011	4.1		1049	3.9
	1616	0.6		1658	0.8
	2225	4.1		2306	3.9
13 SU	0447	0.3	28 M	0508	0.7
	1103	4.2		1128	4.0
	1708	0.4		1735	0.7
●	2319	4.3	O	2346	3.9
14 M	0536	0.3	29 TU	0544	0.7
	1153	4.3		1204	4.0
	1800	0.3		1810	0.7
15 TU	0011	4.3	30 W	0023	3.9
	0622	0.4		0619	0.7
	1242	4.3		1238	3.9
	1849	0.2		1844	0.6

JULY

Day	Time	m	Day	Time	m
1 TH	0059	3.9	16 F	0138	4.3
	0654	0.7		0736	0.6
	1312	3.9		1359	4.2
	1920	0.6		2015	0.2
2 F	0135	3.9	17 SA	0224	4.2
	0729	0.8		0819	0.7
	1348	3.9		1442	4.1
	1958	0.6		2059	0.3
3 SA	0213	3.9	18 SU	0308	4.1
	0806	0.8		0901	0.8
	1426	3.9		1523	4.0
	2037	0.5		2143	0.4
4 SU	0255	3.9	19 M	0352	3.9
	0846	0.8		0944	1.0
	1507	3.8		1606	3.9
	2120	0.6		2227	0.6
5 M	0341	3.8	20 TU	0438	3.7
	0931	0.9		1031	1.1
	1554	3.7		1652	3.7
	2208	0.6		2316	0.8
6 TU	0433	3.7	21 W	0529	3.5
	1025	1.0		1127	1.3
	1647	3.7		1747	3.5
	2304	0.6			
7 W	0532	3.7	22 TH	0011	0.9
	1128	1.1		0628	3.4
	1748	3.6		1234	1.3
				1851	3.4
8 TH	0011	0.7	23 F	0112	1.0
	0637	3.6		0734	3.4
	1240	1.1		1346	1.3
	1854	3.6		1958	3.4
9 F	0125	0.7	24 SA	0214	1.0
	0744	3.7		0837	3.5
	1352	1.0		1453	1.1
	2001	3.7		2100	3.5
10 SA	0234	0.6	25 SU	0310	0.9
	0849	3.8		0932	3.7
	1459	0.8		1548	1.0
	2106	3.8		2155	3.7
11 SU	0336	0.5	26 M	0359	0.8
	0949	4.0		1021	3.9
	1601	0.6		1635	0.8
	2208	4.0		2243	3.8
12 M	0431	0.4	27 TU	0443	0.8
	1046	4.1		1104	4.0
	1658	0.5		1716	0.7
	2306	4.2		2326	3.9
13 TU	0521	0.4	28 W	0523	0.7
	1138	4.2		1144	4.0
	1751	0.3		1754	0.6
●			O		
14 W	0000	4.3	29 TH	0005	4.0
	0608	0.4		0600	0.7
	1228	4.2		1221	4.0
	1841	0.2		1829	0.6
15 TH	0051	4.3	30 F	0042	4.0
	0653	0.5		0636	0.7
	1315	4.3		1256	4.0
	1929	0.2		1905	0.5
31 SA	0118	4.0			
	0712	0.7			
	1331	4.0			
	1942	0.5			

AUGUST

Day	Time	m	Day	Time	m
1 SU	0155	4.1	16 M	0239	4.1
	0748	0.7		0831	0.8
	1407	4.0		1451	4.1
	2019	0.4		2106	0.4
2 M	0235	4.0	17 TU	0314	3.9
	0827	0.7		0907	0.9
	1446	4.0		1525	3.9
	2058	0.4		2142	0.6
3 TU	0318	4.0	18 W	0350	3.8
	0910	0.8		0945	1.0
	1528	3.9		1604	3.8
	2141	0.5		2222	0.8
4 W	0406	3.9	19 TH	0430	3.6
	0958	0.9		1032	1.1
	1618	3.8		1651	3.6
	2232	0.6		2313	1.0
5 TH	0502	3.7	20 F	0520	3.4
	1056	1.0		1133	1.3
	1716	3.7		1751	3.4
	2336	0.7			
6 F	0606	3.6	21 SA	0015	1.1
	1207	1.1		0624	3.3
	1825	3.6		1246	1.3
				1907	3.3
7 SA	0054	0.8	22 SU	0123	1.2
	0716	3.6		0745	3.4
	1328	1.0		1405	1.2
	1940	3.6		2025	3.4
8 SU	0213	0.8	23 M	0230	1.1
	0828	3.7		0856	3.6
	1446	0.9		1515	1.1
	2053	3.7		2128	3.6
9 M	0322	0.7	24 TU	0329	1.0
	0935	3.8		0951	3.8
	1554	0.7		1609	0.9
	2200	3.9		2219	3.8
10 TU	0418	0.6	25 W	0418	0.9
	1034	4.0		1038	3.9
	1651	0.5		1652	0.7
	2259	4.1		2304	4.0
11 W	0508	0.6	26 TH	0459	0.8
	1127	4.2		1120	4.1
	1743	0.3		1731	0.6
●	2351	4.3	O	2344	4.1
12 TH	0553	0.5	27 F	0538	0.7
	1214	4.3		1158	4.1
	1829	0.2		1808	0.5
13 F	0038	4.3	28 SA	0021	4.2
	0635	0.6		0614	0.7
	1259	4.3		1234	4.1
	1912	0.2		1844	0.4
14 SA	0122	4.3	29 SU	0057	4.2
	0715	0.6		0651	0.6
	1339	4.2		1310	4.2
	1953	0.2		1920	0.4
15 SU	0202	4.2	30 M	0134	4.2
	0754	0.7		0728	0.6
	1416	4.2		1346	4.2
	2030	0.3		1956	0.3
31 TU	0213	4.2			
	0808	0.6			
	1424	4.2			
	2034	0.4			

Chart Datum: 2·16 metres below Ordnance Datum (Newlyn)

ENGLAND – WALTON–ON–THE–NAZE

LAT 51°51′N   LONG 1°16′E

TIMES AND HEIGHTS OF HIGH AND LOW WATERS

YEAR **1999**

4

TIME ZONE (UT)
For Summer Time add ONE hour in non-shaded areas

SEPTEMBER

	Time	m		Time	m
1 W	0255 / 0850 / 1506 / 2115	4.1 / 0.7 / 4.1 / 0.5	**16** TH	0305 / 0907 / 1524 / 2133	3.9 / 0.9 / 3.8 / 0.8
2 TH	0342 / 0937 / 1554 / 2204	4.0 / 0.8 / 3.9 / 0.6	**17** F	0342 / 0950 / 1607 / 2219	3.7 / 1.0 / 3.6 / 1.0
3 F	0435 / 1034 / 1653 / 2307	3.8 / 0.9 / 3.7 / 0.9	**18** SA	0427 / 1046 / 1701 / 2323	3.6 / 1.2 / 3.4 / 1.2
4 SA	0539 / 1146 / 1807	3.6 / 1.0 / 3.6	**19** SU	0526 / 1158 / 1813	3.4 / 1.3 / 3.2
5 SU	0031 / 0656 / 1317 / 1931	1.0 / 3.5 / 1.0 / 3.5	**20** M	0037 / 0644 / 1318 / 1943	1.3 / 3.3 / 1.3 / 3.3
6 M	0200 / 0815 / 1441 / 2050	1.0 / 3.6 / 0.9 / 3.7	**21** TU	0151 / 0812 / 1434 / 2057	1.3 / 3.4 / 1.1 / 3.5
7 TU	0310 / 0924 / 1547 / 2156	0.9 / 3.8 / 0.6 / 3.9	**22** W	0256 / 0916 / 1534 / 2151	1.2 / 3.7 / 0.9 / 3.8
8 W	0405 / 1022 / 1641 / 2251	0.8 / 4.0 / 0.4 / 4.2	**23** TH	0347 / 1006 / 1620 / 2236	1.0 / 3.9 / 0.7 / 4.0
9 TH ●	0452 / 1112 / 1728 / 2339	0.7 / 4.2 / 0.3 / 4.3	**24** F	0431 / 1050 / 1702 / 2317	0.8 / 4.1 / 0.5 / 4.2
10 F	0534 / 1157 / 1810	0.6 / 4.3 / 0.3	**25** SA ○	0511 / 1129 / 1741 / 2355	0.7 / 4.2 / 0.4 / 4.3
11 SA	0022 / 0614 / 1239 / 1848	4.3 / 0.6 / 4.3 / 0.3	**26** SU	0549 / 1208 / 1818	0.6 / 4.2 / 0.3
12 SU	0101 / 0651 / 1315 / 1923	4.2 / 0.7 / 4.2 / 0.4	**27** M	0033 / 0628 / 1246 / 1855	4.3 / 0.6 / 4.3 / 0.3
13 M	0136 / 0727 / 1347 / 1956	4.1 / 0.7 / 4.1 / 0.4	**28** TU	0112 / 0708 / 1325 / 1933	4.4 / 0.5 / 4.3 / 0.3
14 TU	0206 / 0800 / 1417 / 2026	4.0 / 0.7 / 4.0 / 0.5	**29** W	0152 / 0749 / 1405 / 2012	4.3 / 0.5 / 4.3 / 0.4
15 W	0235 / 0832 / 1448 / 2057	3.9 / 0.8 / 4.0 / 0.7	**30** TH	0234 / 0833 / 1449 / 2054	4.2 / 0.6 / 4.2 / 0.5

OCTOBER

	Time	m		Time	m
1 F	0320 / 0922 / 1539 / 2143	4.0 / 0.7 / 4.0 / 0.8	**16** SA	0304 / 0918 / 1534 / 2133	3.8 / 0.9 / 3.7 / 1.1
2 SA	0413 / 1021 / 1640 / 2246	3.8 / 0.8 / 3.7 / 1.0	**17** SU	0349 / 1011 / 1624 / 2232	3.7 / 1.1 / 3.5 / 1.3
3 SU	0519 / 1138 / 1758	3.5 / 1.0 / 3.5	**18** M	0444 / 1119 / 1729 / 2351	3.5 / 1.2 / 3.3 / 1.4
4 M	0014 / 0641 / 1312 / 1926	1.2 / 3.4 / 1.0 / 3.5	**19** TU	0556 / 1236 / 1853	3.3 / 1.2 / 3.3
5 TU	0146 / 0802 / 1431 / 2043	1.2 / 3.6 / 0.8 / 3.7	**20** W	0109 / 0721 / 1350 / 2015	1.4 / 3.4 / 1.1 / 3.5
6 W	0254 / 0909 / 1533 / 2144	1.1 / 3.8 / 0.6 / 4.0	**21** TH	0216 / 0833 / 1453 / 2114	1.3 / 3.6 / 0.9 / 3.8
7 TH	0347 / 1004 / 1623 / 2235	0.9 / 4.0 / 0.4 / 4.2	**22** F	0311 / 0927 / 1544 / 2202	1.1 / 3.8 / 0.7 / 4.1
8 F	0432 / 1052 / 1706 / 2319	0.8 / 4.2 / 0.3 / 4.3	**23** SA	0358 / 1014 / 1629 / 2245	0.9 / 4.0 / 0.5 / 4.2
9 SA	0512 / 1135 / 1745 / 2359	0.7 / 4.2 / 0.4 / 4.2	**24** SU ○	0441 / 1058 / 1711 / 2327	0.7 / 4.2 / 0.4 / 4.4
10 SU	0550 / 1213 / 1819	0.7 / 4.2 / 0.4	**25** M	0523 / 1140 / 1752	0.6 / 4.3 / 0.3
11 M	0035 / 0626 / 1248 / 1851	4.1 / 0.7 / 4.1 / 0.5	**26** TU	0008 / 0605 / 1222 / 1832	4.4 / 0.5 / 4.4 / 0.3
12 TU	0106 / 0659 / 1317 / 1920	4.0 / 0.7 / 4.1 / 0.6	**27** W	0049 / 0646 / 1305 / 1912	4.4 / 0.4 / 4.4 / 0.3
13 W	0132 / 0730 / 1346 / 1948	4.0 / 0.7 / 4.0 / 0.7	**28** TH	0132 / 0733 / 1349 / 1953	4.3 / 0.4 / 4.3 / 0.5
14 TH	0158 / 0801 / 1417 / 2018	4.0 / 0.8 / 3.9 / 0.8	**29** F	0215 / 0821 / 1436 / 2038	4.2 / 0.5 / 4.3 / 0.6
15 F	0228 / 0836 / 1453 / 2052	3.9 / 0.8 / 3.8 / 0.9	**30** SA	0303 / 0913 / 1529 / 2128	4.0 / 0.6 / 4.0 / 0.9
			31 SU	0356 / 1015 / 1631 / 2231	3.8 / 0.7 / 3.8 / 1.2

NOVEMBER

	Time	m		Time	m
1 M	0503 / 1132 / 1748 / 2355	3.6 / 0.9 / 3.6 / 1.4	**16** TU	0412 / 1045 / 1655 / 2300	3.5 / 1.1 / 3.5 / 1.4
2 TU	0622 / 1256 / 1909	3.5 / 0.9 / 3.6	**17** W	0517 / 1155 / 1806	3.4 / 1.1 / 3.4
3 W	0121 / 0738 / 1410 / 2021	1.3 / 3.6 / 0.7 / 3.7	**18** TH	0019 / 0632 / 1306 / 1923	1.4 / 3.4 / 1.0 / 3.5
4 TH	0229 / 0843 / 1509 / 2119	1.2 / 3.8 / 0.6 / 4.0	**19** F	0130 / 0744 / 1410 / 2029	1.3 / 3.5 / 0.9 / 3.7
5 F	0323 / 0937 / 1558 / 2209	1.0 / 4.0 / 0.5 / 4.1	**20** SA	0230 / 0844 / 1506 / 2124	1.1 / 3.8 / 0.7 / 4.0
6 SA	0408 / 1025 / 1639 / 2252	0.9 / 4.1 / 0.5 / 4.2	**21** SU	0323 / 0937 / 1556 / 2212	0.9 / 4.0 / 0.5 / 4.2
7 SU	0448 / 1107 / 1716 / 2331	0.8 / 4.1 / 0.5 / 4.1	**22** M	0412 / 1026 / 1643 / 2258	0.7 / 4.2 / 0.4 / 4.3
8 M ●	0526 / 1145 / 1749	0.7 / 4.1 / 0.6	**23** TU ○	0459 / 1113 / 1728 / 2344	0.6 / 4.3 / 0.4 / 4.4
9 TU	0005 / 0601 / 1219 / 1819	4.1 / 0.7 / 4.0 / 0.7	**24** W	0547 / 1200 / 1812	0.4 / 4.4 / 0.4
10 W	0035 / 0634 / 1250 / 1849	4.0 / 0.7 / 4.0 / 0.7	**25** TH	0028 / 0634 / 1248 / 1856	4.4 / 0.4 / 4.5 / 0.4
11 TH	0101 / 0705 / 1320 / 1917	4.0 / 0.7 / 4.0 / 0.8	**26** F	0114 / 0722 / 1336 / 1940	4.3 / 0.4 / 4.4 / 0.5
12 F	0128 / 0737 / 1352 / 1948	4.0 / 0.7 / 3.9 / 0.8	**27** SA	0200 / 0813 / 1426 / 2026	4.2 / 0.4 / 4.3 / 0.7
13 SA	0159 / 0813 / 1428 / 2022	4.0 / 0.8 / 3.9 / 0.9	**28** SU	0248 / 0907 / 1519 / 2115	4.0 / 0.6 / 4.1 / 0.9
14 SU	0236 / 0854 / 1509 / 2101	3.9 / 0.9 / 3.8 / 1.1	**29** M	0340 / 1007 / 1617 / 2213	3.9 / 0.6 / 3.9 / 1.2
15 M	0319 / 0944 / 1557 / 2152	3.7 / 1.0 / 3.6 / 1.2	**30** TU	0441 / 1115 / 1724 / 2323	3.7 / 0.7 / 3.7 / 1.3

DECEMBER

	Time	m		Time	m
1 W	0551 / 1227 / 1836	3.5 / 0.8 / 3.6	**16** TH	0440 / 1112 / 1726 / 2325	3.5 / 0.9 / 3.5 / 1.3
2 TH	0041 / 0701 / 1336 / 1945	1.4 / 3.5 / 0.8 / 3.6	**17** F	0546 / 1219 / 1834	3.5 / 0.9 / 3.5
3 F	0153 / 0806 / 1435 / 2044	1.3 / 3.7 / 0.7 / 3.8	**18** SA	0038 / 0656 / 1326 / 1942	1.2 / 3.5 / 0.8 / 3.7
4 SA	0251 / 0903 / 1525 / 2135	1.1 / 3.8 / 0.7 / 3.9	**19** SU	0146 / 0802 / 1429 / 2045	1.1 / 3.7 / 0.7 / 3.8
5 SU	0340 / 0952 / 1607 / 2220	1.0 / 3.9 / 0.7 / 4.0	**20** M	0248 / 0902 / 1527 / 2141	0.9 / 3.9 / 0.6 / 3.9
6 M	0424 / 1037 / 1645 / 2300	0.8 / 4.0 / 0.7 / 4.0	**21** TU	0345 / 0958 / 1620 / 2233	0.7 / 4.1 / 0.5 / 4.1
7 TU ●	0504 / 1117 / 1720 / 2336	0.8 / 4.0 / 0.7 / 4.0	**22** W ○	0440 / 1051 / 1710 / 2323	0.6 / 4.2 / 0.4 / 4.2
8 W	0540 / 1153 / 1753	0.7 / 4.0 / 0.8	**23** TH	0533 / 1143 / 1757	0.4 / 4.4 / 0.4
9 TH	0008 / 0614 / 1227 / 1823	4.0 / 0.7 / 4.0 / 0.8	**24** F	0011 / 0624 / 1235 / 1843	4.3 / 0.3 / 4.4 / 0.5
10 F	0037 / 0646 / 1300 / 1854	4.0 / 0.7 / 3.9 / 0.8	**25** SA	0059 / 0715 / 1324 / 1928	4.3 / 0.2 / 4.4 / 0.6
11 SA	0106 / 0719 / 1333 / 1927	4.0 / 0.7 / 3.9 / 0.8	**26** SU	0146 / 0806 / 1414 / 2013	4.2 / 0.3 / 4.3 / 0.7
12 SU	0139 / 0756 / 1409 / 2001	3.9 / 0.7 / 3.9 / 0.9	**27** M	0232 / 0857 / 1503 / 2059	4.1 / 0.4 / 4.2 / 0.8
13 M	0216 / 0836 / 1449 / 2040	3.9 / 0.8 / 3.8 / 1.0	**28** TU	0320 / 0950 / 1555 / 2148	4.0 / 0.4 / 4.0 / 1.0
14 TU	0257 / 0921 / 1534 / 2125	3.8 / 0.8 / 3.7 / 1.1	**29** W	0411 / 1045 / 1650 / 2243	3.8 / 0.6 / 3.8 / 1.2
15 W	0344 / 1012 / 1626 / 2219	3.7 / 0.9 / 3.6 / 1.2	**30** TH	0508 / 1144 / 1751 / 2347	3.6 / 0.7 / 3.6 / 1.3
			31 F	0613 / 1246 / 1856	3.5 / 0.8 / 3.5

Chart Datum: 2·16 metres below Ordnance Datum (Newlyn)

RIVERS STOUR, ORWELL AND DEBEN

Rtg 1-1-1

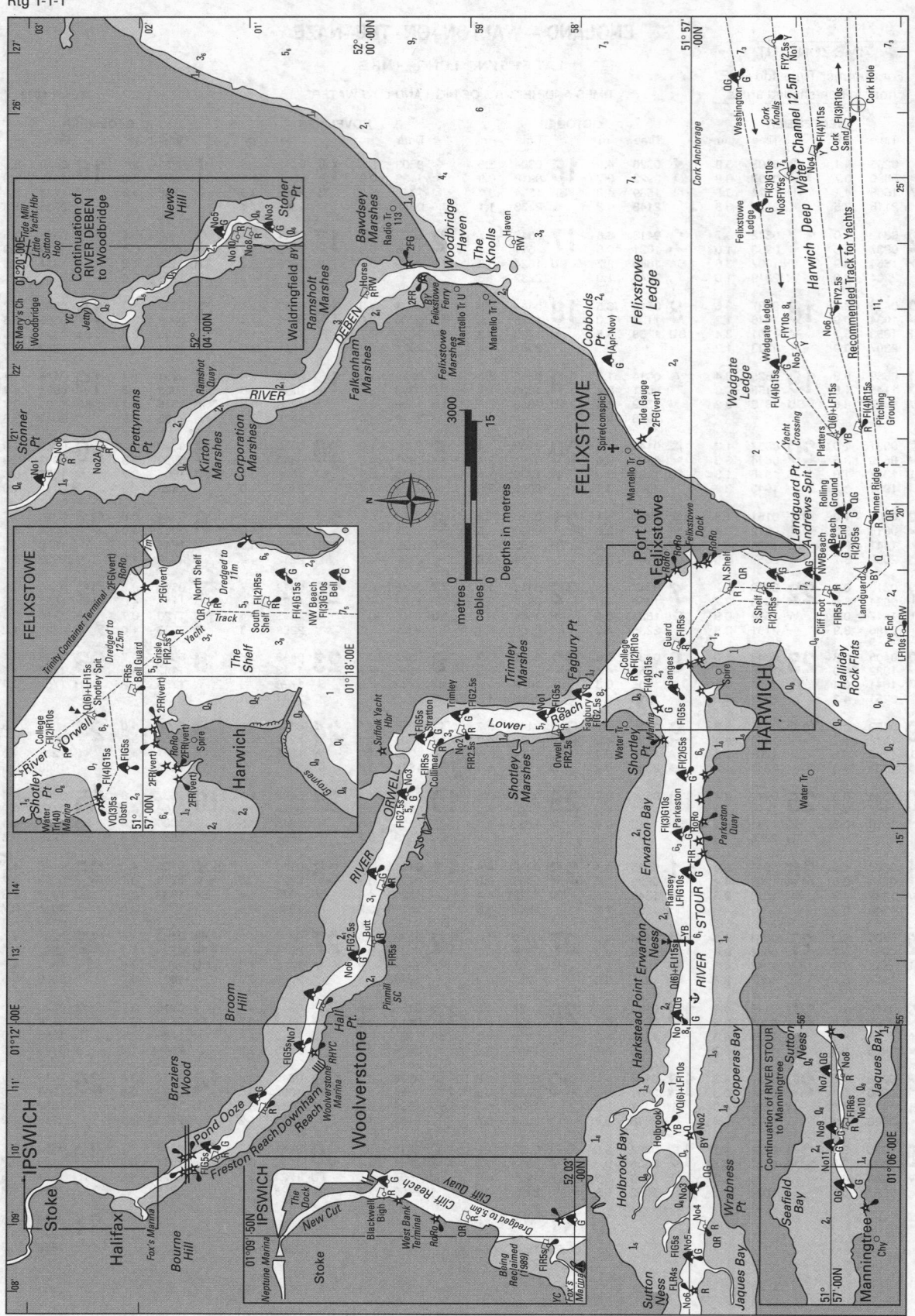

RIVER STOUR   8-4-21

Essex/Suffolk 51°57'·03N 01°17'·88E (Guard PHM buoy)

CHARTS
AC *2693*, 1594, 1491, 1593, *2052*; Imray Y16; Stanfords 5, 6; OS 169

TIDES
Harwich+0050 Dover; ML 2·1; Duration 0630; Zone 0 (UT)

Standard Port WALTON-ON-THE-NAZE (←—)

Times				Height (metres)			
High Water		Low Water		MHWS	MHWN	MLWN	MLWS
0000	0600	0500	1100	4·2	3·4	1·1	0·4
1200	1800	1700	2300				
Differences HARWICH							
+0007	+0002	−0010	−0012	−0·2	0·0	0·0	0·0
WRABNESS							
+0017	+0015	−0010	−0012	−0·1	0·0	0·0	0·0
MISTLEY							
+0032	+0027	−0010	−0012	0·0	0·0	−0·1	−0·1

Note: Although Harwich is a Standard Port, it has only two Secondary Ports referenced to it. Harwich HW and LW times differ by only 5 and 10 minutes from Walton-on-the-Naze.

SHELTER
Good at Shotley Marina; all tide access via chan dredged 2m, outer limits lit, to lock. AB also at Harwich Pound (dries; access only near HW), Mistley, Manningtree (both dry). No yachts at Parkeston Quay. ⚓s off Erwarton Ness, Wrabness Pt, Holbrook Creek and Stutton Ness.

NAVIGATION
WPT Cork Sand PHM lt buoy, Fl (3) R 10s, 51°55'·43N 01°25'·95E, 087°/to position 7ca S of Landguard Pt, 4M. Keep clear of commercial shipping/HSS. Outside the hbr, yachts should cross the DW chan at 90° between Rolling Ground and Platters buoys. See 8.4.5. Stay out of the DW chan by using recommended yacht track, running S and W of DW chan to past Harwich.
Caution: Bkwtr, ESE of Blackman's Hd, covers at HW; it is marked by small inconspic unlit PHM bn, only 5ca W of main chan. The Guard shoal (0·8m), about 2ca S of Guard PHM buoy, lies close to the recommended yacht track. The R Stour is well marked; speed limit 8kn. Beware 'The Horse' 4ca NE and a drying bank 1½ca NW of Wrabness Pt. From Mistley Quay local knowledge is needed for the narrow, tortuous chan to Manningtree.

Special Local Sound Signals
Commercial vessels may use these additional sigs:

Four short and rapid blasts followed by one short blast } = I am turning short around to stbd.

Four short and rapid blasts followed by two short blasts } = I am turning short around to port.

One prolonged blast = I am leaving a dock, quay or ⚓.

LIGHTS AND MARKS
The R Stour to Mistley Quay is lit. At Cattawade, 8M up river, a conspic chy leads 270° through the best water up to Harkstead Pt.
Shotley Marina: a Dir lt at lock indicates the dredged chan (2·0m) by Inogen (or Moiré) visual marker lts which are square, ambered displays; a vert B line indicates on the appr centre line 339°. If off the centre line, arrows indicate the direction to steer to regain it.

RADIO TELEPHONE
Harwich Hbr Radio Ch **71** 11 14 16 (H24). Yachts should monitor Ch 71 for tfc info, but not transmit. Weather, tidal info and possibly help in poor vis may be available on request. The Hbr Patrol launch listens on Ch 11. Hbr Radar Ch 20. Shotley Pt Marina Ch **80** M (lock master).

TELEPHONE (Dial code 01255)
Harwich Hr Mr 243030; Hbr Ops 243000; Marinecall 0891 500455; MRSC 675518; ⌗ 508266/502267 (H24) and (01473) 235704 (H24); Police 241312; Dr 506451; Ⓗ 502446.

FACILITIES
HARWICH: **Town Pier** L, FW, AB (tidal). **Town** EC Wed; P, D, ME, SM, Gas, El, Sh, V, R, Bar, ⊠, Ⓑ, ⇌, ✈ (Cambridge).
SHOTLEY: (01473) **Shotley Marina** (350, visitors welcome) ☎ 788982, 🗲 788868, £14.51, access H24 via lock; FW, AC, D, ▣, ⑁, ME, El, Ⓔ, Sh, BH (30 ton), C, V, BY, CH, SM, Bar, R; **Shotley SC** ☎ 787500, Slip, FW, Bar. WRABNESS: M, FW, V. MISTLEY and MANNINGTREE: AB, M, FW, V, P & D (cans), Gas, Bar. **Stour SC** ☎ (01206) 393924 M, Bar.

RIVER ORWELL   8-4-22

Suffolk 51°57'·03N 01°17'·88E (Guard PHM buoy)   Rtg 1-1-1

CHARTS
AC *2693*, 1491, *2052*; Imray Y16; Stanfords 5, 6; OS 169. A *Yachting Guide to Harwich Harbour and its Rivers* has much useful info, inc Harwich tidal predictions; it can be obtained free from Harwich Haven Authority, Angel Gate, Harwich CO12 3EJ; ☎ (01255) 243000, 🗲 241325.

TIDES
Pin Mill +0100 Dover; Ipswich +0115 Dover; ML 2·4; Duration 0555; Zone 0 (UT)

Standard Port WALTON-ON-THE-NAZE (←—)

Times				Height (metres)			
High Water		Low Water		MHWS	MHWN	MLWN	MLWS
0000	0600	0500	1100	4·2	3·4	1·1	0·4
1200	1800	1700	2300				
Differences IPSWICH							
+0022	+0027	0000	−0012	0·0	0·0	−0·1	−0·1
PIN MILL							
+0012	+0015	−0008	−0012	−0·1	0·0	0·0	0·0

SHELTER
Good. Ent and river well marked, but many unlit moorings line both banks. ⚓s above Shotley Pt on W side, or off Pinmill. No yacht facilities at Felixstowe. Visitors' berths (by pre-arrangement) at Suffolk Yacht Hbr, Woolverstone Marina and Fox's Marina (Ipswich). Ipswich Dock opens from HW −2 to HW+¾; for entry, it is essential first to call *Ipswich Port Radio* Ch 14 before arrival, then call *Neptune Marina* also Ch 14 for alongside berth in 5m.

NAVIGATION
Appr/ent from sea as in 8.4.21. WPT Shotley Spit SCM buoy, Q (6)+L Fl 15s, 51°57'·22N 01°17'·70E, at river ent. Keep clear of the many merchant ships, ferries from/to Harwich, Felixstowe & Ipswich, especially container ships turning between Trinity container terminal and Shotley Spit and Guard buoys. 6kn is max speed in R Orwell.

LIGHTS AND MARKS
Suffolk Yacht Hbr appr marked by four bns and ldg lts: front Iso Y; rear Oc Y 4s. Woolverstone Marina: 2 FR (vert). A14 bridge lts: Centre FY (clearance 38m)

No 9 Pier 2 FR (vert)) shown up and
No 10 Pier 2 FG (vert)) down stream.

Ⓡ and Ⓖ tfc lts control ent to Ipswich Dock (H24).
New Cut, W of Ipswich Dock: 3 FR (vert) = Cut closed, ie a water velocity control structure is raised from the river bed to just below water level; vessels must not proceed.

RADIO TELEPHONE
Call: *Ipswich Port Radio* VHF Ch **14** 16 12 (H24). Once above Shotley Pt, monitor Ch 14 continuously for tfc info. Suffolk Yacht Hbr, Woolverstone Marina, Fox's Marina: Ch 80 M. Neptune Marina: Ch M 14 (0800-1730LT).

TELEPHONE (Dial code 01473)
Orwell Navigation Service 231010 (also Ipswich Hr Mr and Port Radio); MRSC (01255) 675518; ⌗ 235704 (H24); Marinecall 0891 500455; Police 233000; Ⓗ 712233.

FACILITIES
LEVINGTON
Suffolk Yacht Hbr (SYH) (500+ Ⓥ welcome) ☎ 659240, 🗲 659632, £10.93, Slip, ⑁,P, D, FW, ME, El, Ⓔ, Sh, C (15 ton), BH (10/60 ton), CH, V, Gas, Gaz, AC, SM, ▣, ⑁, ▣, Access H24; **Haven Ports YC** ☎ 659658, R, Bar. **Town** ⊠, Ⓑ (Felixstowe), ⇌ (bus to Ipswich), ✈ (Cambridge/Norwich).
PIN MILL
Hr Mr ☎ 780276, M £5, L, CH, C (6 ton), SH, ME, El, FW, D (cans), Bar, R; **Pin Mill SC** ☎ 780271; Facilities at Ipswich.
WOOLVERSTONE
Woolverstone Marina (300 + Ⓥ welcome) ☎ 780206, 🗲 780273, £12.74, D, FW, BY, ME, El, Sh, AC, Gas, Gaz, ▣, ⑁, C (20 ton), SM, CH, Slip, V, R; **Royal Harwich YC** ☎ 780319, R, Bar. **Town** EC Chelmondiston Wed; ⊠, V.
IPSWICH
Fox's Marina (100+some visitors) ☎ 689111, 🗲 601737, £8.50, FW, AC, P & D (cans), BY, Gas, Gaz, BH (26 and 44 ton), C (7 ton), ME, El, Ⓔ, Sh, CH, ACA, Rigging, Bar; **Neptune Marina** (100+100 Ⓥ), ☎ 215204/780366, £12, near city centre, wet Dock (5·8m), access via lock HW −2 to +¾, waiting pontoon, max LOA 114m, FW, AC, D, P (cans), Sh, ME, C (14 ton), BH (40 ton), BY, El, Ⓔ, Gas, Gaz, R, Bar; **Orwell YC** ☎ 602288, Slip, L, FW, Bar.
City No EC; ⊠, Ⓑ, ⇌, ✈ (Cambridge/Norwich).

4

RIVER DEBEN   8-4-23
Suffolk 51°59'·35N 01°23'·69E (Felixstowe Ferry) Rtg 5-2-1

CHARTS
AC *2693, 2052*; Imray C28, Y15; Stanfords 3, 5, 6; OS 169
TIDES
Woodbridge Haven +0025 Dover; Woodbridge +0105
Dover; ML 1·9; Duration 0635; Zone 0 (UT)

Standard Port WALTON-ON-THE-NAZE (⟵)

Times				Height (metres)			
High Water		Low Water		MHWS	MHWN	MLWN	MLWS
0100	0700	0100	0700	4·2	3·4	1·1	0·4
1300	1900	1300	1900				
Differences FELIXSTOWE PIER							
−0005	−0007	−0018	−0020	−0·5	−0·4	0·0	0·0
BAWDSEY							
−0010	−0012	−0028	−0032	−0·8	−0·7	−0·2	−0·2
WOODBRIDGE HAVEN (Ent)							
0000	−0005	−0020	−0025	−0·5	−0·5	−0·1	+0·1
WOODBRIDGE (Town)							
+0045	+0025	+0025	−0020	−0·2	−0·3	−0·2	0·0

SHELTER
Good in Tide Mill Yacht Harbour (TMYH) at Woodbridge.
Ent by No 24 PHM buoy; depth over sill, dries 1·5m, is 1·6m
@ MHWN and 2·5m MHWS, with very accurate tide gauge
and 8 waiting buoys. ⚓s up-river N of Horse Sand, at:
Ramsholt, Waldringfield, Methersgate, Kyson Point and
Woodbridge (9M from ent), keeping clear of moorings.
NAVIGATION
WPT Woodbridge Haven unlit SWM buoy, 51°58'·15N
01°23'·90E, 306°/126° from/to Martello tower T, 0·65M. If
a pilot is required call VHF Ch 08 or dip the burgee when
passing Martello tower T. The shifting shingle bar, with
SHM buoy, may be crossed at HW−4 to HW depending
on draft. Best to enter after half-flood, and leave on the
flood. The ent is only 1ca wide and in strong on-shore
winds gets dangerously choppy; chan is well buoyed/
marked. Keep W until past the SC, then move E of Horse
Sand just up river of the ent. No commercial tfc. Speed
limit is 8kn above Green Reach. For current sketch map
of approach, send SAE (plus 2 1st-class stamps for RNLI)
to: Tidemill Yacht Hbr, Woodbridge, Suffolk IP12 1BP.
LIGHTS AND MARKS
Ldg marks (unlit), between Martello trs T and U, are: Front
W △ on R ■ background, rear R ■; moved according to the
chan. No lights. Bawdsey Radio tower (113m) is conspic.
RADIO TELEPHONE
Pilot Ch 08, call *Late Times* (pilot launch). Tide Mill Yacht
Hbr VHF Ch **80** M (some VHF dead spots down-river).
TELEPHONE (Dial code 01394)
Pilot 270853; MRSC (01255) 675518; Marinecall 0891 500
455; ∰ (01473) 235704 (H24); Police 383377.
FACILITIES
FELIXSTOWE FERRY (01394) **Quay** Slip, M, L, FW, ME, El, Sh,
CH, V, R, Bar; **Felixstowe Ferry SC** ☎ 283785; **Felixstowe
Ferry BY** ☎ 282173, M (200), Gas, Slip.
RAMSHOLT **Services:** M, FW, Bar.
WALDRINGFIELD (01473) **Waldringfield SC** ☎ 736633, Bar;
Services: BY, C, Slip, D, FW, CH, Gas, Gaz, V.
WOODBRIDGE (01394) **Tide Mill Yacht Hbr** (150+50 Ⓥ)
☎ 385745, 🛥 380735, £12, D, L, FW, ME, El, Sh, C (10
ton), AC, V; Tide Mill is conspic daymark. **Services:** CH,
Slip, C, M, ACA; **Deben YC. Town** P, D, L, FW, CH, V, R,
Bar, ✉, Ⓑ, ⇌, ✈ (Cambridge or Norwich).

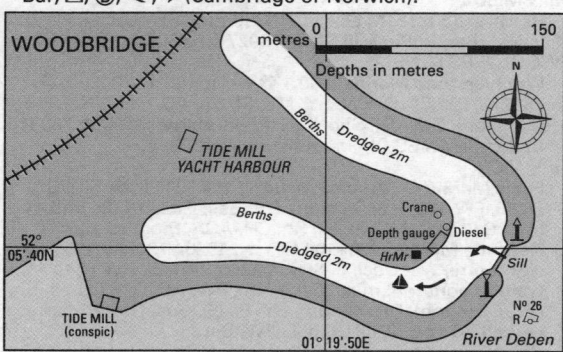

RIVER ORE/ALDE   8-4-24
Suffolk 52°02'·10N 01°27'·60E (Ent) Rtg 4-2-1

CHARTS
AC *2695, 2693*, 1543, *2052*; Imray Y15, C28; Stanfords 3, 6;
OS 169
TIDES
Ent. +0015 Dover Slaughden Quay +0155 Dover; ML1·6;
Duration 0620; Zone 0 (UT)

Standard Port WALTON-ON-THE-NAZE (⟵)

Times				Height (metres)			
High Water		Low Water		MHWS	MHWN	MLWN	MLWS
0100	0700	0100	0700	4·2	3·4	1·1	0·4
1300	1900	1300	1900				
Differences ORFORD HAVEN BAR							
−0015	−0017	−0038	−0042	−1·0	−0·8	−0·2	−0·1
ORFORD QUAY							
+0040	+0040	+0055	+0055	−1·6	−1·3	+0·2	0·0
SLAUGHDEN QUAY							
+0100	+0100	+0115	+0115	−1·3	−1·0	+0·2	0·0
SNAPE							
+0200	+0200	No data		−1·3	−1·0	−0·3	+0·4

SHELTER
Good shelter within the river, but the entrance should not
be attempted in strong E/ESE onshore winds and rough
seas. Good ⚓s as shown and at Iken; also ⚓s between
Martello Tr and Slaughden Quay. Landing on Havergate
Island, a bird sanctuary, is prohib.
NAVIGATION
WPT Orford Haven SWM buoy, 52°01'·44N 01°27'·60E *in
Mar '98*; it does not mark the chan ent and may be moved.
For latest position call Thames CG ☎ (01255) 675518.
The chartlet below (larger scale than that opposite)
depicts a layout of the ent, to which current info can be
referred. It is strongly advised that the latest plan of ent
and directions (£1, plus SAE) is obtained from: 15 Drury
Park, Snape, Suffolk IP17 1TA; or Hill House, Snape
Bridge IP17, ☎ (01728) 688404; or from Aldeburgh YC.

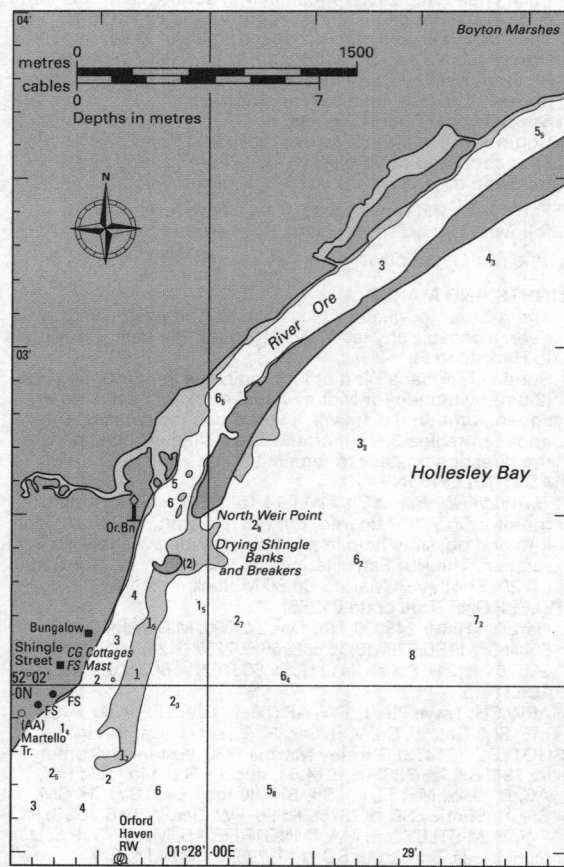

The bar (approx 0·5m) shifts after onshore gales and is dangerous in rough or confused seas. These result from tidal streams offshore running against those within the shingle banks. Sp ebb reaches 6kn. Without local info do not enter before half flood or at night. For a first visit, appr at about LW+2½ in settled conditions and at nps. *Directions only valid March 98:* From Haven buoy track toward Martello Tr AA, brg not less than 315°. Do not get set NE of this brg. About 100m off the shore turn NE into the very narrow chan between the shore and the off-lying small shingle islets; keep about 70m off the shore. Off the orange ◇ bn best water is on W shore.
Beware shoals S & SW of Dove Pt (SW tip of Havergate Island). R Ore (re-named R Alde between Orford and Slaughden Quay) is navigable up to Snape. The upper reaches are shallow and winding, and although marked by withies these may have been damaged.

LIGHTS AND MARKS
Orfordness lt ho, W tr/R bands, Fl 5s, is 5·5M NE of Haven buoy. Ent and river are unlit. Shingle Street, about 2ca S of ent, is identified by Martello tr 'AA', CG Stn, terrace houses and DF aerial. Up-river, Orford Ch and Castle are conspic; also Martello Tr 'CC', 3ca S of Slaughden Quay.

RADIO TELEPHONE
None.

TELEPHONE (Dial codes 01394 Orford; 01728 Aldeburgh)
Hr Mr Orford 450481; Orford River Warden 450267; Hr Mr Aldeburgh 453047; Marinecall 0891 500455; MRSC (01255) 675518; ⌗ (01394) 674777; Police (01473) 613500; Orford Dr 450315 (HO); Aldeburgh Dr 452027 (HO); for Dr outside HO and at weekends, call Ipswich (01474) 299600.

FACILITIES
ORFORD **Orford Quay** Slip, AB (1 hour free, then £10/hour), M £5 night, L, FW, D (cans), C (mobile 5 ton), CH, Sh (small craft), Orford SC (OSC), R, Bar.
Village (¼M). EC Wed; P & D (cans), Gas, Gaz, ✉, V, R, Bar, ⇌ (occas. bus to Woodbridge).
ALDEBURGH **Slaughden Quay** L, FW, Slip, BH (20 ton); CH; **Aldeburgh YC** (AYC) ☎ 452562, Ⓛ. **Slaughden SC** (SSC).
Services: M £4, Sh, Slip, D, ME, BY, Gas, Gaz, P. **Town** (¾M), EC Wed; P, V, R, Bar, ✉, Ⓑ, ⇌ (bus to Wickham Market), ✈ (Norwich).

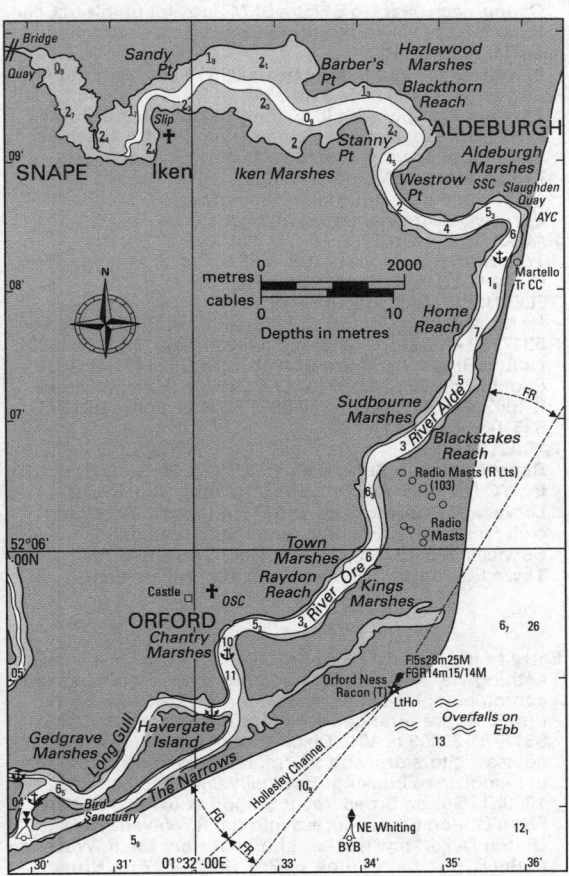

SOUTHWOLD   8-4-25
Suffolk 52°18′·75N 01°40′·65E   Rtg 3-3/4-1

CHARTS
AC *2695*, 1543; Imray C28; Stanfords 3; OS 156
TIDES
–0105 Dover; ML 1·5; Duration 0620; Zone 0 (UT)

Standard Port LOWESTOFT (⟶)

Times				Height (metres)			
High Water		Low Water		MHWS	MHWN	MLWN	MLWS
0300	0900	0200	0800	2·4	2·1	1·0	0·5
1500	2100	1400	2000				
Differences SOUTHWOLD							
+0105	+0105	+0055	+0055	0·0	0·0	–0·1	0·0
MINSMERE							
+0110	+0110	+0110	+0110	0·0	–0·1	–0·2	–0·2
ALDEBURGH (seaward)							
+0120	+0120	+0120	+0110	+0·3	+0·4	–0·1	–0·1
ORFORD NESS							
+0135	+0135	+0135	+0125	+0·4	+0·6	–0·1	0·0

Note: HW time differences (above) for Southwold apply up the hbr. At the ent mean HW is HW Lowestoft +0035.

SHELTER
Good, but the ent is dangerous in strong winds from N through E to S. Visitors berth on a staging 6ca from the ent, on N bank near to the Harbour Inn. If rafted, shore lines are essential due to current.

NAVIGATION
WPT 52°18′·06N 01°41′·80E, 135°/315° from/to N Pier lt, 1M. Enter on the flood since the ebb runs up to 6kn. Some shoals are unpredictable; a sand and shingle bar, extent/depth variable, lies off the hbr ent and a shoal builds inside N Pier. Obtain details of appr chans from Hr Mr before entering (Ch 12 or ☎ 724712). Enter between piers in midstream. When chan widens, at The Knuckle (2 FG vert), turn stbd towards LB House; keep within 10m of quay wall until it ends, when resume midstream. Unlit low footbridge ¾M upstream of ent.

LIGHTS AND MARKS
Ldg lines as chartlet. In addition: Walberswick ⊕ on with N Pier lt = 268°. Hbr ent opens on 300°. 3 FR (vert) at N pier = port closed. Lt ho, W ○ tr, is in Southwold town, 0·86M NNE of hbr ent, Fl (4) WR 20s 37m 18/17/14M; vis R (intens) 204°-220°, W220°-001°, R001°-032°.

RADIO TELEPHONE
Southwold Port Radio Ch 12 16 09 (as required).

TELEPHONE (Dial code 01502)
Hr Mr 724712; MRCC (01493) 851338; ⌗ (01473) 235704 (H24); Marinecall 0891 500455; Weather (01603) 660779; Police 722666; Dr 722326; Ⓗ 723333; Pilot 724712.

FACILITIES
Hbr AB £9.65, FW, D, BY, CH, ME, Sh, Slip, BH (20 ton), SM. **Southwold SC; Town** (¾M), EC Wed (Southwold & Walberswick); Gas, Gaz, Kos, P (cans, 1M), R, V, ✉, Ⓑ, ⇌ (bus to Brampton/Darsham), ✈ (Norwich).

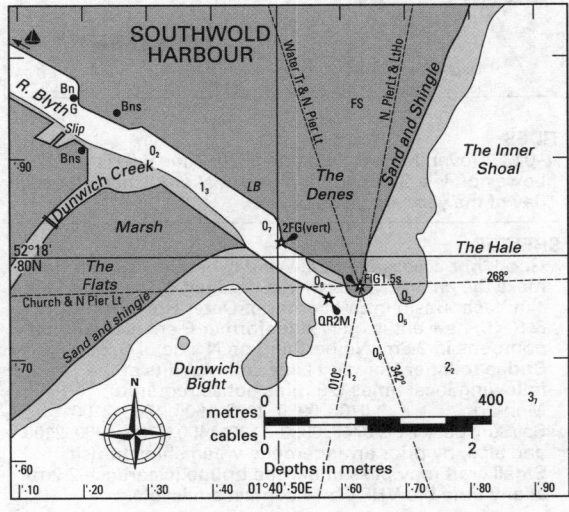

H.W.Hts.m.

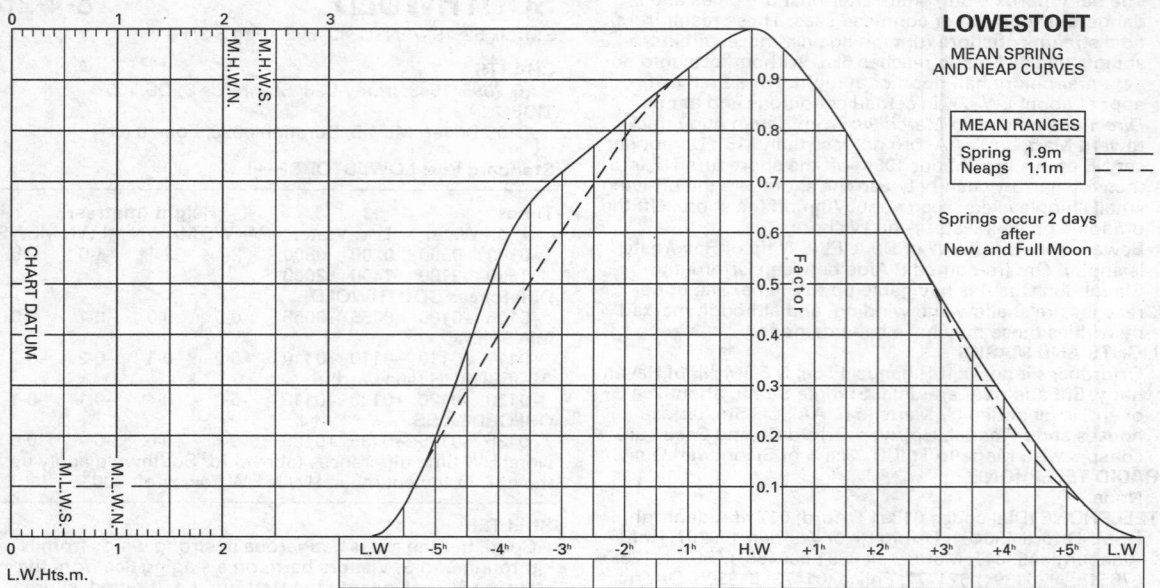

LOWESTOFT
MEAN SPRING
AND NEAP CURVES

MEAN RANGES	
Spring	1.9m
Neaps	1.1m

Springs occur 2 days
after
New and Full Moon

L.W.Hts.m.

LOWESTOFT   8-4-26

Suffolk 52°28'·28N 01°45'·50E   Rtg 1-1-1

CHARTS
AC 1536, 1543; Imray C28; Stanfords 3; OS 156/134

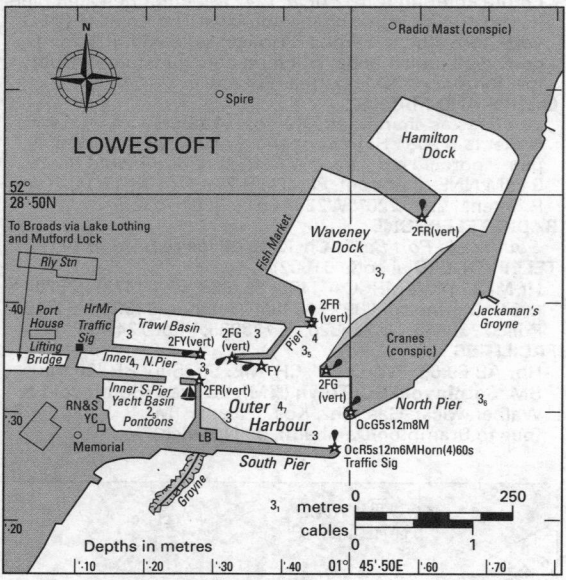

TIDES
–0133 Dover; ML 1·6; Duration 0620; Zone 0 (UT)
Lowestoft is a Standard port and tidal predictions for each
day of the year are given below

SHELTER
Good; hbr accessible H24. Wind over tide, esp ebb, can
make the ent lively. Fairway is dredged 4·7m. Speed limit
4kn.Yacht Basin in SW corner of Outer Hbr is run by RN
& S YC; new ent is on N side (former E ent is closed off)
pontoons in 2·5m. No berthing on N side of S Pier.
Bridge to Inner Hbr (and Lake Lothing) lifts at the
following local times (20 mins notice required):
Mon-Fri   0700, 0930, 1100, 1600, 1900, 2100
Sat/Sun, Bank Hols 0745, 0930, 1100, 1400, 1730, 1900, 2100
and also, by prior arrangement, when ships transit.
Small craft may pass under the bridge (clearance 2·2m)
at any time but VHF Ch 14 contact advisable.

NAVIGATION
Sands continually shift. Beware shoals and drying areas;
do not cross banks in bad weather nor at mid flood/ebb.
From S, WPT is E Barnard ECM buoy, Q (3) 10s, 52°25'·11N
01°46'·50E; thence via Stanford Chan E of Newcome Sand
QR, Stanford Fl R 2.5s and N Newcome Fl (4) R 15s, all PHM
buoys. S Holm SCM, VQ (6)+L Fl 10s, and SW Holm SHM,
Fl (2) G 5s, buoys mark the seaward side of this chan.
From E, WPT is Corton ECM buoy, Q (3) 10s Whis, 52°31'·10N
01°51'·50E; then via Holm Chan (buoyed) into Corton Road.
Or approach direct to S Holm SCM buoy for Stanford Chan.
From N, appr via Yarmouth, Gorleston and Corton Roads.

LIGHTS AND MARKS
N Newcome PHM lt buoy bears 086°/5·5ca from hbr ent.
Lowestoft lt ho, Fl 15s 37m 23M, is 1M N of hbr ent.
Tfc Sigs: Comply with IPTS (only Nos 2 & 5 are shown)
on S pierhead; also get clearance on VHF Ch 14 when
entering or leaving, due to restricted vis in appr and ent.
Bridge Sigs (on N side of bridge):
  Ⓨ = bridge operating, keep 150m clear.
  Ⓖ = vessels may enter/leave Inner Hbr.

RADIO TELEPHONE
Lowestoft Hbr Control (ABP) VHF Ch **14** 16 11 (H24). Pilot
Ch 14. RN & SYC Ch M, 14 (occas).

TELEPHONE (Dial code 01502)
Hr Mr & Bridge Control 572286; Mutford Bridge and Lock
531778 (+Ansafone, checked daily at 0830, 1300 & 1730);
Oulton Broad Yacht Stn 574946; MRCC (01493) 851338;
Pilot 572286 ext 243; ⌗ (01473) 235704 (H24); Weather
(01603) 660779; Marinecall 0891 500455; Police ()01986)
835100; Ⓗ 600611.

FACILITIES
Royal Norfolk & Suffolk YC ☎ 566726, ⚓ 517981, £14.00
inc YC facilities, AB, D, L, FW, C (2 ton), Slip, R, Bar;
Lowestoft Cruising Club ☎ 574376 (occas), AB £9 (no
club facilities), L, FW, Slip (emergency use only);
Services: ME, EI, Sh, CH, SM, Gas, Gaz, Ⓔ, ACA.
Town EC Thurs; V, R, Bar, ✉, Ⓑ, ⇌, ✈ (Norwich).

Entry to the Broads: Passage to Oulton Broad, from Lake
Lothing via two bridges and Mutford Lock (openings are
coordinated; fee £5), is available 7 days/wk in working
hrs HJ as pre-arranged with Mutford Br/Lock ☎ (01502)
531778/523003 or VHF Ch 09 14 (occas), who will also
advise visitors drawing >1·7m. Mutford Control operates
in response to bookings and daily 0800-1100 and 1300-
1600LT. Oulton Broad Yacht Station ☎ (01502) 574946.
From Oulton Broad, access via the R. Waveney is via
Oulton Dyke. New Cut is a short cut from the R. Waveney
to the R Yare for air draft <7·3m. See 8.4.27 for Broads.

ENGLAND – LOWESTOFT

LAT 52°28′N   LONG 1°45′E

TIMES AND HEIGHTS OF HIGH AND LOW WATERS   YEAR **1999**

TIME ZONE (UT)
For Summer Time add ONE hour in non-shaded areas

4

JANUARY

Day	Time	m	Time	m	Time	m	Time	m
1 F	0223	0.6	0822	2.5	1449	0.5	2048	2.5
2 SA ○	0316	0.5	0917	2.5	1536	0.6	2133	2.6
3 SU	0405	0.4	1010	2.5	1620	0.6	2217	2.6
4 M	0451	0.3	1101	2.5	1700	0.7	2259	2.6
5 TU	0536	0.3	1150	2.4	1736	0.8	2339	2.6
6 W	0619	0.4	1238	2.3	1808	0.9		
7 TH	0019	2.6	0702	0.5	1330	2.2	1843	1.0
8 F	0059	2.5	0748	0.6	1425	2.1	1926	1.2
9 SA	0145	2.4	0837	0.7	1522	2.1	2020	1.2
10 SU	0242	2.3	0930	0.9	1618	2.0	2125	1.3
11 M	0351	2.2	1024	0.9	1712	2.1	2231	1.3
12 TU	0500	2.2	1118	1.0	1802	2.1	2335	1.2
13 W	0603	2.2	1210	1.0	1847	2.2		
14 TH	0036	1.1	0658	2.2	1259	0.9	1930	2.3
15 F	0130	1.0	0748	2.3	1344	0.9	2012	2.4
16 SA	0217	0.9	0836	2.3	1426	0.9	2053	2.5
17 SU ●	0301	0.8	0921	2.3	1507	0.9	2131	2.5
18 M	0343	0.7	1005	2.4	1546	0.8	2207	2.5
19 TU	0423	0.6	1046	2.4	1624	0.8	2242	2.6
20 W	0502	0.5	1123	2.4	1702	0.8	2318	2.6
21 TH	0542	0.5	1159	2.4	1742	0.8	2357	2.6
22 F	0623	0.5	1238	2.3	1822	0.8		
23 SA	0040	2.6	0706	0.5	1322	2.2	1906	0.9
24 SU	0128	2.5	0755	0.6	1412	2.2	1956	1.0
25 M	0220	2.4	0854	0.7	1514	2.1	2054	1.0
26 TU	0319	2.3	1015	0.8	1650	2.1	2213	1.1
27 W	0442	2.2	1137	0.8	1757	2.1		
28 TH	0004	1.0	0609	2.2	1247	0.8	1852	2.2
29 F	0117	0.8	0717	2.3	1346	0.7	1943	2.3
30 SA	0215	0.6	0818	2.4	1439	0.7	2031	2.4
31 SU ○	0307	0.4	0914	2.4	1525	0.7	2117	2.5

FEBRUARY

Day	Time	m	Time	m	Time	m	Time	m
1 M	0355	0.3	1004	2.4	1608	0.7	2200	2.6
2 TU	0439	0.3	1051	2.4	1645	0.7	2240	2.6
3 W	0519	0.2	1133	2.3	1717	0.7	2318	2.6
4 TH	0557	0.3	1210	2.2	1744	0.7	2353	2.5
5 F	0633	0.4	1244	2.2	1813	0.9		
6 SA	0029	2.5	0709	0.6	1320	2.1	1847	1.0
7 SU	0109	2.4	0752	0.7	1405	2.0	1930	1.1
8 M	0156	2.3	0843	0.8	1503	2.0	2034	1.2
9 TU	0254	2.2	0940	1.0	1609	2.0	2151	1.2
10 W	0406	2.1	1037	1.0	1711	2.1	2258	1.2
11 TH	0521	2.1	1132	1.0	1808	2.1		
12 F	0001	1.1	0627	2.1	1227	1.0	1859	2.2
13 SA	0102	1.0	0726	2.2	1319	1.0	1945	2.3
14 SU	0157	0.9	0818	2.2	1407	0.9	2028	2.4
15 M	0246	0.7	0905	2.3	1451	0.9	2108	2.5
16 TU ●	0329	0.6	0949	2.4	1532	0.8	2146	2.5
17 W	0410	0.5	1028	2.4	1610	0.7	2223	2.6
18 TH	0449	0.4	1104	2.4	1648	0.7	2302	2.6
19 F	0528	0.3	1139	2.4	1727	0.6	2342	2.6
20 SA	0607	0.4	1216	2.4	1806	0.6		
21 SU	0025	2.6	0647	0.4	1257	2.3	1848	0.7
22 M	0111	2.5	0732	0.6	1344	2.2	1935	0.8
23 TU	0203	2.4	0827	0.7	1440	2.1	2033	0.9
24 W	0307	2.2	0940	0.9	1610	2.0	2150	1.0
25 TH	0443	2.2	1116	0.9	1731	2.1	2354	0.9
26 F	0607	2.2	1239	0.8	1832	2.1		
27 SA	0109	0.7	0715	2.2	1339	0.9	1925	2.2
28 SU	0206	0.5	0814	2.3	1429	0.8	2014	2.3

MARCH

Day	Time	m	Time	m	Time	m	Time	m
1 M	0254	0.3	0906	2.3	1513	0.7	2059	2.4
2 TU ○	0339	0.2	0952	2.4	1552	0.7	2142	2.5
3 W	0420	0.2	1032	2.3	1627	0.7	2220	2.5
4 TH	0457	0.3	1106	2.3	1655	0.7	2254	2.5
5 F	0530	0.3	1133	2.2	1719	0.7	2328	2.5
6 SA	0600	0.5	1159	2.2	1745	0.7		
7 SU	0003	2.4	0630	0.6	1232	2.1	1814	0.8
8 M	0042	2.3	0706	0.7	1311	2.1	1847	0.9
9 TU	0126	2.2	0752	0.9	1359	2.0	1927	1.0
10 W	0218	2.1	0856	1.0	1502	2.0	2106	1.1
11 TH	0325	2.0	1001	1.1	1621	2.0	2226	1.1
12 F	0446	2.0	1102	1.1	1728	2.1	2332	1.1
13 SA	0602	2.1	1200	1.1	1825	2.1		
14 SU	0035	0.9	0706	2.1	1257	1.0	1914	2.2
15 M	0133	0.7	0759	2.2	1348	0.9	1958	2.3
16 TU	0224	0.6	0844	2.3	1434	0.8	2039	2.4
17 W ●	0309	0.5	0925	2.4	1515	0.7	2120	2.5
18 TH	0351	0.3	1004	2.4	1555	0.6	2202	2.6
19 F	0431	0.2	1040	2.5	1634	0.5	2244	2.7
20 SA	0510	0.2	1116	2.4	1712	0.5	2327	2.7
21 SU	0549	0.3	1154	2.4	1752	0.5		
22 M	0011	2.6	0629	0.5	1235	2.3	1834	0.5
23 TU	0059	2.5	0713	0.6	1320	2.2	1923	0.6
24 W	0154	2.3	0807	0.8	1414	2.1	2022	0.8
25 TH	0312	2.2	0915	1.0	1541	2.0	2146	0.8
26 F	0446	2.2	1101	1.1	1705	2.0	2345	0.8
27 SA	0603	2.2	1228	1.0	1809	2.1		
28 SU	0054	0.6	0708	2.3	1325	0.9	1904	2.2
29 M	0148	0.4	0803	2.3	1412	0.8	1954	2.3
30 TU	0235	0.3	0850	2.3	1454	0.8	2039	2.4
31 W ○	0318	0.3	0930	2.3	1532	0.7	2121	2.4

APRIL

Day	Time	m	Time	m	Time	m	Time	m
1 TH	0356	0.3	1005	2.3	1605	0.7	2157	2.4
2 F	0430	0.3	1032	2.3	1632	0.7	2231	2.4
3 SA	0459	0.5	1056	2.3	1655	0.7	2305	2.4
4 SU	0525	0.5	1125	2.3	1721	0.7	2340	2.4
5 M	0552	0.6	1158	2.2	1749	0.7		
6 TU	0019	2.3	0621	0.8	1234	2.2	1820	0.8
7 W	0102	2.3	0654	0.9	1314	2.1	1857	0.9
8 TH	0151	2.1	0742	1.1	1402	2.0	1957	1.0
9 F	0254	2.0	0912	1.2	1501	2.0	2152	1.0
10 SA	0418	2.0	1027	1.2	1633	2.0	2303	1.0
11 SU	0537	2.0	1130	1.2	1740	2.1		
12 M	0006	0.9	0641	2.2	1230	1.1	1833	2.2
13 TU	0104	0.7	0733	2.3	1323	1.0	1921	2.3
14 W	0156	0.5	0817	2.3	1410	0.8	2007	2.4
15 TH	0243	0.3	0857	2.4	1455	0.7	2053	2.5
16 F ●	0327	0.2	0936	2.5	1537	0.5	2140	2.6
17 SA	0409	0.2	1015	2.5	1619	0.4	2226	2.7
18 SU	0450	0.2	1054	2.5	1700	0.4	2312	2.7
19 M	0531	0.3	1134	2.4	1742	0.4	2359	2.6
20 TU	0612	0.4	1215	2.3	1827	0.4		
21 W	0050	2.5	0656	0.6	1302	2.2	1918	0.5
22 TH	0154	2.3	0748	0.9	1357	2.1	2021	0.6
23 F	0317	2.2	0853	1.1	1519	2.1	2147	0.7
24 SA	0439	2.2	1029	1.2	1637	2.1	2322	0.7
25 SU	0549	2.2	1203	1.1	1742	2.1		
26 M	0029	0.6	0650	2.3	1301	1.0	1838	2.2
27 TU	0123	0.5	0741	2.3	1348	0.9	1930	2.3
28 W	0210	0.4	0825	2.3	1430	0.8	2016	2.3
29 TH	0252	0.4	0901	2.3	1508	0.8	2057	2.3
30 F ○	0329	0.5	0931	2.3	1541	0.7	2133	2.3

Chart Datum: 1·50 metres below Ordnance Datum (Newlyn)

ENGLAND – LOWESTOFT

LAT 52°28′N LONG 1°45′E

TIMES AND HEIGHTS OF HIGH AND LOW WATERS

YEAR **1999**

TIME ZONE (UT)
For Summer Time add ONE hour in non-shaded areas

MAY

Day	Time	m		Day	Time	m
1 SA	0359 / 0957 / 1606 / 2208	0.5 / 2.3 / 0.7 / 2.3		16 SU	0348 / 0951 / 1605 / 2209	0.2 / 2.5 / 0.4 / 2.6
2 SU	0425 / 1026 / 1631 / 2244	0.6 / 2.3 / 0.6 / 2.3		17 M	0431 / 1034 / 1650 / 2259	0.2 / 2.5 / 0.3 / 2.6
3 M	0450 / 1058 / 1659 / 2321	0.6 / 2.3 / 0.6 / 2.3		18 TU	0514 / 1116 / 1735 / 2350	0.3 / 2.5 / 0.3 / 2.5
4 TU	0518 / 1131 / 1730 / 2359	0.7 / 2.3 / 0.7 / 2.3		19 W	0556 / 1200 / 1823	0.5 / 2.4 / 0.3
5 W	0548 / 1205 / 1804	0.8 / 2.3 / 0.7		20 TH	0045 / 0640 / 1247 / 1916	2.4 / 0.7 / 2.4 / 0.4
6 TH	0040 / 0623 / 1243 / 1844	2.2 / 0.9 / 2.2 / 0.8		21 F	0152 / 0729 / 1342 / 2019	2.3 / 0.9 / 2.3 / 0.5
7 F	0128 / 0707 / 1326 / 1938	2.1 / 1.1 / 2.2 / 0.9		22 SA	0308 / 0826 / 1453 / 2130	2.2 / 1.1 / 2.2 / 0.6
8 SA	0227 / 0806 / 1417 / 2102	2.1 / 1.2 / 2.1 / 0.9		23 SU	0419 / 0934 / 1604 / 2247	2.2 / 1.2 / 2.2 / 0.6
9 SU	0352 / 0924 / 1515 / 2227	2.0 / 1.2 / 2.1 / 0.9		24 M	0523 / 1116 / 1708 / 2356	2.2 / 1.2 / 2.2 / 0.6
10 M	0508 / 1046 / 1624 / 2333	2.1 / 1.2 / 2.1 / 0.8		25 TU	0621 / 1227 / 1808	2.2 / 1.2 / 2.2
11 TU	0610 / 1153 / 1743	2.2 / 1.1 / 2.2		26 W	0052 / 0711 / 1319 / 1901	0.6 / 2.3 / 1.0 / 2.3
12 W	0032 / 0702 / 1251 / 1842	0.6 / 2.3 / 1.0 / 2.3		27 TH	0141 / 0753 / 1403 / 1948	0.6 / 2.3 / 0.9 / 2.3
13 TH	0126 / 0746 / 1343 / 1936	0.5 / 2.3 / 0.8 / 2.4		28 F	0222 / 0827 / 1442 / 2030	0.6 / 2.3 / 0.9 / 2.3
14 F	0215 / 0828 / 1432 / 2028	0.3 / 2.4 / 0.6 / 2.5		29 SA	0256 / 0857 / 1515 / 2109	0.7 / 2.3 / 0.8 / 2.3
15 SA ●	0303 / 0910 / 1519 / 2119	0.3 / 2.5 / 0.5 / 2.6		30 SU O	0323 / 0929 / 1541 / 2147	0.7 / 2.4 / 0.7 / 2.3
				31 M	0349 / 1003 / 1609 / 2226	0.7 / 2.4 / 0.7 / 2.3

JUNE

Day	Time	m		Day	Time	m
1 TU	0419 / 1037 / 1642 / 2304	0.7 / 2.4 / 0.7 / 2.3		16 W	0459 / 1100 / 1730 / 2342	0.5 / 2.6 / 0.2 / 2.5
2 W	0451 / 1110 / 1716 / 2343	0.8 / 2.4 / 0.7 / 2.3		17 TH	0541 / 1145 / 1818	0.6 / 2.6 / 0.3
3 TH	0524 / 1143 / 1753	0.8 / 2.4 / 0.7		18 F	0037 / 0622 / 1231 / 1908	2.4 / 0.8 / 2.5 / 0.3
4 F	0023 / 0601 / 1220 / 1834	2.2 / 0.9 / 2.3 / 0.7		19 SA	0139 / 0705 / 1321 / 2002	2.3 / 0.9 / 2.4 / 0.4
5 SA	0107 / 0645 / 1302 / 1924	2.2 / 1.0 / 2.3 / 0.8		20 SU	0245 / 0754 / 1419 / 2059	2.2 / 1.1 / 2.3 / 0.6
6 SU	0200 / 0736 / 1350 / 2025	2.1 / 1.1 / 2.2 / 0.8		21 M	0348 / 0849 / 1524 / 2159	2.2 / 1.2 / 2.3 / 0.7
7 M	0314 / 0835 / 1443 / 2142	2.1 / 1.2 / 2.2 / 0.8		22 TU	0448 / 0950 / 1628 / 2303	2.2 / 1.3 / 2.3 / 0.7
8 TU	0432 / 0943 / 1541 / 2254	2.1 / 1.2 / 2.2 / 0.7		23 W	0543 / 1104 / 1731	2.2 / 1.3 / 2.2
9 W	0535 / 1105 / 1651 / 2358	2.2 / 1.1 / 2.2 / 0.6		24 TH	0007 / 0632 / 1239 / 1828	0.8 / 2.2 / 1.2 / 2.2
10 TH	0629 / 1216 / 1809	2.2 / 1.0 / 2.3		25 F	0100 / 0714 / 1332 / 1919	0.8 / 2.3 / 1.1 / 2.2
11 F	0055 / 0717 / 1317 / 1910	0.5 / 2.3 / 0.9 / 2.4		26 SA	0141 / 0751 / 1413 / 2004	0.8 / 2.3 / 1.0 / 2.3
12 SA	0149 / 0802 / 1411 / 2007	0.4 / 2.4 / 0.7 / 2.5		27 SU	0213 / 0827 / 1447 / 2047	0.8 / 2.4 / 0.9 / 2.2
13 SU ●	0240 / 0846 / 1503 / 2102	0.3 / 2.5 / 0.5 / 2.5		28 M O	0243 / 0904 / 1518 / 2129	0.8 / 2.4 / 0.8 / 2.3
14 M	0329 / 0931 / 1553 / 2156	0.3 / 2.5 / 0.4 / 2.6		29 TU	0317 / 0942 / 1552 / 2210	0.8 / 2.5 / 0.4 / 2.6
15 TU	0415 / 1016 / 1642 / 2249	0.4 / 2.6 / 0.3 / 2.5		30 W	0353 / 1019 / 1627 / 2251	0.8 / 2.5 / 0.7 / 2.3

JULY

Day	Time	m		Day	Time	m
1 TH	0428 / 1053 / 1704 / 2330	0.8 / 2.5 / 0.7 / 2.3		16 F	0525 / 1126 / 1805	0.7 / 2.7 / 0.2
2 F	0505 / 1125 / 1742	0.8 / 2.5 / 0.6		17 SA	0022 / 0602 / 1209 / 1849	2.4 / 0.8 / 2.6 / 0.3
3 SA	0007 / 0543 / 1200 / 1821	2.3 / 0.9 / 2.5 / 0.6		18 SU	0114 / 0638 / 1252 / 1934	2.3 / 0.9 / 2.5 / 0.4
4 SU	0046 / 0625 / 1241 / 1906	2.3 / 0.9 / 2.4 / 0.6		19 M	0209 / 0719 / 1337 / 2021	2.2 / 1.0 / 2.4 / 0.6
5 M	0130 / 0711 / 1327 / 1957	2.2 / 1.0 / 2.4 / 0.7		20 TU	0307 / 0809 / 1431 / 2111	2.1 / 1.1 / 2.3 / 0.7
6 TU	0223 / 0803 / 1417 / 2059	2.2 / 1.1 / 2.4 / 0.7		21 W	0403 / 0907 / 1537 / 2202	2.1 / 1.2 / 2.2 / 0.7
7 W	0340 / 0902 / 1513 / 2214	2.1 / 1.1 / 2.3 / 0.7		22 TH	0456 / 1009 / 1645 / 2255	2.1 / 1.3 / 2.2 / 0.9
8 TH	0457 / 1016 / 1619 / 2324	2.1 / 1.1 / 2.3 / 0.6		23 F	0547 / 1113 / 1750 / 2348	2.2 / 1.2 / 2.2 / 0.9
9 F	0557 / 1144 / 1743	2.2 / 1.0 / 2.3		24 SA	0634 / 1220 / 1848	2.2 / 1.2 / 2.2
10 SA	0028 / 0650 / 1255 / 1852	0.6 / 2.3 / 0.9 / 2.4		25 SU	0039 / 0717 / 1327 / 1939	1.0 / 2.3 / 1.0 / 2.2
11 SU	0128 / 0739 / 1356 / 1954	0.6 / 2.4 / 0.7 / 2.4		26 M	0128 / 0759 / 1416 / 2026	0.9 / 2.4 / 0.9 / 2.3
12 M	0223 / 0826 / 1452 / 2053	0.5 / 2.5 / 0.5 / 2.5		27 TU	0212 / 0841 / 1457 / 2112	0.9 / 2.5 / 0.8 / 2.3
13 TU ●	0314 / 0913 / 1544 / 2149	0.5 / 2.6 / 0.3 / 2.5		28 W O	0253 / 0921 / 1603 / 2155	0.9 / 2.5 / 0.8 / 2.3
14 W	0401 / 0959 / 1633 / 2241	0.5 / 2.6 / 0.2 / 2.5		29 TH	0332 / 0959 / 1614 / 2235	0.9 / 2.6 / 0.7 / 2.4
15 TH	0445 / 1043 / 1720 / 2332	0.6 / 2.7 / 0.2 / 2.5		30 F	0410 / 1033 / 1650 / 2313	0.8 / 2.6 / 0.6 / 2.4
				31 SA	0447 / 1106 / 1727 / 2347	0.8 / 2.6 / 0.5 / 2.4

AUGUST

Day	Time	m		Day	Time	m
1 SU	0526 / 1142 / 1805	0.8 / 2.6 / 0.5		16 M	0036 / 0609 / 1219 / 1859	2.3 / 0.9 / 2.6 / 0.5
2 M	0020 / 0605 / 1222 / 1845	2.4 / 0.8 / 2.6 / 0.5		17 TU	0114 / 0644 / 1258 / 1939	2.2 / 1.0 / 2.5 / 0.7
3 TU	0100 / 0648 / 1306 / 1931	2.3 / 0.9 / 2.5 / 0.6		18 W	0157 / 0729 / 1343 / 2027	2.1 / 1.1 / 2.3 / 0.8
4 W	0146 / 0736 / 1355 / 2025	2.2 / 1.0 / 2.5 / 0.7		19 TH	0255 / 0828 / 1440 / 2120	2.1 / 1.2 / 2.2 / 1.0
5 TH	0242 / 0831 / 1451 / 2135	2.2 / 1.0 / 2.4 / 0.7		20 F	0359 / 0935 / 1554 / 2216	2.1 / 1.2 / 2.1 / 1.0
6 F	0409 / 0942 / 1600 / 2255	2.1 / 1.1 / 2.3 / 0.8		21 SA	0500 / 1040 / 1710 / 2311	2.1 / 1.2 / 2.1 / 1.1
7 SA	0527 / 1120 / 1732	2.2 / 1.0 / 2.3		22 SU	0555 / 1143 / 1819	2.2 / 1.2 / 2.1
8 SU	0008 / 0626 / 1242 / 1846	0.8 / 2.3 / 0.9 / 2.3		23 M	0006 / 0645 / 1247 / 1917	1.1 / 2.3 / 1.1 / 2.2
9 M	0115 / 0718 / 1347 / 1950	0.8 / 2.4 / 0.8 / 2.4		24 TU	0059 / 0731 / 1346 / 2007	1.0 / 2.4 / 0.9 / 2.3
10 TU	0212 / 0808 / 1443 / 2049	0.7 / 2.5 / 0.5 / 2.4		25 W	0149 / 0815 / 1434 / 2052	1.0 / 2.5 / 0.8 / 2.4
11 W ●	0303 / 0855 / 1533 / 2142	0.7 / 2.6 / 0.3 / 2.5		26 TH O	0233 / 0855 / 1516 / 2135	0.9 / 2.5 / 0.7 / 2.4
12 TH	0348 / 0941 / 1619 / 2231	0.7 / 2.6 / 0.2 / 2.5		27 F	0314 / 0933 / 1555 / 2214	0.9 / 2.6 / 0.6 / 2.5
13 F	0430 / 1024 / 1703 / 2316	0.7 / 2.7 / 0.2 / 2.4		28 SA	0352 / 1009 / 1632 / 2249	0.8 / 2.6 / 0.5 / 2.5
14 SA	0506 / 1104 / 1743 / 2357	0.7 / 2.7 / 0.2 / 2.4		29 SU	0429 / 1045 / 1708 / 2321	0.7 / 2.7 / 0.4 / 2.5
15 SU	0539 / 1142 / 1821	0.7 / 2.6 / 0.3		30 M	0507 / 1123 / 1745 / 2354	0.7 / 2.7 / 0.4 / 2.5
				31 TU	0547 / 1203 / 1824	0.7 / 2.7 / 0.5

Chart Datum: 1·50 metres below Ordnance Datum (Newlyn)

4

ENGLAND – LOWESTOFT

LAT 52°28'N   LONG 1°45'E

TIMES AND HEIGHTS OF HIGH AND LOW WATERS — YEAR **1999**

SEPTEMBER

Day	Time	m		Day	Time	m
1 W	0032 / 0628 / 1248 / 1906	2.4 / 0.8 / 2.6 / 0.6		**16** TH	0052 / 0649 / 1308 / 1938	2.2 / 1.0 / 2.3 / 0.9
2 TH	0116 / 0714 / 1337 / 1956	2.3 / 0.8 / 2.5 / 0.7		**17** F	0137 / 0743 / 1400 / 2037	2.2 / 1.1 / 2.2 / 1.1
3 F	0207 / 0810 / 1435 / 2103	2.2 / 0.9 / 2.4 / 0.9		**18** SA	0243 / 0903 / 1511 / 2141	2.1 / 1.1 / 2.1 / 1.2
4 SA	0316 / 0924 / 1557 / 2232	2.1 / 1.0 / 2.3 / 1.0		**19** SU	0410 / 1013 / 1636 / 2241	2.2 / 1.2 / 2.1 / 1.2
5 SU	0500 / 1110 / 1733 / 2358	2.2 / 1.0 / 2.3 / 1.2		**20** M	0516 / 1117 / 1753 / 2339	2.2 / 1.2 / 2.1 / 1.2
6 M	0605 / 1235 / 1846	2.2 / 0.8 / 2.3		**21** TU	0612 / 1219 / 1855	2.3 / 1.0 / 2.2
7 TU	0107 / 0659 / 1338 / 1948	0.9 / 2.4 / 0.6 / 2.4		**22** W	0034 / 0700 / 1316 / 1945	1.1 / 2.4 / 0.9 / 2.3
8 W	0202 / 0749 / 1430 / 2042	0.9 / 2.5 / 0.4 / 2.5		**23** TH	0126 / 0743 / 1405 / 2028	1.1 / 2.5 / 0.8 / 2.4
9 TH	0249 / 0836 / 1517 / ● 2130	0.8 / 2.6 / 0.3 / 2.5		**24** F	0211 / 0823 / 1449 / 2109	1.0 / 2.6 / 0.6 / 2.5
10 F	0332 / 0921 / 1600 / 2213	0.8 / 2.6 / 0.2 / 2.5		**25** SA	0253 / 0902 / 1530 / O 2146	0.9 / 2.6 / 0.5 / 2.5
11 SA	0410 / 1002 / 1640 / 2251	0.8 / 2.6 / 0.3 / 2.4		**26** SU	0332 / 0942 / 1609 / 2221	0.8 / 2.7 / 0.4 / 2.6
12 SU	0443 / 1039 / 1716 / 2322	0.8 / 2.6 / 0.3 / 2.4		**27** M	0410 / 1022 / 1647 / 2254	0.7 / 2.8 / 0.4 / 2.6
13 M	0512 / 1114 / 1749 / 2348	0.8 / 2.6 / 0.5 / 2.3		**28** TU	0450 / 1104 / 1724 / 2330	0.6 / 2.8 / 0.4 / 2.5
14 TU	0539 / 1148 / 1820	0.8 / 2.5 / 0.6		**29** W	0530 / 1146 / 1803	0.6 / 2.7 / 0.5
15 W	0016 / 0611 / 1226 / 1854	2.3 / 0.9 / 2.4 / 0.8		**30** TH	0008 / 0612 / 1232 / 1844	2.5 / 0.7 / 2.6 / 0.7

OCTOBER

Day	Time	m		Day	Time	m
1 F	0051 / 0659 / 1323 / 1933	2.4 / 0.8 / 2.5 / 0.9		**16** SA	0052 / 0656 / 1329 / 1911	2.3 / 1.1 / 2.2 / 1.2
2 SA	0141 / 0758 / 1429 / 2038	2.3 / 0.9 / 2.3 / 1.1		**17** SU	0137 / 0818 / 1433 / 2045	2.2 / 1.2 / 2.1 / 1.3
3 SU	0246 / 0920 / 1608 / 2212	2.2 / 0.9 / 2.2 / 1.2		**18** M	0237 / 0944 / 1605 / 2204	2.2 / 1.2 / 2.1 / 1.3
4 M	0433 / 1107 / 1732 / 2350	2.2 / 0.9 / 2.3 / 1.2		**19** TU	0425 / 1049 / 1723 / 2307	2.2 / 1.1 / 2.1 / 1.3
5 TU	0542 / 1223 / 1840	2.3 / 0.7 / 2.4		**20** W	0529 / 1150 / 1826	2.3 / 1.0 / 2.2
6 W	0054 / 0638 / 1321 / 1937	1.1 / 2.4 / 0.6 / 2.4		**21** TH	0005 / 0619 / 1245 / 1916	1.2 / 2.4 / 0.8 / 2.3
7 TH	0145 / 0729 / 1410 / 2026	1.0 / 2.5 / 0.4 / 2.5		**22** F	0058 / 0704 / 1334 / 1959	1.1 / 2.5 / 0.7 / 2.4
8 F	0230 / 0815 / 1455 / 2109	0.9 / 2.5 / 0.4 / 2.5		**23** SA	0144 / 0747 / 1420 / 2039	1.0 / 2.6 / 0.6 / 2.5
9 SA	0310 / 0858 / 1536 / ● 2147	0.8 / 2.6 / 0.4 / 2.4		**24** SU	0228 / 0831 / 1503 / O 2116	0.9 / 2.6 / 0.4 / 2.6
10 SU	0347 / 0938 / 1613 / 2218	0.8 / 2.6 / 0.4 / 2.4		**25** M	0310 / 0915 / 1544 / 2153	0.7 / 2.7 / 0.4 / 2.6
11 M	0418 / 1013 / 1645 / 2243	0.8 / 2.6 / 0.5 / 2.4		**26** TU	0352 / 1001 / 1624 / 2230	0.6 / 2.8 / 0.4 / 2.6
12 TU	0444 / 1047 / 1712 / 2308	0.8 / 2.5 / 0.6 / 2.4		**27** W	0434 / 1046 / 1704 / 2308	0.6 / 2.7 / 0.4 / 2.6
13 W	0511 / 1122 / 1739 / 2339	0.8 / 2.5 / 0.7 / 2.4		**28** TH	0517 / 1132 / 1744 / 2348	0.5 / 2.7 / 0.5 / 2.5
14 TH	0541 / 1200 / 1806	0.8 / 2.4 / 0.9		**29** F	0602 / 1221 / 1826	0.6 / 2.6 / 0.7
15 F	0013 / 0615 / 1241 / 1833	2.4 / 0.8 / 2.3 / 1.0		**30** SA	0031 / 0652 / 1317 / 1914	2.4 / 0.7 / 2.4 / 1.0
				31 SU	0121 / 0754 / 1434 / 2014	2.3 / 0.8 / 2.3 / 1.2

NOVEMBER

Day	Time	m		Day	Time	m
1 M	0227 / 0919 / 1605 / 2140	2.3 / 0.8 / 2.2 / 1.3		**16** TU	0152 / 0859 / 1529 / 2039	2.3 / 1.1 / 2.1 / 1.4
2 TU	0404 / 1051 / 1719 / 2325	2.3 / 0.8 / 2.3 / 1.3		**17** W	0248 / 1013 / 1647 / 2213	2.3 / 1.0 / 2.1 / 1.4
3 W	0514 / 1201 / 1823	2.3 / 0.7 / 2.4		**18** TH	0352 / 1114 / 1750 / 2324	2.3 / 0.9 / 2.2 / 1.3
4 TH	0030 / 0613 / 1257 / 1916	1.2 / 2.4 / 0.6 / 2.4		**19** F	0519 / 1210 / 1842	2.3 / 0.8 / 2.3
5 F	0121 / 0705 / 1346 / 2002	1.1 / 2.5 / 0.5 / 2.4		**20** SA	0022 / 0618 / 1301 / 1927	1.2 / 2.4 / 0.7 / 2.4
6 SA	0206 / 0752 / 1430 / 2042	1.0 / 2.5 / 0.5 / 2.4		**21** SU	0114 / 0711 / 1350 / 2007	1.0 / 2.5 / 0.5 / 2.5
7 SU	0246 / 0836 / 1509 / 2115	0.9 / 2.5 / 0.5 / 2.4		**22** M	0203 / 0802 / 1436 / 2047	0.8 / 2.6 / 0.4 / 2.5
8 M	0322 / 0914 / 1543 / ● 2144	0.8 / 2.5 / 0.6 / 2.4		**23** TU	0250 / 0852 / 1521 / O 2127	0.7 / 2.7 / 0.4 / 2.6
9 TU	0352 / 0950 / 1611 / 2210	0.8 / 2.5 / 0.6 / 2.4		**24** W	0337 / 0942 / 1604 / 2209	0.6 / 2.7 / 0.4 / 2.6
10 W	0417 / 1025 / 1635 / 2239	0.8 / 2.4 / 0.8 / 2.5		**25** TH	0423 / 1032 / 1647 / 2250	0.5 / 2.7 / 0.6 / 2.6
11 TH	0446 / 1101 / 1700 / 2311	0.8 / 2.4 / 0.8 / 2.5		**26** F	0509 / 1122 / 1728 / 2333	0.5 / 2.6 / 0.6 / 2.6
12 F	0518 / 1139 / 1727 / 2344	0.8 / 2.3 / 0.9 / 2.4		**27** SA	0557 / 1214 / 1811	0.5 / 2.5 / 0.8
13 SA	0553 / 1220 / 1757	0.9 / 2.3 / 1.0		**28** SU	0016 / 0649 / 1314 / 1856	2.5 / 0.6 / 2.4 / 1.0
14 SU	0020 / 0631 / 1305 / 1834	2.4 / 1.0 / 2.2 / 1.1		**29** M	0105 / 0750 / 1429 / 1949	2.5 / 0.6 / 2.3 / 1.2
15 M	0103 / 0725 / 1401 / 1926	2.3 / 1.1 / 2.1 / 1.3		**30** TU	0206 / 0903 / 1546 / 2053	2.5 / 0.7 / 2.2 / 1.3

DECEMBER

Day	Time	m		Day	Time	m
1 W	0328 / 1019 / 1654 / 2230	2.3 / 0.7 / 2.3 / 1.4		**16** TH	0216 / 0915 / 1557 / 2058	2.3 / 0.9 / 2.1 / 1.3
2 TH	0440 / 1129 / 1754 / 2356	2.3 / 0.7 / 2.3 / 1.3		**17** F	0310 / 1029 / 1706 / 2215	2.3 / 0.9 / 2.1 / 1.3
3 F	0543 / 1228 / 1847	2.3 / 0.7 / 2.3		**18** SA	0410 / 1131 / 1803 / 2340	2.3 / 0.8 / 2.2 / 1.2
4 SA	0053 / 0639 / 1319 / 1932	1.2 / 2.4 / 0.7 / 2.3		**19** SU	0528 / 1228 / 1853	2.4 / 0.7 / 2.3
5 SU	0141 / 0729 / 1403 / 2010	1.1 / 2.4 / 0.7 / 2.4		**20** M	0044 / 0639 / 1322 / 1937	1.0 / 2.4 / 0.6 / 2.4
6 M	0223 / 0814 / 1441 / 2043	1.0 / 2.4 / 0.7 / 2.4		**21** TU	0141 / 0738 / 1412 / 2021	0.8 / 2.5 / 0.5 / 2.5
7 TU	0259 / 0854 / 1511 / ● 2113	0.9 / 2.4 / 0.8 / 2.4		**22** W	0234 / 0834 / 1501 / O 2105	0.7 / 2.6 / 0.5 / 2.5
8 W	0329 / 0931 / 1535 / 2145	0.8 / 2.4 / 0.8 / 2.5		**23** TH	0326 / 0929 / 1548 / 2150	0.5 / 2.6 / 0.5 / 2.6
9 TH	0356 / 1009 / 1601 / 2218	0.8 / 2.3 / 0.9 / 2.5		**24** F	0416 / 1022 / 1633 / 2234	0.4 / 2.6 / 0.6 / 2.7
10 F	0427 / 1047 / 1631 / 2250	0.8 / 2.3 / 0.9 / 2.5		**25** SA	0504 / 1114 / 1715 / 2318	0.3 / 2.5 / 0.7 / 2.7
11 SA	0501 / 1125 / 1702 / 2323	0.8 / 2.3 / 0.9 / 2.5		**26** SU	0552 / 1207 / 1756	0.3 / 2.5 / 0.8
12 SU	0537 / 1204 / 1735 / 2358	0.8 / 2.3 / 1.0 / 2.5		**27** M	0002 / 0641 / 1305 / 1836	2.6 / 0.4 / 2.4
13 M	0616 / 1245 / 1814	0.8 / 2.2 / 1.1		**28** TU	0048 / 0734 / 1409 / 1920	2.6 / 0.5 / 2.3 / 1.1
14 TU	0038 / 0700 / 1332 / 1900	2.4 / 0.9 / 2.2 / 1.2		**29** W	0138 / 0831 / 1515 / 2011	2.5 / 0.6 / 2.2 / 1.2
15 W	0125 / 0757 / 1430 / 1955	2.4 / 0.9 / 2.1 / 1.3		**30** TH	0242 / 0933 / 1618 / 2111	2.4 / 0.7 / 2.1 / 1.3
				31 F	0356 / 1039 / 1717 / 2224	2.3 / 0.8 / 2.1 / 1.3

Chart Datum: 1·50 metres below Ordnance Datum (Newlyn)

GREAT YARMOUTH 8-4-27

Norfolk 52°34'·33N 01°44'·50E Rtg 3-5-2

CHARTS

AC 1536, 1543; Imray C28; Stanfords 3; OS 134

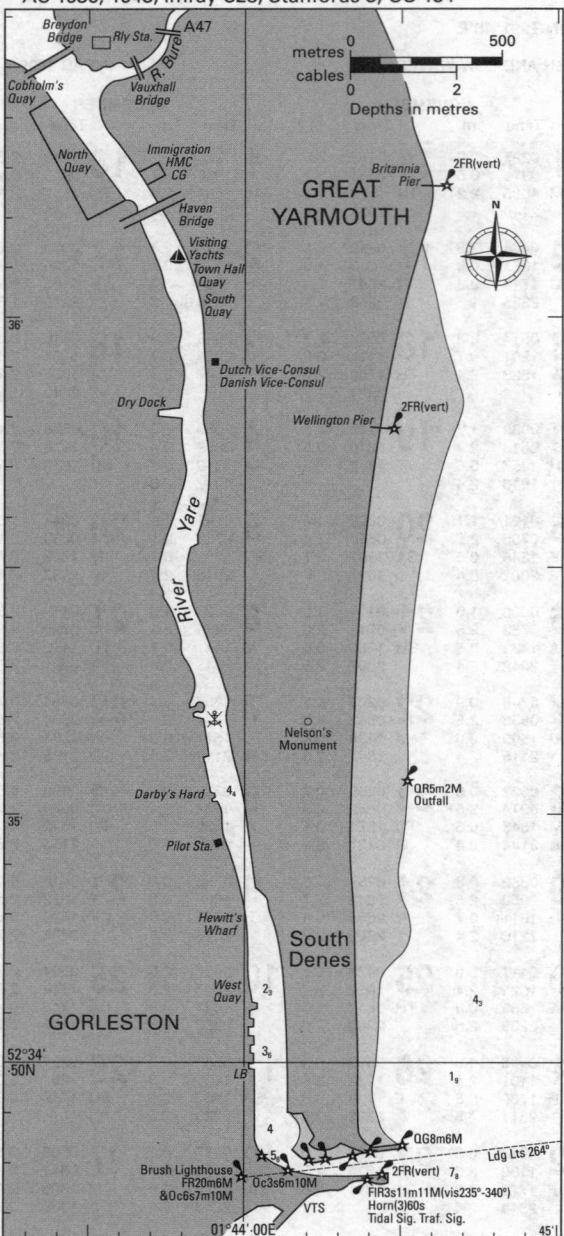

TIDES

−0210 Dover; ML 1·5; Duration 0620; Zone 0 (UT)

Standard Port LOWESTOFT (←—)

Times				Height (metres)			
High Water		Low Water		MHWS	MHWN	MLWN	MLWS
0300	0900	0200	0800	2·4	2·1	1·0	0·5
1500	2100	1400	2000				

Differences GORLESTON (To be used for Great Yarmouth)

−0035	−0035	−0030	−0030	0·0	−0·1	0·0	0·0

CAISTER-ON-SEA

−0130	−0130	−0100	−0100	0·0	−0·1	0·0	0·0

WINTERTON-ON-SEA

−0225	−0215	−0135	−0135	+0·8	+0·5	+0·2	+0·1

Rise of tide occurs mainly during 3½ hours after LW. From HW Lowestoft −3 until HW the level is usually within 0·3m of predicted HW. Flood tide runs until about HW +1½ and Ebb until about LW +2½. See also under NAVIGATION.

SHELTER

Excellent on Town Hall Quay, close S of Haven Bridge; ⚓ prohib in hbr which is a busy commercial port.

NAVIGATION

WPT 52°34'·40N 01°45'·67E, 084°/264° from/to front ldg lt, 1·0M. Access is H24, subject to clearance, but small craft must not attempt ent in strong SE winds which cause dangerous seas, especially on the ebb. Except at local slack water, which occurs at HW+1½ and LW+1¾, tidal streams at the ent are strong. On the flood, the stream eddies NW past S pier, thence up-river; beware being set onto N pier; a QY tidal lt on S pier warns of this D/N. Temp shoaling may occur in the ent during strong E'lies, with depths 1m less than those charted. Beware strong tidal streams that sweep through the Haven Bridge.

LIGHTS AND MARKS

Main lt Fl R 3s 11m 11M, vis 235°-340°, Horn (3) 60s. (Note: Tfc Sigs and the tidal QY are co-located with the Main lt on a R brick bldg, W lower half floodlit, at S pier). Ldg lts 264°: front Oc 3s 6m 10M; rear Oc 6s 7m 10M, (below the FR 20m 6M on Brush lt ho). N pier lt, QG 8m 6M, vis 176°-078° (262°). Ent and bend marked by five x 2 FG and seven x 2FR (all vert).

TRAFFIC SIGNALS

VTS instructions (Ch 12) must always be obeyed. Tfc sigs on S pier: 3 Ⓡ (vert), vis 235°-295° = No entry. VTS office: 3 Ⓡ (vert) = no vessel to go down-river S of the LB shed. Haven and Breydon bridges: 3 Ⓡ (vert) = passage prohib.

RADIO TELEPHONE

Call: *Yarmouth* Ch **12** (both H24) 09. Both bridges Ch 12.

TELEPHONE (Dial code 01493)

Hr Mr & Port Control 335511, ☎ 653464; MRCC 851338; ⌗ (01473) 235704 (H24) or (01493) 843686 (Mon-Fri 0900-1600); Police 336200; Breydon Bridge 651275.

FACILITIES

Town Hall Quay (50m stretch) AB £10, may be limited to only 2 nights in season.
Burgh Castle Marina (on Breydon Water) (90+10 visitors) ☎ 780331, £6, Slip, D, FW, ME, El, Sh, C (35 ton), ▣, Gas, Gaz, CH, V, R, Bar, Access HW ±4; **Services:** BY, P & D, ME, El, FW, Slip, Diving, AB, L, M, Sh, SM, ACA.
Town EC Thurs; P, D, CH, V, R, Bar, ✉, Ⓑ, ⇌, ✈ (Norwich).

Entry to the Broads: Pass up R Yare at slack LW, under Haven Bridge (2·3m MHWS) thence to Breydon Water via Breydon Bridge (4·0m) or to R Bure. Both bridges lift in co-ordination to pass small craft in groups. They are manned 0800-1700 Mon-Thurs, 0800-1600 Fri, but do not open 0800-0900 or 1700-1800. Call the Bridge Officer on VHF Ch 12. R Bure has two fixed bridges (2·3m MHWS).

NORFOLK BROADS: The Broads comprise about 120 miles of navigable rivers and lakes in Norfolk and Suffolk. The main rivers (Bure, Yare and Waveney) are tidal, flowing into the sea at Great Yarmouth. The N Broads have a 2·3m headroom limit. Unlimited headroom restricts cruising to R Yare (Great Yarmouth to Norwich, but note that 3M E of Norwich, Postwick viaduct on S bypass has 8.67m clearance) and River Waveney (Lowestoft to Beccles). The Broads may be entered from sea at Great Yarmouth (as above) or at Lowestoft (8.4.26). Broads Navigation Authority ☎ (01603) 610734.

Tidal data on the rivers and Broads is based on the time of LW at Yarmouth Yacht Stn (mouth of R Bure), which is LW Gorleston +0100 (see TIDES). Add the differences below to time of LW Yarmouth Yacht Stn to get local LW times:

R Bure		R Waveney	
Acle Bridge	+0230	Berney Arms	+0100
Horning	+0300	St Olaves	+0115
Potter Heigham	+0400	Oulton Broad	+0300
R Yare		Beccles	+0320
Reedham	+0115		
Cantley	+0200		
Norwich	+0430		

LW at Breydon (mouth of R Yare) is LW Yarmouth Yacht Stn +0100. Tide starts to flood on Breydon Water whilst still ebbing down from R Bure. Max draft is 1·8m; 2m with care. Tidal range varies from 0·6m to 1·8m.

Licences are compulsory; get temp one from The Broads Authority, 18 Colegate, Norwich NR3 1BQ, ☎ 01603-610734; from Mutford Lock or from River Inspectors. *Hamilton's Guide to the Broads* is recommended.

VOLVO PENTA SERVICE

Area 5

North East England
Blakeney to Berwick-upon-Tweed

5

VOLVO PENTA

8.5.1 Index **Page 323**

8.5.2 Diagram of ports, lights, RDF bns, Coast radio and weather stns **324**

8.5.3 Tidal stream charts **326**

8.5.4 List of coastal lights, fog signals and waypoints **328**

8.5.5 Passage information **331**

8.5.6 Distance table **333**

8.5.7 Blakeney **334**

8.5.8 Wells-next-the-Sea **334**

8.5.9 King's Lynn **335**
Burnham Overy Staithe
Brancaster Staithe
Wisbech

8.5.10 Boston **336**
River Welland
Wainfleet

8.5.11 River Humber (Immingham, Standard Port, tidal curves) **340**

8.5.12 Bridlington **342**
Filey

8.5.13 Scarborough **342**

8.5.14 Whitby **343**
Runswick Bay
River Tees, Middlesbrough

8.5.15 Hartlepool **344**

8.5.16 Seaham **345**

8.5.17 Sunderland **345**

8.5.18 River Tyne/North Shields, Standard Port, tidal curves **346**
Cullercoats

8.5.19 Blyth **350**
Newbiggin

8.5.20 Amble **351**
Boulmer
Craster
Newton Haven and Beadnell Bay
North Sunderland (Seahouses)
Farne Islands

8.5.21 Holy Island **352**

8.5.22 Berwick-upon-Tweed **353**

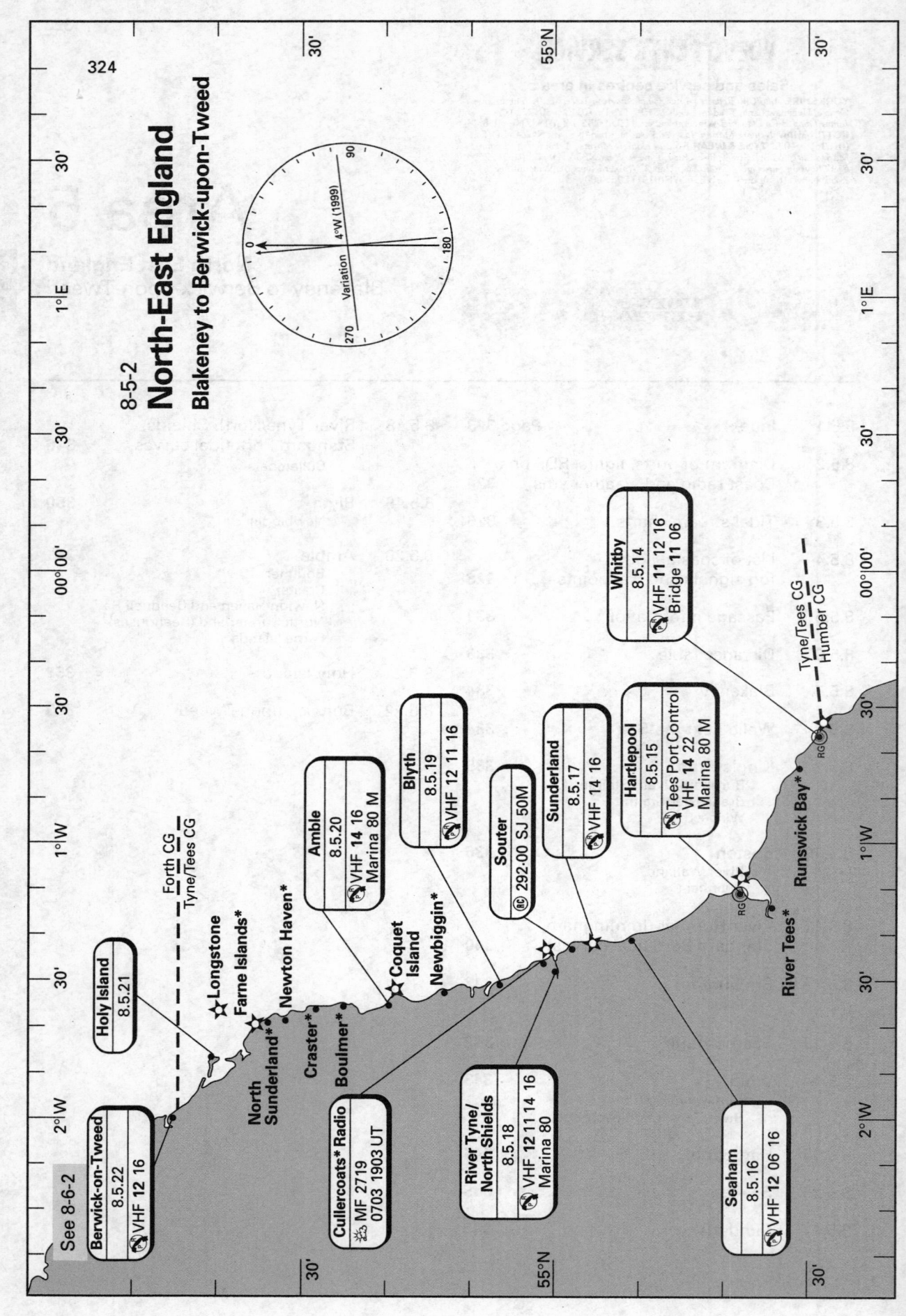

324

8-5-2
North-East England
Blakeney to Berwick-upon-Tweed

Variation 4°W (1999)

See 8-6-2

Berwick-on-Tweed
8.5.22
VHF 12 16

Holy Island
8.5.21

Longstone
Farne Islands*

Forth CG
Tyne/Tees CG

North Sunderland*
Newton Haven*
Craster*
Boulmer*

Cullercoats* Radio
MF 2719
0703 1903 UT

Amble
8.5.20
VHF 14 16
Marina 80 M

Coquet Island
Newbiggin*

Blyth
8.5.19
VHF 12 11 16

**River Tyne/
North Shields**
8.5.18
VHF 12 11 14 16
Marina 80

Souter
292-00 SJ 50M

Sunderland
8.5.17
VHF 14 16

Seaham
8.5.16
VHF 12 06 16

Hartlepool
8.5.15
Tees Port Control
VHF 14 22
Marina 80 M

River Tees*
Runswick Bay*

Whitby
8.5.14
VHF 11 12 16
Bridge 11 06

Tyne/Tees CG
Humber CG

Key to Symbols

- Coast Radio Station: VHF/MF frequencies
- Port, VTS, or marina Radio: VHF frequencies
- Marine RDF beacon
- Aero RDF beacon
- Weather information (Frequencies/times of broadcasts)
- SAR helicopter base
- Selected principal lights
- Light vessel/Light float/Lanby
- ○RG Emergency VHF DF
- * See Area Index

5

54°N

30'

1°E

30'

00°00'

Filey*

Scarborough
8.5.13
VHF 12 16

Flamborough Hd
302·00 FB 70M

Bridlington
8.5.12
VHF 12 14 16

Leconfield

Hull

Immingham

Grimsby
VHF 74 18 79
Marina 09 18 74

Grimsby Radio
VHF 27 16
VHF 27
0733 1933 UT

Humber Radio
VHF 26 16
MF 1925 1869
2684 2810
VHF 26
MF 1869
0733 1933 UT

Humber Lt By

River Humber
8.5.11
VTS 12 14 16

B1D Dowsing

Inner Dowsing

Humber CG
Yarmouth CG

Skegness

Wainfleet*

The Wash

Hunstanton

Brancaster Staithe*

Burnham Overy Staithe*

West Stones

Wisbech* Cut

River Welland*

Boston
8.5.10
VHF 12 16
Grand Sluice 74
Marina M 06

King's Lynn
8.5.9
VHF 14 11 12 16
Docks 14 11 16

Wisbech*
VHF 14 09 16

Blakeney
8.5.7

Sheringham

Wells-next-the-Sea
8.5.8
VHF 12 16

Cromer
313·50 CM 50M

Dudgeon light buoy

Winterton

53°N

2°W

1°W

30'

00°00'

30'

1°E

53°N

30'

8-5-3   AREA 5 TIDAL STREAMS

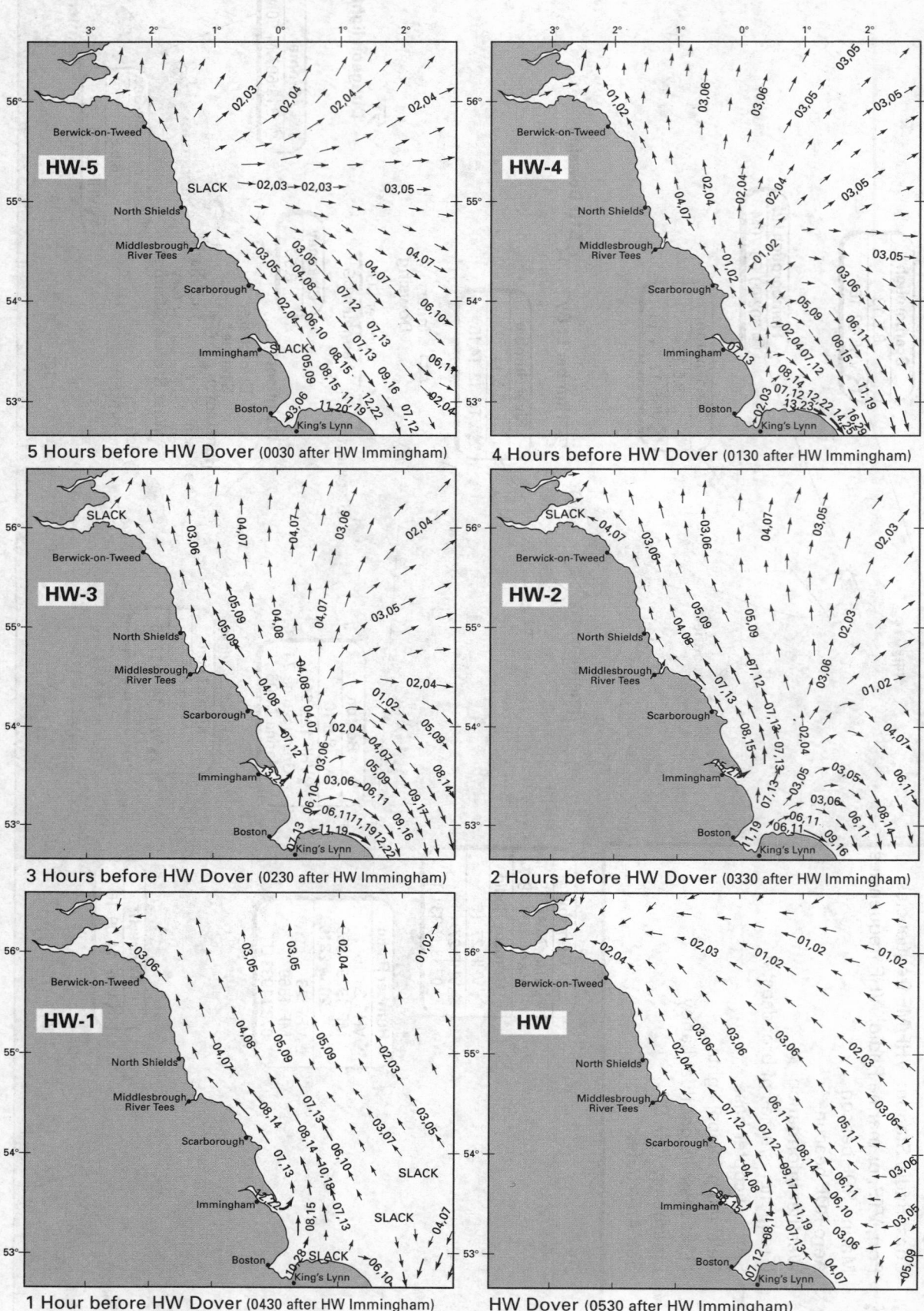

HW-5

5 Hours before HW Dover (0030 after HW Immingham)

HW-4

4 Hours before HW Dover (0130 after HW Immingham)

HW-3

3 Hours before HW Dover (0230 after HW Immingham)

HW-2

2 Hours before HW Dover (0330 after HW Immingham)

HW-1

1 Hour before HW Dover (0430 after HW Immingham)

HW

HW Dover (0530 after HW Immingham)

Northward 8.6.3   Southward 8.4.3

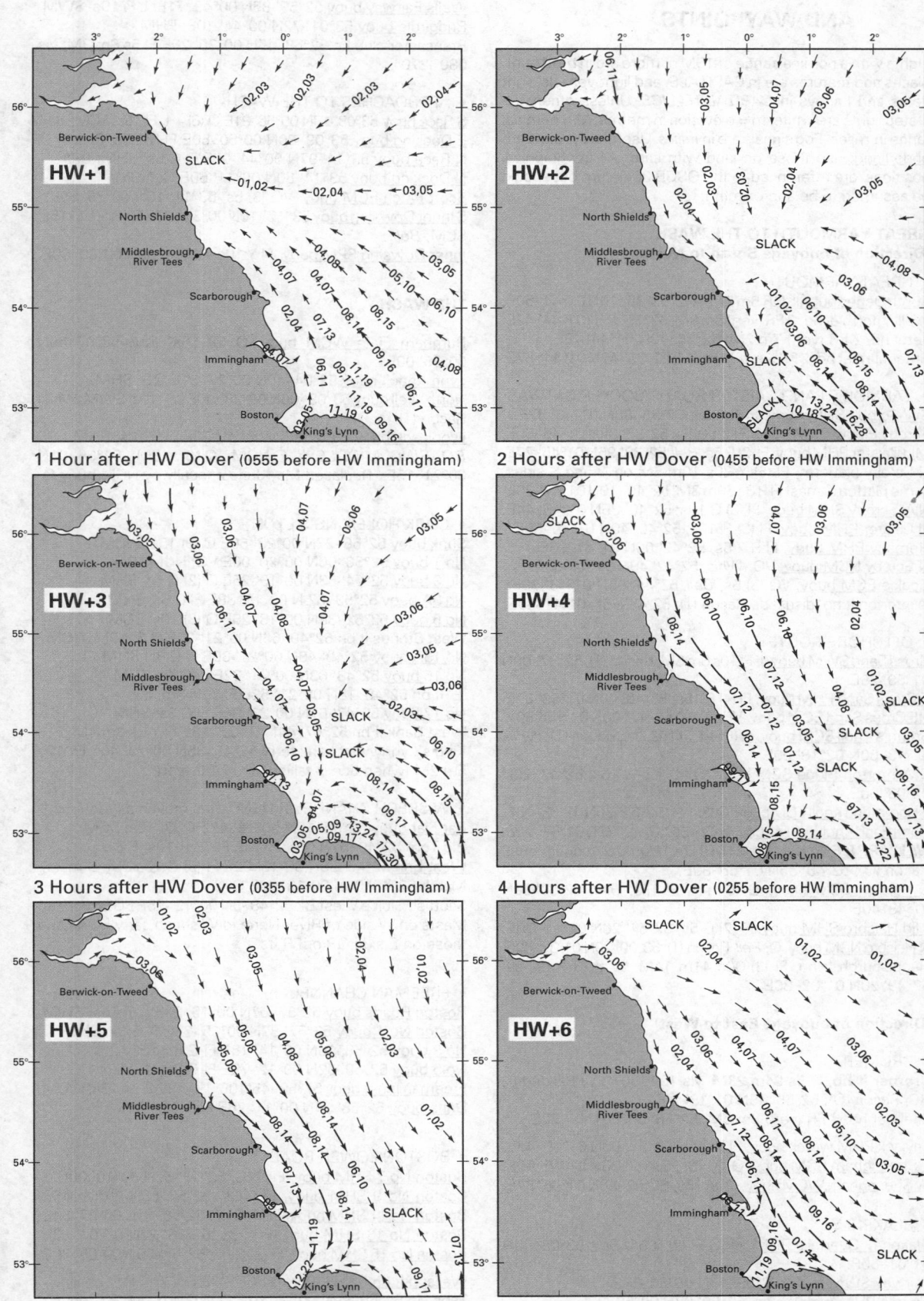

HW+1

1 Hour after HW Dover (0555 before HW Immingham)

HW+2

2 Hours after HW Dover (0455 before HW Immingham)

HW+3

3 Hours after HW Dover (0355 before HW Immingham)

HW+4

4 Hours after HW Dover (0255 before HW Immingham)

HW+5

5 Hours after HW Dover (0155 before HW Immingham)

HW+6

6 Hours after HW Dover (0055 before HW Immingham)

5

8.5.4   COASTAL LIGHTS, FOG SIGNALS AND WAYPOINTS

Lights with a nominal range of 15M or more are in **bold** print, places and features are in CAPITALS, and light-vessels, light floats and Lanbys in *CAPITAL ITALICS*. Unless otherwise stated lights are white. m = elevation in metres; M = nominal range in miles. Fog signals are in *italics*. Useful waypoints are underlined; use those on land with care. All geographical positions are referenced to the OSGB 36 datum but should be assumed to be approximate.

GREAT YARMOUTH TO THE WASH
(Direction of buoyage South to North)

● GREAT YARMOUTH
South Denes outfall, QR 5m 2M, R △; 52°35'·10N 01°44'·50E.
Wellington pier hd, 2 FR (vert) 8m 3M; 52°35'·92N 01°44'·42E.
Jetty hd, 2 FR (vert) 7m 2M; 52°36'·10N 01°44'·48E.
Britannia pier hd, 2 FR (vert) 11m 4M; 52°36'·47N 01°44'·57E.

● YARMOUTH AND CAISTER ROADS/COCKLE GATWAY
SW Scroby SHM buoy, Fl G 2·5s; 52°35'·80N 01°46'·37E.
Scroby Elbow SHM buoy, Fl (2) G 5s; 52°37'·32N 01°46'·50E.
Mid Caister PHM buoy, Fl (2) R 5s, *Bell;* 52°38'·96N 01°45'·77E.
N Scroby platform, Fl (5) Y 20s 10m 5M on N and S sides; same platform, mast Fl R 3s 50m 3M; 52°40'·10N 01°47'·20E.
NW Scroby SHM buoy, Fl (3) G 10s; 52°40'·35N 01°46'·44E.
N Caister PHM buoy, Fl (3) R 10s; 52°40'·40N 01°45'·66E.
Hemsby PHM buoy, Fl R 2·5s; 52°42'·00N 01°44'·95E.
N Scroby NCM buoy, VQ, *Whis;* 52°42'·49N 01°44'·80E.
Cockle ECM buoy, VQ (3) 5s, *Bell;* 52°44'·00N 01°43'·70E.
Winterton lt ho (disused), Racon (T); 52°42'·75N 01°41'·80E.

● OFFSHORE ROUTE
Cross Sand SWM buoy, L Fl 10s 6m 5M, Racon (T); 52°37'·00N 01°59'·25E.
E Cross Sand PHM buoy, Fl (4) R 15s; 52°40'·00N 01°53'·80E.
NE Cross Sand ECM buoy, VQ (3) 5s; 52°43'·00N 01°53'·80E.
Smith's Knoll SCM buoy, Q (6) + L Fl 15s 7M, Racon (T), *Whis;* 52°43'·50N 02°18'·00E.
S Winterton Ridge SCM buoy, Q (6) + L Fl 15s; 52°47'·20N 02°03'·60E.
E Hammond Knoll ECM buoy, Q (3) 10s; 52°52'·30N 01°58'·75E.
Hammond Knoll WCM buoy, Q (9) 15s; 52°49'·72N 01°57'·70E.
NEWARP lt F, Fl 10s 12m **21M** (H24), *Horn 20s* (continuous), Racon (O); 52°48'·35N 01°55'·80E.
S Haisbro SCM buoy, Q (6) + L Fl 15s, *Bell;* 52°50'·80N 01°48'·40E.
Mid Haisbro SHM buoy, Fl (2) G 5s; 52°54'·20N 01°41'·70E.
N Haisbro NCM buoy, Q, *Bell,* Racon (T); 53°00'·20N 01°32'·40E.
Happisburgh lt ho, Fl (3) 30s 41m 14M, W tr, 3 R bands; 52°49'·20N 01°32'·30E.

(Direction of buoyage East to West)

● CROMER
Cromer lt ho, Fl 5s 84m **23M**, vis 102°-307°, W 8-sided tr; RC; Racon (O); 52°55'·45N 01°19'·10E.
Lifeboat ho, 2 FR (vert) 8m 5M; 52°56'·00N 01°18'·20E.

Tayjack PHM wreck buoy, Fl R 2·5s; 52°57'·60N 01°15'·47E.
E Sheringham ECM buoy, Q (3) 10s; 53°02'·20N 01°15'·00E.
W Sheringham WCM buoy, Q (9) 15s; 53°02'·93N 01°06'·87E.

● BLAKENEY
Blakeney Overfalls PHM buoy, Fl (2) R 5s, *Bell;* 53°03'·00N 01°01'·50E.
Fairway SWM buoy, 52°59'·17N 00°56'·38E.
Hjordis PHM wreck buoy 52°58'·97N 00°58'·20E.

● WELLS-NEXT-THE-SEA/BRANCASTER STAITHE
Wells Fairway buoy 52°59'·85N 00°49'·71E, L Fl 10s; SWM.
Bridgirdle buoy 53°01'·72N 00°44'·10E; PHM.
Brancaster club ho 52°58'·45N 00°38'·25E Fl 5s 8m 3M; vis 080°-270°.

● APPROACHES TO THE WASH
S Race buoy 53°08'·18N 00°56'·81E Q (6) + L Fl 15s; SCM; *Bell.*
E Docking buoy 53°09'·80N 00°50'·50E Fl R 2·5s; PHM.
N Race buoy 53°14'·97N 00°44'·00E Fl G 5s; SHM; *Bell.*
N Docking buoy 53°14'·80N 00°41'·60E Q; NCM.
Scott Patch ECM buoy, VQ (3) 5s; 53°11'·10N 00°36'·50E.
S Inner Dowsing buoy 53°12'·10N 00°33'·80E Q (6) + L Fl 15s; SCM; *Bell.*
Inner Dowsing SPM buoy, Fl Y 10s, 53°14'·00N 00°30'·00E.

THE WASH

Burnham Flats WCM buoy, Q (9) 15s, *Bell;* 53°07'·50N 00°35'·00E.
Lynn Knock buoy 53°04'·40N 00°27'·31E QG; SHM.
North Well buoy 53°03'·00N 00°28'·00E L Fl 10s; SWM; *Whis;* Racon (T).
Woolpack buoy 53°02'·65N 00°31'·55E Fl R 10s; PHM.
ROARING MIDDLE lt F NCM, Q 5m 8M; 52°58'·61N 00°21'·15E . Replaced May-June annually by NCM buoy Q.

● CORK HOLE/KING'S LYNN
Sunk buoy 52°56'·27N 00°23'·50E Q (9) 15s; WCM.
No 1 buoy 52°56'·00N 00°20'·00E VQ; NCM; *Bell.*
No 3 buoy 52°54'·63N 00°19'·25E Fl (2) G 6s; SHM.
No 3A buoy 52°53'·67 N 00°18'·38E Fl G 5s; SHM.
No 5 buoy 52°52'·39N 00°18'·26E Q (3) 10s; ECM.
West Stones lt bn 52°49'·66N 00°21'·22E Q 3m 2M; NCM.
No 13A buoy 52°49'·48N 00°21'·30E Fl G 3s; SHM.
No 15 buoy 52°48'·63N 00°21'·22E Fl G 4s; SHM.
'E' lt bn 52°48'·18N 00°21'·52E Fl Y 3s 3m 2M.
No 17 buoy 52°47'·67N 00°21'·94E Fl G 3s; SHM.
West Bank lt bn 52°47'·44N 00°22'·13E Fl·Y 2s 3m 4M.
King's Lynn West bank ferry 52°45'·35N 00°23'·46E Fl Y 2s 5m 2M (when tide is falling) and 2 FG (vert).

● WISBECH CHANNEL/R NENE (Bns moved as required.)
Bar Flat buoy 52°55'·10N 00°16'·47E Q (3) 10s; ECM.
Big Tom 52°49'·57N 00°13'·17E Fl (2) R 10s; R Bn.
West End 52°49'·38N 00°13'·02E Fl (3) G 10s 3M; B mast.
Marsh 52°49'·03N 00°13'·00E QR.
Scottish Sluice West Bk 52°48'·5N 00°12'·75E FG 9m; mast.
Masts on W side of River Nene to Wisbech carry FG lts and those on E side QR or FR lts.

● FREEMAN CHANNEL
Boston Roads buoy 52°57'·67N 00°16'·23E L Fl 10s; SWM.
Boston No 1 buoy 52°57'·87N 00°15'·22E Fl G 3s; SHM.
No 3 buoy 52°58'·10N 00°14'·15E Fl G 6s; SHM.
No 5 buoy 52°58'·52N 00°12'·78E Fl G 3s; SHM.
Freeman Inner buoy 52°58'·45N 00°11'·43E Q (9) 15s; WCM.
Delta buoy 52°58'·34N 00°11'·26E Fl R 6s; PHM.

● BOSTON LOWER ROAD
Boston No 7 SHM buoy, Fl G 3s, 52°58'·57N 00°10'·00E.
Boston No 9 SHM buoy, Fl G 3s, 52°57'·58N 00°08'·45E.
Boston No 11 SHM buoy, Fl (2) G 6s, 52°56'·51N 00°07'·64E.
Boston No 13 SHM buoy, Fl G 3s, 52°56'·22N 00°07'·13E.
Boston No 15 SHM buoy, Fl (2) G 6s, 52°56'·29 N00°05'·70E.

Welland lt bn 52°56'·06N 00°05'·37E QR 5m; R □ on Bn.
Tabs Hd 52°55'·99N 00°05'·01E Q WG 4m 1M; R □ on W mast; vis W shore-251°, G251°-shore; Ra refl.

- BOSTON, NEW CUT AND RIVER WITHAM
Ent N side, Dollypeg lt bn 52°56'·10N 00°05'·15E QG 4m 1M; B △ on Bn; Ra refl.
New Cut 52°55'·97N 00°04'·79E Fl G 3s; △ on pile.
New Cut ldg lts 240°: Front, No 1 52°55'·82N 00°04'·49E F 5m 5M; rear, 90m from front, F 8m 5M.
Boston ldg lts 324°: Front, No 10 52°58'·02N 00°00'·49W F; rear, No 10A 150m from front, F.

- WELLAND CUT/RIVER WELLAND
SE side Iso R 2s; NW side Iso G 2s. Lts QR (to port) and QG (to stbd) mark the chan upstream.
Fosdyke Bridge 52°52'·26N 00°02'·45W FY.

(Direction of buoyage North to South)

- BOSTON DEEP/WAINFLEET ROADS
Wainfleet Range UQ R, with FR on Trs SW & NE.
Scullridge buoy 52°59'·68N 00°14'·00E; SHM.
Friskney buoy 53°00'·48N 00°16'·68E; SHM.
Long Sand buoy 53°01'·10N 00°18'·30E; SHM.
Pompey buoy 53°02'·20N 00°19'·37E; SHM.
Swatchway buoy 53°03'·76N 00°19'·80E; SHM.
Inner Knock buoy 53°04'·85N 00°20'·50E; PHM.
Wainfleet Roads buoy 53°06'·22N 00°21'·55E; PHM.
Skegness S buoy 53°06'·70N 00°23'·35E; SHM.

WASH TO THE RIVER HUMBER
(Direction of buoyage South to North)
Dudgeon buoy 53°16'·60N 01°17'·00E Q (9) 15s 7M; WCM; Racon (O); Whis.
E Dudgeon buoy 53°19'·70N 00°58'·80E Q (3) 10s; ECM; Bell.
Mid Outer Dowsing buoy 53°24'·80N 01°07'·90E Fl (3) G 10s; SHM; Bell.
N Outer Dowsing buoy 53°33'·50N 00°59'·70E Q; NCM.
B.1D Platform Dowsing 53°33'·71N 00°52'·72E Fl (2) 10s 28m **22M**; Morse (U) R 15s 28m 3M; Horn (2) 60s; Racon (T).

- RIVER HUMBER APPROACHES
W Ridge buoy 53°19'·05N 00°44'·60E Q (9) 15s; WCM.
Inner Dowsing lt F 53°19'·50N 00°33'·96E Fl 10s 12m **15M**; Racon (T); Horn 60s.
Protector buoy 53°24'·83N 00°25'·25E Fl R 2·5s; PHM.
DZ No 4 buoy 53°27'·12N 00°19'·17E Fl Y 5s; SPM.
DZ No 3 buoy 53°29'·17N 00°19'·19E Fl Y 2·5s; SPM.
Rosse Spit buoy 53°30'·40N 00°17'·04E Fl (2) R 5s; PHM.
Haile Sand No 2 buoy 53°32'·14N 00°12'·80E Fl (3) R 10s; PHM.
Humber buoy 53°36'·72N 00°21'·60E L Fl 10s; SWM; Whis; Racon (T).
N Binks buoy 53°36'·22N 00°18'·70E Fl Y 2·5s; SPM.
Outer Haile buoy 53°34'·80N 00°18'·70E Fl (4) Y 15s; SPM.
S Binks buoy 53°34'·72N 00°16'·65E Fl Y 5s; SPM.
SPURN lt F 53°33'·54N 00°14'·33E Q (3) 10s 10m 8M; ECM; Horn 20s; Racon (M).
SE CHEQUER lt F 53°33'·37N 00°12'·65E VQ (6) + L Fl 10s 6m 6M; SCM; Ra refl; Horn 30s.
No 3 Chequer buoy 53°33'·05N 00°10'·70E Q (6) + L Fl 15s; SCM.
Tetney Monobuoy 53°32'·34N 00°06'·85E 2 VQ Y (vert); Y SBM; Horn Mo (A) 60s; QY on 290m floating hose.

- RIVER HUMBER/GRIMSBY/HULL
Spurn Pt lt bn 53°34'·36N 00°06'·59E Fl G 3s 11m 5M; G △.
BULL lt F 53°33'·78N 00°05'·65E VQ 8m 6M; NCM; Horn (2) 20s.
North Fort buoy 53°33'·78N 00°04'·29E Q; NCM.
South Fort buoy 53°33'·63N 00°04'·06E Q (6) + L Fl 15s; SCM.
Haile Sand Fort 53°32'·05N 00°02'·14E Fl R 5s 21m 3M.
Haile Chan No 4 buoy 53°33'·63N 00°02'·94E Fl R 4s; PHM.
Middle No 7 lt F VQ (6) + L Fl 10s; SCM; Horn 20s.

Grimsby Royal Dock ent E side 53°35'·06N 00°03'·93W Fl (2) R 6s 10m 8M; Dn.
Killingholme ldg lts in line 292°: Front, 53°38'·78N 00°12'·87W Iso R 2s 10m 14M; rear, 189m from front, Oc R 4s 21m 14M.
Immingham oil terminal SE end 53°37'·68N 00°09'·32W, 2 QR (vert) 8m 5M; Horn Mo (N) 30s.
Clay Huts No 13 lt F 53°38'·52N 00°11'·28W Iso 2s 5m 9M; SWM.
Sand End No 16 lt F 53°42'·52N 00°14'·47W Fl R 4s 5m 3M; PHM.
Hebbles No 21 buoy 53°44'·03N 00°15'·88W Fl G 1·5s; SHM.
Lower W Middle No 24 buoy 53°44'·26N 00°18'·24W Fl R 4s; PHM.
Hull Marina, Humber Dock Basin, E ent 53°44'·22N 00°20'·05W 2 FG (vert).

RIVER HUMBER TO WHITBY
Canada & Giorgios wreck buoy 53°42'·33N 00°07'·22E VQ (3) 5s; ECM.
Hornsea outfall buoy 53°55'·02N 00°08'·27E Fl Y 20s; SPM.
Atwick outfall buoy 53°57'·10N 00°10'·25W Fl Y 10s; SPM.

BRIDLINGTON
SW Smithic buoy 54°02'·40N 00°09'·10W Q (9) 15s; WCM.
N pier hd 54°04'·77N 00°11'·10W Fl 2s 12m 9M; Horn 60s; Tidal lts Fl R or Fl G.
N Smithic buoy 54°06'·20N 00°03'·80W VQ; NCM; Bell.

Flamborough Head 54°06'·97N 00°04'·87W Fl (4) 15s 65m **24M**; W ○ tr; RC; Horn (2) 90s.

- FILEY/SCARBOROUGH/WHITBY
Filey on cliff above CG stn FR 31m 1M; vis 272°-308°.
Filey Brigg buoy 54°12'·73N 00°14'·48W Q (3) 10s; ECM; Bell.
Scarborough E pier hd 54°16'·87N 00°23'·27W QG 8m 3M.
Scarborough pier lt ho, Iso 5s 17m 9M, vis 219°-039°, W ○ tr; and FY 8m, vis 233°-030°; (tide sigs); Dia 60s.
Scalby Ness diffusers buoy 54°18'·60N 00°23'·25W Fl R 5s; PHM.
Whitby NCM buoy Q, Bell; 54°30'·32N 00°36'·48W.
High Lt Ling Hill 54°28'·60N 00°34'·00W Iso RW 10s 73m **18M**; R16M; W 8-sided tr and dwellings; vis R128°-143°, W143°-319°.
Whitby E pier hd 54°29'·63N 00°36'·63W FR 14m 3M; R tr.
Whitby W pier hd 54°29'·63N 00°36'·70W FG (occas) 14m 3M; G tr; Horn 30s.

WHITBY TO RIVER TYNE

- RUNSWICK/REDCAR
Runswick Bay pier 54°31'·99N 00°44'·90W 2 FY (occas).
Boulby outfall buoy 54°34'·51N 00°48'·15W Fl (4) Y 10s; SPM.
Outfall buoy 54°36'·63N 01°00'·30W Fl Y 10s; SPM.
Salt Scar buoy 54°38'·10N 01°00'·00W VQ; NCM; Horn (1) 15s; Bell.
Luff Way ldg lts 197°: Front, on Esplanade, FR 8m 7M; vis 182°-212°; rear, 115m from front, FR 12m 7M; vis 182°-212°.
High Stone. Lade Way ldg lts 247°: Front, 54°37'·15N 01°03'·81W Oc R 2·5s 9m 7M; rear, 43m from front, Oc R 2·5s 11m 7M; vis 232°-262°.

- TEES APPROACHES/HARTLEPOOL
Tees Fairway buoy 54°40'·95N 01°06'·23W Iso 4s 9m 8M; SWM; Racon (B); Horn 5s.
Tees North buoy 54°40'·35N 01°07'·09W Fl G 5s; SHM.
Tees South buoy 54°40'·28N 01°06'·88W Fl R 5s; PHM.

S Gare bkwtr hd 54°38'·83N 01°08'·13W Fl WR 12s 16m **W20M, R17M**; W ○ tr; vis W020°-274°, R274°-357°; Sig stn; *Horn (2) 30s.*
Ldg lts 210·1°: Front, 54°37'·22N 01°10'·08W. Both FR 18/20m 13/**16M**.
Longscar buoy 54°40'·85N 01°09'·80W Q (3) 10s; ECM; *Bell.*
The Heugh 54°41'·80N 01°10'·47W Fl (2) 10s 19m **19M** (H24); W tr.
Hartlepool Old pier hd 54°41'·59N 01°10'·99W QG 13m 7M; B tr.
W Hbr N pier hd 54°41'·31N 01°11'·47W Oc G 5s 12m 2M.
Hartlepool Yacht Haven lock, Dir lt 308° 54°41'·43N 01°11'·80W, Fl WRG 2s 6m 3M; vis G305·5°-307°, W307°-309°, R309°-310·5°.
N Sands, Pipe jetty hd 54°42'·80N 01°12'·40W 2 FR (vert) 1M; *Bell 15s.*

• SEAHAM/SUNDERLAND
Seaham N pier hd 54°50'·25N 01°19'·15W Fl G 10s 12m 5M; W col, B bands; *Dia 30s.*
Sunderland Roker pier hd 54°55'·27N 01°21'·05W Fl 5s 25m**23M**; W ○ tr, 3 R bands and cupola: vis 211°-357°; *Siren 20s.*
Old N pier hd 54°55'·12N 01°21'·52W QG 12m 8M; *Horn 10s.*
Whitburn Steel buoy 54°56'·30N 01°20'·80W; PHM.
Whitburn Firing Range 54°57'·2N 01°21'·3W and 54°57'·7N 01°21'·2W both FR when firing is taking place.
DZ buoys 54°57'·04N 01°18'·81W and 54°58'·58N 01°19'·80W, both Fl Y 2·5s; SPM.

• TYNE ENTRANCE/NORTH SHIELDS
Ent N pier hd 55°00'·87N 01°24'·08W Fl (3) 10s 26m **26M**; Gy ○ tr, W lantern; *Horn 10s.*
S pier hd 55°00'·67N 01°23'·97W Oc WRG 10s 15m W13M, R9M, G8M; Gy ○ tr, R&W lantern; vis W075°-161°, G161°-179° over Bellhues rk, W179°-255°, R255°-075°; *Bell (1) 10s* (TD 1995).
Fish Quay ldg lts 258°: **Front,** 55°00'·54N 01°25'·98W F 25m **20M**; W □ tr; **rear,** 220m from front, F 39m **20M**; W □ tr.
Herd Groyne hd 55°00'·48N 01°25'·34W Oc WR 10s 13m W13M, R11M, R1M; R pile structure, R&W lantern; vis R (unintens) 080°-224°, W224°-255°, R255°-277°; *Bell (1) 5s.*
Saint Peter's Marina ent 54°57'·93N 01°34'·25W (unmarked).

RIVER TYNE TO BERWICK-UPON-TWEED

• CULLERCOATS/BLYTH/NEWBIGGIN
Cullercoats ldg lts 256°: Front, 55°02'·05N 01°25'·77W FR 27m 3M; rear, 38m from front, FR 35m 3M.
Blyth ldg lts 324°: Front, 55°07'·42N 01°29'·72W F Bu 11m 10M; rear, 80m from front, F Bu 17m 10M. Both Or ◊ on tr.
Blyth Fairway buoy 55°06'·58N 01°28'·50W Fl G 3s; SHM; *Bell.*

Blyth E pier hd 55°06'·98N 01°29'·11W Fl (4) 10s 19m **21M**; W tr. FR 13m 13M (same tr); vis 152°-249°; *Horn (3) 30s.*
Blyth W pier hd 55°06'·98N 01°29'·27W 2 FR (vert) 7m 8M; W tr.
Newbiggin bkwtr hd 55°11'·00N 01°30'·22W Fl G 10s 4M.
Newbiggen outfall buoy 55°12'·50N 01°30'·70W Fl R 10s; PHM.

• COQUET ISLAND/WARKWORTH AND AMBLE
Coquet 55°20'·03N 01°32'·28W Fl (3) WR 30s 25m **W23M, R19M**; W □ tr, turreted parapet, lower half Gy; vis R330°-140°, W140°-163°, R163°-180°, W180°-330°; sector boundaries are indeterminate and may appear as Alt WR; *Horn 30s.*
Outfall buoy 55°20'·32N 01°33'·63W Fl R 10s; PHM; *Bell.*
Amble S pier hd 55°20'·38N 01°34'·14W Fl R 5s 9m 5M; W ○ tr, R bands, W base.
N pier hd 55°20'·38N 01°34'·15W Fl G 6s 12m 6M; W pylon.

• BOULMER/CRASTER/NEWTON HAVEN/BEADNELL BAY
Boulmer Haven bn 55°24'·75N 01°34'·40W; SHM.
Craster Hbr 55°28'·37N 01°35'·45W (unmarked).
Newton Rk buoy 55°32'·17N 01°35'·75W; PHM.

• N SUNDERLAND (SEAHOUSES)/BAMBURGH/FARNE IS
The Falls PHM buoy 55°34'·62N 01°37'·02W.
N Sunderland NW pier hd, FG 11m 3M, vis 159°-294°; W tr;tfc sigs; *siren 90s* (occas); 55°35'·03N 01°38'·84W.
N Sunderland bkwtr hd, Fl R 2·5s 6m, 55°35'·05N 01°38'·79W.
Shoreston Outcars buoy 55°35'·88N 01°39'·22W; PHM.

Bamburgh Black Rocks Pt, Oc (2) WRG 15s 12m **W17M**, R13M, G13M, vis G122°-165°, W165°-175°, R175°-191°, W191°-238°, R238°-275°, W275°-289°, G289°-300°; W bldg; 55°37'·00N 01°43'·35W.

Inner Farne, Fl (2) WR 15s 27m W10M, R7M, vis R119°-280°, W280°-119°; W ○ tr; 55°36'·93N 01°39'·25W.
Longstone W side 55°38'·63N 01°36'·55W Fl 20s 23m **24M**; R tr, W band; *Horn (2) 60s.*
Swedman buoy 55°37'·65N 01°41'·52W; SHM.

• HOLY ISLAND
Goldstone buoy 55°40'·25N 01°43'·54W; SHM.
Ridge buoy 55°39'·70N 01°45'·87W; ECM.
Triton Shoal buoy 55°39'·58N 01°46'·72W; SHM.
Old Law E bn (Guile Pt) 55°39'·49N 01°47'·50W Oc WRG 6s 9m 4M; vis G182°-262°,W262°-264°, R264°-shore.
Heugh 55°40'·09N 01°47'·89W Oc WRG 6s 24m 5M; R △ on tr; vis G135°-308°, W308°-311°, R311°-shore°.
Plough Seat buoy 55°40'·37N 01°44'·87W; PHM.

• BERWICK-UPON-TWEED
Bkwtr hd. Fl 5s 15m 10M, vis E of Seal Carr ledges-shore; W ○ tr, R cupola and base; 55°45'·88N 01°58'·95W.
FG (same tr) 8m 1M, vis 010°-154°.

8.5.5 PASSAGE INFORMATION

For directions and pilotage refer to: *The East Coast* (Imray/Bowskill) as far as The Wash; *Tidal Havens of the Wash and Humber* (Imray/Irving) carefully documents the hbrs of this little-frequented cruising ground. N from R Humber see the Royal Northumberland YC's *Sailing Directions, Humber to Rattray Head*. The Admiralty Pilot *North Sea (West)* covers the whole coast. *North Sea Passage Pilot* (Imray/Navin) goes as far N as Cromer and across to Den Helder.

NORTH NORFOLK COAST (charts 106, 108)

The coast of N Norfolk is unfriendly in bad weather, with no hbr accessible when there is any N in the wind. The hbrs all dry, and seas soon build up in the entrances or over the bars, some of which are dangerous even in a moderate breeze and an ebb tide. But in settled weather and moderate offshore winds it is a peaceful area to explore, particularly for boats which can take the ground. At Blakeney and Wells (see 8.5.7 and 8.5.8) chans shift almost every year, so local knowledge is essential and may best be acquired in advance from the Hr Mr; or in the event by following a friendly FV of suitable draft.

Haisborough Sand (buoyed) lies parallel to and 8M off the Norfolk coast at Happisburgh lt ho, with depths of less than 1m in many places, and drying 0·3m near the mid-point. The shoal is steep-to, on its NE side in particular, and there are tidal eddies. Even a moderate sea or swell breaks on the shallower parts. There are dangerous wks near the S end. Haisborough Tail and Hammond Knoll (with wk depth 1m) lie to the E of S end of Haisborough Sand. Newarp lt F is 5M SE. Similar banks lie parallel to and up to 60M off the coast.

The streams follow the generally NW/SE direction of the coast and offshore chans. But in the outer chans the stream is somewhat rotatory: when changing from SE-going to NW-going it sets SW, and when changing from NW-going to SE-going it sets NE, across the shoals. Close S of Haisborough Sand the SE-going stream begins at HW Immingham −0030; the NW-going at HW Immingham +0515, sp rates up to 2·5kn. It is possible to carry a fair tide from Gt Yarmouth to the Wash.

If proceeding direct from Cromer to the Humber, pass S of Sheringham Shoal (buoyed) where the ESE-going stream begins at HW Immingham − 0225, and the WNW-going at + 0430. Proceed to NE of Blakeney Overfalls and Docking Shoal, and to SW of Race Bank, so as to fetch Inner Dowsing lt tr (lt, fog sig). Thence pass E of Protector Overfalls, and steer for Rosse Spit buoy at SE ent to R Humber (8.5.11).

THE WASH (charts 108, 1200)

The Wash is formed by the estuaries of the rivers Great Ouse, Nene, Welland and Witham; it is an area of shifting sands, most of which dry. Important features are the strong tidal streams, the low-lying shore, and the often poor vis. Keep a careful watch on the echo sounder, because buoys may (or may not) have been moved to accommodate changes in the chan. Near North Well, the in-going stream begins at HW Immingham − 0430, and the out-going at HW Immingham + 0130, sp rates about 2kn. The in-going stream is usually stronger than the out-going, but its duration is less. Prolonged NE winds cause an in-going current, which can increase the rate and duration of the in-going stream and raise the water level at the head of the estuary. Do not attempt entry to the rivers too early on the flood, which runs hard in the rivers.

North Well SWM lt buoy and Roaring Middle lt F are the keys to entering the Wash from N or E. But from the E it is also possible to appr via a shallow route N of Stiffkey Overfalls and Bridgirdle PHM buoy; thence via Sledway and Woolpack PHM lt buoy to North Well and into Lynn Deeps. Near north end of Lynn Deeps there are overfalls over Lynn Knock at sp tides. For King's Lynn (8.5.9) and R Nene (Wisbech) follow the buoyed/lit Cork Hole and Wisbech Chans. Boston (8.5.10) and R Welland are reached via Freeman Chan, westward from Roaring Middle; or via Boston Deep, all lit.

The NW shore of The Wash is fronted by mudflats extending 2–3M offshore and drying more than 4m; a bombing range is marked by Y bns and buoys. Wainfleet Swatchway should only be used in good vis; the buoyed chan shifts constantly, and several shoals (charted depths unreliable) off Gibraltar Pt obstruct access to Boston Deep. For Wainfleet, see 8.5.10.

THE WASH TO THE RIVER HUMBER (charts 108, 107)

Inner Dowsing is a narrow N/S sandbank with a least depth of 1·2m, 8M offshore between Skegness and Mablethorpe. There are overfalls off the W side of the bank at the N end. Inner Dowsing lt float (fog sig) is 1M NE of the bank.

In the outer approaches to The Wash and R. Humber there are many offlying banks, but few of them are of direct danger to yachts. The sea however breaks on some of them in bad weather, when they should be avoided. Fishing vessels may be encountered, and there are many oil/gas installations offshore (see below).

RIVER HUMBER (charts 109, 1188, 3497)

R. Humber is formed by R. Ouse and R. Trent, which meet 13M above Kingston-upon-Hull. It is commercially important and gives access to these rivers and inland waterways; it also drains most of Yorkshire and the Midlands. Where the Humber estuary reaches the sea between Northcoates Pt and Spurn Hd it is 4M wide. A VTS scheme is in operation to regulate commercial shipping in the Humber, Ouse and Trent and provide full radar surveillance. Yachts are advised to monitor the appropriate Humber VTS frequency.

Approaching from the S, a yacht should make good Rosse Spit and then Haile Sand No 2, both PHM lt buoys, before altering westward to intercept the buoyed appr chan, which leads SW from the Humber fairway lt buoy to Spurn lt float.

If bound to/from the N, avoid The Binks, a shoal (dries 0·4m in places) extending 3M E from Spurn Hd, with a rough sea when wind is against tide. Depths offshore are irregular and subject to frequent change; it would be best to round the Outer Binks ECM buoy, unless in calm conditions and with local knowledge.

Haile Sand and Bull Sand Forts are both conspic to the SW of Spurn Head; beyond them it is advisable to follow one of the buoyed chans, since shoals are liable to change. Hawke Chan (later Sunk) is the main dredged chan to the N. Haile Chan favours the S side and Grimsby. Bull Chan takes a middle course before merging with Haile Chan. There are good yachting facilities at Grimsby and Hull (8.5.11).

Streams are strong, even fierce at sp; local info suggests that they are stronger than shown in 8.5.3, which is based upon NP 251 (Admiralty Tidal Stream Atlas). 5ca S of Spurn Hd the flood sets NW from about HW Immingham − 0520, sp rate 3·5kn; the ebb sets SE from about HW Immingham, sp rate 4kn. The worst seas are experienced in NW gales against a strong flood tide. 10M E of Spurn Hd the tidal streams are not affected by the river; relative to HW Immingham, the S-going stream begins at − 0455, and the N-going at + 0130. Nearer the entrance the direction of the S-going stream becomes more W'ly, and that of the N-going stream more E'ly.

5

R HUMBER TO HARTLEPOOL (charts 107, 121, 129, 134)

Air gunnery and bombing practice is carried out 3M off Cowden, 17M S of Bridlington. The range is marked by 6 SPM buoys; 3 seaward ones Fl Y 10s, the 3 inner ones Fl Y 2s or 5s. Bridlington Bay (chart 1882) is clear of dangers apart from Smithic Shoals (marked by N and S cardinal lt buoys), about 3M off Bridlington (8.5.12); the seas break on these shoals in strong N or E winds even at HW.

Flamborough Head (lt, fog sig, RC) is a steep, W cliff with conspic lt ho on summit. The lt may be obsc by cliffs when close inshore. An old lt ho, also conspic, is 2½ca WNW. Tides run hard around the Head which, in strong winds against a sp tide, is best avoided by 2M. From here the coast runs NW, with no offshore dangers until Filey Brigg where rky ledges extend 5ca ESE, marked by an ECM lt buoy. There is anch in Filey B (8.5.12) in N or offshore winds. NW of Filey Brigg beware Old Horse Rks and foul ground 5ca offshore; maintain this offing past Scarborough (8.5.13) to Whitby High lt. Off Whitby (8.5.14) beware Whitby Rk and The Scar (dry in places) to E of hbr, and Upgang Rks (dry in places) 1M to WNW; swell breaks heavily on all these rocks.

From Whitby to Hartlepool (8.5.15) there are no dangers more than 1M offshore. Runswick B (8.5.14 and AC 1612), 5M NW of Whitby, provides anch in winds from S and W but is dangerous in onshore winds. 2½M further NW the little hbr of Staithes is more suitable for yachts which can take the ground, and only in good weather and offshore winds.

Redcliff, dark red and 205m high is a conspic feature of this coast which, along to Hunt Cliff, is prone to landslides and is fringed with rky ledges which dry for about 3ca off. There is a conspic radio mast 4ca SSE of Redcliff. Off Redcar and Coatham beware Salt Scar and West Scar, drying rky ledges lying 1 – 8ca offshore. Other ledges lie close SE and S of Salt Scar which has NCM lt buoy. Between R. Tees (8.5.14) and Hartlepool beware Long Scar, detached rky ledge (dries 2m) with extremity marked by ECM lt buoy. Tees and Hartlepool Bays are exposed to strong E/SE winds. The R. Tees and Middlesbrough are highly industrialised and there is a centre specialising in the maintenance of Tall Ships.

HARTLEPOOL TO COQUET ISLAND (charts 134, 152, 156)

From The Heugh an offing of 1M clears all dangers until past Seaham (8.5.16) and approaching Sunderland (8.5.17), where White Stones, rky shoals with depth 2.6m, lie 1.75M SSE of Roker Pier lt ho, and Hendon Rk, depth 0.9m, lies 1.25M SE of the lt ho. 1M N of Sunderland is Whitburn Steel, a rky ledge with less than 2m over it; a dangerous wreck (buoyed) lies 1ca SE of it. A firing range at Souter Pt is marked by R flags (R lts) when active. Along this stretch of coast industrial smoke haze may reduce vis and obscure lights.

The coast N of Tynemouth (8.5.18) is foul, and on passage to Blyth (8.5.19) it should be given an offing of 1M. 3.5M N of Tynemouth is St Mary's Island (with disused lt ho), joined to mainland by causeway. The small, drying hbr of Seaton Sluice, 1M NW of St Mary's Island, is accessible only in offshore winds via a narrow ent.

Proceeding N from Blyth, keep well seaward of The Sow and Pigs rks, and set course to clear Newbiggin Pt and Beacon Pt by about 1M. There are conspic measured mile bns here. Near Beacon Pt are conspic chys of aluminium smelter and power stn. 2M NNW of Beacon Pt is Snab Pt where rks extend 3ca seaward. Further offshore Cresswell Skeres, rky patches with depth 3m, lie about 1.5M NNE of Snab Pt.

COQUET ISLAND TO FARNE ISLANDS (chart 156)

Coquet Is (lt, fog sig) lies about 5ca offshore at SE end of Alnmouth B, and nearly 1M NNE of Hauxley Pt, off which dangerous rks extend 6ca offshore, drying 1.9m. On passage, normally pass 1M E of Coquet Is in the W sector of the lt. Coquet chan may be used in good vis by day; but it is only 2ca wide, not buoyed, has least depth of 0.3m near the centre; and the stream runs strongly: S-going from HW Tyne – 0515 and N-going from HW Tyne + 0045. In S or W winds, there are good anchs in Coquet Road, W and NW of the Island.

Amble (Warkworth) hbr ent (8.5.20) is about 1M W of Coquet Is, and 1.5M SE of Warkworth Castle (conspic). 4ca NE and ENE of ent is Pan Bush, rky shoal with least depth of 0.3m on which dangerous seas can build in any swell. The bar has varying depths, down to less than 1m. The entrance is dangerous in strong winds from N/E when broken water may extend to Coquet Is. Once inside, the hbr is safe.

Between Coquet Is and the Farne Is, 19M to N, keep at least 1M offshore to avoid various dangers. To seaward, Craster Skeres lie 5M E of Castle Pt, and Dicky Shad and Newton Skere lie 1.75M and 4.5M E of Beadnell Pt; these are three rky banks on which the sea breaks heavily in bad weather. For Newton Haven and N Sunderland (Seahouses), see 8.5.20.

FARNE ISLANDS (charts 111, 160)

The coast between N Sunderland Pt (Snook) and Holy Island, 8M NW, has fine hill (Cheviots) scenery fronted by dunes and sandy beaches. The Farne Is and offlying shoals extend 4.5M offshore, and are a mini-cruising ground well worth visiting in good weather. The islands are a bird sanctuary, owned and operated by the National Trust, with large colonies of sea birds and grey seals. AC 111 is essential.

Inner Sound separates the islands from the mainland. In good conditions it is a better N/S route than keeping outside the whole group; but the stream runs at 3kn at sp, and with strong wind against tide there is rough water. If course is set outside Farne Is, pass 1M E of Longstone (lt, fog sig) to clear Crumstone Rk 1M to S, and Knivestone (dries 3.6m) and Whirl Rks (depth 0.6m) respectively 5 and 6ca NE of Longstone lt ho. The sea breaks on these rks.

The islands, rks and shoals are divided by Staple Sound, running NW/SE, into an inner and outer group. The former comprises Inner Farne, W and E Wideopens and Knock's Reef. Inner Farne (lt) is the innermost Is; close NE there is anch called The Kettle, sheltered except from NW, but anch out of stream close to The Bridges connecting Knock's Reef and W Wideopen. 1M NW of Inner Farne Is and separated by Farne Sound, which runs NE/SW, lies the Megstone, a rk 5m high. Beware Swedman reef (dries 0.5m), marked by SHM buoy 4ca WSW of Megstone.

The outer group of Islands comprises Staple and Brownsman Islands, N and S Wamses, the Harcars and Longstone. There is occas anch between Staple and Brownsman Is. Piper Gut and Crafords Gut may be negotiated in calm weather and near HW, stemming the S-going stream.

HOLY ISLAND TO BERWICK (charts 1612, 111, 160)

Near the Farne Is and Holy Is the SE-going stream begins at HW Tyne – 0430, and the NW-going at HW Tyne + 0130. Sp rates are about 2.5kn in Inner Sound, 4kn in Staple Sound and about 3·5kn 1M NE of Longstone, decreasing to seaward. There is an eddy S of Longstone on NW-going stream.

Holy Is (or Lindisfarne; 8.5.21) lies 6M WNW of Longstone, and is linked to mainland by a causeway covered at HW. There is a good anch on S side (chart 1612) with conspic daymarks and dir lts. The castle and a W obelisk at Emanuel Head are also conspic. The stream runs strongly in and out of hbr, W-going from HW Tyne + 0510, and E-going from HW Tyne – 0045. E of Holy Is, Goldstone chan runs N/S between Goldstone Rk (dries) SHM buoy on E side and Plough Seat Reef and Plough Rk (both dry) on W side, with PHM buoy.

Berwick Bay has some offlying shoals. Berwick-upon-Tweed (8.5.22) is easily visible against the low shoreline, which rises again to high cliffs further north. The hbr entrance is restricted by a shallow bar, dangerous in onshore winds.

OIL AND GAS INSTALLATIONS

Any yacht going offshore in the N Sea is likely to encounter oil or gas installations. These are shown on Admiralty charts, where scale permits; the position of mobile rigs is updated in weekly NMs. Safety zones of radius 500m are established round all permanent platforms, mobile exploration rigs, and tanker loading moorings, as described in the Annual Summary of Admiralty Notices to Mariners No 20. Some of these platforms are close together or inter-linked. Unauthorised vessels, including yachts, must not enter these zones except in emergency or due to stress of weather.

Platforms show a main lt, Fl Mo (U) 15s 15M. In addition secondary lts, Fl Mo (U) R 15s 2M, synchronised with the main lt, may mark projections at each corner of the platform if not marked by a W lt. The fog signal is Horn Mo (U) 30s. See the Admiralty List of Lights and Fog Signals, Vol A.

NORTH SEA PASSAGES

See 8.0.10 for Distances across the North Sea. There are also further passage Notes in 8.4.5 for the Southern North Sea TSS; in 8.6.5 for crossing to Norway and the Baltic; in 8.20.5 for crossings from Belgium and the Netherlands; and in 8.21.5 for crossings from the Frisian Is and German Bight.

HARTLEPOOL TO SOUTHERN NETHERLANDS
(charts 2182A, 1191, *1190*, 1503, 1408, 1610, 3371, 110)

From abeam Whitby the passage can, theoretically, be made on one direct course, but this would conflict with oil/gas activities and platforms including Rough and Amethyst fields off Humber, Hewett off Cromer and very extensive fields further offshore. Commercial, oil-rig support and fishing vessels may be met S of Flamborough Hd and particularly off NE Norfolk where it is advisable to follow an inshore track.

After passing Flamborough Hd, Dowsing B1D, Dudgeon lt buoy and Newarp lt F, either:
Proceed SxE'ly to take departure from the Outer Gabbard; thence cross N Hinder South TSS (8.20.36) at right angles before heading for Roompotsluis via Middelbank and subsequent buoyed chan.
Or set course ESE from the vicinity of Cross Sand lt buoy and Smith's Knoll, so as to cross the N/S deep-water traffic routes to the E (see 8.20.5). Thence alter SE toward Hoek van Holland, keeping N of Maas Approaches TSS; see 8.20.21, 8.20.36 and 8.20.37.

HARTLEPOOL TO THE GERMAN BIGHT
(charts 2182A, 1191, 266, 1405)

Taking departure eastward from abeam Whitby High lt, skirt the SW Patch off Dogger Bank, keeping clear S of Gordon Gas Field and then N of German Bight W Approach TSS (8.20.36). Thence head for the Elbe or Helgoland; the latter may also serve as a convenient haven in order to adjust the passage for Elbe tides and streams (8.21.5), without greatly increasing passage distance. Tidal streams are less than 1kn away from the coast and run E/W along much of the route.

8.5.6   DISTANCE TABLE

Approximate distances in nautical miles are by the most direct route, whilst avoiding dangers and allowing for Traffic Separation Schemes. Places in *italics* are in adjoining areas; places in **bold** are in 8.0.10, Distances across the North Sea.

		1	2	3	4	5	6	7	8	9	10	11	12	13	14	15	16	17	18	19	20
1.	*Great Yarmouth*	1																			
2.	Blakeney	44	2																		
3.	**King's Lynn**	85	42	3																	
4.	Boston	83	39	34	4																
5.	Humber Lt Buoy	82	45	55	54	5															
6.	**Grimsby**	99	54	61	58	17	6														
7.	Hull	113	68	75	72	31	14	7													
8.	Bridlington	114	79	87	83	35	44	58	8												
9.	Scarborough	130	96	105	98	50	59	81	20	9											
8.	Whitby	143	101	121	114	66	75	97	35	16	10										
11.	River Tees (ent)	166	122	138	135	87	96	118	56	37	21	11									
12.	**Hartlepool**	169	126	140	137	89	98	122	58	39	24	4	12								
13.	Seaham	175	137	151	145	100	106	133	66	47	33	15	11	13							
14.	Sunderland	180	142	156	149	105	110	138	70	51	36	20	16	5	14						
15.	Tynemouth	183	149	163	154	112	115	145	75	56	41	27	23	12	7	15					
16.	Blyth	190	156	171	162	120	123	153	83	64	49	35	31	20	15	8	16				
17.	Amble	203	170	185	176	126	143	157	102	81	65	46	42	32	27	21	14	17			
18.	Holy Island	225	191	196	198	148	166	180	126	104	88	68	65	54	50	44	37	22	18		
19.	**Berwick-on-Tweed**	232	200	205	205	157	166	189	126	107	91	82	78	67	61	55	47	31	9	19	
20.	*Eyemouth*	240	208	213	213	165	174	197	134	115	99	90	86	75	69	63	55	39	17	8	20

BLAKENEY   8-5-7

Norfolk 52°59'·10N 00°58'·35E   Rtg 4-3-1

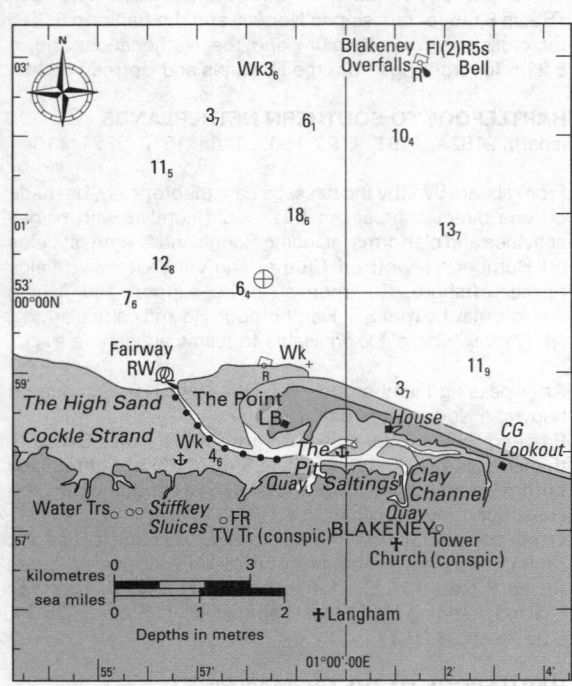

CHARTS
AC 108, 1190; Imray C28; Stanfords 19; OS 133

TIDES
−0445 Dover; ML Cromer 2·8; Duration 0530; Zone 0 (UT)

Standard Port IMMINGHAM (→)

Times				Height (metres)			
High Water		Low Water		MHWS	MHWN	MLWN	MLWS
0100	0700	0100	0700	7·3	5·8	2·6	0·9
1300	1900	1300	1900				
Differences BLAKENEY BAR (approx 52°59'N 00°59'E)							
+0035	+0025	+0030	+0040	−1·6	−1·3		No data
BLAKENEY (approx 52°57'N 01°01'E)							
+0115	+0055	No data		−3·9	−3·8		No data
CROMER							
+0050	+0030	+0050	+0130	−2·1	−1·7	−0·5	−0·1

SHELTER
Very good, but hbr inaccessible with fresh on-shore winds when conditions in the ent deteriorate very quickly, especially on the ebb. Entry, sp HW ±2½, nps HW ±1. Moorings in The Pit or at Stiffkey Sluices. Speed limit 8kn.

NAVIGATION
WPT 53°00'·00N 00°58'·20E, approx 045°/225° 1M from/to Fairway RW buoy (52°59'·17N 00°56'·38E, April-Oct) at ent to chan. Large dangerous wk, about 1·5M E of ent, marked by unlit R PHM buoy. The bar is shallow and shifts often. The chan is marked by 15 unlit G SHM buoys, relaid each spring. Beware mussel lays, drying, off Blakeney Spit.

LIGHTS AND MARKS
Y ldg bns on dunes at Blakeney Pt are erected only when the chan ent moves adjacent to the Point. Conspic marks: Blakeney and Langham churches; a chy on the house on Blakeney Pt neck; TV mast (R lts) approx 2M S of ent.

RADIO TELEPHONE
None.

TELEPHONE (Dial code 01263)
Hr Mr 740362; MRCC (01493) 851338; ⊞ (01473) 235704 (H24); Marinecall 0891 500455; Dr 740314; Pilot 740362.

FACILITIES
Quay AB (Free), Slip, M, D, FW, El, C (15 ton), CH; **Services:** Pilot (☎ 740362), AB, BY, M, P & D (cans), FW, ME, El, Sh, SM, Gas, Gaz, AC. **Village** EC Wed; V, R, Bar, ⊠, Ⓑ, ⇌ (Sherringham), ✈ (Norwich).

WELLS-NEXT-THE-SEA   8-5-8

Norfolk 52°59'·30N 00°49'·75E (ent shifts)   Rtg 4-3-1

CHARTS
AC 108, 1190; Imray C28, Y9; OS 132

TIDES
−0445 Dover; ML 1·2 Duration 0540; Zone 0 (UT)

Standard Port IMMINGHAM (→)

Times				Height (metres)			
High Water		Low Water		MHWS	MHWN	MLWN	MLWS
0100	0700	0100	0700	7·3	5·8	2·6	0·9
1300	1900	1300	1900				
Differences WELLS BAR (approx 52°59'N 00°49'E)							
+0020	+0020	+0020	+0020	−1·3	−1·0		No data
WELLS-NEXT-THE-SEA (approx 52°57'N 00°51'E)							
+0035	+0045	+0340	+0310	−3·8	−3·8		Not below CD

Note: LW time differences at Wells are for the end of a LW stand which lasts about 4 hrs at sp and about 5 hrs at nps.

SHELTER
Good, but in strong N'lies swell renders entry impossible for small craft. Max draft 3m at sp. Access from HW −1½ to HW +1, but best on the flood. Quay berths mostly dry.

NAVIGATION
WPT Fairway SWM buoy, L Fl 10s, 52°59'·85N 00°49'·71E, 015°/175° from/to chan ent, 0·7M. The drying bar and ent vary in depth and position; buoys are altered to suit. Initially keep to W side of chan to counter E-going tide at HW−2; and to E side of chan from No 12 PHM lt buoy to quay. Best to seek Hr Mr's advice (send SAE for latest free plan) or follow FV of appropriate draft.

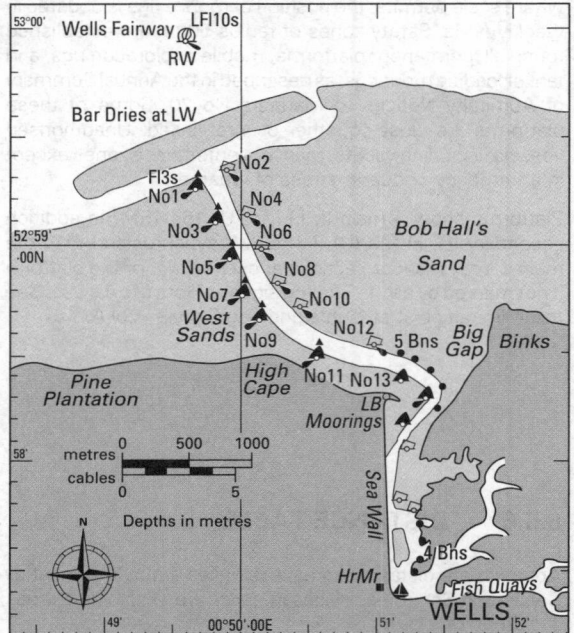

LIGHTS AND MARKS
Chan is marked by No 1 SHM buoy, Fl 3s, and 9 SHM buoys, of which 6 are Fl G 3s; and by 9 PHM buoys of which 6 are Fl R 3s; the rest unlit. Temp buoys may be laid when chan changes. A fir plantation is conspic W of hbr ent; ditto white LB ho with R roof.

RADIO TELEPHONE
Wells Hbr Radio Ch 12 16, HW−2 and when vessel due. Hbr launch may escort visitors into hbr and up to Quay.

TELEPHONE (Dial code 01328 Fakenham)
Hr Mr 711744, ☎ 710623; MRCC (01493) 851338; ⊞ (01473) 235704 (H24); Marinecall 0891 500 455; Police (01692) 402222; Dr 710741; Ⓗ 710218.

FACILITIES
Main Quay AB (£10), M (see Hr Mr), FW, ME, El, Sh, C (5 ton mobile), CH, V, R, Bar; **E Quay** Slip, M; **Wells SC** ☎ 710622, Slip, Bar; **Services:** Ⓔ, ACA. **Town** EC Thurs; P & D (bowser on quay; up to 500 galls), Gas, V, R, Bar, ⊠, Ⓑ, ⇌ (bus to Norwich/King's Lynn), ✈ (Norwich).

KING'S LYNN   8-5-9

Norfolk 52°49'·72N 00°21'·30E (West Stones bn)   Rtg 3-5-2

CHARTS
AC 1200, 108, 1190; Imray Y9; OS 132

TIDES
–0443 Dover; ML 3·6; Duration 0340 Sp, 0515 Np;
Zone 0 (UT)

Standard Port IMMINGHAM (→)

Times				Height (metres)			
High Water		Low Water		MHWS	MHWN	MLWN	MLWS
0100	0700	0100	0700	7·3	5·8	2·6	0·9
1300	1900	1300	1900				
Differences KING'S LYNN							
+0030	+0030	+0305	+0140	–0·5	–0·8	–0·8	+0·1
BURNHAM OVERY STAITHE							
+0045	+0055	No data		–5·0	–4·9		No data
HUNSTANTON							
+0010	+0020	+0105	+0025	+0·1	–0·2	–0·1	0·0
WEST STONES							
+0025	+0025	+0115	+0040	–0·3	–0·4	–0·3	+0·2
WISBECH CUT							
+0020	+0025	+0200	+0030	–0·3	–0·7	–0·4	No data

SHELTER
Port is well sheltered 1½M up river; entry is recommended HW±3. A commercial port with virtually no facilities for yachts which are not encouraged. Some mid-river moorings are free, via Hr Mr, but passage up to Denver (12M) is preferred. Alexandra dock is open from about HW –1½ to HW and yachts can be left there only with the Dockmaster's permission. Drying moorings at S Quay, S side of Boal Quay or at Friars Fleet; keep clear of FV moorings.

NAVIGATION
WPT 52°58'·61N 00°21'·15E, Roaring Middle lt float SWM, L Fl 10s 7m 8M, 013°/193° from/to No 1 NCM lt buoy, Q, 2·58M; thence 1·3M SSW to No 3 ECM buoy, Q (3) 10s, at 52°54'·65N 00°19'·25E, marking the ent to Teetotal Chan, now the main buoyed/lit appr route.
NB: Roaring Middle lt float (WPT) is replaced temporarily every May/Jun by a NCM pillar buoy, Q, for maintenance. Extensive shifting sand banks extend several miles into the Wash. Chans are subject to frequent changes. S of W Stones bn deeper water is on E side of chan. Advice may be obtained from Pilot launches which are often near to 52°56'·92N 00°21'·50E (boarding point); or call VHF Ch 14.

LIGHTS AND MARKS
Conspic white lt ho (disused, 18m) on Hunstanton cliffs. West Stones bn NCM, Q 3m 2M. Lynn Cut ldg lts 155°: front Iso R 2s 11m 3M; rear FW 16m 4M, both on masts.
Entry sigs for Alexandra Dock:
Bu flag or Ⓡ = Vessels can enter;
R flag or Ⓖ = Vessels leaving dock.

RADIO TELEPHONE
Call *KLCB* VHF Ch **14** 16 11 12 (Mon-Fri: 0800-1730 LT. Other times: HW –4 to HW+1).
King's Lynn Docks (ABP) Ch **14** 16 11 (HW–2½ to HW+1).

TELEPHONE (Dial code 01553)
Hr Mr 773411; Dock 691555; MRCC (01493) 851338; Dr via Hr Mr; ⌗ (01473) 235704 (H24); Marinecall 0891 500455.

FACILITIES
Docks ☎ 691555, AB £42 for 48 hrs, FW, C (32 ton);
Services: CH, Sh, ME, El, Ⓔ, D.
Town EC Wed; P, D, V, R, Bar, ✉, Ⓑ, ⇌, ✈ (Humberside or Norwich).
Note: 24M up the Great Ouse river, Ely Marina ☎ (01353) 664622, Slip, M, P, D, FW, ME, El, Sh, C (10 ton), CH. Lock half-way at Denver Sluice ☎ (01366) 382340/VHF Ch 73, and low bridges beyond.

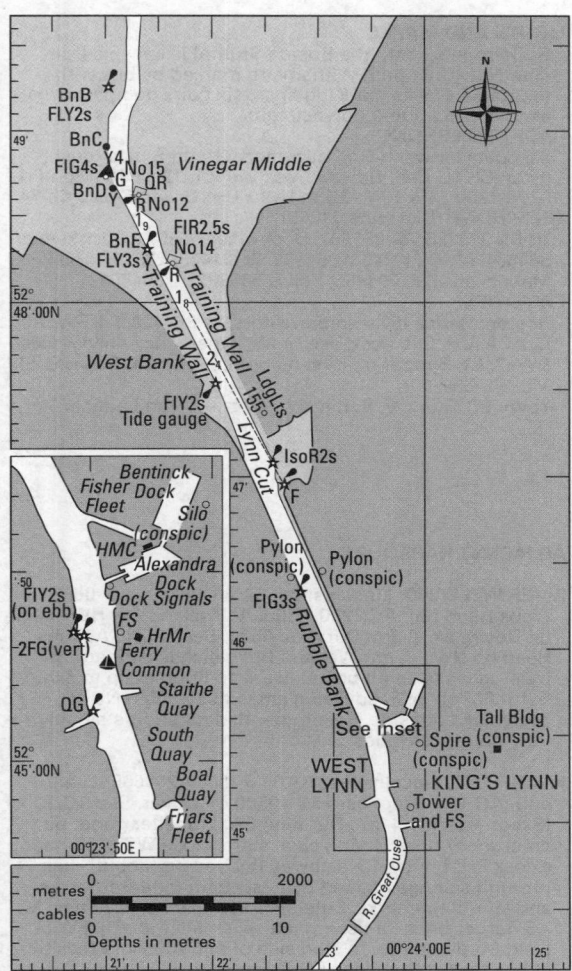

ADJACENT HARBOURS

BURNHAM OVERY STAITHE, Norfolk, 52°59'·00N 00°46'·50E. Rtg 4-5-1. AC 108, 1190. HW –0420 on Dover. See 8·5·9. Small drying hbr; ent chan has 0·3m MLWS. ⚓ off the Staithe only suitable in good weather. No lts. Scolt Hd is conspic to W and Gun Hill to E; Scolt Hd Island is conspic 3M long sandbank which affords some shelter. Chan varies constantly and buoys are moved to suit. Local knowledge advisable. Facilities: (01328) **Burnham Overy Staithe SC** ☎ 738348, M, L; **Services:** CH, M, ME, Sh, Slip, FW; **Burnham Market** EC Wed; Bar, P and D (cans), R, V.

BRANCASTER STAITHE, Norfolk, 52°59'·00N 00°38'·50E. Rtg 4-4-1. AC 108, 1190. HW –0425 on Dover; See 8.5.9. Small drying hbr; dangerous to enter except by day in settled weather. Speed limit 6kn. Appr from due N. Conspic golf club house with lt, Fl 5s 8m 3M, is 0·5M S of chan ent and Fairway buoy. Beware wk shown on chart. Sandbanks vary constantly and buoys changed to suit. Scolt Hd conspic to E. Local knowledge or Pilot advised. ⚓s available occas in The Hole. Hr Mr ☎ (01485) 210638. Facilities: **Brancaster Staithe SC** ☎ 210249, R, Bar; **Services:** BY, CH, El, FW, P & D (cans), ME, R, Sh, Bar, V.

WISBECH, Cambridgeshire, 52°40'·00N 00°09'·65E. Rtg 3-5-3. AC 1200, 1190. HW –0450 on Dover; ML 3·5m; Duration 0520. See 8·5·9. Excellent shelter. Vessels of 4·8m draft can reach Wisbech at sp (3·4m at nps), but depths vary. Ent to R Nene and inland waterways. Landing at W Nene tr; moorings at Sutton Port (W bank 0·5M downstream from Sutton Bridge) or at Wisbech town quay. Ent well marked with lit buoys and bns from RAF No 6 ECM buoy to Nene trs. Best ent HW –3. Big Tom bn, Fl (2) R 10s 10m 3M, to Sutton br is 3½M, thence to Wisbech 6M, with FG lts to stbd. Call on VHF Ch 16 09 **14** or ☎ (01945) 582125, HW –3 to HW. Take care when ships entering or leaving the berthing area. Hr Mr ☎ (01406) 351530 at Sutton Bridge, not H24. **Town** P & D (cans), Bar, R, V, Gas.

BOSTON   8-5-10
Lincs 52°56'·00N 00°05'·00E (Tabs Head bn)   Rtg 3-4-2

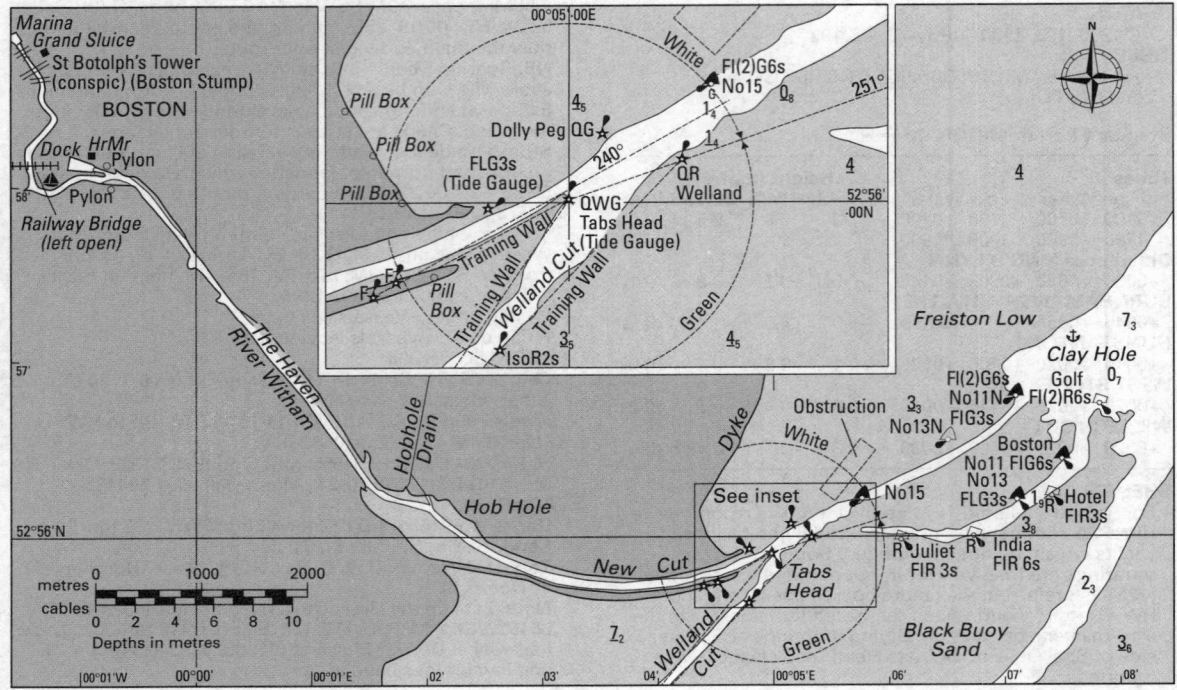

CHARTS
AC 1200, 108; Imray Y9; OS 131
TIDES
−0415 Dover; ML 3·3; Duration Flood 0500, Ebb 0700;
Zone 0 (UT)

Standard Port IMMINGHAM (→)

Times				Height (metres)			
High Water		Low Water		MHWS	MHWN	MLWN	MLWS
0100	0700	0100	0700	7·3	5·8	2·6	0·9
1300	1900	1300	1900				
Differences BOSTON							
0000	+0010	+0140	+0050	−0·5	−1·0	−0·9	−0·5
TABS HEAD (WELLAND RIVER)							
0000	+0005	+0125	+0020	+0·2	−0·2	−0·2	−0·2
SKEGNESS							
+0010	+0015	+0030	+0020	−0·4	−0·2	−0·1	0·0
INNER DOWSING LIGHT TOWER							
0000	0000	+0010	+0010	−0·9	−0·7	−0·1	+0·3

SHELTER
Very good. Except in emergency berthing in the Dock is
prohib. Yachts secure just above Dock ent and see Hr Mr.
The port is administered by Port of Boston Ltd. Moorings
may be possible (on S side) below first fixed bridge.
Yachts which can lower masts should pass the Grand
Sluice lock into fresh water (24 hrs notice required); the
lock is 22·7m x 4·6m and opens approx HW±2. It leads
into the R Witham Navigation which goes 31M to Lincoln.
Marina is to stbd immediately beyond the sluice. British
Waterways have 50 moorings, with FW and AC, beyond
Grand Sluice.
NAVIGATION
WPT Boston Rds SWM lt buoy, L Fl 10s, 52°57'·53N
00°16'·23E, 100°/280° from/to Freeman Chan ent, 0·70M.
Thence Bar Chan is well marked, but liable to change.
SW of Clay Hole a new chan has formed approx 0·5M to
NW of former chan; it is marked by SHM lt buoys Nos
11N, 13N, and 15. Note: former chan is still buoyed ufn.
Tabs Head marks the ent to the river; it should be passed
not earlier than HW−3 to enable the Grand Sluice to be
reached before the start of the ebb. On reaching Boston
Dock, masts should be lowered to negotiate swing bridge
(cannot always be opened) and three fixed bridges. Chan
through town is narrow and un-navigable at LW.

LIGHTS AND MARKS
St Boltoph's ch tr, (the Boston Stump) is conspic from
afar. New Cut and R Witham are marked by bns with
topmarks. FW lts mark ldg lines: six pairs going upstream
and six pairs going downstream.
RADIO TELEPHONE
All boats between Golf buoy and Grand Sluice must
listen Ch 12. Call: Boston Dock VHF Ch 12 11 16 (Mon-Fri
0700-1700 LT & HW −2½ to HW +1½). Grand Sluice Ch 74.
TELEPHONE (Dial code 01205)
Hr Mr 362328, ☎ 351852; Dock office 365571; Lock keeper
364864; MRCC (01493) 851338; ⌗ (01473) 235704 (H24);
Marinecall 0891 500455; Police 366222; Ⓗ 364801.
FACILITIES
Boston Marina (50 + some visitors) ☎ 364420, £4, FW, AC,
D, ACA, CH, C in dock, see Hr Mr (emergency only) Access
HW±2; **BWB** moorings: 1st night free, then £4. **Services:** El,
ME, Sh, Gas.
Town EC Thurs; V, R, Bar, ⊠, Ⓑ, ⇌, ✈ (Humberside).

ADJACENT HARBOURS

RIVER WELLAND, Lincolnshire, 52°56'·00N 00°05'·00E
(Tabs Head bn). AC 1200, 1190. At Welland Cut HW −0440
on Dover; ML 0·3m; Duration 0520. See 8.5.10. At Tabs
Head bn HW ±3, ent Welland Cut which is defined by
training walls and lt bns. Beware sp flood of up to 5kn.
Berth 6M up, at Fosdyke on small quay 300m NE of
bridge on stbd side. Recommended for short stay only.
Very limited facilities.

WAINFLEET, Lincolnshire, 53°04'·77N 00°20'·00E (chan
ent). AC 108. Skegness HW +0500 on Dover. See 8.5.10
(Skegness). ML 4·0m; Duration 0600. Shelter good, but
emergency only. Drying chan starts close WSW of Inner
Knock PHM buoy. Swatchway buoyed but not lit; chan
through saltings marked by posts with radar reflectors
and lateral topmarks. Enter HW ±1½. No lts. Facilities: M,
AB (larger boats at fishing jetties, smaller at YC), FW at
Field Study Centre on stbd side of ent. All shore facilities
at Skegness (3½ miles), EC Thurs.

ENGLAND – IMMINGHAM

LAT 53°38′N   LONG   0°11′W

TIMES AND HEIGHTS OF HIGH AND LOW WATERS

YEAR **1999**

TIME ZONE (UT)
For Summer Time add ONE hour in non-shaded areas

5

JANUARY

Day	Time	m	Day	Time	m
1 F	0447 / 1112 / 1716 / 2341	7.1 / 1.2 / 7.2 / 1.0	**16** SA	0458 / 1110 / 1715 / 2337	6.5 / 1.7 / 6.9 / 1.7
2 SA O	0540 / 1201 / 1801	7.3 / 1.1 / 7.4	**17** SU ●	0539 / 1152 / 1753	6.7 / 1.6 / 7.0
3 SU	0032 / 0630 / 1248 / 1844	0.8 / 7.4 / 1.1 / 7.4	**18** M	0019 / 0619 / 1232 / 1830	1.4 / 6.9 / 1.5 / 7.2
4 M	0120 / 0717 / 1331 / 1926	0.7 / 7.3 / 1.2 / 7.4	**19** TU	0100 / 0658 / 1309 / 1906	1.3 / 6.9 / 1.4 / 7.3
5 TU	0204 / 0802 / 1411 / 2007	0.8 / 7.1 / 1.4 / 7.3	**20** W	0138 / 0737 / 1347 / 1942	1.2 / 7.0 / 1.4 / 7.3
6 W	0246 / 0846 / 1448 / 2046	1.0 / 6.9 / 1.6 / 7.1	**21** TH	0216 / 0816 / 1425 / 2020	1.1 / 6.9 / 1.4 / 7.3
7 TH	0325 / 0928 / 1523 / 2127	1.3 / 6.6 / 1.9 / 6.8	**22** F	0256 / 0856 / 1505 / 2101	1.1 / 6.9 / 1.5 / 7.2
8 F	0403 / 1010 / 1600 / 2210	1.6 / 6.3 / 2.2 / 6.4	**23** SA	0337 / 0940 / 1548 / 2147	1.2 / 6.7 / 1.7 / 7.0
9 SA	0444 / 1057 / 1643 / 2301	2.0 / 6.0 / 2.5 / 6.1	**24** SU	0423 / 1029 / 1637 / 2240	1.4 / 6.4 / 1.9 / 6.8
10 SU	0532 / 1154 / 1737	2.3 / 5.7 / 2.8	**25** M	0517 / 1128 / 1737 / 2344	1.7 / 6.2 / 2.2 / 6.5
11 M	0006 / 0628 / 1259 / 1841	5.8 / 2.5 / 5.7 / 2.9	**26** TU	0623 / 1244 / 1854	2.0 / 6.0 / 2.4
12 TU	0119 / 0732 / 1404 / 1953	5.8 / 2.5 / 5.8 / 2.8	**27** W	0105 / 0742 / 1404 / 2020	6.3 / 2.1 / 6.1 / 2.3
13 W	0228 / 0837 / 1502 / 2104	5.8 / 2.4 / 6.0 / 2.6	**28** TH	0230 / 0859 / 1513 / 2135	6.3 / 2.0 / 6.3 / 2.0
14 TH	0325 / 0935 / 1552 / 2203	6.0 / 2.2 / 6.3 / 2.2	**29** F	0341 / 1003 / 1612 / 2237	6.5 / 1.8 / 6.6 / 1.5
15 F	0414 / 1025 / 1635 / 2253	6.3 / 1.9 / 6.6 / 1.9	**30** SA	0442 / 1059 / 1703 / 2332	6.8 / 1.5 / 7.0 / 1.1
			31 SU O	0536 / 1148 / 1748	7.0 / 1.3 / 7.2

FEBRUARY

Day	Time	m	Day	Time	m
1 M	0021 / 0623 / 1234 / 1830	0.9 / 7.1 / 1.2 / 7.3	**16** TU ●	0002 / 0602 / 1213 / 1810	1.3 / 6.9 / 1.4 / 7.3
2 TU	0107 / 0706 / 1316 / 1910	0.7 / 7.2 / 1.2 / 7.4	**17** W	0045 / 0641 / 1254 / 1847	1.0 / 7.1 / 1.2 / 7.5
3 W	0149 / 0746 / 1353 / 1948	0.7 / 7.1 / 1.3 / 7.3	**18** TH	0125 / 0720 / 1333 / 1925	0.8 / 7.2 / 1.1 / 7.6
4 TH	0226 / 0822 / 1426 / 2023	0.9 / 6.9 / 1.4 / 7.2	**19** F	0203 / 0758 / 1412 / 2004	0.7 / 7.2 / 1.1 / 7.6
5 F	0259 / 0855 / 1457 / 2056	1.1 / 6.7 / 1.6 / 6.9	**20** SA	0242 / 0837 / 1452 / 2045	0.8 / 7.1 / 1.1 / 7.5
6 SA	0331 / 0926 / 1528 / 2130	1.4 / 6.4 / 1.8 / 6.6	**21** SU	0321 / 0918 / 1533 / 2130	0.9 / 6.9 / 1.3 / 7.2
7 SU	0404 / 1000 / 1602 / 2207	1.7 / 6.2 / 2.1 / 6.3	**22** M	0403 / 1004 / 1618 / 2220	1.2 / 6.6 / 1.7 / 6.8
8 M	0443 / 1042 / 1644 / 2254	2.1 / 5.9 / 2.5 / 5.9	**23** TU	0451 / 1058 / 1713 / 2323	1.7 / 6.2 / 2.0 / 6.4
9 TU	0534 / 1139 / 1741	2.4 / 5.6 / 2.8	**24** W	0552 / 1211 / 1828	2.1 / 5.9 / 2.4
10 W	0004 / 0636 / 1300 / 1855	5.6 / 2.7 / 5.5 / 2.9	**25** TH	0049 / 0717 / 1339 / 2005	6.0 / 2.4 / 5.9 / 2.4
11 TH	0135 / 0746 / 1416 / 2012	5.5 / 2.7 / 5.7 / 2.8	**26** F	0221 / 0845 / 1454 / 2126	6.0 / 2.3 / 6.1 / 2.0
12 F	0251 / 0855 / 1517 / 2127	5.7 / 2.5 / 6.0 / 2.4	**27** SA	0337 / 0952 / 1557 / 2228	6.2 / 2.0 / 6.4 / 1.5
13 SA	0349 / 0955 / 1608 / 2227	6.0 / 2.2 / 6.4 / 2.0	**28** SU	0439 / 1047 / 1649 / 2320	6.6 / 1.7 / 6.8 / 1.1
14 SU	0438 / 1046 / 1651 / 2317	6.4 / 1.9 / 6.7 / 1.6			
15 M	0521 / 1131 / 1732	6.7 / 1.6 / 7.0			

MARCH

Day	Time	m	Day	Time	m
1 M	0528 / 1134 / 1733	6.9 / 1.4 / 7.1	**16** TU ●	0500 / 1107 / 1706 / 2338	6.7 / 1.6 / 7.0 / 1.1
2 TU	0006 / 0610 / 1218 / 1813	0.9 / 7.0 / 1.3 / 7.2	**17** W ●	0541 / 1151 / 1746	7.0 / 1.2 / 7.4
3 W	0049 / 0648 / 1257 / 1851	0.7 / 7.1 / 1.2 / 7.3	**18** TH	0022 / 0620 / 1234 / 1825	0.8 / 7.2 / 1.0 / 7.6
4 TH	0127 / 0723 / 1332 / 1926	0.7 / 7.0 / 1.2 / 7.3	**19** F	0104 / 0658 / 1316 / 1905	0.5 / 7.4 / 0.8 / 7.7
5 F	0200 / 0753 / 1403 / 1958	0.9 / 6.9 / 1.4 / 7.1	**20** SA	0144 / 0736 / 1357 / 1946	0.5 / 7.4 / 0.7 / 7.8
6 SA	0230 / 0820 / 1431 / 2027	1.1 / 6.8 / 1.4 / 6.8	**21** SU	0223 / 0815 / 1438 / 2029	0.5 / 7.3 / 0.8 / 7.6
7 SU	0259 / 0846 / 1459 / 2056	1.3 / 6.6 / 1.6 / 6.7	**22** M	0303 / 0856 / 1519 / 2115	0.8 / 7.1 / 1.1 / 7.3
8 M	0327 / 0916 / 1527 / 2128	1.6 / 6.4 / 1.8 / 6.4	**23** TU	0344 / 0941 / 1604 / 2207	1.2 / 6.7 / 1.5 / 6.8
9 TU	0358 / 0951 / 1600 / 2206	2.0 / 6.1 / 2.2 / 6.0	**24** W	0430 / 1035 / 1659 / 2313	1.7 / 6.3 / 1.9 / 6.2
10 W	0439 / 1035 / 1648 / 2258	2.4 / 5.8 / 2.6 / 5.6	**25** TH	0531 / 1147 / 1815	2.3 / 5.9 / 2.5
11 TH	0541 / 1143 / 1803	2.7 / 5.5 / 2.8	**26** F	0045 / 0658 / 1318 / 1956	5.9 / 2.6 / 5.8 / 2.3
12 F	0035 / 0700 / 1329 / 1929	5.4 / 2.9 / 5.5 / 2.8	**27** SA	0215 / 0831 / 1435 / 2113	5.9 / 2.5 / 6.0 / 1.9
13 SA	0217 / 0817 / 1442 / 2050	5.5 / 2.7 / 5.8 / 2.5	**28** SU	0329 / 0937 / 1538 / 2211	6.2 / 2.2 / 6.3 / 1.5
14 SU	0324 / 0924 / 1538 / 2158	5.9 / 2.3 / 6.2 / 2.0	**29** M	0428 / 1029 / 1629 / 2300	6.5 / 1.8 / 6.7 / 1.1
15 M	0416 / 1019 / 1624 / 2252	6.3 / 1.9 / 6.7 / 1.5	**30** TU	0512 / 1114 / 1713 / 2344	6.8 / 1.5 / 6.9 / 0.9
			31 W O	0550 / 1156 / 1752	6.9 / 1.3 / 7.1

APRIL

Day	Time	m	Day	Time	m
1 TH	0024 / 0624 / 1234 / 1828	0.8 / 7.0 / 1.2 / 7.1	**16** F ●	0555 / 1212 / 1802	7.3 / 0.8 / 7.7
2 F	0100 / 0655 / 1308 / 1902	0.9 / 7.0 / 1.1 / 7.1	**17** SA	0039 / 0634 / 1257 / 1845	0.4 / 7.5 / 0.6 / 7.8
3 SA	0132 / 0722 / 1338 / 1932	1.0 / 6.9 / 1.2 / 7.0	**18** SU	0123 / 0714 / 1341 / 1930	0.4 / 7.5 / 0.5 / 7.8
4 SU	0201 / 0747 / 1406 / 2000	1.1 / 6.8 / 1.3 / 6.8	**19** M	0204 / 0755 / 1424 / 2015	0.5 / 7.4 / 0.6 / 7.5
5 M	0228 / 0814 / 1433 / 2029	1.3 / 6.7 / 1.5 / 6.6	**20** TU	0245 / 0838 / 1508 / 2104	0.8 / 7.1 / 0.9 / 7.2
6 TU	0255 / 0843 / 1459 / 2059	1.6 / 6.5 / 1.7 / 6.4	**21** W	0328 / 0924 / 1556 / 2159	1.3 / 6.8 / 1.3 / 6.6
7 W	0322 / 0915 / 1530 / 2136	1.9 / 6.3 / 2.0 / 6.0	**22** TH	0415 / 1018 / 1653 / 2309	1.8 / 6.3 / 1.7 / 6.1
8 TH	0357 / 0954 / 1615 / 2224	2.3 / 5.9 / 2.3 / 5.7	**23** F	0515 / 1129 / 1808	2.4 / 5.9 / 2.1
9 F	0451 / 1049 / 1722 / 2341	2.7 / 5.6 / 2.6 / 5.4	**24** SA	0038 / 0636 / 1255 / 1939	5.9 / 2.7 / 5.8 / 2.1
10 SA	0613 / 1224 / 1850	2.9 / 5.5 / 2.6	**25** SU	0159 / 0805 / 1410 / 2050	5.9 / 2.6 / 5.9 / 1.8
11 SU	0140 / 0738 / 1400 / 2013	5.5 / 2.8 / 5.7 / 2.3	**26** M	0308 / 0911 / 1513 / 2145	6.1 / 2.3 / 6.2 / 1.5
12 M	0253 / 0849 / 1501 / 2123	5.9 / 2.4 / 6.1 / 1.9	**27** TU	0403 / 1003 / 1604 / 2232	6.4 / 1.9 / 6.5 / 1.2
13 TU	0348 / 0948 / 1551 / 2220	6.3 / 2.0 / 6.6 / 1.4	**28** W	0446 / 1048 / 1648 / 2315	6.6 / 1.6 / 6.7 / 1.1
14 W	0434 / 1039 / 1636 / 2309	6.8 / 1.5 / 7.0 / 0.9	**29** TH	0522 / 1129 / 1727 / 2353	6.8 / 1.4 / 6.8 / 1.1
15 TH	0515 / 1126 / 1719 / 2355	7.1 / 1.1 / 7.4 / 0.6	**30** F O	0555 / 1207 / 1803	6.9 / 1.3 / 6.9

Chart Datum: 3·90 metres below Ordnance Datum (Newlyn)

ENGLAND – IMMINGHAM

LAT 53°38′N   LONG 0°11′W

TIMES AND HEIGHTS OF HIGH AND LOW WATERS

YEAR **1999**

TIME ZONE (UT)
For Summer Time add ONE hour in non-shaded areas

MAY

Day	Time	m	Day	Time	m
1 SA	0029 / 0624 / 1242 / 1836	1.1 / 6.9 / 1.2 / 6.9	**16** SU	0016 / 0613 / 1239 / 1828	0.5 / 7.5 / 0.6 / 7.7
2 SU	0102 / 0652 / 1314 / 1907	1.1 / 6.9 / 1.3 / 6.8	**17** M	0102 / 0655 / 1326 / 1917	0.5 / 7.5 / 0.5 / 7.6
3 M	0132 / 0719 / 1344 / 1938	1.2 / 6.9 / 1.3 / 6.7	**18** TU	0147 / 0738 / 1413 / 2006	0.6 / 7.4 / 0.6 / 7.4
4 TU	0201 / 0748 / 1412 / 2009	1.4 / 6.8 / 1.5 / 6.5	**19** W	0230 / 0827 / 1500 / 2057	0.9 / 7.2 / 0.8 / 7.1
5 W	0228 / 0818 / 1440 / 2041	1.6 / 6.6 / 1.6 / 6.3	**20** TH	0315 / 0910 / 1550 / 2153	1.3 / 6.9 / 1.1 / 6.6
6 TH	0257 / 0850 / 1513 / 2119	1.9 / 6.4 / 1.8 / 6.1	**21** F	0402 / 1003 / 1645 / 2301	1.8 / 6.5 / 1.5 / 6.2
7 F	0334 / 0930 / 1557 / 2208	2.2 / 6.1 / 2.1 / 5.8	**22** SA	0456 / 1109 / 1751	2.3 / 6.1 / 1.8
8 SA	0424 / 1021 / 1658 / 2315	2.5 / 5.9 / 2.3 / 5.6	**23** SU	0017 / 0603 / 1224 / 1906	5.9 / 2.6 / 5.9 / 1.9
9 SU	0533 / 1133 / 1816	2.7 / 5.7 / 2.3	**24** M	0128 / 0723 / 1336 / 2014	5.9 / 2.7 / 6.0 / 1.9
10 M	0053 / 0655 / 1305 / 1935	5.6 / 2.7 / 5.8 / 2.1	**25** TU	0232 / 0834 / 1439 / 2110	6.0 / 2.5 / 6.1 / 1.7
11 TU	0214 / 0809 / 1418 / 2045	5.9 / 2.4 / 6.1 / 1.7	**26** W	0327 / 0929 / 1533 / 2158	6.2 / 2.2 / 6.3 / 1.6
12 W	0313 / 0913 / 1515 / 2146	6.3 / 2.0 / 6.6 / 1.3	**27** TH	0412 / 1017 / 1619 / 2241	6.4 / 1.9 / 6.5 / 1.4
13 TH	0403 / 1009 / 1605 / 2239	6.7 / 1.5 / 7.0 / 0.9	**28** F	0450 / 1059 / 1700 / 2320	6.6 / 1.7 / 6.6 / 1.4
14 F	0448 / 1101 / 1654 / 2329	7.1 / 1.1 / 7.3 / 0.6	**29** SA	0524 / 1139 / 1737 / 2357	6.7 / 1.5 / 6.7 / 1.3
15 SA ●	0531 / 1150 / 1741	7.3 / 0.8 / 7.6	**30** SU O	0555 / 1215 / 1812	6.8 / 1.4 / 6.7
			31 M	0032 / 0625 / 1251 / 1846	1.3 / 6.9 / 1.4 / 6.7

JUNE

Day	Time	m	Day	Time	m
1 TU	0107 / 0657 / 1324 / 1920	1.4 / 6.9 / 1.4 / 6.6	**16** W	0132 / 0725 / 1402 / 1959	0.8 / 7.4 / 0.5 / 7.3
2 W	0138 / 0730 / 1356 / 1954	1.5 / 6.8 / 1.5 / 6.5	**17** TH	0217 / 0810 / 1450 / 2049	1.0 / 7.3 / 0.7 / 7.0
3 TH	0209 / 0802 / 1428 / 2030	1.6 / 6.7 / 1.6 / 6.4	**18** F	0301 / 0856 / 1539 / 2142	1.3 / 7.0 / 1.0 / 6.7
4 F	0242 / 0836 / 1504 / 2110	1.8 / 6.6 / 1.7 / 6.2	**19** SA	0345 / 0946 / 1628 / 2239	1.7 / 6.7 / 1.3 / 6.3
5 SA	0320 / 0916 / 1547 / 2157	2.0 / 6.4 / 1.8 / 6.1	**20** SU	0431 / 1041 / 1720 / 2340	2.1 / 6.4 / 1.7 / 6.0
6 SU	0407 / 1005 / 1641 / 2255	2.2 / 6.2 / 1.9 / 5.9	**21** M	0522 / 1144 / 1819	2.4 / 6.1 / 1.9
7 M	0505 / 1105 / 1746	2.4 / 6.1 / 2.0	**22** TU	0043 / 0622 / 1251 / 1922	5.8 / 2.6 / 5.9 / 2.1
8 TU	0007 / 0615 / 1217 / 1858	5.9 / 2.5 / 6.1 / 1.9	**23** W	0144 / 0732 / 1356 / 2023	5.8 / 2.7 / 5.9 / 2.1
9 W	0129 / 0729 / 1333 / 2009	6.0 / 2.3 / 6.2 / 1.7	**24** TH	0241 / 0842 / 1455 / 2117	5.9 / 2.5 / 6.0 / 2.0
10 TH	0235 / 0838 / 1440 / 2114	6.3 / 2.0 / 6.6 / 1.4	**25** F	0331 / 0939 / 1547 / 2204	6.1 / 2.3 / 6.2 / 1.8
11 F	0332 / 0941 / 1539 / 2212	6.6 / 1.6 / 6.9 / 1.1	**26** SA	0414 / 1027 / 1632 / 2247	6.4 / 2.0 / 6.3 / 1.7
12 SA	0423 / 1038 / 1634 / 2306	7.0 / 1.2 / 7.2 / 0.8	**27** SU	0452 / 1119 / 1712 / 2328	6.6 / 1.8 / 6.5 / 1.6
13 SU ●	0510 / 1132 / 1727 / 2356	7.2 / 0.9 / 7.4 / 0.7	**28** M O	0527 / 1152 / 1750	6.7 / 1.6 / 6.6
14 M	0555 / 1223 / 1818	7.4 / 0.6 / 7.5	**29** TU	0007 / 0602 / 1232 / 1827	1.5 / 6.9 / 1.5 / 6.6
15 TU	0045 / 0640 / 1314 / 1908	0.7 / 7.5 / 0.5 / 7.5	**30** W	0045 / 0639 / 1309 / 1905	1.5 / 6.9 / 1.4 / 6.7

JULY

Day	Time	m	Day	Time	m
1 TH	0120 / 0715 / 1346 / 1942	1.5 / 6.9 / 1.4 / 6.7	**16** F	0202 / 0756 / 1437 / 2036	1.1 / 7.4 / 0.6 / 7.1
2 F	0155 / 0750 / 1421 / 2020	1.6 / 6.9 / 1.4 / 6.6	**17** SA	0243 / 0839 / 1520 / 2120	1.3 / 7.2 / 0.9 / 6.8
3 SA	0230 / 0826 / 1457 / 2100	1.7 / 6.8 / 1.4 / 6.5	**18** SU	0322 / 0922 / 1601 / 2205	1.6 / 6.9 / 1.2 / 6.4
4 SU	0308 / 0905 / 1537 / 2143	1.7 / 6.7 / 1.5 / 6.4	**19** M	0400 / 1007 / 1642 / 2251	1.9 / 6.6 / 1.6 / 6.1
5 M	0351 / 0949 / 1624 / 2233	1.9 / 6.6 / 1.6 / 6.2	**20** TU	0440 / 1057 / 1725 / 2343	2.2 / 6.2 / 2.0 / 5.8
6 TU	0441 / 1041 / 1719 / 2332	2.1 / 6.5 / 1.7 / 6.1	**21** W	0527 / 1156 / 1816	2.5 / 5.9 / 2.3
7 W	0542 / 1143 / 1824	2.2 / 6.3 / 1.8	**22** TH	0043 / 0624 / 1303 / 1916	5.7 / 2.7 / 5.7 / 2.4
8 TH	0045 / 0652 / 1257 / 1937	6.1 / 2.3 / 6.3 / 1.8	**23** F	0146 / 0732 / 1411 / 2023	5.7 / 2.8 / 5.8 / 2.4
9 F	0200 / 0807 / 1413 / 2048	6.2 / 2.1 / 6.4 / 1.7	**24** SA	0245 / 0848 / 1512 / 2124	5.9 / 2.6 / 5.9 / 2.2
10 SA	0304 / 0918 / 1521 / 2152	6.4 / 1.8 / 6.7 / 1.4	**25** SU	0337 / 0953 / 1605 / 2216	6.1 / 2.3 / 6.1 / 2.0
11 SU	0402 / 1021 / 1623 / 2249	6.7 / 1.4 / 6.9 / 1.2	**26** M	0422 / 1045 / 1649 / 2302	6.4 / 2.0 / 6.4 / 1.8
12 M	0454 / 1119 / 1719 / 2342	7.0 / 1.1 / 7.2 / 1.0	**27** TU	0502 / 1131 / 1730 / 2345	6.7 / 1.7 / 6.6 / 1.6
13 TU ●	0542 / 1212 / 1813	7.3 / 0.8 / 7.3	**28** W O	0542 / 1214 / 1810	6.9 / 1.5 / 6.7
14 W	0031 / 0627 / 1303 / 1902	0.9 / 7.4 / 0.6 / 7.3	**29** TH	0026 / 0620 / 1255 / 1849	1.5 / 7.0 / 1.3 / 6.8
15 TH	0118 / 0712 / 1351 / 1950	0.7 / 7.4 / 0.5 / 7.2	**30** F	0104 / 0658 / 1334 / 1927	1.4 / 7.1 / 1.2 / 6.9
			31 SA	0140 / 0734 / 1410 / 2005	1.4 / 7.2 / 1.2 / 6.9

AUGUST

Day	Time	m	Day	Time	m
1 SU	0216 / 0811 / 1446 / 2043	1.4 / 7.2 / 1.2 / 6.8	**16** M	0255 / 0853 / 1527 / 2123	1.4 / 7.0 / 1.2 / 6.6
2 M	0254 / 0849 / 1523 / 2123	1.5 / 7.1 / 1.2 / 6.7	**17** TU	0326 / 0930 / 1600 / 2157	1.7 / 6.7 / 1.6 / 6.3
3 TU	0334 / 0931 / 1604 / 2208	1.6 / 7.0 / 1.4 / 6.5	**18** W	0400 / 1009 / 1636 / 2237	2.0 / 6.3 / 2.0 / 6.0
4 W	0419 / 1019 / 1651 / 2301	1.8 / 6.8 / 1.6 / 6.3	**19** TH	0439 / 1056 / 1721 / 2331	2.4 / 5.9 / 2.4 / 5.7
5 TH	0513 / 1118 / 1751	2.1 / 6.5 / 1.9	**20** F	0531 / 1204 / 1820	2.7 / 5.6 / 2.7
6 F	0009 / 0621 / 1232 / 1907	6.1 / 2.3 / 6.3 / 2.1	**21** SA	0045 / 0638 / 1325 / 1930	5.6 / 2.9 / 5.5 / 2.8
7 SA	0130 / 0743 / 1357 / 2028	6.0 / 2.3 / 6.2 / 2.1	**22** SU	0200 / 0756 / 1439 / 2045	5.7 / 2.8 / 5.7 / 2.6
8 SU	0243 / 0903 / 1513 / 2138	6.2 / 2.0 / 6.4 / 1.8	**23** M	0302 / 0919 / 1539 / 2148	6.0 / 2.5 / 6.0 / 2.3
9 M	0346 / 1011 / 1619 / 2238	6.5 / 1.6 / 6.7 / 1.5	**24** TU	0354 / 1021 / 1627 / 2239	6.4 / 2.1 / 6.3 / 1.9
10 TU	0441 / 1110 / 1716 / 2330	6.9 / 1.1 / 7.0 / 1.3	**25** W	0438 / 1109 / 1710 / 2323	6.7 / 1.7 / 6.6 / 1.6
11 W ●	0529 / 1202 / 1807	7.2 / 0.8 / 7.2	**26** TH O	0518 / 1154 / 1750	7.0 / 1.4 / 6.9
12 TH	0018 / 0613 / 1251 / 1852	1.1 / 7.4 / 0.6 / 7.3	**27** F	0005 / 0557 / 1236 / 1829	1.4 / 7.2 / 1.1 / 7.0
13 F	0103 / 0656 / 1335 / 1934	1.0 / 7.4 / 0.5 / 7.2	**28** SA	0044 / 0635 / 1315 / 1907	1.3 / 7.4 / 1.0 / 7.1
14 SA	0144 / 0736 / 1417 / 2013	1.1 / 7.4 / 0.6 / 7.1	**29** SU	0121 / 0712 / 1351 / 1943	1.2 / 7.5 / 0.9 / 7.2
15 SU	0221 / 0816 / 1454 / 2050	1.2 / 7.3 / 0.9 / 6.8	**30** M	0158 / 0750 / 1427 / 2020	1.2 / 7.5 / 0.9 / 7.1
			31 TU	0236 / 0829 / 1503 / 2059	1.2 / 7.4 / 1.0 / 6.9

Chart Datum: 3·90 metres below Ordnance Datum (Newlyn)

ENGLAND – IMMINGHAM

LAT 53°38′N   LONG 0°11′W

TIMES AND HEIGHTS OF HIGH AND LOW WATERS

YEAR **1999**

TIME ZONE (UT)
For Summer Time add ONE hour in non-shaded areas

5

SEPTEMBER

	Time	m		Time	m
1 W	0315 0911 1541 2142	1.4 7.2 1.3 6.7	**16** TH	0322 0925 1549 2141	1.9 6.4 2.0 6.2
2 TH	0358 0959 1625 2232	1.6 6.9 1.7 6.4	**17** F	0356 1003 1627 2225	2.2 6.0 2.4 5.9
3 F	0450 1058 1722 2339	2.0 6.5 2.1 6.0	**18** SA	0442 1100 1725 2340	2.6 5.6 2.8 5.6
4 SA	0558 1217 1844	2.3 6.1 2.4	**19** SU	0551 1239 1843	2.9 5.4 3.0
5 SU	0106 0729 1350 2016	5.9 2.4 6.0 2.4	**20** M	0117 0714 1405 2005	5.6 2.9 5.5 2.9
6 M	0226 0857 1509 2129	6.1 2.1 6.3 2.1	**21** TU	0228 0842 1511 2117	5.9 2.6 5.9 2.5
7 TU	0332 1004 1615 2226	6.4 1.6 6.6 1.8	**22** W	0323 0951 1602 2211	6.3 2.1 6.3 2.1
8 W	0426 1058 1709 2316	6.8 1.1 7.0 1.4	**23** TH	0409 1041 1646 2256	6.7 1.6 6.7 1.7
9 TH ●	0513 1147 1754	7.1 0.8 7.2	**24** F	0451 1126 1726 2338	7.1 1.2 7.0 1.4
10 F	0000 0554 1232 1833	1.2 7.3 0.6 7.2	**25** SA ○	0530 1208 1804	7.4 1.0 7.2
11 SA	0042 0634 1313 1910	1.1 7.4 0.6 7.2	**26** SU	0018 0608 1248 1841	1.2 7.6 0.8 7.3
12 SU	0120 0712 1350 1943	1.1 7.4 0.8 7.1	**27** M	0058 0647 1326 1918	1.0 7.7 0.7 7.4
13 M	0154 0748 1422 2013	1.2 7.3 1.0 6.9	**28** TU	0137 0727 1403 1955	1.0 7.7 0.7 7.3
14 TU	0225 0821 1451 2040	1.4 7.1 1.3 6.7	**29** W	0217 0808 1441 2034	1.0 7.6 0.9 7.1
15 W	0253 0852 1519 2108	1.6 6.8 1.6 6.5	**30** TH	0258 0852 1520 2117	1.2 7.3 1.3 6.8

OCTOBER

	Time	m		Time	m
1 F	0342 0943 1603 2207	1.5 6.9 1.8 6.4	**16** SA	0320 0926 1541 2139	2.1 6.1 2.4 6.1
2 SA	0434 1045 1700 2315	1.9 6.4 2.3 6.0	**17** SU	0402 1014 1630 2233	2.4 5.7 2.8 5.7
3 SU	0546 1211 1824	2.3 6.0 2.7	**18** M	0507 1144 1749	2.8 5.4 3.1
4 M	0046 0722 1343 2002	5.9 2.4 6.0 2.7	**19** TU	0021 0633 1327 1919	5.6 2.8 5.5 3.0
5 TU	0207 0847 1500 2113	6.1 2.0 6.2 2.3	**20** W	0147 0758 1436 2035	5.8 2.6 5.9 2.7
6 W	0313 0948 1603 2207	6.4 1.6 6.6 1.9	**21** TH	0246 0910 1530 2133	6.2 2.1 6.3 2.2
7 TH	0406 1039 1651 2254	6.8 1.2 6.9 1.6	**22** F	0335 1004 1616 2222	6.6 1.6 6.7 1.8
8 F	0451 1124 1731 2337	7.1 0.9 7.1 1.3	**23** SA	0418 1051 1657 2307	7.1 1.2 7.1 1.4
9 SA ●	0532 1206 1807	7.3 0.8 7.2	**24** SU ○	0500 1135 1736 2350	7.4 0.9 7.3 1.1
10 SU	0017 0610 1245 1840	1.2 7.3 0.8 7.1	**25** M	0541 1218 1814	7.7 0.7 7.5
11 M	0054 0646 1319 1910	1.2 7.3 1.0 7.1	**26** TU	0033 0622 1259 1852	0.9 7.8 0.6 7.5
12 TU	0126 0720 1349 1937	1.2 7.2 1.2 7.0	**27** W	0116 0706 1340 1931	0.8 7.8 0.7 7.5
13 W	0155 0751 1416 2002	1.4 7.0 1.4 6.9	**28** TH	0159 0751 1420 2012	0.9 7.6 1.0 7.3
14 TH	0222 0820 1442 2030	1.5 6.8 1.7 6.7	**29** F	0243 0839 1501 2056	1.1 7.3 1.4 7.0
15 F	0250 0851 1509 2101	1.8 6.5 2.0 6.4	**30** SA	0330 0932 1547 2148	1.4 6.9 1.9 6.6
			31 SU	0426 1037 1643 2255	1.8 6.4 2.4 6.2

NOVEMBER

	Time	m		Time	m
1 M	0537 1202 1801	2.2 6.0 2.8	**16** TU	0433 1055 1659 2306	2.5 5.6 2.9 5.8
2 TU	0021 0706 1325 1934	6.0 2.2 6.0 2.8	**17** W	0548 1231 1822	2.6 5.6 3.0
3 W	0140 0823 1436 2046	6.1 2.0 6.2 2.5	**18** TH	0043 0709 1350 1942	5.8 2.5 5.8 2.8
4 TH	0246 0922 1536 2141	6.4 1.6 6.5 2.1	**19** F	0157 0821 1450 2048	6.1 2.1 6.2 2.4
5 F	0340 1011 1623 2228	6.7 1.4 6.7 1.8	**20** SA	0254 0921 1541 2144	6.5 1.7 6.6 1.9
6 SA	0425 1056 1702 2310	6.9 1.2 6.9 1.5	**21** SU	0343 1014 1626 2235	7.0 1.3 7.0 1.5
7 SU	0507 1136 1737 2350	7.1 1.1 7.0 1.4	**22** M	0430 1103 1708 2324	7.3 1.0 7.3 1.1
8 M ●	0545 1213 1810	7.1 1.2 7.1	**23** TU ○	0516 1149 1749	7.6 0.8 7.5
9 TU	0026 0621 1246 1839	1.3 7.1 1.2 7.1	**24** W	0011 0602 1235 1830	0.9 7.7 0.7 7.6
10 W	0058 0654 1316 1906	1.3 7.0 1.4 7.0	**25** TH	0059 0650 1319 1912	0.7 7.7 0.8 7.6
11 TH	0128 0725 1345 1934	1.4 6.9 1.5 6.9	**26** F	0145 0738 1403 1955	0.8 7.6 1.0 7.4
12 F	0157 0757 1412 2003	1.6 6.7 1.7 6.8	**27** SA	0233 0829 1447 2041	0.9 7.3 1.4 7.1
13 SA	0225 0829 1439 2034	1.7 6.5 2.0 6.6	**28** SU	0322 0924 1533 2132	1.2 6.9 1.8 6.8
14 SU	0257 0905 1512 2110	2.0 6.3 2.3 6.3	**29** M	0416 1027 1625 2233	1.6 6.5 2.3 6.4
15 M	0337 0950 1557 2158	2.2 5.9 2.6 6.0	**30** TU	0519 1140 1728 2347	1.9 6.1 2.7 6.2

DECEMBER

	Time	m		Time	m
1 W	0634 1253 1847	2.1 6.0 2.8	**16** TH	0508 1128 1730 2334	2.2 5.8 2.7 6.1
2 TH	0103 0746 1359 2005	6.1 2.0 6.1 2.7	**17** F	0618 1248 1846	2.2 5.9 2.7
3 F	0210 0846 1458 2106	6.2 1.9 6.2 2.4	**18** SA	0050 0731 1402 2001	6.2 2.1 6.1 2.5
4 SA	0307 0938 1547 2157	6.4 1.7 6.4 2.1	**19** SU	0205 0839 1502 2108	6.4 1.8 6.4 2.1
5 SU	0357 1023 1630 2241	6.6 1.5 6.6 1.8	**20** M	0309 0940 1555 2207	6.7 1.5 6.8 1.7
6 M	0441 1103 1707 2322	6.8 1.5 6.8 1.6	**21** TU	0405 1035 1643 2302	7.1 1.2 7.1 1.3
7 TU ●	0521 1141 1741 2359	6.8 1.5 6.9 1.5	**22** W ○	0458 1127 1729 2354	7.4 1.0 7.4 0.9
8 W	0558 1215 1812	6.9 1.5 7.0	**23** TH	0550 1216 1814	7.5 0.9 7.5
9 TH	0034 0632 1248 1843	1.5 6.8 1.5 7.0	**24** F	0045 0640 1304 1858	0.7 7.6 0.9 7.6
10 F	0107 0706 1320 1914	1.5 6.8 1.6 7.0	**25** SA	0135 0731 1349 1943	0.6 7.5 1.1 7.5
11 SA	0139 0740 1349 1946	1.6 6.7 1.7 6.9	**26** SU	0223 0821 1434 2028	0.7 7.3 1.3 7.3
12 SU	0210 0815 1420 2018	1.7 6.5 1.9 6.9	**27** M	0312 0913 1517 2116	0.9 7.0 1.7 7.1
13 M	0243 0851 1454 2053	1.8 6.4 2.1 6.6	**28** TU	0400 1007 1602 2208	1.2 6.6 2.0 6.7
14 TU	0321 0933 1535 2136	1.9 6.2 2.4 6.4	**29** W	0451 1106 1650 2307	1.6 6.2 2.4 6.4
15 W	0409 1024 1626 2229	2.1 6.0 2.5 6.2	**30** TH	0547 1208 1745	1.9 6.0 2.7
			31 F	0014 0649 1311 1853	6.1 2.2 5.9 2.8

Chart Datum: 3·90 metres below Ordnance Datum (Newlyn)

RIVER HUMBER

8-5-11

S bank: NE and N Lincolnshire
Grimsby marina (53°35'·10N 00°03'·87W Rtg 2-2-2).

N bank: E Riding of Yorks and City of Kingston-upon-Hull
Hull marina (53°44'·22N 00°20'·60W Rtg 3-1-1)

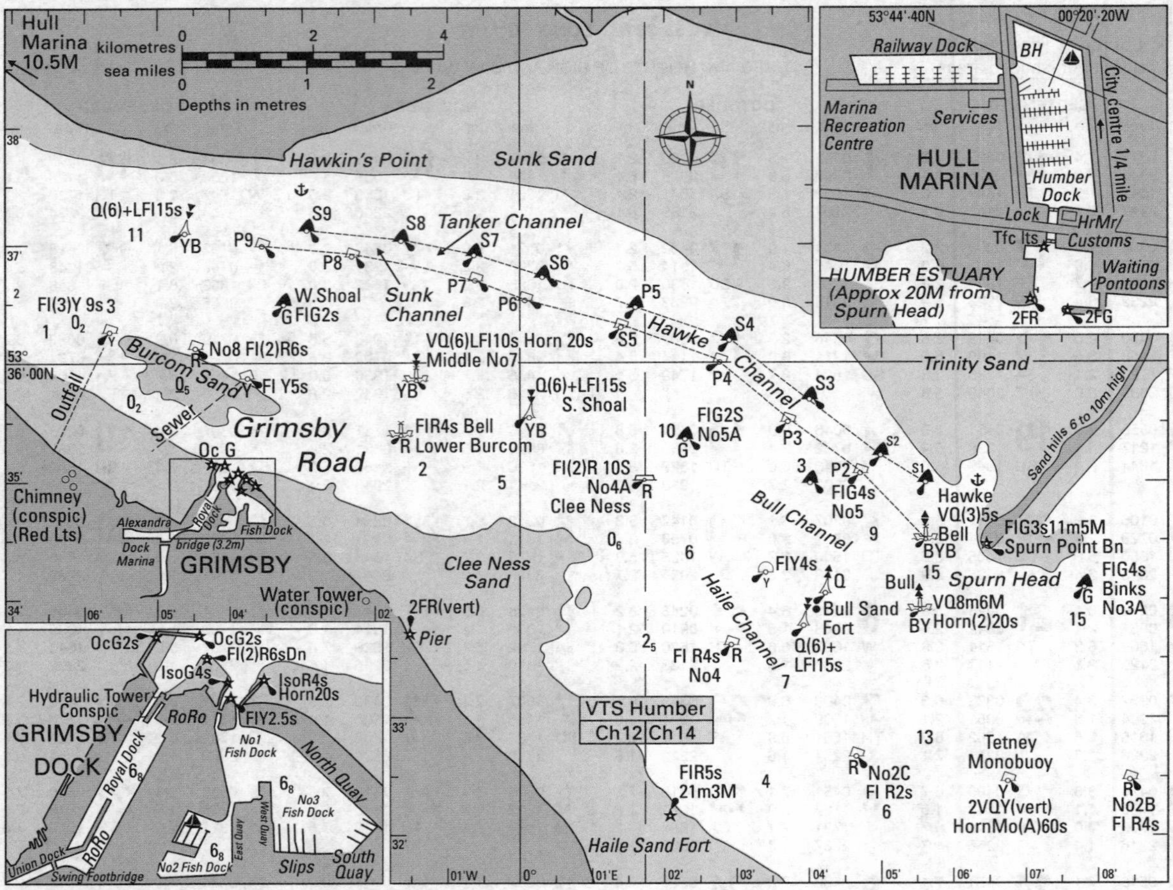

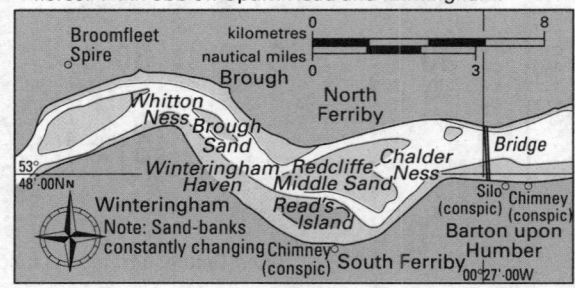

CHARTS
AC 109, 3497, 1188, 1190; Imray C29; OS 107; ABP (local)

TIDES
–0510 Immingham, –0452 Hull, Dover; ML 4·1; Duration 0555; Zone 0 (UT)

Standard Port IMMINGHAM (←—)

Times				Height (metres)			
High Water		Low Water		MHWS	MHWN	MLWN	MLWS
0100	0700	0100	0700	7·3	5·8	2·6	0·9
1300	1900	1300	1900				
Differences BULL SAND FORT							
–0020	–0030	–0035	–0015	–0·4	–0·3	+0·1	+0·2
GRIMSBY							
–0003	–0011	–0015	–0002	–0·3	–0·2	0·0	+0·1
HULL (ALBERT DOCK)							
+0019	+0019	+0033	+0027	+0·3	+0·1	–0·1	–0·2
HUMBER BRIDGE							
+0024	+0022	+0047	+0036	–0·1	–0·4	–0·7	–0·7
BURTON STATHER (R. Trent)*							
+0105	+0045	+0335	+0305	–2·1	–2·3	–2·3	Dries
KEADBY (R. Trent)*							
+0135	+0120	+0425	+0410	–2·5	–2·8	Dries	Dries
BLACKTOFT (R. Ouse)†							
+0100	+0055	+0325	+0255	–1·6	–1·8	–2·2	–1·1
GOOLE (R. Ouse)†							
+0130	+0115	+0355	+0350	–1·6	–2·1	–1·9	–0·6

NOTE: Daily predictions for Immingham are given above.

* Normal river level at Burton Stather is about 0·1m below CD, and at Keadby 0·1m to 0·2m below CD.

† Heights of LW can increase by up to 0·3m at Blacktoft and 0·6m at Goole when river in spate. HW heights are little affected.

SHELTER
R Humber is the estuary of R Ouse and R Trent. ABP is the Authority for the Humber and owns the ports of Hull, Grimsby, Immingham and Goole. Yachts can ⚓ inside Spurn Hd, except in strong SW/NW winds. Immingham should be used by yachts only in emergency. If unable to reach Hull on the tide, in S to W winds there is a good ⚓ off the SW bank 8ca above Killingholme Oil jetty, well out of main chan. In N'lies ⚓ off Hawkin's Pt, N of S9 buoy. The **marinas** at Grimsby, Hull, S Ferriby and the docks at Goole are all entered by lock, access HW±3. S Ferriby should not be attempted without up-to-date ABP charts which cover the ever-changing buoyed chan above Hull. Entry to Winteringham (HW±½) and Brough Havens (HW±1) should not be attempted without first contacting Humber Yawl Club for latest details of approach channel and mooring availability. Both havens dry to soft mud. Winteringham is prone to bad silting, but is dredged.

NAVIGATION
From N, WPT 53°34'·72N 00°16'·65E, S Binks SPM buoy, Fl Y 5s. From S, WPT 53°30'·40N 00°17'·04E, Rosse Spit PHM buoy, Fl (2) R 5s. Best arrival at LW. Sp tides are fierce: 4·4kn ebb off Spurn Head and Immingham.

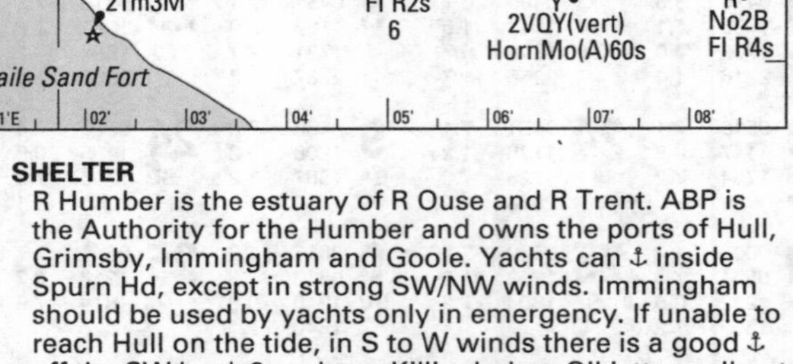

RIVER HUMBER *continued*

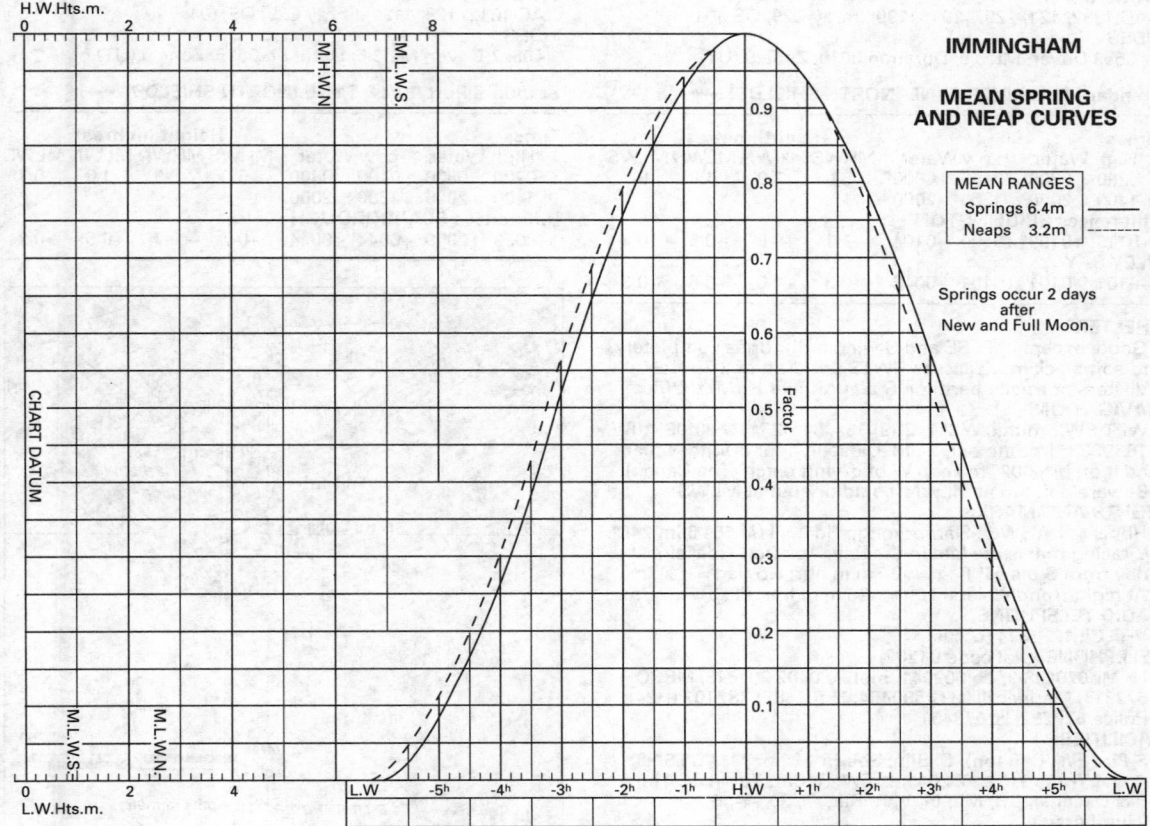

IMMINGHAM

MEAN SPRING AND NEAP CURVES

MEAN RANGES
Springs 6.4m
Neaps 3.2m

Springs occur 2 days after New and Full Moon.

H.W.Hts.m.

CHART DATUM

M.H.W.N
M.L.W.S.

M.L.W.S.
M.L.W.N.

Factor

L.W   -5h -4h -3h -2h -1h H.W +1h +2h +3h +4h +5h L.W

L.W.Hts.m.

From the S WPT, make Haile Sand No 2, then via No 2B, Tetney monobuoy and No 2C into Haile Chan.
From the N WPT, make Outer Binks No 1, passing N of Spurn Lt Float, SE Chequer and Chequer No 3 to make Binks 3A; then enter the estuary to the S of Spurn Hd for Bull Chan. There is a big ship ⚓ S of Spurn Hd. Keep clear of large commercial vessels using Hawke (8·4m) and Sunk (8·8m) Chans; these are marked by S1-S9 SHM buoys, all Fl G 1·5s (S8 is a SHM bn, Fl G 1·5s with tide gauge); and by P2-P9 PHM buoys, all Fl R 1·5s.
Off Kingston-upon-Hull there is a tidal eddy and streams can be rotatory, ie the flood makes W up Hull Roads for ¾hr whilst the ebb is already running down-river over Skitter Sand on the opposite bank (reaches 2½kn at sp). Humber bridge (conspic) has 30m clearance.

LIGHTS AND MARKS
The Humber is well buoyed/lit for its whole length. At Grimsby a conspic tr (94m) marks ent to Royal Dock. IPTS control entry to Grimsby (shown W of ent to Royal Dock), Immingham, Killingholme, Hull and Goole.

RADIO TELEPHONE
Monitor *VTS Humber* (☎ 01482-212191) Ch 14 if seaward of 00°01´·8E (Clee Ness lt float); and on Ch 12 if W of this meridian, up to Gainsborough (R Trent) and to Goole (R Ouse). Weather, nav & tidal information is broadcast on Ch 12/14 every odd H+03; more detailed info, inc height of tide, is available on request.
Other VHF stns: *Grimsby Docks Radio* Ch 74 (H24) 18 79. *Grimsby Marina* Ch 09 18. *Immingham Docks Radio* Ch 19 68 (H24). R Hull Port Ops Service call *Drypool Radio* Ch 22 (Mon-Fri HW–2 to HW+1; Sat 0900-1100 LT). *Hull Marina,* Ch M 80 (H24); *Albert Dock Radio* Ch 09. S Ferriby lock/marina Ch 74. Humber YC, Ch M (if racing). *Goole Docks Radio* Ch 14 (H24) 09 19. *Boothferry Bridge* Ch 09 (H24). Selby Railway and Toll Bridges Ch 09.

TELEPHONE (Dial codes: Grimsby 01472; Hull 01482)
Humber Hr Mr (01482) 327171 controls whole estuary/river. GRIMSBY Port Mgr 359181; ⌨ (01482) 782107 (H24); MRSC

(01262) 672317; Marinecall 0891 500454; Police 359171.
HULL Marina 613451 & lock 593455; MRSC (01262) 672317; ⌨ 782107; Marinecall 0891 500454; Police 26111; Dr contact Humber VTS 212191.

FACILITIES
GRIMSBY (01472; NE Lincs)
Grimsby Marina (150+25 Ⓥ) ☎ 360404, VHF Ch 09 18; D, P (cans), FW, ME, AC, Gas, Gaz, El, Sh, BH (30 ton), R, CH, Bar, (access HW±3 via Royal Dock and Union Dock, but fixed bridge clearance is only 4·45m; marina is just off the SW corner of chartlet).
The **Fish Docks** are entered by lock 300m E of conspic tr. Access is HW±3, with R/G tfc lts, but yachts should enter HW±2, "on the level", after being cleared in by *Fish Dock Island* Ch 74. Inside No 2 Fish Dock is:
Meridian Quay Marina,100 berths + 20 Ⓥ on pontoon along the W quay, £11 inc AC, D, ⛽, ♿. Call Humber Cruising Association ☎ (01472) 268424; usual facilities. Rtg 2-2-2
Grimsby and Cleethorpes YC ☎ 356678, Bar, R, M, FW, ▣.
Town EC Thurs; all facilities, ACA.
HULL (01482: City of Kingston-upon-Hull)
Hull Marina, lock ent 53°44´·28N 00°20´·10W, (310 + 20 Ⓥ), ☎ 613451, ⚓ 224148; £12.34 inc AC, access HW±3 via lock, (wait at pontoons in tidal basin, accessible HW±4½; or at Victoria Pier, 150m to the E). Marina office open 0900-1700 daily; VHF Ch 80 (H24); P, D, FW, AC, CH, Gas, ⌨, ♿, ⛽, ME, El, Sh, BH (50 ton), C (2 ton), ▣, SM, ACA.
SOUTH FERRIBY, N Lincs. Rtg 3-3-2.
Marina (100+20 visitors) ☎ (01652) 635620; access HW±3, £8 inc lock fee, D, P (cans), FW, ME, El, C (30 ton), CH, Gas, Gaz. **Village** V, Bar.
WINTERINGHAM HAVEN, N Lincs (belongs to Humber Yawl Club) ☎ (01724) 734452, ✉.
BROUGH HAVEN, E Riding of Yorkshire, **Humber Yawl Club** ☎ (01482) 667224, Slip, FW, Bar, limited AB; contact club.
NABURN (R Ouse, 4M S of York and 80M above Spurn Pt).
Naburn Marina (450+50 visitors) ☎ (01904) 621021; £6.00; VHF Ch 80 M; CH, P, D, FW, AC, Sh, ME, BH (16 ton), R.

BRIDLINGTON   8-5-12

E Riding of Yorkshire 54°04'·77N 00°11'·12W   Rtg 3-4-1

CHARTS
AC 1882, 121, 129, 1191, 1190; Imray C29; OS 101

TIDES
+0553 Dover; ML 3·6; Duration 0610; Zone 0 (UT)

Standard Port RIVER TYNE (NORTH SHIELDS) (⟶)

Times				Height (metres)			
High Water		Low Water		MHWS	MHWN	MLWN	MLWS
0200	0800	0100	0800	5·0	3·9	1·8	0·7
1400	2000	1300	2000				
Differences BRIDLINGTON							
+0119	+0109	+0109	+0104	+1·1	+0·8	+0·5	+0·4
FILEY BAY							
+0101	+0101	+0101	+0048	+0·8	+1·0	+0·6	+0·3

SHELTER
Good, except in E, SE and S winds. Hbr dries completely to soft black mud; access HW±3 (for draft of 2·7m). Visitors normally berth on S pier or near Hr Mr's Office.

NAVIGATION
WPT SW Smithic WCM, Q (9) 15s, 54°02'·41N 00°09'·10W, 153°/333° from/to ent, 2·6M. Close-in appr is with N pier hd lt on brg 002° to keep W of drying patch (The Canch). Beware bar, 1m at MLWN, could dry out at MLWS.

LIGHTS AND MARKS
Hbr is 4M WSW of Flamborough Hd lt, Fl (4) 15s 65m 24M. Y racing marks are laid in the Bay, Apr-Oct. Tidal sigs, by day from S pier: R flag = >2·7m in hbr; No flag = < 2·7m. At night from N pier: Fl Ⓡ = >2·7m in hbr; Fl Ⓖ = < 2·7m.

RADIO TELEPHONE
VHF Ch **12** 16 14 (occas).

TELEPHONE (Dial code 01262)
Hr Mr 670148/9, 🕿 602041, mobile 0402 201613; MRSC 672317; Marinecall 0891 500454; ⌗ (01482) 782107 (H24); Police 672222; Ⓗ 673451.

FACILITIES
S Pier FW, C (5 ton), C, Slip; See Hr Mr for M, AB £9.38; **Royal Yorks YC** 🕿 672041, L, FW, R, Bar. **Town** EC Thurs; P & D (cans), CH, ME, El, V, R, Bar, ✉, Ⓑ, ⇌, ✈ (Humberside).

ADJACENT ANCHORAGE

FILEY, N Yorkshire, 54°12'·80N 00°16'·10W, AC 1882, 129. HW +0532 on Dover; ML 3·5m; Duration 0605. See 8.5.12. Good ⚓ in winds from S to NNE in 4 – 5m on hard sand. Lt on cliff above CG Stn, G metal column, FR 31m 1M vis 272°-308°. The natural bkwtr, Filey Brigg marked by ECM buoy, Q(3)10s, Bell. Beware Horse Rk, N of Filey Brigg, foul ground extending ½M from shore. Facilities EC Wed; V, R, Bar, L, Ⓗ 🕿 (01723) 68111, ✉, Ⓑ, ⇌.

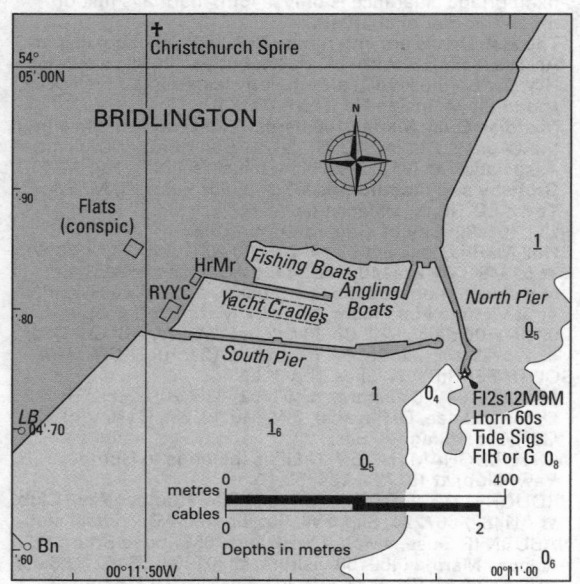

SCARBOROUGH   8-5-13

N. Yorkshire 54°16'·87N 00°23'·28W   Rtg 3-2-1

CHARTS
AC 1612, 129, 1191; Imray C29; OS 101

TIDES
+0527 Dover; ML 3·5; Duration 0615; Zone 0 (UT)

Standard Port RIVER TYNE (NORTH SHIELDS) (⟶)

Times				Height (metres)			
High Water		Low Water		MHWS	MHWN	MLWN	MLWS
0200	0800	0100	0800	5·0	3·9	1·8	0·7
1400	2000	1300	2000				
Differences SCARBOROUGH							
+0059	+0059	+0044	+0044	+0·7	+0·7	+0·5	+0·2

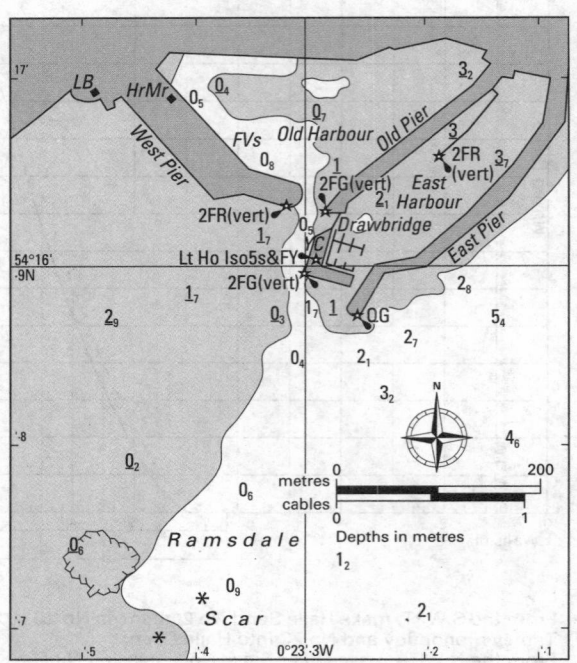

SHELTER
Good in E Hbr, access HW±3 via narrow (10m) ent by E pier, but not in strong E/SE'lies. 7 Ⓥ pontoon berths, (max LOA 10.3m, draft 1.8m), in the SW corner of E Hbr, just below lt ho. 4 Ⓥ drying AB on Old Pier just N of the drawbridge. The Old Hbr is strictly for FVs.

NAVIGATION
WPT 54°16'·50N 00°22'·00W, 122°/302° from/to E pier lt, 0.83M. Appr from the E to avoid Ramsdale Scar, rky shoal 0·9m. Keep careful watch for salmon nets E & SE of ent. Beware rks extending approx 20m SW of E pier head.

LIGHTS AND MARKS
Lt ho (conspic), Iso 5s, Dia 60s, on Old Pier. No ldg lts/marks. All lts, except QG on E Pier, indicate depths at ent to Old Hbr. Lt ho: Iso 5s or B ● = >3·7m; FY = 1·8 - 3·7m. Two sets 2 FG (vert) and, on W pier, 2FR (vert) = >1·8m. Note: E hbr ent has approx 1·5m less water.

RADIO TELEPHONE
Call *Scarborough lt ho* VHF Ch **12** 16 (H24). Watchkeeper will offer guidance to approaching visitors and help them to berth.

TELEPHONE (Dial code 01723)
Hr Mr (HO) 🕿 and 🕿 373530, 360684 (OT); CG 372323; MRSC (01262) 672317; ⌗ (01482) 782107 (H24); Marinecall 0891 500454; Police 500300; Ⓗ 368111.

FACILITIES
East Hbr AB £8.00, M (long waiting list), FW, AC, D, C (3 ton), Slip; **Scarborough YC** 🕿 373821, AB, Slip, M*, L, FW, ME, El, Ⓒ;
Services: ME, El, Sh, CH, P & D (cans), Ⓔ.
Town EC Wed; P, D, V, R, Bar, ✉, Ⓑ, ⇌, ✈ (Humberside).

WHITBY   8-5-14

N. Yorkshire 54°29'.64N 00°36'.68W   Rtg 3-2-1

CHARTS

AC 1612, 134, 129; Imray C29; OS 94

TIDES

+0500 Dover; ML 3·3; Duration 0605; Zone 0 (UT)

Standard Port RIVER TYNE (NORTH SHIELDS) (⟶)

Times				Height (metres)			
High Water		Low Water		MHWS	MHWN	MLWN	MLWS
0200	0800	0100	0800	5·0	3·9	1·8	0·7
1400	2000	1300	2000				
Differences WHITBY							
+0034	+0049	+0034	+0019	+0·6	+0·4	+0·1	+0·1

SHELTER

Good, except in lower hbr in strong NW to NE winds. Hbr is available from HW±4 for drafts of approx 2m. Marina (dredged approx 2m) is 2ca beyond swing bridge; visitor berths at seaward end of long pontoon. Bridge opens on request at ½ hr intervals HW±2; extra openings at weekends as arranged with WYC. FG lts = open; FR lts = shut.

NAVIGATION

WPT 54°30'.20N 00°36'.86W, 349°/169° from/to ent, 0·57M. Hbr can be approached safely from any direction except SE. In strong winds from NW through N to SE the sea breaks a long way out and ent is difficult. From the SE beware Whitby Rk; leave Whitby NCM buoy, Q, to port. Beware strong set to E from HW –2 to HW, when nearing piers. Vessels >37m LOA must embark pilot; via Hr Mr.

LIGHTS AND MARKS

Whitby High lt ho, Iso RW 10s 73m 18/16M, (R128°-143°, W143°-319°), is 2M ESE of hbr ent.

Ldg lines:
(1)   Chapel spire in line 176° with E pier disused lt ho.
(2)   FR lt or 2 bns, seen between disused lt houses, lead 169° into hbr. Continue on this line until bns (W △ and W ○ with B stripe) on E pier (two FY lts) are abeam.
(3)   On course 209° keep these same bns in line astern.

RADIO TELEPHONE

VHF Ch **11** 16 12 (H24). Whitby Bridge Ch **11** 16 06 (listens on Ch 16 HW–2 to HW+2).

TELEPHONE (Dial code 01947)

Hr Mr ☎ & 🛥 602354; MRSC (01262) 672317; ⌗ (01482) 782107 (H24); Marinecall 0891 500454/453; Police 603443; Dr 820888.

FACILITIES

Whitby Marina (200+10 visitors) ☎ 600165, £12.87, AC, D, FW, P (cans), Slip, ME, El, Sh, C, CH; **Fish Quay** M, D, L, FW, C (1 ton), CH, AB, R, Bar; **Whitby YC** ☎ 603623, M, L, Bar; **Services:** ME, El, Sh, CH, BH, ACA, SM, Gas, Gaz. **Town** EC Wed; usual amenities, ✉, Ⓑ, ⇌, ✈ (Teesside).

ADJACENT ANCHORAGE

RUNSWICK BAY, N. Yorkshire, 54°32'.10N 00°44'.10W. AC 1612. HW +0505 on Dover: Differences on R Tyne are approx as Whitby; ML 3·1m; Duration 0605. Good shelter in all winds from NW by W to SSE. Enter bay at 225° keeping clear of many rks at base of cliffs. Two W posts (2FY by night when required by lifeboat) 18m apart are ldg marks 270° to LB ho and can be used to lead into ⚓. Good holding in 6m to 9m in middle of bay. Facilities: **Runswick Bay Rescue Boat Station** ☎ (01947) 840965. **Village** Bar, R, V.

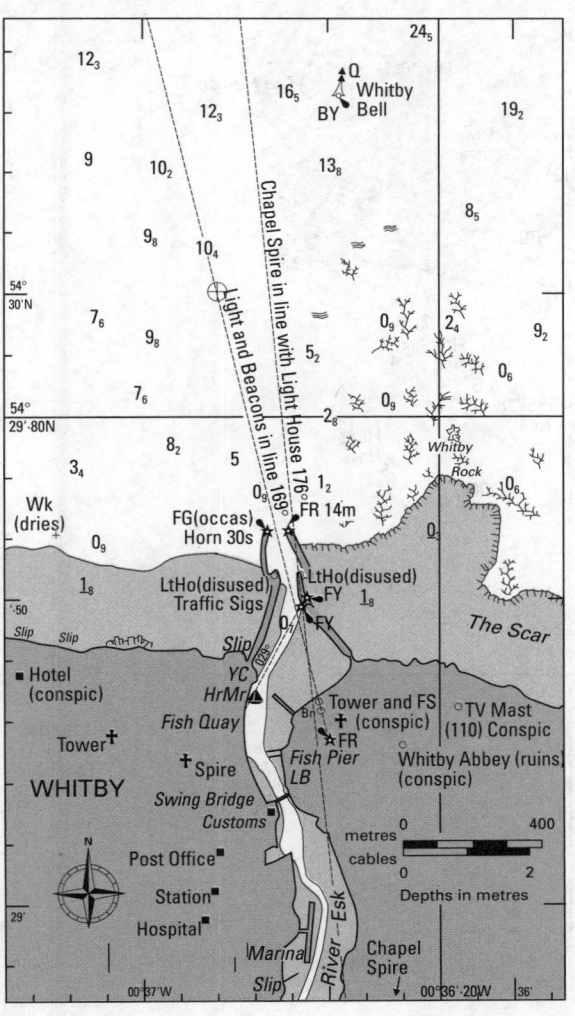

ADJACENT PORT (3M SSE OF HARTLEPOOL)

RIVER TEES/MIDDLESBROUGH, Middlesbrough/Stockton, 54°38'.93N 01°08'.38W. Rtg 4-5-3. AC 2566, 2567, 152; Imray C29; OS 93. HW +0450 Dover; Differences see 8.5.15. ML 3·1; Duration 0605. R. Tees & Middlesbrough are a major industrial area. 5M up-river from hbr ent a Tall Ships Centre is planned in the former Middlesbrough Dock.

Entry to River Tees is not recommended for small craft in heavy weather, especially in strong winds from NE to SE. Tees Fairway SWM buoy, Iso 4s 9m 8M, Horn 5s, Racon, is at 54°40'.93N 01°06'.38W, 030°/2·4M from S Gare bkwtr. The channel is well buoyed from the Fairway buoy to beyond Middlesbrough. Ldg lts 210°, both FR on framework trs. At Old CG stn a Q lt, or 3 Ⓡ (vert), = no entry without Hr Mr's consent. Call: *Tees Port Control* VHF Ch **14** 22 16 12 (H24). Monitor Ch 14; also info Ch 14 22. *Tees Barrage Radio* Ch M (37). Hr Mr ☎ (01642) 452541, 🛥 467855; Police 248184.

Tall Ships Centre (54°34'.74N 01°13'.29W) *provisional information:* ☎ (01642) 677123, 🛥 676123; Access HW±3 via lock; major BY dock facilities inc BH (570 ton), C (40 ton), ME, Sh, El, AB for yachts by prior arrangement. **South Gare Marine Club** ☎ 491039 (occas), M, FW, Slip; **Castlegate Marine Club** ☎ 583299 Slip, M, FW, ME, El, Sh, CH, V; **Tees Motor Boat Club** M; **Services:** El, ME, Ⓔ, ACA. **City** EC Wed; ✉, Ⓑ, ⇌, ✈. Hartlepool marina (8.5.15) lies 3M to the NNW with all yacht facilities.

5

HARTLEPOOL 8-5-15

Hartlepool 54°41'·30N 01°11'·49W (West Hbr ent) Rtg 3-1-2

CHARTS
AC 2566, 2567, 152; Imray C29; OS 93
TIDES
+0437 Dover; ML 3·0; Duration 0600; Zone 0 (UT)

Standard Port RIVER TYNE (NORTH SHIELDS) (→)

Times				Height (metres)			
High Water		Low Water		MHWS	MHWN	MLWN	MLWS
0200	0800	0100	0800	5·0	3·9	1·8	0·7
1400	2000	1300	2000				
Differences HARTLEPOOL							
+0015	+0015	+0008	+0008	+0·4	+0·3	0·0	+0·1
MIDDLESBROUGH							
+0019	+0021	+0014	+0011	+0·6	+0·6	+0·3	+0·1

SHELTER
Excellent in marina (5m), access HW±5 via chan dredged 0·8m and lock (ent 9m wide; pontoon on S side). Speed limit 4kn in W Hbr and marina. Strong E/SE winds raise broken water and swell in the bay, making ent channel hazardous, but possible. In such conditions, call VHF Ch M to shelter in the lock, awaiting tide. Or call *Tees Port Control* Ch 14 for short-stay in Victoria Hbr (commercial dock, not normally for yachts), access H24.

NAVIGATION
WPT Longs
01°09'·79W
Victoria Hb
From S, be
Note: Tees
01°06'·23W
assist the i
LIGHTS AND
The Heugh
6m 3M lead
W307°-309
12m 2M; br
Lock sigs:
Dir lt Iso W
buoyed cha
RADIO TELE
Marina Ch
Hartlepool
TELEPHONE
Marina 865
Tees & Ha
500453; # (

FACILITIES
Hartlepool Marina (262 + Ⓥ) ☎ 865744, 🛥 865947, £13.80, FW, AC, D, P (cans), BY, El, Sh, Ⓤ, Ⓙ, ⟨Ⓔ⟩, BH (40 tons), C (15 ton), Gas, Gaz; **Tees & Hartlepool YC** ☎ 233423, Bar, Slip; **Services:** CH, ME, EL, Sh, C (mobiles).
Town EC Wed; P (cans), V, R, Bar, ✉, Ⓑ, ⇌, ✈ (Teesside).

Chart of Hartlepool harbour showing: DirIsoWRG3s42m, Victoria Harbour, 2FG(vert), Kafiga Landings, 2FG(vert), HARTLEPOOL, 2FR(vert), QR, CH, C, BH, BY, Fuel, H, G, F, HrMr, DirFlWRG2s, West Harbour, Dredged to 0.8m, E, D, C, B, A, Hartlepool Marina, FR, FG, Slip, OcR5s, Tees & Hartlepool YC, OcG5s, South Pier, Middleton Strand, North Pier, Dir Lt 308°, Fl(4)G10s No5, G, QG, R, Fl(4)R10s No6, Dredged to 5.7m, The Heugh Fl(2)10s19m19M, Tower (conspic), Breakwater, Fl(4)G5s No3 G, Fl(4)R5s R No4, Fl G6s No1 G, Fl R6s No2 R, Dir Lt 325°, Q(3)10s Bell Longscar BYB, Long Scar. Scale: metres 0-1000, cables 0-5, Depths in metres.

SEAHAM   8-5-16

Durham 54°50'·23N 01°19'·17W Rtg 3-3-2

CHARTS
AC 1627, 152; Imray C29; OS 88

TIDES
+0435 Dover; ML 3·0; Duration 0600; Zone 0 (UT)

Standard Port RIVER TYNE (NORTH SHIELDS) (→)

Times				Height (metres)			
High Water		Low Water		MHWS	MHWN	MLWN	MLWS
0200	0800	0100	0800	5·0	3·9	1·8	0·7
1400	2000	1300	2000				
Differences SEAHAM							
+0004	+0004	−0001	−0001	+0·2	+0·2	+0·2	0·0

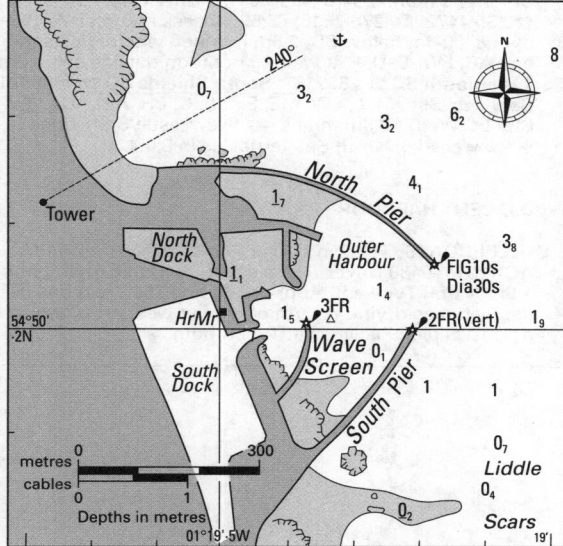

SHELTER
Small boats normally berth in N Dock where shelter is excellent, but it dries. Larger boats may lock into S Dock; gates open from HW −2 to HW+1. Speed limit 5kn. Or ⚓ 2½ca offshore with clock tr in transit 240° with St John's church tr.

NAVIGATION
WPT 54°50'·35N 01°18'·50W (off chartlet), 076°/256° from/to N bkwtr lt ho, 0·40M. Shoals and rks to S of S bkwtr (Liddle Scars). Ent should not be attempted in strong onshore winds.

LIGHTS AND MARKS
No ldg lts, but hbr is easily identified by lt ho (W with B bands) on N pier, Fl G 10s 12m 5M (often shows FG in bad weather), Dia 30s (sounded HW–2½ to +1½). FS at NE corner of S dock on with N lt ho leads in 256° clear of Tangle Rks. 3FR lts on wave screen are in form of a △.
Traffic sigs at S Dock:
® = Vessels enter
Ⓖ = Vessels leave

RADIO TELEPHONE
VHF Ch 12 16 06 (HW–2½ to HW+1½ between 0800-1800 LT Mon-Fri).

TELEPHONE (Dial code 0191)
Hr Mr 581 3246; Hbr Ops Office 581 3877; MRSC 257 2691; ℍ (0191) 257 9441; Marinecall 0891 500453; Police 581 2255; Dr 581 2332.

FACILITIES
S Dock (Seaham Hbr Dock Co) ☎ 5813877, 🛥 5130700, AB £4 but normally no charge for the odd night, L, FW, C (40 ton), AB; **N Dock** M.
Town (½M) EC Wed; P, D, FW, ME, El, CH (5M), V, R, Bar, ✉, Ⓑ, ≋, ✈ (Teesside or Newcastle).

SUNDERLAND   8-5-17

Tyne and Wear 54°55'·22N 01°21'·05W Rtg 1-3-2

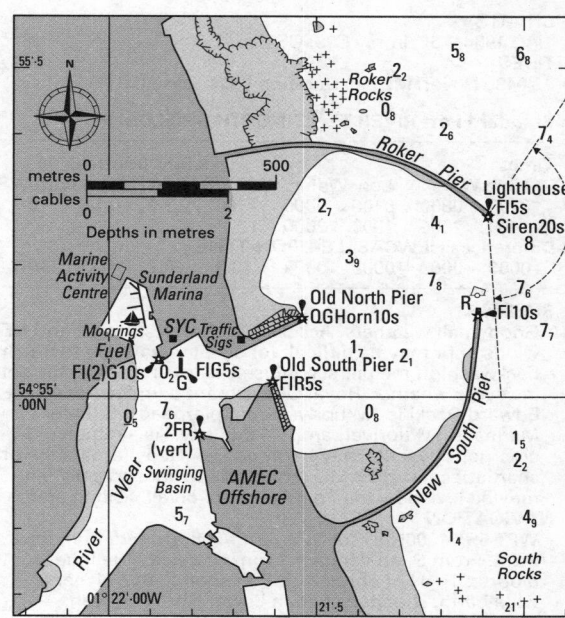

CHARTS
AC 1627, 152; Imray C29; OS 88

TIDES
+0430 Dover; ML 2·9; Duration 0600; Zone 0 (UT)

Standard Port RIVER TYNE (NORTH SHIELDS) (→)

Times				Height (metres)			
High Water		Low Water		MHWS	MHWN	MLWN	MLWS
0200	0800	0100	0800	5·0	3·9	1·8	0·7
1400	2000	1300	2000				
Differences SUNDERLAND							
+0002	−0002	−0002	−0002	+0·2	+0·3	+0·2	+0·1

SHELTER
Very good, but strong E'lies cause heavy swell in ent and outer hbr. There are 88 pontoon berths and 110 fore-and-aft ⚓s in Sunderland Marina (2·3m), protected by floating bkwtr; access H24. App to marina ent is marked by SHM dolphin, Fl G 5s, and E jetty, Fl (2) G 10s.

NAVIGATION
WPT 54°55'·20N 01°20'·00W, 098°/278° from/to Roker Pier lt, 0·61M. Beware wreck at Whitburn Steel about 1M N of ent, and Hendon Rk (0·9m), 1·2M SE of hbr ent.

LIGHTS AND MARKS
3 FL ® at Pilot Stn (Old N Pier) = danger in hbr; no ent/dep.

RADIO TELEPHONE
Sunderland Marina Ch M. Port VHF Ch 14 16 (H24); tide and visibility reports on request.

TELEPHONE (Dial code 0191)
Marina 514 4721; Hr Mr 514 0411 (HO), 567 2626 (OT); MRSC 257 2691; ℍ (0191) 257 9441; Marinecall 0891 500453; Police 5102020; ℍ 565 6256.

FACILITIES
Sunderland Marina (88 pontoon berths, max LOA 15m; and 110 moorings) ☎ 514 4721, 🛥 514 1847, AB £12.90, M £9, &, D, Slip, FW;
Sunderland YC ☎ 567 5133, FW, AB, Bar, Slip (dinghy);
Wear Boating Association ☎ 567 5313, AB.
Town EC Wed; P (cans), Gas, Gaz, CH, El, ME, SM, V, R, Bar, ✉, ▣, Ⓑ, ≋, ✈ (Newcastle).

5

R. TYNE/NORTH SHIELDS   8-5-18
Tyne and Wear 55°00'·78N 01°24'·00W   Rtg 2-2-2

CHARTS
AC 1934, 152; Imray C29; OS 88

TIDES
+0430 Dover; ML 3·0; Duration 0604; Zone 0 (UT)

Standard Port RIVER TYNE (NORTH SHIELDS) (→)

Times				Height (metres)			
High Water		Low Water		MHWS	MHWN	MLWN	MLWS
0200	0800	0100	0800	5·0	3·9	1·8	0·7
1400	2000	1300	2000				
Differences NEWCASTLE-UPON-TYNE							
+0003	+0003	+0008	+0008	+0·3	+0·2	+0·1	+0·1

SHELTER
Good in all weathers. Access H24, but in strong E and NE winds appr may be difficult for smaller craft due to much backwash off the piers; confused seas can build at the ent in severe weather. Royal Quays marina (in former Albert Edward Dock) is 2M upriver from pierheads. St Peter's Marina is 8M upriver, and 1M E of city. As a refuge or in emergency yachts may berth on Fish Quay (at W edge of chartlet); contact Hr Mr. A one-off £10 conservancy fee may be levied by the Port Authority on all visiting craft.

NAVIGATION
WPT 55°01'·00N 01°22'·22W, 078°/258° from/to front ldg lt, 2·2M. From S, no dangers. From N, beware Bellhues Rk (approx 1M N of hbr and ¾M off shore); give N pier a wide berth. Dredged chan in Lower Hbr is buoyed. The six bridges at Newcastle have least clearance 25m, or 4m when swing bridge closed.

LIGHTS AND MARKS
Ldg lts 258°, FW 25/39m 20M, two W trs (off chartlets); but disregard once inside pier heads. Castle conspic on cliff, N of ent.

RADIO TELEPHONE
Call: Tyne Hbr Radio VHF Ch 12 16 11 14 (H24). Royal Quays marina Ch 80. St Peter's Marina Ch 80 M.

TELEPHONE (Dial code 0191)
Hr Mr 257 2080, ☎ 258 3238; Port Ops 257 0407; MRSC 257 2691; ⌗ 257 9441; Marinecall 0891 500453; Met 2326453; Police 232 3451; Dr via Tyne Hbr Radio 257 2080; Ⓗ (Tynemouth) 259 6660; Ⓗ (Newcastle) 232 5131.

FACILITIES (from seaward)
Royal Quays marina 54°59'·78N 01°26'·74W. Phase I = 170 berths in 7·9m depth. S lock (42.5m x 8·0m) operates H24 on request, (N lock closed). Waiting pontoon outside lock. Call mobile ☎ 07771 864611 or Royal Quays marina VHF Ch 80 for latest info. BY, BH (30 ton).
St Peter's marina 54°57'·93N 01°35'·25W (140 + 20 Ⓥ) ☎ 265 4472, ☎ 276 2618; £8.52. Access approx HW±3½ over sill 0·8m below CD; 2·5m retained within; tfc lts at ent; AC, FW, ▣. D, P at waiting pontoon outside ent in 2m.
Tynemouth SC ☎ 2529157; **South Shields SC** ☎ 4565821;
Services: Slip, M, L, FW, ME, EI, Sh, C, CH, AB, ACA, Ⓔ.
City EC Wed; All amenities, ⇌ (Newcastle/S Shields), ✈ (Newcastle). North Sea ferries as in 8.0.4.

ADJACENT HARBOUR

CULLERCOATS, Tyne and Wear, 55°02'·07N 01°25'·71W. AC 1191. +0430 Dover. Tides as 8.5.18. Small drying hbr 1·6M N of R Tyne ent. Appr on ldg line 256°, two bns (FR lts), between drying rks. An occas fair weather ⚓ or dry against S pier. Facilities at Tynemouth.

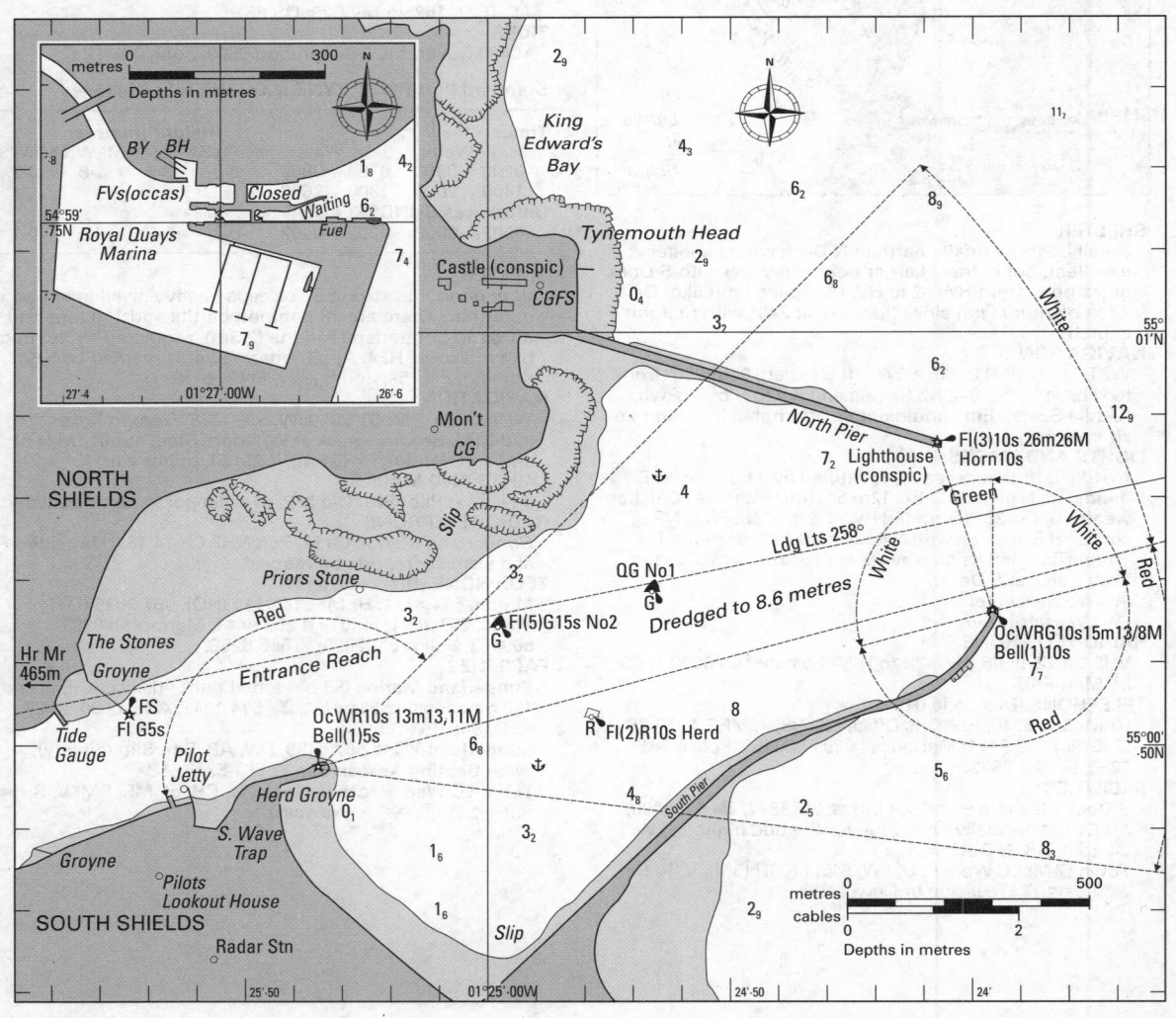

ENGLAND – NORTH SHIELDS

LAT 55°01′N   LONG 1°26′W

TIMES AND HEIGHTS OF HIGH AND LOW WATERS   YEAR 1999

TIME ZONE (UT)
For Summer Time add ONE hour in non-shaded areas

5

JANUARY

Day				
1 F	0211 5.1	0840 0.9	1439 5.1	2105 0.8
2 SA O	0303 5.2	0928 0.8	1525 5.3	2155 0.6
3 SU	0352 5.2	1013 0.9	1609 5.3	2242 0.6
4 M	0440 5.2	1056 1.0	1652 5.3	2327 0.6
5 TU	0526 5.1	1137 1.1	1735 5.2	
6 W	0010 0.7	0611 4.9	1216 1.3	1818 5.0
7 TH	0053 1.0	0656 4.6	1255 1.5	1903 4.8
8 F	0135 1.2	0743 4.4	1337 1.8	1951 4.5
9 SA	0221 1.5	0834 4.2	1427 2.0	2045 4.3
10 SU	0315 1.7	0931 4.0	1530 2.2	2148 4.1
11 M	0418 1.9	1035 4.0	1647 2.2	2258 4.1
12 TU	0527 1.9	1141 4.0	1803 2.1	
13 W	0006 4.1	0629 1.8	1249 4.2	1902 1.9
14 TH	0106 4.3	0721 1.7	1330 4.4	1951 1.7
15 F	0154 4.4	0806 1.5	1412 4.6	2032 1.5
16 SA	0235 4.6	0845 1.4	1449 4.8	2111 1.3
17 SU ●	0313 4.7	0922 1.2	1523 4.9	2147 1.1
18 M	0349 4.8	0958 1.1	1557 5.0	2224 0.9
19 TU	0426 4.9	1034 1.0	1632 5.1	2302 0.8
20 W	0504 4.9	1111 1.0	1709 5.1	2341 0.7
21 TH	0543 4.9	1150 1.1	1748 5.1	
22 F	0022 0.8	0626 4.8	1230 1.2	1831 5.0
23 SA	0105 0.9	0713 4.7	1315 1.3	1920 4.9
24 SU	0154 1.1	0806 4.5	1407 1.5	2016 4.7
25 M	0251 1.3	0908 4.4	1511 1.7	2122 4.6
26 TU	0400 1.4	1018 4.3	1629 1.7	2239 4.5
27 W	0519 1.5	1133 4.3	1752 1.7	2358 4.5
28 TH	0635 1.4	1241 4.5	1906 1.4	
29 F	0108 4.7	0738 1.3	1341 4.7	2007 1.1
30 SA	0208 4.9	0832 1.2	1431 5.0	2100 0.9
31 SU O	0259 5.0	0919 1.0	1516 5.1	2148 0.7

FEBRUARY

Day				
1 M	0345 5.1	1001 1.0	1557 5.2	2231 0.6
2 TU	0427 5.1	1039 1.0	1636 5.3	2310 0.6
3 W	0507 5.0	1115 1.0	1714 5.2	2347 0.7
4 TH	0545 4.9	1149 1.2	1752 5.0	
5 F	0022 0.9	0622 4.7	1222 1.3	1829 4.9
6 SA	0057 1.1	0701 4.5	1255 1.5	1909 4.6
7 SU	0133 1.4	0742 4.3	1334 1.8	1955 4.4
8 M	0216 1.6	0830 4.1	1423 2.0	2049 4.1
9 TU	0311 1.9	0927 3.9	1530 2.2	2154 4.0
10 W	0421 2.0	1036 3.9	1659 2.2	2312 3.9
11 TH	0540 2.1	1150 3.9	1822 2.1	
12 F	0027 4.0	0648 1.9	1254 4.1	1922 1.8
13 SA	0126 4.2	0740 1.7	1344 4.4	2009 1.5
14 SU	0212 4.5	0823 1.4	1424 4.7	2050 1.2
15 M	0252 4.7	0902 1.2	1501 4.9	2128 0.9
16 TU ●	0329 4.9	0940 1.0	1536 5.1	2207 0.6
17 W	0407 5.0	1018 0.8	1612 5.2	2245 0.5
18 TH	0445 5.1	1055 0.7	1650 5.3	2324 0.4
19 F	0524 5.1	1133 0.8	1730 5.3	
20 SA	0004 0.5	0605 5.0	1213 0.9	1813 5.2
21 SU	0046 0.6	0650 4.8	1256 1.0	1901 5.0
22 M	0132 0.7	0740 4.6	1345 1.3	1956 4.8
23 TU	0226 1.2	0839 4.4	1447 1.5	2103 4.5
24 W	0335 1.5	0951 4.2	1609 1.7	2225 4.3
25 TH	0501 1.7	1112 4.2	1742 1.6	2352 4.3
26 F	0626 1.7	1229 4.3	1901 1.4	
27 SA	0107 4.5	0732 1.5	1332 4.6	2002 1.1
28 SU	0205 4.7	0824 1.3	1422 4.8	2052 0.8

MARCH

Day				
1 M	0252 4.8	0907 1.1	1504 5.0	2135 0.7
2 TU	0332 4.9	0945 1.0	1542 5.1	2213 0.6
3 W	0409 5.0	1019 0.9	1617 5.2	2247 0.6
4 TH	0443 5.0	1051 0.9	1651 5.1	2319 0.6
5 F	0516 4.9	1121 1.0	1724 5.0	2349 0.8
6 SA	0549 4.7	1151 1.1	1759 4.9	
7 SU	0019 1.0	0622 4.6	1221 1.3	1834 4.7
8 M	0052 1.2	0658 4.4	1255 1.5	1915 4.4
9 TU	0128 1.5	0739 4.2	1337 1.7	2003 4.2
10 W	0215 1.8	0830 4.0	1433 2.0	2103 3.9
11 TH	0318 2.1	0934 3.8	1553 2.1	2219 3.8
12 F	0444 2.2	1052 3.8	1731 2.1	2343 3.8
13 SA	0610 2.0	1209 4.0	1847 1.8	
14 SU	0052 4.1	0710 1.7	1308 4.2	1939 1.4
15 M	0143 4.4	0757 1.4	1353 4.6	2023 1.1
16 TU	0226 4.7	0838 1.1	1433 4.9	2103 0.7
17 W ●	0305 4.9	0918 0.8	1511 5.1	2143 0.4
18 TH	0343 5.0	0957 0.6	1549 5.3	2224 0.2
19 F	0422 5.2	1036 0.5	1629 5.5	2304 0.2
20 SA	0502 5.2	1115 0.5	1711 5.4	2344 0.3
21 SU	0544 5.1	1156 0.6	1756 5.3	
22 M	0026 0.5	0628 4.9	1240 0.8	1846 5.1
23 TU	0112 0.9	0718 4.6	1331 1.1	1943 4.7
24 W	0206 1.3	0817 4.4	1435 1.3	2053 4.4
25 TH	0317 1.7	0929 4.1	1559 1.5	2217 4.2
26 F	0448 1.9	1054 4.1	1734 1.5	2345 4.2
27 SA	0615 1.8	1213 4.2	1851 1.3	
28 SU	0058 4.4	0724 1.6	1317 4.5	1949 1.0
29 M	0153 4.6	0809 1.3	1406 4.7	2035 0.8
30 TU	0236 4.7	0849 1.2	1446 4.9	2114 0.7
31 W O	0312 4.8	0923 1.0	1521 5.0	2147 0.6

APRIL

Day				
1 TH	0345 4.9	0955 0.9	1554 5.0	2218 0.6
2 F	0416 4.9	1026 0.9	1626 5.0	2248 0.7
3 SA	0447 4.9	1055 0.9	1658 4.9	2317 0.8
4 SU	0517 4.8	1124 1.0	1732 4.8	2346 1.0
5 M	0549 4.6	1154 1.1	1807 4.6	
6 TU	0017 1.2	0622 4.5	1228 1.3	1846 4.4
7 W	0052 1.4	0701 4.3	1308 1.5	1931 4.2
8 TH	0134 1.7	0747 4.1	1358 1.7	2027 3.9
9 F	0231 2.0	0846 3.9	1509 1.9	2138 3.8
10 SA	0352 2.1	0959 3.8	1638 1.9	2259 3.8
11 SU	0523 2.0	1119 3.9	1801 1.6	
12 M	0012 4.0	0632 1.7	1225 4.2	1901 1.3
13 TU	0109 4.4	0724 1.4	1317 4.5	1949 0.9
14 W	0155 4.7	0809 1.1	1401 4.9	2034 0.6
15 TH	0237 5.0	0851 0.8	1443 5.2	2117 0.3
16 F ●	0317 5.2	0933 0.5	1524 5.4	2159 0.1
17 SA	0358 5.3	1015 0.4	1608 5.5	2242 0.1
18 SU	0439 5.3	1057 0.4	1654 5.4	2325 0.3
19 M	0523 5.2	1142 0.4	1743 5.3	
20 TU	0009 0.6	0609 4.9	1230 0.6	1836 5.0
21 W	0057 1.0	0700 4.7	1323 0.9	1936 4.6
22 TH	0152 1.4	0759 4.4	1428 1.2	2045 4.3
23 F	0301 1.7	0909 4.2	1548 1.3	2205 4.1
24 SA	0428 1.9	1030 4.1	1714 1.3	2327 4.1
25 SU	0552 1.8	1148 4.2	1828 1.2	
26 M	0035 4.3	0655 1.6	1252 4.4	1924 1.1
27 TU	0129 4.4	0744 1.4	1341 4.5	2008 0.9
28 W	0210 4.6	0823 1.2	1421 4.7	2045 0.9
29 TH	0246 4.7	0857 1.1	1457 4.8	2117 0.8
30 F O	0318 4.8	0930 1.0	1530 4.8	2148 0.8

Chart Datum: 2·60 metres below Ordnance Datum (Newlyn)

ENGLAND – NORTH SHIELDS

LAT 55°01′N   LONG 1°26′W

TIMES AND HEIGHTS OF HIGH AND LOW WATERS

YEAR 1999

TIME ZONE (UT)
For Summer Time add ONE hour in non-shaded areas

MAY

Day	Time	m	Time	m	Time	m	Time	m
1 SA	0349	4.8	1001	0.9	1603	4.8	2218	0.8
16 SU	0335	5.2	0956	0.4	1550	5.4	2222	0.3
2 SU	0419	4.8	1032	0.9	1636	4.8	2248	0.9
17 M	0419	5.3	1043	0.3	1640	5.3	2308	0.4
3 M	0450	4.8	1103	1.0	1710	4.7	2318	1.0
18 TU	0504	5.2	1131	0.3	1732	5.2	2354	0.7
4 TU	0521	4.7	1134	1.0	1745	4.5	2350	1.2
19 W	0552	5.0	1222	0.5	1827	4.9		
5 W	0555	4.5	1209	1.2	1824	4.4		
20 TH	0042	1.0	0643	4.8	1316	0.7	1926	4.6
6 TH	0025	1.4	0632	4.4	1249	1.3	1908	4.2
21 F	0136	1.4	0741	4.5	1417	1.0	2030	4.3
7 F	0106	1.6	0717	4.2	1338	1.5	2001	4.0
22 SA	0239	1.7	0845	4.3	1525	1.2	2140	4.1
8 SA	0159	1.8	0812	4.1	1440	1.6	2105	3.9
23 SU	0353	1.9	0958	4.2	1640	1.3	2252	4.1
9 SU	0310	2.0	0918	4.0	1555	1.6	2218	3.9
24 M	0511	1.9	1110	4.2	1750	1.3	2358	4.1
10 M	0433	1.9	1031	4.0	1713	1.4	2330	4.1
25 TU	0617	1.7	1215	4.2	1847	1.2		
11 TU	0547	1.7	1140	4.2	1819	1.2		
26 W	0053	4.3	0709	1.6	1308	4.4	1932	1.2
12 W	0030	4.4	0646	1.4	1238	4.5	1913	0.8
27 TH	0138	4.4	0759	1.4	1352	4.5	2011	1.1
13 TH	0122	4.7	0736	1.1	1329	4.9	2003	0.5
28 F	0216	4.6	0829	1.2	1430	4.6	2045	1.0
14 F	0208	4.9	0823	0.8	1416	5.1	2050	0.3
29 SA	0250	4.7	0904	1.1	1506	4.7	2119	1.0
15 SA ●	0252	5.1	0910	0.5	1502	5.3	2136	0.2
30 SU O	0323	4.8	0938	1.0	1541	4.7	2152	0.9
31 M	0355	4.8	1012	1.0	1616	4.7	2224	1.0

JUNE

Day	Time	m	Time	m	Time	m	Time	m
1 TU	0427	4.8	1045	0.9	1651	4.6	2256	1.1
16 W	0449	5.2	1122	0.3	1722	5.1	2340	0.8
2 W	0459	4.7	1119	1.0	1728	4.5	2330	1.2
17 TH	0537	5.1	1212	0.4	1815	4.9		
3 TH	0534	4.6	1155	1.0	1807	4.4		
18 F	0026	1.1	0626	4.9	1303	0.6	1908	4.6
4 F	0006	1.3	0611	4.5	1236	1.1	1849	4.3
19 SA	0115	1.3	0718	4.7	1355	0.9	2004	4.4
5 SA	0048	1.5	0655	4.4	1322	1.2	1938	4.2
20 SU	0207	1.6	0814	4.5	1451	1.1	2103	4.2
6 SU	0137	1.6	0745	4.3	1417	1.3	2036	4.1
21 M	0306	1.8	0916	4.3	1552	1.3	2206	4.1
7 M	0237	1.7	0844	4.2	1520	1.3	2141	4.1
22 TU	0414	1.9	1022	4.2	1656	1.5	2309	4.0
8 TU	0348	1.8	0950	4.2	1630	1.3	2249	4.2
23 W	0525	1.9	1128	4.1	1758	1.5		
9 W	0501	1.6	1058	4.4	1738	1.1	2353	4.4
24 TH	0008	4.1	0626	1.8	1229	4.2	1851	1.4
10 TH	0607	1.4	1202	4.6	1840	0.9		
25 F	0100	4.3	0718	1.6	1320	4.3	1936	1.4
11 F	0050	4.6	0705	1.2	1301	4.8	1936	0.7
26 SA	0145	4.4	0802	1.5	1405	4.4	2016	1.3
12 SA	0142	4.9	0759	0.9	1355	5.0	2028	0.5
27 SU	0224	4.6	0841	1.3	1445	4.5	2054	1.2
13 SU ●	0230	5.1	0851	0.6	1447	5.2	2118	0.5
28 M O	0259	4.7	0918	1.1	1531	4.6	2130	1.1
14 M	0316	5.2	0942	0.4	1538	5.3	2206	0.5
29 TU	0333	4.8	0954	1.0	1559	4.7	2204	1.1
15 TU	0402	5.2	1032	0.3	1630	5.2	2253	0.6
30 W	0406	4.8	1029	0.9	1634	4.7	2239	1.1

JULY

Day	Time	m	Time	m	Time	m	Time	m
1 TH	0440	4.8	1105	0.9	1711	4.7	2314	1.1
16 F	0519	5.2	1156	0.4	1756	4.9		
2 F	0515	4.8	1142	0.9	1749	4.6	2351	1.2
17 SA	0004	1.0	0603	5.1	1240	0.6	1842	4.7
3 SA	0553	4.8	1222	0.9	1830	4.5		
18 SU	0045	1.2	0649	4.9	1323	0.8	1929	4.5
4 SU	0031	1.3	0634	4.7	1305	1.0	1915	4.4
19 M	0127	1.5	0737	4.6	1408	1.1	2018	4.3
5 M	0116	1.4	0721	4.6	1353	1.1	2007	4.3
20 TU	0214	1.7	0829	4.4	1457	1.4	2111	4.1
6 TU	0208	1.5	0814	4.5	1449	1.2	2106	4.3
21 W	0310	1.9	0928	4.2	1554	1.6	2211	4.0
7 W	0309	1.6	0916	4.5	1553	1.2	2212	4.3
22 TH	0420	2.0	1034	4.1	1700	1.8	2316	4.0
8 TH	0420	1.6	1024	4.5	1703	1.2	2320	4.4
23 F	0537	2.0	1144	4.0	1806	1.8		
9 F	0533	1.5	1134	4.6	1812	1.1		
24 SA	0018	4.1	0642	1.9	1248	4.1	1902	1.7
10 SA	0024	4.5	0641	1.3	1242	4.7	1915	1.0
25 SU	0112	4.3	0735	1.6	1340	4.3	1950	1.5
11 SU	0122	4.7	0743	1.0	1343	4.9	2013	0.8
26 M	0157	4.5	0820	1.4	1424	4.5	2031	1.4
12 M	0214	4.9	0840	0.7	1439	5.1	2105	0.8
27 TU	0236	4.6	0859	1.2	1503	4.6	2109	1.2
13 TU ●	0302	5.1	0933	0.5	1531	5.2	2153	0.7
28 W O	0312	4.8	0936	1.0	1540	4.7	2146	1.1
14 W	0348	5.2	1023	0.4	1621	5.2	2239	0.7
29 TH	0346	4.9	1012	0.8	1615	4.8	2221	1.0
15 TH	0434	5.3	1110	0.3	1709	5.1	2323	0.9
30 F	0420	4.9	1049	0.7	1651	4.9	2257	1.0
31 SA	0455	5.0	1126	0.7	1729	4.8	2334	1.0

AUGUST

Day	Time	m	Time	m	Time	m	Time	m
1 SU	0532	5.0	1204	0.7	1808	4.8		
16 M	0012	1.2	0616	5.0	1246	0.9	1849	4.6
2 M	0012	1.1	0612	5.0	1245	0.8	1851	4.7
17 TU	0047	1.4	0657	4.7	1322	1.2	1930	4.4
3 TU	0054	1.2	0656	4.9	1329	0.9	1939	4.5
18 W	0125	1.6	0742	4.5	1403	1.5	2016	4.2
4 W	0141	1.4	0747	4.7	1419	1.1	2034	4.4
19 TH	0213	1.9	0835	4.2	1454	1.8	2111	4.0
5 TH	0237	1.5	0847	4.6	1521	1.3	2139	4.3
20 F	0316	2.1	0939	4.0	1559	2.0	2217	3.9
6 F	0348	1.6	0958	4.5	1635	1.4	2252	4.3
21 SA	0440	2.0	1055	3.9	1718	2.0	2330	4.0
7 SA	0510	1.6	1117	4.5	1754	1.4		
22 SU	0605	2.0	1212	4.0	1830	1.9		
8 SU	0004	4.4	0629	1.4	1234	4.6	1904	1.3
23 M	0037	4.2	0708	1.8	1315	4.2	1924	1.7
9 M	0109	4.6	0736	1.1	1339	4.8	2004	1.2
24 TU	0129	4.4	0756	1.5	1401	4.4	2009	1.5
10 TU	0203	4.9	0834	0.8	1435	5.0	2055	1.0
25 W	0210	4.6	0837	1.2	1441	4.6	2048	1.3
11 W ●	0251	5.1	0924	0.6	1523	5.1	2140	0.9
26 TH O	0247	4.9	0914	0.9	1517	4.8	2124	1.1
12 TH	0335	5.2	1010	0.4	1608	5.1	2222	0.9
27 F	0321	5.0	0950	0.7	1552	4.9	2200	0.9
13 F	0416	5.3	1053	0.4	1650	5.1	2301	0.9
28 SA	0355	5.2	1027	0.5	1628	5.0	2237	0.8
14 SA	0457	5.3	1132	0.4	1730	5.0	2337	1.0
29 SU	0431	5.3	1104	0.5	1705	5.1	2313	0.8
15 SU	0536	5.1	1209	0.6	1810	4.8		
30 M	0508	5.3	1142	0.5	1744	5.0	2351	0.9
31 TU	0549	5.2	1221	0.6	1825	4.9		

Chart Datum: 2·60 metres below Ordnance Datum (Newlyn)

ENGLAND – NORTH SHIELDS

LAT 55°01′N   LONG 1°26′W

TIMES AND HEIGHTS OF HIGH AND LOW WATERS   YEAR 1999

TIME ZONE (UT)
For Summer Time add ONE hour in non-shaded areas

5

SEPTEMBER

	Time	m		Time	m
1 W	0031 / 0634 / 1304 / 1912	1.0 / 5.1 / 0.9 / 4.7	**16** TH	0046 / 0702 / 1315 / 1927	1.5 / 4.5 / 1.5 / 4.3
2 TH	0118 / 0726 / 1353 / 2006	1.2 / 4.9 / 1.2 / 4.5	**17** F	0128 / 0752 / 1400 / 2017	1.8 / 4.2 / 1.8 / 4.1
3 F	0214 / 0828 / 1456 / 2113	1.5 / 4.6 / 1.5 / 4.3	**18** SA	0224 / 0852 / 1502 / 2120	2.0 / 4.0 / 2.1 / 3.9
4 SA	0329 / 0944 / 1617 / 2232	1.6 / 4.4 / 1.7 / 4.2	**19** SU	0343 / 1008 / 1626 / 2236	2.2 / 3.8 / 2.2 / 3.9
5 SU	0500 / 1112 / 1746 / 2351	1.6 / 4.3 / 1.7 / 4.4	**20** M	0520 / 1132 / 1753 / 2354	2.1 / 3.9 / 2.2 / 4.1
6 M	0625 / 1233 / 1859	1.4 / 4.5 / 1.6	**21** TU	0635 / 1242 / 1855	1.8 / 4.1 / 1.9
7 TU	0059 / 0732 / 1337 / 1956	4.6 / 1.1 / 4.7 / 1.3	**22** W	0053 / 0810 / 1332 / 1941	4.3 / 1.2 / 4.4 / 1.6
8 W	0154 / 0825 / 1428 / 2043	4.9 / 0.8 / 4.9 / 1.2	**23** TH	0138 / 0852 / 1412 / 2021	4.6 / 1.0 / 4.7 / 1.3
9 TH ●	0239 / 0911 / 1511 / 2123	5.1 / 0.6 / 5.1 / 1.0	**24** F	0217 / 0846 / 1449 / 2058	4.9 / 0.9 / 4.9 / 1.1
10 F	0318 / 0952 / 1549 / 2200	5.2 / 0.5 / 5.1 / 0.9	**25** SA O	0252 / 0923 / 1525 / 2136	5.1 / 0.6 / 5.1 / 0.8
11 SA	0355 / 1029 / 1625 / 2235	5.3 / 0.5 / 5.1 / 0.9	**26** SU	0328 / 1001 / 1601 / 2213	5.3 / 0.4 / 5.3 / 0.7
12 SU	0432 / 1103 / 1700 / 2307	5.3 / 0.6 / 5.0 / 1.0	**27** M	0405 / 1039 / 1639 / 2251	5.5 / 0.3 / 5.3 / 0.7
13 M	0507 / 1135 / 1734 / 2339	5.2 / 0.7 / 4.9 / 1.1	**28** TU	0445 / 1118 / 1718 / 2331	5.5 / 0.4 / 5.2 / 0.7
14 TU	0543 / 1206 / 1809	5.0 / 1.0 / 4.7	**29** W	0528 / 1158 / 1801	5.4 / 0.6 / 5.0
15 W	0011 / 0621 / 1239 / 1845	1.3 / 4.8 / 1.2 / 4.5	**30** TH	0013 / 0636 / 1242 / 1848	0.9 / 5.2 / 0.9 / 4.8

OCTOBER

	Time	m		Time	m
1 F	0102 / 0711 / 1333 / 1943	1.1 / 4.9 / 1.3 / 4.6	**16** SA	0055 / 0718 / 1317 / 1933	1.7 / 4.3 / 1.9 / 4.2
2 SA	0202 / 0817 / 1438 / 2052	1.4 / 4.5 / 1.7 / 4.3	**17** SU	0146 / 0814 / 1413 / 2031	1.9 / 4.0 / 2.1 / 4.0
3 SU	0321 / 0939 / 1605 / 2215	1.6 / 4.3 / 1.9 / 4.2	**18** M	0255 / 0924 / 1532 / 2143	2.1 / 3.9 / 2.3 / 3.9
4 M	0455 / 1109 / 1737 / 2338	1.6 / 4.3 / 1.9 / 4.4	**19** TU	0425 / 1045 / 1705 / 2302	2.1 / 3.9 / 2.3 / 4.0
5 TU	0618 / 1227 / 1848	1.4 / 4.5 / 1.7	**20** W	0548 / 1159 / 1816	1.8 / 4.1 / 2.0
6 W	0045 / 0720 / 1327 / 1942	4.6 / 1.1 / 4.7 / 1.5	**21** TH	0008 / 0646 / 1254 / 1906	4.3 / 1.5 / 4.4 / 1.7
7 TH	0139 / 0810 / 1413 / 2025	4.9 / 0.9 / 4.9 / 1.3	**22** F	0059 / 0732 / 1338 / 1949	4.6 / 1.2 / 4.7 / 1.4
8 F	0222 / 0852 / 1451 / 2102	5.0 / 0.7 / 5.0 / 1.1	**23** SA	0142 / 0813 / 1418 / 2029	4.9 / 0.8 / 4.9 / 1.1
9 SA ●	0259 / 0928 / 1526 / 2136	5.2 / 0.6 / 5.1 / 1.0	**24** SU O	0221 / 0854 / 1456 / 2109	5.2 / 0.6 / 5.2 / 0.8
10 SU	0333 / 1000 / 1558 / 2209	5.2 / 0.6 / 5.1 / 1.0	**25** M	0301 / 0934 / 1534 / 2149	5.4 / 0.4 / 5.4 / 0.7
11 M	0407 / 1031 / 1630 / 2240	5.2 / 0.7 / 5.0 / 1.0	**26** TU	0342 / 1015 / 1613 / 2231	5.5 / 0.3 / 5.3 / 0.6
12 TU	0441 / 1102 / 1702 / 2311	5.1 / 0.9 / 4.9 / 1.1	**27** W	0425 / 1056 / 1655 / 2314	5.5 / 0.5 / 5.3 / 0.6
13 W	0515 / 1131 / 1734 / 2342	4.9 / 1.1 / 4.8 / 1.3	**28** TH	0512 / 1139 / 1740	5.4 / 0.7 / 5.1
14 TH	0552 / 1202 / 1808	4.7 / 1.3 / 4.6	**29** F	0000 / 0604 / 1226 / 1828	0.8 / 5.2 / 1.0 / 4.9
15 F	0015 / 0631 / 1236 / 1846	1.4 / 4.5 / 1.6 / 4.4	**30** SA	0053 / 0702 / 1319 / 1925	1.0 / 4.8 / 1.4 / 4.6
			31 SU	0156 / 0810 / 1425 / 2034	1.2 / 4.5 / 1.8 / 4.4

NOVEMBER

	Time	m		Time	m
1 M	0312 / 0930 / 1549 / 2154	1.4 / 4.3 / 2.0 / 4.3	**16** TU	0219 / 0844 / 1443 / 2054	1.8 / 4.0 / 2.2 / 4.1
2 TU	0439 / 1053 / 1716 / 2315	1.5 / 4.3 / 2.0 / 4.4	**17** W	0332 / 0956 / 1606 / 2207	1.9 / 4.0 / 2.2 / 4.1
3 W	0557 / 1206 / 1826	1.3 / 4.4 / 1.8	**18** TH	0450 / 1108 / 1723 / 2316	1.8 / 4.1 / 2.0 / 4.3
4 TH	0023 / 0658 / 1304 / 1919	4.6 / 1.2 / 4.6 / 1.6	**19** F	0557 / 1209 / 1824	1.5 / 4.4 / 1.8
5 F	0117 / 0746 / 1349 / 2002	4.8 / 1.0 / 4.8 / 1.4	**20** SA	0015 / 0651 / 1301 / 1913	4.6 / 1.2 / 4.7 / 1.4
6 SA	0200 / 0826 / 1427 / 2039	4.9 / 0.9 / 4.9 / 1.2	**21** SU	0106 / 0739 / 1346 / 1959	4.9 / 0.9 / 5.0 / 1.1
7 SU	0237 / 0900 / 1500 / 2112	5.0 / 0.9 / 5.0 / 1.1	**22** M	0152 / 0825 / 1428 / 2044	5.2 / 0.7 / 5.2 / 0.9
8 M ●	0312 / 0931 / 1532 / 2145	5.0 / 0.9 / 5.0 / 1.1	**23** TU O	0237 / 0910 / 1510 / 2129	5.4 / 0.5 / 5.3 / 0.7
9 TU	0345 / 1002 / 1603 / 2217	5.0 / 0.9 / 5.0 / 1.1	**24** W	0323 / 0954 / 1552 / 2215	5.5 / 0.5 / 5.3 / 0.6
10 W	0419 / 1033 / 1634 / 2248	4.9 / 1.0 / 5.0 / 1.1	**25** TH	0411 / 1039 / 1636 / 2303	5.5 / 0.6 / 5.4 / 0.5
11 TH	0454 / 1103 / 1706 / 2320	4.9 / 1.2 / 4.9 / 1.2	**26** F	0502 / 1125 / 1723 / 2353	5.4 / 0.8 / 5.2 / 0.6
12 F	0530 / 1134 / 1739 / 2354	4.7 / 1.4 / 4.7 / 1.4	**27** SA	0556 / 1213 / 1814	5.2 / 1.1 / 5.0
13 SA	0609 / 1207 / 1816	4.5 / 1.6 / 4.6	**28** SU	0047 / 0654 / 1306 / 1909	0.8 / 4.9 / 1.5 / 4.8
14 SU	0033 / 0652 / 1247 / 1858	1.5 / 4.3 / 1.8 / 4.4	**29** M	0147 / 0758 / 1407 / 2012	1.1 / 4.6 / 1.8 / 4.6
15 M	0120 / 0743 / 1336 / 1951	1.7 / 4.1 / 2.0 / 4.2	**30** TU	0254 / 0908 / 1518 / 2124	1.3 / 4.4 / 2.0 / 4.4

DECEMBER

	Time	m		Time	m
1 W	0408 / 1021 / 1637 / 2240	1.4 / 4.3 / 2.0 / 4.4	**16** TH	0248 / 0909 / 1510 / 2116	1.6 / 4.1 / 2.0 / 4.3
2 TH	0522 / 1131 / 1750 / 2349	1.4 / 4.3 / 1.9 / 4.4	**17** F	0356 / 1016 / 1624 / 2224	1.6 / 4.2 / 2.0 / 4.4
3 F	0625 / 1230 / 1848	1.4 / 4.4 / 1.8	**18** SA	0506 / 1123 / 1735 / 2331	1.5 / 4.3 / 1.8 / 4.5
4 SA	0046 / 0715 / 1319 / 1935	4.6 / 1.3 / 4.6 / 1.6	**19** SU	0610 / 1223 / 1837	1.3 / 4.6 / 1.6
5 SU	0134 / 0756 / 1400 / 2015	4.7 / 1.3 / 4.7 / 1.4	**20** M	0032 / 0708 / 1316 / 1932	4.8 / 1.1 / 4.8 / 1.3
6 M	0215 / 0832 / 1436 / 2051	4.8 / 1.2 / 4.8 / 1.3	**21** TU	0128 / 0801 / 1405 / 2024	4.9 / 0.9 / 5.1 / 1.0
7 TU	0253 / 0905 / 1509 / 2126	4.8 / 1.2 / 4.9 / 1.2	**22** W O	0220 / 0851 / 1451 / 2115	5.2 / 0.7 / 5.2 / 0.7
8 W	0328 / 0938 / 1541 / 2159	4.9 / 1.1 / 5.0 / 1.2	**23** TH	0312 / 0940 / 1537 / 2206	5.4 / 0.5 / 5.4 / 0.5
9 TH	0403 / 1010 / 1613 / 2232	4.9 / 1.2 / 4.9 / 1.2	**24** F	0403 / 1027 / 1623 / 2256	5.4 / 0.7 / 5.4 / 0.4
10 F	0438 / 1042 / 1645 / 2305	4.8 / 1.3 / 4.9 / 1.2	**25** SA	0455 / 1114 / 1710 / 2346	5.3 / 0.9 / 5.3 / 0.5
11 SA	0513 / 1114 / 1718 / 2339	4.7 / 1.4 / 4.8 / 1.2	**26** SU	0547 / 1201 / 1759	5.2 / 1.1 / 5.2
12 SU	0550 / 1148 / 1753	4.6 / 1.5 / 4.7	**27** M	0037 / 0640 / 1249 / 1850	0.6 / 4.9 / 1.3 / 5.0
13 M	0017 / 0630 / 1225 / 1832	1.3 / 4.4 / 1.7 / 4.6	**28** TU	0129 / 0736 / 1339 / 1945	0.9 / 4.6 / 1.6 / 4.8
14 TU	0100 / 0715 / 1309 / 1919	1.4 / 4.3 / 1.8 / 4.4	**29** W	0224 / 0834 / 1435 / 2046	1.1 / 4.4 / 1.8 / 4.5
15 W	0149 / 0807 / 1403 / 2013	1.6 / 4.2 / 2.0 / 4.3	**30** TH	0324 / 0937 / 1542 / 2153	1.4 / 4.2 / 2.0 / 4.4
			31 F	0430 / 1042 / 1656 / 2303	1.6 / 4.1 / 2.1 / 4.3

Chart Datum: 2·60 metres below Ordnance Datum (Newlyn)

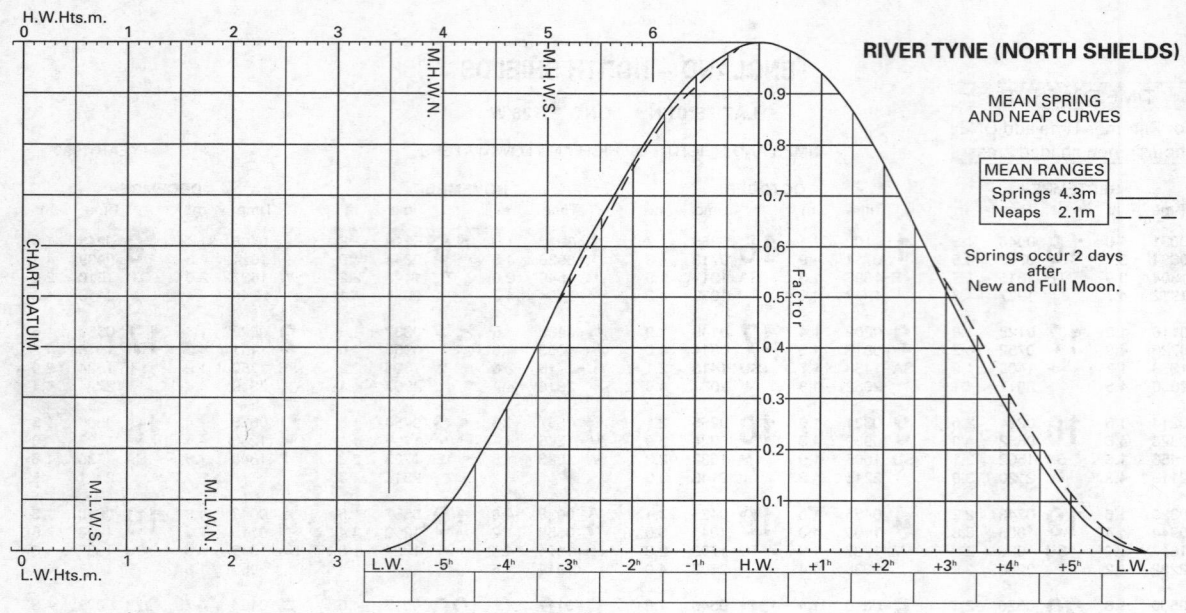

H.W. Hts. m.

RIVER TYNE (NORTH SHIELDS)

MEAN SPRING
AND NEAP CURVES

MEAN RANGES	
Springs	4.3m
Neaps	2.1m

Springs occur 2 days
after
New and Full Moon.

CHART DATUM

Factor

M.H.W.N.   M.H.W.S.

M.L.W.S.   M.L.W.N.

L.W. -5ʰ -4ʰ -3ʰ -2ʰ -1ʰ H.W. +1ʰ +2ʰ +3ʰ +4ʰ +5ʰ L.W.

L.W. Hts. m.

BLYTH   8-5-19

Northumberland 55°06′·98N 01° 29′·17W   Rtg 2-4-2

CHARTS
AC 1626, 152, 156; Imray C29; OS 81, 88

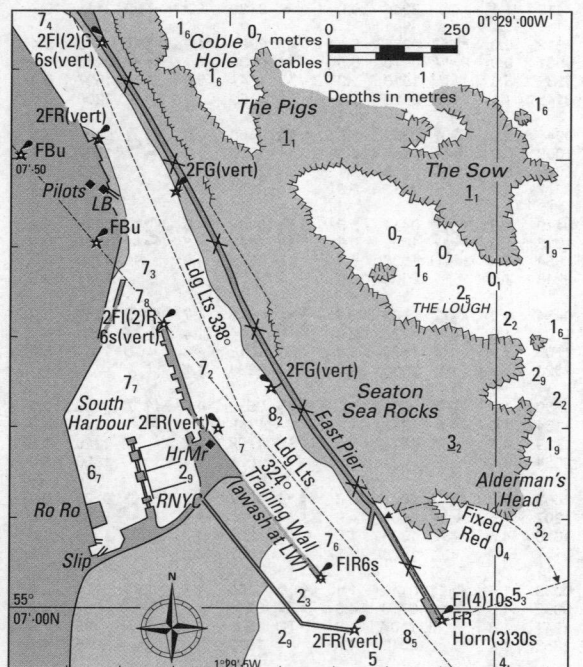

TIDES
+0430 Dover; ML 2·8; Duration 0558; Zone 0 (UT)

Standard Port RIVER TYNE (NORTH SHIELDS) (←)

Times				Height (metres)			
High Water		Low Water		MHWS	MHWN	MLWN	MLWS
0200	0800	0100	0800	5·0	3·9	1·8	0·7
1400	2000	1300	2000				
Differences BLYTH							
+0005	−0007	−0001	+0009	0·0	0·0	−0·1	+0·1

SHELTER
Very good; access H24. Yachts go to SE part of South Hbr; visitors may find berth on RNYC pontoons on E side of Middle Jetty (4·4m least depth) or pick up RNYC mooring.

NAVIGATION
WPT Fairway SHM buoy, Fl G 3s, Bell, 55°06′·58N 01°28′·50W, 140°/320° from/to E pier lt, 0·53M. From N, beware The Pigs, The Sow and Seaton Sea Rks. No dangers from S. At LW in strong SE winds, seas break across ent.

LIGHTS AND MARKS
7 wind turbines (X on chartlet) are conspic on the E pier, plus 2 just off N edge of chartlet. Outer ldg lts 324°, F Bu 11/17m 10M, Or ◊ on framework trs. Inner ldg lts 338°, F Bu 5/11m 10M, front W 6-sided tr; rear W △ on mast. The following SPM unlit spar buoys are laid Apr-Oct:
Meggies   55°06′·61N 01°29′·29W; and
Sow and Pigs 55°07′·50N 01°28′·50W.

RADIO TELEPHONE
Call: Blyth Hbr Control VHF Ch 12 11 16 (H24).

TELEPHONE (Dial code 01670)
Hr Mr 352678; MRSC (0191) 257 2691; ⌗ (0191) 257 9441; Marinecall 0891 500453; Police (01661) 872555; Dr 363334.

FACILITIES
R Northumberland YC ☎ 353636, (50) AB £10, M, FW, C (1½ ton), Bar; South Hbr ☎ 352678, FW, C (30 ton), Slip. Town EC Wed; P & D (cans), V, R, Bar, ✉, Ⓑ, bus to Newcastle ⇌ ✈.

ADJACENT ANCHORAGE

NEWBIGGIN, Northumberland, 55°10′·75N 01°30′·00W. AC 156. Tides approx as for Blyth, 3·5M to the S. Temp, fair weather ⚓ in about 4m in centre of Bay, sheltered from SW to N winds. Caution: offlying rky ledges to N and S. Two pairs of framework trs (marking a measured mile) bracket the bay. Conspic church on N side of bay; bkwtr lt Fl G 10s 4M. Facilities: SC (dinghies). Town V, R, Bar.

AMBLE   8-5-20

Northumberland 55°20'·37N 01°34'·15W   Rtg 3-2-1

CHARTS

AC 1627, 156; Imray C29; OS 81

TIDES

+0412 Dover; ML 3·1; Duration 0606; Zone 0 (UT)

Standard Port RIVER TYNE (NORTH SHIELDS) (←)

Times				Height (metres)			
High Water		Low Water		MHWS	MHWN	MLWN	MLWS
0200	0800	0100	0800	5·0	3·9	1·8	0·7
1400	2000	1300	2000				
Differences AMBLE							
–0023	–0015	–0023	–0014	0·0	+0·2	+0·2	+0·1
COQUET ISLAND							
–0010	–0010	–0020	–0020	+0·1	+0·1	0·0	+0·1

SHELTER

The hbr (also known as Warkworth Hbr) is safe in all weathers, but ent is dangerous in strong N to E winds or in swell which causes heavy breakers on Pan Bush shoal and on the bar at the hbr ent; least depth 0·1m at hbr ent. Once inside the bkwtr, beware drying banks to stbd, ie on S side of ruined N jetty; chan favours the S quays. Visitors should go to Amble marina on S bank of R Coquet, approx 5ca from ent, access HW±4 via sill (0·75m above CD); the sill is marked by PHM and ECM buoys, both unlit. 4kn speed limit in hbr.

NAVIGATION

WPT 55°21'·00N 01°33'·00W, 045°/225° from/to hbr ent, 0·9M. Ent recommended from NE, passing N and W of Pan Bush. A wreck, 3·0m, lies 1·5ca ENE of N pier hd. The S-going stream sets strongly across ent. In NE'ly gales, when broken water can extend to Coquet Island, keep E of island and go to Blyth where app/ent may be safer. Coquet Chan (min depth 0·3m) is not buoyed and should only be used with local knowledge, by day, in fair weather and with adequate rise of tide.

LIGHTS AND MARKS

Coquet Island Lt ho, (conspic) W □ tr, turreted parapet, lower half grey; Fl (3) WR 30s 25m 23/19M R330°-140°, W140°-163°, R163°-180°, W180°-330°. Sector boundaries are indeterminate and may appear as Al WR. Horn 30s.

RADIO TELEPHONE

Call *Amble Marina* Ch 80 (H24). *Warkworth Hbr* VHF, listens Ch 16, works Ch 14 (Mon-Fri 0900-1700 LT). Coquet YC Ch M (occas).

TELEPHONE (Dial code 01665)

Hr Mr 710306; MRSC (0191) 257 9441; local CG 710575; ⌗ (0191) 257 9441 (H24); Marinecall 0891 500453; Ⓗ (01670) 521212.

FACILITIES

Amble Marina (210+40 visitors) ☎ 712168, 🖷 713363, £13.65, AC, BY, C, Gas, FW, D, P, R, Gaz, Slip, BH (20 ton), ME, El, Sh, Ⓔ, SM, Bar, V, CH, Ⓓ, &; **Hbr** D, AB; **Coquet YC** ☎ 711179 Slip, Bar, M, FW, L; **Services**: ME, Slip, CH, El, Sh, SM, Ⓔ. **Town** EC Wed; V, R, Bar, ✉, ⇌ (Alnmouth), ✈ (Newcastle).

HARBOURS AND ANCHORAGES BETWEEN AMBLE AND HOLY ISLAND

BOULMER, Northumberland, 55°25'·00N 01°33'·80W. AC 156. Tides approx as for Amble, 4·5M to the S. A small haven almost enclosed by N and S Rheins, rky ledges either side of the narrow (30m) ent, Mar mouth; only advised in settled offshore weather. 2 unlit bns lead approx 262° through the ent, leaving close to stbd a bn on N Rheins. ⚓ just inside in about 1·5m or dry out on sand at the N end. Few facilities: Pub, ✉ in village. Alnwick is 4M inland.

CRASTER, Northumberland, 55°28'·40N 01°35'·20W. AC 156. Tidal differences: interpolate between Amble (8.5.20) and N Sunderland (8.5.21). Strictly a fair weather ⚓ in offshore winds, 1M S of the conspic Dunstanburgh Castle (ru). The ent, 40m wide, is N of Muckle Carr and S of Little Carr which partly covers and has a bn on its S end. ⚓ in about 3·5m just inshore of these 2 rocky outcrops; or berth at the E pier on rk/sand inside the tiny drying hbr. Facilities: V, R, Bar.

NEWTON HAVEN and BEADNELL BAY, Northumberland, 55°30'·90N 01° 36'·60W. AC 156. HW +0342 on Dover; Tidal differences: interpolate between Amble (8.5.20) and N Sunderland (8.5.21). ML 2·6m; Duration 0625. A safe ⚓ in winds from NNW to SE via S but susceptible to swell. Ent to S of Newton PHM buoy and Newton Pt. Beware Fills Rks. ⚓ between Fills Rks and Low Newton by the Sea in 4/5m. A very attractive ⚓ with no lts, marks or facilities except a pub. Further ⚓ S of Beadnell Pt (1M N of Newton Pt) in 4-6m; small, private hbr; Beadnell SC. Village 0·5M.

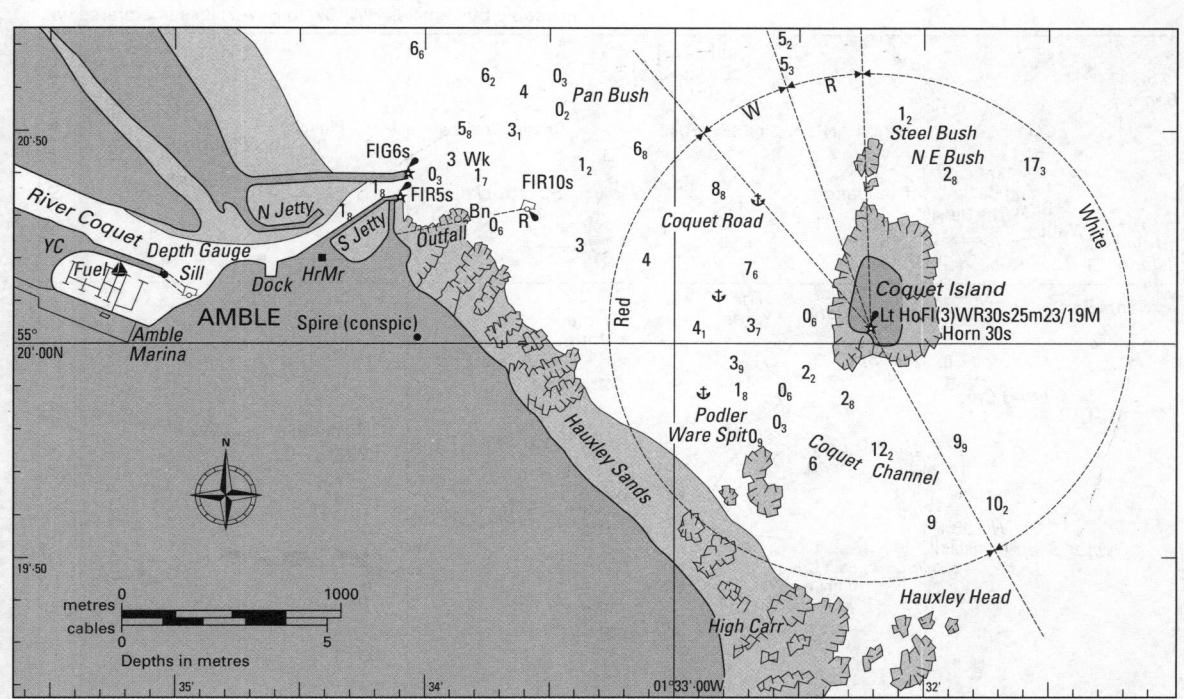

Continued

NORTH SUNDERLAND (Seahouses), Northumberland, 55°35′.04N 01°38′.81W. AC 1612. HW +0340 on Dover; ML No data; Duration 0618. See 8.5.21. Good shelter except in on-shore winds when swell makes outer hbr berths (0·7m) very uncomfortable and dangerous. Access HW±3. Inner hbr has excellent berths but usually full of FVs. Beware The Tumblers (rks) to the W of ent and rks protruding NE from bkwtr hd Fl R 2·5s 6m; NW pier hd FG 11m 3M; vis 159°-294°, on W tr; traffic sigs; Siren 90s when vessels expected. When it is dangerous to enter a Ⓡ is shown over the FG lt (or R flag over a Bu flag) on NW pier hd. Facilities: EC Wed; Gas; all facilities.

FARNE ISLANDS, Northumberland, 55°37′.00N 01°39′.00W. AC 111, 156, 160. HW +0345 on Dover; ML 2·6m; Duration 0630. See 8.5.21. The islands are a NT nature reserve in a beautiful area; they should only be attempted in good weather. Landing is only allowed on Farne Island, Staple Is and Longstone. In the inner group, ⚓ in The Kettle on the NE side of Inner Farne; near the Bridges (which connect Knocks Reef to West Wideopen); or to the S of West Wideopen. In the outer group, ⚓ in Pinnacle Haven (between Staple Is and Brownsman). Beware turbulence over Knivestone and Whirl Rks and eddy S of Longstone during NW tidal streams. Lts and marks: Black Rocks Pt, Oc (2) WRG 15s 12m 17/13M; G122°-165°, W165°-175°, R175°-191°, W191°-238°, R238°-275°, W275°-289°, G289°-300°. Bamburgh Castle is conspic 6ca to the SE. Farne Is lt ho at SW Pt, Fl (2) WR 15s 27m 8/6M; W ○ tr; R119°-280°, W280°-119°. Longstone Fl 20s 23m 24M, R tr with W band (conspic), RC, horn (2) 60s. Caution: reefs extend about 7ca seaward. No facilities.

HISTORICAL NOTE: 161 years ago ...

On 7 September 1838 the merchant ship *Forfarshire*, out of Hull for Dundee, was wrecked on the Farne Islands in a storm. The keeper of the Longstone light house, William Darling, and his 23 year old daughter Grace rowed out to the wreck in a coble despite tremendous seas. They brought back 9 survivors in two sorties. The remaining 43 crew were drowned.
Father and daughter were awarded the Gold Medal of the Royal Humane Society for their courage. Grace Darling died of consumption four years later.

HOLY ISLAND   8-5-21

Northumberland 55°40′.00N 01°48′.00W   Rtg 3-5-1

CHARTS
AC 1612, 111; Imray C24; OS 75
TIDES
+0344 Dover; ML No data; Duration 0630; Zone 0 (UT)

Standard Port RIVER TYNE (NORTH SHIELDS) (←——)

Times				Height (metres)			
High Water		Low Water		MHWS	MHWN	MLWN	MLWS
0200	0800	0100	0800	5·0	3·9	1·8	0·7
1400	2000	1300	2000				
Differences HOLY ISLAND							
−0043	−0039	−0105	−0110	−0·2	−0·2	−0·2	0·0
NORTH SUNDERLAND (Seahouses)							
−0048	−0044	−0058	−0102	−0·7	−0·6	−0·4	−0·2

SHELTER
Good S of The Heugh in 3-6m, but ⚓ is uncomfortable in fresh W/SW winds esp at sp flood. Better shelter in The Ouse on sand/mud if able to dry out; but not in S/SE winds.
NAVIGATION
WPT 55°39′.76N 01°44′.78W, 080°/260° from/to Old Law E bn 1·55M. From N identify Emanuel Hd, conspic W △ bn, then appr via Goldstone Chan leaving Plough Seat PHM buoy to stbd. From S, clear Farne Is thence to WPT. Outer ldg bns lead 260° close past Ridge End ECM and Triton Shoal SHM buoys. Possible overfalls in chan across bar (2·1m) with sp ebb up to 4kn. Inner ldg marks lead 310° to ⚓. Inshore route, round Castle Pt via Hole Mouth and The Yares, may be more sheltered, but is not for strangers.
LIGHTS AND MARKS
Outer ldg marks/lts are Old Law bns (conspic), 2 reddish obelisks 21/25m on 260°; E bn has dir lt, Oc WRG 6s 9m 4M, G182°-2620°, W262°-264°, R264°-shore. Inner ldg marks/lts are The Heugh tr, R △, on with St Mary's ch belfry 310°. The Heugh has dir lt, Oc WRG 6s 24m 5M, G135°-308°, W308°-311°, R311°-shore. Dir lts Oc WRG are aligned on 263° and 309·5° respectively.
RADIO TELEPHONE
None.
TELEPHONE (Dial code 01289)
Hr Mr 389217; MRSC 0191-257 2691.
FACILITIES
Limited. FW on village green, R, Bar, limited V, P & D from Beal (5M); bus (occas) to Berwick. Note Lindisfarne is ancient name; Benedictine Abbey (ruins) and Castle (NT) are worth visiting. Causeway to mainland covers at HW. It is usable by vehicles HW+3½ to HW−2; less in adverse wx.

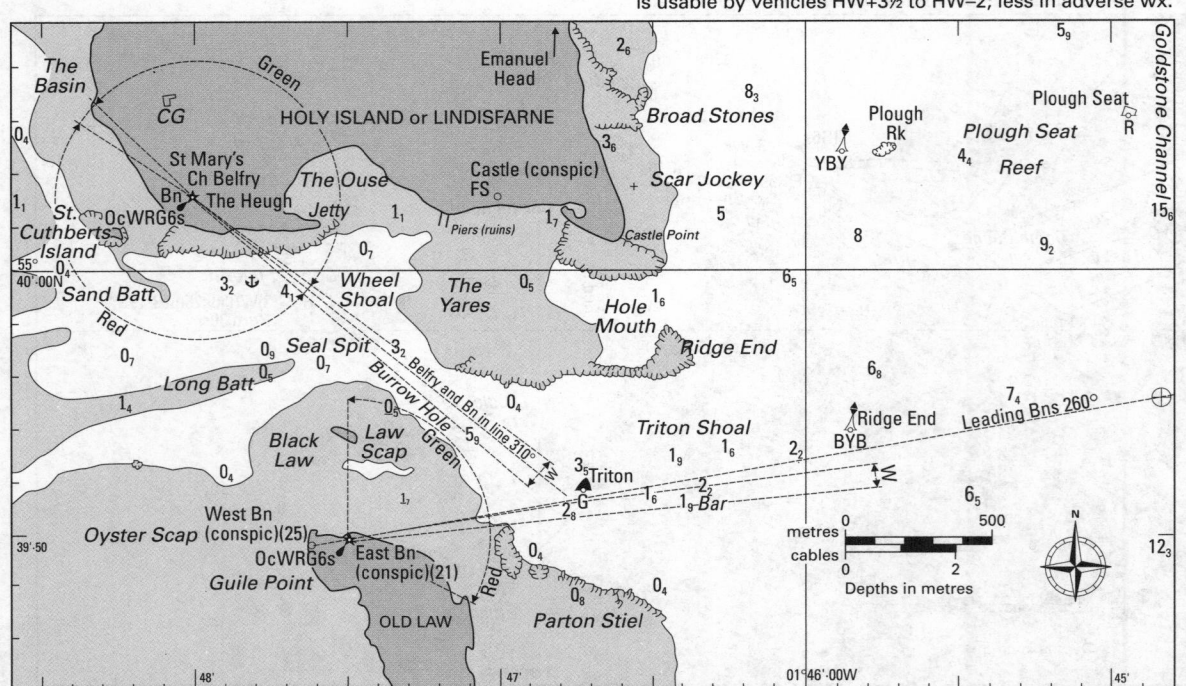

BERWICK-UPON-TWEED 8-5-22

Northumberland 55°45'·87N 01°58'·95W   Rtg 3-3-2

CHARTS

AC 1612, 111, 160; OS 75

TIDES

+0348 Dover; ML 2·5; Duration 0620; Zone 0 (UT)

Standard Port RIVER TYNE (NORTH SHIELDS) (←)

Times				Height (metres)			
High Water		Low Water		MHWS	MHWN	MLWN	MLWS
0200	0800	0100	0800	5·0	3·9	1·8	0·7
1400	2000	1300	2000				
Differences BERWICK-UPON-TWEED							
–0053	–0053	–0109	–0109	–0·3	–0·1	–0·5	–0·1

SHELTER

Good shelter or ⚓ except in strong E/SE winds. Yachts lie in Tweed Dock (the dock gates have been removed; 0·6m in ent, approx 1·2m inside at MLWS) or temporarily at W end of Fish Jetty (1·2m).

NAVIGATION

WPT 55°45'·65N 01°58'·00W, 114°/294° from/to bkwtr lt ho, 0·58M. On-shore winds and ebb tides cause very confused state over the bar (0·6m). Access HW ±4 at sp. From HW–2 to HW+1 strong flood tide sets S across the ent; keep well up to bkwtr. The sands at the mouth of the Tweed shift so often that local knowledge is essential. The Berwick bridge (first and lowest) has about 3m clearance.

LIGHTS AND MARKS

Town hall clock tr and lt ho in line at 294°. When past Crabwater Rk, keep bns at Spittal in line at 207°. Bns are B and Orange with △ top marks (both FR). Caution: The 207° ldg line did not clear (1997) the sands off Spittal Point which have encroached W'wards; best water is further W.

RADIO TELEPHONE

Hr Mr VHF Ch 12 16 (HO).

TELEPHONE (Dial code 01289)

Hr Mr 307404; MRSC 01333 450666; ⌗ 307547 or (01482) 782107 (H24); Marinecall 0891 500453/452; Police 307111; Dr 307484.

FACILITIES

Tweed Dock ☎ 307404, AB £4.00, M, P, D, FW, ME, El, Sh, C (Mobile 3 ton), Slip, SM.
Town EC Thurs; P, V, R, Bar, ✉, Ⓑ, ⇌ and ✈ (Newcastle or Edinburgh).

AGENTS WANTED

If you are interested in becoming our agent for any of the following ports, please write to: The Editor, Edington House, Trent, Sherborne, Dorset DT9 4SR, England – and get your free copy of the Almanac annually. You do not have to live in a port to be the agent, but should at least be a fairly regular visitor.

Plymouth	Port Haliguen
Walton-on-the-Naze	La Trinité-sur-Mer
Hopeman	Piriac
Burghead	St Nazaire/Loire
Findhorn	Pornic
Nairn	St Gilles-Croix-de-Vie
Inverness	Les Sables d'Olonne
Loch Aline	River Seudre
Craobh	Port Bloc/Gironde
Workington	Anglet/Bayonne
Lough Swilly	St Jean-de-Luz
Portbail	Hendaye
St Malo/Dinard	Grandcamp-Maisy
Le Légué/St Brieuc	Port-en-Bessin
Lampaul	Ouistreham/Caen
L'Aberildut	Dives
Douarnenez	St Valéry-en-Caux
Lorient	Dunkerque
River Étel	Emden
Le Palais (Belle Ile)	Langeoog

5

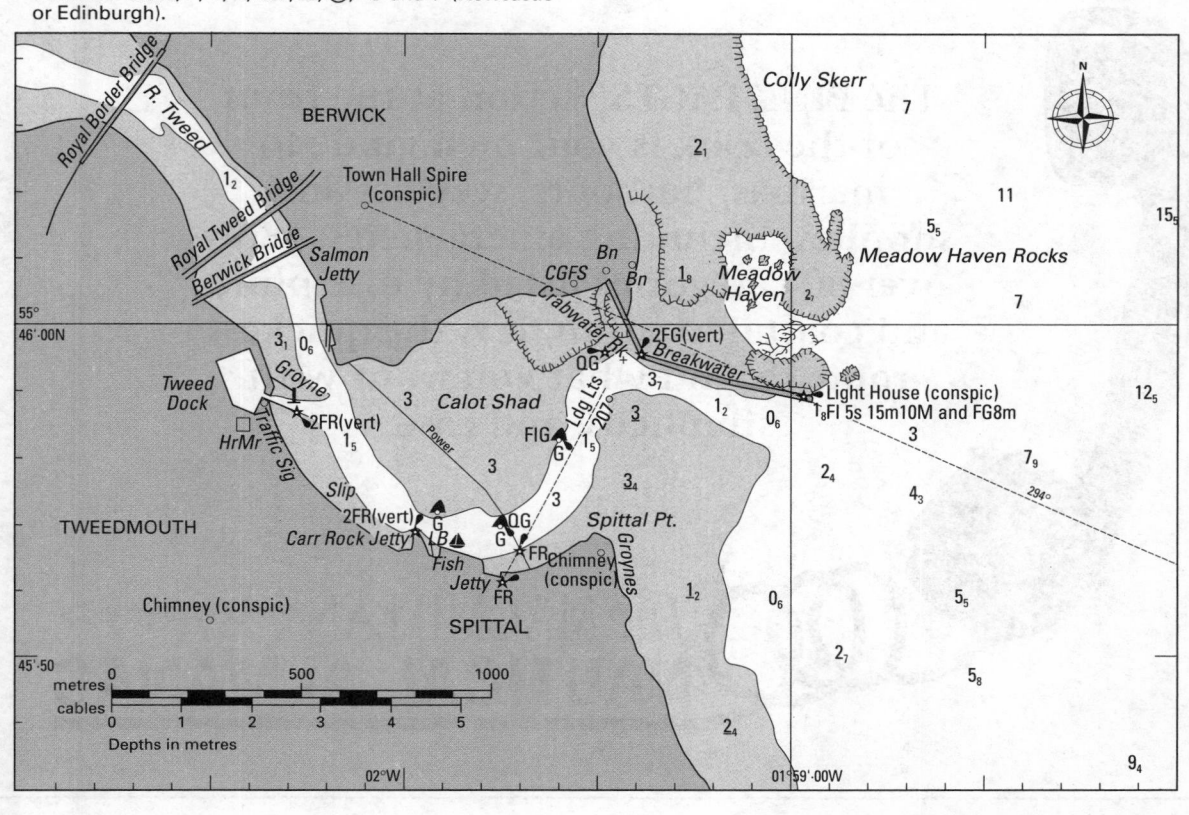

Depths in metres

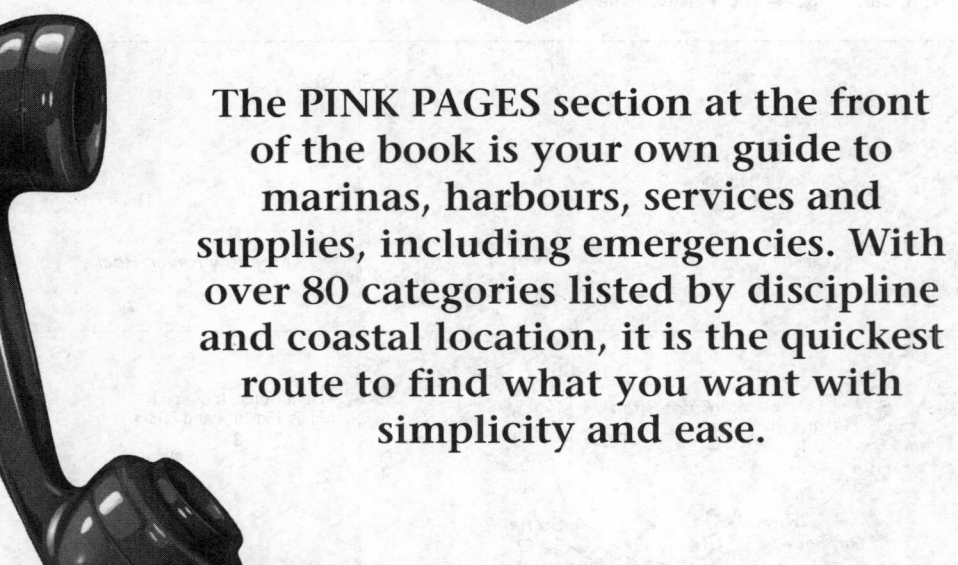

VOLVO PENTA SERVICE

Sales and service centres in area 6
LOTHIAN *Ferry Marine Ltd*, Port Edgar Marina, South Queensferry, Nr.
Edinburgh EH30 9SQ Tel 0131-331 1233

Area 6

South-East Scotland
Eyemouth to Rattray Head

6

**VOLVO
PENTA**

8.6.1	Index	**Page 355**
8.6.2	Diagram of ports, lts, RDF bns, Coast radio and weather stns	356
8.6.3	Tidal stream charts	358
8.6.4	List of coastal lights, fog signals and waypoints	360
8.6.5	Passage information	363
8.6.6	Distance table	365
8.6.7	Eyemouth Burnmouth	365
8.6.8	Dunbar St Abbs	366
8.6.9	Firth of Forth, Leith, Standard Port, tidal curves North Berwick Fisherrow Cramond Inchcolm Aberdour Elie St Monans Pittenweem Crail Isle of May	366
8.6.10	Burntisland	372
8.6.11	Methil Kirkcaldy	373
8.6.12	Anstruther	373
8.6.13	River Tay Perth St Andrews	374
8.6.14	Arbroath	375
8.6.15	Montrose	375
8.6.16	Stonehaven Johnshaven Gourdon	376
8.6.17	Aberdeen, Standard Port, tidal curves	377
8.6.18	Peterhead Boddam	381

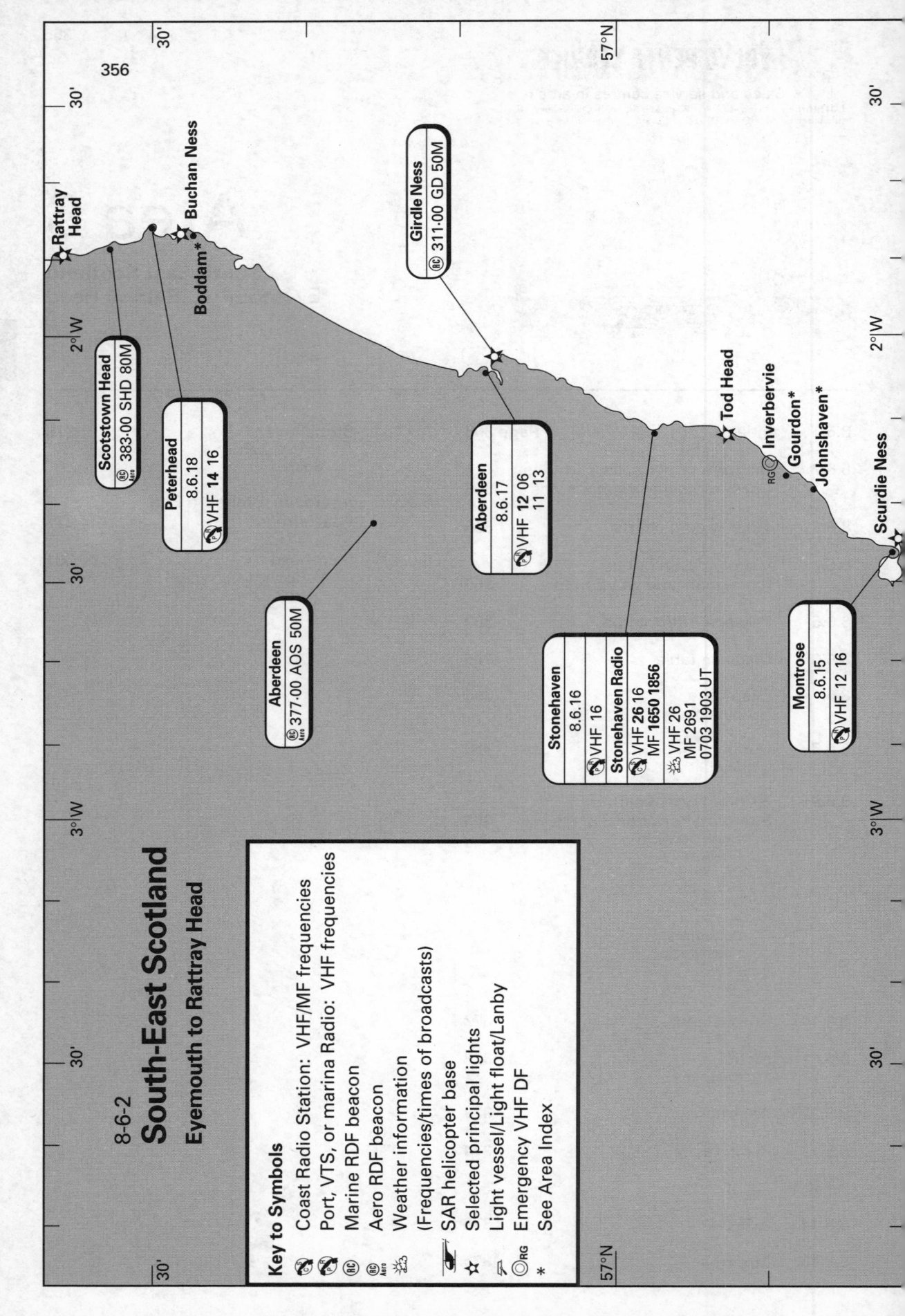

356

8·6·2
South-East Scotland
Eyemouth to Rattray Head

Rattray Head

Buchan Ness

Boddam*

Scotstown Head
ⓇⒸ 383·00 SHD 80M
Aero

Peterhead
8.6.18
📞 VHF 14 16

Girdle Ness
ⓇⒸ 311·00 GD 50M

Aberdeen
ⓇⒸ 377·00 AOS 50M
Aero

Aberdeen
8.6.17
📞 VHF 12 06
   11 13

Tod Head

Inverbervie

Gourdon*

Johnshaven*

Ⓡ RG

Scurdie Ness

Stonehaven
8.6.16
📞 VHF 16
Stonehaven Radio
📞 VHF 26 16
   MF 1650 1856
📡 VHF 26
   MF 2691
   0703 1903 UT

Montrose
8.6.15
📞 VHF 12 16

2°W

3°W

30'

30'

30'

30'

57°N

57°N

Key to Symbols
📞 📞 Coast Radio Station: VHF/MF frequencies
Port, VTS, or marina Radio: VHF frequencies
Ⓡ Marine RDF beacon
Ⓡ Aero RDF beacon
Aero
📡 Weather information
(Frequencies/times of broadcasts)
🚁 SAR helicopter base
⭐ Selected principal lights
⬗ Light vessel/Light float/Lanby
Ⓞ RG Emergency VHF DF
* See Area Index

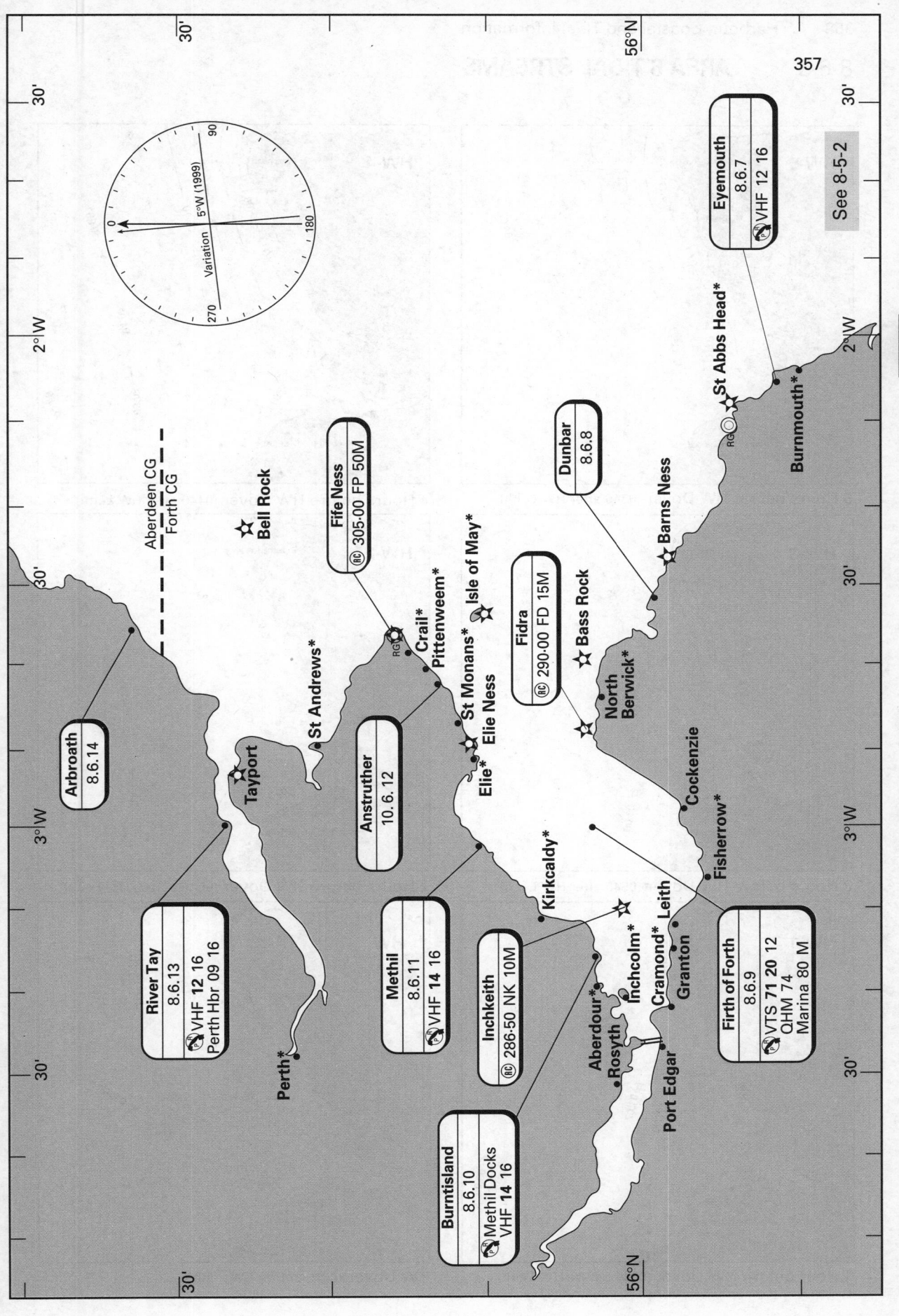

357

6

See 8·5·2

Eyemouth
8.6.7
VHF 12 16

St Abbs Head*
RG

Burnmouth*

Dunbar
8.6.8

Barns Ness

Fidra
290·00 FD 15M

Bass Rock

North
Berwick*

Cockenzie

Fisherrow*

Leith

Granton

Cramond*

Port Edgar

Firth of Forth
8.6.9
VTS 71 20 12
QHM 74
Marina 80 M

Inchcolm*

Rosyth

Aberdour*

Inchkeith
286·50 NK 10M

Kirkcaldy*

Methil
8.6.11
VHF 14 16

Burntisland
8.6.10
Methil Docks
VHF 14 16

Anstruther
10.6.12

Elie*   Elie Ness

St Monans*

Isle of May*

Pittenweem*

Crail*
RG

St Andrews*

Fife Ness
305·00 FP 50M

Bell Rock

Tayport

Arbroath
8.6.14

Aberdeen CG
Forth CG

River Tay
8.6.13
VHF 12 16
Perth Hbr 09 16

Perth*

56°N

2°W

3°W

30'

30'

30'

30'

30'

30'

30'

90

0

180

270

Variation 5°W (1999)

8-6-3   **AREA 6 TIDAL STREAMS**

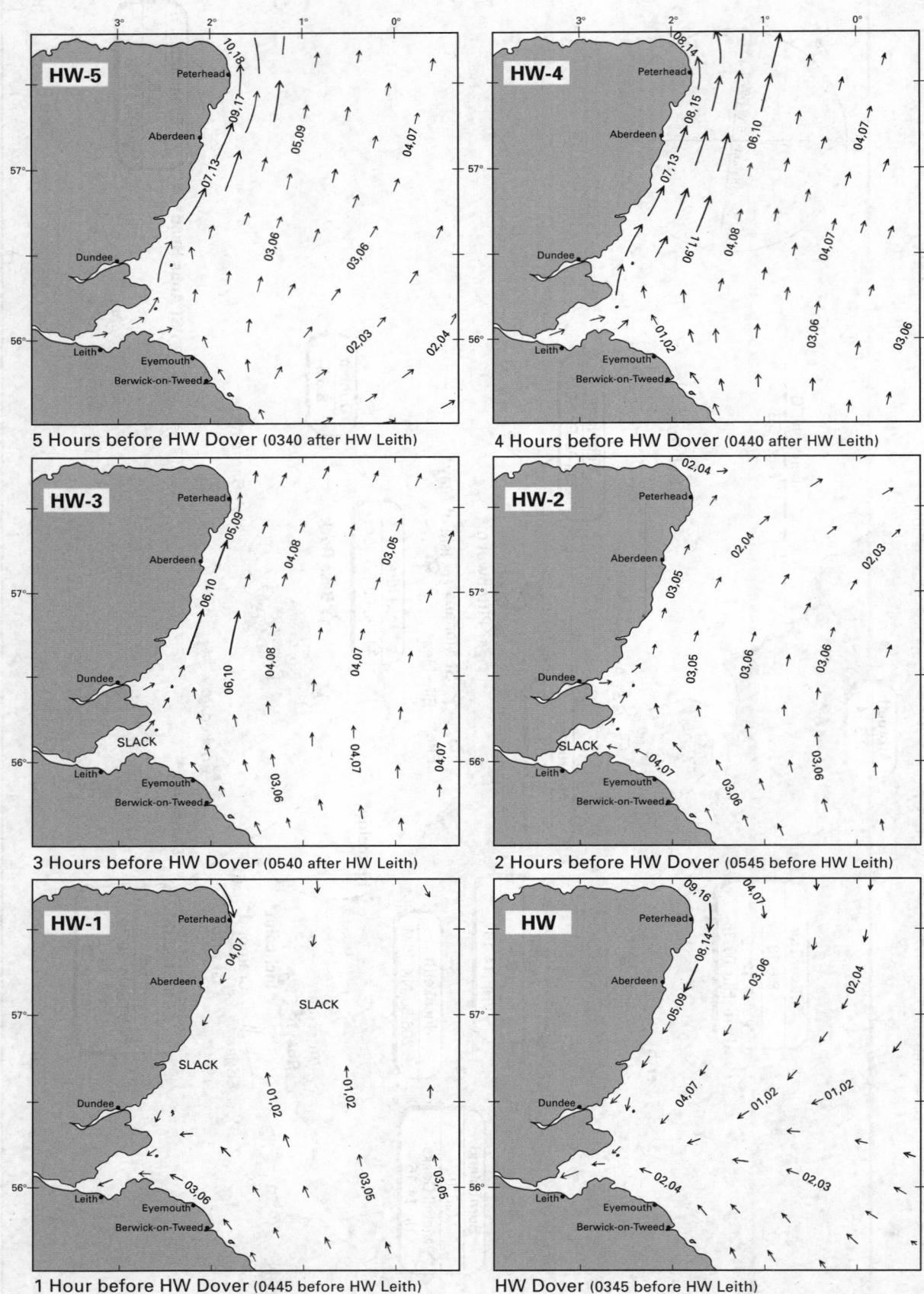

5 Hours before HW Dover (0340 after HW Leith)

4 Hours before HW Dover (0440 after HW Leith)

3 Hours before HW Dover (0540 after HW Leith)

2 Hours before HW Dover (0545 before HW Leith)

1 Hour before HW Dover (0445 before HW Leith)

HW Dover (0345 before HW Leith)

Northward 8.7.3   Southward 8.5.3

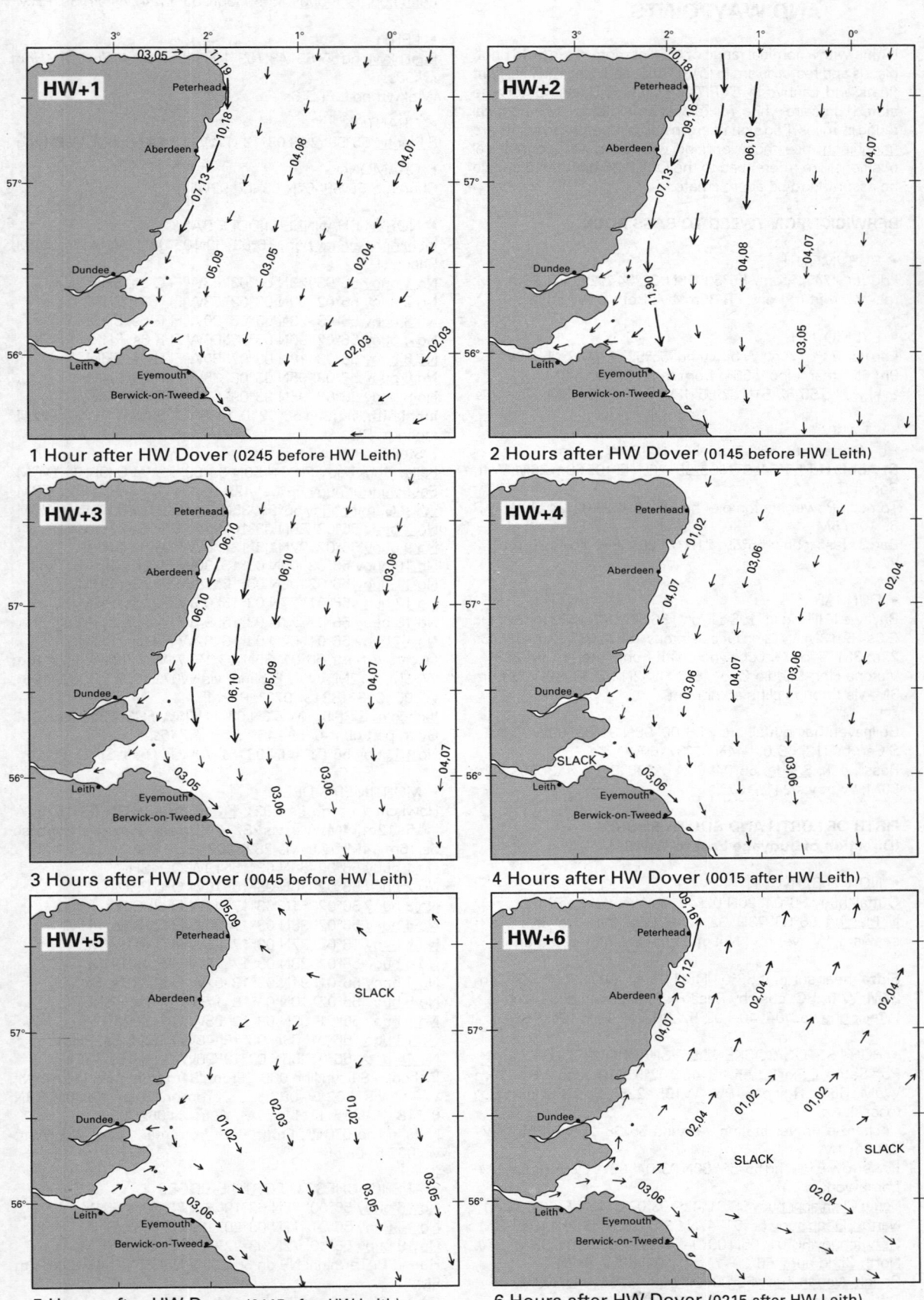

1 Hour after HW Dover (0245 before HW Leith)

2 Hours after HW Dover (0145 before HW Leith)

3 Hours after HW Dover (0045 before HW Leith)

4 Hours after HW Dover (0015 after HW Leith)

5 Hours after HW Dover (0115 after HW Leith)

6 Hours after HW Dover (0215 after HW Leith)

8.6.4 COASTAL LIGHTS, FOG SIGNALS AND WAYPOINTS

Lights with a nominal range of 15M or more are in **bold** print, places and features are in CAPITALS, and light-vessels, light floats and Lanbys in *CAPITAL ITALICS*. Unless otherwise stated lights are white. m = elevation in metres; M = nominal range in miles. Fog signals are in *italics*. Useful waypoints are underlined; use those on land with care. All geographical positions are referenced to the OSGB 36 datum but should be assumed to be approximate.

BERWICK-UPON-TWEED TO BASS ROCK

● BURNMOUTH
Ldg Its 274°: Front, 55°50'·55N 02°04'·12W FR 29m 4M; rear, 45m from front, FR 35m 4M. Both on W posts.

● EYEMOUTH
Ldg Its 174°. Front, W bkwtr hd, 55°52'·47N 02°05'·18W FG 9m 6M; rear, elbow 55m from front, FG 10m 6M.
E bkwtr hd 55°52'·51N 02°05'·18W Iso R 2s 8m 8M; *Siren 30s.*

● ST ABB'S
Hd of inner jetty 55°53'·95N 02°07'·60W FR 4m 1M.
St Abb's Hd 55°54'·97N 02°08'·20W Fl 10s 68m **26M**; W tr; Racon (T).
Torness Power station pier hd 55°58'·40N 02°24'·32W Fl R 5s 10m 5M.
Barns Ness lt bn tr 55°59'·21N 02°26'·68W Iso 4s 36m 10M; W ○ tr.

● DUNBAR
Bayswell Hill ldg Its 198°: Front, 56°00'·26N 02°31'·08W Oc G 6s 15m 3M; W △ on Or col; intens 188°-208°; rear, Oc G 6s 22m 3M; ▽ on Or col; synch with front, intens 188°-208°.
Victoria Hbr, Middle Quay, 56°00'·32N 02°30'·80W QR 6m 3M; vis through cliffs at hbr ent.

Bellhaven Bay outfall buoy 56°00'·98N 02°33'·00W; SPM.
S Carr bn (12) 56°03'·44N 02°37'·60W.
Bass Rock, S side, 56°04'·60N 02°38'·37W Fl (3) 20s 46m 10M; W tr; vis 241°-107°.

FIRTH OF FORTH AND SOUTH SHORE
(Direction of buoyage East to West)

● NORTH BERWICK
Outfall buoy 56°04'·30N 02°40'·70W Fl Y 5s; SPM.
N Pier hd 56°03'·73N 02°42'·92W F WR 7m 3M; vis R seaward, W over hbr. Not lit if ent closed by weather.

Fidra, near summit 56°04'·40N 02°47'·00W Fl (4) 30s 34m **24M**; W tr; RC; obsc by Bass Rk, Craig Leith and Lamb Is.
Wreck buoy 56°04'·40N 02°52'·30W Fl (2) R 10s; PHM.

● PORT SETON/COCKENZIE/FISHERROW/SOUTH CHAN
Port Seton, E Pier hd, 55°58'·40N 02°57'·10W Iso WR 4s 10m W9M, R6M; R shore-105°, W105°-225°, R225°-shore; *Bell (occas).*
Cockenzie Power station, jetty hd 55°58'·25N 02°58'·32W QR 6m 1M.
Fisherrow E Pier hd 55°58'·80N 03°04'·03W Oc W 6s 5m 6M; framework tr.
South Chan appr buoy 56°01'·42N 03°02'·15W L Fl 10s; SWM.
Narrow Deep buoy 56°01'·47N 03°04'·50W Fl (2) R 10s; PHM.
Herwit buoy 56°01'·05N 03°06'·43W Fl (3) G 10s; SHM; *Bell.*
North Craig buoy 56°00'·75N 03°03'·80W; SHM.
Craigh Waugh buoy 56°00'·27N 03°04'·38W Q; NCM.
Diffuser hds buoy (outer) 55°59'·81N 03°07'·75W; NCM.

Diffuser hds buoy (Inner) 55°59'·38N 03°07'·94W; SCM.
Leith approach buoy 55°59'·95N 03°11'·42W Fl R 3s; PHM.

● LEITH
East bkwtr hd 55°59'·48N 03°10'·85W Iso R 4s 7m 9M; *Horn (3) 30s.*
W bkwtr hd L Fl G 6s.

● GRANTON
E Pier hd 55°59'·28N 03°13'·17W Fl R 2s 5m 6M; W ■ Bldg.

● CRAMOND
Church tr 55°58'·67N 03°17'·92W.

● NORTH CHANNEL/MIDDLE BANK
Inchkeith Fairway buoy 56°03'·50N 03°00'·00W Iso 2s; SWM; Racon (T).
No 1 buoy 56°03'·23N 03°03'·63W Fl G 9s; SHM.
No 2 buoy 56°02'·90N 03°03'·63W Fl R 9s; PHM.
No 3 buoy 56°03'·23N 03°06'·00W Fl G 6s; SHM.
No 4 buoy 56°02'·90N 03°06'·00W Fl R 6s; PHM.
No 5 buoy 56°03'·18N 03°07'·80W Fl G 3s; SHM.
No 6 buoy 56°03'·05N 03°08'·35W Fl R 3s; PHM.
No 8 buoy 56°02'·95N 03°09'·54W Fl R 9s; PHM.
Inchkeith, summit 56°02'·01N 03°08'·09W Fl 15s 67m **22M**; stone tr; RC.
E Stell Pt *Horn 15s.*
Pallas Rock buoy 56°01'·50N 03°09'·22W VQ (9) 10s; WCM.
East Gunnet buoy 56°01'·42N 03°10'·30W Q (3) 10s; ECM.
West Gunnet buoy 56°01'·35N 03°10'·97W Q (9) 15s; WCM.
No 7 buoy 56°02'·80N 03°10'·87W QG; *Bell;* Racon (T).
No 9 buoy 56°02'·37N 03°13'·38W Fl G 6s; SHM.
No 10 buoy 56°02'·05N 03°13'·30W Fl R 6s; PHM.
No 11 buoy 56°02'·08N 03°15'·15W Fl G 3s; SHM.
No 12 buoy 56°01'·77N 03°15'·05W Fl R 3s; PHM.
No 13 buoy 56°01'·77N 03°16'·94W Fl G 9s; SHM.
No 14 buoy 56°01'·52N 03°16'·82W Fl R 9s; PHM.
Oxcars lt bn tr 56°01'·36N 03°16'·74W Fl (2) WR 7s 16m W13M, R12M; W tr, R band; vis W072°-087°, R087°-196°, W196°-313°, R313°-072°; Ra refl.
Inchcolm E Pt 56°01'·73N 03°17'·75W Fl (3) 15s 20m 10M; Gy tr; part obsc 075°-145°; *Horn (3) 45s.*
No 15 buoy 56°01'·43N 03°18'·70W Fl G 6s; SHM.

● MORTIMER'S DEEP.
Hawkcraig Pt ldg Its 292°: Front, 56°03'·03N 03°16'·97W Iso 5s 12m 14M; W tr; vis 282°-302°; rear, 96m from front, Iso 5s 16m 14M; W tr; vis 282°-302°.
No 1 buoy 56°02'·68N 03°15'·19W QG; SHM.
No 2 buoy 56°02'·70N 03°15'·76W QR; PHM.
No 3 buoy 56°02'·51N 03°17'·44W Fl (2) G 5s; SHM.
No 4 buoy 56°02'·38N 03°17'·35W Fl (2) R 5s; PHM.
No 5 buoy 56°02'·37N 03°17'·86W Fl G 4s; SHM.
No 6 buoy 56°02'·28N 03°17'·78W Fl R 4s; PHM.
No 7 buoy 56°01'·94N 03°18'·92W Fl (2) G 5s; SHM.
No 8 buoy 56°02'·10N 03°18'·17W Fl R 2s; PHM.
No 9 buoy 56°01'·69N 03°19'·08W QG; SHM.
No 10 buoy 56°01'·83N 03°18'·48W Fl (2) R 5s; PHM.
No 14 buoy 56°01'·56N 03°18'·96W Q (9) 15s; WCM.
Inchcolm S Its in line 066°: Front, 84m from rear, Q 7m 7M; W tr; vis 062·5°-082·5°. Common Rear, 56°01'·80N 03°18'·13W Iso 5s 11m 7M; W tr; vis 062°-082°.
N Its in line 076·7°: Front, 80m from rear, Q 7m 7M; W tr; vis 062·5°-082·5°.

● APPROACHES TO FORTH BRIDGES
No 16 buoy 56°00'·75N 03°19'·81W Fl R 3s; PHM.
No 17 buoy 56°01'·17N 03°20'·12W Fl G 10s; SHM.
No 19 buoy 56°00'·72N 03°22'·40W Fl G 9s; SHM.
Hound Pt Terminal NE dn 56°00'·48N 03°21'·14W 2 FR 7m 5M.

Centre Pier 2 Aero FR 47m 5M.

Hound Pt SW dn 56°00'·28N 03°21'·83W FR 7m 5M.
Inch Garvie, NW end 56°00'·01N 03°23'·29W L Fl 5s 9m 11M; B ● bn, W lantern.
N Queensferry. Oc 5s and QR or QG tfc signals.
Forth Rail Bridge. Centres of spans have W lts and ends of cantilevers R lts, defining N and S chans.
Forth Road Bridge. N suspension tr Iso G 4s 7m 6M on E and W sides; 2 Aero FR 155m 11M and 2 FR 109m 7M on same tr. Main span, N part QG 50m 6M on E and W sides. Main span, centre Iso 4s 52m 8M on E and W sides. Main span, S part QR 50m 6M on E and W sides. S suspension tr Iso R 4s 7m 6M on E and W sides; 2 Aero FR 155m and 2 Fr 109m 7M on same tr.

• PORT EDGAR
Dir lt 244°. W bkwtr hd 55°59'·85N 03°24'·69W Dir Fl R 4s 4m 8M; W blockhouse; 4 QY mark floating bkwtr.
3 x 2 FR (vert) mark N ends of marina pontoons inside hbr.

Beamer Rk lt bn tr 56°02'·28N 03°24'·66W Fl 3s 6m 9M; W tr, R top.

FIRTH OF FORTH – NORTH SHORE (INWARD)

• BURNTISLAND
W Pier outer hd 56°03'·2N 03°22'·2W Fl (2) R 6s 7m; W tr.
E Pier outer hd 56°03'·23N 03°14'·08W Fl (2) G 6s 7m 5M.

• ABERDOUR/BRAEFOOT BAY/INCHCOLM
Hawkcraig Pt (see MORTIMER'S DEEP above)
Aberdour Bay outfall bn 56°02'·97N 03°17'·62W; Y bn.
Braefoot Bay Terminal, W jetty. Ldg lts 247·25°: **Front,** 56°02'·15N 03°18'·63W Fl 3s 6m **15M**; W △ on E dolphin; vis 237·2°-257·2°; four dolphins marked by 2 FG (vert); **rear,** 88m from front, Fl 3s 12m **15M**; W ▽ on appr gangway; vis 237·2°-257·2°; synch with front.
Inchcolm Abbey tr 56°01'·81N 03°18'·02W.

• INVERKEITHING BAY
St David's dir lt bn 56°01'·37N 03°22'·20W Dir 098° Fl G 5s 3m 7M; Or □, on pile.
Channel buoy 56°01'·43N 03°22'·94W QG; SHM.
Channel buoy 56°01'·44N 03°23'·30W QR; PHM.

• ROSYTH DOCKYARD
Main chan dir lt 323·5°. bn 'A' 56°01'·19N 03°25'·53W Dir Oc WRG 7m 4M; R ■ on W post with R bands, on B&W diagonal ■ on W bn; vis G318°-321°, W321°-326°, R326°-328° (H24).
Dir lt 115°, bn 'C' 56°00'·61N 03°24'·17W Dir Oc WRG 6s 7m 4M; W ▽ on W bn; vis R110°-113°, W113°-116·5°, G116·5°-120°.
Dir lt 295°, bn 'E' 56°01'·30N 03°26'·83W Dir Oc 6s 11m 4M; vis 293·5°-296·5°.
No 1 buoy 56°00'·54N 03°24'·48W Fl (2) G 10s; SHM.
Whale Back No 2 buoy 56°00'·70N 03°25'·10W Q (3) 10s; ECM.
No 3 buoy 56°00'·87N 03°24'·98W Fl G 5s; SHM.
No 4 buoy 56°00'·82N 03°25'·18W Fl R 3s; PHM.
No 5 buoy 56°01'·08N 03°25'·80W QG; SHM.
No 6 buoy 56°01'·01N 03°25'·94W QR; PHM.
S Arm jetty hd 56°01'·08N 03°26'·48W L Fl (2) WR 12s 5m W9M; R6M; vis W010°-280°, R280°-010°; Siren 20s (occas).

RIVER FORTH

• ROSYTH TO GRANGEMOUTH
Dhu Craig buoy 56°00'·76N 03°27'·15W Fl G 5s; SHM.
Blackness buoy 56°01'·07N 03°30'·22W QR; PHM.
Charlestown. Lts in line: Front 56°02'·20N 03°30'·60W FG 4m 10M; Y △ on Y pile; vis 017°-037°; marks line of HP gas main; rear FG 6m 10M; Y ▽ on Y pile; vis 017°-037°.

Crombie jetty, downstream dolphin 56°01'·94N 03°31'·76W 2 FG (vert) 8m 4M; Horn (2) 60s.
Crombie Jetty, upstream dolphin 56°02'·00N 03°32'·03W 2 FG (vert) 8m 4M.
Tancred Bank buoy 56°01'·59N 03°31'·83W Fl (2) R 10s; PHM.
Dods Bank buoy 56°02'·03N 03°33'·99W Fl R 3s; PHM.
Bo'ness buoy 56°02'·23N 03°35'·31W Fl R 10s; PHM.
Bo'ness. Carriden outfall 56°01'·32N 03°33'·62W Fl Y 5s 3M; Y ■ on Y bn.
Torry 56°02'·47N 03°35'·20W Fl G 10s 5m 7M; G ● structure.
Bo'ness platform 56°01'·84N 03°36'·13W QR 3m 2M; R pile bn.

• GRANGEMOUTH
Grangemouth app No 1 pile 56°02'·13N 03°38'·01W Fl (3) R 20s 4m 6M.
Hen & Chickens buoy 56°02'·37N 03°38'·00W Fl (3) G 20s; SHM.
No 2 pile 56°02'·35N 03°39'·13W Fl G 5s 4m 6M; G ■ on pile.
No 3 pile 56°02'·26N 03°39'·13W Fl R 5s 4m 6M.
No 4 pile 56°02'·39N 03°39'·83W Fl G 2s 4m 5M.
No 5 pile 56°02'·25N 03°39'·82W Fl R 2s 4m 5M.
Grangemouth W buoy 56°02'·38N 03°40'·50W QG; SHM.
Dock entrance, E jetty; Horn 30s; docking signals.

Longannet Power Station, intake L Fl G 10s 5m 6M.
Inch Brake buoy 56°03'·62N 03°43'·19W; SHM.

• KINCARDINE
Swing bridge 56°03'·9N 03°43'·5W FW at centre of each span; FR lts mark each side of openings.

FIRTH OF FORTH – NORTH SHORE (OUTWARD)

• KIRKCALDY
East Pier hd 56°06'·78N 03°08'·81W Fl WG 10s 12m 8M; vis G156°-336°, W336°-156°.

W Rockheads buoy 56°07'·00N 03°06'·90W; SHM.
E Rockheads buoy 56°07'·15N 03°06'·33W; SHM.
Kirkcaldy wreck buoy 56°07'·26N 03°05'·20W Fl (3) G 18s; SHM.

• METHIL
Outer Pier hd 56°10'·77N 03°00'·39W Oc G 6s 8m 5M; W tr; vis 280°-100°.

• ELIE
Thill Rk buoy 56°10'·88N 02°49'·60W; PHM.
Elie Ness 56°11'·05N 02°48'·65W Fl 6s 15m **18M**; W tr.

• ST MONANCE
Bkwtr hd 56°12'·20N 02°45'·80W Oc WRG 6s 5m W7M, R4M, G4M; vis G282°-355°, W355°-026°, R026°-038°.
E Pier hd 2 FG (vert) 6m 4M; Or tripod; Bell (occas).
W Pier near hd, 2 FR (vert) 6m 4M.

• PITTENWEEM
Ldg lts 037° Middle Pier hd: Front, FR 4m 5M; rear, FR 8m 5M. Both Gy Cols, Or stripes.
E bkwtr hd 56°12'·36N 02°43'·36W Fl (2) RG 5s 9m R9M, G6M; vis R265°-345°, G345°-055°.
Beacon Rk lt bn QR 3m 2M.
W Pier elbow, Horn 90s (occas).

• ANSTRUTHER EASTER
Ldg lts 019°: Front 56°13'·29N 02°41'·68W FG 7m 4M; rear, 38m from front, FG 11m 4M, (both W masts).
W Pier hd 2 FR (vert) 5m 4M; Gy mast; Horn (3) 60s (occas).
E Pier hd 56°13'·15N 02°41'·72W Fl G 3s 6m 4M.

- MAY ISLAND

Isle of May, summit 56°11'·13N 02°33'·30W Fl (2) 15s 73m **22M**; □ tr on stone dwelling.

- CRAIL

Ldg lts 295°: Front, 56°15'·48N 02°37'·70W FR 24m 6M (not lit when hbr closed); rear, 30m from front, FR 30m 6M.

Fife Ness lt 56°16'·73N 02°35'·10W Iso WR 10s 12m **W21M**, **R20M**; W bldg; vis W143°-197°, R197°-217°, W217°-023°; RC.

FIFE NESS TO MONTROSE

N Carr buoy 56°18'·07N 02°32'·85W Q (3) 10s; ECM.
Bell Rk lt tr 56°26'·05N 02°23'·07W Fl 5s 28m **18M**; W ○ tr; Racon (M).

- RIVER TAY/TAYPORT/DUNDEE/PERTH

Tay Fairway buoy 56°29'·25N 02°38'·15W L Fl 10s; SWM; *Bell*.
Middle Green buoy (N) 56°28'·45N 02°39'·25W Fl (3) G 18s; SHM.
Middle Red buoy (S) 56°28'·33N 02°38'·80W Fl (2) R 12s; PHM.
Abertay N buoy 56°27'·44N 02°40'·55W Q (3) 10s; ECM; Racon (T).
Abertay S (Elbow) buoy 56°27'·17N 02°40'·00W Fl R 6s;PHM.

High Lt Ho Dir Lt 269°, 56°27'·17N 02°53'·85W Dir Iso WRG 3s 24m **W22M**, **R17M**, **G16M**; W tr; vis G267°-268°, W268°-270°, R270°-271°.
Inner buoy 56°27'·10N 02°44'·23W Fl (2) R 12s; PHM.
N Lady buoy 56°27'·43N 02°46'·56W Fl (3) G 18s; SHM.
S Lady buoy 56°27'·20N 02°46'·76W Fl (3) R 18s; PHM.
Pool buoy 56°27'·15N 02°48'·50W Fl R 6s; PHM.
Tentsmuir Pt 56°26'·6N 02°49'·5W Fl Y 5s; Y bn; vis 198°-208°; marks gas pipeline.
Monifieth 56°28'·9N 02°47'·8W Fl Y 5s; Y bn; vis 018°-028°; marks gas pipeline.
Horse Shoe buoy 56°27'·28N 02°50'·11W VQ (6) + L Fl 15s; SCM.
Larick Scalp buoy 56°27'·19N 02°51'·50W Fl (2) R 12s; PHM; *Bell*.
Broughty Castle 56°27'·76N 02°52'·10W 2 FG (vert) 10m 4M; Gy col; FR is shown at foot of old lt ho at Buddon Ness, 4M to E, and at other places on firing range when practice is taking place.
Craig buoy 56°27'·48N 02°52'·94W QR; PHM.
Newcombe Shoal buoy 56°27'·73N 02°53'·50W Fl R 6s; PHM.
Dundee tidal basin E ent 56°27'·92N 02°55'·92W 2 FG (vert).
Middle Bank buoy 56°27'·40N 02°56'·39W Q (3) 10s; ECM.
West Deep buoy 56°27'·15N 02°56'·15W Fl R 3s; PHM.
Tay road bridge N navigation span, centre 56°27'·03N 02°56'·44W 2 x VQ 27m.
Tay road bridge S navigation span, centre 56°27'·01N 02°56'·38W 2 x VQ 28m.
Tay railway bridge navigation 56°26'·28N 02°59'·20W 2 x 2 F (vert) 23m.
Jock's Hole 56°21'·75N 03°12'·10W QR 8m 2M.
Pipeline S by Elcho Castle 56°22'·50N 03°20'·80W Iso R 4s 4m 4M.

- ARBROATH

Outfall buoy 56°32'·64N 02°34'·97W Fl Y 3s; SPM.
Ldg lts 299·2°: Front, 56°33'·30N 02°35'·07W FR 7m 5M; W col; rear, 50m from front, FR 13m 5M; W col.
W bkwtr E end, VQ (2) 6s 6m 4M; W post.

E Pier S elbow 56°33'·26N 02°34'·89W Fl G 3s 8m 5M; W tr; shows FR when hbr closed; *Siren (3) 60s* (occas).

- MONTROSE

Scurdie Ness 56°42'·12N 02°26'·15W Fl (3) 20s 38m **23M**; W tr; Racon (T).
Ldg lts 271·5°: Front, FR 11m 5M; W twin pillars, R bands; rear, 272m from front, FR 18m 5M; W tr, R cupola.
Scurdie Rks buoy 56°42'·15N 02°25'·19W QR; PHM.
Annat buoy 56°42'·24N 02°25'·85W Fl G 3s; SHM.
Annat Shoal buoy 56°42'·38N 02°25'·09W QG; SHM.

MONTROSE TO RATTRAY HEAD

- JOHNSHAVEN

Ldg lts 316°: Front, 56°47'·65N 02°20'·05W FR 5m; R structure; rear, 85m from front, FG 20m; G structure; shows R when unsafe to enter hbr.

- GOURDON HARBOUR

Ldg lts 358°: Front, 56°49'·70N 02°17'·10W FR 5m 5M; W tr; shows G when unsafe to enter; *Siren (2) 60s* (occas); rear, 120m from front, FR 30m 5M; W tr.
W Pier hd 56°49'·62N 02°17'·15W Fl WRG 3s 5m W9M, R7M, G7M; vis G180°-344°, W344°-354°, R354°-180°.
E bkwtr hd Q 3m 7M.

Todhead 56°53'·00N 02°12'·85W Fl (4) 30s 41m **18M**; W tr.

- STONEHAVEN

Outer Pier hd 56°57'·59N 02°11'·89W Iso WRG 4s 7m W11M, R7M, G8M; vis G214°-246°, W246°-268°, R268°-280°.

Girdle Ness 57°08'·35N 02°02'·82W Fl (2) 20s 56m **22M**; W ○ tr; obsc by Greg Ness when brg more than about 020°; RC; Racon (G).

- ABERDEEN

Fairway buoy 57°09'·33N 02°01'·85W Mo (A); SWM; Racon (T).
Ldg lts 235·7°: Front, 57°08'·39N 02°04'·41W FR or G 14m 5M; W tr; R when ent safe, FG when dangerous to navigation; vis 195°-279°; rear, 205m from front, FR 19m 5M; W tr; vis 195°-279°.
S bkwtr hd 57°08'·70N 02°03'·23W Fl (3) R 8s 23m 7M.
N Pier hd 57°08'·75N 02°03'·58W Oc WR 6s 11m 9M; W tr; vis W145°-055°, R055°-145°. In fog FY 10m (same tr) vis 136°-336°; *Bell (3) 12s*.

Buchan Ness 57°28'·23N 01°46'·37W Fl 5s 40m **28M**; W tr, R bands; Racon (O); *Horn (3) 60s*.
Cruden Scaurs buoy 57°23'·25N 01°50'·00W Fl R 10s; PHM; *Bell*.

- PETERHEAD

Kirktown ldg lts 314°: Front, 57°30'·23N 01°47'·10W FR 13m 8M; R mast, W △ on Or mast; rear, 91m from front, FR 17m 8M; W ▽ on Or mast.
S bkwtr hd 57°29'·81N 01°46'·43W Fl (2) R 12s 24m 7M; W ○ tr with B base.
N bkwtr hd 57°29'·85N 01°46'·22W Iso RG 6s 19m 11M; W tripod; vis R165°-230°, G230°-165°; *Horn 30s*.
Marina W bkwtr hd, QG 5m 2M, vis 120°-005°; 57°29'·83N 01°47'·34W.
Marina S bkwtr hd, Fl R 3s 6m 2M; 57°29'·82N 01°47'·33W.

Rattray Hd. Ron Rk 57°36'·62N 01°48'·90W Fl (3) 30s 28m **24M**; W tr; Racon (M); *Horn (2) 45s*.

8.6.5 PASSAGE INFORMATION

For these waters refer to the Admiralty *North Sea (West) Pilot*; R Northumberland YC's *Sailing Directions Humber to Rattray Head*, and the *Forth Yacht Clubs Association Pilot Handbook*, which covers the Firth of Forth in detail.

BERWICK-UPON-TWEED TO BASS ROCK (charts 160, 175)

From Berwick-upon-Tweed to the Firth of Forth there is no good hbr which can be approached with safety in strong onshore winds. So, if on passage with strong winds from N or E, plan accordingly and keep well to seaward. In late spring and early summer fog (haar) is likely in onshore winds.

The coast N from Berwick is rky with cliffs rising in height to Burnmouth, then diminishing gradually to Eyemouth (8.6.7). Keep 5ca offshore to clear outlying rks. Burnmouth, although small, has more alongside space than Eyemouth, which is a crowded fishing hbr. 2M NW is St Abb's Hbr (8.6.8), with temp anch in offshore winds in Coldingham B close to the S.

St Abb's Hd (lt) is a bold, steep headland, 92m high, with no offlying dangers. The stream runs strongly round the Hd, causing turbulence with wind against tide; this can be largely avoided by keeping close inshore. The ESE-going stream begins at HW Leith – 0345, and the WNW-going at HW Leith + 0240. There is a good anch in Pettico Wick, on NW side of Hd, in S winds, but dangerous if the wind shifts onshore. There are no off-lying dangers between St Abb's Hd and Fast Castle Hd, 3M WNW. Between Fast Castle Hd and Barns Ness, about 8M NW, is the attractive little hbr of Cove; but it dries and should only be approached in ideal conditions.

Torness Power Station (conspic; lt on bkwtr) is 1·75M SE of Barns Ness (lt) which lies 2·5M ESE of Dunbar (8.6.8) and is fringed with rks; tidal streams as for St Abb's Hd. Conspic chys are 7½ca WSW inland of Barns Ness. Between here and Dunbar keep at least 2½ca offshore to clear rky patches. Sicar Rk (7·9m depth) lies about 1·25M ENE of Dunbar, and sea breaks on it in onshore gales.

The direct course from Dunbar to Bass Rk (lt) is clear of all dangers; inshore of this line beware Wildfire Rks (dry) on NW side of Bellhaven B. In offshore winds there is anch in Scoughall Road. Great Car is ledge of rks, nearly covering at HW, 1M ESE of Gin Hd, with Car bn (stone tr surmounted by cross) at its N end. Drying ledges of rks extend 1M SE of Great Car, up to 3ca offshore. Keep at least 5ca off Car bn in strong onshore winds. Tantallon Castle (ruins) is on cliff edge 1M W of Great Car. Bass Rk (lt) lies 1·25M NNE of Gin Hd, and is a sheer, conspic rk (115m) with no offlying dangers; landing difficult due to swell.

FIRTH OF FORTH, SOUTH SHORE (chart 734, 735)

Westward of Bass Rk, Craigleith (51m), Lamb Is (24m) and Fidra (31m) lie 5ca or more offshore, while the coast is generally foul. Craigleith is steep-to, and temporary anchorage can be found on SE and SW sides; if passing inshore of it keep well to N side of chan. N Berwick hbr (dries) lies S of Craigleith, but is unsafe in onshore winds. Between Craigleith and Lamb Is, beware drying rks up to 3ca from land. Lamb Is is 1·5M WNW of N Berwick (8.6.9) and has a rky ledge extending 2½ca SW. Fidra Is (lt, RC) is a bird reserve, nearly connected to the shore by rky ledges, and should be passed to the N; passage and anch on S side are tricky. Anchor on E or W sides, depending on wind, in good weather.

In the B between Fidra and Edinburgh some shelter can be found in SE winds in Aberlady B and Gosford B. The best anch is SW of Craigielaw Pt. Port Seton is a drying fishing hbr 7½ca E of the conspic chys of Cockenzie Power Station; the E side of the hbr can be entered HW ±3, but not advisable in strong onshore wind or sea. Cockenzie (dries) is close to power station; beware Corsik Rk 400m to E. Access HW ± 2·5, but no attractions except boatyard. For Fisherrow, see 8.6.9.

There are no dangers on the direct course from Fidra to Inchkeith (lt, RC), which stands between the buoyed deep water chans. Rks extend 7½ca SE from Inchkeith, and 5ca off the W side where there is a small hbr below the lt ho; landing is forbidden without permission. N Craig and Craig Waugh (least depth 0·6m) are buoyed shoals 2·5M SE from Inchkeith lt ho. For Cramond and Inchcolm, see 8.6.9.

In N Chan, close to Inchkeith the W-going (flood) stream begins about HW Leith – 0530, and the E-going at HW Leith + 0030, sp rates about 1kn. The streams gather strength towards the Forth bridges, where they reach 2·25kn and there may be turbulence.

Leith is wholly commercial; Granton has yacht moorings in the E hbr; Port Edgar (8.6.9) is a major yacht hbr close W of Forth road bridge. Hound Point oil terminal is an artificial 'island-jetty' almost in mid-stream, connected to the shore by underwater pipeline (no ⚓). Yachts may pass the terminal on either side at least 30m off and well clear of tankers berthing.

RIVER FORTH TO KINCARDINE (charts 736, 737, 738)

The main shipping chan under the N span of the rail bridge is busy with commercial traffic for Grangemouth and warships to/from Rosyth dockyard. In the latter case a Protected Chan may be activated; see 8.6.9 for details. W of Beamer Rk the Firth widens as far as Bo'ness (small drying hbr) on the S shore where the chan narrows between drying mudbanks. Charlestown (N bank) dries, but is a secure hbr. Grangemouth is industrially conspic. Caution: gas carriers, tankers, cargo vessels; no yacht facilities. Few yachts go beyond Kincardine swing bridge, clearance 9m, which is no longer opened.

FIRTH OF FORTH, NORTH SHORE (charts 734, 190)

From Burntisland (8.6.10) the N shore of Firth of Forth leads E to Kinghorn Ness. 1M SSW of Kinghorn Ness Blae Rk (SHM lt buoy) has least depth of 4·1m, and seas break on it in E gales. Rost Bank lies halfway between Kinghorn Ness and Inchkeith, with tide rips at sp tides or in strong winds.

From Kinghorn Ness to Kirkcaldy, drying rks lie up to 3ca offshore. Kirkcaldy hbr (8.6.11) is effectively closed, but yachts can enter inner dock near HW by arrangement; ent is dangerous in strong E'lies, when seas break a long way out.

Between Kirkcaldy and Methil (8.6.11) the only dangers more than 2ca offshore are The Rockheads, extending 4ca SE of Dysart, and marked by 2 SHM buoys. Largo B is anch, well sheltered from N and E, but avoid gaspipes near E side. Close SW of Elie, beware W Vows (dries) and E Vows (dries, bn). There is anch close W of Elie Ness (8.6.9). Ox Rk (dries 2m) lies 5ca ENE of Elie Ness, and 2½ca offshore; otherwise there are no dangers more than 2ca offshore past St Monans, Pittenweem (8.6.9) and Anstruther (8.6.12), but in bad weather the sea breaks on Shield Rk 4ca off Pittenweem. From Anstruther to Crail (8.6.9) and on to Fife Ness keep 3ca offshore to clear Caiplie Rk and other dangers.
May Island (lt) (8.6.9) lies about 5M S of Fife Ness; its shores are bold except at NW end where rks extend 1ca off. Anch near N end at E or W Tarbert, on lee side according to winds; in good weather it is possible to land. Lt ho boats use Kirkhaven, close SE of lt ho

FIFE NESS TO MONTROSE (chart 190)

Fife Ness is fringed by rky ledges, and a reef extends 1M NE to N Carr Rk (dries 1·4m, marked by bn). In strong onshore winds keep to seaward of N Carr ECM lt buoy. From here keep 5ca offshore to clear dangers entering St Andrews B, where there is anch; the little hbr (8.6.13) dries, and should not be approached in onshore winds.

Northward from Firth of Forth to Rattray Hd the coast is mostly rky and steep-to, and there are no out-lying dangers within 2M of the coast except those off R. Tay and Bell Rk. But in an onshore blow there are few safe havens; both yachts and crews need to be prepared for offshore cruising rather than coast-crawling.

R. Tay (8.6.13 and chart 1481) is approached from the NE via Fairway buoy; it is dangerous to cut corners from the S. The Bar, NE of Abertay lt buoy, is dangerous in heavy weather, particularly in strong onshore wind or swell. Abertay Sands extend nearly 4M E of Tentsmuir Pt on S side of chan (buoyed); Elbow is a shoal extension eastward. Gaa Sands running 1.75M E from Buddon Ness, are marked by Abertay lt buoy (Racon) on N side of chan. Passage across Abertay and Gaa Sands is very dangerous. The estuary is shallow, with many shifting sandbanks; Tayport is a good passage stop and best yacht hbr (dries) in the Tay. S of Buddon Ness the W-going (flood) stream begins about HW Aberdeen – 0400, and the E-going at about HW Aberdeen + 0230, sp rates 2kn.

Bell Rk (lt, Racon) lies about 11·5M E of Buddon Ness. 2M E of Bell Rk the S-going stream begins HW Aberdeen – 0220, and the N-going at HW Aberdeen + 0405, sp rates 1kn. W of Bell Rk the streams begin earlier.

N from Buddon Ness the coast is sandy. 1·25M SW of Arbroath (8.6.14) beware Elliot Horses, rky patches with depth 1·9m, which extend about 5ca offshore. Between Whiting Ness and Scurdie Ness, 9·5M NNE, the coast is clear of out-lying dangers, but is mostly fringed with drying rks up to 1ca off. In offshore winds there is temp anch in SW of Lunan B, off Ethie Haven.

Scurdie Ness (lt, Racon) is conspic on S side of ent to Montrose (8.6.15). Scurdie Rks (dry) extend 2ca E of the Ness. On N side of chan Annat Bank dries up to about 5ca E of the shore, opposite Scurdie Ness (chart 1438). The in-going stream begins at HW Aberdeen – 0500, and the outgoing at HW Aberdeen + 0115; both streams are very strong, up to 7kn at sp, and there is turbulence off the ent on the ebb. The ent is dangerous in strong onshore winds, with breaking seas extending to Scurdie Ness on the ebb. In marginal conditions the last quarter of the flood is best time to enter.

MONTROSE TO ABERDEEN (chart 210)

N from Montrose the coast is sandy for 5M to Milton Ness, where there is anch on S side in N winds. Johnshaven (8.6.16), 2M NE, is a small hbr (dries) with tight entrance, which should not be approached with onshore wind or swell. 5ca NE, off Brotherton Cas, drying rks extend 4ca offshore. Gourdon (8.6.16) has a small hbr (mostly dries) approached on ldg line between rky ledges; inner hbr has storm gates. Outside the hbr rks extend both sides of entrance, and the sea breaks heavily in strong E winds. Keep a sharp lookout for lobster pot dan buoys between Montrose and Stonehaven.

North to Inverbervie the coast is fringed with rky ledges up to 2ca offshore. Just N of Todhead Pt (lt) is Catterline, a small B which forms a natural anch in W winds, but open to E. Downie Pt, SE of Stonehaven (8.6.16) should be

rounded 1ca off. The Bay is encumbered by rky ledges up to 2ca from shore and exposed to the E; anch 6ca E of Bay Hotel or berth afloat in outer hbr.

From Garron Pt to Girdle Ness the coast is mostly steep-to. Fishing nets may be met off headlands during fishing season. Craigmaroinn and Seal Craig (dry) are parts of reef 3ca offshore SE of Portlethen, a fishing village with landing sheltered by rks. Cove B has a very small fishing hbr, off which there is anch in good weather; Mutton Rk (dries 2·1m) lie 1½ca offshore. From Cove to Girdle Ness keep 5ca offshore, avoiding Hasman Rks (dries 3·4m) 1ca off Altens .

Greg Ness and Girdle Ness (lt, RC, Racon), at SE corner of Aberdeen B (8.6.17), are fringed by rks. Girdlestone is a rky patch, depth less than 2m, 2ca ENE of lt ho. A drying patch lies 2ca SE of lt ho. Off Girdle Ness the S-going stream begins at HW Aberdeen – 0430, and the N-going at HW Aberdeen + 0130, sp rates 2·5kn. A race forms on S-going stream.

ABERDEEN TO RATTRAY HEAD (chart 213)

From Aberdeen there are few offshore dangers to Buchan Ness. R. Ythan, 1·75M SSW of Hackley Hd, is navigable by small craft, but chan shifts constantly. 3M North is the very small hbr of Collieston (mostly dries), only accessible in fine weather. 4·75M NNE of Hackley Head lie The Skares, rks (marked by PHM lt buoy) extending 3½ca from S point of Cruden B, where there is anch in offshore winds. On N side of Cruden B is Port Erroll (dries 2·5m).

Buchan Ness (lt, fog sig, Racon) is a rky peninsula. 2ca N is Meikle Mackie islet, close W of which is the small hbr of Boddam (dries) (8.6.18). 3ca NE of Meikle Mackie is The Skerry, a rk 6m high on S side of Sandford B; rks on which the sea breaks extend 2ca NNE. The chan between The Skerry and the coast is foul with rks and not advised. Peterhead (8.6.18) is easy to enter in almost all conditions and is an excellent passage port with marina at SW corner of the Bay.

Rattray Hd (with lt, fog sig on The Ron, rk 2ca E of Hd) has rky foreshore, drying for 2ca off. Rattray Briggs is a detached reef, depth 0·2m, 2ca E of lt ho. Rattray Hard is a rky patch, depth 10·7m, 1·5M ENE of lt ho, which raises a dangerous sea during onshore gales. Off Rattray Hd the S-going stream begins at HW Aberdeen – 0420, and the N-going at HW Aberdeen + 0110, sp rates 3kn. In normal conditions keep about 1M E of Rattray Hd, but pass 5M off in bad weather, preferably at slack water. Conspic radio masts with R lts lie 2·5M WNW and 2·2M W of lt ho.

For notes on offshore oil/gas installations, see 8.5.5.

NORTH SEA PASSAGE
For distances across the N Sea, see 8.0.10.

FORTH TO NORWAY AND BALTIC (charts 2182B, 2182C)

Heading ENE'ly from the Firth of Forth the main hazards result from offshore industrial activities and their associated traffic. In summer particularly, oil/gas exploration, movement of drilling rigs, pipe laying etc create situations which could endanger other vessels. Rig movements and many of the more intense activities are published in Notices to Mariners, but even so it is wise to avoid the gas and oil fields where possible and never to approach within 500m of installations (see 8.5.5). There are TSS to be avoided off the S and SW coast of Norway. Strong currents and steep seas may be experienced in the approaches to the Skagerrak.

8.6.6   DISTANCE TABLE

Approximate distances in nautical miles are by the most direct route, whilst avoiding dangers and allowing for Traffic Separation Schemes. Places in *italics* are in adjoining areas; places in **bold** are in 8.0.10, Distances across the North Sea.

		1	2	3	4	5	6	7	8	9	10	11	12	13	14	15	16	17	18	19	20
1.	*Great Yarmouth*	**1**																			
2.	**Berwick-on-Tweed**	232	**2**																		
3.	Eyemouth	240	10	**3**																	
4.	Dunbar	257	26	17	**4**																
5.	North Berwick	266	35	25	9	**5**															
6.	Granton	285	54	44	27	19	**6**														
7.	**Port Edgar**	290	58	50	34	26	7	**7**													
8.	Burntisland	283	53	43	26	18	5	8	**8**												
9.	Methil	276	45	36	20	13	14	20	12	**9**											
8.	Anstruther	269	38	29	14	10	23	29	22	11	**10**										
11.	Fife Ness	269	38	29	17	14	28	34	27	16	5	**11**									
12.	Bell Rock	276	43	36	27	25	40	47	39	28	17	12	**12**								
13.	**Dundee**	289	58	49	37	34	48	54	47	36	25	20	20	**13**							
14.	Arbroath	284	51	44	34	31	45	51	44	33	22	17	10	15	**14**						
15.	Montrose	291	59	51	43	41	55	61	54	43	32	27	17	27	12	**15**					
16.	Stonehaven	300	72	66	60	58	72	78	71	60	49	44	32	45	30	20	**16**				
17.	**Aberdeen**	308	82	78	73	70	84	90	83	72	61	56	44	57	42	32	13	**17**			
18.	Peterhead	318	105	98	93	95	106	108	105	94	83	78	68	80	64	54	35	25	**18**		
19.	*Fraserburgh*	334	121	114	109	108	122	128	121	110	99	94	83	96	79	68	51	39	16	**19**	
20.	*Wick*	391	178	171	166	165	179	185	178	167	156	151	140	153	136	125	108	96	72	57	**20**

EYEMOUTH   8-6-7

Borders 55°52'·51N 02°05'·19W   Rtg 3-3-1

CHARTS
AC 1612, 160; OS 67

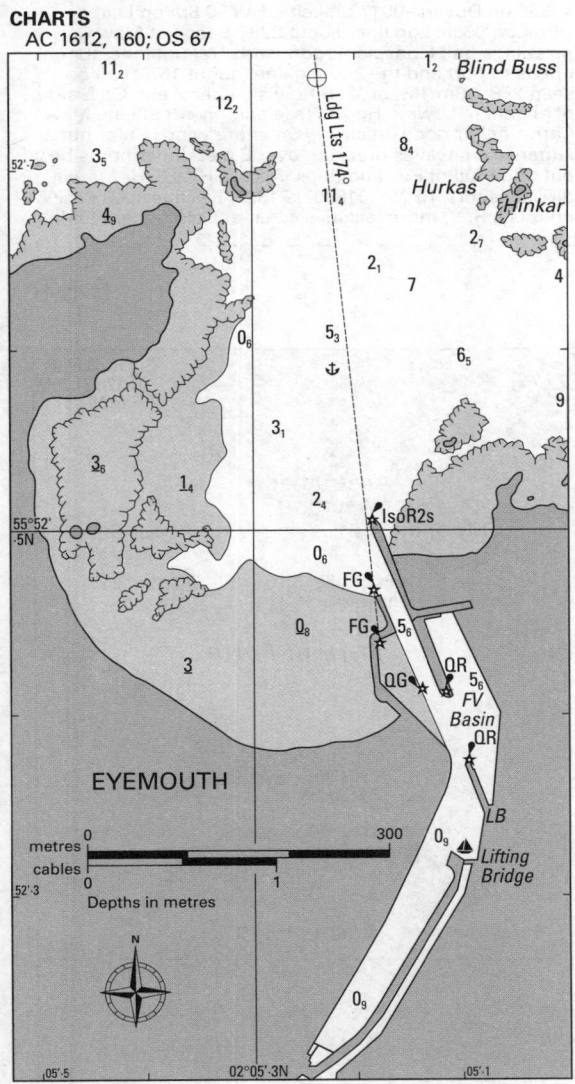

TIDES
+0330 Dover; ML No data; Duration 0610; Zone 0 (UT)

Standard Port LEITH (→)

Times				Height (metres)			
High Water		Low Water		MHWS	MHWN	MLWN	MLWS
0300	0900	0300	0900	5·6	4·5	2·1	0·8
1500	2100	1500	2100				
Differences EYEMOUTH							
–0015	–0025	–0014	–0004	–0.9	–0.8		No data

SHELTER
Good in all weathers but entry should not be attempted in strong N/E'lies. Busy FV hbr, but yachts are welcome. Expect to berth at E quay knuckle, near lifting bridge in about 2m; or as directed by Hr Mr. A new FV basin (5·6m) on E side of ent was due to be completed in late 1998; more room for yachts is available in old hbr. ⚓ in bay only in off-shore winds.

NAVIGATION
WPT 55°52'·75N 02°05'·24W, 354°/174° from/to E bkwtr lt, 2½ca. Appr can be made N or S of Hurkar Rks; from the N, beware Blind Buss 1·2m. From the S there are no ldg marks; keep in mid-chan. Hbr ent is dredged to 5·6m and carries at least 2·5m at MLWS.

LIGHTS AND MARKS
St. Abbs Hd lt ho Fl 10s 68m 26M is 3M NW. Ldg lts 174° both FG 9/10m 6M, orange columns on W pier. Ⓡ or R flag = unsafe to enter.

RADIO TELEPHONE
VHF Ch 16 12 (No regular watch).

TELEPHONE (Dial code 018907)
Hr Mr 50223; MRSC (01333) 450666; ⌗ (0141) 887 9369 (H24); Marinecall 0891 500452; Police 50217; Dr 50599.

FACILITIES
Jetty AB £4.00, FW, D (see Hr Mr for 25 ltr containers or larger quantities by delivery), P (cans), Slip;
Services: BY, ME, Sh, El, C (12 ton mobile), Ⓔ.
Town EC Wed; LB, P, D, CH, V, R, Bar, ✉, Ⓞ, Gas, Gaz, Ⓑ, ⇌ (bus to Berwick-on-Tweed), ✈ (Edinburgh).

ADJACENT HARBOUR

BURNMOUTH, Borders, 55°50'·60N 02°04'·00W. AC 160. HW +0315 on Dover; –0025 on Leith; Duration 0615. Use Eyemouth tides 8.6.7. From S beware Quarry Shoal Rks; and E & W Carrs from N. 2 W posts (FR 29/35m 4M) 45m apart, lead 253° to close N of the hbr; as hbr mouth opens, enter on about 185° with outer hbr ent in line with 2FG (vert). Min depth at ent at LWS is 0·6m. Shelter is good especially in inner hbr (dries). With on-shore winds, swell makes outer hbr uncomfortable. Hr Mr (018907) 81283. Facilities: AB £4, FW, limited V, Bar at top of valley.

DUNBAR 8-6-8

East Lothian 56°00'·39N 02°31'·00W   Rtg 3-4-1

CHARTS
AC 734, 175; Imray 27; OS 67

TIDES
+0330 Dover; ML 3·0; Duration 0600; Zone 0 (UT)

Standard Port LEITH (→)

Times				Height (metres)			
High Water		Low Water		MHWS	MHWN	MLWN	MLWS
0300	0900	0300	0900	5·6	4·5	2·1	0·8
1500	2100	1500	2100				
Differences DUNBAR							
–0005	–0010	+0010	+0017	–0·4	–0·3	–0·1	–0·1
FIDRA							
+0006	+0006	–0006	–0006	–0·2	–0·2	0·0	0·0

SHELTER
Outer (Victoria) Hbr is subject to surge in strong NW to NE winds. N side dries; berth on S quay and contact Hr Mr. Inner (Old or Cromwell) Hbr dries, but is safe except in strong onshore winds near HWS when swell enters: entry is through a bridge, lifted on request to Hr Mr.

NAVIGATION
WPT 56°00'·70N 02°30'·80W, 018°/198° from/to front ldg lt 198°, 0·50M. Beware Outer Buss Rk (0·6m), 4ca to E. Ent is unsafe in heavy on-shore swell. Min depth at ent 0·9m. Keep to port on entry to avoid rockfall off castle.

LIGHTS AND MARKS
Church and Castle ruin both conspic. From NE, ldg lts, Oc G 6s 15/22m 3M, synch, intens 188°-208°, 2 W △ on Or cols, lead 198° through the outer rks to the Roads; thence narrow ent opens with QR brg 132°. From NW, appr on brg 132° between bns on Wallaces Head and Half Ebb Rk.

RADIO TELEPHONE
None.

TELEPHONE (Dial code 01368)
Hr Mr 863206; MRSC (01333) 450666; ⌗ (0141) 887 9369 (H24); Police 862718; Marinecall 0891 500452; Dr 862327; Ⓗ (031) 2292477.

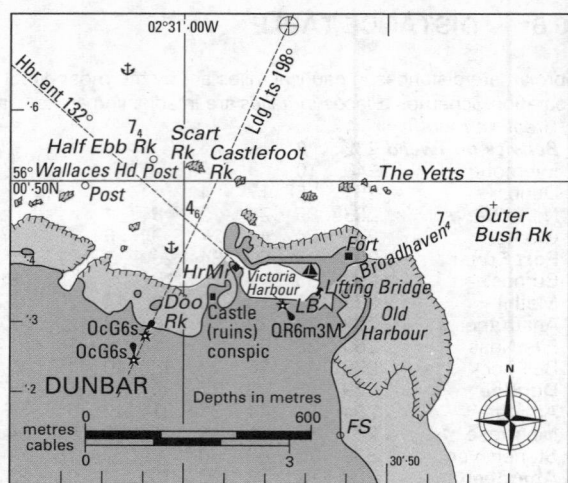

FACILITIES
Quay AB £7.50, Slip, FW, D (delivery), P (cans); **N Wall** M, AB; **Inner Hbr** Slip, AB; **Services** ME, Gas, Gaz.
Town EC Wed; LB, P, ▣, V, R, Bar, ✉, Ⓑ, ⇌, ✈ Edinburgh.

ADJACENT HARBOUR

ST ABBS, Borders, 55°54'·100N 02°07'·65W. AC 175. HW +0330 on Dover, –0017 on Leith; HW –0·6m on Leith; Duration 0605. Ldg line (about 228°) S face of Maw Carr on village hall (conspic R roof) leads SW until the hbr ent opens to port and the 2nd ldg line (about 167°) can be seen 2FR 4/8m 1M, or Y LB ho visible thru' ent. On E side of ent chan, beware Hog's Nose and on W side the Maw Carr. Shelter good. In strong on-shore winds outer hbr suffers from waves breaking over E pier. Inner hbr is best but often full of FVs and dries. Access HW±3. Hr Mr. will direct visitors. Hr Mr (018907) 71323. Facilities: AB £6, FW on quay, R, V, more facilities & bar at Coldingham (5M).

FIRTH OF FORTH 8-6-9

E and W Lothian/City of Edinburgh/Fife

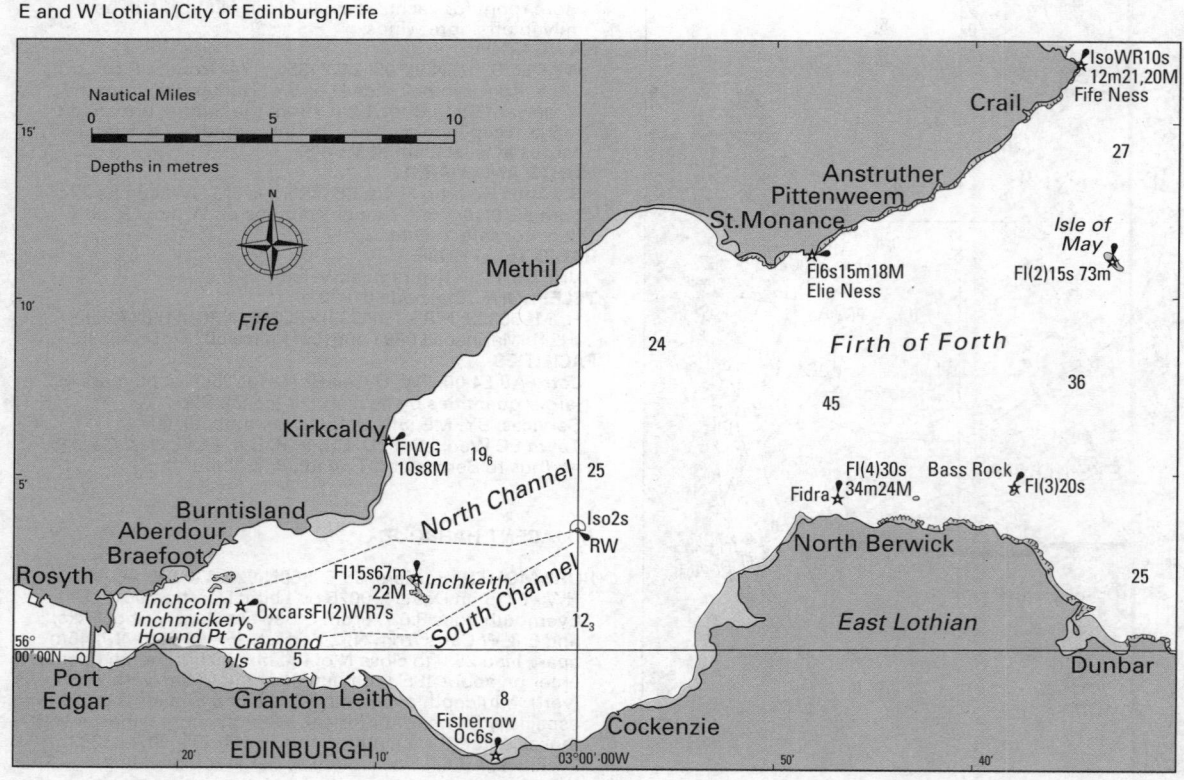

FIRTH OF FORTH *continued*

CHARTS
AC 734, 735, 736; Imray C27; OS 66, 59

TIDES
+0350 (Granton) Dover; ML 3·3; Duration 0620; Zone 0 (UT)

Standard Port LEITH (→)

Times				Height (metres)			
High Water		Low Water		MHWS	MHWN	MLWN	MLWS
0300	0900	0300	0900	5·6	4·5	2·1	0·8
1500	2100	1500	2100				

Differences COCKENZIE

–0007	–0015	–0013	–0005	–0·2	0·0	No data	

GRANTON: Same as LEITH

GRANGEMOUTH

+0025	+0010	–0052	–0015	–0·1	–0·2	–0·3	–0·3

KINCARDINE

+0015	+0030	–0030	–0030	0·0	–0·2	–0·5	–0·3

ALLOA

+0040	+0040	+0025	+0025	–0·2	–0·5	No data	–0·7

STIRLING

+0100	+0100	No data		–2·9	–3·1	–2·3	–0·7

Leith is a Standard Port and tidal predictions for each day of the year are given below.

SHELTER
Granton mostly dries and is open to swell in N'lies, but there are pontoons on E side of Middle pier in about 2m with 20 visitors' berths. Pilot boats berth at seaward end. W hbr is mainly commercial and for FVs.
Port Edgar marina offers good shelter, but prone to silting; do not enter E of wavebreak; 3kn speed limit. Leith is wholly commercial. Rosyth Naval Base should only be used in emergency.
Note: Forth Ports plc controls the Firth of Forth, Granton Hbr and all commercial impounded docks.

NAVIGATION
WPT Granton 56°00'·00N 03°13'·22W, 000°/180° from/to ent, 0·72M.
WPT Port Edgar 56°N 03°24'·2W, 064°/244° from/to Dir Lt, Fl R 4s, on W bkwtr, 3ca. Beware Hound Pt terminal; Forth railway and road bridges; HM Ships entering and leaving Rosyth Naval Base. On N shore, no vessel may enter Mortimer's Deep (Braefoot gas terminal) without prior approval from Forth Navigation Service. 12kn speed limit W of Forth Rly Bridge.
A Protected Chan 150m wide extends from Nos 13 and 14 lt buoys (NNW of Oxcars) under the bridges (N of Inch Garvie and Beamer Rk), to the ent of Rosyth Naval Base. When the Protected Chan is in operation all other vessels must clear the chan for naval traffic.

LIGHTS AND MARKS
Granton: R flag with W diagonal cross (or Ⓖ lt) on signal mast at middle pier hd = Entry prohib.
Port Edgar: On W pier Dir lt Fl R 4s 4m 8M 244°; 4 QY lts mark floating bkwtr; 3 x 2 FR (vert) mark N ends of marina pontoons.

RADIO TELEPHONE
Call *Forth Navigation* (at Leith) Ch **71** (calling and short messages, H24) 16; **20** 12 will be requested if necessary. Traffic, nav and weather info available on request. Leith Hbr Radio Ch 12. Granton marina, call *Boswell* Ch M. Port Edgar Marina Ch M **80** (Apl-Sept 0900-1930; Oct-Mar 0900-1630 LT). Rosyth Naval Base, call *QHM* Ch 74 13 73 (Mon-Fri: 0730-1700). Grangemouth Docks Ch 14 (H24).

TELEPHONE (Dial code 0131)
Forth Navigation Service 554 6473; QHM Rosyth (01383) 425050; MRSC (01333) 450666; ⌗ (0141) 887 9369 (H24); Weather (0141) 248 3451; Marinecall 0891 500452; Police (S. Queensferry) 331 1798; Ⓗ Edinburgh Royal Infirmary 229-2477; Flag Officer Scotland/Northern Ireland (01436) 674321 ext 3206, for Naval activities off N and E Scotland; Forth Yacht Clubs Ass'n 552 3452.

FACILITIES
GRANTON
Hr Mr via Leith, ☎ 554 3661, AB £11.50, Access HW±3½, FW, Slip; **Royal Forth YC** ☎ 552 3006, ⚓ 552 8560, Slip, M, L, FW, C (5 ton), D, El, Bar; **Forth Corinthian YC** ☎ 552 5939, Slip, M, L, Bar; **Services:** Gas, Gaz, Sh, CH, ME.
Town D, P, V, R, Bar, ⊠, Ⓑ, ⇌, ✈ (Buses to Edinburgh).
SOUTH QUEENSFERRY
Port Edgar Marina (300+8 visitors) ☎ 331 3330, ⚓ 331 4878, £12.33, Access H24, M, Slip, AC, CH, D, C (5 ton) on N end of main pier, El, Ⓔ, ME, Sh, SM, Gas, Gaz, FW, R; Port Edgar YC, Bar. **Town** EC Wed; P, V, R, Bar, ⊠, Ⓑ, ⇌ (Dalmeny), ✈ Edinburgh.
EDINBURGH: ACA.
Note: It is planned to open the Forth & Clyde Canal to navigation by Easter 2001. It will link the Rivers Forth and Clyde and will be navigable by craft with max LOA of 20m, beam 5·79m, draught 1·83m and air draft 3·0m.

Continued overleaf

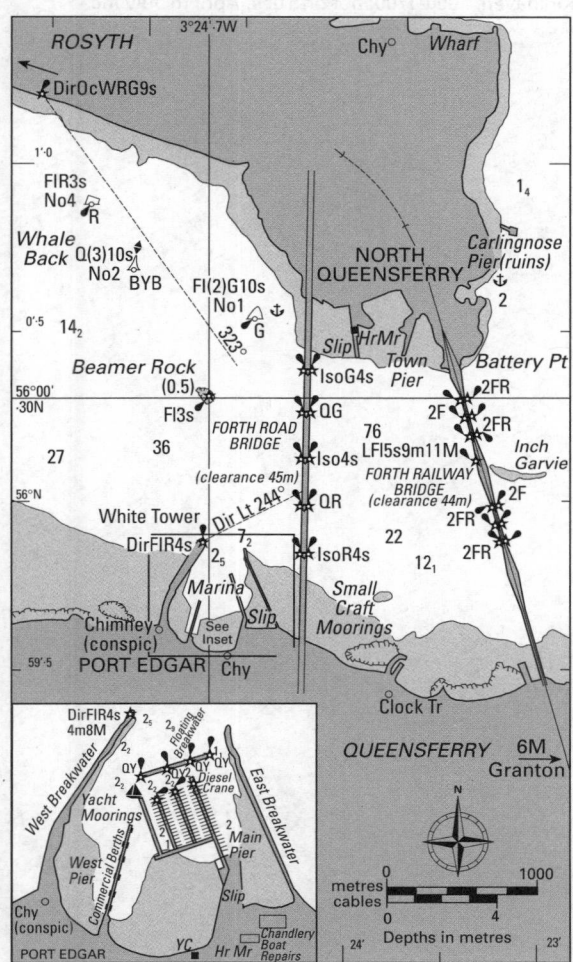

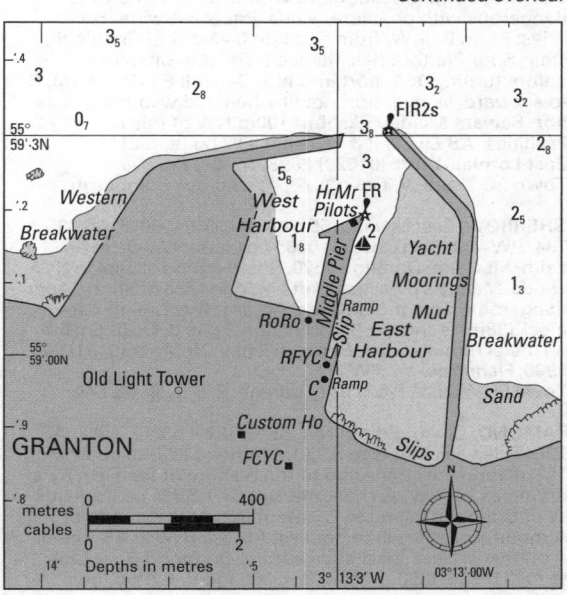

HARBOURS AND ANCHORAGES ON THE NORTH SHORE OF THE FIRTH OF FORTH

INCHCOLM, Fife, 56°01'·85N, 03°17'·80W. AC 736. Tides see 8.6.8. Best ⚓ in 4m, N of abbey (conspic); appr from NW or ESE, to land at pier close E (small fee). Meaduslse Rks (dry) on N side. Ends of island foul. At SE end, lt Fl (3) 15s, obsc 075°-145°, horn (3) 45s. No facilities. ☎ 0131-244 3101. Keep clear of large ships under way in Mortimer's Deep.

ABERDOUR, Fife, 56°03'·00N 03°17'·40W. AC 735, 736. HW +0345 on Dover; +0005 on Leith; HW 0·5m on Leith; ML 3·3m; Duration 0630. See 8.6.8. Good shelter except in SE winds when a swell occurs. The ⚓ between The Little Craigs and the disused pier is good but exposed to winds from E to SW. Temp berths £2 are available in hbr (dries) alongside the quay wall. Beware Little Craigs (dries 2·2m) and outfall 2ca N marked by bn. There are no lts/ marks. Hr Mr ☎ (01383) 860452. Facilities: FW (tap on pier), P, R, V, Bar in village, EC Wed; **Aberdour BC** ☎ (01592) 202827.

BURNTISLAND: See 8.6.10
KIRKCALDY: See 8.6.11
METHIL: See 8.6.11

ELIE, Fife, 56°11'·20N 02°49'·20W. AC 734. HW +0325 on Dover, −0015 on Leith; HW −0·1m on Leith; ML 3·0m; Duration 0620; Elie B provides good shelter from N winds for small craft but local knowledge is needed. Hbr dries; 3 short term waiting buoys available. Beware ledge off end of pier which dries. From E beware Ox Rk (dries 1m) 5M ENE of Elie Ness; from W beware rks off Chapel Ness, W Vows, E Vows (surmounted by cage bn) and Thill Rk, marked by PHM buoy. Lt: Elie Ness Fl 6s 15m 18M, W tr. Hr Mr (01333) 330502; AB (3) drying £5, M, AC, FW, CH, SC, Slip. Police 310333. Dr ☎ 330302; **Services:** P & D (tanker), Gas, Gaz. El. In Elie & Earlsferry: R, V, Bar, ✉, Ⓑ.

ST MONANS, Fife, 56°12'·25N 02°45'·85W. AC 734. HW +0335 on Dover, −0020 on Leith; HW −0·1m on Leith; ML 3·0m; Duration 0620. Shelter good except in strong SE to SW winds when scend occurs in the hbr (dries). Berth alongside E pier until contact with Hr Mr. From NE keep at least 2½ca from coast. Bkwtr hd Oc WRG 6s 5m 7/4M; E pier hd 2 FG (vert) 6m 4M. W pier hd 2 FR (vert) 6m 4M. Facilities: Hr Mr ☎ (01333) 730428; AB £5.10, FW, AC, El; **Services:** Gas, P & D (tanker), AC. **Village** R, Bar, V, ✉, Ⓑ.

PITTENWEEM, Fife, 56°12'·60N 02°43'·70W. AC 734. HW +0325 Dover; −0015 and −0.1m on Leith; ML 3m. Duration 0620. Busy fishing hbr, dredged 1-2m, access all tides, but not in onshore winds. Yachts not encouraged; contact Hr Mr for berth at W end of inner hbr, but only for emergency use. Outer hbr dries to rock; is only suitable for temp stop in calm weather. Appr 037° on ldg marks/lts, Gy cols/Y stripe, both FR 3/8m 5M. Rks to port marked by bn, QR 3m 2M, and 3 unlit bns. E bkwtr lt Fl (2) RG 5s 9m 9/6M, R265°-345°, G345°-055°. No VHF. Hr Mr ☎ (01333) 312591. Facilities: FW, CH, D & P (tanker), Gas, V, Bar.

ANSTRUTHER: See 8.6.12

CRAIL, Fife, 56°15'·35N 02°37'·20W. AC 175. HW +0320 on Dover, −0020 on Leith; HW −0·2m on Leith; ML 3·0m; Duration 0615. Good shelter but only for boats able to take the ground alongside. Appr between S pier and bn on rks to S following ldg line 295°, two W concrete pillars with FR lts, 24/30m 6M. Turn 150° to stbd for ent. Call Forth CG on VHF Ch 16 before entering. Hr Mr ☎ (01333) 450820. Facilities: AB £5.10, El, FW, AC, Slip, P. **Village** EC Wed; Bar, R, V, ✉, Ⓑ.

ISLE OF MAY, Fife, 56°11'·40N 02°33'·60W. AC 734. HW +0325 on Dover, −0025 on Leith. In settled weather only, and depending on the wind, ⚓ at E or W Tarbert in 4m; landing at Altarstanes. Near the SE tip there is a tiny hbr at Kirkhaven, with narrow, rky ent; yachts can moor fore-and-aft to rings in rks, in about 1-1·5m. SDs are needed. Beware Norman Rk to N of Island, and Maiden Hair Rk to S. At the summit, a ☐ tr on stone ho, Fl (2) 15s 73m 22M. The island is a bird sanctuary, owned by Scottish Natural Heritage ☎ (01334) 654038. Avoid the breeding season, mid-Mar to end Jul. Landing only at Altarstanes or Kirkhaven, 1000-1700; not on Tues, April to July inc.

HARBOURS AND ANCHORAGES ON THE SOUTH SHORE OF THE FIRTH OF FORTH

NORTH BERWICK, East Lothian, 56°03'·74N 02°42'·95W. AC 734. Fidra HW +0344 on Dover; ML 3·0m; Duration 0625. See 8.6.8 Fidra. Shelter good with winds from S to W but dangerous with on-shore winds. Ent is 8m wide. Hbr dries. From E or W, from position 0·25M S of Craigleith, steer S for Plattock Rks, thence SSW 40m off bkwtr before turning 180° port into hbr. Bkwtr lt F WR 7m 3M, R to seaward, W over hbr; not lit when bad weather closes hbr. Beware Maiden Rks (bn) 100m NW of this lt. Facilities: AB £5.70, P & D (cans), FW on pier, CH; **East Lothian YC** ☎ (01620) 2698, M, ⚓s, Bar. **Town** EC Thurs; V, Gas, Ⓑ, ✉, ⇌ and bus Edinburgh.

FISHERROW, East Lothian, 55°56'·79N 03°04'·00W. AC 735, 734. HW +0345 on Dover, −0005 on Leith; HW −0·1m on Leith; ML 3·0m; Duration 0620. Shelter good except in NW winds. Mainly a pleasure craft hbr, dries 5ca offshore. Appr dangerous in on-shore winds. Access HW±2. High-rise block (38m) is conspic 9ca W of hbr. E pier lt, Oc 6s 5m 6M on metal framework tr. Berth on E pier. Hr Mr ☎ (0131) 665 5900; **Fisherrow YC** FW. **Town** EC Wed; V, P & D from garage, R, Bar, Ⓑ, ✉, SM.

CRAMOND, City of Edinburgh, 55°59'·80N 03°17'·40W. AC 736. Tides as Leith (see 8.6.9). Cramond Island, approx 1M offshore, is connected to the S shore of the Firth by a drying causeway. A chan, marked by 7 SHM posts, leads W of Cramond Island to Cramond hbr at the mouth of R Almond, conspic white houses. Access HW±2; AB free or ⚓ off the Is. Seek local advice from: **Cramond Boat Club** ☎ (0131) 336 1356, FW, M, Bar. **Village** V, R, Pub, Bus.

SCOTLAND – LEITH

LAT 55°59′N   LONG 3°11′W

TIMES AND HEIGHTS OF HIGH AND LOW WATERS

YEAR **1999**

TIME ZONE (UT)
For Summer Time add ONE hour in non-shaded areas

JANUARY

Day	Time	m	Time	m	Day	Time	m	Time	m
1 F	0119	5.6	1347	5.6	**16** SA	0147	5.0	1401	5.2
	0735	1.0	1958	0.8		0724	1.5	1951	1.3
2 SA O	0211	5.7	1435	5.7	**17** SU ●	0226	5.2	1439	5.3
	0824	0.9	2050	0.6		0803	1.3	2031	1.1
3 SU	0300	5.8	1522	5.8	**18** M	0303	5.3	1516	5.4
	0910	0.9	2138	0.5		0842	1.1	2111	0.9
4 M	0349	5.7	1608	5.7	**19** TU	0340	5.4	1551	5.5
	0952	1.0	2223	0.6		0921	1.0	2151	0.8
5 TU	0436	5.6	1655	5.6	**20** W	0417	5.4	1627	5.5
	1030	1.1	2302	0.8		1001	1.0	2231	0.7
6 W	0523	5.4	1742	5.4	**21** TH	0456	5.4	1705	5.5
	1059	1.4	2335	1.1		1040	1.1	2310	0.8
7 TH	0609	5.2	1829	5.1	**22** F	0538	5.3	1748	5.4
	1123	1.6				1118	1.2	2349	1.0
8 F	0003	1.3	1158	1.9	**23** SA	0625	5.2	1835	5.3
	0655	4.9	1917	4.9		1158	1.4		
9 SA	0041	1.6	1247	2.1	**24** SU	0030	1.2	1247	1.6
	0743	4.7	2009	4.7		0716	5.1	1929	5.1
10 SU	0134	1.9	1356	2.3	**25** M	0120	1.4	1352	1.8
	0835	4.5	2104	4.6		0814	4.9	2033	4.9
11 M	0245	2.0	1525	2.4	**26** TU	0230	1.6	1516	1.9
	0930	4.5	2204	4.5		0921	4.8	2148	4.9
12 TU	0406	2.1	1642	2.3	**27** W	0405	1.7	1644	1.8
	1030	4.5	2309	4.5		1034	4.8	2304	4.9
13 W	0512	2.0	1741	2.1	**28** TH	0529	1.7	1757	1.5
	1134	4.6				1144	5.0		
14 TH	0012	4.6	1232	4.8	**29** F	0014	5.1	1246	5.2
	0602	1.8	1829	1.8		0633	1.5	1859	1.2
15 F	0104	4.8	1320	5.0	**30** SA	0114	5.3	1339	5.4
	0644	1.6	1911	1.6		0725	1.3	1953	0.9
					31 SU O	0206	5.5	1427	5.6
						0812	1.1	2042	0.7

FEBRUARY

Day	Time	m	Time	m	Day	Time	m	Time	m
1 M	0252	5.6	1511	5.7	**16** TU ●	0242	5.4	1454	5.5
	0854	1.0	2126	0.5		0826	1.0	2056	0.7
2 TU	0335	5.6	1554	5.7	**17** W	0319	5.5	1530	5.7
	0933	0.9	2205	0.5		0907	0.8	2137	0.5
3 W	0417	5.5	1635	5.6	**18** TH	0356	5.6	1607	5.7
	1007	1.0	2238	0.7		0947	0.7	2217	0.4
4 TH	0457	5.4	1715	5.4	**19** F	0435	5.6	1646	5.7
	1032	1.2	2302	0.9		1026	0.7	2256	0.5
5 F	0536	5.2	1754	5.2	**20** SA	0517	5.5	1729	5.6
	1053	1.3	2325	1.1		1104	0.8	2332	0.7
6 SA	0616	5.0	1834	5.0	**21** SU	0603	5.3	1816	5.5
	1120	1.6	2356	1.4		1140	1.1		
7 SU	0658	4.8	1918	4.8	**22** M	0008	1.0	1222	1.4
	1156	1.8				0651	5.1	1909	5.2
8 M	0037	1.7	1244	2.1	**23** TU	0052	1.4	1321	1.7
	0743	4.6	2008	4.5		0748	4.9	2014	4.9
9 TU	0133	2.0	1357	2.4	**24** W	0158	1.8	1453	1.9
	0834	4.4	2105	4.4		0856	4.7	2132	4.7
10 W	0252	2.2	1546	2.4	**25** TH	0350	2.0	1637	1.8
	0932	4.3	2211	4.3		1013	4.6	2254	4.7
11 TH	0425	2.2	1709	2.2	**26** F	0522	1.9	1756	1.5
	1038	4.3	2325	4.4		1131	4.8		
12 F	0532	2.1	1807	2.0	**27** SA	0010	4.9	1239	5.0
	1149	4.5				0625	1.7	1856	1.2
13 SA	0031	4.6	1250	4.8	**28** SU	0111	5.2	1333	5.3
	0622	1.8	1853	1.6		0715	1.4	1946	0.9
14 SU	0122	4.9	1337	5.1					
	0705	1.5	1935	1.3					
15 M	0203	5.1	1417	5.3					
	0745	1.3	2016	1.0					

MARCH

Day	Time	m	Time	m	Day	Time	m	Time	m
1 M	0159	5.3	1418	5.5	**16** TU	0135	5.1	1349	5.3
	0757	1.2	2028	0.7		0724	1.2	1955	0.8
2 TU O	0240	5.5	1458	5.6	**17** W ●	0215	5.4	1427	5.6
	0835	1.0	2106	0.6		0805	0.9	2036	0.4
3 W	0318	5.5	1536	5.6	**18** TH	0253	5.6	1505	5.8
	0910	0.9	2140	0.5		0847	0.6	2117	0.2
4 TH	0354	5.5	1612	5.5	**19** F	0332	5.8	1544	5.8
	0941	0.9	2208	0.6		0928	0.4	2158	0.1
5 F	0429	5.4	1646	5.4	**20** SA	0413	5.8	1626	5.9
	1005	1.0	2230	0.8		1009	0.4	2237	0.3
6 SA	0503	5.2	1721	5.2	**21** SU	0456	5.6	1711	5.8
	1026	1.1	2253	1.0		1048	0.6	2315	0.6
7 SU	0539	5.0	1757	5.0	**22** M	0541	5.4	1801	5.5
	1049	1.3	2319	1.3		1127	1.0	2351	1.0
8 M	0617	4.8	1837	4.8	**23** TU	0631	5.2	1856	5.2
	1116	1.6	2352	1.6		1209	1.2		
9 TU	0659	4.6	1923	4.5	**24** W	0033	1.5	1309	1.5
	1151	1.8				0727	4.8	2003	4.8
10 W	0035	2.0	1243	2.2	**25** TH	0144	1.9	1447	1.8
	0745	4.4	2015	4.3		0836	4.6	2121	4.6
11 TH	0143	2.3	1423	2.4	**26** F	0342	2.1	1633	1.7
	0841	4.2	2119	4.2		0955	4.5	2243	4.6
12 F	0331	2.4	1629	2.3	**27** SA	0510	2.0	1748	1.4
	0946	4.2	2234	4.2		1116	4.7		
13 SA	0500	2.2	1739	2.0	**28** SU	0000	4.8	1225	4.9
	1102	4.3	2351	4.5		0610	1.7	1844	1.2
14 SU	0556	1.9	1830	1.6	**29** M	0059	5.1	1318	5.1
	1212	4.6				0656	1.5	1929	0.9
15 M	0049	4.8	1306	5.0	**30** TU	0144	5.2	1401	5.3
	0642	1.5	1913	1.2		0735	1.2	2006	0.8
					31 W O	0222	5.3	1439	5.4
						0810	1.0	2039	0.6

APRIL

Day	Time	m	Time	m	Day	Time	m	Time	m
1 TH	0256	5.4	1514	5.4	**16** F ●	0226	5.7	1439	5.8
	0843	0.9	2109	0.6		0823	0.4	2054	0.1
2 F	0328	5.4	1547	5.4	**17** SA	0308	5.8	1522	6.0
	0913	0.8	2136	0.6		0907	0.3	2137	0.1
3 SA	0400	5.3	1620	5.3	**18** SU	0350	5.8	1608	5.9
	0940	0.9	2200	0.8		0952	0.3	2219	0.3
4 SU	0433	5.2	1653	5.2	**19** M	0435	5.7	1656	5.8
	1003	1.0	2224	1.0		1036	0.4	2300	0.6
5 M	0507	5.1	1729	5.0	**20** TU	0522	5.5	1749	5.5
	1024	1.2	2248	1.2		1119	0.7	2341	1.1
6 TU	0543	4.9	1807	4.8	**21** W	0613	5.2	1847	5.2
	1047	1.4	2315	1.5		1207	1.0		
7 W	0622	4.7	1849	4.6	**22** TH	0026	1.6	1309	1.4
	1117	1.6	2349	1.9		0712	4.9	1953	4.8
8 TH	0705	4.5	1939	4.4	**23** F	0138	2.0	1441	1.6
	1201	1.9				0821	4.6	2106	4.6
9 F	0047	2.2	1322	2.1	**24** SA	0321	2.2	1615	1.6
	0758	4.3	2039	4.2		0936	4.6	2222	4.6
10 SA	0236	2.4	1530	2.1	**25** SU	0443	2.0	1725	1.4
	0902	4.2	2149	4.2		1052	4.6	2335	4.8
11 SU	0418	2.2	1658	1.9	**26** M	0542	1.8	1819	1.2
	1016	4.3	2305	4.4		1159	4.8		
12 M	0522	1.9	1755	1.5	**27** TU	0033	4.9	1253	5.0
	1130	4.5				0627	1.5	1900	1.1
13 TU	0010	4.8	1228	4.9	**28** W	0119	5.1	1337	5.1
	0611	1.5	1842	1.0		0705	1.3	1935	0.9
14 W	0102	5.2	1315	5.3	**29** TH	0157	5.2	1415	5.2
	0656	1.1	1926	0.7		0740	1.1	2006	0.8
15 TH	0145	5.5	1358	5.6	**30** F O	0230	5.2	1450	5.3
	0739	0.7	2010	0.3		0814	0.9	2035	0.8

6

Chart Datum: 2·90 metres below Ordnance Datum (Newlyn)

SCOTLAND – LEITH

LAT 55°59′N   LONG 3°11′W

TIMES AND HEIGHTS OF HIGH AND LOW WATERS

YEAR **1999**

TIME ZONE (UT)
For Summer Time add ONE hour in non-shaded areas

MAY

Day	Time	m	Time	m	Time	m	Time	m
1 SA	0302	5.3	0846	0.9	1523	5.3	2104	0.8
2 SU	0334	5.2	0916	0.9	1556	5.2	2132	0.9
3 M	0406	5.2	0944	1.0	1630	5.1	2159	1.0
4 TU	0440	5.1	1008	1.1	1705	5.0	2225	1.2
5 W	0515	4.9	1032	1.2	1743	4.8	2250	1.5
6 TH	0553	4.8	1102	1.4	1824	4.7	2323	1.8
7 F	0634	4.6	1147	1.6	1911	4.5		
8 SA	0017	2.0	0724	4.4	1257	1.8	2007	4.4
9 SU	0153	2.2	0825	4.3	1434	1.9	2113	4.4
10 M	0329	2.1	0935	4.4	1606	1.7	2224	4.5
11 TU	0440	1.8	1046	4.6	1712	1.4	2330	4.8
12 W	0535	1.5	1149	4.9	1806	1.0		
13 TH	0026	5.2	0624	1.1	1242	5.3	1855	0.7
14 F	0115	5.5	0712	0.8	1329	5.6	1944	0.4
15 SA ●	0200	5.7	0800	0.5	1415	5.8	2031	0.2
16 SU	0244	5.8	0849	0.3	1503	5.9	2118	0.2
17 M	0330	5.8	0938	0.2	1552	5.9	2204	0.4
18 TU	0417	5.7	1026	0.3	1644	5.8	2249	0.7
19 W	0506	5.5	1114	0.6	1738	5.5	2332	1.2
20 TH	0559	5.2	1204	0.9	1835	5.2		
21 F	0019	1.6	0658	5.0	1302	1.2	1937	4.9
22 SA	0119	1.9	0802	4.8	1416	1.4	2041	4.7
23 SU	0239	2.1	0910	4.6	1538	1.5	2148	4.6
24 M	0357	2.1	1017	4.6	1646	1.5	2255	4.6
25 TU	0458	1.9	1122	4.7	1739	1.4	2355	4.8
26 W	0548	1.7	1219	4.8	1822	1.3		
27 TH	0045	4.9	0630	1.5	1307	4.9	1857	1.2
28 F	0127	5.0	0709	1.3	1348	5.0	1930	1.1
29 SA	0203	5.1	0746	1.1	1425	5.1	2002	1.0
30 SU O	0237	5.2	0821	1.0	1500	5.1	2035	1.0
31 M	0310	5.2	0854	1.0	1534	5.1	2107	1.0

JUNE

Day	Time	m	Time	m	Time	m	Time	m
1 TU	0344	5.2	0927	1.0	1609	5.1	2139	1.1
2 W	0418	5.1	0958	1.0	1645	5.0	2210	1.2
3 TH	0453	5.0	1029	1.1	1722	4.9	2242	1.4
4 F	0530	4.9	1104	1.2	1802	4.8	2317	1.6
5 SA	0611	4.8	1147	1.4	1848	4.7		
6 SU	0008	1.8	0658	4.7	1244	1.5	1940	4.6
7 M	0120	1.9	0754	4.6	1354	1.6	2041	4.5
8 TU	0240	1.9	0858	4.6	1513	1.5	2147	4.7
9 W	0354	1.8	1007	4.7	1627	1.3	2253	4.9
10 TH	0457	1.5	1112	4.9	1730	1.1	2354	5.1
11 F	0554	1.2	1212	5.2	1828	0.8		
12 SA	0048	5.4	0648	0.9	1306	5.5	1921	0.6
13 SU ●	0138	5.6	0742	0.6	1357	5.7	2013	0.5
14 M	0225	5.7	0835	0.4	1448	5.8	2103	0.5
15 TU	0313	5.6	0927	0.3	1539	5.8	2150	0.6
16 W	0402	5.7	1017	0.3	1631	5.7	2236	0.8
17 TH	0452	5.6	1106	0.4	1724	5.5	2319	1.1
18 F	0545	5.4	1153	0.7	1818	5.3	2359	1.4
19 SA	0640	5.1	1239	1.0	1913	5.1		
20 SU	0042	1.7	0737	4.9	1331	1.3	2008	4.8
21 M	0140	2.0	0835	4.7	1435	1.6	2105	4.6
22 TU	0252	2.1	0935	4.6	1544	1.7	2204	4.5
23 W	0404	2.1	1037	4.6	1646	1.7	2306	4.6
24 TH	0504	1.9	1138	4.6	1736	1.6		
25 F	0003	4.7	0555	1.7	1234	4.7	1818	1.5
26 SA	0053	4.8	0640	1.5	1320	4.9	1857	1.4
27 SU	0135	5.0	0720	1.3	1401	5.0	1934	1.2
28 M O	0212	5.1	0758	1.2	1438	5.1	2010	1.2
29 TU	0248	5.2	0835	1.0	1513	5.1	2046	1.1
30 W	0324	5.2	0911	1.0	1549	5.2	2123	1.1

JULY

Day	Time	m	Time	m	Time	m	Time	m
1 TH	0359	5.2	0948	0.9	1625	5.1	2159	1.1
2 F	0434	5.2	1025	0.9	1702	5.1	2236	1.2
3 SA	0510	5.1	1103	1.0	1742	5.0	2314	1.3
4 SU	0550	5.1	1143	1.1	1826	5.0	2357	1.5
5 M	0635	5.0	1228	1.2	1915	4.9		
6 TU	0049	1.6	0726	4.9	1322	1.3	2011	4.8
7 W	0155	1.8	0825	4.8	1427	1.4	2114	4.8
8 TH	0310	1.8	0933	4.8	1544	1.4	2221	4.9
9 F	0424	1.6	1043	4.9	1702	1.3	2327	5.0
10 SA	0532	1.4	1150	5.1	1809	1.1		
11 SU ●	0027	5.2	0633	1.1	1251	5.4	1910	0.9
12 M	0121	5.6	0732	0.8	1346	5.6	2000	0.8
13 TU ●	0211	5.6	0827	0.5	1438	5.7	2049	0.7
14 W	0259	5.7	0918	0.3	1528	5.8	2136	0.7
15 TH	0348	5.6	1006	0.3	1617	5.7	2219	0.8
16 F	0436	5.6	1050	0.4	1705	5.5	2257	1.0
17 SA	0525	5.5	1130	0.6	1753	5.3	2329	1.3
18 SU	0614	5.3	1204	0.9	1841	5.1	2359	1.6
19 M	0703	5.0	1237	1.3	1929	4.8		
20 TU	0039	1.8	0754	4.8	1320	1.6	2018	4.6
21 W	0138	2.1	0847	4.6	1421	1.8	2111	4.5
22 TH	0258	2.2	0945	4.5	1539	2.0	2209	4.4
23 F	0420	2.2	1049	4.4	1650	1.9	2312	4.5
24 SA	0524	2.0	1155	4.5	1745	1.8		
25 SU	0014	4.6	0615	1.8	1251	4.7	1829	1.6
26 M	0106	4.8	0659	1.5	1337	4.9	1910	1.5
27 TU	0148	5.0	0739	1.3	1415	5.1	1948	1.3
28 W	0227	5.2	0817	1.1	1452	5.2	2027	1.1
29 TH	0303	5.3	0856	0.9	1528	5.3	2106	1.0
30 F	0339	5.4	0935	0.7	1604	5.3	2145	0.9
31 SA	0414	5.4	1014	0.7	1641	5.3	2224	0.9

AUGUST

Day	Time	m	Time	m	Time	m	Time	m
1 SU	0449	5.4	1052	0.7	1720	5.3	2301	1.1
2 M	0528	5.4	1129	0.8	1803	5.2	2339	1.2
3 TU	0612	5.3	1207	1.0	1850	5.1		
4 W	0021	1.4	0701	5.1	1251	1.2	1943	4.9
5 TH	0117	1.7	0758	5.0	1349	1.5	2044	4.8
6 F	0233	1.8	0908	4.8	1513	1.7	2154	4.8
7 SA	0403	1.8	1025	4.9	1648	1.6	2306	4.9
8 SU	0523	1.5	1139	5.0	1801	1.5		
9 M	0013	5.1	0629	1.2	1245	5.2	1858	1.3
10 TU	0111	5.4	0727	0.9	1340	5.5	1949	1.0
11 W ●	0201	5.6	0819	0.5	1429	5.6	2034	0.9
12 TH	0247	5.7	0906	0.3	1514	5.7	2117	0.8
13 F	0332	5.8	0948	0.3	1558	5.7	2156	0.8
14 SA	0416	5.7	1027	0.4	1641	5.5	2229	0.7
15 SU	0459	5.6	1059	0.6	1723	5.3	2254	1.2
16 M	0541	5.4	1123	0.9	1804	5.1	2317	1.4
17 TU	0624	5.1	1149	1.2	1846	4.9	2349	1.7
18 W	0708	4.9	1224	1.6	1931	4.7		
19 TH	0033	2.0	0757	4.6	1315	1.9	2020	4.5
20 F	0142	2.3	0852	4.4	1429	2.2	2115	4.4
21 SA	0329	2.3	0956	4.3	1604	2.3	2218	4.4
22 SU	0456	2.2	1108	4.3	1715	2.1	2328	4.5
23 M	0555	1.9	1218	4.6	1806	1.9		
24 TU	0032	4.7	0640	1.6	1309	4.8	1848	1.6
25 W	0120	5.0	0720	1.3	1350	5.1	1928	1.3
26 TH O	0201	5.3	0759	1.0	1427	5.3	2007	1.1
27 F	0238	5.5	0837	0.7	1503	5.5	2047	0.9
28 SA	0314	5.6	0916	0.5	1540	5.6	2126	0.7
29 SU	0349	5.7	0955	0.4	1617	5.6	2205	0.7
30 M	0426	5.7	1033	0.5	1657	5.6	2243	0.8
31 TU	0506	5.6	1109	0.6	1739	5.4	2319	1.0

Chart Datum: 2·90 metres below Ordnance Datum (Newlyn)

TIME ZONE (UT)
For Summer Time add ONE hour in non-shaded areas

SCOTLAND – LEITH

LAT 55°59′N   LONG 3°11′W

TIMES AND HEIGHTS OF HIGH AND LOW WATERS   YEAR **1999**

6

SEPTEMBER

Day	Time	m	Time	m	Time	m	Time	m
1 W	0551	5.5	1144	0.9	1826	5.2	2358	1.3
16 TH	0626	4.9	1137	1.6	1846	4.7	2341	1.9
2 TH	0641	5.3	1223	1.3	1918	5.0		
17 F	0712	4.6	1219	2.0	1933	4.5		
3 F	0051	1.6	0740	5.0	1321	1.7	2020	4.8
18 SA	0033	2.2	0805	4.4	1324	2.3	2027	4.4
4 SA	0214	1.8	0853	4.8	1459	2.0	2134	4.7
19 SU	0214	2.4	0906	4.2	1510	2.5	2129	4.3
5 SU	0359	1.8	1015	4.8	1645	1.9	2252	4.8
20 M	0422	2.3	1018	4.3	1643	2.4	2241	4.4
6 M	0524	1.6	1135	4.9	1755	1.7		
21 TU	0530	2.0	1135	4.5	1740	2.1	2352	4.7
7 TU	0004	5.1	0628	1.2	1241	5.2	1849	1.5
22 W	0616	1.6	1234	4.8	1824	1.7		
8 W	0103	5.3	0721	0.9	1334	5.4	1934	1.2
23 TH	0046	1.3	0656	1.3	1319	5.1	1904	1.3
9 TH ●	0150	5.5	0806	0.6	1417	5.6	2015	1.0
24 F	0130	5.3	0734	0.9	1358	5.4	1943	1.0
10 F	0233	5.7	0847	0.4	1457	5.6	2053	0.8
25 SA O	0208	5.6	0813	0.6	1436	5.6	2023	0.8
11 SA	0313	5.7	0924	0.4	1536	5.6	2128	0.8
26 SU	0245	5.8	0853	0.3	1513	5.8	2104	0.6
12 SU	0352	5.7	0956	0.5	1613	5.5	2158	0.9
27 M	0322	5.9	0932	0.3	1552	5.8	2144	0.6
13 M	0430	5.5	1022	0.7	1649	5.4	2221	1.1
28 TU	0402	5.9	1011	0.3	1633	5.7	2224	0.7
14 TU	0507	5.4	1043	0.9	1726	5.2	2241	1.3
29 W	0446	5.8	1049	0.6	1716	5.6	2303	0.9
15 W	0545	5.1	1107	1.2	1804	5.0	2307	1.6
30 TH	0533	5.6	1124	1.0	1804	5.3	2345	1.2

OCTOBER

Day	Time	m	Time	m	Time	m	Time	m
1 F	0626	5.3	1204	1.5	1857	5.1		
16 SA	0636	4.7	1133	2.0	1851	4.6	2350	2.0
2 SA	0042	1.6	0729	5.0	1307	1.9	2002	4.8
17 SU	0726	4.5	1226	2.3	1943	4.4		
3 SU	0211	1.8	0845	4.8	1457	2.2	2120	4.7
18 M	0109	2.3	0824	4.3	1410	2.6	2045	4.4
4 M	0359	1.8	1007	4.7	1636	2.1	2240	4.8
19 TU	0318	2.3	0932	4.3	1557	2.5	2156	4.4
5 TU	0518	1.5	1126	4.9	1742	1.9	2351	5.1
20 W	0448	2.0	1046	4.5	1703	2.1	2307	4.7
6 W	0618	1.2	1230	5.2	1832	1.6		
21 TH	0540	1.6	1151	4.8	1752	1.8		
7 TH	0048	5.3	0705	0.9	1320	5.4	1913	1.3
22 F	0006	5.0	0623	1.3	1242	5.2	1834	1.4
8 F	0135	5.5	0745	0.7	1400	5.5	1950	1.1
23 SA	0055	5.3	0704	0.9	1326	5.5	1916	1.0
9 SA ●	0214	5.6	0821	0.6	1436	5.6	2025	0.9
24 SU O	0137	5.6	0745	0.6	1406	5.7	1958	0.7
10 SU	0251	5.6	0853	0.6	1510	5.6	2059	0.9
25 M	0217	5.9	0827	0.4	1446	5.9	2040	0.6
11 M	0327	5.6	0922	0.7	1544	5.5	2128	1.0
26 TU	0258	6.0	0909	0.3	1527	5.9	2124	0.5
12 TU	0402	5.5	0946	0.8	1617	5.4	2151	1.1
27 W	0342	6.0	0951	0.4	1610	5.8	2208	0.6
13 W	0436	5.3	1008	1.0	1652	5.2	2212	1.3
28 TH	0429	5.9	1033	0.7	1656	5.7	2253	0.8
14 TH	0513	5.1	1032	1.3	1728	5.0	2235	1.5
29 F	0519	5.7	1113	1.1	1745	5.4	2342	1.1
15 F	0552	4.9	1059	1.6	1807	4.8	2306	1.7
30 SA	0616	5.4	1158	1.6	1841	5.1		
31 SU	0042	1.4	0720	5.0	1304	2.0	1949	4.9

NOVEMBER

Day	Time	m	Time	m	Time	m	Time	m
1 M	0207	1.7	0833	4.8	1441	2.3	2104	4.8
16 TU	0035	2.0	0748	4.5	1318	2.4	2004	4.5
2 TU	0343	1.7	0950	4.8	1610	2.2	2220	4.8
17 W	0207	2.1	0851	4.4	1458	2.4	2112	4.5
3 W	0458	1.7	1104	4.9	1715	2.0	2328	5.0
18 TH	0343	2.0	0959	4.6	1615	2.2	2221	4.7
4 TH	0555	1.3	1207	5.1	1804	1.7		
19 F	0451	1.7	1106	4.8	1712	1.8	2324	5.0
5 F	0025	5.2	0640	1.1	1256	5.3	1845	1.5
20 SA	0544	1.3	1204	5.2	1801	1.5		
6 SA	0113	5.4	0717	1.0	1337	5.4	1922	1.3
21 SU	0018	5.3	0631	1.0	1254	5.5	1847	1.2
7 SU	0153	5.4	0750	0.9	1412	5.4	1957	1.1
22 M	0106	5.6	0717	0.7	1339	5.7	1933	0.9
8 M ●	0230	5.5	0820	0.9	1445	5.5	2031	1.1
23 TU O	0152	5.8	0803	0.5	1422	5.9	2020	0.6
9 TU	0304	5.5	0848	0.9	1517	5.4	2101	1.1
24 W	0237	6.0	0849	0.5	1505	5.9	2109	0.5
10 W	0338	5.4	0915	1.0	1550	5.4	2128	1.1
25 TH	0325	6.0	0935	0.5	1551	5.9	2159	0.5
11 TH	0412	5.3	0941	1.2	1623	5.3	2153	1.3
26 F	0415	5.9	1021	0.8	1639	5.7	2248	0.7
12 F	0448	5.1	1007	1.4	1659	5.1	2218	1.4
27 SA	0508	5.7	1106	1.2	1730	5.5	2339	0.9
13 SA	0526	5.0	1033	1.6	1736	4.9	2249	1.6
28 SU	0605	5.4	1153	1.6	1828	5.2		
14 SU	0608	4.8	1106	1.9	1817	4.8	2331	1.7
29 M	0035	1.2	0707	5.1	1249	2.0	1932	5.0
15 M	0655	4.6	1152	2.2	1906	4.6		
30 TU	0144	1.5	0812	4.9	1402	2.2	2041	4.9

DECEMBER

Day	Time	m	Time	m	Time	m	Time	m
1 W	0306	1.6	0920	4.8	1524	2.3	2149	4.9
16 TH	0119	1.8	0813	4.6	1356	2.2	2027	4.7
2 TH	0420	1.6	1027	4.8	1633	2.1	2255	4.9
17 F	0233	1.8	0916	4.7	1517	2.2	2134	4.7
3 F	0520	1.6	1131	4.9	1728	1.9	2355	5.0
18 SA	0352	1.7	1023	4.8	1627	2.0	2241	4.9
4 SA	0607	1.5	1224	5.0	1813	1.7		
19 SU	0500	1.5	1126	5.0	1727	1.7	2344	5.2
5 SU	0046	5.1	0644	1.4	1309	5.2	1854	1.5
20 M	0600	1.2	1223	5.3	1821	1.3		
6 M	0130	5.2	0717	1.3	1348	5.3	1931	1.4
21 TU	0040	5.4	0653	1.0	1314	5.6	1914	1.0
7 TU	0209	5.2	0748	1.2	1422	5.3	2007	1.2
22 W O	0132	5.7	0745	0.8	1402	5.7	2008	0.7
8 W	0245	5.3	0819	1.2	1455	5.3	2040	1.2
23 TH	0223	5.9	0835	0.7	1448	5.8	2100	0.5
9 TH	0319	5.3	0850	1.2	1528	5.3	2111	1.2
24 F	0313	6.0	0924	0.7	1535	5.9	2152	0.4
10 F	0353	5.2	0921	1.3	1602	5.2	2141	1.2
25 SA	0404	5.9	1011	0.9	1625	5.8	2242	0.5
11 SA	0428	5.2	0952	1.4	1636	5.2	2212	1.3
26 SU	0456	5.7	1055	1.1	1716	5.6	2330	0.7
12 SU	0505	5.1	1022	1.5	1712	5.1	2246	1.4
27 M	0550	5.5	1137	1.4	1811	5.4		
13 M	0544	4.9	1055	1.7	1750	4.9	2325	1.5
28 TU	0017	1.0	0645	5.2	1218	1.7	1908	5.2
14 TU	0628	4.8	1136	1.9	1835	4.8		
29 W	0106	1.3	0742	5.0	1307	2.0	2008	5.0
15 W	0015	1.7	0717	4.7	1235	2.1	1926	4.7
30 TH	0203	1.6	0840	4.8	1414	2.2	2110	4.8
31 F	0314	1.8	0940	4.7	1533	2.3	2212	4.7

Chart Datum: 2·90 metres below Ordnance Datum (Newlyn)

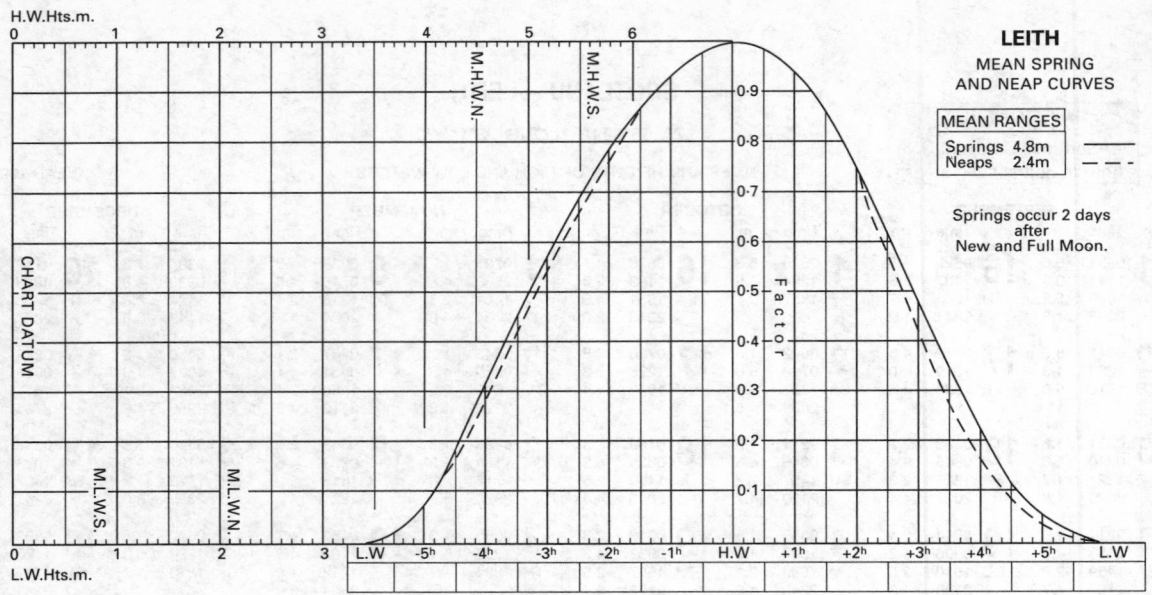

LEITH
MEAN SPRING
AND NEAP CURVES

MEAN RANGES	
Springs	4.8m
Neaps	2.4m

Springs occur 2 days after
New and Full Moon.

BURNTISLAND   8-6-10

Fife 56°03'·23N 03°14'·12W   Rtg 3-5-3

CHARTS
AC 733, 739, 735; Imray C27; OS 66

TIDES
+0340 Dover; ML 3·3; Duration 0625; Zone 0 (UT)

Standard Port LEITH (←—)

Times				Height (metres)			
High Water		Low Water		MHWS	MHWN	MLWN	MLWS
0300	0900	0300	0900	5·6	4·5	2·1	0·8
1500	2100	1500	2100				
Differences BURNTISLAND							
+0002	−0002	+0002	−0003	0·0	0·0	+0·1	+0·1

SHELTER
Outer hbr gives only fair shelter, not suitable for yachts in strong winds. Island Jetty is unsafe. Good shelter in the industrial docks; E Dock access HW−3 to HW, but only in emergency.

NAVIGATION
WPT 56°03'·00N 03°14'·00W, 163°/343° from/to ent, 0·23M. To the E, beware Black Rks (off chartlet) and to the W, Familars Rks. Keep clear of ships using DG ranges SW of port. Commercial barge operations can cause delays.

LIGHTS AND MARKS
Conspic marks: Radio mast 1·1M N of hbr ent; shed to NW; lt tr on W pier head; radar tr at root of E pier. Lts as chartlet. Tfc sigs are for E dock only.

RADIO TELEPHONE
Forth Navigation Ch **71** 16 12 20 (H24), for ent to E Dock.

TELEPHONE (Dial code 01592)
Hr Mr (01333) 426725; MRSC (01333) 450666; ☰ (01324) 665988 (HO) or (0141) 887 9369 (H24); Marinecall 0891 500452; Police 204444; Dr 872761.

FACILITIES
Dock ☎ 872236, AB (limited) £21.32, FW, C (10 ton); **Outer Hbr** Slip, FW, AB (limited); **Burntisland YC** M or AB for small fee, if room in Boat Shelter; FW; **Services**: D, ME ☎ 872939, El, Ⓔ, Sh, BY, C (80 & 30 ton), CH, Gas, Gaz. **Town** EC Wed; P, D, ME, El, C, V, R, Bar, ✉, Ⓑ, ⇌, Ⓗ Kirkcaldy, ✈ Edinburgh.

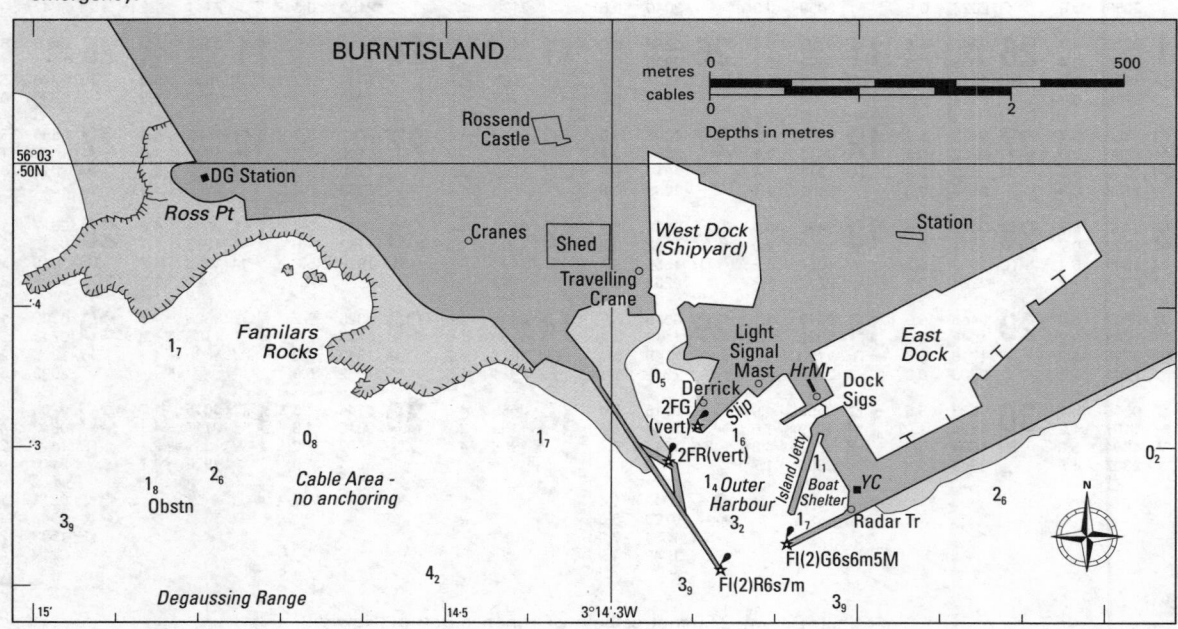

METHIL   8-6-11

Fife 56°10'·76N 03°00'·45W   Rtg 3-5-3

CHARTS

AC 739, 734; Imray C27; OS 59

TIDES

+0330 Dover; ML 3·0; Duration 0615; Zone 0 (UT)

Standard Port LEITH (⟵)

Times				Height (metres)			
High Water		Low Water		MHWS	MHWN	MLWN	MLWS
0300	0900	0300	0900	5·6	4·5	2·1	0·8
1500	2100	1500	2100				
Differences METHIL							
+0007	+0007	−0007	−0007	0·0	0·0	+0·1	+0·1
KIRKCALDY							
+0009	+0009	−0009	−0009	−0·3	−0·3	−0·2	−0·2

SHELTER

Commercial port, but good emergency shelter in No 2 dock.

NAVIGATION

WPT 56°10'·50N 03°00'·00W, 140°/320° from/to pier hd lt, 0·34M. Beware silting. A sand bar forms rapidly to seaward of the lt ho and dredged depth is not always maintained.

LIGHTS AND MARKS

By day and night (vert lts):

Ⓡ
Ⓖ   =   Dangerous to enter; Bring up in roads.

Ⓡ
Ⓦ   =   Clear to enter No 2 dock.

Ⓡ   =   Remain in roads until another signal is made.

RADIO TELEPHONE

Methil Docks Radio VHF Ch 14 16 (HW−3 to +1). Forth Navigation Ch 71 (H24).

TELEPHONE (Dial code 01592)

Hr Mr (Port Manager) (01333) 426725; MRSC (01333) 450666; ⌗ (01324) 665988 (HO) or (0141) 887 9369 (H24); Marinecall 0891 500452; Police 712881; Dr (01333) 426913.

FACILITIES

Hbr No 2 Dock £21.32, FW, C (10 ton).
Town EC Thurs; P, D, Gas, Gaz, V, R, Bar, ✉, Ⓑ, ⇌ (bus to Markinch or Kirkcaldy), Ⓗ Kirkcaldy, ✈ Edinburgh.

ADJACENT HARBOUR, 6M to SW.

KIRKCALDY, Fife, 56°06'·81N 03°08'·86W. AC 739. HW +0345 on Dover, −0005 on Leith; HW −0·1m on Leith; ML 3·2m; Duration 0620. See 8.6.11. Shelter good except in strong E winds; an emergency refuge. Officially the hbr is closed (no commercial tfc, but some local FVs) and not manned; depths may be less than charted due to silting. The only hbr light is on E Pier head, Fl WG 10s 12m 8M. Small craft should contact Forth Ports Authority ☎ (01333) 426725, or call Forth Navigation Ch 71 (H24) or *Methil Docks Radio* Ch 16 14 for advice.

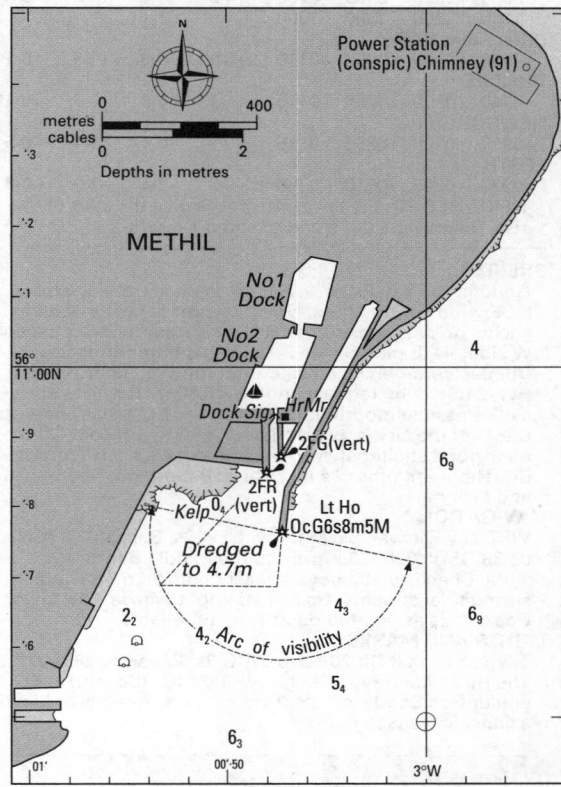

ANSTRUTHER   8-6-12

Fife 56°13'·16N 02°41'·72W   Rtg 3-2-2

CHARTS

AC 734, 175; Imray C27; OS 59

TIDES

+0315 Dover; ML 3·1; Duration 0620; Zone 0 (UT)

Standard Port LEITH (⟵)

Times				Height (metres)			
High Water		Low Water		MHWS	MHWN	MLWN	MLWS
0300	0900	0300	0900	5·6	4·5	2·1	0·8
1500	2100	1500	2100				
Differences ANSTRUTHER EASTER							
−0010	−0035	−0020	−0020	−0·1	−0·1	−0·1	−0·1

SHELTER

Good, but dangerous to enter in strong E & S winds. Hbr dries; access approx HW±2. Caution: ledge at base of W pier. No ⚓ to W of hbr; do not go N of W pier lt due to rks.

NAVIGATION

WPT 56°12'·60N 02°42'·10W, 199°/019° from/to ent, 0·60M. Beware lobster pots and FVs.

LIGHTS AND MARKS

Conspic tr on W pier. Ldg lts 019°, both FG 7/11m 4M. Pier lts as chartlet. Horn (3) 60s in conspic tr.

RADIO TELEPHONE

Call *Anstruther Hbr* VHF Ch 11 (HO) or Forth CG (OT).

TELEPHONE (Dial code 01333)

Hr Mr 310836; MRSC (01333) 450666; ⌗ (01324) 665988 (HO) or (0141) 887 9369 (H24); Marinecall 0891 500452; Police 592100; Dr 310352.

FACILITIES

Hbr AB £8.00, £12.00 >10m LOA, Slip, FW, AC, ⌂, Shwrs; **Services:** D (tanker), CH, ACA, ME, Gas, Gaz, El, Ⓔ, ◙, LB.
Town EC Wed; P, V, R, Bar, ✉, Ⓑ, ⇌ (bus Cupar or Leuchars), Ⓗ St Andrews, ✈ Edinburgh/Dundee.

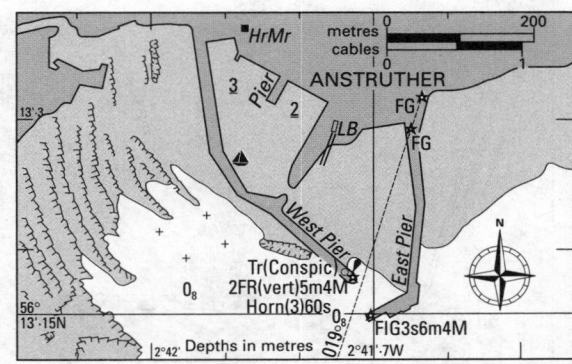

RIVER TAY   8-6-13
Fife/Angus Tayport (56°27'·11N 02°52'·78W) Rtg 3-3-2

CHARTS
AC 1481, 190; OS 54, 59
TIDES
+0401 (Dundee) Dover; ML 3·1; Duration 0610; Zone 0 (UT)

Standard Port ABERDEEN (→)

Times				Height (metres)			
High Water		Low Water		MHWS	MHWN	MLWN	MLWS
0000	0600	0100	0700	4·3	3·4	1·6	0·6
1200	1800	1300	1900				
Differences BAR							
+0100	+0100	+0050	+0110	+0·9	+0·8	+0·3	+0·1
DUNDEE							
+0140	+0120	+0055	+0145	+1·1	+0·9	+0·3	+0·1
NEWBURGH							
+0215	+0200	+0250	+0335	−0·2	−0·4	−1·1	−0·5
PERTH							
+0220	+0225	+0510	+0530	−0·9	−1·4	−1·2	−0·3

NOTE: At Perth LW time differences give the start of the rise, following a LW stand of about 4 hours.

SHELTER
Good in the Tay Estuary, but ent is dangerous in strong E/SE winds or on-shore swell. **Tayport** is best place for yachts on passage, access HW±4. Hbr partly dries except W side of NE pier; S side is full of yacht moorings. At **Dundee** commercial dock (Camperdown), gates open HW−2 to HW by request and fee £5.50 (Fl R lt = no entry/exit). Possible moorings off Royal Tay YC. ‡s as chartlet: the ‡ off the city is exposed and landing difficult. Off S bank good shelter at Woodhaven and ♦s from Wormit BC. There are other ‡s up river at Balmerino, Newburgh and Inchyra.

NAVIGATION
WPT Tay Fairway SWM buoy, L Fl 10s, Bell, 56°29'·25N 02°38'·15W, 029°/209° from/to the Middle Bar buoys, 1·0M. Chan is well buoyed, least depth 5·2m. Beware strong tidal streams. Do not attempt to cross Abertay or Gaa Sands as charted depths are unreliable.

LIGHTS AND MARKS
Tayport High lt Dir 269° Iso WRG 3s, W sector 268°-270°. The HFP "Abertay" ECM buoy, Q (3) 10s (Racon), at E end of Gaa Sands is a clear visual mark. Keep N of Larick, a conspic disused lt bn.

RADIO TELEPHONE
Dundee Hbr Radio VHF Ch **12** 16 (H24); local nav warnings, weather, vis and tides on request. Royal Tay YC, Ch M.
TELEPHONE (Dial code 01382)
Hr Mr (Dundee) 224121/📠 200834; Hr Mr (Perth) (01738) 624056; MRSC (01333) 450666; ⌗ 200822; Marinecall 0891 500452; Tayport Boatowners' Ass'n 553679; Police (Tayport) 552222, (Dundee) 223200; Dr 221953; Ⓗ 223125.
FACILITIES
N BANK: **Camperdown Dock**, AB £15.50, FW, ME, El, C (8 ton); **Victoria Dock** FW, ME, C (8 ton), AB; **Royal Tay YC** (Broughty Ferry) ☎ 477516, ♦s free, L, R, Bar;
Services: CH, L, ME, El, Sh, C (2 ton), ACA.
Dundee City EC Wed; P, D, CH, V, R, Bar, ✉, Ⓑ, ⇌, ✈.
S BANK: **Tayport Hbr** ☎ 553679 AB £6.60, Slip, L, FW, AC;
Wormit Boating Club ☎ 541400 ♦s free, Slip, L, FW, V.

ADJACENT HARBOURS

PERTH, Perth & Kinross, 56°22'·90N 03°25'·65W. AC 1481; OS 53, 58. Tides, see 8.6.13. FYCA Pilot Handbook is needed. Leave Tay rly bridge at about HW Dundee −2 to carry a fair tide the 16·5M to Perth. The buoyed/lit chan favours the S bank for 9M to Newburgh. Here care is needed due to mudbanks in mid-stream; keep S of Mugdrum Is. Up-river, power cables have clearance of 33m and Friarton bridge 26m. Keep S of Willow Is, past the gasworks to hbr on the W bank. Hbr has approx 1·5m; keep clear of coasters. See Hr Mr, ☎ (01738) 624056, for berth. VHF Ch 09 16. FW, D & P (cans), usual city amenities, ⇌, ✈.

ST ANDREWS, Fife, 56°20'·33N 02°46'·70W. AC 190. HW −0015 Leith. Small drying hbr 7M S of Tay Estuary and 8M NW of Fife Ness. In strong onshore winds breaking seas render appr/ent impossible. Appr at HW±2 on 270°; N bkwtr bn in transit with conspic cathedral tr; no lights. Keep about 10m S of the bkwtr for best water. Berth on W side of inner hbr (drying 2·5m). 8m wide ent has lock gates, usually open, and retractable footbridge. Facilities: FW, SC. EC Thurs; All amenities of university town, inc golf course.

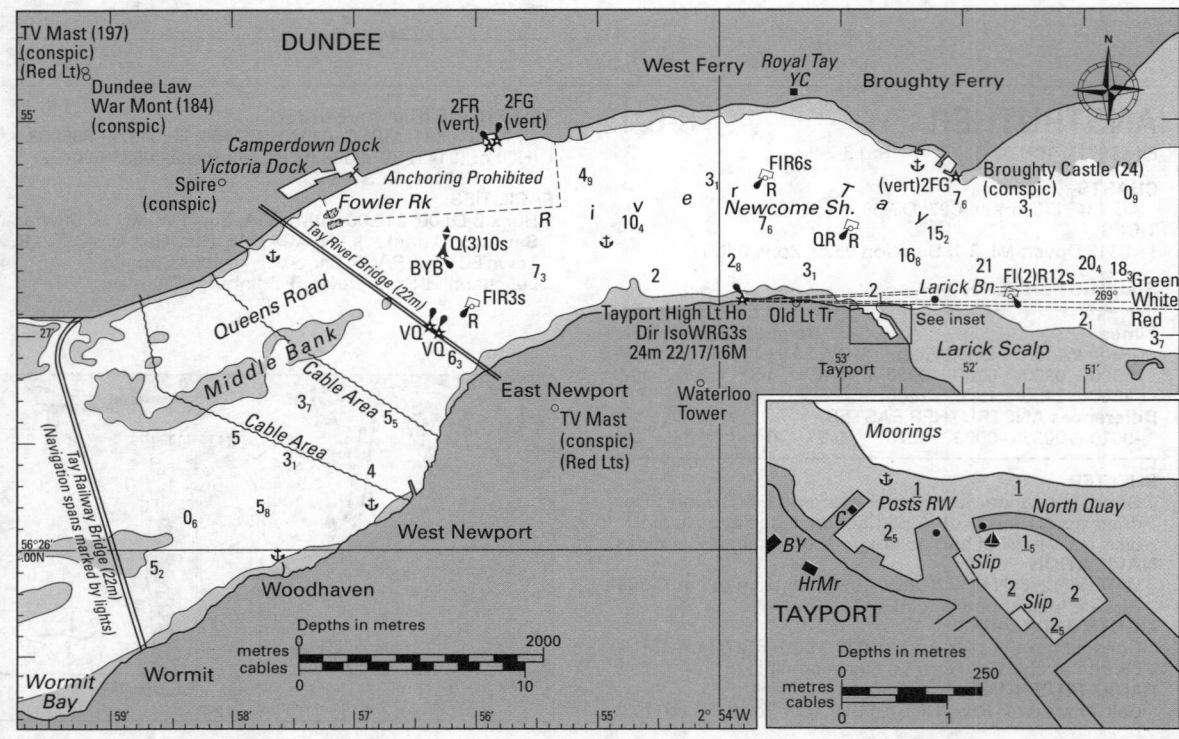

ARBROATH

8-6-14

Angus 56°33'·24N 02°34'·88W   Rtg 3-4-2

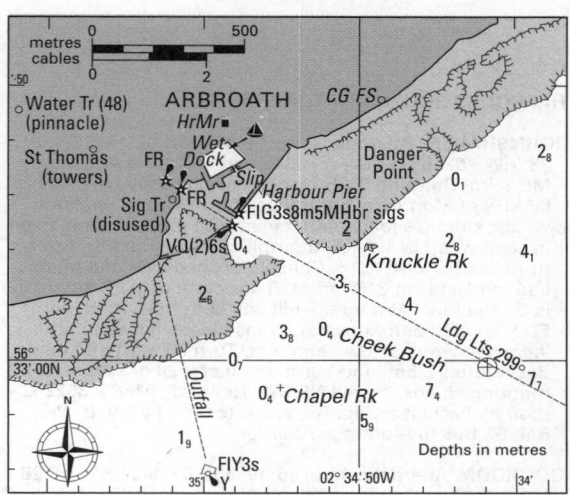

CHARTS
AC 1438, 190; OS 54

TIDES
+0317 Dover; ML 2·9; Duration 0620; Zone 0 (UT)

Standard Port ABERDEEN (→)

Times				Height (metres)			
High Water		Low Water		MHWS	MHWN	MLWN	MLWS
0000	0600	0100	0700	4·3	3·4	1·6	0·6
1200	1800	1300	1900				
Differences ARBROATH							
+0056	+0037	+0034	+0055	+0·7	+0·7	+0·2	+0·1

SHELTER
Good, especially in Wet Dock, but ent can be dangerous in moderate SE swell. Dock gates normally remain open, but will be closed on request. Or small craft can dry out in the SW corner of inner hbr; inside ent, turn stbd and stbd again.

NAVIGATION
WPT 56°33'·00N 02°34'·10W, 119°/299° from/to ent, 0·5M. Entry should not be attempted LW±2½. Beware Knuckle rks to stbd and Cheek Bush rks to port on entering.

LIGHTS AND MARKS
Ldg lts 299°, both FR 7/13m 5M; or twin trs of St Thomas' ✠ visible between N pier lt ho and W bkwtr bn.
Hbr entry sigs: Fl G 3s on E pier = Entry safe. Same lt shows FR when hbr closed, entry dangerous. Siren (3) 60s at E pier lt is occas, for FVs.

RADIO TELEPHONE
None.

TELEPHONE (Dial code 01241)
Hr Mr 872166; MRSC (01224) 592334; ⌗ (0141) 887 9369 (H24); Marinecall 0891 500452; Police 722222; Dr 876836.

FACILITIES
Pier AB £11, Slip, D, FW; **Services:** BY, Slip, L, ME, EI, Sh, C (8 ton) Ⓔ, M, Gas, CH.
Town EC Wed; P, D, V, R, Bar, ✉, Ⓑ, ⇌, ✈ (Dundee).

MONTROSE

8-6-15

Angus 56°42'·21N 02°26'·49W   Rtg 3-4-2

CHARTS
AC 1438, 190; OS 54

TIDES
+0320 Dover; ML 2·9; Duration 0645; Zone 0 (UT)

Standard Port ABERDEEN (→)

Times				Height (metres)			
High Water		Low Water		MHWS	MHWN	MLWN	MLWS
0000	0600	0100	0700	4·3	3·4	1·6	0·6
1200	1800	1300	1900				
Differences MONTROSE							
+0055	+0055	+0030	+0040	+0·5	+0·4	+0·2	0·0

SHELTER
Good; yachts are welcome in this busy commercial port. Contact Hr Mr for AB, usually available, but beware wash from other traffic. Double mooring lines advised due to strong tidal streams (up to 6kn).

NAVIGATION
WPT 56°42'·20N 02°25'·00W, 091°/271° from/to front ldg lt, 1·25M. Beware Annat Bank to N and Scurdie Rks to S of ent chan. In quiet weather best access is LW to LW+1, but in strong onshore winds only safe access would be from HW –2 to HW. Ent is dangerous with strong onshore winds against ebb tide when heavy overfalls develop.

LIGHTS AND MARKS
Scurdie Ness lt ho Fl (3) 20s 38m 23M (conspic). Two sets of ldg lts: Outer 271·5°, both FR 11/18m 5M, front W twin pillars, R bands; rear W tr, R cupola. Inner 265°, both FG 21/33m 5M, Orange △ front and ▽ rear. For positions of outer PHM and SHM chan buoys (off chartlet), see 8.6.4.

RADIO TELEPHONE
VHF Ch 12 16 (H24).

TELEPHONE (Dial code 01674)
Hr Mr 672302; MRCC (01224) 592334; Marinecall 0891 500 452; ⌗ (01224) 844844; Police 672222; Dr 672554/673400.

FACILITIES
N Quay ☎ 672302, AB £6.00, D (by tanker via Hr Mr), FW, ME, EI, C (1½ to 40 ton), CH, Gas.
Town EC Wed; V, R, P, Bar, ✉, Ⓑ, ⇌, ✈ (Aberdeen).

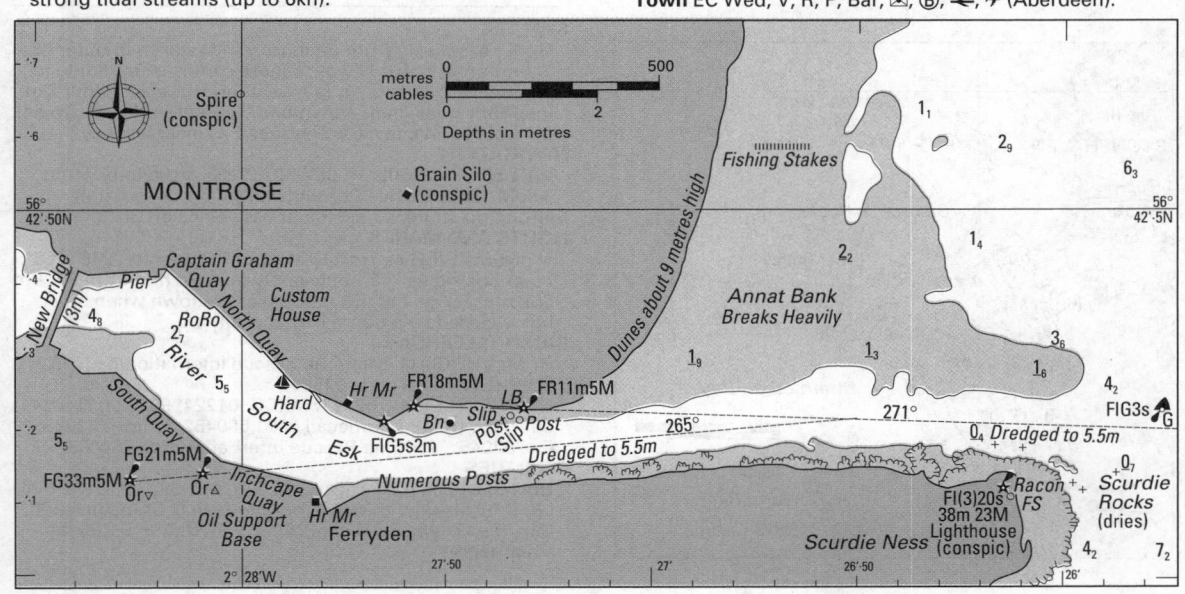

HARBOURS SOUTH OF STONEHAVEN

JOHNSHAVEN, Aberdeenshire, 56°47'·61N 02°19'·96W. AC
28. HW +0245 on Dover; +0045 and +0·4m on Aberdeen;
ML 2·7m; Duration 0626. Very small, attractive drying hbr
6·5M N of Montrose. Ent impossible in strong onshore
winds; strictly a fair weather visit with great caution. Even
in calm weather swell is a problem inside the hbr. Appr
from 5ca SE at HW±2½. Conspic W shed at N end of hbr.
Ldg marks/lts on 316°: front, R structure with FR 5m; rear
is G structure, 20m up the hill and 85m from front, with
FG (FR when entry unsafe). Transit leads between rky
ledges to very narrow (20m) ent. Turn 90° port into Inner
Basin (dries 2·5m) and berth on outer wall or secure to
mooring chains, rigged NE/SW. Hr Mr ☎ (01561) 362262
(home). Facilities: Slip, AB, AC, C (5 ton), FW, V, R, ME,
Bar, ✉. Bus to Montrose/Aberdeen.

GOURDON, Aberdeenshire, 56°49'·50N 02°17'·10W. AC 28.
HW +0240 on Dover; +0035 on Aberdeen; HW +0·4m on
Aberdeen; ML 2·7m; Duration 0620. Shelter good in inner
W hbr (drys about 2m; protected by storm gates); access
from about mid-flood. E (or Gutty) hbr is rky, with
difficult access. Beware rky ledges marked by bn and
extending 200m S from W pier end. A dangerous rk dries
on the ldg line about 1½ca S of pier heads. Ldg marks/lts
358°, both FR 5/30m 5M, 2 W trs; front lt shows G when
not safe to enter. W pier hd Fl WRG 3s 5m 9/7M, vis
G180°-344°, W344°-354° (10°), R354°-180°. E bkwtr hd Q
3m 7M. Hr Mr ☎ (01569) 762741 (part-time, same as
8.6.16). Facilities: Slip, FW from standpipe, D, ME, AC, M,
V, R, Bar. Fish market held Mon-Fri 1130 and 1530.

BERTHING FEES. Aberdeenshire and Moray Councils offer
a "single entry" Rover fee (£8 inc VAT) valid for 1 week
from date of first entry at any or all of the following hbrs:
Johnshaven, Gourdon, Stonehaven; and in Area 7
(Moray Firth): Rosehearty, Banff, Portsoy, Cullen,
Portknockie, Findochty, Hopeman and Burghead. Berths
are of course subject to availability.

AGENTS WANTED

If you are interested in becoming our agent for any of the
following ports, please write to: The Editor, Edington House,
Trent, Sherborne, Dorset DT9 4SR, England – and get your
free copy of the Almanac annually. You do not have to live in
a port to be the agent, but should at least be a fairly regular
visitor.

Plymouth	Port Haliguen
Walton-on-the-Naze	La Trinité-sur-Mer
Hopeman	Piriac
Burghead	St Nazaire/Loire
Findhorn	Pornic
Nairn	St Gilles-Croix-de-Vie
Inverness	Les Sables d'Olonne
Loch Aline	River Seudre
Craobh	Port Bloc/Gironde
Workington	Anglet/Bayonne
Lough Swilly	St Jean-de-Luz
Portbail	Hendaye
St Malo/Dinard	Grandcamp-Maisy
Le Légué/St Brieuc	Port-en-Bessin
Lampaul	Ouistreham/Caen
L'Aberildut	Dives
Douarnenez	St Valéry-en-Caux
Lorient	Dunkerque
River Étel	Emden
Le Palais (Belle Ile)	Langeoog

STONEHAVEN   8-6-16

Aberdeenshire 56°57'·58N 02°11'·91WZ   Rtg 3-4-2

CHARTS
AC 1438, 210; OS 45
TIDES
+0235 Dover; ML 2·6; Duration 0620; Zone 0 (UT)

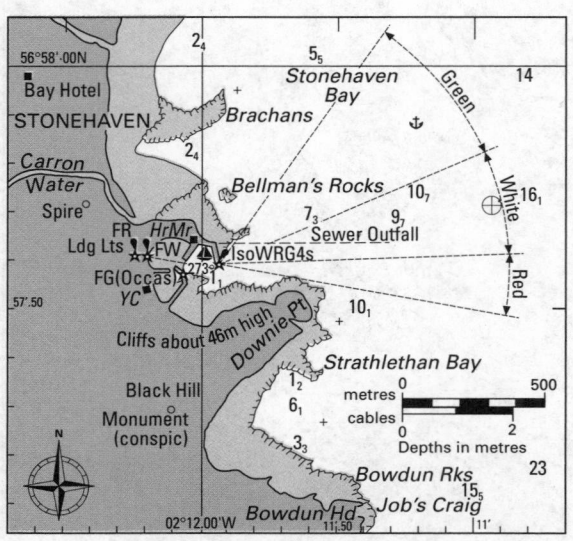

Standard Port ABERDEEN (→)

Times				Height (metres)			
High Water		Low Water		MHWS	MHWN	MLWN	MLWS
0000	0600	0100	0700	4·3	3·4	1·6	0·6
1200	1800	1300	1900				
Differences STONEHAVEN							
+0013	+0008	+0013	+0009	+0·2	+0·2	+0·1	0·0

SHELTER
Good, especially from offshore winds. Berth in outer hbr
(1·0m) on bkwtr or N wall; sandbank forms in middle to
W side. Or ‡ outside in fair weather. Hbr speed limit 3kn.
Inner hbr dries 3·4m and in bad weather is closed. Do not
go S of ldg line, to clear rks close E of inner hbr wall.
NAVIGATION
WPT 56°57'·70N 02°11'·00W, 078°/258° from/to bkwtr lt,
0·50M. Give Downie Pt a wide berth. Do not enter in
strong on-shore winds. Radar assistance on Ch 16 in fog.
LIGHTS AND MARKS
N pier Iso WRG 4s 7m 11/7M; appr in W sector, 246°-268°.
Inner hbr ldg lts 273°, only apply to inner hbr: front FW 6m
5M; rear FR 8m 5M. FG on SE pier is shown when inner
hbr is closed by a boom in bad weather.
RADIO TELEPHONE
Hr Mr VHF Ch 11. Maritime Rescue International Ch 16.
TELEPHONE (Dial code 01569)
Hr Mr (part-time) 762741; MRCC (01224) 592334; ₪ (0141)
887 9369 (H24); Marinecall 0891 500452; Police 762963;
Dr 762945; Maritime Rescue International ☎ 764065.
FACILITIES
Hbr AB £10.00 for 7 days, L, M, FW, AC, Slip, ⓛ, C (1·5 ton),
LB, D by tanker, Fri early am; **Aberdeen & Stonehaven YC**
Slip, Bar. **Town** EC Wed; P, Gas, V, R, Bar, Ⓗ, ✉, Ⓑ, ⇌, ✈
(Aberdeen).

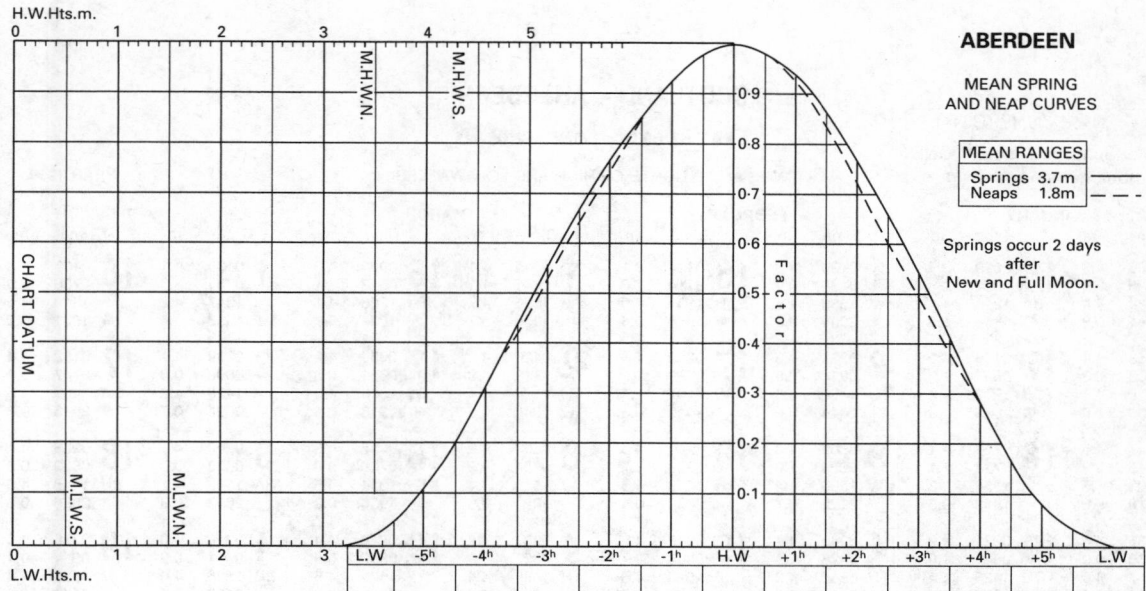

ABERDEEN

MEAN SPRING
AND NEAP CURVES

MEAN RANGES
Springs 3.7m
Neaps 1.8m

Springs occur 2 days
after
New and Full Moon.

ABERDEEN   8-6-17

Aberdeenshire 57°08'·72N 02°03'·48W   Rtg 2-5-2

CHARTS
AC 1446, 210; OS 38

TIDES
+0231 Dover; ML 2·5; Duration 0620; Zone 0 (UT)
Note: Aberdeen is a Standard Port and tidal predictions
for each day of the year are given below.

SHELTER
Good in hbr; open at all tides, but do not enter in strong
NE/ESE winds. For berthing instructions call Hr Mr VHF
Ch 12 or berth at Pocra Quay first. Yachts usually lie in
Upper Dock or on N side of Albert Basin alongside
floating linkspan, but are not encouraged in this busy
commercial port. ‡ in Aberdeen Bay gives some shelter
from S and W winds.

NAVIGATION
WPT Fairway SWM buoy, Mo (A) 5s, Racon, 57°09'·32N
02°01'·83W, 056°/236° from/to hbr ent 1·05M. Give Girdle
Ness a berth of at least ¼M (more in bad weather) and do
not pass close round pier hds. Strong tidal streams and,
with river in spate, possible overfalls. Chan dredged to
6m on ldg line.

LIGHTS AND MARKS
Ldg lts 236° (FR = port open; FG = port closed).
Traffic sigs at root of N pier:

Ⓖ	=	Entry prohib
Ⓡ	=	Dep prohib
Ⓡ & Ⓖ	=	Port closed

RADIO TELEPHONE
VHF Ch 06 11 **12** 13 16 (H24).

TELEPHONE (Dial code 01224)
Hr Mr 597000, ☎ 571507; MRCC 592334, ☎ 575920; ⌗
844844; Weather 722334; Marinecall 0891 500 452/0839
406189; Police 639111.

FACILITIES
Services: AB £16 for a period of up to 5 days , EI, Ⓔ, CH,
ME, ACA.
City EC Wed/Sat; all amenities, ⇌, ✈.

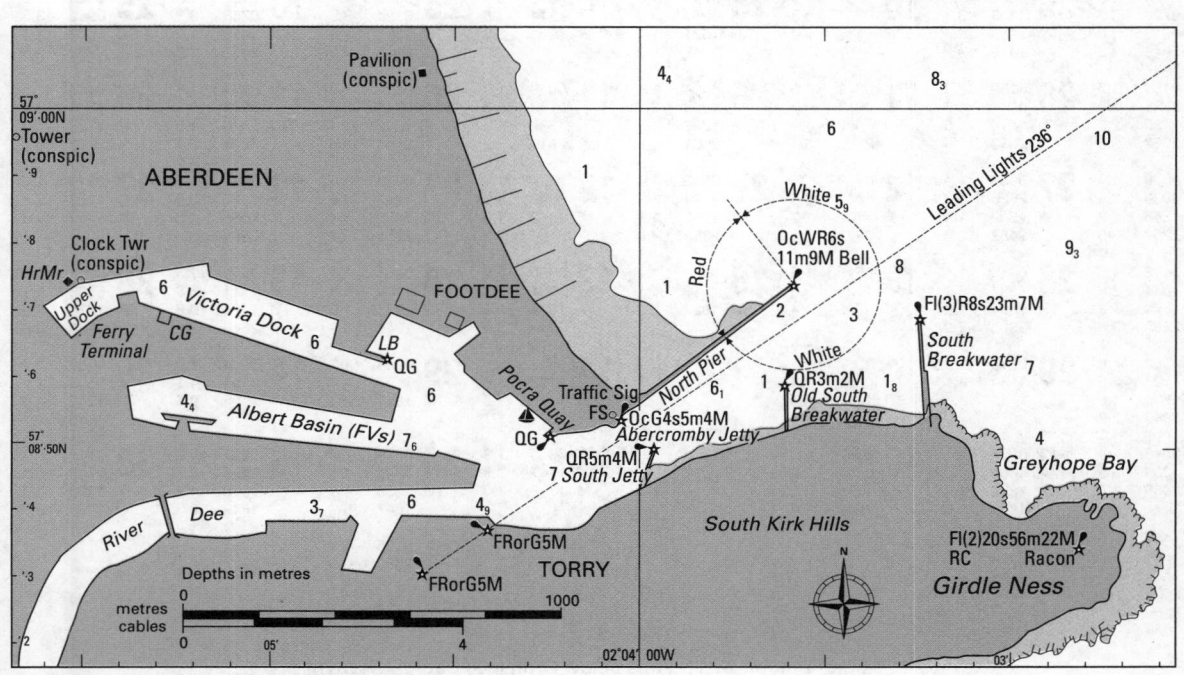

▲ After berthing at Pocra Quay report to HrMr

SCOTLAND – ABERDEEN

LAT 57°09′N   LONG   2°05′W

TIMES AND HEIGHTS OF HIGH AND LOW WATERS   YEAR **1999**

TIME ZONE (UT)
For Summer Time add ONE hour in non-shaded areas

JANUARY

Day	Time	m	Day	Time	m
1 F	0006	4.3	16 SA	0029	3.9
	0615	0.9		0621	1.3
	1234	4.4		1241	4.1
	1841	0.8		1846	1.2
2 SA O	0058	4.4	17 SU ●	0108	4.0
	0703	0.8		0657	1.2
	1319	4.5		1317	4.2
	1930	0.6		1922	1.0
3 SU	0147	4.5	18 M	0144	4.1
	0747	0.9		0733	1.1
	1403	4.5		1351	4.3
	2016	0.6		1959	0.8
4 M	0235	4.4	19 TU	0221	4.2
	0830	0.9		0809	1.0
	1447	4.5		1426	4.4
	2101	0.6		2037	0.7
5 TU	0321	4.3	20 W	0259	4.2
	0911	1.1		0847	1.0
	1530	4.4		1503	4.4
	2145	0.7		2116	0.7
6 W	0407	4.1	21 TH	0339	4.1
	0952	1.2		0925	1.0
	1613	4.3		1543	4.3
	2228	0.9		2157	0.8
7 TH	0453	3.9	22 F	0421	4.1
	1032	1.4		1006	1.1
	1658	4.1		1626	4.3
	2312	1.1		2241	0.9
8 F	0541	3.7	23 SA	0508	4.0
	1117	1.6		1052	1.3
	1747	3.9		1714	4.2
	2359	1.4		2331	1.0
9 SA	0632	3.6	24 SU	0602	3.8
	1208	1.8		1146	1.4
	1841	3.7		1810	4.0
10 SU	0054	1.6	25 M	0030	1.2
	0728	3.5		0703	3.7
	1313	2.0		1253	1.6
	1943	3.6		1916	3.9
11 M	0159	1.7	26 TU	0139	1.3
	0831	3.4		0814	3.7
	1430	2.0		1410	1.6
	2052	3.5		2033	3.8
12 TU	0309	1.7	27 W	0257	1.4
	0936	3.5		0928	3.7
	1546	1.9		1532	1.5
	2201	3.5		2152	3.9
13 W	0412	1.7	28 TH	0413	1.4
	1034	3.6		1037	3.9
	1644	1.8		1644	1.3
	2259	3.6		2303	4.0
14 TH	0502	1.6	29 F	0516	1.3
	1123	3.8		1134	4.1
	1730	1.6		1744	1.1
	2347	3.8			
15 F	0543	1.4	30 SA	0002	4.1
	1204	3.9		0608	1.1
	1809	1.4		1224	4.2
				1835	0.8
			31 SU O	0053	4.3
				0653	1.0
				1309	4.4
				1922	0.7

FEBRUARY

Day	Time	m	Day	Time	m
1 M	0139	4.3	16 TU ●	0124	4.1
	0735	0.9		0714	1.0
	1350	4.5		1331	4.3
	2004	0.6		1940	0.6
2 TU	0221	4.3	17 W	0202	4.2
	0814	0.9		0752	0.8
	1430	4.5		1407	4.4
	2044	0.6		2019	0.5
3 W	0302	4.3	18 TH	0240	4.3
	0850	1.0		0829	0.7
	1509	4.4		1445	4.5
	2122	0.7		2058	0.4
4 TH	0340	4.1	19 F	0319	4.3
	0925	1.1		0908	0.7
	1546	4.3		1525	4.4
	2157	0.8		2138	0.5
5 F	0418	4.0	20 SA	0400	4.2
	0959	1.2		0947	0.8
	1624	4.1		1607	4.4
	2233	1.0		2220	0.6
6 SA	0456	3.8	21 SU	0444	4.1
	1035	1.4		1031	1.0
	1704	3.9		1655	4.3
	2311	1.3		2307	0.9
7 SU	0538	3.7	22 M	0534	3.9
	1115	1.6		1122	1.2
	1750	3.7		1750	4.1
	2355	1.5			
8 M	0626	3.5	23 TU	0003	1.2
	1206	1.8		0633	3.7
	1844	3.5		1227	1.4
				1857	3.8
9 TU	0050	1.7	24 W	0113	1.4
	0723	3.4		0746	3.6
	1314	2.0		1349	1.5
	1950	3.4		2019	3.7
10 W	0201	1.9	25 TH	0239	1.6
	0831	3.3		0907	3.6
	1442	2.0		1521	1.5
	2107	3.4		2147	3.7
11 TH	0322	1.9	26 F	0404	1.7
	0944	3.4		1023	3.7
	1606	1.9		1639	1.3
	2223	3.4		2301	3.8
12 F	0429	1.8	27 SA	0509	1.4
	1047	3.6		1124	3.9
	1702	1.7		1739	1.0
	2321	3.6		2358	4.0
13 SA	0519	1.6	28 SU	0559	1.2
	1136	3.8		1213	4.1
	1746	1.4		1827	0.8
14 SU	0007	3.8			
	0559	1.4			
	1218	4.0			
	1824	1.1			
15 M	0047	4.0			
	0637	1.2			
	1255	4.2			
	1902	0.9			

MARCH

Day	Time	m	Day	Time	m
1 M	0045	4.1	16 TU	0020	4.0
	0641	1.1		0613	1.1
	1256	4.3		1228	4.1
	1908	0.7		1837	0.7
2 TU O	0126	4.2	17 W ●	0059	4.2
	0719	0.9		0651	0.8
	1334	4.4		1306	4.3
	1946	0.6		1916	0.4
3 W	0202	4.2	18 TH	0138	4.3
	0754	0.9		0730	0.6
	1410	4.4		1344	4.5
	2021	0.6		1956	0.3
4 TH	0237	4.2	19 F	0216	4.4
	0827	0.9		0809	0.5
	1445	4.4		1424	4.6
	2054	0.6		2036	0.2
5 F	0310	4.1	20 SA	0256	4.4
	0858	0.9		0848	0.5
	1519	4.3		1505	4.6
	2125	0.8		2116	0.3
6 SA	0342	4.1	21 SU	0337	4.3
	0928	1.0		0929	0.6
	1553	4.1		1550	4.5
	2156	1.0		2159	0.5
7 SU	0416	3.9	22 M	0422	4.1
	1000	1.2		1014	0.7
	1629	3.9		1640	4.3
	2228	1.2		2246	0.8
8 M	0452	3.7	23 TU	0511	3.9
	1034	1.4		1107	1.0
	1710	3.7		1737	4.0
	2307	1.4		2343	1.2
9 TU	0534	3.6	24 W	0611	3.7
	1117	1.6		1213	1.2
	1759	3.5		1848	3.7
	2354	1.6			
10 W	0626	3.4	25 TH	0055	1.5
	1214	1.8		0724	3.5
	1901	3.3		1337	1.4
				2013	3.6
11 TH	0059	1.9	26 F	0224	1.7
	0730	3.3		0848	3.5
	1336	1.9		1512	1.4
	2017	3.2		2141	3.6
12 F	0224	1.9	27 SA	0353	1.6
	0848	3.3		1007	3.6
	1513	1.8		1629	1.2
	2141	3.3		2253	3.7
13 SA	0350	1.8	28 SU	0456	1.4
	1004	3.4		1109	3.8
	1627	1.6		1725	1.0
	2249	3.5		2346	3.9
14 SU	0449	1.6	29 M	0544	1.2
	1102	3.6		1157	4.0
	1716	1.3		1810	0.8
	2339	3.7			
15 M	0533	1.3	30 TU	0029	4.0
	1147	3.8		0623	1.1
	1758	1.0		1238	4.1
				1847	0.7
			31 W O	0105	4.1
				0658	0.9
				1314	4.2
				1921	0.6

APRIL

Day	Time	m	Day	Time	m
1 TH	0138	4.1	16 F ●	0111	4.3
	0731	0.8		0706	0.5
	1347	4.2		1319	4.5
	1953	0.6		1931	0.2
2 F	0209	4.1	17 SA	0152	4.4
	0802	0.8		0747	0.4
	1420	4.2		1403	4.6
	2024	0.7		2013	0.2
3 SA	0240	4.1	18 SU	0233	4.4
	0832	0.8		0829	0.3
	1452	4.1		1448	4.6
	2053	0.8		2056	0.3
4 SU	0310	4.0	19 M	0316	4.3
	0901	0.9		0914	0.4
	1525	4.0		1536	4.4
	2122	0.9		2141	0.6
5 M	0341	3.9	20 TU	0402	4.1
	0932	1.0		1003	0.6
	1601	3.9		1629	4.2
	2153	1.1		2230	0.9
6 TU	0416	3.8	21 W	0453	3.9
	1005	1.2		1059	0.8
	1641	3.7		1730	3.9
	2229	1.3		2328	1.2
7 W	0455	3.6	22 TH	0553	3.7
	1045	1.4		1205	1.0
	1727	3.5		1842	3.6
	2312	1.5			
8 TH	0542	3.4	23 F	0038	1.5
	1137	1.5		0704	3.5
	1824	3.3		1325	1.2
				2002	3.5
9 F	0011	1.8	24 SA	0203	1.7
	0641	3.3		0824	3.5
	1249	1.7		1453	1.2
	1935	3.2		2124	3.5
10 SA	0132	1.9	25 SU	0329	1.6
	0755	3.2		0942	3.5
	1418	1.7		1607	1.1
	2057	3.2		2232	3.6
11 SU	0301	1.8	26 M	0432	1.5
	0914	3.3		1044	3.7
	1540	1.5		1702	1.0
	2209	3.4		2323	3.7
12 M	0410	1.6	27 TU	0519	1.3
	1020	3.5		1133	3.8
	1638	1.2		1744	0.9
	2304	3.7			
13 TU	0501	1.3	28 W	0004	3.8
	1111	3.8		0558	1.1
	1725	0.8		1214	3.9
	2349	3.9		1820	0.8
14 W	0544	1.0	29 TH	0039	3.9
	1155	4.1		0633	1.0
	1808	0.5		1249	4.0
				1853	0.7
15 TH	0031	4.2	30 F O	0111	4.0
	0625	0.7		0706	0.9
	1238	4.3		1323	4.0
	1849	0.3		1924	0.7

Chart Datum: 2·25 metres below Ordnance Datum (Newlyn)

TIME ZONE (UT)
For Summer Time add ONE hour in non-shaded areas

SCOTLAND – ABERDEEN

LAT 57°09′N LONG 2°05′W

TIMES AND HEIGHTS OF HIGH AND LOW WATERS

YEAR **1999**

6

MAY

Day	Time	m	Day	Time	m
1 SA	0142 / 0738 / 1356 / 1955	4.0 / 0.8 / 4.0 / 0.7	**16** SU	0129 / 0728 / 1345 / 1953	4.4 / 0.3 / 4.5 / 0.3
2 SU	0212 / 0809 / 1429 / 2024	4.0 / 0.8 / 4.0 / 0.8	**17** M	0213 / 0815 / 1434 / 2039	4.4 / 0.3 / 4.5 / 0.4
3 M	0242 / 0839 / 1503 / 2054	4.0 / 0.9 / 3.9 / 0.9	**18** TU	0258 / 0904 / 1526 / 2127	4.3 / 0.3 / 4.3 / 0.7
4 TU	0314 / 0910 / 1539 / 2126	3.9 / 1.0 / 3.8 / 1.1	**19** W	0345 / 0955 / 1621 / 2217	4.2 / 0.5 / 4.1 / 0.9
5 W	0348 / 0945 / 1619 / 2202	3.8 / 1.0 / 3.7 / 1.2	**20** TH	0437 / 1051 / 1722 / 2312	4.0 / 0.7 / 3.9 / 1.2
6 TH	0426 / 1025 / 1704 / 2244	3.7 / 1.2 / 3.5 / 1.4	**21** F	0535 / 1153 / 1827	3.8 / 0.9 / 3.6
7 F	0510 / 1114 / 1757 / 2338	3.5 / 1.3 / 3.4 / 1.6	**22** SA	0015 / 0641 / 1302 / 1937	1.5 / 3.6 / 1.1 / 3.5
8 SA	0605 / 1218 / 1902	3.4 / 1.4 / 3.3	**23** SU	0129 / 0753 / 1419 / 2050	1.6 / 3.5 / 1.2 / 3.4
9 SU	0051 / 0712 / 1335 / 2015	1.7 / 3.3 / 1.4 / 3.3	**24** M	0248 / 0905 / 1531 / 2156	1.7 / 3.5 / 1.2 / 3.5
10 M	0212 / 0825 / 1451 / 2126	1.7 / 3.4 / 1.3 / 3.4	**25** TU	0356 / 1010 / 1627 / 2250	1.6 / 3.6 / 1.1 / 3.6
11 TU	0325 / 0934 / 1556 / 2226	1.5 / 3.5 / 1.0 / 3.7	**26** W	0447 / 1102 / 1711 / 2333	1.4 / 3.7 / 1.0 / 3.7
12 W	0423 / 1032 / 1650 / 2317	1.3 / 3.8 / 0.8 / 3.9	**27** TH	0530 / 1145 / 1749	1.3 / 3.8 / 1.0
13 TH	0513 / 1123 / 1738	1.0 / 4.0 / 0.5	**28** F	0009 / 0607 / 1224 / 1823	3.8 / 1.1 / 3.8 / 0.9
14 F	0002 / 0558 / 1211 / 1823	4.1 / 0.7 / 4.3 / 0.3	**29** SA	0044 / 0642 / 1300 / 1857	3.9 / 1.0 / 3.9 / 0.9
15 SA ●	0046 / 0643 / 1258 / 1908	4.3 / 0.5 / 4.4 / 0.2	**30** SU ○	0116 / 0716 / 1336 / 1929	4.0 / 0.9 / 3.9 / 0.9
			31 M	0148 / 0749 / 1410 / 2001	4.0 / 0.9 / 3.9 / 0.9

JUNE

Day	Time	m	Day	Time	m
1 TU	0219 / 0821 / 1445 / 2033	4.0 / 0.9 / 3.9 / 1.0	**16** W	0243 / 0855 / 1517 / 2114	4.4 / 0.3 / 4.3 / 0.8
2 W	0252 / 0855 / 1522 / 2107	3.9 / 0.9 / 3.8 / 1.1	**17** TH	0331 / 0946 / 1610 / 2201	4.3 / 0.4 / 4.1 / 1.0
3 TH	0326 / 0931 / 1601 / 2143	3.9 / 1.0 / 3.7 / 1.2	**18** F	0420 / 1037 / 1705 / 2251	4.1 / 0.6 / 3.9 / 1.2
4 F	0404 / 1011 / 1644 / 2225	3.8 / 1.0 / 3.6 / 1.3	**19** SA	0513 / 1131 / 1801 / 2344	3.9 / 0.8 / 3.7 / 1.4
5 SA	0447 / 1058 / 1734 / 2315	3.7 / 1.1 / 3.5 / 1.5	**20** SU	0611 / 1228 / 1901	3.8 / 1.0 / 3.5
6 SU	0538 / 1154 / 1832	3.6 / 1.2 / 3.4	**21** M	0044 / 0712 / 1331 / 2003	1.6 / 3.6 / 1.2 / 3.4
7 M	0017 / 0637 / 1300 / 1937	1.6 / 3.5 / 1.2 / 3.4	**22** TU	0153 / 0818 / 1438 / 2107	1.7 / 3.5 / 1.3 / 3.4
8 TU	0129 / 0744 / 1409 / 2045	1.6 / 3.5 / 1.2 / 3.5	**23** W	0306 / 0925 / 1541 / 2206	1.7 / 3.5 / 1.4 / 3.5
9 W	0241 / 0852 / 1516 / 2149	1.5 / 3.6 / 1.0 / 3.7	**24** TH	0409 / 1025 / 1633 / 2256	1.6 / 3.5 / 1.3 / 3.6
10 TH	0345 / 0956 / 1617 / 2246	1.3 / 3.8 / 0.8 / 3.8	**25** F	0459 / 1115 / 1717 / 2339	1.5 / 3.6 / 1.2 / 3.7
11 F	0443 / 1055 / 1711 / 2337	1.1 / 4.0 / 0.7 / 4.1	**26** SA	0542 / 1159 / 1756	1.3 / 3.7 / 1.2
12 SA	0536 / 1150 / 1802	0.8 / 4.2 / 0.5	**27** SU	0017 / 0620 / 1240 / 1832	3.8 / 1.2 / 3.8 / 1.1
13 SU ●	0024 / 0626 / 1242 / 1851	4.2 / 0.6 / 4.4 / 0.5	**28** M ○	0053 / 0656 / 1317 / 1907	3.9 / 1.0 / 3.9 / 1.0
14 M	0111 / 0715 / 1333 / 1939	4.3 / 0.4 / 4.4 / 0.5	**29** TU	0127 / 0731 / 1354 / 1941	4.0 / 0.9 / 3.9 / 1.0
15 TU	0156 / 0805 / 1425 / 2026	4.3 / 0.3 / 4.4 / 0.6	**30** W	0200 / 0806 / 1429 / 2015	4.0 / 0.9 / 3.9 / 1.0

JULY

Day	Time	m	Day	Time	m
1 TH	0233 / 0841 / 1506 / 2051	4.0 / 0.8 / 3.9 / 1.0	**16** F	0313 / 0930 / 1552 / 2140	4.4 / 0.4 / 4.2 / 1.0
2 F	0309 / 0918 / 1544 / 2128	4.0 / 0.8 / 3.8 / 1.1	**17** SA	0359 / 1015 / 1639 / 2222	4.3 / 0.6 / 4.0 / 1.1
3 SA	0346 / 0957 / 1626 / 2208	4.0 / 0.8 / 3.8 / 1.2	**18** SU	0445 / 1059 / 1726 / 2306	4.1 / 0.8 / 3.8 / 1.4
4 SU	0427 / 1041 / 1711 / 2253	3.9 / 0.9 / 3.7 / 1.3	**19** M	0533 / 1145 / 1815 / 2355	3.9 / 1.1 / 3.6 / 1.6
5 M	0514 / 1130 / 1803 / 2347	3.8 / 1.0 / 3.6 / 1.4	**20** TU	0626 / 1236 / 1909	3.7 / 1.3 / 3.6
6 TU	0608 / 1227 / 1902	3.7 / 1.1 / 3.6	**21** W	0053 / 0724 / 1336 / 2008	1.7 / 3.5 / 1.5 / 3.4
7 W	0050 / 0709 / 1332 / 2007	1.5 / 3.7 / 1.1 / 3.6	**22** TH	0205 / 0831 / 1444 / 2112	1.8 / 3.4 / 1.6 / 3.4
8 TH	0201 / 0817 / 1441 / 2115	1.5 / 3.7 / 1.1 / 3.7	**23** F	0323 / 0941 / 1551 / 2214	1.8 / 3.4 / 1.6 / 3.5
9 F	0313 / 0929 / 1550 / 2219	1.4 / 3.8 / 1.0 / 3.8	**24** SA	0428 / 1044 / 1646 / 2306	1.7 / 3.5 / 1.5 / 3.6
10 SA	0421 / 1037 / 1653 / 2317	1.2 / 4.0 / 0.9 / 4.0	**25** SU	0518 / 1135 / 1731 / 2350	1.5 / 3.6 / 1.4 / 3.8
11 SU	0521 / 1138 / 1749	1.0 / 4.1 / 0.8	**26** M	0559 / 1219 / 1811	1.3 / 3.8 / 1.3
12 M	0009 / 0616 / 1234 / 1840	4.2 / 0.7 / 4.3 / 0.7	**27** TU	0029 / 0637 / 1259 / 1847	3.9 / 1.1 / 3.9 / 1.2
13 TU ●	0057 / 0708 / 1326 / 1928	4.3 / 0.5 / 4.4 / 0.7	**28** W ○	0106 / 0712 / 1335 / 1922	4.0 / 0.8 / 4.0 / 1.1
14 W	0143 / 0757 / 1416 / 2014	4.4 / 0.4 / 4.4 / 0.7	**29** TH	0140 / 0748 / 1411 / 1957	4.1 / 0.8 / 4.0 / 1.0
15 TH	0228 / 0845 / 1504 / 2057	4.3 / 0.3 / 4.3 / 0.8	**30** F	0214 / 0824 / 1447 / 2033	4.2 / 0.7 / 4.1 / 0.9
			31 SA	0249 / 0901 / 1524 / 2110	4.2 / 0.6 / 4.1 / 1.0

AUGUST

Day	Time	m	Day	Time	m
1 SU	0326 / 0939 / 1604 / 2148	4.2 / 0.7 / 4.0 / 1.0	**16** M	0412 / 1022 / 1645 / 2226	4.2 / 0.9 / 3.9 / 1.3
2 M	0406 / 1019 / 1646 / 2230	4.1 / 0.7 / 3.9 / 1.1	**17** TU	0453 / 1059 / 1726 / 2306	4.0 / 1.1 / 3.7 / 1.5
3 TU	0451 / 1104 / 1734 / 2318	4.1 / 0.9 / 3.8 / 1.3	**18** W	0538 / 1142 / 1813 / 2355	3.8 / 1.4 / 3.5 / 1.7
4 W	0542 / 1157 / 1830	4.0 / 1.0 / 3.7	**19** TH	0632 / 1234 / 1908	3.6 / 1.6 / 3.4
5 TH	0018 / 0641 / 1300 / 1935	1.4 / 3.9 / 1.2 / 3.6	**20** F	0100 / 0736 / 1341 / 2012	1.9 / 3.4 / 1.8 / 3.4
6 F	0130 / 0753 / 1414 / 2048	1.6 / 3.8 / 1.3 / 3.6	**21** SA	0226 / 0852 / 1502 / 2124	1.9 / 3.3 / 1.9 / 3.4
7 SA	0251 / 0913 / 1533 / 2200	1.5 / 3.8 / 1.3 / 3.8	**22** SU	0353 / 1009 / 1615 / 2230	1.8 / 3.4 / 1.8 / 3.5
8 SU	0410 / 1030 / 1644 / 2304	1.3 / 3.9 / 1.2 / 3.9	**23** M	0452 / 1109 / 1706 / 2322	1.6 / 3.6 / 1.6 / 3.7
9 M	0515 / 1135 / 1742 / 2358	1.0 / 4.0 / 1.1 / 4.1	**24** TU	0536 / 1156 / 1748	1.4 / 3.7 / 1.4
10 TU	0611 / 1229 / 1832	0.8 / 4.2 / 1.0	**25** W	0003 / 0614 / 1236 / 1824	3.9 / 1.1 / 3.9 / 1.2
11 W ●	0045 / 0700 / 1319 / 1916	4.3 / 0.6 / 4.3 / 0.9	**26** TH ○	0041 / 0649 / 1312 / 1900	4.1 / 0.9 / 4.1 / 1.1
12 TH	0129 / 0745 / 1403 / 1957	4.4 / 0.4 / 4.3 / 0.8	**27** F	0116 / 0725 / 1348 / 1936	4.3 / 0.7 / 4.2 / 0.9
13 F	0211 / 0828 / 1445 / 2036	4.5 / 0.4 / 4.3 / 0.9	**28** SA	0151 / 0801 / 1423 / 2012	4.4 / 0.5 / 4.3 / 0.8
14 SA	0252 / 0907 / 1526 / 2113	4.5 / 0.5 / 4.2 / 0.9	**29** SU	0227 / 0838 / 1500 / 2048	4.5 / 0.5 / 4.3 / 0.8
15 SU	0332 / 0945 / 1606 / 2149	4.5 / 0.6 / 4.0 / 1.1	**30** M	0304 / 0916 / 1539 / 2126	4.5 / 0.5 / 4.2 / 0.8
			31 TU	0345 / 0955 / 1621 / 2207	4.4 / 0.6 / 4.1 / 1.0

Chart Datum: 2·25 metres below Ordnance Datum (Newlyn)

TIME ZONE (UT)
For Summer Time add ONE hour in non-shaded areas

SCOTLAND – ABERDEEN

LAT 57°09′N   LONG 2°05′W

TIMES AND HEIGHTS OF HIGH AND LOW WATERS

YEAR 1999

SEPTEMBER

Day	Time	m	Day	Time	m
1 W	0429 / 1039 / 1707 / 2254	4.3 / 0.8 / 4.0 / 1.1	16 TH	0457 / 1053 / 1721 / 2307	3.8 / 1.4 / 3.7 / 1.6
2 TH	0521 / 1130 / 1802 / 2354	4.1 / 1.1 / 3.8 / 1.3	17 F	0547 / 1139 / 1812	3.6 / 1.7 / 3.5
3 F	0623 / 1235 / 1909	3.9 / 1.4 / 3.7	18 SA	0004 / 0648 / 1242 / 1915	1.8 / 3.4 / 1.9 / 3.4
4 SA	0111 / 0740 / 1356 / 2028	1.5 / 3.7 / 1.6 / 3.6	19 SU	0125 / 0804 / 1406 / 2031	2.0 / 3.3 / 2.0 / 3.4
5 SU	0241 / 0909 / 1525 / 2147	1.5 / 3.7 / 1.6 / 3.7	20 M	0306 / 0928 / 1536 / 2147	1.9 / 3.3 / 2.0 / 3.5
6 M	0406 / 1029 / 1639 / 2254	1.3 / 3.8 / 1.5 / 3.9	21 TU	0419 / 1037 / 1637 / 2246	1.7 / 3.5 / 1.8 / 3.7
7 TU	0511 / 1132 / 1734 / 2347	1.0 / 4.0 / 1.3 / 4.1	22 W	0506 / 1126 / 1720 / 2332	1.4 / 3.7 / 1.5 / 3.9
8 W	0603 / 1222 / 1820	0.8 / 4.2 / 1.1	23 TH	0545 / 1207 / 1758	1.1 / 4.0 / 1.3
9 TH ●	0032 / 0647 / 1306 / 1900	4.3 / 0.6 / 4.3 / 1.0	24 F	0010 / 0621 / 1244 / 1834	4.1 / 0.8 / 4.2 / 1.0
10 F	0113 / 0727 / 1344 / 1937	4.4 / 0.5 / 4.3 / 0.9	25 SA O	0047 / 0657 / 1320 / 1910	4.3 / 0.6 / 4.3 / 0.8
11 SA	0150 / 0804 / 1420 / 2011	4.5 / 0.5 / 4.3 / 0.9	26 SU	0124 / 0735 / 1356 / 1947	4.5 / 0.4 / 4.4 / 0.7
12 SU	0227 / 0839 / 1455 / 2045	4.5 / 0.6 / 4.2 / 0.9	27 M	0202 / 0813 / 1434 / 2025	4.6 / 0.3 / 4.5 / 0.6
13 M	0303 / 0911 / 1529 / 2117	4.4 / 0.7 / 4.1 / 1.1	28 TU	0242 / 0851 / 1514 / 2105	4.6 / 0.4 / 4.4 / 0.7
14 TU	0339 / 0943 / 1604 / 2149	4.2 / 0.9 / 4.0 / 1.2	29 W	0325 / 0932 / 1556 / 2148	4.5 / 0.6 / 4.3 / 0.8
15 W	0416 / 1016 / 1640 / 2224	4.0 / 1.2 / 3.8 / 1.4	30 TH	0412 / 1016 / 1643 / 2238	4.4 / 0.9 / 4.1 / 1.0

OCTOBER

Day	Time	m	Day	Time	m
1 F	0507 / 1110 / 1739 / 2341	4.1 / 1.2 / 3.9 / 1.3	16 SA	0513 / 1055 / 1726 / 2324	3.6 / 1.7 / 3.6 / 1.7
2 SA	0614 / 1218 / 1849	3.9 / 1.5 / 3.7	17 SU	0610 / 1152 / 1825	3.4 / 1.9 / 3.4
3 SU	0101 / 0736 / 1344 / 2011	1.4 / 3.7 / 1.7 / 3.6	18 M	0035 / 0721 / 1311 / 1938	1.8 / 3.3 / 2.1 / 3.4
4 M	0235 / 0906 / 1517 / 2133	1.4 / 3.7 / 1.7 / 3.7	19 TU	0205 / 0842 / 1443 / 2056	1.8 / 3.3 / 2.0 / 3.4
5 TU	0359 / 1023 / 1628 / 2239	1.3 / 3.8 / 1.6 / 3.9	20 W	0329 / 0954 / 1555 / 2202	1.7 / 3.5 / 1.8 / 3.6
6 W	0500 / 1122 / 1720 / 2332	1.0 / 4.0 / 1.4 / 4.1	21 TH	0425 / 1049 / 1644 / 2253	1.4 / 3.7 / 1.6 / 3.9
7 TH	0548 / 1208 / 1802	0.8 / 4.1 / 1.2	22 F	0509 / 1133 / 1726 / 2336	1.1 / 4.0 / 1.3 / 4.1
8 F	0014 / 0628 / 1246 / 1839	4.3 / 0.6 / 4.2 / 1.0	23 SA	0549 / 1212 / 1805	0.8 / 4.2 / 1.0
9 SA ●	0052 / 0703 / 1320 / 1913	4.4 / 0.6 / 4.3 / 0.9	24 SU O	0016 / 0628 / 1251 / 1844	4.4 / 0.6 / 4.4 / 0.8
10 SU	0127 / 0736 / 1353 / 1946	4.4 / 0.6 / 4.3 / 0.9	25 M	0057 / 0707 / 1329 / 1923	4.6 / 0.4 / 4.5 / 0.6
11 M	0202 / 0808 / 1424 / 2018	4.4 / 0.7 / 4.2 / 1.0	26 TU	0138 / 0747 / 1409 / 2004	4.7 / 0.4 / 4.6 / 0.6
12 TU	0236 / 0838 / 1455 / 2048	4.3 / 0.8 / 4.2 / 1.0	27 W	0222 / 0829 / 1450 / 2048	4.7 / 0.5 / 4.5 / 0.6
13 W	0310 / 0908 / 1527 / 2119	4.2 / 1.0 / 4.1 / 1.2	28 TH	0309 / 0912 / 1535 / 2135	4.6 / 0.7 / 4.4 / 0.7
14 TH	0346 / 0939 / 1601 / 2153	4.0 / 1.2 / 3.9 / 1.3	29 F	0400 / 1000 / 1624 / 2229	4.4 / 1.0 / 4.2 / 0.9
15 F	0426 / 1013 / 1640 / 2232	3.8 / 1.4 / 3.8 / 1.5	30 SA	0459 / 1056 / 1721 / 2334	4.1 / 1.3 / 3.9 / 1.2
			31 SU	0608 / 1204 / 1831	3.8 / 1.6 / 3.8

NOVEMBER

Day	Time	m	Day	Time	m
1 M	0051 / 0728 / 1326 / 1950	1.3 / 3.7 / 1.8 / 3.7	16 TU	0642 / 1223 / 1849	3.4 / 2.0 / 3.5
2 TU	0219 / 0851 / 1454 / 2110	1.4 / 3.7 / 1.8 / 3.7	17 W	0111 / 0753 / 1345 / 2001	1.7 / 3.4 / 2.0 / 3.5
3 W	0339 / 1004 / 1605 / 2217	1.3 / 3.8 / 1.7 / 3.9	18 TH	0229 / 0904 / 1501 / 2110	1.6 / 3.5 / 1.9 / 3.6
4 TH	0438 / 1101 / 1657 / 2310	1.1 / 3.9 / 1.5 / 4.0	19 F	0335 / 1005 / 1601 / 2210	1.4 / 3.7 / 1.6 / 3.9
5 F	0525 / 1145 / 1739 / 2353	1.0 / 4.0 / 1.4 / 4.2	20 SA	0428 / 1056 / 1650 / 2300	1.1 / 4.0 / 1.3 / 4.1
6 SA	0603 / 1221 / 1816	0.9 / 4.1 / 1.2	21 SU	0515 / 1141 / 1736 / 2347	0.9 / 4.2 / 1.1 / 4.4
7 SU	0030 / 0636 / 1254 / 1850	4.2 / 0.9 / 4.2 / 1.1	22 M	0559 / 1223 / 1820	0.6 / 4.4 / 0.8
8 M ●	0105 / 0708 / 1326 / 1923	4.3 / 0.9 / 4.2 / 1.0	23 TU O	0033 / 0643 / 1305 / 1903	4.6 / 0.5 / 4.5 / 0.6
9 TU	0139 / 0739 / 1356 / 1955	4.3 / 0.9 / 4.2 / 1.0	24 W	0120 / 0727 / 1348 / 1949	4.7 / 0.5 / 4.6 / 0.5
10 W	0213 / 0809 / 1427 / 2026	4.2 / 1.0 / 4.2 / 1.1	25 TH	0208 / 0812 / 1432 / 2037	4.7 / 0.6 / 4.5 / 0.5
11 TH	0247 / 0839 / 1458 / 2057	4.1 / 1.1 / 4.1 / 1.1	26 F	0258 / 0859 / 1518 / 2128	4.6 / 0.8 / 4.4 / 0.6
12 F	0323 / 0911 / 1531 / 2131	4.0 / 1.3 / 4.0 / 1.3	27 SA	0352 / 0948 / 1608 / 2223	4.4 / 1.1 / 4.3 / 0.8
13 SA	0402 / 0945 / 1608 / 2210	3.8 / 1.4 / 3.9 / 1.4	28 SU	0451 / 1042 / 1704 / 2324	4.1 / 1.4 / 4.1 / 1.0
14 SU	0447 / 1025 / 1651 / 2257	3.7 / 1.6 / 3.7 / 1.5	29 M	0556 / 1144 / 1809	3.9 / 1.6 / 3.9
15 M	0539 / 1115 / 1744 / 2357	3.5 / 1.8 / 3.6 / 1.7	30 TU	0031 / 0706 / 1254 / 1920	1.2 / 3.7 / 1.8 / 3.8

DECEMBER

Day	Time	m	Day	Time	m
1 W	0146 / 0819 / 1413 / 2034	1.3 / 3.6 / 1.8 / 3.8	16 TH	0028 / 0707 / 1252 / 1910	1.5 / 3.5 / 1.9 / 3.7
2 TH	0302 / 0930 / 1527 / 2144	1.3 / 3.7 / 1.8 / 3.8	17 F	0136 / 0813 / 1405 / 2019	1.5 / 3.6 / 1.8 / 3.7
3 F	0405 / 1028 / 1626 / 2241	1.3 / 3.8 / 1.7 / 3.9	18 SA	0244 / 0919 / 1514 / 2125	1.4 / 3.7 / 1.7 / 3.9
4 SA	0454 / 1115 / 1712 / 2328	1.3 / 3.9 / 1.5 / 4.0	19 SU	0347 / 1019 / 1615 / 2227	1.2 / 3.9 / 1.4 / 4.1
5 SU	0534 / 1154 / 1752	1.2 / 4.0 / 1.4	20 M	0444 / 1112 / 1710 / 2323	1.0 / 4.1 / 1.2 / 4.3
6 M	0008 / 0609 / 1229 / 1828	4.0 / 1.1 / 4.1 / 1.2	21 TU	0536 / 1200 / 1801	0.8 / 4.3 / 0.9
7 TU ●	0046 / 0643 / 1302 / 1903	4.1 / 1.1 / 4.2 / 1.1	22 W O	0016 / 0625 / 1247 / 1850	4.4 / 0.7 / 4.5 / 0.7
8 W	0121 / 0715 / 1334 / 1937	4.1 / 1.1 / 4.2 / 1.1	23 TH	0108 / 0713 / 1332 / 1940	4.6 / 0.7 / 4.6 / 0.5
9 TH	0156 / 0747 / 1405 / 2009	4.1 / 1.1 / 4.2 / 1.1	24 F	0159 / 0801 / 1417 / 2030	4.6 / 0.7 / 4.6 / 0.5
10 F	0231 / 0819 / 1436 / 2042	4.1 / 1.2 / 4.2 / 1.1	25 SA	0250 / 0848 / 1504 / 2120	4.5 / 0.9 / 4.5 / 0.6
11 SA	0307 / 0851 / 1510 / 2116	4.0 / 1.3 / 4.1 / 1.2	26 SU	0343 / 0935 / 1553 / 2212	4.4 / 1.0 / 4.4 / 0.6
12 SU	0344 / 0926 / 1545 / 2154	3.9 / 1.4 / 4.0 / 1.2	27 M	0437 / 1024 / 1645 / 2304	4.2 / 1.3 / 4.3 / 0.8
13 M	0425 / 1004 / 1626 / 2237	3.8 / 1.5 / 3.9 / 1.3	28 TU	0533 / 1115 / 1740	4.0 / 1.5 / 4.1
14 TU	0512 / 1048 / 1712 / 2327	3.7 / 1.7 / 3.8 / 1.4	29 W	0000 / 0631 / 1213 / 1841	1.1 / 3.8 / 1.7 / 3.9
15 W	0605 / 1143 / 1807	3.6 / 1.8 / 3.7	30 TH	0101 / 0734 / 1319 / 1948	1.3 / 3.6 / 1.9 / 3.7
			31 F	0208 / 0840 / 1434 / 2058	1.5 / 3.6 / 1.9 / 3.7

Chart Datum: 2·25 metres below Ordnance Datum (Newlyn)

PETERHEAD   8-6-18

Aberdeenshire 57°29'·83N 01°46'·31W   Rtg 1-4-2

CHARTS
AC 1438, 213; OS 30

TIDES
+0140 Dover; ML 2·3; Duration 0620; Zone 0 (UT)

Standard Port ABERDEEN (←)

Times				Height (metres)			
High Water		Low Water		MHWS	MHWN	MLWN	MLWS
0000	0600	0100	0700	4·3	3·4	1·6	0·6
1200	1800	1300	1900				
Differences PETERHEAD							
–0035	–0045	–0035	–0040	–0·5	–0·3	–0·1	–0·1

SHELTER
Good in marina (2·8m). A useful passage hbr, also a major fishing and oil/gas industry port. Access any weather/tide.

NAVIGATION
WPT 57°29'·46N 01°45'·64W, 134°/314° from/to ent, 0·5M. No dangers. 5kn speed limit in Bay; 4kn in marina. Chan between marina bkwtr and SHM lt buoy is <30m wide.

LIGHTS AND MARKS
Power stn chy (183m) is conspic 1·25M S of ent, with Fl W lts H24. Ldg marks 314°, front △, rear ▽ on Y cols; lts as chartlet. Marina bkwtr ✦ Fl R 3s 6m 2M is atop 2·5m high ⚓ symbol; new N bkwtr hd, QG 5m 2M, vis 120°-005°.

RADIO TELEPHONE
All vessels, including yachts, must call *Peterhead Harbour Radio* VHF Ch **14** 9 16 for clearance to enter/depart the Bay.

TELEPHONE (Dial code 01779)
Hr Mr (Bay Authority) 474020, ☎ 475712; Hr Control (H24) 474281; MRCC (01224) 592334; ⌗ (01224) 212666; Marinecall 0891 500452; Police 472571; Dr 474841; Ⓗ 472316.

FACILITIES
Marina ☎ via 474020 (HO)/☎ 475712, 92 berths, max LOA 17m; access all tides, 2·3m at ent, D, Gas, AC, FW, V and ◎ at caravan site; **Peterhead SC** ☎ (011358) 751340 (Sec); **Services:** D available in S Hbr, Slip, ME, El, Ⓔ, Sh, C, Gas. **Town** EC Wed; P, D, V, R, ✉, bus to Aberdeen for ⇌ & ✈.

ADJACENT HARBOUR

BODDAM, Aberdeenshire, 57°28'·38N 01°46'·30W. AC 213. HW +0145 on Dover; Tides as 8.6.18. Good shelter in the lee of Meikle Mackie, the island just N of Buchan Ness, Fl 5s 40m 28M Horn (3) 60s. Hbr dries/unlit. Beware rks around Meikle Mackie and to the SW of it. Appr from 1½ca NW of The Skerry. Yachts lie alongside N wall. All facilities at Peterhead, 4 miles N.

6

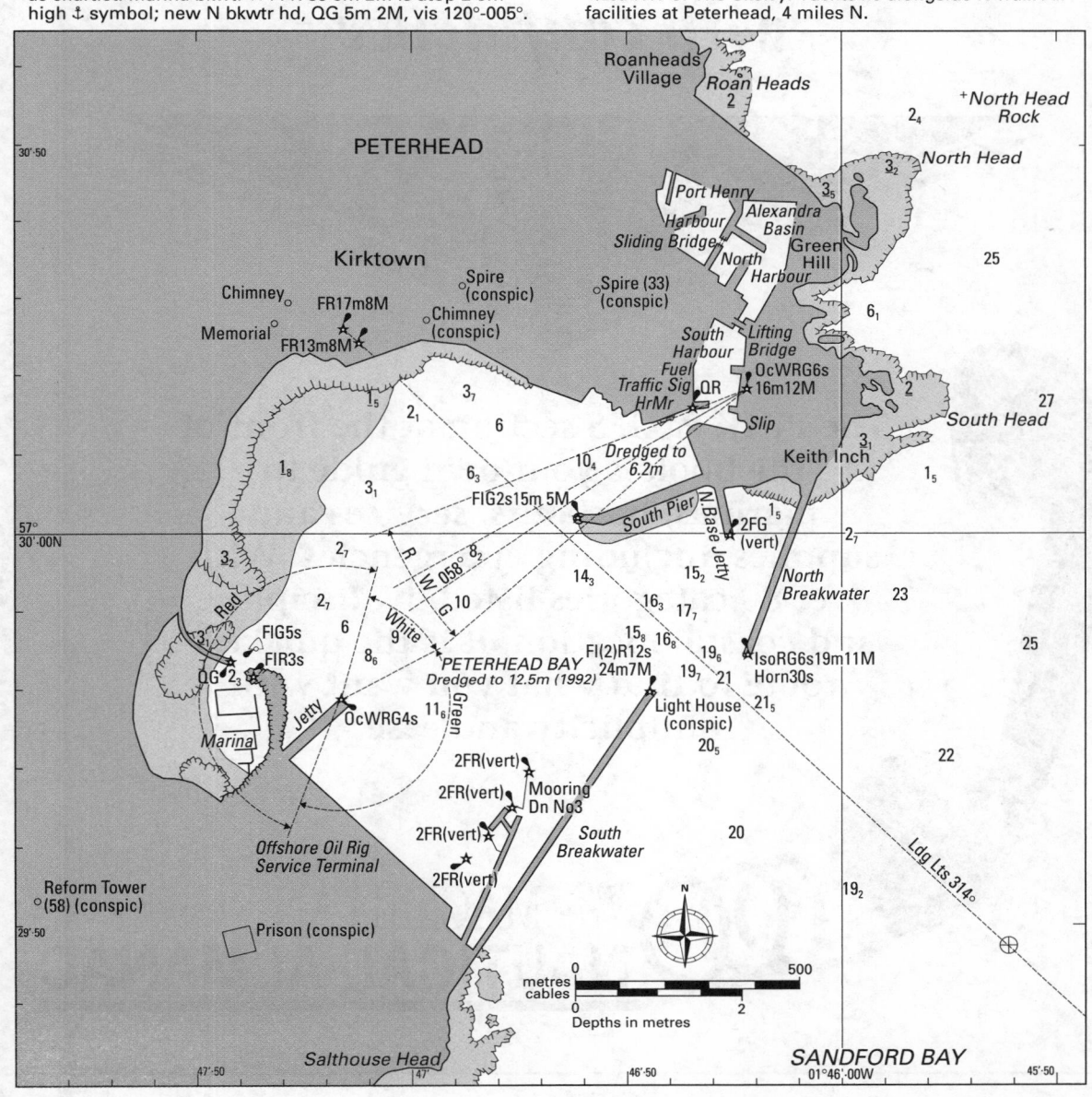

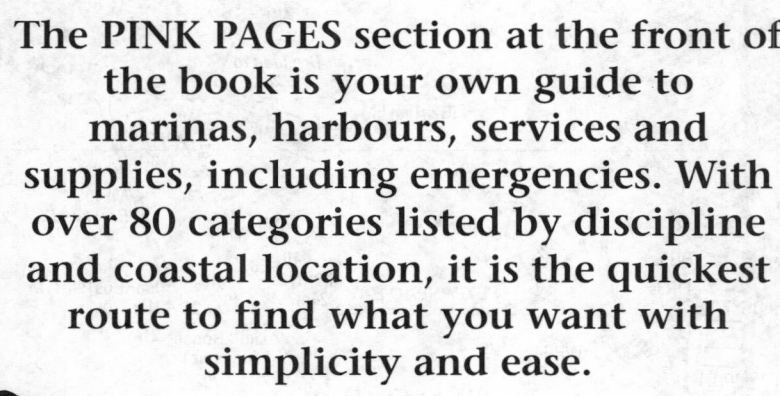

VOLVO PENTA

Area 7

North-East Scotland
Rattray Head to Cape Wrath
including Orkney and Shetland Islands

7

8.7.1	Index	**Page 383**
8.7.2	Diagram of ports, lights, RDF bns, Coast radio and weather stns	**384**
8.7.3	Tidal stream charts	**386**
8.7.4	List of coastal lights, fog signals and waypoints	**388**
8.7.5	Passage information	**392**
8.7.6	Distance table	**393**
8.7.7	Fraserburgh Rosehearty	**394**
8.7.8	Macduff and Banff	**394**
8.7.9	Whitehills Portsoy Cullen Portknockie Findochty	**395**
8.7.10	Buckie	**395**
8.7.11	Lossiemouth	**396**
8.7.12	Hopeman	**396**
8.7.13	Burghead	**397**
8.7.14	Findhorn	**397**
8.7.15	Nairn	**398**
8.7.16	Inverness Caledonian Canal Fortrose Avoch	**398**
8.7.17	Portmahomack Cromarty Firth Dornoch Firth Golspie	**400**
8.7.18	Helmsdale Lybster	**401**
8.7.19	Wick, Standard Port, tidal curves	**401**
8.7.20	Scrabster Kyle of Tongue Loch Eriboll	**405**
8.7.21	Orkney Islands Houton Bay Shapinsay Auskerry	**406**
8.7.22	Stromness	**407**
8.7.23	Kirkwall	**408**
8.7.24	Stronsay Pierowall	**408**
8.7.25	Shetland Islands	**412**
8.7.26	Lerwick, Standard Port, tidal curves Fair Isle Foula Scalloway Vaila Sound (Walls) Balta Sound	**413**

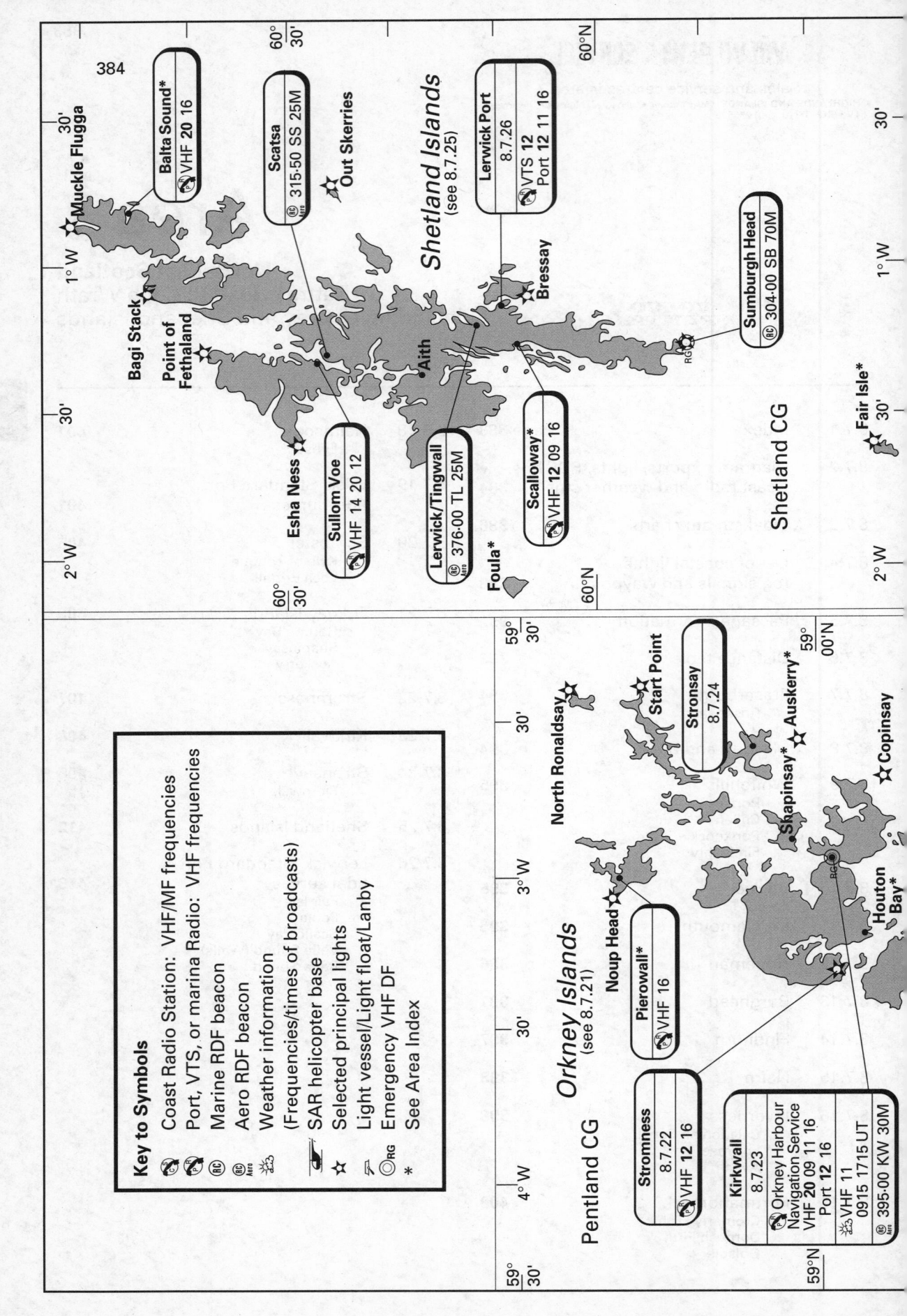

384

Key to Symbols

Coast Radio Station: VHF/MF frequencies
Port, VTS, or marina Radio: VHF frequencies
Marine RDF beacon
Aero RDF beacon
Weather information
(Frequencies/times of broadcasts)
SAR helicopter base
Selected principal lights
Light vessel/Light float/Lanby
Emergency VHF DF
See Area Index

Shetland Islands
(see 8.7.25)

Muckle Flugga

Balta Sound*
VHF 20 16

Scatsa
315·50 SS 25M

Out Skerries

Bagi Stack

Point of
Fethaland

Esha Ness

Sullom Voe
VHF 14 20 12

Aith

Bressay

Lerwick Port
8.7.26
VTS 12
Port 12 11 16

Lerwick/Tingwall
376·00 TL 25M

Scalloway*
VHF 12 09 16

Foula*

Sumburgh Head
304·00 SB 70M

Fair Isle*

Shetland CG

Orkney Islands
(see 8.7.21)

Pentland CG

North Ronaldsay

Start Point

Stronsay
8.7.24

Shapinsay* Auskerry*

Copinsay

Noup Head

Pierowall*
VHF 16

Stromness
8.7.22
VHF 12 16

Kirkwall
8.7.23
Orkney Harbour
Navigation Service
VHF 20 09 11 16
Port 12 16
VHF 11
0915 1715 UT
395·00 KW 30M

Houton
Bay*

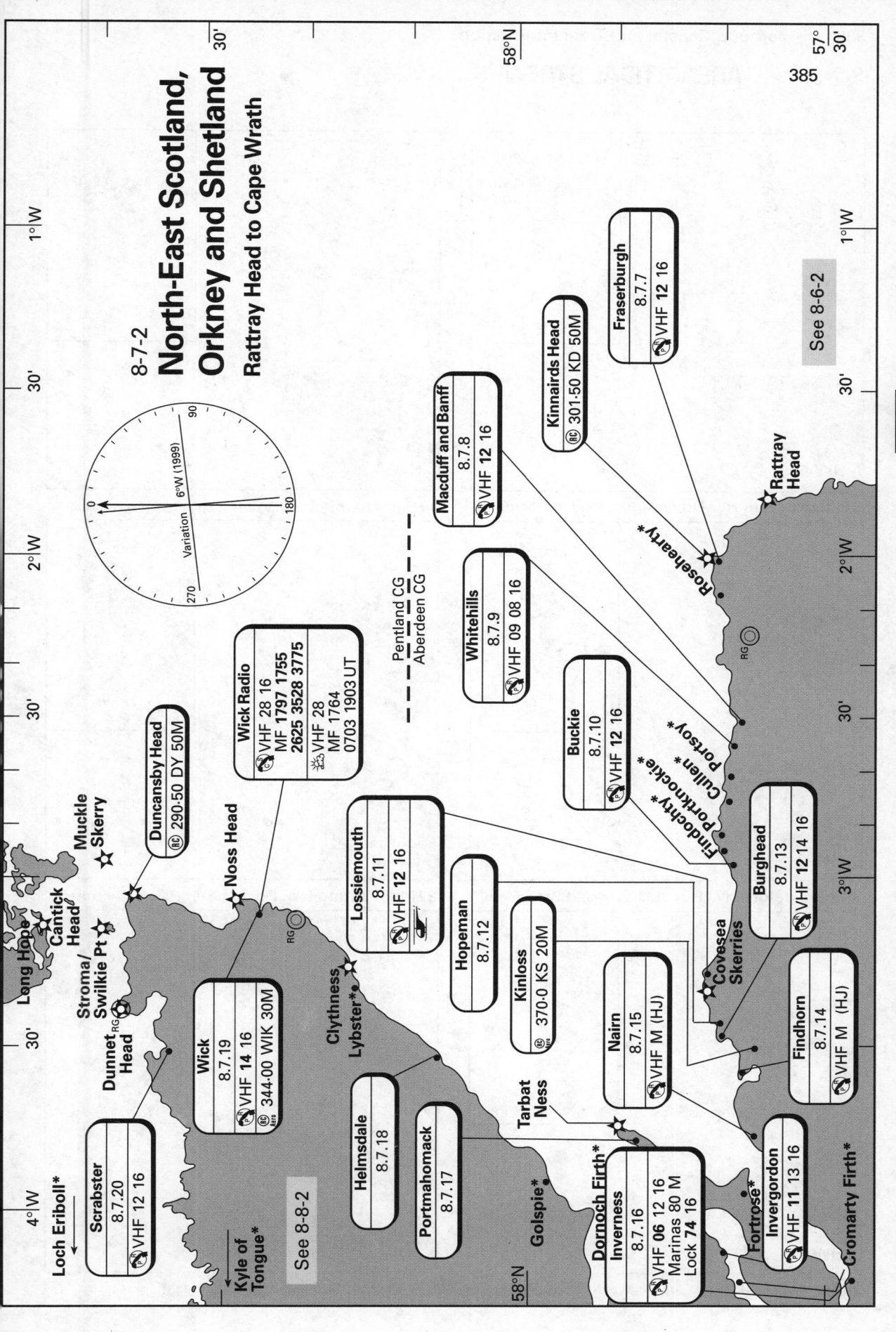

8-7-2
North-East Scotland, Orkney and Shetland
Rattray Head to Cape Wrath

385

See 8-6-2

Variation 6°W (1999)

Pentland CG
Aberdeen CG

Fraserburgh
8.7.7
VHF 12 16

Kinnairds Head
RC 301·50 KD 50M

Macduff and Banff
8.7.8
VHF 12 16

Whitehills
8.7.9
VHF 09 08 16

Buckie
8.7.10
VHF 12 16

Burghead
8.7.13
VHF **12** 14 16

Rosehearty*

Rattray Head

RG

Findochty*
Portknockie*
Cullen*
Portsoy*

Covesea Skerries

Duncansby Head
RC 290·50 DY 50M

Wick Radio
VHF 28 16
MF 1797 1755
2625 3528 3775
VHF 28
MF 1764
0703 1903 UT

Lossiemouth
8.7.11
VHF **12** 16

Hopeman
8.7.12

Kinloss
RC 370·0 KS 20M

Nairn
8.7.15
VHF M (HJ)

Findhorn
8.7.14
VHF M (HJ)

Muckle Skerry

Noss Head

RG

Tarbat Ness

Long Hope

Cantick Head

Stroma/ Swilkie Pt

Dunnet Head RG

Wick
8.7.19
VHF **14** 16
RC 344·00 WIK 30M

Clythness, Lybster*

Scrabster
8.7.20
VHF 12 16

Loch Eriboll*

Kyle of Tongue*

See 8-8-2

Helmsdale
8.7.18

Portmahomack
8.7.17

Golspie*

Dornoch Firth*

Inverness
8.7.16
VHF **06** 12 16
Marinas 80 M
Lock 74 16

Fortrose*

Invergordon
8.7.11 13 16

Cromarty Firth*

7

58°N

57° 30'

1°W

30'

2°W

30'

1°W

30'

2°W

30'

3°W

30'

4°W

30'

58°N

8-7-3   AREA 7 TIDAL STREAMS

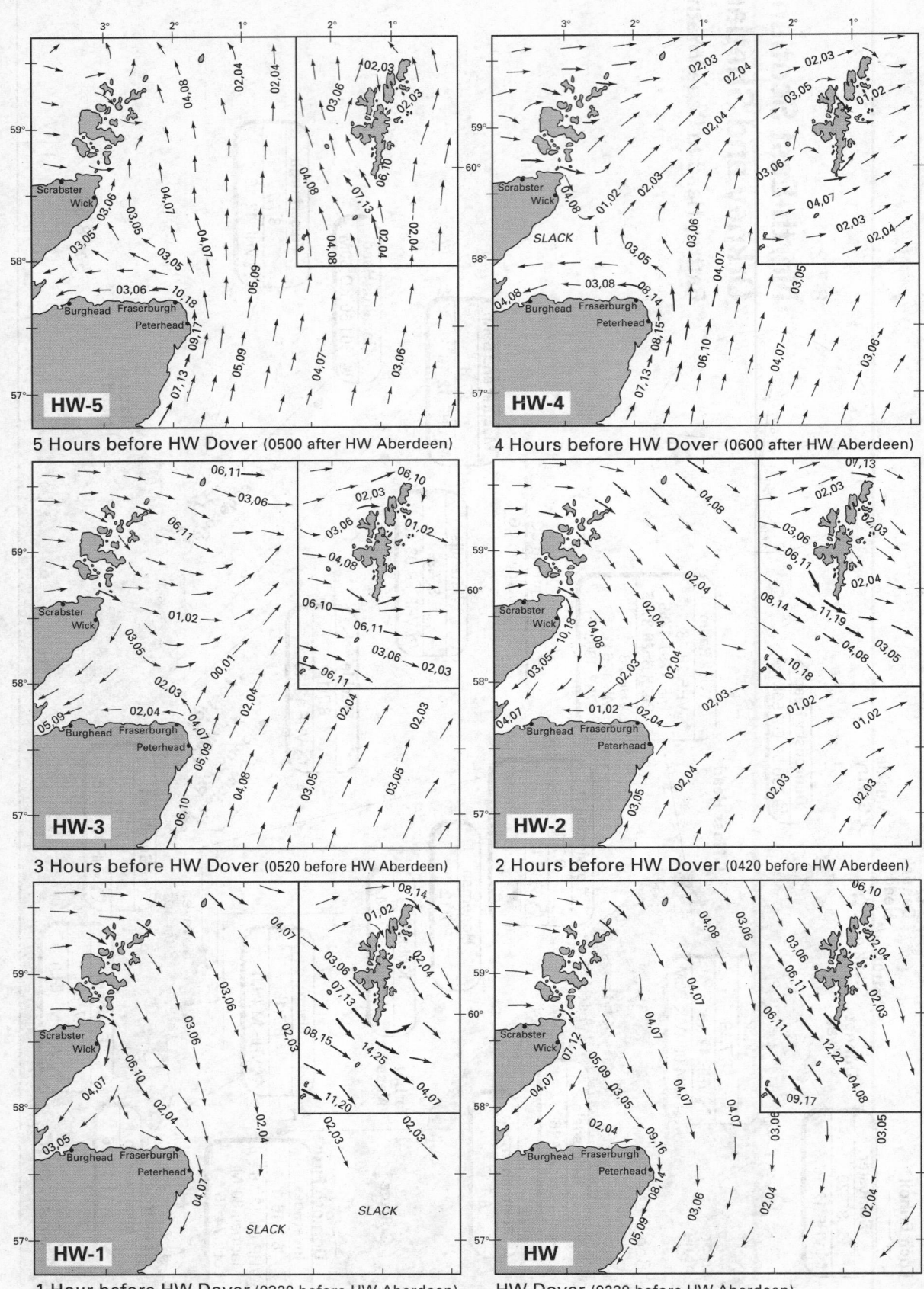

HW-5
5 Hours before HW Dover (0500 after HW Aberdeen)

HW-4
4 Hours before HW Dover (0600 after HW Aberdeen)

HW-3
3 Hours before HW Dover (0520 before HW Aberdeen)

HW-2
2 Hours before HW Dover (0420 before HW Aberdeen)

HW-1
1 Hour before HW Dover (0320 before HW Aberdeen)

HW
HW Dover (0220 before HW Aberdeen)

Southward 8.6.3   Westward 8.8.3

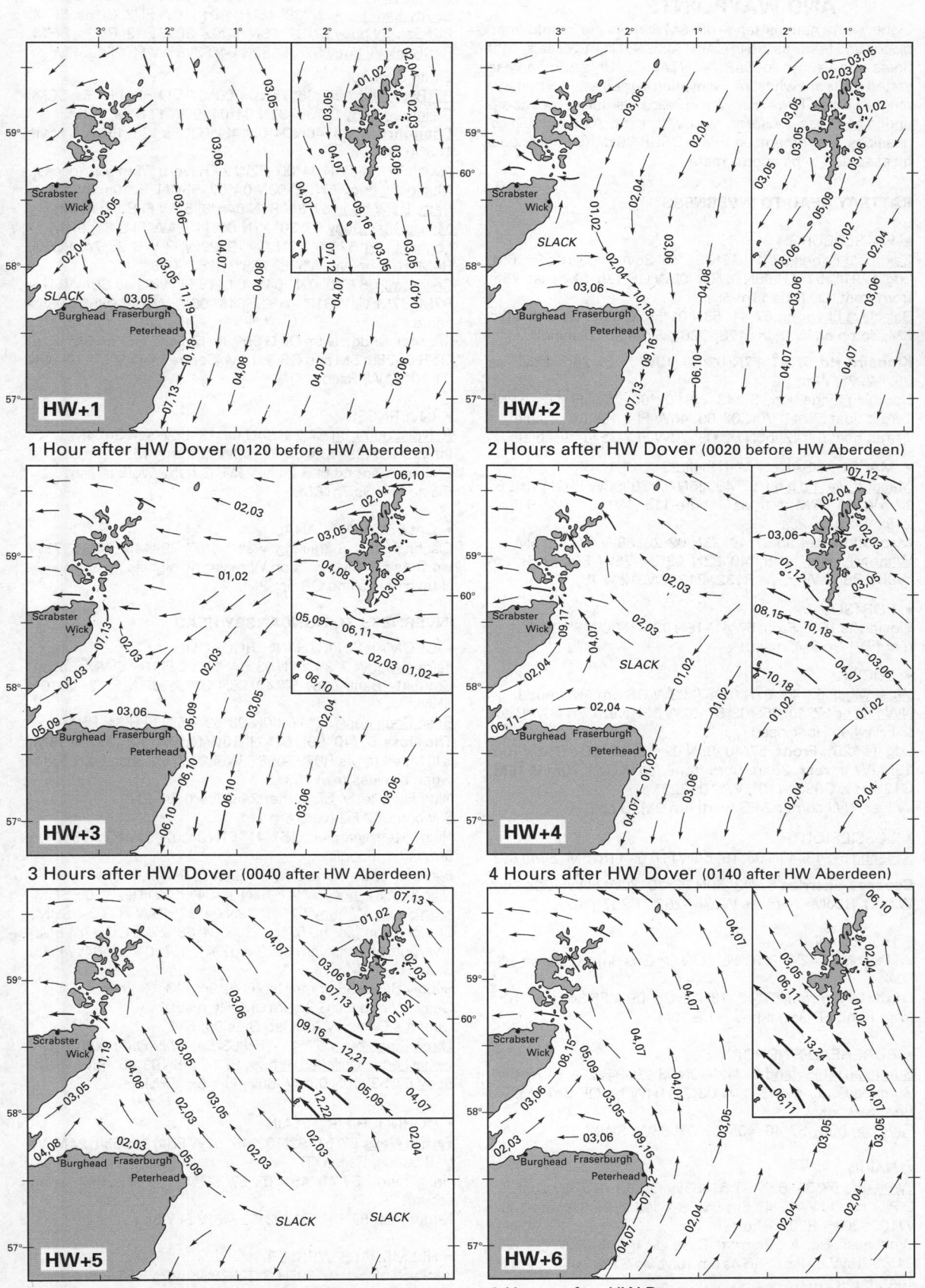

1 Hour after HW Dover (0120 before HW Aberdeen)

2 Hours after HW Dover (0020 before HW Aberdeen)

3 Hours after HW Dover (0040 after HW Aberdeen)

4 Hours after HW Dover (0140 after HW Aberdeen)

5 Hours after HW Dover (0240 after HW Aberdeen)

6 Hours after HW Dover (0340 after HW Aberdeen)

7

8.7.4 COASTAL LIGHTS, FOG SIGNALS AND WAYPOINTS

Lights with a nominal range of 15M or more are in **bold** print, places and features are in CAPITALS, and light-vessels, light floats and Lanbys in *CAPITAL ITALICS*. Unless otherwise stated lights are white. m = elevation in metres; M = nominal range in miles. Fog signals are in *italics*. Useful waypoints are underlined; use those on land with care. All geographical positions are referenced to the OSGB 36 datum but should be assumed to be approximate.

RATTRAY HEAD TO INVERNESS

• FRASERBURGH
Cairnbulg Briggs 57°41'·12N 01°56'·35W Fl (2) 10s 9m 6M.
Ldg lt 291°: 57°41'·58N 02°00'·03W QR 12m 5M; rear, 75m from front, Oc R 6s 17m 5M.
Balaclava bkwtr hd 57°41'·53N 01°59'·63W Fl (2) G 8s 26m 6M; dome on W tr; vis 178°-326°; *Siren 20s* (fishing).

Kinnaird Hd 57°41'·87N 02°00'·15W Fl 5s 25m **22M**; vis 092°-297°; W tr; RC.
Bombing range buoy 57°43'·80N 02°00'·75W Fl Y 5s; SPM.
Target float 57°41'·70N 02°09'·40W Fl Y 10s (unreliable).
Target float 57°42'·60N 02°09'·70W Fl Y 3s (unreliable).

• MACDUFF/BANFF/WHITEHILLS
Macduff Pier hd lt ho 57°40'·26N 02°29'·90W Fl (2) WRG 6s 12m W9M, R7M; W tr; vis G shore-115°, W115°-174°, R174°-210°; *Horn (2) 20s*.
Macduff W Pier hd 57°40'·23N 02°29'·88W QG 4m 5M.
Whitehills Pier hd 57°40'·82N 02°34'·75W Fl WR 3s 7m W9M, R6M; W tr; vis R132°-212°, W212°-245°.

• PORTSOY
Pier ldg lts 160°: Front 57°41'·18N 02°41'·30W F 12m 5M; tr; rear FR 17m 5M; mast.

• BUCKIE
West Muck 57°41'·07N 02°57'·93W QR 5m 7M; tripod.
NW Pier hd 57°40'·85N 02°57'·62W 2 FR (vert) 7m 11M; R col. (3 FR when Hbr closed.)
Ldg lts 125°: **Front**, 57°40'·85N 02°57'·56W Oc R 10s 15m **15M**; W tr; **rear**, 365m from front, Iso WG 2s 20m **W16M**, G12M; vis G090°-110°, W110°-225°.
W Pier, NW corner 2 FG (vert) 4m 9M; G col.

• LOSSIEMOUTH
S Pier hd 57°43'·44N 03°16'·59W Fl R 6s 11m 5M; *Siren 60s*.

Covesea Skerries 57°43'·50N 03°20'·30W Fl WR 20s 49m **W24M**, **R20M**; W tr; vis W076°-267°, R267°-282°.

• HOPEMAN
W Pier hd 57°42'·71N 03°26'·20W Oc G 4s 8m 4M shown 1/8-30/4.
Ldg lts 081°: Front, 57°42'·73N 03°26'·09W FR 3m; rear, 10m from front, FR 3m. Shown 1/8-30/4.

• BURGHEAD/FINDHORN
Burghead N bkwtr hd 57°42'·10N 03°29'·94W Oc 8s 7m 5M.
Burghead spur 57°42'·11N 03°29'·94W hd QR 3m 5M; vis from SW only.
Findhorn buoy 57°40'·40N 03°37'·65W; SWM.

• NAIRN
W Pier hd 57°35'·62N 03°51'·56W QG 5m 1M; Gy post.
E Pier hd Oc WRG 4s 6m 5M; 8-sided tr; vis Gshore-100°, W100°-207°, R207°-shore.
Whiteness Hd, McDermott Base dir lt 142·5° 57°35'·88N 04°00'·15W dir Iso WRG 4s 6m 10M; vis G138°-141°, W141°-144°, R144°-147°.

• INVERNESS FIRTH
Riff Bank E buoy 57°38'·40N 03°58'·07W Fl Y 10s; SPM.
Navity Bank buoy 57°38'·18N 04°01'·10W Fl (3) G 15s; SHM.
Riff Bank N buoy 57°37'·18N 04°02'·30W Fl (2) R 12s; PHM.
Riff Bank W buoy 57°35'·80N 04°03'·95W Fl Y 5s; SPM.

South Channel
Riff Bank S buoy 57°36'·75N 04°00'·87W Q (6) + LFl 15s; SCM.
Craigmee buoy 57°35'·32N 04°04'·90W Fl R 6s; PHM.
Chanonry 57°34'·46N 04°05'·48W Oc 6s 12m **15M**; W tr; vis 148°-073°.
Avoch 57°34'·04N 04°09'·82W 2 FR (vert) 7/5m 5M; (occas).
Munlochy buoy 57°32'·93N 04°07'·55W L Fl 10s; SWM.
Petty Bank buoy 57°31'·83N 04°08'·51W Fl R 5s; PHM.
Meikle Mee buoy 57°30'·27N 04°11'·94W Fl G 3s; SHM.
Longman Pt 57°30'·02N 04°13'·22W Fl WR 2s 7m W5M, R4M; R ▲ bn; vis W078°-258°, R258°-078°.
Craigton Pt 57°30'·07N 04°14'·01W Fl WRG 4s 6m W11M, R7M, G7M; vis W312°-048°, R048°-064°, W064°-085°, G085°-shore.
Kessock Bridge N trs Oc G 6s 28m 5M and QG 3m 3M; S trs Oc R 6s 28m 5M and QR 3m 3M. Centre mark ▽ 57°29'·99N 04°13'·71W; Racon (K).

• INVERNESS
R. Ness outer bn 57°29'·84N 04°13'·85W QR 3m 4M.
Inner bn 57°29'·73N 04°14'·02W QR 3m 4M.
Embankment hd Fl G 2s 8m 4M; G framework tr.
E side Fl R 3s 7m 6M.

• CALEDONIAN CANAL
Clachnaharry, S training wall hd 57°29'·44N 04°15'·78W Iso G 4s 5m 2M; W △ on W mast; tfc signals.
N training wall hd QR 5m 2M.

INVERNESS TO DUNCANSBY HEAD

• CROMARTY FIRTH/INVERGORDON
Fairway buoy 57°39'·98N 03°54'·10W L Fl 10s; SWM; Racon.
Cromarty Bank buoy 57°40'·68N 03°56'·69W Fl (2) G 10s; SHM.
Buss Bank buoy 57°41'·00N 03°59'·45W Fl R 3s; PHM.
The Ness 57°40'·99N 04°02'·10W Oc WR 10s 18m **W15M**, R11M; W tr; vis R079°-088°, W088°-275°, obsc by N Sutor when brg less than 253°.
Nigg Ferry jetty, SE corner 2 FG (vert) 6m 2M.
SW corner 2 FG (vert) 6m 2M.
Nigg oil terminal pier hd 57°41'·57N 04°02'·51W Oc G 5s 31m 5M; Gy tr, floodlit.
E and W ends marked by 2 FG (vert) 9 4M.
Nigg Sands E buoy 57°41'·62N 04°04'·25W Fl (2) G 10s; SHM.
Nigg Sands W buoy 57°41'·29N 04°07'·15W Fl G 3s; SHM.
British Alcan pier hd 57°41'·30N 04°08'·27W QG 17m 5M.
Invergordon Dockyard pier hd 57°41'·17N 04°09'·64W Fl (3) G 10s 15m 4M.
Supply Base, SE corner Iso G 4s 9m 6M; Gy mast.
Quay, W end Oc G 8s 9m 6M; Gy mast.
Queen's Dock, W Arm Iso G 2s 9m 6M.
Three Kings buoy 57°43'·75N 03°54'·17W Q (3) 10s; ECM.
Tarbat Ledge/Culloden Rk buoy 57°52'·45N 03°45'·45W; PHM.
Buoy 57°53'·00N 03°47'·00W Fl Y 5s; SPM.

• DORNOCH FIRTH/TAIN
Tarbat Ness 57°51'·92N 03°46'·52W Fl (4) 30s 53m **24M**; W tr, R bands; Racon (T).
Firing range 57°49'·45N 03°57'·50W Fl R 5s, when firing occurs.
Target float 57°51'·59N 03°52'·46W Fl Y 5s.

• HELMSDALE/LYBSTER
Ben-a-chielt 58°19'·80N 03°22'·20W, Aero 5 FR (vert), from 265 to 448m high; radio mast.

Lybster, S pier hd 58°17'·80N 03°17'·25W Oc R 6s 10m 3M; W tr; (occas).
Clythness 58°18'·70N 03°12'·50W Fl (2) 30s 45m **16M**; W tr, R band.

• WICK
S pier hd 58°26'·36N 03°04'·64W Fl WRG 3s 12m W12M, R9M, G9M; W 8-sided tr; vis G253°-270°, W270°-286°, R286°-329°; *Bell (2) 10s* (occas).
Dir lt 288·5°, 58°26'·56N 03°05'·26W, Iso WRG 4s 9m W10M, R7M, G7M; column on N end of bridge; vis G283·5°-287·2°, W287·2°-289·7°, R289·7°-293·5°.
Noss Hd 58°28'·75N 03°02'·90W Fl WR 20s 53m **W25M, R 21M**; W tr; vis R shore-191°, W191°-shore.

DUNCANSBY HEAD TO CAPE WRATH

Duncansby Hd 58°38'·62N 03°01'·44W Fl 12s 67m **22M**; W tr; RC; Racon (T).
Pentland Skerries 58°41'·43N 02°55'·39W Fl (3) 30s 52m **23M**; W tr; *Horn 45s.*
Lother Rock 58°43'·80N 02°58'·58W Q 11m 6M; Racon.
S Ronaldsay, Burwick bkwtr hd 2 FR (vert) 8m 5M.
Swona, near SW end 58°44'·28N 03°04'·13W Fl 8s 17m 9M; W col; vis 261°-210°.
Swona N hd 58°45'·13N 03°03'·00W Fl (3) 10s 16m 10M.
Stroma, Swilkie Pt 58°41'·78N 03°06'·92W Fl (2) 20s 32m **26M**; W tr; *Horn (2) 60s.*
Inner sound, John O'Groats, Pier hd 58°38'·73N 03°04'·12W Fl R 3s 4m 2M; W post; Ra refl.
Dunnet Hd 58°40'·31N 03°22'·48W Fl (4) 30s 105m **23M**; W tr; RG.

• THURSO/SCRABSTER
Holburn (Little) Hd 58°36'·90N 03°32'·28W Fl WR 10s 23m **W15M**, R11M; W tr; vis W198°-358°, R358°-shore.
Thurso bkwtr hd 58°35'·97N 03°30'·63W QG 5m 4M; G post; shown 1/9-30/4.
Thurso ldg lts 195°: Front, 58°35'·98N 03°30'·65W FG 5m 4M; Gy post; rear, FG 6m 4M; Gy mast.
Scrabster outer pier hd 58°36'·63N 03°32'·48W QG 6m 4M.

Strathy Pt 58°36'·10N 04°01'·00W Fl 20s 45m **26M**; W tr on W dwelling.
Sule Skerry 59°05'·10N 04°24'·30W Fl (2) 15s 34m **21M**; W tr; Racon (T).
North Rona 59°07'·30N 05°48'·80W Fl (3) 20s 114m **24M**; W tr.
Sula Sgeir 59°05'·65N 06°09'·50W Fl 15s 74m 11M; ■ structure.
Loch Eriboll, White hd 58°31'·10N 04°38'·80W Fl WR 3s 18m W13M, R12M; W tr and bldg; vis W030°-172°, R172°-191°, W191°-212°.
Cape Wrath 58°37'·55N 04°59'·87W Fl (4) 30s 122m **24M**; W tr; *Horn (3) 45s.*

ORKNEY ISLANDS

Tor Ness 58°46'·71N 03°17'·70W Fl 3s 21m 10M; W tr.
S Walls, SE end, **Cantick Hd** 58°47'·25N 03°07'·76W Fl 20s 35m **18M**; W tr.

• SCAPA FLOW AND APPROACHES
Ruff Reef, off Cantick Hd 58°47'·48N 03°07'·68W Fl (2) 10s 10m 6M; B bn.
Long Hope, S Ness Pier Hd, 58°48'·08N 03°12'·22W Fl WRG 3s 6m W7M, R5M, G5M; vis G082°-242°, W242°-252°, R252°-082°.

Hoxa Hd 58°49'·35N 03°01'·93W Fl WR 3s 15m W9M, R6M; W tr; vis W026°-163°, R163°-201°, W201°-215°.
Stanger Hd 58°48'·98N 03°04'·60W Fl R 5s 25m 8M.
Roan Hd 58°50'·75N 03°03'·81W Fl (2) R 6s 12m 7M.
Nevi Skerry 58°50'·70N 03°02'·60W Fl (2) 6s 7m 6M; IDM.
Calf of Flotta 58°51'·30N 03°03'·90W QR 8m 4M.
Flotta Terminal, N end of E Jetty. 2 FR (vert) 10m 3M.
West jetty 2 FR (vert) 10m 3M; *Bell (1)10s.*
Mooring dolphins, E and W, both QR 8m 3M.
SPM tr No 1, Fl Y 5s 12m 3M, *Horn Mo (A) 60s;* 58°52'·20N 03°07'·37W.
SPM tr No 2, Fl (4) Y 15s 12m 3M, *Horn Mo (N) 60s;* 58°52'·27N 03°05'·82W; .
Gibraltar Pier 58°50'·29N 03°07'·77W 2 FG (vert) 7m 3M.
Golden Wharf, N end 58°50'·16N 03°11'·36W 2 FR (vert) 7m 3M.
Lyness Wharf, S end 58°50'·04N 03°11'·31W 2 FR (vert) 7m 3M.
St Margaret's Hope, Needle Pt Reef 58°50'·12N 02°57'·38W Fl G 3s 6m 3M; ◊ on post.
Pier hd 2 FG (vert) 6m 2M.
Ldg lts 196°, both FR 7/11m.
Rose Ness 58°52'·36N 02°49'·80W Fl 6s 24m 8M; W tr.
Scapa Pier W end 58°57'·44N 02°58'·32W Fl G 3s 6m 8M; W mast.
Barrel of Butter 58 53'·45N 03°07'·47W Fl (2) 10s 6m 7M; Gy platform on ○ tr.
Cava lt tr 58°53'·26N 03°10'·58W Fl WR 3s 11m W10M, R8M; W ○ tr; vis W351°-143°, R143°-196°, W196°-251°, R251°- 271°, W271°-298°.
Houton Bay ldg lts 316°: Front, 58°55'·00N 03°11'·46W Fl G 3s 8m; rear, 200m from front, FG 16m; both R ▲ on W pole, B bands, vis 312°-320°.
Ro-Ro terminal, S end Iso R 4s 7m 5M.

• CLESTRAN SOUND
Peter Skerry buoy 58°55'·28N 03°13'·42W Fl G 6s; SHM.
Riddock Shoal buoy 58°55'·90N 03°15'·07W Fl (2) R 12s; PHM.

• HOY SOUND
Ebbing Eddy Rks buoy 58°56'·62N 03°16'·90W Q; NCM.
Graemsay Is ldg lts 104°: **Front**, 58°56'·46N 03°18'·50W Iso 3s 17m **15M**; W tr; vis 070°-255°; **rear**, 1·2M from front, Oc WR 8s 35m **W20M, R16M**; W tr; vis R097°-112°, W112°-163°, R163°-178°, W178°-332°; obsc on Ldg line within 0·5M.
Skerry of Ness 58°56'·98N 03°17'·73W Fl WG 4s 7m W7M, G4M; vis W shore-090°, G090°-shore.

• STROMNESS
Stromness Can buoy 58°57'·27N 03°17'·52W QR; PHM.
Stromness Conical buoy 58°57'·43N 03°17'·55W Fl G 3s.
Ldg lts 317°: Front, 58°57'·64N 03°18'·06W FR 29m 11M; post on W tr; rear, 55m from front FR 39m 11M; both vis 307°-327°.
N Pier hd 58°57'·78N 03°17'·62W Fl R 3s 8m 5M.

• AUSKERRY.
Copinsay 58°53'·82N 02°40'·25W Fl (5) 30s 79m **21M**; W tr; *Horn (4) 60s.* Fog det lt UQ, vis 192°.
Auskerry 59°01'·58N 02°34'·25W Fl 20s 34m **18M**; W tr.

Helliar Holm, S end 59°01'·17N 02°53'·95W Fl WRG 10s 18m W14M, R10M; W tr; vis G256°-276°, W276°-292°, R292°-098°, W098°-116°, G116°-154°.
Balfour Pier, Shapinsay 59°01'·89N 02°54'·40W Q WRG 5m W3M, R2M, G2M; vis G270°-010°, W010°-020°, R020°-090°.

• KIRKWALL
Scargun Shoal buoy 59°00'·83N 02°58'·57W; SHM.
Pier N end 58°59'·32N 02°57'·62W Iso WRG 5s 8m **W15M**, R13M, G13M; W tr; vis G153°-183°, W183°-192°, R192°-210°.

7

● WIDE FIRTH
Linga Skerry buoy 59°02'·42N 02°57'·45W Q (3) 10s; ECM.
Boray Skerries buoy 59°03'·68N 02°57'·55W Q (6) + L Fl 15s; SCM.
Skertours buoy 59°04'·15N 02°56'·61W Q; NCM.
Galt Skerry buoy 59°05'·25N 02°54'·10W Q; NCM.
Brough of Birsay 59°08'·25N 03°20'·30W Fl (3) 25s 52m **18M**; W castellated tr and bldg.
Papa Stronsay NE end, The Ness 59°09'·38N 02°34'·80W Iso 4s 8m 9M; W tr.

● STRONSAY, PAPA SOUND
Quiabow buoy 59°09'·85N 02°36'·20W Fl (2) G 12s; SHM.
No 1 buoy (off Jacks Reef) 59°09'·20N 02°36'·40W Fl G 5s; SHM.
No 2 buoy 59°08'·95N 02°36'·50W Fl R 5s; PHM.
No 3 buoy 59°08'·73N 02°36'·08W Fl (2) G 5s; SHM.
No 4 buoy 59°08'·80N 02°36'·37W Fl (2) R 5s; PHM.
Whitehall pier 50°08'·61N 02°35'·79W 2 FG (vert) 8m 4M.

● SANDAY ISLAND/NORTH RONALDSAY
Start Pt 59°16'·70N 02°22'·50W Fl (2) 20s 24m **19M**; W tr, B stripes.
Kettletoft pier hd, Fl WRG 3s 7m W7M, R/G5M, vis W351°-011°, R011°-180°, G180°-351°; W tr; 59°13'·90N 02°35'·72W.
N Ronaldsay near NE end, Fl 10s 43m **24M**; R tr, W bands; Racon; *Horn 60s;* 59°23'·40N 02°22'·80W.
Nouster pier hd, QR 5m, 59°21'·32N 02°26'·35W.

● EDAY/EGILSAY
Calf Sound 59°14'·30N 02°45'·70W Iso WRG 5s 8m W8M, R7M, G6M; W tr; vis R shore-216°, W216°-223°, G223°-302°, W302°-307°.
Backaland pier 59°09'·45N 02°44'·75W Fl R 3s 5m 4M; vis 192°-250°.
Egilsay Graand buoy 59°06'·90N 02°54'·30W Q(6) + L Fl 15s; SCM.
Egilsay Pier, S end 59°09'·32N 02°56'·65W Fl G 3s 4m 4M.

● WESTRAY/PIEROWALL.
Noup Hd 59°19'·90N 03°04'·10W Fl 30s 79m **22M**; W tr; vis 335°-242°, 248°-282°; obsc on E bearings within 0·8M, part obsc 240°-275°.
Pierowall E pier hd 59°19'·39N 02°58'·41W Fl WRG 3s 7m W11M, R7M, G7M; vis G254°-276°, W276°-291°, R291°-308°, G308°-215°.
Papa Westray, Moclett Bay pier hd 59°19'·65N 02°53'·40W Fl WRG 5s 7m W5M, R3M, G3M; vis G306°-341°, W341°-040°, R040°-074°.

SHETLAND ISLES

● FAIR ISLE
Skadan, S end 59°30'·85N 01°39'·08W Fl (4) 30s 32m **22M**; W tr; vis 260°-146°, obsc inshore 260°-282°; *Horn (2) 60s.*
Skroo, N end 59°33'·16N 01°36'·49W Fl (2) 30s 80m **22M**; W tr; vis 086·7°-358°; *Horn (3) 45s.*

● MAINLAND, SOUTH
Sumburgh Hd 59°51'·30N 01°16'·37W Fl (3) 30s 91m **23M**; W tr; RC.
Pool of Virkie, marina E bkwtr hd 59°53'·05N 01°17'·00W 2 FG (vert) 6m 5M.
Mousa, Perie Bard 59°59'·85N 01°09'·40W Fl 3s 20m 10M; W tr.
Aithsvoe 60°02'·30N 01°12'·83W Fl R 3s 3m 2M.

● BRESSAY/LERWICK
Kirkabister Ness 60°07'·25N 01°07'·18W Fl (2) 20s 32m **23M**; W tr.
Cro of Ham 60°08'·20N 01°07'·40W Fl 3s 3M.
Twageos Pt 60°08'·95N 01°07'·83W L Fl 6s 8m 6M; W bn.

Maryfield, ferry terminal 60°09'·47N 01°07'·32W Oc WRG 6s 5m 5M; vis W008°-013°, R013°-111°, G111°-008°.
Bkwtr N hd 60°09'·27N 01°08'·29W 2 FR (vert) 5m 4M.
N Ness 60°09'·60N 01°08'·66W Iso WG 4s 4m 5M; vis G158°-216°, W216°-158°.
Loofa Baa 60°09'·75N 01°08'·67W Q (6) + L Fl 15s 4m 5M; SCM.
Soldian Rock buoy 60°12'·54N 01°04'·61W VQ(6) + L Fl 15s; SCM.
N ent dir Lt 215° 60°10'·49N 01°09'·40W Dir Oc WRG 6s 27m 8M; Y ▲, Or stripe; vis R211°-214°, W214°-216°, G216°-221°.
Gremista marina S bkwtr hd 60°10'·23N 01°09'·49W   Iso R 4s 3m 2M.
Greenhead 60°10'·87N 01°08'·98W Q (4) R 10s 4m 3M.
Rova hd 60°11'·45N 01°08'·45W Fl (3) WRG 18s 10m W8M, R7M, G6M; W tr; vis R shore-180°, W180°-194°, G194°-213°, R213°-241°, W241°-261·5°, G261·5°-009°, W009°-shore.
The Brethren Rk buoy 60°12'·38N 01°08'·12W Q (9) 15s; WCM.
The Unicorn Rk buoy 60°13'·54N 01°08'·35W VQ (3) 5s; ECM.
Dales Voe 60°11'·82N 01°11'·10W Fl (2) WRG 8s 5m W4M, R3M, G3M; vis G220°-227°, W227°-233°, R233°-240°.
Dales Voe Quay 60°11'·60N 01°10'·48W 2 FR (vert) 9m 3M.
Laxfirth Pier hd 60°12'·77N 01°12'·01W 2 FG (vert) 4m 2M.
Hoo Stack 60°14'·99N 01°05'·25W Fl (4) WRG 12s 40m W7M, R5M, G5M; W pylon; vis R169°-180°, W180°-184°, G184°-193°, W193°-169°. Dir lt 182°. Dir Fl (4) WRG 12s 33m W9M, R6M, G6M; same structure; vis R177°-180°, W180°-184°, G184°-187°; synch with upper lt.
Mull (Moul) of Eswick 60°15'·80N 01°05'·80W Fl WRG 3s 50m W9M, R6M, G6M; W tr; vis R028°-200°, W200°-207°, G207°-018°, W018°-028°.

● WHALSAY/SKERRIES
Symbister Ness 60°20'·46N 01°02'·15W Fl (2) WG 12s 11m W8M, G6M; W tr; vis W shore-203°, G203°-shore.
Symbister Bay S bkwtr hd 60°20'·60N 01°01'·50W QG 4m 2M.
N bkwtr hd 60°20'·67N 01°01'·60W Oc G 7s 3m 3M.
E bkwtr hd Oc R 7s 3m 3M.
Marina N pontoon 60°20'·50N 01°01'·40W 2 FG (vert) 2m 3M.
Skate of Marrister 60°21'·42N 01°01'·25W Fl G 6s 4m 4M; G mast with platform.
Suther Ness 60°22'·15N 01°00'·05W Fl WRG 3s 8m W10M, R8M, G7M; vis W shore-038°, R038°-173°, W173°-206°, G206°-shore.
Mainland, Laxo Voe ferry terminal 60°21'·1N 01°10'·0W 2 FG (vert) 4m 2M.
Bound Skerry 60°25'·50N 00°43'·50W Fl 20s 44m **20M**; W tr.
South Mouth. Ldg lts 014°: Front, 60°25'·37N 00°44'·89W FY 3m 2M; rear, FY 12m 2M.
Bruray bn D Fl (3) G 6s 3m 3M.
Bruray bn B VQ G 3m 3M.
Housay bn A VQ R 3m 3M.
Bruray ferry berth 60°25'·4N 00°45'·10W 2 FG (vert) 6m 4M.
Muckle Skerry 60°26'·40N 00°51'·70W Fl (2) WRG 10s 13m W7M, R5M, G5M; W tr; vis W046°-192°, R192°-272°, G272°-348°, W348°-353°, R353°-046°.

● YELL SOUND
S ent, Lunna Holm 60°27'·38N 01°02'·39W Fl (3) WRG 15s 19m W10M, R7M, G7M; W ○ tr; vis R shore-090°, W090°-094°, G094°-209°, W209°-275°, R275°-shore.
Firths Voe, N shore 60°27'·24N 01°10'·50W Oc WRG 8s 9m **W15M**, R10M, G10M; W tr; vis W189°-194°, G194°-257°, W257°-261°, R261°-339°, W339°-066°.
Linga Is. Dir lt 60°26'·83N 01°09'·00W Dir Q (4) WRG 8s 10m W9M, R9M, G9M; concrete col; vis R145°-148°, W148°-152°, G152°-155°. Q (4) WRG 8s 10m W7M, R4M, G4M; same structure; vis R052°-146°, G154°-196°, W196°-312°; synch with dir lt.
The Rumble bn 60°28'·20N 01°07'·12W R bn; Racon (O).

Yell, Ulsta ferry terminal bkwtr hd 60°29'·78N 01°09'·40W Oc RG 4s 7m R5M, G5M; vis G shore-354°, R044°-shore. Same structure; Oc WRG 4s 5m W8M, R5M, G5M; vis G shore-008°, W008°-036°, R036°-shore.

Toft ferry terminal 60°28'·06N 01°12'·26W 2 FR (vert) 5m 2M.

Ness of Sound, W side 60°31'·38N 01°11'·15W Iso WRG 5s 18m W9M, R6M, G6M; vis G shore-345°, W345°-350°, R350°-160°, W160°-165°, G165°-shore.

Brother Is. Dir lt 329° 60°30'·99N 01°13'·99W dir Fl (4) WRG 8s 16m W10M, R7M, G7M; vis G323·5°-328°, W328°-330°, R330°-333·5°.

Mio Ness 60°29'·70N 01°13'·55W Q (2) WR 10s 12m W7M, R4M; W ○ tr; W282°-238°, R238°-282°.

Tinga Skerry 60°30'·52N 01°14'·73W Q (2) G 10s 9m 5M; W ○ tr.

● YELL SOUND, NORTH ENTRANCE
Bagi Stack 60°43'·55N 01°07'·40W Fl (4) 20s 45m 10M; W tr.
Gruney Is 60°39'·20N 01°18'·03W Fl WR 5s 53m W8M, R6M; W tr; vis R064°-180°, W180°-012°; Racon (T).
Point of Fethaland 60°38'·09N 01°18'·58W Fl (3) WR 15s 65m **W24M**, **R20M**; W tr; vis R080°-103°, W103°-160°, R160°-206°, W206°-340°.
Muckle Holm 60°34'·85N 01°15'·90W Fl (4) 10s 32m 10M; W tr.
Little Holm 60°33'·46N 01°15'·75W Iso 4s 12m 6M; W tr.
Outer Skerry 60°33'·08N 01°18'·20W Fl 6s 12m 8M; W col, B bands.
Quey Firth 60°31'·48N 01°19'·46W Oc WRG 6s 22m W12M, R8M, G8M; W tr; vis W shore (through S and W-290°, G290°-327°, W327°-334°, R334°-shore.
Lamba, S side 60°30'·76N 01°17'·70W Fl WRG 3s 30m W8M, R5M, G5M; W tr; vis G shore-288°, W288°-293°, R293°-327°, W327°-044°, R044°-140°, W140°-shore. Dir lt 290·5° dir Fl WRG 3s 24m W10M, R7M, G7M; vis 285·5°-288°, W288°-293°, R293°-295·5°.

● SULLOM VOE
Gluss Is ldg lts 194·7° (H24): **Front**, 60°29'·81N 01°19'·31W F 39m **19M**; ■ on Gy tr. **Rear**, 0·75M from front, F 69m **19M**; ■ on Gy tr. Both lts 9M by day.
Little Roe 60°30'·05N 01°16'·35W Fl (3) WR 10s 16m W5M, R4M; Y and W structure; vis R036°-095·5°, W095·5°-036°.
Skaw Taing 60°29'·13N 01°16'·72W Fl (2) WRG 5s 21m W8M, R5M, G5M; Or and W structure; vis W049°-078°, G078°-147°, W147°-154°, R154°-169°, W169°-288°.
Ness of Bardister 60°28'·22N 01°19'·50W Oc WRG 8s 20m W9M, R6M, G6M; Or and W structure; vis W180·5°-240°, R240°-310·5°, W310·5°-314·5°, G314·5°-030·5°.
Vats Houllands 60°27'·97N 01°17'·48W Oc WRGY 3s 73m 6M; Gy tr; vis W343·5°-029·5°, Y029·5°-049°, G049°-074·5°, R074·5°-098·5°, G098·5°-123·5°, Y123·5°-148°, W148°-163·5°.
Fugla Ness. Lts in line 212·3°; rear, 60°27'·3N 01°19'·7W Iso 4s 45m 14M. Common front 60°27'·48N 01°19'·43W Iso 4s 27m 14M; synch with rear lts. Lts in line 203°; rear, 60°27'·3N 01°19'·6W Iso 4s 45m 14M.
Sella Ness. Upper lt 60°26'·92N 01°16'·52W Q WRG 14m 7M; Gy tr; vis G084·5°-098·7°, W098·7°-099·7°, W126°-128·5°, R128·5°-174·5°; by day F WRG 2M (occas). Lower lt. Q WRG 10m 7M; vis: G084·5°-106·5°, W106·5°-115°, R115°-174·5°; by day F WRG 2M (occas).
Tug jetty finger, pier hd 60°26'·79N 01°16'·25W Iso G 4s 4m 3M.
Garth Pier N arm hd 60°26'·72N 01°16'·22W Fl (2) 5s 4m 3M.
Scatsa Ness upper lt 60°26'·52N 01°18'·13W Oc WRG 5s 14m 7M; Gy tr; vis G161·5°-187·2°, W187·2°-188·2°, W207·2°-208·2°, R208·2°-251·5°; by day F WRG 2M (occas).

Lower lt Oc WRG 5s 10m 7M; vis G161·5°-197·2°, W197·2°-202·2°, R202·2°-251·5°; by day F WRG 2M (occas).
Ungam Is 60°27'·27N 01°18'·50W VQ (2) 5s 2m 2M; W col; Ra refl.

● EAST YELL /UNST/BALTA SOUND
Whitehill 60°34'·85N 01°00'·01W Fl WR 3s 24m W9M, R6M; vis W shore-163°, R163°-211°, W211°-349°, R349°-shore.
Uyea Sound 60°41'·19N 00°55'·37W Fl (2) 8s 8m 7M; R & W tr.
Balta Sound 60°44'·47N 00°47'·56W Fl WR 10s 17m 10M, R7M; vis W249°-010°, R010°-060°, W060°-154°; Q lt (occas) marks Unst Aero RC 0·7M W.
Balta marina bkwtr hd 60°45'·60N 00°50'·20W Fl R 6s 2m 2M.
Holme of Skaw 60°49'·92N 00°46'·19W Fl 5s 8m 8M.
Muckle Flugga 60°51'·33N 00°53'·00W Fl (2) 20s 66m **22M**; W tr.
Yell. Cullivoe bkwtr hd 60°41'·91N 00°59'·66W Oc R 7s 5m 2M; Gy col.

● MAINLAND, WEST
Esha Ness 60°29'·35N 01°37'·55W Fl 12s 61m **25M**; W □tr.
Hillswick, S end of Ness 60°27'·20N 01°29'·70W Fl (4) WR 15s 34m W9M, R6M; W house: vis W217°-093°, R093°-114°.
Muckle Roe, Swarbacks Minn, 60°21'·05N 01°26'·90W Fl WR 3s 30m W9M, R6M; vis W314°-041°, R041°-075°, W075°-137°.
W Burra Firth outer lt 60°17'·84N 01°33'·47W Oc WRG 8s 27m W9M, R7M, G7M; vis G136°-142°, W142°-150°, R150°-156°.
W Burra Firth inner lt 60°17'·84N 01°32'·03W F WRG 9m W15M, R9M, G9M; vis G095°-098°, W098°-102°, W098°-102°, R102°-105°.
Aith bkwtr. RNLI berth 60°17'·20N 01°22'·30W QG 5m 3M.
W Burra Firth transport pier hd 60°17'·75N 01°32'·30W Iso G 4s 4m 4M.
Ve Skerries 60°22'·40N 01°48'·67W Fl (2) 20s 17m 11M; W tr; Racon (T).
Rams Hd 60°12'·00N 01°33'·40W Fl WG 8s 16m W9m, G6M, R6M; W house; vis G265°-355°, W355°-012°, R012°-090°, W090°-136°, obsc by Vaila Is when brg more than 030°.
Vaila pier 60°13'·47N 01°34'·00W 2 FR (vert) 4m.
Skeld Voe, Skeld pier hd 60°11'·20N 01°26'·10W 2 FR (vert) 4m 3M.
North Havra 60°09'·88N 01°20'·17W Fl WRG 12s 24m W7M, R5M, G5M; W tr; vis G001°-053·5°, W053·5°-060·5°, G274°-334°, W334°-337·5°, R337·5°-001°.

● SCALLOWAY
Pt of the Pund 60°08'·02N 01°18'·20W Fl WRG 5s 20m W7M, R5M, G5M; W tr; vis R350°-090°, G090°-111°, R111°-135°, W135°-140°, G140°-177°, W267°-350°.
Whaleback Skerry buoy 60°07'·98N 01°18'·79W Q; NCM.
Moores slipway jetty hd 60°08'·21N 01°16'·72W 2 FR (vert) 4m 1M.
Centre pier 60°08'·06N 01°16'·47W Oc WRG 10s 10m W11M, G8M, R8M; vis G052°-063·5°, W063·5°-065·5°, R065·5°-077°.

Fugla Ness 60°06'·40N 01°20'·75W Fl (2) WRG 10s 20m W10M, R7M, G7M; W tr; vis G014°-032°, W032°-082°, R082°-134°, W134°-shore.

● FOULA
60°06'·78N 02°03'·72W Fl (3) 15s 36m **18M**; W tr. Obscured 123°-221°.

7

8.7.5 PASSAGE INFORMATION

Refer to the *N Coast of Scotland Pilot*; the CCC's SDs (3 vols) for *N and NE coasts of Scotland; Orkney;* and *Shetland.*

MORAY FIRTH: SOUTH COAST (charts 115, 222, 223)

Crossing the Moray Firth from Rattray Hd (lt, fog sig) to Duncansby Hd (lt,RC, Racon) heavy seas may be met in strong W winds. Most hbrs in the Firth are exposed to NE-E winds. For oil installations, see 8.5.5; the Beatrice Field is 20M S of Wick. Tidal streams attain 3kn at sp close off Rattray Hd, but 5M NE of the Head the NE-going stream begins at HW Aberdeen + 0140, and the SE-going stream at HW Aberdeen – 0440, sp rates 2kn. Streams are weak elsewhere in the Moray Firth, except in the inner part. In late spring/early summer fog (haar) is likely in onshore winds.

In strong winds the sea breaks over Steratan Rk and Colonel Rk, respectively 3M E and 1M ENE of Fraserburgh (8.7.7). Rosehearty firing range is N & W of Kinnairds Hd (lt); tgt buoys often partially submerged. Banff B is shallow; N of Macduff (8.7.8) beware Collie Rks. Banff hbr dries, and should not be approached in fresh NE-E winds, when seas break well offshore; Macduff would then be a feasible alternative.

From Meavie Pt to Scar Nose dangers extend up to 3ca from shore in places. Beware Caple Rk (depth 0.2m) 7½ca W of Logie Hd. Spey B is clear of dangers more than 7½ca from shore; anch here, but only in offshore winds. Beware E Muck (dries) 5ca SW of Craigenroan, an above-water rky patch 5ca SW of Craig Hd, and Middle Muck and W Muck in approach to Buckie (8.7.10); Findochty & Portknockie are 2 and 3.5M ENE. Halliman Skerries (dry; bn) lie 1.5M WNW of Lossiemouth (8.7.11). Covesea Skerries (dry) lie 5ca NW of their lt ho.

Inverness Firth is approached between Nairn (8.7.15) and S Sutor. In heavy weather there is a confused sea with overfalls on Guillam Bank, 9M S of Tarbat Ness. The sea also breaks on Riff Bank (S of S Sutor) which dries in places. Chans run both N and S of Riff Bank. Off Fort George, on E side of ent to Inverness Firth (chart 1078), the SW-going stream begins HW Aberdeen + 0605, sp rate 2.5kn; the NE-going stream begins at HW Aberdeen – 0105, sp rate 3.5kn. There are eddies and turbulence between Fort George and Chanonry Pt when stream is running hard. Much of Inverness Firth is shallow, but a direct course from Chanonry Pt to Kessock Bridge, via Munlochy SWM and Meikle Mee SHM lt buoys, carries a least depth of 2.1m. Meikle Mee bank dries 0.2m. For Fortrose and Avoch, see 8.7.16.

MORAY FIRTH: NORTH WEST COAST (chart 115)

Cromarty Firth (charts 1889, 1890) is entered between N Sutor and S Sutor, both fringed by rks, some of which dry. Off the entrance the in-going stream begins at HW Aberdeen + 0605, and the out-going at HW Aberdeen – 0105, sp rates 1.5 kn. Good sheltered anchs within the firth, see 8.7.17.

The coast NE to Tarbat Ness (lt) is fringed with rks. Beware Three Kings (dries) about 3M NE of N Sutor. Culloden Rk, a shoal with depth of 1.8m, extends 2½ca NE of Tarbat Ness, where stream is weak. Beware salmon nets between Tarbat Ness and Portmahomack (8.7.17). Dornoch Firth (8.7.17) is shallow, with shifting banks, and in strong E winds the sea breaks heavily on the bar E of Dornoch Pt.

At Lothbeg Pt, 5M SW of Helmsdale (8.7.18), a rky ledge extends 5ca offshore. Near Berriedale, 7M NE of Helmsdale, The Pinnacle, a detached rk 61m high, stands close offshore. The Beatrice oil field lies on Smith Bank, 28M NE of Tarbat Ness, and 11M off Caithness coast. Between Dunbeath and Lybster (8.7.18) there are no dangers more than 2ca offshore. Clyth Ness (lt) is fringed by detached and drying rks. From here to Wick (8.7.19) the only dangers are close inshore. There is anch in Sinclair's B in good weather, but Freswick B further N is better to await the tide in Pentland Firth (beware wreck in centre of bay). Stacks of Duncansby and Baxter Rk (depth 2.7m) lie 1M and 4ca S of Duncansby Hd.

PENTLAND FIRTH (charts 2162, 2581)

This potentially dangerous chan should only be attempted with moderate winds (less than F4), good vis, no swell and a fair np tide; when it presents few problems. A safe passage depends on a clear understanding of tidal streams and correct timing. The Admiralty Tidal Stream Atlas for Orkney and Shetland (NP 209) gives large scale vectors and is essential. Even in ideal conditions the races off Duncansby Hd, Swilkie Pt (N end of Stroma), and Rks of Mey (Merry Men of Mey) must be avoided as they are always dangerous to small craft. Also avoid the Pentland Skerries, Muckle Skerry, Old Head, Lother Rock (S Ronaldsay), and Dunnet Hd on E-going flood. For passages across the Firth see CCC *SDs for Orkney.*

At E end the Firth is entered between Duncansby Hd and Old Hd (S Ronaldsay), between which lie Muckle Skerry and the Pentland Skerries. Near the centre of Firth are the Islands of Swona (N side) and Stroma (S side). Outer Sound (main chan, 2.5M wide) runs between Swona and Stroma; Inner Sound (1.5M wide) between Stroma and the mainland. Rks of Mey extend about 2ca N of St John's Pt. The W end of the Firth is between Dunnet Hd and Tor Ness (Hoy).

Tidal streams reach 8-9kn at sp in the Outer Sound, and 9-12kn between Pentland Skerries and Duncansby Hd. The resultant dangerous seas, very strong eddies and violent races should be avoided by yachts at all costs. Broadly the E-going stream begins at HW Aberdeen + 0500, and the W-going at HW Aberdeen – 0105. **Duncansby Race** extends ENE towards Muckle Skerry on the SE-going stream, but by HW Aberdeen – 0440 it extends NW from Duncansby Hd. Note: HW at Muckle Skerry is the same time as HW Dover. A persistent race off **Swilkie Pt** at N end of Stroma, is very dangerous with a strong W'ly wind over a W-going stream. The most dangerous and extensive race in the Firth is **Merry Men of Mey**, which forms off St John's Pt on W-going stream at HW Aberdeen – 0150 and for a while extends right across to Tor Ness with heavy breaking seas even in fine weather.

Passage Westward: This is the more difficult direction due to prevailing W winds. Freswick B, 3.5M S of Duncansby Hd, is a good waiting anch; here an eddy runs N for 9 hrs. Round Duncansby Hd close in at HW Aberdeen –0220, as the ebb starts to run W. Take a mid-course through the Inner Sound to appr the Rks of Mey from close inshore. Gills Bay is a temp anch if early; do not pass Rks of Mey until ebb has run for at least 2 hrs. Pass 100m N of the Rks (awash).

Passage Eastward: With a fair wind and tide, no race forms and the passage is easier. Leave Scrabster at local LW+1 so as to be close off Dunnet Hd at HW Aberdeen +0240 as the E-going flood starts to make. If late, give the Hd a wide berth. Having rounded the Rks of Mey, steer S initially to avoid being set onto the rky S tip of Stroma, marked by unlit SCM bn. Then keep mid-chan through the Inner Sound and maintain this offing to give Duncansby Hd a wide berth.

PENTLAND FIRTH TO CAPE WRATH (chart 1954)

Dunnet B, S of Dunnet Hd (lt) gives temp anch in E or S winds, but dangerous seas enter in NW'lies. On W side of Thurso B is Scrabster (8.7.20) sheltered from S and W. Between Holborn Hd and Strathy Pt the E-going stream begins at HW Ullapool – 0150, and the W-going at HW Ullapool + 0420, sp rates 1.8kn. Close to Brims Ness off Ushat Hd the sp rate is 3kn, and there is often turbulence.
SW of Ushat Hd the Dounreay power stn is conspic, near shore. Dangers extend 2½ca seaward off this coast.

Along E side of Strathy Pt (lt) an eddy gives almost continuous N-going stream, but there is usually turbulence off the Pt where this eddy meets the main E or W stream. Several small B's along this coast give temp anch in offshore winds, but must not be used or approached with wind in a N quarter.

Kyle of Tongue (8.7.20) is entered from E through Caol Raineach, S of Eilean nan Ron, or from N between Eilean Iosal and Cnoc Glass. There is no chan into the kyle W of Rabbit Is, to which a drying spit extends 0·5M NNE from the mainland shore. Further S there is a bar across entrance to inner part of kyle. There are anchs on SE side of Eilean nan Ron, SE side of Rabbit Is, off Skullomie, or S of Eilean Creagach off Talmine. Approach to the latter runs close W of Rabbit Islands, but beware rks to N and NW of them.

Loch Eriboll, (chart 2076 and 8.7.20), provides secure anchs, but in strong winds violent squalls blow down from mountains. Eilean Cluimhrig lies on W side of entrance; the E shore is fringed with rks up to 2ca offshore. At White Hd (lt) the loch narrows to 6ca. There are chans W and E of Eilean Choraidh. Best anchs in Camas an Duin (S of Ard Neackie) or in Rispond B close to entrance (but not in E winds, and beware Rispond Rk which dries).

The coast to C. Wrath (8.8.5) is indented, with dangers extending 3ca off the shore and offlying rks and Is. Once a yacht has left Loch Eriboll she is committed to a long and exposed passage until reaching Loch Inchard. The Kyle of Durness is dangerous if the wind or sea is onshore. Give Cape Wrath a wide berth when wind-against-tide which raises a severe sea. A firing exercise area extends 8M E of C. Wrath, and 4M offshore. When in use, R flags or pairs of R lts (vert) are shown from E and W limits, and yachts should keep clear.

ORKNEY ISLANDS (8.7.21 and charts 2249, 2250)

The Islands are mostly indented and rky, but with sandy beaches especially on NE sides. Pilotage is easy in good vis, but in other conditions great care is needed since tides run strongly. For details refer to Clyde Cruising Club's *Orkney Sailing Directions* and the Admiralty Tidal Atlas NP 209.

When cruising in Orkney it is essential to understand and use the tidal streams to the best advantage, avoiding the various tide races and overfalls, particularly near sp. A good engine is needed since, for example, there are many places where it is dangerous to get becalmed. Swell from the Atlantic or North Sea can contribute to dangerous sea conditions, or penetrate to some of the anchorages. During summer months winds are not normally unduly strong, and can be expected to be Force 7 or more on about two days a month. But in winter the wind reaches this strength for 10-15 days per month, and gales can be very severe in late winter and early spring. Cruising conditions are best near midsummer, when of course the hours of daylight are much extended.

Stronsay Firth and Westray Firth run SE/NW through the group. The many good anchs, include: Deer Sound (W of Deer Ness); B of Firth, B of Isbister, and off Balfour in Elwick B (all leading from Wide Firth); Rysa Sound, B of Houton, Hunda Sound (in Scapa Flow); Rousay Sound; and Pierowall Road (Westray). Plans for some of these are on chart 2622. For Houton Bay, Shapinsay and Auskerry, see 8.7.21; for Pierowall see 8.7.24. There is a major oil terminal and prohibited area at Flotta, on the S side of Scapa Flow.

Tide races or dangerous seas occur at the entrances to most of the firths or sounds when the stream is against strong winds. This applies particularly to Hoy Sound, Eynhallow Sound, Papa Sound (Westray), Lashy Sound, and North Ronaldsay Firth. Also off Mull Head, over Dowie Sand, between Muckle Green Holm and War Ness (where violent turbulence may extend right across the firth), between Faraclett Head and Wart Holm, and off Sacquoy Hd. Off War Ness the SE-going stream begins at HW Aberdeen + 0435, and the NW-going at HW Aberdeen – 0200, sp rates 7kn.

SHETLAND ISLANDS (8.7.25 and charts 3281, 3282, 3283)

These Islands mostly have bold cliffs and are relatively high, separated by narrow sounds through which the tide runs strongly, so that in poor vis great care is needed. Avoid sp tides, swell and wind against tide conditions. Although there are many secluded and attractive anchs, remember that the weather can change very quickly, with sudden shifts of wind. Also beware salmon fisheries and mussel rafts (unlit) in many Voes, Sounds and hbrs. Lerwick (8.7.26) is the busy main port and capital; for Scalloway, Vaila Sound and Balta Sound see 8.7.26. Refer to the CCC's *Shetland Sailing Directions*.

Coming from the S, beware a most violent and dangerous race (roost) off Sumburgh Hd (at S end of Mainland) on both streams. Other dangerous areas include between Ve Skerries and Papa Stour; the mouth of Yell Sound with strong wind against N-going stream; and off Holm of Skaw (N end of Unst). Tidal streams run mainly NW/SE and are not strong except off headlands and in the major sounds; the Admiralty Tidal Atlas NP 209 gives detail. The sp range is about 2m.

The 50M passage from Orkney can conveniently be broken by a stop at Fair Isle (North Haven). Note that races form off both ends of the Is, especially S (Roost of Keels); see 8.7.26. Recommended Traffic Routes: NW-bound ships pass to the NE (no closer than 10M to Sumburgh Hd) or SW of Fair Isle; SE-bound ships pass no closer than 5M off N Ronaldsay (Orkney). Lerwick to Bergen, Norway is about 210M.

7

8.7.6   DISTANCE TABLE

Approximate distances in nautical miles are by the most direct route, whilst avoiding dangers and allowing for Traffic Separation Schemes. Places in *italics* are in adjoining areas; places in **bold** are in 8.0.10, Distances across the North Sea.

		1	2	3	4	5	6	7	8	9	10	11	12	13	14	15	16	17	18	19	20
1.	*Peterhead*	**1**																			
2.	**Fraserburgh**	16	**2**																		
3.	Banff/Macduff	33	18	**3**																	
4.	Buckie	46	31	15	**4**																
5.	Lossiemouth	56	41	25	11	**5**															
6.	Findhorn	69	54	38	24	13	**6**														
7.	Nairn	79	64	48	34	23	10	**7**													
8.	**Inverness**	90	75	59	45	34	23	13	**8**												
9.	Tarbat Ness	72	57	41	27	18	14	17	27	**9**											
8.	Helmsdale	74	59	44	33	26	28	32	43	16	**10**										
11.	**Wick**	72	57	50	46	44	51	58	69	42	29	**11**									
12.	Duncansby Head	82	67	62	58	57	64	71	81	54	41	13	**12**								
13.	Scrabster	100	85	80	76	75	82	89	99	72	59	31	18	**13**							
14.	**Kirkwall**	115	100	95	91	90	97	104	114	87	74	46	34	50	**14**						
15.	*Stromness*	104	89	84	80	79	85	92	103	76	63	35	22	25	32	**15**					
16.	Fair Isle	122	111	116	118	120	130	137	148	121	108	79	68	85	55	77	**16**				
17.	**Lerwick**	160	150	156	160	162	172	170	190	162	148	120	109	124	95	110	42	**17**			
18.	Loch Eriboll (ent)	137	122	117	113	112	119	126	136	109	96	68	55	37	80	50	110	150	**18**		
19.	Cape Wrath	145	130	125	121	120	127	126	144	117	104	76	63	47	79	58	120	155	13	**19**	
20.	*Ullapool*	198	183	178	174	173	180	179	197	170	157	129	116	100	132	111	173	208	66	53	**20**

FRASERBURGH   8-7-7

Aberdeenshire 57°41'·52N 01°59'·70W   Rtg 1-2-3

CHARTS
AC 1462, 222,115; OS 30
TIDES
+0120 Dover; ML 2·3; Duration 0615; Zone 0 (UT)

Standard Port ABERDEEN (←—)

Times				Height (metres)			
High Water		Low Water		MHWS	MHWN	MLWN	MLWS
0000	0600	0100	0700	4·3	3·4	1·6	0·6
1200	1800	1300	1900				
Differences FRASERBURGH							
–0105	–0115	–0120	–0110	–0·6	–0·5	–0·2	0·0

SHELTER
A safe refuge, but ent is dangerous in NE/SE gales. A very busy FV hbr; yachts are not encouraged but may find a berth in S Hbr (3.2m). FVs come and go H24.
NAVIGATION
WPT 57°41'·32N 01°58'·71W, 111°/291° from/to ent, 0·57M. The ent chan is dredged 5·9m. Good lookout on entering/leaving. Yachts can enter under radar control in poor vis.
LIGHTS AND MARKS
Kinnairds Hd lt ho, Fl 5s 25m 22M, is 0·45M NNW of ent. Cairnbulg Briggs bn, Fl (2) 10s 9m 6M, is 1·8M ESE of ent. Ldg lts 291°: front QR 12m 5M; rear Oc R 6s 17m 5M.
RADIO TELEPHONE
Call on approach VHF Ch 12 16 (H24) for directions/berth.
TELEPHONE (Dial code 01346)
Port Office 515858; Watch Tr 515926; MRCC (01224) 592334; ⌖ (0141) 887 9369 (H24); Marinecall 0891 500 451; Police 513151; Dr 518088.
FACILITIES
Port ☎ 515858, AB £10 (in S Hbr), Slip, P (cans), D, FW, CH, ME, El, Sh, C (30 ton & 70 ton mobile), SM, V, R, Bar; **Town** EC Wed; ✉, Ⓑ, ⇌, ✈ (bus to Aberdeen).

ADJACENT HARBOURS

ROSEHEARTY, Aberdeen, 57°42'·10N 02°06'·78W. Rtg 4-5-2. AC 222, 213. HW Aberdeen –1. E pier and inner hbr dry, but end of W pier is accessible at all tides. Ent exposed in N/E winds; in E/SE winds hbr can be uncomfortable. Ldg marks B/W on approx 220°; rks E of ldg line. When 30m from pier, steer midway between ldg line and W pier. Port Rae, close to E, has unmarked rks; local knowledge. Hr Mr ☎ (01346) 571292 (home), AB £8. **Town** V, R, Bar, ✉. Firing range: for info ☎ (01436) 571634; see also 8.7.5.
Pennan Bay, 5M W: ⚓ on sand between Howdman (2·9m) and Tamhead (2·1m) rks, 300m N of hbr (small craft only).
Gardenstown (Gamrie Bay). Appr from E of Craig Dagerty rk (4m, conspic). Access HW±3 to drying hbr or ⚓ off.

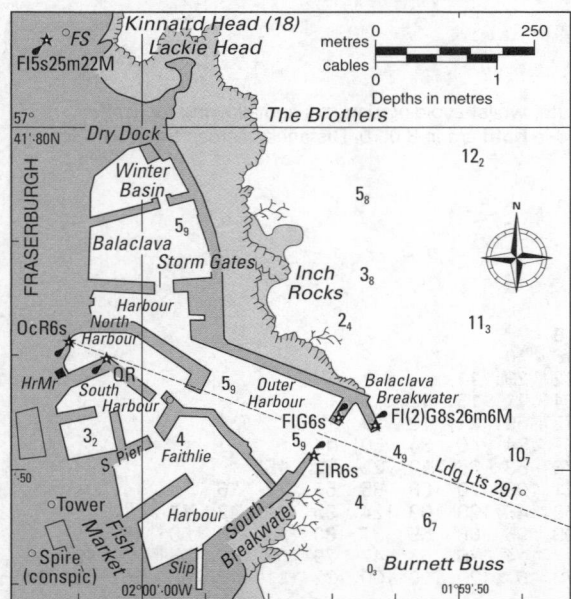

MACDUFF/BANFF   8-7-8

Aberdeenshire Macduff 57°40'·27N 02°29'·94W   Rtg 2-3-2
             Banff   57°40'·24N 02°31'·18W   Rtg 4-4-2

CHARTS
AC 1462, 222, 115; OS 29
TIDES
+ 0055 Dover; ML 2·0; Duration 0615; Zone 0 (UT)

Standard Port ABERDEEN (←—)

Times				Height (metres)			
High Water		Low Water		MHWS	MHWN	MLWN	MLWS
0200	0900	0400	0900	4·3	3·4	1·6	0·6
1400	2100	1600	2100				
Differences BANFF							
–0100	–0150	–0150	–0050	–0·4	–0·2	–0·1	+0·2

SHELTER
Macduff: Reasonably good, but ent not advised in strong NW/N winds. Slight/moderate surge in outer hbr with N/NE gales. Hbr ent is 17m wide with 3 basins; approx 2·6m in outer hbr and 2m inner hbr. A busy cargo/fishing port with limited space for yachts.
Banff: Popular hbr (dries); access HW±4. When Macduff ent is very rough in strong NW/N winds, Banff can be a safe refuge; berth in outer basin and contact Hr Mr. In strong N/ENE winds Banff is unusable.
NAVIGATION
WPT 57°40'·50N 02°30'·50W, 307°/127° from/to **Macduff** ent, 0·4M. Same WPT 056°/236° from/to **Banff** ent, 0·44M. Beware Feachie Craig, Collie Rks and rky coast N and S of hbr ent.
LIGHTS AND MARKS
Macduff: Ldg lts/marks 127° both FR 44/55m 3M, orange △s. Pier hd lt, Fl (2) WRG 6s 12m 9/7M, W tr; W115°-174°, Horn (2) 20s. **Banff**: W bn (unlit) at head of N pier.

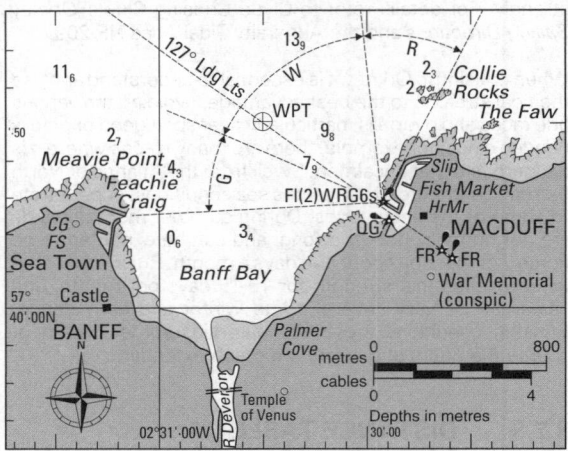

RADIO TELEPHONE
Macduff VHF Ch 12 16 (H24); **Banff** Ch 14 (part time).
TELEPHONE (Dial code 01261)
Hr Mr (**Macduff**) 832236, ⛟ 833612, Watch tr 833962; Hr Mr (**Banff**) 815544 (part time); MRCC (01224) 592334; ⌖ (0141) 887 9369 (H24); Marinecall 0891 500 451; Police 812555; Dr (**Banff**) 812027.
FACILITIES
MACDUFF: **Hbr** Slip, P (cans), D, FW, ME, El, Sh, CH. **Town** EC Wed; V, R, Bar, ✉, ⇌ (bus to Keith). BANFF: **Hbr** £8, FW, AC, Slip, new toilet block; **Banff SC**: showers. **Town**, P, D, V, R, Bar, ⇌, Ⓑ, ✈ (Aberdeen).

WHITEHILLS   8-7-9

Aberdeenshire 57°40'·82N 02°34'·78W   Rtg 2-4-2

CHARTS
AC 222, 115; OS 29
TIDES
+0050 Dover; ML 2·4; Duration 0610; Zone 0 (UT)

Standard Port ABERDEEN (←)

Times				Height (metres)			
High Water		Low Water		MHWS	MHWN	MLWN	MLWS
0200	0900	0400	0900	4·3	3·4	1·6	0·6
1400	2100	1600	2100				
Differences WHITEHILLS							
–0122	–0137	–0117	–0127	–0·4	–0·3	+0·1	+0·1

SHELTER
Safe. In strong NW/N winds beware surge in the narrow ent and outer hbr (2·4m), when ent is best not attempted. See Hr Mr for vacant pontoon berth (1·2m), or berth on N or E walls of inner hbr (1·8m) as space permits.

NAVIGATION
WPT 57°42'·00N 02°34'·80W, 000°/180° from/to bkwtr lt, 1·2M. Reefs on S side of chan marked by 2 rusty/white SHM bns. Beware fishing floats.

LIGHTS AND MARKS
Fl WR 3s (timing is unreliable) on pier hd, vis R132°–212°, W212°–245°; appr in R sector.

RADIO TELEPHONE
Whitehills Hbr Radio VHF Ch 09 08 16.

TELEPHONE (Dial code 01261)
Hr Mr 861291; MRCC (01224) 592334; ⌗ (0141) 887 9369 (H24); Marinecall 0891 500451; Police (01542) 32222; Dr 812027.

FACILITIES
Harbour AB £5, P, D, FW, ME, El, CH.
Town V, R, Bar, ⊠, Ⓑ (AM only), ⇌ (bus to Keith), ✈ (Aberdeen).

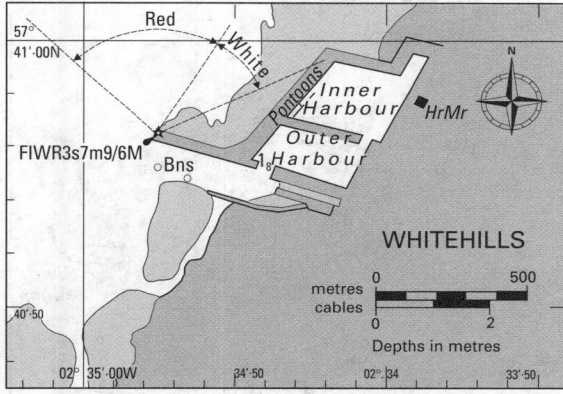

WHITEHILLS

ADJACENT HARBOURS

PORTSOY, Aberdeenshire, 57°41'·36N 02°41'·50W. Rtg 4-5-1. AC 222. HW +0047 on Dover; –0132 and Ht –0·3m on Aberdeen. Small drying hbr; ent exposed to NW/NE'lies. New Hbr to port of ent partially dries; inner hbr dries to clean sand. Ldg lts 160°, front FW 12m 5M on twr; rear FR 17m 5M. Hr Mr ☎ (01261) 815544. Facilities: few. AB, FW, Slip, V, R, Bar, ⊠. **Sandend Bay**, 1·7M W (57°41'N 02°44'·5W). ⚓ on sand E of hbr.

CULLEN, Moray, 57°41'·65N 02°49'·20W. Rtg 5-4-2. AC 222. HW +0045 on Dover, HW –0135 & –0·3m on Aberdeen; Duration 0555; ML 2·4m. Shelter good, but ent hazardous in strong W/N winds. Appr on 180° toward conspic viaduct and W bn on N pier. Caple Rk, 0·2m, is 5ca NE of hbr. Access HW ±2 approx to small drying unlit hbr, best for shoal draft. Moor S of Inner jetty if < 1m draft. Beware moorings across inner basin ent. Y ⚓s (10 ton max) about 400m WNW of hbr in 1·5m, 57°41'·7N 02°49'·5W. Hr Mr ☎ (01261) 842477 (home, part-time), £8. **Town** V, R, Bar, ⊠.

PORTKNOCKIE, Moray, 57°42'·30N 02°51'·70W. Rtg 2-5-1. AC 222. HW +0045 on Dover; –0135 and ht –0·3m Aberdeen; ML 2·3m; Duration 0555; access H24. Good shelter in one of the safest hbrs on S side of Moray Firth, but scend is often experienced; care needed in strong NW/N winds. FW ldg lts, on white-topped poles, lead approx 143°, to ent. Orange street lts surround the hbr. Berth N quay of outer hbr on firm sand; most of inner hbr dries. Hr Mr ☎ (01542) 840833; Facilities: Slip, AB £8, FW, Sh; Dr ☎ 840272. **Town** EC Wed; Ⓑ, P & D, ⊠, V, Bar.

ADJACENT HARBOUR (2M ENE of BUCKIE)

FINDOCHTY, Moray, 57°41'·96N 02°54'·20W. AC 222. HW +0045 on Dover, HW –0140 & ht –0·2m on Aberdeen; ML 2·3m; Duration 0550. Ent is about 2ca W of conspic church belfry. 1ca N of ent, leave Beacon Rock (3m high) to stbd. Y ⚓ is in 5m, 150m N of hbr ent, close E of Beacon Rock. Ldg lts, FW, lead approx 166° into Outer Basin which dries 0·2m and has many rky outcrops; access HW ±2 for 1·5m draft. Ent faces N and is 20m wide; unlit white bn at hd of W pier. Good shelter in inner basin for 100 yachts on 3 pontoons (the 2 W'ly pontoons dry); AB £8. Hr Mr ☎ (01542) 831466 (home, part-time). **Town** V, R, Bar, ⊠, Ⓑ.

BUCKIE   8-7-10

Moray 57°40'·84N 02°57'·63W   Rtg 3-1-2

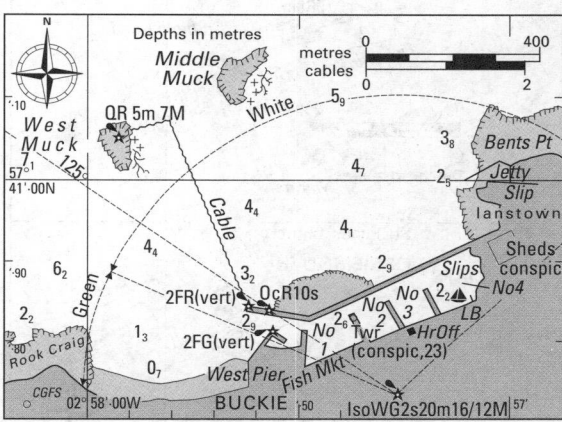

BUCKIE

CHARTS
AC 1462, 222, 115; OS 28

TIDES
+0040 Dover; ML 2·4; Duration 0550; Zone 0 (UT)

Standard Port ABERDEEN (←)

Times				Height (metres)			
High Water		Low Water		MHWS	MHWN	MLWN	MLWS
0200	0900	0400	0900	4·3	3·4	1·6	0·6
1400	2100	1600	2100				
Differences BUCKIE							
–0130	–0145	–0125	–0140	–0·2	–0·2	0·0	+0·1

SHELTER
Good in all weathers, but in strong NNW to NE winds there is a dangerous swell over the bar at hbr ent; access H24. Berth in No 4 basin as directed by Hr Mr.

NAVIGATION
WPT 57°41'·32N 02°58'·80W, 306°/126° from/to ent, 0·80M. Beware W Muck (QR 5m tripod, 7M), Middle Muck and E Muck Rks, 3ca off shore.

LIGHTS AND MARKS
The Oc R 10s 15m 15M, W tr on N bkwtr, in line 125° with Iso WG 2s 20m 16/12M, W tr, R top, leads clear of W Muck. NB: this line does not lead into hbr ent; but the transit of 2FG (vert) on W pier with same Iso WG 2s does lead 119° to ent (24m wide). White tr of ice plant on pier No. 2 is conspic. Entry sigs on N pier:
3 Ⓡ lts = hbr closed. Traffic is controlled by VHF.

RADIO TELEPHONE
VHF Ch 12 16 (H24).

TELEPHONE (Dial code 01542)
Hr Mr 831700, ⛴ 834742; MRCC (01224) 592334; ⌗ (0141) 887 9369 (H24); Marinecall 0891 500 451; Police 832222; Dr 831555.

FACILITIES
No 4 Basin AB £12, FW; **Services:** D & P (delivery), BY, ME, El, Sh, CH, Slip, C (15 ton), Gas.
Town EC Wed; V, Bar, Ⓑ, ⊠, ⊡ at Strathlene caravan site 1·5M E, ⇌ (bus to Elgin), ✈ (Aberdeen or Inverness).

LOSSIEMOUTH   8-7-11

Moray 57°43'·43N 03°16'·54W   Rtg 3-4-2

CHARTS
AC 1462, 223; OS 28
TIDES
+0040 Dover; ML 2·3; Duration 0605; Zone 0 (UT)

Standard Port ABERDEEN (←—)

Times				Height (metres)			
High Water		Low Water		MHWS	MHWN	MLWN	MLWS
0200	0900	0400	0900	4·3	3·4	1·6	0·6
1400	2100	1600	2100				
Differences LOSSIEMOUTH							
–0125	–0200	–0130	–0130	–0·2	–0·2	0·0	0·0

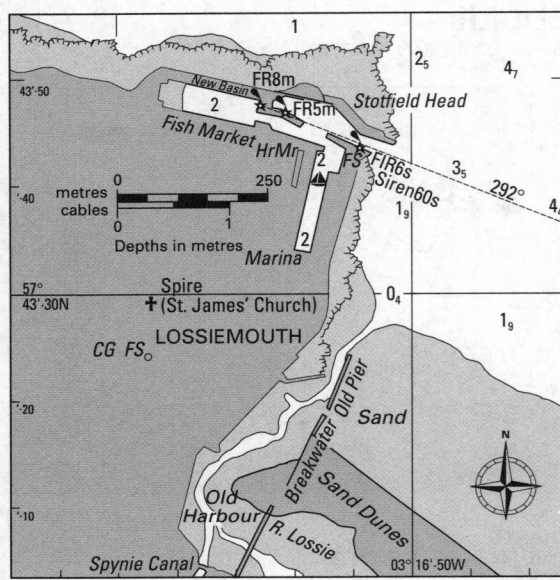

SHELTER
Very good in winds from SSE to NW. In N to SE winds >F6 appr to ent can be dangerous, with swell in outer hbr. Turn hard port for marina in S Basin, dredged 2m; access HW±4. But chan and Basin are prone to silting; a vessel drawing 2m would have little clearance at LWS ±1. West (or New) Basin is for commercial and FVs. 2 Y ⚓s have been laid in 4m at 57°43'·41N 03°16'·18W, 350m E of the hbr ent.
NAVIGATION
WPT 57°43'·40N 03°16'·00W, 097°/277° from/to ent, 0·30M. Rks to N and S of hbr ent; appr from E. Near ent, beware current from R Lossie setting in N'ly direction, causing confused water in N to SE winds at sp.
LIGHTS AND MARKS
Covesea Skerries, W lt ho, Fl WR 20s 49m 24M, is 2M W of the hbr ent; a SPM buoy, Fl Y 5s, is 5ca NE of hbr. Ldg lts 292°, both FR 5/8m (for FVs); S pier hd Fl R 6s 11m 5M. Traffic sigs: B ● at S pier (® over Fl R 6s) = hbr shut.
RADIO TELEPHONE
VHF Ch 12 16 HO. Call before ent/dep due to restricted visibility in entrance.
TELEPHONE (Dial code 01343)
Hr Mr ☎/📞 813066; MRCC (01224) 592334; ♯ (0141) 887 9369 (H24); Marinecall 0891 500451; Police 812022; Dr 812277.
FACILITIES
Marina (43), ☎ 813066, £16.00 inc AC, FW, ▣, ♿; Hbr ME, El, Sh, C, SM; Lossiemouth CC ☎ (01309) 672956; Lossiemouth SC ☎ 812928 (dinghies, at West Beach); Hbr Service Stn ☎ 813001, Mon-Fri 0800-2030, Sat 0800-1800, Sun 0930-1730, P & D cans, Gas. Town EC Thurs; CH, V, R, Bar, ✉, ®, ≋ (bus to Elgin), ✈ (Inverness).

HOPEMAN   8-7-12

Moray 57°42'·72N 03°26'·22W   Rtg 3-4-2

CHARTS
AC 1462, 223; OS 28
TIDES
+0050 Dover; ML 2·4; Duration 0610; Zone 0 (UT)

Standard Port ABERDEEN (←—)

Times				Height (metres)			
High Water		Low Water		MHWS	MHWN	MLWN	MLWS
0200	0900	0400	0900	4·3	3·4	1·6	0·6
1400	2100	1600	2100				
Differences HOPEMAN							
–0120	–0150	–0135	–0120	–0·2	–0·2	0·0	0·0

SHELTER
Once in SW basin, shelter good from all winds; but hbr dries, access HW ± 2 (for 1·5m draft). Ent is difficult in winds from NE to SE. A popular yachting hbr with AB and good facilities; run by Moray Council.
NAVIGATION
WPT 57°42'·68N, 03°26'·50W, 263°/083° from/to ent, 0·17M. Dangerous rks lie off hbr ent. Do not attempt entry in heavy weather. Beware salmon stake nets E and W of hbr (Mar to Aug) and lobster pot floats.

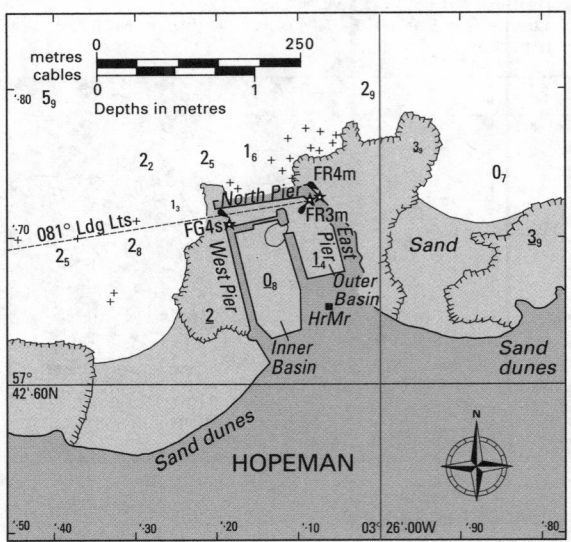

LIGHTS AND MARKS
Ldg lts 081°, FR 3/4m; S pier hd FG 4s 8m 4M. All lit only 1 Aug – 30 Apr.
RADIO TELEPHONE
Call Burghead Radio Ch 14 (HX).
TELEPHONE (Dial code 01343)
Hr Mr 835337; MRCC (01224) 592334; ♯ (0141) 887 9369 (H24); Marinecall 0891 500 451; Police 830222; Dr 543141.
FACILITIES
Hbr AB £10, D, FW, Slip.
Services: CH, ME, Gas, Sh, El, P (cans).
Town EC Wed; V, R, Bar, ✉, ®, ≋ (bus to Elgin), ✈ (Inverness).

BERTHING FEES. Aberdeenshire and Moray Councils offer a "single entry" Rover fee (£8 inc VAT) valid for 1 week from date of first entry to any or all of the following hbrs: Rosehearty, Banff, Portsoy, Cullen, Portknockie, Findochty, Hopeman and Burghead; and in Area 6: Johnshaven, Gourdon and Stonehaven. Berths are of course subject to availability.

BURGHEAD   8-7-13

Moray 57°42'·08N 03°29'·93W   Rtg 3-4-2

CHARTS
AC 1462, 223; OS 28

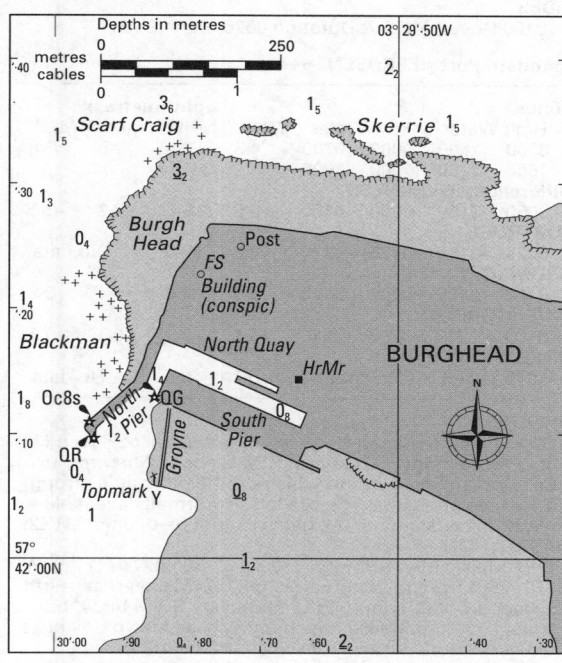

TIDES
+0035 Dover; ML 2·4; Duration 0610; Zone 0 (UT)

Standard Port ABERDEEN (⟵)

Times				Height (metres)			
High Water		Low Water		MHWS	MHWN	MLWN	MLWS
0200	0900	0400	0900	4·3	3·4	1·6	0·6
1400	2100	1600	2100				
Differences BURGHEAD							
–0120	–0150	–0135	–0120	–0·2	–0·2	0·0	0·0

SHELTER
One of the few Moray Firth hbrs open in strong E winds. 1·2m depth in ent chan and hbr. Go alongside where available and contact Hr Mr. Can be very full with FVs.

NAVIGATION
WPT 57°42'·30N 03°30'·30W, 317°/137° from/to N pier lt QR, 0·28M. Chan is variable due to sand movement. Appr from SW. Access HW ±4.

LIGHTS AND MARKS
No ldg lts but night ent is safe after identifying the N pier lts: QR 3m 5M and Oc 8s 7m 5M. S pier hd QG 3m 5M.

RADIO TELEPHONE
Call *Burghead Radio* VHF Ch 12 **14** 16 (HO and when vessel due).

TELEPHONE (Dial code 01343)
Hr Mr 835337; MRCC (01224) 592334; ☷ (0141) 887 9369 (H24); Marinecall 0891 500 451; Dr 812277.

FACILITIES
Hbr £10, D, FW, AB, C (50 ton mobile), L, Slip, BY, Sh.
Town EC Thurs; Bar, ✉, V, P (cans), Ⓑ, ⇌ (bus to Elgin), ✈ (Inverness).

FINDHORN   8-7-14

Moray 57°39'·66N 03°37'·38W   Rtg 3-3-1

CHARTS
AC 223; OS 27

TIDES
+0110 Dover; ML 2·5; Duration 0615; Zone 0 (UT)

Standard Port ABERDEEN (⟵)

Times				Height (metres)			
High Water		Low Water		MHWS	MHWN	MLWN	MLWS
0200	0900	0400	0900	4·3	3·4	1·6	0·6
1400	2100	1600	2100				
Differences FINDHORN							
–0120	–0150	–0135	–0130	0·0	–0·1	0·0	+0·1

SHELTER
⚓ in pool off boatyard or off N pier or dry out alongside, inside piers and ask at YC; or pick up Y ⚓ off N pier. Do not attempt entry in strong NW/NE winds or with big swell running; expect breakers/surf either side of ent. THE OLD BAR. The original mouth of Findhorn River 4M SW of Findhorn gives excellent shelter in all weathers. Chan changes; local knowledge needed.

NAVIGATION
WPT 57°40'·31N 03°38'·55W, SWM spar buoy, 313°/133° from/to Ee Point, 0·85M. Access HW±2. 100m SE of the spar buoy there are 2 Y waiting ⚓s in 4m. From WPT, proceed SSE to the buoys marking the gap in the sand bar; thence ESE via SHM buoy to 3 poles with PHM topmarks to be left a boat's length to port. Once past The Ee, turn port inside G buoys. The S part of Findhorn Bay dries extensively.

LIGHTS AND MARKS
Unlit. There is a windsock on FS by The Ee. Boatyard building is conspic.

RADIO TELEPHONE
VHF Ch M *Chadwick Base* (when racing in progress).

TELEPHONE (Dial code 01309)
MRCC (01224) 592334; ☷ (0141) 887 9369 (H24); Findhorn Pilot (G. Mackenzie) 690546; Marinecall 0891 500 451; Police 672224; Dr 672221.

FACILITIES
Royal Findhorn YC ☎ 690247, M, FW, Bar;
Services: BY, L, M, AC, FW, Slip, C (16 ton), P & D (cans), El, ME, CH, ACA, Gas, Sh.
Town V, R, Bar, ✉, Ⓑ, ⇌ (Forres), ✈ (Inverness).

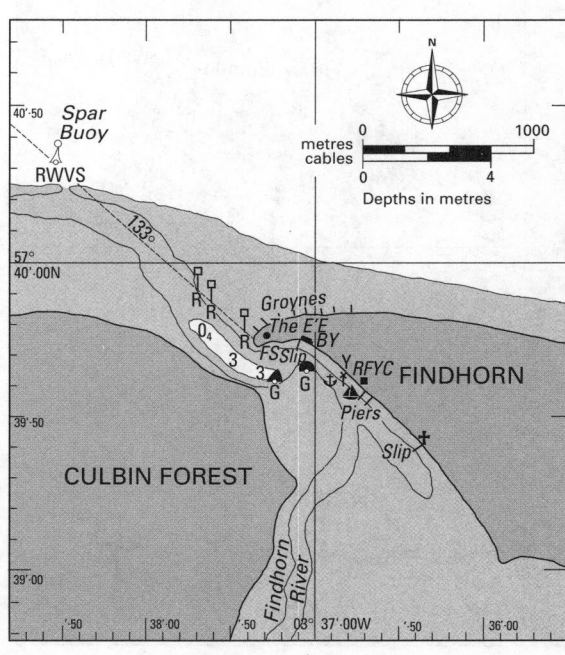

NAIRN 8-7-15

Highland 57°35'·63N 03°51'·56W   Rtg 3-4-2

CHARTS
AC 1462, 223; OS 27

TIDES
+0110 Dover; ML 2·2; Duration 0615; Zone 0 (UT)

Standard Port ABERDEEN (←)

Times				Height (metres)			
High Water		Low Water		MHWS	MHWN	MLWN	MLWS
0200	0900	0400	0900	4·3	3·4	1·6	0·6
1400	2100	1600	2100				
Differences NAIRN							
–0120	–0150	–0135	–0130	0·0	–0·1	0·0	+0·1
McDERMOTT BASE							
–0110	–0140	–0120	–0115	–0·1	–0·1	+0·1	+0·3

SHELTER
Good, but entry difficult in fresh NNE'ly. Pontoons in hbr with ❶ berths. Best entry HW ± 1½. Two Y ⚓s are close to the WPT, approx 400m NNW of the pierheads; the W'ly buoy in 2·5m, the E'ly in 1·5m. No commercial shipping.

NAVIGATION
WPT 57°35'·90N 03°51'·80W, 335°/155° from/to ent, 0·3M. The approach dries to 100m off the pierheads. Inside, the best water is to the E side of the river chan.

LIGHTS AND MARKS
Lt ho on E pier hd, Oc WRG 4s 6m 5M, vis G shore-100°, W100°-207°, R207°-shore. Keep in W sector. McDermott Base, 4·5M to the W, has a large conspic cream-coloured building; also useful if making for Inverness Firth.

RADIO TELEPHONE
None. Ch M (weekends only).

TELEPHONE (Dial code 01667)
Hr Mr 454704; MRCC (01224) 592334; ∰ (0141) 887 9369 (H24); Clinic 455092; Marinecall 0891 500 451; Police 452222; Dr 453421.

FACILITIES
Nairn Basin AB £10, FW (standpipes), Slip, AC (110 volts), P, D; **Nairn SC** ☎ 453897, Bar.
Town EC Wed; V, R, Bar, ⊠, Ⓑ, ⇌, ✈ (Inverness).

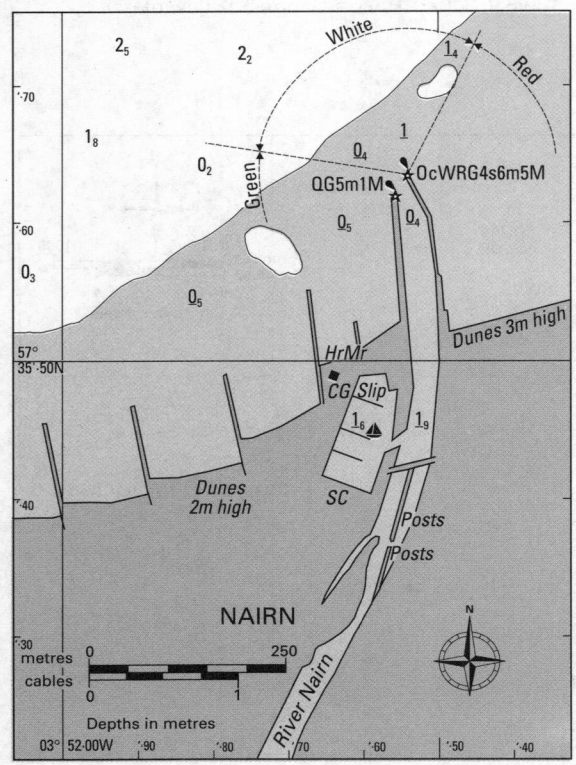

INVERNESS 8-7-16

Highland 57°29'·75N 04°14'·08W   Rtg 3-2-2

CHARTS
AC 1078, 1077, 223; OS 26/27

TIDES
+0100 Dover; ML 2·7; Duration 0620; Zone 0 (UT)

Standard Port ABERDEEN (←)

Times				Height (metres)			
High Water		Low Water		MHWS	MHWN	MLWN	MLWS
0300	1000	0000	0700	4·3	3·4	1·6	0·6
1500	2200	1200	1900				
Differences INVERNESS							
–0050	–0150	–0200	–0150	+0·5	+0·3	+0·2	+0·1
FORTROSE							
–0125	–0125	–0125	–0125	0·0	0·0	No data	
CROMARTY							
–0120	–0155	–0155	–0120	0·0	0·0	+0·1	+0·2
INVERGORDON							
–0105	–0200	–0200	–0110	+0·1	+0·1	+0·1	+0·1
DINGWALL							
–0045	–0145	No data		+0·1	+0·2	No data	

SHELTER
Good in all weathers. Berth at Longman Yacht Haven (3m at LW) or alongside quays in R Ness; or at 2 marinas in Caledonian Canal, ent to which can be difficult in strong tides (see opposite). The sea lock is normally available HW±4 in canal hours; the gates cannot be opened LW±2.

NAVIGATION
WPT Meikle Mee SHM By Fl G 3s, 57°30'·28N 04°11'·93W, 070°/250° from/to Longman Pt bn, 0·74M. Inverness Firth is deep from Chanonry Pt to Munlochy SWM buoy, but shoal (2·1m) to Meikle Mee buoy. Meikle Mee partly dries. Beware marine farms S of Avoch (off chartlet). Tidal streams are strong S of Craigton Pt (E-going stream at sp exceeds 5kn). Ent to R Ness is narrow but deep. For the ent to Caledonian Canal, keep to N Kessock bank until clear of unmarked shoals on S bank.

LIGHTS AND MARKS
Longman Pt bn Fl WR 2s 7m 5/4M, vis W078°-258°, R258°-078°. Craigton Pt lt, Fl WRG 4s 6m 11/7M vis W312°-048°, R048°-064°, W064°-085°, G085°-shore. Caledonian Canal ent marked by QR and Iso G 4s on ends of training walls.

RADIO TELEPHONE
Call: *Inverness Hbr Office* VHF Ch 06 12 16 (Mon-Fri: 0900 -1700 LT). Inverness Boat Centre Ch 80 M (0900-1800 LT). Caledonian Canal: Ch 74 is used by all stations. Call: *Clachnaharry Sea Lock*; or for office: *Caledonian Canal.*

TELEPHONE (Dial code 01463)
Hr Mr 715715; Clachnaharry Sea Lock 713896; Canal Office 233140; MRCC (01224) 592334; ∰ 222787; Marinecall 0891 500 451; Police 239191; Dr 234151.

FACILITIES
Longman Yacht Haven L-shaped pontoon, (15+5 visitors), £10, ☎ 715715, FW, access H24 (3m at LW);
Citadel and Shore Street Quays (R Ness) ☎ 715715, AB £10, P, D, FW, ME, El; (used mainly by commercial ships).
Services: Slip, M, ME, El, C (100 ton), CH, FW, P, SM, Gas.
Town EC Wed; V, R, Bar, ⊠, Ⓑ, ⇌, ✈.

MINOR HARBOURS IN INVERNESS FIRTH

FORTROSE, Highland, 57°34'·73N 04°07'·95W. AC 1078. Tides 8.7.16. HW +0055 on Dover; ML 2·5m; Duration 0620. Small drying unlit hbr, well protected by Chanonry Ness to E; access HW±2, limited space. Follow ldg line 296°, Broomhill Ho (conspic on hill to NW) in line with school spire until abeam SPM buoy; then turn W to avoid Craig an Roan rks (1·8m) ESE of ent. Chanonry Pt lt, Oc 6s 12m 15M, obscd 073°-shore. Hr Mr ☎ (01381) 620861; Dr ☎ 620909. Facilities: EC Thurs; AB £3, L, M, P, D, Slip, Gas, R, V, ⊠, Ⓑ; **Chanonry SC** (near pier) ☎ 62108.

AVOCH, Highland, 57°34'·05N 04°09'·85W. AC 1078. Tides as Fortrose (1·25M to the ENE). Hbr dries, mostly on the N side, but is bigger than Fortrose; access HW±2. Small craft may stay afloat at nps against the S pier, which has 2FR (vert) at E-facing ent. Facilities: AB, FW. **Village**: ⊠, V, R, Bar, P & D (cans), ME.

INVERNESS *continued*

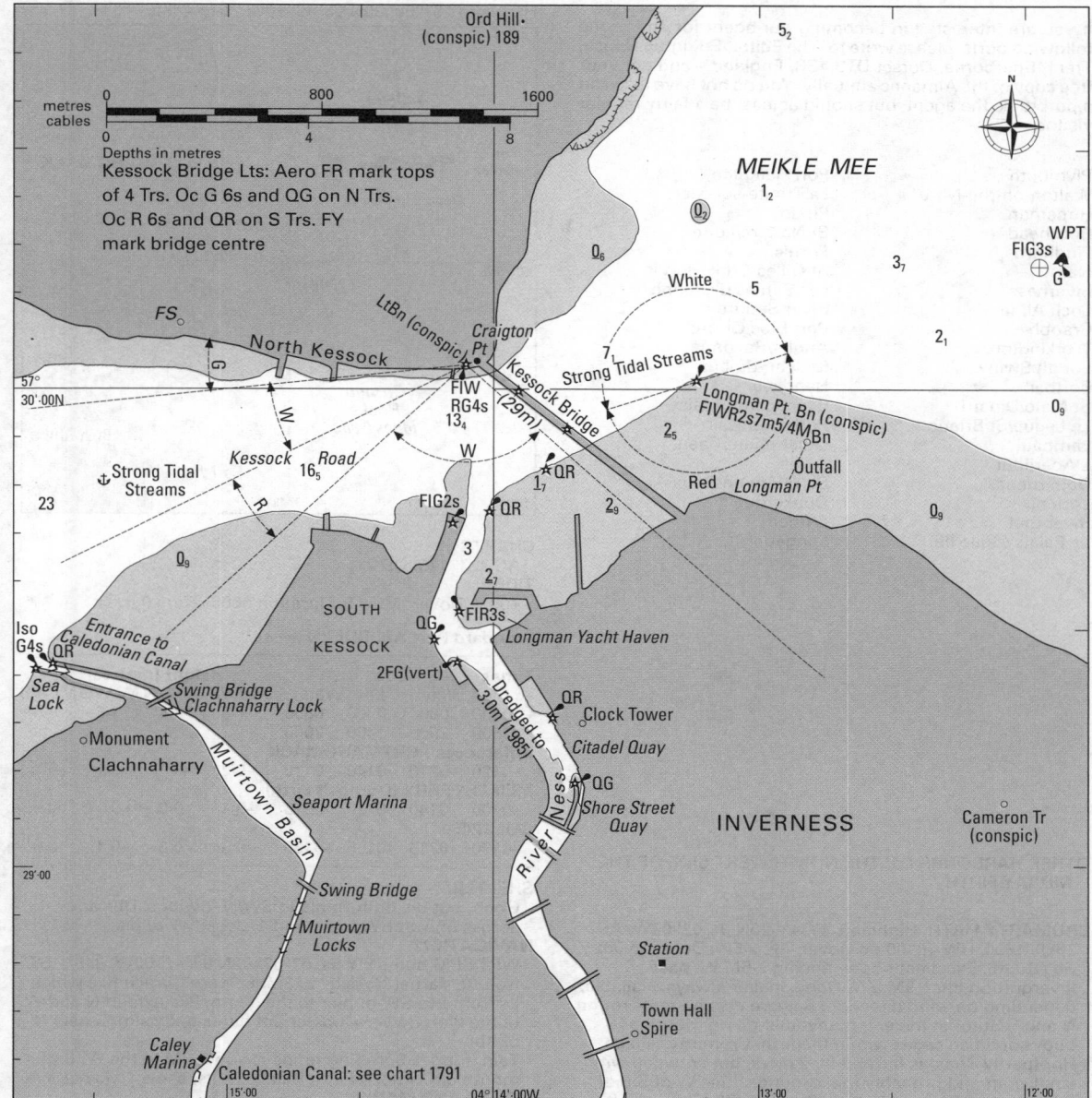

CALEDONIAN CANAL (Sea lock 57°29'·46N 04°15'·75W)
These notes are for the convenience of those entering
the Canal at Inverness, qv. They supplement and partly
duplicate the main information and chartlet in 8.8.18.
CHARTS
AC 1078, 1791; OS 26, 27, 34, 41. *Skipper's Guide* advised.
TIDES
Differences: Clachnaharry +0116 on Dover; see 8.7.16.
SHELTER
Clachnaharry sea lock operates HW±4 (sp) within canal
hours. The road and rail swing bridges may cause delays
up to 25 mins. Seaport and Caley marinas: see Facilities.
NAVIGATION
The 60M Caledonian Canal consists of 38M through three
lochs, (Lochs Ness, Oich and Lochy), connected by 22M
through canals. It can take vessels 45m LOA, 10m beam,
4m draft and max mast ht 27·4m. The passage normally
takes two full days, possibly longer in the summer; 14 hrs
is absolute minimum. Speed limit is 5kn in canal sections.
There are 10 swing bridges; road tfc has priority at peak
hrs. Do not pass bridges without the keeper's instructions.
From Clachnaharry sea lock to Loch Ness (Bona Ferry lt
ho) is approx 7M, via Muirtown and Dochgarroch locks.

LOCKS
All 29 locks are manned and operate early May to early
Oct, 0800-1800LT daily. Dues: see 8.8.18. For regulations
and *Skipper's Guide* apply: Canal Manager, Muirtown
Wharf, Inverness IV3 5LS, ☎ (01463) 233140; 📠 710942.
LIGHTS & MARKS
Chans are marked by posts, cairns and unlit buoys, PHM
on the NW side of the chan and SHM on the SE side.
BOAT SAFETY SCHEME
Transient/visiting vessels will be checked for apparent
dangerous defects eg leaking gas or fuel, damaged
electrical cables, taking in water, risk of capsize. £1M 3rd
party insurance is required. For details see 8.8.18.
RADIO TELEPHONE
Sea locks and main lock flights operate VHF Ch **74** (HO).
TELEPHONE
Clachnaharry sea lock (01463) 713896; Canal Office,
Inverness (01463) 233140.
FACILITIES
Seaport marina (20 + 20 Ⓥ), £6, ☎ (01463) 239475, AC,
FW, D, El, ME, Sh, Gas, Gaz, 🛢, C (40 ton), ⚓, ♿.
Caley marina (25+25 Ⓥ) ☎ (01463) 236539, £6.50, FW, CH,
D, ME, El, Sh, AC, C (20 ton), ACA.

AGENTS WANTED

If you are interested in becoming our agent for any of the following ports, please write to: The Editor, Edington House, Trent, Sherborne, Dorset DT9 4SR, England – and get your free copy of the Almanac annually. You do not have to live in a port to be the agent, but should at least be a fairly regular visitor.

Plymouth	Port Haliguen
Walton-on-the-Naze	La Trinité-sur-Mer
Hopeman	Piriac
Burghead	St Nazaire/Loire
Findhorn	Pornic
Nairn	St Gilles-Croix-de-Vie
Inverness	Les Sables d'Olonne
Loch Aline	River Seudre
Craobh	Port Bloc/Gironde
Workington	Anglet/Bayonne
Lough Swilly	St Jean-de-Luz
Portbail	Hendaye
St Malo/Dinard	Grandcamp-Maisy
Le Légué/St Brieuc	Port-en-Bessin
Lampaul	Ouistreham/Caen
L'Aberildut	Dives
Douarnenez	St Valéry-en-Caux
Lorient	Dunkerque
River Étel	Emden
Le Palais (Belle Ile)	Langeoog

OTHER HARBOURS ON THE NORTH WEST SIDE OF THE MORAY FIRTH

CROMARTY FIRTH, Highland, 57°41'·20N 04°02'·00W. AC 1889, 1890. HW +0100 on Dover; ML 2·5m; Duration 0625. See 8.7.16. Excellent hbr extending 7·5M W, past Invergordon, then 9M SW. Good shelter always available, depending on wind direction. Beware rks and reefs round N and S Sutor at the ent; many unlit oil rig mooring buoys and fish cages within the firth. Cromarty Village Hbr (partly dries) is formed by 2 piers, but crowded with small craft and probably foul ground; ⚓ 2ca W of S pier hd in approx 6m. Hr Mr ☎ (01381) 600479. Cromarty lt ho, on the Ness, Oc WR 10s 18m 15/11M, R079°–088°, W088°–275°, obsc by N Sutor when brg < 253°. *Cromarty Firth Port Control* VHF Ch 11 16 13 (H24) ☎ (01349) 852308; ▦ 852221. **Invergordon Boat Club** Hon Sec ☎ 877612. Facilities: AB, Bar, C (3 ton), D, FW, ✉, P, R, V, Gas, L; EC Wed. Ferry: Local to Nigg; also Invergordon-Kirkwall.

DORNOCH FIRTH, Highland. 57°51'·30N 03°59'·30W. AC 223, 115. HW +0115 on Dover; ML 2·5m; Duration 0605; see 8.7.17. Excellent shelter but difficult ent. There are many shifting sandbanks, especially near the ent, from N edge of Whiteness Sands to S edge of Gizzen Briggs. ⚓s in 7m ¾M ESE of Dornoch Pt (sheltered from NE swell by Gizzen Briggs); in 7m 2ca SSE of Ard na Cailc; in 3·3m 1M below Bonar Bridge. Firth extends 15M inland, but AC coverage ceases ¼M E of Ferry Pt. The A9 road bridge, 3·3M W of Dornoch Pt, with 11m clearance, has 3 spans lit on both sides; span centres show Iso 4s, N bank pier Iso G 4s, S bank pier Iso R 4s and 2 midstream piers QY. Tarbat Ness lt ho Fl (4) 30s 53m 24M. Fl R 5s lt shown when Tain firing range active. Very limited facilities at Ferrytown and Bonar Bridge. CG ☎ (01862) 810016. **Dornoch**: EC Thur; V, P, ✉, Dr, Ⓑ, R, Bar.

PORTMAHOMACK   8-7-17
Highland 57°50'·30N 03°49'·70W   Rtg 4-5-2

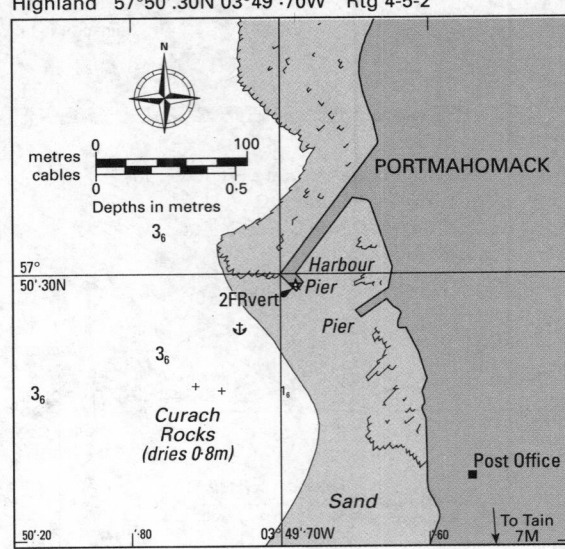

CHARTS
AC 223, 115; OS 21

TIDES
+0035 Dover; ML 2·5; Duration 0600; Zone 0 (UT)

Standard Port ABERDEEN (←—)

Times				Height (metres)			
High Water		Low Water		MHWS	MHWN	MLWN	MLWS
0300	0800	0200	0800	4·3	3·4	1·6	0·6
1500	2000	1400	2000				
Differences PORTMAHOMACK							
–0120	–0210	–0140	–0110	–0·2	–0·1	+0·1	+0·1
MEIKLE FERRY (Dornoch Firth)							
–0100	–0140	–0120	–0055	+0·1	0·0	–0·1	0·0
GOLSPIE							
–0130	–0215	–0155	–0130	–0·3	–0·3	–0·1	0·0

SHELTER
Good, but uncomfortable in SW/NW winds. Hbr dries, access only at HW, but good ⚓ close SW of pier.

NAVIGATION
WPT SPM buoy, Fl Y 5s, 57°53'·03N 03°47'·02W, 346°/166° from/to Tarbat Ness lt, 1·13M. Beware Curach Rks which lie from 2ca SW of pier to the shore. Rks extend N and W of the pier. Beware lobster pot floats and salmon nets N of hbr.
Tain firing & bombing range is about 3M to the W, S of mouth of Dornoch Firth; R flags, R lts, shown when active.

LIGHTS AND MARKS
Tarbert Ness lt ho Fl (4) 30s 53m 24M, W twr R bands, is 2·6M to NE of hbr. Pier hd 2 FR (vert) 7m 5M.

RADIO TELEPHONE
None.

TELEPHONE (Dial code 01862)
Hr Mr 871441; MRCC (01224) 592334; ▦ (0141) 887 9369 (H24); Marinecall 0891 500 451; Dr 892759.

FACILITIES
Hbr, AB £13, M, L, FW. **Town** EC Wed; R, V, Bar, ✉, ⇌ (bus to Tain), ✈ (Inverness).

GOLSPIE, Highland, 57°58'·73N 03°56'·70W. AC 223. HW +0045 on Dover; ML 2·3m; Duration 068. See 8.7.17. Golspie pier projects 60m SE across foreshore with arm projecting SW at the hd, giving shelter during NE winds. Beware The Bridge, a bank (0·3m to 1·8m) running parallel to the shore ¼M to seaward of pier hd. Seas break heavily over The Bridge in NE winds. There are no lts. To enter, keep Duke of Sutherland's Memorial in line 316° with boathouse SW of pier, until church spire in village is in line 006° with hd of pier, then keep on those marks. Hbr gets very congested; good ⚓ off pier.
Town EC Wed; Bar, D, Dr, Ⓗ, L, M, P, Gas, ✉, R, ⇌, V, Ⓑ.

HELMSDALE   8-7-18

Highland 58°06'·85N 03°38'·80W   Rtg 3-4-2

CHARTS
AC 1462, 115; OS 17

TIDES
+0035 Dover; ML 2·2; Duration 0615; Zone 0 (UT)

Standard Port WICK (→)

Times				Height (metres)			
High Water		Low Water		MHWS	MHWN	MLWN	MLWS
0000	0700	0200	0700	3·5	2·8	1·4	0·7
1200	1900	1400	1900				
Differences HELMSDALE							
+0025	+0015	+0035	+0030	+0·4	+0·3	+0·1	0·0

SHELTER
Good, except in strong E/SE'lies. AB on NW pier, approx 1m.

NAVIGATION
WPT 58°06'·61N 03°38'·3W, 133°/313° from/to ent, 0·35M. Beware spate coming down river after heavy rain. Shoal both sides of chan and bar builds up when river in spate.

LIGHTS AND MARKS
Ldg lts 313°. Front FG (= hbr open) or FR (= hbr closed); rear FG; both on W masts. By day Or disc on each mast.

RADIO TELEPHONE
VHF Ch 12 16.

TELEPHONE (Dial code 01431)
Hr Mr 821347; MRCC (01224) 592334; ⌗ (01955) 603650; Marinecall 0891 500 451; Dr 821221, or 821225 (Home).

FACILITIES
Hbr AB £13, M (See Hr Mr), FW, Slip.
Town EC Wed; P, D, Gas, V, R, Bar, ✉, Ⓑ (Brora), ⇌ (Wick).

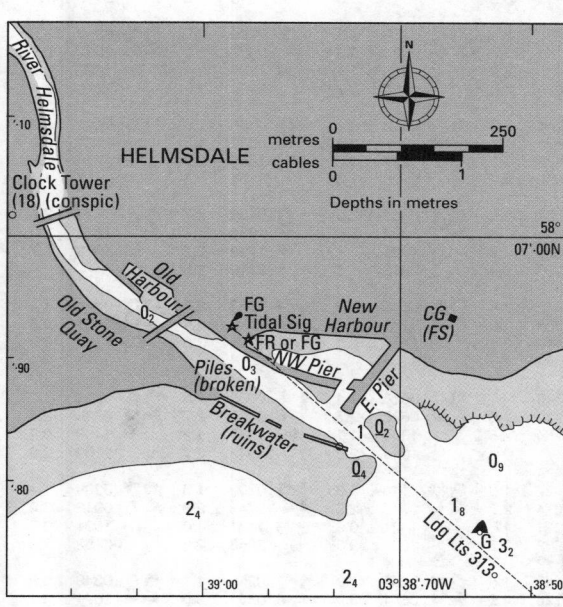

ADJACENT HARBOUR

LYBSTER, Highland, 58°17'·75N 03°17'·30W. AC 115. HW +0020 on Dover; HW −0150 sp, −0215 np; HW ht −0·6m on Aberdeen; ML 2·1m; Duration 0620. Excellent shelter in basin (SW corner of inner hbr); AB on W side of pier in about 1·2m. Most of hbr dries to sand/mud and is much used by FVs; no bollards on N wall. Appr on about 350°. Beware rks close on E side of ent; narrow (10m) ent is difficult in strong E to S winds. Min depth 2·5m in ent. S pier hd, Oc R 6s 10m 3M, occas in fishing season. AB £16.25, FW on W quay. **Town** EC Thurs; Bar, D, P, R, V.

WICK   8-7-19

Highland 58°26'·38N 03°04'·63W   Rtg 3-4-2

CHARTS
AC 1462, 115; OS 12

TIDES
+0010 Dover; ML 2·0; Duration 0625; Zone 0 (UT). Wick is a Standard Port. Daily tidal predictions are given below.

Standard Port WICK (→)

Times				Height (metres)			
High Water		Low Water		MHWS	MHWN	MLWN	MLWS
0000	0700	0200	0700	3·5	2·8	1·4	0·7
1200	1900	1400	1900				
Differences DUNCANSBY HEAD							
−0115	−0115	−0110	−0110	−0·4	−0·4		No data

SHELTER
Good, except in strong NNE to SSE winds. A good hbr to await right conditions for W-bound passage through the Pentland Firth (see 8.7.5). Berth where directed in the Inner Hbr, 2·4m. NB: The River Hbr (commercial) is leased and must *not* be entered without prior approval.

NAVIGATION
WPT 58°26'·20N 03°03'·30W, 104°/284° from/to S pier, 0·72M. From the N, open up hbr ent before rounding North Head so as to clear drying Proudfoot Rks. Hbr ent is dangerous in strong E'lies as boats have to turn port 90° at the end of S pier. On S side of bay, an unlit NCM bn, 300m ENE of LB slip, marks end of ruined bkwtr.

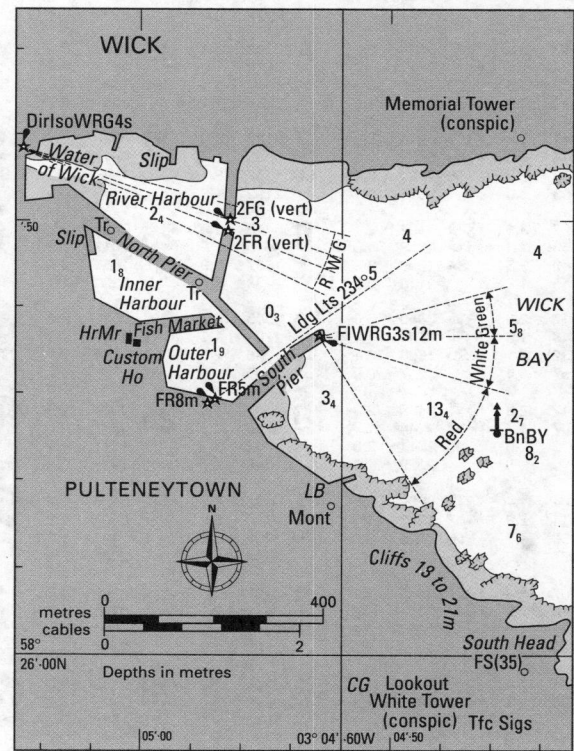

LIGHTS AND MARKS
S pier lt, Fl WRG 3s 12m 12/9M, G253°-270°, W270°-286°, R286°-329°, Bell (2) 10s (fishing). Ldg lts , both FR 5/8m, lead 234° into outer hbr. Traffic signals:
B ● (Ⓖ) at CG stn on S Head = hbr closed by weather.
B ● (Ⓡ) at S pier head = caution; hbr temp obstructed.

RADIO TELEPHONE
VHF Ch 14 16 (when vessel expected).

TELEPHONE (Dial code 01955)
Hr Mr 602030; MRSC (01856) 873268; ⌗ 603650; Police 603551; Ⓗ 602434, 602261.

FACILITIES
Inner Hbr AB (£5 day, £10 week; see Hr Mr), Slip, ME;
Fish Jetty D, FW, CH; **Services:** ME, El, Sh, Slip, Gas, C (15/ 100 ton). **Town** EC Wed; P, V, R, Bar, ✉, Ⓑ, ⇌, ✈.

SCOTLAND – WICK

LAT 58°26′N   LONG   3°05′W

TIMES AND HEIGHTS OF HIGH AND LOW WATERS

YEAR **1999**

TIME ZONE (UT)
For Summer Time add ONE hour in non-shaded areas

JANUARY

Day	Time	m	Day	Time	m
1 F	0401 / 1029 / 1632 / 2251	0.8 / 3.5 / 0.7 / 3.5	**16** SA	0407 / 1034 / 1637 / 2257	1.1 / 3.3 / 1.0 / 3.2
2 SA O	0449 / 1116 / 1720 / 2341	0.8 / 3.7 / 0.6 / 3.6	**17** SU ●	0444 / 1110 / 1713 / 2335	1.0 / 3.4 / 0.8 / 3.3
3 SU	0533 / 1201 / 1806	0.8 / 3.8 / 0.6	**18** M	0520 / 1146 / 1749	0.9 / 3.4 / 0.7
4 M	0028 / 0615 / 1245 / 1850	3.6 / 0.9 / 3.8 / 0.6	**19** TU	0012 / 0556 / 1223 / 1825	3.3 / 0.9 / 3.5 / 0.6
5 TU	0113 / 0655 / 1327 / 1933	3.5 / 1.0 / 3.7 / 0.7	**20** W	0051 / 0633 / 1300 / 1902	3.3 / 0.8 / 3.5 / 0.6
6 W	0157 / 0734 / 1409 / 2017	3.4 / 1.1 / 3.6 / 0.9	**21** TH	0131 / 0711 / 1338 / 1941	3.3 / 0.9 / 3.5 / 0.6
7 TH	0241 / 0814 / 1453 / 2103	3.2 / 1.3 / 3.5 / 1.0	**22** F	0214 / 0752 / 1420 / 2025	3.2 / 0.9 / 3.4 / 0.7
8 F	0327 / 0856 / 1540 / 2155	3.1 / 1.5 / 3.3 / 1.2	**23** SA	0301 / 0838 / 1509 / 2116	3.1 / 1.0 / 3.3 / 0.8
9 SA	0417 / 0948 / 1632 / 2257	2.9 / 1.6 / 3.1 / 1.4	**24** SU	0355 / 0934 / 1606 / 2217	3.0 / 1.2 / 3.1 / 0.9
10 SU	0512 / 1107 / 1732	2.8 / 1.7 / 2.9	**25** M	0456 / 1044 / 1711 / 2329	2.9 / 1.3 / 3.0 / 1.0
11 M	0004 / 0614 / 1230 / 1837	1.4 / 2.8 / 1.7 / 2.9	**26** TU	0602 / 1202 / 1823	2.8 / 1.3 / 3.0
12 TU	0107 / 0719 / 1337 / 1944	1.4 / 2.8 / 1.6 / 2.9	**27** W	0045 / 0711 / 1321 / 1937	1.1 / 2.9 / 1.2 / 3.0
13 W	0201 / 0820 / 1433 / 2044	1.4 / 2.9 / 1.5 / 2.9	**28** TH	0159 / 0820 / 1434 / 2049	1.0 / 3.0 / 1.0 / 3.1
14 TH	0247 / 0911 / 1519 / 2134	1.3 / 3.0 / 1.3 / 3.0	**29** F	0302 / 0922 / 1536 / 2151	1.0 / 3.2 / 0.8 / 3.2
15 F	0328 / 0955 / 1600 / 2217	1.2 / 3.2 / 1.1 / 3.1	**30** SA	0354 / 1016 / 1627 / 2245	0.9 / 3.4 / 0.7 / 3.3
			31 SU O	0440 / 1103 / 1713 / 2332	0.8 / 3.5 / 0.5 / 3.4

FEBRUARY

Day	Time	m	Day	Time	m
1 M	0520 / 1147 / 1754	0.8 / 3.6 / 0.5	**16** TU ●	0504 / 1125 / 1732 / 2354	0.8 / 3.5 / 0.5 / 3.4
2 TU	0015 / 0558 / 1229 / 1833	3.4 / 0.8 / 3.7 / 0.5	**17** W	0541 / 1203 / 1809	0.7 / 3.6 / 0.4
3 W	0055 / 0634 / 1308 / 1909	3.4 / 0.9 / 3.7 / 0.6	**18** TH	0033 / 0617 / 1242 / 1845	3.4 / 0.6 / 3.6 / 0.4
4 TH	0133 / 0708 / 1346 / 1944	3.3 / 0.9 / 3.6 / 0.7	**19** F	0112 / 0655 / 1321 / 1923	3.4 / 0.6 / 3.6 / 0.4
5 F	0210 / 0741 / 1424 / 2019	3.2 / 1.1 / 3.5 / 0.9	**20** SA	0153 / 0735 / 1403 / 2005	3.3 / 0.7 / 3.5 / 0.5
6 SA	0248 / 0816 / 1504 / 2056	3.1 / 1.2 / 3.3 / 1.1	**21** SU	0236 / 0819 / 1450 / 2051	3.2 / 0.8 / 3.4 / 0.9
7 SU	0327 / 0855 / 1547 / 2139	3.0 / 1.4 / 3.1 / 1.3	**22** M	0326 / 0911 / 1545 / 2148	3.0 / 1.0 / 3.2 / 0.9
8 M	0413 / 0945 / 1637 / 2238	2.8 / 1.6 / 2.9 / 1.5	**23** TU	0424 / 1017 / 1650 / 2302	2.9 / 1.1 / 3.0 / 1.1
9 TU	0505 / 1101 / 1736	2.7 / 1.7 / 2.8	**24** W	0532 / 1141 / 1806	2.8 / 1.2 / 2.9
10 W	0005 / 0606 / 1252 / 1845	1.5 / 2.7 / 1.7 / 2.7	**25** TH	0029 / 0647 / 1311 / 1929	1.2 / 2.8 / 1.1 / 2.8
11 TH	0123 / 0717 / 1402 / 2002	1.5 / 2.8 / 1.5 / 2.7	**26** F	0155 / 0804 / 1431 / 2046	1.2 / 2.9 / 1.0 / 2.9
12 F	0221 / 0827 / 1455 / 2106	1.4 / 2.9 / 1.3 / 2.9	**27** SA	0300 / 0909 / 1531 / 2146	1.1 / 3.0 / 0.8 / 3.1
13 SA	0308 / 0922 / 1540 / 2155	1.2 / 3.0 / 1.1 / 3.0	**28** SU	0348 / 1002 / 1618 / 2235	1.0 / 3.2 / 0.6 / 3.2
14 SU	0349 / 1006 / 1619 / 2237	1.1 / 3.2 / 0.9 / 3.1			
15 M	0427 / 1047 / 1656 / 2316	0.9 / 3.3 / 0.7 / 3.3			

MARCH

Day	Time	m	Day	Time	m
1 M	0428 / 1048 / 1659 / 2318	0.9 / 3.4 / 0.5 / 3.3	**16** TU	0405 / 1017 / 1631 / 2253	0.9 / 3.3 / 0.6 / 3.3
2 TU O	0504 / 1130 / 1735 / 2357	0.8 / 3.5 / 0.4 / 3.3	**17** W ●	0443 / 1100 / 1709 / 2332	0.7 / 3.5 / 0.4 / 3.4
3 W	0537 / 1209 / 1809	0.7 / 3.6 / 0.5	**18** TH	0521 / 1141 / 1747	0.6 / 3.6 / 0.3
4 TH	0032 / 0609 / 1246 / 1840	3.3 / 0.7 / 3.6 / 0.5	**19** F	0011 / 0558 / 1222 / 1824	3.5 / 0.5 / 3.7 / 0.2
5 F	0106 / 0641 / 1321 / 1910	3.3 / 0.8 / 3.5 / 0.6	**20** SA	0051 / 0637 / 1304 / 1903	3.5 / 0.4 / 3.7 / 0.3
6 SA	0138 / 0712 / 1355 / 1941	3.2 / 0.9 / 3.4 / 0.8	**21** SU	0131 / 0718 / 1347 / 1945	3.5 / 0.5 / 3.6 / 0.5
7 SU	0216 / 0745 / 1430 / 2013	3.1 / 1.0 / 3.2 / 1.0	**22** M	0214 / 0803 / 1435 / 2030	3.3 / 0.6 / 3.4 / 0.7
8 M	0244 / 0821 / 1509 / 2050	3.0 / 1.2 / 3.0 / 1.2	**23** TU	0302 / 0855 / 1531 / 2126	3.1 / 0.8 / 3.2 / 1.0
9 TU	0324 / 0903 / 1555 / 2136	2.9 / 1.4 / 2.9 / 1.4	**24** W	0359 / 1003 / 1638 / 2242	2.9 / 1.0 / 2.9 / 1.3
10 W	0413 / 0958 / 1649 / 2241	2.8 / 1.5 / 2.7 / 1.6	**25** TH	0509 / 1131 / 1758	2.8 / 1.1 / 2.8
11 TH	0510 / 1130 / 1754	2.7 / 1.6 / 2.6	**26** F	0018 / 0628 / 1304 / 1924	1.4 / 2.7 / 1.1 / 2.8
12 F	0027 / 0614 / 1321 / 1909	1.6 / 2.7 / 1.5 / 2.6	**27** SA	0148 / 0747 / 1421 / 2038	1.3 / 2.8 / 0.9 / 2.8
13 SA	0148 / 0726 / 1422 / 2028	1.5 / 2.7 / 1.4 / 2.8	**28** SU	0251 / 0851 / 1517 / 2133	1.2 / 3.0 / 0.7 / 3.0
14 SU	0241 / 0836 / 1510 / 2125	1.3 / 2.9 / 1.1 / 2.9	**29** M	0334 / 0943 / 1600 / 2218	1.0 / 3.1 / 0.6 / 3.1
15 M	0325 / 0931 / 1552 / 2211	1.1 / 3.1 / 0.8 / 3.1	**30** TU	0409 / 1028 / 1636 / 2257	0.9 / 3.3 / 0.5 / 3.1
			31 W O	0441 / 1108 / 1709 / 2333	0.8 / 3.3 / 0.5 / 3.2

APRIL

Day	Time	m	Day	Time	m
1 TH	0513 / 1145 / 1739	0.7 / 3.4 / 0.5	**16** F ●	0457 / 1117 / 1722 / 2348	0.5 / 3.7 / 0.2 / 3.6
2 F	0006 / 0543 / 1221 / 1808	3.2 / 0.7 / 3.4 / 0.6	**17** SA	0538 / 1202 / 1803	0.4 / 3.8 / 0.2
3 SA	0037 / 0613 / 1254 / 1837	3.2 / 0.7 / 3.3 / 0.7	**18** SU	0029 / 0619 / 1247 / 1844	3.6 / 0.3 / 3.8 / 0.3
4 SU	0106 / 0645 / 1327 / 1907	3.2 / 0.8 / 3.2 / 0.8	**19** M	0111 / 0703 / 1333 / 1927	3.6 / 0.4 / 3.7 / 0.5
5 M	0135 / 0718 / 1400 / 1940	3.1 / 0.9 / 3.1 / 1.0	**20** TU	0155 / 0750 / 1424 / 2013	3.4 / 0.6 / 3.4 / 0.8
6 TU	0207 / 0753 / 1438 / 2015	3.0 / 1.0 / 3.0 / 1.2	**21** W	0243 / 0846 / 1521 / 2109	3.2 / 0.8 / 3.2 / 1.1
7 W	0246 / 0833 / 1523 / 2056	2.9 / 1.2 / 2.8 / 1.3	**22** TH	0341 / 0957 / 1629 / 2226	3.0 / 0.9 / 2.9 / 1.4
8 TH	0333 / 0922 / 1616 / 2151	2.8 / 1.3 / 2.7 / 1.5	**23** F	0449 / 1121 / 1746 / 2357	2.9 / 1.0 / 2.8 / 1.5
9 F	0430 / 1034 / 1718 / 2316	2.7 / 1.4 / 2.6 / 1.6	**24** SA	0606 / 1244 / 1908	2.8 / 1.0 / 2.7
10 SA	0533 / 1220 / 1828	2.7 / 1.4 / 2.6	**25** SU	0121 / 0721 / 1357 / 2016	1.4 / 2.8 / 0.9 / 2.8
11 SU	0058 / 0640 / 1337 / 1943	1.5 / 2.7 / 1.2 / 2.7	**26** M	0224 / 0824 / 1450 / 2109	1.2 / 2.9 / 0.8 / 2.9
12 M	0203 / 0748 / 1431 / 2048	1.3 / 2.8 / 1.0 / 2.9	**27** TU	0308 / 0916 / 1531 / 2152	1.1 / 3.0 / 0.7 / 3.0
13 TU	0252 / 0851 / 1517 / 2139	1.1 / 3.0 / 0.8 / 3.1	**28** W	0343 / 1001 / 1606 / 2229	0.9 / 3.1 / 0.6 / 3.0
14 W	0335 / 0944 / 1600 / 2225	0.9 / 3.3 / 0.5 / 3.3	**29** TH	0415 / 1041 / 1637 / 2304	0.8 / 3.2 / 0.6 / 3.1
15 TH	0417 / 1032 / 1642 / 2307	0.7 / 3.5 / 0.3 / 3.5	**30** F O	0446 / 1119 / 1708 / 2337	0.7 / 3.2 / 0.6 / 3.1

Chart Datum: 1·71 metres below Ordnance Datum (Local)

SCOTLAND – WICK

LAT 58°26′N   LONG 3°05′W

TIMES AND HEIGHTS OF HIGH AND LOW WATERS

YEAR **1999**

TIME ZONE (UT)
For Summer Time add ONE hour in non-shaded areas

Chart Datum: 1·71 metres below Ordnance Datum (Local)

MAY

	Time	m		Time	m
1 SA	0518 / 1154 / 1737	0.7 / 3.2 / 0.7	**16** SU	0519 / 1144 / 1743	0.4 / 3.7 / 0.3
2 SU	0008 / 0549 / 1228 / 1807	3.2 / 0.7 / 3.2 / 0.7	**17** M	0010 / 0604 / 1233 / 1827	3.6 / 0.3 / 3.7 / 0.5
3 M	0037 / 0621 / 1301 / 1839	3.2 / 0.7 / 3.1 / 0.8	**18** TU	0054 / 0652 / 1322 / 1911	3.6 / 0.4 / 3.6 / 0.7
4 TU	0106 / 0655 / 1335 / 1912	3.1 / 0.8 / 3.0 / 0.9	**19** W	0140 / 0742 / 1414 / 1959	3.5 / 0.5 / 3.4 / 0.9
5 W	0139 / 0731 / 1413 / 1948	3.1 / 0.9 / 2.9 / 1.1	**20** TH	0229 / 0839 / 1510 / 2053	3.4 / 0.7 / 3.2 / 1.2
6 TH	0217 / 0811 / 1458 / 2028	3.0 / 1.1 / 2.8 / 1.3	**21** F	0324 / 0946 / 1613 / 2202	3.2 / 0.8 / 3.0 / 1.4
7 F	0303 / 0858 / 1551 / 2119	2.9 / 1.2 / 2.7 / 1.4	**22** SA	0427 / 1059 / 1722 / 2320	3.0 / 1.0 / 2.8 / 1.5
8 SA	0358 / 1003 / 1651 / 2231	2.8 / 1.2 / 2.6 / 1.5	**23** SU	0535 / 1211 / 1833	2.9 / 1.0 / 2.7
9 SU	0500 / 1126 / 1756 / 2359	2.7 / 1.2 / 2.7 / 1.4	**24** M	0035 / 0644 / 1317 / 1938	1.5 / 2.9 / 0.9 / 2.7
10 M	0605 / 1244 / 1905	2.7 / 1.0 / 2.7	**25** TU	0140 / 0747 / 1411 / 2033	1.4 / 2.9 / 0.9 / 2.8
11 TU	0114 / 0711 / 1347 / 2009	1.3 / 2.9 / 0.8 / 2.9	**26** W	0231 / 0842 / 1455 / 2118	1.2 / 3.0 / 0.8 / 2.9
12 W	0212 / 0814 / 1440 / 2105	1.1 / 3.0 / 0.6 / 3.1	**27** TH	0311 / 0930 / 1532 / 2158	1.1 / 3.0 / 0.8 / 3.0
13 TH	0302 / 0912 / 1528 / 2155	0.9 / 3.3 / 0.5 / 3.3	**28** F	0348 / 1013 / 1606 / 2235	0.9 / 3.1 / 0.8 / 3.0
14 F	0349 / 1005 / 1614 / 2242	0.6 / 3.5 / 0.3 / 3.5	**29** SA	0422 / 1052 / 1638 / 2310	0.8 / 3.1 / 0.7 / 3.1
15 SA ●	0434 / 1055 / 1659 / 2326	0.5 / 3.6 / 0.3 / 3.6	**30** SU ○	0455 / 1129 / 1710 / 2342	0.8 / 3.1 / 0.7 / 3.2
			31 M	0529 / 1204 / 1742	0.7 / 3.1 / 0.8

JUNE

	Time	m		Time	m
1 TU	0012 / 0603 / 1239 / 1816	3.2 / 0.7 / 3.0 / 0.8	**16** W	0039 / 0643 / 1311 / 1858	3.6 / 0.4 / 3.5 / 0.7
2 W	0044 / 0638 / 1314 / 1851	3.2 / 0.8 / 3.0 / 0.9	**17** TH	0126 / 0733 / 1402 / 1943	3.6 / 0.5 / 3.4 / 0.9
3 TH	0118 / 0715 / 1354 / 1927	3.1 / 0.8 / 2.9 / 1.0	**18** F	0213 / 0826 / 1453 / 2031	3.5 / 0.6 / 3.2 / 1.1
4 F	0155 / 0755 / 1438 / 2007	3.0 / 0.9 / 2.8 / 1.1	**19** SA	0303 / 0923 / 1547 / 2126	3.3 / 0.8 / 3.0 / 1.3
5 SA	0239 / 0841 / 1529 / 2055	3.0 / 1.0 / 2.8 / 1.2	**20** SU	0357 / 1025 / 1645 / 2231	3.1 / 0.9 / 2.8 / 1.5
6 SU	0330 / 0939 / 1626 / 2158	2.9 / 1.0 / 2.7 / 1.3	**21** M	0457 / 1128 / 1746 / 2342	3.0 / 1.0 / 2.7 / 1.5
7 M	0430 / 1048 / 1727 / 2313	2.8 / 1.0 / 2.7 / 1.3	**22** TU	0600 / 1230 / 1848	2.9 / 1.1 / 2.7
8 TU	0534 / 1159 / 1831	2.8 / 0.9 / 2.8	**23** W	0050 / 0704 / 1327 / 1947	1.5 / 2.8 / 1.1 / 2.7
9 W	0026 / 0638 / 1305 / 1933	1.2 / 2.9 / 0.8 / 2.9	**24** TH	0150 / 0804 / 1416 / 2039	1.3 / 2.9 / 1.0 / 2.8
10 TH	0132 / 0742 / 1404 / 2033	1.1 / 3.1 / 0.6 / 3.1	**25** F	0240 / 0858 / 1459 / 2125	1.2 / 2.9 / 1.0 / 3.0
11 F	0230 / 0844 / 1459 / 2128	0.9 / 3.2 / 0.5 / 3.2	**26** SA	0323 / 0945 / 1537 / 2206	1.1 / 2.9 / 0.9 / 3.0
12 SA	0324 / 0942 / 1551 / 2219	0.7 / 3.4 / 0.5 / 3.4	**27** SU	0402 / 1028 / 1613 / 2244	0.8 / 3.0 / 0.9 / 3.1
13 SU ●	0416 / 1037 / 1640 / 2307	0.6 / 3.5 / 0.5 / 3.5	**28** M ○	0439 / 1107 / 1648 / 2319	0.8 / 3.0 / 0.8 / 3.2
14 M	0506 / 1130 / 1727 / 2354	0.6 / 3.6 / 0.5 / 3.6	**29** TU	0514 / 1144 / 1723 / 2352	0.8 / 3.0 / 0.8 / —
15 TU	0555 / 1221 / 1813	0.3 / 3.6 / 0.6	**30** W	0549 / 1220 / 1758	0.7 / 3.1 / 0.8

JULY

	Time	m		Time	m
1 TH	0025 / 0625 / 1257 / 1834	3.2 / 0.7 / 3.0 / 0.8	**16** F	0109 / 0718 / 1344 / 1922	3.7 / 0.4 / 3.4 / 0.9
2 F	0100 / 0702 / 1336 / 1911	3.2 / 0.7 / 3.0 / 0.9	**17** SA	0153 / 0803 / 1428 / 2002	3.6 / 0.5 / 3.3 / 1.1
3 SA	0136 / 0741 / 1419 / 1950	3.2 / 0.7 / 2.9 / 1.0	**18** SU	0237 / 0849 / 1514 / 2044	3.4 / 0.7 / 3.1 / 1.2
4 SU	0217 / 0824 / 1506 / 2035	3.1 / 0.7 / 2.9 / 1.1	**19** M	0323 / 0939 / 1602 / 2132	3.3 / 0.9 / 2.9 / 1.4
5 M	0305 / 0915 / 1559 / 2129	3.0 / 0.8 / 2.8 / 1.1	**20** TU	0414 / 1036 / 1654 / 2237	3.1 / 1.1 / 2.8 / 1.5
6 TU	0401 / 1015 / 1657 / 2236	3.0 / 0.8 / 2.8 / 1.2	**21** W	0511 / 1138 / 1751 / 2357	2.9 / 1.3 / 2.7 / 1.6
7 W	0504 / 1122 / 1758 / 2348	2.9 / 0.8 / 2.8 / 1.2	**22** TH	0615 / 1241 / 1854	2.8 / 1.3 / 2.7
8 TH	0610 / 1229 / 1901	2.9 / 0.8 / 2.8	**23** F	0110 / 0722 / 1339 / 1956	1.5 / 2.7 / 1.3 / 2.8
9 F	0058 / 0716 / 1335 / 2004	1.1 / 3.0 / 0.8 / 3.0	**24** SA	0211 / 0826 / 1429 / 2051	1.4 / 2.8 / 1.2 / 2.9
10 SA	0206 / 0823 / 1438 / 2105	0.9 / 3.1 / 0.7 / 3.1	**25** SU	0302 / 0920 / 1513 / 2138	1.2 / 2.9 / 1.1 / 3.0
11 SU	0309 / 0927 / 1535 / 2200	0.8 / 3.2 / 0.7 / 3.3	**26** M	0344 / 1006 / 1552 / 2220	1.0 / 2.9 / 1.0 / 3.1
12 M	0406 / 1027 / 1627 / 2252	0.6 / 3.4 / 0.7 / 3.5	**27** TU	0423 / 1047 / 1629 / 2257	0.9 / 3.0 / 0.9 / 3.2
13 TU ●	0458 / 1121 / 1715 / 2339	0.4 / 3.5 / 0.7 / 3.6	**28** W ○	0459 / 1125 / 1706 / 2331	0.8 / 3.1 / 0.9 / 3.3
14 W	0547 / 1211 / 1759	0.4 / 3.5 / 0.7	**29** TH	0534 / 1202 / 1742	0.7 / 3.1 / 0.8
15 TH	0025 / 0633 / 1258 / 1841	3.7 / 0.4 / 3.5 / 0.8	**30** F	0005 / 0609 / 1239 / 1817	3.3 / 0.6 / 3.2 / 0.8
			31 SA	0040 / 0646 / 1316 / 1854	3.4 / 0.5 / 3.2 / 0.8

AUGUST

	Time	m		Time	m
1 SU	0117 / 0723 / 1357 / 1932	3.4 / 0.5 / 3.1 / 0.8	**16** M	0207 / 0809 / 1437 / 2004	3.5 / 0.8 / 3.2 / 1.1
2 M	0156 / 0803 / 1440 / 2014	3.3 / 0.6 / 3.0 / 0.9	**17** TU	0247 / 0846 / 1517 / 2042	3.3 / 1.0 / 3.0 / 1.3
3 TU	0240 / 0850 / 1529 / 2104	3.2 / 0.7 / 2.9 / 1.0	**18** W	0331 / 0929 / 1601 / 2130	3.1 / 1.2 / 2.9 / 1.5
4 W	0333 / 0945 / 1625 / 2205	3.1 / 0.8 / 2.9 / 1.1	**19** TH	0421 / 1025 / 1652 / 2242	2.9 / 1.4 / 2.8 / 1.6
5 TH	0436 / 1050 / 1727 / 2319	3.0 / 0.9 / 2.8 / 1.2	**20** F	0520 / 1145 / 1751	2.8 / 1.5 / 2.7
6 F	0546 / 1203 / 1834	2.9 / 1.0 / 2.8	**21** SA	0028 / 0631 / 1301 / 1901	1.6 / 2.7 / 1.5 / 2.7
7 SA	0037 / 0658 / 1318 / 1943	1.1 / 2.9 / 1.0 / 2.9	**22** SU	0142 / 0751 / 1401 / 2012	1.5 / 2.7 / 1.4 / 2.8
8 SU	0155 / 0814 / 1428 / 2049	1.0 / 3.0 / 1.0 / 3.1	**23** M	0237 / 0855 / 1450 / 2108	1.3 / 2.8 / 1.3 / 3.0
9 M	0304 / 0922 / 1528 / 2147	0.8 / 3.1 / 0.9 / 3.3	**24** TU	0322 / 0944 / 1532 / 2152	1.1 / 3.0 / 1.2 / 3.1
10 TU	0401 / 1021 / 1618 / 2238	0.6 / 3.3 / 0.8 / 3.4	**25** W	0402 / 1026 / 1610 / 2230	0.9 / 3.1 / 1.0 / 3.3
11 W ●	0451 / 1112 / 1702 / 2325	0.5 / 3.4 / 0.8 / 3.6	**26** TH ○	0438 / 1103 / 1646 / 2306	0.7 / 3.2 / 0.9 / 3.4
12 TH	0535 / 1157 / 1742	0.4 / 3.4 / 0.8	**27** F	0514 / 1140 / 1722 / 2342	0.6 / 3.3 / 0.8 / 3.5
13 F	0008 / 0616 / 1240 / 1819	3.7 / 0.3 / 3.4 / 0.8	**28** SA	0549 / 1216 / 1758	0.5 / 3.4 / 0.7
14 SA	0049 / 0655 / 1320 / 1855	3.7 / 0.4 / 3.4 / 0.9	**29** SU	0018 / 0625 / 1254 / 1834	3.6 / 0.4 / 3.4 / 0.7
15 SU	0128 / 0732 / 1358 / 1930	3.6 / 0.6 / 3.3 / 1.0	**30** M	0056 / 0702 / 1332 / 1912	3.6 / 0.4 / 3.3 / 0.7
			31 TU	0135 / 0741 / 1414 / 1953	3.5 / 0.5 / 3.2 / 0.8

7

SCOTLAND – WICK

LAT 58°26′N   LONG   3°05′W

TIMES AND HEIGHTS OF HIGH AND LOW WATERS

YEAR **1999**

TIME ZONE (UT)
For Summer Time add ONE hour in non-shaded areas

SEPTEMBER

Day	Time	m	Day	Time	m
1 W	0219 / 0825 / 1500 / 2041	3.4 / 0.7 / 3.1 / 1.0	**16** TH	0250 / 0837 / 1511 / 2048	3.1 / 1.3 / 3.0 / 1.5
2 TH	0311 / 0918 / 1555 / 2142	3.2 / 0.9 / 3.0 / 1.1	**17** F	0336 / 0922 / 1559 / 2145	2.9 / 1.5 / 2.9 / 1.6
3 F	0415 / 1025 / 1700 / 2301	3.2 / 1.1 / 2.8 / 1.2	**18** SA	0432 / 1029 / 1655 / 2331	2.8 / 1.7 / 2.8 / 1.7
4 SA	0530 / 1147 / 1813	2.9 / 1.2 / 2.8	**19** SU	0539 / 1217 / 1801	2.7 / 1.7 / 2.8
5 SU	0030 / 0652 / 1314 / 1929	1.2 / 2.9 / 1.3 / 2.9	**20** M	0106 / 0701 / 1330 / 1916	1.6 / 2.7 / 1.6 / 2.8
6 M	0155 / 0813 / 1428 / 2038	1.0 / 2.9 / 1.2 / 3.1	**21** TU	0206 / 0821 / 1423 / 2025	1.4 / 2.8 / 1.5 / 3.0
7 TU	0302 / 0919 / 1523 / 2135	0.8 / 3.1 / 1.0 / 3.3	**22** W	0253 / 0915 / 1507 / 2116	1.2 / 3.0 / 1.3 / 3.1
8 W	0354 / 1013 / 1606 / 2223	0.6 / 3.2 / 0.9 / 3.4	**23** TH	0333 / 0957 / 1546 / 2158	0.9 / 3.2 / 1.1 / 3.3
9 TH ●	0437 / 1058 / 1645 / 2307	0.5 / 3.3 / 0.8 / 3.6	**24** F	0411 / 1036 / 1623 / 2238	0.7 / 3.3 / 0.9 / 3.5
10 F	0516 / 1139 / 1720 / 2347	0.4 / 3.4 / 0.8 / 3.6	**25** SA O	0448 / 1114 / 1659 / 2317	0.5 / 3.5 / 0.8 / 3.7
11 SA	0551 / 1216 / 1753	0.4 / 3.4 / 0.8	**26** SU	0524 / 1151 / 1736 / 2356	0.4 / 3.6 / 0.7 / 3.8
12 SU	0025 / 0624 / 1251 / 1825	3.7 / 0.5 / 3.4 / 0.8	**27** M	0601 / 1229 / 1814	0.4 / 3.6 / 0.6
13 M	0101 / 0656 / 1325 / 1857	3.6 / 0.7 / 3.3 / 0.9	**28** TU	0035 / 0639 / 1308 / 1853	3.8 / 0.4 / 3.6 / 0.7
14 TU	0136 / 0728 / 1358 / 1930	3.5 / 0.8 / 3.2 / 1.1	**29** W	0117 / 0719 / 1349 / 1935	3.7 / 0.6 / 3.5 / 0.8
15 W	0212 / 0800 / 1433 / 2006	3.3 / 1.1 / 3.1 / 1.3	**30** TH	0203 / 0803 / 1435 / 2025	3.6 / 0.8 / 3.3 / 0.9

OCTOBER

Day	Time	m	Day	Time	m
1 F	0256 / 0855 / 1530 / 2128	3.3 / 1.1 / 3.1 / 1.1	**16** SA	0301 / 0841 / 1517 / 2108	3.0 / 1.5 / 3.0 / 1.6
2 SA	0402 / 1007 / 1638 / 2254	3.1 / 1.4 / 2.9 / 1.3	**17** SU	0355 / 0938 / 1613 / 2227	2.8 / 1.7 / 2.9 / 1.7
3 SU	0523 / 1140 / 1757	2.9 / 1.5 / 2.9	**18** M	0459 / 1112 / 1716	2.7 / 1.8 / 2.8
4 M	0027 / 0651 / 1312 / 1916	1.2 / 2.9 / 1.5 / 2.9	**19** TU	0017 / 0613 / 1248 / 1825	1.6 / 2.7 / 1.7 / 2.9
5 TU	0150 / 0810 / 1421 / 2023	1.0 / 3.0 / 1.3 / 3.1	**20** W	0124 / 0732 / 1347 / 1934	1.4 / 2.9 / 1.6 / 3.0
6 W	0250 / 0910 / 1510 / 2118	0.8 / 3.1 / 1.2 / 3.3	**21** TH	0214 / 0834 / 1434 / 2033	1.2 / 3.0 / 1.4 / 3.2
7 TH	0337 / 0957 / 1548 / 2204	0.7 / 3.2 / 1.0 / 3.4	**22** F	0258 / 0922 / 1516 / 2123	0.9 / 3.2 / 1.1 / 3.4
8 F	0415 / 1038 / 1622 / 2245	0.6 / 3.3 / 0.9 / 3.5	**23** SA	0339 / 1005 / 1555 / 2208	0.7 / 3.4 / 0.9 / 3.6
9 SA ●	0449 / 1114 / 1654 / 2323	0.6 / 3.4 / 0.8 / 3.6	**24** SU O	0419 / 1046 / 1635 / 2251	0.6 / 3.6 / 0.8 / 3.8
10 SU	0521 / 1148 / 1726 / 2359	0.6 / 3.4 / 0.8 / 3.6	**25** M	0458 / 1126 / 1714 / 2334	0.5 / 3.7 / 0.6 / 3.9
11 M	0552 / 1221 / 1757	0.7 / 3.4 / 0.9	**26** TU	0537 / 1206 / 1754	0.4 / 3.8 / 0.6
12 TU	0033 / 0621 / 1252 / 1829	3.5 / 0.8 / 3.4 / 0.9	**27** W	0017 / 0617 / 1247 / 1836	3.9 / 0.5 / 3.7 / 0.6
13 W	0107 / 0652 / 1323 / 1902	3.4 / 1.0 / 3.3 / 1.1	**28** TH	0103 / 0700 / 1330 / 1922	3.8 / 0.7 / 3.6 / 0.7
14 TH	0140 / 0724 / 1355 / 1937	3.3 / 1.1 / 3.2 / 1.2	**29** F	0151 / 0745 / 1416 / 2014	3.6 / 0.9 / 3.4 / 0.9
15 F	0217 / 0759 / 1432 / 2017	3.1 / 1.3 / 3.1 / 1.4	**30** SA	0247 / 0839 / 1512 / 2121	3.4 / 1.3 / 3.2 / 1.1
			31 SU	0354 / 0952 / 1619 / 2247	3.1 / 1.5 / 3.1 / 1.2

NOVEMBER

Day	Time	m	Day	Time	m
1 M	0514 / 1124 / 1736	2.9 / 1.6 / 3.0	**16** TU	0428 / 1014 / 1638 / 2312	2.8 / 1.7 / 2.9 / 1.5
2 TU	0012 / 0638 / 1249 / 1852	1.2 / 2.9 / 1.6 / 3.0	**17** W	0534 / 1145 / 1744	2.8 / 1.7 / 2.9
3 W	0128 / 0752 / 1357 / 1959	1.1 / 3.0 / 1.5 / 3.1	**18** TH	0029 / 0643 / 1258 / 1849	1.3 / 2.9 / 1.6 / 3.0
4 TH	0226 / 0848 / 1446 / 2053	0.9 / 3.1 / 1.3 / 3.3	**19** F	0128 / 0748 / 1354 / 1951	1.2 / 3.0 / 1.4 / 3.2
5 F	0310 / 0932 / 1523 / 2139	0.8 / 3.2 / 1.2 / 3.4	**20** SA	0219 / 0844 / 1442 / 2048	1.0 / 3.2 / 1.2 / 3.4
6 SA	0346 / 1011 / 1557 / 2220	0.8 / 3.3 / 1.0 / 3.4	**21** SU	0305 / 0933 / 1527 / 2140	0.8 / 3.4 / 1.0 / 3.6
7 SU	0419 / 1046 / 1630 / 2258	0.8 / 3.3 / 0.9 / 3.4	**22** M	0350 / 1019 / 1611 / 2228	0.6 / 3.6 / 0.8 / 3.7
8 M ●	0450 / 1120 / 1702 / 2334	0.8 / 3.4 / 0.9 / 3.4	**23** TU O	0433 / 1103 / 1655 / 2316	0.6 / 3.7 / 0.7 / 3.8
9 TU	0521 / 1152 / 1734	0.8 / 3.4 / 0.9	**24** W	0517 / 1146 / 1740	0.6 / 3.8 / 0.6
10 W	0008 / 0551 / 1224 / 1806	3.4 / 0.9 / 3.4 / 1.0	**25** TH	0003 / 0600 / 1230 / 1825	3.9 / 0.7 / 3.8 / 0.6
11 TH	0042 / 0622 / 1254 / 1840	3.3 / 1.0 / 3.4 / 1.0	**26** F	0052 / 0645 / 1315 / 1914	3.8 / 0.8 / 3.8 / 0.7
12 F	0115 / 0656 / 1326 / 1916	3.2 / 1.2 / 3.3 / 1.2	**27** SA	0143 / 0732 / 1403 / 2008	3.6 / 1.1 / 3.6 / 0.8
13 SA	0152 / 0732 / 1403 / 1956	3.1 / 1.3 / 3.2 / 1.3	**28** SU	0239 / 0825 / 1456 / 2112	3.4 / 1.3 / 3.4 / 1.0
14 SU	0235 / 0812 / 1446 / 2042	3.0 / 1.5 / 3.1 / 1.4	**29** M	0341 / 0930 / 1557 / 2226	3.2 / 1.5 / 3.3 / 1.1
15 M	0327 / 0902 / 1538 / 2145	2.9 / 1.6 / 3.0 / 1.5	**30** TU	0451 / 1049 / 1706 / 2341	3.0 / 1.7 / 3.1 / 1.2

DECEMBER

Day	Time	m	Day	Time	m
1 W	0605 / 1206 / 1816	2.9 / 1.7 / 3.1	**16** TH	0458 / 1043 / 1704 / 2330	2.8 / 1.6 / 3.0 / 1.2
2 TH	0050 / 0714 / 1315 / 1923	1.1 / 2.9 / 1.6 / 3.1	**17** F	0602 / 1159 / 1809	2.9 / 1.6 / 3.0
3 F	0149 / 0813 / 1411 / 2021	1.1 / 3.0 / 1.4 / 3.1	**18** SA	0037 / 0705 / 1306 / 1913	1.1 / 3.0 / 1.4 / 3.1
4 SA	0236 / 0900 / 1455 / 2111	1.0 / 3.1 / 1.3 / 3.2	**19** SU	0138 / 0805 / 1406 / 2015	1.0 / 3.1 / 1.2 / 3.3
5 SU	0315 / 0941 / 1534 / 2155	1.0 / 3.2 / 1.2 / 3.3	**20** M	0233 / 0902 / 1501 / 2115	0.9 / 3.3 / 1.0 / 3.4
6 M	0350 / 1018 / 1610 / 2235	1.0 / 3.3 / 1.0 / 3.3	**21** TU	0325 / 0954 / 1553 / 2210	0.8 / 3.5 / 0.8 / 3.6
7 TU ●	0424 / 1055 / 1644 / 2313	1.0 / 3.3 / 1.0 / 3.3	**22** W O	0414 / 1043 / 1643 / 2303	0.7 / 3.7 / 0.7 / 3.8
8 W	0456 / 1129 / 1718 / 2349	1.0 / 3.4 / 0.9 / 3.3	**23** TH	0502 / 1131 / 1731 / 2354	0.7 / 3.8 / 0.6 / 3.8
9 TH	0528 / 1202 / 1752	1.0 / 3.4 / 1.0	**24** F	0548 / 1216 / 1820	0.8 / 3.8 / 0.5
10 F	0023 / 0601 / 1234 / 1826	3.2 / 1.0 / 3.4 / 1.0	**25** SA	0044 / 0633 / 1303 / 1908	3.7 / 0.9 / 3.8 / 0.6
11 SA	0057 / 0636 / 1307 / 1902	3.2 / 1.1 / 3.3 / 1.0	**26** SU	0134 / 0719 / 1349 / 1959	3.6 / 1.0 / 3.8 / 0.7
12 SU	0134 / 0712 / 1342 / 1940	3.1 / 1.2 / 3.3 / 1.1	**27** M	0225 / 0806 / 1438 / 2053	3.4 / 1.2 / 3.6 / 0.8
13 M	0215 / 0750 / 1421 / 2022	3.0 / 1.3 / 3.2 / 1.2	**28** TU	0318 / 0858 / 1530 / 2153	3.2 / 1.4 / 3.4 / 1.0
14 TU	0302 / 0834 / 1507 / 2113	2.9 / 1.5 / 3.1 / 1.2	**29** W	0415 / 1000 / 1628 / 2258	3.0 / 1.6 / 3.2 / 1.1
15 W	0357 / 0930 / 1602 / 2218	2.9 / 1.6 / 3.0 / 1.3	**30** TH	0517 / 1112 / 1731	2.9 / 1.7 / 3.1
			31 F	0004 / 0621 / 1225 / 1838	1.2 / 2.8 / 1.6 / 3.0

Chart Datum: 1·71 metres below Ordnance Datum (Local)

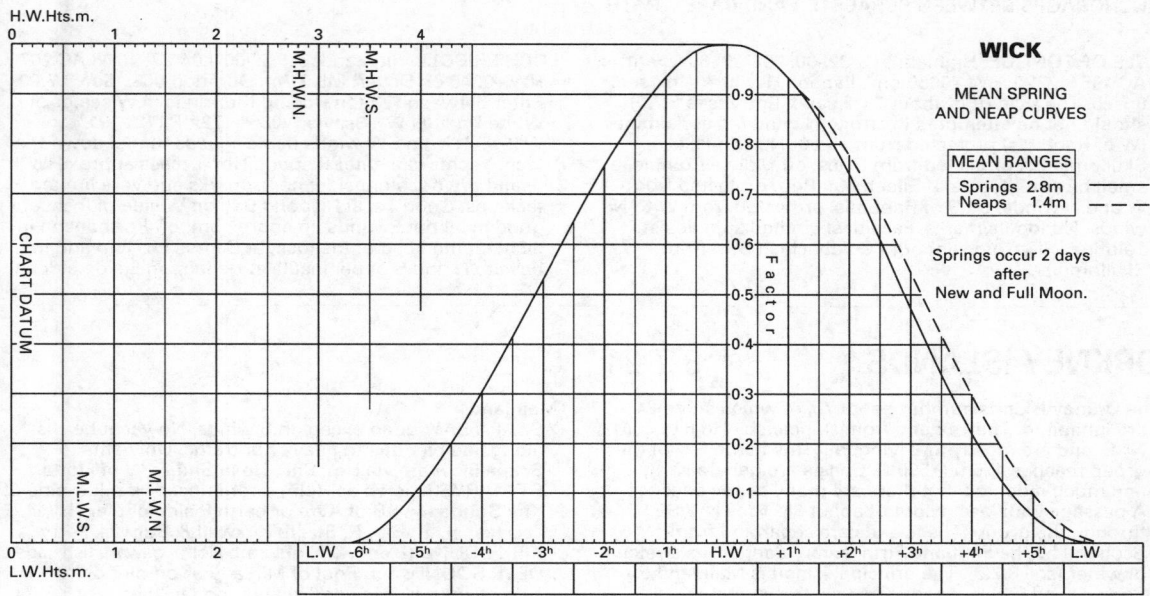

H.W.Hts.m.

WICK

MEAN SPRING
AND NEAP CURVES

MEAN RANGES	
Springs	2.8m
Neaps	1.4m

Springs occur 2 days
after
New and Full Moon.

CHART DATUM

Factor

M.H.W.N.
M.H.W.S.
M.L.W.S.
M.L.W.N.

L.W.Hts.m.

7

SCRABSTER   8-7-20

Highland 58°36'·63N 03°32'·52W   Rtg 1-4-1

CHARTS
AC 1462, 2162, 1954; OS 12
TIDES
-0240 Dover; ML 3·2; Duration 0615; Zone 0 (UT)

Standard Port WICK (←)

Times				Height (metres)			
High Water		Low Water		MHWS	MHWN	MLWN	MLWS
0200	0700	0100	0700	3·5	2·8	1·4	0·7
1400	1900	1300	1900				
Differences SCRABSTER							
−0255	−0225	−0240	−0230	+1·5	+1·2	+0·8	+0·3
GILLS BAY							
−0150	−0150	−0202	−0202	+0·7	+0·7	+0·6	+0·3
STROMA							
−0115	−0115	−0110	−0110	−0·4	−0·5	−0·1	−0·2
LOCH ERIBOLL (Portnancon) (overleaf)							
−0340	−0255	−0315	−0255	+1·6	+1·3	+0·8	+0·4
KYLE OF DURNESS (overleaf)							
−0350	−0350	−0315	−0315	+1·1	+0·7	+0·4	−0·1
SULE SKERRY (59°05'N 04°24'W)							
−0320	−0255	−0315	−0250	+0·4	+0·3	+0·2	+0·1
RONA (59°08'N 05°49'W)							
−0410	−0345	−0330	−0340	−0·1	−0·2	−0·2	−0·1

SHELTER
Very good except for swell in NW and N winds. Yachts usually lie in the Inner (0·9 - 1·2m) or Centre Basins (0·9 - 2·7m). ⚓ is not advised. A good hbr to await the right conditions for E-bound passage through Pentland Firth (see 8.7.5). Beware floating creel lines E and W of hbr ent.
NAVIGATION
WPT 58°36'·60N 03°32'·00W, 098°/278° from/to E pier lt, 0·25M. Can be entered at all tides in all weathers. Beware FVs, merchant ships and the Orkney ferries.
LIGHTS AND MARKS
No ldg marks/lts. Entry is simple once the conspic ice plant tr and/or the pier lt, QG 6m 4M, have been located. Do not confuse hbr lts with the shore lts of Thurso.
RADIO TELEPHONE
Call Hr Mr VHF Ch 12 16 (H24) for berthing directions, before entering hbr. From the W reception is very poor due to masking by Holborn Head.

TELEPHONE (Dial code 01847)
Hr Mr 892779, ⚓ 892353; MRSC (01856) 873268; ⌗ (01955) 603650; Marinecall 0891 500 451; Police 893222; Dr 893154.
FACILITIES
Hbr AB £4.66 (£5.70 for 4th and subsequent days), FW, D, P (cans), ME, EI, C (15, 30 & 100 ton mobiles), Slip, CH; **Pentland Firth YC** M, R, Bar, Showers (keys held by Duty Hr Mr). **Thurso** EC Thurs; V, R, Bar, ✉, Ⓑ, ⇌, ✈ (Wick). Ferry to Stromness.

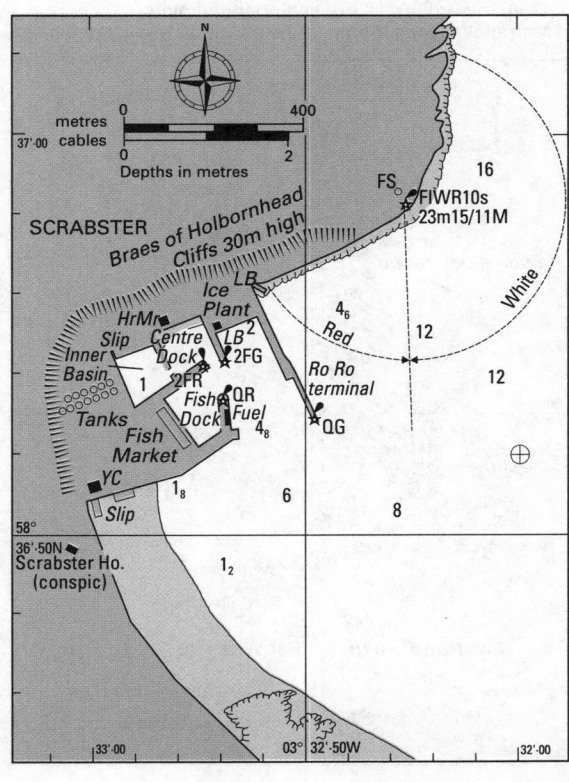

metres   0   400
cables
Depths in metres   2

SCRABSTER
Braes of Holbornhead
Cliffs 30m high

FS
FlWR10s
23m15/11M

16

White

LB
Ice Plant
HrMr
Slip   Centre   LB 2FG
Dock   2FG
Inner   2FR
Basin   1   Fish   QR   Fuel
Dock   4₈
Tanks   Fish
Market
YC   1₈
Slip   6

Red   4₆   12

Ro Ro terminal   12
QG

8

58°
36'·50N
Scrabster Ho.
(conspic)   1₂

33'·00   03° 32'·50W   32'·00

ANCHORAGES BETWEEN SCRABSTER AND CAPE WRATH

KYLE OF TONGUE, Highland, 58°32'·00N 04°22'·60W (ent). AC 1954, 2720. HW +0050 on Ullapool; HW ht −0·4m; see 8.7.20. The Kyle runs about 7M inland. Entry (see 8.7.5) should not be attempted in strong N winds. ‡ at Talmine (W of Rabbit Is) protected from all but NE winds; at Skullomie Hr, protected from E'lies; off Mol na Coinnle, a small bay on SE side of Eilean nan Ron, protected from W and N winds; off S of Rabbit Is, protected from W to N winds. No ldg lts/marks. Facilities: Limited supplies at Talmine (½M from slip) or at Coldbachie (1½M from Skullomie).

LOCH ERIBOLL, Highland, 58°32'·60N 04°37'·40W. AC 2076. HW −0345 on Dover; ML 2·7m; Duration 068. See 8.7.20. Enter between Whiten Hd and Klourig Is in W sector of White Hd lt, Fl WR 3s, vis W030°-172°, R172°-191°, W191°-212°. In SW winds fierce squalls funnel down the loch. Yachts can enter Rispond Hbr, access approx HW ± 3, and dry out alongside; no lts/marks and very limited facilities. Good ‡s: at Rispond Bay on W side of loch, ent good in all but E winds, in approx 5m; off Portnancon in 5·5m; at the head of the loch; at Camus an Duin and in bays to N and S of peninsula at Heilam on E side of loch.

ORKNEY ISLANDS   8-7-21

The Orkney Islands number about 70, of which some 24 are inhabited. They extend from Duncansby Hd 5 to 50M NNE, and are mostly low-lying, but Hoy in the SW of the group reaches 475m (1560ft). Coasts are generally rky and much indented, but there are many sandy beaches. A passage with least width of about 3M runs NW/SE through the group. The islands are separated from Scotland by the Pentland Firth, a very dangerous stretch of water (see 8.7.5). The principal island is Mainland (or Pomona) on which stands Kirkwall, the capital.
Severe gales blow in winter and early spring (see 8.7.5). The climate is mild but windy, and very few trees grow. There are LBs at Longhope, Stromness and Kirkwall. There is a CG MRSC at Kirkwall, ☎ (01856) 873268, with Auxiliary (Watch & Rescue) Stns at Longhope (S Walls), Brough Ness (S Ronaldsay), Stromness and Deerness (both Mainland), Westray, Papa Westray, N Ronaldsay, Sanday, and all inhabited isles except Egilsay and Wyre.

CHARTS
AC 2249, 2250 and 2162 at medium scale. For larger scale charts, see under individual hbrs. OS sheets 5 and 6.

TIDES
Aberdeen (8.6.17) is the Standard Port. Tidal streams are strong, particularly in Pentland Firth and in the firths and sounds among the islands (see 8.7.5).

SHELTER
There are piers (fender board advised) at all main islands. Yachts can pay 4 or 14 day hbr dues (£10.00 or £20.00 in 1998) to berth on all Council-operated piers, except St Margaret's Hope. Some of the many ‡s are listed below:

Mainland
SCAPA BAY: good except in S winds. No yacht berths alongside pier due to heavy hbr traffic. Only ents to Scapa Flow are via Hoy Snd, Hoxa Snd or W of Flotta.
ST MARYS (known as Holm, pronounced Ham): N side of Kirk Sound; ‡ in B of Ayre or berth E side of pier HW±4. P & D (cans), ⊠, Bar, R, Bus to Kirkwall & Burwick Ferry.
KIRK SOUND (E ent): ‡ N of Lamb Holm; beware fish cages.
DEER SOUND: ‡ in Pool of Mirkady or off pier on NW side of sound; very good shelter, no facilities.

Burray
E WEDDEL SOUND: ‡ to E of pier in E'lies, sheltered by No 4 Churchill Barrier; pier is exposed in strong W'lies. P & D (cans), BY, Slip, V, ⊠, Bar, R, Bus to Kirkwall.
HUNDA SOUND: good ‡ in all winds.

S Ronaldsay
ST MARGARET'S HOPE: Rtg 3-4-2. ‡ in centre of bay; or AB £6.50 at pier, beware salmon farm. Hr Mr ☎ 831454; Dr 831206. FW, P & D (cans), V, R, Bar, ⊠, Bus Kirkwall.
WIDEWALL BAY: ‡ sheltered from all but SW winds.

Flotta
Berth on Sutherland Pier, SW of oil terminal. Hr Mr ☎ 701411. P & D (cans), V, ⊠.

Hoy
LONG HOPE: ‡ E of S Ness pier, used by steamers, or berth on pier (safest at slack water) ☎ 701273; Dr 701209. Facilities: FW, P & D (cans), ⊠, V, Bar.
LYNESS: berth on pier; keep clear of disused piles. Also ‡ in Ore Bay. Hr Mr ☎ 791228. FW, P & D (cans), Bar, ⊠. Beware fish cages
PEGAL B: good ‡ except in strong W winds.

Rousay
WYRE SOUND: ‡ E of Rousay pier, or berth on it ⊠, V, R.

Eday
FERSNESS Bay: good holding, sheltered from S winds.
BACKALAND Bay: berth on pier clear of ferry or ‡ to NW. Beware cross tides. FW, P & D, V, ⊠.
CALF SND: ‡ in Carrick B; good shelter from SW-NW'lies.

Papa Westray
B OF MOCLETT: Good ‡ but open to S.
SOUTH WICK: ‡ off the old pier or ESE of pier off Holm of Papa. Backaskaill: P & D (cans), V, ⊠.

Sanday
LOTH B: berth on pier, clear of ferry. Beware strong tides.
KETTLETOFT B: ‡ in bay or berth on pier; very exposed to SE'lies. Hr Mr ☎ 600227. P & D (cans), FW, Gas, ⊠, ⑧, V, hotel.
NORTH BAY: on NW side of island, exposed to NW.
OTTERSWICK: good ‡ except in N or E winds.

N Ronaldsay
SOUTH B: ‡ in middle of bay or berth on pier; open to S and W, and subject to swell. V, ⊠.
LINKLET B: ‡ off jetty at N of bay, open to E.

NAVIGATION
From the mainland, appr from Scrabster to Stromness and Scapa Flow via Hoy Mouth and Hoy Sound. From the Moray Firth (Wick) keep well E of the Pentland Skerries if going N to Kirkwall. Or, if bound for Scapa Flow via Hoxa Sound, keep close to Duncansby Head, passing W of the Pentland Skerries and between Swona and S Ronaldsay. Keep well clear of Lother Rk (dries 1·8m; lt, Q, Racon) off SW tip of S Ronaldsay. Time this entry for slack water in the Pentland Firth (about HW Aberdeen −1¾ and +4). Be aware of tankers off Flotta oil terminal and in the S part of Scapa Flow.

Elsewhere in Orkney navigation is easy in clear weather, apart from the strong tidal streams in all the firths and sounds. Beware races and overfalls off Brough of Birsay (Mainland), Noup Head (Westray) and Dennis Head (N Ronaldsay); see also 8.7.5. Keep a good lookout for the many lobster pots (creels).

LIGHTS AND MARKS
The main hbrs and sounds are well lit; for details see 8.7.4. Powerful lts are shown offshore from Cantick Hd, Graemsay Island, Copinsay, Auskerry, Kirkwall, Brough of Birsay, Sanday Island, N Ronaldsay and Noup Hd.

RADIO TELEPHONE
Orkney Hbrs Navigation Service (call: *Orkney Hbr Radio*, Ch 09 11 20 16 (H24)) covers Scapa Flow and appr's, Wide Firth, Shapinsay Sound and Kirkwall Bay. It also broadcasts Orkney, Scapa and Pentland Firth forecasts for 12 hrs and outlook for further 12 hrs on Ch 11 at 0915 and 1715. For other local stations see individual hbrs.
TELEPHONE Area Code for islands SW of Stronsay and Westray Firths is 01856; islands to the NE are 01857.

MEDICAL SERVICES
Doctors are available at Kirkwall, Stromness, Rousay, Hoy, Shapinsay, Eday, S and N Ronaldsay, Stronsay, Sanday and Westray (Pierowall); Papa Westray is looked after by Westray. The only hospital (and dentist) are at Kirkwall. Serious cases are flown to Aberdeen (1 hour).

FISH FARMS
Fish cages/farms may be found anywhere in sheltered waters within anchoring depths. Some are well buoyed, others are marked only by poles. Those known are listed:

Beware **salmon cages** (may be marked by Y buoys/lts) at:

Rysa Sound	St Margaret's Hope
Bring Deeps	Backaland Bay (Eday)
Pegal Bay (Hoy)	Hunda Sound
Lyrawa Bay	Kirk Sound
Ore Bay (Hoy)	Carness Bay
Widewall Bay (S Ronaldsay)	Bay of Ham
	Bay of London (Eday)

Beware **oysters and longlines** at:

Widewall Bay	Bay of Firth
Swandister Bay	Damsay Sound
Water Sound	Millburn Bay (Gairsay)
Hunda Sound	Pierowall
Deer Sound	Bay of Skaill (Westray)
Inganess Bay	Longhope

MINOR HARBOURS IN THE ORKNEY ISLANDS

HOUTON BAY, Mainland, 58°54'·88N 03°11'·23W. AC 2568, 35. HW –0140 on Dover, –0400 on Aberdeen; HW ht +0·3m on Kirkwall; ML 1·8m; Duration 0615. ⚓ in the bay in approx 5·5m at centre, sheltered from all winds. The ent is to the E of the island Holm of Houton; ent chan dredged 3·5m for 15m each side of ldg line. Keep clear of merchant vessels/ferries plying to Flotta.
Ldg lts 316°: front Fl G 3s 8m, rear FG 16m; both R △ on W pole, B bands. Ro Ro terminal in NE corner marked by Iso R 4s. Bus to Kirkwall; Slip close E of piers. Yachtsmen may contact **M. Grainger** ☎ 811356 for help.

SHAPINSAY, Orkney Islands, 59°02'·00N 02°54'·00W. AC 2584, 2249. HW –0015 on Dover, –0330 on Aberdeen; HW ht –1·0m on Aberdeen. Good shelter in Elwick Bay off Balfour on SW end of island in 2·5-3m. Enter bay passing W of Helliar Holm which has lt Fl WRG 10s on S end. Keep mid-chan. Balfour Pier lt Q WRG 5m 3/2M; vis G270°–010°, W010°–020°, R020°–090°. Tides in The String reach 5kn at sp. Facilities: FW, P & D (cans), ✉, shop, Bar.

AUSKERRY, Orkney Islands, 59°02'·05N 02°34'·55W. AC 2250. HW –0010 on Dover, –0315 on Aberdeen, HW ht –1m on Aberdeen. Small island at ent to Stronsay Firth with small hbr on W side. Safe ent and good shelter except in SW winds. Ent has 3·5m; 1·2m alongside pier. Yachts can lie secured between ringbolts at ent and the pier. Auskerry Sound and Stronsay Firth are dangerous with wind over tide. Auskerry lt at S end, Fl 20s 34m 18M, W tr. No facilities.

See overleaf for **Pierowall** and **Rapness** on **Westray**.

STROMNESS   8-7-22
Orkney Islands, Mainland 58°57'·81N 03°17'·62W   Rtg 2-2-1

CHARTS
AC 2568, 2249; OS 6
TIDES
-0145 Dover; ML 2·0; Duration 0620; Zone 0 (UT)

Standard Port WICK (⟵)

Times				Height (metres)			
High Water		Low Water		MHWS	MHWN	MLWN	MLWS
0000	0700	0200	0700	3·5	2·8	1·4	0·7
1200	1900	1400	1900				
Differences STROMNESS							
–0225	–0135	–0205	–0205	+0·1	–0·1	0·0	0·0
ST MARY'S (Scapa Flow)							
–0140	–0140	–0140	–0140	–0·2	–0·2	0·0	–0·1
BURRAY NESS (Burray)							
+0005	+0005	+0015	+0015	–0·2	–0·3	–0·1	–0·1
WIDEWALL BAY (S Ronaldsay)							
–0155	–0150	–0150	–0150	+0·1	–0·1	–0·1	–0·3
BUR WICK (S Ronaldsay)							
–0100	–0100	–0150	–0150	–0·1	–0·1	+0·2	+0·1
MUCKLE SKERRY (Pentland Firth)							
–0025	–0025	–0020	–0020	–0·9	–0·8	–0·4	–0·3

SHELTER
Very good. Northern Lights Board have sole use of pier near to ldg lts. ⚓ in hbr or berth at ferry piers further N.
NAVIGATION
WPT 58°57'·00N 03°16'·90W, 137°/317° from/to front ldg lt, 0·88M. Entry from the W should not be attempted with strong wind against tide due to heavy overfalls; if entering against the ebb, stand on to avoid being swept onto Skerry of Ness. Tides in Hoy Sound are very strong (>7kn sp). No tidal stream in hbr.
LIGHTS AND MARKS
For Hoy Sound, ldg lts 104° on Graemsay Is: front Iso 3s 17m 15M, W tr; rear Oc WR 8s 35m 20/16M, ldg sector is R097°-112°. Skerry of Ness, Fl WG 4s 7m 7/4M; W shore-090°, G090°-shore.
Hbr ldg lts 317°, both FR 29/39m 11M (H24), W trs, vis 307°-327°.
RADIO TELEPHONE
VHF Ch 12 16 (0900-1700 LT). (See also Kirkwall.)
TELEPHONE (Dial code 01856)
Hr Mr 850744; Fuel 851286; MRSC 873268; ⌗ 872108; Marinecall 0891 500 451; Police 850222; Dr 850205.
FACILITIES
Services: FW, Sh, El, Ⓔ, ME, C (mobile, 30 ton), Slip.
Town EC Thurs; FW, D, V, R, Bar, Gas, ✉, ◎, Ⓑ, ⇌ (ferry to Scrabster, bus to Thurso), ✈ (Kirkwall).
Yachtsmen may contact for help/advice: **Mr J. Stout** ☎ 850100, **Mr S. Mowat** ☎ 850624 or **Capt A. Johnston** ☎ 850366.

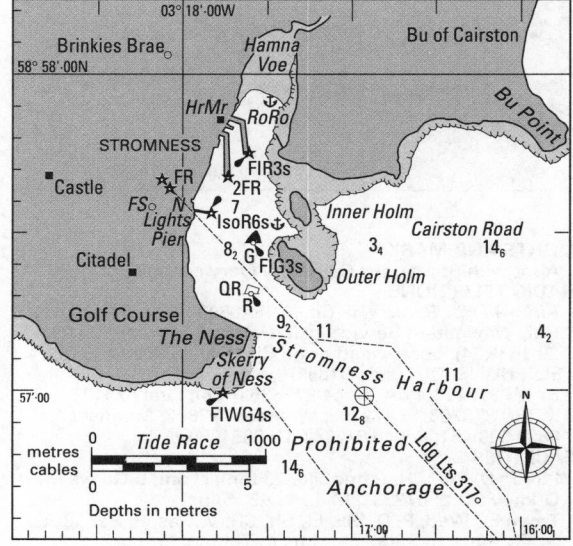

KIRKWALL   8-7-23

Orkney Islands, Mainland 58°59'·33N 02°57'·60W Rtg 2-3-1

CHARTS
AC 1553, 2584, 2249, 2250; OS 6

TIDES
−0045 Dover; ML 1·8; Duration 0620; Zone 0 (UT)

Standard Port WICK (←)

Times				Height (metres)			
High Water		Low Water		MHWS	MHWN	MLWN	MLWS
0000	0700	0200	0700	3·5	2·8	1·4	0·7
1200	1900	1400	1900				
Differences KIRKWALL							
−0042	−0042	−0041	−0041	−0·5	−0·4	−0·1	−0·1
DEER SOUND							
−0040	−0040	−0035	−0035	−0·3	−0·3	−0·1	−0·1
TINGWALL							
−0200	−0125	−0145	−0125	−0·4	−0·4	−0·1	−0·1

SHELTER
Good except in N winds or W gales when there is a surge at the ent. At SW end of main pier, enter inner hbr (very full in Jun/Jul); or safe ⚓ between pier and Crow Ness Pt.

NAVIGATION
WPT 59°01'·40N 02°57'·00W, 008°/188° from/to pier hd lt, 2·2M. Appr in W sector of pier hd lt. Bay is shoal to SW.

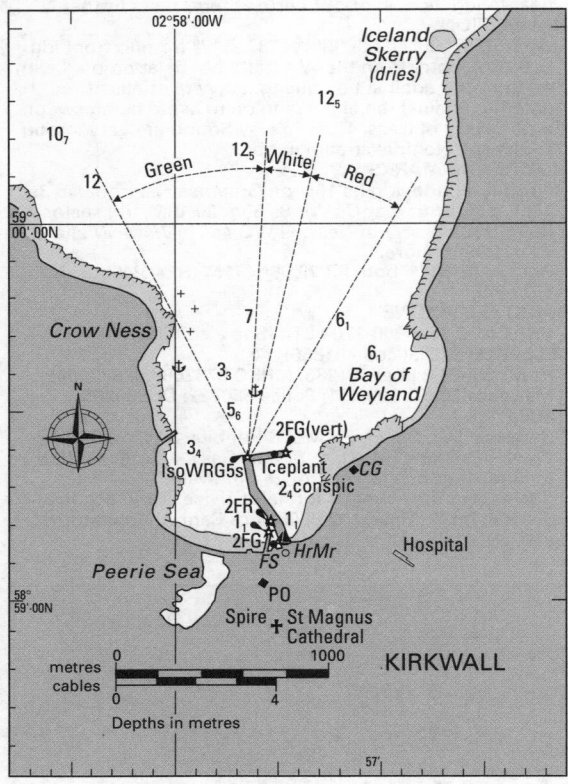

LIGHTS AND MARKS
Appr with St Magnus Cathedral (very conspic) brg 190°.

RADIO TELEPHONE
Kirkwall Hbr Radio VHF Ch 12 16 (0800-1700 LT). Orkney Hbrs Navigation Service, call: *Orkney Hbr Radio* Ch 09 11 20 16 (H24). Local weather on Ch 11 at 0915 and 1715 LT.

TELEPHONE (Dial code 01856)
Hr Mr 872292; Port Office 873636 (H24); Fuel 873105; MRSC 873268; ⌗ 872108; Weather 873802; Marinecall 0891 500 451; Police 872241; Dr 885400 (Ⓗ).

FACILITIES
Pier P, D, FW, CH, C (mobile, 25 ton); **N and E Quays** M; **Orkney SC** ☎ 872331, M, L, C, AB, Slip.
Town EC Wed; P, D, ME, El, Sh, CH, V, Gas, R, Bar, Ⓑ, ◎, ✉, ⇌ (ferry to Scrabster, bus to Thurso), ✈.

STRONSAY   8-7-24

Orkney Islands, Stronsay 59°08'·60N 02°35'·90W Rtg 3-4-2

CHARTS
AC 2622, 2250; OS 6

TIDES
−0140 Dover; ML 1·7; Duration 0620; Zone 0 (UT)

Standard Port WICK (←)

Times				Height (metres)			
High Water		Low Water		MHWS	MHWN	MLWN	MLWS
0000	0700	0200	0700	3·5	2·8	1·4	0·7
1200	1900	1400	1900				
Differences LOTH (Sanday)							
−0052	−0052	−0058	−0058	−0·1	0·0	+0·3	+0·4
KETTLETOFT PIER (Sanday)							
−0025	−0025	−0015	−0015	0·0	0·0	+0·2	+0·2
RAPNESS (Westray)							
−0205	−0205	−0205	−0205	+0·1	0·0	+0·2	0·0
PIEROWALL (Westray)							
−0150	−0150	−0145	−0145	+0·2	0·0	0·0	−0·1

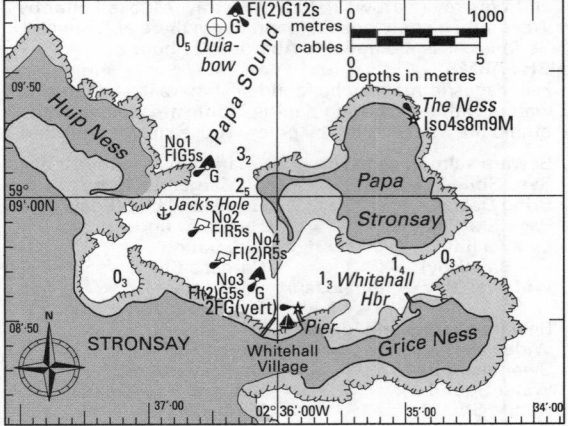

SHELTER
Good from all winds. Good ⚓ between seaward end of piers, or berth on outer end of W pier and contact Hr Mr. The extended E pier head is berth for Ro-Ro ferry. There are many other sheltered ⚓s around the bay.

NAVIGATION
WPT 59°09'·85N 02°36'·20W, Quiabow SHM By, Fl (2) G 12s, 009°/189° from/to No 1 lt buoy, 6·5ca. 800m NE of Huip Ness is Quiabow, a submerged rk. Jack's Reef extends 400m E from Huip Ness, and is marked by No 1 SHM buoy Fl G 5. A bank extends 350m SW from Papa Stronsay. Crampie Shoal is in mid-chan, marked by No 3 buoy. The buoyed chan to Whitehall pier is dredged 3·5m. Spit to E of Whitehall pier extends 400m N. The E ent is narrow and shallow and should not be attempted.

LIGHTS AND MARKS
As chartlet. Pier hd lts, 2FG (vert).

RADIO TELEPHONE
See Kirkwall.

TELEPHONE (Dial code 01857)
Hr Mr 616257; MRSC (01856) 873268; ⌗ (01856) 872108; Marinecall 0891 500451; Police (01856) 872241; Dr 616321.

FACILITIES
W Pier M, L, AB; **Main (E) Pier** M, L, FW, AB clear of ferry.
Village (Whitehall) EC Thurs; P, D, V, Bar, ✉, Ⓑ, ⇌ (ferry to Scrabster, bus to Thurso), ✈.

PIEROWALL, Westray, 59°19'·35N 02°58'·41W. AC 2622, 2250. HW −0135 on Dover; ML 2·2m; Duration 0620. See 8·7·24. The bay is a good ⚓ in 2-7m and well protected. Deep water AB at Gill Pt piers may be available; see Hr Mr. From S, beware Skelwick Skerry rks, and from the N the rks extending approx 1ca off Vest Ness. The N ent via Papa Sound needs local knowledge; tide race on the ebb. A dangerous tide race runs off Mull Hd at the N of Papa Westray. Lights: E pier hd Fl WRG 3s 7m 11/7M, G254°-276°, W276°-291°, R291°-308°, G308°-215°. W pier hd 2 FR (vert) 4/6m 3M. VHF Ch 16. Hr Mr ☎ (01857) 677273. Facilities: FW (Gill Pier), P & D (cans), Gas, Bar, ✉, Ⓑ, R, V.
RAPNESS: Berth on pier, clear of Ro-Ro. Open to SSW.

SCOTLAND – LERWICK

LAT 60°09′N   LONG 1°08′W

TIMES AND HEIGHTS OF HIGH AND LOW WATERS

YEAR **1999**

TIME ZONE (UT)
For Summer Time add ONE hour in non-shaded areas

7

JANUARY

Day	Time	m	Time	m	Time	m	Time	m
1 F	0345	0.8	1006	2.4	1612	0.7	2233	2.4
2 SA O	0432	0.8	1053	2.5	1700	0.6	2321	2.4
3 SU	0516	0.8	1137	2.5	1746	0.6		
4 M	0007	2.4	0559	0.8	1220	2.5	1831	0.6
5 TU	0052	2.3	0641	0.9	1302	2.5	1916	0.6
6 W	0135	2.2	0722	1.0	1344	2.4	2000	0.7
7 TH	0218	2.1	0803	1.1	1427	2.2	2046	0.9
8 F	0303	2.0	0846	1.2	1513	2.1	2135	1.0
9 SA	0351	1.9	0938	1.2	1605	2.0	2234	1.1
10 SU	0445	1.9	1057	1.3	1705	1.9	2350	1.1
11 M	0545	1.9	1232	1.3	1812	1.9		
12 TU	0056	1.2	0648	1.9	1334	1.2	1920	1.9
13 W	0148	1.1	0748	2.0	1422	1.2	2019	2.0
14 TH	0233	1.1	0839	2.1	1504	1.1	2108	2.1
15 F	0314	1.1	0923	2.2	1543	1.0	2151	2.2
16 SA	0353	1.0	1002	2.3	1622	0.9	2231	2.2
17 SU ●	0431	0.9	1039	2.4	1659	0.8	2309	2.3
18 M	0507	0.9	1115	2.4	1736	0.7	2347	2.3
19 TU	0542	0.9	1151	2.5	1812	0.7		
20 W	0025	2.3	0618	0.9	1230	2.5	1849	0.7
21 TH	0106	2.3	0656	0.9	1311	2.4	1931	0.7
22 F	0149	2.2	0850	0.9	1355	2.4	2016	0.7
23 SA	0235	2.2	0938	1.0	1443	2.3	2106	0.8
24 SU	0326	2.1	0919	1.1	1537	2.2	2203	0.9
25 M	0424	2.0	1023	1.1	1641	2.2	2313	1.0
26 TU	0535	2.0	1145	1.2	1803	2.1		
27 W	0041	1.1	0658	2.1	1318	1.1	1931	2.1
28 TH	0154	1.0	0809	2.2	1424	1.0	2040	2.2
29 F	0250	1.0	0906	2.3	1518	0.8	2136	2.3
30 SA	0338	0.9	0956	2.4	1606	0.7	2226	2.4
31 SU O	0422	0.9	1041	2.5	1651	0.6	2311	2.4

FEBRUARY

Day	Time	m	Time	m	Time	m	Time	m
1 M	0504	0.9	1124	2.5	1733	0.6	2353	2.4
2 TU	0543	0.9	1203	2.5	1813	0.6		
3 W	0032	2.3	0619	0.9	1242	2.5	1850	0.6
4 TH	0109	2.3	0655	0.9	1318	2.4	1927	0.7
5 F	0146	2.2	0730	1.0	1356	2.3	2003	0.8
6 SA	0224	2.1	0808	1.1	1436	2.2	2042	1.0
7 SU	0306	2.0	0850	1.2	1521	2.1	2125	1.1
8 M	0352	2.0	0938	1.3	1613	2.0	2217	1.2
9 TU	0446	1.9	1049	1.3	1717	1.9	2337	1.3
10 W	0551	1.9	1252	1.3	1831	1.9		
11 TH	0110	1.3	0659	1.9	1355	1.2	1943	1.9
12 F	0208	1.2	0803	2.0	1442	1.1	2042	2.0
13 SA	0253	1.1	0855	2.1	1523	1.0	2130	2.1
14 SU	0333	1.0	0939	2.2	1601	0.8	2211	2.2
15 M	0411	0.9	1018	2.3	1638	0.7	2250	2.3
16 TU ●	0447	0.8	1056	2.4	1715	0.6	2328	2.4
17 W	0522	0.8	1133	2.5	1751	0.5		
18 TH	0007	2.4	0559	0.7	1213	2.5	1829	0.5
19 F	0047	2.4	0638	0.7	1255	2.5	1911	0.6
20 SA	0129	2.3	0721	0.8	1339	2.5	1955	0.7
21 SU	0213	2.2	0807	0.8	1426	2.4	2043	0.8
22 M	0301	2.2	0859	0.9	1519	2.1	2137	0.9
23 TU	0355	2.1	1000	1.1	1621	2.1	2246	1.1
24 W	0502	2.0	1131	1.1	1747	2.0		
25 TH	0032	1.1	0636	2.0	1315	1.0	1929	2.0
26 F	0148	1.1	0758	2.2	1419	0.9	2038	2.1
27 SA	0243	1.0	0857	2.2	1511	0.8	2131	2.2
28 SU	0328	1.0	0945	2.3	1556	0.7	2216	2.2

MARCH

Day	Time	m	Time	m	Time	m	Time	m
1 M	0409	0.9	1029	2.4	1636	0.6	2257	2.3
2 TU O	0447	0.8	1108	2.4	1714	0.5	2334	2.3
3 W	0522	0.8	1145	2.4	1748	0.5		
4 TH	0008	2.3	0554	0.7	1218	2.4	1820	0.6
5 F	0041	2.2	0627	0.8	1251	2.3	1852	0.7
6 SA	0113	2.2	0700	0.8	1326	2.2	1926	0.7
7 SU	0147	2.1	0736	0.9	1402	2.1	2002	0.9
8 M	0224	2.0	0815	1.0	1441	2.0	2042	1.0
9 TU	0303	1.9	0858	1.1	1525	1.9	2126	1.1
10 W	0348	1.9	0950	1.2	1625	1.8	2222	1.2
11 TH	0450	1.8	1124	1.2	1747	1.7		
12 F	0018	1.2	0610	1.8	1321	1.1	1907	1.8
13 SA	0139	1.2	0724	1.8	1413	1.0	2013	1.9
14 SU	0227	1.1	0823	1.9	1456	0.8	2104	2.0
15 M	0308	0.9	0911	2.1	1534	0.7	2147	2.1
16 TU	0345	0.8	0953	2.2	1611	0.5	2227	2.2
17 W ●	0421	0.7	1033	2.3	1648	0.4	2306	2.3
18 TH	0459	0.6	1114	2.4	1727	0.3	2345	2.3
19 F	0538	0.5	1155	2.5	1807	0.3		
20 SA	0026	2.3	0619	0.5	1239	2.5	1849	0.4
21 SU	0108	2.3	0703	0.5	1324	2.4	1933	0.5
22 M	0152	2.2	0750	0.6	1412	2.3	2021	0.7
23 TU	0239	2.1	0842	0.7	1505	2.1	2115	0.9
24 W	0331	2.0	0946	0.9	1609	1.9	2228	1.0
25 TH	0437	1.9	1131	0.9	1744	1.8		
26 F	0024	1.1	0618	1.8	1304	0.8	1925	1.8
27 SA	0135	1.0	0744	1.9	1406	0.7	2029	1.9
28 SU	0228	0.9	0842	2.0	1455	0.6	2117	2.0
29 M	0312	0.7	0929	2.1	1537	0.5	2159	2.0
30 TU	0351	0.7	1011	2.1	1615	0.5	2237	2.1
31 W O	0426	0.7	1049	2.2	1648	0.5	2311	2.1

APRIL

Day	Time	m	Time	m	Time	m	Time	m
1 TH	0458	0.6	1122	2.2	1718	0.5	2341	2.1
2 F	0529	0.6	1153	2.2	1748	0.5		
3 SA	0010	2.1	0600	0.6	1224	2.1	1819	0.5
4 SU	0041	2.1	0634	0.6	1257	2.0	1853	0.6
5 M	0113	2.0	0710	0.7	1332	2.0	1929	0.7
6 TU	0147	1.9	0747	0.8	1409	1.8	2007	0.8
7 W	0221	1.8	0829	0.9	1450	1.7	2049	0.9
8 TH	0259	1.7	0917	1.0	1543	1.6	2141	1.0
9 F	0350	1.7	1022	1.0	1704	1.6	2254	1.1
10 SA	0507	1.6	1224	1.0	1830	1.6		
11 SU	0054	1.0	0637	1.6	1333	0.8	1939	1.7
12 M	0151	0.9	0744	1.8	1419	0.6	2032	1.8
13 TU	0234	0.8	0838	1.9	1500	0.5	2118	1.9
14 W	0314	0.6	0925	2.1	1540	0.3	2201	2.1
15 TH	0353	0.5	1009	2.2	1620	0.2	2242	2.1
16 F ●	0434	0.4	1053	2.3	1701	0.2	2323	2.2
17 SA	0517	0.3	1138	2.3	1744	0.2		
18 SU	0005	2.2	0600	0.3	1224	2.3	1828	0.3
19 M	0049	2.2	0647	0.3	1311	2.2	1913	0.4
20 TU	0134	2.1	0736	0.4	1401	2.1	2002	0.6
21 W	0221	2.0	0831	0.5	1456	1.9	2057	0.8
22 TH	0314	1.8	0939	0.6	1602	1.7	2214	0.9
23 F	0419	1.7	1119	0.7	1734	1.6		
24 SA	0001	0.9	0552	1.7	1242	0.6	1906	1.6
25 SU	0111	0.9	0718	1.7	1341	0.6	2007	1.7
26 M	0204	0.8	0817	1.8	1430	0.5	2054	1.7
27 TU	0249	0.7	0905	1.8	1511	0.4	2134	1.8
28 W	0327	0.6	0947	1.9	1546	0.4	2210	1.9
29 TH	0401	0.5	1024	1.9	1618	0.4	2242	1.9
30 F O	0433	0.5	1057	1.9	1647	0.5	2311	1.9

Chart Datum: 1·22 metres below Ordnance Datum (Local)

TIME ZONE (UT)
For Summer Time add ONE hour in non-shaded areas

SCOTLAND – LERWICK

LAT 60°09′N   LONG 1°08′W

TIMES AND HEIGHTS OF HIGH AND LOW WATERS

YEAR **1999**

MAY

Day	Time/m	Time/m	Time/m	Time/m
1 SA	0504 0.5	1127 1.9	1718 0.4	2340 1.9
2 SU	0537 0.4	1159 1.9	1751 0.5	
3 M	0011 1.9	0611 0.5	1233 1.9	1825 0.5
4 TU	0044 1.9	0648 0.5	1309 1.8	1901 0.6
5 W	0117 1.8	0726 0.6	1346 1.7	1939 0.7
6 TH	0151 1.8	0807 0.6	1428 1.6	2021 0.8
7 F	0231 1.7	0855 0.7	1520 1.5	2112 0.9
8 SA	0319 1.6	0952 0.7	1627 1.5	2214 0.9
9 SU	0422 1.6	1107 0.7	1747 1.5	2336 0.9
10 M	0543 1.6	1234 0.6	1858 1.6	
11 TU	0057 0.8	0700 1.6	1334 0.5	1956 1.7
12 W	0153 0.7	0802 1.8	1423 0.4	2046 1.8
13 TH	0240 0.5	0856 1.9	1508 0.2	2133 1.9
14 F	0326 0.4	0946 2.1	1553 0.2	2217 2.0
15 SA	0412 0.2	1034 2.2	1638 0.2	● 2302 2.1
16 SU	0458 0.2	1122 2.2	1723 0.2	2346 2.1
17 M	0546 0.1	1211 2.2	1809 0.3	
18 TU	0031 2.1	0634 0.2	1301 2.1	1856 0.4
19 W	0118 2.0	0726 0.2	1352 1.9	1945 0.5
20 TH	0206 1.9	0822 0.3	1447 1.8	2040 0.7
21 F	0259 1.8	0928 0.4	1549 1.6	2150 0.8
22 SA	0359 1.7	1050 0.5	1702 1.5	2322 0.9
23 SU	0513 1.6	1206 0.5	1824 1.5	
24 M	0035 0.8	0635 1.6	1307 0.5	1929 1.5
25 TU	0132 0.8	0741 1.6	1357 0.5	2019 1.6
26 W	0219 0.7	0833 1.7	1438 0.5	2101 1.7
27 TH	0300 0.6	0917 1.7	1514 0.5	2138 1.7
28 F	0335 0.5	0955 1.7	1546 0.5	2211 1.8
29 SA	0408 0.4	1030 1.8	1618 0.5	2241 1.9
30 SU	0442 0.4	1103 1.8	1652 0.5	O 2313 1.9
31 M	0518 0.4	1137 1.8	1727 0.5	2345 1.9

JUNE

Day	Time/m	Time/m	Time/m	Time/m
1 TU	0554 0.4	1213 1.8	1803 0.5	
2 W	0019 1.9	0631 0.4	1250 1.7	1839 0.6
3 TH	0053 1.8	0709 0.5	1329 1.7	1917 0.6
4 F	0130 1.8	0750 0.5	1411 1.6	1959 0.7
5 SA	0211 1.7	0835 0.5	1500 1.6	2048 0.8
6 SU	0258 1.7	0928 0.5	1557 1.5	2144 0.8
7 M	0354 1.6	1029 0.5	1703 1.5	2249 0.8
8 TU	0501 1.6	1138 0.5	1813 1.6	
9 W	0003 0.8	0617 1.7	1248 0.5	1917 1.6
10 TH	0113 0.7	0728 1.8	1348 0.4	2015 1.8
11 F	0211 0.5	0830 1.9	1441 0.3	2107 1.9
12 SA	0304 0.4	0926 2.0	1530 0.3	2156 1.9
13 SU	0355 0.3	1019 2.1	1618 0.3	● 2243 2.1
14 M	0444 0.2	1110 2.1	1706 0.3	2330 2.2
15 TU	0534 0.1	1159 2.1	1753 0.4	
16 W	0016 2.2	0623 0.2	1249 2.0	1840 0.5
17 TH	0103 2.1	0714 0.2	1339 1.9	1928 0.6
18 F	0150 2.0	0806 0.3	1430 1.8	2018 0.7
19 SA	0239 1.9	0903 0.4	1523 1.7	2114 0.8
20 SU	0331 1.8	1007 0.5	1620 1.6	2224 0.8
21 M	0429 1.7	1117 0.6	1722 1.5	2344 0.8
22 TU	0535 1.6	1221 0.6	1828 1.5	
23 W	0051 0.8	0646 1.6	1316 0.6	1928 1.6
24 TH	0146 0.8	0749 1.6	1402 0.7	2018 1.6
25 F	0231 0.7	0841 1.6	1441 0.7	2100 1.7
26 SA	0311 0.7	0924 1.7	1517 0.6	2138 1.8
27 SU	0348 0.6	1004 1.8	1554 0.6	2214 1.9
28 M	0424 0.5	1041 1.8	1632 0.6	O 2249 1.9
29 TU	0502 0.5	1118 1.8	1709 0.6	2323 2.0
30 W	0539 0.5	1154 1.8	1746 0.6	2357 2.0

JULY

Day	Time/m	Time/m	Time/m	Time/m
1 TH	0616 0.4	1231 1.8	1822 0.6	
2 F	0033 2.0	0653 0.4	1311 1.8	1858 0.6
3 SA	0111 1.9	0732 0.4	1352 1.8	1939 0.7
4 SU	0153 1.9	0815 0.5	1437 1.7	2025 0.7
5 M	0239 1.9	0904 0.5	1528 1.7	2116 0.8
6 TU	0331 1.8	0958 0.5	1625 1.7	2216 0.8
7 W	0431 1.8	1100 0.6	1730 1.7	2325 0.8
8 TH	0542 1.8	1210 0.6	1841 1.7	
9 F	0041 0.8	0700 1.8	1321 0.6	1947 1.8
10 SA	0152 0.7	0811 1.9	1422 0.6	2046 1.9
11 SU	0251 0.5	0913 2.0	1515 0.5	2139 2.1
12 M	0345 0.4	1008 2.1	1605 0.5	2228 2.2
13 TU	0435 0.3	1059 2.1	1652 0.5	● 2315 2.2
14 W	0523 0.3	1148 2.1	1738 0.5	
15 TH	0001 2.3	0610 0.3	1235 2.1	1822 0.5
16 F	0045 2.2	0656 0.2	1320 2.0	1905 0.6
17 SA	0129 2.1	0742 0.3	1405 1.9	1949 0.7
18 SU	0213 2.0	0828 0.4	1449 1.8	2033 0.8
19 M	0258 1.9	0916 0.6	1535 1.7	2122 0.9
20 TU	0347 1.8	1008 0.7	1625 1.6	2224 0.9
21 W	0442 1.7	1111 0.8	1720 1.6	2354 1.0
22 TH	0545 1.6	1222 0.9	1821 1.6	
23 F	0108 1.0	0655 1.6	1323 0.9	1923 1.7
24 SA	0203 0.9	0801 1.7	1411 0.9	2020 1.8
25 SU	0248 0.8	0855 1.7	1454 0.8	2107 1.9
26 M	0328 0.7	0941 1.8	1535 0.8	2149 1.9
27 TU	0406 0.6	1021 1.9	1614 0.7	2226 2.0
28 W	0444 0.6	1058 1.9	1651 0.7	O 2301 2.1
29 TH	0521 0.5	1135 1.9	1727 0.6	2336 2.1
30 F	0557 0.4	1211 2.0	1802 0.6	
31 SA	0012 2.1	0633 0.4	1249 2.0	1838 0.6

AUGUST

Day	Time/m	Time/m	Time/m	Time/m
1 SU	0051 2.2	0711 0.4	1329 2.0	1918 0.7
2 M	0133 2.1	0753 0.4	1412 1.9	2002 0.7
3 TU	0218 2.1	0839 0.5	1459 1.9	2051 0.8
4 W	0308 2.0	0930 0.6	1552 1.8	2148 0.8
5 TH	0406 1.9	1030 0.7	1653 1.8	2257 0.9
6 F	0516 1.9	1143 0.8	1808 1.8	
7 SA	0024 0.9	0643 1.9	1307 0.8	1927 1.9
8 SU	0145 0.8	0803 1.9	1414 0.8	2033 2.0
9 M	0247 0.6	0907 2.0	1507 0.7	2128 2.1
10 TU	0338 0.5	1001 2.1	1555 0.7	2217 2.2
11 W	0425 0.4	1049 2.1	1639 0.6	● 2302 2.3
12 TH	0509 0.3	1133 2.2	1721 0.6	2344 2.3
13 F	0552 0.3	1215 2.1	1801 0.6	
14 SA	0024 2.3	0632 0.3	1255 2.1	1839 0.6
15 SU	0103 2.2	0711 0.4	1333 2.0	1916 0.7
16 M	0142 2.1	0749 0.5	1411 1.9	1955 0.8
17 TU	0222 2.0	0828 0.7	1451 1.9	2036 0.9
18 W	0306 1.9	0909 0.8	1536 1.8	2124 1.0
19 TH	0357 1.8	0958 0.9	1627 1.7	2230 1.1
20 F	0458 1.7	1107 1.0	1728 1.7	
21 SA	0025 1.1	0609 1.6	1243 1.1	1836 1.7
22 SU	0136 1.0	0725 1.7	1346 1.0	1943 1.8
23 M	0225 0.9	0829 1.8	1433 1.0	2038 1.9
24 TU	0306 0.8	0917 1.9	1515 0.9	2123 2.0
25 W	0344 0.7	0958 2.0	1553 0.8	2202 2.1
26 TH	0421 0.6	1036 2.0	1629 0.7	O 2238 2.2
27 F	0457 0.5	1111 2.1	1705 0.6	2313 2.3
28 SA	0532 0.4	1147 2.1	1740 0.6	2351 2.3
29 SU	0609 0.4	1224 2.2	1817 0.6	
30 M	0030 2.3	0647 0.4	1305 2.1	1857 0.6
31 TU	0113 2.3	0729 0.5	1347 2.1	1941 0.7

Chart Datum: 1·22 metres below Ordnance Datum (Local)

SCOTLAND – LERWICK

LAT 60°09′N   LONG 1°08′W

TIMES AND HEIGHTS OF HIGH AND LOW WATERS

YEAR **1999**

TIME ZONE (UT)
For Summer Time add ONE hour in non-shaded areas

SEPTEMBER

Day	Time	m	Time	m	Time	m	Time	m
1 W	0159	2.2	0814	0.6	1433	2.0	2029	0.8
16 TH	0228	1.9	0825	0.9	1449	1.9	2044	1.0
2 TH	0249	2.1	0904	0.7	1523	1.9	2126	0.9
17 F	0314	1.8	0908	1.0	1536	1.8	2137	1.1
3 F	0346	2.0	1004	0.9	1623	1.9	2239	0.9
18 SA	0414	1.7	1003	1.1	1637	1.7	2319	1.1
4 SA	0500	1.9	1128	1.0	1744	1.8		
19 SU	0531	1.6	1155	1.2	1752	1.7		
5 SU	0025	0.9	0643	1.8	1306	1.0	1918	1.9
20 M	0103	1.1	0652	1.7	1319	1.1	1906	1.7
6 M	0145	0.8	0805	1.9	1410	0.9	2025	2.0
21 TU	0157	0.9	0800	1.7	1409	1.0	2006	1.8
7 TU	0241	0.7	0904	2.0	1459	0.8	2118	2.1
22 W	0238	0.8	0850	1.9	1450	0.9	2053	2.0
8 W	0328	0.5	0952	2.1	1543	0.7	2205	2.2
23 TH	0316	0.7	0931	2.0	1527	0.8	2134	2.1
9 TH ●	0411	0.4	1035	2.1	1623	0.7	2247	2.3
24 F	0353	0.5	1009	2.1	1603	0.7	2212	2.2
10 F	0451	0.4	1115	2.2	1701	0.6	2325	2.3
25 SA O	0429	0.4	1045	2.2	1639	0.6	2250	2.3
11 SA	0528	0.4	1151	2.2	1736	0.6		
26 SU	0505	0.3	1122	2.2	1716	0.5	2330	2.4
12 SU	0001	2.3	0602	0.4	1225	2.1	1810	0.6
27 M	0544	0.3	1200	2.3	1755	0.5		
13 M	0035	2.2	0636	0.5	1258	2.1	1845	0.7
28 TU	0011	2.4	0623	0.4	1241	2.2	1837	0.5
14 TU	0110	2.2	0710	0.6	1332	2.0	1921	0.7
29 W	0056	2.3	0706	0.5	1324	2.2	1922	0.6
15 W	0147	2.0	0746	0.7	1409	1.9	2000	0.9
30 TH	0143	2.2	0752	0.6	1410	2.1	2013	0.7

OCTOBER

Day	Time	m	Time	m	Time	m	Time	m
1 F	0234	2.1	0842	0.8	1500	2.0	2112	0.8
16 SA	0237	1.8	0829	1.0	1444	1.8	2102	1.0
2 SA	0334	1.9	0945	1.0	1601	1.9	2235	0.9
17 SU	0332	1.7	0919	1.1	1535	1.7	2210	1.1
3 SU	0457	1.8	1128	1.1	1729	1.8		
18 M	0452	1.6	1035	1.2	1656	1.7		
4 M	0024	0.9	0649	1.8	1259	1.0	1909	1.9
19 TU	0015	1.0	0615	1.6	1239	1.2	1821	1.7
5 TU	0135	0.7	0801	1.9	1358	1.0	2014	2.0
20 W	0118	0.9	0723	1.7	1335	1.0	1926	1.8
6 W	0227	0.6	0853	2.0	1445	0.9	2104	2.1
21 TH	0204	0.8	0815	1.8	1418	0.9	2018	1.9
7 TH	0312	0.5	0937	2.0	1526	0.8	2148	2.2
22 F	0244	0.6	0859	2.0	1457	0.8	2103	2.1
8 F	0351	0.5	1016	2.1	1604	0.7	2228	2.2
23 SA	0322	0.5	0939	2.1	1534	0.6	2145	2.2
9 SA ●	0427	0.4	1052	2.1	1638	0.6	2303	2.2
24 SU O	0400	0.4	1018	2.2	1613	0.5	2228	2.4
10 SU	0500	0.4	1124	2.1	1712	0.6	2336	2.2
25 M	0439	0.3	1058	2.3	1653	0.4	2311	2.4
11 M	0532	0.5	1154	2.1	1744	0.6		
26 TU	0520	0.3	1138	2.3	1736	0.4	2355	2.4
12 TU	0007	2.2	0603	0.6	1224	2.1	1818	0.6
27 W	0602	0.4	1220	2.3	1821	0.4		
13 W	0041	2.1	0636	0.7	1256	2.1	1854	0.7
28 TH	0041	2.4	0646	0.5	1305	2.2	1909	0.5
14 TH	0116	2.0	0711	0.8	1331	2.0	1932	0.8
29 F	0131	2.2	0733	0.7	1351	2.2	2002	0.6
15 F	0154	1.9	0748	0.9	1406	1.9	2013	0.9
30 SA	0225	2.2	0825	0.9	1443	2.0	2105	0.7
31 SU	0328	1.9	0931	1.0	1545	1.9	2233	0.8

NOVEMBER

Day	Time	m	Time	m	Time	m	Time	m
1 M	0453	1.8	1114	1.1	1711	1.9		
16 TU	0407	1.7	0947	1.2	1557	1.8	2251	1.0
2 TU	0007	0.8	0635	1.8	1238	1.1	1847	1.9
17 W	0527	1.7	1114	1.2	1721	1.8		
3 W	0113	0.7	0742	1.8	1336	1.0	1952	2.0
18 TH	0022	0.9	0637	1.7	1244	1.1	1838	1.8
4 TH	0205	0.7	0832	1.9	1424	0.9	2042	2.0
19 F	0120	0.8	0735	1.9	1337	1.0	1939	2.0
5 F	0249	0.6	0914	2.0	1505	0.8	2126	2.1
20 SA	0207	0.7	0824	2.0	1423	0.8	2032	2.1
6 SA	0327	0.6	0952	2.1	1543	0.7	2205	2.1
21 SU	0250	0.6	0909	2.1	1506	0.7	2121	2.3
7 SU	0401	0.6	1026	2.1	1617	0.7	2240	2.1
22 M	0332	0.5	0953	2.3	1550	0.6	2208	2.4
8 M ●	0433	0.6	1056	2.1	1650	0.6	2312	2.2
23 TU O	0415	0.5	1036	2.4	1635	0.5	2255	2.4
9 TU	0503	0.6	1124	2.2	1723	0.6	2343	2.1
24 W	0459	0.5	1120	2.4	1721	0.5	2343	2.4
10 W	0535	0.7	1154	2.2	1757	0.7		
25 TH	0544	0.5	1204	2.4	1810	0.4		
11 TH	0016	2.1	0609	0.7	1227	2.1	1833	0.7
26 F	0031	2.4	0630	0.6	1250	2.4	1859	0.5
12 F	0052	2.0	0644	0.8	1300	2.1	1910	0.8
27 SA	0123	2.3	0718	0.8	1338	2.3	1954	0.6
13 SA	0130	1.9	0720	0.9	1334	2.0	1951	0.9
28 SU	0216	2.1	0811	0.9	1429	2.2	2056	0.9
14 SU	0211	1.8	0800	1.0	1411	1.9	2037	0.9
29 M	0316	2.0	0913	1.1	1527	2.1	2213	0.9
15 M	0301	1.7	0847	1.1	1456	1.8	2133	1.0
30 TU	0428	1.8	1040	1.1	1639	2.0	2335	0.8

DECEMBER

Day	Time	m	Time	m	Time	m	Time	m
1 W	0555	1.8	1203	1.1	1806	1.9		
16 TH	0432	1.8	1015	1.2	1628	1.9	2308	0.9
2 TH	0041	0.8	0707	1.8	1306	1.1	1918	1.9
17 F	0543	1.8	1129	1.2	1744	2.0		
3 F	0136	0.8	0801	1.9	1358	1.0	2014	2.0
18 SA	0023	0.9	0650	1.9	1247	1.1	1859	2.1
4 SA	0221	0.8	0845	2.0	1442	0.9	2100	2.0
19 SU	0128	0.8	0749	2.0	1350	1.0	2003	2.2
5 SU	0301	0.8	0924	2.1	1522	0.9	2141	2.1
20 M	0221	0.8	0842	2.2	1443	0.8	2100	2.3
6 M	0336	0.8	0958	2.1	1558	0.8	2217	2.1
21 TU	0310	0.7	0931	2.3	1534	0.7	2153	2.4
7 TU ●	0408	0.8	1029	2.2	1632	0.8	2251	2.1
22 W O	0358	0.7	1018	2.4	1623	0.6	2244	2.5
8 W	0441	0.8	1059	2.2	1707	0.8	2323	2.1
23 TH	0444	0.7	1104	2.5	1711	0.5	2333	2.5
9 TH	0515	0.8	1131	2.2	1742	0.8	2358	2.1
24 F	0531	0.7	1150	2.5	1801	0.5		
10 F	0549	0.9	1204	2.2	1819	0.8		
25 SA	0022	2.4	0617	0.8	1237	2.5	1850	0.5
11 SA	0034	2.1	0624	0.9	1238	2.2	1855	0.8
26 SU	0112	2.3	0704	0.8	1324	2.5	1942	0.6
12 SU	0112	2.0	0700	1.0	1312	2.1	1933	0.8
27 M	0202	2.2	0753	1.0	1412	2.3	2037	0.7
13 M	0152	2.0	0738	1.0	1350	2.1	2016	0.9
28 TU	0254	2.1	0846	1.1	1503	2.2	2138	0.8
14 TU	0237	1.9	0822	1.1	1433	2.0	2104	0.9
29 W	0350	2.0	0950	1.2	1601	2.1	2249	0.9
15 W	0329	1.8	0914	1.2	1525	2.0	2200	0.9
30 TH	0453	1.9	1113	1.2	1708	2.0	2359	1.0
31 F	0604	1.9	1228	1.2	1826	2.0		

Chart Datum: 1·22 metres below Ordnance Datum (Local)

7

SHETLAND ISLANDS   8-7-25

The Shetland Islands consist of approx 100 islands, holms and rks of which fewer than 20 are inhabited. They lie 90 to 150M NNE of the Scottish mainland. By far the biggest island is Mainland with Lerwick (8.7.26), the capital, on the E side and Scalloway (overleaf), the only other town and old capital, on the W side. At the very S is Sumburgh airport and there are airstrips at Baltasound, Scalsta and Tingwall. Two islands of the Shetland group not shown on the chartlet are Fair Isle (see overleaf), 20M SSW of Sumburgh Hd and owned by the NT for Scotland, and Foula (see below) 12M WSW of Mainland.
  There are LBs at Lerwick and Aith. The CG MRSC is at Lerwick ☎ (01595) 692976, with a Sector Base at Sella Ness (Sullom Voe) and an Auxiliary Station (Watch & Rescue) at Fair Isle.

CHARTS
AC: Med scale 3281, 3282, 3283; larger scale 3290, 3291, 3292, 3293, 3294, 3295, 3297, 3298; OS sheets 1-4.

TIDES
Lerwick is the Standard Port. Tidal streams run mostly N/ S or NW/SE and in open waters to the E and W are mostly weak. But rates >6kn can cause dangerous disturbances at the N and S extremities of the islands and in the two main sounds (Yell Sound and BlueMull/ Colgrave Sounds). Keep 3M off Sumburgh Head to clear a dangerous race (roost) or pass close inshore.

SHELTER
Weather conditions are bad in winter; yachts should only visit Apr – Sept. Around mid-summer it is day light H24. Some 12 small, non-commercial "marinas" are asterisked below; they are mostly full of local boats but supposedly each reserves 1 berth for visitors. Often only 1 boat lies between 2 fingers so that she can be held off by warps all round. Of the many ‡s, the following are safe to enter in most weathers:
Mainland (anti-clockwise from Sumburgh Head)
GRUTNESS VOE*: 1·5M N of Sumburgh Hd, a convenient passage ‡, open to NE. Beware 2 rks awash in mid-ent.
CAT FIRTH: excellent shelter, ‡ in approx 6m. Facilities: ✉ (Skellister), FW, V (both at Lax Firth).
GRUNNA VOE: off S side of Dury Voe, good shelter and holding, ‡ in 5-10m; beware prohib ‡ areas. Facilities: V, FW, ✉ (Lax Firth).
WHALSAY*: FV hbr at Symbister. FW, D, V, ✉.
OUT SKERRIES*: Quay and ‡ at Bruray. FW, D, V, ✉.
S OF YELL SOUND*: Tides –0025 on Lerwick. W of Lunna Ness, well-protected ‡s with good holding include: Boatsroom Voe, W Lunna Voe (small hotel, FW), Colla Firth* (excellent pier) and Dales Voe. Facilities: none.
SULLOM VOE: tides –0130 on Lerwick. 6·5M long deep water voe, partly taken over by the oil industry. ‡ S of the narrows. Facilities at Brae: FW, V, ✉, D, ME, El, Sh, Bar.
HAMNA VOE: Tides –0200 on Lerwick; very good shelter. Ldg line 153° old house on S shore with prominent rk on pt of W shore 3ca within ent. Almost land-locked; ‡ in 6m approx, but bottom foul with old moorings. Facilities: ✉ (0·5M), Vs, D (1·5M), L (at pier).
URA FIRTH: NE of St Magnus Bay, ‡ off Hills Wick on W side or in Hamar Voe on E side, which has excellent shelter in all weathers and good holding, but no facilities. Facilities: Hills Wick FW, ✉, D, ME, El, Sh, V, R, Bar.
OLNA FIRTH: NE of Swarbacks Minn, beware rk 1ca off S shore which dries. ‡ in firth, 4-8m or in Gon Firth or go alongside pier at Voe. Facilities: (Voe) FW, V, D, ✉, Bar.
SWARBACKS MINN*: a large complex of voes and isles SE of St Magnus Bay. Best ‡ Uyea Sound or Aith Voe*, both well sheltered and good holding. Facilities: former none; Aith FW, ✉, V, Bar, LB.
VAILA SOUND: on SW of Mainland, ent via Easter Sound (do not attempt Wester Sound); very good shelter, ‡ N of Salt Ness in 4-5m in mud. See WALLS* overleaf: FW, V, ✉.
GRUTING VOE*: HW –0150 on Lerwick, ‡ in main voe or in Seli, Scutta or Browland* voes. Facilities: V and ✉ at Bridge of Walls (hd of Browland Voe).
Yell. MID YELL VOE: tides –0040 on Lerwick, enter through S Sd or Hascosay Sd, good ‡ in wide part of voe 2·5-10m. Facilities: ✉, FW at pier on S side, D, V, ME, Sh, El.
BASTA VOE: good ‡ above shingle bank in 5-15m; good holding in places. Facilities: FW, V, Hotel, ✉.
BLUE MULL SND*: ‡ at Cullivoe, pier and slip. D, FW, V.
Foula: Ham Voe on E side has tiny hbr/pier, unsafe in E'ly; berth clear of mailboat. Avoid Hoevdi Grund, 2M ESE.

NAVIGATION
A careful lookout must be kept for salmon farming cages, mostly marked by Y buoys and combinations of Y lts. The Clyde Cruising Club's *Shetland Sailing Directions and Anchorages* are essential for visitors. For general passage information see 8.7.5. Weather forecasting and the avoidance of wind-over-tide conditions assume yet more significance than elsewhere in the UK. Local magnetic anomalies may be experienced.
Note: There are two Historic Wrecks (*Kennemerland* and *Wrangels Palais*) on Out Skerries at 60°25'·2N 00°45'·0W and 60°25'·5N 00°43'·27W (see 8.0.3h).

LIGHTS AND MARKS
See 8.7.4. Powerful lights show offshore from Fair Isle, Sumburgh Head, Kirkabister Ness, Bound Skerry, Muckle Flugga, Pt of Fethaland, Esha Ness and Foula.

RADIO TELEPHONE
For Port Radio services see 8.7.26. There is no Coast Radio Station.

TELEPHONE (Dial code 01595; 01806 for Sullom Voe) MRSC 692976; Sullom Voe Port Control (01806) 242551; Weather 692239; Forecaster (01806) 242069; Sumburgh Airport (01950) 460654.

FACILITIES
See SHELTER. All stores can be obtained in Lerwick and to a lesser extent in Scalloway. Elsewhere in Shetland there is little available and yachts should be stored for extended offshore cruising.

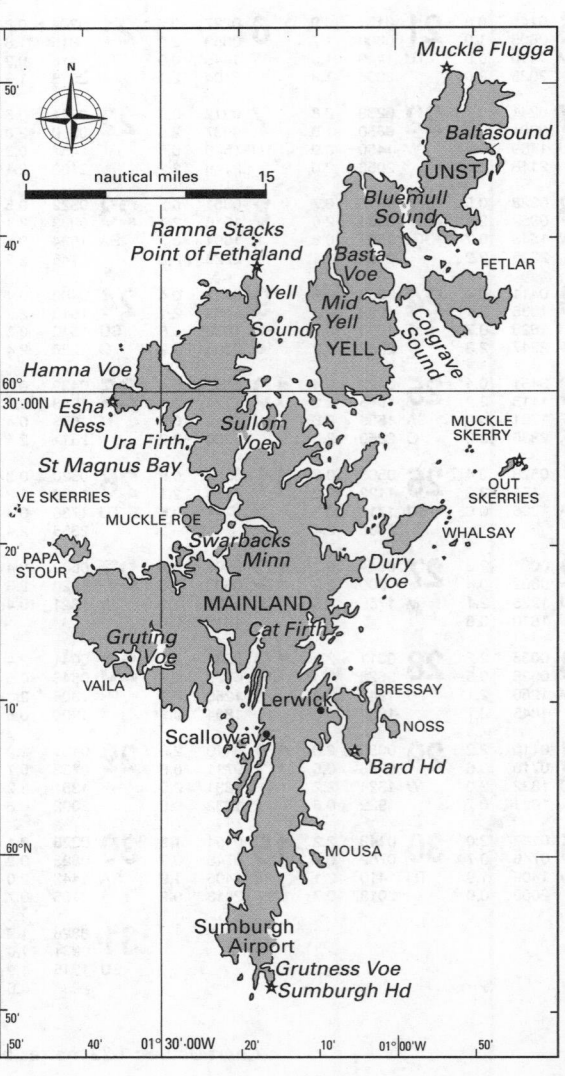

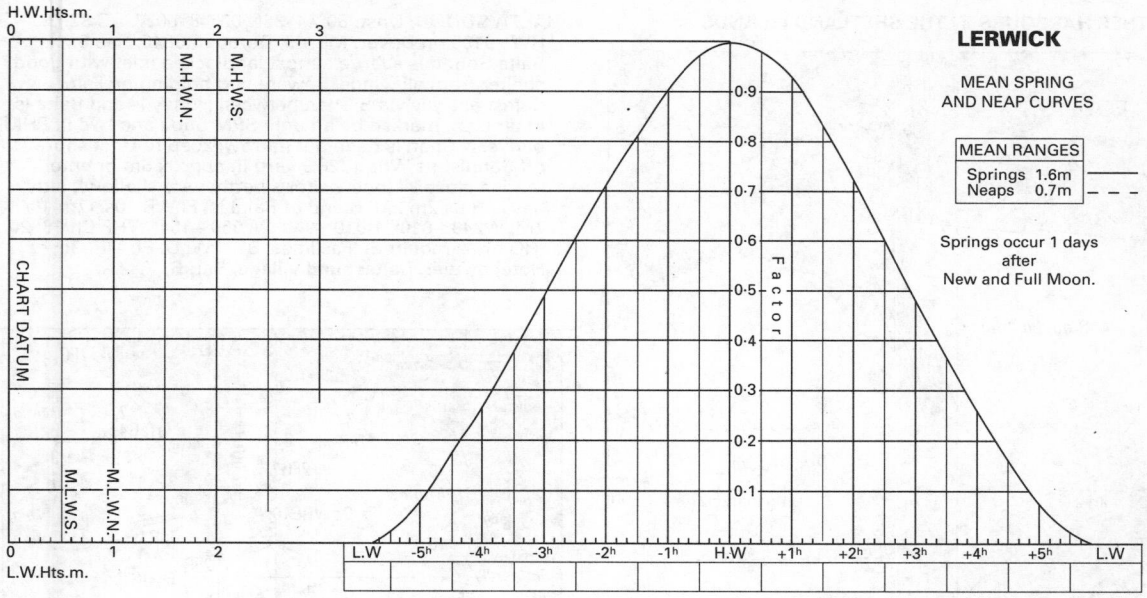

LERWICK

MEAN SPRING
AND NEAP CURVES

MEAN RANGES
Springs 1.6m ——
Neaps 0.7m - - -

Springs occur 1 days
after
New and Full Moon.

7

LERWICK
8-7-26

Shetland Is, Mainland 60°09'·29N 01°08'·30W Rtg 1-3-2

CHARTS
AC 3290, 3291, 3283; OS 4
TIDES
−0001 Dover; ML 1·4; Duration 0620; Zone 0 (UT)

Standard Port LERWICK (←—)

Times				Height (metres)			
High Water		Low Water		MHWS	MHWN	MLWN	MLWS
0000	0600	0100	0800	2·2	1·7	1·0	0·6
1200	1800	1300	2000				
Differences FAIR ISLE							
−0006	−0015	−0031	−0037	0·0	0·0	0·0	0·0
SUMBURGH (Grutness Voe)							
+0006	+0008	+0004	−0002	−0·4	−0·3	−0·3	−0·2
DURY VOE							
−0015	−0015	−0010	−0010	−0·1	−0·1	−0·1	−0·3
BURRA VOE (YELL SOUND)							
−0025	−0025	−0025	−0025	+0·2	+0·2	0·0	0·0
BALTA SOUND							
−0055	−0055	−0045	−0045	+0·1	+0·2	−0·1	−0·1
BLUE MULL SOUND							
−0135	−0135	−0155	−0155	+0·4	+0·2	−0·1	−0·1
SULLOM VOE							
−0135	−0125	−0135	−0120	0·0	0·0	−0·2	−0·2
HILLSWICK (URA FIRTH)							
−0220	−0220	−0200	−0200	0·0	−0·4	−0·4	−0·1
SCALLOWAY							
−0150	−0150	−0150	−0150	−0·6	−0·3	−0·3	0·0
FOULA (23M West of Scalloway)							
−0140	−0130	−0140	−0120	−0·2	−0·1	−0·1	−0·1

Lerwick is a Standard Port and tidal predictions for each day
of the year are given below.

SHELTER
Good. Hr Mr allocates berths in Small Dock or Albert
Dock. FVs occupy most alongside space. ⚓ prohib for
about 2ca off the waterfront. Gremista marina in N hbr, is
mainly for local boats, and is about 1M from the town.
NAVIGATION
WPT 60°06'·00N 01°08'·50W, 190°/010° from/to Maryfield
lt, 3·5M, in W sector. From S, Bressay Sound is clear of
dangers. From N, WPT 60°11'·60N 01°07'·88W, 035°/215°
from/to N ent Dir lt, 1·34M; lt Oc WRG 6s, W sector 214°-
216°. Beware Soldian Rk (dries), Nive Baa (0·6m), Green
Holm (10m) and The Brethren (two rks 2m and 1·5m).

LIGHTS AND MARKS
Kirkabister Ness, Fl (2) 20s 32m 23M; Cro of Ham, Fl 3s
3M; Maryfield, Oc WRG 6s, W 008°-013°; all on Bressay.
Twageos Pt, L Fl 6s 8m 6M. Loofa Baa SCM lt bn, as on
chartlet. 2 SHM lt buoys mark Middle Ground in N Hbr.
RADIO TELEPHONE
Lerwick Harbour VHF Ch **12** 11 16 (H24) for VTS, radar
and information.
Other stns: *Sullom Voe Hbr Radio* broadcasts traffic info
and local forecasts on request Ch **14** 12 20 16 (H24).
TELEPHONE (Dial code 01595)
Hr Mr 692991; MRSC 692976; ⌗ 696166; Weather 692239;
Police 692110; Dr 693201.
FACILITIES
Hbr Slip, M, P, D, L, FW, ME, Sh, Gas; **Lerwick Hbr Trust**
☎ 692991, AB £17 for 5 days (£1.70/metre), M, FW, D, P;
Lerwick Boating Club ☎ 692407, L, C, Bar, Ⓠ;
Services: ME, El, Ⓔ, Sh, Slip, BY, CH, SM, Gas, ACA.
Town EC Wed (all day); V, R, Bar, ✉, Ⓑ, ⇌, (ferry to
Aberdeen), ✈.

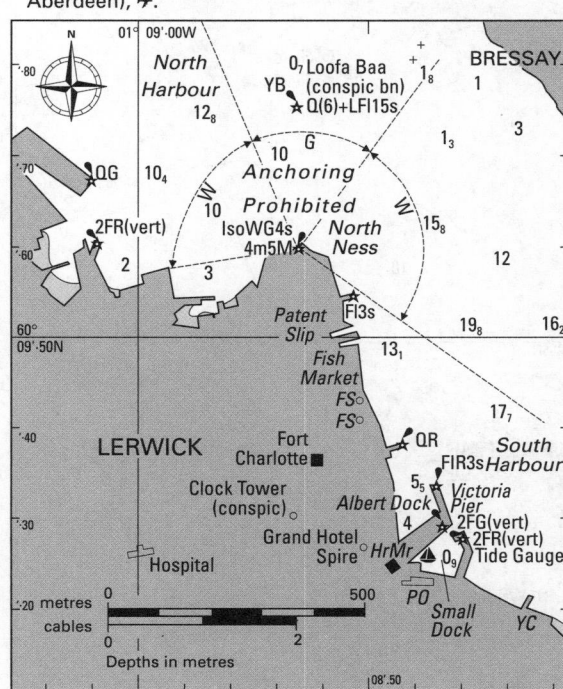

OTHER HARBOURS IN THE SHETLAND ISLANDS

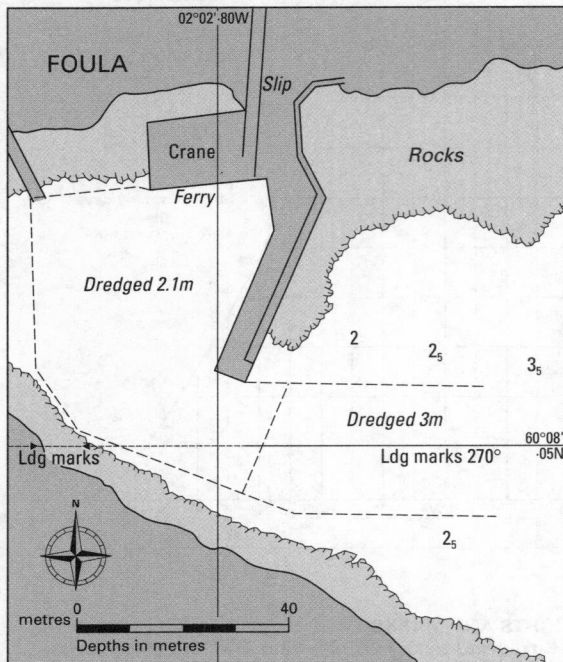

FOULA, Shetland Islands, 60°08'·05N 02°02'·80W (Ham Voe). AC 3283. HW −0150 on Dover; ML 1·3m. See 8.7.26. Foula is 12M WSW of Mainland. Highest ground is 416m. S Ness lt ho, Fl (3) 15s, is at the S tip. Beware Foula Shoal (7·6m) and Hœvdi Grund (1·4m), respectively 4·3M E and 2M SE of Ham Voe. Ham Voe is a narrow inlet on the E coast with a quay; rks on both sides. Two R ▲ ldg marks, approx 270°, are hard to see. Berthing or landing is only possible in settled weather with no swell. Take advice from mail boat skipper out of Walls and call Foula ✉, ☎ (01595) 753222 for prior approval. Small ✈. No facilities.

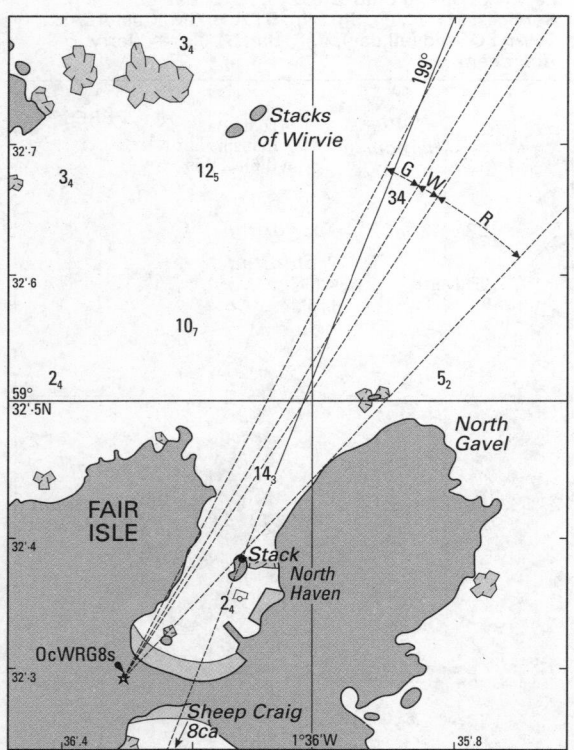

BALTA SOUND, Unst, 60°44'·35N 00°48'·00W. AC 3293. HW −0105 on Dover; ML 1·3; Duration 0640. See 8.7.26. Balta Sound is a large almost landlocked inlet with good shelter from all winds. Beware bad holding on kelp. Safest entry is via S Chan between Huney Is and Balta Is; inner chan marked by an unlit SPM buoy and two lit PHM buoys. N Chan is deep but narrow; keep to Unst shore. ⚓ off Sandisons Wharf (2FG vert) in approx 6m or enter marina close W (one visitor's berth, very shallow); jetty has Fl R 6s 2m 2M. S end of Balta Is, Fl WR 10s 17m 10/7M, W249°−010°, R010°−060°, W060°−154°. VHF Ch 16; 20 (HO or as required). Facilities: BY, FW, D, El, ME, Sh; Hotel by pier. **Baltasound village**, Bar, R, V, ✉.

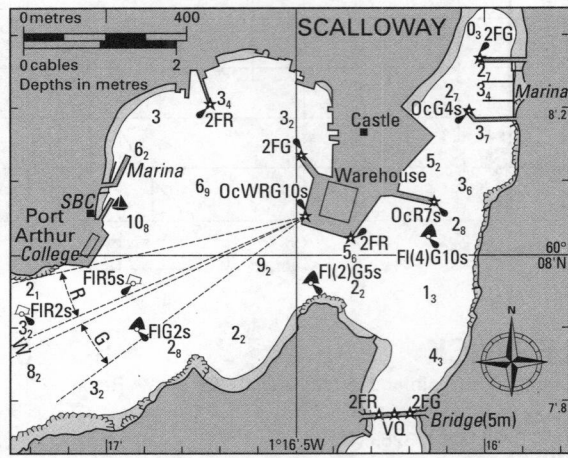

SCALLOWAY, Mainland, 60°08'·05N 01°16'·47W. AC 3294. HW −0200 on Dover; ML 0·9m; Duration 0620. See 8.7.26. A busy fishing port; good shelter and ⚓ in all weathers. Care is needed negotiating the islands in strong SW'lies. The N Chan is easier and safer than the S Chan, both are well lit and marked. Castle and warehouse (both conspic) lead 054° through S Chan. Dir Oc WRG 10s on hbr quay leads 064·5° into hbr. Hbr lts as chartlet. Ⓥ pontoon in 3m off SBC is best option; marina close N or new marina in E Voe. ⚓s in hbr 6 -10m or in Hamna Voe (W Burra). Call *Scalloway Hbr Radio* VHF Ch **12** 09 16 (Mon-Fri 0600-1800; Sat 0600-1230LT). Hr Mr/Port Control ☎ (01595) 880574 (H24). Facilities: **Scalloway Boat Club** (SBC) ☎ 880409 welcomes visitors; AB (free), Bar. **Town** EC Thurs; Slip, P, D, FW, SM, BY, CH, C, El, ME, Sh, ✉, R, V, Bar.

VAILA SOUND (WALLS), Mainland, 60°13'·68N 01°33'·75W. AC 3295. Tides approx as Scalloway (above); see 8.7.26. Appr to E of Vaila island (do not attempt Wester Sound) in the W sector (355°-012°) of Rams Head lt, Fl WRG 8s 16m 9/6M. Gruting Voe lies to the NE. Enter Easter Sound and go N for 1·5M, passing E of Linga islet, to Walls at the head of Vaila Voe. Navigate by echo sounder. Beware fish farms. Temp'y AB on Bayhaa pier (covers). Close E of this, AB £1 on pontoon of Peter Georgeson **marina**; Sec ☎ (01595) 809273, FW. **Walls Regatta Club** welcomes visitors; showers, Bar, Slip. **Village**: P & D (cans), V, ✉.

FAIR ISLE, Shetland Islands, 59°32'·40N 01°36'·10W (North Haven). AC 2622. HW −0030 on Dover; ML 1·4m; Duration 0620. See 8.7.26 Good shelter in North Haven, except in NE winds. AB on pier or ⚓ in approx 2m. Beware strong cross-tides in the apprs; beware also rocks all round Fair Isle, particularly in S Haven and South Hbr which are not recommended.
Ldg marks 199° into North Haven: front, Stack of N Haven (only visible as a dark "tooth" sticking up from the jumble of blocks which form the bkwtr) in transit with conspic summit of Sheep Craig (rear). Dir lt, 209·5° into N Haven, Oc WRG 8s 10m 6M, vis G204°-208°, W208°- 211°, R211°-221°. Other lts: At N tip, Skroo Fl (2) 30s 80m **22M**, vis 086·7°−358°, Horn (3) 45s. At S tip, Skadan Fl (4) 30s 32m **22M**, vis 260°−110°, but obscd close inshore from 260°−282°, Horn (2) 60s. **Facilities:** V, ✉ at N Shriva, ✈ and a bi-weekly mail boat ("Good Shepherd") to Shetland.

Area 8

North-West Scotland
Cape Wrath to Crinan Canal

8

8.8.1	Index	**Page 415**
8.8.2	Diagram of ports, lights, RDF bns, Coast radio and weather stns	**416**
8.8.3	Tidal stream charts	**418**
8.8.4	List of coastal lights, fog signals and waypoints	**420**
8.8.5	Passage information	**423**
8.8.6	Distance table	**424**
8.8.7	Stornoway, Standard Port, tidal curves	**425**
	Loch Shell (Lewis)	
	Shiant Islands	
	E Loch Tarbert (Harris)	
	Loch Maddy (N Uist)	
	Loch Skipport (S Uist)	
	Loch Boisdale (S Uist)	
	Castlebay (Barra)	
	St Kilda	
8.8.8	Kinlochbervie	**431**
	Loch Laxford	
	Loch Inver	
8.8.9	Ullapool, Standard Port, tidal curves	**432**
	Summer Isles	
	Loch Ewe	
	Loch Gairloch	
8.8.10	Portree	**436**
	Loch Torridon	
	Loch A'Bhraige (Rona)	
	Around Skye:	
	Loch Dunvegan	
	Loch Harport	
	Soay	
	Crowlin Islands	
8.8.11	Plockton	**437**
	Loch Carron	
8.8.12	Loch Alsh	**437**
	Kyle of Lochalsh	
	Kyleakin	
8.8.13	Mallaig	**438**
	Sound of Sleat	
	Loch Hourn	
	Loch Nevis	
	Armadale Bay (Skye)	
	Small Islands: Canna, Rhum, Eigg and Muck	
	Arisaig	
8.8.14	Loch Sunart	**439**
	Arinagour (Coll)	
	Gott Bay (Tiree)	
8.8.15	Tobermory	**440**
	Sound of Mull	
8.8.16	Loch Aline	**440**
	Around Mull: Treshnish Isles	
	Staffa, Gometra	
	Loch na Keal	
	Loch Lathaich	
	Sound of Iona, Tinker's Hole	
	Carsaig Bay	
	Loch Spelve	
8.8.17	Fort William/Corpach	**441**
	Lynn of Lorn	
	Loch Creran	
	Loch Leven	
	Corran Narrows	
8.8.18	Caledonian Canal	**442**
8.8.19	Oban, Standard Port, tidal curves	**446**
	Dunstaffnage Bay	
	Loch Etive	
	Loch Feochan	
	Puilladobhrain	
	Cuan Sound	
8.8.20	Loch Melfort	**448**
	Ardinamar	
8.8.21	Craobh Marina (Loch Shuna)	**449**
8.8.22	Loch Craignish	**449**
8.8.23	Submarine exercise areas	**450**
8.8.24	Ferries on the West coast	**450**

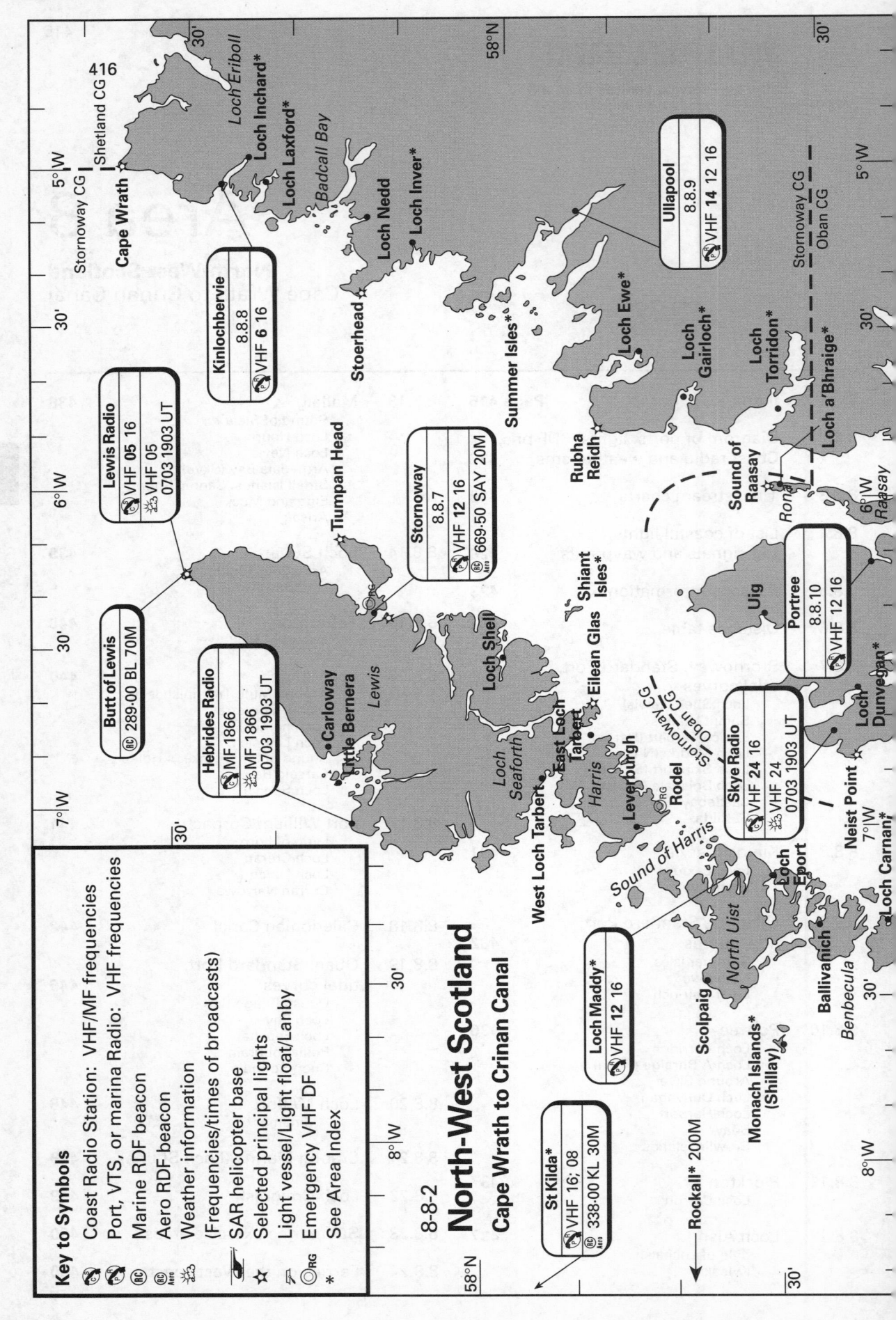

416

Loch Eriboll

Loch Inchard*

Loch Laxford*

Badcall Bay

Stornoway CG   Cape Wrath

5°W

Loch Nedd

Loch Inver*

Stoerhead

Kinlochbervie
8.8.8
VHF 6 16

30'

Loch Ewe*

Loch Gairloch*

Loch Torridon*

Loch a'Bhraige*

Ullapool
8.8.9
VHF 14 12 16

Summer Isles*

Rubha Reidh

Lewis Radio
VHF 05 16
VHF 05
0703 1903 UT

6°W

Tiumpan Head

Stornoway
8.8.7
VHF 12 16
669·50 SAY 20M

Stornoway CG   Oban CG

5°W

Sound of Raasay

Rona

6°W   Raasay

Butt of Lewis
289·00 BL 70M

30'

Carloway
Little Bernera

Hebrides Radio
MF 1866
MF 1866
0703 1903 UT

Lewis

Loch Seaforth

Loch Shell

East Loch Tarbert

Shiant Isles*

Eilean Glas

Harris

Leverburgh

Rodel

Stornoway CG
Oban CG

Uig

Portree
8.8.10
VHF 12 16

7°W

West Loch Tarbert

Sound of Harris

Skye Radio
VHF 24 16
VHF 24
0703 1903 UT

Loch Dunvegan*

Neist Point

Loch Eport

7°W   Loch Carnan*

30'

Loch Maddy*
VHF 12 16

Scolpaig

North Uist

Ballivanich

Benbecula

30'

8°W

Monach Islands*
(Shillay)

Rockall* 200M

St Kilda*
VHF 16; 08
338·00 KL 30M

58°N

8°W

30'

30'

58°N

5°W

30'

30'

Key to Symbols

Coast Radio Station: VHF/MF frequencies

Port, VTS, or marina Radio: VHF frequencies

Marine RDF beacon

Aero RDF beacon

Weather information
(Frequencies/times of broadcasts)

SAR helicopter base

Selected principal lights

Light vessel/Light float/Lanby

Emergency VHF DF

See Area Index

8-8-2   **North-West Scotland**

Cape Wrath to Crinan Canal

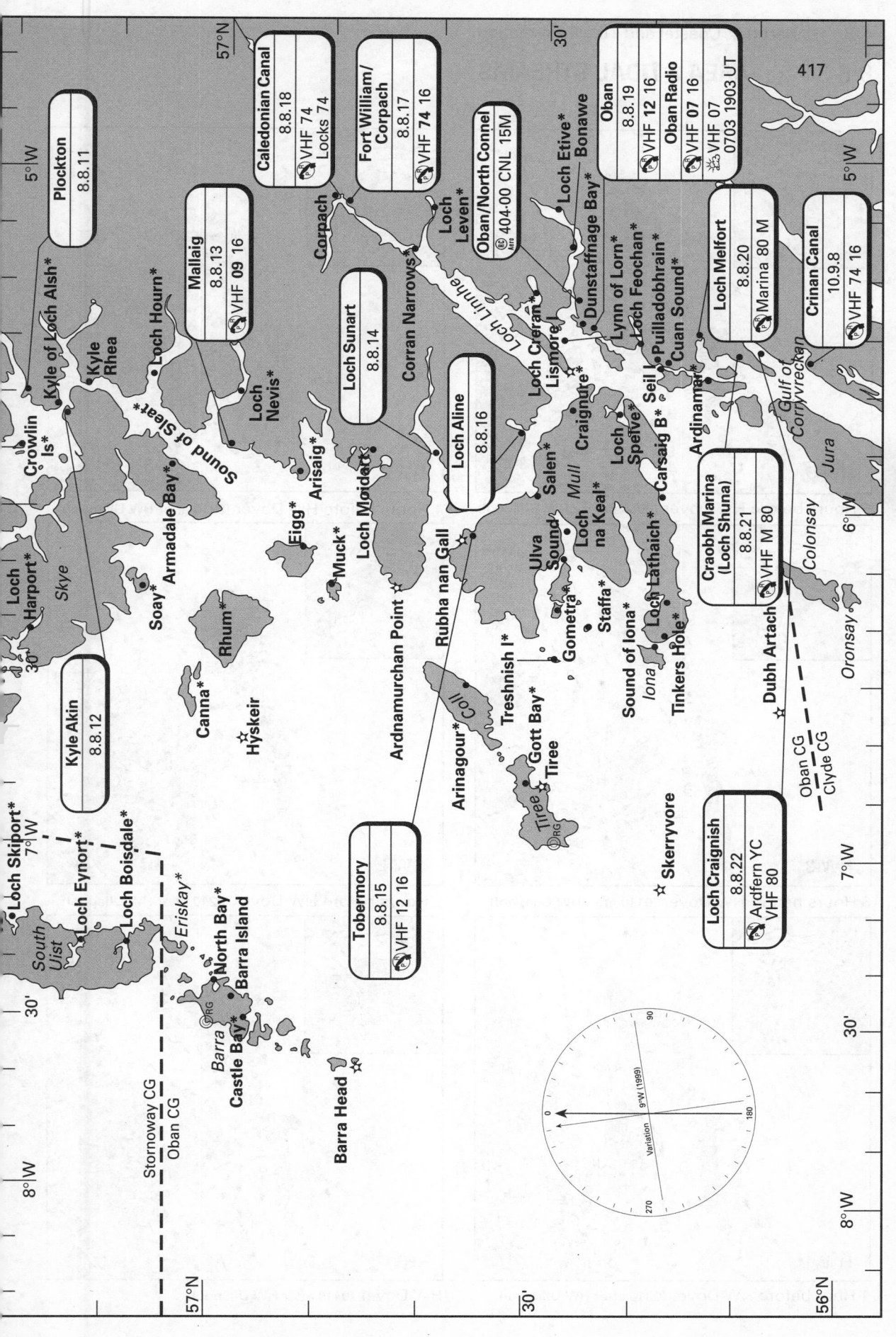

8

Plockton
8.8.11

Kyle of Loch Alsh*
Crowlin Is*
Kyle Rhea
Loch Hourn*
Loch Nevis*
Sound of Sleat*
Skye
Loch Harport*
Soay*
Armadale Bay*
Arisaig*
Eigg*
Muck*
Loch Moidart
Rhum*
Canna*
Hyskeir

Caledonian Canal
8.8.18
VHF 74
Locks 74

Fort William/
Corpach
8.8.17
VHF 74 16

Corpach
Loch Leven*

Oban/North Connel
404·00 CNL 15M

Loch Etive*
Bonawe

Oban
8.8.19
VHF 12 16

Oban Radio
VHF 07 16
0703 1903 UT

Dunstaffnage Bay*
Lynn of Lorn*
Loch Feochan*
Pulладobhrain*
Seil
Cuan Sound*
Loch Creran*
Lismore*
Craignure*

Loch Melfort
8.8.20
Marina 80 M

Crinan Canal
10.9.8
VHF 74 16

Ardinamar

Gulf of Corryvreckan

Jura

Colonsay

Mallaig
8.8.13
VHF 09 16

Loch Sunart
8.8.14

Corran Narrows*
Loch Linnhe

Loch Aline
8.8.16

Salen
Mull
Craobh Marina
(Loch Shuna)
8.8.21
VHF M 80

Dubh Artach

Oban CG
Clyde CG

Rubha nan Gall
Ardnamurchan Point

Treshnish I*
Coll
Arinagour*
Gott Bay*
Tiree
Tiree
RG

Ulva Sound
Gometra*
Staffa*
Sound of Iona
Iona
Tinkers Hole
Loch na Keal*
Loch Spelve*
Loch Lathaich*
Carsaig B*

Kyle Akin
8.8.12

Loch Skiport*
Loch Eynort*
Loch Boisdale*
South Uist
Eriskay*

Stornoway CG
Oban CG

Barra
North Bay*
Castle Bay*
Barra Island
Barra Head

Tobermory
8.8.15
VHF 12 16

Skerryvore

Loch Craignish
8.8.22
Ardfern YC
VHF 80

Oronsay

Variation
9°W (1999)

8-8-3   AREA 8 TIDAL STREAMS

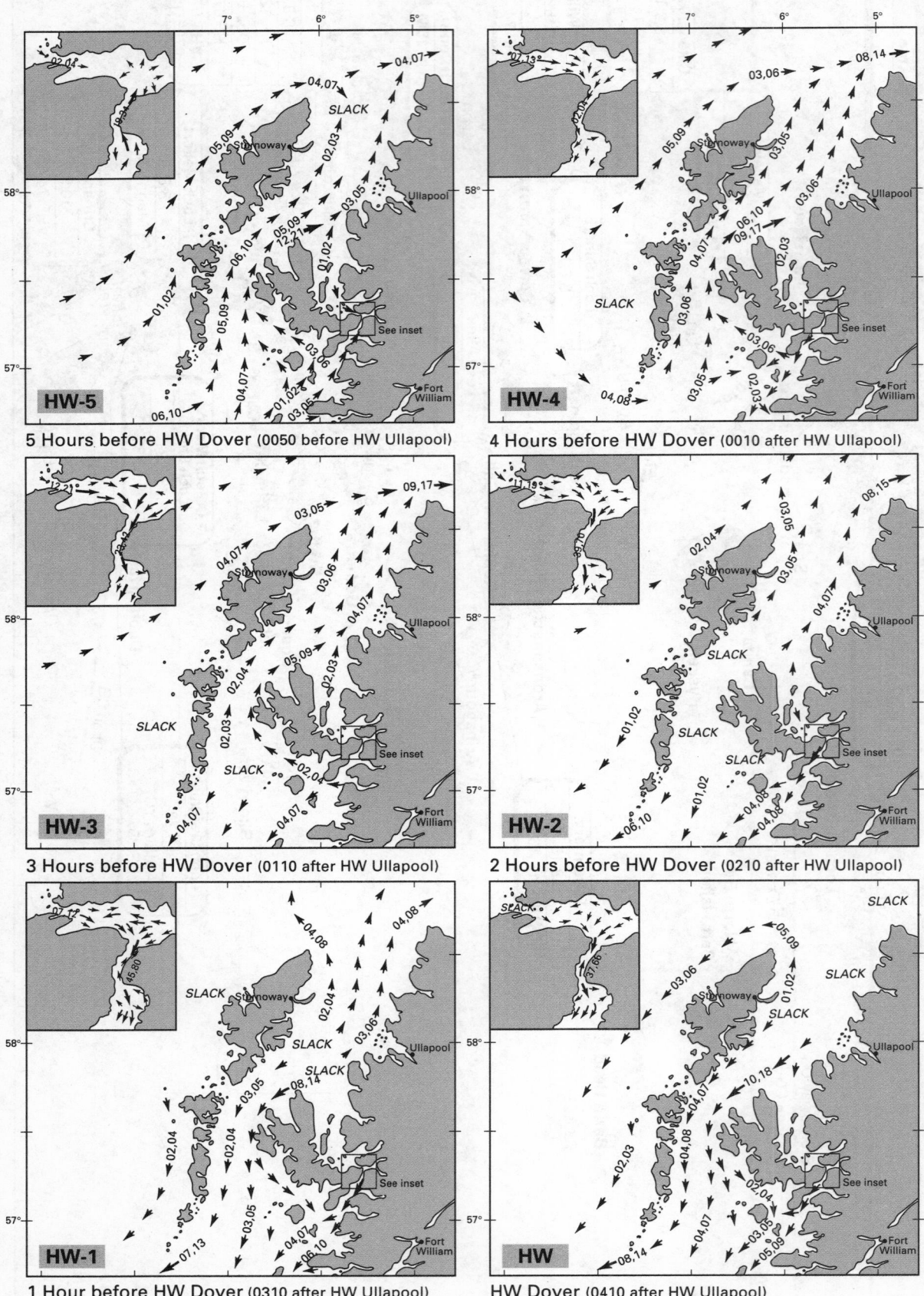

HW-5 — 5 Hours before HW Dover (0050 before HW Ullapool)

HW-4 — 4 Hours before HW Dover (0010 after HW Ullapool)

HW-3 — 3 Hours before HW Dover (0110 after HW Ullapool)

HW-2 — 2 Hours before HW Dover (0210 after HW Ullapool)

HW-1 — 1 Hour before HW Dover (0310 after HW Ullapool)

HW — HW Dover (0410 after HW Ullapool)

Eastward 8.7.3   Southward 8.9.3   Mull of Kintyre 8.9.12

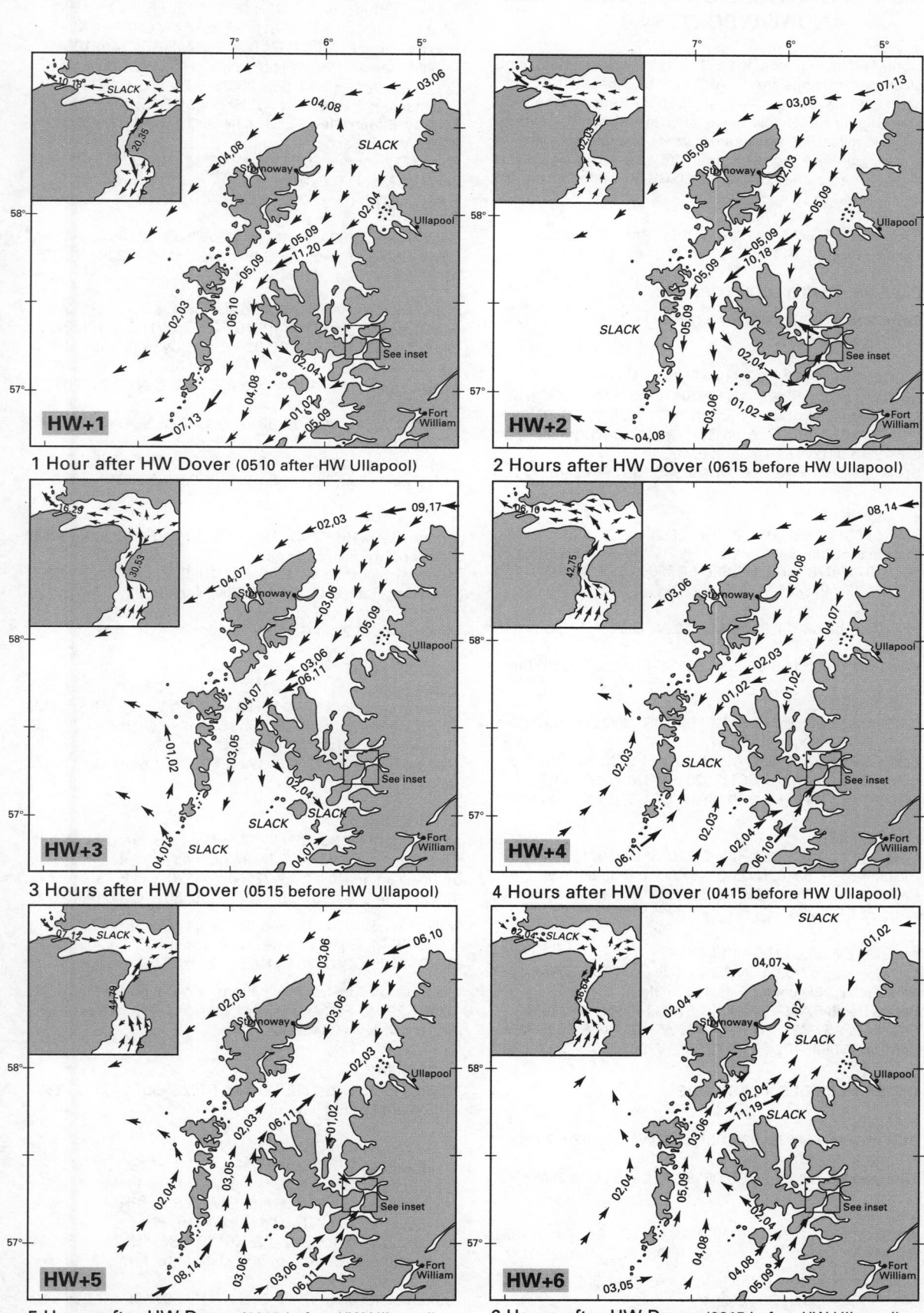

8

1 Hour after HW Dover (0510 after HW Ullapool)

2 Hours after HW Dover (0615 before HW Ullapool)

3 Hours after HW Dover (0515 before HW Ullapool)

4 Hours after HW Dover (0415 before HW Ullapool)

5 Hours after HW Dover (0315 before HW Ullapool)

6 Hours after HW Dover (0215 before HW Ullapool)

8.8.4 COASTAL LIGHTS, FOG SIGNALS AND WAYPOINTS

Lights with a nominal range of 15M or more are in **bold** print, places and features are in CAPITALS, and light-vessels, light floats and Lanbys in *CAPITAL ITALICS*. Unless otherwise stated lights are white. m – elevation in metres; M – nominal range in miles. Fog signals are in *italics*. Useful waypoints are underlined – use those on land with care. All geographical positions are referenced to the OSGB 36 datum but should be assumed to be approximate.

Rockall 57°35'·8N 13°41'·3W Fl 15s 19m 13M (unreliable). Extinguished (T) 1997.

CAPE WRATH TO LOCH TORRIDON

Cape Wrath 58°37'·55N 04°59'·87W Fl (4) 30s 122m **17M**; W tr; *Horn (3) 45s.*

• LOCH INCHARD/LOCH LAXFORD
Rubha na Lecaig 58°27'·43N 05°04'·51W Fl (2) 10s 30m 8M. Kinlochbervie ldg lts 327°: Front, 58°27'·52N 05°03'·01W Oc G 8s 16m 9M W □, Or △ on Gy tr; rear, 330m from front, Oc G 8s 26m 9M; W □, Or ▽ on Gy tr.
Stoer hd 58°14'·43N 05°24'·08W Fl 15s 59m **24M**; W tr.

• LOCH INVER
Soyea I 58°08'·58N 05°19'·59W Fl (2) 10s 34m 6M; Y post. Glas Leac 58°08'·69N 05°16'·28W Fl WRG 3s 7m 5M; Gy col; vis W071°-078°, R078°-090°, G090°-103°, W103°-111°, R111°-243°, W243°-247°, G247°-071°.

Hbr bkwtr hd 58°08'·91N 05°15'·02W QG 3m 1M; B col, W bands.
Culag Hbr pier hd 58°08'·93N 05°14'·61W 2 FG (vert) 6m.

• SUMMER ISLES
Old Dornie, new pier hd 58°02'·59N 05°25'·31W Fl G 3s 5m.

Rubha Cadail 57°55'·53N 05°13'·30W Fl WRG 6s 11m W9M, R6M, G6M; W tr; vis G311°-320°, W320°-325°, R325°-103°, W103°-111°, G111°-118°, W118°-127°, R127°-157°, W157°-199°.

• ULLAPOOL
Ullapool Pt buoy 57°53'·43N 05°10'·35W QR; PHM. Ullapool Pt 57°53'·62N 05°09'·67W Iso R 4s 8m 6M. Cailleach hd 57°55'·83N 05°24'·15W Fl (2) 12s 60m 9M; W tr; vis 015°-236°.

• LOCH EWE/LOCH GAIRLOCH
Fairway buoy 57°52'·00N 05°40'·02W L Fl 10s; SWM. NATO jetty, NW corner Fl G 4s 5m 3M.
Rubha Reidh 57°51'·55N 05°48'·61W Fl (4) 15s 37m **24M**. Glas Eilean 57°42'·82N 05°42'·36W Fl WRG 6s 9m W6M, R4M; vis W080°-102°, R102°-296°, W296°-333°, G333°-080°.

OUTER HEBRIDES – EAST SIDE

• LEWIS
Butt of Lewis 58°30'·93N 06°15'·72W Fl 5s 52m **25M**; R tr; vis 056°-320°; RC.
Tiumpan Hd 58°15'·6N 06°08'·3W Fl (2) 15s 55m **25M**; W tr.

• STORNOWAY
Arnish Pt 58°11'·50N 06°22'·17W Fl WR 10s 17m **W19M, R15M**; W ○ tr; vis W088°-198°, R198°-302°, W302°-013°.

Sandwick Bay, NW side Oc WRG 6s 10m 9M; vis G334°-341°, W341°-347°, R347°-354°.
Eitshal 58°10'·7N 06°35'·0W 4 FR (vert) on radio mast.

• LOCH ERISORT/LOCH SHELL/EAST LOCH TARBERT
Tabhaidh Bheag 58°07'·22N 06°23'·15W Fl 3s 13m 3M. Eilean Chalabrigh 58°06'·81N 06°26'·62W QG 5m 3M. Gob na Milaid Pt 58°01'·0N 06°21'·8W Fl 15s 14m 10M. Rubh' Uisenis 57°56'·2N 06°28'·2W Fl 5s 24m 11M; W tr. Sgeir Inoe buoy 57°50'·95N 06°33'·90W Fl G 6s; SHM. Shiants buoy 57°54'·60N 06°25'·60W QG; SHM. Scalpay, **Eilean Glas** 57°51'·43N 06°38'·45W Fl (3) 20s 43m **23M**; W tr, R bands; Racon (T). Scalpay N Hbr buoy 57°52'·58N 06°42'·16W Fl G 2s; SHM. Dun Cor Mòr Fl R 5s 10m 5M. Sgeir Graidach buoy 57°50'·38N 06°41'·31W Q (6) + L Fl 15s; SCM. Sgeir Ghlas 57°52'·38N 06°45'·18W Iso WRG 4s 9m W9M, R6M, G6M; W ○ tr; vis G282°-319°, W319°-329°, R329°-153°, W153°-164°, G164°-171°.

• SOUND OF HARRIS/LEVERBURGH
Stumbles Rk buoy 57°45'·15N 07°01'·75W Fl (2) R 10s; PHM. Dubh Sgeir 57°45'·54N 07°02'·56W Q (2) 5s 9m 6M; R tr, B bands. Leverburgh ldg lts 014·7°. Front, 57°46'·25N 07°01'·98W Q 10m 4M; rear, Oc 3s 12m 4M. Jane's tr 57°45'·79N 07°02'·05W Q (2) G 5s 6m 4M; obsc 273°-318°. Leverburgh pier hd 57°46'·04N 07°01'·56W Oc WRG 8s 5m 2M; Gy col; vis G305°-059°, W059°-066°, R066°-125°.

• BERNERAY
W side, **Barra Hd** 57°47'·13N 07°39'·18W Fl 15s 208m **18M**; W tr; obsc by islands to NE. Berneray bkwtr hd 57°42'·9N 07°10'·0W Iso R 4s 6m 4M. Drowning Rock Q (2) G 8s 2m 2M; G pillar. Reef Chan No 1 QG 2m 4M. Reef Chan No 2 Iso G 4s 2m 4M.

• NORTH UIST
Eilean Fuam 57°41'·9N 07°10'·6W Q 6m 2M; W col. Newton jetty Root 57°41'·5N 07°11'·5W 2 FG (vert) 9m 4M. Griminish Hbr ldg lts 183°: Front, 57°39'·41N 07°26'·62W QG 6m 4M; rear, 110m from front, QG 7m 4M. Pier hd 57°39'·3N 07°26'·3W 2 FG (vert) 6m 4M; Gy col (shown Mar-Oct).

• LOCH MADDY
Weaver's Pt 57°36'·51N 07°05'·95W Fl 3s 21m 7M; W hut. Glas Eilean Mòr 57°35'·97N 07°06'·64W Fl G 4s 8m 5M. Rubna Nam Pleàc 57°35'·78N 07°06'·70W Fl R 4s 7m 5M. Ruigh Liath E Islet 57°35'·74N 07°08'·36W QG 6m 5M.

Vallaquie Island 57°35'·52N 07°09'·34W Fl (3) WRG 8s 11m W7M, R5M, G5M; W pillar; vis G shore-205°, W205°-210°, R210°-240°, G240°-254°, W254°-257°, R257°-shore (P).

Lochmaddy ldg lts 298°: Front, Ro-Ro pier 57°35'·79N 07°09'·29W 2 FG (vert) 8m 4M; rear, 110m from front, Oc G 8s 10m 4M; vis 284°-304°.

• GRIMSAY
Kallin Hbr bkwtr, NE corner 57°28'·90N 07°12'·25W 2 FR (vert) 6m 5M; Gy col.

• SOUTH UIST, LOCH CARNAN
Landfall buoy 57°22'·30N 07°11'·45W L Fl 10s; SWM. No 2 buoy 57°22'·41N 07°14'·87W Fl R 2s; PHM. No 3 buoy 57°22'·33N 07°15'·54W Fl R 5s; PHM. No 4 buoy 57°22'·27N 07°15'·82W QR; PHM. Ldg lts 222°: Front 57°22'·02N 07°16'·28W Fl R 2s 7m 5M; W ◊ on post; rear, 58m from front, Iso R 10s 11m 5M; W ◊ on post.
Ushenish (S Uist) 57°17'·91N 07°11'·50W Fl WR 20s 54m **W19M, R15M**; W tr; vis W193°-356°, R356°-013°.

- LOCH BOISDALE
Calvay E end 57°08'·55N 07°15'·32W Fl (2) WRG 10s 16m W7M, R4M, G4M; W tr; vis W111°-190°, G190°-202°, W202°-286°, R286°-111°.
N side 57°08'·99N 07°16'·98W Fl G 6s 3m 3M.
Eilean Dubh 57°09'·09N 07°18'·13W Fl (2) R 5s 2m 3M.
Gasay Is Fl WR 5s 10m W7M, R4M; W tr; vis W120°-284°, R284°-120°.
Channel buoy 57°09'·04N 07°17'·38W QG; SHM.
Sgeir Rk buoy 57°09'·11N 07°17'·70W Fl G 3s; SHM.
Ro-Ro jetty hd 57°09'·15N 07°18'·17W Iso RG 4s 8m 2M; vis G shore-283°, R283°-shore; 2 FG (vert) 8m 3M on dn 84m W.
Sgeir Dhearg buoy 57°00'·75N 05°49'·43W QG; SHM.

- LUDAIG
Ludaig Dir lt 297° 57°06'·2N 07°19'·7W Dir Oc WRG 6s   8m W7M, R4M, G4M; vis G287°-296°, W296°-298°, R298°-307°.
Stag Rk 57°05'·88N 07°18'·31W Fl (2) 8s 7m 4M.
The Witches buoy 57°05'·75N 07°20'·77W Fl R 5s; PHM.
Ludaig pier 2 FG (vert) 5m 3M.

- ERISKAY
Bank Rk 57°05'·60N 07°17'·51W Q (2) 4s 5m 4M.
Haun Dir lt 236° Dir Oc WRG 3s 9m W7M, R4M, G4M; vis G226°-234·5°, W234·5°-237·5°, R237·5°-246°.
Pier 2 FG (vert) 5m 5M.
Acairseid Mhor ldg lts 285°: Front, 57°03'·92N 07°17'·18W Oc R 6s 9m 4M; rear, 24m from front, Oc R 6s 10m 4M.

- BARRA/CASTLEBAY, VATERSAY SOUND
Drover Rks buoy 57°04'·18N 07°23'·58W Fl (2) 10s; IDM.
Curachan buoy 56°58'·58N 07°20'·45W Q (3) 10s; ECM.
Ardveenish 57°00'·23N 07°24'·37W Oc WRG 6m 9/6M; vis G300°-304°, W304°-306°, R306°-310°.
Bo Vich Chuan buoy 56°56'·17N 07°23'·27W Q (6) + L Fl 15s; SCM; Racon (M).
Channel Rk lt bn 56°56'·25N 07°28'·88W Fl WR 6s 4m W6M, R4M; vis W121·5°-277°, R277°-121·5°.
Sgeir Dubh 56°56'·42N 07°28'·86W Q (3) WG 6s 6m W6M, G4M; vis W280°-117°, G117°-280°. In line 283° with Sgeir Leadh (Liath) below.
Sgeir Leadh (Liath) 56°56'·65N 07°30'·72W Fl 3s 7m 8M.
Castlebay 56°57'·23N 07°29'·22W Fl R 5s 2m 3M.
Rubha Glas. Ldg lts 295°: Front, 56°56'·78N 07°30'·59W FG 9m 11M; Or △ on W tr; rear, 457m from front, FG 15m 11M; Or ▽ on W tr.

OUTER HEBRIDES – WEST SIDE

Flannan Is, Eilean Mór 58°17'·32N 07°35'·23W Fl (2) 30s 101m **20M**; W tr; obsc in places by Is to W of Eilean Mór.

- EAST LOCH ROAG
Aird Laimishader Carloway 58°17'·06N 06°49'·50W L Fl 12s 61m 8M; W hut; obsc on some brgs.
Ardvanich Pt 58°13'·48N 06°47'·68W Fl G 3s 4m 2M.
Tidal Rk 58°13'·45N 06°47'·57W Fl R 3s 2m 2M (synch with Ardvanich Pt above).
Gt Bernera Kirkibost jetty 2 FG (vert) 7m 2M.
Grèinam 58°13'·30N 06°46'·16W Fl WR 6s 8m W8M, R7M; W bn; vis R143°-169°, W169°-143°.
Whale Rk ECM buoy, Q (3) 10s, 57°54'·90N 08°00'·70W.

- NORTH UIST/SOUTH UIST
Valley Island 57°39'·70N 07°26'·10W Fl WRG 3s 8M; vis W206°-085°, G085°-140°, W140°-145°, R145°-206°.
Falconet tr 57°21'·5N 07°23'·6W FR 25m 8M (3M by day); shown 1h before firing, changes to Iso R 2s 15 min before firing until completion.

- ST KILDA
Ldg lts 270°: Front, 57°48'·36N 08°34'·27W Oc 5s 26m 3M; rear, 100m from front, Oc 5s 38m 3M; synch.

SKYE AND ADJACENT WATERS
Eilean Trodday 57°43'·65N 06°17'·87W Fl (2) WRG 10s 49m W12M, R9M, G9M; W bn; vis W062°-088°, R088°-130°, W130°-322°, G322°-062°.

- RONA/LOCH A'BHRAIGE
NE Point 57°34'·71N 05°57'·48W Fl 12s 69m **19M**; W tr;   vis 050°-358°.
Sgeir Shuas 57°35'·04N 05°58'·54W Fl R 2s 6m 3M; vis 070°-199°.
Jetty, NE end 57°34'·68N 05°57'·86W 2 FR (vert).
Rock 57°34'·62N 05°57'·94W Fl R 5s 4m 3M.
Ldg lts 136·5°: Front, No 9 bn 57°34'·43N 05°58'·02W   Q WRG 3m W4M, R3M; W and Or bn; vis W135°-138°, R138°-318°, G318°-135°; rear, No 10 Iso 6s 28m 5M; W bn.
No 1 bn Fl G 3s 91m 3M, Or bn.
Rubha Chùiltairbh Fl 3s 6m 5M; W bn.
No 11 bn QY 6m 4M; Or bn.
No 3 bn Fl (2) 10s 9m 4M; W bn and Or stripes.
No 12 bn QR 5m 3M; Or bn.
Garbh Eilean SE Pt No 8 bn Fl 3s 8m 5M; W bn.

- INNER SOUND
Ru Na Lachan 57°29'·04N 05°52'·07W Oc WR 8s 21m 10M; tr; vis W337°-022°, R022°-117°, W117°-162°.

- SOUND OF RAASAY, PORTREE
Portree pier hd 57°24'·66N 06°11'·34W 2 FR (vert) 6m 4M; (occas).

- CROWLIN ISLANDS
Eilean Beag 57°21'·23N 05°51'·33W Fl 6s 32m 6M; W bn.

- RAASAY/LOCH SLIGACHAN
Suisnish 2 FG (vert) 8m 2M.
Eyre Pt 57°20'·03N 06°01'·22W Fl WR 3s 5m W9M, R6M; W tr; vis W215°-266°, R266°-288°, W288°-063°.
Sconser ferry terminal 57°18'·9N 06°06'·6W QR 8m 3M.
McMillan's Rk buoy 57°21'·13N 06°06'·24W Fl (2) G 12s; SHM.

- LOCH CARRON
No 1 buoy 57°21'·43N 05°38'·82W Fl G 3s; SHM.
Old lt ho 57°20'·97N 05°38'·81W (unlit).

- KYLE AKIN AND KYLE OF LOCH ALSH
Kyle Akin lt ho 57°16'·68N 05°44'·48W (unlit).
Carragh Rk buoy 57°17'·20N 05°45'·30W Fl (2) G 12s; SHM; Racon (T).
Bow Rk buoy 57°16'·78N 05°45'·85W Fl (2) R 12s; PHM.
Fork Rks buoy 57°16'·86N 05°44'·87W Fl G 6s; SHM.
Black Eye Rk buoy 57°16'·73N 05°45'·24W Fl R 6s; PHM.
Kyle Akin bridge centre 57°16'·58N 05°44'·51W Oc 6s.
Eileanan Dubha E 57°16'·58N 05°42'·25W Fl (2) 10s 9m 8M; vis obscured 104°-146°.
Eileanan Dubha W 57°16'·62N 05°42'·61W Fl G 6s 5m 4M.
String Rk buoy 57°16'·51N 05°42'·82W Fl R 6s; PHM.
Allt-an-Avaig jetty 2 FR (vert) 10m; vis 075°-270°.
S shore, ferry slipway QR 6m (vis in Kyle of Loch Alsh).
Mooring dolphin 57°16'·38N 05°43'·36W Q 5m 3M.
Ferry pier, W and E sides, 2 FG (vert) 6/5m 5/4M.
Butec jetty W end, N corner 57°16'·77N 05°42'·36W Oc G 6s 5m 3M each end, synch.
Sgeir-na-Caillich 57°15'·63N 05°38'·83W Fl (2) R 6s 3m 4M.

- SOUND OF SLEAT
Kyle Rhea 57°14'·24N 05°39'·85W Fl WRG 3s 7m W11M, R9M, G8M; W bn; vis R shore-219°, W219-228°, G228°-338°, W338°-346°, R346°-shore.
Sandaig Is, NW point Fl 6s 12m 8M; W 8-sided tr.
Ornsay, N end 57°09'·10N 05°46'·5W Fl R 6s 8m 4M; W tr.
Ornsay, **SE end** 57°08'·60N 05°46'·80W Oc 8s 18m **15M**; W tr; vis 157°-030°.
Eilean Iarmain, off pier hd 2 FR (vert) 3m 2M.
Armadale Bay pier Centre Oc R 6s 6m 6M.

8

Pt of Sleat 57°01'·11N 06° 01'·00W Fl 3s 20m 9M; W tr.
Elgol 57°08'·80N 06°06'·43W Fl G 3s 4m 4M.

- MALLAIG, ENTRANCE TO LOCH NEVIS

Sgeir Dhearg buoy 57°00'·75N 05°49'·43W QG; SHM.
Northern pier E end 57°00'·48N 05°49'·43W Iso WRG 4s 6m
W9M, R6M, G6M; Gy tr; vis G181°-185°, W185°-197°, R197°-
201°. Fl G 3s 14m 6M; same structure.
Sgeir Dhearg 57°00'·64N 05°49'·53W Fl (2) WG 8s 6m 5M;
Gy bn; vis G190°-055°, W055°-190°.

- NW SKYE, UIG/LOCH DUNVEGAN/LOCH HARPORT
Uig, Edward pier hd 57°35'·14N 06°22'·22W Iso WRG 4s 9m
W7M, R4M, G4M; vis W180°-008°, G008°-052°, W052°-075°,
R075°-180°.
Waternish Pt 57°36'·5N 06°38'·0W Fl 20s 21m 8M; W tr.
Loch Dunvegan, Uiginish Pt 57°26'·8N 06°36'·5W Fl WG
3s 14m W7M, G5M; W hut; vis G040°-128°, W128°-306°,
obsc by Fiadhairt Pt when brg more than 148°.
Neist Pt 57°25'·4N 06°47'·2W Fl 5s 43m **16M**; W tr.
Loch Harport, Ardtreck Pt 57°20'·4N 06°25'·8W Iso 4s 17m
9M; small W tr.

SMALL ISLES AND WEST OF MULL

- CANNA, RHUM
E end, Sanday Is 57°02'·84N 06°27'·92W Fl 6s 32m 9M; W
tr; vis 152°-061°.

- ÒIGH SGEIR/EIGG/ARISAIG
Humla buoy 57°00'·43N 06°37'·40W Fl G 6s; SHM.
S end, **Hyskeir** 56°58'·13N 06°40'·80W Fl (3) 30s 41m **24M**;
W tr. N end *Horn 30s.*
SE point of Eigg (Eilean Chathastail) 56°52'·25N 06°07'·20W
Fl 6s 24m 8M; W tr; vis 181°-shore.
Bo Faskadale buoy 56°48'·18N 06°06'·35W Fl (3) G 18s; SHM.
Ardnamurchan 56°43'·64N 06°13'·46W Fl (2) 20s 55m **24M**;
Gy tr; vis 002°-217°; *Horn (2) 20s.*
Cairns of Coll, Suil Ghorm 56°42'·27N 06°26'·70W Fl 12s 23m
10M; W tr.

- COLL/ARINAGOUR
Loch Eatharna, Bogha Mor buoy 56°36'·67N 06°30'·90W   Fl
G 6s; SHM.
Arinagour pier 2 FR (vert) 12m.

- TIREE
Roan Bogha buoy 56°32'·25N 06°40'·10W Q (6) + L Fl 15s; SCM.
Placaid Bogha buoy 56°33'·24N 06°43'·93W Fl G 4s; SHM.
Scarinish, S side of ent 56°30'·02N 06°48'·20W Fl 3s 11m
16M; W □ tr; vis 210°-030°.
Gott Bay ldg lts 286·5°: Front 56°30'·63N 06°47'·75W FR 8m;
rear 30m from front FR 11m.
Skerryvore 56°19'·40N 07°06'·75W Fl 10s 46m **23M**; Gy tr;
Racon (M); *Horn 60s.*

- LOCH NA LÀTHAICH (LOCH LATHAICH)
Eileanan na Liathanaich, SE end 56°20'·58N 06°16'·30W
Fl WR 6s 12m W8M, R6M; vis R088°-108°, W108°-088°.
Dubh Artach 56°07'·95N 06°37'·95W Fl (2) 30s 44m **20M**;
Gy tr, R band; *Horn 45s.*

SOUND OF MULL

- LOCH SUNART/TOBERMORY/LOCH ALINE
Ardmore Pt 56°39'·39N 06°07'·62W Fl (2) 10s 17m 8M.
New Rks buoy 56°39'·07N 06°03'·22W Fl G 6s; SHM.
Rubha nan Gall 56°38'·33N 06°03'·91W Fl 3s 17m **15M**;
W tr.
Bogha Bhuilg buoy 56°36'·15N 05°59'·07W; SHM.
Hispania wk buoy 56°34'·70N 05°59'·30W Fl (2) R 10s; PHM.
Bo Rks buoy 56°31'·54N 05°55'·47W; SHM.
Eileanan Glasa, Green Is (Dearg Sgeir) 56°32'·27N 05°54'·72W
Fl 6s 7m 8M; W ○ tr.
Fuinary Spit buoy 56°32'·66N 05°53'·09W Fl G 6s; SHM.

Avon Rk buoy 56°30'·80N 05°46'·72W; PHM.
Lochaline buoy 56°32'·99N 05°46'·41W QR; PHM.
Lochaline ldg lts 356°: Front, 56°32'·40N 05°46'·40W F 2M;
rear, 88m from front, F 4M; H24.
Ardtornish Pt 56°31'·10N 05°45'·15W Fl (2) WRG 10s 7m
W8M, R5M, G5M; W tr; vis G shore-302°, W302°-310°,
R310°-342°, W342°-057°, R057°-095°, W095°-108°, G108°-
shore.
Yule Rk buoy 56°30'·03N 05°43'·88W; PHM.
Glas Eileanan Gy Rks 56°29'·78N 05°42'·76W Fl 3s 11m 6M;
W ○ tr on W base.
Craignure ldg lts 240·9°: Front, 56°28'·30N 05°42'·21W FR 10m;
rear, 150m from front, FR 12m; vis 225·8°-255·8° (on req).

MULL TO CALEDONIAN CANAL AND OBAN

Lismore, SW end 56°27'·35N 05°36'·38W Fl 10s 31m **19M**;
W tr; vis 237°-208°.

Lady's Rk 56°26'·91N 05°36'·98W Fl 6s 12m 5M; R ○ on W bn.
Duart Pt 56°26'·85N 05°38'·69W Fl (3) WR 18s 14m W5M,
R3M; vis W162°-261°, R261°-275°, W275°-353°, R353°-shore.

- LOCH LINNHE
Ent W side, Corran Pt 56°43'·27N 05°14'·47W Iso WRG 4s
12m W10M, R7M; W tr; vis R shore-195°, W195°-215°,
G215°-305°, W305°-030°, R030°-shore.
Corran Narrows NE 56°43'·62N 05°13'·83W Fl 5s 4m 4M;
W tr; vis S shore-214°.
Jetty 56°43'·42N 05°14'·56W Fl R 5s 7m 3M; Gy mast.

- FORT WILLIAM/CALEDONIAN CANAL
Corpach, Caledonian Canal lock ent Iso WRG 4s 6m 5M;
W tr; vis G287°-310°, W310°-335°, R335°-030°.

- LYNN OF LORN
Sgeir Bhuidhe Appin 56°33'·65N 05°24'·57W Fl (2) WR 7s 7m
9M; W bn; vis R184°-220°, W220°-184°.
Dearg Sgeir (Eileanan Glasa = Green Island), off Aird's Point
lt bn, Fl W 6s 7m 8M; W ○ tr; 56°32'·22N 05°25'·15W.
Eriska NE Pt, QG 2m 2M; G col; vis 128°-329°.

- DUNSTAFFNAGE BAY
Pier hd, NE end 56°27'·22N 05°26'·10W 2 FG (vert) 4m 2M.

- OBAN
N spit of Kerrera 56°25'·50N 05°29'·50W Fl R 3s 9m 5M;
W col, R bands.
Dunollie 56°25'·39N 05°28'·98W Fl (2) WRG 6s 7m W5M,
G4M, R4M; vis G351°-009°, W009°-047°, R047°-120°, W120°-
138°, G138°-143°.
Rubbh'a' Chruidh 56°25'·33N 05°29'·22W QR 3m 2M.

OBAN TO LOCH CRAIGNISH

Kerrera Sound, Dubh Sgeir 56°22'·82N 05°32'·20W Fl (2) 12s
7m 5M; W ○ tr.

Fladda 56°14'·90N 05°40'·75W Fl (2) WRG 9s 13m W11M,
R9M, G9M; W tr; vis R169°-186°, W186°-337°, G337°-344°.
W344°-356°, R356°-026°.
Dubh Sgeir (Luing) 56°14'·78N 05°40'·12W Fl WRG 6s 9m
W6M, R4M. G4M; W tr; vis W000°-010°, R010°-025°, W025°-
199°, G199°-000°; Racon (M).
The Garvellachs, Eileach an Naoimh, SW end 56°13'·05N
05°48'·97W Fl 6s 21m 9M; W bn; vis 240°-215°.

- LOCH MELFORT/CRAOBH HAVEN
Fearnach Bay pier 56°16'·15N 05°30'·11W 2 FR (vert) 6/5m
3M; (Private shown 1/4 to 31/10).
Craobh Haven bkwtr hd 56°12'·79N 05°33'·44W Iso WRG 5s
10m 5/3M; vis G114°-162°, W162°-183°, R183°-200°.

For Colonsay, and Sounds of Jura and Islay see 8.9.4.

8.8.5   PASSAGE INFORMATION

It is essential to carry large scale charts, and current Pilots, ie Admiralty *W Coast of Scotland Pilot*; Clyde Cruising Club's *Sailing Directions, Pt 2 Kintyre to Ardnamurchan* and *Pt 3 Ardnamurchan to Cape Wrath*; and the *Yachtsman's Pilot to W Coast of Scotland (Vol 2 Crinan to Canna)*, *(Vol 3 The Western Isles)*, *(Vol 4 Skye & NW Scotland)*, Lawrence/Imray. See 8.9.5 for some of the more relevant terms in Gaelic.

The West coast of Scotland provides splendid, if sometimes boisterous, sailing and matchless scenery. In summer the long daylight hours and warmth of the Gulf Stream compensate for the lower air temperatures and higher wind speeds experienced when depressions run typically north of Scotland. Inshore winds are often unpredictable, due to geographical effects of lochs, mountains and islands offshore; calms and squalls can alternate rapidly. Good anchors, especially on kelp/weed, are essential. HIE and public ⚓s are listed, but it should not be assumed that these will always be available. Particularly in N of area, facilities are very dispersed. VHF communications with shore stations may be limited by high ground. Beware ever more fish farms in many inlets. Local magnetic anomalies occur in Kilbrannan Sound, Passage of Tiree, Sound of Mull, Canna, and East Loch Roag. Submarines exercise throughout these waters; see 8.8.23.

CAPE WRATH TO ULLAPOOL (charts 1785, 1794)

C Wrath (lt, fog sig) is a steep headland (110m). To N of it the E-going stream begins at HW Ullapool – 0350, and W- going at HW Ullapool + 0235, sp rates 3kn. Eddies close inshore cause almost continuous W-going stream E of Cape, and N-going stream SW of it. Where they meet is turbulence, with dangerous seas in bad weather. Duslic Rk, 7ca NE of lt ho, dries 3·4m. 6M SW of C Wrath, islet of Am Balg (45m)is foul for 2ca around.

There are anchs in Loch Inchard (chart 2503), the best shelter being in Kinochbervie (8.8.8) on N shore; also good anchs among Is along S shore of Loch Laxford, entered between Ardmore Pt and Rubha Ruadh (see 8.8.8). Handa Is to WSW is a bird sanctuary. Handa Sound is navigable with care, but beware Bogha Morair in mid-chan and associated overfalls. Tide turns 2hrs earlier in the Sound than offshore.

Strong winds against tide raise a bad sea off Pt of Stoer. The best shelter is 8M S at Loch Inver (8.8.8 and chart 2504), with good anch off hotel near head of loch. S lies Enard Bay.

ULLAPOOL TO LOCH TORRIDON (charts 1794, 2210)

The Summer Isles (chart 2501), 12M NW of the major fishing port of Ullapool (8.8.9), offer some sheltered anchs and tight approaches. The best include the Bay on E side of Tanera Mor; off NE of Tanera Beg (W of Eilean Fada Mor); and in Caolas Eilean Ristol, between the Is and mainland.

Loch Ewe (8.8.9 and chart 3146) provides good shelter and easy access. Best anchs are in Poolewe Bay (beware Boor Rks off W shore) and in SW corner of Loch Thuirnaig (entering, keep close to S shore to avoid rks extending from N side). Off Rubha Reidh (lt) seas can be dangerous. The NE-going stream begins at HW Ullapool – 0335; the SW-going at HW Ullapool + 0305. Sp rates 3kn, but slacker to SW of point.

Longa Is lies N of ent to Loch Gairloch (8.8.9 and chart 2528). The chan N of it is navigable but narrow at E end. Outer loch is free of dangers, but exposed to swell. Best anch is on S side of loch in Caolas Bad a' Chrotha, W of Eilean Horrisdale.

Entering L Torridon (chart 2210) from S or W beware Murchadh Breac (dries 1·5m) 3ca NNW of Rubha na Fearna. Best anchs are SW of Eilean Mor (to W of Ardheslaig); in Loch a 'Chracaich, 7ca further SE; E of Shieldaig Is; and near head of Upper L Torridon. Streams are weak except where they run 2-3 kn in narrows between L Shieldaig and Upper L Torridon.

OUTER HEBRIDES (charts 1785, 1794, 1795)

The E sides of these Is have many good, sheltered anchs, but W coasts give little shelter. The CCC's *Outer Hebrides SDs* or *The Western Isles* (Imray) are advised. The Minches and Sea of the Hebrides can be very rough, particularly in the Little Minch between Skye and Harris, and around Shiant Is where tide runs locally 4kn at sp, and heavy overfalls can be met. The NE-going stream begins at HW Ullapool – 0335; the SW-going stream at HW Ullapool + 0250, sp rates 2·5kn.

From N to S, the better hbrs in Outer Hebrides include:
Lewis. Stornoway (8.8.7); Loch Grimshader (beware Sgeir a'Chaolais, dries in entrance); Loch Erisort; Loch Odhairn; Loch Shell (8.8.7). Proceeding S from here, or to E Loch Tarbert beware Sgeir Inoe (dries 2·3m) 3M ESE of Eilean Glas lt ho at SE end of Scalpay.
Harris. E Loch Tarbert; Loch Scadaby; Loch Stockinish; Loch Finsby; W Loch Tarbert; Loch Rodel (HIE ⚓). A well buoyed/lit ferry chan connects Leverburgh (South Harris) to Berneray.
N Uist. Loch Maddy (HIE ⚓); Loch Eport, Kallin Hbr (HIE ⚓).
S Uist. Loch Carnan (HIE ⚓); Loch Skiport; Loch Eynort; Loch Boisdale (HIE ⚓).
Barra. Castlebay (HIE ⚓), see 8.8.7, and Berneray, on N side, E of Shelter Rk.

Activity at the Hebrides Range, S. Uist ☎ (01870) 604441, is broadcast daily at 0950LT and Mon-Fri 1100-1700LT on VHF Ch **12** (Ch 73 in emergency) and on MF 2660 kHz.

SKYE TO ARDNAMURCHAN PT (charts 1795, 2210, 2209, 2208, 2207)

Skye and the islands around it provide many good and attractive anchs, of which the most secure are: Acairseid Mhor on the W side of Rona; Portree (8.8.10); Isleornsay; Portnalong, near the ent to Loch Harport, and Carbost at the head; Loch Dunvegan; and Uig Bay in Loch Snizort. HIE ⚓s at Stein (Loch Dunvegan), Portree, Acairseid Mhor (Rona), Churchton Bay (Raasay) and Armadale Bay (S tip).

Tides are strong off Rubha Hunish at N end of Skye, and heavy overfalls occur with tide against fresh or strong winds. Anch behind Fladday Is near the N end of Raasay can be squally and uncomfortable; and Loch Scavaig (S. Skye, beneath the Cuillins) more so, though the latter is so spectacular as to warrant a visit in fair weather. Soay Is has a small, safe hbr on its N side, but the bar at ent almost dries at LW sp.

Between N Skye and the mainland there is the choice of Sound of Raasay or Inner Sound. **The direction of buoyage in both Sounds is Northward.** In the former, coming S from Portree, beware Sgeir Chnapach (3m) and Ebbing Rk (dries 2·9m), both NNW of Oskaig Pt. At the Narrows (chart 2534) the SE- going stream begins at HW Ullapool – 0605, and the NW-going at HW Ullapool + 0040; sp rate 1·4kn in mid-chan, but more near shoals each side. Beware McMillan's Rk (0·4m depth) in mid-chan, marked by SHM lt buoy.

The chan between Scalpay and Skye narrows to 2½ca with drying reefs each side and least depth 0·1m. Here the E-going stream begins at HW Ullapool + 0550, and W-going at HW Ullapool – 0010, sp rate 1kn.

Inner Sound, which is a Submarine exercise area, is wider and easier than Sound of Raasay; the two are connected by Caol Rona and Caol Mor, respectively N and S of Raasay. Dangers extend about 1M N of Rona, and Cow Is lies off the mainland 8M to S; otherwise approach from N is clear to Crowlin Is, which should be passed to W. There is a good anch between Eilean Mor and Eilean Meadhonach, see 8.8.8.

A torpedo range in the Inner Sound does not normally restrict passage, but vessels may be requested to keep to the E side of the Sound if the range is active. Range activity is broadcast at 0800 and 1600LT on VHF Ch 08, 16 and is indicated by R Flags and International Code NE4 flown at the range building at Applecross, by all range vessels and at the naval pier at Kyle of Lochalsh (8.8.12), ☎ (01599) 534262.

Approaching Kyle Akin (chart 2540) from W, beware dangerous rks to N, off Bleat Is (at S side of entrance to Loch Carron); on S side of chan, Bogha Beag (dries 0·6m) and Black Eye Rk (depth 3·8m), respectively 6ca and 4ca W of bridge. For Plockton (Loch Carron), see 8.8.11. Pass at least 100m N or S of Eileanan Dubha in Kyle Akin. On S side of chan String Rk (dries) is marked by PHM lt buoy. For Loch Alsh, see 8.8.12.

Kyle Rhea connects Loch Alsh with NE end of Sound of Sleat. The tidal streams are very strong: N-going stream begins HW Ullapool + 0600, sp rate 6-7kn; S-going stream begins at HW Ullapool, sp rate 8kn. Eddies form both sides of the Kyle and there are dangerous overfalls off S end in fresh S'ly winds on S-going stream. Temp anch in Sandaig Bay, 3M to SW.

The Sound of Sleat widens to 4M off Point of Sleat and is exposed to SW winds unless Eigg and Muck give a lee. Mallaig (8.8.13) is a busy fishing and ferry hbr, convenient for supplies. Further S the lochs require intricate pilotage. 6M NE of Ardnamurchan Pt (lt, fog sig) are Bo Faskadale rks, drying 0·5m and marked by SHM lt buoy, and Elizabeth Rk with depth of 0·7m. Ardnamurchan Pt is an exposed headland onto which the ebb sets. With onshore winds, very heavy seas extend 2M offshore and it should be given a wide berth. Here the N-going stream begins at HW Oban − 0525, and the S-going at HW Oban + 0100, sp rates 1·5kn.

THE SMALL ISLES (charts 2207, 2208)

These consist of Canna, Rhum, Eigg (8.8.13) and Muck. Dangers extend SSW from Canna: at 1M Jemina Rk (depth 1·5m) and Belle Rk (depth 3·6m); at 2M Humla Rk (5m high), marked by buoy and with offlying shoals close W of it; at 5M Oigh Sgeir (lt, fog sig), the largest of a group of small islands; and at 7M Mill Rks (with depths of 1·8m).

The tide runs hard here, and in bad weather the sea breaks heavily up to 15M SW of Canna. Between Skerryvore and Neist Pt the stream runs generally N and S, starting N-going at HW Ullapool + 0550, and S-going at HW Ullapool − 008. It rarely exceeds 1kn, except near Skerryvore, around headlands of The Small Isles, and over rks and shoals.

1M off the N side of Muck are Godag Rks, some above water but with submerged dangers extending 2ca further N. Most other dangers around the Small Isles are closer inshore, but there are banks on which the sea breaks heavily in bad weather. A local magnetic anomaly exists about 2M E of Muck. The hbrs at Eigg (SE end), Rhum (Loch Scresort) and Canna (between Canna and Sanday) are all exposed to E'lies; Canna has best shelter and is useful for the Outer Hebrides.

ARDNAMURCHAN TO CRINAN (charts 2171, 2169)

S of Ardnamurchan the route lies either W of Mull via Passage of Tiree (where headlands need to be treated with respect in bad weather); or via the more sheltered Sound of Mull and Firth of Lorne. The former permits a visit to Coll and Tiree, where best anchs are at Arinagour (HIE ⚓s) and Gott Bay respectively. Beware Cairns of Coll, off the N tip.

The W coast of Mull is rewarding in settled weather, but careful pilotage is needed. Beware tide rip off Caliach Pt (NW corner) and Torran Rks off SW end of Mull (large scale chart 2617 required). Apart from the attractions of Iona and of Staffa (Fingal's Cave), the remote Treshnish Is are worth visiting. The best anchs in this area are at Ulva, Gometra, Bull Hole and Tinker's Hole in Iona Sound. The usual passage through Iona Sound avoids overfalls W of Iona, but heed shoal patches. Loch Lathaich on the N side of Ross of Mull is 5M to the E; a good base with anch and boatyard at Bunessan.

The Sound of Mull gives access to Tobermory (8.8.15, HIE ⚓), Dunstaffnage Bay, Oban (8.8.19), and up Loch Linnhe through Corran Narrows (where tide runs strongly) to Fort William (8.8.17) and to Corpach for the Caledonian Canal (8.8.18). But, apart from these places, there are dozens of lovely anchs in the sheltered lochs inside Mull, as for example in Loch Sunart (8.8.14) with HIE ⚓s at Kilchoan; also at Craignure and Salen Bays on Sound of Mull. For Loch Aline see 8.8.16.

On the mainland shore Puilladobhrain is a sheltered anch. Cuan Sound (see 8.8.19 for details) is a useful short cut to Loch Melfort, (8.8.20) and Craobh Marina (8.8.21). Good shelter, draft permitting, in Ardinamar B, SW of Torsa.

Sound of Luing (chart 2326) between Fladda (lt), Lunga and Scarba on the W side, and Luing and Dubh Sgeir (lt) on the E side, is the normal chan to or from Sound of Jura, despite dangers at the N end and strong tidal streams. The N and W-going flood begins at HW Oban + 0430; the S and E-going ebb at HW Oban −0155. Sp rates are 2·5kn at S end of Sound, increasing to 6kn or more in Islands off N entrance, where there are eddies, races and overfalls.

At N end of Sound of Jura (chart 2326) is Loch Craignish (8.8.22). From the N, beware very strong streams, eddies and whirlpools in Dorus Mór, off Craignish Pt. Streams begin to set W and N away from Dorus Mór at HW Oban + 0345, and E and S towards Dorus Mór at HW Oban − 0215, sp rates 7kn.

For Gulf of Corryvreckan, Colonsay, Islay, Loch Crinan and passage south through the Sound of Jura, see 8.9.5.

8.8.6 DISTANCE TABLE

Approximate distances in nautical miles are by the most direct route, keeping East of Skye and Mull where appropriate, and avoiding dangers. Places in *italics* are in adjoining areas.

	1	2	3	4	5	6	7	8	9	10	11	12	13	14	15	16	17	18	19	20
1. *Cape Wrath*	1																			
2. Ullapool	54	2																		
3. Stornoway	53	45	3																	
4. East Loch Tarbert	75	56	33	4																
5. Portree	83	57	53	42	5															
6. Loch Harport	110	82	65	45	66	6														
7. Kyle of Lochalsh	91	63	62	63	21	53	7													
8. Mallaig	112	82	83	84	42	33	21	8												
9. Eigg	123	98	97	75	54	34	35	14	9											
10. Castlebay (Barra)	133	105	92	69	97	43	76	59	46	10										
11. Tobermory	144	114	115	87	74	52	53	32	20	53	11									
12. Loch Aline	157	127	128	100	87	65	66	45	33	66	13	12								
13. Fort William	198	161	162	134	121	99	98	75	63	96	43	34	13							
14. Oban	169	138	139	111	100	76	77	56	44	77	24	13	29	14						
15. Loch Lathaich	160	130	124	98	91	62	67	49	35	56	31	53	77	48	15					
16. Loch Melfort	184	154	155	117	114	92	93	69	61	92	40	27	45	18	45	16				
17. Craobh Haven	184	155	155	117	114	93	92	70	60	93	40	27	50	21	43	5	17			
18. Loch Craignish	188	158	159	131	118	95	96	76	64	98	44	31	55	26	46	17	14	18		
19. *Crinan*	187	157	158	129	112	95	95	74	63	97	42	30	54	25	45	14	9	6	19	
20. *Mull of Kintyre*	232	203	189	175	159	133	143	121	105	120	89	87	98	72	78	62	57	54	51	20

STORNOWAY   8-8-7
Lewis (Western Isles) 58°11'·60N 06°21'·75W   Rtg 2-3-2

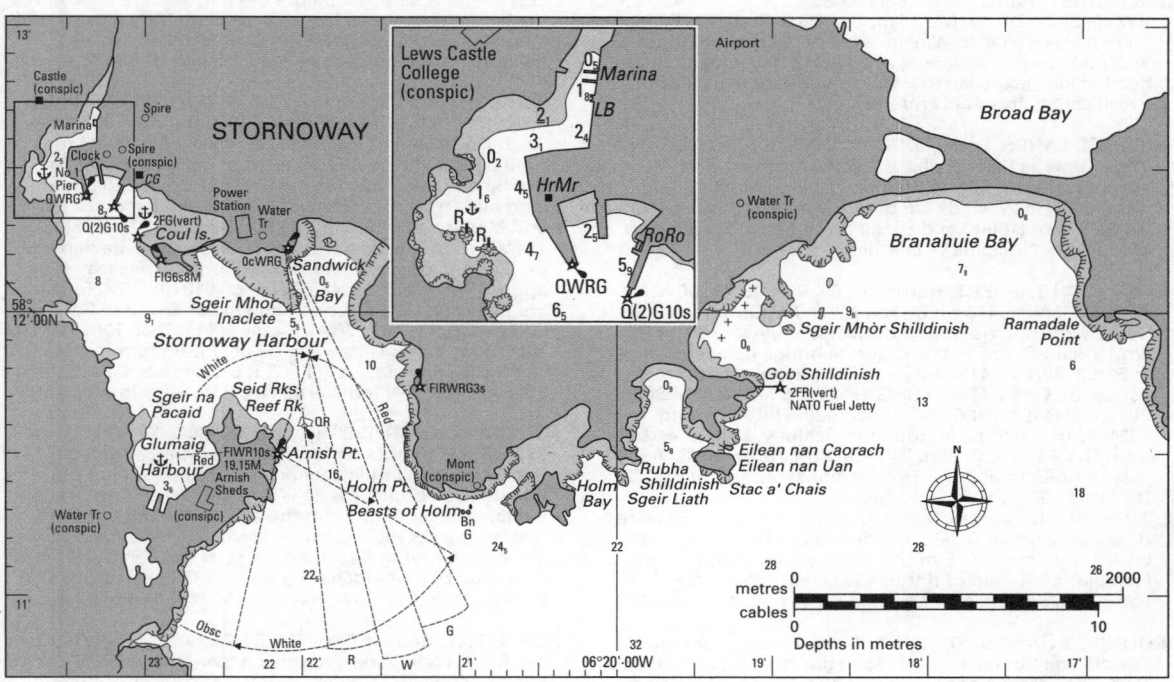

CHARTS
AC 2529, 1794, 1785; OS 8

TIDES
–0428 Dover; ML 2·8; Duration 0610; Zone 0 (UT)

Standard Port STORNOWAY (→)

Times				Height (metres)			
High Water		Low Water		MHWS	MHWN	MLWN	MLWS
0100	0700	0300	0900	4·8	3·7	2·0	0·7
1300	1900	1500	2100				

East side of Outer Hebrides, N to S

Differences LOCH SHELL (Harris)
–0013	0000	0000	–0017	0·0	–0·1	–0·1	0·0

EAST LOCH TARBERT (Harris)
–0025	–0010	–0010	–0020	+0·2	0·0	+0·1	+0·1

LEVERBURGH (Sound of Harris)
–0041	–0020	–0015	–0025	–0·2	–0·2	–0·1	–0·1

LOCH MADDY (N Uist)
–0044	–0014	–0016	–0030	0·0	–0·1	–0·1	0·0

LOCH CARNAN (S Uist)
–0050	–0010	–0020	–0040	–0·3	–0·5	–0·1	–0·1

LOCH SKIPPORT (S Uist)
–0100	–0025	–0024	–0024	–0·2	–0·4	–0·3	–0·2

LOCH BOISDALE (S Uist)
–0055	–0020	–0020	–0040	–0·7	–0·7	–0·3	–0·2

BARRA (North Bay)
–0103	–0031	–0034	–0048	–0·6	–0·5	–0·2	–0·1

CASTLEBAY (Barra)
–0115	–0040	–0045	–0100	–0·5	–0·6	–0·3	–0·1

BARRA HEAD (Berneray)
–0115	–0040	–0045	–0055	–0·8	–0·7	–0·2	+0·1

West side of Outer Hebrides, N to S

CARLOWAY (W Lewis)
–0040	+0020	–0035	–0015	–0·6	–0·5	–0·4	–0·1

LITTLE BERNERA (W Lewis)
–0021	–0011	–0017	–0027	–0·5	–0·6	–0·4	–0·2

WEST LOCH TARBERT (W Harris)
–0015	–0015	–0046	–0046	–1·1	–0·9	–0·5	0·0

SCOLPAIG (W North Uist)
–0033	–0033	–0040	–0040	–1·0	–0·9	–0·5	0·0

SHILLAY (Monach Islands)
–0103	–0043	–0047	–0107	–0·6	–0·7	–0·7	–0·3

BALIVANICH (W Benbecula)
–0103	–0017	–0031	–0045	–0·7	–0·6	–0·5	–0·2

SHELTER
Good. A small marina, max LOA 12m, at the N end of the Inner Hbr, beyond the LB berth, has depths 1·4 - 3·3m. Or AB for larger boats on adjacent Cromwell St Quay, close S; or lie alongside FVs in the inner hbr. Visitors should report to Hr Mr. Ullapool ferries use the new No 3 pier and commercial vessels on Nos 1 and 2 Piers.
S'ly swells can make anchoring uncomfortable. Much of the hbr is foul with old wire hawsers. ⚓s as on chartlet at: Poll nam Portan on the W side of inner chan, opposite No 1 Pier; Glumaig Hbr is best ⚓, but oil works may preclude this; in bay NW of Coul Island (Eilean na Gobhail).

NAVIGATION
WPT 58°10'·00N 06°20'·80W, 163°/343° from/to Oc WRG lt, 2·3M. Reef Rk, N of Arnish Pt on W side of ent, is marked by PHM buoy, QR. At the E side of ent an unlit G bn marks the Beasts of Holm, a rky patch off Holm Pt, on which is a conspic memorial. A local magnetic anomaly exists over a small area in mid-hbr, 1·75ca N of Seid Rks PHM bn.

LIGHTS AND MARKS
Arnish sheds are conspic 3ca SW of Arnish Pt lt, Fl WR 10s 17m 19/15M, W tr; W sector 302°-013° covers ent. Then in turn follow W sectors of: Sandwick B lt, (close E of water tr, 3 power stn chys and fuel tanks; all conspic) Oc WRG 6s 10m 9M, W341°-347°; then Stoney Field Fl WRG 3s 8m 11M, vis W102°-109° across hbr; and finally No 1 Pier, Q WRG 5m 11M, W335°-352°.

RADIO TELEPHONE
VHF Ch 12 16 (H24).

TELEPHONE (Dial code 01851)
Hr Mr 702688; MRSC 702013; ☰ 703626; Marinecall 0891 500464; Police 702222; Dr 703145.

FACILITIES
Marina 27 berths, inc 8 Ⓥ, £8 via Hr Mr Ch 12; FW, AC.
Nos 1 & 2 Piers FW, C (10 ton), CH, AB, Slip, P.
Services: ACA, ME, El, Sh.
Town EC Wed; P (cans), D, El, V, R, Bar, Gas, ✉, Ⓑ, ⇌ (ferry to Ullapool, bus to Garve), ✈.

HARBOURS AND ANCHORAGES ON THE EAST SIDE OF THE OUTER HEBRIDES (Western Isles), from N to S:

LOCH SHELL, Harris, 58°00′·00N 06°25′·00W. AC 1794. HW −0437 on Dover; ML 2·7m. See 8.8.7. Pass S of Eilean Iuvard; beware rks to W of Is. ⚓ in Tob Eishken, 2½M up loch on N shore (beware rk awash on E side of ent), or at head of loch (exposed to E winds; dries some distance). Facilities: ⊠/Stores at Lemreway.

SHIANT ISLANDS, Lewis, 57°53′·70N 06°21′·30W. AC 1794, 1795. Tides as Loch Shell 8.8.7. Beware strong tidal streams and overfalls in Sound of Shiant. Strictly a fair weather ⚓; in W winds ⚓ E of Mol Mor, isthmus between Garbh Eileen (160m) and Eileen an Tighe. In E winds ⚓ W of Mol Mor. No lights or facilities.

EAST LOCH TARBERT, Harris, 57°50′·00N 06°41′·00W. AC 2905. HW −0446 on Dover; ML 3·0m; Duration 0605. See 8.8.7. Appr via Sound of Scalpay; beware Elliot Rk (2m) 2½ca SSW of Rubha Crago. A bridge (20m clearance) at 57°52′·80N 06°41′·73W joins Scalpay to Harris. Bridge lts: Centre Oc 6s; N side Oc G 4s 40m; S side Oc R 4s 40m. Eilean Glas lt ho at E end of Scalpay, Fl (3) 20s 43m 23M; W tr, R bands. In Sound of Scalpay, stream sets W from HW +3, and E from HW −3. ⚓ off Tarbert WSW of steamer pier in about 2·5m. Facilities: EC Thurs; Bar, D, Dr, FW, P, ⊠, R, V, ferry to Uig.
Alternatively Scalpay N Hbr gives good shelter. Beware rk 5ca off Aird an Aiseig, E side of ent. SHM buoy marks wk off Coddem; 5ca E of the buoy is a rk, depth 1·1m. Fish pier at SE end of hbr has 2FG (vert) lts; ⚓ 7ca N, in about 3m. Facilities: FW at pier, ⊠, V, ferry to Harris.

SOUND OF HARRIS, 57°43′N 06°58′W. Passages through this difficult Sound are detailed in the *W Coast of Scotland Pilot*. The Stanton and Outer Stromay Chans off the Harris shore are the most feasible for yachts. AC 2642 shows the newly marked ferry routes from Leverburgh to Berneray.

LOCH MADDY, North Uist, 57°36′·00N 07°06′·00W. AC 2825 HW −0500 on Dover. See 8.8.7. With strong wind against tide there can be bad seas off ent. Appr clear, but from S beware submerged rk ½ca N of Leacnam Madadh. Lts: Weaver's Pt Fl 3s 21m 7M; Glas Eilean Mor Fl (2) G 4s 8m 5M; Rubna Nam Pleac Fl R 4s 7m 5M. Inside loch: Ruigh Liath QG 6m 5M; Vallaquie Is dir Fl (3) WRG 8s. Ferry pier ldg lts 298°: front 2FG(vert) 4M; rear Oc G 8s 10m 4M, vis 284°-304°. 2 ⚓s Bagh Aird nam Madadh; 2 ⚓s W of and 4 ⚓s SW of ferry pier ☎ (01870) 602425; 2 ⚓s E of Oronsay. ⚓s: clear S of ferry pier; NE of Vallaquie Is; Charles Hbr; Oronsay (⚓ not advised due to moorings), tidal berth on private pier; Sponish Hbr; Loch Portain. VHF Ch 12 16. Port Manager ☎ (01876) 5003337 (day), 5003226 (night). Facilities: Lochmaddy, EC Wed; Shop, ⑧, Gas, ⊠, P, D, FW; Loch Portain ⊠, Shop.

LOCH EPORT, North Uist, 57°33′·47N 07°08′·05W. AC 2825, but not the head of loch. Tides, approx as L Maddy; 3kn sp stream. On the S side of ent are rks, some drying. The ent proper is clean but very narrow (about 100m) for 5ca, then widens. Follow the charted clearing line 082°. Best ⚓s are: Bàgh a' Bhiorain (S of chan); and Acairseid Lee (N bank) E or W of Deer Is. V, R, Bar, ⊠ at Clachan, hd of loch.

LOCH CARNAN, South Uist, 57°22′·05N 07°16′·32W. AC 2825. Tides, see 8.8.7. SWM buoy, L Fl 10s, at 57°22′·30N 07°11′·57W is almost 2M E of app chan proper, marked by Nos 1 and 2 buoys, Fl G 2·5s and Fl R 2s, at 57°22′·45N 07°14′·90W. Round No 3 PHM buoy, Fl R 5s, between Gasay and Taigh Iamain, then pick up ldg lts 222° to Sandwick quay; front Fl R 2s, rear Iso R 10s, both 5M, W ◊s on posts. Power stn and 2 chys are conspic close to SE of quay. Call ☎ (01870) 602425 for permission to berth on the quay (MoD property). There is ⚓ or 2 ⚓s about 2ca WNW of the quay in deep water. The passage S of Gasay is unmarked and needs careful pilotage. FW, D available.

LOCH SKIPPORT, South Uist, 57°20′·00N 07°13′·60W. AC 2825, 2904. HW −0602 on Dover; see 8.8.7. Easy ent 3M NNE of Hecla (604m). No lights, but 2¼M SSE is Usinish lt ho Fl WR 20s 54m 19/15M. ⚓s at: Wizard Pool in 7m; beware Float Rk, dries 2·3m; on N side of Caolas Mor in 7m; Bagh Charmaig in 5m. Linne Arm has narrow ent, many fish farms and poor holding. No facilities.

LOCH EYNORT, South Uist, 57°13′·15N 07°16′·80W. AC 2825. Tides: interpolate between Lochs Skipport and Boisdale, see 8.8.7. ⚓s in the outer loch at Cearcdal Bay and on the N side just before the narrows are exposed to the E. The passage to Upper L Eynort is very narrow and streams reach 5-7kn; best not attempted unless local fishermen offer guidance. Good ⚓ inside at Bàgh Lathach.

LOCH BOISDALE, South Uist, 57°08′·80N 07°16′·00W. AC 2770. HW −0455 on Dover; ML 2·4m; Duration 0600. See 8.8.7. Good shelter except in SE gales when swell runs right up the 2M loch. From N, appr between Rubha na Cruibe and Calvay Is; ldg line 245°: Hollisgeir (0·3m) on with pier (ru). From S beware Clan Ewan Rk, dries 1·2m, and McKenzie Rk (2·4m), marked by PHM lt buoy Fl (3) R 15s. Chan to Boisdale Hbr lies N of Gasay Is; beware rks off E end. ⚓ off pier in approx 4m, or SW of Gasay Is in approx 9m. 4 HIE ⚓s NE of pier ☎ (01870) 602425. There are fish cages W of Rubha Bhuailt. Lts: E end of Calvay Is Fl (2) WRG 10s 16m 7/4M. Gasay Is Fl WR 5s 10m 7/4M. N side of loch, opp Gasay Is, Fl G 6s. Ro-Ro terminal Iso RG 4s 8m 2M; and close SE, Fl (2) R 5s. See 8.8.4. Facilities: EC Tues; Bar, FW (on pier), P, ⊠, R, V, ferry to mainland.

ACAIRSEID MHÓR, Eriskay, ⊕ 57°03′·80N 07°16′·28W. AC 2770. Tides approx as for North Bay (Barra), see 8.8.7. Ben Scrien (183m) is conspic, pointed peak N of hbr. Ldg lts 285°, both Oc R 6s 9/10m 4M, W △ ▽ on orange posts, lead for 0·5M from the above lat/long between two drying rks into the outer loch. A SHM buoy, Fl G 6s, marks a rk drying 3m. 3 ⚓s are at 57°03′·95N 07°17′·40W on S side of inner loch, opp pier, 2 FG (vert). ☎ (01870) 602425. V, R, Bar, ⊠ at Haun, 1·5M at N end of island.

NORTH BAY, Barra, 57°00′·13N 07°24′·60W. AC 2770. Tides see 8.8.7. Well marked approach to inlet sheltered from S and W winds. WPT 56°58′·68N 07°20′·31W is about 200m NE of Curachan ECM buoy, Q (3) 10s, and in the white sector (304°-306°) of Ardveenish dir ☆ 305°, Oc WRG 3s, 2·5M to the WNW. ⚓ 1ca WNW of Black Island or in N part of Bay Hirivagh where there are ⚓s; or tempy AB on the quay in 4·5m. FW, Bar, V, bus to Castlebay.

CASTLEBAY, Barra, 56°56′·80N 07°29′·60W. AC 2769. HW −0525 on Dover; ML 2·3m; Duration 0600. See 8.8.7. Very good shelter & holding. Best ⚓ in approx 8m NW of Kiessimul Castle (on an island); NE of castle are rks. 8 HIE ⚓s lie to W of pier ☎ (01870) 602425. Or ⚓ in Vatersay Bay in approx 9m. W end of Vatersay Sound is closed by a causeway. Beware rks NNW of Sgeir Dubh a conspic W/G tr, Fl (2) WG 6s 6m 7/5M, vis W280°-117°, G117°-280°; which leads 283° in transit with Sgeir Liath, Fl 3s 7m 8M. Chan Rk, 2ca to the S, is marked by Fl WR 6s 4m 6/4M. Close-in ldg lts 295°, both FG 11M on W framework trs: front 9m Or △ on Rubha Glas; rear, 457m from front, 15m Or ▽. Facilities: Bar, D, FW, P, ⊠, R, V, Ferry to mainland.

HIE ⚓s are also located in the Outer Hebrides at:
Loch Rodel, Harris. AC 2642. 3 ⚓s at 57°44′·2N 06°57′·4W in Poll an Tigh-mhàil; enter from SW past jetties. No lts. ☎ (01851) 703773.
Kallin, Grimsay. AC 2904. 1 ⚓ at 57°28′·9N 07°12′·2W, NE of hbr. 3 chan lt buoys and 2 FR (vert) on hbr bkwtr. ☎ (01870) 602425.

The Skipper must not only know his vessel and how to handle her, but he must be able to navigate her and must know the sea. He must be watchful and careful. He needs 'nerve', coolness and endurance, this endurance being a mental rather than a physical quality. Above all he must not be liable to panic in a sudden emergency.

I have known men who, faced with an awkward situation and knowing exactly what should be done, lose their heads and do something quite different – perhaps run for a difficult harbour on a lee shore, thereby taking a risk twenty times greater than that which they are trying to avoid. They, fortunately, are exceptions.

Of the average man R.L.Stevenson has truly said:
'It is a commonplace that we cannot answer for ourselves until we have been tried. But it is not so common a reflection, and surely more consoling, that we usually find ourselves a great deal braver and better than we thought. I believe this is every one's experience.'

Yacht Cruising: Claud Worth 1910.

SCOTLAND – STORNOWAY

LAT 58°12′N   LONG 6°23′W

TIMES AND HEIGHTS OF HIGH AND LOW WATERS

YEAR **1999**

TIME ZONE (UT)
For Summer Time add ONE hour in non-shaded areas

Chart Datum: 2·71 metres below Ordnance Datum (Newlyn)

JANUARY

Day	Time	m	Day	Time	m
1 F	0558 / 1223 / 1819	4.8 / 0.9 / 4.8	**16** SA	0007 / 0606 / 1227 / 1827	1.3 / 4.4 / 1.3 / 4.2
2 SA O	0036 / 0642 / 1312 / 1904	0.8 / 4.9 / 0.7 / 4.8	**17** SU	0044 / 0638 / 1305 / 1901	1.1 / 4.6 / 1.0 / 4.3
3 SU	0121 / 0725 / 1357 / 1949	0.7 / 5.0 / 0.6 / 4.8	**18** M	0119 / 0712 / 1341 / 1935	0.9 / 4.7 / 0.8 / 4.4
4 M	0204 / 0807 / 1441 / 2032	0.8 / 5.0 / 0.7 / 4.6	**19** TU	0155 / 0746 / 1419 / 2009	0.8 / 4.8 / 0.7 / 4.4
5 TU	0245 / 0849 / 1524 / 2115	0.9 / 4.9 / 0.8 / 4.4	**20** W	0231 / 0822 / 1457 / 2046	0.8 / 4.8 / 0.6 / 4.4
6 W	0325 / 0931 / 1607 / 2200	1.1 / 4.7 / 1.0 / 4.2	**21** TH	0308 / 0901 / 1536 / 2126	0.8 / 4.7 / 0.7 / 4.2
7 TH	0407 / 1017 / 1651 / 2250	1.3 / 4.4 / 1.3 / 3.9	**22** F	0348 / 0945 / 1620 / 2214	0.9 / 4.5 / 0.8 / 4.1
8 F	0451 / 1109 / 1738 / 2349	1.6 / 4.2 / 1.5 / 3.7	**23** SA	0432 / 1039 / 1708 / 2315	1.1 / 4.3 / 1.0 / 3.9
9 SA	0540 / 1211 / 1832	1.9 / 3.9 / 1.8	**24** SU	0523 / 1144 / 1803	1.4 / 4.2 / 1.2
10 SU	0100 / 0638 / 1324 / 1936	3.6 / 2.1 / 3.7 / 1.9	**25** M	0030 / 0626 / 1257 / 1906	3.7 / 1.6 / 4.0 / 1.4
11 M	0215 / 0751 / 1440 / 2049	3.5 / 2.2 / 3.7 / 1.9	**26** TU	0146 / 0742 / 1411 / 2021	3.7 / 1.7 / 4.0 / 1.5
12 TU	0321 / 0911 / 1544 / 2154	3.6 / 2.1 / 3.7 / 1.8	**27** W	0300 / 0908 / 1523 / 2140	3.8 / 1.6 / 4.0 / 1.4
13 W	0413 / 1015 / 1635 / 2246	3.8 / 2.0 / 3.8 / 1.7	**28** TH	0406 / 1024 / 1628 / 2247	4.0 / 1.4 / 4.1 / 1.3
14 TH	0456 / 1105 / 1717 / 2329	4.0 / 1.8 / 3.9 / 1.5	**29** F	0502 / 1126 / 1723 / 2341	4.3 / 1.2 / 4.3 / 1.1
15 F	0533 / 1148 / 1754	4.2 / 1.5 / 4.0	**30** SA	0550 / 1218 / 1811	4.5 / 0.9 / 4.5
			31 SU O	0028 / 0632 / 1304 / 1853	0.9 / 4.7 / 0.7 / 4.6

FEBRUARY

Day	Time	m	Day	Time	m
1 M	0111 / 0711 / 1346 / 1932	0.7 / 4.9 / 0.5 / 4.6	**16** TU ●	0101 / 0653 / 1323 / 1917	0.8 / 4.8 / 0.6 / 4.6
2 TU	0150 / 0748 / 1425 / 2009	0.7 / 4.9 / 0.5 / 4.6	**17** W	0138 / 0728 / 1400 / 1951	0.6 / 5.0 / 0.4 / 4.7
3 W	0228 / 0823 / 1502 / 2045	0.7 / 4.9 / 0.6 / 4.4	**18** TH	0214 / 0803 / 1437 / 2026	0.5 / 5.0 / 0.3 / 4.7
4 TH	0304 / 0858 / 1539 / 2121	0.8 / 4.7 / 0.7 / 4.3	**19** F	0251 / 0841 / 1516 / 2104	0.5 / 5.0 / 0.3 / 4.5
5 F	0340 / 0934 / 1616 / 2159	1.0 / 4.5 / 0.9 / 4.0	**20** SA	0329 / 0923 / 1557 / 2147	0.6 / 4.8 / 0.5 / 4.3
6 SA	0417 / 1014 / 1654 / 2244	1.3 / 4.2 / 1.3 / 3.8	**21** SU	0411 / 1013 / 1642 / 2240	0.8 / 4.5 / 0.8 / 4.0
7 SU	0458 / 1101 / 1737 / 2339	1.6 / 3.9 / 1.6 / 3.6	**22** M	0459 / 1116 / 1732 / 2355	1.1 / 4.2 / 1.1 / 3.8
8 M	0544 / 1200 / 1827	1.8 / 3.6 / 1.9	**23** TU	0558 / 1235 / 1834	1.4 / 3.9 / 1.5
9 TU	0051 / 0640 / 1319 / 1932	3.5 / 2.1 / 3.5 / 2.0	**24** W	0121 / 0716 / 1358 / 1954	3.6 / 1.7 / 3.8 / 1.7
10 W	0221 / 0755 / 1459 / 2101	3.5 / 2.2 / 3.4 / 2.1	**25** TH	0244 / 0858 / 1517 / 2129	3.7 / 1.7 / 3.8 / 1.7
11 TH	0334 / 0932 / 1606 / 2214	3.6 / 2.1 / 3.5 / 1.9	**26** F	0356 / 1021 / 1624 / 2241	3.9 / 1.5 / 3.9 / 1.5
12 F	0426 / 1038 / 1655 / 2304	3.8 / 1.9 / 3.7 / 1.7	**27** SA	0454 / 1121 / 1718 / 2334	4.1 / 1.2 / 4.1 / 1.2
13 SA	0508 / 1126 / 1735 / 2346	4.0 / 1.6 / 3.9 / 1.4	**28** SU	0541 / 1209 / 1801	4.4 / 0.9 / 4.3
14 SU	0545 / 1207 / 1810	4.3 / 1.3 / 4.2			
15 M	0024 / 0619 / 1246 / 1844	1.1 / 4.6 / 0.9 / 4.4			

MARCH

Day	Time	m	Day	Time	m
1 M	0017 / 0619 / 1251 / 1838	1.0 / 4.6 / 0.7 / 4.4	**16** TU	0554 / 1220 / 1821	4.6 / 0.8 / 4.6
2 TU O	0057 / 0654 / 1328 / 1911	0.8 / 4.8 / 0.5 / 4.5	**17** W ●	0037 / 0630 / 1259 / 1855	0.8 / 5.0 / 0.5 / 4.8
3 W	0133 / 0726 / 1403 / 1943	0.6 / 4.8 / 0.5 / 4.6	**18** TH	0115 / 0705 / 1337 / 1929	0.5 / 5.2 / 0.2 / 4.9
4 TH	0207 / 0757 / 1436 / 2014	0.6 / 4.8 / 0.5 / 4.5	**19** F	0153 / 0742 / 1415 / 2005	0.3 / 5.3 / 0.1 / 4.9
5 F	0240 / 0827 / 1508 / 2046	0.7 / 4.7 / 0.7 / 4.4	**20** SA	0231 / 0821 / 1454 / 2043	0.3 / 5.2 / 0.2 / 4.8
6 SA	0313 / 0858 / 1540 / 2119	0.9 / 4.5 / 0.9 / 4.2	**21** SU	0311 / 0904 / 1534 / 2126	0.4 / 5.0 / 0.4 / 4.5
7 SU	0347 / 0932 / 1615 / 2157	1.1 / 4.2 / 1.2 / 4.0	**22** M	0354 / 0954 / 1618 / 2218	0.7 / 4.6 / 0.8 / 4.2
8 M	0423 / 1012 / 1653 / 2245	1.4 / 3.9 / 1.5 / 3.7	**23** TU	0442 / 1100 / 1707 / 2335	1.0 / 4.2 / 1.2 / 3.9
9 TU	0504 / 1105 / 1737 / 2348	1.7 / 3.6 / 1.8 / 3.5	**24** W	0541 / 1224 / 1808	1.4 / 3.9 / 1.6
10 W	0553 / 1217 / 1833	2.0 / 3.4 / 2.1	**25** TH	0105 / 0705 / 1349 / 1935	3.7 / 1.7 / 3.7 / 1.9
11 TH	0106 / 0656 / 1354 / 1951	3.4 / 2.2 / 3.3 / 2.2	**26** F	0229 / 0850 / 1510 / 2118	3.7 / 1.7 / 3.7 / 1.9
12 F	0234 / 0829 / 1530 / 2132	3.5 / 2.2 / 3.4 / 2.1	**27** SA	0344 / 1012 / 1617 / 2229	3.9 / 1.5 / 3.8 / 1.6
13 SA	0345 / 1003 / 1626 / 2234	3.7 / 2.0 / 3.7 / 1.8	**28** SU	0442 / 1108 / 1707 / 2318	4.1 / 1.2 / 4.0 / 1.4
14 SU	0435 / 1057 / 1709 / 2319	4.0 / 1.6 / 3.9 / 1.5	**29** M	0526 / 1152 / 1746 / 2359	4.3 / 0.9 / 4.2 / 1.1
15 M	0517 / 1141 / 1746 / 2359	4.3 / 1.2 / 4.3 / 1.1	**30** TU	0602 / 1230 / 1819	4.5 / 0.7 / 4.4
			31 W O	0036 / 0633 / 1305 / 1848	0.9 / 4.6 / 0.6 / 4.5

APRIL

Day	Time	m	Day	Time	m
1 TH	0111 / 0702 / 1337 / 1917	0.8 / 4.7 / 0.6 / 4.6	**16** F ●	0051 / 0643 / 1311 / 1907	0.6 / 5.2 / 0.2 / 5.1
2 F	0144 / 0730 / 1407 / 1946	0.7 / 4.7 / 0.6 / 4.5	**17** SA	0131 / 0722 / 1351 / 1945	0.4 / 5.3 / 0.1 / 5.1
3 SA	0215 / 0758 / 1437 / 2015	0.7 / 4.6 / 0.7 / 4.5	**18** SU	0212 / 0804 / 1432 / 2025	0.3 / 5.2 / 0.2 / 5.0
4 SU	0247 / 0828 / 1508 / 2047	0.8 / 4.4 / 0.9 / 4.3	**19** M	0255 / 0850 / 1513 / 2111	0.4 / 5.0 / 0.5 / 4.7
5 M	0319 / 0901 / 1540 / 2123	1.0 / 4.2 / 1.2 / 4.1	**20** TU	0340 / 0944 / 1558 / 2207	0.7 / 4.6 / 0.9 / 4.4
6 TU	0354 / 0938 / 1616 / 2207	1.3 / 3.9 / 1.5 / 3.9	**21** W	0431 / 1052 / 1647 / 2324	1.0 / 4.2 / 1.3 / 4.1
7 W	0433 / 1026 / 1657 / 2306	1.6 / 3.6 / 1.8 / 3.7	**22** TH	0533 / 1213 / 1749	1.4 / 3.9 / 1.7
8 TH	0518 / 1139 / 1749	1.8 / 3.4 / 2.0	**23** F	0048 / 0655 / 1334 / 1914	3.9 / 1.7 / 3.7 / 2.0
9 F	0020 / 0618 / 1308 / 1900	3.5 / 2.0 / 3.3 / 2.2	**24** SA	0207 / 0829 / 1453 / 2051	3.8 / 1.7 / 3.7 / 2.0
10 SA	0138 / 0739 / 1440 / 2035	3.5 / 2.1 / 3.4 / 2.2	**25** SU	0321 / 0948 / 1600 / 2202	3.9 / 1.5 / 3.8 / 1.8
11 SU	0253 / 0913 / 1548 / 2152	3.7 / 1.9 / 3.7 / 1.9	**26** M	0419 / 1043 / 1649 / 2252	4.1 / 1.3 / 3.9 / 1.5
12 M	0354 / 1019 / 1636 / 2244	4.0 / 1.6 / 4.0 / 1.6	**27** TU	0504 / 1126 / 1725 / 2334	4.2 / 1.1 / 4.1 / 1.3
13 TU	0442 / 1107 / 1716 / 2328	4.3 / 1.2 / 4.3 / 1.2	**28** W	0539 / 1203 / 1756	4.3 / 0.9 / 4.3
14 W	0524 / 1150 / 1754	4.7 / 0.8 / 4.7	**29** TH	0011 / 0610 / 1238 / 1824	1.1 / 4.4 / 0.8 / 4.4
15 TH	0009 / 0603 / 1231 / 1830	0.9 / 5.0 / 0.4 / 4.9	**30** F O	0046 / 0638 / 1309 / 1852	1.0 / 4.5 / 0.8 / 4.5

SCOTLAND – STORNOWAY

LAT 58°12′N   LONG 6°23′W

TIMES AND HEIGHTS OF HIGH AND LOW WATERS

YEAR **1999**

TIME ZONE (UT)
For Summer Time add ONE hour in non-shaded areas

MAY

Day	Time	m	Time	m	Time	m	Time	m
1 SA	0119	0.9	0706	4.5	1340	0.8	1920	4.5
2 SU	0151	0.9	0734	4.4	1409	0.8	1950	4.5
3 M	0223	0.9	0805	4.3	1440	1.0	2023	4.4
4 TU	0256	1.1	0839	4.1	1512	1.2	2100	4.2
5 W	0331	1.3	0918	3.9	1547	1.4	2142	4.0
6 TH	0410	1.5	1006	3.7	1627	1.7	2237	3.8
7 F	0455	1.7	1114	3.5	1716	1.9	2346	3.7
8 SA	0552	1.8	1234	3.4	1822	2.1		
9 SU	0057	3.7	0704	1.9	1352	3.5	1944	2.1
10 M	0206	3.8	0823	1.7	1441	3.7	2102	1.9
11 TU	0309	4.0	0933	1.5	1558	4.0	2203	1.6
12 W	0404	4.3	1029	1.1	1644	4.3	2253	1.3
13 TH	0453	4.7	1118	0.8	1726	4.7	2340	1.0
14 F	0538	4.9	1203	0.5	1806	4.9		
15 SA •	0026	0.7	0621	5.1	1247	0.4	1846	5.1
16 SU	0111	0.5	0706	5.2	1330	0.3	1928	5.1
17 M	0157	0.4	0752	5.1	1413	0.4	2012	5.0
18 TU	0243	0.5	0841	4.9	1457	0.6	2101	4.8
19 W	0332	0.7	0937	4.6	1542	1.0	2158	4.5
20 TH	0424	1.0	1041	4.2	1632	1.4	2307	4.3
21 F	0525	1.3	1152	3.9	1731	1.7		
22 SA	0022	4.1	0634	1.5	1306	3.7	1844	2.0
23 SU	0135	3.9	0752	1.6	1420	3.6	2008	2.0
24 M	0245	3.9	0906	1.6	1528	3.7	2121	1.9
25 TU	0346	4.0	1005	1.5	1619	3.8	2217	1.7
26 W	0434	4.0	1052	1.3	1658	4.0	2303	1.5
27 TH	0513	4.1	1133	1.2	1731	4.1	2344	1.4
28 F	0547	4.2	1209	1.1	1802	4.3		
29 SA	0021	1.2	0618	4.2	1243	1.0	1831	4.4
30 SU O	0056	1.1	0647	4.2	1315	1.0	1900	4.5
31 M	0130	1.0	0718	4.2	1346	1.0	1931	4.5

JUNE

Day	Time	m	Time	m	Time	m	Time	m
1 TU	0203	1.0	0751	4.2	1418	1.0	2005	4.4
2 W	0238	1.1	0827	4.0	1451	1.1	2043	4.3
3 TH	0314	1.2	0906	3.9	1527	1.3	2124	4.1
4 F	0353	1.3	0953	3.7	1606	1.5	2214	4.0
5 SA	0438	1.4	1052	3.6	1653	1.7	2314	3.9
6 SU	0531	1.5	1200	3.5	1751	1.9		
7 M	0020	3.8	0633	1.5	1309	3.6	1901	1.9
8 TU	0125	3.8	0741	1.5	1416	3.7	2014	1.8
9 W	0229	4.0	0849	1.3	1518	3.9	2121	1.6
10 TH	0329	4.3	0951	1.1	1612	4.2	2220	1.3
11 F	0424	4.5	1047	0.9	1700	4.5	2314	1.1
12 SA	0516	4.7	1138	0.7	1746	4.7		
13 SU •	0006	0.8	0605	4.9	1227	0.6	1830	4.9
14 M	0057	0.6	0654	4.9	1314	0.5	1915	5.0
15 TU	0146	0.5	0743	4.9	1359	0.6	2001	5.0
16 W	0234	0.5	0832	4.7	1444	0.7	2049	4.9
17 TH	0323	0.6	0924	4.5	1529	1.0	2140	4.7
18 F	0413	0.8	1019	4.2	1616	1.3	2238	4.4
19 SA	0505	1.1	1119	4.0	1707	1.6	2343	4.2
20 SU	0602	1.4	1224	3.7	1806	1.8		
21 M	0051	4.0	0705	1.6	1334	3.6	1915	2.0
22 TU	0200	3.8	0813	1.7	1442	3.6	2029	1.9
23 W	0305	3.8	0918	1.7	1541	3.7	2136	1.9
24 TH	0400	3.8	1014	1.6	1628	3.8	2230	1.8
25 F	0447	3.8	1101	1.5	1706	4.0	2317	1.6
26 SA	0526	3.9	1142	1.3	1741	4.1	2358	1.4
27 SU	0602	4.0	1219	1.2	1813	4.3		
28 M O	0035	1.3	0634	4.1	1255	1.1	1844	4.4
29 TU	0112	1.1	0707	4.1	1328	1.0	1916	4.5
30 W	0146	1.0	0741	4.1	1401	1.0	1950	4.5

JULY

Day	Time	m	Time	m	Time	m	Time	m
1 TH	0222	1.0	0816	4.1	1435	1.0	2026	4.4
2 F	0259	0.9	0854	4.0	1511	1.1	2104	4.3
3 SA	0338	1.0	0935	3.9	1549	1.2	2148	4.2
4 SU	0420	1.1	1024	3.8	1631	1.4	2240	4.1
5 M	0508	1.2	1123	3.7	1722	1.6	2343	4.0
6 TU	0602	1.3	1229	3.6	1823	1.7		
7 W	0049	4.0	0703	1.3	1336	3.7	1932	1.7
8 TH	0155	4.1	0810	1.3	1443	3.8	2046	1.6
9 F	0301	4.1	0919	1.2	1545	4.0	2156	1.4
10 SA	0404	4.3	1024	1.1	1641	4.3	2259	1.2
11 SU	0502	4.4	1122	1.0	1731	4.6	2356	0.9
12 M	0555	4.6	1214	0.8	1819	4.8		
13 TU •	0048	0.7	0645	4.7	1303	0.7	1903	4.9
14 W	0138	0.5	0732	4.7	1348	0.7	1947	5.0
15 TH	0224	0.5	0818	4.7	1430	0.7	2031	4.9
16 F	0308	0.5	0903	4.5	1512	0.9	2115	4.8
17 SA	0352	0.7	0948	4.3	1554	1.1	2201	4.5
18 SU	0436	1.0	1037	4.0	1637	1.4	2252	4.3
19 M	0522	1.2	1132	3.8	1724	1.7	2353	4.0
20 TU	0613	1.5	1236	3.6	1819	1.9		
21 W	0104	3.8	0712	1.8	1349	3.5	1926	2.1
22 TH	0219	3.6	0822	1.9	1457	3.6	2047	2.1
23 F	0326	3.6	0933	1.9	1555	3.7	2158	2.0
24 SA	0421	3.6	1030	1.7	1641	3.9	2252	1.8
25 SU	0507	3.7	1117	1.6	1720	4.1	2337	1.6
26 M	0546	3.9	1158	1.4	1755	4.2		
27 TU	0017	1.4	0621	4.0	1236	1.2	1827	4.4
28 W O	0053	1.1	0654	4.1	1310	1.1	1859	4.6
29 TH	0128	0.9	0726	4.2	1344	0.9	1932	4.6
30 F	0204	0.8	0800	4.3	1418	0.9	2006	4.7
31 SA	0240	0.7	0834	4.3	1453	0.9	2041	4.6

AUGUST

Day	Time	m	Time	m	Time	m	Time	m
1 SU	0317	0.7	0911	4.2	1529	1.0	2121	4.5
2 M	0357	0.7	0953	4.1	1609	1.1	2208	4.4
3 TU	0441	0.9	1046	3.9	1655	1.3	2308	4.2
4 W	0531	1.1	1152	3.8	1751	1.5		
5 TH	0019	4.0	0628	1.3	1305	3.7	1859	1.7
6 F	0133	3.9	0737	1.4	1418	3.8	2022	1.7
7 SA	0246	4.1	0856	1.5	1528	3.9	2147	1.5
8 SU	0356	4.1	1013	1.4	1630	4.2	2255	1.3
9 M	0456	4.2	1115	1.2	1723	4.5	2351	1.0
10 TU	0549	4.4	1206	1.0	1809	4.7		
11 W •	0041	0.7	0635	4.6	1252	0.8	1850	4.9
12 TH	0126	0.5	0717	4.7	1334	0.7	1930	5.0
13 F	0207	0.5	0757	4.7	1413	0.7	2007	5.0
14 SA	0245	0.5	0835	4.6	1450	0.8	2044	4.8
15 SU	0323	0.7	0913	4.4	1527	1.0	2121	4.6
16 M	0401	0.9	0952	4.2	1605	1.3	2201	4.3
17 TU	0440	1.2	1037	3.9	1644	1.6	2248	4.0
18 W	0522	1.6	1131	3.7	1729	1.9	2350	3.7
19 TH	0610	1.9	1242	3.6	1824	2.1		
20 F	0119	3.5	0712	2.1	1406	3.5	1939	2.3
21 SA	0250	3.5	0843	2.1	1517	3.6	2123	2.2
22 SU	0355	3.5	1000	2.0	1612	3.8	2229	2.0
23 M	0446	3.7	1053	1.8	1656	4.0	2316	1.7
24 TU	0526	3.9	1135	1.6	1732	4.3	2355	1.4
25 W	0601	4.1	1213	1.3	1806	4.5		
26 TH O	0030	1.1	0633	4.3	1248	1.1	1837	4.8
27 F	0106	0.8	0705	4.5	1322	0.9	1910	4.9
28 SA	0141	0.6	0737	4.6	1356	0.7	1943	5.0
29 SU	0216	0.5	0810	4.7	1431	0.7	2018	5.0
30 M	0253	0.4	0845	4.6	1508	0.7	2056	4.8
31 TU	0332	0.6	0925	4.4	1547	0.9	2142	4.6

Chart Datum: 2·71 metres below Ordnance Datum (Newlyn)

TIME ZONE (UT)
For Summer Time add ONE hour in non-shaded areas

SCOTLAND – STORNOWAY

LAT 58°12'N   LONG 6°23'W

TIMES AND HEIGHTS OF HIGH AND LOW WATERS

YEAR 1999

SEPTEMBER

Date	Time	m	Date	Time	m
1 W	0415 1014 1632 2241	0.8 4.2 1.2 4.3	16 TH	0437 1037 1650 2251	1.6 3.9 1.8 3.7
2 TH	0502 1122 1725 2359	1.1 3.9 1.5 4.0	17 F	0520 1141 1739	1.9 3.7 2.1
3 F	0559 1243 1836	1.4 3.8 1.7	18 SA	0012 0614 1301 1843	3.5 2.2 3.6 2.4
4 SA	0122 0711 1404 2015	3.9 1.7 3.8 1.8	19 SU	0203 0734 1427 2026	3.4 2.4 3.6 2.4
5 SU	0242 0847 1520 2149	3.9 1.8 4.0 1.6	20 M	0323 0924 1534 2158	3.5 2.3 3.8 2.1
6 M	0354 1011 1624 2253	4.0 1.6 4.2 1.3	21 TU	0418 1024 1623 2247	3.7 2.1 4.1 1.8
7 TU	0453 1109 1715 2344	4.2 1.4 4.5 1.0	22 W	0459 1107 1703 2326	4.0 1.8 4.4 1.5
8 W	0541 1156 1757	4.4 1.1 4.8	23 TH	0534 1145 1738	4.3 1.4 4.7
9 TH ●	0028 0621 1237 1834	0.8 4.6 0.9 4.9	24 F	0002 0606 1221 1811	1.1 4.6 1.1 5.0
10 F	0107 0657 1315 1908	0.6 4.7 0.8 5.0	25 SA O	0038 0639 1256 1845	0.8 4.8 0.9 5.2
11 SA	0143 0731 1351 1940	0.5 4.7 0.8 5.0	26 SU	0114 0712 1332 1920	0.5 5.0 0.7 5.3
12 SU	0218 0804 1425 2012	0.6 4.7 0.8 4.9	27 M	0151 0745 1409 1956	0.4 5.0 0.6 5.3
13 M	0251 0836 1459 2043	0.7 4.5 1.0 4.6	28 TU	0228 0822 1447 2036	0.4 4.9 0.7 5.1
14 TU	0325 0910 1533 2117	1.0 4.3 1.2 4.4	29 W	0308 0902 1528 2124	0.5 4.7 0.9 4.8
15 W	0359 0948 1609 2157	1.3 4.1 1.5 4.0	30 TH	0350 0952 1614 2225	0.9 4.4 1.2 4.4

OCTOBER

Date	Time	m	Date	Time	m
1 F	0437 1104 1709 2350	1.3 4.1 1.5 4.1	16 SA	0440 1058 1704 2329	2.0 3.9 2.1<>3.6
2 SA	0535 1231 1827	1.7 4.0 1.8	17 SU	0532 1212 1804	2.2 3.7 2.3
3 SU	0116 0654 1353 2014	3.9 2.0 3.9 1.9	18 M	0105 0642 1329 1926	3.5 2.4 3.7 2.4
4 M	0237 0841 1510 2144	3.9 2.0 4.1 1.6	19 TU	0234 0822 1441 2104	3.6 2.4 3.8 2.2
5 TU	0349 1002 1614 2243	4.0 1.8 4.3 1.3	20 W	0338 0941 1540 2205	3.8 2.2 4.1 1.8
6 W	0444 1055 1703 2329	4.2 1.5 4.5 1.1	21 TH	0423 1030 1626 2249	4.1 1.9 4.4 1.5
7 TH	0527 1138 1742	4.4 1.3 4.7	22 F	0501 1110 1706 2328	4.4 1.5 4.7 1.1
8 F	0008 0602 1217 1815	0.9 4.6 1.1 4.9	23 SA	0537 1149 1744	4.7 1.2 5.0
9 SA ●	0044 0704 1252 1845	0.8 4.7 1.0 4.9	24 SU O	0007 0611 1229 1820	0.8 5.0 0.9 5.3
10 SU	0117 0704 1314 1914	0.7 4.7 0.9 4.9	25 M	0046 0647 1308 1858	0.5 5.2 0.7 5.4
11 M	0148 0734 1359 1942	0.8 4.7 0.9 4.8	26 TU	0126 0723 1348 1939	0.4 5.2 0.6 5.4
12 TU	0219 0803 1431 2012	0.9 4.7 1.1 4.6	27 W	0205 0803 1430 2023	0.6 5.1 0.7 5.2
13 W	0251 0835 1504 2044	1.1 4.5 1.3 4.4	28 TH	0247 0846 1514 2114	0.6 4.9 0.9 4.8
14 TH	0323 0911 1539 2121	1.3 4.3 1.5 4.1	29 F	0330 0940 1603 2219	1.0 4.6 1.2 4.5
15 F	0359 0956 1618 2211	1.6 4.1 1.8 3.8	30 SA	0419 1053 1702 2342	1.4 4.3 1.5 4.1
31 SU	0517 1216 1821	1.8 4.1 1.8			

NOVEMBER

Date	Time	m	Date	Time	m
1 M	0102 0637 1334 1956	3.9 2.1 4.1 1.8	16 TU	0018 0602 1240 1844	3.5 2.3 3.8 2.1
2 TU	0221 0818 1449 2120	3.9 2.2 4.1 1.7	17 W	0135 0721 1346 2001	3.6 2.4 3.9 2.0
3 W	0332 0937 1554 2220	4.0 2.0 4.3 1.4	18 TH	0244 0840 1448 2111	3.8 2.2 4.1 1.8
4 TH	0427 1031 1643 2304	4.2 1.7 4.4 1.2	19 F	0339 0942 1543 2206	4.0 1.9 4.3 1.4
5 F	0507 1114 1722 2342	4.3 1.5 4.6 1.1	20 SA	0425 1032 1631 2253	4.4 1.6 4.7 1.1
6 SA	0541 1152 1754	4.5 1.3 4.6	21 SU	0506 1118 1715 2337	4.7 1.3 4.9 0.8
7 SU	0017 0611 1228 1823	1.0 4.6 1.2 4.7	22 M	0545 1202 1758	4.9 1.0 5.2
8 M ●	0050 0640 1302 1851	1.0 4.7 1.1 4.7	23 TU O	0021 0625 1247 1841	0.6 5.1 0.8 5.3
9 TU	0121 0708 1335 1919	1.0 4.7 1.1 4.6	24 W	0104 0706 1332 1926	0.5 5.2 0.7 5.2
10 W	0152 0738 1408 1949	1.0 4.7 1.1 4.5	25 TH	0147 0749 1418 2014	0.6 5.2 0.7 5.1
11 TH	0223 0810 1441 2022	1.1 4.6 1.3 4.3	26 F	0231 0836 1506 2108	0.7 5.0 0.8 4.8
12 F	0255 0846 1516 2101	1.3 4.4 1.5 4.1	27 SA	0316 0931 1557 2210	1.0 4.8 1.0 4.5
13 SA	0331 0929 1555 2148	1.6 4.2 1.7 3.8	28 SU	0405 1037 1655 2321	1.4 4.5 1.3 4.2
14 SU	0410 1024 1640 2257	1.8 4.0 1.9 3.6	29 M	0501 1150 1802	1.7 4.3 1.6
15 M	0459 1132 1735	2.1 3.9 2.1	30 TU	0034 0610 1303 1918	3.9 2.0 4.2 1.7

DECEMBER

Date	Time	m	Date	Time	m
1 W	0148 0733 1414 2036	3.8 2.1 4.1 1.7	16 TH	0041 0631 1257 1911	3.6 2.1 3.9 1.7
2 TH	0259 0853 1520 2141	3.8 2.1 4.1 1.6	17 F	0148 0742 1400 2019	3.7 2.0 4.0 1.6
3 F	0358 0956 1615 2232	4.0 1.9 4.2 1.5	18 SA	0251 0851 1501 2122	3.9 1.9 4.2 1.4
4 SA	0442 1045 1658 2313	4.1 1.7 4.3 1.3	19 SU	0347 0954 1558 2220	4.2 1.6 4.4 1.2
5 SU	0517 1127 1734 2350	4.3 1.5 4.4 1.2	20 M	0437 1049 1651 2312	4.5 1.4 4.7 1.0
6 M	0550 1205 1806	4.4 1.4 4.3	21 TU	0523 1142 1741	4.7 1.1 4.9
7 TU ●	0025 0620 1242 1836	1.2 4.5 1.2 4.4	22 W O	0001 0608 1233 1830	0.8 5.0 0.8 5.0
8 W	0059 0650 1317 1905	1.1 4.6 1.2 4.4	23 TH	0049 0653 1322 1918	0.7 5.1 0.7 5.0
9 TH	0131 0721 1351 1937	1.1 4.6 1.2 4.3	24 F	0135 0739 1411 2007	0.6 5.2 0.6 4.9
10 F	0203 0754 1425 2011	1.1 4.6 1.2 4.2	25 SA	0220 0826 1459 2057	0.7 5.1 0.6 4.8
11 SA	0236 0830 1500 2049	1.2 4.5 1.3 4.1	26 SU	0305 0916 1547 2149	0.9 4.9 0.8 4.5
12 SU	0311 0909 1539 2131	1.4 4.3 1.4 3.9	27 M	0351 1010 1638 2247	1.1 4.7 1.0 4.2
13 M	0349 0955 1621 2225	1.6 4.1 1.5 3.7	28 TU	0440 1111 1732 2352	1.4 4.4 1.3 3.9
14 TU	0433 1051 1710 2331	1.8 4.0 1.7 3.6	29 W	0535 1218 1832	1.7 4.2 1.5
15 W	0527 1153 1807	2.0 3.9 1.7	30 TH	0101 0639 1328 1939	3.7 2.0 4.0 1.7
			31 F	0212 0754 1438 2049	3.7 2.1 3.9 1.8

Chart Datum: 2·71 metres below Ordnance Datum (Newlyn)

8

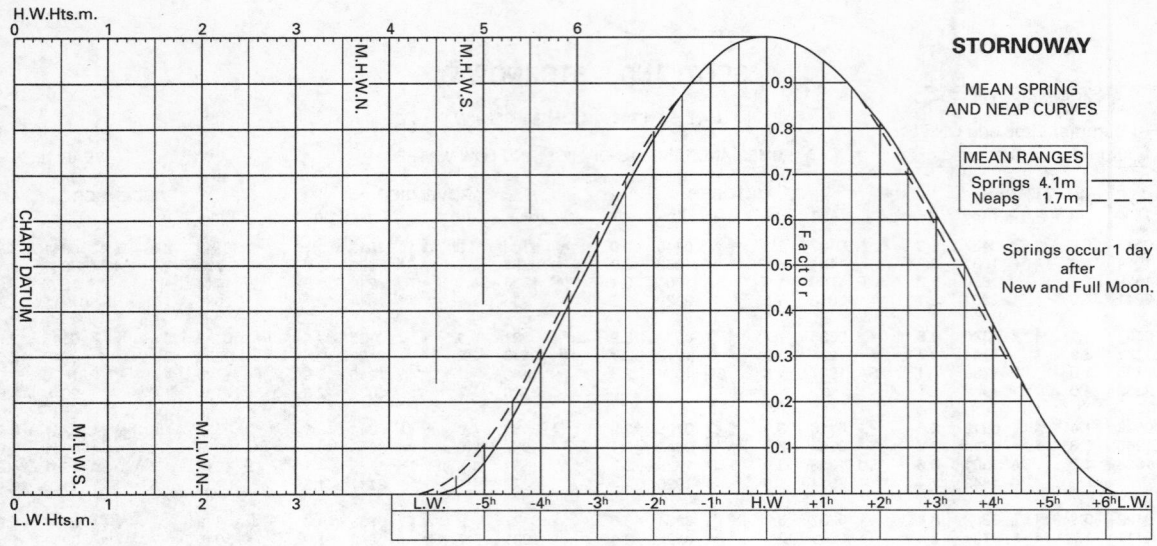

STORNOWAY

MEAN SPRING
AND NEAP CURVES

MEAN RANGES

Springs	4.1m
Neaps	1.7m

Springs occur 1 day
after
New and Full Moon.

ISLANDS WEST OF THE OUTER HEBRIDES (N to S)

TIDES

Standard Port ULLAPOOL (→)

Times				Height (metres)			
High Water		Low Water		MHWS	MHWN	MLWN	MLWS
0000	0600	0300	0900	5·2	3·9	2·1	0·7
1200	1800	1500	2100				
FLANNAN ISLES							
−0036	−0026	−0026	−0036	−1·3	−0·9	−0·7	−0·2
VILLAGE BAY (St Kilda)							
−0050	−0050	−0055	−0055	−1·8	−1·4	−0·9	−0·3
ROCKALL							
−0105	−0105	−0115	−0115	−2·2	−1·7	−1·0	−0·2

FLANNAN ISLES, Western Isles, centred on 58°17′·30N 07°35′·20W (Eilean Mór). AC 2524, 2721. Tides, as above. Uninhabited group of several rky islets, 18M WNW of Gallan Head (Lewis). The main islet is Eilean Mór where landing can be made on SW side in suitable conditions. Lt ho, Fl (2) 30s 101m 20M, is a 23m high W tr on NE tip of Eilean Mór; the lt is obscured by islets to the W which are up to 57m high. No recommended ‡s and the few charted depths are by lead-line surveys.

ST KILDA, Western Isles, 57°48′·30N 08°33′·00W. AC 2524, 2721. Tides at Village Bay, Hirta: HW −0510 on Dover; ML 1·9m; Duration 0615; see above. A group of four isles and three stacks, the main island is Hirta from which the Army withdrew in April 1998 after 30 years. The facility is now manned by a civilian company, Serco ☎ (01870) 604443, based at South Uist. Hirta is owned by National Trust for Scotland and leased to Scottish National Heritage whose Warden lives at Village Bay. ‡ in Village Bay, SE-facing, in approx 5m about 1·5ca off the pier. Ldg lts 270°, both Oc 5s 26/38m 3M. If wind is between NE and SSW big swells enter the bay; good holding, but untenable if winds strong. Levenish Is (55m) is 1·5M E of Hirta with offlying rks. Call *Kilda Radio* VHF Ch 16 08 (HJ) for permission to land; ☎ (01870) 602384. Alternative ‡ at Glen Bay on N side is only safe in S & E winds. Facilities: FW from wells near landings.

ROCKALL, 57°35′·7N 13°41′·2W. AC 2524, 1128. Tides, as above. A 19m high granite rock, 200M W of N Uist. Best access by helicopter. Lt, Fl 15s 13M, is often extinguished for long periods due to weather damage. Helen's Reef, 1·4m, on which the sea breaks is 2M ENE.

MONACH ISLANDS (or Heisker Is), centred on 57°31′·30N 07°38′·00W. AC 2721, 2721. Tides, see 8.8.7 Shillay. The group lies 5M SW of N Uist and 8M WNW of Benbecula. The 5 main islands (W-E) are Shillay, Ceann Iar, Shivinish, Ceann Ear and Stockay; all uninhabited. There are many rky offliers from NW through N to SE of the group. On Shillay there is a conspic, disused, red brick lt ho. ‡s at: E of disused lt ho; Croic Hbr, bay N of Shivinish; and S Hbr on W side of Shivinish. Detailed directions required.

KINLOCHBERVIE   8-8-8

Highland 58°27'·28N 05°02'·70W   Rtg 1-3-2

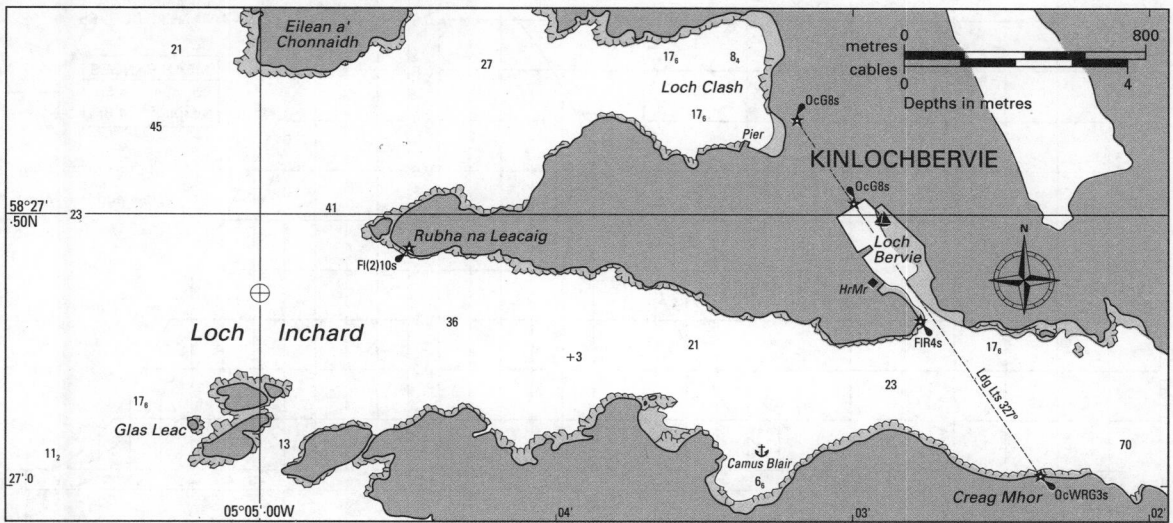

CHARTS
AC 2503, 1785, 1954; OS 9
TIDES
–0400 Dover; ML 2·7; Duration 0610; Zone 0 (UT)

Standard Port ULLAPOOL (→)

Times				Height (metres)			
High Water		Low Water		MHWS	MHWN	MLWN	MLWS
0000	0600	0300	0900	5·2	3·9	2·1	0·7
1200	1800	1500	2100				
Differences LOCH BERVIE							
+0030	+0010	+0010	+0020	–0·3	–0·3	–0·2	0·0
LOCH LAXFORD							
+0015	+0015	+0005	+0005	–0·3	–0·4	–0·2	0·0
BADCALL BAY							
+0005	+0005	+0005	+0005	–0·7	–0·5	–0·5	+0·2
LOCH NEDD							
0000	0000	0000	0000	–0·3	–0·2	0·0	0·0
LOCH INVER							
–0005	–0005	–0005	–0005	–0·2	0·0	0·0	+0·1

SHELTER
Very good in Kinlochbervie Hbr off the N shore of Loch Inchard. A useful passage port, only 14.5 track miles S of Cape Wrath. It is also a very busy FV port, but in NNE corner yachts AB on 18m long pontoon in 4m on SW side only; NE side is shoal/foul. If full, ‡ at Loch Clash, open to W; landing jetty in 2·7m. Other ‡s at: Camus Blair on S shore, 5ca SW of hbr ent, and up the loch at L Sheigra, Achriesgill Bay and 5ca short of the head of the loch.

NAVIGATION
WPT 58°27'·36N 05°05'·00W (at mouth of Loch Inchard), 280°/100° from/to hbr ent, 1·3M. The sides of the loch are clean, but keep to N side of Loch Inchard to clear a rk (3m depth) almost in mid-chan.

LIGHTS AND MARKS
From offshore in good vis Ceann Garbh, a conspic mountain 899m (6M inland) leads 110° toward ent of Loch Inchard. Rubha na Leacaig, Fl (2) 10s 30m 8M, marks N side of ent to loch. Creag Mhòr, Dir Oc lt WRG 2.8s 16m 9M, is on S shore of loch aligned 147°/327° with hbr ent chan; sectors G136·5°-146·5°, W146·°5-147·5°, R147·5°-157·5°. Ldg lts 327°into hbr, both Oc G 8s 16/26m 9M; front daymark is orange △ on white □; rear orange ▽ on white □. The 25m wide ent chan (and hbr) is dredged 4m and marked by 2 PHM poles, Fl R 4s and QR, and by a SHM pole, Fl G 4s.

RADIO TELEPHONE
VHF Ch **14** 16 HX. Ch 06 is used by FVs in the Minches.
TELEPHONE (Dial code 01971)
Hr Mr ☎ 521235, 📠 521718; MRSC (01851) 702013; ☷ (0141) 887 9369 (H24); Marinecall 0891 500 464; Police 521222; Dr 502002.
FACILITIES
FW, D at FV quay, P (cans), Gas, CH, Sh, ME, ✉, Bar, V, R. Showers (Mission), ♿. In summer, bus to Inverness.

ANCHORAGE/HARBOUR BETWEEN KINLOCHBERVIE AND ULLAPOOL

LOCH LAXFORD, Highland, 58°24'·80N 05°07'·10W. AC 2503. HW –0410 on Dover. ML 2·7m. See 8.8.8. Ent between Rubha Ruadh and Ardmore Pt, 1M ENE, clearly identified by 3 isolated mountains (N-S) Ceann Garbh, Ben Arkle and Ben Stack. The many ‡s in the loch include: Loch a'Chadh-fi, on N/NE sides of islet (John Ridgeway's Adventure School on Pt on W side of narrows has moorings); Bagh nah-Airde Beag, next bay to E, (beware rk 5ca off SE shore which covers at MHWS); Weaver's Bay on SW shore, 3M from ent (beware drying rk off NW Pt of ent); Bagh na Fionndalach Mor on SW shore (4-6m); Fanagmore Bay on SW shore (beware head of bay foul with old moorings). Beware many fish farming cages. Facilities: none, nearest stores at Scourie (5M).

LOCH INVER, Highland, 58°09'·00N 05°15'·00W. AC 2504. HW –0433 on Dover; ML 3·0m. See 8.8.8. Good shelter in all weathers at head of loch in busy fishing hbr on S side. Appr N or S of Soyea Is, Fl (2) 10s 34m 6M; beware rk drying 1·7m about 50m off Kirkaig Point (S side of ent). Glas Leac, a small islet 7ca WSW of hbr, may be passed on either side. Its ☆, Fl WRG 3s, has 3 WRG sectors (see 8.8.4) covering the chans N and S of Soyea Is and into the hbr. The church, hotel (S side) and white ho (N side) are all conspic. A pontoon for yachts, <12m LOA, is in 5m between the bkwtr (QG) and the first FV pier. Or, in W'ly gales, ‡ in the lee of bkwtr in about 8m; or where Hr Mr directs. Other ‡s on S shore of Loch Inver. VHF Ch 09 16. Hr Mr ☎ (01571) 844247. **Facilities:** FW, P, D, V, ✉, Gas.

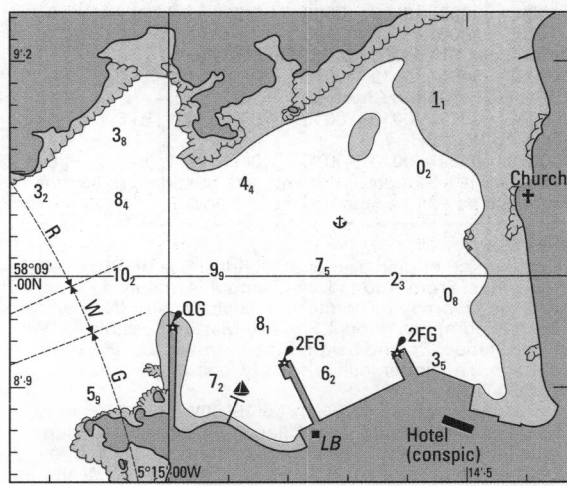

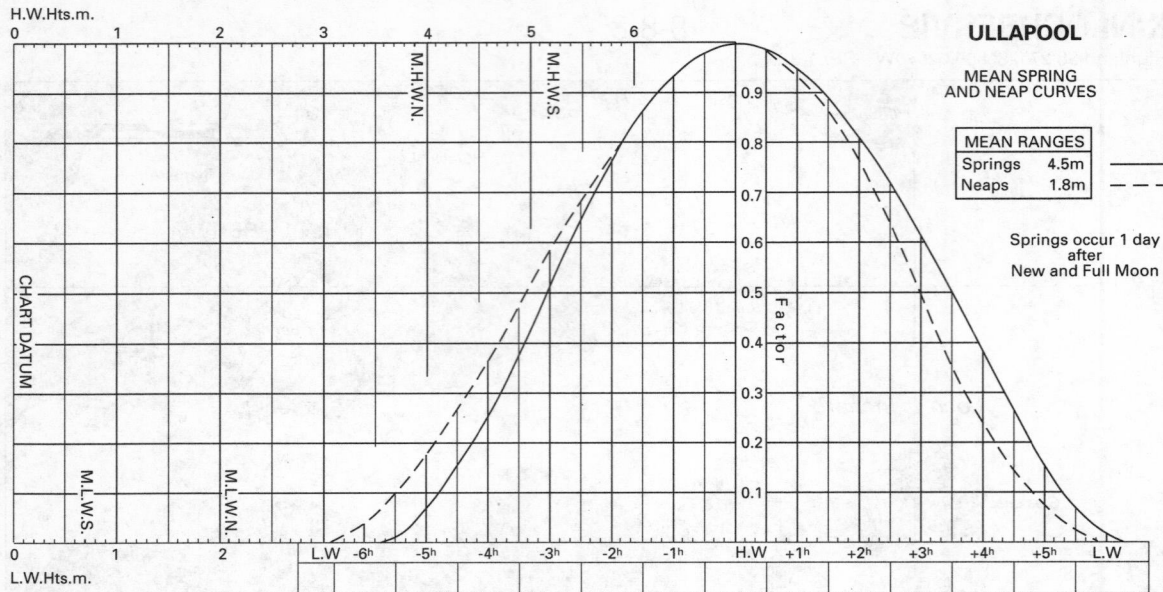

H.W.Hts.m.

ULLAPOOL

MEAN SPRING
AND NEAP CURVES

MEAN RANGES	
Springs	4.5m ———
Neaps	1.8m -----

Springs occur 1 day
after
New and Full Moon

CHART DATUM

M.H.W.N.   M.H.W.S.

M.L.W.S.   M.L.W.N.

Factor

L.W. -6h -5h -4h -3h -2h -1h H.W. +1h +2h +3h +4h +5h L.W.

L.W.Hts.m.

ULLAPOOL   8-8-9

Highland 57°53′·72N 05°09′·30W   Rtg 2-4-2

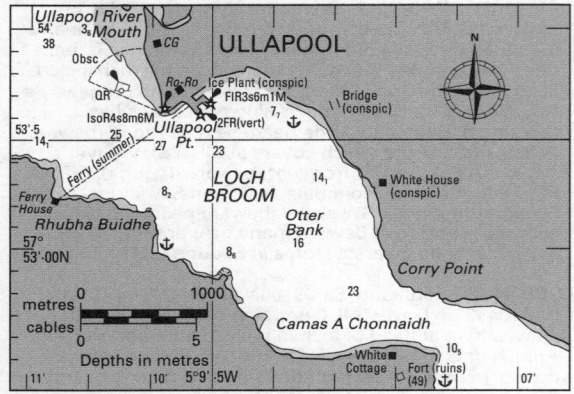

CHARTS
AC 2500, 2501, 2509, 1794; OS 19

TIDES
–0415 Dover; ML 3·0; Duration 0610; Zone 0 (UT)

Standard Port ULLAPOOL (→)

Times				Height (metres)			
High Water		Low Water		MHWS	MHWN	MLWN	MLWS
0000	0600	0300	0900	5·2	3·9	2·1	0·7
1200	1800	1500	2100				
Differences SUMMER ISLES (Tanera Mor)							
–0005	–0005	–0010	–0010	–0.1	+0.1	0.0	+0.1
LOCH EWE (Mellon Charles)							
–0010	–0010	–0010	–0010	–0.1	–0.1	–0.1	0.0
LOCH GAIRLOCH							
–0020	–0020	–0010	–0010	0.0	+0.1	–0.3	–0.1

Ullapool is a Standard Port and detailed tidal predictions
for each day of the year are given below.

SHELTER
Good in ⚓ E of pier; access at all tides. See Hr Mr for temp
moorings. From Aug to Mar Ullapool is mainly a FV port
and the pier may be congested. Loch Kanaird (N of ent to
Loch Broom) has good ⚓ E of Isle Martin. Possible ⚓s 6ca
S of Ullapool Pt, and beyond the narrows 3ca ESE of W
cottage. The upper loch is squally in strong winds.

NAVIGATION
WPT L Broom ent 57°55′·80N 05°15′·00W, 309°/129° from/
to Ullapool Pt lt, 3.5M. N of Ullapool Pt extensive drying
flats off the mouth of Ullapool R are marked by QR buoy.
Beware fish pens and unlit buoys SE of narrows off W shore.

LIGHTS AND MARKS
Rhubha Cadail, N of L. Broom ent, Fl WRG 6s 11m 9/6M.
Cailleach Hd, W of ent, Fl (2) 12s 60m 9M. Ullapool Pt Iso
R 4s 8m 6M; grey mast, vis 258°-108°.

RADIO TELEPHONE
VHF Ch 14 16 12 (July-Nov: H24. Dec-June: HO).

TELEPHONE (Dial code 01854)
Hr Mr 612091/612165; MRSC (01851) 702013; ⌗ (0141) 887
9369; Marinecall 0891 500464; Police 612017; Dr 612015.

FACILITIES
Pier AB £5 for 1 or more nights, D, FW, CH; **Ullapool YC** Gas;
Services: ME, EI, Ⓔ, Sh. **Town** EC Tues (winter); P, Ⓞ, V, R,
Bar, ✉, Ⓑ, ⇌ (bus to Garve). Daily buses to Inverness (✈),
ferries twice daily (summer) to Stornoway.

ADJACENT ANCHORAGES

SUMMER ISLES, High. 58°01′N 05°25′W. AC 2501, 2509. HW
–0425 Dover; See 8.8.9; streams are weak and irregular. In
the N apps to Loch Broom some 30 islands and rks, the main
ones being Eilean Mullagrach, Isle Ristol, Glas-leac Mor,
Tanera Beg, Eilean a' Char, Eilean Fada Mor. ⚓s: Isle Ristol,
⚓ to the S of drying causeway; close to slip is lt Fl G 3s.
Tanera Beg, ⚓ in the chan to the E inside Eilean Fada Mor
(beware bys, nets and drying rks). Tanera Mor on E side, ⚓
in bay (the "Cabbage Patch"); new pier but many moorings;
or in NW, ⚓ close E of Eilean na Saille, but N of drying rk.
Temp ⚓ at Badentarbat B for Achiltibuie on mainland.
Facilities: V, R, Gas, FW, D (emerg) ☎ (01854) 622261.

LOCH EWE, Highland, 57°52′·00N 05°40′·00W. AC 3146, 2509.
Tides: See 8.8.9; HW –0415 on Dover; ML 2·9m; Duration
068. Shelter in all winds. Easy ent with no dangers in loch.
Rhubha Reidh lt, Fl (4) 15s 37m 24M, W tr, is 4·5M W of ent.
Loch approx 7M long with Isle Ewe and 2 small islets about
2M from ent in centre; can be passed on either side. Beware
unlit buoys E side Isle Ewe. Excellent ⚓ in Loch Thurnaig to
S. Aultbea Pier, partly derelict, to NE. Beware fish farms.
Boor Rks on W shore about 7ca from loch hd. Fairway buoy
SWM L Fl 10s; No 1 lt buoy Fl (3) G 10s; NATO fuelling jetty
and dolphins, all Fl G 4s. Facilities: Dr, P, ✉, R, V, Bar. S of
Poolewe Bay (3·5m): **Inverewe Gdns** FW, D, L on pier, P (at
garage), ✉, R, Bar, V, Gas; **Aultbea** V.

LOCH GAIRLOCH, Highland, 57°43′·00N   05°45′·00W. AC
2528, 228. HW –0440 on Dover. See 8.8.9. A wide loch facing
W. Ent clear of dangers. Quite heavy seas enter in bad
weather. Good shelter in Badachro, SW of Eilean Horrisdale
on S side of loch or in Loch Shieldaig at SE end of the loch.
Or ⚓ in approx 6m near Gairloch pier (NB: proposed marina
at river mouth). Lts: Glas Eilean Fl WRG 6s 9m 6/4M, W080°-
102°, R102°-296°, W296°-333°, G333°-080°. Pier hd, QR 9m.
Hr Mr ☎ (01445) 712140. VHF Ch 16 (occas). Gairloch Pier:
AB fees charged. Facilities: P, D, FW, Hotel, Gas, V.

SCOTLAND – ULLAPOOL

LAT 57°54′N   LONG 5°10′W

TIMES AND HEIGHTS OF HIGH AND LOW WATERS

YEAR **1999**

TIME ZONE (UT)
For Summer Time add ONE hour in non-shaded areas

JANUARY

Day	Time	m	Day	Time	m
1 F	0001	1.0	**16** SA	0015	1.5
	0606	5.3		0611	4.8
	1232	1.0		1234	1.5
	1829	5.3		1831	4.7
2 SA O	0047	0.9	**17** SU	0052	1.3
	0648	5.4		0644	5.0
	1320	0.8		1311	1.2
	1915	5.4		●1904	4.8
3 SU	0132	0.8	**18** M	0127	1.2
	0729	5.5		0717	5.2
	1405	0.7		1347	1.0
	1959	5.3		1938	4.9
4 M	0215	0.9	**19** TU	0202	1.0
	0810	5.4		0752	5.2
	1449	0.8		1424	0.9
	2044	5.2		2016	4.9
5 TU	0256	1.0	**20** W	0239	1.0
	0852	5.3		0829	5.2
	1533	0.9		1503	0.8
	2130	4.9		2056	4.9
6 W	0337	1.2	**21** TH	0318	1.0
	0935	5.0		0909	5.1
	1616	1.1		1544	0.9
	2218	4.7		2139	4.7
7 TH	0419	1.5	**22** F	0359	1.1
	1022	4.8		0954	5.0
	1700	1.4		1628	1.0
	2310	4.4		2229	4.6
8 F	0503	1.8	**23** SA	0444	1.3
	1116	4.5		1045	4.8
	1747	1.7		1716	1.2
				2326	4.4
9 SA	0007	4.2	**24** SU	0536	1.6
	0550	2.0		1146	4.6
	1220	4.2		1810	1.4
	1839	2.0			
10 SU	0110	4.0	**25** M	0033	4.2
	0646	2.3		0636	1.8
	1330	4.1		1258	4.4
	1940	2.1		1914	1.7
11 M	0214	4.0	**26** TU	0149	4.2
	0754	2.4		0750	1.9
	1438	4.0		1417	4.4
	2051	2.2		2031	1.8
12 TU	0317	4.0	**27** W	0308	4.3
	0910	2.4		0917	1.9
	1541	4.1		1535	4.4
	2158	2.1		2152	1.7
13 W	0411	4.2	**28** TH	0417	4.5
	1018	2.2		1035	1.6
	1634	4.2		1642	4.6
	2252	1.9		2258	1.5
14 TH	0457	4.4	**29** F	0513	4.8
	1111	2.0		1134	1.3
	1719	4.4		1736	4.8
	2336	1.7		2351	1.2
15 F	0537	4.6	**30** SA	0600	5.0
	1154	1.7		1225	1.0
	1757	4.5		1823	5.0
			31 SU	0037	1.0
				0640	5.2
				1311	0.8
				O ●1904	5.1

FEBRUARY

Day	Time	m	Day	Time	m
1 M	0121	0.9	**16** TU ●	0109	1.0
	0717	5.3		0656	5.2
	1354	0.7		1328	0.8
	1943	5.2		●1918	5.0
2 TU	0200	0.8	**17** W	0145	0.8
	0752	5.3		0732	5.4
	1433	0.7		1405	0.5
	2021	5.1		1955	5.1
3 W	0238	0.8	**18** TH	0221	0.6
	0828	5.3		0808	5.4
	1511	0.7		1444	0.4
	2059	4.9		2034	5.1
4 TH	0315	1.0	**19** F	0300	0.6
	0904	5.1		0848	5.4
	1548	0.9		1524	0.5
	2138	4.7		2115	5.0
5 F	0351	1.1	**20** SA	0341	0.7
	0940	4.8		0930	5.2
	1624	1.1		1606	0.6
	2218	4.5		2201	4.8
6 SA	0428	1.4	**21** SU	0425	0.9
	1017	4.6		1019	4.9
	1702	1.4		1652	0.9
	2302	4.2		2255	4.5
7 SU	0507	1.7	**22** M	0513	1.2
	1100	4.3		1119	4.6
	1744	1.8		1743	1.3
	2356	4.0			
8 M	0551	2.0	**23** TU	0000	4.3
	1158	4.0		0610	1.6
	1832	2.0		1233	4.3
				1843	1.7
9 TU	0106	3.8	**24** W	0121	4.1
	0643	2.3		0722	1.9
	1329	3.8		1401	4.1
	1937	2.3		2003	1.9
10 W	0223	3.8	**25** TH	0251	4.1
	0758	2.4		0902	1.8
	1455	3.8		1529	4.2
	2108	2.3		2139	1.9
11 TH	0333	3.9	**26** F	0409	4.3
	0936	2.4		1029	1.7
	1604	3.9		1639	4.4
	2222	2.1		2249	1.6
12 F	0429	4.1	**27** SA	0507	4.5
	1045	2.1		1128	1.3
	1657	4.1		1732	4.6
	2313	1.8		2342	1.4
13 SA	0513	4.4	**28** SU	0552	4.8
	1133	1.8		1217	1.0
	1737	4.4		1814	4.8
	2355	1.5			
14 SU	0550	4.7			
	1214	1.4			
	1811	4.6			
15 M	0033	1.2			
	0623	5.0			
	1252	1.1			
	1844	4.9			

MARCH

Day	Time	m	Day	Time	m
1 M	0026	1.1	**16** TU	0009	1.2
	0629	5.0		0556	5.0
	1259	0.8		1227	0.9
	1850	5.0		1820	4.9
2 TU	0107	0.9	**17** W	0046	0.8
	0701	5.1		0632	5.3
	1338	0.6		1305	0.5
	O 1923	5.0		●1856	5.2
3 W	0143	0.8	**18** TH	0123	0.5
	0732	5.2		0709	5.5
	1413	0.6		1343	0.3
	1955	5.0		1933	5.0
4 TH	0217	0.7	**19** F	0201	0.4
	0803	5.2		0747	5.6
	1446	0.6		1422	0.2
	2028	4.9		2011	5.3
5 F	0250	0.8	**20** SA	0241	0.3
	0834	5.0		0827	5.5
	1517	0.8		1503	0.2
	2059	4.8		2053	5.2
6 SA	0323	0.9	**21** SU	0323	0.4
	0903	4.8		0911	5.3
	1550	1.0		1545	0.5
	2131	4.6		2138	4.9
7 SU	0357	1.1	**22** M	0407	0.7
	0935	4.6		1002	4.9
	1623	1.3		1630	0.8
	2205	4.3		2231	4.6
8 M	0432	1.4	**23** TU	0456	1.1
	1010	4.3		1103	4.5
	1659	1.6		1720	1.3
	2248	4.1		2337	4.3
9 TU	0510	1.7	**24** W	0553	1.5
	1054	4.0		1222	4.2
	1739	1.9		1821	1.7
	2348	3.8			
10 W	0555	2.1	**25** TH	0103	4.0
	1200	3.7		0707	1.8
	1830	2.2		1355	4.0
				1944	2.0
11 TH	0118	3.7	**26** F	0237	4.0
	0654	2.3		0853	1.9
	1356	3.6		1525	4.0
	2000	2.4		2125	2.0
12 F	0246	3.7	**27** SA	0357	4.2
	0840	2.4		1020	1.6
	1531	3.7		1632	4.2
	2148	2.2		2237	1.7
13 SA	0353	3.9	**28** SU	0455	4.4
	1013	2.1		1117	1.3
	1631	3.9		1721	4.4
	2246	1.9		2329	1.4
14 SU	0442	4.3	**29** M	0538	4.6
	1106	1.7		1202	1.0
	1712	4.3		1759	4.6
	2330	1.5			
15 M	0521	4.6	**30** TU	0011	1.2
	1148	1.3		0612	4.8
	1747	4.6		1241	0.8
				1830	4.8
			31 W	0048	1.0
				0640	4.9
				1316	0.7
				O ●1859	4.9

APRIL

Day	Time	m	Day	Time	m
1 TH	0122	0.8	**16** F	0059	0.5
	0709	5.0		0647	5.5
	1348	0.6		1319	0.2
	1929	4.9		●1911	5.4
2 F	0154	0.8	**17** SA	0140	0.3
	0738	5.0		0728	5.6
	1418	0.7		1400	0.1
	1958	4.9		1951	5.4
3 SA	0225	0.8	**18** SU	0223	0.2
	0806	4.9		0811	5.5
	1447	0.8		1442	0.2
	2026	4.8		2034	5.3
4 SU	0257	0.9	**19** M	0307	0.4
	0834	4.7		0859	5.2
	1518	0.9		1526	0.5
	2055	4.6		2121	5.0
5 M	0330	1.0	**20** TU	0353	0.6
	0905	4.5		0953	4.9
	1550	1.2		1612	0.9
	2129	4.4		2215	4.7
6 TU	0404	1.3	**21** W	0444	1.0
	0941	4.3		1058	4.5
	1623	1.5		1703	1.3
	2211	4.2		2324	4.4
7 W	0440	1.6	**22** TH	0543	1.4
	1024	4.0		1216	4.2
	1701	1.8		1805	1.8
	2306	3.9			
8 TH	0524	1.9	**23** F	0048	4.1
	1125	3.7		0657	1.7
	1749	2.1		1344	4.0
				1925	2.0
9 F	0025	3.7	**24** SA	0217	4.0
	0619	2.1		0832	1.7
	1302	3.5		1508	4.0
	1859	2.3		2100	2.0
10 SA	0154	3.7	**25** SU	0334	4.1
	0742	2.2		0956	1.6
	1445	3.6		1613	4.1
	2101	2.3		2214	1.8
11 SU	0307	3.9	**26** M	0432	4.3
	0929	2.0		1054	1.3
	1555	3.9		1701	4.3
	2210	1.9		2306	1.6
12 M	0402	4.2	**27** TU	0516	4.4
	1030	1.6		1138	1.1
	1640	4.2		1738	4.5
	2257	1.6		2347	1.3
13 TU	0447	4.6	**28** W	0549	4.6
	1116	1.2		1216	1.0
	1719	4.6		1807	4.6
	2339	1.2			
14 W	0528	4.9	**29** TH	0024	1.1
	1158	0.8		0617	4.7
	1756	5.0		1250	0.9
				1835	4.8
15 TH	0019	0.8	**30** F	0058	1.0
	0607	5.3		0646	4.8
	1238	0.4		1321	0.8
	1833	5.2		O ●1904	4.8

8

Chart Datum: 2·75 metres below Ordnance Datum (Newlyn)

SCOTLAND – ULLAPOOL

LAT 57°54′N   LONG 5°10′W

TIMES AND HEIGHTS OF HIGH AND LOW WATERS   YEAR **1999**

TIME ZONE (UT)
For Summer Time add ONE hour in non-shaded areas

MAY

Day	Time	m	Day	Time	m
1 SA	0130 / 0715 / 1350 / 1932	0.9 / 4.8 / 0.8 / 4.8	**16** SU	0122 / 0713 / 1341 / 1936	0.4 / 5.4 / 0.3 / 5.4
2 SU	0202 / 0744 / 1420 / 2000	0.9 / 4.7 / 0.9 / 4.8	**17** M	0208 / 0800 / 1425 / 2020	0.3 / 5.4 / 0.4 / 5.3
3 M	0234 / 0813 / 1451 / 2031	1.0 / 4.6 / 1.0 / 4.7	**18** TU	0254 / 0851 / 1510 / 2108	0.4 / 5.2 / 0.6 / 5.1
4 TU	0307 / 0846 / 1523 / 2107	1.1 / 4.4 / 1.2 / 4.5	**19** W	0343 / 0947 / 1557 / 2204	0.6 / 4.9 / 0.9 / 4.8
5 W	0342 / 0924 / 1557 / 2149	1.3 / 4.2 / 1.5 / 4.2	**20** TH	0435 / 1050 / 1648 / 2309	0.9 / 4.5 / 1.3 / 4.5
6 TH	0420 / 1010 / 1635 / 2242	1.5 / 4.0 / 1.7 / 4.0	**21** F	0533 / 1200 / 1747	1.2 / 4.2 / 1.7
7 F	0503 / 1110 / 1723 / 2351	1.7 / 3.8 / 2.0 / 3.9	**22** SA	0024 / 0639 / 1318 / 1857	4.2 / 1.5 / 4.0 / 2.0
8 SA	0557 / 1229 / 1827	1.9 / 3.6 / 2.2	**23** SU	0144 / 0755 / 1435 / 2016	4.1 / 1.6 / 4.0 / 2.1
9 SU	0107 / 0707 / 1353 / 1958	3.8 / 2.0 / 3.7 / 2.2	**24** M	0258 / 0913 / 1540 / 2133	4.1 / 1.6 / 4.0 / 2.0
10 M	0218 / 0834 / 1507 / 2121	3.9 / 1.8 / 3.9 / 1.9	**25** TU	0358 / 1016 / 1630 / 2231	4.1 / 1.5 / 4.2 / 1.8
11 TU	0319 / 0945 / 1603 / 2218	4.2 / 1.5 / 4.2 / 1.6	**26** W	0444 / 1105 / 1708 / 2317	4.2 / 1.4 / 4.3 / 1.6
12 W	0412 / 1039 / 1649 / 2306	4.5 / 1.2 / 4.6 / 1.2	**27** TH	0520 / 1145 / 1740 / 2356	4.3 / 1.3 / 4.5 / 1.4
13 TH	0459 / 1127 / 1732 / 2352	4.9 / 0.8 / 4.9 / 0.9	**28** F	0552 / 1220 / 1811	4.4 / 1.2 / 4.6
14 F	0544 / 1212 / 1813	5.2 / 0.5 / 5.2	**29** SA	0032 / 0625 / 1253 / 1842	1.3 / 4.5 / 1.1 / 4.7
15 SA ●	0036 / 0628 / 1257 / 1853	0.6 / 5.4 / 0.3 / 5.4	**30** SU O	0106 / 0657 / 1324 / 1912	1.1 / 4.6 / 1.1 / 4.8
			31 M	0140 / 0728 / 1356 / 1942	1.1 / 4.6 / 1.1 / 4.8

JUNE

Day	Time	m	Day	Time	m
1 TU	0214 / 0759 / 1429 / 2015	1.1 / 4.5 / 1.1 / 4.7	**16** W	0244 / 0842 / 1457 / 2056	0.5 / 5.1 / 0.7 / 5.1
2 W	0249 / 0835 / 1502 / 2052	1.1 / 4.4 / 1.2 / 4.6	**17** TH	0333 / 0935 / 1543 / 2147	0.6 / 4.9 / 1.0 / 4.9
3 TH	0325 / 0915 / 1538 / 2134	1.2 / 4.3 / 1.4 / 4.4	**18** F	0423 / 1031 / 1631 / 2244	0.8 / 4.6 / 1.3 / 4.6
4 F	0404 / 1001 / 1617 / 2223	1.3 / 4.1 / 1.6 / 4.2	**19** SA	0514 / 1130 / 1723 / 2348	1.1 / 4.3 / 1.6 / 4.3
5 SA	0448 / 1055 / 1704 / 2321	1.4 / 3.9 / 1.8 / 4.1	**20** SU	0609 / 1235 / 1820	1.4 / 4.1 / 1.8
6 SU	0538 / 1159 / 1801	1.6 / 3.8 / 1.9	**21** M	0056 / 0709 / 1343 / 1924	4.1 / 1.6 / 3.9 / 2.0
7 M	0026 / 0638 / 1310 / 1911	4.0 / 1.7 / 3.8 / 2.0	**22** TU	0205 / 0814 / 1448 / 2034	4.0 / 1.7 / 3.9 / 2.1
8 TU	0133 / 0747 / 1421 / 2028	4.0 / 1.6 / 3.9 / 1.9	**23** W	0309 / 0922 / 1546 / 2143	4.0 / 1.8 / 4.0 / 2.0
9 W	0237 / 0858 / 1526 / 2136	4.2 / 1.5 / 4.2 / 1.6	**24** TH	0403 / 1021 / 1632 / 2240	4.0 / 1.7 / 4.1 / 1.8
10 TH	0338 / 1002 / 1621 / 2235	4.5 / 1.2 / 4.5 / 1.3	**25** F	0448 / 1110 / 1712 / 2326	4.1 / 1.6 / 4.3 / 1.7
11 F	0433 / 1058 / 1710 / 2328	4.7 / 1.0 / 4.8 / 1.0	**26** SA	0528 / 1151 / 1748	4.2 / 1.5 / 4.5
12 SA	0525 / 1149 / 1756	5.0 / 0.7 / 5.1	**27** SU	0007 / 0605 / 1228 / 1823	1.5 / 4.3 / 1.4 / 4.6
13 SU ●	0018 / 0614 / 1238 / 1840	0.7 / 5.2 / 0.6 / 5.3	**28** M O	0045 / 0640 / 1303 / 1855	1.3 / 4.4 / 1.3 / 4.7
14 M	0108 / 0703 / 1325 / 1924	0.5 / 5.3 / 0.5 / 5.3	**29** TU	0121 / 0713 / 1337 / 1927	1.2 / 4.5 / 1.2 / 4.7
15 TU	0156 / 0752 / 1411 / 2009	0.4 / 5.2 / 0.6 / 5.3	**30** W	0156 / 0746 / 1411 / 2000	1.1 / 4.5 / 1.1 / 4.8

JULY

Day	Time	m	Day	Time	m
1 TH	0232 / 0821 / 1445 / 2036	1.0 / 4.5 / 1.1 / 4.7	**16** F	0317 / 0913 / 1524 / 2122	0.5 / 4.9 / 0.9 / 5.0
2 F	0308 / 0900 / 1522 / 2115	1.0 / 4.4 / 1.2 / 4.6	**17** SA	0402 / 1001 / 1607 / 2209	0.7 / 4.7 / 1.1 / 4.7
3 SA	0347 / 0943 / 1601 / 2159	1.1 / 4.3 / 1.3 / 4.5	**18** SU	0446 / 1051 / 1651 / 2302	0.9 / 4.4 / 1.4 / 4.4
4 SU	0429 / 1031 / 1645 / 2249	1.1 / 4.2 / 1.5 / 4.4	**19** M	0531 / 1145 / 1738	1.2 / 4.2 / 1.7
5 M	0516 / 1127 / 1736 / 2347	1.2 / 4.1 / 1.6 / 4.3	**20** TU	0002 / 0619 / 1245 / 1830	4.2 / 1.6 / 4.2 / 1.9
6 TU	0609 / 1230 / 1836	1.4 / 4.0 / 1.8	**21** W	0108 / 0713 / 1349 / 1931	4.0 / 1.8 / 3.8 / 2.1
7 W	0052 / 0709 / 1340 / 1945	4.2 / 1.5 / 4.0 / 1.8	**22** TH	0215 / 0818 / 1454 / 2045	3.8 / 2.0 / 3.8 / 2.2
8 TH	0201 / 0818 / 1452 / 2059	4.2 / 1.5 / 4.1 / 1.7	**23** F	0320 / 0931 / 1554 / 2201	3.8 / 2.0 / 3.9 / 2.1
9 F	0310 / 0929 / 1557 / 2210	4.3 / 1.4 / 4.4 / 1.5	**24** SA	0417 / 1034 / 1644 / 2259	3.9 / 1.9 / 4.1 / 1.9
10 SA	0415 / 1035 / 1654 / 2312	4.5 / 1.2 / 4.7 / 1.2	**25** SU	0506 / 1124 / 1726 / 2344	4.0 / 1.7 / 4.3 / 1.7
11 SU ●	0513 / 1133 / 1744	4.8 / 1.0 / 4.9	**26** M	0547 / 1205 / 1803	4.2 / 1.5 / 4.5
12 M	0007 / 0605 / 1225 / 1829	0.9 / 5.0 / 0.8 / 5.2	**27** TU	0024 / 0622 / 1243 / 1836	1.4 / 4.4 / 1.3 / 4.7
13 TU ●	0058 / 0654 / 1313 / 1912	0.7 / 5.1 / 0.7 / 5.3	**28** W O	0101 / 0655 / 1318 / 1907	1.2 / 4.5 / 1.2 / 4.9
14 W	0146 / 0741 / 1358 / 1955	0.5 / 5.2 / 0.7 / 5.3	**29** TH	0136 / 0726 / 1352 / 1939	1.0 / 4.6 / 1.0 / 5.0
15 TH	0233 / 0827 / 1442 / 2037	0.7 / 5.1 / 0.7 / 5.2	**30** F	0212 / 0801 / 1427 / 2014	0.9 / 4.7 / 1.0 / 5.0
			31 SA	0248 / 0838 / 1503 / 2051	0.8 / 4.7 / 0.9 / 4.9

AUGUST

Day	Time	m	Day	Time	m
1 SU	0326 / 0918 / 1541 / 2131	0.7 / 4.6 / 1.0 / 4.8	**16** M	0411 / 1006 / 1617 / 2210	0.9 / 4.5 / 1.2 / 4.5
2 M	0407 / 1003 / 1623 / 2218	0.8 / 4.5 / 1.2 / 4.6	**17** TU	0449 / 1051 / 1656 / 2257	1.2 / 4.3 / 1.5 / 4.2
3 TU	0451 / 1054 / 1710 / 2313	1.0 / 4.3 / 1.4 / 4.4	**18** W	0529 / 1145 / 1740	1.6 / 4.0 / 1.8
4 W	0540 / 1154 / 1805	1.2 / 4.2 / 1.6	**19** TH	0002 / 0615 / 1252 / 1832	3.9 / 1.9 / 3.8 / 2.1
5 TH	0020 / 0637 / 1306 / 1911	4.3 / 1.4 / 4.1 / 1.8	**20** F	0123 / 0715 / 1405 / 1945	3.7 / 2.2 / 3.8 / 2.3
6 F	0135 / 0745 / 1426 / 2032	4.2 / 1.6 / 4.1 / 1.8	**21** SA	0240 / 0839 / 1516 / 2123	3.7 / 2.3 / 3.8 / 2.3
7 SA	0254 / 0905 / 1542 / 2159	4.1 / 1.6 / 4.3 / 1.6	**22** SU	0349 / 1003 / 1615 / 2234	3.7 / 2.2 / 4.0 / 2.1
8 SU	0407 / 1023 / 1644 / 2306	4.4 / 1.5 / 4.5 / 1.3	**23** M	0444 / 1059 / 1702 / 2322	3.9 / 1.9 / 4.3 / 1.8
9 M	0508 / 1123 / 1736	4.6 / 1.3 / 4.8	**24** TU	0526 / 1142 / 1740	4.2 / 1.6 / 4.6
10 TU	0000 / 0559 / 1215 / 1819	1.0 / 4.8 / 1.0 / 5.1	**25** W	0001 / 0600 / 1220 / 1812	1.4 / 4.4 / 1.4 / 4.8
11 W ●	0049 / 0643 / 1300 / 1859	0.7 / 5.0 / 0.8 / 5.3	**26** TH O	0037 / 0630 / 1255 / 1843	1.1 / 4.7 / 1.1 / 5.0
12 TH	0134 / 0725 / 1343 / 1937	0.5 / 5.1 / 0.7 / 5.3	**27** F	0112 / 0701 / 1329 / 1915	0.8 / 4.9 / 0.9 / 5.2
13 F	0215 / 0805 / 1423 / 2014	0.5 / 5.1 / 0.7 / 5.2	**28** SA	0147 / 0736 / 1404 / 1949	0.6 / 5.0 / 0.7 / 5.3
14 SA	0255 / 0844 / 1501 / 2051	0.5 / 5.0 / 0.8 / 5.1	**29** SU	0223 / 0812 / 1440 / 2025	0.5 / 5.0 / 0.7 / 5.2
15 SU	0333 / 0924 / 1539 / 2130	0.7 / 4.8 / 1.0 / 4.8	**30** M	0302 / 0851 / 1519 / 2105	0.5 / 4.9 / 0.7 / 5.1
			31 TU	0342 / 0934 / 1601 / 2151	0.6 / 4.8 / 0.9 / 4.9

Chart Datum: 2·75 metres below Ordnance Datum (Newlyn)

SCOTLAND – ULLAPOOL

LAT 57°54′N   LONG 5°10′W

TIMES AND HEIGHTS OF HIGH AND LOW WATERS

YEAR **1999**

TIME ZONE (UT)
For Summer Time add ONE hour in non-shaded areas

SEPTEMBER

	Time	m		Time	m
1 W	0425 1024 1647 2247	0.8 4.5 1.2 4.6	**16** TH	0444 1037 1658 2245	1.6 4.2 1.8 4.0
2 TH	0513 1125 1740 2358	1.2 4.3 1.5 4.3	**17** F	0524 1142 1743	1.9 3.9 2.2
3 F	0609 1242 1848	1.5 4.1 1.8	**18** SA	0009 0615 1316 1846	3.7 2.3 3.8 2.4
4 SA	0123 0720 1411 2020	4.1 1.8 4.1 1.9	**19** SU	0200 0742 1437 2042	3.6 2.5 3.8 2.5
5 SU	0251 0853 1533 2158	4.1 1.9 4.2 1.7	**20** M	0321 0930 1543 2206	3.7 2.4 4.0 2.2
6 M	0407 1017 1638 2302	4.3 1.7 4.5 1.3	**21** TU	0419 1031 1632 2254	3.9 2.1 4.3 1.8
7 TU	0505 1115 1727 2352	4.6 1.4 4.8 1.0	**22** W	0501 1114 1710 2333	4.2 1.7 4.6 1.4
8 W	0551 1203 1808	4.8 1.2 5.1	**23** TH	0533 1152 1743	4.5 1.4 4.9
9 TH ●	0036 0630 1245 1843	0.7 5.0 0.9 5.2	**24** F	0009 0603 1228 1815	1.1 4.8 1.1 5.2
10 F ○	0116 0705 1324 1915	0.6 5.1 0.8 5.3	**25** SA ○	0044 0635 1303 1849	0.7 5.1 0.8 5.4
11 SA	0153 0738 1400 1947	0.5 5.1 0.7 5.2	**26** SU	0120 0710 1339 1925	0.5 5.3 0.6 5.5
12 SU	0228 0812 1435 2020	0.6 5.0 0.8 5.1	**27** M	0158 0747 1418 2002	0.4 5.3 0.5 5.5
13 M	0301 0845 1509 2051	0.7 4.9 0.9 4.9	**28** TU	0237 0826 1458 2044	0.4 5.2 0.6 5.3
14 TU	0334 0919 1543 2123	0.9 4.7 1.2 4.6	**29** W	0318 0909 1541 2132	0.5 5.0 0.8 5.0
15 W	0408 0954 1619 2159	1.2 4.4 1.5 4.3	**30** TH	0402 1000 1628 2231	0.9 4.8 1.2 4.6

OCTOBER

	Time	m		Time	m
1 F	0450 1103 1723 2350	1.3 4.5 1.5 4.3	**16** SA	0444 1052 1708 2318	2.0 4.1 2.1 3.8
2 SA	0547 1228 1835	1.7 4.2 1.9	**17** SU	0529 1221 1805	2.3 3.9 2.4
3 SU	0121 0703 1401 2018	4.1 2.1 4.2 2.0	**18** M	0110 0639 1350 1945	3.6 2.6 3.9 2.5
4 M	0250 0844 1523 2152	4.1 2.1 4.3 1.7	**19** TU	0242 0844 1500 2123	3.7 2.5 4.0 2.2
5 TU	0402 1007 1626 2251	4.3 1.9 4.6 1.4	**20** W	0344 0953 1552 2217	4.0 2.2 4.3 1.9
6 W	0455 1102 1714 2337	4.5 1.6 4.8 1.1	**21** TH	0427 1040 1634 2259	4.3 1.9 4.7 1.4
7 TH	0538 1146 1752	4.8 1.3 5.0	**22** F	0502 1120 1711 2338	4.6 1.5 5.0 1.1
8 F	0018 0612 1226 1823	0.9 5.0 1.1 5.2	**23** SA	0535 1158 1748	5.0 1.1 5.3
9 SA ●	0054 0642 1302 1853	0.7 5.1 1.0 5.2	**24** SU ○	0015 0610 1237 1825	0.7 5.3 0.8 5.6
10 SU	0128 0711 1335 1922	0.7 5.1 0.9 5.2	**25** M	0054 0647 1316 1904	0.5 5.5 0.6 5.7
11 M	0159 0741 1408 1952	0.8 5.1 0.9 5.1	**26** TU	0134 0725 1357 1945	0.4 5.5 0.6 5.6
12 TU	0229 0811 1441 2021	0.9 5.0 1.0 4.9	**27** W	0215 0806 1440 2030	0.4 5.5 0.7 5.4
13 W	0300 0841 1514 2050	1.1 4.8 1.2 4.6	**28** TH	0258 0851 1525 2122	0.6 5.3 0.9 5.1
14 TH	0333 0914 1548 2125	1.3 4.6 1.5 4.4	**29** F	0343 0943 1615 2227	1.0 5.0 1.2 4.7
15 F	0406 0955 1625 2210	1.6 4.3 1.8 4.1	**30** SA	0432 1040 1713 2346	1.4 4.6 1.5 4.4
			31 SU	0531 1214 1826	1.9 4.4 1.8

NOVEMBER

	Time	m		Time	m
1 M	0112 0647 1343 2002	4.2 2.2 4.3 1.9	**16** TU	0016 0559 1253 1849	3.8 2.4 4.0 2.3
2 TU	0236 0822 1503 2130	4.2 2.2 4.4 1.7	**17** W	0140 0731 1403 2022	3.8 2.5 4.1 2.2
3 W	0344 0944 1605 2229	4.4 2.1 4.6 1.5	**18** TH	0251 0900 1503 2130	4.0 2.3 4.4 1.9
4 TH	0437 1040 1654 2314	4.6 1.8 4.7 1.3	**19** F	0344 0958 1554 2221	4.3 2.0 4.7 1.5
5 F	0518 1124 1731 2354	4.7 1.6 4.9 1.1	**20** SA	0428 1045 1639 2305	4.7 1.6 5.0 1.2
6 SA	0551 1202 1802	4.9 1.4 5.0	**21** SU	0508 1129 1722 2348	5.0 1.3 5.3 0.9
7 SU	0028 0619 1238 1831	1.0 5.0 1.2 5.1	**22** M	0548 1212 1805	5.3 1.0 5.4
8 M ●	0101 0647 1311 1901	1.0 5.1 1.1 5.0	**23** TU ○	0030 0628 1256 1849	0.6 5.5 0.7 5.6
9 TU	0131 0716 1344 1931	1.0 5.1 1.1 5.0	**24** W	0114 0709 1341 1934	0.5 5.6 0.6 5.6
10 W	0201 0745 1417 2000	1.1 5.1 1.2 4.8	**25** TH	0157 0753 1427 2023	0.5 5.6 0.7 5.4
11 TH	0233 0815 1451 2031	1.2 4.9 1.3 4.7	**26** F	0242 0839 1515 2118	0.8 5.4 0.8 5.2
12 F	0305 0850 1525 2108	1.4 4.8 1.5 4.4	**27** SA	0329 0932 1606 2220	1.1 5.2 1.1 4.8
13 SA	0339 0932 1602 2153	1.7 4.5 1.8 4.2	**28** SU	0419 1034 1703 2330	1.4 4.9 1.4 4.5
14 SU	0416 1024 1645 2255	1.9 4.3 2.0 3.9	**29** M	0515 1148 1809	1.8 4.6 1.7
15 M	0500 1133 1737	2.2 4.1 2.2	**30** TU	0046 0622 1310 1925	4.3 2.1 4.4 1.8

DECEMBER

	Time	m		Time	m
1 W	0203 0740 1427 2047	4.3 2.3 4.4 1.8	**16** TH	0041 0634 1305 1918	4.0 2.3 4.3 2.0
2 TH	0311 0901 1533 2153	4.3 2.2 4.4 1.7	**17** F	0151 0751 1410 2031	4.1 2.3 4.4 1.9
3 F	0407 1006 1625 2243	4.4 2.0 4.5 1.6	**18** SA	0256 0906 1512 2138	4.3 2.1 4.6 1.6
4 SA	0451 1055 1706 2325	4.6 1.8 4.6 1.5	**19** SU	0353 1009 1609 2234	4.5 1.8 4.8 1.4
5 SU	0526 1137 1740	4.7 1.7 4.7	**20** M	0444 1103 1701 2324	4.9 1.4 5.1 1.1
6 M	0002 0556 1215 1812	1.3 4.8 1.5 4.8	**21** TU	0530 1153 1751	5.2 1.1 5.3
7 TU ●	0036 0627 1251 1845	1.3 5.0 1.4 4.8	**22** W ○	0012 0614 1242 1839	0.9 5.4 0.9 5.5
8 W	0108 0657 1325 1917	1.3 5.0 1.3 4.8	**23** TH	0059 0658 1330 1927	0.7 5.6 0.7 5.5
9 TH	0140 0728 1359 1948	1.3 5.0 1.3 4.8	**24** F	0144 0743 1417 2016	0.7 5.6 0.6 5.4
10 F	0212 0800 1433 2020	1.3 5.0 1.4 4.7	**25** SA	0230 0828 1506 2107	0.8 5.5 0.7 5.2
11 SA	0246 0835 1509 2057	1.4 4.9 1.5 4.5	**26** SU	0316 0917 1555 2202	1.0 5.3 0.9 5.0
12 SU	0320 0915 1546 2140	1.6 4.7 1.6 4.3	**27** M	0403 1010 1646 2301	1.3 5.1 1.1 4.7
13 M	0357 1000 1627 2231	1.8 4.5 1.7 4.2	**28** TU	0453 1111 1740	1.6 4.8 1.4
14 TU	0439 1054 1714 2332	2.0 4.4 1.9 4.0	**29** W	0005 0547 1220 1840	4.4 1.9 4.5 1.7
15 W	0530 1157 1810	2.2 4.3 2.0	**30** TH	0112 0649 1334 1946	4.2 2.1 4.3 1.9
			31 F	0220 0759 1445 2058	4.1 2.3 4.2 2.0

8

Chart Datum: 2·75 metres below Ordnance Datum (Newlyn)

PORTREE　　　　　　　8-8-10
Skye (Highland) 57°24'·75N 06°11'·00W　Rtg 2-4-1

CHARTS
AC 2534, 2209; Imray C66; OS 23

TIDES
–0445 Dover; ML no data; Duration 0610; Zone 0 (UT)

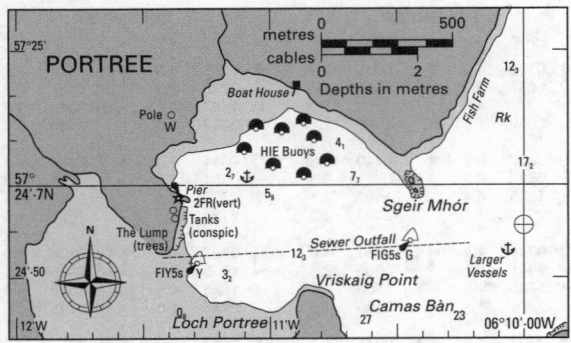

Standard Port ULLAPOOL (←—)

Times				Height (metres)			
High Water		Low Water		MHWS	MHWN	MLWN	MLWS
0000	0600	0300	0900	5·2	3·9	2·1	0·7
1200	1800	1500	2100				
Differences PORTREE (Skye)							
–0025	–0025	–0025	–0025	+0·1	–0·2	–0·2	0·0
SHIELDAIG (Loch Torridon)							
–0020	–0020	–0015	–0015	+0·4	+0·3	+0·1	0·0
LOCH A'BHRAIGE (Rona)							
–0020	0000	–0010	0000	–0·1	–0·1	–0·1	–0·2
PLOCKTON (Loch Carron)							
+0005	+0025	–0005	–0010	+0·5	+0·5	+0·5	+0·2
LOCH SNIZORT (Uig Bay, Skye)							
–0045	–0020	–0005	–0025	+0·1	–0·4	–0·2	0·0
LOCH DUNVEGAN (Skye)							
–0105	–0030	–0020	–0040	0·0	–0·1	0·0	0·0
LOCH HARPORT (Skye)							
–0115	–0035	–0020	–0100	–0·1	–0·1	0·0	+0·1
SOAY (Camus nan Gall)							
–0055	–0025	–0025	–0045	–0·4	–0·2	No data	
KYLE OF LOCHALSH							
–0040	–0020	–0005	–0025	+0·1	0·0	+0·1	+0·1
DORNIE BRIDGE (Loch Alsh)							
–0040	–0010	–0005	–0020	+0·1	–0·1	0·0	0·0
GLENELG BAY (Kyle Rhea)							
–0105	–0035	–0035	–0055	–0·4	–0·4	–0·9	–0·1
LOCH HOURN							
–0125	–0050	–0040	–0110	–0·2	–0·1	–0·1	+0·1

SHELTER
Secure in all but strong SW'lies, when Camas Bàn is more sheltered. In the N of the bay there are 8 HIE ⚓s for <15 tons.

NAVIGATION
WPT 57°24'·60N 06°10'·00W, 095°/275° from/to pier, 0·72M. From the S, avoid rks off An Tom Pt (1·5M to E, off chartlet).

LIGHTS AND MARKS
Only lts are a SHM buoy Fl G 5s marking Sgeir Mhór, 2 FR (vert) 6m 4M (occas) on the pier and a SPM buoy Fl Y 5s.

RADIO TELEPHONE
VHF Ch 16 12 (occas).

TELEPHONE (Dial code 01478)
Hr Mr ☎ 612926; Moorings 612341; MRSC (01631) 563720; ⌗ (0141) 887 9369; Marinecall 0891 500464; Police 612888; Dr 612013; Ⓗ 612704.

FACILITIES
Pier D (cans), L, FW. **Town** EC Wed; P, V, Gas, Gaz, ⌾, R, Bar, ✉, Ⓑ, ⇌ (bus/ferry to Kyle of Lochalsh).

ANCHORAGES AROUND OR NEAR SKYE

LOCH TORRIDON, Highland, 57°36'N 05°49'W. AC 228. Tides, see 8.8.8. Three large lochs: ent to outer loch (Torridon) is 3M wide, with isolated Sgeir na Trian (2m) almost in mid-chan; ⚓s on SW side behind Eilean Mór and in L Beag. L Sheildaig is middle loch with good ⚓ between the Is and village. 1M to the N, a 2ca wide chan leads into Upper L Torridon; many fish cages and prone to squalls. Few facilities, except Shieldaig: FW, V, R, Bar, ✉, Garage.

LOCH A'BHRAIGE, Rona (Highland), 57°34'·63N 05°57'·87W. AC 2534, 2479. HW –0438 on Dover; ML 2·8m; Duration 0605. See 8.8.8. A good ⚓ in NW of the island, safe except in NNW winds. Beware rks on NE side up to 1ca off shore. Hbr in NE corner of loch head. Ldg lts 137°, see 8.8.4. Facilities: jetty, FW and a helipad, all owned by MOD (DRA). Before ent, call *Rona* VHF Ch 16. **Acarseid Mhor** is ⚓ on W of Rona. App S of Eilean Garbh marked by W arrow. SD sketch of rks at ent is necessary. FW (cans), showers. At **Churchton Bay,** SW tip of Raasay, there are 4 HIE ⚓s; ☎ (01478) 612341; Slip, showers, R.

LOCH DUNVEGAN, 4 HIE ⚓s off Stein, 57°30'·9N 06°34'·5W. 3 HIE ⚓s off Dunvegan, 57°26'·3N 06°35'·2W. Fuel, FW, R. ☎ (01478) 612341.

LOCH HARPORT, Skye (Highland), 57°20'·60N 06°25'·80W. AC 1795. HW –0447 (sp), –0527 (np) on Dover. See 8.8.8. On E side of Loch Bracadale, entered between Oronsay Is and Ardtreck Pt (W lt ho, Iso 4s 17m 9M). SW end of Oronsay has conspic rk pillar, called The Castle; keep ¼M off-shore here and off E coast of Oronsay which is joined to Ullinish Pt by drying reef. ⚓ Oronsay Is, N side of drying reef (4m), or on E side, but beware rk (dries) 0·5ca off N shore of Oronsay. Fiskavaig Bay 1M S of Ardtreck (7m); Loch Beag on N side of loch, exposed to W winds; Port na Long E of Ardtreck, sheltered except from E winds (beware fish farm); Carbost on SW shore. Facilities: EC Wed (Carbost); V (local shop), Bar, R, P (garage), ✉, FW. (Port na Long) Bar, FW, V (shop).

SOAY HARBOUR, Skye (Highland), 57°09'·50N 06°13'·40W. AC 2208. Tides see 8.8.8. Narrow inlet on NW side of Soay; enter from Soay Sound above half flood to clear bar, dries 0·6m. Appr on 135° from 5ca out to avoid reefs close each side of ent. Cross bar slightly E of mid-chan, altering 20° stbd for best water; ent is 15m wide between boulder spits. ⚓ in 3m mid-pool or shoal draft boats can enter inner pool. Good shelter and holding. Camas nan Gall (poor holding) has public ☎; no other facilities.

CROWLIN ISLANDS, Highland, 57°21'·08N 05°50'·59W. AC 2498, 2209. HW –0435 on Dover, –0020 on Ullapool; HW +0·3m on Ullapool. See 8.8.8. ⚓ between Eilean Meadhonach and Eilean Mor, appr from N, keep E of Eilean Beg. Excellent shelter except in strong N winds. There is an inner ⚓ with 3½m but ent chan dries. Eilean Beg lt ho Fl 6s 32m 6M, W tr. There are no facilities.

Sing me a song of a lad that is gone,
Say, could that lad be I?
Merry of soul he sailed on a day
Over the sea to Skye.

Mull was astern, Rum on the port,
Eigg on the starboard bow;
Glory of youth glowed in his soul:
Where is that glory now?

Billow and breeze, islands and seas,
Mountains of rain and sun,
All that was good, all that was fair,
All that was me is gone.

Robert Louis Stevenson (1850-1894)

PLOCKTON   8-8-11

Highland 57°20´·54N 05°38´·40W   Rtg 3-4-1

CHARTS
AC 2528, 2209; Imray C66; OS 24, 33

TIDES
−0435 Dover; ML 3·5m; Duration 0600; See 8.8.10

SHELTER
Good, exposed only to N/NE'lies. ‡ in centre of bay in approx 3·5m or find a vacant mooring. Inner part of bay shoals and dries to the SW.

NAVIGATION
WPT 57°21´·41N 05°39´·36W; thence steer ENE between Sgeir Bhuidhe and Sgeir Golach (3·8m). When past the latter alter for Duncraig Castle 170°, between Bogha Dubh Sgeir (1·5m, PHM bn) and Hawk Rk (0·1m, E of Cat Is). A shorter appr is SE between a PHM bn (S of Sgeir Golach) and Cat Is. Beware Plockton Rks (3·1m) on E side of bay.

LIGHTS AND MARKS
No lts or buoys. Old lt ho (13m) on Cat Is is conspic, as is Duncraig Castle with white △ bn.

RADIO TELEPHONE
None.

TELEPHONE
Hr Mr ☎/📠 (01599) 534167 at Kyle of Lochalsh, mobile 0802 367253; MRSC (01631) 563720; ⌗ (0141) 887 9369; Marinecall 0891 500 464; Police/Dr via Hr Mr.

FACILITIES
Village FW, M, L at 24m long pontoon, D (cans), CH, V, R, Bar, ✉, ⇌, Gas, airstrip, (bus to Kyle of Lochalsh).

LOCH CARRON. Strome Narrows are no longer buoyed or lit. At head of loch are 3 Y ⚓s (max LOA 14m) in 3m off drying jetty at 57°23´·95N 05°29´·0W; call ☎ 01520 722321. Appr on 328° between Sgeir Chreagach and Sgeir Fhada.

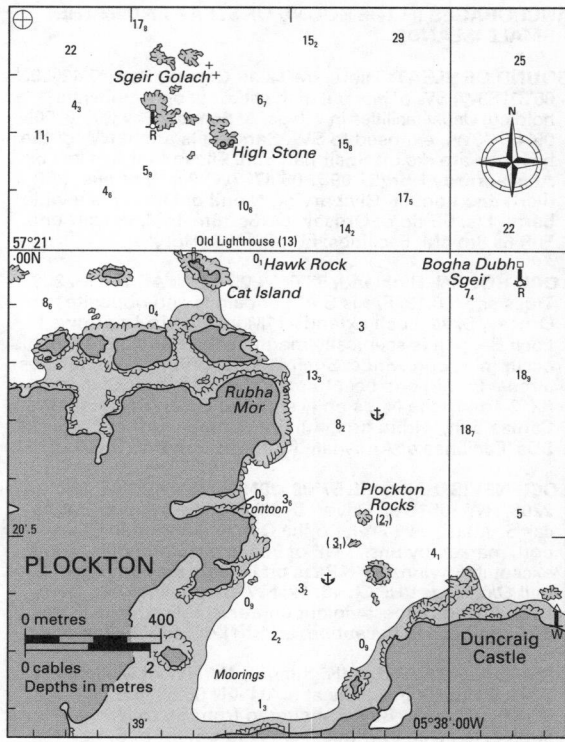

LOCH ALSH   8-8-12

Highland 57°16´·70N 05°42´·80W   Rtg 2-4-1

CHARTS
AC 2540, 2541; Imray C66; OS 33

TIDES
−0450 Dover; ML 3·0m; Duration 0555; See 8.8.10

SHELTER
At **Kyle (of Lochalsh)** AB on Railway Pier, with FVs, or on 40m pontoon planned for summer 97, close W of Railway Pier; or ‡ off the hotel there in 11m. Off **Kyleakin** 4 ⚓s, as shown, are free but subject to tidal stream. A pontoon was planned for late 97 on S side of hbr; up to 8 ⚓s in bay 3ca E of hbr are planned for March 1998. Safe ‡s, depending on winds, are (clockwise from Kyle): Avernish B, (2ca N of Racoon Rk) in 3m clear of power cables, open to SW; NW of Eilean Donnan Castle (conspic); in Ratagan B at head of L Duich in 7m; in Totaig B facing Loch Long ent in 3·5m; on S shore in Ardintoul B in 5·5m; at head of Loch na Béiste in 7m close inshore and W of fish cages.

NAVIGATION
WPT (from Inner Sound) 57°17´·00N 05°45´·70W, 303°/123° from/to bridge, 7½ca. Chan to bridge is marked by 2 PHM and 2 SHM lt buoys. Bridge to Skye, 30m clearance, is lit Oc 6s in centre of main span, Iso R 4s on S pier and Iso G4s on N pier. The secondary NE span is lit, but has only 4.5m clearance.

LIGHTS AND MARKS
Lts/marks as chartlet. Direction of buoyage is N in Kyle Rhea, thence E up Loch Alsh; but W through Kyle Akin and the bridge, ie SHMs are on N side of chan.

RADIO TELEPHONE
VHF Ch 11 16.

TELEPHONE (Dial code 01599)
Hr Mr ☎/📠 534167; MRSC (01631) 563720; ⌗ (0141) 887 9369; Marinecall 0891 500 464; Police, Dr, Ⓗ : via Hr Mr.

FACILITIES
Kyle of Lochalsh: AB, FW, D (Fish pier), P (cans), ME, Ⓔ, CH, ✉, Ⓑ, R, Bar, V, Gas, ⇌ (useful railhead), Bus to Glasgow & Inverness; buses every ½hr to/from Kyleakin.
Kyleakin: AB, M, FW, V, R, Bar.

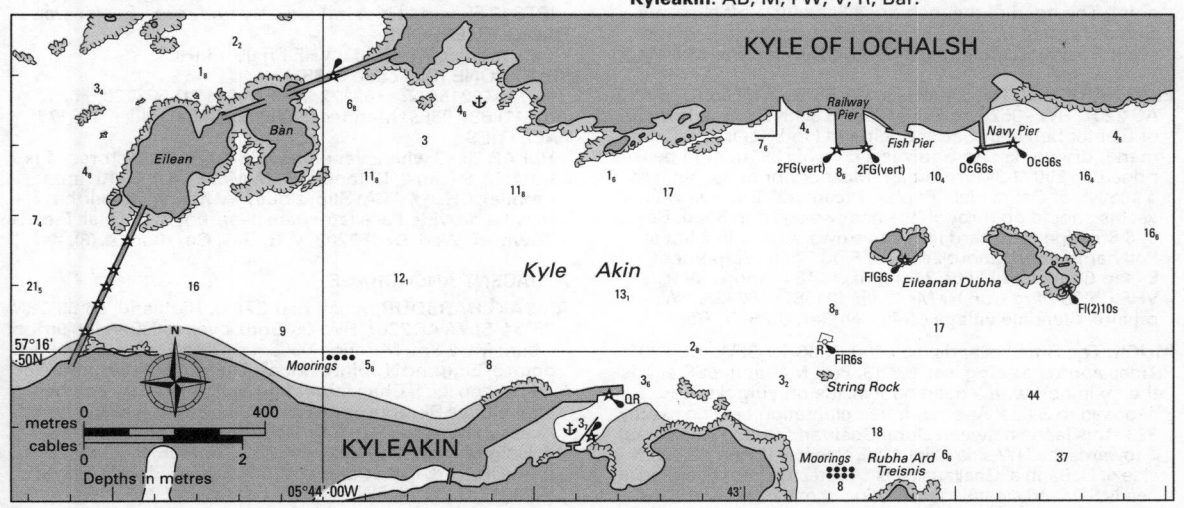

ANCHORAGES IN THE SOUND OF SLEAT AND IN THE SMALL ISLANDS

SOUND OF SLEAT: There are ⚓s at: **Glenelg Bay** (57°12'·58N 05°37'·88W) SW of pier out of the tide, but only moderate holding. Usual facilities in village. At **Sandaig Bay** (57°10'·00N 05°41'·43W), exposed to SW. Sandaig Is are to NW of the bay; beware rks off Sgeir nan Eun. Eilean Mór has lt Fl 6s. At **Isleornsay Hbr** (57°09'N 05°47'·7W) 2ca N of pier, 2FR (vert) and floodlit. Give drying N end of Ornsay Is a wide berth. Lts: SE tip of Ornsay, Oc 8s 18m 15M, W tr; N end, Fl R 6s 8m 4M. Facilities: FW, P, V, ⊠, Hotel.

LOCH HOURN, Highland, 57°08'N 05°42'W. AC 2541, 2208. Tides see 8.8.13. Ent is S of Sandaig Is and opposite Isle Ornsay, Skye. Loch extends 11M inland via 4 narrows to Loch Beag; it is scenically magnificent, but violent squalls occur in strong winds. Sgeir Ulibhe, drying 2·1m, bn, lies almost in mid-ent; best to pass S of it to clear Clansman Rk, 2·1m, to the N. ⚓s on N shore at Eilean Ràrsaidh and Camas Bàn, within first 4M. For pilotage further E, consult SDs. Facilities at Arnisdale (Camas Bàn): FW, V, R, Bar, ⊠.

LOCH NEVIS, Highland, 57°02'·20N 05°43'·34W. AC 2541, 2208. HW –0515 on Dover. See 8.8.13. Beware rks Bogha cas Sruth (dries 1·8m), Bogha Don and Sgeirean Glasa both marked by bns. ⚓ NE of Eilean na Glascoille, good except in S winds; or 6 R ⚓s off Inverie, £5, 10m max LOA. Call *Old Forge* VHF Ch 16, 12; FW, Bar, R, showers, ⊡. In strong winds expect violent unpredictable squalls. Enter the inner loch with caution, and ⚓ N or SE of Eilean Maol.

ARMADALE BAY, Skye (Highland), 4M NW of Mallaig. AC 2208. 6 HIE ⚓s in 2 trots at 57°04'·0N 05°53'·6W (☎ (01478) 612341). Bay is sheltered from SE to N winds but subject to swell in winds from N to SE. From S, beware the Eilean Maol and Sgorach rocks. Ferry pier, Oc R 6s 6m 6M, with conspic W shed. Facilities: FW at ferry pier or on charter (☎ 01471 844216) moorings from long hose on old pier; D (cans), V, Gas, showers at Ardvasar ¾ mile; P (cans), Gaz at ¼ mile; R, Bar, ferry to Mallaig for ⇌.

CANNA, The Small Islands, 57°03'·30N 06°29'·40W. AC 2208, 1796. HW –0457 (Sp), –0550 (Np) on Dover; HW –0035 and –0·4m on Ullapool; Duration 0605. Good holding and shelter, except in strong E'lies, in hbr between Canna and Sanday Is. Appr along Sanday shore, keeping N of Sgeir a' Phuirt, dries 4·6m. Ldg marks as in SDs. ⚓ in 3 - 4m W of Canna pier, off which beware drying rky patch. ⚓ Lt is advised due to FVs. Conspic W lt bn, Fl 6s 32m 9M, vis 152°-061°, at E end of Sanday Is. Magnetic anomaly off NE Canna. Facilities: FW only. Note: National Trust for Scotland runs island; please do not ditch rubbish.

RHUM, The Small Islands, 57°00'·08N 06°15'·70W. AC 2207, 2208. HW –0500 on Dover; –0035 and –0·3m on Ullapool; ML 2·4m; Duration 0600. Nature Conservancy Council owns Is. The mountains (809m) are unmistakeable. Landing is only allowed at L Scresort on E side; no dogs. Beware drying rks 1ca off N point of ent and almost 3ca off S point. The head of the loch dries 2ca out; ⚓ off slip on S side or further in, to NE of jetty. Hbr is open to E winds/ swell. Facilities: Hotel, ⊠, FW, V, R, Bar, ferry to Mallaig.

EIGG HARBOUR, The Small Islands, 56°52'·64N 06°07'·60W. AC 2207. HW –0523 on Dover. See 8.8.13. Coming from N or E enter between Garbh Sgeir and Flod Sgeir (bn, ○ topmark), drying rks. An Sgùrr is a conspic 391m high peak/ ridge brg 290°/1·3M from pier. Most of hbr dries, but good ⚓ 1ca NE of Galmisdale Pt pier, except in NE winds when yachts should go through the narrows and ⚓ in South Bay in 6-8m; tide runs hard in the narrows. Also ⚓ in 2·5m at Poll nam Partan, about 2ca N of Flod Sgeir. SE point of Eilean Chathastail Fl 6s 24m 8M, vis 181°-shore, W tr. VHF Ch 08 *Eigg Hbr.* Hr Mr ☎ via (01687) 482428. FW, repairs. **Cleadale village** (2M to N) Bar, ⊠, R, V, Gas.

MUCK, The Small Islands, 56°49'·80N 06°13'·33W. AC 2207. Tides approx as Eigg, see 8.8.13. Port Mór at the SE end is the main hbr, with a deep pool inside offlying rks, but exposed to S'lies. Appr with tree plantation bearing exactly 329°; this leads between Dubh Sgeir and Bogha Ruadh rks. ⚓ towards the NW side of inlet; NE side has drying rks. On N side of Is, Bagh a' Ghallanaich is ⚓ protected from S; entrance needs SDs and careful identification of marks. Few facilities.

MALLAIG   8-8-13

Highland 57°00'·48N 05°49'·40W   Rtg 1-2-2

CHARTS
AC 2541, 2208; Imray C65, C66; OS 40
TIDES
–0515 Dover; ML 2·9; Duration 0605; Zone 0 (UT)

Standard Port OBAN (→)

Times				Height (metres)			
High Water		Low Water		MHWS	MHWN	MLWN	MLWS
0000	0600	0100	0700	4·0	2·9	1·8	0·7
1200	1800	1300	1900				
Differences MALLAIG							
+0017	+0017	+0017	+0017	+1·0	+0·7	+0·3	+0·1
INVERIE BAY (Loch Nevis)							
+0030	+0020	+0035	+0020	+1·0	+0·9	+0·2	0·0
BAY OF LAIG (Eigg)							
+0015	+0030	+0040	+0005	+0·7	+0·6	–0·2	–0·2
LOCH MOIDART							
+0015	+0015	+0040	+0020	+0·8	+0·6	–0·2	–0·2

SHELTER
Good in SW'lies but open to N. Access H24. ⚓ in SE part of hbr or find a berth on Fish Pier. No ⚓s. Hbr is often full of FVs; also Skye ferry. WIP on new N bkwtr and FV basin.
NAVIGATION
WPT 57°00'·76N 05°49'·42W, 011°/191° from/to Steamer Pier lt, 540m, passing E of Sgeir Dhearg lt bn. The former W chan is now permanently closed to navigation.

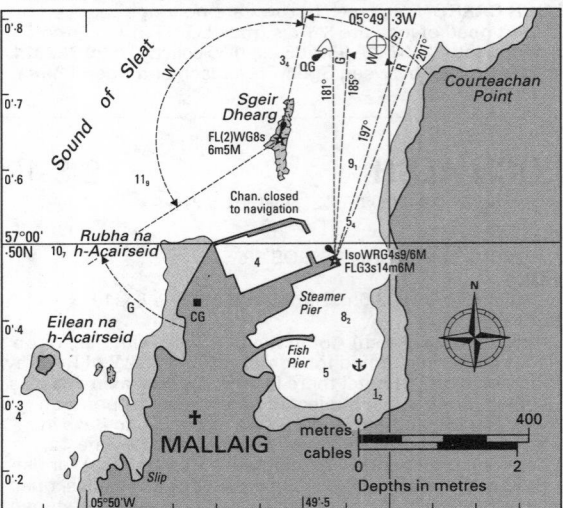

No visitors moorings

LIGHTS AND MARKS
As chartlet & 8.8.4. Town lts may obscure Sgeir Dhearg lt. IPTS (3 FR vert at pier hd) are only for ferries, Easter-Oct.
RADIO TELEPHONE
Call: *Mallaig Hbr Radio* VHF Ch 09 16 (HO).
TELEPHONE (Dial code 01687)
Hr Mr 462154, 🖰 462172; MRSC (01631) 563720; ⌗ (0141) 887 9369; Marinecall 0891 500464; Police 462177.
FACILITIES
Hbr AB £5.87 whenever alongside for FW/fuel/stores (⚓ is free), M, P (cans), D (tanker), FW, ME, EI, Sh, C (10 ton mobile), CH, Ⓔ, ACA, Slip; a busy FV hbr, yacht berths may be provided at a later date near root of the Fish Pier.
Town EC Wed; Dr 462202. V, R, Gas, Gaz, Bar, ⊠, Ⓑ, ⇌.

ADJACENT ANCHORAGE

ARISAIG HARBOUR, (Loch nan Ceall), Highland, 56°53'·78N 05°54'·50W. AC 2207. HW–0515 on Dover;+0030 and +0·9m on Oban; ML 2·9m; Duration 0605. Ldg line 256° into loch is S point of Eigg and N point of Muck. There are many unmarked rks, but no lts. S Chan is winding, but marked by perches. ⚓ above Cave Rk, approx 1M within the ent, is well sheltered. Access HW –3 to +2. Call *Arisaig Hbr* VHF Ch 12 16, M. **Arisaig Marine** ☎ (01687) 450224, 🖰 450678, 20 ⚓s, C (10 ton), CH, D & FW at pier (HW), P (cans), EI, ME, Sh, Slip. **Village** EC Thurs; FW at hotel, Bar, ⊠, R, Gas, V, ⇌.

LOCH SUNART   8-8-14
Highland 56°39'·50N 06°00'·00W

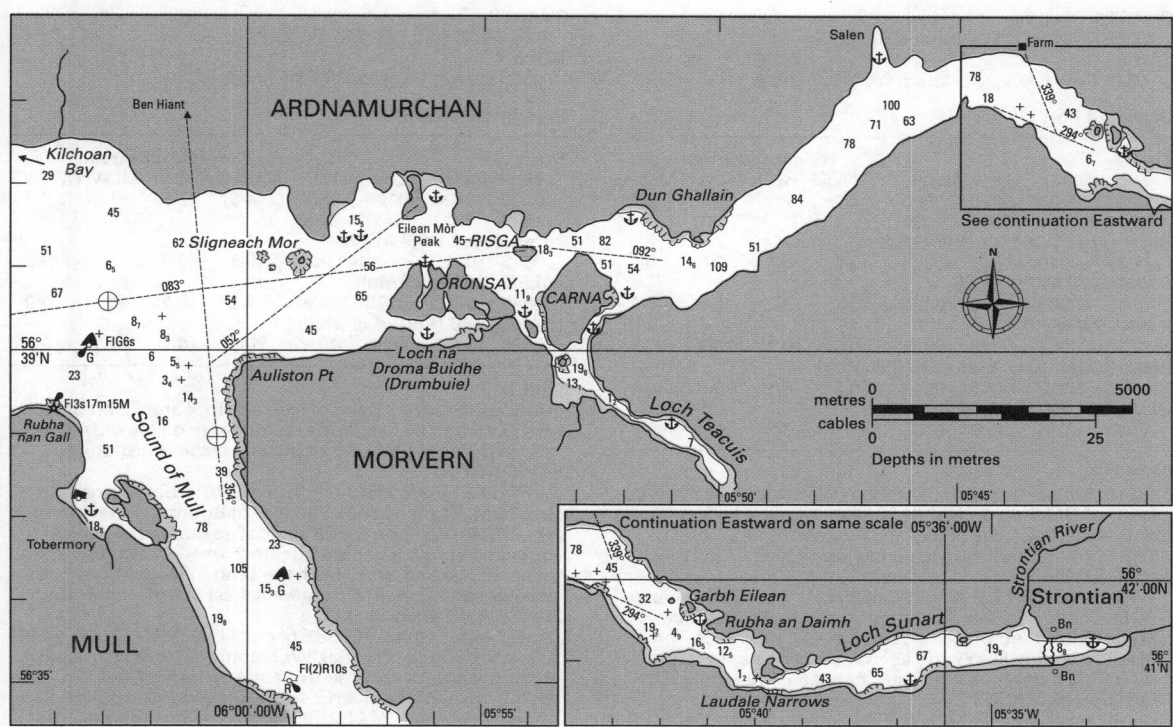

CHARTS
AC 2394, 2392, *2171*; Imray C65; OS 45, 47, 49
TIDES
Salen –0500 Dover; ML 2·0; Zone 0 (UT)

Standard Port OBAN (→)

Times				Height (metres)			
High Water		Low Water		MHWS	MHWN	MLWN	MLWS
0100	0700	0100	0800	4·0	2·9	1·8	0·7
1300	1900	1300	2000				
Differences SALEN (Loch Sunart)							
–0015	+0015	+0010	+0005	+0·6	+0·5	–0·1	–0·1
LOCH EATHARNA (Coll)							
+0025	+0010	+0010	+0025	+0·4	+0·3	No data	
GOTT BAY (Tiree)							
0000	+0010	+0005	+0010	0·0	+0·1	0·0	0·0

SHELTER
8 HIE Øs at Kilchoan B (56°24'·5N 06°07'·3W); ☎ (01972) 510209. ‡s in Loch na Droma Buidhe (S of Oronsay) sheltered in all winds; in Sailean Mór (N of Oronsay) convenient and easy ent; between Oronsay and Carna; in Loch Teacuis (very tricky ent); E of Carna; Salen Bay, with Øs and jetty; Garbh Eilean (NW of Rubha an Daimh), and E of sand spit by Strontian R.
NAVIGATION
West WPT, 56°39'·70N 06°03'·00W, 263°/083° from/to Creag nan Sgarbh (NW tip of Orinsay), 3·7M.
South WPT, 56°38'·00N 06°00'·65W, 1M S of Auliston Pt; there are extensive rky reefs W of this pt. Chart 2394 and detailed directions are needed to navigate the 17M long loch, particularly in its upper reaches. Beware Ross Rk, S of Risga; Broad Rk, E of Risga; Dun Ghallain Rk; shoals extending 3ca NNW from Eilean mo Shlinneag off S shore; drying rk 1ca W of Garbh Eilean and strong streams at sp in Laudale Narrows.
LIGHTS AND MARKS
Unlit. Transits as on the chart: from W WPT, Risga on with N tip of Oronsay at 083°; N pt of Carna on with top of Risga 092°. From S WPT, Ben Hiant bearing 354°, thence Eilean Mor Peak at 052°. Further up the loch, 339° and 294°, as on chartlet, are useful. Many other transits are shown on AC 2394.

RADIO TELEPHONE
None.
TELEPHONE (Dial code 01967)
MRSC (01631) 563720; ∰ (0141) 887 9369; Marinecall 0891 500463; Dr 431231.
FACILITIES
SALEN BAY Jetty ☎ 01967 431333, access HW±2; two Øs £10, FW, D by hose, CH, Gas, Gaz, Diver, ME, El, limited V, R, Bar.
Acharacle (2½M), P, V, ✉, Ⓑ (Tues/Wed, mobile), ⇌ (bus to Loch Ailort/Fort William), ✈ (Oban).
STRONTIAN
FW, P, V, hotel, ✉, Gas, Gaz, Bar. Bus to Fort William.

ANCHORAGES IN COLL AND TIREE (Argyll and Bute)

ARINAGOUR, Loch Eatharna, Coll, 56°37'·00N 06°31'·20W. AC 2474, 2171. HW –0530 on Dover; ML 1·4m; Duration 0600; see 8.8.14. Good shelter except with SE swell or strong winds from ENE to SSW. Enter at SHM buoy, Fl G 6s, marking Bogha Mòr. Thence NW to Arinagour ferry pier, 2 FR(vert) 10m. Beware McQuarrie's Rk (dries 2·9m) 1ca E of pier hd and unmarked drying rks further N on E side of fairway. Ch and hotel are conspic ahead. Continue N towards old stone pier; ‡ S of it or pick up a buoy. Six HIE Øs on W side of hbr, between the two piers. Also ‡ E of Eilean Eatharna. Piermaster ☎ (01879) 230347; VHF Ch 31. Facilities: **HIE Trading Post** ☎ 230349, M, D, FW, Gas, V, CH, R. **Village** Ⓞ, FW, P, ✉, ferry to Oban (⇌).

GOTT BAY, Tiree, 56°30'·75N 06°48'·00W. AC 2474. Tides as 8.8.14; HW –0540 on Dover. Adequate shelter in calm weather, but exposed in winds ENE to S. The bay, at NE end of island, can be identified by conspic latticed tr at Scarinish about 8ca SW of ent, with lt Fl 3s 11m 16M close by (obscd over hbr). Appr on NW track, keeping to SW side of bay which is obstructed on NE side by Soa Is and drying rks. The ferry pier at S side of ent has FR ldg lts 286½°. ‡ about 1ca NW of pier head in 3m on sand; dinghy landing at pier. Facilities: P & D (cans), Gas, V, R, Bar, ✉ at Scarinish (½M), ferry to Oban (⇌).

TOBERMORY   8-8-15

Mull (Argyll and Bute) 56°37'·60N 06°03'·15W   Rtg 2-4-1

CHARTS
AC 2474, *2390, 2171*; Imray C65; OS 47

TIDES
–0519 Dover; ML 2·4; Duration 0610; Zone 0 (UT)

Standard Port OBAN (→)

Times				Height (metres)			
High Water		Low Water		MHWS	MHWN	MLWN	MLWS
0100	0700	0100	0800	4·0	2·9	1·8	0·7
1300	1900	1300	2000				
Differences TOBERMORY (Mull)							
+0025	+0010	+0015	+0025	+0·4	+0·4	0·0	0·0
CARSAIG BAY (S Mull)							
–0015	–0005	–0030	+0020	+0·1	+0·2	0·0	–0·1
IONA (SW Mull)							
–0010	–0005	–0020	+0015	0·0	+0·1	–0·3	–0·2
BUNESSAN (Loch Lathaich, SW Mull)							
–0015	–0015	–0010	+0015	+0·3	+0·1	0·0	–0·1
ULVA SOUND (W Mull)							
–0010	–0015	0000	–0005	+0·4	+0·3	0·0	–0·1

SHELTER
Good, but some swell in strong N/NE winds. 8 Bu HIE ⚓s are S of Old Pier. ⚓ clear of fairway, marked by Y buoys; or in Aros Bay (clear of pier and fish farms); at SE end of The Doirlinn; or in restricted bay on W side of Calve Is.

NAVIGATION
WPT 56°38'·00N 06°02'·00W, 058°/238° from/to ferry pier, 1·1M. N ent is wide and clear of dangers. From SE beware Sgeir Calve 1·8m on NE side of Calve Is. S ent via The Doirlinn is only 80m wide at HW, and dries at LW; at HW±2 least depth is 2m. Enter between 2 bns on 300°.

LIGHTS AND MARKS
Rhubha nan Gall, Fl 3s 17m 15M, W tr is 1M N of ent. Ch spire and hotel turret are both conspic.

RADIO TELEPHONE
VHF Ch 16 12 (HO), M.

TELEPHONE (Dial code 01688)
Hr Mr 302017; MRSC (01631) 563720; Local CG 302200; Marinecall 0891 500463; Police 302016; Dr 302013.

FACILITIES
Ferry Pier, temp AB for P, D, FW £2; **Western Isles YC** ☎ 302207; **Services**: ME, CH, ACA, Gaz, Gas, Divers. **Town** EC Wed (winter); FW, P, Dr, V, R, Bar, ✉, Ⓑ, Ⓞ, ≋ ·(ferry to Oban), ✈ (grass strip; helipad on golf course).

SOUND OF MULL. 8M SE of Tobermory at **Salen Bay** (Mull, 56°31'·45N 05°56'·75W) are 8 HIE ⚓s. Beware drying rks 6ca E of the bay; ent on SE side. Land at jetty in SW corner. At **Craignure**, (Mull, 56°28'·37N 05°42'·25W) 9M SE, are 8 more HIE ⚓s, N of ferry pier; ldg lts 241°, both FR 10/12m. Facilities: V, Bar, ✉, Gas, ferry to Oban. Tides, see 8.8.13. There are 2 Historic Wrecks at the SE end of the Sound: *Dartmouth* at 56°30'·19N 05°41'·95W on W side of Eilean Rubha an Ridire; and *Speedwell* on Duart Point at 56°27'·45N 05°39'·32W. See 8.0.3h.

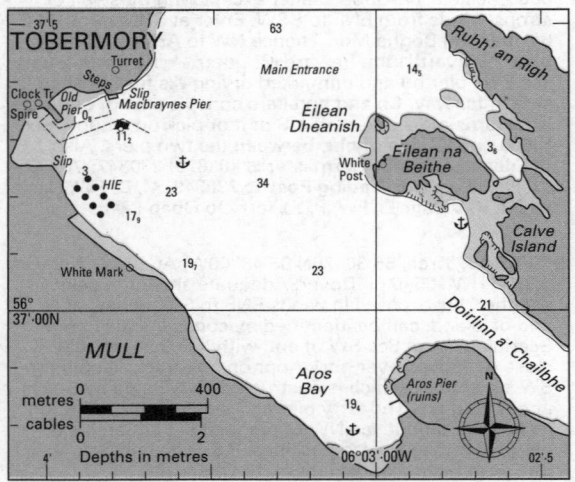

LOCH ALINE   8-8-16

Highland 56°32'·10N 05°46'·40W   Rtg 2-5-1

CHARTS
AC *2390*; Imray C65; OS 49

TIDES
–0523 Dover; Duration 0610; Zone 0 (UT)

Standard Port OBAN (→)

Times				Height (metres)			
High Water		Low Water		MHWS	MHWN	MLWN	MLWS
0100	0700	0100	0800	4·0	2·9	1·8	0·7
1300	1900	1300	2000				
Differences LOCH ALINE							
+0012	+0012	No data		+0·5	+0·3	No data	
SALEN (Sound of Mull)							
+0045	+0015	+0020	+0030	+0·2	+0·2	–0·1	0·0
CRAIGNURE (Sound of Mull)							
+0030	+0005	+0010	+0015	0·0	+0·1	–0·1	–0·1

SHELTER
Very good. ⚓s in SE end of loch and in N and E part of loch are restricted by fish farms. Temp berth on the old stone slip in the ent on W side, depth and ferries permitting.

NAVIGATION
WPT 56°31'·50N 05°46'·30W, 356°/176° from/to front ldg bn, 0·9M. Bns lead 356°, 100m W of Bogha Lurcain, drying rk off Bolorkle Pt on E side of ent. The buoyed ent is easy, but narrow with a bar (min depth 2·1m); stream runs 2½kn at sp. Beware coasters from the sand mine going to/from the jetty and ferries to/from Mull. Last 5ca of loch dries.

LIGHTS AND MARKS
Ardtornish Pt lt ho, 1M SSE of ent, Fl (2) WRG 10s 7m 8/5M. Lts and buoys as chartlet. War memorial cross (conspic, 9m high) stands on W side of ent. Ldg lts are FW 2/4m (H24). 1M up the loch on E side a Y bn with ● topmark marks a reef, and ½M further up similar bn marks a larger reef on W side. Clock tr is conspic at head of loch.

RADIO TELEPHONE
None.

TELEPHONE (Dial code 01967)
MRSC (01631) 563720; ✠ (0141) 887 9369; Marinecall 0891 500463; Ⓗ (01631) 563727; Dr 421252.

FACILITIES
Village Gas, V, R, Bar, P, ✉, (Ⓑ, ≋, ✈ at Oban), Ferry to Fishnish Bay (Mull).

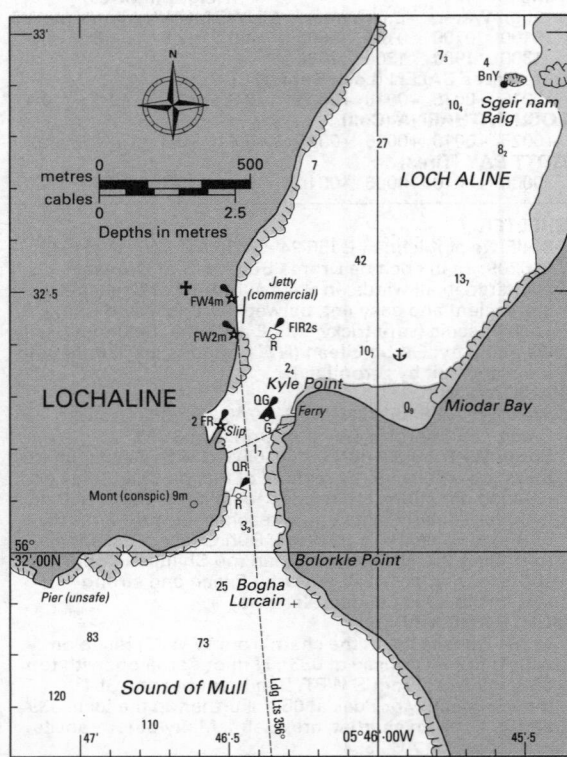

ANCHORAGES on WEST and SOUTH COASTS OF MULL
(Anti-clockwise from the North. SDs essential)

TRESHNISH ISLES, 56°30'N 06°24'W. AC 2652. The main Is (N to S) are: Cairn na Burgh, Fladda, Lunga, Bac Mòr and Bac Beag. Tides run hard and isles are exposed to swell, but merit a visit in calm weather. Appr with caution on ldg lines as in CCC SDs; temp ‡ off Lunga's N tip in 4m.

STAFFA, 56°25'·97N 06°20'·27W. AC 2652. Spectacular isle with Fingal's Cave, but same caveats as above. Very temp ‡ off SE tip where there is landing; beware unmarked rks.

GOMETRA, 56°28'·86N 06°16'W. AC 2652. Tides as 8.8.15. The narrow inlet between Gometra and Ulva Is offers sheltered ‡, except in S'lies. Appr on 020° between Staffa and Little Colonsay, or N of the former. Beware rks drying 3·2m, to stbd and 5ca S of ent. Inside, E side is cleaner.

LOCH NA KEAL, 56°27'N 06°11'W (ent). AC 2652. Tides in 8.8.15. Appr S of Geasgill Is and N of drying rks off **Inch Kenneth**; E of this Is and in **Sound of Ulva** are sheltered ‡s, except in S'lies. Beware MacQuarrie's Rk, dries 0·8m.

LOCH LATHAICH, Mull, 56°19'·30N 06°15'·40W. AC 2617. HW –0545 on Dover; ML 2·4. See 8.8.15. Excellent shelter with easy access; good base for cruising W Mull. Eilean na Liathanaich (a group of islets) lie off the ent, marked by a W bn at the E end, Fl WR 6s 12m 8/6M, R088°-108°, W108°-088°. Keep to W side of loch and ‡ off Bendoran BY in SW, or SE of Eilean Ban off the pier in approx 5m. Facilities: (Bunessan) Shop, ⊠, Bar, R, FW.

SOUND OF IONA, 56°19'·46N 06°23'·05W. AC 2617. Tides see 8.8.15. From N, enter in mid-chan; from S keep clear of Torran Rks. Cathedral brg 012° closes the Iona shore past 2 SHM buoys and SCM buoy. Beware a bank 0·1m in mid-sound, between cathedral and Fionnphort; also tel cables and ferries. ‡ S of ferry close in to Iona, or in Bull Hole. Consult SDs. Crowded in season; limited facilities.

TINKER'S HOLE, Ross of Mull, 56°17'·50N 06°23'·00W. AC 2617. Beware Torran Rks, reefs extending 5M S and SW of Erraid. Usual app from S, avoiding Rankin's Rks, drying 0·8m, and rk, dries 2·3m, between Eilean nam Muc and Erraid. Popular ‡ in mid-pool twixt Eilean Dubh and Erraid.

CARSAIG BAY, Ross of Mull, 56°19'·20N 05°59'·00W. Tides see 8.8.15. AC 2386. Temp, fair weather ‡s to N of Gamhnach Mhòr, reef 2m high, or close into NW corner of bay. Landing at stone quay on NE side. No facilities.

LOCH SPELVE, Mull, 56°23'N 05°41'W. AC 2387. Tides as Oban. Landlocked water, prone to squalls off surrounding hills. Ent narrows to ½ca due to shoal S side and drying rk N side, 56°23'·24N 05°41'·95W, ☆ QG 3m 2M, G pole. CCC SDs give local ldg lines. ‡s in SW and NW arms, clear of fish farms. Pier at Croggan; no facilities.

ANCHORAGES ALONG LOCH LINNHE (AC 2378, 2379, 2380)

LYNN OF LORN, 56°33'N 05°25'·2W: At NE end are ‡s off **Port Appin**, clear of ferry and cables (beware Appin Rks); and in **Airds Bay**, open to SW. At NW tip of Lismore, **Port Ramsey** offers good ‡s between the 3 main islets.

LOCH CRERAN, 56°32'·15N 05°25'·15W. Tides 8.8.17. Ent at Airds Pt, Dir lt 050°, Fl WRG 2s, W vis 041-058°. Chan turns 90° stbd and streams runs 4kn. Sgeir Callich, rky ridge juts out NE to SHM By, Fl G 3s; ‡ W of it. ⚓s (max LOA 7m) off Barcaldine; also off Creagan Inn, ☎ (01631) 573250, 3 ⚓s max LOA 9m. Bridge has 12m clearance.

LOCH LEVEN, 56°41'·62N 05°12'W. Tides 8.8.17. Fair weather ‡s in Ballachulish Bay at Kentallen B (deep), Onich and off St Brides on N shore. App bridge (17m clnce) on 114°; 4ca ENE of br are moorings and ‡ at Poll an Dùnan, entered W of perch. Facilities at Ballachulish: Hotels, V, R, ⊠, Ⓑ. Loch is navigable 7M to Kinlochleven.

CORRAN NARROWS, 56°43'·28N 05°14'·27W. AC 2372. Sp rate 6kn. Well buoyed; Corran Pt lt ho, Iso WRG 4s, and lt bn 5ca NE. ‡ 5ca NW of Pt, off Camas Aiseig pier/slip.

FORT WILLIAM/CORPACH 8-8-17
Highland 56°49'·00N 05°07'·00W (off Fort William)

CHARTS
AC 2372, 2380; Imray C65; OS 41
TIDES
–0535 Dover; ML 2·3; Duration 0610; Zone 0 (UT)

Standard Port OBAN (→)

Times				Height (metres)			
High Water		Low Water		MHWS	MHWN	MLWN	MLWS
0100	0700	0100	0800	4·0	2·9	1·8	0·7
1300	1900	1300	2000				
Differences CORPACH							
0000	+0020	+0040	0000	0·0	0·0	–0·2	–0·2
LOCH EIL (Head)							
+0025	+0045	+0105	+0025	No data		No data	
CORRAN NARROWS							
+0007	+0007	+0004	+0004	+0·4	+0·4	–0·1	0·0
LOCH LEVEN (Head)							
+0045	+0045	+0045	+0045	No data		No data	
LOCH LINNHE (Port Appin)							
–0005	–0005	–0030	0000	+0·2	+0·2	+0·1	+0·1
LOCH CRERAN (Barcaldine Pier)							
+0010	+0020	+0040	+0015	+0·1	+0·1	0·0	+0·1
LOCH CRERAN (Head)							
+0015	+0025	+0120	+0020	–0·3	–0·3	–0·4	–0·3

SHELTER
Exposed to winds SW thro' N to NE. ‡s off Fort William pier; in Camus na Gall; SSW of Eilean A Bhealaidh; and off Corpach Basin, where there is also a waiting pontoon; or inside the canal. The sea lock is normally available HW±4 during canal hrs. For Caledonian Canal see 8.8.18.
NAVIGATION
Corpach WPT 56°50'·30N 05°07'·00W, 135°/315° from/to lock ent, 0·30M. Beware McLean Rk, dries 0·3m, buoyed, 8ca N of Fort William. Lochy Flats dry 3ca off the E bank. In Annat Narrows at ent to Loch Eil streams reach 5kn.
LIGHTS AND MARKS
Iso WRG 4s lt is at N jetty of sea-lock ent, W310°-335°. A long pier/viaduct off Ft William is unlit.
RADIO TELEPHONE
Call: *Corpach Lock* VHF Ch **74** 16 (during canal hours).
TELEPHONE (Dial code 01397)
Hr Mr 772249 (Corpach); MRSC (01631) 563720; ⌗ 702948; Marinecall 0891 500463; Police 702361; Dr 703136.
FACILITIES
FORT WILLIAM. Pier ☎ 703881, AB; **Services:** Slip, L, CH, ACA. **Town** EC Wed; P, ME, El, Sh, YC, V, R, Bar, Ⓗ, ⊠, Ⓑ, ⇌. **CORPACH. Corpach Basin** ☎ 772249, AB, L, FW; **Lochaber YC** ☎ 703576, M, FW, L, Slip; **Services:** ME, El, Sh, D (cans), M, CH, C, (18 ton), Slip, Divers. **Village** P, V, R, Bar, ⊠, Ⓑ, ⇌.

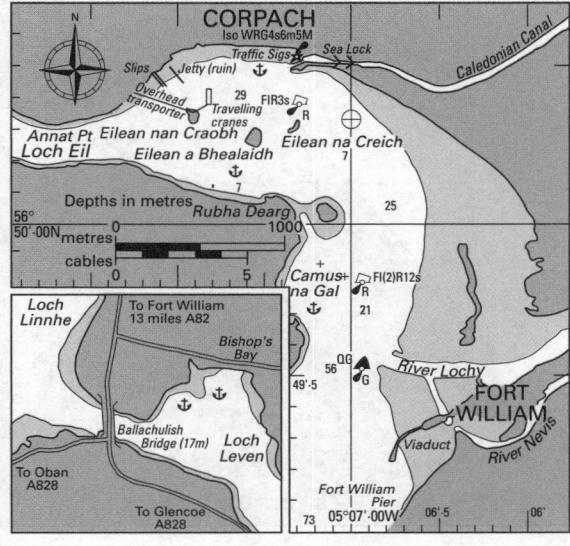

CALEDONIAN CANAL   8-8-18

Highland   Rtg 3-2-1

CHARTS
AC 1791; OS 41, 34, 26

TIDES
Tidal differences: Corpach –0455 on Dover; See 8.8.14.
Clachnaharry: +0116 on Dover; See 8.7.16.

SHELTER
Corpach is at the SW ent of the Caledonian Canal, which is
available for vessels up to 45m LOA, 10m beam, 4m draft
and max mast ht 27·4m. Access from HW–4 to HW+4 (sp);
H24 (nps); the sea locks at both ends do not open LW±2 at
springs. For best shelter transit the sea lock and lie above
the double lock. Numerous pontoons along the canal; cost
is included in the canal dues. For Inverness see 8.7.16.

NAVIGATION
The 60M canal consists of 38M through 3 lochs, (Lochs
Lochy, Oich and Ness), connected by 22M through canals.
Loch Oich is part of a hydro-electric scheme which may
vary the water level. The passage normally takes two full
days, possibly longer in the summer; absolute minimum
is 14 hrs. Speed limit is 5kn in the canal sections. There
are 10 swing bridges; road tfc has priority at peak hrs. Do
not pass bridges without the keeper's instructions.

LOCKS
There are 29 locks: 14 between Loch Linnhe (Corpach), via
Lochs Lochy and Oich up to the summit (106´ above sea
level); and 15 locks from the summit down via Loch Ness
to Inverness. All locks are manned and operate early May
to early Oct, 0800-1730LT daily. Contact canal office for
reduced hrs in autumn, winter and spring; shut Christmas
and New Year. The Sea locks are normally available HW±4
during canal hrs; they will open outside hrs for extra fees.
Last lockings start ½ hr before the canal closes for the day.
Dues, payable at Corpach, at 1998 rates, inc VAT: £7.72
per metre for 1 day; £12.74 for 3 days, plus special offers.
For regulations and useful booklet *Skipper's Guide* apply:
Canal Manager, Canal Office, Seaport Marina, Muirtown
Wharf, Inverness IV3 5LS, ☎ (01463) 233140/📠 710942.

LIGHTS & MARKS
See 8.8.17 and 8.7.16 for ent lts. Channel is marked by posts,
cairns and unlit buoys, PHM on the NW side of the chan and
SHM on the SE side.

BOAT SAFETY SCHEME
BWB, who operate the Caledonian & Crinan Canals,
require compulsory safety and seaworthiness checks for
craft based on these waterways. Transient/visiting
vessels will be checked for apparent dangerous defects
eg leaking gas or fuel, damaged electrical cables,
taking in water, risk of capsize. £1M 3rd party
insurance is required. For details contact:
Boat Safety Scheme, Willow Grange,
Church Road, Watford WD1 3QA.
☎ 01923 226422; 📠 226081.

RADIO TELEPHONE
Sea locks and main lock flights operate VHF Ch **74** (HO).

TELEPHONE
Corpach Sea Lock/Basin (01397) 772249; Canal Office,
Inverness (01463) 233140; Clachnaharry Sea Lock (01463)
713896.

FACILITIES
For details see *Skipper's Guide* (using the maps).
- Corpach see 8.8.17.
- Banavie (Neptune's Staircase; one-way locking takes
  1½ hrs) AC, 60m jetty, V, ✉, ⚓, ♿.
- Gairlochy AB, R.
- NE end of Loch Lochy V, M, AB, R.
- Oich (Laggan) Bridge D, AB, R.
- Invergarry V, L, FW, AB.
- Fort Augustus AB, FW, D, P, ME, El, V, ✉, ⚓, Dr, Bar.
- Urquhart B. (L. Ness) FW, AC, AB £6, 3m depth, V, Bar.
- Dochgarroch FW, AC, P, V.

At Inverness (8.7.16):
- Caley Marina (25+25 visitors) ☎ (01463) 236539, FW,
  CH, D, ME, El, Sh, AC, C (20 ton), ACA.
- Seaport Marina (20 + 20 Ⓥ), £6, ☎ (01463) 239475, FW,
  AC, D, El, ME, Sh, Gas, Gaz, ▣, ⚓, ♿, C (40 ton).

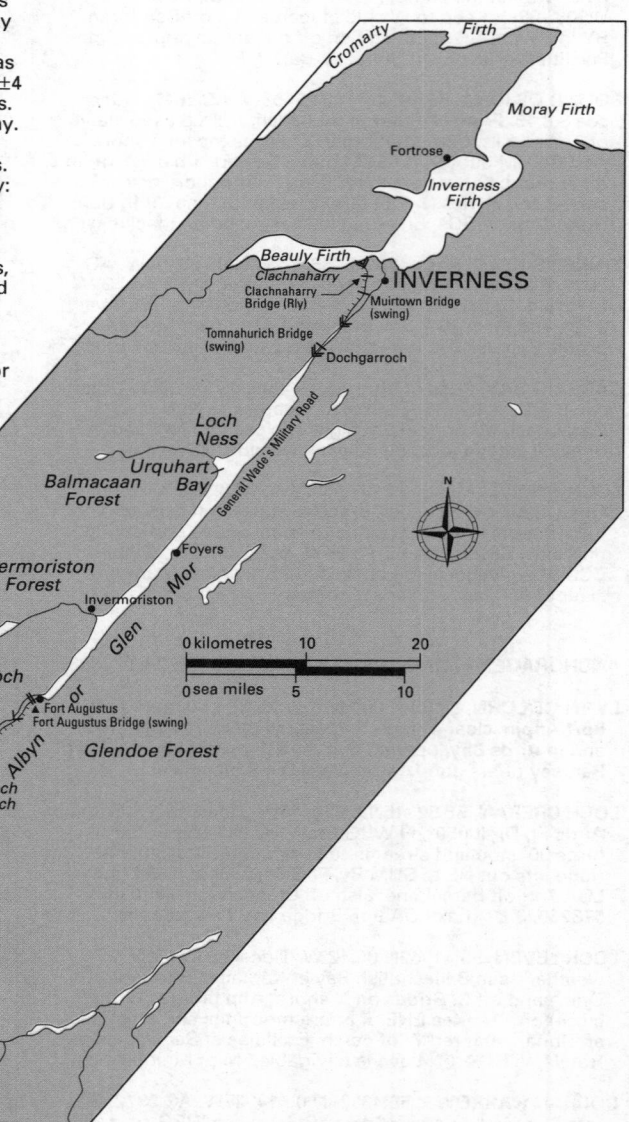

TIME ZONE (UT)
For Summer Time add ONE hour in non-shaded areas

SCOTLAND – OBAN

LAT 56°25′N   LONG 5°29′W

TIMES AND HEIGHTS OF HIGH AND LOW WATERS

YEAR 1999

JANUARY

Time	m	Time	m
1 0443 / 1115 / F 1717 / 2325	3.9 / 0.9 / 4.0 / 0.8	**16** 0459 / 1106 / SA 1714 / 2333	3.7 / 1.4 / 3.7 / 1.2
2 0527 / 1204 / SA 1758 / O	4.1 / 0.8 / 4.1	**17** 0538 / 1147 / SU 1751 / ●	3.8 / 1.2 / 3.8
3 0009 / 0608 / SU 1251 / 1838	0.7 / 4.1 / 0.8 / 4.0	**18** 0007 / 0613 / M 1226 / 1824	1.0 / 3.9 / 1.1 / 3.9
4 0053 / 0650 / M 1335 / 1918	0.7 / 4.1 / 0.9 / 3.9	**19** 0041 / 0647 / TU 1304 / 1855	0.9 / 4.0 / 1.0 / 3.9
5 0136 / 0730 / TU 1419 / 1956	0.7 / 4.1 / 1.1 / 3.8	**20** 0116 / 0720 / W 1341 / 1928	0.9 / 4.0 / 1.0 / 3.8
6 0218 / 0809 / W 1501 / 2034	0.9 / 3.9 / 1.3 / 3.6	**21** 0152 / 0756 / TH 1419 / 2004	0.9 / 3.9 / 1.0 / 3.7
7 0300 / 0848 / TH 1544 / 2113	1.0 / 3.7 / 1.5 / 3.4	**22** 0230 / 0835 / F 1501 / 2045	0.9 / 3.8 / 1.1 / 3.6
8 0343 / 0929 / F 1630 / 2157	1.3 / 3.5 / 1.7 / 3.2	**23** 0314 / 0920 / SA 1550 / 2132	1.0 / 3.7 / 1.3 / 3.4
9 0430 / 1014 / SA 1721 / 2251	1.5 / 3.3 / 1.9 / 3.0	**24** 0406 / 1014 / SU 1648 / 2227	1.2 / 3.5 / 1.4 / 3.2
10 0520 / 1112 / SU 1822	1.7 / 3.1 / 2.0	**25** 0510 / 1123 / M 1757 / 2341	1.4 / 3.3 / 1.5 / 3.1
11 0012 / 0617 / M 1235 / 1934	3.0 / 1.8 / 3.0 / 2.0	**26** 0627 / 1306 / TU 1911	1.5 / 3.2 / 1.5
12 0146 / 0719 / TU 1406 / 2048	3.0 / 1.9 / 3.1 / 1.9	**27** 0121 / 0749 / W 1439 / 2024	3.1 / 1.5 / 3.3 / 1.5
13 0248 / 0827 / W 1507 / 2142	3.1 / 1.8 / 3.2 / 1.8	**28** 0251 / 0910 / TH 1544 / 2129	3.2 / 1.4 / 3.5 / 1.3
14 0337 / 0931 / TH 1553 / 2223	3.3 / 1.7 / 3.4 / 1.6	**29** 0353 / 1018 / F 1635 / 2225	3.5 / 1.2 / 3.7 / 1.1
15 0419 / 1023 / F 1635 / 2259	3.5 / 1.5 / 3.6 / 1.4	**30** 0439 / 1112 / SA 1717 / 2314	3.7 / 1.0 / 3.8 / 0.9
		31 0520 / 1158 / SU 1754 / O 2358	3.9 / 0.9 / 3.9 / 0.7

FEBRUARY

Time	m	Time	m
1 0559 / 1240 / M 1830	4.1 / 0.8 / 4.0	**16** 0558 / 1210 / TU 1809 / ●	4.0 / 0.8 / 3.9
2 0039 / 0637 / TU 1321 / 1904	0.6 / 4.1 / 0.9 / 3.9	**17** 0021 / 0632 / W 1247 / 1839	0.7 / 4.1 / 0.7 / 3.9
3 0119 / 0713 / W 1359 / 1937	0.6 / 4.1 / 1.0 / 3.9	**18** 0058 / 0705 / TH 1324 / 1910	0.5 / 4.1 / 0.6 / 3.9
4 0157 / 0747 / TH 1435 / 2009	0.7 / 4.0 / 1.1 / 3.7	**19** 0135 / 0742 / F 1401 / 1946	0.5 / 4.1 / 0.6 / 3.8
5 0234 / 0820 / F 1509 / 2041	0.9 / 3.8 / 1.3 / 3.6	**20** 0215 / 0817 / SA 1442 / 2026	0.6 / 3.9 / 0.8 / 3.7
6 0311 / 0854 / SA 1546 / 2115	1.1 / 3.6 / 1.6 / 3.4	**21** 0259 / 0859 / SU 1528 / 2109	0.7 / 3.7 / 0.9 / 3.5
7 0350 / 0929 / SU 1628 / 2155	1.4 / 3.4 / 1.8 / 3.2	**22** 0350 / 0949 / M 1622 / 2200	0.9 / 3.4 / 1.2 / 3.2
8 0435 / 1009 / M 1719 / 2246	1.6 / 3.2 / 1.9 / 3.0	**23** 0451 / 1053 / TU 1727 / 2309	1.2 / 3.1 / 1.4 / 3.0
9 0527 / 1102 / TU 1822	1.8 / 3.0 / 2.0	**24** 0607 / 1245 / W 1842	1.4 / 3.0 / 1.5
10 0012 / 0628 / W 1253 / 1937	2.9 / 1.9 / 2.9 / 2.0	**25** 0059 / 0734 / TH 1433 / 2001	2.9 / 1.5 / 3.0 / 1.5
11 0209 / 0738 / TH 1443 / 2100	2.9 / 2.0 / 3.0 / 1.6	**26** 0247 / 0912 / F 1545 / 2115	3.1 / 1.4 / 3.2 / 1.3
12 0316 / 0855 / F 1540 / 2158	3.1 / 1.8 / 3.1 / 1.6	**27** 0352 / 1020 / SA 1634 / 2214	3.3 / 1.2 / 3.4 / 1.1
13 0403 / 1003 / SA 1622 / 2238	3.3 / 1.6 / 3.4 / 1.4	**28** 0433 / 1108 / SU 1710 / 2301	3.6 / 1.0 / 3.6 / 0.9
14 0444 / 1051 / SU 1701 / 2314	3.6 / 1.3 / 3.6 / 1.1		
15 0522 / 1132 / M 1737 / 2347	3.8 / 1.0 / 3.7 / 0.9		

MARCH

Time	m	Time	m
1 0509 / 1148 / M 1742 / 2343	3.8 / 0.9 / 3.8 / 0.7	**16** 0459 / 1110 / TU 1715 / 2323	3.8 / 0.9 / 3.7 / 0.7
2 0545 / 1225 / TU 1813 / O	4.0 / 0.8 / 3.9	**17** 0536 / 1148 / W 1747 / ● 2359	3.9 / 0.6 / 3.9 / 0.4
3 0022 / 0618 / W 1300 / 1843	0.6 / 4.1 / 0.8 / 3.9	**18** 0611 / 1224 / TH 1817	4.2 / 0.4 / 4.0
4 0059 / 0651 / TH 1333 / 1913	0.6 / 4.1 / 0.9 / 3.9	**19** 0037 / 0644 / F 1302 / 1850	0.3 / 4.2 / 0.3 / 4.0
5 0134 / 0722 / F 1405 / 1942	0.7 / 4.0 / 1.0 / 3.9	**20** 0118 / 0720 / SA 1341 / 1927	0.2 / 4.1 / 0.4 / 3.8
6 0206 / 0752 / SA 1435 / 2011	0.8 / 3.8 / 1.2 / 3.6	**21** 0200 / 0759 / SU 1423 / 2006	0.3 / 4.0 / 0.5 / 3.8
7 0239 / 0821 / SU 1507 / 2042	1.1 / 3.7 / 1.4 / 3.5	**22** 0246 / 0841 / M 1509 / 2050	0.6 / 3.7 / 0.7 / 3.5
8 0314 / 0851 / M 1543 / 2117	1.3 / 3.4 / 1.6 / 3.3	**23** 0338 / 0930 / TU 1602 / 2140	0.8 / 3.3 / 1.0 / 3.2
9 0354 / 0923 / TU 1629 / 2158	1.6 / 3.2 / 1.8 / 3.1	**24** 0440 / 1034 / W 1705 / 2248	1.1 / 3.0 / 1.3 / 3.0
10 0443 / 1004 / W 1730 / 2256	1.8 / 3.0 / 2.0 / 2.9	**25** 0554 / 1237 / TH 1818	1.4 / 2.8 / 1.5
11 0547 / 1107 / TH 1844	2.0 / 2.8 / 2.0	**26** 0046 / 0729 / F 1426 / 1939	2.8 / 1.5 / 2.8 / 1.5
12 0118 / 0702 / F 1418 / 2005	2.8 / 2.0 / 2.8 / 1.9	**27** 0237 / 0912 / SA 1538 / 2058	3.0 / 1.4 / 3.0 / 1.3
13 0252 / 0825 / SA 1523 / 2120	3.0 / 1.8 / 3.0 / 1.7	**28** 0340 / 1011 / SU 1620 / 2156	3.2 / 1.2 / 3.2 / 1.1
14 0341 / 0940 / SU 1604 / 2208	3.2 / 1.5 / 3.2 / 1.3	**29** 0415 / 1054 / M 1649 / 2242	3.5 / 1.0 / 3.5 / 0.9
15 0422 / 1029 / M 1641 / 2247	3.5 / 1.2 / 3.5 / 1.0	**30** 0448 / 1129 / TU 1718 / 2322	3.7 / 0.9 / 3.7 / 0.7
		31 0522 / 1202 / W 1748 / O 2359	3.8 / 0.8 / 3.8 / 0.7

APRIL

Time	m	Time	m
1 0554 / 1233 / TH 1818 / ●	4.0 / 0.8 / 3.9	**16** 0546 / 1200 / F 1753 / ●	4.2 / 0.3 / 4.0
2 0034 / 0625 / F 1304 / 1846	0.7 / 4.0 / 0.9 / 3.9	**17** 0017 / 0623 / SA 1240 / 1830	0.2 / 4.2 / 0.2 / 4.0
3 0107 / 0655 / SA 1334 / 1915	0.7 / 3.9 / 1.0 / 3.9	**18** 0101 / 0701 / SU 1321 / 1909	0.2 / 4.1 / 0.3 / 4.0
4 0139 / 0724 / SU 1404 / 1944	0.9 / 3.8 / 1.1 / 3.8	**19** 0147 / 0742 / M 1405 / 1951	0.3 / 3.9 / 0.4 / 3.8
5 0210 / 0753 / M 1433 / 2014	1.1 / 3.7 / 1.3 / 3.6	**20** 0235 / 0826 / TU 1452 / 2036	0.5 / 3.6 / 0.6 / 3.6
6 0242 / 0821 / TU 1503 / 2048	1.3 / 3.5 / 1.5 / 3.4	**21** 0329 / 0916 / W 1545 / 2127	0.8 / 3.3 / 0.9 / 3.3
7 0317 / 0851 / W 1540 / 2126	1.6 / 3.2 / 1.7 / 3.2	**22** 0430 / 1022 / TH 1645 / 2234	1.1 / 2.9 / 1.2 / 3.0
8 0402 / 0929 / TH 1638 / 2217	1.8 / 3.0 / 1.9 / 3.0	**23** 0543 / 1222 / F 1753	1.4 / 2.7 / 1.4
9 0510 / 1027 / F 1754 / 2349	1.9 / 2.8 / 2.0 / 2.8	**24** 0024 / 0720 / SA 1403 / 1911	2.9 / 1.5 / 2.8 / 1.4
10 0631 / 1326 / SA 1912	2.0 / 2.7 / 1.9	**25** 0209 / 0852 / SU 1512 / 2029	3.0 / 1.4 / 2.9 / 1.4
11 0211 / 0754 / SU 1450 / 2027	3.0 / 1.8 / 2.9 / 1.7	**26** 0311 / 0948 / M 1551 / 2129	3.1 / 1.3 / 3.1 / 1.2
12 0308 / 0906 / M 1535 / 2126	3.2 / 1.5 / 3.1 / 1.3	**27** 0347 / 1029 / TU 1618 / 2216	3.3 / 1.2 / 3.3 / 1.0
13 0351 / 0958 / TU 1612 / 2212	3.5 / 1.1 / 3.4 / 1.0	**28** 0420 / 1103 / W 1648 / 2256	3.5 / 1.0 / 3.5 / 0.9
14 0431 / 1041 / W 1646 / 2254	3.8 / 0.8 / 3.7 / 0.6	**29** 0453 / 1134 / TH 1719 / 2332	3.7 / 1.0 / 3.7 / 0.8
15 0508 / 1121 / TH 1719 / 2335	4.1 / 0.5 / 3.9 / 0.4	**30** 0526 / 1204 / F 1750 / O	3.8 / 1.0 / 3.8

8

Chart Datum: 2·10 metres below Ordnance Datum (Newlyn)

SCOTLAND – OBAN

LAT 56°25′N   LONG 5°29′W

TIMES AND HEIGHTS OF HIGH AND LOW WATERS

YEAR 1999

TIME ZONE (UT)
For Summer Time add ONE hour in non-shaded areas

MAY

Day	Time	m	Time	m	Time	m	Time	m
1 SA	0006	0.8	0558	3.9	1234	0.9	1820	3.9
2 SU	0040	0.9	0630	3.8	1305	1.0	1850	3.9
3 M	0113	1.0	0701	3.8	1336	1.1	1921	3.8
4 TU	0145	1.2	0730	3.6	1405	1.3	1953	3.6
5 W	0217	1.4	0800	3.4	1434	1.4	2027	3.5
6 TH	0251	1.5	0832	3.3	1507	1.6	2105	3.3
7 F	0334	1.7	0912	3.1	1555	1.7	2154	3.1
8 SA	0438	1.8	1009	2.9	1704	1.8	2304	3.0
9 SU	0558	1.8	1138	2.8	1819	1.8		
10 M	0100	3.0	0717	1.7	1355	2.9	1932	1.6
11 TU	0223	3.3	0826	1.5	1453	3.1	2038	1.3
12 W	0314	3.5	0922	1.1	1535	3.4	2135	1.0
13 TH	0359	3.8	1010	0.8	1613	3.6	2225	0.7
14 F	0441	4.0	1053	0.6	1652	3.8	2313	0.5
15 SA ●	0522	4.1	1136	0.4	1732	4.0		
16 SU	0000	0.3	0603	4.2	1219	0.3	1813	4.1
17 M	0047	0.3	0646	4.1	1303	0.3	1855	4.0
18 TU	0136	0.4	0730	3.9	1348	0.4	1939	3.9
19 W	0226	0.6	0816	3.6	1436	0.6	2025	3.6
20 TH	0319	0.9	0906	3.3	1527	0.9	2116	3.4
21 F	0418	1.2	1009	3.0	1623	1.1	2217	3.1
22 SA	0526	1.4	1147	2.8	1724	1.3	2340	3.0
23 SU	0650	1.5	1318	2.8	1833	1.4		
24 M	0119	3.0	0814	1.5	1424	2.9	1945	1.4
25 TU	0226	3.1	0913	1.5	1508	3.0	2050	1.4
26 W	0311	3.2	0957	1.4	1542	3.2	2142	1.3
27 TH	0348	3.3	1033	1.3	1615	3.4	2224	1.2
28 F	0423	3.5	1116	1.2	1649	3.6	2302	1.1
29 SA	0459	3.6	1134	1.1	1724	3.7	2338	1.1
30 SU O	0534	3.7	1206	1.1	1757	3.8		
31 M	0013	1.1	0609	3.7	1239	1.1	1830	3.8

JUNE

Day	Time	m	Time	m	Time	m	Time	m
1 TU	0050	1.1	0643	3.7	1312	1.1	1904	3.8
2 W	0125	1.2	0715	3.6	1343	1.2	1937	3.7
3 TH	0200	1.3	0747	3.5	1414	1.3	2012	3.6
4 F	0236	1.4	0822	3.3	1448	1.4	2051	3.4
5 SA	0318	1.6	0903	3.2	1531	1.5	2138	3.3
6 SU	0412	1.6	0955	3.0	1626	1.6	2236	3.2
7 M	0521	1.7	1101	2.9	1733	1.6	2353	3.2
8 TU	0635	1.6	1226	2.9	1845	1.5		
9 W	0125	3.3	0744	1.4	1355	3.1	1956	1.4
10 TH	0235	3.5	0846	1.2	1458	3.3	2102	1.1
11 F	0330	3.7	0940	1.0	1546	3.5	2201	0.9
12 SA	0419	3.9	1030	0.7	1632	3.8	2256	0.7
13 SU ●	0506	4.0	1116	0.5	1716	3.9	2347	0.5
14 M	0551	4.0	1202	0.4	1801	4.0		
15 TU	0037	0.5	0635	4.0	1248	0.4	1845	4.0
16 W	0127	0.5	0720	3.8	1334	0.5	1929	3.9
17 TH	0216	0.7	0806	3.6	1421	0.6	2014	3.8
18 F	0307	0.9	0853	3.4	1508	0.8	2101	3.5
19 SA	0359	1.2	0945	3.1	1557	1.0	2150	3.3
20 SU	0456	1.4	1048	3.0	1650	1.3	2247	3.1
21 M	0601	1.6	1211	2.8	1746	1.4	2359	3.0
22 TU	0714	1.7	1323	2.9	1847	1.5		
23 W	0121	3.0	0824	1.7	1419	2.9	1952	1.6
24 TH	0225	3.0	0919	1.6	1504	3.1	2054	1.5
25 F	0313	3.1	1001	1.5	1545	3.3	2147	1.5
26 SA	0355	3.3	1037	1.4	1624	3.5	2231	1.4
27 SU	0436	3.5	1110	1.2	1702	3.6	2311	1.3
28 M O	0516	3.6	1143	1.1	1740	3.7	2351	1.2
29 TU	0554	3.6	1217	1.1	1816	3.8		
30 W	0030	1.2	0630	3.7	1252	1.1	1851	3.8

JULY

Day	Time	m	Time	m	Time	m	Time	m
1 TH	0109	1.2	0704	3.6	1325	1.1	1925	3.8
2 F	0147	1.2	0736	3.6	1356	1.1	2000	3.7
3 SA	0223	1.2	0810	3.5	1430	1.2	2037	3.6
4 SU	0302	1.3	0849	3.3	1510	1.3	2119	3.5
5 M	0348	1.4	0935	3.2	1559	1.3	2210	3.4
6 TU	0446	1.5	1030	3.1	1658	1.4	2313	3.3
7 W	0554	1.5	1139	3.0	1808	1.4		
8 TH	0036	3.3	0706	1.4	1306	3.0	1924	1.4
9 F	0205	3.4	0814	1.3	1428	3.2	2038	1.3
10 SA	0314	3.5	0917	1.1	1531	3.4	2147	1.1
11 SU	0410	3.7	1012	0.9	1622	3.7	2247	0.9
12 M	0500	3.8	1103	0.7	1709	3.9	2340	0.7
13 TU ●	0545	3.9	1150	0.6	1753	4.0		
14 W	0030	0.6	0628	3.9	1236	0.5	1836	4.1
15 TH	0118	0.7	0710	3.8	1320	0.5	1918	4.0
16 F	0203	0.8	0751	3.7	1403	0.6	1958	3.9
17 SA	0248	0.9	0831	3.5	1446	0.8	2038	3.7
18 SU	0332	1.2	0911	3.3	1528	1.0	2118	3.5
19 M	0417	1.4	0953	3.2	1612	1.2	2200	3.3
20 TU	0506	1.6	1043	3.0	1700	1.4	2249	3.1
21 W	0601	1.8	1155	2.9	1753	1.6	2354	2.9
22 TH	0708	1.8	1322	2.9	1852	1.8		
23 F	0123	2.9	0825	1.8	1429	3.0	1956	1.8
24 SA	0240	3.0	0928	1.7	1521	3.1	2105	1.7
25 SU	0335	3.1	1014	1.5	1605	3.3	2205	1.6
26 M	0420	3.3	1051	1.3	1646	3.5	2252	1.4
27 TU	0502	3.5	1126	1.2	1726	3.7	2334	1.2
28 W O	0542	3.6	1200	1.0	1803	3.8		
29 TH	0014	1.1	0618	3.7	1233	0.9	1838	3.9
30 F	0053	1.0	0650	3.7	1305	0.9	1911	3.9
31 SA	0130	0.9	0719	3.7	1338	0.8	1943	3.9

AUGUST

Day	Time	m	Time	m	Time	m	Time	m
1 SU	0206	1.0	0751	3.6	1412	0.9	2018	3.8
2 M	0243	1.0	0828	3.5	1451	1.0	2058	3.7
3 TU	0325	1.1	0910	3.4	1537	1.1	2145	3.5
4 W	0417	1.3	1000	3.2	1633	1.3	2242	3.3
5 TH	0522	1.4	1104	3.0	1743	1.4		
6 F	0003	3.2	0635	1.5	1236	3.0	1904	1.5
7 SA	0153	3.2	0750	1.4	1422	3.1	2027	1.4
8 SU	0313	3.3	0900	1.2	1533	3.4	2145	1.2
9 M	0413	3.5	1001	1.0	1624	3.6	2246	1.0
10 TU	0501	3.7	1053	0.8	1706	3.9	2336	0.8
11 W ●	0542	3.8	1139	0.6	1745	4.0		
12 TH	0021	0.7	0619	3.9	1223	0.5	1823	4.1
13 F	0103	0.7	0654	3.9	1304	0.5	1900	4.1
14 SA	0143	0.8	0729	3.8	1343	0.6	1935	4.0
15 SU	0221	0.9	0802	3.7	1420	0.7	2009	3.8
16 M	0258	1.1	0834	3.6	1457	1.0	2042	3.6
17 TU	0335	1.4	0907	3.4	1536	1.2	2116	3.4
18 W	0416	1.6	0946	3.2	1619	1.5	2154	3.2
19 TH	0505	1.8	1036	3.0	1709	1.7	2242	3.0
20 F	0607	1.9	1204	2.9	1808	1.9		
21 SA	0012	2.8	0722	1.9	1401	2.9	1916	2.0
22 SU	0218	2.8	0851	1.8	1505	3.1	2035	1.9
23 M	0325	3.0	0951	1.6	1551	3.3	2150	1.7
24 TU	0409	3.3	1032	1.4	1631	3.5	2238	1.4
25 W	0448	3.5	1107	1.1	1709	3.8	2318	1.1
26 TH O	0525	3.7	1139	0.9	1745	3.9	2356	0.9
27 F	0559	3.8	1210	0.8	1819	4.1		
28 SA	0032	0.8	0629	3.8	1243	0.6	1850	4.1
29 SU	0108	0.7	0656	3.8	1317	0.6	1922	4.1
30 M	0143	0.7	0728	3.8	1353	0.6	1956	4.0
31 TU	0221	0.8	0804	3.7	1434	0.8	2035	3.8

Chart Datum: 2·10 metres below Ordnance Datum (Newlyn)

SCOTLAND – OBAN

LAT 56°25′N   LONG 5°29′W

TIMES AND HEIGHTS OF HIGH AND LOW WATERS

YEAR **1999**

TIME ZONE (UT)
For Summer Time add ONE hour in non-shaded areas

SEPTEMBER

Day	Time	m	Time	m	Time	m	Time	m		Day	Time	m	Time	m	Time	m	Time	m
1 W	0303	0.9	0846	3.5	1520	1.0	2120	3.5		**16** TH	0333	1.6	0905	3.4	1542	1.6	2109	3.3
2 TH	0354	1.1	0934	3.3	1617	1.2	2217	3.2		**17** F	0420	1.8	0948	3.1	1632	1.9	2147	3.0
3 F	0457	1.3	1037	3.1	1730	1.5	2345	3.0		**18** SA	0521	2.0	1053	2.9	1734	2.1	2247	2.8
4 SA	0612	1.5	1223	2.9	1855	1.6				**19** SU	0635	2.0	1337	2.9	1848	2.1		
5 SU	0156	3.0	0731	1.5	1429	3.1	2031	1.5		**20** M	0208	2.8	0804	1.9	1449	3.1	2013	2.0
6 M	0316	3.2	0848	1.3	1535	3.4	2152	1.3		**21** TU	0312	3.0	0918	1.7	1533	3.3	2130	1.7
7 TU	0412	3.4	0950	1.1	1620	3.6	2244	1.1		**22** W	0351	3.2	1003	1.4	1610	3.6	2216	1.4
8 W	0453	3.6	1040	0.9	1655	3.9	2326	0.9		**23** TH	0427	3.5	1039	1.2	1645	3.8	2255	1.1
9 TH ●	0527	3.8	1124	0.7	1729	4.1				**24** F	0501	3.7	1111	0.9	1720	4.1	2331	0.8
10 F	0005	0.8	0559	3.9	1205	0.5	1802	4.2		**25** SA O	0533	3.9	1144	0.7	1753	4.2		
11 SA	0041	0.8	0630	4.0	1243	0.5	1835	4.2		**26** SU	0006	0.6	0601	4.0	1218	0.5	1825	4.3
12 SU	0116	0.8	0701	4.0	1318	0.6	1906	4.1		**27** M	0042	0.5	0631	4.0	1255	0.5	1858	4.2
13 M	0149	0.9	0730	3.9	1352	0.8	1937	3.9		**28** TU	0119	0.5	0704	4.0	1335	0.5	1934	4.1
14 TU	0222	1.1	0759	3.8	1426	1.0	2007	3.7		**29** W	0159	0.6	0742	3.8	1419	0.7	2014	3.8
15 W	0255	1.3	0830	3.6	1501	1.3	2037	3.5		**30** TH	0243	0.8	0825	3.6	1509	0.9	2100	3.5

OCTOBER

Day	Time	m	Time	m	Time	m	Time	m		Day	Time	m	Time	m	Time	m	Time	m
1 F	0334	1.0	0914	3.4	1609	1.3	2157	3.2		**16** SA	0339	1.8	0916	3.3	1558	2.0	2112	3.1
2 SA	0436	1.3	1019	3.1	1722	1.5	2340	2.9		**17** SU	0436	2.0	1011	3.1	1703	2.1	2205	2.9
3 SU	0550	1.5	1228	3.0	1852	1.6				**18** M	0548	2.1	1231	3.0	1820	2.2		
4 M	0152	2.9	0711	1.5	1423	3.1	2040	1.6		**19** TU	0125	2.8	0708	2.0	1417	3.1	1944	2.0
5 TU	0309	3.1	0831	1.4	1525	3.4	2147	1.3		**20** W	0242	3.0	0826	1.8	1503	3.4	2055	1.8
6 W	0400	3.3	0933	1.2	1602	3.6	2231	1.1		**21** TH	0323	3.2	0920	1.6	1540	3.6	2143	1.4
7 TH	0433	3.5	1021	1.0	1633	3.9	2308	1.0		**22** F	0358	3.5	1001	1.2	1615	3.9	2224	1.1
8 F	0502	3.7	1103	0.8	1705	4.0	2341	0.9		**23** SA	0431	3.7	1038	0.9	1650	4.1	2301	0.8
9 SA ●	0532	3.9	1141	0.7	1736	4.1				**24** SU O	0502	3.9	1115	0.7	1725	4.3	2338	0.6
10 SU	0013	0.9	0602	4.0	1218	0.7	1806	4.1		**25** M	0533	4.1	1154	0.5	1800	4.4		
11 M	0045	0.9	0631	4.0	1252	0.8	1837	4.1		**26** TU	0015	0.4	0607	4.1	1236	0.5	1836	4.3
12 TU	0117	1.0	0700	4.0	1324	1.0	1907	4.0		**27** W	0056	0.4	0644	4.1	1320	0.5	1915	4.1
13 W	0148	1.1	0729	3.9	1357	1.2	1936	3.8		**28** TH	0139	0.5	0725	4.0	1407	0.7	1957	3.9
14 TH	0221	1.3	0800	3.7	1431	1.5	2006	3.5		**29** F	0225	0.7	0810	3.8	1500	1.0	2045	3.5
15 F	0257	1.6	0835	3.5	1510	1.7	2036	3.4		**30** SA	0317	1.0	0901	3.5	1600	1.3	2144	3.2
										31 SU	0417	1.3	1006	3.2	1712	1.6	2327	2.9

NOVEMBER

Day	Time	m	Time	m	Time	m	Time	m		Day	Time	m	Time	m	Time	m	Time	m
1 M	0526	1.5	1207	3.1	1843	1.7				**16** TU	0451	2.0	1052	3.1	1744	2.1	2303	2.9
2 TU	0132	2.9	0643	1.5	1400	3.2	2023	1.6		**17** W	0604	2.0	1310	3.2	1900	2.0		
3 W	0248	3.1	0802	1.5	1502	3.4	2125	1.5		**18** TH	0143	2.9	0717	1.9	1418	3.4	2008	1.8
4 TH	0335	3.3	0906	1.3	1537	3.6	2208	1.3		**19** F	0240	3.1	0823	1.7	1503	3.6	2103	1.5
5 F	0405	3.5	0956	1.0	1606	3.7	2243	1.2		**20** SA	0320	3.4	0917	1.4	1542	3.9	2148	1.2
6 SA	0432	3.7	1038	1.0	1637	3.9	2315	1.1		**21** SU	0356	3.7	1004	1.1	1620	4.1	2230	0.9
7 SU	0502	3.9	1116	1.0	1708	4.0	2344	1.1		**22** M	0431	3.9	1049	0.8	1659	4.3	2311	0.7
8 M ●	0534	4.0	1151	1.0	1739	4.1				**23** TU O	0509	4.1	1134	0.6	1738	4.3	2353	0.5
9 TU	0015	1.0	0604	4.1	1225	1.0	1810	4.0		**24** W	0549	4.2	1220	0.6	1819	4.3		
10 W	0047	1.1	0634	4.1	1259	1.2	1842	4.0		**25** TH	0036	0.5	0630	4.2	1308	0.6	1901	4.1
11 TH	0120	1.2	0706	4.0	1332	1.4	1914	3.8		**26** F	0122	0.5	0714	4.1	1358	0.8	1946	3.9
12 F	0154	1.4	0739	3.8	1407	1.6	1944	3.7		**27** SA	0210	0.7	0800	3.9	1451	1.0	2034	3.6
13 SA	0227	1.6	0814	3.7	1445	1.8	2016	3.4		**28** SU	0301	0.9	0851	3.7	1549	1.3	2130	3.3
14 SU	0303	1.8	0854	3.5	1529	2.0	2053	3.2		**29** M	0356	1.2	0950	3.4	1655	1.5	2248	3.0
15 M	0349	1.9	0942	3.3	1630	2.1	2143	3.0		**30** TU	0458	1.4	1112	3.2	1813	1.7		

DECEMBER

Day	Time	m	Time	m	Time	m	Time	m		Day	Time	m	Time	m	Time	m	Time	m
1 W	0042	2.9	0606	1.5	1307	3.2	1941	1.7		**16** TH	0501	1.9	1119	3.3	1804	1.9	2335	3.0
2 TH	0200	3.0	0719	1.5	1420	3.3	2049	1.6		**17** F	0611	1.8	1256	3.3	1914	1.8		
3 F	0253	3.1	0828	1.5	1504	3.4	2137	1.5		**18** SA	0111	3.1	0724	1.7	1415	3.5	2017	1.6
4 SA	0328	3.3	0924	1.4	1537	3.5	2215	1.4		**19** SU	0228	3.3	0833	1.5	1510	3.7	2112	1.3
5 SU	0400	3.5	1010	1.3	1610	3.7	2247	1.3		**20** M	0321	3.5	0935	1.2	1557	3.9	2203	1.0
6 M	0434	3.7	1050	1.3	1643	3.8	2318	1.3		**21** TU	0408	3.8	1030	1.0	1642	4.1	2250	0.8
7 TU ●	0508	3.9	1126	1.2	1717	3.9	2350	1.2		**22** W O	0453	4.0	1122	0.8	1726	4.2	2336	0.6
8 W	0542	4.0	1202	1.3	1751	3.9				**23** TH	0537	4.1	1212	0.7	1809	4.2		
9 TH	0023	1.2	0616	4.0	1238	1.3	1826	3.9		**24** F	0022	0.5	0621	4.2	1301	0.7	1853	4.1
10 F	0059	1.2	0650	4.0	1314	1.4	1859	3.8		**25** SA	0109	0.5	0706	4.2	1350	0.8	1937	3.9
11 SA	0133	1.3	0725	3.9	1350	1.5	1932	3.7		**26** SU	0156	0.6	0751	4.0	1440	1.0	2023	3.7
12 SU	0205	1.5	0800	3.8	1426	1.7	2005	3.5		**27** M	0244	0.8	0838	3.8	1532	1.2	2110	3.4
13 M	0237	1.6	0837	3.6	1504	1.8	2041	3.4		**28** TU	0333	1.0	0927	3.6	1626	1.4	2204	3.2
14 TU	0313	1.7	0919	3.5	1552	1.9	2125	3.2		**29** W	0425	1.2	1022	3.3	1726	1.7	2313	3.0
15 W	0400	1.8	1010	3.4	1653	2.0	2221	3.1		**30** TH	0522	1.4	1132	3.2	1835	1.8		
										31 F	0042	2.9	0623	1.6	1307	3.1	1952	1.8

8

Chart Datum: 2·10 metres below Ordnance Datum (Newlyn)

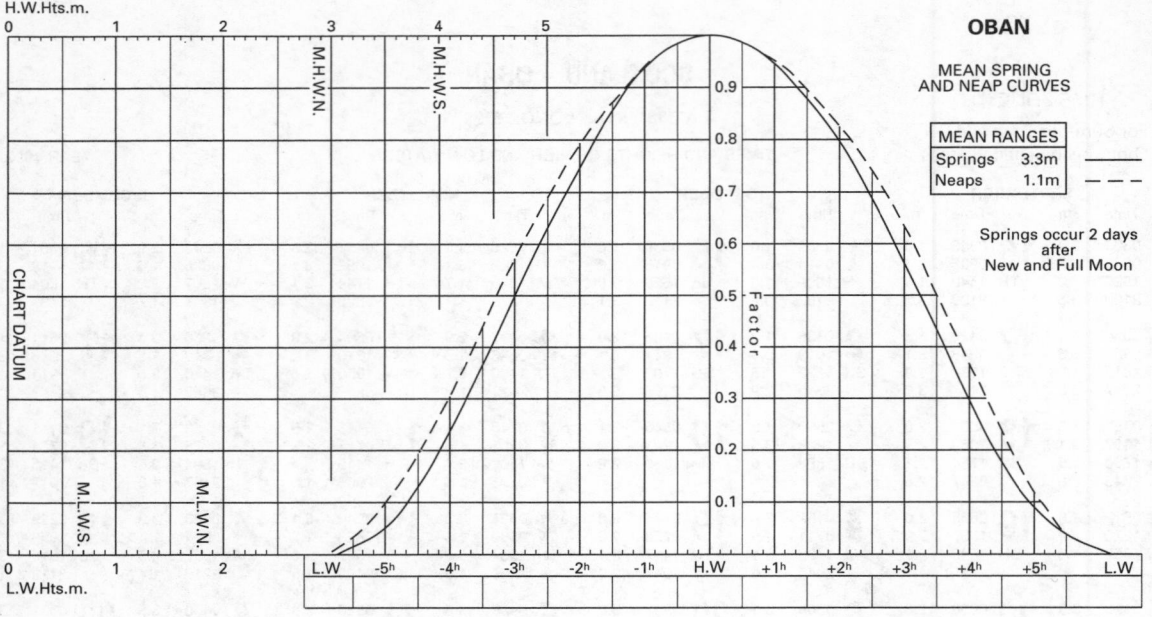

OBAN

MEAN SPRING
AND NEAP CURVES

MEAN RANGES	
Springs	3.3m
Neaps	1.1m

Springs occur 2 days
after
New and Full Moon

ADJACENT ANCHORAGES/HAVEN

DUNSTAFFNAGE BAY, Argyll & Bute, 56°27′·05N 05°25′·90W. Rtg 3-2-1. AC 2378, 2387. HW −0530 on Dover; see 8.8.19. Good shelter at marina pontoons, SE side of bay entered 'twixt Rubha Garbh and Eilean Mór; little room to ‡, but 7 Y ⚓s available. No navigational hazards; W and SW sides of bay dry. Private pier on NW side has 2 FG (vert) 4m 2M. **Dunstaffnage Marina** ☎ (01631) 566555, 🖅 567422, VHF Ch 80, AB £8.74, FW, Slip, BH (10 ton), SM, R, Bar; **Alba Yachts** ☎ 565630, VHF Ch M call *Alba*, ME, El, Sh, CH, Gas. Facilities: P & D (cans, ¾M), V (½M), Bus, ⇌ Oban (2M) & Connel (airstrip). In the bay 8ca to E, 37 ⚓s and landing pontoon are approved.

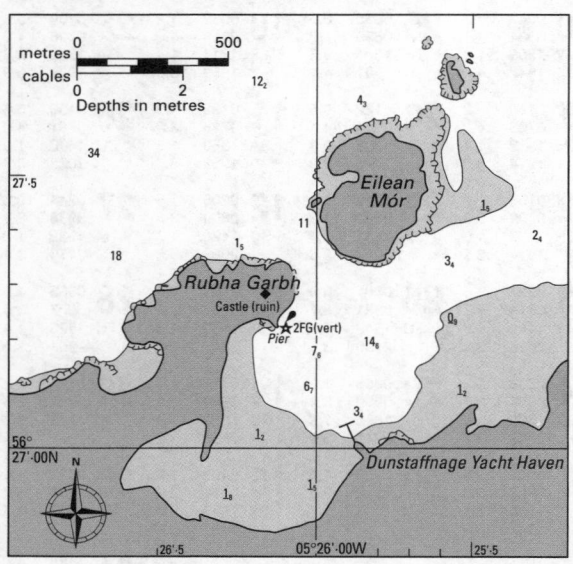

LOCH ETIVE, AC 2378 to Bonawe, thence AC 5076. Connel Bridge, 15m clrnce, and Falls of Lora can be physical and tidal barriers. HT cables at Bonawe have 13m clrnce. See CCC SDs.

OBAN   8-8-19

Argyll and Bute 56°25′·00N 05°29′·00W   Rtg 1-2-2

CHARTS
AC 1790, 2387, *2171*; Imray C65; OS 49
TIDES
−0530 Dover; ML 2·4; Duration 0610; Zone 0 (UT)

Standard Port OBAN (←—)

Times				Height (metres)			
High Water		Low Water		MHWS	MHWN	MLWN	MLWS
0100	0700	0100	0800	4·0	2·9	1·8	0·7
1300	1900	1300	2000				
Differences DUNSTAFFNAGE BAY							
+0005	0000	0000	+0005	+0·1	+0·1	+0·1	+0·1
CONNEL							
+0020	+0005	+0010	+0015	−0·3	−0·2	−0·1	+0·1
BONAWE							
+0150	+0205	+0240	+0210	−2·0	−1·7	−1·3	−0·5

Oban is a Standard Port and tidal predictions for each day of the year are given above.

SHELTER
Good except in strong SW/NW winds, but Ardantrive Bay (20 ⚓s, some pontoon berths and water taxi 0800-2300) is sheltered from these winds. See chartlet for ⚓s. ‡s off town, but in deep water. ‡ or M off Brandystone and in Kerrera Sound at: Horseshoe Bay, Gallanachbeg (rk dries 0·3m) and Little Horseshoe Bay.
Dunstaffnage Bay, 3M NE: see facing column.

NAVIGATION
WPT 56°25′·80N 05°30′·00W, 306°/126° from/to Dunollie lt, 0·71M. Beware Sgeir Rathaid, buoyed, in middle of the bay; also CalMac ferries running to/from Railway Quay.

LIGHTS AND MARKS
N Spit of Kerrera Fl R 3s 9m 5M, W col, R bands. Dunollie Fl (2) WRG 6s 7m 5/4M; G351°-009°, W009°-047°, R047°-120°, W120°-138°, G138°-143°. N Pier 2FG (vert). S Quay 2FG (vert). Northern Lights Wharf Oc G 6s.

RADIO TELEPHONE
Call *North Pier* Ch 12 16 (0900-1700). For Railway Quay, call *CalMac* Ch 06 12 16. For Ardantrive Bay, call *Oban Yachts* Ch 80.

TELEPHONE (Dial code 01631)
Pier 562892; Marinecall 0891 500 463; ☎ 563079; MRSC 563720; Police 562213; Dr 563175.

OBAN *continued*

FACILITIES
N Pier ☎ 562892, L, FW, C (15 ton mobile) via Piermaster;
Rly Quay, L, Slip, D, FW, CH;
Services: BY, Slip, ACA, Gas, ME, EI, divers;
Oban Yachts (Ardantrive Bay) ☎ 565333, 🕿 565888, AB
£12.24, M, D, FW, ME, Sh, C, CH, Slip, BH (16 ton), Gas.
Town EC Thurs; P, V, R, Bar, ✉, Ⓑ, ⊚, ⇌, ✈.

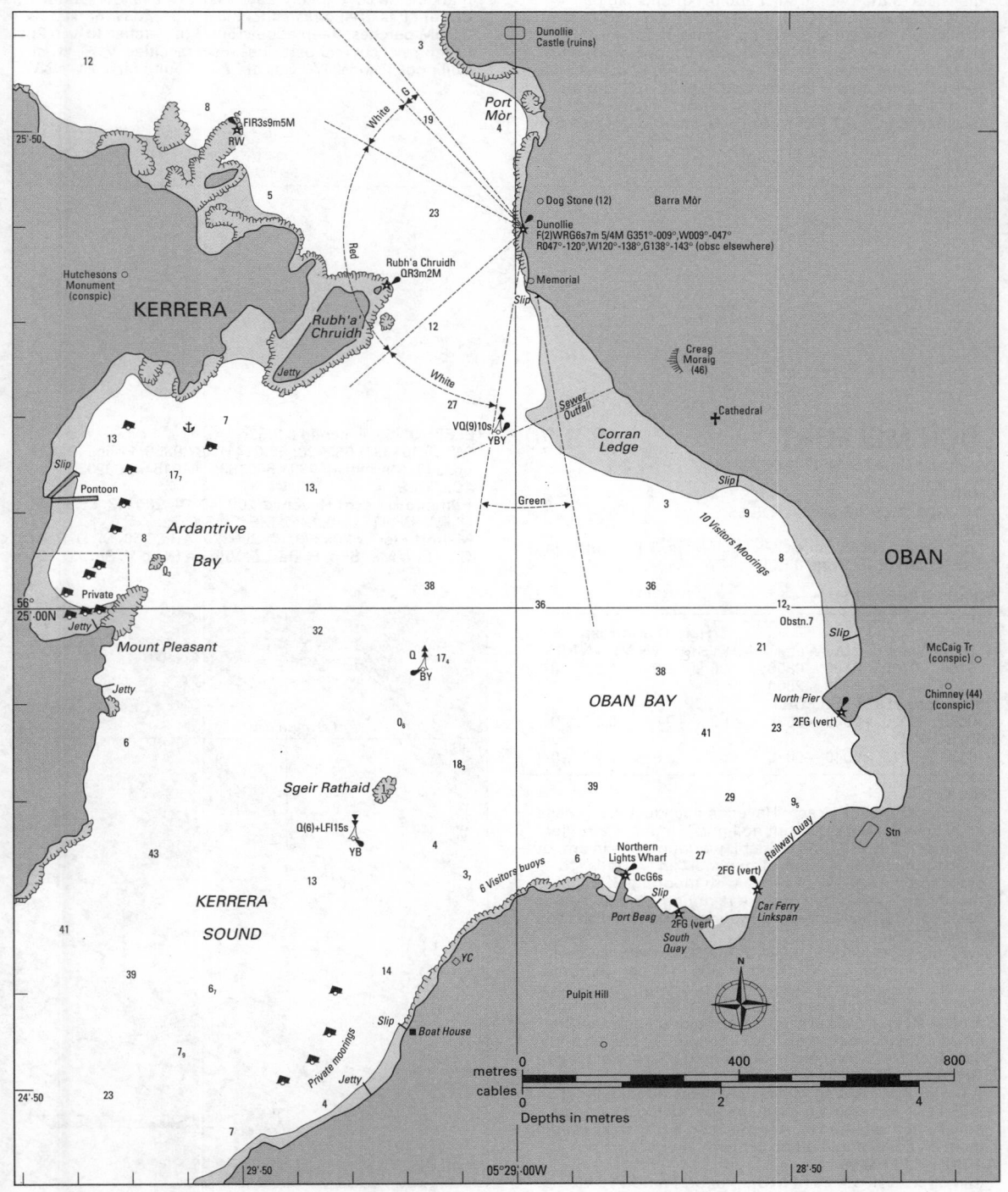

ANCHORAGES ON MAINLAND SHORE OF FIRTH OF LORN

LOCH FEOCHAN, Argyll and Bute, 56°21'·40N 05°29'·70W. AC 2387. HW = HW Oban; flood runs 4 hrs, ebb for 8 hrs. Caution: strong streams off Ardentallan Pt. Good shelter, 5M S of Oban and 1·5M SE of Kerrera. Best appr at local slack LW = LW Oban +0200. Narrow chan marked by 3 PHM buoys, 2 PHM perches on shore and 5 SHM buoys. ⚓ off pier, or moor/berth at **Ardoran Marine** ☎ (01631) 566123, 🛥 566611 AB, M, D, FW, ME, Gas, Sh, Slip, CH, Showers, V. **Royal Highland YC**, Ardentallan Ho ☎ (01631) 563309.

PUILLADOBHRAIN, Argyll & Bute, 56°19'·48N 05°35'·15W. AC 2386/2387. Tides as Oban. Popular ⚓ on the SE shore of the Firth of Lorne, approx 7M S of Oban, sheltered by the islets to the W of it. At N end of Ardencaple Bay identify Eilean Dùin (18m) and steer SE keeping 1½ca off to clear a rk awash at its NE tip. Continue for 4ca between Eilean nam Beathach, with Orange drum on N tip, and Dun Horses rks drying 2·7m. Two W cairns on E side of Eilean nam Freumha lead approx 215° into the inner ⚓ in about 4m. Landing at head of inlet. Nearest facilities: Bar, P at Clachan Br (½M); ☎, ✉ at Clachan Seil.

CUAN SOUND, Argyll & Bute, 56°15'·85N 05°37'·40W. AC 2326, 2386. Tides see 8.8.20 Seil Sound. Streams reach 6kn at sp; N-going makes at HW Oban +0420, S-going at HW Oban –2. The Sound is a useful doglegged short cut from Firth of Lorne to Lochs Melfort and Shuna, but needs care due to rks and tides. There are ⚓s at either end to await the tide. At the 90° dogleg, pass close N of Cleit Rk onto which the tide sets; it is marked by a Y △ perch. The chan is only ¾ca wide here due to rks off Seil. Overhead cables (35m) cross from Seil to Luing. There are ⚓s out of the tide to the S of Cleit Rk. No lts/facilities. See CCC SDs.

ARDINAMAR, Luing/Torsa, 56°14'·93N 05°36'·97W. AC 2326. HW –0555 on Dover; ML 1·7m; see 8.8.20 SEIL SOUND. A small cove and popular ⚓ between Luing and Torsa, close W of ent to L. Melfort. Appr with conspic W paint mark inside cove on brg 290°. Narrow, shallow (about 1m CD) ent has drying rks either side, those to N marked by 2 SHM perches. Keep about 15m S of perches to ⚓ in 2m in centre of cove; S part dries. Few facilities: V, ✉, ☎, at Cullipool 1½M WNW. Gas at Cuan Sound ferry 2M NNW.

LOCH MELFORT   8-8-20

Argyll and Bute 56°14'·60N 05°34'·00W   Rtg 2-2-1

CHARTS
AC 2326, 2169; Imray C65; OS 55

TIDES
Loch Shuna –0615 Dover; ML Loch Melfort 1·7; Duration Seil Sound 0615; Zone 0 (UT)

Standard Port OBAN (←)

Times				Height (metres)			
High Water		Low Water		MHWS	MHWN	MLWN	MLWS
0100	0700	0100	0800	4·0	2·9	1·8	0·7
1300	1900	1300	2000				
Differences LOCH MELFORT							
–0055	–0025	–0040	–0035	–1·2	–0·8	–0·5	–0·1
SEIL SOUND							
–0035	–0015	–0040	–0015	–1·3	–0·9	–0·7	–0·3

SHELTER
Good at Kilmelford Yacht Haven in Loch na Cille; access at all tides for 3m draft, but no lights. Or at Melfort Pier (Fearnach Bay at N end of loch): pier/pontoons in 2m, but chan to inner hbr has only 1m; good ⚓ in N winds. ⚓s sheltered from S – W at: a bay with moorings ½M inside the ent on S shore, but beware rk drying 1·5m; in Kames Bay (1·5M further E) clear of moorings, rks and fish farm.

NAVIGATION
WPT 56°14'·00N 05°35'·00W, 210°/030° from/to summit Eilean Gamhna, 4ca. Pass either side of Eilean Gamhna. 8ca NE lies Campbell Rk (1·8m). A rk drying 1m lies 1½ca ESE of the FS on Eilean Coltair. The S side of L Melfort is mostly steep-to, except in Kames Bay. At Loch na Cille, beware drying reef ¾ca off NE shore (PHM perch), and rk near S shore (SHM perch); boats may obscure perches.

LIGHTS AND MARKS
A Dir FR ☆ 6m 3M on Melfort pier (also depth gauge) and a Dir FG ☆ close NE on the shore are not ldg lts, nor do they form a safe transit. Approach on a N'ly track keeping them an equal angle off each bow.

RADIO TELEPHONE
Kilmelford VHF Ch **80** M (HO). *Melfort Pier* Ch 12 16.

TELEPHONE (Dial code 01852)
MRSC (01631) 563720; ⌖ (0141) 887 9369; Police (01631) 562213; Marinecall 0891 500463; Ⓗ (01546) 602323.

FACILITIES
Kilmelford Yacht Haven ☎ 200248, 🛥 200343, £8.80, M, D, FW, BH (12 ton), Slip, ME, El, Sh, Gas, ⚓;
Melfort Pier ☎ 200333, 🛥 200329, AB £8.50, M, D, P, AC, Gas, FW, ME, Slip, R, Bar, ⓞ. **Village** (¾M) V, Bar, ✉.

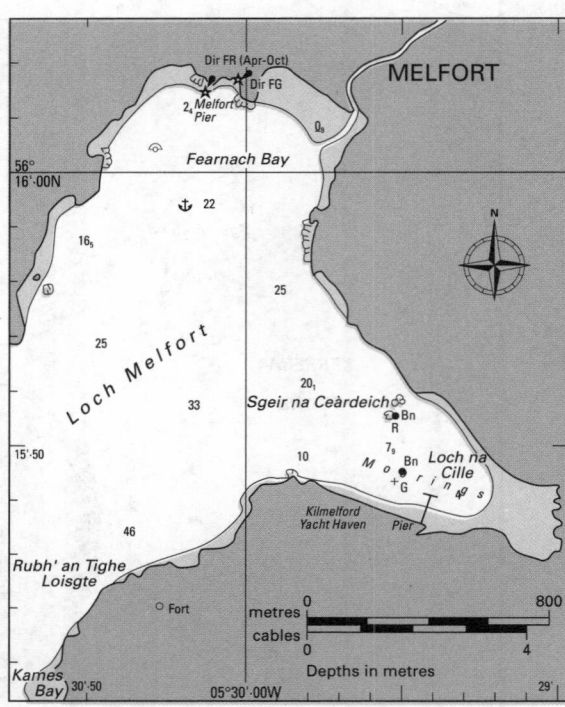

CRAOBH MARINA (Loch Shuna)

Argyll & Bute 56°12'·81N 05°33'·47W Rtg 1-1-1   8-8-21

CHARTS
AC *2326, 2169*; Imray C65; OS 55

TIDES
HW Loch Shuna –0615 Dover; Seil Sound Duration 0615, ML 1·4; Zone 0 (UT). For tidal figures see 8.8.20.

SHELTER
Very good. Craobh (pronounced Croove) Marina (access H24) on SE shore of Loch Shuna is enclosed by N and S causeways between islets. The ent is between 2 bkwtrs on the N side. In the marina, a shoal area S of the E bkwtr is marked by PHM buoys. A pink perch in W corner of hbr marks a spit; elsewhere ample depth. There are ⌇s in Asknish Bay 1M to the N, and in the bays E of Eilean Arsa and at Bàgh an Tigh-Stòir, S of Craobh.

NAVIGATION
WPT 56°13'·02N 05°33'·50W, 353°/173° from/to ent, 2ca. Tidal streams in Loch Shuna are weak. Beware lobster pots in appr's and unmarked rks (dr 1·5m) 4ca NNE of ent. An unlit SHM buoy marks a rk (1m) 150m NNW of the W bkwtr. 1M N of marina, Eich Donna, an unmarked reef (dr 1·5m), lies between Eilean Creagach and Arduaine Pt.

LIGHTS AND MARKS
The W sector, 162°-183°, of Dir Lt, Iso WRG 5s 10m 5/3M, on E bkwtr hd leads 172° between the close-in rks above.

RADIO TELEPHONE
VHF Ch M, 80 (summer 0830-2000LT; winter 0830-1800).

TELEPHONE (Dial code 01852)
Hr Mr 500222; MRSC (01631) 563720; ⌗ (0141) 887 9369; Marinecall 0891 500463; Police (01546) 602222; Ⓗ (01546) 602323.

FACILITIES
Craobh Marina (200+50 Ⓥ) ☎ 500222, ⥥ 500252, £14.49, AC, D, FW, SM, BY, CH, Slip, BH (15 ton), C (12 ton), Gas, Gaz, ME, El, Sh, R, SC, Ⓔ, Ⓞ, Divers. **Village** V, Bar, Ⓑ (Wed), ✉ (Kilmelford), ⇌ (Oban by bus), ✈ (Glasgow).

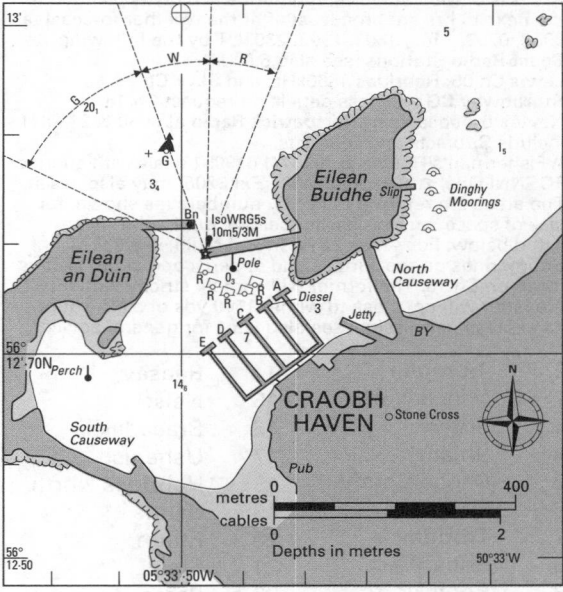

LOCH CRAIGNISH   8-8-22

Argyll and Bute 56°08'·00N 05°35'·00W   Rtg (Ardfern) 2-1-1

CHARTS
AC *2326, 2169*; Imray C63, C65; OS 55

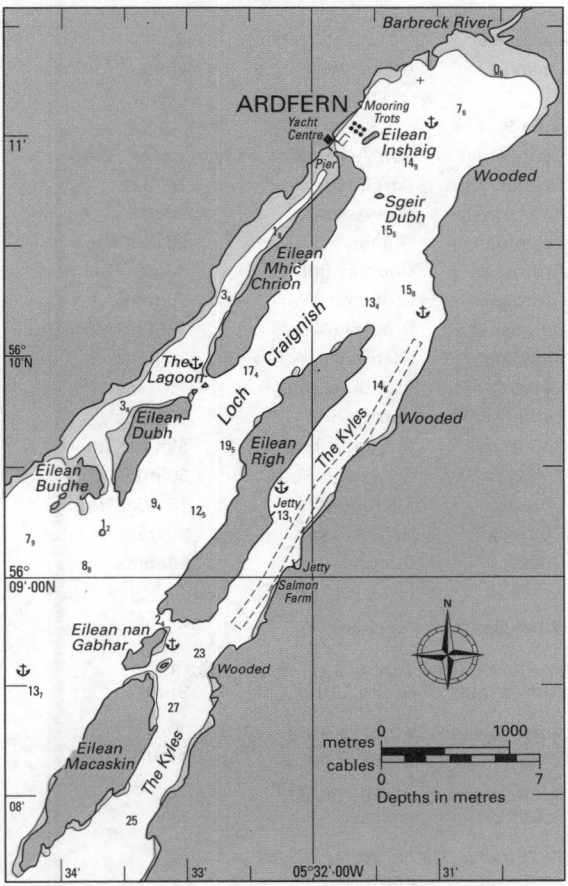

TIDES
+0600 Dover; ML (Loch Beag)1·2; Duration (Seil Sound) 0615; Zone 0 (UT)

Standard Port OBAN (←)

Times				Height (metres)			
High Water		Low Water		MHWS	MHWN	MLWN	MLWS
0100	0700	0100	0800	4·0	2·9	1·8	0·7
1300	1900	1300	2000				

Differences LOCH BEAG (Sound of Jura)

–0110	–0045	–0035	–0045	–1·6	–1·2	–0·8	–0·4

Note: HW Ardfern is approx HW Oban –0045; times/heights much affected by local winds and barometric pressure

SHELTER
Good at Ardfern, 56°11'·0N 05°31'·8W, access H24; ⌇s at:
– Eilean nan Gabhar; appr from E chan and ⌇ E of island.
– Eilean Righ; midway up the E side of the island.
– Bàgh na Cille, NNE of Craignish Pt.
– Eilean Dubh in the "lagoon" between the Is and mainland. Beware squalls in E'lies, especially on E side of loch.

NAVIGATION
WPT 56°07'·60N 05°35'·30W (off chartlet) between Dorus Mór and Liath-sgier Mhòr. Beware: strong tidal streams (up to 8kn) in Dorus Mór; a reef extending 1ca SSW of the SE chain of islands; rk 1½ca SSW of Eilean Dubh; fish cages especially on E side of loch; a drying rk at N end of Ardfern ⌇ with a rk awash ¼ca E of it. (These 2 rks are ½ca S of the more S'ly of little islets close to mainland). The main fairway is free from hazards, except for Sgeir Dhubh, a rk 3½ca SSE of Ardfern, with a reef extending about ½ca all round. Ardfern is 1ca W of Eilean Inshaig.

LIGHTS AND MARKS
No lts.

RADIO TELEPHONE
Ardfern Yacht Centre VHF Ch 80 M (office hrs).

TELEPHONE (Dial code 01852)
Hr Mr (Yacht Centre) 500247/500636; MRSC (01631) 563720; Marinecall 0891 500 463; ⌗ (0141) 887 9369; Dr (01546) 602921; Ⓗ (01546) 602449.

FACILITIES
Ardfern Yacht Centre (87+20 visitors); ☎ 500247/500636, ⥥ 500624, AB £11, M, FW, AC, D, BH (20 ton), Slip, ME, El, Sh, ACA, C (12 ton), CH, ⌂, Gas, Gaz.
Village R, V, Ⓑ (Wed), ✉, ⇌ (Oban), ✈ (Glasgow).

SUBMARINE EXERCISE AREAS (SUBFACTS)   8-8-23

Areas N of Mull in which submarine activity is planned for the next 16 hrs are broadcast after the weather forecast at 0303, 0703, 1103, 1503, 1903, 2303UT by the following **Coast Radio Stations** (see also 6.5.1):
Lewis Ch 05; **Hebrides** 1866kHz; and **Skye** Ch 24.
Stornoway CG will pass details on request Ch 16.
Navtex broadcasts by **Portpatrick Radio** at 0930 & 2130UT include Subfacts and Gunfacts.
A Fisherman's Hotline ☎ (01374) 613097 deals with queries.
FOSNNI Ops, ☎ (01436) 674321 Ext 3206, may also assist.
The areas are referred to not by numbers (as shown, for lack of space, on the chartlet below), but by the names listed below. For Areas 22 – 81 (S of Mull), see 8.9.24.
Submarines on the surface and at periscope depth always listen on Ch 16. The former will comply strictly with IRPCS; the latter will not close to within 1500 yds of a FV without its express permission; see also 8.5.1 for general advice.

1	Tiumpan	14	Raasay
2	Minch North	15	Neist
3	Stoer	16	Bracadale
4	Shiant	17	Ushenish
5	Minch South	18	Hebrides North
6	Ewe	19	Canna
7	Troddday	20	Rhum
8	Rona West	21	Sleat
9	Rona North	22	Barra
10	Lochmaddy	23	Hebrides Central
11	Dunvegan	24	Hawes
12	Portree	25	Eigg
13	Rona South	26	Hebrides South

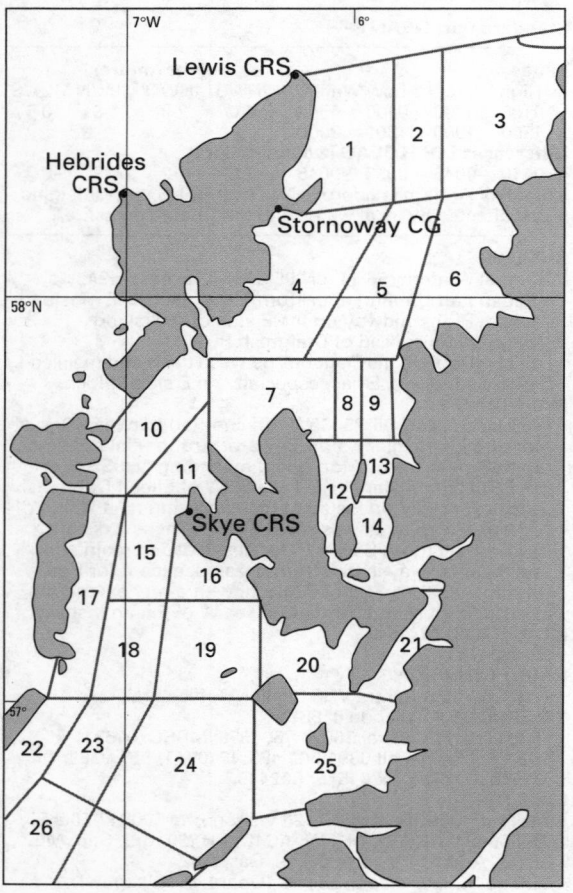

FERRIES ON THE WEST COAST OF SCOTLAND   8-8-24

The following is a brief summary of the many ferries plying between mainland and island harbours. It supplements the UK and Continental ferry services listed in 8.0.4, and may prove useful when cruise plans or crews change, often in remote places. It covers Area 8 (Stornoway to Oban) and Area 9 (Jura to the Clyde).
The major operator is Caledonian MacBrayne: Head Office, The Ferry Terminal, Gourock PA19 1QP; ☎ 0990-650000 for reservations, ☎ (01475) 637607. Many routes are very short and not be pre-bookable; seasonal routes are *asterisked.

From	To	Time	Remarks
Area 8			
Ullapool	Stornoway	2¾ hrs	See 8.0.4
Kyles Scalpay	Scalpay (Lewis)	10 mins	Not Sun
Uig (Skye)	Tarbert (Harris)	1¾ hrs	Not Sun
Uig	Lochmaddy (N Uist)	1¾ hrs	
Tarbert	Lochmaddy	1¾ hrs	Not Sun
Oban/Mallaig	Castlebay/Lochboisdale	5 hrs/1hr 50m	
Sconser (Skye)	Raasay	15 mins	Not Sun
Mallaig*	Kyle of Lochalsh	2 hrs	Fri only
Mallaig*	Armadale (Skye)	30 mins	
Mallaig	Eigg-Muck-Rhum-Canna	Varies	Not Sun
Oban	Tobermory-Coll-Tiree	Varies	Not Sun
Tobermory	Kilchoan	35 mins	
Fionnphort	Iona	5 mins	
Lochaline	Fishnish (Mull)	15 mins	
Oban	Craignure (Mull)	40 mins	
Oban	Lismore	50 mins	Not Sun
Areas 8/9			
Oban	Colonsay	2h10m	M/W/Fri
Area 9			
Kennacraig	Port Askaig/Colonsay	Varies	Wed
Kennacraig	Port Ellen	2h 10m	
Kennacraig	Port Askaig	2 hrs	
Tayinloan	Gigha	20 mins	
Ardrossan*	Douglas (IoM)	8 hrs	Sat/Sun
Ardrossan	Brodick	55 mins	
Rothesay*	Brodick (Arran)	1h50m	Mon/Thur
Claonaig	Lochranza (Arran)	30 mins	
Largs	Cumbrae Slip	15 mins	
Tarbert (L Fyne)	Portavadie*	20 mins	
Colintraive	Rhubodach (Bute)	5 mins	
Wemyss Bay	Rothesay (Bute)	30 mins	
Gourock	Kilcreggan	10 mins	Not Sun
Gourock	Helensburgh	30 mins	Not Sun
Gourock	Dunoon	20 mins	

Other Operators/services

Western Ferries (Argyll Ltd), ☎ *0141 332 8766:*
Port Askaig   Feolin (Jura)   Short

Argyll & Bute Council ☎ *01631 562125:*
Seil   Luing   Short

D.J.Rodgers, ☎ *01878 720261:*
South Uist   Eriskay

W. Rusk, ☎ *01878 720233:*
South Uist   Barra

VOLVO PENTA SERVICE

Sales and service centres in area 9
STRATHCLYDE *J. N. MacDonald & Co Ltd*, 47-49 Byron Street, Glasgow
G11 6LP Tel 0141-334 6171 **RENFREWSHIRE** *J. N. MacDonald & Co Ltd*,
Units B & C, The Yacht Harbour, Inverkip, Greenock, PA16 0AS
Tel (01475) 522450

VOLVO PENTA

Area 9

South-West Scotland
Crinan Canal to Mull of Galloway

9

8.9.1	Index	**Page 451**
8.9.2	Diagram of ports, lights, RDF bns, Coast radio and weather stns	452
8.9.3	Tidal stream charts	454
8.9.4	List of coastal lights, fog signals and waypoints	456
8.9.5	Passage information	459
8.9.6	Distance table	460
8.9.7	Port Ellen	461
	Scalasaig (Colonsay)	
	Loch Tarbert (Jura)	
	Port Askaig (Islay)	
	Craighouse (Jura)	
	Loch Sween	
	West Loch Tarbert (Kintyre)	
	Gigha Island	
8.9.8	Crinan Canal	462
8.9.9	Ardrishaig	463
8.9.10	Tarbert, Loch Fyne	463
	Loch Fyne	
8.9.11	Campbeltown	464
	Carradale Bay	
8.9.12	Tidal stream charts for Mull of Kintyre	465
8.9.13	Lamlash	466
	Brodick (Arran)	
	Loch Ranza (Arran)	
	St Ninian's Bay (Bute)	
	West Kyle	
	Caladh Harbour	
	Loch Riddon	
	Burnt Islands	
	Kames Bay (Bute)	
	Kilchattan Bay (Bute)	
8.9.14	Rothesay	467
8.9.15	Largs	467
	Millport (Cumbraes)	
8.9.16	Inverkip (Kip marina)	468
	Dunoon	
8.9.17	Clyde area waypoints	468
8.9.18	Firth of Clyde area	469
8.9.19	Gareloch/Rhu	470
	Loch Long/Loch Goil	
8.9.20	Greenock, Standard Port, tidal curves/Gourock	471
8.9.21	Ardrossan	475
	Irvine	
8.9.22	Troon	476
	Ayr	
	Girvan	
	Loch Ryan	
8.9.23	Portpatrick	477
8.9.24	Submarine exercise areas	478

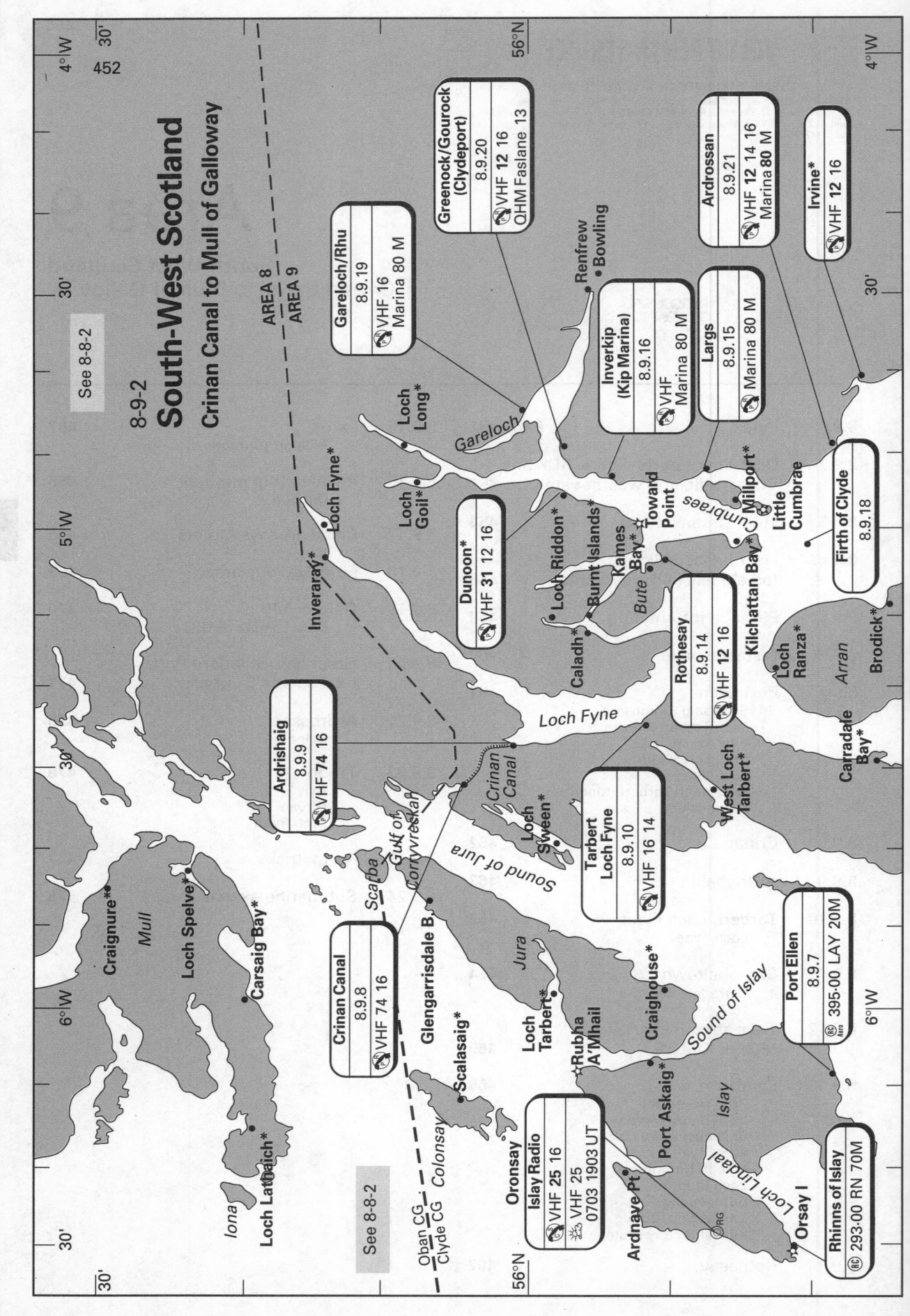

452

8-9-2
South-West Scotland
Crinan Canal to Mull of Galloway

See 8-8-2

AREA 8
AREA 9

Gareloch/Rhu
8.9.19
☎ VHF 16
Marina 80 M

Greenock/Gourock (Clydeport)
8.9.20
☎ VHF 12 16
⚓ QHM Faslane 13

Ardrossan
8.9.21
☎ VHF 12 14 16
Marina 80 M

Irvine*
☎ VHF 12 16

Inverkip (Kip Marina)
8.9.16
☎ VHF
Marina 80 M

Largs
8.9.15
Marina 80 M

Renfrew • Bowling

Loch Long*

Gareloch

Loch Goil*

Millport*

Toward Point

Cumbrae

Little Cumbrae

Firth of Clyde
8.9.18

Dunoon*
☎ VHF 31 12 16

Loch Fyne*

Inveraray*

Loch Riddon*

Burnt Islands*

Kames Bay*

Caladh*

Bute

Kilchattan Bay*

Rothesay
8.9.14
☎ VHF 12 16

Loch Ranza*

Brodick*

Arran

Ardrishaig
8.9.9
☎ VHF 74 16

Loch Fyne

Scarba

Gulf of Corryvreckan

Crinan Canal

Loch Sween*

Sound of Jura

Tarbert Loch Fyne
8.9.10
☎ VHF 16 14

West Loch Tarbert*

Carradale Bay*

Crinan Canal
8.9.8
☎ VHF 74 16

Glengarrisdale B.

Jura

Loch Tarbert*

Rubha A'Mhail

Craighouse*

Scalasaig*

Colonsay

Port Ellen
8.9.7
⚓RC Aero 395·00 LAY 20M

Sound of Islay

6°W

Craignure**

Mull

Loch Spelve*

Carsaig Bay*

Iona

Loch Lathaich*

See 8-8-2

Oban CG
Clyde CG

Oronsay

Islay Radio
☎ VHF 25 16
☼ VHF 25
0703 1903 UT

Ardnave Pt

Port Askaig*

Islay

Loch Indaal

Orsay I

Rhinns of Islay
⚓RC 293·00 RN 70M

RG

56°N

30'

30'

30'

30'

30'

30'

4°W

5°W

6°W

56°N

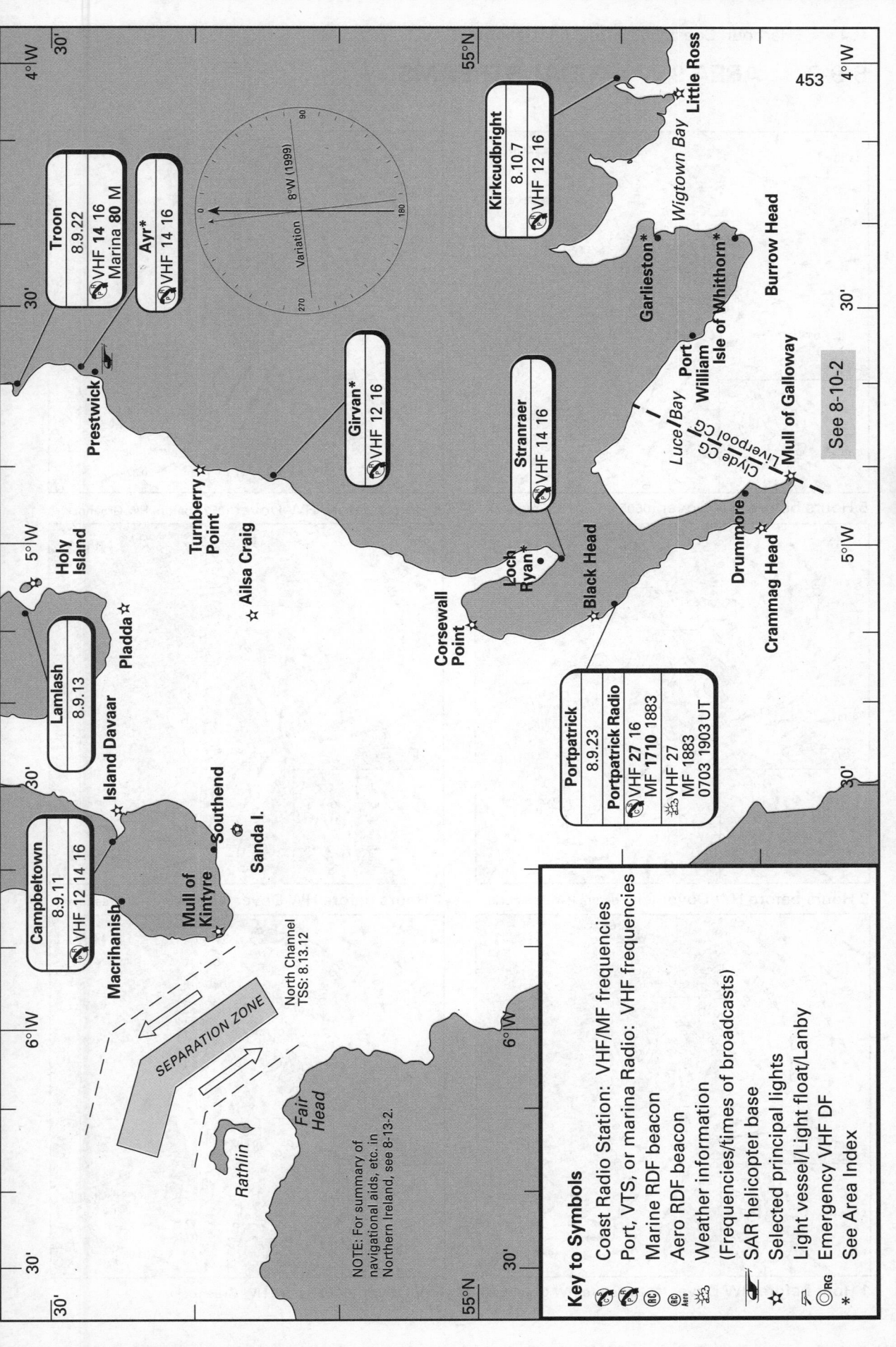

Key to Symbols

Coast Radio Station: VHF/MF frequencies

Port, VTS, or marina Radio: VHF frequencies

Marine RDF beacon

Aero RDF beacon

Weather information
(Frequencies/times of broadcasts)

SAR helicopter base

Selected principal lights

Light vessel/Light float/Lanby

Emergency VHF DF

See Area Index

Troon 8.9.22 — VHF 14 16 Marina 80 M

Ayr* — VHF 14 16

Girvan* — VHF 12 16

Stranraer — VHF 14 16

Kirkcudbright 8.10.7 — VHF 12 16

Campbeltown 8.9.11 — VHF 12 14 16

Lamlash 8.9.13

Portpatrick 8.9.23
Portpatrick Radio — VHF 27 16 MF **1710** 1883 — VHF 27 MF 1883 0703 1903 UT

Variation 8°W (1999)

Prestwick

Turnberry Point

Ailsa Craig

Holy Island

Pladda

Island Davaar

Mull of Kintyre

Macrihanish

Southend

Sanda I.

Fair Head

Rathlin

SEPARATION ZONE

North Channel TSS: 8.13.12

NOTE: For summary of navigational aids, etc. in Northern Ireland, see 8-13-2.

Corsewall Point

Loch Ryan*

Black Head

Drummore

Crammag Head

Mull of Galloway

Clyde CG
Liverpool CG

Luce Bay

Port William

Isle of Whithorn*

Garlieston*

Wigtown Bay

Burrow Head

Little Ross

Kirkcudbright

See 8-10-2

453

9

8-9-3   AREA 9   TIDAL STREAMS

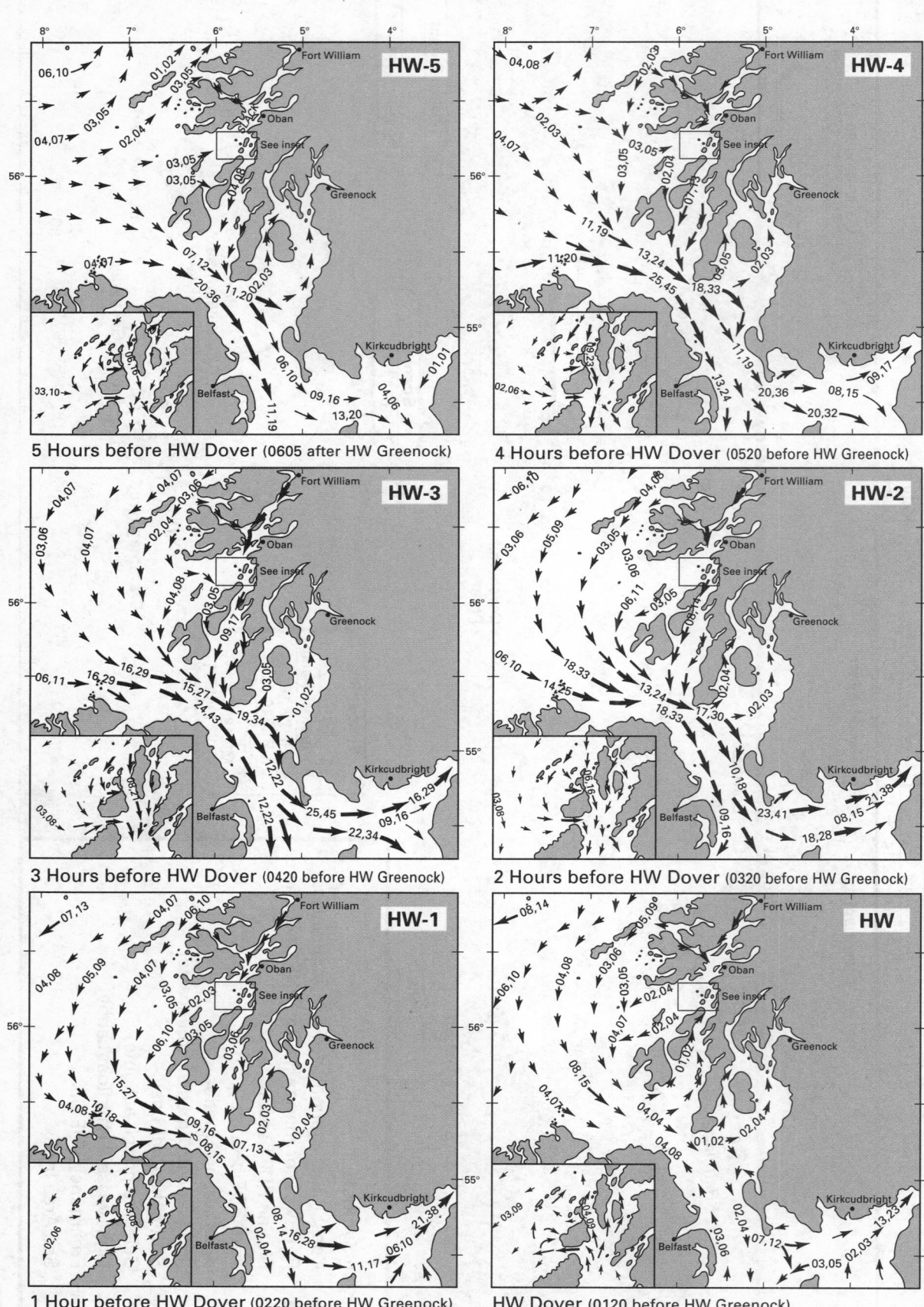

HW-5 — 5 Hours before HW Dover (0605 after HW Greenock)

HW-4 — 4 Hours before HW Dover (0520 before HW Greenock)

HW-3 — 3 Hours before HW Dover (0420 before HW Greenock)

HW-2 — 2 Hours before HW Dover (0320 before HW Greenock)

HW-1 — 1 Hour before HW Dover (0220 before HW Greenock)

HW — HW Dover (0120 before HW Greenock)

Northward 8.8.3   8.9.12 Mull of Kintyre
Irish Sea 8.10.3   North Ireland 8.13.3

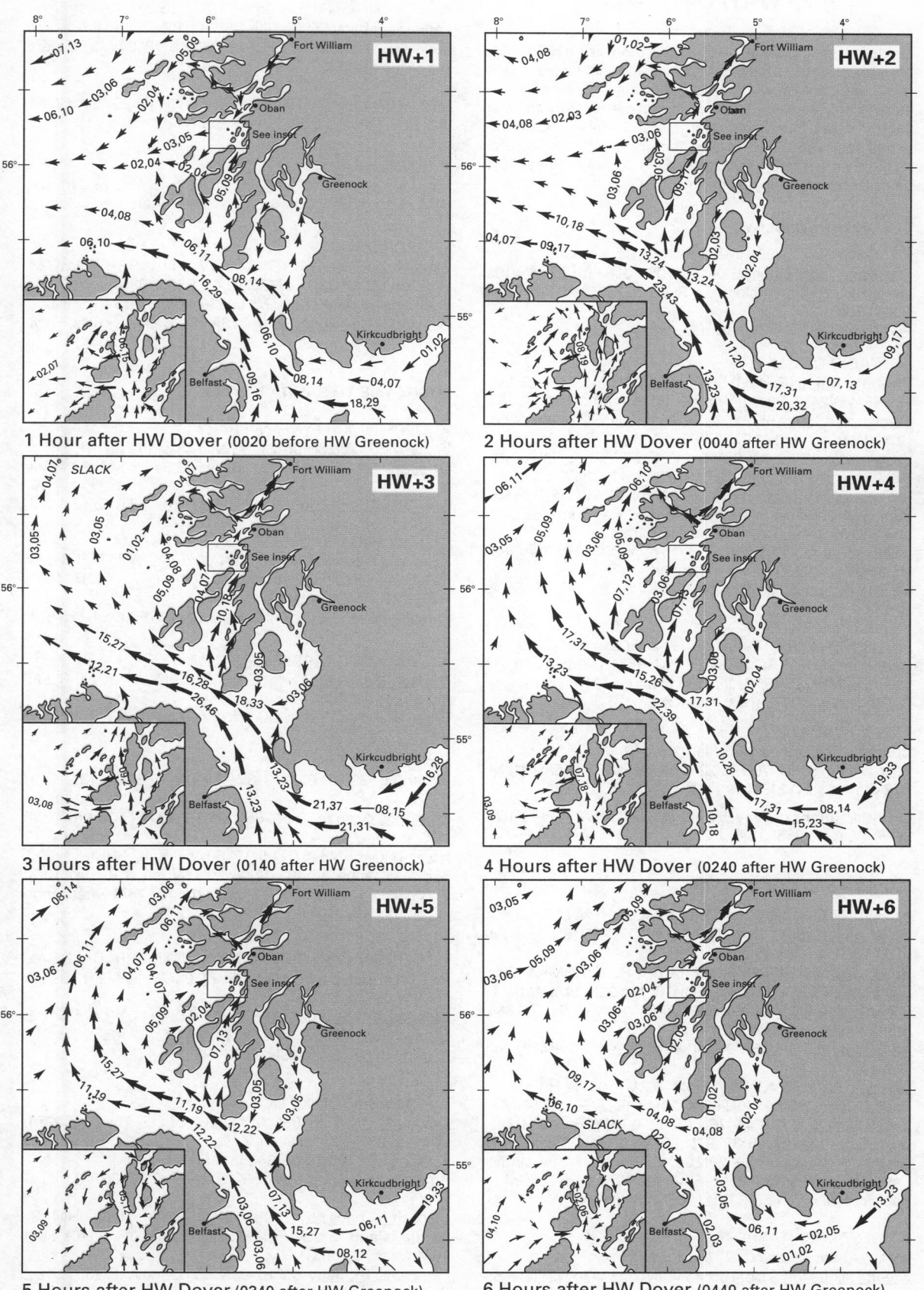

1 Hour after HW Dover (0020 before HW Greenock)

2 Hours after HW Dover (0040 after HW Greenock)

3 Hours after HW Dover (0140 after HW Greenock)

4 Hours after HW Dover (0240 after HW Greenock)

5 Hours after HW Dover (0340 after HW Greenock)

6 Hours after HW Dover (0440 after HW Greenock)

8.9.4   COASTAL LIGHTS, FOG SIGNALS AND WAYPOINTS

Lights with a nominal range of 15M or more are in **bold** print, places and features are in CAPITALS, and light-vessels, light floats and Lanbys in *CAPITAL ITALICS*. Unless otherwise stated lights are white. m = elevation in metres; M = nominal range in miles. Fog signals are in *italics*. Useful waypoints are underlined; use those on land with care. All geographical positions are referenced to the OSGB 36 datum but should be assumed to be approximate.

COLONSAY TO ISLAY

- COLONSAY
Scalasaig, Rubha Dubh 56°04'·02N 06°10'·83W Fl (2) WR 10s 6m W8M, R5M; W bldg; vis R shore-230°, W230°-337°, R337°-354°.
Pier hd ldg lts 262° FR 8/10m (occas).

- SOUND OF ISLAY
Rhubh' a Mhàil (Ruvaal) 55°56'·20N 06°07'·35W Fl (3) WR 15s 45m **W24M**, **R21M**; W tr; vis R075°-180°, W180°-075°.
Carragh an t'Struith 55°52'·3N 06°05'·7W Fl WG 3s 8m W9M, G6M; W tr; vis W354°-078°, G078°-170°, W170°-185°.
Carraig Mòr 55°50'·4N 06°06'·0W Fl (2) WR 6s 7m W8M, R6M; W tr; vis R shore-175°, W175°-347°, R347°-shore.
McArthur's Hd, S end 55°45'·85N 06°02'·80W Fl (2) WR 10s 39m W14M, R11M; W tr; W in Sound of Islay from NE coast-159°, R159°-244°, W244°-E coast of Islay.
Eilean a Chùirn 55°40'·14N 06°01'·15W Fl (3) 18s 26m 8M; W bn; obsc when brg more than 040°.
Otter Rock buoy 55°33'·92N 06°07'·80W Q (6) + L Fl 15s; SCM.

- PORT ELLEN
Port Ellen buoy 55°37'·00N 06°12'·22W QG; SHM.
Carraig Fhada Fl WRG 3s 20m W8M, R6M, G6M; W □ tr; vis W shore-248°, G248°-311°, W311°-340°, R340°-shore.
Ro-Ro terminal 2 FG (vert) 7/6m 3M.

- LOCH INDAAL
Bruichladdich pier hd 2 FR (vert) 6m 5M.
Rubh'an Dùin 55°44'·70N 06°22'·35W Fl (2) WR 7s 15m W13M, R12M; W tr; vis W218°-249°, R249°-350°, W350°-036°.

Orsay Is, **Rhinns of Islay** 55°40'·38N 06°30'·70W Fl 5s 46m **24M**; W tr; vis 256°-184°; RC.

JURA TO MULL OF KINTYRE

- SOUND OF JURA/CRAIGHOUSE/LOCH SWEEN/GIGHA
Reisa an t-Struith, S end of Is 56°07'·78N 05°38'·84W Fl (2) 12s 12m 7M; W col.
Ruadh Sgeir 56°04'·32N 05°39'·69W Fl 6s 13m 8M; W ○ tr.
Skervuile 55°52'·47N 05°49'·80W Fl 15s 22m 9M; W tr.
Eilean nan Gabhar 55°50'·05N 05°56'·15W Fl 5s 7m 8M; framework tr; vis 225°-010°.
Na Cùiltean 55°48'·65N 05°54'·85W Fl 10s 9m 9M; col on W bldg.
Gamhna Gigha 55°43'·78N 05°41'·02W Fl (2) 6s 7m 5M.
Badh Rk buoy 55°42'·30N 05°41'·18W Fl (2) G 12s; SHM.
Sgeir Nuadh buoy 55°41'·78N 05°42'·00W Fl R 6s; PHM.
Sgeir Gigalum buoy 55°39'·97N 05°42'·60W Fl G 6s; SHM.
Gigalum Rks buoy 55°39'·20N 05°43'·62W Q (9) 15s; WCM.
Cathsgeir buoy 55°39'·66N 05°47'·43W Q (9) 15s; WCM.
Caolas Gigalum bn 55°39'·16N 05°44'·50W; NCM.

- WEST LOCH TARBERT
Dunskeig Bay, N end Q (2) 10s 11m 8M.
Eileen Tráighe (off S side) 55°45'·40N 05°35'·70W Fl (2) R 5s 5m 3M; R post; Ra refl.

Corran Pt 55°46'·12N 05°34'·28W QG 3m 3M; G post.
Sgeir Mhein 55°47'·06N 05°32'·33W QR 3m 3M; R post.
Black Rocks 55°47'·91N 05°30'·07W QG 3M; G post.
Kennacraig buoy 55°48'·67N 05°29'·10W QR; PHM.
Kennacraig ferry terminal 55°48'·42N 05°28'·94W 2 FG (vert) 7m 3M; silver post.

Mull of Kintyre 55°18'·6N 05°48'·1W Fl (2) 20s 91m **24M**; W tr on W bldg; vis 347°-178°; *Horn Mo (N) 90s.*

- CRINAN CANAL
E of lock ent 56°05'·48N 05°33'·30W Fl WG 3s 8m 4M; W tr, R band; vis W shore-146°, G146°-shore.

- ARDRISHAIG
Bkwtr hd 56°00'·76N 05°26'·53W L Fl WRG 6s 9m 4M; W tr; vis G287°-339°, W339°-350°, R350°-035°.
Sgeir Sgalag No 49 buoy 56°00'·36N 05°26'·23W; SHM.
Gulnare Rk No 48 buoy 56°00'·18N 05°26'·24W Fl R 4s; PHM.

LOCH FYNE TO SANDA ISLAND

- UPPER LOCH FYNE/INVERARY
'P' buoy 56°00'·23N 05°21'·98W Fl R 3s; PHM.
Otter Spit 56°00'·63N 05°21'·03W Fl G 3s 7m 8M; G tank on pyramid.
Glas Eilean, S end 56°01'·10N 05°21'·10W Fl R 5s 12m 7M; R col on pedestal.
'Q' buoy 56°00'·97N 05°20'·60W Fl R 3s; PHM.
Sgeir an Eirionnaich 56°06'·49N 05°13'·47W Fl WR 3s 7m 8M; B tr on B ○ tr, W stripes; vis R044°-087°, W087°-192°, R192°-210°, W210°-044°.
Furnace Wharf 56°09'·06N 05°10'·38W 2 FR (vert) 9m 5M.

- EAST LOCH TARBERT
Madadh Maol, ent S side 55°52'·02N 05°24'·18W Fl R 2·5s 4m 3M; R col.
Eilean a'Choic, SE side QG 3m 2M; G col.

- PORTAVADIE
Bkwtr 55°52'·52N 05°19'·16W 2 FG (vert) 6/4m 4M.

Sgat Mór (S end) 55°50'·85N 05°18'·42W Fl 3s 9m 12M; W ○ tr.
No 51 buoy 55°45'·57N 05°19'·60W Fl R 4s; PHM.
Skipness range 55°46'·7N 05°19'·0W Iso R 8s 7m 10M; Y ◊ on bldg; vis 292·2°-312·2°. Oc (2) Y 10s **24M** when range in use (occas).

- KILBRANNAN SOUND/CRANNAICH/CARRADALE BAY
Port Crannaich bkwtr hd 55°35'·7N 05°27'·8W Fl R 10s 5m 6M; vis 099°-279°.
Crubon Rk buoy 55°34'·48N 05°27'·00W Fl (2) R 12s; PHM.
Otterard buoy 55°27'·07N 05°31'·04W Q (3) 10s; ECM.
Smerby buoy 55°26'·89N 05°31'·92; PHM.

- CAMPBELTOWN LOCH
Davaar N Pt 55°25'·69N 05°32'·37W Fl (2) 10s 37m **23M**; W tr; vis 073°-330°; *Horn (2) 20s.*
'C' buoy 55°25'·30N 05°34'·35W Fl (2) 6s; IDM.
Arranman's Barrels buoy 55°19'·40N 05°32'·80W Fl (2) R 12s; PHM.
Macosh Rk buoy 55°17'·95N 05°36'·90W Fl R 6s; PHM.
Sanda Island, S side 55°16'·50N 05°34'·90W Fl 10s 50m **15M**; W tr; Racon (T).
Patersons Rk buoy 55°16'·90N 05°32'·40W Fl (3) R 18s; PHM.

KYLES OF BUTE TO RIVER CLYDE

- ### KYLES OF BUTE/CALADH
Ardlamont Pt No 47 buoy 55°49'·59N 05°11'·68W Fl R 4s; PHM.

Carry Pt No 46 buoy 55°51'·42N 05°12'·17W Fl R 4s; PHM.
Rubha Ban buoy 55°54'·95N 05°12'·33W Fl R 4s; PHM.
Burnt Is buoy (NE of Eilean Fraoich) 55°55'·79N 05°10'·43W Fl G 3s; SHM.
Burnt Islands No 42 buoy (S of Eilean Buidhe) 55°55'·77N 05°10'·32W Fl R 2s; PHM.
Creyke Rk No 45 buoy 55°55'·67N 05°10'·80W; PHM.
Beere Rk No 44 buoy 55°55'·56N 05°10'·56W; SHM.
Wood Farm Rk No 43 buoy 55°55'·43N 05°10'·25W; SHM.
Rubha Bodach buoy 55°55'·39N 05°09'·53W Fl G; SHM.
Ardmaleish Pt No 41 buoy 55°53'·02N 05°04'·62W Q; NCM.

- ### ROTHESAY
Front Pier, E end 55°50'·32N 05°03'·03W 2 FG (vert) 7m 5M.
Pier W end 2 FR (vert) 7m 5M.

- ### FIRTH OF CLYDE
Ascog Patches No 13 lt bn 55°49'·71N 05°00'·17W Fl (2) 10s 5m 5M; IDM.
Toward Pt 55°51'·73N 04°58'·73W Fl 10s 21m **22M**; W tr.
No 34 buoy 55°51'·43N 04°59'·03W; ECM.
Toward Bank No 35 buoy 55°51'·04N 04°59'·93W Fl G 3s; SHM.
Skelmorlie buoy 55°51'·65N 04°56'·27W Iso 5s; SWM.

- ### WEMYSS BAY/INVERKIP
Pier 55°52'·57N 04°53'·39W 2 FG (vert) 7/5m 5M.
No 12 55°52'·96N 04°53'·70W Oc (2) Y 10s 5m 3M; SPM.
Inverkip oil jetty, S and N ends 2 FG (vert) 11m 2M.
'M' buoy 55°53'·53N 04°54'·35W Fl G 5s; SHM.
Kip buoy 55°54'·49N 04°52'·95W QG; SHM.
Cowal buoy 55°56'·00N 04°54'·75W L Fl 10s; SWM.
Lunderston Bay No 8 55°55'·5N 04°52'·9W Fl (4) Y 10s 5m 3M.

The Gantocks 55°56'·45N 04°55'·00W Fl R 6s 12m 6M; ● tr.

- ### DUNOON
Pier, S end and N end 2 FR (vert) 5m 6M.
Cloch Pt 55°56'·55N 04°52'·67W Fl 3s 24m 8M; W ● tr, B band, W dwellings.
McInroy's Pt, Ro-Ro terminal 55°57'·09N 04°51'·20W 2 FG (vert) 5/3m 6M.
No 5 55°56'·97N 04°51'·62W Oc (2) Y 10s 5m 3M; SPM.

- ### HOLY LOCH
Hunter's Quay, Ro-Ro terminal 55°58'·27N 04°54'·42W 2 FR (vert) 6/4m 6M.

- ### LOCH LONG/LOCH GOIL
Loch Long buoy 55°59'·17N 04°52'·33W Oc 6s; SWM.
Baron's Pt No 3 55°59'·2N 04°51'·0W Oc (2) Y 10s 5m 3M.
Ravenrock Pt 56°02'·17N 04°54'·32W Fl 4s 12m 10M; W tr on W col. Dir lt 204°, Dir WRG 9m (same tr); vis R201·5°-203°, Al WR203°-203·5° (W phase incr with brg), F W203·5°-204·5°, Al WG204·5°-205° (G phase incr with brg), FG205°-206·5°.
Port Dornaige 56°03·76N 04°53'·60W Fl 6s 8m 11M; W col; vis 026°-206°.
Carraig nan Ron (Dog Rock) 56°06'·01N 04°51'·60W Fl 2s 7m 11M; W col.
The Perch, ldg lts 318° Front, 56°06'·90N 04°54'·20W Dir Fl WRG 3m 5M; vis: G311°-317°, W317°-320°, R320°-322°. Same structure, Fl R 3s 3m 3M; rear, 700m from front, F 7m 5M; vis 312°-322·5°.
Rubha Ardnahein 56°06'·20N 04°53'·50W Fl R 5s 3m 3M.

Finnart Oil Terminal, Cnap Pt 56°07'·41N 04°49'·88W ldg lts 031°: Front, Q 8m 10M; W col; rear, 87m from front F 13m; R line on W tr.
Ashton buoy 55°58'·12N 04°50'·58W Iso 5s; SWM.

- ### GOUROCK
Railway pier hd 55°57'·8N 04°49'·0W 2 FG (vert) 10/8m 3M; Gy tr.
Kempock Pt No 4 55°57'·72N 04°49'·27W Oc (2) Y 10s   6m 3M.
Whiteforeland buoy 55°58'·12N 04°47'·20W L Fl 10s; SWM.
Rosneath Patch, S end 55°58'·52N 04°47'·37W Fl (2) 10s 5m 10M.

- ### ROSNEATH/RHU NARROWS/GARELOCH
Ldg lts 356°: **Front, No 7N** 56°00'·06N 04°45'·28W Dir lt 356°. Dir WRG 5m **W16M**, R13M, G13M; vis Al G/W 353°-355°, FW 355°-357°, Al W/R 357°-000° .
Dir lt 115° WRG 3m **W16M**, R13M, G13M; vis Al WG 111°-114°; F 114°-116°, Al W/R 116°-119°; FR 119°-121°. Passing lt Oc G 6s 3m 3M; vis: 360°; G △ on G pile structure.
Rear, Ardencaple Castle, 56°00'·55N 04°45'·35W 2 FG (vert) 26m 12M; tr on castle NW corner; vis 335°-020°.
No 8N lt bn. Dir lt 080° 55°59'·09N 04°44'·13W Dir WRG 3m; vis F & Al **W16M**, R13M, G13M; vis FG 075°-077·5°,   Al WG077·5°-079·5°, FW079·5°-080·5°, Alt WR080·5°-082·5°, FR082·5°-085°. Dir lt 138° WRG 3m F & Al; **W16M**, R13M, G13M; vis FG132°-134°, Al WG134°-137°, FW 137°-139°, Al WR139°-142°. Fl Y 3s 3m 3M; vis: 360°; Y ✖ on Y pile.
Gareloch No 1 lt bn 55°59'·12N 04°43'·81W VQ (4) Y 5s 9m; Y ✖ on Y structure.
Row buoy 55°59'·85N 04°45'·05W Fl G 5s; SHM.
Cairndhu buoy 56°00'·36N 04°45'·93W Fl G 2·5s; SHM.
Castle Pt 56°00'·20N 04°46'·43W Fl (2) R 10s 8m 6M; R mast.
Lt buoy 56°00'·62N 04°46'·47W Fl G 4s; SHM.

No 3 N lt bn 56°00'·08N 04°46'·64W Dir lt 149° WRG 9m **W16M**, R13M, G13M F & Al ; vis FG144°-145°, AlWG145°-148°,F148°-150°, Al WR150°-153°, FR153°-154°. Passing lt Oc R 8s 9m 3M.
Rosneath DG jetty 56°00'·40N 04°47'·43W 2 FR (vert) 5M; W col; vis 150°-330°.
Rhu SE buoy 56°00'·65N 04°47'·09W Fl G 3s; SHM.
Rhu Pt 56°00'·96N 04°47'·12W Q (3) WRG 6s 9m W10M, R7M, G7M; vis G270°-000°,W000°-114°, R114°-188°.
Dir lt 318° Dir WRG **W16M**, R13M,G13M; vis Al WG 315°-317°, F317°-319°, Al WR319°-321°, FR321°-325°.
Limekiln No 2N lt bn 56°00'·67N 04°47'·64W Dir lt 295° WRG 5m **W16M**, R13M, G13M F & Al; R ☐ on R bn; vis Al WG291°-294°,F294°-296°, Al WR 296°-299°, FR299°-301°.
Rhu NE buoy 56°01'·03N 04°47'·50W QG; SHM.
Rhu Spit lt bn 56°00'·85N 04°47'·27W Fl 3s 6m 6M.
Mambeg dir lt 331° 56°03'·77N 04°50'·39W Dir Q (4) WRG 8s 8m 14M; W l; vis G328·5°-330°, W330°-332°, R332°-333°; shown H24.
Faslane Base, jetty, S elbow 56°03'·17N 04°49'·12W Fl G 5s 11m 5M.
Floating barrier 56°03'·85N 04°49'·54W Fl Y 5s 3M.
Garelochhead, S fuel jetty 56°04'·23N 04°49'·62W 2 FG (vert) 10m 5M.
N fuel jetty, elbow 56°04'·35N 04°49'·66W Iso WRG 4s 10m 14M; vis G351°-356°, W356°-006°, R006°-011°.

- ### GREENOCK
Anchorage lts in line 196°: Front, 55°57'·6N 04°46'·5W FG 7m 12M; Y col; rear, 32m from front, FG 9m 12M. Y col.
Lts in line 194·5°: Front, 55°57'·4N 04°45'·8W FG 18m; rear, 360m from front, FG 33m.
Clydeport container terminal NW corner QG 8m 8M.
Victoria Hbr ent W side 2 FG 5m (vert).

9

Garvel Embankment, W end 55°56'·81N 04°43'·48W Oc G 10s 9m 4M.
E end, Maurice Clark Pt 55°56'·61N 04°42'·78W QG 7m 2M; G tr.

● PORT GLASGOW
Beacon off ent 55°56'·25N 04°41'·18W FG 7m 9M; B&W chequered tr and cupola.
Steamboat Quay, W end FG 12m 12M; B&W chequered col; vis 210°-290°. From here to Glasgow lts on S bank are Fl G and lts on N bank are Fl R.

CLYDE TO MULL OF GALLOWAY

● LARGS
Marina S bkwtr hd 55°46'·35N 04°51'·67W Oc G 10s 4m 4M.
W bkwtr hd Oc R 10s 4m 4M; R □ on col.
Approach buoy 55°46'·40N 04°51'·78W L Fl 10s; SWM.
Largs pier hd N end 2 FG (vert) 7/5m 5M (H24).

● FAIRLIE
Hunterston jetty, S end 55°45'·10N 04°52'·80W 2 FG (vert).
Pier N end 2 FG (vert) 7m 5M.
NATO pier hd 2 FG (vert) N and S ends.

● MILLPORT, GREAT CUMBRAE
The Eileans, W end 55°44'·89N 04°55'·52W QG 5m 2M; (shown 1/9-30/4.)

Ldg lts 333°. pier hd front, 55°45'·04N 04°55'·78W FR 7m 5M; rear, 137m from front, FR 9m 5M.

Mountstuart buoy 55°48'·00N 04°57'·50W L Fl 10s; SWM.
Portachur buoy 55°44'·35N 04°58'·44W Fl G 3s; SHM.
Runnaneun Pt (Rubha'n Eun) 55°43'·79N 05°00'·17W Fl R 6s 8m 12M; W tr.

Little Cumbrae, Cumbrae Elbow 55°43'·27N 04°57'·95W Fl 3s 31m **23M**; W tr; vis 334°-210°. Shown by day when))) operating.

● ARDROSSAN
Approach dir lt 055° 55°38'·66N 04°49'·14W Dir F WRG 15m W14M, R11M, G11M; vis FG 050°-051·2°, Alt WG 051·2°-053·8°, W phase increasing with Brg; FW 053·8°-056·2°; Alt WR 056·2°-058·8°. R phase increasing with brg; FR 058·8°-060°. FR 13m 6M; vis 325°-145°.

N bkwtr hd Fl WR 2s 7m 5M; R gantry; vis R041°-126°, W126°-041°.
Lighthouse pier hd 55°38'·47N 04°49'·50W Iso WG 4s 11m 9M; W tr; vis W035°-317°, G317°-035°.
Eagle Rk buoy 55°38'·22N 04°49'·62W Fl G 5s; SHM.

● IRVINE
Ent N side 55°36'·21N 04°42'·01W Fl R 3s 6m 5M; R col.
S side Fl G 3s 6m 5M; G col.
Ldg lts 051°: Front, 55°36'·41N 04°41'·50W FG 10m 5M; rear, 101m from front, FR 15m 5M; G masts, vis 019°-120°.

● TROON
Troon buoy 55°33'·07N 04°41'·28W Fl G 4s; SHM.
West pier hd 55°33'·07N 04°40'·95W Fl (2) WG 5s 11m 9M; W tr; vis G036°-090°, W090°-036°.
E pier hd Fl R 10s 6m 3M.

Lady Island 55°31'·63N 04°43'·95W Fl (4) 30s 19m 8M; W bn.

● ARRAN/RANZA/LAMLASH/BRODICK
Hamilton Rk buoy 55°32'·63N 05°04'·83W Fl R 6s; PHM.
Brodick Bay, pier hd 2 FR (vert) 9m 4M.
Pillar Rk Pt (Holy Island), 55°31'·05N 05°03'·57W Fl (2) 20s 38m **25M**; W □ tr.
Holy Island SW end Fl G 3s 14m 10M; W tr; vis 282°-147°.
Pladda 55°25'·50N 05°07'·07W Fl (3) 30s 40m **17M**; W tr.

● AYR
Bar buoy 55°28'·12N 04°39'·38W Fl G 2s; SHM.
N bkwtr hd 55°28'·22N 04°38'·71W QR 9m 5M.
S pier hd Q 7m 7M; R tr; vis 012°-161°. FG 5m 5M; same tr; vis 012°-082°.
Ldg lts 098°: Front, 55°28'·16N 04°38'·31W FR 10m 5M; R tr; rear, 130m from front Oc R 10s 18m 9M.

Turnberry Pt, near castle ruins 55°19'·55N 04°50'·60W Fl 15s 29m **24M**; W tr.
Ailsa Craig 55°15'·12N 05°06'·42W Fl 4s 18m **17M**; W tr; vis 145°-028°.

● GIRVAN
N groyne hd 55°14'·71N 04°51'·64W Iso 4s 3m 4M.
S pier hd 2 FG (vert) 8m 4M; W tr.
N bkwtr hd 55°14'·74N 04°51'·77W Fl (2) R 6s 7m 4M.

● LOCH RYAN
Cairn Pt 54°58'·48N 05°01'·77W Fl (2) R 10s 14m 12M; W tr.
Cairnryan 54°57'·77N 05°00'·92W Fl R 5s 5m 5M.
Forbes Shoal buoy 54°59'·48N 05°02'·88W QR; PHM.
Loch Ryan W buoy 54°59'·23N 05°03'·17W QG; SHM.

Stranraer No 1 bn 54°56'·69N 05°01'·30W Oc G 6s; SHM.
No 3 bn 54°55'·89N 05°01'·52W QG; SHM.
No 5 54°55'·09N 05°01'·80W Fl G 3s; SHM.

● STRANRAER
Ross pier hd 2 F Bu (vert).
E pier hd 54°54'·62N 05°01'·52W 2 FR (vert) 9m.
W pier hd 2 FG (vert) 8m 4M; Gy col.

Corsewall Pt 55°00'·43N 05°09'·50W Fl (5) 30s 34m **22M**; W tr; vis 027°-257°.
Killantringan, Black Hd 54°51'·71N 05°08'·75W Fl (2) 15s 49m **25M**; W tr.

● PORTPATRICK
Ldg lts 050·5°: Front, 54°50'·50N 05°06'·95W FG (occas); rear, 68m from front, FG 8m (occas).

Crammag Hd 54°39'·90N 04°57'·80W Fl 10s 35m **18M**; W tr.
Mull of Galloway, SE end 54°38'·05N 04°51'·35W Fl 20s 99m **28M**; W tr; vis 182°-105°.

8.9.5 PASSAGE INFORMATION

Although conditions in the South-West of Scotland are in general less rugged than from Mull northwards, some of the remarks at the start of 8.8.5 are equally applicable to this area. Refer to the Admiralty *West Coast of Scotland Pilot*; to *Yachtsman's Pilot to the W Coast of Scotland, Clyde to Colonsay* (Imray/Lawrence) and to the Clyde Cruising Club's SDs. Submarines exercise throughout these waters; see 8.8.23 and 8.9.24 for information on active areas (Subfacts).

Some of the following more common Gaelic terms may help with navigation: *Acairseid*: anchorage. *Ailean*: meadow. *Aird, ard*: promontory. *Aisir, aisridh*: passage between rocks. *Beag*: little. *Beinn*: mountain. *Bo, boghar, bodha*: rock. *Cala*: harbour. *Camas*: channel, bay. *Caol*: strait. *Cladach*: shore, beach. *Creag*: cliff. *Cumhamn*: narrows. *Dubh, dhubh*: black. *Dun*: castle. *Eilean, eileanan*: island. *Garbh*: rough. *Geal, gheal*: white. *Glas, ghlas*: grey, green. *Inis*: island. *Kyle*: narrow strait. *Linn, Linne*: pool. *Mor, mhor*: large. *Mull*: promontory. *Rinn, roinn*: point. *Ruadh*: red, brown. *Rubha, rhu*: cape. *Sgeir*: rock. *Sruth*: current. *Strath*: river valley. *Tarbert*: isthmus. *Traigh*: beach. *Uig*: bay.

CORRYVRECKAN TO CRINAN (charts *2326*, 2343)

Between Scarba and Jura is the Gulf of Corryvreckan (chart 2343) which is best avoided, and should never be attempted by yachts except at slack water and in calm conditions. (In any event the Sound of Luing is always a safer and not much longer alternative). The Gulf has a least width of 6ca and is free of dangers, other than its very strong tides which, in conjunction with a very uneven bottom, cause extreme turbulence. This is particularly dangerous with strong W winds over a W-going (flood) tide which spews out several miles to seaward of the gulf, with overfalls extending 5M from the W of ent (The Great Race). Keep to the S side of the gulf to avoid the worst turbulence and the whirlpool known as The Hag, caused by depths of only 29m, as opposed to more than 100m in the fairway. The W-going stream in the gulf begins at HW Oban + 0410, and the E-going at HW Oban – 028. Sp rate W-going is 8·5kn, and E-going about 6kn.

The range of tide at sp can vary nearly 2m between the E end of the gulf (1·5m) and the W end (3·4m), with HW ½ hr earlier at the E end. Slack water occurs at HW Oban +4 and –2½ and lasts almost 1 hr at nps, but only 15 mins at sps. On the W-going (flood) stream eddies form both sides of the gulf, but the one on the N (Scarba) shore is more important. Where this eddy meets the main stream off Camas nam Bairneach there is violent turbulence, with heavy overfalls extending W at the division of the eddy and the main stream. There are temp anchs with the wind in the right quarter in Bàgh Gleann a' Mhaoil in the SE corner of Scarba, and in Bàgh Gleann nam Muc at N end of Jura but the latter has rks in approaches E and SW of Eilean Beag.

SE of Corryvreckan is Loch Crinan, which leads to the Crinan Canal (8.9.8). Beware Black Rk, 2m high and 2ca N of the canal sea lock, and dangers extending 100m from the rk.

WEST OF JURA TO ISLAY (charts 2481, 2168)

The W coasts of Colonsay and Oronsay (chart *2169*) are fringed with dangers up to 2M offshore. The two islands are separated by a narrow chan which dries and has an overhead cable (10m). There are HIE ⚓s at Scalasaig; see 8.9.7.

The Sound of Islay presents no difficulty; hold to the Islay shore, where all dangers are close in. The N-going stream begins at HW Oban + 0440, and the S-going at HW Oban – 0140. The sp rates are 2·5kn at N entrance and 1·5kn at S entrance, but reaching 5kn in the narrows off Port Askaig.

There are anchs in the Sound, but mostly holding ground is poor. The best places are alongside at Port Askaig (8.9.7), or at anch off the distillery in Bunnahabhain B, 2·5M to N. There are overfalls off McArthur's Hd (Islay side of S entrance) during the S-going stream.

The N coast of Islay and Rhinns of Islay are very exposed. In the N there is anch SE of Nave Island at entrance to Loch Gruinart; beware Balach Rks which dry, just to N. To the SW off Orsay (lt), Frenchman's Rks and W Bank there is a race and overfalls which should be cleared by 3M. Here the NW-going stream begins at HW Oban + 0530, and the SE-going at HW Oban – 0040; sp rates are 6-8kn inshore, but decrease to 3kn 5M offshore. Loch Indaal gives some shelter; beware rks extending from Laggan Pt on E side of ent. Off the Mull of Oa there are further overfalls. Port Ellen, the main hbr on Islay, has HIE ⚓s; there are some dangers in approach, and it is exposed to S; see 8.9.7 and chart 2474.

SOUND OF JURA TO GIGHA (charts 2397, 2396, 2168)

From Crinan to Gigha the Sound of Jura is safe if a mid-chan course is held. Ruadh Sgeir (lt) are rky ledges in mid-fairway, about 3M W of Crinan. Loch Sween (chart 2397) can be approached N or SE of MacCormaig Islands, where there is an attractive anch on NE side of Eilean Mor, but exposed to NE. Coming from N beware Keills Rk and Danna Rk. Sgeirean a Mhain is a rk in fairway 1·5M NE of Castle Sween (conspic on SE shore). Anch at Tayvallich, near head of loch on W side. See 8.9.7.

W Loch Tarbert (chart 2477) is long and narrow, with good anchs and lts near ent, but unmarked shoals. On entry give a berth of at least 2½ca to Eilean Traighe off N shore, E of Ardpatrick Pt. Dun Skeig, an isolated hill, is conspic on S shore. Good anch near head of loch, 1M by road from E Loch Tarbert; Loch Fyne; see 8.9.7.

On W side of Sound, near S end of Jura, are The Small Is (chart 2396) across the mouth of Loch na Mile. Beware Goat Rk (dries 0·3m) 1½ca off southernmost Is, Eilean nan Gabhar, behind which is good anch. Also possible to go alongside Craighouse Pier (HIE ⚓) (8.9.7). Another anch is in Lowlandman's B, about 3M to N, but exposed to S winds; Ninefoot Rks with depth of 2·4m and ECM lt buoy lie off ent. Skervuile (lt) is a reef to the E, in middle of the Sound.

S of W Loch Tarbert, and about 2M off the Kintyre shore, is Gigha Is (chart 2475 and 8.9.7). Good anchs on E side in Druimyeon B and Ardminish B (HIE ⚓s), respectively N and S of Ardminish Pt. Outer and Inner Red Rks (least depth 2m) lie 2M SW of N end of Gigha Is. Dangers extend 1M W off S end of Gigha Is. Gigalum Is and Cara Is are off the S end. Gigha Sound needs very careful pilotage, since there are several dangerous rks, some buoyed/lit, others not. The N-going stream begins at HW Oban + 0430, and S-going at HW Oban – 0155, sp rates 1·3kn.

MULL OF KINTYRE (charts 2126, 2199, 2798)

From Crinan to Mull of Kintyre is about 50M. This long peninsula much affects the tidal streams in North Chan. Off Mull of Kintyre (lt, fog sig) the N-going stream begins at HW Oban + 0400, and the S-going at HW Oban – 0225, sp rate 5kn. A strong race and overfalls exist S and SW of Mull of Kintyre, dangerous in strong S winds against S-going tide. Careful timing is needed, especially W-bound (8.9.12). The Traffic Separation Scheme in the North Channel, see 8.13.12, is only 2M W of the Mull and may limit sea-room in the ITZ.

Sanda Sound separates Sanda Is (lt) and its rks and islets, from Kintyre. On the mainland shore beware Macosh Rks (dry, PHM lt buoy) forming part of Barley Ridges, 2ca offshore; Arranman Barrels, drying and submerged, marked by PHM lt buoy; and Blindman Rk (depth 2m) 1·3M N of Ru Stafnish, where 3 radio masts are 5ca inland. Sanda Is has Sheep Is 3ca to the N; Paterson's Rk (dries) is 1M E. There is anch in Sanda hbr on N side. In Sanda Sound the E-going stream begins at HW Greenock + 0340, and the W-going at HW Greenock − 0230, sp rates 5kn. Tide races extend W, N and NE from Sanda, and in strong S or SW winds the Sound is dangerous. In these conditions pass 2M S of Mull of Kintyre and Sanda and E of Paterson's Rk.

MULL OF KINTYRE TO UPPER LOCH FYNE
(charts *2126*, 2383, 2381, 2382).

Once E of Mull of Kintyre, tidal conditions and pilotage much improve. Campbeltown (8.9.11) is entered N of Island Davaar (lt, fog sig). 1·5M N of lt ho is Otterard Rk (depth 3·8m), with Long Rk (dries 1·1m) 5ca W of it; both are buoyed. E of Island Davaar tide runs 3kn at sp, and there are overfalls.

Kilbrannan Sound runs 21M from Island Davaar to Skipness Pt, where it joins Inchmarnock Water, Lower Loch Fyne and Bute Sound. There are few dangers apart from overfalls on Erins Bank, 10M S of Skipness, on S-going stream. Good anch in Carradale B (8.9.11), off Torrisdale Castle. There are overfalls off Carradale Pt on S-going stream.

Lower L. Fyne (chart 2381) is mainly clear of dangers to East L. Tarbert (8.9.10). On E shore beware rks off Ardlamont Pt; 4M to NW is Skate Is which is best passed to W. 3M S of Ardrishaig (8.9.9) beware Big Rk (depth 2·1m). Further N, at entrance to Loch Gilp (mostly dries) note shoals (least depth 1·5m) round Gulnare Rk, PHM lt buoy; also Duncuan Is with dangers extending SW to Sgeir Sgalag (depth 0·6m), buoyed.

Where Upper L. Fyne turns NE (The Narrows) it is partly obstructed by Otter Spit (dries 0·9m), extending 8ca WNW from E shore and marked by lt bn. The stream runs up to 2kn here. A buoyed/lit rk, depth less than 2m, lies about 7ca SW of Otter Spit bn. In Upper L. Fyne (chart 2382) off Minard Pt, the chan between rks and islands in the fairway is buoyed/lit. For Inveraray, see 8.9.10.

ARRAN, BUTE AND FIRTH OF CLYDE (charts 1906, 1907)

Bute Sound leads into Firth of Clyde, and is clear in fairway. Arran's mountains tend to cause squalls or calms, but it has good anchs at Lamlash (8.9.13), Brodick and Loch Ranza. Sannox Rock (depth 1·5m) is 2½ca off Arran coast 8M N of Lamlash (8.9.12). 1ca off W side of Inchmarnock is Tra na-h-uil, a rk drying 1·5m. In Inchmarnock Sound, Shearwater Rk (depth 0·9m) lies in centre of S entrance.

Kyles of Bute are attractive chan N of Bute from Inchmarnock Water to Firth of Clyde, and straightforward apart from Burnt Islands. Here it is best to take the north channel, narrow but well buoyed, passing S of Eilean Buidhe, and N of Eilean Fraoich and Eilean Mor. Care is needed, since sp stream may reach 5kn. Caladh Hbr is a beautiful anch 7ca NW of Burnt Is.

In contrast, the N lochs in Firth of Clyde are less attractive. Loch Goil is worth a visit but Loch Long is squally and has few anchs, while Gareloch (8.9.19) has little to attract cruising yachts other than Rhu marina. Navigation in Firth of Clyde is easy since tidal streams are weak, seldom exceeding 1kn and chans are well marked; but beware commercial and naval shipping and also unlit moorings, see 8.9.19. There are marinas on the mainland at Largs (8.9.15) and Inverkip (8.9.16). Rothesay hbr (8.9.14) on E Bute, and Kilchattan B (anch 6M to S) are both sheltered from SSE to WNW.

FIRTH OF CLYDE TO MULL OF GALLOWAY
(charts *2131*, *2126*, 2199, 2198)

Further S the coast is less inviting, with mostly commercial hbrs until reaching Ardrossan (8.9.21) and Troon (8.9.22), NW of which there are various dangers: beware Troon Rk (depth 5·6m, but sea can break), Lappock Rk (dries 0·6m, marked by bn), and Mill Rk (dries 0·4m, buoyed). Lady Isle (lt), shoal to NE, is 2M WSW of Troon.

There is a severe race off Bennane Hd (8M SSE of Ailsa Craig, conspic) when tide is running strongly. Loch Ryan offers little for yachtsmen but there is anch S of Kirkcolm Pt, inside the drying spit which runs in SE direction 1·5M from the point. There is also useful anch in Lady Bay, sheltered except from NE. Between Corsewall Pt and Mull of Galloway the S-going stream begins HW Greenock + 0310, and the N-going at HW Greenock − 0250. Sp rate off Corsewall Pt is 2-3 kn, increasing to 5kn off and S of Black Hd. Portpatrick (8.9.23) is a useful passage hbr, but not in onshore winds. Races occur off Morroch B, Money Hd and Mull of Logan.

A race SSE of Crammag Hd is bad if wind against tide. Mull of Galloway (lt) is a high (82m), steep-to headland. Beware dangerous race extending nearly 3M to S. On E-going stream the race extends NNE into Luce B; on W-going stream it extends SW and W. Best to give the race a wide berth, or pass close inshore at slack water nps and calm weather. SW wind >F4 against W-going stream, do not attempt inshore route.

See 8.10.5 for continuation E into Solway Firth and S into the Irish Sea. For notes on crossing the Irish Sea, see 8.13.5.

8.9.6   DISTANCE TABLE

Approximate distances in nautical miles are by the most direct route, whilst avoiding dangers and allowing for Traffic Separation Schemes. Places in *italics* are in adjoining areas; places in **bold** are in 8.0.9, Distances across the Irish Sea.

Place	1	2	3	4	5	6	7	8	9	10	11	12	13	14	15	16	17	18	19	20
1. *Loch Craignish*	1																			
2. **Port Ellen (Islay)**	42	2																		
3. Crinan	5	39	3																	
4. Ardrishaig	14	48	9	4																
5. East Loch Tarbert	24	58	19	10	5															
6. **Campbeltown**	55	47	50	39	31	6														
7. Mull of Kintyre	56	27	51	54	45	20	7													
8. Lamlash	48	61	43	34	25	24	34	8												
9. Largs	48	94	43	34	24	39	47	17	9											
10. Rothesay	49	95	44	35	25	43	48	23	9	10										
11. Kip Marina	53	85	48	39	28	50	58	25	10	8	11									
12. Greenock	59	90	54	45	36	53	63	31	16	14	6	12								
13. Rhu (Helensburgh)	62	94	57	48	37	59	67	33	19	17	9	4	13							
14. **Troon**	54	71	49	40	33	33	44	16	20	25	29	34	38	14						
15. Girvan	67	58	62	53	43	29	31	20	33	40	46	49	51	21	15					
16. Stranraer	89	62	84	75	65	34	35	39	56	63	69	65	74	44	23	16				
17. **Portpatrick**	88	63	83	74	66	39	36	44	61	67	68	77	77	49	28	23	17			
18. **Mull of Galloway**	104	78	99	90	82	56	52	60	78	82	84	93	93	65	62	39	16	18		
19. *Kirkcudbright*	136	111	131	122	114	88	84	92	110	114	116	124	125	97	94	71	48	32	19	
20. *Douglas (IoM)*	146	120	141	132	124	106	94	102	141	130	126	141	135	107	104	84	60	42	45	20

HARBOURS AND ANCHORAGES IN COLONSAY, JURA, ISLAY AND THE SOUND OF JURA

SCALASAIG, Colonsay, 56°04´·15N 06°10´·80W. AC 2474, *2169*. HW +0542 on Dover; ML 2·2m. See 8.9.7. Conspic monument ½M SW of hbr. Beware group of rks N of pier hd marked by bn. 2 HIE ❶ berths on N side of pier, inner end approx 2·5m. Inner hbr to SW of pier is safe, but dries. Ldg lts 262°, both FR 8/10m on pier. Also ⚓ clear of cable in **Loch Staosnaig**; SW of Rubha Dubh lt, Fl (2) WR 10s 6m 8/5M; R shore-230°, W230°-337°, R337°-354°. Facilities: D, P, V (all at ✉), FW, Hotel ☎ (01951) 200316.

LOCH TARBERT, W Jura, 55°57´·70N 06°00´·00W. AC 2481, *2169*. Tides as Rubha A'Mhàil (N tip of Islay). See 8.9.7. HW −0540 on Dover; ML 2·1m; Duration 0600. Excellent shelter inside the loch, but subject to squalls in strong winds; ⚓ outside in Glenbatrick Bay in approx 6m in S winds, or at Bagh Gleann Righ Mor in approx 2m in N winds. To enter inner loch via Cumhann Beag, there are four pairs of ldg marks (W stones) at approx 120°, 150°, 077°, and 188°, the latter astern, to be used in sequence; pilot book required. There are no facilities.

PORT ASKAIG, Islay, 55°50´·88N 06°06´·20W. AC 2481, 2168. HW +0610 on Dover; ML 1·2m. See 8.9.7. Hbr on W side of Sound of Islay. ⚓ close inshore in 4m or secure to ferry pier. Beware strong tide/eddies. ☆ FR at LB. Facilities: FW (hose on pier), Gas, P, R, Hotel, V, ✉, ferries to Jura and Kintyre. Other ⚓s in the Sound at: Bunnahabhain (2M N); Whitefarland Bay, Jura, opp Caol Ila distillery; NW of Am Fraoch Eilean (S tip of Jura); Aros Bay, N of Ardmore Pt.

CRAIGHOUSE, SE Jura, 55°50´·00N 05°56´·25W. AC 2396, 2481, 2168. HW +0600 on Dover; ML 0·5m; Duration 0640 np, 0530 sp. See 8.9.7. Good shelter, but squalls occur in W winds. Enter between lt bn on SW end of Eilean nan Gabhar, Fl 5s 7m 8M vis 225°-010°, and unlit bn close SW. There are 8 HIE ⚓s N of pier (☎ (01496) 810332), where yachts may berth alongside; or ⚓ in 5m in poor holding at the N end of Loch na Mile. Facilities: very limited, Bar, FW, ✉, R, V, Gas, P & D (cans). **Lowlandman's Bay** is 1M further N, with ECM buoy, Q (3) 10s, marking Nine Foot Rk (2·4m) off the ent. ⚓ to SW of conspic houses, off stone jetty.

LOCH SWEEN, Argyll and Bute, 55°55´·70N 05°41´·20W. AC 2397. HW +0550 on Dover; ML 1·5m; Duration 068. See 8.9.8 Carsaig Bay. Off the ent to loch, **Eilean Mòr** (most SW'ly of MacCormaig Isles) has tiny ⚓ on N side in 3m; local transit marks keep clear of two rks, 0·6m and 0·9m. Inside the loch, beware Sgeirean a'Mhain, a rk in mid-chan to S of Taynish Is, 3M from ent. Good shelter in Loch a Bhealaich (⚓ outside **Tayvallich** in approx 7m on boulders) or enter inner hbr to ⚓ W of central reef. There are no lts. Facilities: Gas, Bar, ✉, FW (🚰 by ✉), R, V. Close to NE are ⚓s at **Caol Scotnish** and **Fairy Is**, the former obstructed by rks 3ca from ent.

WEST LOCH TARBERT, Argyll and Bute, (Kintyre), 55°45´N 05°36´W. AC 2477. Tides as Gigha Sound, 8.9.7. Good shelter. Ent is S of Eilean Traighe, Fl (2) R 5s, and NW of Dun Skeig, Q (2) 10s, where there is also conspic conical hill (142m). Loch is lit for 5M by 3 bns, QG, QR and QG in sequence, up to Kennacraig ferry pier, 2FG (vert). PHM buoy, QR, is 2½ca NW of pier. Caution: many drying rks and fish farms outside the fairway and near head of loch. ⚓s are NE of Eilean Traighe (beware weed & ferry wash); near Rhu Pt, possible ⚓s; NE of Eilean dà Gallagain, and at loch hd by pier (ru). Tarbert (8.9.10) is 1·5M walk/bus.

GIGHA ISLAND, Argyll and Bute, 55°40´·60N 05°44´·00W. AC 2475, 2168. HW +0600 on Dover; ML 0·9m; Duration 0530. See 8.9.7. Main ⚓ is **Ardminish Bay**: 12 HIE ⚓s in the centre. Reefs extend off both points, the S'ly reef marked by an unlit PHM buoy. Kiln Rk (dries 1·5m) is close NE of the old ferry jetty. **Druimyeon Bay** is more sheltered in E'lies, but care needed entering from S. ⚓s sheltered from winds in ( ): Port Mór (S-W), Bàgh na Dòirlinne (SE-S), W Tarbert Bay (NE). Caolas Gigalum (⚓ 50m SE of pier) is safe in all but NE-E winds. Beware many rks in Gigha Sound. Lts: Fl (2) 6s, on Gamhna Gigha (off NE tip) & WCM buoy Fl (9) 15s marks Gigalum Rks, at S end of Gigha. **Ardminish** ☎/⛽ (01583) 505254: FW, Gas, P & D (cans), ⬛, ✉, Bar, R, V.

PORT ELLEN   8-9-7

Islay (Argyll and Bute) 55°37´·30N 06°12´·20W   Rtg 3-4-2

CHARTS
AC 2474, 2168
TIDES
HW +0620 np, +0130 sp on Dover; ML 0·6. Sea level is much affected by the weather, rising by 1m in S/E gales; at nps the tide is sometimes diurnal and range negligible.

Standard Port OBAN (◄──)

Times				Height (metres)			
High Water		Low Water		MHWS	MHWN	MLWN	MLWS
0100	0700	0100	0800	4·0	2·89	1·8	0·7
1300	1900	1300	2000				
Differences PORT ELLEN (S Islay)							
−0530	−0050	−0045	−0530	−3·1	−2·1	−1·3	−0·4
SCALASAIG (E Colonsay)							
−0020	−0005	−0015	+0005	−0·1	−0·2	−0·2	−0·2
GLENGARRISDALE BAY (N Jura)							
−0020	0000	−0010	0000	−0·4	−0·2	0·0	−0·2
CRAIGHOUSE (SE Jura)							
−0230	−0250	−0150	−0230	−3·0	−2·4	−1·3	−0·6
RUBHA A'MHÀIL (N Islay)							
−0020	0000	+0005	−0015	−0·3	−0·1	−0·3	−0·1
ARDNAVE POINT (NW Islay)							
−0035	+0010	0000	−0025	−0·4	−0·2	−0·3	−0·1
ORSAY ISLAND (SW Islay)							
−0110	−0110	−0040	−0040	−1·4	−0·6	−0·5	−0·2
BRUICHLADDICH (Islay, Loch Indaal)							
−0100	−0005	−0110	−0040	−1·7	−1·4	−0·4	+0·1
PORT ASKAIG (Sound of Islay)							
−0110	−0030	−0020	−0020	−1·9	−1·4	−0·8	−0·3
GIGHA SOUND (Sound of Jura)							
−0450	−0210	−0130	−0410	−2·5	−1·6	−1·0	−0·1
MACHRIHANISH							
−0520	−0350	−0340	−0540		Mean range 0·5 metres.		

SHELTER
Good shelter close S of pier and clear of ferries/FVs, but in S winds swell sets into the bay. 10 HIE ⚓s to W of Rubha Glas; adjacent rks are marked by 3 perches with reflective topmarks. Inner hbr dries. In W'lies ⚓ in Kilnaughton Bay, N of Carraig Fhada lt ho; or 4M ENE at Loch-an-t-Sàilein.
NAVIGATION
WPT 55°36´·70N 06°12´·00W, 146°/326° from/to Carraig Fhada lt ho, 0·63M. Beware Otter Rk 4M SE of hbr, and rks closer in on both sides of ent and in NE corner of bay.

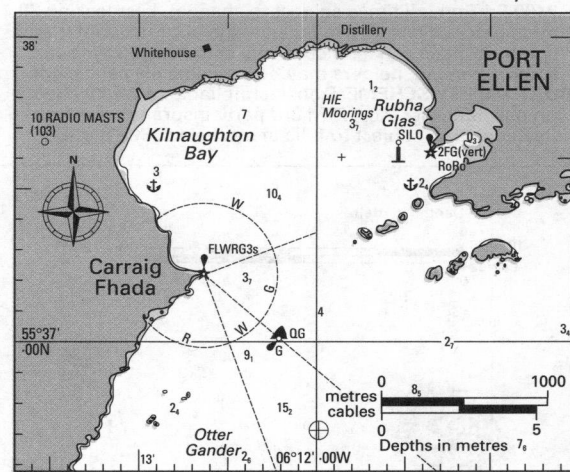

LIGHTS AND MARKS
On W side 10 Radio masts (103m) and Carraig Fhada lt ho (conspic), Fl WRG 3s 20m 8/6M; W shore-248°, G248°-311°, W311°-340°, R340°-shore; keep in W sector until past the SHM buoy, QG. Ro-Ro pier shows 2 FG (vert).
RADIO TELEPHONE
None.
TELEPHONE (Dial code 01496)
Moorings 810332; ⚕ 810337; MRCC (01475) 729988.
FACILITIES
Village Bar, FW, ✉, R, V, Gas.

9

CRINAN CANAL   8-9-8

Argyll and Bute 56°05'·50N 05°33'·31W   Crinan Rtg 3-3-1

CHARTS
AC 2320, *2326*; Imray C65; OS 55

TIDES
–0608 Dover; ML 2·1; Duration 0605; Zone 0 (UT)
HW Crinan is at HW Oban –0045

Standard Port OBAN (←)

Times				Height (metres)			
High Water		Low Water		MHWS	MHWN	MLWN	MLWS
0100	0700	0100	0800	4·0	2·89	1·8	0·7
1300	1900	1300	2000				

Differences CARSAIG BAY (4·5M SSW of Loch Crinan)
–0105 –0040 –0050 –0050   –2·1 –1·6 –1·0 –0·4
Note: In the Sound of Jura, S of Loch Crinan, the rise of tide occurs mainly during the 3½hrs after LW; the fall during the 3½hrs after HW. At other times the changes in level are usually small and irregular.

SHELTER
Complete shelter in canal basin; yachts are welcome, but often full of FVs. Good shelter in Crinan Hbr (E of Eilean da Mheinn) but full of moorings. Except in strong W/N winds, ‡ E of the canal ent, clear of fairway. Gallanach Bay on N side of L Crinan has good holding in about 3m. Berths may be reserved at Bellanoch Bay (see chartlet).

NAVIGATION
WPT 56°05'·70N 05°33'·57W, 326°/146° from/to Fl WG 3s lt, 0·27M. Beware Black Rock (2m high) in appr NE of ldg line 146° to dir Fl WG 3s lt. Off NW corner of chartlet, no ‡ in a nearly rectangular shellfish bed, 6ca by 6ca. SPM lt buoys mark each corner: Fl (4) Y 12s at the NE and NW corners, Fl Y 6s at the SW and SE corners; the latter being about 100m NE of Black Rk.

CANAL
Canal is 9M long and has 15 locks. Least transit time is 5 to 6 hrs, observing the 4kn speed limit. Entry at all tides. Sea locks open 0800-2100 daily in season, but only HW±3 in drought. Sea lock outer gates are left open after hours for yachts to shelter in the locks. All 7 bridges open. Max size: 26·5m LOA, 6m beam, 2·9m draught, mast ht 28.9m. Vessels NW-bound have right of way. Canal dues can be paid at Ardrishaig or Crinan sea locks. Total transit/lock fee in 1998 was £8.65/metre, inc VAT, for 3 days = £77.85 for 30'/9.14m LOA. Inland locks and bridges operate 0800-1800 daily; lock 14 and Crinan Bridge open 0800-2100 Fri-Sun (all times subject to change). Last locking 30 mins before close. For reduced hrs in autumn, winter and spring, contact canal office. Canal shut Xmas/New Year. If short-handed, helpers may be available via canal staff.

BOAT SAFETY SCHEME Transit craft liable to safety checks on gas, fuel, electrics; £1M 3rd party insurance required. Resident craft subject to full safety checks. See 8.8.18.

LIGHTS AND MARKS
Crinan Hotel is conspic W bldg. A conspic chy, 3ca SW of hotel, leads 187° into Crinan Hbr. E of sea-lock: Dir Fl WG 3s 8m 4M, vis W 114°-146°, G146°-280°. Ent: 2 FG (vert) and 2FR (vert).

RADIO TELEPHONE
VHF Ch **74** (throughout the canal) 16.

TELEPHONE (Dial code 01546)
Sea lock 830285; Canal HQ 603210; MRCC (01475) 729988; ‡ (0141) 887 9369 (H24); Marinecall 0891 500463; Police 602222; Dr 602921.

FACILITIES
Canal HQ ☎ 603210, M, L, FW; **Sea Basin** AB £18.36, D; **Services:** BY, Slip, ME, El, Sh, Gas, ACA, C (5 ton), ⊚, CH, P (cans), V, R, Bar.
Village ✉, Ⓑ (Ardrishaig), ⇌ (Oban), ✈ (Glasgow or Macrihanish). There is a wintering park, plus BY and CH, at Cairnbaan for yachts <10m LOA.

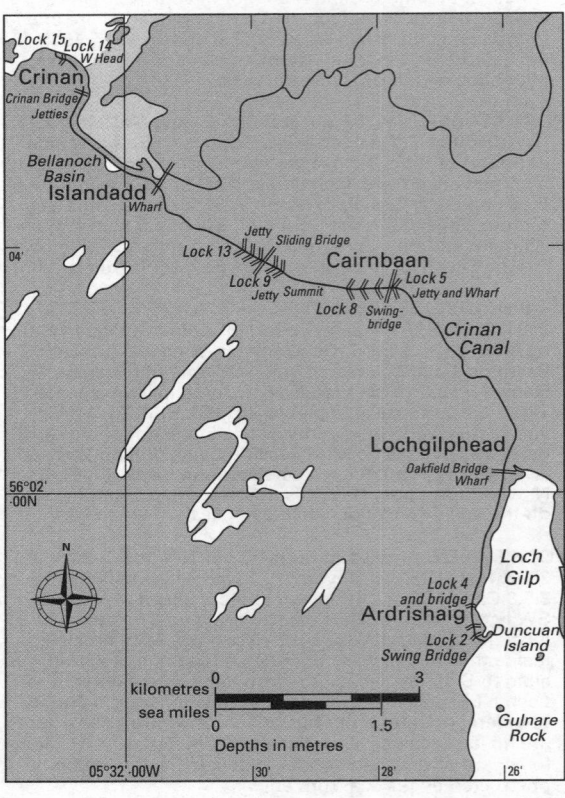

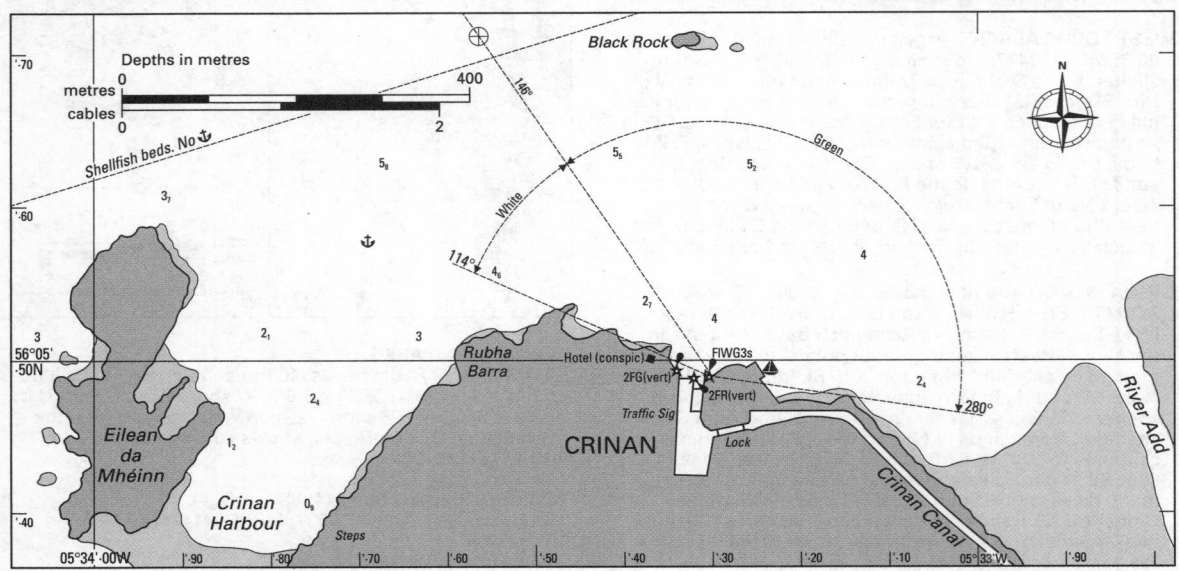

ARDRISHAIG   8-9-9

Argyll and Bute 56°00'·78N 05°26'·55W   Rtg 3-3-2

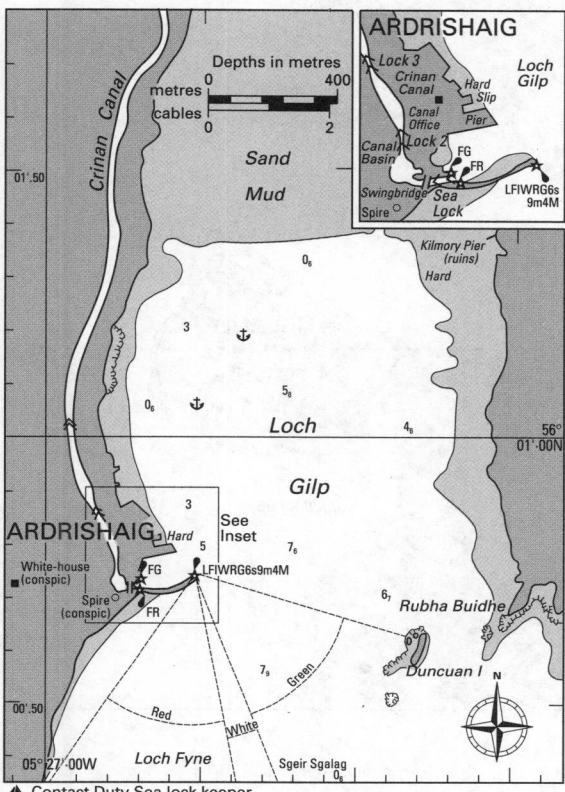

▲ Contact Duty Sea lock keeper

CHARTS
AC 2381, *2131*; Imray C63; OS 55
TIDES
+0120 Dover; ML 1·9; Duration 0640; Zone 0 (UT)

Standard Port GREENOCK (→)

Times				Height (metres)			
High Water		Low Water		MHWS	MHWN	MLWN	MLWS
0000	0600	0000	0600	3·4	2·8	1·0	0·3
1200	1800	1200	1800				
Differences ARDRISHAIG							
+0006	+0006	-0015	+0020	0·0	0·0	+0·1	−0·1
INVERARAY							
+0011	+0011	+0034	+0034	−0·1	+0·1	−0·5	−0·2

SHELTER
Hbr is sheltered except from strong E'lies; do not berth on
pier or ⌘ due to commercial vessels H24. Sea lock into the
Crinan Canal is usually left open; access at all tides.
Complete shelter in the canal basin, or beyond lock No 2;
see 8.9.8. Also ⌘ 2ca N of hbr, off the W shore of L Gilp.
NAVIGATION
WPT No 48 PHM buoy, Fl R 4s, 56°00'·18N 05°26'·24W,
165°/345° from/to bkwtr lt, 0·61M. Dangerous drying rks to
E of appr chan are marked by No 49 unlit SHM buoy.
LIGHTS AND MARKS
Conspic W Ho on with block of flats leads 315°between
Nos 48 & 49 buoys. Bkwtr lt, L Fl WRG 6s, W339°-350°.
RADIO TELEPHONE
VHF Ch **74** 16.
TELEPHONE (Dial code 01546)
Hr Mr 603210; MRCC (01475) 729988; ☷ (0141) 887 9369
(H24); Marinecall 0891 500462; Police 603233; Dr 602921.
FACILITIES
Pier/Hbr ☎ 603210, AB, Slip, FW; **Sea Lock** ☎ 602458, AB
£16.65; **Crinan Canal** AB, M, L, FW, R, Bar; see 8.9.8.
Services: BY, ME, El, Sh, CH, D (cans), Gas; C (20 ton) at
Lochgilphead (2M). **Village** EC Wed; P & D (cans), V, R, Bar,
✉, Ⓑ, ⇌ (bus to Oban), ✈ (Glasgow or Campbeltown).

TARBERT, LOCH FYNE   8-9-10

Argyll and Bute 55°52'·05N 05°24'·15W   Rtg 2-2-2

CHARTS
AC 2381, *2131*; Imray C63; OS 62
TIDES
+0120 Dover; ML 1·9; Duration 0640; Zone 0 (UT)

Standard Port GREENOCK (→)

Times				Height (metres)			
High Water		Low Water		MHWS	MHWN	MLWN	MLWS
0000	0600	0000	0600	3·4	2·8	1·0	0·3
1200	1800	1200	1800				
Differences EAST LOCH TARBERT							
+0005	+0005	−0020	+0015	0·0	0·0	+0·1	−0·1

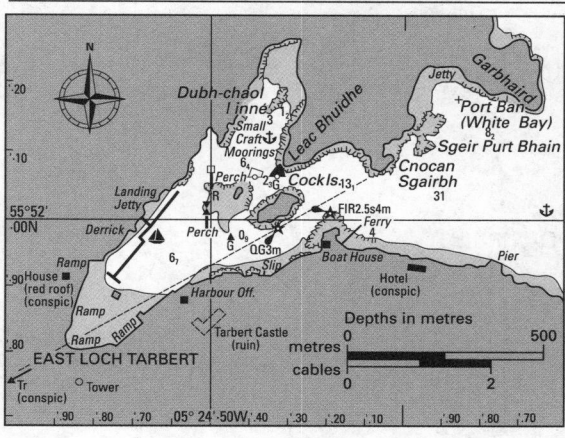

SHELTER
Very good in all weathers but gets crowded. Access H24.
Visitors berth only on SE side of yacht pontoons in 5m.
Note: also known as East Loch Tarbert.
NAVIGATION
WPT 55°52'·02N 05°22'·96W, 090°/270° from/to Fl R 2·5s
lt, 0·70M. Ent is very narrow. Cock Isle divides the ent in
half: Main hbr to the S, Buteman's Hole to the N, where
⌘s are fouled by heavy moorings and lost chains.
LIGHTS AND MARKS
Outer ldg lts 252° to S ent: Fl R 2·5s on with Cock Is lt QG.
Inner ldg line 239°: same QG, G column, on with conspic
✠ tr. Note: The W sector, 065°-078°, of Eilean na Beithe ☆,
Fl WRG 3s 7m 5M (on E shore of Lower Loch Fyne), could
be used to position for the initial appr to Tarbert.
RADIO TELEPHONE
Call VHF Ch 16; work Ch 14 (0900-1700LT).
TELEPHONE (Dial code 01880)
Hr Mr 820344, ☎ 820719; MRCC (01475) 729988; ☷ (0141)
887 9369 (H24); Marinecall 0891 500462; Police 820200;
Ⓗ (01546) 602323.
FACILITIES
Yacht Berthing Facility 100 visitors, AB £10.75, FW, AC;
Old Quay D, FW; **Tarbert YC** Slip, L;
Services: SM, ▣, ACA, Sh, CH.
Town EC Wed; P & D (cans), Gas, Gaz, L, V, R, Bar, ✉, Ⓑ,
⇌ (bus to Glasgow), ✈ (Glasgow/Campbeltown).

ANCHORAGES IN LOCH FYNE

INVERARAY, Argyll and Bute, 56°13'·95N 05°04'·00W. AC
2382, *2131*. HW +0126 on Dover. See 8.9.9. For Upper
Loch Fyne see 8.9.5. Beyond Otter Spit, are ⌘s on NW
bank at Port Ann, Loch Gair and Minard Bay; and on SE
bank at Otter Ferry, Strachur Bay (5 ⚓s off Creggans Inn,
☎ (01369) 860279) and St Catherine's.
Inveraray: beware An Oitir drying spit 2ca offshore, ½M S
of pier. Some ⚓s or ⌘ SSW of pier in 4m or dry out NW of
the pier. FW (on pier), ✉, V, R, Bar, Gas, bus to Glasgow.
In Lower L Fyne, 6M NNE of East Loch Tarbert there is a ⚓
at Kilfinan Bay, ☎ (01700) 821201.

9

CAMPBELTOWN   8-9-11
Argyll & Bute 55°25'·90N 05°32'·50W (Hbr ent) Rtg 1-2-1

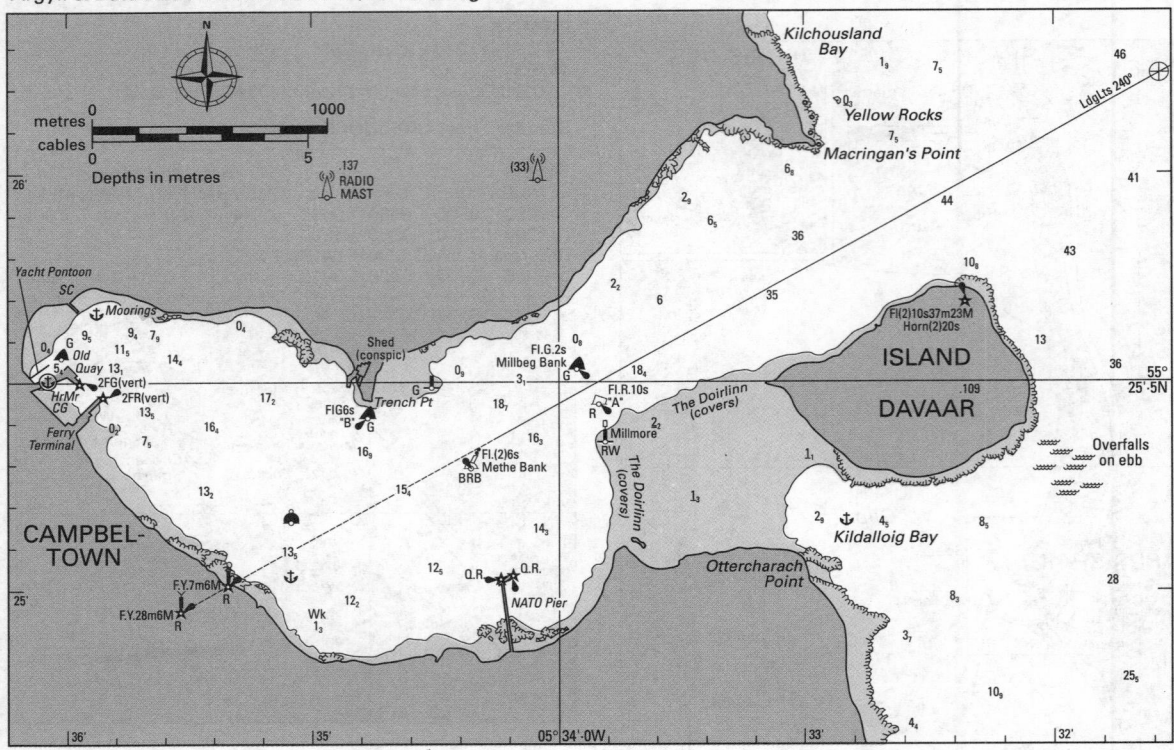

CHARTS
AC 1864, *2126*; Imray C63; OS 68
TIDES
+0125 Dover; ML 1·8; Duration 0630; Zone 0 (UT)

Standard Port GREENOCK (⟶)

Times				Height (metres)			
High Water		Low Water		MHWS	MHWN	MLWN	MLWS
0000	0600	0000	0600	3·4	2·8	1·0	0·3
1200	1800	1200	1800				
Differences CAMPBELTOWN							
−0025	−0005	−0015	+0005	−0·5	−0·3	+0·1	+0·2
CARRADALE BAY							
−0015	−0005	−0005	+0005	−0·3	−0·2	+0·1	+0·1
SOUTHEND, (Mull of Kintyre)							
−0030	−0010	+0005	+0035	−1·3	−1·2	−0·5	−0·2

SHELTER
Good, but gusts off the hills in strong SW'lies. Yacht pontoon (6+34 visitors) dredged 3·0m is close NW of Old Quay and gives excellent sheltered berthing. Yachts >12m LOA should pre-notify ETA to Berthing Master by ☎ (below). Excellent ⚓ close E of front ldg lt (240°), also near moorings NNE of the hbr. S of Island Davaar there is a temp ⚓ in Kildalloig Bay, but no access to the loch.
NAVIGATION
WPT 55°26'·24N 05°31'·55W, 060°/240° from/to first chan buoys, 1·4M. The ent is easily identified by radio masts N and NE of Trench Pt (conspic W bldg) and conspic lt ho on N tip of Island Davaar off which streams are strong (4kn sp). Caution: The Dhorlin, a bank drying 2·5m which covers at HW, is close S of the ldg line.
LIGHTS AND MARKS
Davaar Fl (2) 10s 37m 23M. Otterard Rk (3·8m depth, off chartlet, 1·5M NNE of Island Davaar), is marked by ECM buoy Q (3) 10s. Ldg lts 240°, both FY 7/28m 6M, are sodium vapour lts, H24. The ☆ 2FR (vert) at the NE end of the ferry terminal pier is on a dolphin, standing clear of the pier head.

RADIO TELEPHONE
VHF Ch 12 13 16 (Mon-Thur 0845-1645; Fri 0845-1600LT).
TELEPHONE (Dial code 01586)
Hr Mr 552552, ⛴ 554739; Yacht pontoon Berthing Master ☎ & ⛴ 554381, mobile 04985 24821, night 554782; MRCC (01475) 729988; ⌗ 552261; Marinecall 0891 500462; Police 552253; Dr 552105.
FACILITIES
Yacht pontoon £10, FW, AC; Bath/shower in hotel opposite.
Old Quay ☎ 552552, D, FW, AB, LB;
New Quay Slip, Ro-Ro ferry to Ballycastle (N Ireland);
Campbeltown SC Slip (dinghies), Bar, regular racing.
Town EC Wed; BY, ME, ACA, C (25 ton), CH, P, D, El, Ⓔ, Gas, Gaz, V (2 supermarkets), R, Bar, ✉, Ⓑ, Ⓞ, Ⓗ, ♿ toilet about 100m from yacht pontoon, key at Tourist office or police station (H24).
Bus thrice daily to Glasgow, ✈ twice daily to Glasgow, ⇌ (nearest is Arrochar, 90 miles N by road). Car hire/taxi.
Almost an Island – Always a Welcome.

ADJACENT ANCHORAGE IN KILBRANNAN SOUND

CARRADALE BAY, Argyll and Bute, 55°34'·40N 05°28'·60W. AC *2131*, HW+0115 on Dover. ML 1·8m. See 8.9.11. Good ⚓ in 7m off Torrisdale Castle in SW corner of Carradale Bay. In N & E winds ⚓ in NE corner of bay, W of Carradale Pt. 3ca E of this Pt, a PHM buoy Fl (2) R 12s marks Cruban Rk. With S & SE winds a swell sets into bay, when good shelter can be found 1M N in **Carradale Harbour** (Port Crannaich); if full of FVs, ⚓ 100m N of Hbr. Bkwtr lt, Fl R 10s 5m 6M. Piermaster ☎ (01586) 431228. Facilities: FW on pier, D & P (cans), Gas, V, R, Bar, ✉.

TIDAL STREAMS AROUND THE MULL OF KINTYRE

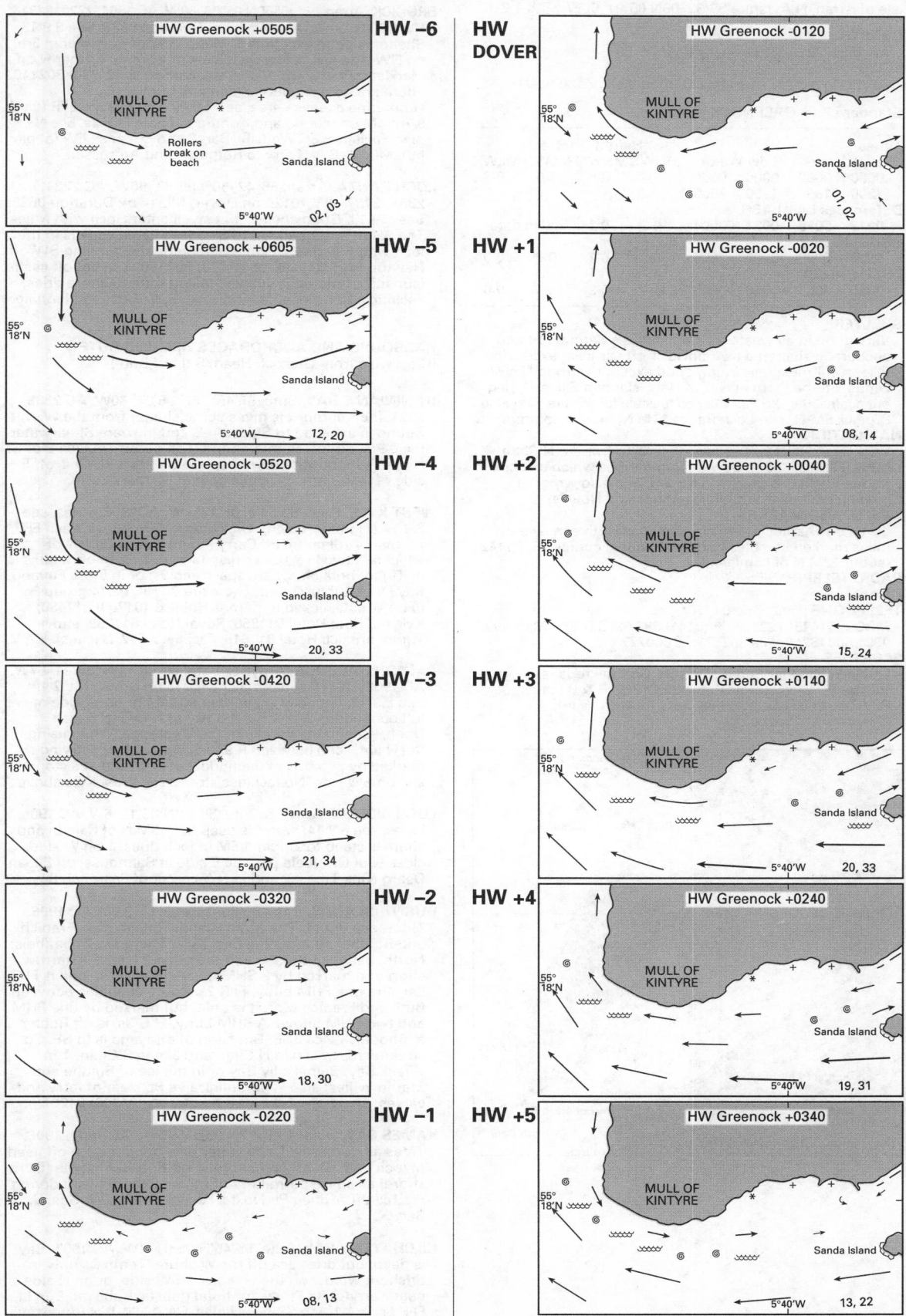

HW –6 — HW Greenock +0505	HW DOVER — HW Greenock -0120
HW –5 — HW Greenock +0605	HW +1 — HW Greenock -0020
HW –4 — HW Greenock -0520	HW +2 — HW Greenock +0040
HW –3 — HW Greenock -0420	HW +3 — HW Greenock +0140
HW –2 — HW Greenock -0320	HW +4 — HW Greenock +0240
HW –1 — HW Greenock -0220	HW +5 — HW Greenock +0340

9

LAMLASH   8-9-13

Isle of Arran, N Ayrshire 55°32'.00N 05°07'.00W   Rtg 1-2-1

CHARTS
AC 1864, 2220, *2131*; Imray C63; OS 69
TIDES
+0115 Dover; ML no data; Duration 0635; Zone 0 (UT)

Standard Port GREENOCK (→)

Times				Height (metres)			
High Water		Low Water		MHWS	MHWN	MLWN	MLWS
0000	0600	0000	0600	3·4	2·8	1·0	0·3
1200	1800	1200	1800				
Differences LAMLASH							
−0016	−0036	−0024	−0004	−0·2	−0·2	No data	
BRODICK BAY							
0000	0000	+0005	+0005	−0·2	−0·2	0·0	0·0
LOCH RANZA							
−0015	−0005	−0010	−0005	−0·4	−0·3	−0·1	0·0

SHELTER
Very good in all weathers. Lamlash is a natural hbr and anchorage sheltered as follows: ‡ off Lamlash except in E'lies; off Kingscross Point, good except in strong N/NW winds; off the Farm at NW of Holy Island in E'lies. Drying out against the Old Pier may be feasible for repairs. See also Brodick 5M N, and Loch Ranza 14M N, in next column.
NAVIGATION
WPT 55°32'.63N 05°03'.00W, 090°/270° from/to N Chan buoy (FI R 6s), 1·0M. Beware submarines which exercise frequently in this area (see 8.9.24), and also wreck of landing craft (charted) off farmhouse on Holy Is.
LIGHTS AND MARKS
Lts as on chartlet. There are two consecutive measured miles marked by poles north of Sannox, courses 322°/142° (about 12M N of Lamlash).
RADIO TELEPHONE
None.
TELEPHONE (Dial code 01770)
MRCC (01475) 729988; ☰ (0141) 887 9369 (H24); Marinecall 0891 500462; Police 302573; ⊞ 600777.
FACILITIES
Lamlash Old Pier Slip, L, FW, CH, Sh (hull repairs); **Village** EC Wed (Lamlash/Brodick); ME, P & D (cans), Bar, R, V, ✉, ⇌ (bus to Brodick, ferry to Ardrossan), ✈ (Glasgow or Prestwick).

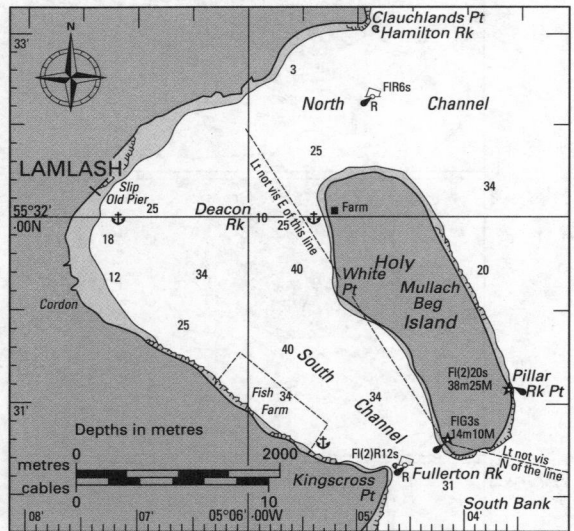

OTHER HARBOURS ON ARRAN

BRODICK, Arran, 55°35'.50N 05°08'.60W. AC 1864, 2220, *2131*. HW +0115 on Dover; ML 1·8m; Duration 0635. See 8.9.13. Shelter is good except in E winds. ‡ W of ferry pier in 3m; on NW side just below the Castle in 4·5m, or further N off Merkland Pt in 3-4m. Also 5 ⚓s: contact ☎ (01770) 302140. There are no navigational dangers but the bay is in a submarine exercise area; see 8.9.22. Only lts are 2FR (vert) 9/7m 4M on pier hd and Admiralty buoy, FI Y 2s, 5ca N of pier. Facilities: EC Wed; ⒷBar, P and D (cans), FW (at pier hd), ME, ✉, R, V. Ferry to Rothesay and Ardrossan.

LOCH RANZA, Arran, 55°42'.60N 05°17'.90W. AC 2221, 2383, *2131*. HW +0120 on Dover; ML 1·7m; Duration 0635. See 8.9.13. Good shelter, but swell enters loch with N'lies. The 850m mountain 4M to S causes fierce squalls in the loch with S winds. Beware Screda Reef extending SW off Newton Pt. 5 ⚓s; call ☎ (01770) 302140. ‡ in 5m off castle (conspic); holding is suspect in soft mud. S shore dries. Facilities: Bar, FW at ferry slip, ✉, R, V. Ferry to Claonaig.

HARBOURS AND ANCHORAGES AROUND BUTE
(Clockwise from Garroch Head, S tip of Bute)

ST NINIAN'S BAY, Bute, 55°48'.15N 05°07'.80W. AC 2383, 2221. Inchmarnock Is gives some shelter from the W, but Sound is exposed to S'lies. At S end, beware Shearwater Rk, 0·9m, almost in mid-sound. ‡ in about 7m, 2ca E of St Ninian's Pt; beware drying spit to S of this Pt. Or ‡ off E side of Inchmarnock, close abeam Midpark Farm.

WEST KYLE, Bute, 55°54'N 05°12'.7W. AC1906. Tides, see 8.9.14 (Tighnabruaich). On W bank PHM buoys, each FI R 4s, mark Ardlamont Pt, Carry Pt and Rubha Ban; N of which are two FI Y buoys (fish farms). ‡ close off Kames or Tighnabruaich, where space allows; or in Black Farland Bay (N of Rubha Dubh). There are 24 HIE ⚓s (4 groups of 6) on W side, linked to Kames Hotel ☎ (01700) 811489; Kyles of Bute Hotel 811350; Royal Hotel 811239; and Tighnabruaich Hotel 811615. Facilities: FW, D (cans), BY, V.

CALADH HARBOUR, Argyll & Bute, 55°56'.00N, 05°11'.67W. AC 1906. HW (Tighnabruaich) +0015 on Dover; ML 2·1m. See 8.9.14. Perfectly sheltered natural hbr on W side of ent to Loch Riddon. Enter Caladh Hbr to N or S of Eilean Dubh; keep to the middle of the S passage. When using the N ent, keep between R and G bns to clear a drying rk marked by perch. ‡ in the middle of hbr; land at a stone slip on SW side. No facilities/stores; see West Kyle above.

LOCH RIDDON, Argyll & Bute, 55°57'N 05°11'.6W. AC 1906. Tides, see 8.9.14. Water is deep for 1·3M N of Caladh and shore is steep-to; upper 1·5M of loch dries. ‡ on W side close N of Ormidale pier; on E side at Salthouse; off Eilean Dearg (One Tree Is); and at NW corner of Fearnoch Bay.

BURNT ISLANDS, Bute, 55°55'.76N 05°10'.33W. AC 1906. Tides, see 8.9.14. The three islands (Eilean Mor, Fraoich and Buidhe) straddle the East Kyle. There are 2 channels: North, between Buidhe and the other 2 islets, is narrow, short and marked by 2 SHM buoys (the NW'ly one is FI G 3s), and one PHM buoy, FI R 2s. South chan lies between Bute and Fraoich/Mor; it is unlit, but marked by one PHM and two SHM buoys. A SHM buoy, FI G 3s, is off Rubha a' Bhodaich, 4ca ESE. Direction of buoyage is to SE. Sp streams reach 5kn in N Chan and 3kn in S Chan. ‡ in Wreck Bay, Balnakailly Bay or in the lee of Buidhe and Mor in W'lies; also W of Colintraive Pt, clear of ferry and cables. There are 4 ⚓s off the hotel, ☎ (01700) 84207.

KAMES BAY, Bute, 55°51'.7N 05°04'.75W. AC 1867, 1906. Tides as Rothesay. Deep water bay, but dries 2ca off head of loch and 1ca off NW shore. ‡ off Port Bannatyne (S shore) as space permits W of ruined jetty. Beware drying rks 1ca off Ardbeg Pt. No lts. Facilities: BY, FW, Gas, V, Bar, ✉.

KILCHATTAN BAY, Bute, 55°45'N 05°01'.1W. AC 1907. Bay is deep, but dries 3ca off the W shore. Temp ‡s only in offshore winds: off the village on SW side, or on N side near Kerrytonlia Pt. ⚓s for hotel guests. Rubh' an Eun Lt, FI R 6s, is 1·1M to SSE. Facilities: FW, V, ✉, bus Rothesay.

ROTHESAY   8-9-14

Isle of Bute, Argyll & Bute 55°50′·32N 05°03′·01W   Rtg 2-3-1

CHARTS
AC 1867, 1906, 1907, *2131*; Imray C63; OS 63

TIDES
+0100 Dover; ML 1·9; Duration 0640; Zone 0 (UT)

Standard Port GREENOCK (→)

Times				Height (metres)			
High Water		Low Water		MHWS	MHWN	MLWN	MLWS
0000	0600	0000	0600	3·4	2·8	1·0	0·3
1200	1800	1200	1800				

Differences ROTHESAY BAY

−0020	−0015	−0010	−0002	+0·2	+0·2	+0·2	+0·2

RUBHA A'BHODAICH (Burnt Is)

−0020	−0010	−0007	−0007	−0·2	−0·1	+0·2	+0·2

TIGHNABRUAICH

+0007	−0010	−0002	−0015	0·0	+0·2	+0·4	+0·5

SHELTER
Good on yacht pontoons in Outer Hbr (2m) and at W end inside the Front pier (2m). 40 ⚓s WNW of pier or good ⚓ in bay ¼M W, off Isle of Bute SC; except in strong N/NE'lies when Kyles of Bute or Kames Bay offer better shelter.

NAVIGATION
WPT 55°51′·00N 05°02′·69W, 014°/194° from/to Outer hbr ent, 0·69M. From E keep 1ca off Bogany Pt, and off Ardbeg Pt from N.

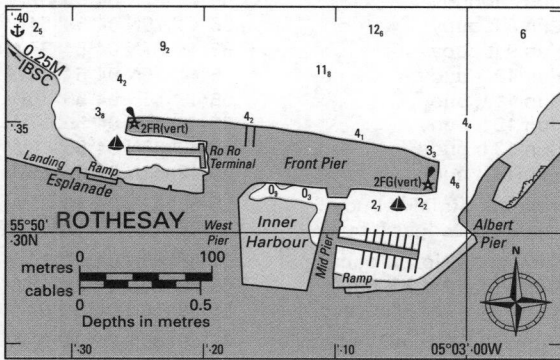

LIGHTS AND MARKS
Lts as chartlet, hard to see against shore lts. Conspic Ch spire leads 190° to outer hbr; at night beware large, unlit Admiralty buoy "MK" on this brg 5½ca from hbr. 3½ca N of hbr is Rothesay 'A' mooring buoy, Fl Y 2s.

RADIO TELEPHONE
VHF Ch 12 16 (1 May-30 Sept: 0600-2100; 1 Oct-30 Apl: 0600-1900 LT).

TELEPHONE (Dial code 01700)
Hr Mr 503842; Moorings 504750; MRCC (01475) 729988; ⊞ (0141) 887 9369 (H24); Marinecall 0891 500462; Police 502121; Dr 503985; Ⓗ 503938.

FACILITIES
Outer Hbr AB £11, AC, FW, Slip, D*, L, FW, ME, EI, CH, ⬚;
Inner Hbr L, FW, AB, NB: Dredging had not begun in 1998;
Front Pier (W) FW, AC, R, ⬚; **Albert Pier** D*, L, FW, C (4 ton mobile).
Town EC Wed; P, D, CH, V, R, Bar, ⬚, Ⓑ, ⇌ (ferry to Wemyss Bay), ✈ (Glasgow).
*By arrangement (min 200 galls).

GREAT CUMBRAE ISLAND

MILLPORT, Great Cumbrae, N Ayrshire, 55°45′·00N 04°55′·75W. AC 1867, 1907. HW +0100 on Dover; ML 1·9m; Duration 0640. See 8.9.15. Good shelter, except in S'lies. Berth at pontoon N side of pier hd or ⚓ in approx 3m S of pier or E of the Eileans. 12 HIE ⚓s 1½ca SSE of pier; call ☎ (01475) 530741. Ldg marks: pier hd on with ⊕ twr 333°; or ldg lts 333°, both FR 7/9m 5M, between the Spoig and the Eileans, QG. Unmarked, drying rk is close E of ldg line. Hr Mr ☎ (01475) 530826.
Town EC Wed; CH, Bar, Gas, D, P, FW, ⬚, R, Slip, V.

LARGS   8-9-15

N Ayrshire 55°46′·40N 04°51′·77W   Rtg 2-1-2

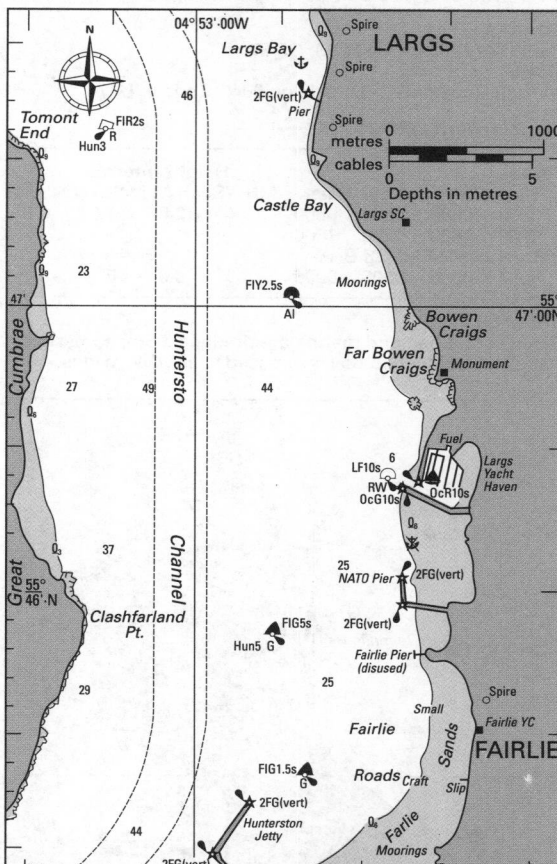

CHARTS
AC 1867, 1907, *2131*; Imray C63; OS 63

TIDES
+0105 Dover; ML 1·9; Duration 0640; Zone 0 (UT)

Standard Port GREENOCK (→)

Times				Heights (metres)			
High Water		Low Water		MHWS	MHWN	MLWN	MLWS
0000	0600	0000	0600	3·4	2·8	1·0	0·3
1200	1800	1200	1800				

Differences MILLPORT

−0005	−0025	−0025	−0005	0·0	−0·1	0·0	+0·1

SHELTER
Excellent in Yacht Haven (1·4M S of Largs Pier), access all tides (3·5m in ent & deep berths; 2·5m elsewhere). Largs Chan is sheltered from W'lies by Cumbrae Is, but open to winds from S or N. Temp'y ⚓ in 10m about ½ca N of pier.

NAVIGATION
WPT 55°46′·40N 04°51′·77W, SWM buoy, L Fl 10s, off yacht haven. From S beware Hunterston and Southannan sands and outfalls from Hunterston Power Stn (conspic). From S bkwtr to the NATO pier is a restricted, no ⚓ area.

LIGHTS AND MARKS
"Pencil" monument (12m) is conspic 4ca N of ent. Lts as on chartlet. Largs Pier, 2 FG (vert) when vessel expected.

RADIO TELEPHONE
Marina Ch 80 M (H24).

TELEPHONE (Dial code 01475)
Yacht Haven 675333; MRCC 729988; ⊞ (0141) 887 9369 (H24); Dr 673380; Ⓗ 733777; Marinecall 0891 500 462; Police 674651.

FACILITIES
Largs Yacht Haven (600, some Ⓥ) ☎ 675333, ⬚ 672245, £14.82, FW, D, P, AC, ⬚, SM, BY, C (17 ton), BH (40 ton), ME, Divers, EI, Sh, Ⓔ,CH, ⬚, Gas, Gaz, Slip (access H24), Bar, R; **Largs SC; Fairlie YC; Town** EC Wed; V, R, Bar, ⬚, Ⓑ, ⇌, ✈ (Glasgow).

9

INVERKIP (KIP MARINA)   8-9-16
Inverclyde 55°54'·50N 04°53'·00W   Rtg 2-1-2

CHARTS
AC 1907, 2131; Imray C63; OS 63

TIDES
+0110 Dover; ML 1·8; Duration 0640; Zone 0 (UT)

Standard Port GREENOCK (→)

Times				Height (metres)			
High Water		Low Water		MHWS	MHWN	MLWN	MLWS
0000	0600	0000	0600	3·4	2·8	1·0	0·3
1200	1800	1200	1800				
Differences WEMYSS BAY							
−0005	−0005	−0005	−0005	0·0	0·0	+0·1	+0·1

SHELTER
Excellent. Chan and marina are dredged 3·5m; accessible at all tides. Inverkip Bay is exposed to SW/NW winds.

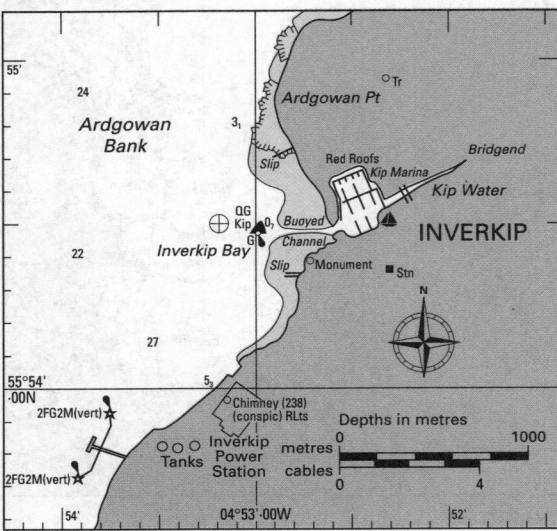

NAVIGATION
WPT 55°54'·48N 04°52'·95W, Kip SHM buoy, QG, at ent to buoyed chan; beware shifting bank to the N.

LIGHTS AND MARKS
Ent is ½M N of conspic chey (238m). SPM buoy marks sewer outfall off Ardgowan Pt. From Kip SHM buoy, 3 SHM and 3 PHM buoys mark 365m long appr chan.

RADIO TELEPHONE
VHF Ch 80 M (H24).

TELEPHONE (Dial code 01475)
Hr Mr 521485; MRCC 729988; ⌗ (0141) 887 9369 (H24); Marinecall 0891 500462; Police 521222; Dr 520248; Ⓗ 33777.

FACILITIES
Kip Marina (700+40 Ⓥ), ☎ 521485, ⚓ 521298, £13.90, AC, FW, D, P (cans), Sh, C, ME, El, Ⓔ, SM, CH, Diver, BH (40 ton), V, R, Bar, Ⓖ, Gas, Gaz, YC.
Town EC Wed; ✉, Ⓑ (Gourock), ⇌, ✈ (Glasgow).

ADJACENT ANCHORAGE
DUNOON, Argyll and Bute, 55°56'·70N 04°55'·20W. AC 1994, 1907, 2131. Use Greenock tides. Temp ⚓ in West or East Bays (S and N of Dunoon Pt). The former is open to the S; the latter more shoal. Six HIE ⚓s (free) in each bay; call ☎ (01369) 703785. The Gantocks, drying rks 3ca SE of Dunoon Pt, have W ○ bn tr, Fl R 6s 12m 6M. 2FR (vert) on ferry pier. Facilities: P & D (cans), V, R, Bar, ✉, Gas, ferry to Gourock. 3 ⚓s off Inellan, 3·7M S of Dunoon, ☎ (01369) 830445.

CLYDE WAYPOINTS   8-9-17
The following selected waypoints in the Firth of Clyde area supplement those in 8.9.4; there is no duplication. All positions are referenced to OSGB 36.

AE lt buoy	55°51'·68N 05°02'·32W
Ardgowan outfall buoy	55°54'·92N 04°53'·04W
Ardmore No 4 lt buoy	55°58'·75N 04°48'·30W
Ardmore No 5 lt buoy	55°58'·67N 04°47'·43W
Ardmore No 8 lt buoy	55°58'·95N 04°46'·67W
Ardmore No 10 lt buoy	55°59'·03N 04°45'·62W
Ardyne lt buoy	55°52'·10N 05°03'·12W
Big Rock lt buoy	55°57'·89N 05°25'·27W
Burnt Islands No. 43 lt buoy	55°55'·43N 05°10'·27W
Burnt Islands No. 44 lt buoy	55°55'·56N 05°10'·57W
Dunoon Bank lt buoy	55°56'·65N 04°54'·08W
Eilean Buidhe lt buoy	55°55'·77N 05°10'·32W
Eilean Fraoich lt buoy	55°55'·78N 05°10'·43W
Fairlie Patch lt buoy	55°45'·37N 04°52'·27W
Fullerton Rock lt buoy	55°30'·65N 05°04'·50W
Green Isle lt buoy	55°59'·40N 04°45'·47W
Hun 1 lt buoy	55°48'·12N 04°54'·14W
Hun 3 lt buoy	55°47'·61N 04°53'·44W
Hun 5 lt buoy	55°45'·87N 04°52'·45W
Hun 7 lt buoy	55°44'·97N 04°53'·87W
Hun 8 lt buoy	55°44'·79N 04°53'·64W
Hun 9 lt buoy	55°44'·67N 04°54'·37W
Hun 10 lt buoy	55°44'·16N 04°54'·79W
Hun 11 lt buoy	55°43'·46N 04°55'·10W
Hun 12 lt buoy	55°43'·46N 04°55'·57W
Hun 13 lt buoy	55°42'·53N 04°55'·10W
Hun 14 lt buoy	55°42'·53N 04°55'·56W
Ironotter outfall lt buoy	55°58'·37N 04°48'·33W
Iron Rock Ledges lt buoy	55°26'·83N 05°18'·80W
Kilcreggan No 1 lt buoy	55°58'·68N 04°50'·20W
Kilcreggan No 3 lt buoy	55°59'·20N 04°51'·38W
Kilcreggan No 3 lt beacon	55°59'·18N 04°51'·03W
Lamlash S Channel lt buoy	55°30'·66N 05°04'·50W
Methe Bank lt buoy	55°25'·30N 05°34'·36W
Millbeg Bank lt buoy	55°25'·53N 05°33'·93W
Outer St Nicholas lt buoy	55°28'·11N 04°39'·37W
Outfall lt buoy	55°43'·58N 04°54'·70W
Pillar Rock lt house	55°31'·05N 05°03'·57W
Perch Rock buoy	55°59'·45N 04°45'·58W
Pladda lt house	55°25'·50N 05°07'·07W
Rosneath Patch No 27 lt buoy	55°58'·31N 04°47'·19W
Skelmorlie Bank lt buoy	55°51'·64N 04°55'·84W
Skelmorlie 'A' lt buoy	55°46'·50N 04°57'·70W
Skelmorlie 'B' lt buoy	55°47'·13N 04°57'·47W
Skelmorlie 'C' lt buoy	55°48'·11N 04°55'·23W
Skelmorlie 'D' lt buoy	55°47'·85N 04°56'·22W
Skelmorlie 'F' lt buoy	55°48'·63N 04°54'·90W
Skelmorlie 'G' lt buoy	55°49'·00N 04°54'·15W
Skelmorlie 'H' lt buoy	55°49'·00N 04°54'·63W
Skelmorlie 'J' lt buoy	55°51'·53N 04°54'·63W
Skelmorlie 'L' lt buoy	55°52'·38N 04°54'·42W
Skelmorlie 'M' lt buoy	55°53'·53N 04°54'·35W
Skelmorlie 'N' lt buoy	55°53'·80N 04°55'·10W
Skelmorlie 'O' lt buoy	55°54'·55N 04°54'·47W
Strone lt buoy	55°58'·77N 04°53'·77W
Tann Spit (No 38) buoy	55°44'·42N 04°57'·06W
Warden Bank lt buoy	55°55'·78N 04°54'·48W
West Crinan lt buoy	55°38'·47N 04°49'·82W
7N lt beacon	56°00'·06N 04°45'·28W

FIRTH OF CLYDE AREA   8-9-18

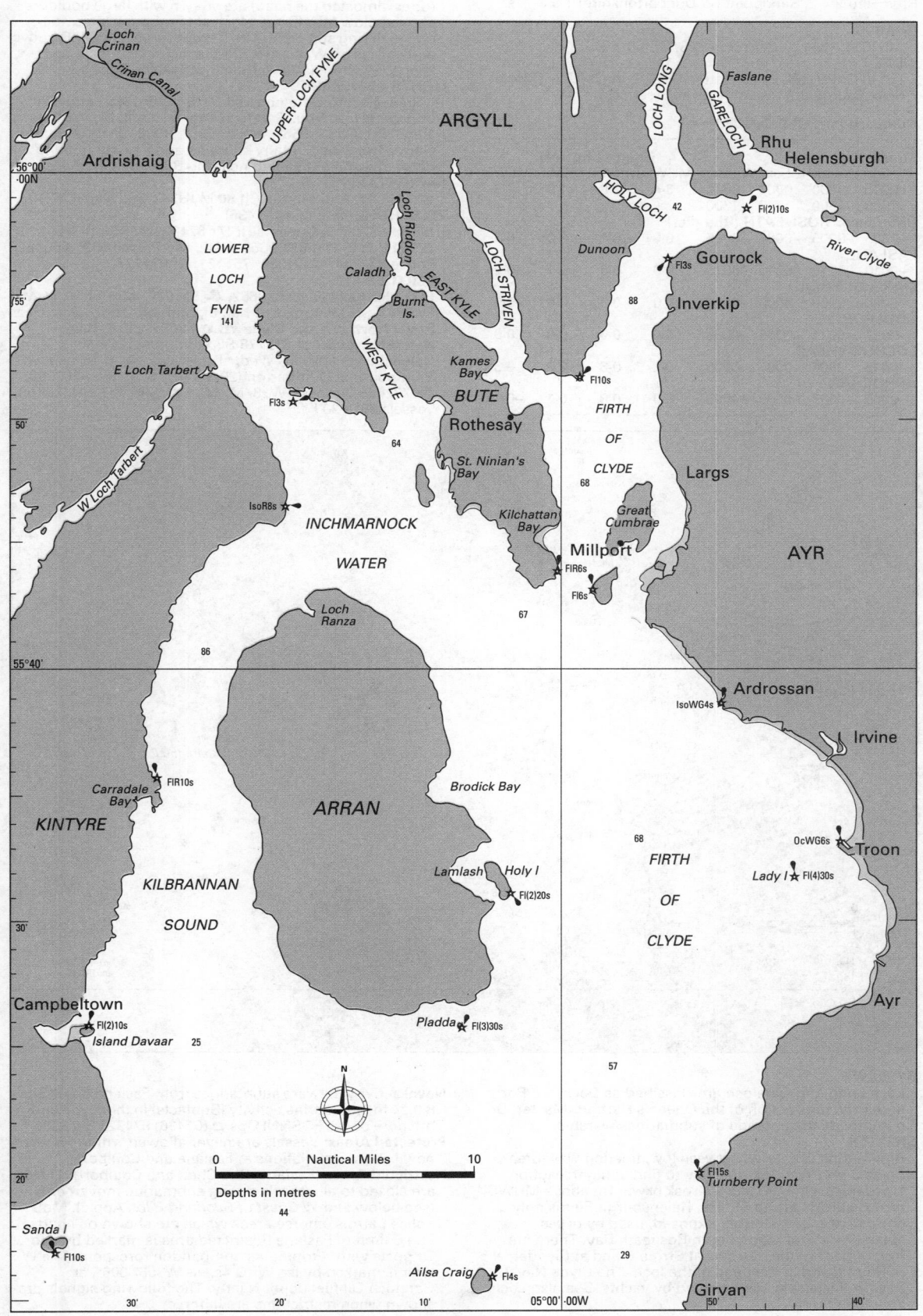

Loch Crinan

Crinan Canal

UPPER LOCH FYNE

ARGYLL

LOCH LONG

GARELOCH

Faslane

Rhu

Helensburgh

Ardrishaig

56°00'
-00N

HOLY LOCH

42

Fl(2)10s

River Clyde

LOWER LOCH FYNE 141

Loch Riddon

LOCH STRIVEN

Dunoon

Fl3s

Gourock

55'

Caladh

EAST KYLE

88

Inverkip

Burnt Is.

Kames Bay

E Loch Tarbert

50'

Fl3s

WEST KYLE

BUTE

Fl10s

FIRTH OF CLYDE

W Loch Tarbert

Rothesay

64

68

Largs

St. Ninian's Bay

IsoR8s

INCHMARNOCK

Kilchattan Bay

Great Cumbrae

AYR

WATER

Millport

Loch Ranza

67

FIR6s

Fl6s

55°40'

86

68

FIRTH OF CLYDE

Carradale Bay

FIR10s

ARRAN

Brodick Bay

Ardrossan

IsoWG4s

Irvine

KINTYRE

68

OcWG6s

Troon

KILBRANNAN

Lamlash

Holy I

FIRTH

Lady I

Fl(4)30s

SOUND

Fl(2)20s

OF

30'

Campbeltown

CLYDE

Ayr

Fl(2)10s

Island Davaar   25

Pladda

Fl(3)30s

57

50'

20'

N

Fl15s

Turnberry Point

0   Nautical Miles   10

Depths in metres

44

29

Sanda I

Fl10s

Ailsa Craig

Fl4s

Girvan

30'   20'   10'   05°00'·00W   40'

9

GARELOCH/RHU   8-9-19

Argyll & Bute 56°00'·71N 04°46'·50W (Rhu marina)
Rtgs: Rhu 2-4-2; Sandpoint (W Dunbartonshire) 1-5-3

CHARTS
AC 2000, 1994, *2131*; Imray C63; OS 56, 63

TIDES
+0110 Dover; ML 1·9; Duration 0640; Zone 0 (UT). Tides at Helensburgh are the same as at Greenock

Standard Port GREENOCK (→)

Times				Height (metres)			
High Water		Low Water		MHWS	MHWN	MLWN	MLWS
0000	0600	0000	0600	3·4	2·8	1·0	0·3
1200	1800	1200	1800				
Differences ROSNEATH (Rhu pier)							
–0005	–0005	–0005	–0005	0·0	–0·1	0·0	0·0
FASLANE							
–0010	–0010	–0010	–0010	0·0	0·0	–0·1	–0·2
GARELOCHHEAD							
0000	0000	0000	0000	0·0	0·0	0·0	–0·1
COULPORT							
–0011	–0011	–0008	–0008	0·0	0·0	0·0	0·0
LOCHGOILHEAD							
+0015	0000	–0005	–0005	–0·2	–0·3	–0·3	–0·3
ARROCHAR							
–0005	–0005	–0005	–0005	0·0	0·0	–0·1	–0·1

NAVIGATION
WPT 55°59'·30N 04°45'·19W, 176°/356° from/to bn No 7, 1·3M. Beaches between Cairndhu Pt and Helensburgh Pier (dries almost to the head) are strewn with large boulders above/below MLWS. Gareloch ent is about 225m wide due to drying spit off Rhu Pt. Beware large unlit MoD buoys and barges off W shore of Gareloch; for Garelochhead keep to W shore until well clear of Faslane Base area.

LIGHTS AND MARKS
Ldg/dir lts into Gareloch 356°, 318°, 295°, 329° and 331°. Conspic ✠ tr at Rhu. Gareloch Fuel Depot lt, Iso WRG 4s 10m 14M, G351°-356°, W356°-006°, R006°-011°, is clearly visible from the S. Many shore lts and an unlit floating boom make night sailing near the Base area inadvisable.

RADIO TELEPHONE
VHF Ch 16. Rhu Marina Ch **80** M (H24). See also 8.19.19.

TELEPHONE (Dial code 01436)
Marina 820652; Queen's Hr Mr 674321; MRCC (01475) 729014; ⌗ (0141) 887 9369 (H24); Marinecall 0891 500462; Police 672141; Ⓗ (01389) 754121; Dr 672277.

FACILITIES
Rhu Marina (200) ☎ 820652, 🛥 821039, AB £14.10, D, M, FW, AC, BH (35 ton), CH, ME, El, Slip, M, C hire, Gas, Gaz; **Royal Northern and Clyde YC** ☎ 820322, L, R, Bar; **Helensburgh SC** ☎ 672778 Slip (dinghies) L, FW; **Helensburgh** (1M) EC Wed; all services, 🚆, ✈ (Glasgow). **Sandpoint**, at Dumbarton (20, £5.88), ☎ (01389) 762396, 🛥 732605, Access HW±3, M, AC, FW, Slip, CH, BH (20 ton, vessels 80' x 20').

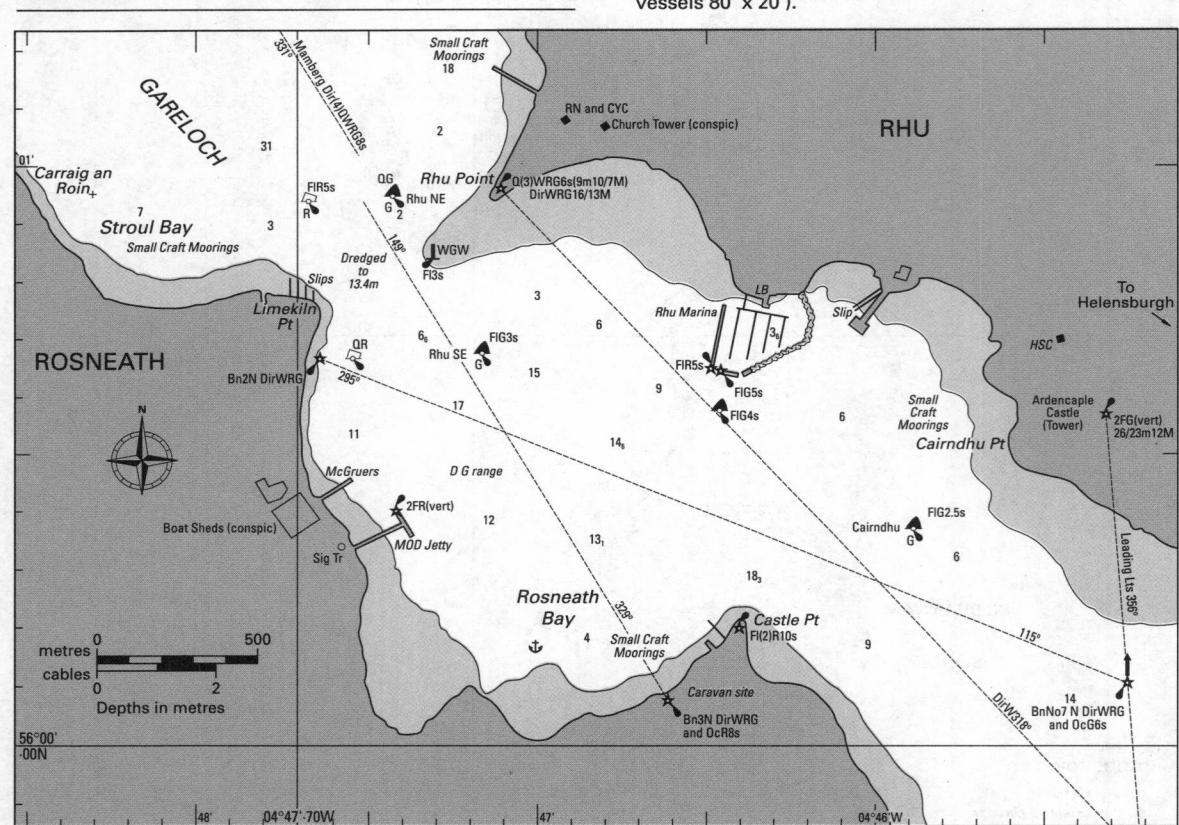

BYELAWS
Loch Long and Gareloch are classified as Dockyard Ports under the jurisdiction of the Queen's Harbour Master. Do not impede the passage of submarines/warships.

SHELTER
Rhu Marina is entered between low, floating wavebreaks on its S and W sides, not easy to find at night; caution cross-tides. On E/SE sides a rock bkwtr 1m above MHWS protects from strong SE'lies. Helensburgh Pier is only a temp drying berth, rather exposed, used by occas steamers. ⌕ E of marina or in Rosneath Bay. There are moorings N of the narrows at Stroul B and at Clynder; N of Rhu Pt; and at the head of the loch. The Clyde Naval Base at Faslane is best avoided by yachts. See also Loch Long/Loch Goil.

Naval activity: Beware submarines from Faslane Base. See 8.9.24 for submarine activity (Subfacts) in the Clyde and offshore or call FOSNNI Ops ☎ (01436) 674321 Ext 3206.

Protected Areas: Vessels are never allowed within 150m of naval shore installations at Faslane and Coulport.

Restricted Areas (Faslane, Rhu Chan and Coulport): These are closed to all vessels during submarine movements (see below and *W Coast of Scotland Pilot*, App 2). MoD Police patrols enforce areas which are shown on charts. The S limit of Faslane Restricted area is marked by two Or posts with X topmarks on Shandon foreshore. The W limit is marked by Iso WRG 4s, vis W356°-006°, at Gareloch Oil fuel depot N jetty. The following signals are shown when restrictions are in force:

1. Entrance to Gareloch
   by day : ⓡ ⓖ ⓖ (vert), supplemented by R flag with
   W diagonal bar.
   by night : ⓡ ⓖ ⓖ (vert).·
2. Faslane and Coulport
   by day : 3 ⓖ (vert), supplemented by International
   Code pendant over pendant Nine.
   by night : 3 ⓖ (vert) in conspic position.

HOLY LOCH, Argyll & Bute, 55°58'·5N 04°54'·0W is no more
a restricted or protected area. There are some moorings
on the S side, and AB for about 4 boats on former USN
jetty. ⚓ not advised as the bottom is reported to be foul.

LOCH LONG/LOCH GOIL, Argyll and Bute, approx 56°00'N
04°52'·5W to 56°12'·00N 04°45'·00W. AC 3746. Tides: See
8.9·19 for differences. ML 1·7m; Duration 0645. **Shelter**:
Loch Long is about 15M long. Temp ⚓s (S→N) at Cove,
Blairmore (not in S'lies), Ardentinny, Portincaple,
Coilessan (about 1M S of Ardgartan Pt), and near head of
loch (Arrochar) on either shore.
In Loch Goil ⚓ at Swines Hole and off Carrick Castle (S of
the pier, in N'lies a swell builds). Avoid ⚓ near Douglas
Pier. The head of the loch is crowded with private/dinghy
moorings, and is either too steep-to or too shallow to ⚓.
Lights: Coulport Jetty, 2FG (vert) each end and two Fl G
12s on N jetty; Port Dornaige Fl 6s 8m 11M, vis 026°-206°;
Dog Rock (Carraig nan Ron) Fl 2s 11M; Finnart Oil
Terminal has FG lts and ldg lts 031° QW/FW on Cnap Pt.
Upper Loch Long is unlit.
Loch Goil ent is marked by 2 PHM buoys (Fl R 3s and
QR), a SHM buoy (QG) and ldg lts 318°: front (The Perch)
Dir FWRG and Fl R 3s; rear FW. Rubha Ardnahein Fl R5s.
Facilities: Loch Long (Cove), Cove SC, FW, Bar; V, FW
(pier); (Portincaple) shops, hotel, ⊠, FW; (Ardentinny)
shop, V, R, hotel, M; (Blairmore) shops, ⊠, Slip, FW;
(Arrochar) shops, hotel, FW, Gas, ⊠.
Loch Goil (Carrick Castle) has ⊠, shop, hotel;
(Lochgoilhead) has a store, ⊠, hotel, FW, Gas.

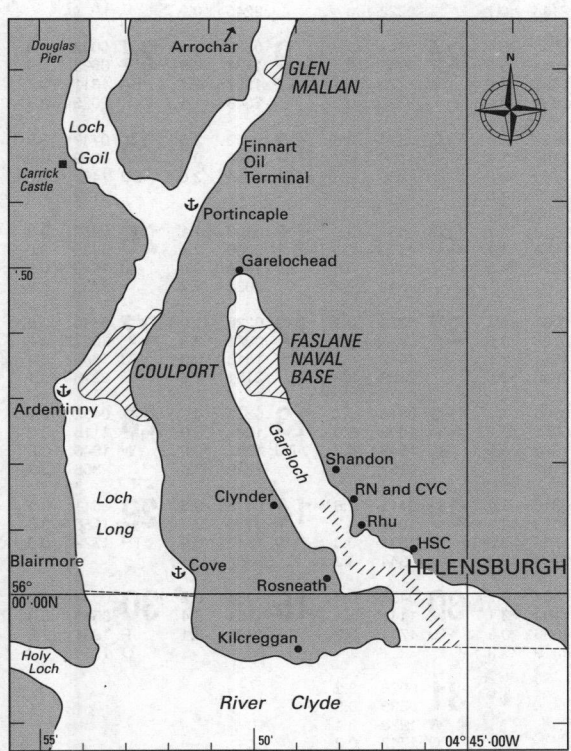

░░ Restricted Area-Max speed 7Kn
----- Southern limit of Dockyard Port

GREENOCK/GOUROCK 8-9-20

Inverclyde 55°58'·00N 04°49'·00W (As WPT) Rtg 1-5-3

CHARTS
AC 1994, *2131*; Imray C63; OS 63
TIDES
+0122 Dover; ML 2·0; Duration 0640; Zone 0 (UT)

Standard Port GREENOCK (⟶)

Times				Height (metres)			
High Water		Low Water		MHWS	MHWN	MLWN	MLWS
0000	0600	0000	0600	3·4	2·8	1·0	0·3
1200	1800	1200	1800				
Differences PORT GLASGOW							
+0010	+0005	+0010	+0020	+0·2	+0·1	0·0	0·0
BOWLING							
+0020	+0010	+0030	+0055	+0·6	+0·5	+0·3	+0·1
RENFREW							
+0025	+0015	+0035	+0100	+0·9	+0·8	+0·5	+0·2
GLASGOW							
+0025	+0015	+0035	+0105	+1·3	+1·2	+0·6	+0·4

Greenock is a Standard Port and tidal predictions for each
day of the year are given below.

SHELTER
Gourock: good ⚓ in West Bay, but open to N/NE winds.
Greenock is a commercial port. Up-river, possible AB at
Dumbarton (McAlister's BY), Bowling Hbr and at Renfrew
Hbr, but the R Clyde is only suitable for laying-up/repairs.
Hbrs are controlled by Clyde Port Authority.

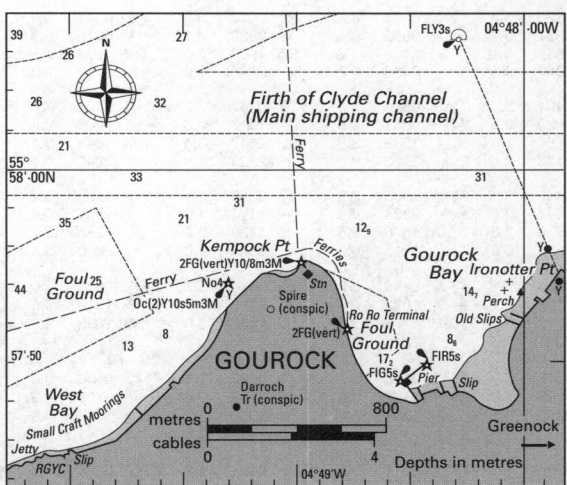

NAVIGATION
Gourock WPT 55°58'·00N 04°49'·00W, 000°/180° from/to
Kempock Pt lt, 0·22M. No navigational dangers, but much
shipping and ferries in the Clyde. Beware foul ground in
Gourock Bay. Cardwell Bay pier (lit) is disused.
LIGHTS AND MARKS
As chartlet. Note Ashton and Whiteforeland SWM buoys.
RADIO TELEPHONE
Call: *Clydeport Estuary Radio* VHF Ch 12 16 (H24). Info on
weather and traffic available on request.
TELEPHONE (Dial codes: Gourock/Greenock 01475;
Glasgow 0141)
General Mgr Marine 725775; Estuary Control 726221;
MRCC 729988; ⌗ (0141) 308 3618; Police 724444;
Marinecall 0891 500462; Dr 634617.
FACILITIES
GOUROCK: **Royal Gourock YC** ☎ 632983 M, L, FW, ME, V,
R, Bar; **Services:** SM.
Town EC Wed; P, D, V, R, Bar, ⊠, Ⓑ, ⇌, ✈ (Glasgow).
GREENOCK: All facilities, but small craft not particularly
encouraged. **Services:** AB, FW, AC, D, CH, Gas, ME, Sh,
El, Ⓔ, SM, C (45 ton).
GLASGOW (0141): Clyde Yacht Clubs Association is at 8 St
James St, Paisley, ☎ 887 8296. Clyde Cruising Club is at
Suite 408, Pentagon Centre, 36 Washington St, Glasgow
G3 8AZ, ☎ 221 2774, ✆ 221 2775. **Services:** ACA, CH.

9

SCOTLAND – GREENOCK

LAT 55°57′N   LONG   4°46′W

TIMES AND HEIGHTS OF HIGH AND LOW WATERS

YEAR **1999**

TIME ZONE (UT)
For Summer Time add ONE hour in non-shaded areas

JANUARY

Day	Time	m	Day	Time	m
1 F	0442 / 1141 / 1707	0.4 / 3.6 / 0.4	16 SA	0455 / 1202 / 1726	0.7 / 3.4 / 0.6
2 SA O	0013 / 0531 / 1227 / 1753	3.5 / 0.4 / 3.7 / 0.3	17 SU ●	0003 / 0530 / 1236 / 1800	3.1 / 0.7 / 3.4 / 0.4
3 SU	0104 / 0618 / 1311 / 1838	3.5 / 0.4 / 3.8 / 0.3	18 M	0042 / 0605 / 1308 / 1834	3.2 / 0.6 / 3.5 / 0.3
4 M	0152 / 0705 / 1353 / 1923	3.5 / 0.5 / 3.9 / 0.3	19 TU	0121 / 0642 / 1343 / 1911	3.2 / 0.5 / 3.5 / 0.3
5 TU	0237 / 0751 / 1434 / 2008	3.5 / 0.6 / 3.9 / 0.4	20 W	0202 / 0722 / 1420 / 1952	3.2 / 0.5 / 3.6 / 0.4
6 W	0320 / 0837 / 1515 / 2052	3.4 / 0.7 / 3.9 / 0.5	21 TH	0243 / 0805 / 1459 / 2035	3.2 / 0.4 / 3.6 / 0.2
7 TH	0401 / 0923 / 1556 / 2139	3.4 / 0.8 / 3.8 / 0.6	22 F	0324 / 0851 / 1538 / 2123	3.3 / 0.5 / 3.6 / 0.2
8 F	0443 / 1011 / 1638 / 2229	3.3 / 0.9 / 3.6 / 0.8	23 SA	0405 / 0939 / 1620 / 2215	3.2 / 0.5 / 3.5 / 0.3
9 SA	0528 / 1105 / 1722 / 2327	3.1 / 1.1 / 3.4 / 1.0	24 SU	0449 / 1032 / 1707 / 2313	3.2 / 0.7 / 3.3 / 0.4
10 SU	0616 / 1208 / 1810	3.0 / 1.2 / 3.2	25 M	0538 / 1132 / 1801	3.1 / 0.8 / 3.2
11 M	0036 / 0709 / 1320 / 1904	1.1 / 2.9 / 1.2 / 3.1	26 TU	0017 / 0635 / 1239 / 1910	0.6 / 3.0 / 0.9 / 3.0
12 TU	0144 / 0818 / 1426 / 2008	1.1 / 2.9 / 1.2 / 3.0	27 W	0126 / 0748 / 1353 / 2052	0.6 / 2.9 / 0.9 / 3.0
13 W	0244 / 0943 / 1522 / 2129	1.0 / 3.0 / 1.0 / 2.9	28 TH	0236 / 0928 / 1507 / 2214	0.6 / 3.0 / 0.8 / 3.1
14 TH	0334 / 1041 / 1610 / 2236	0.9 / 3.1 / 0.8 / 3.0	29 F	0340 / 1035 / 1609 / 2315	0.6 / 3.2 / 0.6 / 3.2
15 F	0417 / 1125 / 1650 / 2323	0.8 / 3.3 / 0.7 / 3.1	30 SA	0434 / 1128 / 1659	0.5 / 3.4 / 0.4
			31 SU O	0008 / 0522 / 1215 / 1744	3.3 / 0.4 / 3.6 / 0.3

FEBRUARY

Day	Time	m	Day	Time	m
1 M	0058 / 0607 / 1259 / 1825	3.4 / 0.4 / 3.7 / 0.2	16 TU ●	0024 / 0545 / 1247 / 1815	3.1 / 0.4 / 3.4 / 0.1
2 TU	0143 / 0649 / 1340 / 1906	3.4 / 0.4 / 3.7 / 0.2	17 W	0105 / 0623 / 1325 / 1852	3.2 / 0.3 / 3.5 / 0.0
3 W	0224 / 0730 / 1419 / 1945	3.4 / 0.4 / 3.8 / 0.3	18 TH	0145 / 0702 / 1403 / 1931	3.2 / 0.3 / 3.6 / 0.0
4 TH	0300 / 0810 / 1456 / 2024	3.3 / 0.5 / 3.8 / 0.4	19 F	0224 / 0745 / 1442 / 2014	3.3 / 0.2 / 3.6 / 0.0
5 F	0335 / 0849 / 1532 / 2103	3.3 / 0.6 / 3.7 / 0.5	20 SA	0302 / 0829 / 1522 / 2100	3.3 / 0.2 / 3.6 / 0.0
6 SA	0410 / 0930 / 1609 / 2144	3.3 / 0.7 / 3.6 / 0.6	21 SU	0341 / 0915 / 1602 / 2149	3.3 / 0.3 / 3.5 / 0.4
7 SU	0447 / 1013 / 1647 / 2228	3.2 / 0.8 / 3.4 / 0.8	22 M	0422 / 1006 / 1646 / 2245	3.3 / 0.4 / 3.4 / 0.4
8 M	0528 / 1103 / 1729 / 2320	3.1 / 1.0 / 3.2 / 1.0	23 TU	0507 / 1104 / 1736 / 2350	3.2 / 0.6 / 3.2 / 0.6
9 TU	0614 / 1205 / 1817	2.9 / 1.1 / 3.0	24 W	0559 / 1213 / 1839	3.0 / 0.8 / 2.9
10 W	0026 / 0708 / 1330 / 1913	1.1 / 2.8 / 1.2 / 2.8	25 TH	0106 / 0706 / 1337 / 2041	0.8 / 2.9 / 0.9 / 2.8
11 TH	0151 / 0821 / 1447 / 2023	1.2 / 2.8 / 1.1 / 2.8	26 F	0226 / 0907 / 1500 / 2211	0.8 / 2.8 / 0.8 / 2.9
12 F	0300 / 0959 / 1542 / 2150	1.1 / 2.9 / 0.9 / 2.8	27 SA	0332 / 1022 / 1601 / 2310	0.7 / 3.1 / 0.5 / 3.1
13 SA	0351 / 1055 / 1626 / 2257	0.9 / 3.1 / 0.7 / 2.9	28 SU	0426 / 1115 / 1649	0.5 / 3.3 / 0.4
14 SU	0433 / 1136 / 1704 / 2343	0.7 / 3.2 / 0.5 / 3.0			
15 M	0510 / 1211 / 1740	0.6 / 3.3 / 0.3			

MARCH

Day	Time	m	Day	Time	m
1 M	0000 / 0511 / 1201 / 1730	3.2 / 0.4 / 3.5 / 0.2	16 TU	0444 / 1142 / 1713	0.5 / 3.2 / 0.1
2 TU O	0046 / 0552 / 1243 / 1808	3.3 / 0.3 / 3.5 / 0.2	17 W ●	0002 / 0521 / 1222 / 1749	3.1 / 0.3 / 3.4 / 0.0
3 W	0127 / 0630 / 1323 / 1844	3.3 / 0.3 / 3.6 / 0.2	18 TH	0044 / 0600 / 1303 / 1828	3.2 / 0.2 / 3.5 / −0.1
4 TH	0203 / 0706 / 1359 / 1919	3.3 / 0.3 / 3.6 / 0.2	19 F	0124 / 0640 / 1344 / 1909	3.3 / 0.1 / 3.6 / −0.2
5 F	0234 / 0740 / 1433 / 1953	3.3 / 0.4 / 3.6 / 0.3	20 SA	0202 / 0722 / 1425 / 1952	3.4 / 0.0 / 3.6 / −0.1
6 SA	0304 / 0815 / 1506 / 2028	3.3 / 0.4 / 3.6 / 0.3	21 SU	0240 / 0807 / 1505 / 2038	3.4 / 0.2 / 3.6 / 0.2
7 SU	0335 / 0852 / 1540 / 2105	3.2 / 0.5 / 3.5 / 0.5	22 M	0317 / 0853 / 1546 / 2127	3.5 / 0.1 / 3.6 / 0.2
8 M	0408 / 0931 / 1615 / 2144	3.2 / 0.6 / 3.4 / 0.7	23 TU	0357 / 0944 / 1630 / 2222	3.4 / 0.3 / 3.4 / 0.4
9 TU	0445 / 1014 / 1655 / 2228	3.1 / 0.8 / 3.2 / 0.9	24 W	0441 / 1043 / 1720 / 2329	3.2 / 0.5 / 3.1 / 0.7
10 W	0527 / 1107 / 1740 / 2322	2.9 / 1.0 / 3.0 / 1.0	25 TH	0534 / 1156 / 1826	3.0 / 0.7 / 2.8
11 TH	0619 / 1214 / 1836	2.7 / 1.1 / 2.8	26 F	0051 / 0640 / 1329 / 2041	0.9 / 2.9 / 0.8 / 2.7
12 F	0031 / 0725 / 1354 / 1943	1.2 / 2.6 / 1.1 / 2.7	27 SA	0212 / 0845 / 1447 / 2202	0.9 / 2.8 / 0.7 / 2.9
13 SA	0205 / 0851 / 1506 / 2107	1.1 / 2.7 / 0.9 / 2.7	28 SU	0318 / 1003 / 1545 / 2257	0.7 / 3.0 / 0.5 / 3.0
14 SU	0316 / 1013 / 1555 / 2227	1.0 / 2.9 / 0.6 / 2.8	29 M	0411 / 1056 / 1631 / 2344	0.6 / 3.2 / 0.3 / 3.2
15 M	0404 / 1102 / 1636 / 2319	0.7 / 3.1 / 0.4 / 3.0	30 TU	0455 / 1141 / 1711	0.4 / 3.4 / 0.2
			31 W O	0026 / 0533 / 1223 / 1747	3.2 / 0.3 / 3.4 / 0.2

APRIL

Day	Time	m	Day	Time	m
1 TH	0104 / 0608 / 1300 / 1819	3.2 / 0.3 / 3.4 / 0.3	16 F ●	0018 / 0536 / 1239 / 1803	3.2 / 0.1 / 3.5 / −0.2
2 F	0136 / 0640 / 1335 / 1851	3.2 / 0.3 / 3.4 / 0.3	17 SA	0100 / 0618 / 1324 / 1846	3.4 / 0.1 / 3.6 / −0.2
3 SA	0205 / 0711 / 1407 / 1923	3.2 / 0.3 / 3.4 / 0.4	18 SU	0140 / 0702 / 1408 / 1931	3.5 / −0.1 / 3.6 / −0.1
4 SU	0233 / 0744 / 1439 / 1956	3.2 / 0.3 / 3.4 / 0.4	19 M	0219 / 0747 / 1451 / 2019	3.5 / −0.1 / 3.6 / 0.0
5 M	0302 / 0819 / 1512 / 2032	3.3 / 0.3 / 3.3 / 0.5	20 TU	0258 / 0835 / 1534 / 2110	3.6 / 0.1 / 3.5 / 0.2
6 TU	0333 / 0857 / 1548 / 2111	3.2 / 0.4 / 3.2 / 0.6	21 W	0338 / 0928 / 1621 / 2206	3.5 / 0.2 / 3.3 / 0.5
7 W	0408 / 0939 / 1627 / 2154	3.1 / 0.6 / 3.1 / 0.7	22 TH	0423 / 1028 / 1716 / 2313	3.3 / 0.5 / 3.0 / 0.8
8 TH	0447 / 1029 / 1712 / 2245	2.9 / 0.8 / 2.9 / 0.9	23 F	0516 / 1145 / 1830	3.1 / 0.6 / 2.8
9 F	0537 / 1131 / 1807 / 2348	2.8 / 0.9 / 2.7 / 1.1	24 SA	0032 / 0623 / 1311 / 2025	0.9 / 2.9 / 0.7 / 2.7
10 SA	0642 / 1248 / 1914	2.6 / 0.9 / 2.6	25 SU	0147 / 0809 / 1422 / 2139	0.9 / 2.9 / 0.6 / 2.9
11 SU	0103 / 0800 / 1416 / 2032	1.1 / 2.6 / 0.8 / 2.7	26 M	0252 / 0935 / 1518 / 2233	0.8 / 3.0 / 0.5 / 3.0
12 M	0226 / 0923 / 1515 / 2151	1.0 / 2.8 / 0.5 / 2.8	27 TU	0346 / 1029 / 1606 / 2318	0.6 / 3.2 / 0.4 / 3.1
13 TU	0327 / 1022 / 1601 / 2249	0.7 / 3.0 / 0.2 / 3.0	28 W	0432 / 1115 / 1646 / 2358	0.4 / 3.2 / 0.3 / 3.1
14 W	0413 / 1110 / 1642 / 2335	0.5 / 3.2 / 0.0 / 3.1	29 TH	0511 / 1156 / 1722	0.3 / 3.3 / 0.3
15 TH	0456 / 1154 / 1722	0.2 / 3.4 / −0.1	30 F O	0034 / 0545 / 1234 / 1754	3.2 / 0.3 / 3.2 / 0.3

Chart Datum: 1·62 metres below Ordnance Datum (Newlyn)

SCOTLAND – GREENOCK

LAT 55°57′N   LONG   4°46′W

TIMES AND HEIGHTS OF HIGH AND LOW WATERS

YEAR 1999

TIME ZONE (UT)
For Summer Time add ONE hour in non-shaded areas

MAY

Day	Time	m	Day	Time	m
1 SA	0108	3.2	16 SU	0037	3.4
	0616	0.3		0559	-0.1
	1308	3.2		1304	3.5
	1824	0.4		1826	-0.1
2 SU	0137	3.2	17 M	0120	3.5
	0646	0.3		0644	-0.1
	1340	3.2		1352	3.5
	1855	0.4		1914	0.0
3 M	0205	3.2	18 TU	0201	3.6
	0717	0.3		0732	-0.1
	1412	3.2		1439	3.5
	1929	0.4		2004	0.1
4 TU	0233	3.3	19 W	0243	3.6
	0752	0.4		0821	0.1
	1446	3.2		1527	3.4
	2006	0.5		2057	0.3
5 W	0304	3.2	20 TH	0325	3.6
	0830	0.4		0915	0.2
	1524	3.1		1618	3.2
	2046	0.5		2153	0.5
6 TH	0338	3.2	21 F	0411	3.5
	0913	0.5		1015	0.4
	1604	3.0		1714	3.1
	2131	0.6		2255	0.7
7 F	0416	3.0	22 SA	0503	3.3
	1003	0.6		1125	0.6
	1651	2.9		1821	2.9
	2221	0.8			
8 SA	0503	2.8	23 SU	0003	0.9
	1103	0.7		0605	3.1
	1745	2.8		1241	0.6
	2320	0.9		1944	2.8
9 SU	0604	2.7	24 M	0112	0.9
	1212	0.7		0723	3.0
	1849	2.7		1348	0.6
				2100	2.8
10 M	0027	0.9	25 TU	0218	0.9
	0719	2.7		0851	3.0
	1325	0.6		1445	0.5
	1959	2.7		2157	2.9
11 TU	0139	0.9	26 W	0315	0.7
	0837	2.8		0954	3.0
	1430	0.4		1534	0.5
	2112	2.8		2244	3.0
12 W	0245	0.7	27 TH	0404	0.6
	0944	3.0		1043	3.1
	1523	0.2		1618	0.4
	2215	3.0		2326	3.1
13 TH	0341	0.5	28 F	0446	0.4
	1038	3.2		1126	3.1
	1611	0.0		1656	0.4
	2307	3.1			
14 F	0429	0.2	29 SA	0005	3.1
	1127	3.4		0523	0.4
	1656	-0.1		1205	3.1
	2353	3.3		1729	0.5
15 SA	0515	0.1	30 SU	0040	3.2
	1215	3.5		0555	0.3
	1741	-0.2 ●		1240	3.1
			O	1801	0.5
			31 M	0111	3.2
				0626	0.3
				1312	3.1
				1833	0.5

JUNE

Day	Time	m	Day	Time	m
1 TU	0140	3.2	16 W	0148	3.6
	0657	0.3		0719	0.0
	1346	3.1		1431	3.4
	1908	0.5		1951	0.2
2 W	0209	3.3	17 TH	0231	3.7
	0732	0.3		0808	0.1
	1423	3.1		1521	3.3
	1946	0.5		2042	0.4
3 TH	0241	3.3	18 F	0314	3.7
	0811	0.3		0859	0.2
	1503	3.0		1610	3.2
	2028	0.5		2134	0.5
4 F	0316	3.2	19 SA	0358	3.6
	0854	0.4		0954	0.4
	1546	3.0		1701	3.1
	2113	0.5		2228	0.7
5 SA	0355	3.1	20 SU	0446	3.4
	0943	0.4		1054	0.5
	1633	2.9		1754	3.0
	2203	0.6		2327	0.8
6 SU	0438	3.0	21 M	0539	3.2
	1040	0.5		1202	0.6
	1725	2.8		1851	2.9
	2257	0.7			
7 M	0533	2.9	22 TU	0637	3.1
	1143	0.5		1309	0.7
	1822	2.8		1954	2.8
	2358	0.7			
8 TU	0641	2.8	23 W	0137	0.9
	1248	0.4		0745	2.9
	1925	2.8		1408	0.7
				2105	2.8
9 W	0102	0.8	24 TH	0240	0.8
	0756	2.9		0902	2.9
	1351	0.3		1501	0.7
	2032	2.8		2204	2.9
10 TH	0208	0.7	25 F	0335	0.7
	0909	3.0		1006	2.9
	1450	0.2		1549	0.6
	2141	2.9		2253	3.0
11 F	0310	0.5	26 SA	0422	0.6
	1011	3.2		1055	3.0
	1543	0.1		1631	0.6
	2240	3.1		2336	3.1
12 SA	0406	0.3	27 SU	0502	0.5
	1105	3.3		1137	3.0
	1634	0.0		1708	0.6
	2331	3.3			
13 SU	0456	0.1	28 M	0014	3.2
	1157	3.4		0537	0.4
	1722	0.0 ●		1214	3.0
			O	1742	0.5
14 M	0018	3.4	29 TU	0049	3.2
	0543	0.0		0610	0.3
	1249	3.4		1248	3.0
	1811	0.0		1815	0.5
15 TU	0104	3.5	30 W	0118	3.2
	0631	0.0		0642	0.3
	1341	3.4		1324	3.0
	1900	0.1		1850	0.5

JULY

Day	Time	m	Day	Time	m
1 TH	0149	3.3	16 F	0218	3.7
	0716	0.3		0751	0.1
	1404	3.0		1509	3.3
	1929	0.5		2022	0.5
2 F	0222	3.3	17 SA	0300	3.7
	0754	0.3		0837	0.2
	1446	3.0		1552	3.2
	2011	0.4		2108	0.5
3 SA	0258	3.3	18 SU	0341	3.6
	0836	0.2		0924	0.2
	1528	3.0		1634	3.2
	2055	0.4		2155	0.6
4 SU	0337	3.2	19 M	0423	3.5
	0923	0.3		1014	0.5
	1613	3.0		1717	3.1
	2142	0.5		2246	0.7
5 M	0419	3.2	20 TU	0507	3.3
	1015	0.3		1112	0.7
	1700	2.9		1802	3.0
	2233	0.5		2342	0.9
6 TU	0507	3.1	21 W	0554	3.1
	1114	0.3		1218	0.8
	1751	2.9		1850	2.9
	2329	0.6			
7 W	0604	3.0	22 TH	0048	1.0
	1216	0.4		0646	2.9
	1846	2.9		1326	0.9
				1947	2.8
8 TH	0030	0.7	23 F	0200	1.0
	0714	2.9		0748	2.8
	1319	0.3		1427	0.9
	1950	2.8		2107	2.8
9 F	0136	0.7	24 SA	0304	0.9
	0836	2.9		0908	2.8
	1422	0.3		1520	0.8
	2107	2.9		2219	2.9
10 SA	0244	0.6	25 SU	0357	0.7
	0949	3.1		1023	2.8
	1522	0.3		1607	0.8
	2217	3.0		2309	3.0
11 SU	0348	0.4	26 M	0441	0.5
	1051	3.2		1113	2.9
	1617	0.2		1648	0.7
	2314	3.2		2351	3.1
12 M	0443	0.3	27 TU	0519	0.4
	1146	3.3		1153	2.9
	1709	0.2		1724	0.6
13 TU	0004	3.4	28 W	0026	3.2
	0532	0.1		0553	0.3
	1241	3.3		1230	3.0
	1758	0.2 ●	O	1757	0.5
14 W	0051	3.5	29 TH	0058	3.2
	0619	0.0		0625	0.3
	1333	3.0		1307	3.0
	1847	0.5		1832	0.5
15 TH	0136	3.6	30 F	0129	3.3
	0705	0.0		0659	0.2
	1423	3.3		1347	3.0
	1935	0.3		1909	0.4
			31 SA	0204	3.3
				0735	0.2
				1427	3.1
				1950	0.4

AUGUST

Day	Time	m	Day	Time	m
1 SU	0241	3.4	16 M	0318	3.6
	0815	0.1		0849	0.4
	1508	3.1		1600	3.3
	2033	0.3		2117	0.6
2 M	0319	3.4	17 TU	0354	3.6
	0859	0.2		0930	0.6
	1549	3.1		1637	3.2
	2118	0.4		2200	0.7
3 TU	0359	3.3	18 W	0432	3.4
	0948	0.2		1015	0.8
	1631	3.1		1716	3.1
	2207	0.4		2247	0.9
4 W	0442	3.2	19 TH	0513	3.2
	1044	0.3		1108	1.0
	1716	3.0		1759	3.0
	2301	0.6		2345	1.0
5 TH	0532	3.1	20 F	0600	3.0
	1146	0.5		1220	1.1
	1807	3.0		1849	2.8
6 F	0001	0.7	21 SA	0109	1.1
	0635	2.9		0656	2.8
	1253	0.5		1347	1.2
	1907	2.9		1952	2.8
7 SA	0110	0.8	22 SU	0231	1.1
	0806	2.9		0807	2.7
	1402	0.6		1451	1.1
	2034	2.9		2133	2.8
8 SU	0227	0.7	23 M	0329	0.9
	0940	2.9		0944	2.7
	1510	0.5		1542	1.0
	2201	3.0		2240	3.0
9 M	0339	0.6	24 TU	0416	0.7
	1047	3.1		1052	2.9
	1609	0.5		1624	0.8
	2301	3.2		2324	3.1
10 TU	0436	0.4	25 W	0455	0.5
	1143	3.3		1135	3.0
	1700	0.4		1701	0.7
	2352	3.4			
11 W	0524	0.2	26 TH	0000	3.2
	1235	3.3		0529	0.3
	1747	0.3 ●	O	1213	3.1
				1734	0.6
12 TH	0038	3.5	27 F	0034	3.3
	0607	0.1		0602	0.2
	1324	3.3		1249	3.1
	1831	0.3		1809	0.5
13 F	0122	3.6	28 SA	0108	3.4
	0648	0.1		0635	0.1
	1409	3.3		1327	3.2
	1914	0.4		1845	0.4
14 SA	0202	3.7	29 SU	0144	3.5
	0729	0.2		0711	0.1
	1449	3.3		1406	3.2
	1956	0.4		1925	0.3
15 SU	0241	3.7	30 M	0221	3.5
	0809	0.3		0750	0.1
	1525	3.3		1444	3.3
	2037	0.5		2007	0.3
			31 TU	0300	3.5
				0834	0.1
				1522	3.3
				2052	0.3

Chart Datum: 1·62 metres below Ordnance Datum (Newlyn)

SCOTLAND – GREENOCK

LAT 55°57′N   LONG   4°46′W

TIMES AND HEIGHTS OF HIGH AND LOW WATERS

YEAR **1999**

TIME ZONE (UT)
For Summer Time add ONE hour in non-shaded areas

SEPTEMBER

Day	Time	m		Day	Time	m
1 W	0339 / 0921 / 1601 / 2140	3.5 / 0.2 / 3.3 / 0.4		**16** TH	0400 / 0927 / 1633 / 2200	3.4 / 0.8 / 3.2 / 0.9
2 TH	0420 / 1015 / 1643 / 2234	3.3 / 0.4 / 3.2 / 0.6		**17** F	0438 / 1010 / 1714 / 2250	3.2 / 1.0 / 3.1 / 1.1
3 F	0507 / 1117 / 1733 / 2337	3.1 / 0.7 / 3.1 / 0.8		**18** SA	0523 / 1106 / 1803 / 2358	3.0 / 1.3 / 2.9 / 1.2
4 SA	0607 / 1232 / 1833	2.9 / 0.8 / 3.0		**19** SU	0619 / 1228 / 1904	2.8 / 1.4 / 2.8
5 SU	0052 / 0752 / 1352 / 2006	0.9 / 2.8 / 0.9 / 2.9		**20** M	0149 / 0729 / 1412 / 2024	1.2 / 2.7 / 1.3 / 2.8
6 M	0222 / 0943 / 1503 / 2150	0.8 / 2.9 / 0.8 / 3.1		**21** TU	0256 / 0858 / 1510 / 2159	1.0 / 2.7 / 1.2 / 3.0
7 TU	0334 / 1046 / 1601 / 2249	0.6 / 3.1 / 0.7 / 3.3		**22** W	0344 / 1024 / 1554 / 2249	0.7 / 2.9 / 1.0 / 3.2
8 W	0427 / 1137 / 1649 / 2338	0.4 / 3.3 / 0.5 / 3.5		**23** TH	0424 / 1110 / 1632 / 2328	0.5 / 3.1 / 0.8 / 3.3
9 TH ●	0511 / 1224 / 1732	0.3 / 3.3 / 0.4		**24** F	0500 / 1149 / 1707	0.3 / 3.2 / 0.6
10 F	0022 / 0550 / 1308 / 1812	3.6 / 0.2 / 3.4 / 0.4		**25** SA ○	0004 / 0534 / 1226 / 1742	3.4 / 0.2 / 3.3 / 0.4
11 SA	0104 / 0626 / 1347 / 1850	3.6 / 0.2 / 3.4 / 0.4		**26** SU	0042 / 0608 / 1304 / 1819	3.5 / 0.1 / 3.4 / 0.3
12 SU	0142 / 0702 / 1421 / 1926	3.7 / 0.3 / 3.4 / 0.5		**27** M	0122 / 0645 / 1341 / 1859	3.6 / 0.0 / 3.4 / 0.3
13 M	0217 / 0737 / 1452 / 2002	3.7 / 0.4 / 3.4 / 0.5		**28** TU	0201 / 0726 / 1418 / 1942	3.6 / 0.1 / 3.5 / 0.3
14 TU	0251 / 0812 / 1524 / 2038	3.6 / 0.5 / 3.4 / 0.6		**29** W	0241 / 0810 / 1456 / 2028	3.7 / 0.2 / 3.5 / 0.3
15 W	0325 / 0848 / 1557 / 2117	3.5 / 0.7 / 3.3 / 0.7		**30** TH	0320 / 0857 / 1535 / 2117	3.6 / 0.4 / 3.5 / 0.5

OCTOBER

Day	Time	m		Day	Time	m
1 F	0402 / 0951 / 1617 / 2212	3.4 / 0.6 / 3.4 / 0.7		**16** SA	0409 / 0933 / 1635 / 2212	3.3 / 1.1 / 3.2 / 1.0
2 SA	0450 / 1056 / 1706 / 2319	3.2 / 0.9 / 3.3 / 0.9		**17** SU	0454 / 1024 / 1723 / 2312	3.1 / 1.3 / 3.1 / 1.2
3 SU	0553 / 1218 / 1808	2.9 / 1.1 / 3.1		**18** M	0549 / 1131 / 1823	2.9 / 1.4 / 2.9
4 M	0045 / 0804 / 1342 / 1948	1.0 / 2.8 / 1.1 / 3.0		**19** TU	0036 / 0658 / 1300 / 1935	1.2 / 2.8 / 1.5 / 2.9
5 TU	0215 / 0939 / 1451 / 2133	0.9 / 3.0 / 1.0 / 3.2		**20** W	0207 / 0819 / 1421 / 2059	1.1 / 2.8 / 1.3 / 3.0
6 W	0320 / 1035 / 1546 / 2231	0.7 / 3.2 / 0.8 / 3.4		**21** TH	0303 / 0941 / 1514 / 2204	0.8 / 3.0 / 1.1 / 3.2
7 TH	0410 / 1123 / 1633 / 2318	0.5 / 3.4 / 0.6 / 3.5		**22** F	0347 / 1036 / 1558 / 2251	0.5 / 3.2 / 0.8 / 3.3
8 F	0452 / 1205 / 1713	0.4 / 3.4 / 0.5		**23** SA	0426 / 1119 / 1637 / 2334	0.3 / 3.3 / 0.6 / 3.5
9 SA ●	0001 / 0528 / 1245 / 1750	3.6 / 0.3 / 3.4 / 0.5		**24** SU ○	0503 / 1159 / 1716	0.2 / 3.4 / 0.4
10 SU	0041 / 0602 / 1319 / 1824	3.6 / 0.4 / 3.4 / 0.5		**25** M	0016 / 0541 / 1238 / 1755	3.6 / 0.1 / 3.5 / 0.3
11 M	0117 / 0634 / 1350 / 1857	3.6 / 0.5 / 3.4 / 0.5		**26** TU	0059 / 0621 / 1317 / 1837	3.7 / 0.1 / 3.6 / 0.3
12 TU	0151 / 0704 / 1420 / 1930	3.6 / 0.5 / 3.5 / 0.6		**27** W	0142 / 0704 / 1356 / 1921	3.7 / 0.1 / 3.7 / 0.3
13 W	0223 / 0739 / 1450 / 2004	3.6 / 0.6 / 3.5 / 0.6		**28** TH	0225 / 0750 / 1435 / 2009	3.7 / 0.3 / 3.8 / 0.3
14 TH	0256 / 0814 / 1521 / 2042	3.5 / 0.7 / 3.5 / 0.7		**29** F	0307 / 0840 / 1515 / 2100	3.6 / 0.5 / 3.7 / 0.5
15 F	0331 / 0851 / 1556 / 2123	3.4 / 0.9 / 3.4 / 0.8		**30** SA	0352 / 0935 / 1559 / 2157	3.5 / 0.8 / 3.6 / 0.7
				31 SU	0445 / 1041 / 1649 / 2307	3.2 / 1.0 / 3.4 / 0.9

NOVEMBER

Day	Time	m		Day	Time	m
1 M	0556 / 1201 / 1752	3.0 / 1.2 / 3.2		**16** TU	0524 / 1057 / 1743 / 2348	3.0 / 1.3 / 3.0 / 1.1
2 TU	0033 / 0754 / 1319 / 1923	1.0 / 2.9 / 1.2 / 3.1		**17** W	0628 / 1208 / 1851	2.9 / 1.4 / 3.0
3 W	0152 / 0917 / 1426 / 2103	0.9 / 3.1 / 1.1 / 3.2		**18** TH	0103 / 0739 / 1321 / 2005	1.0 / 2.9 / 1.3 / 3.0
4 TH	0254 / 1012 / 1522 / 2204	0.7 / 3.3 / 0.9 / 3.4		**19** F	0210 / 0852 / 1426 / 2117	0.8 / 3.0 / 1.1 / 3.2
5 F	0344 / 1058 / 1610 / 2253	0.6 / 3.4 / 0.7 / 3.5		**20** SA	0303 / 0956 / 1520 / 2215	0.6 / 3.2 / 0.9 / 3.3
6 SA	0427 / 1139 / 1651 / 2336	0.5 / 3.5 / 0.6 / 3.5		**21** SU	0350 / 1047 / 1607 / 2305	0.5 / 3.3 / 0.7 / 3.5
7 SU	0504 / 1216 / 1728	0.5 / 3.5 / 0.6		**22** M	0434 / 1132 / 1652 / 2352	0.2 / 3.5 / 0.5 / 3.6
8 M ●	0015 / 0537 / 1250 / 1801	3.5 / 0.6 / 3.5 / 0.6		**23** TU ○	0517 / 1214 / 1735	0.2 / 3.6 / 0.3
9 TU	0052 / 0609 / 1322 / 1833	3.5 / 0.6 / 3.5 / 0.6		**24** W	0039 / 0600 / 1257 / 1819	3.7 / 0.2 / 3.8 / 0.3
10 W	0125 / 0639 / 1351 / 1904	3.5 / 0.7 / 3.6 / 0.6		**25** TH	0126 / 0646 / 1338 / 1906	3.7 / 0.3 / 3.8 / 0.3
11 TH	0157 / 0712 / 1421 / 1938	3.4 / 0.7 / 3.6 / 0.6		**26** F	0213 / 0735 / 1420 / 1955	3.6 / 0.4 / 3.9 / 0.3
12 F	0231 / 0747 / 1452 / 2015	3.4 / 0.8 / 3.6 / 0.7		**27** SA	0300 / 0827 / 1503 / 2047	3.6 / 0.6 / 3.9 / 0.4
13 SA	0307 / 0826 / 1526 / 2057	3.4 / 0.9 / 3.5 / 0.8		**28** SU	0349 / 0923 / 1548 / 2144	3.5 / 0.8 / 3.8 / 0.6
14 SU	0346 / 0909 / 1604 / 2144	3.3 / 1.0 / 3.4 / 0.9		**29** M	0444 / 1024 / 1638 / 2250	3.3 / 1.0 / 3.6 / 0.8
15 M	0431 / 0958 / 1648 / 2240	3.1 / 1.2 / 3.2 / 1.0		**30** TU	0551 / 1134 / 1737	3.1 / 1.2 / 3.4

DECEMBER

Day	Time	m		Day	Time	m
1 W	0005 / 0714 / 1245 / 1847	0.9 / 3.0 / 1.2 / 3.3		**16** TH	0554 / 1130 / 1807	3.0 / 1.1 / 3.1
2 TH	0118 / 0836 / 1352 / 2014	0.8 / 3.1 / 1.2 / 3.2		**17** F	0016 / 0654 / 1235 / 1914	0.8 / 2.9 / 1.1 / 3.1
3 F	0220 / 0937 / 1452 / 2128	0.8 / 3.2 / 1.0 / 3.3		**18** SA	0120 / 0802 / 1341 / 2030	0.7 / 3.0 / 1.1 / 3.1
4 SA	0313 / 1026 / 1543 / 2223	0.8 / 3.3 / 0.9 / 3.4		**19** SU	0221 / 0912 / 1443 / 2140	0.6 / 3.1 / 0.9 / 3.2
5 SU	0359 / 1109 / 1628 / 2309	0.7 / 3.4 / 0.7 / 3.4		**20** M	0317 / 1015 / 1540 / 2239	0.4 / 3.3 / 0.7 / 3.4
6 M	0440 / 1148 / 1708 / 2351	0.7 / 3.5 / 0.6 / 3.4		**21** TU	0408 / 1107 / 1631 / 2333	0.3 / 3.4 / 0.5 / 3.5
7 TU ●	0516 / 1224 / 1743	0.7 / 3.5 / 0.6		**22** W ○	0457 / 1155 / 1719	0.3 / 3.5 / 0.3
8 W	0028 / 0544 / 1258 / 1815	3.3 / 0.8 / 3.6 / 0.6		**23** TH	0024 / 0544 / 1241 / 1806	3.6 / 0.3 / 3.7 / 0.2
9 TH	0102 / 0620 / 1329 / 1846	3.3 / 0.8 / 3.6 / 0.6		**24** F	0116 / 0633 / 1325 / 1854	3.6 / 0.3 / 3.9 / 0.2
10 F	0135 / 0652 / 1358 / 1920	3.3 / 0.8 / 3.6 / 0.6		**25** SA	0206 / 0723 / 1409 / 1943	3.6 / 0.4 / 3.9 / 0.2
11 SA	0210 / 0728 / 1430 / 1956	3.3 / 0.8 / 3.6 / 0.6		**26** SU	0255 / 0814 / 1453 / 2034	3.5 / 0.6 / 3.9 / 0.3
12 SU	0247 / 0808 / 1504 / 2036	3.3 / 0.8 / 3.5 / 0.7		**27** M	0344 / 0906 / 1537 / 2126	3.5 / 0.7 / 3.9 / 0.5
13 M	0327 / 0850 / 1541 / 2122	3.2 / 0.9 / 3.4 / 0.7		**28** TU	0434 / 1000 / 1624 / 2222	3.4 / 0.8 / 3.8 / 0.6
14 TU	0411 / 0937 / 1622 / 2213	3.1 / 1.0 / 3.3 / 0.8		**29** W	0526 / 1059 / 1714 / 2326	3.2 / 1.0 / 3.6 / 0.8
15 W	0459 / 1030 / 1710 / 2312	3.0 / 1.1 / 3.2 / 0.8		**30** TH	0622 / 1204 / 1809	3.1 / 1.1 / 3.4
				31 F	0035 / 0725 / 1312 / 1910	0.9 / 3.0 / 1.1 / 3.2

Chart Datum: 1·62 metres below Ordnance Datum (Newlyn)

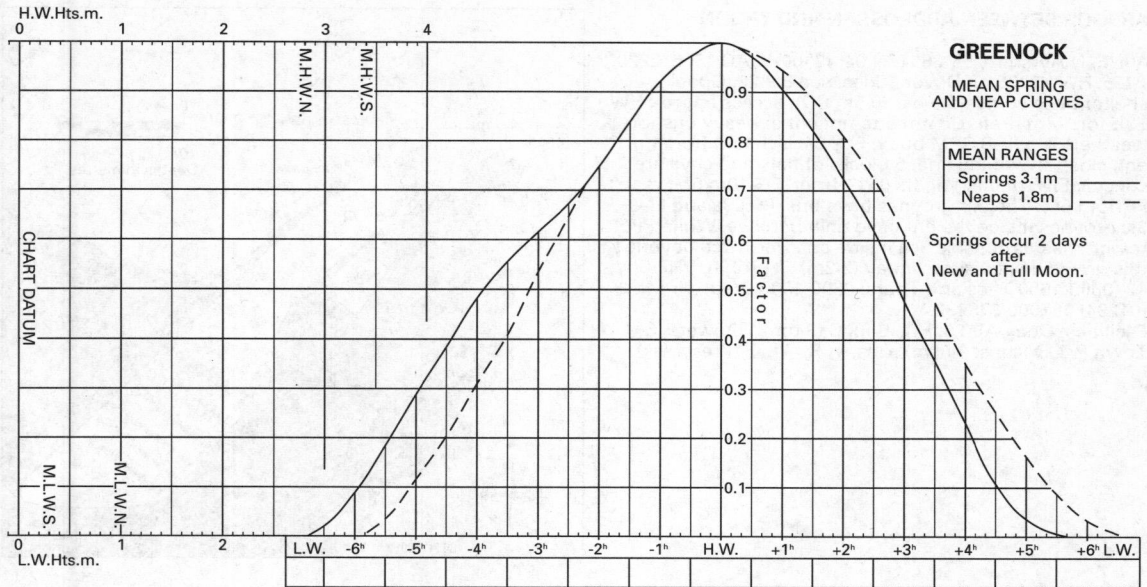

H.W.Hts.m.

GREENOCK

MEAN SPRING
AND NEAP CURVES

MEAN RANGES	
Springs 3.1m	——
Neaps 1.8m	- - -

Springs occur 2 days
after
New and Full Moon.

ARDROSSAN   8-9-21

N Ayrshire 55°38'·50N 04°49'·54W   Rtg 2-2-2

CHARTS
AC 1866, 2491, 2221, *2126*; Imray C63; OS 63/70
TIDES
+0055 Dover; ML 1·9; Duration 0630; Zone 0 (UT)

Standard Port GREENOCK (←)

Times				Height (metres)			
High Water		Low Water		MHWS	MHWN	MLWN	MLWS
0000	0600	0000	0600	3·4	2·8	1·0	0·3
1200	1800	1200	1800				
Differences ARDROSSAN							
–0020	–0010	–0010	–0010	–0·2	–0·2	+0·1	+0·1
IRVINE							
–0020	–0020	–0030	–0010	–0·3	–0·3	–0·1	0·0

SHELTER
Good in marina (formerly Eglinton Dock), access at all
tides over sill, 5·2m least depth. A storm gate is fitted;
max acceptable beam is 8·6m (28ft). Strong SW/NW winds
cause heavy seas in the apprs and the hbr may be closed
in SW gales. Ferries berth on both sides of Winton Pier.
NAVIGATION
WPT 55°38'·13N 04°50'·48W, 235°/055° from/to hbr ent,
0·65M. From the W/NW keep clear of low-lying Horse Isle
(conspic W tower on its S end) ringed by drying ledges.
The passage between Horse Isle and the mainland is
obstructed by drying rks and should not be attempted.
Be aware of following dangers: From the S/SE, Eagle Rk
3ca S of hbr ent, marked by SHM buoy, Fl G 5s. 3ca SE of
Eagle Rk lies unmarked Campbell Rk (0·2m). W Crinan Rk
(1·1m) is 300m W of hbr ent, marked by PHM buoy, Fl R 4s.
LIGHTS AND MARKS
Dir It WRG 15m W14M, R/G11M (see 8.9.4); W sector
leads 055° to hbr ent between It ho and detached bkwtr.
Lt ho Iso WG 4s 11m 9M, G317°-035°, W elsewhere. On S
end of detached bkwtr, Fl WR 2s 7m 5M, R041°-126°, W
elsewhere.
Tfc signals, shown from control twr at ent to marina:
3 F®️ lts (vert) = hbr and marina closed; no entry/exit for
commercial and pleasure vessels.
3 F©️ lts (vert) = marina open, hbr closed; pleasure craft
may enter/exit the marina, no commercial movements.
2 F®️ lts over 1 F©️ = hbr open, marina closed; in severe
weather marina storm gate is closed. Commercial
vessels may enter/exit hbr, subject to approval by Hbr
Control on VHF. Pleasure craft must clear the approach
channel, ferry turning area (between the detached bkwtr
and Winton Pier) and the outer basin.

RADIO TELEPHONE
Marina VHF Ch **80** M. Ardrossan Hr Mr Ch 12 14 16 (H24).
TELEPHONE (Dial code 01294)
Marina 607077, ☎ 607076; Hr Mr 63972; MRCC (01475)
729988; ⌗ (0141) 887 9369 (H24); Marinecall 0891 500462;
Police 468236; Dr 463838; Ⓗ (01563) 521133.
FACILITIES
Clyde Marina (250+50 visitors) ☎ 607077, ☎ 607076,
£12.88, access all tides. D, AC, FW, ME, El, Ⓔ, CH, BH (20
ton). **Town** EC Wed; V, R, Bar, ☺, Gas, Gaz, ✉, Ⓑ, ⇌, ✈
(Prestwick/Glasgow). Ferries to Brodick (Arran) and
Douglas (IOM).

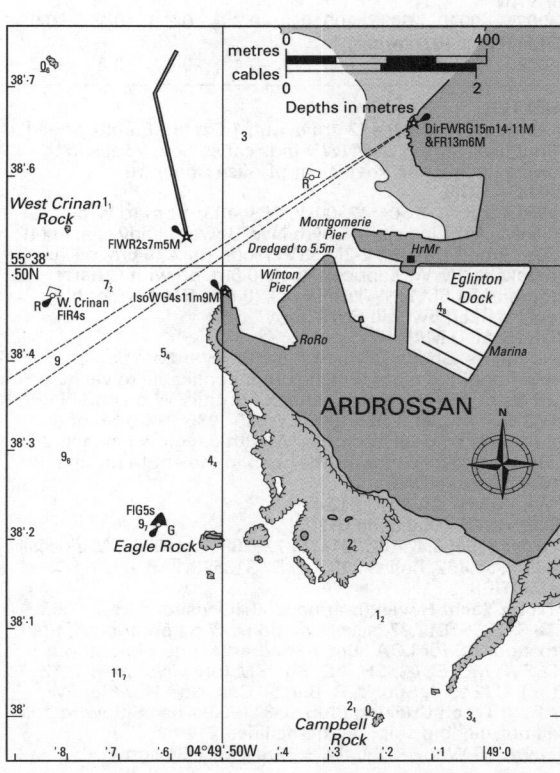

9

HARBOUR BETWEEN ARDROSSAN AND TROON

IRVINE, N Ayrshire, 55°36'·17N 04°42'·00W. AC 1866, 2220, *2126*. HW +0055 on Dover. Tides: see 8.9.21. Good shelter once across the bar (0·5m CD); access approx HW ±3½ for 1·4m draft. Do not attempt ent in heavy onshore weather. The IB-B SPM buoy, Fl Y 3s, is 1·15M from hbr ent, close NW of ldg line. 5 blocks of flats and chys are conspic ENE of ent. Ldg lts 051°: front, FG 10m 5M; rear, FR 15m 5M. The ent groynes have bns, Fl R 3s and Fl G 3s; groynes inside the ent have unlit perches. White Pilot tr with mast is conspic 3ca inside ent. Berth 2ca beyond this on S side at visitors' quay (2·2m). ⚓ prohib. VHF Ch 12 (0800-1600 Tues and Thurs; 0800-1300 Wed). Hr Mr ☎ (01294) 487000/278132.
Facilities: **Quay** AB £5, FW, Slip, C (3 ton), Showers, SM.
Town P & D (cans, 1·5km), Gas, V, R, ⇌, ✈ (Prestwick).

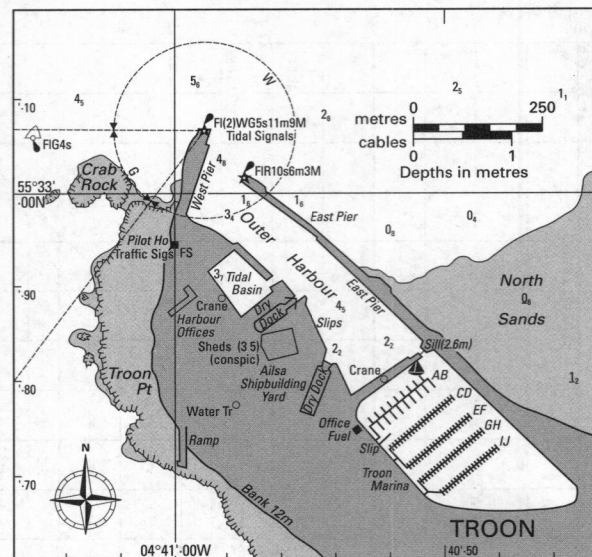

TROON   8-9-22

S Ayrshire 55°33'·10N 04°40'·90W   Rtg 2-1-2

CHARTS
AC 1866, 2220, *2126*; Imray C63; OS 70
TIDES
+0050 Dover; ML 1·9; Duration 0630; Zone 0 (UT)

Standard Port GREENOCK (←)

Times				Height (metres)			
High Water		Low Water		MHWS	MHWN	MLWN	MLWS
0000	0600	0000	0600	3·4	2·8	1·0	0·3
1200	1800	1200	1800				
Differences TROON							
−0025	−0025	−0020	−0020	−0·2	−0·2	0·0	0·0
AYR							
−0025	−0025	−0030	−0015	−0·4	−0·3	+0·1	+0·1
GIRVAN							
−0025	−0040	−0035	−0010	−0·3	−0·3	−0·1	0·0
LOCH RYAN (Stranraer)							
−0020	−0020	−0017	−0017	−0·4	−0·4	−0·4	−0·2

SHELTER
Complete in marina (2·4m at ent, 1·6m at SE end); speed limit 5kn. Strong SW/NW winds cause heavy seas in the apprs. Inside hbr, keep clear of Ailsa Shipyard.
NAVIGATION
WPT 55°33'·20N 04°42'·00W, 283°/103° from/to W pier lt, 0·61M. Appr in sector SW to NW. Beware Lady Isle, Fl (4) 30s 19m 8M, W bn, 2·2M SW; Troon Rock (5·6m, occas breaks) 1·1M W; Lappock Rock (0·6m, bn with G barrel topmark) 1·6M NNW; Mill Rock (0·4m) ½M NNE of hbr ent, marked by unlit PHM buoy.
LIGHTS AND MARKS
No ldg lts. Sheds (35m) at Ailsa Shipyard are conspic and floodlit at night. Ent sigs (not applicable to yachts): 2B ●s or 2F®⃝ lts (vert) = ent/exit prohib. W pier hd Fl (2) WG 5s 11m 9M, G036°-090°, W090°-036°. 14m SE of this lt there is a floodlit dolphin, W with dayglow patches. A SHM lt buoy, FG, marks the chan in the ent to marina.
RADIO TELEPHONE
Marina VHF Ch 80 M (H24).
TELEPHONE (Dial code 01292)
Hr Mr 315553; MRCC (01475) 729988; ⌗ 478548; Marinecall 0891 500 462; Police 313100; Dr 313593; Ⓗ 610553.
FACILITIES
Troon Yacht Haven (marina: 250+50 visitors) ☎ 315553, ⇌ 312836, £12.97, access all tides. Ⓥ on pontoon A, first to stbd. AB for LOA 36m x 3m draft at end of pontoons. D, FW, ME, El, Ⓔ, CH, AC, Sh , SM (dly pick-up), BH (12 ton), C (2 ton), Slip, V, R, Bar, ▣, Gas, Gaz; **Hbr Pier** FW, AB, V; **Troon Cruising Club** ☎ 311908; **Ailsa Shipyard** has all normal 'big ship' repair facilities.
Town EC Wed; ✉, Ⓑ, ⇌, ✈ (Prestwick/Glasgow).

HARBOURS ON THE FIRTH OF CLYDE SOUTH OF TROON

AYR, S Ayrshire, 55°28'·22N 04°38'·71W. AC 1866, 2220, *2126*. HW +0050 on Dover; ML 1·8m. Duration 0630. See 8.9.22. Good shelter in the dock on S side of ent chan, which is open to W'lies. After heavy rains large amounts of debris may be washed down the R Ayr. From the W, hbr ent lies between conspic gasholder to the N and townhall spire to the S. Outer St Nicholas SHM buoy, Fl G 2s, warns of shoals and eponymous Rock (0·8m) 150m S of ent. Ldg lts 098°: front, by Pilot Stn, FR 10m 5M R tr, also tfc sigs; rear (130m from front), Oc R 10s 18m 9M. N bkwtr hd, QR 9m 5M. S pier hd, Q 7m 7M, vis 012°-161°, and FG 5m 5M, same structure, vis 012°-082°, over St Nicholas Rk. Tfc sigs (near front ldg lt): 2 B ●s (vert) or 2FR (vert) = hbr closed; 1 B ● (1 Ⓡ or 1 Ⓖ) = proceed with care. Hr Mr ☎ (01292) 281687; VHF Ch 14 16; ⌗ 478548; **Ayr Y & CC** at S dock, M. **Services:** Sh, ME, El, CH. **Town** EC Wed; Ⓑ, Bar, Gas, P & D, FW, ✉, R, ⇌, V.

GIRVAN, S Ayrshire, 55°14'·77N 04°51'·80W. AC 1866, 2199. HW +0043 on Dover; ML 1·8m; Duration 0630. See 8.9.22. Good shelter at inner hbr for 16 yachts on 60m pontoon (1·7m) beyond LB. Coasters and FVs berth on adjacent quay. No access LW±2 over bar 1·5m. Beware Girvan Patch, 1·7m, 4ca SW of ent, and Brest Rks, 3·5M N of hbr extending 6ca offshore. Ch spire (conspic) brg 104° leads between N bkwtr, Fl (2) R 6s 7m 4M, and S pier, 2 FG (vert) 8m 4M. Inner N groyne, Iso 4s 3m 4M. Tfc sigs at root of S pier: 2 B discs (hor), at night 2 Ⓡ (hor) = hbr shut. VHF Ch 12 16 (HO). Hr Mr ☎ (01465) 713048; FW, Slip. **Town** EC Wed; Ⓑ, ✉, V, R, ⇌, P & D (cans).

ANCHORAGES WITHIN LOCH RYAN

LOCH RYAN, Dumfries and Galloway, 55°01'·00N 05°05'·00W. AC 1403, 2198. HW (Stranraer) +0055 on Dover; ML 1·6m; Duration 0640. See 8.9.22. Very good shelter except in strong NW winds. Ent between Milleur Pt and Finnarts Pt. ⚓s in Lady Bay, 1·3M SSE of Milleur Pt, but exposed to heavy wash from fast catamaran ferries; in The Wig in 3m (avoid weed patches); or off Stranraer 3ca NW of W pier hd. Larger yachts berth on NE side of E pier, by arrangement with Hr Mr, VHF Ch 14 (H24) or ☎ (01776) 702460. Beware The Beef Barrel, rk 1m high 6ca SSE of Milleur Pt; the sand spit running 1·5M to SE from W shore opposite Cairn Pt lt ho Fl (2) R 10s 14m 12M. Lt at Cairnryan ferry terminal Fl R 5s 5m 5M. Lts at Stranraer: centre pier hd 2FBu (vert), E pier hd 2FR (vert), W pier hd 2 FG (vert) 8m 4M. Facilities (Stranraer): EC Wed; Ⓑ, Bar, D, FW, P, ✉, R, ⇌, V.

PORTPATRICK   8-9-23

Dumfries and Galloway 54°50'·42N 05°07'·11W   Rtg 3-4-2

CHARTS
AC 2198, *2724*; Imray C62; OS 82
TIDES
+0032 Dover; ML 2·1; Duration 0615; Zone 0 (UT)

Standard Port LIVERPOOL (→)

Times				Heights (metres)			
High Water		Low Water		MHWS	MHWN	MLWN	MLWS
0000	0600	0200	0800	9·3	7·4	2·9	0·9
1200	1800	1400	2000				
Differences PORTPATRICK							
+0018	+0026	0000	−0035	−5·5	−4·4	−2·0	−0·6

SHELTER
Good in tiny Inner hbr, but ent is difficult in strong SW/NW winds. Beware cross tides off ent, up to 3kn springs.
NAVIGATION
WPT 54°50'·00N 05°08'·00W, 235°/055° from/to ent, 0·70M. Ent to outer hbr by short narrow chan with hazards either side, including rky shelf covered at HW. Barrel buoy (not unlike a mooring buoy) marks end of Half Tide Rk; do not cut inside.
LIGHTS AND MARKS
Killantringan lt ho, Fl (2) 15s 49m 25M, is 1.6M NW of ent. Ldg lts 050°, FG (H24) 6/8m: Front on sea wall; rear on bldg; 2 vert orange stripes by day. Conspic features include: TV mast 1M NE, almost on ldg line; large hotel on cliffs about 1½ca NNW of hbr ent; Dunskey Castle (ru) 4ca SE of hbr.
RADIO TELEPHONE
None. Portpatrick Coast Radio Stn VHF Ch 27 16.
TELEPHONE (Dial code 01776)
Hr Mr 810355; MRSC (01475) 729988; ⌗ (0141) 887 9369 (H24); Marinecall 0891 500462; Police 810222; Ⓗ 702323.
FACILITIES
Hbr Slip (small craft), AB £6, M, FW, L. Note: Pontoons are planned in inner hbr, to be dredged approx 2·5m.
Village EC Thurs; P (cans), D (bulk tanker), Gas, V, R, Bar, ✉, Ⓑ (Stranraer), ⇌ (bus to Stranraer), ✈ (Carlisle).

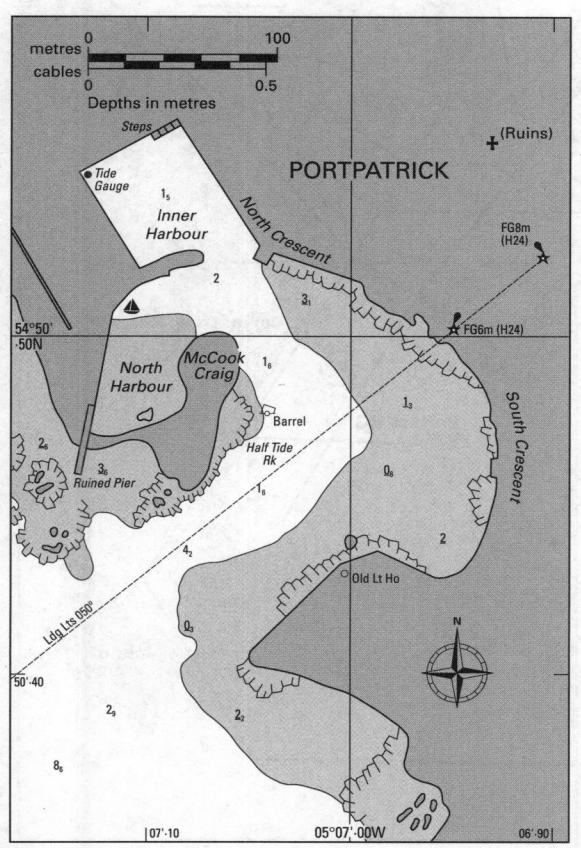

AGENTS WANTED

If you are interested in becoming our agent for any of the following ports, please write to: The Editor, Edington House, Trent, Sherborne, Dorset DT9 4SR, England – and get your free copy of the Almanac annually. You do not have to live in a port to be the agent, but should at least be a fairly regular visitor.

Plymouth	Port Haliguen
Walton-on-the-Naze	La Trinité-sur-Mer
Hopeman	Piriac
Burghead	St Nazaire/Loire
Findhorn	Pornic
Nairn	St Gilles-Croix-de-Vie
Inverness	Les Sables d'Olonne
Loch Aline	River Seudre
Craobh	Port Bloc/Gironde
Workington	Anglet/Bayonne
Lough Swilly	St Jean-de-Luz
Portbail	Hendaye
St Malo/Dinard	Grandcamp-Maisy
Le Légué/St Brieuc	Port-en-Bessin
Lampaul	Ouistreham/Caen
L'Aberildut	Dives
Douarnenez	St Valéry-en-Caux
Lorient	Dunkerque
River Étel	Emden
Le Palais (Belle Ile)	Langeoog

SUBFACT AREAS (see 8.9.24 overleaf). The numbered areas, as shown on the chartlet overleaf, are referred to in broadcasts by their names; these are listed below. For areas 1-26, North of Mull, see 8.8.23.

22	Barra	52	Boyle
23	Hebrides Central	53	Orsay
24	Hawes	54	Islay
25	Eigg	55	Otter
26	Hebrides South	56	Gigha
27	Ford	57	Earadale
28	Tiree	58	Lochranza
29	Staffa	59	Davaar
30	Mackenzie	60	Brodick
31	Mull	61	Irvine
32	Linnhe	62	Lamlash
33	Jura Sound	63	Ayr
34	Fyne	64	Skerries
35	Minard	65	Rathlin
36	Tarbert	66	Kintyre
37	Skipness	67	Sanda
38	West Kyle	68	Stafnish
39	Striven	69	Pladda
40	East Kyle	70	Turnberry
41	Goil	71	Torr
42	Long	72	Mermaid
43	Cove	73	Ailsa
44	Gareloch	74	Maiden
45	Rosneath	75	Corsewall
46	Cumbrae	76	Ballantrae
47	Garroch	77	Magee
48	Laggan	78	Londonderry
49	Blackstone	79	Beaufort
50	Place	80	Ardglass
51	Colonsay	81	Peel

9

SUBMARINE EXERCISE AREAS (SUBFACTS)

Those areas in which submarine activity is planned for the next 16 hrs are broadcast by Coast Radio Stations at the times and on the VHF channels shown below. The areas are referred to not by numbers, but by names as listed on the previous page; see also 8.8.23 for areas to the N of Mull.

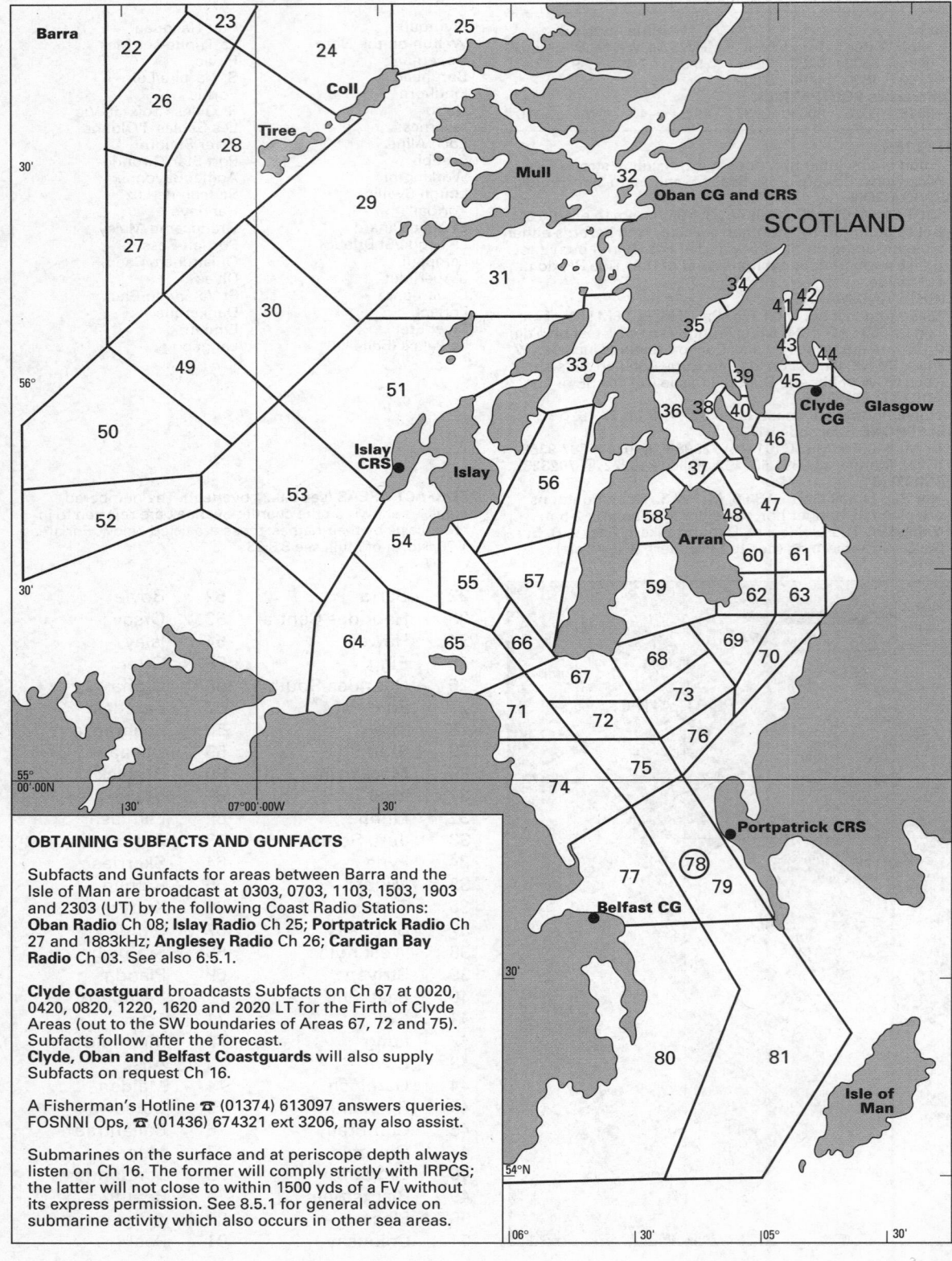

OBTAINING SUBFACTS AND GUNFACTS

Subfacts and Gunfacts for areas between Barra and the Isle of Man are broadcast at 0303, 0703, 1103, 1503, 1903 and 2303 (UT) by the following Coast Radio Stations: **Oban Radio** Ch 08; **Islay Radio** Ch 25; **Portpatrick Radio** Ch 27 and 1883kHz; **Anglesey Radio** Ch 26; **Cardigan Bay Radio** Ch 03. See also 6.5.1.

Clyde Coastguard broadcasts Subfacts on Ch 67 at 0020, 0420, 0820, 1220, 1620 and 2020 LT for the Firth of Clyde Areas (out to the SW boundaries of Areas 67, 72 and 75). Subfacts follow after the forecast.
Clyde, Oban and Belfast Coastguards will also supply Subfacts on request Ch 16.

A Fisherman's Hotline ☎ (01374) 613097 answers queries. FOSNNI Ops, ☎ (01436) 674321 ext 3206, may also assist.

Submarines on the surface and at periscope depth always listen on Ch 16. The former will comply strictly with IRPCS; the latter will not close to within 1500 yds of a FV without its express permission. See 8.5.1 for general advice on submarine activity which also occurs in other sea areas.

VOLVO PENTA SERVICE

Sales and service centres in area 10
CUMBRIA *Shepherds (Windermere) Ltd*, Bowness Bay, Windermere LA23 3HE
Tel (015394) 44031 **MERSEYSIDE** *James Troop & Co Ltd*, Pleasant Hill Street,
Liverpool L8 5SZ Tel 0151-709 0581 **GWYNEDD** *Abersoch Land & Sea*,
Abersoch, Pwllheli, Gwynedd LL53 7AH (01758) 713434 *Arfon Oceaneering*,
Victoria Dock Slipway, Balaclava Road, Caernarfon LL55 1TG Tel (01286)
676055 *Llyn Marine Services*, Pwllheli Marine Centre, Glandon, Pwllheli,
Gwynedd LL53 5YT Tel (01758) 612606

VOLVO PENTA

Area 10

North-West England, Isle of Man and North Wales
Mull of Galloway to Bardsey Island

10

8.10.1	Index	**Page 479**
8.10.2	Diagram of ports, lights, RDF bns, Coast radio and weather stns	480
8.10.3	Tidal stream charts	482
8.10.4	List of coastal lights, fog signals and waypoints	484
8.10.5	Passage information	487
8.10.6	Distance table	488
8.10.7	Kirkcudbright Isle of Whithorn Garlieston Kippford	489
8.10.8	Maryport Silloth	490
8.10.9	Workington Harrington	490
8.10.10	Whitehaven Ravenglass	491
8.10.11	Glasson Dock Barrow-in-Furness Heysham	492
8.10.12	Fleetwood	493
8.10.13	River Ribble/Preston	494
8.10.14	Liverpool, Standard Port, tidal curves River Alt	494
8.10.15	Isle of Man Port Erin Castletown Laxey	499
8.10.16	Peel	499
8.10.17	Port St Mary	500
8.10.18	Douglas	500
8.10.19	Ramsey	501
8.10.20	Conwy	501
8.10.21	Menai Strait Beaumaris, Bangor The Swellies Port Dinorwic Caernarfon	502
8.10.22	Holyhead, Standard Port, tidal curves Off Skerries TSS Porth Dinllaen	504

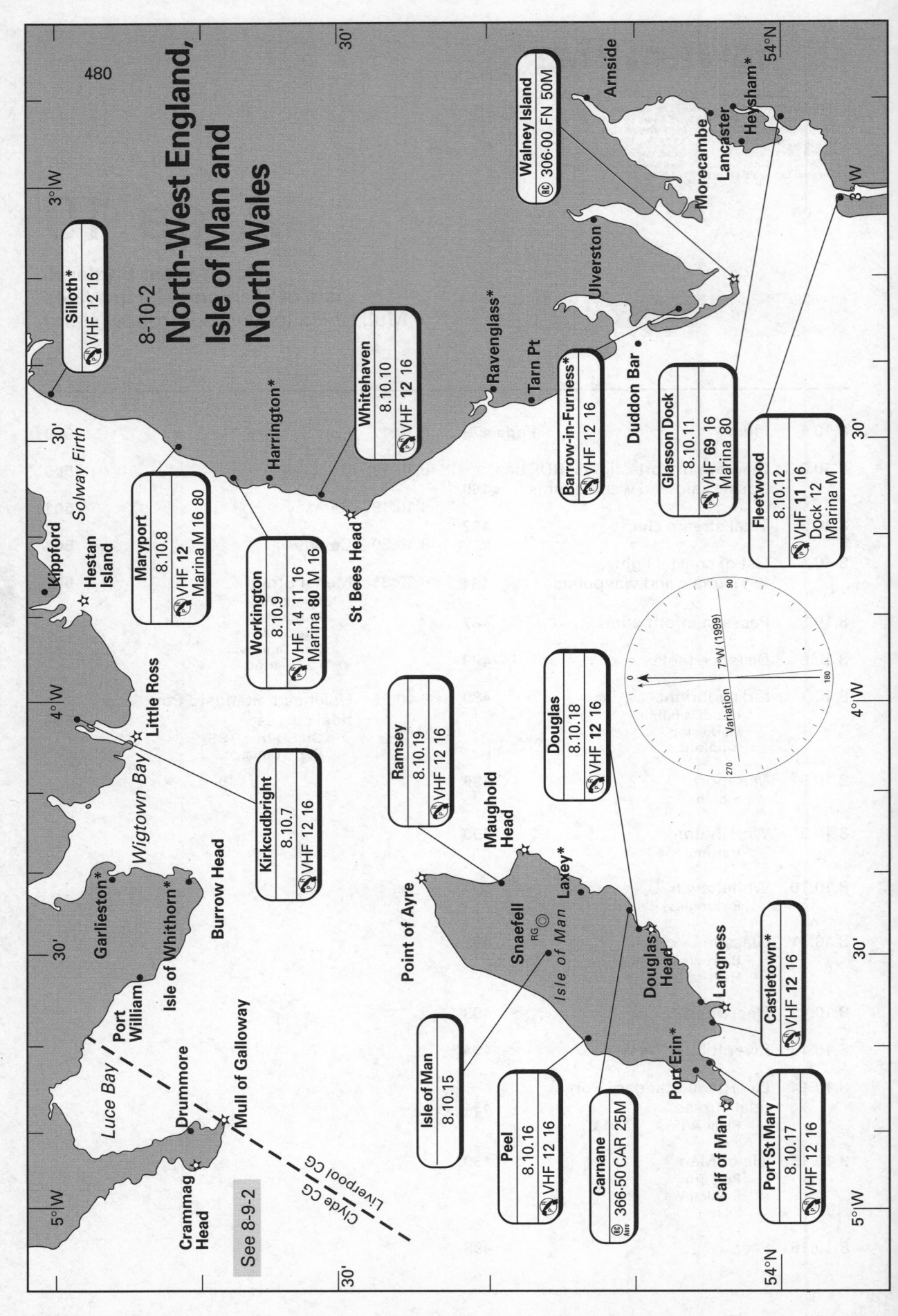

480

8-10-2 **North-West England, Isle of Man and North Wales**

Silloth*
📻 VHF 12 16

Maryport
8.10.8
📻 VHF 12
Marina M 16 80

Workington
8.10.9
📻 VHF 14 11 16
Marina 80 M 16

Whitehaven
8.10.10
📻 VHF 12 16

Walney Island
🔘 306·00 FN 50M

Barrow-in-Furness*
📻 VHF 12 16

Glasson Dock
8.10.11
📻 VHF 69 16
Marina 80

Fleetwood
8.10.12
📻 VHF 11 16
Dock 12
Marina M

Kirkcudbright
8.10.7
📻 VHF 12 16

Ramsey
8.10.19
📻 VHF 12 16

Douglas
8.10.18
📻 VHF 12 16

Isle of Man
8.10.15

Peel
8.10.16
📻 VHF 12 16

Carnane
366·50 CAR 25M

Port St Mary
8.10.17
📻 VHF 12 16

Castletown*
📻 VHF 12 16

Variation 7°W (1999)

Kippford
Hestan Island
Solway Firth
Harrington*
St Bees Head
Ravenglass*
Tarn Pt
Duddon Bar
Ulverston
Arnside
Morecambe
Lancaster
Heysham*

Little Ross
Wigtown Bay
Burrow Head
Garlieston*
Isle of Whithorn*
Port William
Drummore
Mull of Galloway
Crammag Head
Luce Bay

Point of Ayre
Maughold Head
Snaefell RG
Isle of Man
Laxey*
Douglas Head
Langness
Port Erin*
Calf of Man

Clyde CG / Liverpool CG

See 8-9-2

54°N
30'
3°W
30'
4°W
30'
5°W

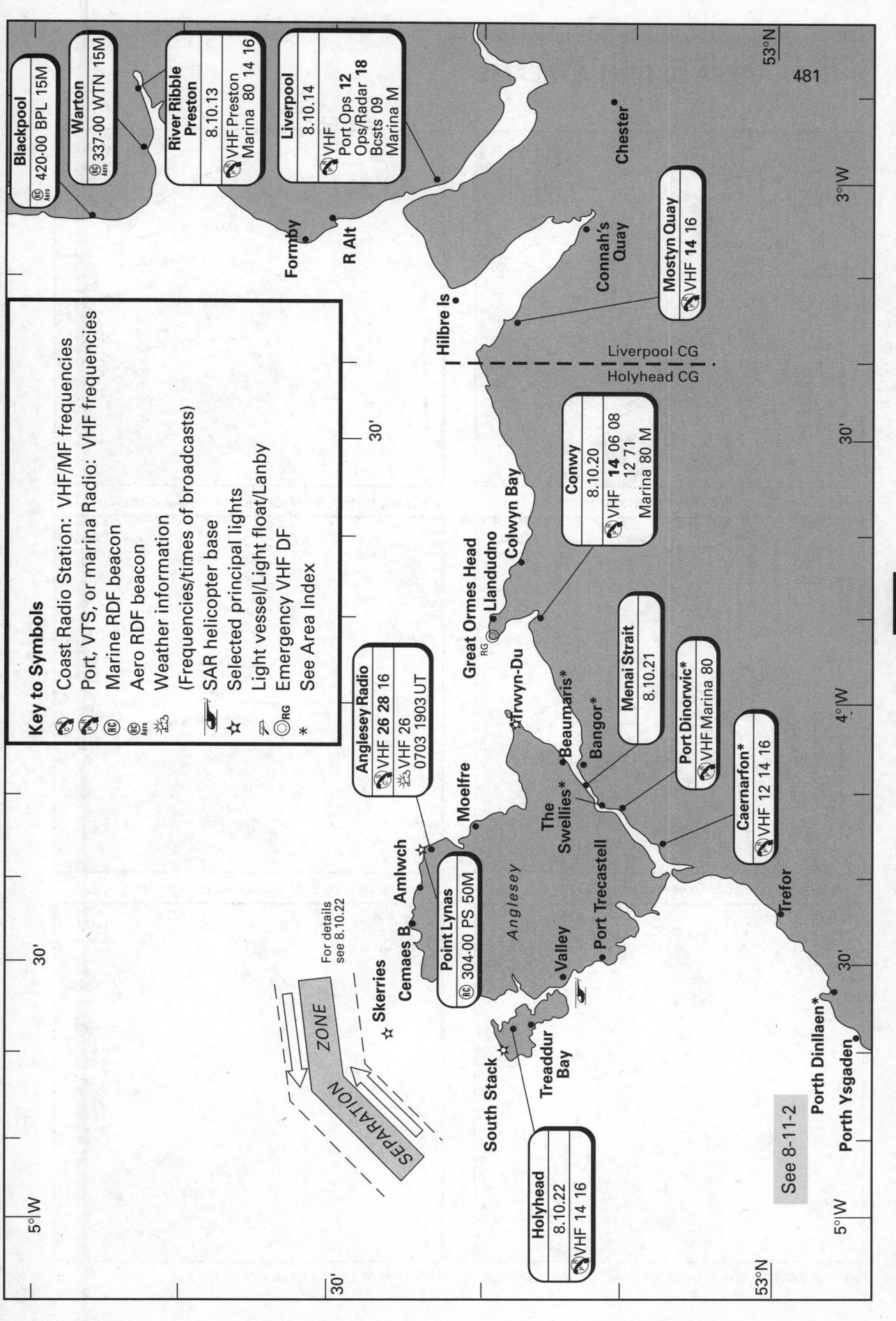

Key to Symbols

📡 Coast Radio Station: VHF/MF frequencies
📡 Port, VTS, or marina Radio: VHF frequencies
Ⓡⓒ Marine RDF beacon
Ⓡⓒ Aero RDF beacon
📻 Weather information
   (Frequencies/times of broadcasts)
🚁 SAR helicopter base
☆ Selected principal lights
Light vessel/Light float/Lanby
Ⓡ RG Emergency VHF DF
* See Area Index

Blackpool
Ⓡⓒ Aero 420·00 BPL 15M

Warton
Ⓡⓒ Aero 337·00 WTN 15M

River Ribble Preston
8.10.13
📡 VHF Preston Marina 80 14 16

Liverpool
8.10.14
📡 VHF Port Ops **12** Ops/Radar **18** Bcsts 09 Marina M

Mostyn Quay
📡 VHF 14 16

Conwy
8.10.20
📡 VHF **14** 06 08 12 71 Marina 80 M

Anglesey Radio
📡 VHF **26** 28 16
📻 VHF 26 0703 1903 UT

Point Lynas
Ⓡⓒ 304·00 PS 50M

Menai Strait
8.10.21

Port Dinorwic*
📡 VHF Marina 80

Caernarfon*
📡 VHF 12 14 16

Holyhead
8.10.22
📡 VHF 14 16

Liverpool CG
Holyhead CG

Chester

Connah's Quay

Formby

R Alt

Hilbre Is

Colwyn Bay

Great Ormes Head
RG Llandudno

Trwyn-Du

Beaumaris*

Bangor*

The Swellies*

Port Trecastell

Moelfre

Anglesey

Valley

Treaddur Bay

South Stack

Skerries

Cemaes B Amlwch

Trefor

Porth Dinllaen*

Porth Ysgaden

SEPARATION ZONE

For details see 8.10.22

See 8-11-2

481

10

53°N   3°W   30'   4°W   30'   5°W   30'   53°N

8-10-3   AREA 10 TIDAL STREAMS

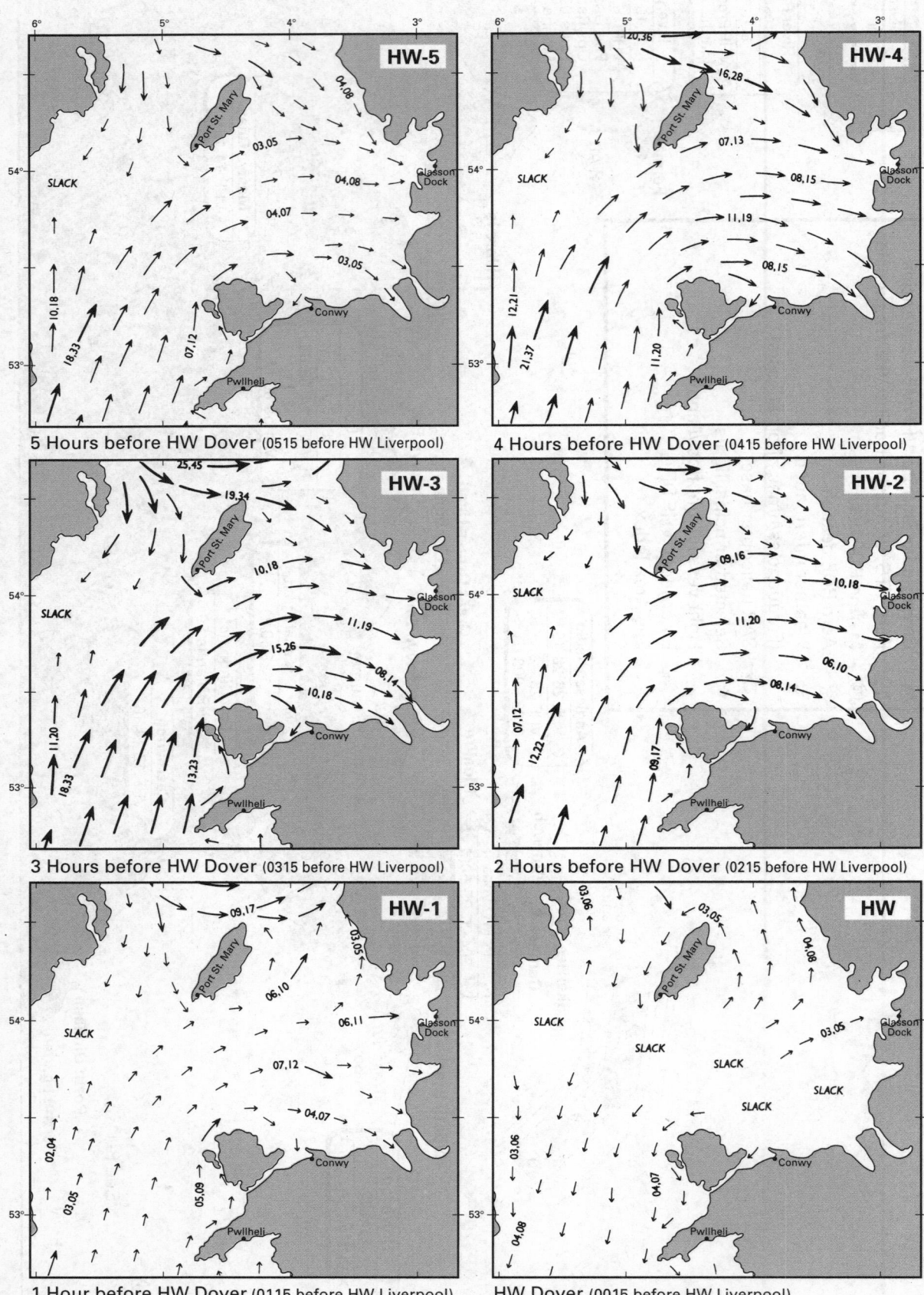

5 Hours before HW Dover (0515 before HW Liverpool)

4 Hours before HW Dover (0415 before HW Liverpool)

3 Hours before HW Dover (0315 before HW Liverpool)

2 Hours before HW Dover (0215 before HW Liverpool)

1 Hour before HW Dover (0115 before HW Liverpool)

HW Dover (0015 before HW Liverpool)

Northward 8.9.3   Southward 8.11.3   North Ireland 8.13.3   Mull of Kintyre 8.9.12   South Ireland 8.12.3

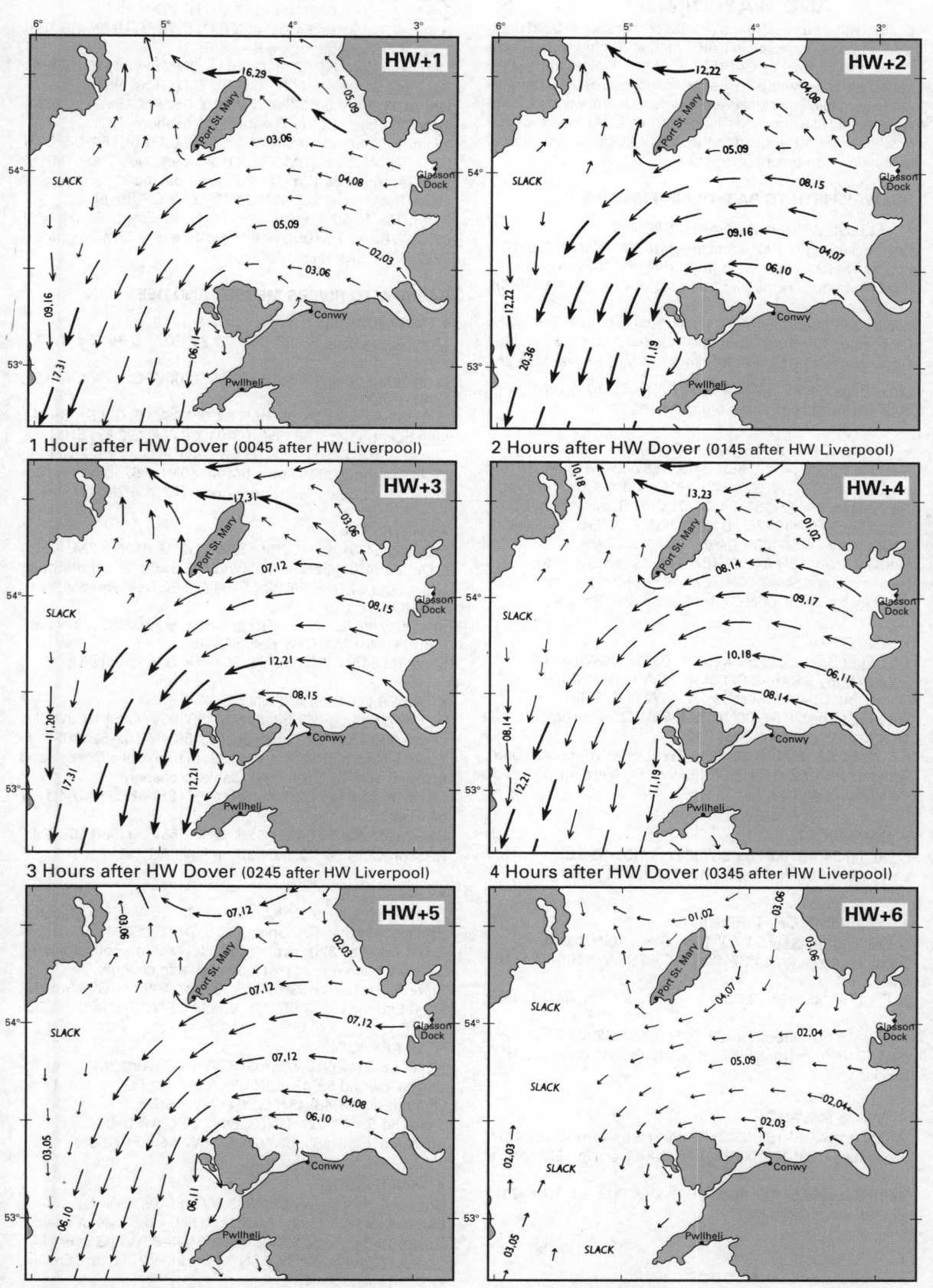

1 Hour after HW Dover (0045 after HW Liverpool)

2 Hours after HW Dover (0145 after HW Liverpool)

3 Hours after HW Dover (0245 after HW Liverpool)

4 Hours after HW Dover (0345 after HW Liverpool)

5 Hours after HW Dover (0445 after HW Liverpool)

6 Hours after HW Dover (0545 after HW Liverpool)

8.10.4 COASTAL LIGHTS, FOG SIGNALS AND WAYPOINTS

Lights with a nominal range of 15M or more are in **bold** print, places and features are in CAPITALS, and light-vessels, light floats and Lanbys in *CAPITAL ITALICS*. Unless otherwise stated lights are white. m = elevation in metres; M = nominal range in miles. Fog signals are in *italics*. Useful waypoints are underlined; use those on land with care. All geographical positions are referenced to the OSGB 36 datum but should be assumed to be approximate.

SOLWAY FIRTH TO BARROW-IN-FURNESS

• ISLE OF WHITHORN/GARLIESTON
Port William ldg lts 105°. Front, pier hd 54°45'·65N 04°35'·10W Fl G 3s 7m 3M; rear, 130m from front, FG 10m 2M.
Isle of Whithorn Hbr E pier hd 54°41'·8N 04°21'·7W QG 4m 5M; Gy col.
Ldg lts 335°. Front, 54°42'·01N 04°22'·00W Oc R 8s 7m 7M; Or ◆; rear, 35m from front, Oc R 8s 9m 7M; Or ◆, synch.
Garlieston pier hd 54°47'·30N 04°21'·70W 2 FR (vert) 8m 3M.

Little Ross 54°45'·93N 04°05'·02W Fl 5s 50m 12M; W tr; obsc in Wigtown B when brg more than 103°.

• KIRKCUDBRIGHT BAY/KIPPFORD
No 1 LB House 54°47'·68N 04°03'·66W Fl WRG 3s 7m 3M; vis Gshore-037°, W037°-043°, R043°-080°, G080°-shore.
No 12 buoy 54°49'·13N 04°04'·76W Fl R 3s.
Perch No 14 54°49'·25N 04°04'·76W Fl 3s 5m.
No 22 buoy 54°50'·08N 04°03'·93W Fl R 3s.
Outfall 54°50'·18N 04°03'·76W Fl Y 5s 3m 2M; Y tr.
Hestan ls, E end 54°49'·90N 03°48'·40W Fl (2) 10s 42m 9M; W tr.
Barnkirk Pt 54°58'·00N 03°15'·90W Fl 2s 18m 2M.

• SILLOTH
Two Feet Bank buoy 54°42'·40N 03°44'·40W; WCM.
Solway buoy 54°46'·80N 03°30'·05W Fl G; SHM.
Corner buoy 54°48'·90N 03°29'·45W Fl G; SHM.
Lees Scar lt bn 54°51'·80N 03°24'·75W QG 11m 8M; W structure on piles; vis 005°-317°.
E Cote 54°52'·78N 03°22'·78W FG 15m 12M; vis 046°-058°.
Groyne hd 54°52'·14N 03°23'·84W 2 FG (vert) 4m 4M; Fl Bu tfc signals close by.

• MARYPORT
S pier hd 54°43'·06N 03°30'·56W Fl 1·5s 10m 6M.
Outfall SHM bn Fl G 5s, 54°42'·75N 03°31'·35W.

• WORKINGTON/HARRINGTON
N Workington buoy 54°40'·10N 03°38'·10W; NCM.
S Workington buoy 54°37'·00N 03°38'·50W VQ (6) + L Fl 10s; SCM.
S Pier 54°39'·13N 03°34'·71W Fl 5s 11m 8M; R bldg; *Siren 20s.*
Ldg lts 131·8°. Front, 54°38'·92N 03°34'·12W FR 10m 3M; rear, 134m from front, FR 12m 3M; both on W pyramidal tr, Or bands.

• WHITEHAVEN
W pier hd 54°33'·16N 03°35'·84W Fl G 5s 16m 13M; W ○ tr.
N pier hd 54°33'·17N 03°35'·67W 2 FR (vert) 8m 9M; W ○ tr.

Saint Bees Hd 54°30'·80N 03°38'·15W Fl (2) 20s 102m **21M**; W ○ tr; obsc shore-340°.

• RAVENGLASS
Blockhouse 54°20'·15N 03°25'·27W FG.
Selker buoy 54°16'·13N 03°29'·50W Fl (3) G 10s; SHM; *Bell.*

• BARROW-IN-FURNESS
Lightning Knoll buoy 53°59'·83N 03°14'·20W L Fl 10s; SWM; *Bell.*
Sea 1 buoy 53°59'·73N 03°11'·79W Fl G 2·5s; SHM.
Halfway Shoal lt bn 54°01'·46N 03°11'·79W Fl R 5s; QR 16m 10M; R & Y cheqered bn; Racon (B).
Outer Bar buoy 54°02'·00N 03°11'·05W Fl (4) R 10s; PHM.
Bar buoy 54°02'·32N 03°10'·14W Fl (2) R 5s; PHM.
Isle of Walney 54°02'·92N 03°10'·65W Fl 15s 21m **23M**; stone tr; obsc 122°-127° within 3M of shore; RC.
Walney Chan ldg lts 040·7°. No.1 Front, 54°03'·33N 03°08'·93W Q 7m 10M; Pile, Or daymark. No 2 Rear, 0·61M from front, Iso 2s 13m 10M; Pile, Or daymark.
Haws Pt W bn 54°02'·98N 03°10'·03W QR 8m 6M.
Rampside Sands ldg lts 005·1°. No 3 Front, 54°04'·40N 03°09'·70W Q 7m10M; W ● tr. No 4 Rear, 0·77M from front, Iso 2s 13m 6M; R col, W face.

BARROW TO RIVERS MERSEY AND DEE

• MORECAMBE
Morecambe buoy 53°52'·00N 03°24'·00W Q (9) 15s; WCM; *Whis.*
Lune Deep buoy 53°55'·80N 03°11'·00W Q (6) + L Fl 15s; SCM; *Whis;* Racon.
Shell Wharf buoy 53°55'·45N 03°08'·88W Fl G 2·5s; SHM.
King Scar buoy 53°56'·95N 03°04'·30W Fl G 2·5s; SHM.
Sewer outfall 54°04'·33N 02°53'·74W Fl G 2s 4m 2M; tr.
Lts in line about 090°. Front, 54°04'·40N 02°52'·52W FR 10m 2M; G mast; rear, 140m from front, FR 14m 2M; G mast.

• HEYSHAM
S Outfall 54°01'·73N 02°55'·73W Fl (2) G 10s 5m 2M.
N Outfall 54°01'·85N 02°55'·69W Fl G 5s 5m 2M; metal post.
S bkwtr hd 54°01'·90N 02°55'·64W 2 FG (vert) 9m 5M; W tr; Ra refl; *Siren 30s.*
SW Quay ldg lts 102·2°. Front, 54°01'·90N 02°55'·13W both F Bu 11/14m 2M; Or & B ◆ on masts.
S pier hd 54°01'·90N 02°55'·35W Oc G 7·5s 9m 6M.

• RIVER LUNE/GLASSON DOCK
R Lune No 1 buoy 53°58'·62N 02°59'·99W Q (9) 15s; WCM.
Ldg lts 083·7°. Front, Plover Scar 53°58'·87N 02°52'·88W Fl 2s 6m 6M; W tr, B lantern; rear, 854m from front, Cockersand Abbey F 18m 8M; R tr (chan liable to change).
Crook perch, No 7 53°59'·45N 02°52'·28W Fl G 5s 3M; G ▲ on mast.
Bazil perch, No.16 54°00'·19N 02°51'·58W Fl (3) R 10s 3M.
Glasson Quay 54°00'·02N 02°50·94W FG 1M.

• FLEETWOOD
Fairway No 1 buoy 53°57'·56N 03°02'·25W Q; NCM; *Bell.*
Esplanade ldg lts 156°. Front, 53°55'·70N 03°00'·47W Fl G 2s 14m; rear, 320m from front, Fl G 4s 28m. Both stone trs. Vis on ldg line only. (H24) (chan liable to change).
Steep Breast perch 53°55'·73N 03°00'·49W Iso G 2s 3m 2M.
Knott End slip Hd 53°55'·72N 03°00'·02W 2 FR (vert) 3m 2M.

• BLACKPOOL
N pier hd 53°49'·16N 03°03'·83W 2 FG (vert) 3M.
Central pier hd 53°48'·65N 03°03'·55W 2 FG (vert) 4M.
Obstn buoy 53°48'·45N 03°04'·22W; SHM.
S pier hd 53°47'·72N 03°03'·60W 2 FG (vert) 4M.
Blackpool tr 53°48'·95N 03°03'·26W Aero FR 158m.

• RIVER RIBBLE
Gut buoy 53°41'·75N 03°08'·90W L Fl 10s; SWM.
Perches show Fl R on N side, and Fl G on S side of chan.
S side, 14·3M perch 53°42'·75N 03°04'·85W Fl G 5s 6m 3M.
Southport pier hd 52°39'·35N 03°01'·25W 2 FG (vert) 6m 5M; W post; vis 033°-213°.
Jordan's Spit buoy 53°35'·75N 03°19'·20W Q (9) 15s; WCM.

FT buoy 53°34'·55N 03°13'·12W Q; NCM.
Spoil Ground buoy 53°34'·25N 03°17'·30W Fl Y 3s; SPM.

• RIVER MERSEY/LIVERPOOL
BAR lt F 53°32'·00N 03°20'·90W Fl 5s 10m 12M; R structure on buoy; Racon (T); *Horn (2) 20s.*
Q1 lt F 53°31'·00N 03°16'·62W VQ; NCM.
Q2 lt F 53°31'·47N 03°14'·87W VQ R; PHM.
Q3 buoy 53°30'·95N 03°15'·00W Fl G 3s; SHM.
Burbo trs buoy 53°30'·41N 03°17'·52W Fl (3) G 9s; SHM.
FORMBY Lt F 53°31'·10N 03°13'·45W Iso 4s 11m 6M; R hull, W stripes.
C4 lt F 53°31'·82N 03°08'·42W Fl R 3s; PHM.
CROSBY Lt F 53°30'·72N 03°06'·21W Oc 5s 11m 8M; R hull, W stripes.
C14 lt F 53°29'·91N 03°05'·27W Fl R 3s; PHM.
BRAZIL Lt F 53°26'·83N 03°02'·18W QG; SHM.
Seacombe Ferry N and S corners 53°24'·6N 03°00'·8W 3 FG 5m 5M; near N corner FY 8m 6M; *Bell (3) 20s .*
Birkenhead, Woodside landing stage N end 53°23'·7N 03°00'·4W 3 FG 5m 4M and S end 2 FG (vert) with *Bell (4) 15s.*
Cammell Laird slip, SE corner 53°23'·96N 03°00'·22W Fl (2) G 6s 5m 5M.
Pluckington Bk buoy 53°22'·99N 02°59'·48W VQ (9) 10s; WCM.
Brombro buoy 53°21'·81N 02°58'·59W Q (3) 10s; ECM.
Eastham Locks E dn 53°19'·57N 02°56'·92W Fl (2) R 6s 5m 8M.
Garston NW dn 53°20'·87N 02°54'·54W 2 FG (vert) 12m 9M; *Horn 11s.*

• RIVER DEE
HE1 buoy 53°26'·31N 03°18'·00W Q (9) 15s; WCM.
HE2 buoy 53°25'·11N 03°13'·09W Q (3) 10s; ECM.
HE3 buoy 53°24'·75N 03°12'·90W; SHM.
Hilbre Is 53°22'·97N 03°13'·70W Fl R 3s 14m 5M; W tr.
HE4 buoy 53°22'·30N 03°14'·20W; SHM.

• MOSTYN/CONNAH'S QUAY
Mostyn training wall hd 53°19'·52N 03°15'·62W 2 FR (vert) 10m 3M; B mast.
Mostyn ldg lts 215·7°. Front, 53°19'·18N 03°16'·15W FR 12m; W ◆ on B mast; rear, 135m from front, FR 22m; W ◆ on B mast.
Flint Sands, N training wall hd 53°15'·05N 03°06'·40W Fl R 3s 4m 6M; tr.
Connah's Quay, S trg wall hd 53°13'·75N 03°04'·02W Fl G 5s 3m 6M.

• WELSH CHANNEL
Bank buoy 53°20'·31N 03°15'·96W Fl R 5s; PHM.
Mostyn buoy 53°21'·00N 03°16'·40W Fl (4) G 15s; SHM.
NE Mostyn buoy 53°21'·48N 03°17'·73W Fl (3) G 10s; SHM.
Air buoy 53°21'·83N 03°19'·20W SHM.
Dee buoy 53°21'·97N 03°18'·78W Q (6) + L Fl 15s; SCM.
E Hoyle buoy 53°22'·03N 03°21'·03W Fl (4) R 15s; PHM.
Earwig buoy 53°21'·37N 03°23'·50W Fl (2) G 5s; SHM.
S Hoyle buoy 53°21'·40N 03°24'·78W Fl (3) R 10s; PHM.
Mid Hoyle buoy 53°22'·90N 03°19'·63W; PHM.
Hoyle buoy 53°23'·14N 03°21'·30W QR; PHM.
NW Hoyle buoy 53°23'·30N 03°23'·80W Fl R 2·5s; PHM.
N Hoyle buoy 53°26'·67N 03°30'·50W VQ; NCM.

ISLE OF MAN
Point of Ayre 54°24'·95N 04°22'·03W Fl (4) 20s 32m **19M**; W tr, two R bands; Racon (M); *Horn (3) 60s.*
Low lt 54°25'·05N 04°21'·80W Fl 3s 10m 8M; R tr, lower part W, on B Base; part obsc 335°-341°.

• JURBY/PEEL
Cronk y Cliwe 54°22'·30N 04°31'·40W 2 Fl R 5s (vert); synch.
Orrisdale 54°19'·30N 04°34'·10W 2 Fl R 5s (vert); synch.
Peel bkwtr hd 54°13'·67N 04°41'·62W Oc 7s 11m 6M; W tr;

Bell (4) 12s (occas).
Peel Groyne Hd 54°13'·55N 04°41'·60W Iso R 2s 4m.

• PORT ERIN
Ldg lts 099·1°. Front, 54°05'·23N 04°45'·49W FR 10m 5M; W tr, R band; rear, 39m from front, FR 19m 5M; W col, R band.
Raglan pier hd 54°05'·11N 04°45'·79W Oc G 5s 8m 5M.
Thousla Rk 54°03'·71N 04°47'·97W Fl R 3s 9m 4M.
Calf of Man W Pt 54°03'·20N 04°49'·70W Fl 15s 93m **26M**; W 8-sided tr; vis 274°-190°; *Horn 45s.*
Chicken Rk 54°02'·30N 04°50'·20W Fl 5s 38m 13M; tr; *Horn 60s.*

• PORT ST MARY
The Carrick 54°04'·30N 04°42'·60W Q (2) 5s 6m 3M; IDM.
Alfred pier hd 54°04'·32N 04°43'·74W Oc R 10s 8m 6M; W tr, R band.
Inner pier hd 54°04'·42N 04°44'·07W Oc R 3s 8m 5M.

• CASTLETOWN/DERBY HAVEN
buoy 54°03'·72N 04°38'·54W Fl R 3s; PHM; *Bell.*
New pier hd 54°04'·32N 04°38'·89W Oc R 15s 8m 5M.
Langness, Dreswick Pt 54°03'·28N 04°37'·45W Fl (2) 30s 23m 12M; W tr.
Derby Haven, bkwtr SW end 54°04'·57N 04°36'·98W   Iso G 2s 5m 5M; W tr, G band.

• DOUGLAS
Douglas Hd 54°08'·58N 04°27'·88W Fl 10s 32m **24M**; W tr; obsc brg more than 037°. FR lts on radio masts 1 and 3M West.
No 1 buoy 54°09'·03N 04°27'·61W Q (3) G 5s; SHM.
Princess Alexandra pier hd 54°08'·85N 04°27'·80W Fl R 5s 16m 8M; R mast; *Whis (2) 40s.*
Ldg lts 229·3°, Front, 54°08'·71N 04°28'·17W Oc 10s 9m 5M; W △ R border on mast; rear, 62m from front, Oc 10s 12m 5M; W ▽ on R border; synch with front.
Victoria pier hd 54°08'·83N 04°28'·01W Oc G 8s 10m 3M; W col; vis 225°-327°; Intnl Port Tfc Signals.

• LAXEY
Pier hd 54°13'·45N 04°23'·20W Oc R 3s 7m 5M; W tr, R band; obsc when brg less than 318°.
Bkwtr hd 54°13'·50N 04°23'·30W Oc G 3s 7m; W tr, G band.
Maughold Hd 54°17'·70N 04°18'·50W Fl (3) 30s 65m **21M**.
Bahama buoy 54°20'·00N 04°08'·50W VQ (6) + L Fl 10s; SCM; *Bell.*

• RAMSEY
Queens Pier dn 54°19'·27N 04°21'·87W Fl R 5s.
S pier hd 54°19'·42N 04°22'·43W QR 8m 10M; W tr, R band, B base.
N pier hd 54°19'·48N 04°22'·43W QG 9m 10M; W tr, B base.
Whitestone Bk buoy 54°24'·55N 04°20'·20W Q (9) 15s; WCM.
King William Bk buoy 54°26'·00N 04°00'·00W Q (3) 10s; ECM.

WALES – NORTH COAST
Chester Flat buoy 53°21'·65N 03°27'·40W Fl (2) R 5s; PHM.
Mid Patch Spit buoy 53°21'·80N 03°31'·50W Fl R 5s; PHM.
N Rhyl buoy 53°22'·75N 03°34'·50W Q; NCM.
W Constable buoy 53°23'·13N 03°49'·17W Q (9) 15s; WCM.

• RHYL/LLANDUDNO/CONWY
River Clwyd bkwtr hd 53°19'·50N 03°30'·30W QR 7m 2M.
Llanddulas, Llysfaen Jetty 53°17'·55N 03°39'·45W Fl G 10s.
Raynes Quarry jetty hd 53°17'·60N 03°40'·28W 2 FG (vert).
Llandudno pier hd 53°19'·90N 03°49'·40W 2 FG (vert) 8m 4M.
Great Ormes Hd lt Ho 53°20'·55N 03°52'·10W (unlit).

Conwy Fairway buoy 53°17'·92N 03°55'·47W; SWM.
Conway R ent S side 53°17'·98N 03°50'·90W Fl WR 5s 5m 2M; vis W076°-088°, R088°-171°, W171°-319°, R319°-076°.

ANGLESEY
Pilot Station Pier 53°24'·90N 04°17'·20W 2 FR (vert).
Pt Lynas 53°24'·97N 04°17'·30W Oc 10s 39m **20M**; W castellated tr; vis 109°-315°; (H24). Fog Det lt F 25m 16M vis 211·8°-214·3°; RC; *Horn 45s.*

• AMLWCH
Main bkwtr 53°25'·01N 04°19'·80W Fl G 15s 11m 3M; W mast; vis 141°-271°.
Inner bkwtr 53°24'·98N 04°19'·85W 2 FR (vert) 12m 5M; W mast; vis 164°-239°.
Inner Hbr 53°24'·94N 04°19'·90W F 9m 8M; W post; vis 233°-257°.

Wylfa power station 53°25'·06N 04°29'·17W 2 FG (vert) 13m 6M.
Furlong buoy 53°25'·40N 04°30'·40W; SHM.
Archdeacon Rk buoy 53°26'·70N 04°30'·80W; NCM.
Victoria Bank buoy 53°25'·60N 04°31'·30W; NCM.
Coal Rk buoy 53°25'·90N 04°32'·72W; SCM.
Ethel Rk buoy 53°26'·63N 04°33'·60W; NCM.
W Mouse bn 53°25'·03N 04°33'·20W; SWM.
The Skerries 53°25'·25N 04°36'·45W Fl (2) 10s 36m **22M**; W ● tr, R band; Racon (T). FR 26m **16M**; same tr; vis 231°-254°; *Horn (2) 20s.*
Langdon buoy 53°22'·74N 04°38'·58W Q (9) 15s; WCM.
Bolivar Rk buoy 53°21'·50N 04°35'·23W; SHM.
Wk buoy 53°20'·43N 04°36'·42W Fl (2) R 10s; PHM.
Clipera buoy 53°20'·08N 04°36'·15W Fl (4) R 15s; PHM; *Bell.*

• HOLYHEAD
Bkwtr hd 53°19'·83N 04°37'·08W Fl (3) G 15s 21m 14M; W □ tr, B band; *Siren 20s.*
Old Hbr, Admiralty Pier dn 53°18'·85N 04°37'·00W 2 FG (vert) 8m 5M; *Horn 15s* (occas).

S Stack 53°18'·39N 04°41'·91W Fl 10s 60m **27M**; (H24); W ○ tr; obsc to N by N Stack and part obsc in Penrhos bay. *Horn 30s.* Fog det lt vis 145°-325°.
Llanddwyn Is lt 53°08'·00N 04°24'·70W Fl WR 2·5s 12m W7M, R4M; W tr; vis R280°-013°, W015°-120°.

MENAI STRAIT TO BARDSEY ISLAND
Trwyn-Du 53°18'·76N 04°02'·38W Fl 5s 19m 12M; W ○ castellated tr, B bands; vis 101°-023°; *Bell (1) 30s,* sounded continuously. FR on radio mast 2M SW.
Ten Feet Bank buoy 53°19'·45N 04°02'·66W; PHM.
Dinmor buoy 53°19'·33N 04°03'·20W; SHM.

• BEAUMARIS/BANGOR
(Direction of buoyage NE to SW)
Perch Rk bn 53°18'·73N 04°02'·09W; PHM.
B2 buoy 53°18'·32N 04°02'·00W Fl (2) R 5s; PHM.
B1 buoy 53°18'·12N 04°02'·23W Fl (2) G 10s; SHM.

B3 buoy 53°17'·44N 04°02'·33W QG; SHM.
B8 buoy 53°16'·48N 04°04'·40W; PHM.
B5 buoy 53°17'·77N 04°04'·83W Fl G 5s; SHM.
B6 buoy 53°17'·14N 04°03'·42W Fl R 3s; PHM.
Beaumaris Pier 53°15'·67N 04°05'·33W F WG 5m 6M; vis G212°-286°, W286°-014°, G014°-071°.
B10 buoy 53°15'·59N 04°05'·15W Fl (2) R 10s; PHM.
B12 buoy 53°15'·26N 04°05'·30W QR; PHM.
B7 buoy 53°15'·05N 04°06'·03W Fl (2) G 5s; SHM.
Bangor buoy 53°14'·47N 04°07'·00W; PHM.
St George's Pier 53°13'·53N 04°09'·50W Fl G 10s.
E side of chan 53°13'·20N 04°09'·53W QR 4m; R mast; vis 064°-222°. (1cable E of Menai Suspension Bridge.)
Price's Pt 53°13'·10N 04°10'·44W Fl WR 2s 5m 3M; W bn; vis R059°-239°, W239°-259°.
Britannia tubular bridge, S chan ldg lts 231° E side. Front, 53°12'·90N 04°10'·97W FW; rear, 45m from front, FW. Centre span of bridge Iso 5s 27m 3M, one either side. SE end of bridge, FR 21m 3M either side, NW end of bridge section FG 21m 3M either side.

• PORT DINORWIC
Port Dinorwic buoy 53°11'·22N 04°13'·64W Fl R; PHM.
pier hd 53°11'·18N 04°12'·56W F WR 5m 2M; vis R225°-357°, W357°-225°.
C9 buoy 53°10'·63N 04°13'·91W; SHM.
Channel buoy 53°10'·34N 04°15'·19W; SHM.
C14 buoy 53°10'·17N 04°15'·31W; PHM.
C11 buoy 53°09'·90N 04°15'·61W; SHM.
C13 buoy 53°09'·50N 04°15'·87W; SHM.

(Direction of buoyage SW to NE)
Change buoy 53°08'·80N 04°16'·67W; SCM.

• CAERNARFON
Caernarfon N pier hd 53°08'·59N 04°16'·60W 2 FG (vert) 5m 2M.
C10 buoy 53°07'·94N 04°18'·20W QR; PHM.
Abermenai Pt 53°07'·60N 04°19'·64W Fl WR 3·5s 6m 3M; W mast; vis R065°-245°, W245°-065°.
Mussel Bk buoy 53°07'·23N 04°20'·85W Fl (2) R 5s; PHM.
C6 buoy 53°07'·07N 04°22'·25W Fl R 5s; PHM.
C5 buoy 53°07'·04N 04°22'·60W; SHM.
C4 buoy 53°07'·21N 04°23'·06W QR; PHM.
C3 buoy 53°07'·33N 04°23'·80W QG; SHM.
C1 buoy 53°07'·18N 04°24'·37W Fl G 5s; SHM.
C2 buoy 53°07'·28N 04°24'·42W Fl R 10s; PHM.
Poole buoy 53°00'·00N 04°34'·00W Fl Y 6s; SPM (Apr-Oct).

• PORTH DINLLÄEN
CG Stn 52°56'·80N 04°33'·81W FR when firing taking place 10M North.
Careg y Chwislen 52°56'·96N 04°33'·44W; IDM (unlit).

Bardsey Island 52°44'·97N 04°47'·93W Fl (5) 15s 39m **26M**; W □ tr, R bands; obsc by Bardsey I 198°-250° and in tremadoc B when brg less than 260°; *Horn Mo (N) 45s.*

8.10.5   PASSAGE INFORMATION

For detailed directions covering these waters and harbours refer to the Admiralty Pilot *W Coast of England and Wales*; *A Cruising Guide to NW England & Wales* (Griffiths/Imray) and *Lundy and Irish Sea Pilot* (Taylor/Imray). *Solway SDs* cover from Loch Ryan to Ravenglass; by post £5.60 from: Matheson, Decca Stn, Kidsdale, Whithorn, Newton Stewart DG8 8HZ.

SCOTLAND – SW COAST

The Scares, two groups of rocks, lie at the mouth of Luce Bay which elsewhere is clear more than 3ca offshore; but the whole bay is occupied by a practice bombing range, marked by 12 DZ SPM lt buoys. Good anch at E Tarbert B to await the tide around the Mull of Galloway, or dry out alongside in shelter of Drummore. Off Burrow Hd there is a bad race in strong W winds with W-going tide. In Wigtown B the best anch is in Isle of Whithorn B, but exposed to S. It is also possible to dry out in Garlieston, see 8.10.7.

A tank firing range, between the E side of ent to Kirkcudbright Bay (8.10.7) and Abbey Hd, 4M to E, extends 14M offshore. If unable to avoid the area, cross it at N end close inshore. For information contact Range Control ☎ (01557) 323236 or call the Range safety boat "Gallovidian" on VHF Ch 16, 73. The range operates 0900-1600LT Mon-Fri, but weekend and night firing may also occur.

SOLWAY FIRTH (chart 1346)

Between Abbey Head and St Bees Head lies the Solway Firth, most of which is encumbered by shifting sandbanks. The *Solway SDs* (see above) are virtually essential. Off the entrances to the Firth, and in the approaches to Workington (8.10.9) beware shoals over which strong W winds raise a heavy sea. There are navigable, buoyed chans as far as Annan on the N shore, but buoys are laid primarily for the aid of Pilots. Local knowledge is required, particularly in the upper Firth, where streams run very strongly in the chans when the banks are dry, and less strongly over the banks when covered. In Powfoot for example the in-going stream begins at HW Liverpool – 0300, and the outgoing at HW Liverpool + 0100, sp rates up to 6kn. For Silloth and Maryport see 8.10.8; Workington and Harrington 8.10.9, Whitehaven and Ravenglass 8.10.10. South along the Cumbrian coast past St Bees Hd to Walney Is there are no dangers more than 2M offshore, but no shelter either.

BARROW TO CONWY (AC 2010, 1981, *1978*)

Ent to Barrow-in-Furness (8.10.11 and chart 3164) is about 1M S of Hilpsford Pt at S end of Walney Island where the lt ho (RC) is prominent. The stream sets across the narrow chan, which is well marked but shallow in patches. W winds cause rough sea in the ent. Moorings and anch off Piel and Roa Islands, but space is limited and stream runs hard on ebb. Coming from the S it is possible with sufficient rise of tide to cross the sands between Fleetwood and Barrow.

Lune Deep, 2M NW of Rossall Pt, is ent to Morecambe B (chart 2010), and gives access to the ferry/commercial port of Heysham, Glasson Dock (8.10.11), and Fleetwood (8.10.12); it is well buoyed. Streams run 3·5kn at sp. Most of Bay is encumbered with drying sands, intersected by chans which are subject to change. S of Morecambe B, beware shoals extending 3M W of Rossall Pt. Further S, R. Ribble (8.10.13) gives access via a long drying chan to the marina at Preston.

Queen's Chan and Crosby Chan (charts 1951 and *1978*) are entered E of the Bar Lanby. They are well buoyed, dredged and preserved by training banks, and give main access to R. Mersey and Liverpool (8.10.14). Keep clear of commercial shipping. From the N the old Formby chan is abandoned, but possible near HW. Towards HW and in moderate winds a yacht can cross the training bank (level of which varies between 2m and 3m above CD) E of Great Burbo Bank, if coming from the W. Rock Chan, parts of which dry and which is unmarked, may also be used but beware wrecks.

In good weather and at nps, the Dee Estuary (charts 1953, *1978*) is accessible for boats able to take the ground. But most of estuary dries and banks extend 6M seaward. Chans shift, and buoys are moved as required. Stream runs hard in chans when banks are dry. Main ent is Welsh Chan, but if coming from N, Hilbre Swash runs W of Hilbre Is (lit).

Sailing W from the Dee on the ebb, it is feasible to take the Inner Passage (buoyed) S of West Hoyle Spit, and this enjoys some protection from onshore winds at half tide or below. Rhyl is a tidal hbr, not accessible in strong onshore winds, but gives shelter for yachts able to take the ground. Abergele Road, Colwyn B and Llandudno B are possible anchs in settled weather and S winds. Conwy (8.10.20) offer good shelter in both marina and harbour. Between Point of Ayr and Great Ormes Head the E-going stream begins at HW Liverpool + 0600, and the W-going at HW Liverpool – 0015, sp rates 3kn.

ISLE OF MAN (IOM) (charts 2094, 2696)

For general pilotage information, tidal streams and hbr details of IOM, see *IOM Sailing Directions*, *Tidal Streams and Anchorages*, published by the Manx Sailing and Cruising Club. For notes on crossing the Irish Sea, see 8.13.5.

There are four choices when rounding South of Isle of Man: **a**, In bad weather, or at night, keep S of Chicken Rk (lt, fog sig). **b**, In good conditions, take the chan between Chicken Rk and Calf of Man (lt, fog sig). **c**, Alternatively, with winds of Force 3 or less and a reliable engine capable of producing a speed of at least 5kn, by day only use Calf Sound between Calf of Man and IOM, passing W of Kitterland Island but E of Thousla Rock, which is marked by lt bn and is close to Calf of Man shore. **d**, Little Sound, a minor chan, runs E of Kitterland Is.

The stream runs strongly through Calf Sound, starting N-going at HW Liverpool – 0145, and S-going at HW Liverpool + 0345, sp rates 3·5kn. W of Calf of Man the stream runs N and S, but changes direction off Chicken Rk and runs W and E between Calf of Man and Langness Pt 6M to E. Overfalls extend E from Chicken Rk on E-going stream, which begins at HW Liverpool + 0610, and N from the rk on W-going stream, which begins at HW Liverpool.

Off Langness Pt (lt) the Skerranes (dry) extend 1ca SW, and tidal stream runs strongly, with eddies and a race. E side of Langness peninsula is foul ground, over which a dangerous sea can build in strong winds. Here the NE-going stream begins at HW Liverpool + 0545, and the SW-going at HW Liverpool – 0415, sp rates 2·25kn.

There is anch in Derby Haven, N of St Michael's Is, but exposed to E. From here to Douglas (8.10.18) and on to Maughold Hd (lt), there are no dangers more than 4ca offshore. Near the coast the SW-going stream runs for 9 hours and the NE-going for 3 hours, since an eddy forms during the second half of the main NE-going stream. Off Maughold Hd the NE-going stream begins at HW Liverpool + 0500, and the SW-going at HW Liverpool – 0415.

SE, E and NW of Pt of Ayre are dangerous banks, on which seas break in bad weather. These are Whitestone Bk (least depth 2·0m), Bahama Bk (1·5m, buoy), Ballacash Bk (2·7m), King William Bks (3·3m, buoy), and Strunakill Bk (6·7m).

The W coast of IOM has few pilotage hazards. A spit with depth of 1·4m runs 2ca offshore from Rue Pt. Jurby Rk (depth 2·7m) lies 3ca off Jurby Hd. Craig Rk (depth 4 m) and shoals lie 2·5M NNE of Peel (8.10.16).

MENAI STRAIT (8.10.21 and chart *1464*)

The main features of this narrow chan include: Puffin Is, seaward of NE end; Beaumaris; Garth Pt at Bangor, where NE end of Strait begins; Menai Suspension Bridge (30·5m); The Swellies, a narrow 1M stretch with strong tide and dangers mid-stream; Britannia Rail Bridge (27·4m), with cables close W at elevation of 22m; Port Dinorwic and Caernarfon (8.10.21); Abermenai Pt and Fort Belan, where narrows mark SW end of Strait; and Caernarfon Bar.

10

The following brief notes only cover very basic pilotage. For detailed directions see *W Coasts of England and Wales Pilot*, or *Cruising Anglesey and N Wales* (NW Venturers Yacht Club). The Swellies should be taken near local HW slack, and an understanding of tidal streams is essential. The tide is about 1 hour later, and sp range about 2·7m more, at NE end of Strait than at SW end. Levels differ most at about HW +1 (when level at NE end is more than 1·8m above level at SW end); and at about HW – 0445 (when level at NE end is more than 1·8m below level at SW end). Normally the stream runs as follows (times referred to HW Holyhead). HW – 0040 to HW + 0420: SW between Garth Pt and Abermenai Pt. HW + 0420 to HW + 0545: outwards from about The Swellies, ie NE towards Garth Pt and SW towards Abermenai Pt. HW + 0545 to HW – 0040: NE between Abermenai Pt and Garth Pt. Sp rates are generally about 3kn, but more in narrows, e.g. 5kn off Abermenai Pt, 6kn between the bridges, and 8kn at The Swellies. The timings and rates of streams may be affected by strong winds in either direction.

From NE, enter chan W of Puffin Island, taking first of ebb to rerach the Swellies at slack HW (HW Holyhead – 0100). Slack HW only lasts about 20 mins at sps, a little more at nps. Pass under centre of suspension bridge span, and steer to leave Platters (dry) on mainland shore to port and Swellies lt bn close to stbd. From Swellies lt bn to Britannia Bridge hold mainland shore, leaving bn on Price Pt to port, and Gored Goch and Gribbin Rk to stbd. Leave Britannia Rk (centre pier of bridge) to stbd. Thence to SW hold to buoyed chan near mainland shore. (A Historic Wreck (see 8.0.3h) is 4ca SW of Britannia Bridge at 53°12'·77N 04°11'·72W). Port Dinorwic is useful to await right tidal conditions for onward passage in either direction.

Note: Direction of buoyage becomes NE off Caernarfon. Caernarfon Bar is impassable even in moderately strong winds against ebb, but narrows at Abermenai Pt demand a fair tide, or slackish water, since tide runs strongly here. Going seaward on first of ebb, when there is water over the banks, it may not be practicable to return to the Strait if conditions on the bar are bad. Then it is best to anch near Mussel Bank buoy and await slack water, before returning to Caernarfon (say). Leaving Abermenai Pt on last of ebb means banks to seaward are exposed and there is little water in chan or over bar.

Going NE'ward it is safe to reach the Swellies with last of flood, leaving Caernarfon about HW Holyhead – 0230. Do not leave too late, or full force of ebb will be met before reaching Bangor.

ANGLESEY TO BARDSEY ISLAND (AC *1977*, 1970, 1971)

On N coast of Anglesey, a race extends 5ca off Pt Lynas (lt, fog sig, RC) on E-going stream. Amlwch is a small hbr (partly dries) 1·5M W of Pt Lynas. A drying rk lies 100m offshore on W side of appr, which should not be attempted in strong onshore winds. From here to Carmel Hd beware E Mouse (and shoals to SE), Middle Mouse, Harry Furlong's Rks (dry), Victoria Bank (least depth 1·8m), Coal Rk (awash), and W Mouse (with dangers to W and SW). The outermost of these dangers is 2M offshore. There are overfalls and races at headlands and over many rks and shoals along this coast.

Between Carmel Hd and The Skerries (lt, fog sig, Racon) the NE-going stream begins at HW Holyhead + 0550, and the SW-going at HW Holyhead – 0010, sp rates 5kn. 1M NW of Skerries the stream turns 1½ hours later, and runs less strongly. Simplest passage, or at night or in bad weather, is to pass 1M off Skerries, in the TSS ITZ, see 8.10.22. In good conditions by day and at slack water, Carmel Hd can be rounded close inshore; but beware short, steep, breaking seas here in even moderate winds against tide.

Holyhead (8.10.22) is a port of refuge, access H24 in all weathers, with new marina in New Hbr; beware fast ferries. Races occur off N Stack and (more severe) off S Stack (lt, fog sig), up to 1·5M offshore on NNE-going stream which begins at HW Holyhead – 0605, sp rate 5kn. Races do not extend so far on SSW-going stream which begins at HW Holyhead + 0020, sp rate 5kn. The W coast of Anglesey is rugged with rks, some drying, up to 1·5M offshore. There are races off Penrhyn Mawr and Rhoscolyn Hd. Pilot's Cove, E of Llanddwyn Is, is good anch to await the right conditions for Menai Strait.

On the Lleyn Peninsula Porth Dinllaen (8.10.22) is good anch, but exposed to N and NE. Braich y Pwll is the steep, rky point at end of Lleyn Peninsula (chart 1971). About 1M N of it and up to 1M offshore lie The Tripods, a bank on which there are overfalls and a bad sea with wind against tide.

Bardsey Sound, 1·5M wide, can be used by day in moderate winds. Stream reaches 6kn at sp, and passage should be made at slack water, – 0015 HW or + 0035 LW Holyhead. Avoid Carreg Ddu on N side and Maen Bugail Rk (dries 4·1m) on S side of Sound, where there are dangerous races. If passing outside Bardsey Is (lt, fog sig) make a good offing to avoid overfalls which extend 1·5M W and 2·5M S of Island. Turbulence occurs over Bastram Shoal, Devil's Tail and Devil's Ridge, which lie SSE and E of Bardsey Is.

8.10.6   DISTANCE TABLE

Approximate distances in nautical miles are by the most direct route, whilst avoiding dangers and allowing for Traffic Separation Schemes. Places in *italics* are in adjoining areas; places in **bold** are in 8.0.9, Distances across the Irish Sea.

		1	2	3	4	5	6	7	8	9	10	11	12	13	14	15	16	17	18	19	20
1.	*Portpatrick*	1																			
2.	*Mull of Galloway*	16	2																		
3.	**Kirkcudbright**	48	32	3																	
4.	**Maryport**	65	49	26	4																
5.	Workington	63	47	25	6	5															
6.	Ravenglass	70	54	40	30	23	6														
7.	**Point of Ayre**	38	22	28	37	31	34	7													
8.	Peel	41	26	46	55	49	52	18	8												
9.	**Port St Mary**	56	41	61	63	57	50	35	18	9											
8.	Douglas	60	42	46	50	44	39	19	30	13	10										
11.	Ramsey	44	28	34	41	35	34	6	24	27	15	11									
12.	Glasson Dock	101	85	74	66	60	37	64	85	69	63	61	12								
13.	**Fleetwood**	95	79	68	59	53	30	58	80	63	57	55	10	13							
14.	**Liverpool**	118	102	97	89	83	60	80	86	76	70	77	52	46	14						
15.	Conwy	111	95	95	92	86	58	72	72	57	59	68	62	56	46	15					
16.	Beaumaris	109	93	94	95	89	72	71	73	58	58	70	66	60	49	12	16				
17.	Caernarfon	117	103	104	105	99	82	81	73	68	68	80	76	70	59	22	10	17			
18.	**Holyhead**	93	81	94	96	90	69	68	62	46	50	65	79	73	68	36	32	26	18		
19.	Bardsey Island	127	113	129	129	123	114	107	94	80	88	98	107	101	90	53	41	31	43	19	
20.	*Fishguard*	171	158	175	175	169	160	153	140	126	134	144	153	147	136	100	88	78	89	45	20

KIRKCUDBRIGHT 8-10-7

Dumfries and Galloway 54°50'·30N 04°03'·40W   Rtg 3-2-1

CHARTS
AC1344, 1346, 2094, *1826*; Imray C62; OS 84

TIDES
+0030 Dover; ML 4·1; Duration 0545; Zone 0 (UT)

Standard Port LIVERPOOL (⟶)

Times				Height (metres)			
High Water		Low Water		MHWS	MHWN	MLWN	MLWS
0000	0600	0200	0800	9·3	7·4	2·9	0·9
1200	1800	1400	2000				
Differences KIRKCUDBRIGHT BAY							
+0015	+0015	+0010	+0000	−1·8	−1·5	−0·5	−0·1
DRUMMORE							
+0030	+0040	+0015	+0020	−3·4	−2·5	−0·9	−0·3
PORT WILLIAM							
+0030	+0030	+0025	0000	−2·9	−2·2	−0·8	No data
GARLIESTON							
+0025	+0035	+0030	+0005	−2·3	−1·7	−0·5	No data
ISLE OF WHITHORN							
+0020	+0025	+0025	+0005	−2·4	−2·0	−0·8	−0·2
HESTAN ISLET (Kippford)							
+0025	+0025	+0020	+0025	−1·0	−1·1	−0·5	0.0
SOUTHERNESS POINT							
+0030	+0030	+0030	+0010	−0·7	−0·7		No data
ANNAN WATERFOOT							
+0050	+0105	+0220	+0310	−2·2	−2·6	−2·7	*
TORDUFF POINT							
+0105	+0140	+0520	+0410	−4·1	−4·9	*Not below CD	
REDKIRK							
+0110	+0215	+0715	+0445	−5·5	−6·2	*Not below CD	

Notes: At Annan Waterfoot, Torduff Pt and Redkirk the LW time differences are for the start of the rise, which at sp is very sudden. *At LW the tide does not usually fall below CD.

SHELTER
Very good. There is adequate depth at LW: 1-1·5m at the floating pontoon/jetty, and 1-3m on pile moorings. Also drying out on ⚓s or against town quay. The River Dee has many shoal patches of 0·3m or less. Down-river there are good ⚓s behind Ross Is and ½ca N of Torrs Pt, except in S'lies which raise heavy swell.

NAVIGATION
WPT 54°45'·50N 04°04'·00W, 185°/005° from/to Torrs Pt, 1·4M. The Bar is 1ca N of Torrs Pt; access HW±3. Spring tides run up to 3-4kn. A firing range crosses the ent; call Range Safety Officer ☎ (01557) 323236 or VHF 16 73.

LIGHTS AND MARKS
Little Ross lt ho, W of ent, Fl 5s 50m 12M, (obscured in Wigtown bay when brg more than 103°). No 1 lt bn, Fl WRG 3s, is atop the LB shed (54°47'·70N); vis G080°-037°, W037°-043°, R043°-080°. The river is well lit/buoyed. There are Fl G lts on the mooring piles off the town.

RADIO TELEPHONE
VHF Ch 12 16 (0730-1700). *Range Control* Ch 16 73.

TELEPHONE (Dial code 01557)
Hr Mr 331135; ⌗ (0141) 887 9369; MRCC 0151-931 3341; Marinecall 0891 500 461; Police 330600; Dr 330755.

FACILITIES
Pontoon/jetty £7.10, AC, FW; **Town Quay** P (hose), D (road tanker), FW, El, C (15 ton) CH, ME. **KYC** ☎ 330963; **SC** ☎ 330032, Slip, M, FW; **Town** EC Thur; V, R, Bar, ✉, Ⓑ, ⇌ (Dumfries 30M), ✈ (Glasgow 100M).

OTHER HARBOURS ON THE COASTS OF DUMFRIES AND GALLOWAY

ISLE OF WHITHORN, Dumfries and Galloway, 54°41'·90N 04°21'·80W. AC 2094, *1826*. HW +0035 on Dover; ML 3·7m; Duration 0545. Shelter good but hbr dries, having approx 2·5m at HW±3. On W side of ent beware the Skerries, a ledge with pole/radar reflector. St Ninian's Tr (W ☐ tr) is conspic at E side of ent. E pier hd has QG 4m 5M; ldg lts 335°, both Oc R 8s 7/9m 7M, synch, Or masts and ◊. Hr Mr ☎ (01988) 500246; Facilities: AB on quay £3, Slip, P, D, FW, ME, Sh, CH, V, Bar, ✉, VHF Ch 80 (occas).
Luce Bay Firing Range (D402/403) lies to the NW. For info on activity ☎ (01776) 888792.

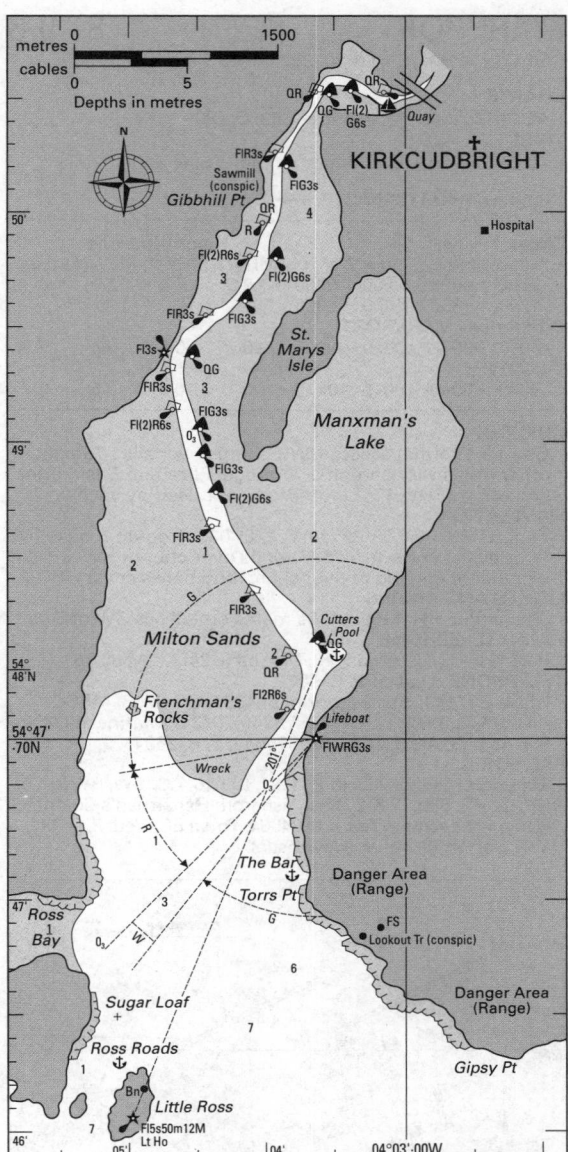

GARLIESTON, Dumfries and Galloway, 54°47'·35N 04°21'·75W. AC 2094, *1826*. HW +0035 on Dover; ML no data; Duration 0545. See 8.10.7. Hbr affords complete shelter but dries. Access (2m) HW±3. Pier hd lt 2FR (vert) 5m 3M. Beware rky outcrops in W side of bay marked by a perch. Hr Mr ☎ (01988) 600274. Facilities: M £3, FW, AC on quay, Slip. **Town:** V, ME, P, D.

KIPPFORD, Dumfries & Galloway, 54°52'·35N 03°48'·85W. AC 1346, *1826*. HW +0040 on Dover; ML 4·2m (Hestan Is). See 8.10.7. Good shelter on drying moorings/pontoons off Kippford, 2·75M up drying Urr Estuary from Hestan Is lt ho Fl (2) 10s 42m 9M. Access HW±2 via marked, unlit chan. CCC or Solway SDs (from Solway YC) are strongly advised. Beware Craig Roan on E side of ent. Temp ⚓s NE or W of Hestan Is to await tide. VHF: Ch M call *Kippford Startline* (YC) HW±2 in season. Ch 16 *Kippford Slipway* (Pilotage). Facilities: **Solway YC** (01556) 620249, AB, AC, FW, M; **Services:** AB £6, M, Slip, D (cans), CH, BY, ME. **Town** P, SM, V, ✉, Bar, Slip

MARYPORT   8-10-8

Cumbria 54°43'·03N 03°30'·38W   Rtg 3-2-1

CHARTS
AC 2013, 1346, *1826*; Imray C62; OS 89
TIDES
+0038 Dover; ML no data; Duration 0550; Zone 0 (UT)

Standard Port LIVERPOOL (→)

Times				Height (metres)			
High Water		Low Water		MHWS	MHWN	MLWN	MLWS
0000	0600	0200	0800	9·3	7·4	2·9	0·9
1200	1800	1400	2000				
Differences MARYPORT							
+0017	+0032	+0020	+0005	–0·7	–0·8	–0·4	0·0
SILLOTH							
+0030	+0040	+0045	+0055	–0·1	–0·3	–0·6	–0·1

SHELTER
Good in marina, access HW ±2½ nps over sill 1·75m; at other times Workington is a refuge. Elizabeth Basin dries 2m, access HW±1½; commercial, not used by yachts.
NAVIGATION
WPT 54°43'·08N 03°32'·39W, 270°/090° from/to S pier, 1M. Overfalls at ent with W/SW winds over ebb. At HW–3 1·8m over bar at ent and in river chan; mud banks cover HW –2.
LIGHTS AND MARKS
As chartlet. SHM bn Fl G 5s marks outfall 6ca SW of S pier.
RADIO TELEPHONE
Port VHF Ch 12 (occas) 16. Marina (H24) Ch M 80 16.
TELEPHONE (Dial code 01900)
Hr Mr 817440; Hbr Authority 604351; CG 2238; MRSC (0151) 931 3341; ☖ (01482) 782107 (H24); Marinecall 0891 500 461; Police 812601; Dr 815544; Ⓗ 812634.
FACILITIES
Maryport Marina (200) ☎ 813331, £11.16, AC, FW, BY, BH, El, CH, ☖, ME, Slip, (P & D, fresh fish from Fisherman's Co-op); **Maryport Yachting Ass'n** ☎ 64964. **Town** EC Wed; P, D, ME, V, R, Bar, ✉, Ⓑ, ≋, ✈ (Newcastle).

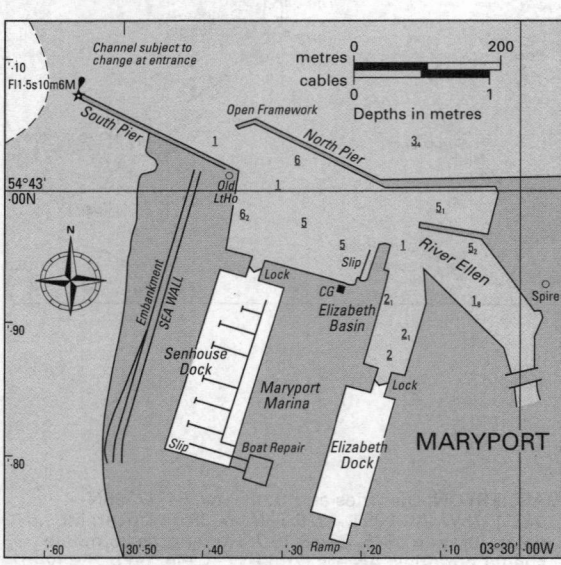

MINOR HARBOUR 10M NNE OF MARYPORT

SILLOTH, Cumbria, 54°52'·15N 03°23'·78W. AC 2013, 1346, *1826*. HW –0050 on Dover; ML no data; Duration 0520. See 8·10·8. Appr via English or Middle Chans, approx 8M long, requires local knowledge. Beware constantly shifting chans and banks. Yachts are not encouraged. ⚓ SW of ent in about 4m off Lees Scar, QG 11m 8M; exposed to SW winds. Outer hbr dries; lock into New Dock, which is mainly commercial. East Cote Dir lt 052° FG 15m 12M; vis 046°-058°, intens 052°. Ldg lts, both F, 115°. Groyne 2 FG (vert). Tfc sigs on mast at New Dock: no entry unless Y signal arm raised by day or Q Bu lt by night. VHF Ch 16 12 (HW–2½ to HW+1½). Hr Mr ☎ (016973) 31358; ☖ (01900) 604611. Facilities: EC Tues; FW, Ⓑ, Bar, ✉, R, V.

WORKINGTON   8-10-9

Cumbria 54°39'·02N 03°34'·30W   Rtg 2-4-3

CHARTS
AC 2013, 1346, *1826*; Imray C62; OS 89
TIDES
+0025 Dover; ML 4·5; Duration 0545; Zone 0 (UT)

Standard Port LIVERPOOL (→)

Times				Height (metres)			
High Water		Low Water		MHWS	MHWN	MLWN	MLWS
0000	0600	0200	0800	9·3	7·4	2·9	0·9
1200	1800	1400	2000				
Differences WORKINGTON							
+0020	+0020	+0020	+0010	–1·2	–1·1	–0·3	0·0

SHELTER
Good; ent and chan to Prince of Wales Dock are dredged 1·8m. Berth where you can (free) or ⚓ in Turning Basin. Lock (HW±1½) into PoW Dock 1·8m (for coasters). Low (1·8m) fixed railway bridge across ent to inner tidal hbr.
NAVIGATION
WPT 54°39'·58N 03°35'·30W, 311°/131° from/to front ldg lt, 1·0M. Tide sets strongly across ent. In periods of heavy rain a strong freshet from R Derwent may be encountered in the hbr ent.
LIGHTS AND MARKS
Workington Bank, least depth 5·5m, is 2M W of hbr ent; it is marked by an unlit NCM buoy and a SCM buoy, VQ (6) + L Fl 10s, (see 8.10.4). A SHM buoy, Fl G 5s, 1·3M NW of hbr ent is a mark for English Chan. Ldg lts 132°, both FR 10/12m 3M, on W pyramidal trs with Y bands. Two sets of F Bu lts in line mark NE and SW edges of chan. There are 16 wind-turbines between ¾M and 2M NE of hbr ent.
RADIO TELEPHONE
VHF Ch 11 14 16 (HW–2½ to HW+2).
TELEPHONE (Dial code 01900)
Hr Mr 602301; CG 2238; ☖ (01482) 782107 (H24); MRSC (0151) 931 3341; Marinecall 0891 500 461; Police 812601; Dr 64866; Ⓗ 602244.
FACILITIES
Dock D, FW, ME, El; **Vanguard SC** ☎ 826886, M, FW. **Town** EC Thurs; P, V, R, Bar, ✉, Ⓑ, ≋, ✈ (Carlisle).

MINOR HARBOUR 2M SOUTH OF WORKINGTON

HARRINGTON, Cumbria, 54°36'·76N 03°34'·21W. AC 2013, 1346, *1826*. HW +0025 on Dover; Duration 0540; Use Diff's Workington 8.10.9. Good shelter in small hbr only used by local FVs and yachts; dries 3ca offshore. Ent difficult in strong W winds. Berth on N wall of inner hbr (free). Call ☎ (01946) 823741 Ext 148 for moorings. Limited facilities. **SC**.

AGENTS WANTED

If you are interested in becoming our agent for any of the following ports, please write to: The Editor, Edington House, Trent, Sherborne, Dorset DT9 4SR, England – and get your free copy of the Almanac annually. You do not have to live in a port to be the agent, but should at least be a fairly regular visitor.

Plymouth	Port Haliguen
Walton-on-the-Naze	La Trinité-sur-Mer
Hopeman	Piriac
Burghead	St Nazaire/Loire
Findhorn	Pornic
Nairn	St Gilles-Croix-de-Vie
Inverness	Les Sables d'Olonne
Loch Aline	River Seudre
Craobh	Port Bloc/Gironde
Workington	Anglet/Bayonne
Lough Swilly	St Jean-de-Luz
Portbail	Hendaye
St Malo/Dinard	Grandcamp-Maisy
Le Légué/St Brieuc	Port-en-Bessin
Lampaul	Ouistreham/Caen
L'Aberildut	Dives
Douarnenez	St Valéry-en-Caux
Lorient	Dunkerque
River Étel	Emden
Le Palais (Belle Ile)	Langeoog

WORKINGTON *continued*

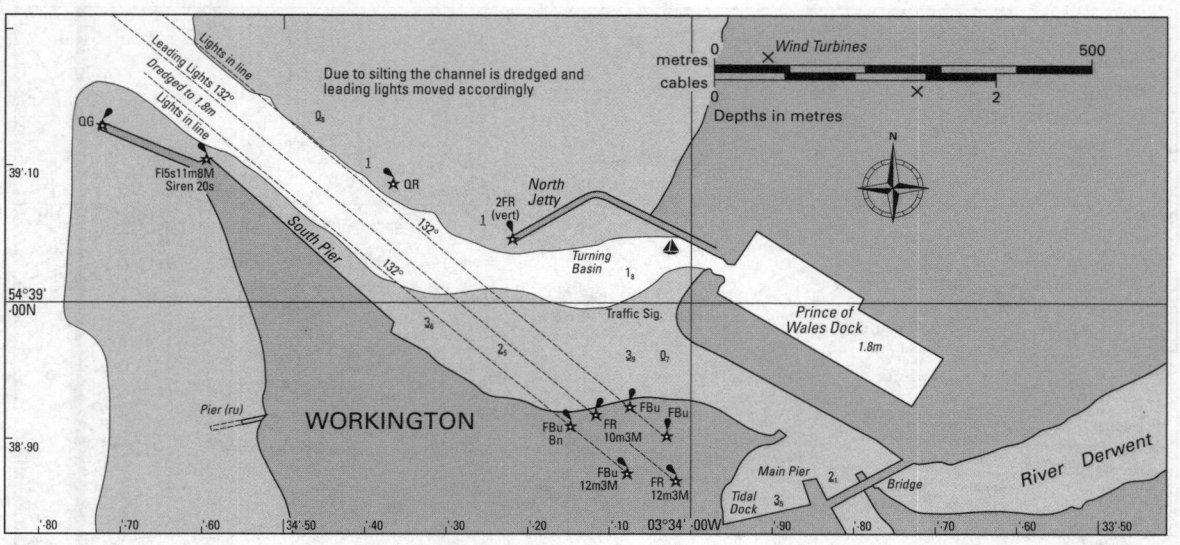

WHITEHAVEN   8-10-10

Cumbria 54°33'·17N 03°35'·74W   Rtg 2-3-2

CHARTS
AC 2013, 1346, *1826*; Imray C62; OS 89

TIDES
+0015 Dover; ML 4·5; Duration 0550; Zone 0 (UT)

Standard Port LIVERPOOL (→)

Times				Height (metres)			
High Water		Low Water		MHWS	MHWN	MLWN	MLWS
0000	0600	0200	0800	9·3	7·4	2·9	0·9
1200	1800	1400	2000				
Differences WHITEHAVEN							
+0005	+0015	+0010	+0005	−1·3	−1·1	−0·5	+0·1
TARN POINT (3M S of Ravenglass)							
+0005	+0005	+0010	0000	−1·0	−1·0	−0·4	0·0
DUDDON BAR (54°09'N 03°20'W)							
+0003	+0003	+0008	+0002	−0·8	−0·8	−0·3	0·0

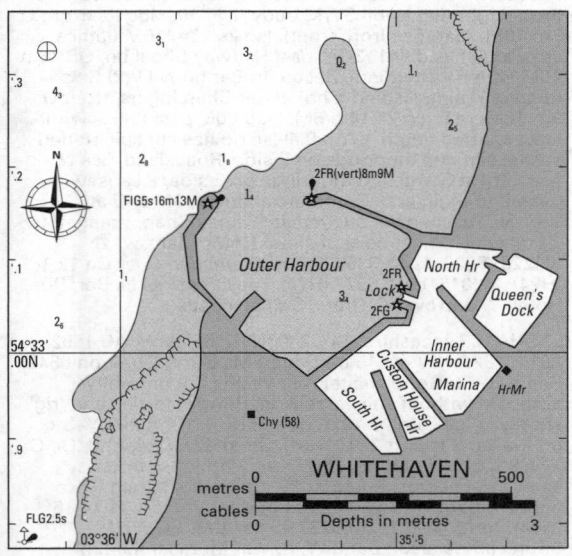

SHELTER
Very good, entry safe in most weathers. A new marina in the Inner Hbr was completed in autumn 1998 making Whitehaven one of the more accessible ports of refuge in NW England. Appr chan across the outer hbr is dredged to 1·0m above CD giving access approx HW+4. Sea lock (30m x 13.7m), with sill at CD, maintains 5·5m within inner hbr. Yacht pontoons are in Inner Hbr. Queens Dock (from which the lock gates have been removed) and N Hbr remain for commercial and FV use. *Further details will be in the Supplements.*

NAVIGATION
WPT 54°33'·33N 03°36'·13W, 313°/133° from/to W pier hd, 4½ca. There are no hazards in the offing. Keep close to W pier when entering on the flood, due to strong E'ly set.

LIGHTS AND MARKS
Several tall chimneys are charted within 1·5M S of hbr. St Bees Head, Fl (2) 20s 102m 21M, is 2·7M SSW of hbr ent. W pier Fl G 5s 16m 13M; N pier 2 FR (vert) 8m 9M; Sea lock 2 FR (vert) 8m 2M, and 2 FG (vert) 8m 2M. SHM bn, Fl G 2·5s, 4½ca S of W pierhead marks sewer outfall.

RADIO TELEPHONE
Hr Mr VHF Ch 12 16 (as for access times).

TELEPHONE (Dial code 01946)
Hr Mr 692435, ☎ 691135; ✠ (01482) 782107 (H24); MRSC (0151) 931 3341; Marinecall 0891 500 461.

FACILITIES
Marina (100) ☎ 692435, AC, FW, D at N Hbr wall, Slip, **SC**. **Town** EC Wed, Market days Thurs, Sat; P (cans), Bar, Ⓑ, ✉, R, V.

MINOR HARBOUR BETWEEN ST BEES HEAD AND MORECAMBE BAY

RAVENGLASS, Cumbria, 54°20'·00N 03°26'·80W (drying line). AC 1346, *1826*. HW +0020 on Dover; ML no data; Duration 0545. See 8.10.10 (Tarn Point). Large drying hbr, into which R's Mite, Irt and Esk flow; has approx 2·5m in ent at HW−2. Sellafield power stn with WCM lt buoy and outfall buoys are 5M NNW. FG ☆ (occas) is on blockhouse at S side of ent. *Solway Sailing Directions* with pilotage notes by Ravenglass Boating Ass'n or local knowledge are advised. From N beware Drigg Rk and from S Selker Rks, marked by SHM buoy Fl (3) G 10s, 5M SSW of ent. Firing range D406 is close S at Eskmeals; Mon-Thur 0800-1600LT (1500 Fri). When in use R flags flown, R lts at night; call *Eskmeals Gun Range* VHF Ch 16 13, ☎ (01229) 717631 Ext 245/6. **Village**: EC Wed; FW, Slip, Bar, V, ✉.

10

GLASSON DOCK   8-10-11

Lancashire 53°59'·97N 02°50'·85W   Rtg 3-1-2

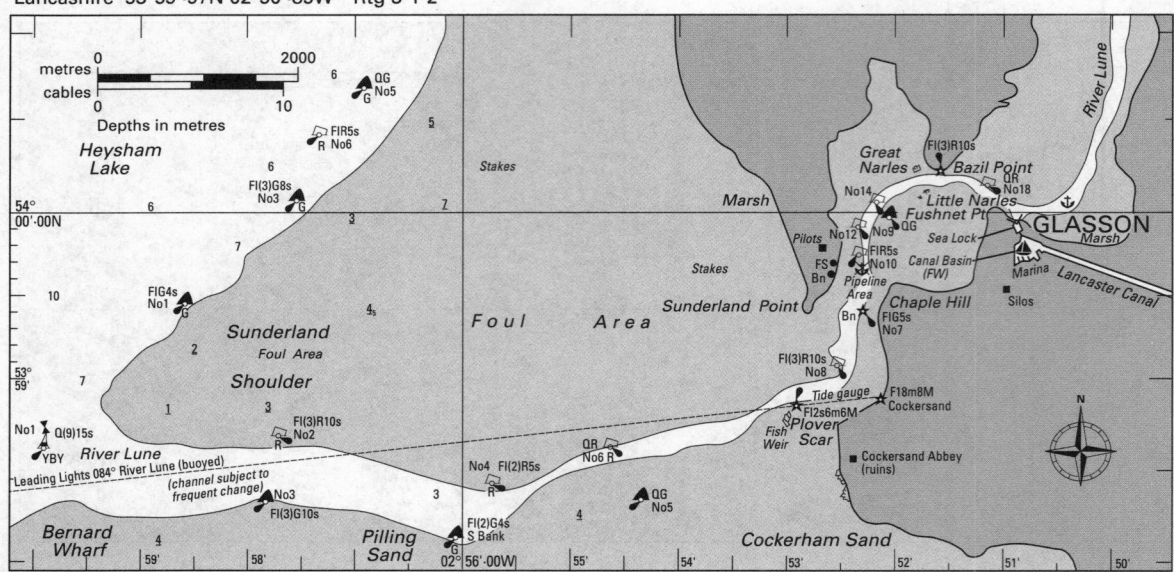

CHARTS
AC 1552, 2010, *1826*; Imray C62; OS 102, 97

TIDES
+0020 Dover; ML No data; Duration 0535; Zone 0 (UT)

Standard Port LIVERPOOL (→)

Times				Height (metres)			
High Water		Low Water		MHWS	MHWN	MLWN	MLWS
0000	0600	0200	0700	9·3	7·4	2·9	0·9
1200	1800	1400	1900				

Differences BARROW-IN-FURNESS (Ramsden Dock)

+0015	+0015	+0015	+0015	0·0	−0·3	+0·1	+0·2
ULVERSTON							
+0020	+0040	No data		0·0	−0·1	No data	
ARNSIDE							
+0100	+0135	No data		+0·5	+0·2	No data	
MORECAMBE							
+0005	+0010	+0030	+0015	+0·2	0·0	0·0	+0·2
HEYSHAM							
+0005	+0005	+0015	0000	+0·1	0·0	0·0	+0·2
GLASSON DOCK							
+0020	+0030	+0220	+0240	−2·7	−3·0	No data	
LANCASTER							
+0110	+0030	No data		−5·0	−4·9	Dries out	

Note: At Glasson Dock LW time differences give the end of a LW stand which lasts up to 2 hours at sp.

SHELTER
Very good in marina; also sheltered ⚓ in R Lune to await sea lock, opens HW Liverpool −0045 to HW, into Glasson Dock. Inner lock/swing bridge lead into BWB basin.

NAVIGATION
WPT 53°58'·40N 03°00'·00W (2ca S of R Lune No 1 WCM By), 264°/084° from/to front ldg lt 084°, 4·2M. Leave WPT at HW−2 via buoyed/lit chan. Plover Scar lt bn has a tide gauge showing depth over the lock sill at Glasson Dock. ⚓ is prohib between Sutherland Pt and No 10 PHM lt buoy. Beyond this a training wall, marked by PHM lt buoys/bn, extends to lock ent. R Lune is navigable to Lancaster.

LIGHTS AND MARKS
Ldg lts (hard to see from WPT): Plover Scar, Fl 2s, on with Cockersand, FW, leads 084° up to Nos 2 /3 buoys; thence follow buoyed chan which shifts.

Tfc Sigs by day (night) at E side of lock:

1 ● (Ⓡ)	= lock manned, but shut
R flag (Ⓡ over Ⓦ)	= lock open, clear to enter
R flag over ● (2 Ⓡ vert)	= lock open, vessels leaving

RADIO TELEPHONE
VHF Ch 69 16 (HW−2 to HW+1). Marina Ch 80.

TELEPHONE (Dial code 01524)
Hr Mr 751724; MRSC 0151-931 3341; ⌗ (0161) 912 6977 (H24); Marinecall 0891 500 461; Police 791239; Ⓗ 765944.

FACILITIES
Marina (240+20 visitors) ☎ 751491, £7.50, Slip, D, FW, AC, ME, El, Ⓔ, Sh, C, (50 ton), BH (50 ton), CH, ⚓;
Glasson Basin, M, AB; **Glasson SC** ☎ 751089 Slip, M, C;
Lune CC Access HW±2.
Town EC Lancaster Wed; P (cans), V, R, Bar, ✉, Ⓑ (Lancaster), ⇌ (bus to Lancaster 4M), ✈ (Blackpool).

ADJACENT HARBOURS IN MORECAMBE BAY

BARROW-IN-FURNESS, Cumbria, 54°05'·63N 03°13'·36W. AC 3164, 2010, *1826*. HW +0030 on Dover; See 8·10·11. ML 5·0m; Duration 0530. Good shelter but open to SE'lies. Drying moorings off Piel and Roa Islands or ⚓ clear of fairway. Marks/lts: Walney Island lt ho (conspic stone tr), Fl 15s 21m 23M (obsc 122°-127° within 3M of shore), RC. From Lightning Knoll SWM buoy (L Fl 10s) ldg lts, front Q 7m 10M; rear (6ca from front), Iso 2s 13m 10M (lattice structures) lead 041°/3·7M past Halfway Shoal bn, QR 16m 10M with RY chequers, Racon, to Bar buoy Fl (2) R 5s (abeam Walney Island lt ho). Inner Chan ldg lts, front Q 9m 10M, rear Iso 2s 14m 6M, lead 006° past Piel Is with least charted depth 1·7m. Piel Island has conspic ruined castle, slip and moorings on E side. Roa Island, 5ca N, has jetty at S end and moorings on E side; a causeway joins it to mainland. Commercial docks, 3M NW at Barrow, reached via buoyed/lit Walney Chan, dredged to 2·5m, which must be kept clear. Hr Mr (Barrow) ☎ (01229) 822911, 📠 835822; VHF *Ramsden Dock* Ch 12 16 (H24). ⌗ (0161) 912 6977 (H24). Facilities: Piel Is, Bar; Roa, Hotel, V. **Barrow** EC Thurs; SM, all needs.

HEYSHAM, Lancashire, 54°02'·00N 02°55'·88W. AC 1552, 2010, *1826*. HW +0015 on Dover; ML 5·1m; Duration 0545. See 8·10·11. Good shelter, but yachts not normally accepted without special reason. Beware ferries and 'rig' supply ships. Ldg lts 102°, both F Bu 11/14m 2M, Y+B ◊ on masts. S jetty lt 2 FG (vert). Siren 30s. S pier hd, Oc G 7·5s 9m 6M. N pier hd, 2FR (vert) 11m, obsc from seaward. Ent sigs: R flag or Ⓡ = no entry; no sig = no dep; 2 R flags or 2 Ⓡ = no ent or dep. VHF Ch 14 74 16 (H24). Hr Mr ☎ (01524) 52373. Facilities: EC Wed (Morecambe also); Bar, FW, R, V at Morecambe (2M).

FLEETWOOD   8-10-12

Lancashire 53°55'·48N 03°00'·07W   Rtg 1 (hbr) -2-2

CHARTS
AC 1552, 2010, *1826*; Imray C62; OS 102

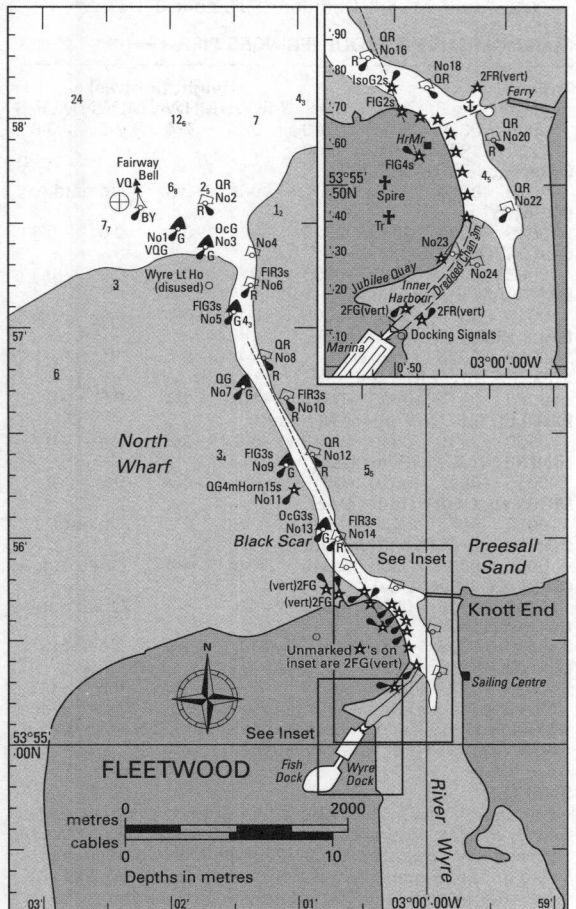

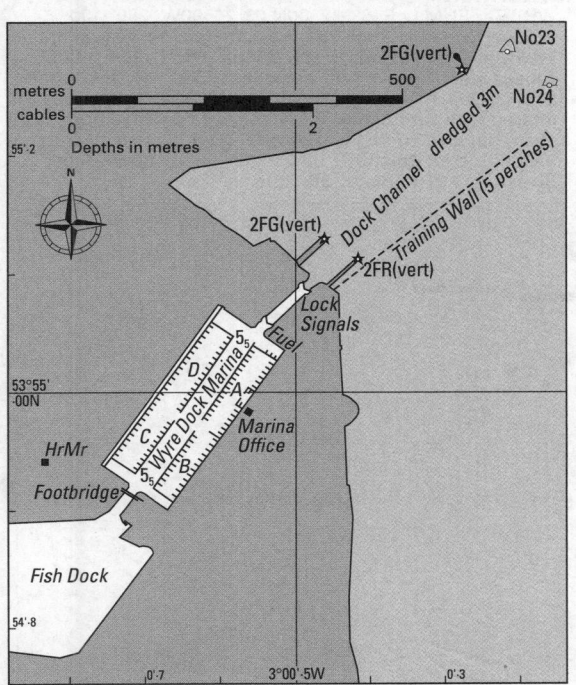

TIDES
+0015 Dover; ML 5.0; Duration 0530; Zone 0 (UT)

Standard Port LIVERPOOL (→)

Times				Height (metres)			
High Water		Low Water		MHWS	MHWN	MLWN	MLWS
0000	0600	0200	0700	9·3	7·4	2·9	0·9
1200	1800	1400	1900				
Differences WYRE LIGHTHOUSE							
–0010	–0010	+0005	0000	–0.1	–0.1	No data	
FLEETWOOD							
0000	0000	+0005	0000	–0.1	–0.1	+0.1	+0.3
BLACKPOOL							
–0015	–0005	–0005	–0015	–0.4	–0.4	–0.1	+0.1

SHELTER
Very good in Wyre Dock Marina 5·5m. Sheltered ⚓ off Knott End pier on E bank to await tide. Passage up-river to Skippool (5M) needs local knowledge and shoal draft; access HW±1 (if ht of tide is >8·0m).

NAVIGATION
WPT 53°57'·57N 03°02'·25W, Fairway NCM lt buoy, 290°/110° from/to No 1 SHM lt buoy, 3ca; here the appr chan turns SE then S. Caution: avoid ferries and dredgers turning in lower hbr, dredged 4·5m. Further up the hbr, Nos 23 SHM and 24 PHM buoys mark start of marina ent chan dredged to drying height of 3m, giving access HW±2 to lock. For best water keep 15m NW of the 300m long training wall (5 Y perches, △ topmarks).

LIGHTS AND MARKS
Chan is well buoyed/lit. Ldg lts, front Fl G 2s; rear Fl G 4s, 156° (only to be used between Nos 8 and 13 buoys). Lock sigs (only enter on instructions): 1 ● (1 ®) = Gates open for entry; 2 ● (2 ®) = open for departures.

RADIO TELEPHONE
Call *Fleetwood Hbr Control* Ch 11, when ferries under way. Call *Fleetwood Dock* Ch 12 16, HW±2 for marina/Fish Dock.

TELEPHONE (Dial code 01253)
Hr Mr (ABP) 872323, 🖇 777549; MRSC (0151) 931 3341/3; ⌗ (0151) 922 9161 and (0161) 912 6977 (H24); Marinecall 0891 500 461; Police 876611; Dr 873312.

FACILITIES
Marina (210) ☎ 872323, 🖇 777549, £13.51, D, FW, AC, Ⓞ, C (25 ton), CH, SM, ACA, ME, El, Sh, Ⓔ, C (mobile 50 ton by arrangement).
Wardley's YC ☎ 700429, 1 Ⓥ.
Blackpool & Fleetwood YC (Skippool) ☎ 884205, AB, Slip, FW, Bar; **Town** EC Wed; P & D (cans), ME, El, Sh, CH, V, R, Bar, ✉, Ⓑ, ⇌ (Poulton-le-Fylde or Blackpool), ✈ (Blackpool).

10

RIVER RIBBLE/PRESTON: *See overleaf*

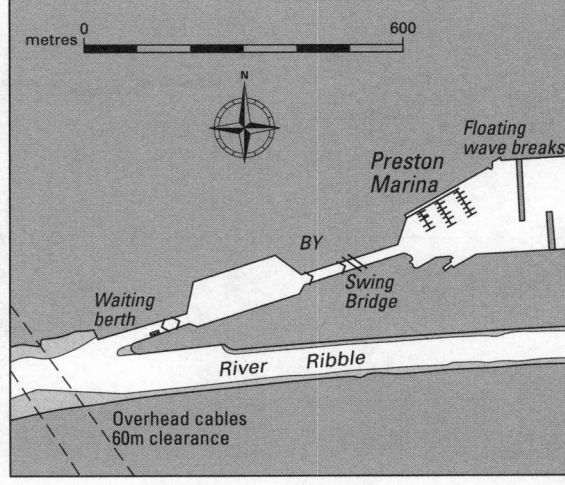

RIVER RIBBLE/PRESTON   8-10-13

Lancashire 53°43´·50N 03°00´·00W   Rtg 3-1-2

CHARTS
AC 1981, *1826*; Imray C62; OS 102
TIDES
+0013 Dover; ML No data; Duration 0520; Zone 0 (UT)

Standard Port LIVERPOOL (→)

Times				Height (metres)			
High Water		Low Water		MHWS	MHWN	MLWN	MLWS
0000	0600	0200	0700	9·3	7·4	2·9	0·9
1200	1800	1400	1900				
Differences PRESTON							
+0010	+0010	+0335	+0310	−4·0	−4·1	−2·8	−0·8

LW time differences give the end of a LW stand lasting 3½ hrs.

SHELTER
Good in Preston marina (5m depth; see chartlet overleaf)
15M upriver. Lock in HW±1½, (no commercial tfc); lay-by
berth outside No 1 Lock for 2m draft. Swing bridge opens
in unison with locks. Possible drying berths on the N bank
at Lytham or Freckleton, or 2M up R Douglas access HW±1.
NAVIGATION
WPT Ⓐ 53°41´·75N 03°08´·90W, Gut SWM buoy, L Fl 10s.
The seaward 2·5M of original lit chan has silted up; best
water is now via South Gut chan (liable to shift), navigable
HW±2. Not before HW Liverpool −2, leave WPT Ⓐ tracking
2M E to WPT Ⓑ 53°41´·80N 03°05´·50W, at the ent to S
Gut chan. Thence the transit of 11½M perch, Fl (2) R 10s,
with conspic W Dome leads 055° to a gap in the south
training wall at WPT Ⓒ 53°43´·30N 03°01´·85W. Enter via
the gap, leaving 11½M perch 100m to port. The river
trends 080° between training walls, drying <u>3</u>m, marked by
perches, lit as below, but night appr not advised.
Note: The chartlet shows only the seaward end of the
estuary. The rest of the 15M long chan is straightforward.
A chartlet of the marina entrance is shown overleaf.
LIGHTS AND MARKS
14½M perch, Fl G 5s, is the most seaward chan mark. Up-
river from 11½M perch there is a PHM buoy and perch
(off chartlet), both Fl R 5s. 4 SHM perches, Fl G 5s, lead to
5M perch, Fl (2) G 10s, marking mouth of unlit R Douglas.
3M and 2M perches are Fl G 5s; 1M perch is Fl G 10s. Tfc
lts at locks into marina. Warton airfield beacon, Mo (WQ)
G 9s, is N abeam 5M perch, Fl G 5s.
RADIO TELEPHONE
At Preston, for locks call *Riversway* Ch 16 14; Marina Ch **80**,
both (HW−3 to +1½). Douglas BY Ch 16 when vessel due.
TELEPHONE (Dial code 01772)
Preston Locks 726711; ⌗ (0161) 912 6977; MRSC (0151)
9313341; Marinecall 0891 500461; Police 203203; Ⓗ 710408.
FACILITIES
Douglas BY, ☎/⛴ 812462, AB, C (7 ton), CH, D, FW, Sh,
Slip, ME. **Preston Marina** (250) ☎ 733595, ⛴ 731881, £5,
AC, FW, D, CH, ME, Sh, Gas, C (50 ton), R, V, ACA.
Ribble Cruising Club ☎ (01253) 739983. ACA at Southport.

See chartlet of Preston marina overleaf.

LIVERPOOL   8-10-14

Merseyside 53°24´·20N 03°00´·20W (Liver Bldg)   Rtg 2-1-2

CHARTS
AC 3490, 1951, *1978, 1826*; Imray C62; OS 108
TIDES
+0015 Dover; ML 5·2; Duration 0535; Zone 0 (UT)

Standard Port LIVERPOOL (PRINCES PIER) (→)

Times				Height (metres)			
High Water		Low Water		MHWS	MHWN	MLWN	MLWS
0000	0600	0200	0700	9·3	7·4	2·9	0·9
1200	1800	1400	1900				
Differences SOUTHPORT							
−0020	−0010	No data		−0·3	−0·3	No data	
FORMBY							
−0015	−0010	−0020	−0020	−0·3	−0·1	0·0	+0·1
GLADSTONE DOCK							
−0003	−0003	−0003	−0003	−0·1	−0·1	0·0	−0·1
EASTHAM (River Mersey)							
+0010	+0010	+0009	+0009	+0·3	+0·1	−0·1	−0·3
HALE HEAD (River Mersey)							
+0030	+0025	No data		−2·4	−2·5	No data	
WIDNES (River Mersey)							
+0040	+0045	+0400	+0345	−4·2	−4·4	−2·5	−0·3
FIDDLER'S FERRY (River Mersey)							
+0100	+0115	+0540	+0450	−5·9	−6·3	−2·4	−0·4
HILBRE ISLAND (River Dee)							
−0015	−0012	−0010	−0015	−0·3	−0·2	+0·2	+0·4
MOSTYN QUAY (River Dee)							
−0020	−0015	−0020	−0020	−0·8	−0·7	No data	
CONNAH'S QUAY (River Dee)							
0000	+0015	+0355	+0340	−4·6	−4·4	Dries out	
CHESTER (River Dee)							
+0105	+0105	+0500	+0500	−5·3	−5·4	Dries out	
COLWYN BAY							
−0035	−0025	No data		−1·5	−1·3	No data	
LLANDUDNO							
−0035	−0025	−0025	−0035	−1·9	−1·5	−0·5	−0·2

NOTE: LW time differences at Connah's Quay give the end
of a LW stand lasting about 3¾hrs at sp and 5hrs at nps. A
bore occurs in the R Dee at Chester.

SHELTER
Good at marina in the Coburg and Brunswick docks. Ent is
1M S of Liver Bldg and abeam the Pluckington Bank WCM;
access HW ±2 approx, 0600-2200 Mar-Oct. Good shelter
also in Canning and Albert Docks but access HW−2 to HW.
‡ on the SW side of river but only in fair weather.
NAVIGATION
WPT Bar PHM Lt F 53°32´·00N 03°20´·90W, 280°/100°
from/to Queen's Chan, 3M. From Bar Lt F to marina ent is
17M via Queen's and Crosby Chans. Wind against tide
causes steep seas in outer reaches of Mersey. The whole
area (R Dee, R Mersey to R Alt and N to Morecambe B) is
littered with sandbanks. R Mersey is safe inside buoyed
chan, but elsewhere local knowledge and great caution
needed. For **R Dee:** WPT 53°26´·20N 03°16´·80W, Hilbre
Swash HE2 PHM buoy, QR, (chan shifts).

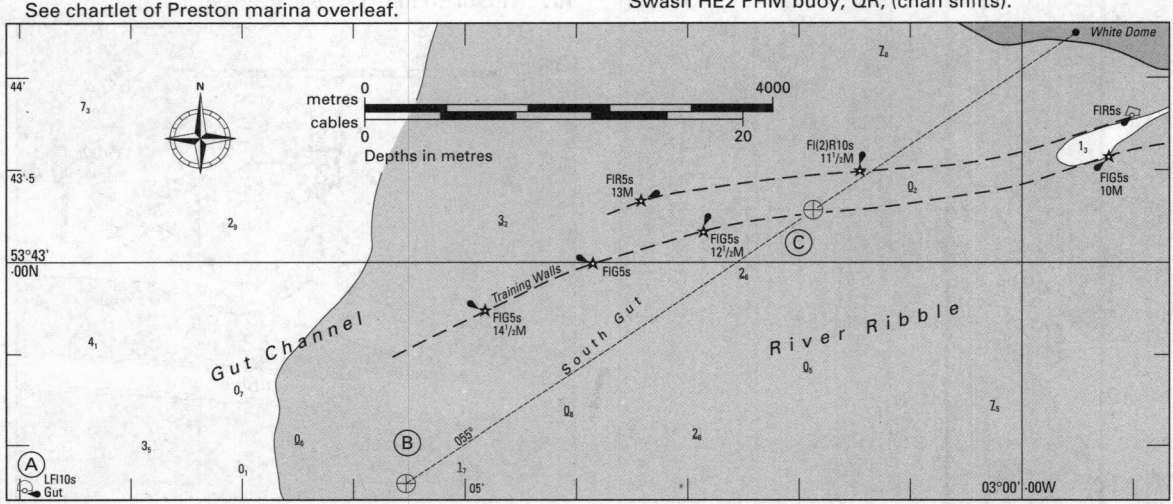

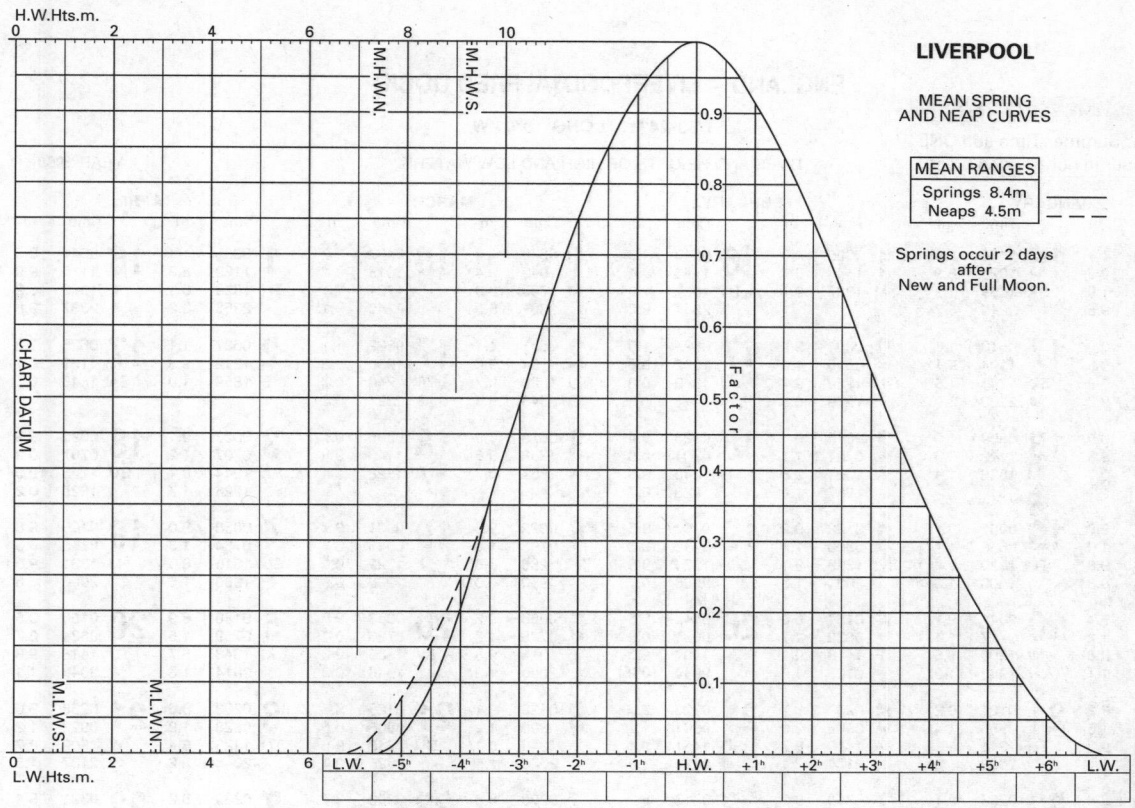

H.W.Hts.m.

LIVERPOOL

MEAN SPRING
AND NEAP CURVES

MEAN RANGES	
Springs	8.4m
Neaps	4.5m

Springs occur 2 days
after
New and Full Moon.

10

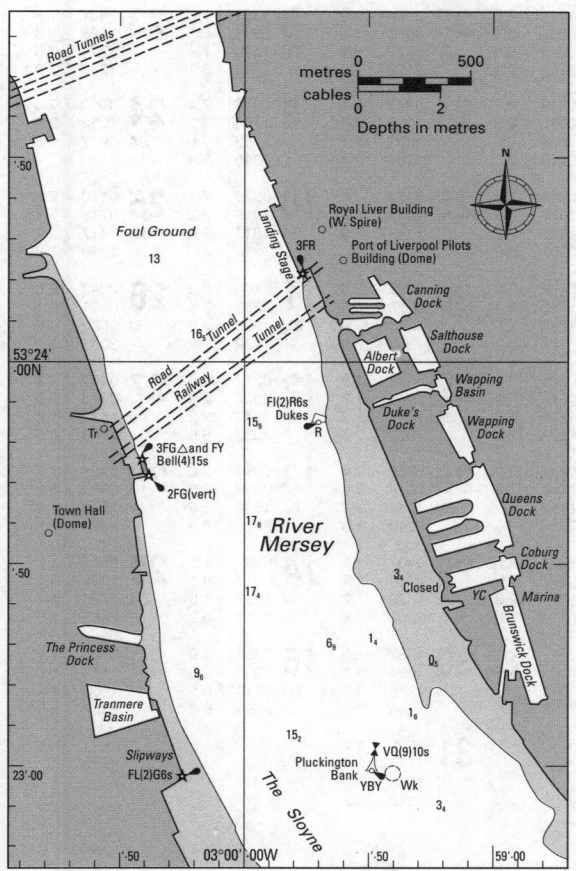

LIGHTS AND MARKS

The ent to R Mersey is at the Bar PHM lt F, Fl 5s 12m 21M, Horn (2) 20s, Racon. Queen's Chan and Crosby Chan are marked by Boat lt bns to port, normal buoys to stbd. Formby and Crosby lt Floats are mid-chan SWMs. See also 8.10.4. Both chans have training banks which cover. Conspic black control bldg at lock ent has 3 R/G lts (vert).

RADIO TELEPHONE

Call: *Mersey Radio* VHF **Ch 12** 16 (H24). Radar Ch 18. Marina Ch M. Traffic movements, nav warnings and weather reports broadcast on Ch 09 at HW–3 and –2. Local nav and gale warnings are broadcast on receipt on Ch 12. Eastham Locks Ch 07 (H24). Manchester Ship Canal Ch 14.

TELEPHONE (Dial code 0151)

Port Ops 949 6134/5; MRSC 931 3341; ⊞ (0161) 912 6977; Marinecall 0891 500 461; Police 709 6010; Ⓗ 709 0141.

FACILITIES

Marina (300 + 50) ☎ 708 5228, (0600-2130 Mar–Oct), 🛥 709 8731. Ent via Brunswick Dock lock, min depth 3·5m. £11.63, D, P (½M), AC, FW, BH (60 ton), Slip, CH, SM, Bar, ⬛, ♿,R, V; **Albert Dock** ☎ 236 6090, VHF Ch M when ent manned, AB, FW, AC;
Royal Mersey YC ☎ 645 3204, Slip, M, P, D, L, FW, R, Bar.
W Kirby SC ☎ 625 5579, AB (at HW), Slip, M (in Dee Est), L, FW, C (30ton), Bar; **Hoylake SC** ☎ 632 2616, Slip, M, FW, Bar; **Services:** CH, SM, ME, El, Sh, ACA, Ⓔ.
City EC Wed; ✉, Ⓑ, ⇌, ✈.
Note: Access to E Coast via Leeds & Liverpool Canal (BWB), ent at Stanley Dock. Max draft 1·0m, air draft 2·2m, beam 4·3m, LOA 18·3m. Liverpool to Goole 161M, 103 locks.

ADJACENT ANCHORAGE

RIVER ALT, Merseyside, 53°31′·40N 03°03′·72W. AC 1951, *1978*. HW –0008 on Dover; see 8·10·14. Good shelter but only for LOA <8·5m x 1·2m draft on a HW of at least 8m. Mersey E training wall can be crossed HW±2. Ent to chan (shifts frequently) is E of C14 PHM lt float, thence marked by locally-laid Y Fairway buoy and perches on the training wall. Unsafe to ⚓ in R Alt; pick up a free mooring off the SC and contact club. Local knowledge advised. Facilities very limited. **Blundellsands SC** ☎ (0151) 929 2101 (occas), Slip, L (at HW), FW, Bar.

ENGLAND – LIVERPOOL (ALFRED DOCK)

LAT 53°24′N   LONG 3°01′W

TIMES AND HEIGHTS OF HIGH AND LOW WATERS

YEAR **1999**

TIME ZONE (UT)
For Summer Time add ONE hour in non-shaded areas

Chart Datum: 4·93 metres below Ordnance Datum (Newlyn)

JANUARY

Day	Time	m	Day	Time	m
1 F	0439 / 1017 / 1710 / 2243	1.1 / 9.5 / 1.0 / 9.6	16 SA	0438 / 1026 / 1659 / 2245	1.9 / 8.9 / 1.9 / 8.7
2 SA O	0528 / 1106 / 1801 / 2331	0.9 / 9.8 / 0.8 / 9.7	17 SU ●	0518 / 1104 / 1741 / 2323	1.6 / 9.1 / 1.6 / 8.9
3 SU	0615 / 1152 / 1849	0.9 / 9.8 / 0.7	18 M	0559 / 1142 / 1823	1.5 / 9.3 / 1.4
4 M	0017 / 0659 / 1237 / 1934	9.6 / 1.0 / 9.8 / 0.8	19 TU	0001 / 0638 / 1220 / 1903	9.1 / 1.4 / 9.4 / 1.3
5 TU	0102 / 0741 / 1320 / 2017	9.4 / 1.2 / 9.6 / 1.1	20 W	0041 / 0717 / 1300 / 1943	9.1 / 1.4 / 9.5 / 1.2
6 W	0145 / 0821 / 1402 / 2058	9.2 / 1.6 / 9.3 / 1.4	21 TH	0121 / 0756 / 1341 / 2022	9.2 / 1.4 / 9.5 / 1.2
7 TH	0226 / 0900 / 1443 / 2138	8.8 / 2.0 / 8.9 / 1.9	22 F	0203 / 0836 / 1424 / 2102	8.9 / 1.5 / 9.4 / 1.4
8 F	0308 / 0939 / 1525 / 2219	8.4 / 2.4 / 8.5 / 2.3	23 SA	0247 / 0917 / 1510 / 2145	8.9 / 1.8 / 9.1 / 1.7
9 SA	0353 / 1022 / 1612 / 2306	7.9 / 2.8 / 8.0 / 2.7	24 SU	0335 / 1005 / 1602 / 2236	8.6 / 2.1 / 8.8 / 2.0
10 SU	0446 / 1115 / 1710	7.5 / 3.2 / 7.6	25 M	0432 / 1103 / 1703 / 2340	8.2 / 2.4 / 8.4 / 2.4
11 M	0001 / 0553 / 1217 / 1820	3.0 / 7.3 / 3.4 / 7.4	26 TU	0540 / 1215 / 1814	7.9 / 2.6 / 8.2
12 TU	0104 / 0707 / 1324 / 1933	3.1 / 7.4 / 3.3 / 7.5	27 W	0055 / 0657 / 1338 / 1931	2.5 / 7.9 / 2.6 / 8.2
13 W	0208 / 0811 / 1430 / 2034	2.9 / 7.7 / 3.0 / 7.8	28 TH	0218 / 0812 / 1501 / 2043	2.4 / 8.2 / 2.3 / 8.5
14 TH	0306 / 0902 / 1527 / 2124	2.6 / 8.1 / 2.6 / 8.1	29 F	0331 / 0915 / 1608 / 2143	2.0 / 8.7 / 1.7 / 8.9
15 F	0354 / 0947 / 1616 / 2206	2.2 / 8.5 / 2.2 / 8.5	30 SA	0430 / 1008 / 1703 / 2235	1.5 / 9.2 / 1.2 / 9.3
			31 SU O	0520 / 1056 / 1752 / 2321	1.2 / 9.5 / 0.9 / 9.5

FEBRUARY

Day	Time	m	Day	Time	m
1 M	0605 / 1140 / 1837	1.0 / 9.7 / 0.7	16 TU ●	0543 / 1123 / 1807 / 2344	1.3 / 9.4 / 1.0 / 9.2
2 TU	0004 / 0646 / 1222 / 1919	9.5 / 1.0 / 9.7 / 0.8	17 W	0624 / 1202 / 1849	1.0 / 9.6 / 0.8
3 W	0045 / 0724 / 1301 / 1957	9.4 / 1.1 / 9.6 / 1.0	18 TH	0023 / 0704 / 1243 / 1928	9.4 / 0.9 / 9.8 / 0.7
4 TH	0122 / 0800 / 1338 / 2031	9.2 / 1.4 / 9.4 / 1.3	19 F	0104 / 0743 / 1324 / 2006	9.5 / 0.8 / 9.8 / 0.7
5 F	0157 / 0832 / 1413 / 2103	9.0 / 1.7 / 9.1 / 1.6	20 SA	0145 / 0821 / 1407 / 2044	9.5 / 0.9 / 9.7 / 0.9
6 SA	0233 / 0902 / 1449 / 2134	8.7 / 2.0 / 8.7 / 2.1	21 SU	0228 / 0901 / 1451 / 2124	9.3 / 1.2 / 9.4 / 1.3
7 SU	0310 / 0935 / 1528 / 2210	8.3 / 2.4 / 8.3 / 2.5	22 M	0313 / 0946 / 1540 / 2211	8.9 / 1.6 / 8.9 / 1.8
8 M	0352 / 1018 / 1614 / 2258	7.8 / 2.9 / 7.8 / 3.0	23 TU	0405 / 1040 / 1638 / 2311	8.3 / 2.2 / 8.3 / 2.4
9 TU	0446 / 1117 / 1712	7.4 / 3.2 / 7.3	24 W	0512 / 1151 / 1752	7.8 / 2.6 / 7.8
10 W	0002 / 0556 / 1228 / 1827	3.2 / 7.1 / 3.4 / 7.1	25 TH	0028 / 0636 / 1321 / 1919	2.8 / 7.6 / 2.7 / 7.8
11 TH	0113 / 0719 / 1341 / 1950	3.3 / 7.3 / 3.2 / 7.3	26 F	0201 / 0800 / 1455 / 2036	2.7 / 7.9 / 2.3 / 8.1
12 F	0222 / 0828 / 1449 / 2054	3.0 / 7.7 / 2.8 / 7.7	27 SA	0324 / 0906 / 1602 / 2135	2.3 / 8.4 / 1.7 / 8.6
13 SA	0323 / 0920 / 1548 / 2143	2.5 / 8.2 / 2.3 / 8.2	28 SU	0423 / 0958 / 1654 / 2224	1.8 / 9.0 / 1.2 / 9.0
14 SU	0414 / 1004 / 1638 / 2225	2.1 / 8.7 / 1.8 / 8.6			
15 M	0500 / 1044 / 1724 / 2305	1.6 / 9.1 / 1.4 / 9.0			

MARCH

Day	Time	m	Day	Time	m
1 M	0510 / 1043 / 1739 / 2307	1.4 / 9.4 / 0.9 / 9.3	16 TU	0437 / 1018 / 1701 / 2240	1.6 / 9.1 / 1.1 / 9.1
2 TU O	0551 / 1124 / 1820 / 2346	1.1 / 9.6 / 0.7 / 9.4	17 W ●	0522 / 1059 / 1746 / 2321	1.1 / 9.5 / 0.7 / 9.4
3 W	0629 / 1202 / 1857	1.0 / 9.6 / 0.7	18 TH	0605 / 1140 / 1828	0.7 / 9.8 / 0.4
4 TH	0022 / 0703 / 1238 / 1930	9.3 / 1.0 / 9.5 / 0.9	19 F	0001 / 0646 / 1222 / 1908	9.7 / 0.5 / 10.0 / 0.3
5 F	0056 / 0735 / 1311 / 2000	9.2 / 1.2 / 9.3 / 1.2	20 SA	0043 / 0726 / 1305 / 1946	9.8 / 0.4 / 10.0 / 0.3
6 SA	0128 / 0803 / 1343 / 2026	9.1 / 1.4 / 9.1 / 1.5	21 SU	0125 / 0806 / 1348 / 2025	9.7 / 0.5 / 9.8 / 0.6
7 SU	0200 / 0829 / 1417 / 2051	8.8 / 1.7 / 8.8 / 1.9	22 M	0208 / 0846 / 1433 / 2105	9.4 / 0.8 / 9.4 / 1.1
8 M	0234 / 0857 / 1453 / 2121	8.5 / 2.1 / 8.4 / 2.3	23 TU	0254 / 0931 / 1522 / 2152	9.0 / 1.3 / 8.8 / 1.8
9 TU	0312 / 0935 / 1534 / 2203	8.1 / 2.5 / 7.9 / 2.8	24 W	0345 / 1026 / 1621 / 2251	8.4 / 2.0 / 8.1 / 2.4
10 W	0358 / 1027 / 1625 / 2307	7.6 / 3.0 / 7.3 / 3.3	25 TH	0452 / 1138 / 1739	7.8 / 2.5 / 7.6
11 TH	0458 / 1140 / 1733	7.2 / 3.3 / 7.0	26 F	0009 / 0620 / 1311 / 1908	2.9 / 7.5 / 2.6 / 7.5
12 F	0025 / 0618 / 1259 / 1857	3.4 / 7.0 / 3.3 / 7.0	27 SA	0147 / 0744 / 1443 / 2022	2.9 / 7.7 / 2.3 / 7.9
13 SA	0141 / 0744 / 1412 / 2018	3.2 / 7.3 / 2.9 / 7.4	28 SU	0312 / 0848 / 1547 / 2119	2.4 / 8.3 / 1.6 / 8.4
14 SU	0250 / 0847 / 1518 / 2114	2.7 / 7.9 / 2.3 / 8.0	29 M	0407 / 0940 / 1636 / 2206	1.9 / 8.8 / 1.2 / 8.8
15 M	0347 / 0935 / 1613 / 2159	2.1 / 8.5 / 1.7 / 8.6	30 TU	0452 / 1024 / 1718 / 2246	1.5 / 9.1 / 0.9 / 9.1
			31 W O	0530 / 1103 / 1755 / 2323	1.2 / 9.3 / 0.8 / 9.2

APRIL

Day	Time	m	Day	Time	m
1 TH	0605 / 1139 / 1829 / 2356	1.1 / 9.3 / 0.9 / 9.2	16 F ●	0541 / 1115 / 1803 / 2337	0.5 / 9.9 / 0.2 / 9.8
2 F	0637 / 1212 / 1859	1.1 / 9.3 / 1.0	17 SA	0625 / 1159 / 1845	0.3 / 10.1 / 0.1
3 SA	0027 / 0707 / 1244 / 1926	9.1 / 1.2 / 9.1 / 1.2	18 SU	0020 / 0707 / 1245 / 1925	9.9 / 0.2 / 10.0 / 0.2
4 SU	0058 / 0734 / 1315 / 1950	9.0 / 1.3 / 8.9 / 1.5	19 M	0105 / 0750 / 1331 / 2006	9.8 / 0.3 / 9.8 / 0.6
5 M	0130 / 0759 / 1348 / 2014	8.9 / 1.5 / 8.7 / 1.8	20 TU	0150 / 0834 / 1418 / 2048	9.5 / 0.7 / 9.3 / 1.1
6 TU	0203 / 0828 / 1423 / 2044	8.6 / 1.8 / 8.4 / 2.2	21 W	0238 / 0922 / 1509 / 2137	9.0 / 1.2 / 8.7 / 1.8
7 W	0239 / 0904 / 1502 / 2123	8.2 / 2.3 / 7.9 / 2.7	22 TH	0331 / 1018 / 1608 / 2236	8.4 / 1.8 / 8.1 / 2.4
8 TH	0321 / 0951 / 1550 / 2219	7.8 / 2.7 / 7.4 / 3.1	23 F	0437 / 1128 / 1724 / 2350	7.9 / 2.3 / 7.6 / 2.9
9 F	0416 / 1100 / 1653 / 2340	7.4 / 3.1 / 7.0 / 3.4	24 SA	0600 / 1252 / 1847	7.6 / 2.4 / 7.5
10 SA	0529 / 1219 / 1811	7.1 / 3.2 / 7.0	25 SU	0120 / 0718 / 1417 / 1956	2.9 / 7.7 / 2.2 / 7.7
11 SU	0100 / 0652 / 1335 / 1932	3.3 / 7.3 / 2.8 / 7.3	26 M	0243 / 0821 / 1520 / 2052	2.6 / 8.1 / 1.8 / 8.2
12 M	0212 / 0804 / 1443 / 2036	2.8 / 7.8 / 2.2 / 8.0	27 TU	0339 / 0913 / 1609 / 2139	2.1 / 8.5 / 1.5 / 8.6
13 TU	0314 / 0859 / 1542 / 2126	2.2 / 8.5 / 1.6 / 8.6	28 W	0424 / 0958 / 1649 / 2219	1.7 / 8.8 / 1.2 / 8.8
14 W	0407 / 0946 / 1633 / 2211	1.5 / 9.1 / 1.0 / 9.2	29 TH	0501 / 1037 / 1724 / 2255	1.5 / 9.0 / 1.1 / 9.0
15 TH	0455 / 1031 / 1719 / 2254	1.0 / 9.6 / 0.5 / 9.6	30 F O	0536 / 1113 / 1756 / 2327	1.3 / 9.0 / 1.1 / 9.0

ENGLAND – LIVERPOOL (ALFRED DOCK)

LAT 53°24′N   LONG 3°01′W

TIMES AND HEIGHTS OF HIGH AND LOW WATERS   YEAR **1999**

TIME ZONE (UT)
For Summer Time add ONE hour in non-shaded areas

MAY

Day	Time	m	Day	Time	m
1 SA	0608 / 1145 / 1826 / 2359	1.3 / 9.0 / 1.2 / 9.0	**16** SU	0604 / 1138 / 1822 / 2359	0.3 / 10.0 / 0.3 / 9.9
2 SU	0638 / 1217 / 1853	1.3 / 8.9 / 1.3	**17** M	0651 / 1226 / 1906	0.2 / 9.9 / 0.4
3 M	0030 / 0706 / 1249 / 1918	8.9 / 1.4 / 8.8 / 1.5	**18** TU	0046 / 0737 / 1315 / 1950	9.8 / 0.4 / 9.7 / 0.7
4 TU	0103 / 0735 / 1323 / 1946	8.8 / 1.5 / 8.6 / 1.8	**19** W	0135 / 0825 / 1405 / 2035	9.5 / 0.7 / 9.3 / 1.2
5 W	0137 / 0806 / 1358 / 2019	8.6 / 1.8 / 8.4 / 2.1	**20** TH	0224 / 0915 / 1456 / 2124	9.1 / 1.1 / 8.8 / 1.8
6 TH	0214 / 0843 / 1438 / 2057	8.4 / 2.1 / 8.1 / 2.5	**21** F	0317 / 1010 / 1553 / 2220	8.6 / 1.6 / 8.2 / 2.4
7 F	0255 / 0928 / 1524 / 2148	8.0 / 2.5 / 7.7 / 2.9	**22** SA	0418 / 1111 / 1659 / 2325	8.1 / 2.0 / 7.7 / 2.8
8 SA	0347 / 1028 / 1622 / 2258	7.7 / 2.8 / 7.4 / 3.2	**23** SU	0529 / 1220 / 1812	7.8 / 2.3 / 7.5
9 SU	0452 / 1141 / 1732	7.5 / 2.9 / 7.2	**24** M	0038 / 0640 / 1332 / 1919	2.9 / 7.7 / 2.3 / 7.6
10 M	0017 / 0606 / 1255 / 1847	3.2 / 7.5 / 2.6 / 7.5	**25** TU	0153 / 0744 / 1438 / 2017	2.8 / 7.9 / 2.2 / 7.9
11 TU	0129 / 0718 / 1404 / 1954	2.8 / 7.9 / 2.2 / 8.0	**26** W	0257 / 0839 / 1530 / 2105	2.5 / 8.2 / 1.9 / 8.3
12 W	0235 / 0819 / 1507 / 2050	2.2 / 8.5 / 1.6 / 8.6	**27** TH	0346 / 0926 / 1612 / 2147	2.1 / 8.4 / 1.7 / 8.5
13 TH	0334 / 0913 / 1602 / 2140	1.6 / 9.1 / 1.1 / 9.2	**28** F	0426 / 1008 / 1649 / 2225	1.9 / 8.6 / 1.6 / 8.7
14 F	0427 / 1003 / 1651 / 2227	1.0 / 9.6 / 0.6 / 9.6	**29** SA	0503 / 1045 / 1722 / 2259	1.6 / 8.7 / 1.5 / 8.8
15 SA ●	0516 / 1051 / 1738 / 2313	0.6 / 9.9 / 0.3 / 9.8	**30** SU ○	0537 / 1120 / 1753 / 2332	1.5 / 8.7 / 1.5 / 8.9
			31 M	0610 / 1153 / 1823	1.5 / 8.7 / 1.5

JUNE

Day	Time	m	Day	Time	m
1 TU	0006 / 0642 / 1227 / 1853	8.9 / 1.5 / 8.6 / 1.6	**16** W	0031 / 0727 / 1302 / 1936	9.7 / 0.5 / 9.6 / 0.9
2 W	0040 / 0715 / 1302 / 1926	8.8 / 1.6 / 8.6 / 1.8	**17** TH	0120 / 0816 / 1351 / 2022	9.5 / 0.7 / 9.3 / 1.3
3 TH	0116 / 0751 / 1339 / 2001	8.7 / 1.7 / 8.4 / 2.0	**18** F	0208 / 0904 / 1439 / 2108	9.3 / 1.0 / 8.9 / 1.7
4 F	0154 / 0830 / 1419 / 2041	8.6 / 1.9 / 8.3 / 2.3	**19** SA	0258 / 0953 / 1529 / 2156	8.9 / 1.4 / 8.4 / 2.2
5 SA	0236 / 0913 / 1504 / 2127	8.4 / 2.2 / 8.0 / 2.6	**20** SU	0350 / 1044 / 1623 / 2249	8.4 / 1.9 / 7.9 / 2.6
6 SU	0325 / 1005 / 1556 / 2226	8.1 / 2.4 / 7.8 / 2.8	**21** M	0448 / 1138 / 1725 / 2349	8.0 / 2.3 / 7.6 / 2.9
7 M	0423 / 1106 / 1659 / 2334	8.0 / 2.5 / 7.7 / 2.9	**22** TU	0553 / 1237 / 1831	7.7 / 2.5 / 7.5
8 TU	0530 / 1213 / 1808	7.9 / 2.4 / 7.8	**23** W	0053 / 0658 / 1339 / 1933	3.0 / 7.6 / 2.6 / 7.6
9 W	0045 / 0637 / 1323 / 1915	2.7 / 8.2 / 2.1 / 8.1	**24** TH	0159 / 0759 / 1439 / 2027	2.9 / 7.8 / 2.5 / 7.9
10 TH	0155 / 0742 / 1430 / 2017	2.3 / 8.5 / 1.7 / 8.6	**25** F	0258 / 0851 / 1529 / 2114	2.6 / 8.0 / 2.2 / 8.2
11 F	0301 / 0842 / 1531 / 2113	1.8 / 9.0 / 1.3 / 9.1	**26** SA	0347 / 0938 / 1611 / 2156	2.3 / 8.2 / 2.0 / 8.5
12 SA	0400 / 0938 / 1626 / 2204	1.2 / 9.4 / 0.9 / 9.5	**27** SU	0429 / 1019 / 1649 / 2234	2.0 / 8.4 / 1.8 / 8.7
13 SU ●	0454 / 1031 / 1716 / 2253	0.8 / 9.6 / 0.6 / 9.7	**28** M ○	0508 / 1057 / 1724 / 2310	1.8 / 8.5 / 1.7 / 8.8
14 M	0546 / 1121 / 1804 / 2342	0.5 / 9.8 / 0.6 / 9.8	**29** TU	0545 / 1132 / 1759 / 2345	1.7 / 8.6 / 1.7 / 8.9
15 TU	0637 / 1212 / 1851	0.4 / 9.7 / 0.7	**30** W	0623 / 1208 / 1835	1.6 / 8.6 / 1.7

JULY

Day	Time	m	Day	Time	m
1 TH	0021 / 0701 / 1245 / 1911	8.9 / 1.6 / 8.6 / 1.7	**16** F	0103 / 0802 / 1333 / 2005	9.6 / 0.7 / 9.3 / 1.3
2 F	0059 / 0739 / 1323 / 1948	8.9 / 1.6 / 8.6 / 1.8	**17** SA	0148 / 0846 / 1416 / 2046	9.4 / 0.9 / 9.0 / 1.6
3 SA	0138 / 0818 / 1403 / 2027	8.8 / 1.7 / 8.6 / 2.0	**18** SU	0231 / 0927 / 1458 / 2126	9.1 / 1.3 / 8.6 / 2.0
4 SU	0219 / 0859 / 1445 / 2110	8.8 / 1.8 / 8.5 / 2.1	**19** M	0314 / 1008 / 1541 / 2208	8.7 / 1.8 / 8.2 / 2.5
5 M	0305 / 0943 / 1533 / 2159	8.6 / 1.9 / 8.3 / 2.4	**20** TU	0400 / 1052 / 1630 / 2257	8.2 / 2.3 / 7.7 / 2.9
6 TU	0357 / 1035 / 1628 / 2258	8.5 / 2.1 / 8.1 / 2.5	**21** W	0453 / 1142 / 1729 / 2355	7.7 / 2.7 / 7.4 / 3.1
7 W	0457 / 1135 / 1732	8.3 / 2.2 / 8.0	**22** TH	0558 / 1240 / 1839	7.4 / 2.9 / 7.3
8 TH	0006 / 0603 / 1245 / 1841	2.6 / 8.3 / 2.2 / 8.1	**23** F	0101 / 0710 / 1342 / 1946	3.2 / 7.4 / 2.9 / 7.5
9 F	0120 / 0712 / 1357 / 1949	2.4 / 8.4 / 2.0 / 8.4	**24** SA	0207 / 0815 / 1443 / 2042	3.0 / 7.5 / 2.7 / 7.9
10 SA	0234 / 0819 / 1506 / 2052	2.0 / 8.7 / 1.7 / 8.8	**25** SU	0307 / 0909 / 1535 / 2130	2.7 / 7.9 / 2.4 / 8.3
11 SU	0341 / 0921 / 1607 / 2148	1.6 / 9.0 / 1.3 / 9.2	**26** M	0358 / 0955 / 1620 / 2212	2.3 / 8.2 / 2.1 / 8.6
12 M	0440 / 1017 / 1701 / 2239	1.1 / 9.3 / 1.0 / 9.5	**27** TU	0443 / 1036 / 1701 / 2250	1.9 / 8.4 / 1.8 / 8.9
13 TU ●	0535 / 1109 / 1740 / 2329	0.8 / 9.5 / 1.0 / 9.7	**28** W ○	0525 / 1114 / 1740 / 2327	1.7 / 8.6 / 1.7 / 9.0
14 W	0627 / 1159 / 1838	0.6 / 9.6 / 0.9	**29** TH	0606 / 1151 / 1819	1.5 / 8.7 / 1.5
15 TH	0016 / 0716 / 1247 / 1923	9.7 / 0.5 / 9.5 / 1.0	**30** F	0003 / 0646 / 1228 / 1857	9.1 / 1.4 / 8.8 / 1.5
			31 SA	0041 / 0725 / 1306 / 1935	9.2 / 1.3 / 8.9 / 1.5

AUGUST

Day	Time	m	Day	Time	m
1 SU	0120 / 0804 / 1344 / 2012	9.2 / 1.3 / 8.9 / 1.5	**16** M	0200 / 0854 / 1423 / 2051	9.1 / 1.3 / 8.7 / 1.9
2 M	0201 / 0842 / 1425 / 2052	9.2 / 1.3 / 8.8 / 1.7	**17** TU	0236 / 0927 / 1459 / 2124	8.8 / 1.8 / 8.4 / 2.3
3 TU	0244 / 0921 / 1509 / 2135	9.0 / 1.5 / 8.6 / 2.0	**18** W	0315 / 1002 / 1540 / 2204	8.3 / 2.3 / 7.9 / 2.8
4 W	0332 / 1007 / 1600 / 2228	8.8 / 1.9 / 8.4 / 2.3	**19** TH	0359 / 1046 / 1628 / 2300	7.8 / 2.8 / 7.5 / 3.2
5 TH	0428 / 1103 / 1700 / 2335	8.4 / 2.2 / 8.0 / 2.6	**20** F	0454 / 1145 / 1733	7.3 / 3.2 / 7.2
6 F	0534 / 1212 / 1813	8.1 / 2.4 / 7.9	**21** SA	0010 / 0608 / 1253 / 1856	3.4 / 7.0 / 3.3 / 7.2
7 SA	0054 / 0649 / 1332 / 1930	2.6 / 8.1 / 2.4 / 8.1	**22** SU	0123 / 0735 / 1401 / 2009	3.3 / 7.1 / 3.1 / 7.6
8 SU	0218 / 0805 / 1451 / 2040	2.3 / 8.3 / 2.1 / 8.5	**23** M	0232 / 0841 / 1503 / 2104	2.9 / 7.5 / 2.7 / 8.1
9 M	0333 / 0912 / 1551 / 2139	1.8 / 8.7 / 1.7 / 9.0	**24** TU	0331 / 0931 / 1555 / 2149	2.4 / 8.0 / 2.3 / 8.6
10 TU	0434 / 1009 / 1652 / 2230	1.3 / 9.1 / 1.3 / 9.4	**25** W	0420 / 1014 / 1640 / 2228	1.9 / 8.4 / 1.9 / 8.9
11 W ●	0527 / 1059 / 1741 / 2317	0.9 / 9.4 / 1.1 / 9.7	**26** TH ○	0505 / 1052 / 1722 / 2305	1.5 / 8.7 / 1.5 / 9.2
12 TH	0615 / 1146 / 1825	0.6 / 9.5 / 1.0	**27** F	0547 / 1129 / 1802 / 2342	1.2 / 8.9 / 1.3 / 9.4
13 F	0001 / 0700 / 1229 / 1906	9.7 / 0.5 / 9.4 / 1.0	**28** SA	0628 / 1206 / 1841	1.0 / 9.1 / 1.1
14 SA	0043 / 0741 / 1309 / 1944	9.7 / 0.7 / 9.3 / 1.2	**29** SU	0019 / 0706 / 1244 / 1918	9.5 / 0.9 / 9.2 / 1.1
15 SU	0122 / 0819 / 1347 / 2019	9.5 / 0.9 / 9.0 / 1.5	**30** M	0059 / 0744 / 1323 / 1956	9.6 / 0.9 / 9.2 / 1.1
			31 TU	0140 / 0821 / 1403 / 2034	9.5 / 1.0 / 9.1 / 1.3

10

Chart Datum: 4·93 metres below Ordnance Datum (Newlyn)

ENGLAND – LIVERPOOL (ALFRED DOCK)

LAT 53°24′N   LONG   3°01′W

TIMES AND HEIGHTS OF HIGH AND LOW WATERS   YEAR 1999

TIME ZONE (UT)
For Summer Time add ONE hour in non-shaded areas

SEPTEMBER

Day	Time	m	Day	Time	m
1 W	0223 / 0859 / 1446 / 2115	9.3 / 1.3 / 8.9 / 1.7	16 TH	0236 / 0912 / 1458 / 2118	8.3 / 2.3 / 8.1 / 2.6
2 TH	0310 / 0943 / 1535 / 2206	8.9 / 1.8 / 8.5 / 2.1	17 F	0317 / 0950 / 1542 / 2208	7.8 / 2.9 / 7.7 / 3.1
3 F	0405 / 1037 / 1635 / 2314	8.4 / 2.3 / 8.0 / 2.6	18 SA	0407 / 1134 / 1639 / 2322	7.3 / 2.9 / 7.2 / 3.4
4 SA	0514 / 1149 / 1752	7.9 / 2.7 / 7.7	19 SU	0514 / 1206 / 1757	6.9 / 3.6 / 7.0
5 SU	0041 / 0638 / 1317 / 1919	2.8 / 7.7 / 2.8 / 7.8	20 M	0042 / 0645 / 1323 / 1928	3.4 / 6.9 / 3.4 / 7.3
6 M	0215 / 0801 / 1446 / 2033	2.5 / 8.0 / 2.5 / 8.3	21 TU	0157 / 0809 / 1431 / 2032	3.1 / 7.3 / 3.0 / 7.9
7 TU	0329 / 0907 / 1552 / 2130	1.9 / 8.5 / 1.9 / 8.9	22 W	0301 / 0903 / 1528 / 2119	2.5 / 7.9 / 2.4 / 8.5
8 W	0426 / 1000 / 1644 / 2218	1.2 / 9.0 / 1.5 / 9.4	23 TH	0354 / 0946 / 1616 / 2200	1.9 / 8.4 / 1.9 / 9.0
9 TH ●	0514 / 1046 / 1728 / 2301	0.8 / 9.3 / 1.1 / 9.6	24 F	0440 / 1024 / 1659 / 2238	1.3 / 8.9 / 1.4 / 9.4
10 F	0558 / 1127 / 1808 / 2341	0.6 / 9.4 / 1.0 / 9.7	25 SA O	0522 / 1101 / 1740 / 2316	0.9 / 9.2 / 1.0 / 9.6
11 SA	0638 / 1206 / 1845	0.6 / 9.4 / 1.0	26 SU	0604 / 1139 / 1820 / 2355	0.7 / 9.4 / 0.8 / 9.8
12 SU	0019 / 0714 / 1242 / 1918	9.6 / 0.8 / 9.3 / 1.2	27 M	0644 / 1219 / 1900	0.5 / 9.6 / 0.7
13 M	0054 / 0747 / 1315 / 1949	9.4 / 1.1 / 9.1 / 1.4	28 TU	0036 / 0722 / 1300 / 1938	9.8 / 0.6 / 9.5 / 0.8
14 TU	0127 / 0817 / 1348 / 2017	9.1 / 1.4 / 8.8 / 1.8	29 W	0119 / 0800 / 1342 / 2018	9.7 / 0.8 / 9.4 / 1.0
15 W	0201 / 0844 / 1421 / 2044	8.8 / 1.9 / 8.5 / 2.1	30 TH	0204 / 0839 / 1426 / 2101	9.4 / 1.2 / 9.0 / 1.5

OCTOBER

Day	Time	m	Day	Time	m
1 F	0252 / 0923 / 1516 / 2153	8.9 / 1.8 / 8.5 / 2.0	16 SA	0244 / 0907 / 1506 / 2130	7.9 / 2.8 / 8.0 / 2.9
2 SA	0349 / 1019 / 1617 / 2303	8.2 / 2.4 / 8.0 / 2.5	17 SU	0331 / 1000 / 1557 / 2238	7.4 / 3.3 / 7.4 / 3.3
3 SU	0502 / 1134 / 1739	7.7 / 2.9 / 7.6	18 M	0432 / 1106 / 1706	7.0 / 3.6 / 7.1
4 M	0035 / 0633 / 1308 / 1909	2.7 / 7.6 / 3.0 / 7.8	19 TU	0001 / 0552 / 1240 / 1831	3.4 / 6.9 / 3.6 / 7.2
5 TU	0209 / 0753 / 1438 / 2019	2.4 / 7.9 / 2.6 / 8.3	20 W	0117 / 0720 / 1352 / 1946	3.1 / 7.2 / 3.2 / 7.7
6 W	0318 / 0853 / 1540 / 2114	1.8 / 8.5 / 2.0 / 8.8	21 TH	0224 / 0823 / 1453 / 2040	2.5 / 7.8 / 2.5 / 8.4
7 TH	0411 / 0943 / 1627 / 2200	1.2 / 8.9 / 1.6 / 9.3	22 F	0321 / 0910 / 1545 / 2125	1.9 / 8.5 / 1.9 / 9.0
8 F	0455 / 1026 / 1708 / 2241	0.9 / 9.2 / 1.3 / 9.5	23 SA	0410 / 0951 / 1631 / 2207	1.3 / 9.0 / 1.4 / 9.5
9 SA ●	0534 / 1104 / 1745 / 2319	0.8 / 9.3 / 1.1 / 9.5	24 SU O	0455 / 1032 / 1715 / 2249	0.8 / 9.4 / 0.9 / 9.8
10 SU	0610 / 1139 / 1819 / 2353	0.6 / 9.3 / 1.1 / 9.4	25 M	0537 / 1112 / 1758 / 2331	0.5 / 9.7 / 0.6 / 10.0
11 M	0643 / 1211 / 1851	1.0 / 9.2 / 1.3	26 TU	0619 / 1154 / 1840	0.4 / 9.8 / 0.5
12 TU	0025 / 0713 / 1243 / 1919	9.2 / 1.2 / 9.1 / 1.5	27 W	0015 / 0659 / 1238 / 1922	10.0 / 0.5 / 9.8 / 0.6
13 W	0057 / 0740 / 1315 / 1945	9.0 / 1.6 / 8.9 / 1.7	28 TH	0101 / 0740 / 1323 / 2006	9.8 / 0.8 / 9.6 / 0.9
14 TH	0129 / 0804 / 1348 / 2012	8.7 / 1.9 / 8.6 / 2.0	29 F	0149 / 0822 / 1411 / 2052	9.4 / 1.3 / 9.2 / 1.3
15 F	0205 / 0831 / 1424 / 2045	8.4 / 2.3 / 8.3 / 2.4	30 SA	0239 / 0910 / 1502 / 2147	8.9 / 1.8 / 8.7 / 1.9
			31 SU	0338 / 1007 / 1604 / 2257	8.3 / 2.5 / 8.1 / 2.4

NOVEMBER

Day	Time	m	Day	Time	m
1 M	0451 / 1120 / 1723	7.7 / 2.9 / 7.8	16 TU	0358 / 1034 / 1627 / 2317	7.3 / 3.5 / 7.5 / 3.2
2 TU	0021 / 0616 / 1248 / 1846	2.5 / 7.6 / 3.0 / 7.8	17 W	0507 / 1151 / 1739	7.2 / 3.5 / 7.5
3 W	0147 / 0730 / 1413 / 1954	2.3 / 7.9 / 2.7 / 8.2	18 TH	0031 / 0624 / 1304 / 1851	3.0 / 7.3 / 3.2 / 7.8
4 TH	0254 / 0829 / 1515 / 2049	1.9 / 8.3 / 2.3 / 8.6	19 F	0140 / 0733 / 1410 / 1954	2.6 / 7.8 / 2.7 / 8.4
5 F	0346 / 0918 / 1603 / 2136	1.5 / 8.7 / 1.9 / 9.0	20 SA	0242 / 0829 / 1509 / 2048	2.0 / 8.5 / 2.1 / 8.9
6 SA	0429 / 1000 / 1643 / 2217	1.2 / 9.0 / 1.6 / 9.2	21 SU	0337 / 0918 / 1601 / 2136	1.4 / 9.0 / 1.5 / 9.5
7 SU	0506 / 1038 / 1718 / 2254	1.1 / 9.2 / 1.4 / 9.2	22 M	0426 / 1003 / 1650 / 2223	0.9 / 9.5 / 1.0 / 9.8
8 M ●	0539 / 1112 / 1751 / 2327	1.1 / 9.2 / 1.4 / 9.2	23 TU O	0512 / 1048 / 1737 / 2310	0.6 / 9.8 / 0.7 / 10.0
9 TU	0611 / 1144 / 1823 / 2358	1.3 / 9.2 / 1.4 / 9.0	24 W	0557 / 1134 / 1824 / 2358	0.5 / 10.0 / 0.5 / 10.0
10 W	0640 / 1215 / 1853	1.4 / 9.1 / 1.6	25 TH	0641 / 1220 / 1911	0.6 / 9.9 / 0.6
11 TH	0030 / 0707 / 1248 / 1920	8.9 / 1.7 / 8.9 / 1.7	26 F	0046 / 0725 / 1309 / 1958	9.8 / 0.8 / 9.7 / 0.8
12 F	0104 / 0734 / 1322 / 1950	8.7 / 1.9 / 8.8 / 2.0	27 SA	0137 / 0811 / 1358 / 2048	9.5 / 1.3 / 9.4 / 1.2
13 SA	0140 / 0804 / 1358 / 2024	8.4 / 2.3 / 8.5 / 2.3	28 SU	0228 / 0859 / 1451 / 2142	9.0 / 1.8 / 9.0 / 1.6
14 SU	0218 / 0841 / 1438 / 2107	8.1 / 2.7 / 8.2 / 2.7	29 M	0325 / 0954 / 1548 / 2243	8.5 / 2.3 / 8.5 / 2.1
15 M	0303 / 0928 / 1526 / 2204	7.7 / 3.1 / 7.8 / 3.0	30 TU	0429 / 1057 / 1656 / 2352	8.0 / 2.8 / 8.1 / 2.4

DECEMBER

Day	Time	m	Day	Time	m
1 W	0543 / 1209 / 1810	7.7 / 3.0 / 7.9	16 TH	0428 / 1103 / 1656 / 2342	7.6 / 3.2 / 7.9 / 2.8
2 TH	0106 / 0654 / 1327 / 1918	2.4 / 7.7 / 3.0 / 8.0	17 F	0536 / 1213 / 1804	7.6 / 3.1 / 8.0
3 F	0215 / 0756 / 1436 / 2017	2.3 / 8.0 / 2.7 / 8.3	18 SA	0052 / 0645 / 1323 / 1910	2.6 / 7.7 / 2.8 / 8.3
4 SA	0311 / 0847 / 1530 / 2107	2.0 / 8.4 / 2.3 / 8.5	19 SU	0201 / 0750 / 1431 / 2013	2.2 / 8.3 / 2.3 / 8.8
5 SU	0357 / 0932 / 1613 / 2151	1.8 / 8.7 / 2.0 / 8.8	20 M	0304 / 0848 / 1533 / 2110	1.7 / 8.9 / 1.8 / 9.2
6 M	0435 / 1011 / 1650 / 2229	1.6 / 8.9 / 1.8 / 8.9	21 TU	0400 / 0940 / 1629 / 2203	1.2 / 9.4 / 1.3 / 9.6
7 TU ●	0509 / 1047 / 1725 / 2304	1.6 / 9.0 / 1.7 / 8.9	22 W O	0452 / 1030 / 1721 / 2255	0.9 / 9.7 / 0.9 / 9.9
8 W	0541 / 1120 / 1758 / 2337	1.6 / 9.1 / 1.7 / 8.9	23 TH	0540 / 1118 / 1813 / 2345	0.7 / 9.9 / 0.6 / 9.9
9 TH	0613 / 1153 / 1831	1.6 / 9.1 / 1.7	24 F	0628 / 1207 / 1903	0.7 / 10.0 / 0.6
10 F	0010 / 0642 / 1227 / 1902	8.8 / 1.7 / 9.0 / 1.8	25 SA	0035 / 0715 / 1257 / 1952	9.8 / 0.9 / 9.9 / 0.7
11 SA	0045 / 0713 / 1302 / 1935	8.7 / 1.9 / 8.9 / 1.9	26 SU	0125 / 0801 / 1346 / 2041	9.6 / 1.1 / 9.7 / 0.9
12 SU	0121 / 0747 / 1339 / 2011	8.6 / 2.1 / 8.7 / 2.1	27 M	0214 / 0848 / 1434 / 2129	9.2 / 1.5 / 9.3 / 1.3
13 M	0159 / 0824 / 1418 / 2052	8.4 / 2.4 / 8.5 / 2.3	28 TU	0304 / 0935 / 1525 / 2219	8.8 / 2.0 / 8.9 / 1.8
14 TU	0241 / 0908 / 1502 / 2139	8.1 / 2.7 / 8.3 / 2.6	29 W	0357 / 1026 / 1619 / 2313	8.3 / 2.5 / 8.4 / 2.2
15 W	0329 / 1000 / 1554 / 2236	7.9 / 3.0 / 8.1 / 2.8	30 TH	0456 / 1122 / 1721	7.8 / 2.9 / 8.0
			31 F	0012 / 0604 / 1226 / 1830	2.6 / 7.6 / 3.1 / 7.7

Chart Datum: 4·93 metres below Ordnance Datum (Newlyn)

ISLE OF MAN   8-10-15

CHARTS
AC 2696 (ports), 2094 (small scale). Irish Sea *1826, 1411*

The Isle of Man is one of the British Islands, set in the Irish Sea almost equidistant from England, Scotland and Ireland but it is not part of the UK. It has a large degree of self-government. The IOM comes under the same customs umbrella as the rest of the UK, and there are no formalities on landing from or returning to UK.

Harbours and anchorages. Manx hbrs are administered by the IOM Government and lights are maintained by the Commissioners of Northern Lighthouses in Scotland. Besides the four main hbrs given below, there are good ⚓s at Castletown in the SE, Laxey Bay in the E and Port Erin in the SW; see below. There are also good ⚓s in Derby Haven in the SE; this is a rather bleak area and the inner hbr dries. Most of the hbrs are on the E and S sides but a visit to the W coast with its characteristic cliffs is worth while. All IOM hbrs charge the same overnight berthing fee, ie £6.71 regardless of LOA; or £32.50 weekly fee allows use of all hbrs (1998 figures, inc VAT).

Passage information. Including Calf Sound, see 8.10.5.

R/T. If contact with local Hr Mrs cannot be established on VHF, vessels should call *Douglas Hbr Control* Ch 12 16 for urgent messages or other info.

Coastguard. Call Liverpool MRSC Ch 16 67; there is no loss of VHF coverage as the Snaefell (IoM) aerial is linked to Liverpool by land line.

Weather. Forecasts can be obtained from Manx Radio, see Table 5 (1); or direct from the forecaster at Ronaldsway Met Office ☎ 0696 888 200, (0700-2030LT). Recorded shipping forecast (updated 3 times daily) ☎ 0696 888 322; recorded general forecast ☎ 0696 888 320.

Directions. The *Isle of Man SDs, Tidal streams and Anchorages* by the Manx Sailing and Cruising Club in Ramsey, ☎ 01624-813494, are recommended.

Distances. See 8.10.6 for distances between ports in Area 10 and 10.0.6 for distances across the Irish Sea, North Channel and St George's Channel.

MINOR HARBOURS IN THE ISLE OF MAN

PORT ERIN, Isle of Man, 54°05'·30N 04°46'·27W. AC 2696, 2094. HW −0020 on Dover; ML 2·9m; Duration 0555. See 8.10.16. The bay has good ⚓ in 3-8m, but exposed to all W winds. Ldg lts, both FR 10/19m 5M, lead 099° into the bay. Beware the ruined bkwtr extending N from the SW corner, marked by an unlit SHM buoy. A small hbr on the S side dries 0·8m. Raglan Pier (E arm of hbr) Oc G 5s 8m 5M. Two ⚓s W of Raglan Pier; call Hr Mr Port St. Mary (VHF Ch 12). Facilities: EC Thurs; Bar, D, P, FW, R, Slip, V.

CASTLETOWN, Isle of Man, 54°03'·50N 04°38'·50W. AC 2696, 2094. HW +0025 on Dover; ML 3·4m; Duration 0555. See 8.10.17. Hbr dries (level sand). Access HW±2½. Berth in Outer hbr or go via swing bridge (manually operated) into Inner Hbr below fixed bridge. ⚓ between Lheeah-rio Rks and pier in 3m; off Langness Pt; or in Derby Haven (dries). The bay gives good shelter except in SE to SW winds. Beware Lheeah-rio Rks in W of bay, marked by PHM Fl R 3s, Bell. Keep inside the race off Dreswick Pt, or give it a wide berth. Langness lt , on Dreswick Pt, Fl (2) 30s 23m 12M. S side of ent: New Pier Oc R 15s 8m 5M; then Irish Quay, Oc R 4s 5m 5M, vis 142°-322°. 150m NW is swing bridge marked by 2 FR (hor). N side of ent Oc G 4s 3m (W metal post on concrete column). VHF Ch 12 16 (when vessel due). Hr Mr ☎ 823549. Facilities: **Outer Hbr** Slip, L, C (20 ton) AB; **Irish Quay** AB, C, FW; **Inner Hbr** AB, C, FW; **Services**: P, D, Gas, ME. **Town** EC Thurs; Dr 823597.

LAXEY, Isle of Man, 54°13'·45N 04°23'·25W. AC 2094. HW +0025 on Dover; +0010 and −2·0m on Liverpool; ML 4·0m; Duration 0550. The bay gives good shelter in SW to N winds. The hbr dries 3·0m to rk and is only suitable for small yachts; access HW±3 for 1·5m draft. Beware rks on N side of the narrow ent. Keep close to pier after entering to avoid training wall to N. Pier hd lt Oc R 3s 7m 5M, obsc when brg <318°. Bkwtr hd lt Oc G 3s 7m. Hr Mr ☎ 861663. Facilities: FW, R, ✉, Ⓑ, Bar.

PEEL   8-10-16
Isle of Man 54°13'·60N 04°41'·61W   Rtg 3-3-1

CHARTS
AC 2696, 2094; Imray C62; Y70; OS 95

TIDES
+0005 Dover; ML 2·9; Duration 0545; Zone 0 (UT)

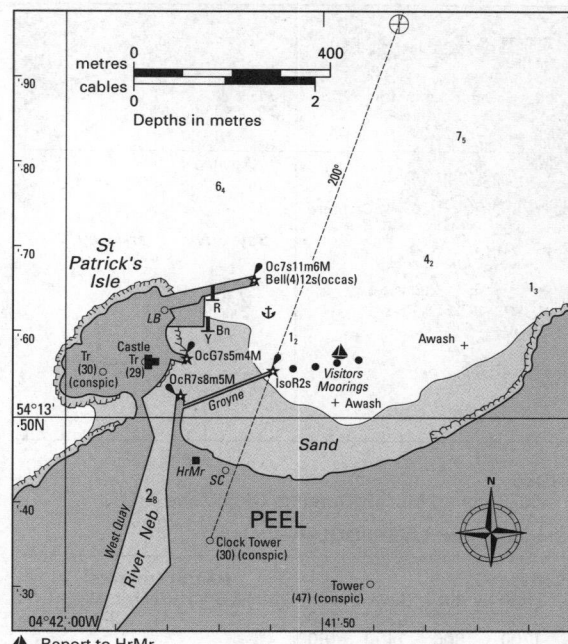

♠ Report to HrMr

Standard Port LIVERPOOL (←)

Times				Height (metres)			
High Water		Low Water		MHWS	MHWN	MLWN	MLWS
0000	0600	0200	0700	9·3	7·4	2·9	0·9
1200	1800	1400	1900				
Differences PEEL							
−0015	+0010	0000	−0010	−4·0	−3·2	−1·4	−0·4
PORT ERIN							
−0005	+0015	−0010	−0050	−4·1	−3·2	−1·3	−0·5

SHELTER
Good, except in strong NW to NE winds when ent should not be attempted. 3 R ⚓s off S groyne in about 2m. Fin keelers may be able to berth on N bkwtr in 5m. Hbr dries; very crowded Jun-Oct. Inner hbr dries approx 2·8m to flat sand; access HW±3, possible AB on W quay.

NAVIGATION
WPT 54°13'·96N 04°41'·36W, 020°/200° from/to groyne lt, 0·42M. When approaching, a rky coastline indicates that you are S of Peel; a sandy coastline means you are to the N. When close in, beware groyne on S side of hbr ent, submerged at half tide.

LIGHTS AND MARKS
Power stn chy (80m, grey with B top) at S end of inner hbr is conspic from W and N; chy brg 203° leads to hbr ent. Groyne lt and Clock Tr (conspic) in transit 200° are almost on same line. Peel Castle and 2 twrs are conspic on St Patrick's Isle to NW of hbr. No ldg lts. N bkwtr Oc 7s 11m 6M. Groyne Iso R 2s 4m. S pier hd Oc R 7s 8m 5M; vis 156°-249°. Castle jetty Oc G 7s 5m 4M.

RADIO TELEPHONE
VHF Ch 12 16 (when vessel expected; at other times call *Douglas Hbr Control* Ch 12).

TELEPHONE (Dial code 01624)
Hr Mr ☎/📠 842338; MRSC 0151-931 3341; ⌗ 674321; Weather 0696 888322; Marinecall 0891 500 461; Police 842208; Dr 843636.

FACILITIES
Outer & Inner Hbrs, AB £6.71 (see 8.10.15), M, Slip, FW, ME, El, Sh, C (30 ton mobile); **Peel Sailing and Cruising Club** ☎ 842390, P & D (cans), R, Ⓒ, Bar; **Services**: Gas, BY, CH, ACA. **Town** EC Thurs; V, R, Bar, ✉, Ⓑ, ⇌ (bus to Douglas, ferry to Heysham & Liverpool), ✈ Ronaldsway.

PORT ST MARY   8-10-17

Isle of Man 54°04'·42N 04°43'·64W   Rtg 3-3-2

CHARTS
AC 2696, 2094; Imray C62; Y70; OS 95

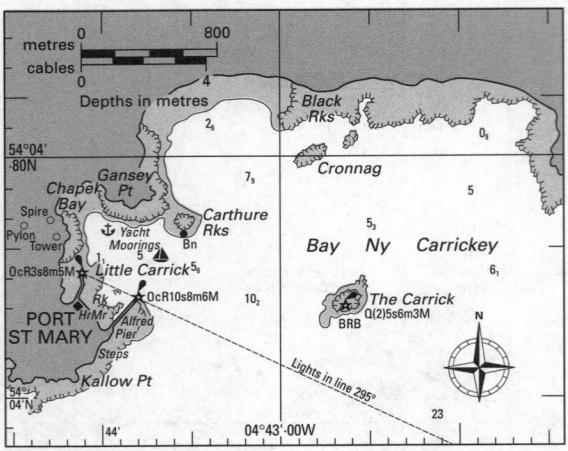

TIDES
+0020 Dover; ML 3·2; Duration 0605; Zone 0 (UT)

Standard Port LIVERPOOL (←—)

Times				Height (metres)			
High Water		Low Water		MHWS	MHWN	MLWN	MLWS
0000	0600	0200	0700	9·3	7·4	2·9	0·9
1200	1800	1400	1900				
Differences PORT ST MARY							
+0005	+0015	−0010	−0030	−3·4	−2·7	−1·2	−0·3
CALF SOUND							
+0005	+0005	−0015	−0025	−3·2	−2·6	−0·9	−0·3

SHELTER
Very good except in E or SE winds. Inner hbr dries 2·4m on sand. ↓ S of Gansey Pt, but poor holding. 8 R ♠s in same area.

NAVIGATION
WPT 54°04'·20N 04°43'·30W, 115°/295° from/to Alfred Pier lt, 0·30M. Rky outcrops to SE of pier to 2ca offshore. Beware lobster/crab pots, especially between Calf Island and Langness Pt.

LIGHTS AND MARKS
Alfred Pier, Oc R 10s 8m 6M. Inner pier, Oc R 3s 8m 5M; both lts on W trs + R band, in transit 295° lead clear S of The Carrick Rk, in centre of bay, which is marked by IDM bn, Q (2) 5s 6m 3M. A conspic TV mast (133m), 5ca WNW of hbr, in transit with Alfred Pier lt leads 290° towards the hbr and also clears The Carrick rock.

RADIO TELEPHONE
Call *Port St Mary Hbr* VHF Ch 12 16 (when vessel due or through Douglas Hbr Control Ch 12).

TELEPHONE (Dial code 01624)
Hr Mr 833206; MRSC 0151-931 3341; ⌗ 674321; Marinecall 0891 500 461; Police 822222; Dr 832281.

FACILITIES
Alfred Pier AB £6.71 (see 8.10.15), Slip, D (road tanker), L, FW, C (20 ton mobile);
Inner Hbr AB, Slip, D, L, FW; **Isle of Man YC** ☎ 832088, FW, Bar; **Services:** ME, CH, D, EI, SM.
Town EC Thurs; CH, V, R, Bar, ✉, Ⓑ, ⇌ (bus to Douglas, ferry to Heysham), ✈ Ronaldsway.

DOUGLAS   8-10-18

Isle of Man 54°08'·86N 04°27'·89W   Rtg 2-4-1

CHARTS
AC 2696, 2094; Imray C62; Y70; OS 95
TIDES
+0009 Dover; ML 3·8; Duration 0600; Zone 0 (UT)

Standard Port LIVERPOOL (←—)

Times				Height (metres)			
High Water		Low Water		MHWS	MHWN	MLWN	MLWS
0000	0600	0200	0700	9·3	7·4	2·9	0·9
1200	0800	1400	1900				
Differences DOUGLAS							
−0004	−0004	−0022	−0032	−2·4	−2·0	−0·5	−0·1

SHELTER
Good except in NE winds. Very heavy seas run in during NE gales. Close NW of front ldg lt the Dept of Transport provides a B can ♠, to which yachts should moor stern-to, bower ↓ laid out radially. About 6 yachts can raft up on small pontoon at inner end of Battery Pier; untenable in NE/E winds. Complete shelter, but very full in summer, at drying inner hbr W of swing bridge which opens 2300-0700 for shipping, and on request HW±3. Victoria and King Edward VIII piers are for commercial vessels/ferries.

NAVIGATION
WPT 54°09'·00N 04°27'·60W (abeam No 1 SHM buoy, Q (3) G 5s), 049°/229° from/to front ldg lt, 0·47M. Appr from NE of No 1 buoy (to avoid overfalls E of Princess Alexandra Pier) and await port entry sig, or call on VHF Ch 12. There is no bar. Keep clear of large vessels and ferries. Beware swing bridge and also concrete step at end of dredged area (◇ mark on King Edward Pier).

LIGHTS AND MARKS
Douglas Head Fl 10s 32m 24M. Ldg lts 229°, both Oc 10s 9/12m 5M, synch; front W △; rear W ▽, both on R border. IPTS Nos 2, 3 & 5 shown from mast on Victoria Pier. Dolphin at N end of Alexandra Pier 2FR (vert).

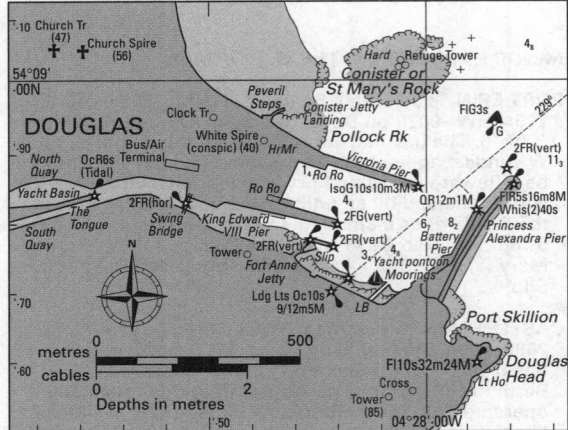

RADIO TELEPHONE
Douglas Hbr Control VHF Ch **12** 16 (H24); also broadcasts nav warnings for IoM coastal waters on Ch 12 at 0133, 0533, 0733, 0933, 1333, 1733 and 2133; weather and tidal info on request.
TELEPHONE (Dial code 01624)
Hr Mr 686628 (H24); MRSC 0151-931 3341; ⌗ 674321; Marinecall 0891 500 461; Police 631212; Ⓗ 642642.
FACILITIES
Outer Hbr AB £6.71 (see 8.10.15), M, FW at pontoon, P & D (cans) across the road from pontoon, ME, EI, Sh, C (10, 5 ton), Slip;
Inner Hbr (N and S Quays) AB, M, AC, FW, ME, C, EI, Sh, CH, Slip;
Douglas Bay YC (S side of inner hbr) ☎ 673965, Bar, Slip, L, showers 0900-2300.
Services: P & D (cans), CH, ACA, EI, Divers, Gas, Gaz, Kos.
Town EC Thurs; V, R, Bar, ✉, Ⓑ, ▣, Ferry to Heysham; also in summer to Belfast and Liverpool; ✈ Ronaldsway.

RAMSEY   8-10-19

Isle of Man 54°19'·43N 04°22'·42W   Rtg 3-3-2

CHARTS
AC 2696, 2094; Imray C62; Y70; OS 95

TIDES
+0020 Dover; ML 4·2; Duration 0545; Zone 0 (UT)

Standard Port LIVERPOOL (←—)

Times				Height (metres)			
High Water		Low Water		MHWS	MHWN	MLWN	MLWS
0000	0600	0200	0700	9·3	7·4	2·9	0·9
1200	1800	1400	1900				
Differences RAMSEY							
+0005	+0015	−0005	−0015	−1·7	−1·5	−0·6	+0·1

SHELTER
Very good except in strong NE/SE winds. Hbr dries 1·8m-6m. Access and ent only permitted HW −2½ to HW +2. Berth on Town quay (S side) or as directed by Hr Mr on entry. There are Y ⚓s SE of Queens Pier hd (summer only). Note: Landing on Queens Pier is prohibited.

NAVIGATION
WPT 54°19'·43N 04°21'·80W, 090°/270° from/to ent, 0·37M. The foreshore dries out 1ca to seaward of the pier hds.

LIGHTS AND MARKS
No ldg lts/marks. Relative to hbr ent, Pt of Ayre, Fl (4) 20s 32m 19M, is 5·5M N; Maughold Hd, Fl (3) 30s 65m 21M, is 3M SE; Albert Tr (□ stone tr 14m, on hill 130m) is conspic 7ca S; and Snaefell (617m) bears 220°/5M. The Iso G 4s, G SHM post, inside the hbr marks the S tip of Mooragh Bank; it is not visible from seaward. 2FR (hor) on each side mark the centre of swing bridge.

RADIO TELEPHONE
Ramsey Hbr VHF Ch 12 16 (0730-1600LT and when a vessel is due); OT call *Douglas Hbr Control* Ch 12.

TELEPHONE (Dial code 01624)
Hr Mr (non-resident) 812245; MRSC 0151-931 3341; ∰ 674321; Marinecall 0891 500 461; Police 812234; Dr 813881; Ⓗ 813254.

FACILITIES
Outer Hbr: E Quay ☎ 812245, AB (but mainly commercial and FVs), FW;
Town Quay (S side) AB £6.71 (see 8.10.15), AC, FW, C*;
Inner Hbr, W Quay AB, AC, FW, Slip (Grid); **N Quay** AB, FW;
Shipyard Quay Slip; **Old Hbr** AB, Slip, M;
Manx Sailing & Cruising Club ☎ 813494, Bar.
Services: P & D (cans) from garages; none located at hbr. Gas, ME, El, Ⓔ, Sh, ⬡.
Town EC Wed; V, R, Gas, Gaz, Kos, Bar, ◻, ✉, Ⓑ, ⇌ (bus to Douglas, ferry to Heysham), ✈ Ronaldsway.
*Mobile cranes for hire from Douglas.

CONWY   8-10-20

Conwy 53°17'·25N 03°50'·00W (marina)   Rtg 3-2-1

CHARTS
AC *1978, 1977, 1826*; Imray C61; OS 115

TIDES
−0015 Dover; ML 4·3; Duration 0545; Zone 0 (UT)

Standard Port HOLYHEAD (—→)

Times				Height (metres)			
High Water		Low Water		MHWS	MHWN	MLWN	MLWS
0000	0600	0500	1100	5·6	4·4	2·0	0·7
1200	1800	1700	2300				
Differences CONWY							
+0020	+0020	No data	+0050	+2·1	+1·6	+0·3	No data

NOTE: HW Conwy is approx HW Liverpool −0040 sp and −0020 nps.

SHELTER
Good, except in strong NW'lies. Marina is to stbd past the Narrows or berth on pontoon between marina and castle or ask Hr Mr for ⚓. 10kn speed limit above Perch lt.

NAVIGATION
WPT Fairway SWM By, 53°17'·95N 03°55'·54W, 291°/111° from/to No 2 PHM lt By, 0·90M. Access HW±2; if Conwy Sands (to N) are covered, there is enough water in chan for 2m draft boat. Chan is marked by 4 PHM buoys (No 2: Fl (2) R 10s; No 6: Fl (6) R 30s; No 8: Fl (8) R 30s) and 3 unlit SHM buoys, all with radar reflectors. After No 6 lt buoy, stand on for approx 20m to clear The Scabs (gravel patch, 0·1m depth); then alter 030° for No 8 buoy. Leave Perch lt approx 30m to stbd. Beware unlit moorings. Sp ebb reaches 5kn. The "Inshore Passage" (close SW of Gt Orme's Hd) is only advised with local knowledge.

LIGHTS AND MARKS
Ent chan is mainly within W sector of Perch lt, Fl WR 5s 5m 2M, vis W076°-088°, R088°-171°, W171°-319°, R319°-076°. Unlit PHM buoy at the Narrows, then marina bkwtr marked by Fl G lt; ent between SHM pile and PHM buoy.

RADIO TELEPHONE
Hr Mr Ch 14 06 08 12 71 80 16 (Summer 09-1700LT every day; winter, same times Mon-Fri). Conwy Marina Ch 80 (H24). N Wales CC Ch M, water taxi. Conwy YC Ch M.

TELEPHONE (Dial code 01492)
Hr Mr 596253; MRSC (01407) 762051; ∰ (01407) 762714; Marinecall 0891 500 460; Police 2222; Dr 592424.

FACILITIES
Marina (420) ☎ 593000, ⛴ 572111, £13.98, AC, FW, D & P (0700-2359), BH (30 ton), ⬧, CH, Gas, ◻, R, Bar;
Harbour ☎ 596253, Pontoon AB £8.00, Quay AB dries (12·3m max LOA; short stay for loading), M, D, FW, ⬡;
Deganwy Dock (dries), AB, Slip, FW, C (mobile);
Conwy YC ☎ 583690, Slip, M, L, FW, R, Bar;
N Wales Cruising Club ☎ 593481, AB, M, FW, Bar.
Services: ME, Gas, Gaz, Sh, El, Ⓔ. **Town** EC Wed; P & D (cans), V, R, Bar, ✉, Ⓑ, ⇌, ✈ (Liverpool).

10

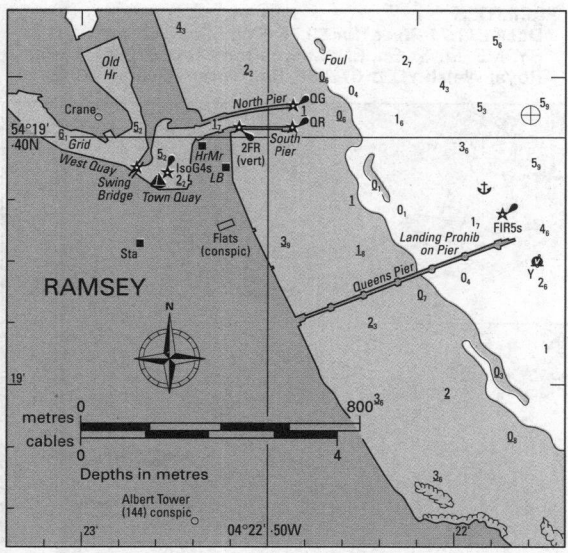

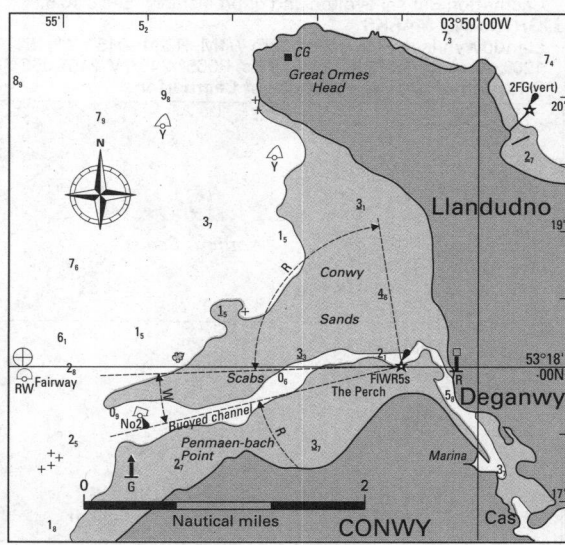

MENAI STRAIT   8-10-21

Gwynedd/Isle of Anglesey

CHARTS
AC 1464, Imray C61; OS 114, 115. NOTE: The definitive
Pilot book is Cruising Anglesey and the North Wales Coast
by R Morris, 5th edition 1995: North West Venturers YC

TIDES
Beaumaris –0025 Dover; ML Beaumaris 4·2; Duration 0540
Standard Port HOLYHEAD (⟶)

Times				Height (metres)			
High Water		Low Water		MHWS	MHWN	MLWN	MLWS
0000	0600	0500	1100	5·6	4·4	2·0	0·7
1200	1800	1700	2300				
Differences BEAUMARIS							
+0025	+0010	+0055	+0035	+2·0	+1·6	+0·5	+0·1
MENAI BRIDGE							
+0030	+0010	+0100	+0035	+1·7	+1·4	+0·3	0·0
PORT DINORWIC							
–0015	–0025	+0030	0000	0·0	0·0	0·0	+0·1
CAERNARFON							
–0030	–0030	+0015	–0005	–0·4	–0·4	–0·1	–0·1
FORT BELAN							
–0040	–0015	–0025	–0005	–1·0	–0·9	–0·2	–0·1
LLANDDWYN ISLAND							
–0115	–0055	–0030	–0020	–0·7	–0·5	–0·1	0·0

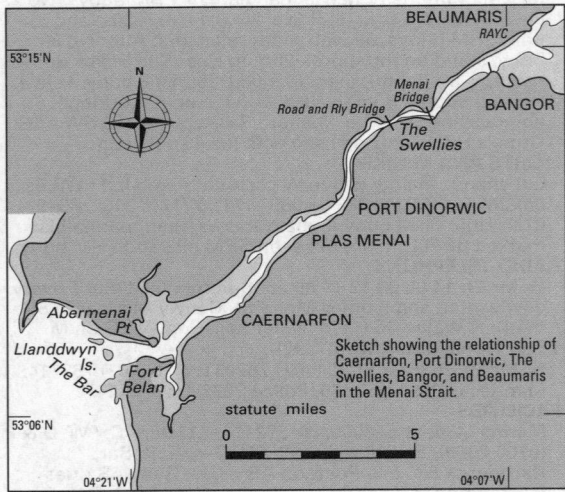

Sketch showing the relationship of
Caernarfon, Port Dinorwic, The
Swellies, Bangor, and Beaumaris
in the Menai Strait.

SOUTH WEST ENTRANCE
NAVIGATION
WPT 53°07'·60N 04°26'·00W, 270°/090° from/to Abermenai Pt,
3·8M. A dangerous sea can build in even a moderate breeze
against tide, especially if a swell is running in the Irish Sea.
Caernarfon Bar shifts often and unpredictably. See 8.10.5.
LIGHTS AND MARKS
Llanddwyn Is lt, Fl WR 2·5s 12m 7/4M, R280°-015°, W015°-
120°. Abermenai Pt lt, Fl WR 3·5s; R065°-245°, W245°-065°.
Direction of buoyage changes at Caernarfon.

PORT DINORWIC 53°11'·22N 04°13'·62W

TELEPHONE (Dial code 01248)
Hr Mr 670441; MRSC (01407) 762051; Dr 670423.
FACILITIES
Port Dinorwic Marina (230 berths in fresh water). Call
Dinorwic Marina VHF Ch **80** M (HO). **Tidal basin** dries at
sp; lock opens HW±2. ☎ 671500, D, P (cans), AC, CH, SM;
Pier hd F WR 5m 2M, vis R225°-357°, W357°-225°.
Services: SM, ME, El, Sh, Slip, C, CH. **Town** Ⓔ, ✉
(Bangor or Caernarfon), Ⓑ, ⇌ (Bangor), ✈ (Liverpool).
Note: Between Port Dinorwic and Caernarfon is **Plas
Menai** ☎ 670964, the Sport Council for Wales Sailing and
Sports Centre. Menai Base Ch **80** M. Day moorings only.
All facilities for the disabled.

CAERNARFON 53°08'·50N 04°16'·75W   Rtg 3-1-1
Direction of buoyage changes at Caernarfon.

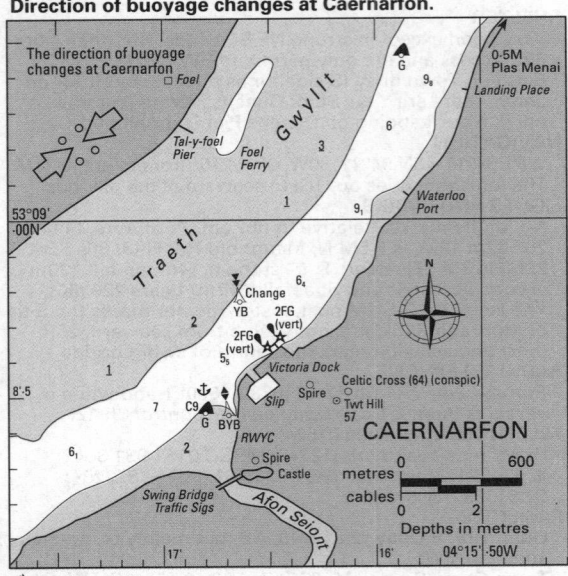

⚓ Apply to HrMr
SHELTER
Good in Victoria Dock marina, access HW±2 via gates;
pontoons at SW end in 2m. Or in river hbr (S of conspic
castle), dries to mud/gravel, access HW±3 via swing
bridge; for opening sound B (─···). ⚓ off Foel Ferry, with
local knowledge; or temp ⚓ in fair holding off Abermenai
Pt, sheltered from W'lies, but strong streams.
RADIO TELEPHONE
Victoria Dock marina VHF Ch 80. Port Ch 14 16 (HJ).
TELEPHONE (Dial code 01286)
Hr Mr 672118, ☎ 678729, Mobile 0410 541364; Police
673333; Dr 672236; Ⓗ 384384.
FACILITIES
Dock £11.21 **River Hbr** £9.75, FW, Slip, C (2 ton), V, D at
BY, ME, El, Ⓔ, Sh, CH; **Caernarfon SC** ☎ 672861, L, Bar;
Royal Welsh YC ☎ 672599, Bar; **Town** P (cans), ✉, Ⓑ.

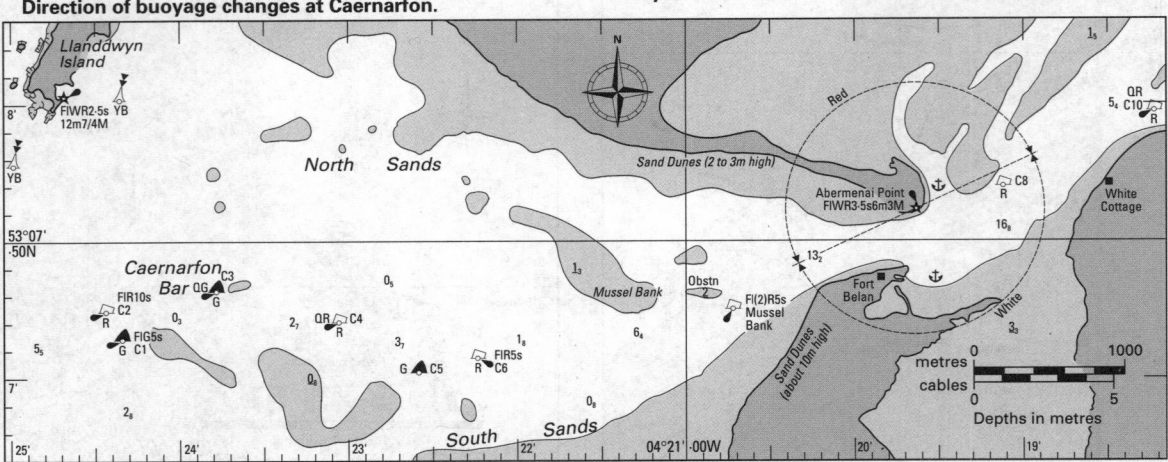

NORTH EAST ENTRANCE

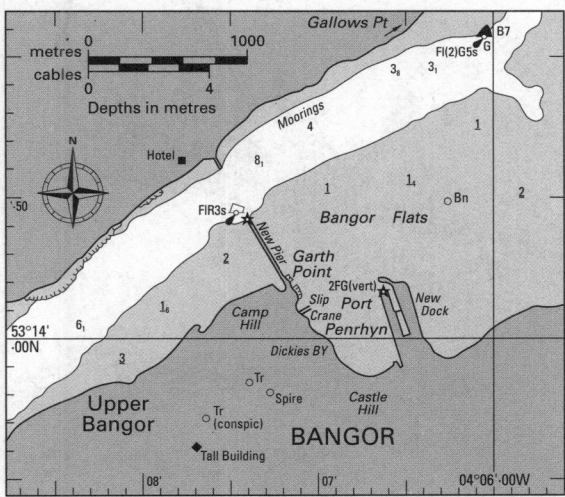

NAVIGATION
WPT 53°19'·47N 04°03'·20W, 317°/137° from/to Perch Rk PHM bn, 1·0M. In N'ly gales seas break on Ten Foot Bank. In N Strait keep to buoyed chan, nearer Anglesey. Night pilotage not advised due to many unlit buoys/moorings.

LIGHTS AND MARKS
At NE end of Strait, Trwyn-Du lt, W tr/B bands, Fl 5s 19m 12M, vis 101°-023° (282°). Conspic tr on Puffin Is. Chan is laterally buoyed, some lit. Beaumaris pier has FWG sectored lt (see 8.10.4).

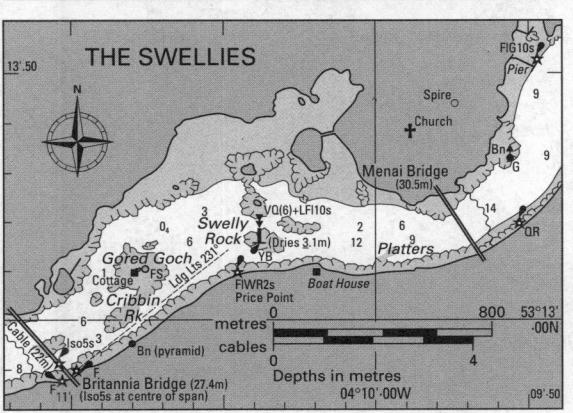

MENAI BRIDGE/BEAUMARIS 53°15'·65N 04°05'·30W

SHELTER
Reasonable off Beaumaris except from NE winds. ⚓ S of B10 PHM buoy or call YCs for mooring. At Menai Bridge, call Hr Mr VHF Ch 69 16 for mooring or temp'y berth on St George's Pier (S of which a marina is planned).

TELEPHONE (Dial code 01248)
Hr Mr Menai 712312, mobile 0378 253178; MRSC (01407) 762051; Marinecall 0891 500 460; ⌗ (01407) 762714; Police (01407) 762323; Dr 810501.

FACILITIES
St George's Pier (Fl G 10s) L at all tides; **Royal Anglesey YC** ☎ 810295, Slip, M, L, R, Bar, P; **North West Venturers YC** ☎ 810023, M, L, FW, water taxi at w/ends only; **Menai Bridge SC. Services:** Slip, P & D (cans), FW, ME, BH (20 ton), Sh, C (2 ton), CH, El, Ⓔ, Gas.
Both towns EC Wed; ✉, Ⓑ, ⇌ (bus to Bangor), ✈ (Liverpool).

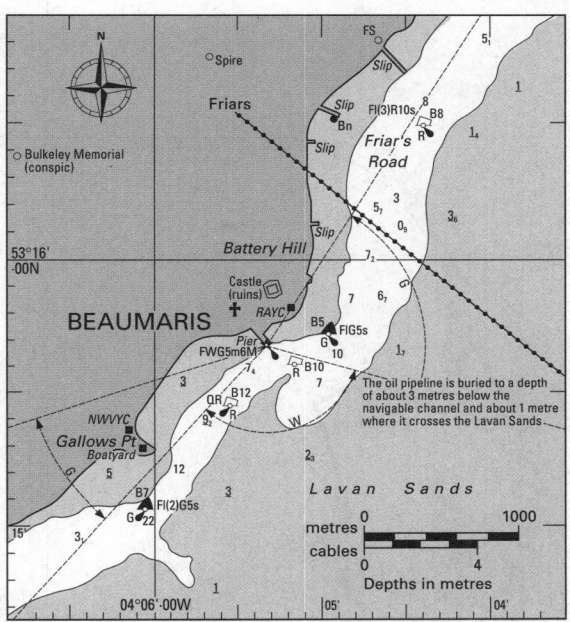

⚓ Apply to Royal Anglesey YC

BANGOR 53°14'·45N 04°07'·50W

SHELTER
Good, except in E'lies, at Dickies BY or Port Penrhyn dock (both dry; access HW±2).

RADIO TELEPHONE
Dickies VHF Ch 09 M 16, all year.

TELEPHONE (Dial code 01248)
Penrhyn Hr Mr 352525; MRSC (01407) 762051; ⌗ (01407) 762714; Dr 362055.

FACILITIES
Services: Slip, D, P (cans), FW, ME, El, Sh, C, CH, Ⓔ, SM, BH (30 ton), Gas, Gaz, ACA; **Port Penrhyn**, Slip, AB, D.
Town ✉, Ⓑ, ⇌, ✈ (Chester).

THE SWELLIES 53°13'·13N 04°10'·38W

NAVIGATION
For pilotage notes, see 8·10·5. The passage should only be attempted at slack HW, which is –0200 HW Liverpool. The shallow rky narrows between the bridges are dangerous for yachts at other times, when the stream can reach 8kn. At slack HW there is 3m over The Platters and the outcrop off Price Pt, which can be ignored. For shoal-draft boats passage is also possible at slack LW nps, but there are depths of 0·5m close E of Britannia Bridge. The bridges and power cables have a least clearance of 22m at MHWS. Night passage is not recommended.

LIGHTS AND MARKS
SE side of chan QR 4m, R mast, vis 064°-222°. Price Pt, Fl WR 2s 5m 3M, vis R059°-239°, W239°-259°. Britannia Bridge, E side, ldg lts 231°, both FW. Bridge lts, both sides: Centre span Iso 5s 27m 3M; S end, FR 21m 3M; N end, FG 21m 3M.

10

HOLYHEAD   8-10-22
Isle of Anglesey 53°19'·70N 04°37'·00W   Rtg 1-2-2

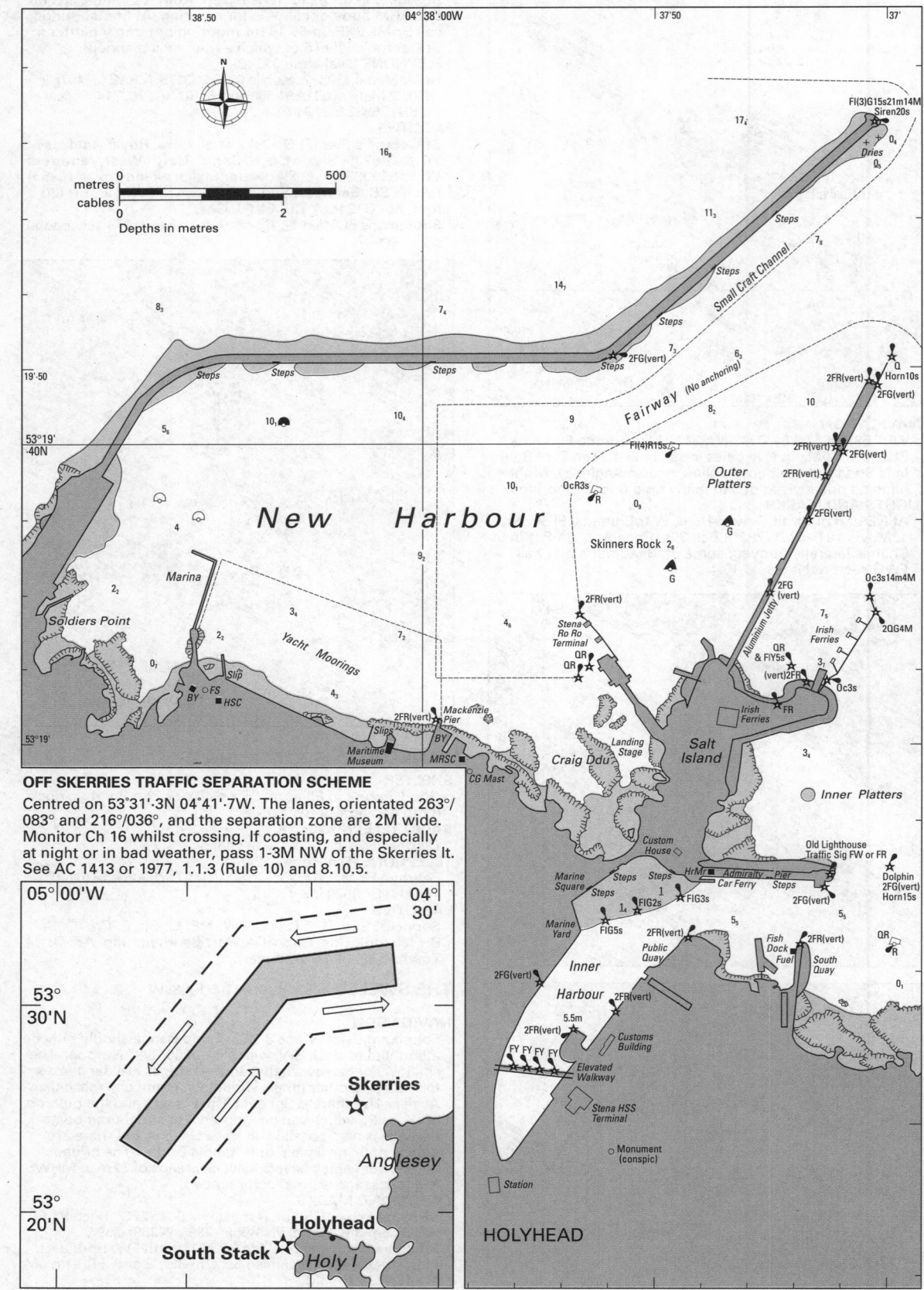

OFF SKERRIES TRAFFIC SEPARATION SCHEME

Centred on 53°31'·3N 04°41'·7W. The lanes, orientated 263°/ 083° and 216°/036°, and the separation zone are 2M wide. Monitor Ch 16 whilst crossing. If coasting, and especially at night or in bad weather, pass 1-3M NW of the Skerries lt. See AC 1413 or 1977, 1.1.3 (Rule 10) and 8.10.5.

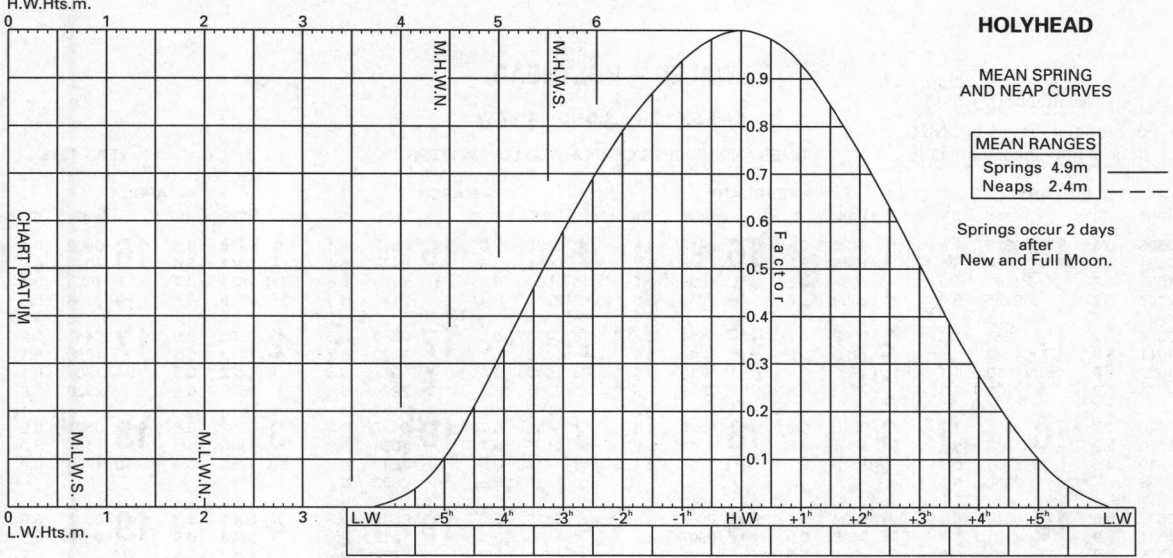

HOLYHEAD

MEAN SPRING
AND NEAP CURVES

MEAN RANGES	
Springs	4.9m
Neaps	2.4m

Springs occur 2 days
after
New and Full Moon.

CHARTS
AC 2011, 1413, *1977*, 1970, *1826*; Imray C61; OS 114

TIDES
–0035 Dover; ML 3·2; Duration 0615; Zone 0 (UT)

Standard Port HOLYHEAD (⟶)

Times				Height (metres)			
High Water		Low Water		MHWS	MHWN	MLWN	MLWS
0000	0600	0500	1100	5·6	4·4	2·0	0·7
1200	1800	1700	2300				
Differences TRWYN DINMOR (W of Puffin Is)							
+0025	+0015	+0050	+0035	+1·9	+1·5	+0·5	+0·2
MOELFRE (NE Anglesey)							
+0025	+0020	+0050	+0035	+1·9	+1·4	+0·5	+0·2
AMLWCH (N Anglesey)							
+0020	+0010	+0035	+0025	+1·6	+1·3	+0·5	+0·2
CEMAES BAY (N Anglesey)							
+0020	+0025	+0040	+0035	+1·0	+0·7	+0·3	+0·1
TREARDDUR BAY (W Anglesey)							
–0045	–0025	–0015	–0015	–0·4	–0·4	0·0	+0·1
PORTH TRECASTELL (SW Anglesey)							
–0045	–0025	–0005	–0015	–0·6	–0·6	0·0	0·0
TREFOR (Lleyn peninsula)							
–0115	–0100	–0030	–0020	–0·8	–0·9	–0·2	–0·1
PORTH DINLLAEN (Lleyn peninsula)							
–0120	–0105	–0035	–0025	–1·0	–1·0	–0·2	–0·2
PORTH YSGADEN (Lleyn peninsula)							
–0125	–0110	–0040	–0035	–1·1	–1·0	–0·1	–0·1
BARDSEY ISLAND							
–0220	–0240	–0145	–0140	–1·2	–1·2	–0·5	–0·1

Holyhead is a Standard Port and tidal predictions for each
day of the year are given below.

SHELTER
Good in marina. ⚓ or moor off HSC; or temp AB on bkwtr; or
in Fish Dock. Strong NE winds raise an uncomfortable sea.

NAVIGATION
WPT 53°20'·10N 04°37'·20W, 345°/165° from/to bkwtr lt ho,
0·28M. Beware very fast catamaran ferries in approaches.
Yachts entering New Hbr should use the Small Craft Chan,
parallel to and within 70m of the bkwtr; but beware shoal,
drying 0·5m, which extends 35m SE of bkwtr head. Keep
clear of the Aluminium Jetty (Ore terminal), Outer Platters
(buoyed) and 3 large unlit mooring buoys at W end of
New Hbr. No anchoring in fairways.
Ferries comply with a mini-TSS at the hbr ent by entering
within 2½ca of bkwtr hd for the Ro-Ro terminal in New Hbr
or the Inner Hbr; outbound ferries pass within 2½ca WSW
of Clipera PHM buoy, Fl (4) R 15s. Yachts to keep clear.

LIGHTS AND MARKS
Ldg marks 165°, bkwtr lt ho on with chy (127m) R lts.
Tfc sigs from old lt ho at E end of Admty pier: Ⓡ = Ent to
Inner hbr is impracticable. Ⓦ = Ent to Inner hbr is clear.

RADIO TELEPHONE
Call *Holyhead* VHF Ch 14 16 (H24) before entering and to
monitor ferry traffic. Daily Info broadcast at 1200UT on Ch
14 includes local nav info/warnings. Marina and Holyhead
SC: Ch M.

TELEPHONE (Dial code 01407)
Marina 764242; Port Control 606700; MRSC 762051; ⌗
762714; Marinecall 0891 500 460; Police 762323; Dr via
MRSC.

FACILITIES
Marina ☎ 764242, FW, AC, D.
Holyhead SC (HSC) ☎ 762526, M, L, FW, Slip, launch, R
(season only), Bar;
Fish Dock ☎ 760139 AB on pontoons, FW, D by hose.
Inner Hbr ☎ 762304, used by Stena HSS; not advised for
yachts.
Services: BY, ACA, CH, ME, El, Sh, C (100 ton), BH, Slip, Ⓔ.
Town EC Tues; P, V, R, Bar, ▣, ✉, Ⓑ, ➤, ✈ (Liverpool/
Manchester). Ferry/Fast Cat to Dun Laoghaire and Dublin.
Trearddur Bay (3M south) M (small craft only), L; **BY** ☎
860501, D, FW, Sh, CH. **Village** P, V, R, Bar.

MINOR HARBOUR ON THE LLEYN PENINSULA

PORTH DINLLAEN, Gwynedd, 52°56'·66N 04°33'·59W. AC
1512, 1971. HW –0240 on Dover; ML 2·5m; Duration 0535.
See 8.10.22. Shelter good in S to W winds but strong
NNW to NNE winds cause heavy seas in the bay. Beware
Carreg-y-Chad (1·8m) 0·75M SW of the point, and Carreg-
y-Chwislen (dries, with unlit IDM Bn) 2ca ENE of the
point. From N, Garn Fadryn (369m) brg 182° leads into
the bay. Best ⚓ 1ca S of LB ho in approx 2m, or ⚓ 1½ca E
of ruined jetty. Hr Mr ☎ (01758) 720295; CG ☎ 720204.
Facilities: EC Wed; Bar, V by landing stage. At Morfa
Nefyn (1M), Bar, P, R, V.

*At last about tea-time, when land began to loom vaguely to
port, to starboard, and also ahead, we realized that we were
near the head of Cardigan Bay, two points off course and
some forty miles from Holyhead. Currents, the compass,
the helmsman, even the navigator, may be responsible for
these anomalies. It is not, however, for the navigator to
accept responsibility for them or to show surprise, or he
may sap what confidence the crew have in him. Attack is the
best form of defence. A few remarks about the impossibility
of navigating the ship if it is not steered straight will restore
his own confidence and subdue and mystify the crew.*

Mostly Mischief: H.W.Tilman

With acknowledgements to the Executors of the estate of
H.W.Tilman and to Hollis & Carter (Publishers 1966).

10

WALES – HOLYHEAD

LAT 53°19′N   LONG   4°37′W

TIMES AND HEIGHTS OF HIGH AND LOW WATERS

YEAR **1999**

TIME ZONE (UT)
For Summer Time add ONE hour in non-shaded areas

JANUARY

Date	Time	m	Date	Time	m
1 F	0306 0924 1535 2147	0.8 5.7 0.7 5.7	**16** SA	0323 0934 1543 2155	1.4 5.3 1.3 5.2
2 SA O	0354 1011 1623 2235	0.7 5.8 0.6 5.8	**17** SU ●	0358 1009 1619 2230	1.2 5.5 1.1 5.3
3 SU	0440 1056 1710 2323	0.7 5.9 0.5 5.7	**18** M	0434 1045 1655 2306	1.1 5.6 0.9 5.4
4 M	0525 1141 1756	0.8 5.9 0.6	**19** TU	0510 1121 1733 2344	0.9 5.7 0.8 5.4
5 TU	0009 0608 1226 1841	5.6 0.9 5.8 0.8	**20** W	0547 1200 1812	0.9 5.7 0.8
6 W	0054 0651 1310 1927	5.4 1.1 5.6 1.0	**21** TH	0023 0626 1241 1853	5.4 0.9 5.7 0.9
7 TH	0138 0734 1353 2013	5.1 1.4 5.3 1.3	**22** F	0106 0709 1324 1937	5.3 1.0 5.6 0.9
8 F	0223 0820 1438 2102	4.9 1.7 5.0 1.6	**23** SA	0151 0755 1412 2027	5.2 1.2 5.4 1.1
9 SA	0312 0911 1529 2158	4.6 2.0 4.8 1.9	**24** SU	0243 0849 1506 2125	5.0 1.4 5.2 1.3
10 SU	0410 1012 1630 2301	4.4 2.2 4.6 2.0	**25** M	0344 0953 1611 2233	4.8 1.6 5.1 1.4
11 M	0519 1122 1741	4.4 2.3 4.5	**26** TU	0458 1108 1727 2348	4.7 1.7 4.9 1.5
12 TU	0007 0629 1233 1851	2.1 4.5 2.3 4.5	**27** W	0617 1226 1844	4.8 1.6 5.0
13 W	0109 0729 1334 1950	2.0 4.6 2.1 4.7	**28** TH	0100 0727 1336 1953	1.4 5.0 1.4 5.1
14 TH	0201 0817 1424 2038	1.8 4.9 1.8 4.9	**29** F	0205 0826 1437 2052	1.3 5.2 1.1 5.3
15 F	0244 0858 1505 2119	1.6 5.1 1.6 5.0	**30** SA	0259 0917 1529 2142	1.1 5.5 0.9 5.5
			31 SU O	0346 1002 1616 2227	0.9 5.7 0.7 5.6

FEBRUARY

Date	Time	m	Date	Time	m
1 M	0429 1045 1658 2309	0.8 5.8 0.6 5.6	**16** TU ●	0414 1025 1636 2248	0.9 5.7 0.7 5.5
2 TU	0509 1125 1739 2349	0.7 5.8 0.6 5.5	**17** W	0451 1102 1713 2325	0.7 5.8 0.6 5.6
3 W	0548 1204 1818	0.7 5.8 0.7	**18** TH	0528 1141 1752	0.6 5.9 0.4
4 TH	0027 0625 1242 1856	5.4 0.9 5.6 0.9	**19** F	0003 0607 1222 1832	5.6 0.5 5.9 0.4
5 F	0104 0702 1319 1934	5.2 1.2 5.4 1.2	**20** SA	0045 0649 1304 1915	5.5 0.6 5.8 0.6
6 SA	0141 0740 1355 2013	5.0 1.4 5.1 1.5	**21** SU	0129 0734 1351 2003	5.4 0.8 5.6 0.9
7 SU	0219 0821 1436 2057	4.8 1.7 4.9 1.8	**22** M	0217 0826 1443 2058	5.1 1.1 5.3 1.2
8 M	0305 0909 1524 2151	4.6 2.0 4.6 2.0	**23** TU	0314 0928 1548 2206	4.9 1.4 5.0 1.5
9 TU	0404 1012 1631 2301	4.4 2.3 4.3 2.2	**24** W	0429 1047 1709 2328	4.6 1.7 4.7 1.7
10 W	0521 1131 1757	4.3 2.4 4.3	**25** TH	0556 1213 1837	4.6 1.7 4.7
11 TH	0017 0640 1251 1915	2.2 4.4 2.2 4.4	**26** F	0049 0716 1330 1952	1.7 4.8 1.5 4.9
12 F	0125 0743 1353 2014	2.0 4.6 1.9 4.6	**27** SA	0158 0820 1432 2050	1.5 5.1 1.2 5.1
13 SA	0218 0832 1441 2059	1.8 4.9 1.6 4.9	**28** SU	0252 0909 1521 2136	1.2 5.3 0.9 5.3
14 SU	0300 0912 1522 2137	1.5 5.2 1.3 5.1			
15 M	0338 0949 1559 2212	1.2 5.4 0.9 5.3			

MARCH

Date	Time	m	Date	Time	m
1 M	0336 0951 1604 2215	1.0 5.6 0.7 5.4	**16** TU	0312 0922 1533 2148	1.1 5.4 0.8 5.4
2 TU O	0415 1029 1641 2250	0.8 5.7 0.6 5.5	**17** W ●	0350 1000 1611 2224	0.8 5.7 0.5 5.6
3 W	0451 1105 1717 2325	0.7 5.7 0.6 5.5	**18** TH	0427 1038 1649 2302	0.5 5.9 0.2 5.7
4 TH	0525 1140 1751 2358	0.7 5.7 0.7 5.4	**19** F	0506 1118 1729 2341	0.3 6.0 0.2 5.8
5 F	0558 1213 1824	0.8 5.6 0.9	**20** SA	0547 1200 1811	0.3 6.0 0.2
6 SA	0031 0631 1246 1857	5.3 1.0 5.4 1.1	**21** SU	0023 0629 1245 1854	5.7 0.4 5.9 0.4
7 SU	0104 0705 1319 1931	5.1 1.2 5.2 1.3	**22** M	0108 0716 1333 1942	5.5 0.6 5.6 0.8
8 M	0137 0742 1355 2009	4.9 1.5 4.9 1.6	**23** TU	0156 0809 1427 2038	5.2 0.9 5.2 1.2
9 TU	0217 0824 1437 2055	4.7 1.8 4.6 2.0	**24** W	0254 0913 1534 2147	4.9 1.3 4.9 1.6
10 W	0306 0917 1534 2156	4.5 2.1 4.3 2.2	**25** TH	0408 1034 1700 2312	4.7 1.6 4.6 1.9
11 TH	0414 1031 1659 2320	4.3 2.3 4.1 2.4	**26** F	0539 1202 1832	4.6 1.6 4.6
12 F	0543 1201 1836	4.2 2.2 4.2	**27** SA	0037 0702 1319 1946	1.9 4.7 1.4 4.8
13 SA	0043 0701 1316 1944	2.2 4.4 2.0 4.5	**28** SU	0146 0806 1419 2040	1.6 5.0 1.2 5.0
14 SU	0145 0758 1406 2032	1.9 4.8 1.6 4.8	**29** M	0239 0854 1506 2121	1.4 5.2 1.0 5.2
15 M	0232 0843 1454 2112	1.5 5.1 1.2 5.1	**30** TU O	0320 0933 1544 2155	1.1 5.4 0.8 5.3
			31 W O	0356 1007 1619 2227	0.9 5.5 0.7 5.4

APRIL

Date	Time	m	Date	Time	m
1 TH	0428 1041 1651 2258	0.8 5.6 0.7 5.4	**16** F ●	0402 1013 1624 2238	0.4 6.0 0.1 5.8
2 F	0500 1113 1722 2329	0.8 5.5 0.8 5.4	**17** SA	0443 1056 1706 2320	0.2 6.1 0.1 5.9
3 SA	0532 1145 1753	0.8 5.4 0.9	**18** SU	0527 1141 1750	0.2 6.0 0.2
4 SU	0001 0603 1217 1824	5.3 0.9 5.3 1.1	**19** M	0003 0612 1229 1836	5.8 0.3 5.9 0.5
5 M	0033 0636 1249 1857	5.2 1.1 5.1 1.3	**20** TU	0050 0702 1319 1926	5.6 0.5 5.6 0.8
6 TU	0106 0711 1324 1932	5.1 1.4 4.9 1.6	**21** W	0141 0758 1416 2022	5.3 0.8 5.2 1.3
7 W	0142 0751 1404 2015	4.9 1.6 4.6 1.9	**22** TH	0240 0903 1525 2130	5.0 1.2 4.8 1.7
8 TH	0227 0840 1455 2110	4.6 1.9 4.4 2.1	**23** F	0352 1021 1648 2252	4.8 1.5 4.6 1.9
9 F	0326 0946 1610 2227	4.4 2.1 4.2 2.3	**24** SA	0516 1143 1814	4.7 1.5 4.5
10 SA	0447 1112 1716 2354	4.3 2.1 4.2 2.2	**25** SU	0013 0636 1256 1925	1.9 4.7 1.4 4.7
11 SU	0613 1231 1905	4.4 1.9 4.4	**26** M	0122 0740 1355 2017	1.8 4.9 1.2 4.9
12 M	0104 0717 1331 1958	1.9 4.7 1.5 4.8	**27** TU	0215 0828 1441 2057	1.5 5.1 1.1 5.0
13 TU	0157 0807 1419 2040	1.5 5.1 1.0 5.1	**28** W	0256 0908 1519 2130	1.3 5.2 1.0 5.2
14 W	0241 0850 1506 2119	1.1 5.4 0.6 5.3	**29** TH	0332 0942 1552 2201	1.1 5.3 0.9 5.3
15 TH	0322 0931 1543 2158	0.7 5.7 0.3 5.7	**30** F O	0404 1015 1624 2232	1.0 5.4 0.9 5.4

Chart Datum: 3·05 metres below Ordnance Datum (Newlyn)

WALES – HOLYHEAD

LAT 53°19′N   LONG   4°37′W

TIMES AND HEIGHTS OF HIGH AND LOW WATERS

YEAR 1999

TIME ZONE (UT)
For Summer Time add ONE hour in non-shaded areas

MAY

Day	Time	m	Time	m	Time	m	Time	m
1 SA	0436	0.9	1047	5.3	1654	0.9	2303	5.4
2 SU	0507	0.9	1119	5.3	1725	1.0	2334	5.4
3 M	0539	1.0	1151	5.2	1757	1.1		
4 TU	0006	5.3	0612	1.1	1225	5.1	1830	1.3
5 W	0041	5.1	0648	1.3	1301	4.9	1906	1.5
6 TH	0118	5.0	0729	1.5	1341	4.7	1948	1.7
7 F	0201	4.8	0816	1.7	1431	4.5	2039	2.0
8 SA	0256	4.6	0915	1.8	1537	4.3	2146	2.1
9 SU	0405	4.5	1029	1.8	1700	4.3	2306	2.1
10 M	0523	4.6	1145	1.7	1818	4.5		
11 TU	0018	1.9	0632	4.8	1250	1.4	1917	4.8
12 W	0118	1.5	0728	5.1	1343	1.0	2006	5.1
13 TH	0207	1.1	0817	5.4	1431	0.6	2050	5.4
14 F	0253	0.7	0903	5.7	1516	0.4	2132	5.6
15 SA ●	0338	0.4	0949	5.9	1600	0.2	2216	5.8
16 SU	0423	0.3	1036	6.0	1646	0.2	2301	5.9
17 M	0510	0.2	1125	5.9	1732	0.3	2347	5.8
18 TU	0600	0.3	1215	5.8	1821	0.6		
19 W	0036	5.7	0651	0.5	1309	5.5	1911	0.9
20 TH	0129	5.4	0747	0.8	1406	5.1	2007	1.3
21 F	0226	5.2	0850	1.1	1510	4.8	2110	1.6
22 SA	0331	4.9	0959	1.3	1623	4.6	2222	1.9
23 SU	0444	4.8	1112	1.5	1739	4.5	2337	2.0
24 M	0558	4.7	1220	1.5	1848	4.6		
25 TU	0044	1.9	0702	4.8	1320	1.4	1942	4.7
26 W	0141	1.7	0754	4.9	1409	1.3	2025	4.9
27 TH	0227	1.5	0837	5.0	1449	1.2	2102	5.0
28 F	0305	1.4	0915	5.1	1525	1.1	2135	5.2
29 SA	0340	1.2	0950	5.1	1557	1.1	2207	5.3
30 SU O	0413	1.1	1023	5.1	1629	1.1	2239	5.3
31 M	0446	1.1	1056	5.2	1701	1.1	2311	5.3

JUNE

Day	Time	m	Time	m	Time	m	Time	m
1 TU	0519	1.1	1130	5.1	1734	1.2	2345	5.3
2 W	0554	1.1	1205	5.0	1809	1.3		
3 TH	0021	5.2	0631	1.2	1243	4.9	1846	1.4
4 F	0100	5.1	0711	1.3	1324	4.8	1928	1.5
5 SA	0143	5.0	0757	1.4	1412	4.6	2016	1.7
6 SU	0233	4.9	0851	1.5	1509	4.5	2115	1.8
7 M	0332	4.8	0954	1.5	1618	4.5	2224	1.9
8 TU	0441	4.8	1103	1.5	1731	4.6	2335	1.8
9 W	0550	4.9	1209	1.3	1837	4.8		
10 TH	0039	1.5	0652	5.1	1309	1.0	1933	5.1
11 F	0137	1.2	0748	5.3	1403	0.8	2024	5.3
12 SA	0229	0.9	0840	5.6	1453	0.6	2111	5.6
13 SU ●	0319	0.6	0931	5.7	1542	0.4	2158	5.7
14 M	0409	0.4	1022	5.8	1630	0.4	2246	5.8
15 TU	0458	0.3	1112	5.8	1718	0.5	2334	5.8
16 W	0549	0.3	1204	5.6	1806	0.7		
17 TH	0023	5.7	0640	0.5	1256	5.4	1855	0.9
18 F	0114	5.6	0732	0.7	1349	5.2	1946	1.2
19 SA	0206	5.4	0828	1.0	1445	4.9	2041	1.5
20 SU	0302	5.1	0927	1.3	1545	4.6	2142	1.8
21 M	0402	4.8	1030	1.5	1650	4.5	2249	2.0
22 TU	0508	4.7	1134	1.7	1757	4.5	2356	2.0
23 W	0614	4.6	1235	1.7	1858	4.5		
24 TH	0059	2.0	0714	4.7	1330	1.6	1948	4.7
25 F	0153	1.8	0805	4.7	1417	1.5	2031	4.9
26 SA	0238	1.6	0849	4.9	1457	1.4	2109	5.1
27 SU	0317	1.4	0927	5.0	1533	1.3	2144	5.2
28 M O	0353	1.3	1003	5.0	1607	1.2	2218	5.3
29 TU	0427	1.2	1038	5.1	1641	1.2	2252	5.4
30 W	0502	1.1	1113	5.1	1715	1.1	2327	5.4

JULY

Day	Time	m	Time	m	Time	m	Time	m
1 TH	0538	1.1	1148	5.1	1751	1.2		
2 F	0003	5.4	0615	1.1	1227	5.0	1828	1.2
3 SA	0043	5.3	0654	1.1	1307	5.0	1909	1.3
4 SU	0125	5.2	0737	1.1	1352	4.9	1955	1.4
5 M	0211	5.1	0826	1.2	1442	4.8	2047	1.6
6 TU	0303	5.0	0922	1.3	1541	4.7	2147	1.7
7 W	0404	5.0	1025	1.3	1650	4.7	2257	1.7
8 TH	0513	4.9	1134	1.3	1801	4.8		
9 F	0007	1.5	0622	5.0	1241	1.2	1906	5.0
10 SA	0113	1.3	0727	5.2	1342	1.0	2004	5.2
11 SU	0213	1.0	0826	5.4	1438	0.8	2057	5.4
12 M	0308	0.8	0920	5.5	1529	0.7	2146	5.6
13 TU ●	0359	0.6	1012	5.6	1618	0.6	2234	5.8
14 W	0448	0.4	1102	5.7	1704	0.7	2321	5.8
15 TH	0536	0.4	1150	5.6	1750	0.7		
16 F	0007	5.8	0623	0.5	1237	5.4	1835	0.9
17 SA	0053	5.7	0710	0.7	1323	5.2	1920	1.1
18 SU	0139	5.4	0757	1.0	1409	5.0	2006	1.4
19 M	0225	5.2	0846	1.3	1458	4.7	2056	1.7
20 TU	0314	4.9	0939	1.6	1551	4.5	2152	2.0
21 W	0410	4.6	1038	1.8	1654	4.4	2259	2.2
22 TH	0517	4.5	1142	2.0	1803	4.4		
23 F	0010	2.2	0628	4.4	1247	1.9	1907	4.5
24 SA	0116	2.1	0732	4.5	1343	1.8	2000	4.7
25 SU	0210	1.8	0825	4.7	1431	1.7	2044	4.9
26 M	0255	1.6	0908	4.8	1511	1.5	2122	5.1
27 TU	0333	1.4	0945	5.0	1547	1.3	2157	5.3
28 W O	0409	1.2	1020	5.1	1621	1.2	2232	5.4
29 TH	0443	1.0	1054	5.2	1656	1.0	2307	5.5
30 F	0519	0.9	1130	5.3	1732	1.0	2344	5.6
31 SA	0556	0.8	1207	5.3	1809	1.0		

AUGUST

Day	Time	m	Time	m	Time	m	Time	m
1 SU	0022	5.6	0633	0.8	1246	5.2	1848	1.0
2 M	0103	5.5	0715	0.9	1328	5.1	1931	1.1
3 TU	0147	5.4	0800	1.0	1415	5.0	2020	1.3
4 W	0236	5.2	0852	1.2	1509	4.9	2117	1.5
5 TH	0334	5.1	0953	1.3	1615	4.7	2227	1.6
6 F	0445	4.9	1105	1.5	1733	4.7	2345	1.6
7 SA	0603	4.9	1220	1.5	1848	4.9		
8 SU	0059	1.5	0717	5.0	1330	1.3	1953	5.1
9 M	0205	1.2	0821	5.2	1429	1.1	2048	5.4
10 TU	0302	0.9	0916	5.4	1521	0.9	2137	5.6
11 W ●	0351	0.6	1004	5.5	1559	0.8	2221	5.8
12 TH	0437	0.5	1048	5.6	1649	0.7	2304	5.9
13 F	0519	0.4	1131	5.6	1730	0.7	2346	5.8
14 SA	0601	0.5	1211	5.4	1810	0.8		
15 SU	0026	5.7	0641	0.7	1251	5.3	1848	1.0
16 M	0106	5.5	0720	1.0	1330	5.1	1928	1.3
17 TU	0145	5.2	0801	1.3	1409	4.8	2010	1.6
18 W	0225	4.9	0844	1.6	1454	4.6	2058	1.9
19 TH	0312	4.6	0936	2.0	1549	4.4	2158	2.2
20 F	0415	4.4	1042	2.2	1701	4.3	2315	2.3
21 SA	0538	4.2	1158	2.2	1820	4.4		
22 SU	0035	2.3	0700	4.3	1308	2.1	1926	4.6
23 M	0141	2.0	0802	4.6	1404	1.9	2017	4.9
24 TU	0230	1.7	0848	4.8	1447	1.6	2058	5.1
25 W	0310	1.4	0925	5.0	1524	1.3	2133	5.4
26 TH O	0345	1.1	0958	5.2	1559	1.1	2208	5.6
27 F	0420	0.8	1032	5.4	1633	0.9	2243	5.7
28 SA	0455	0.7	1106	5.5	1709	0.8	2320	5.8
29 SU	0532	0.6	1143	5.5	1746	0.7	2359	5.8
30 M	0610	0.6	1222	5.5	1825	0.8		
31 TU	0039	5.7	0650	0.7	1303	5.4	1908	0.9

10

Chart Datum: 3·05 metres below Ordnance Datum (Newlyn)

WALES – HOLYHEAD

LAT 53°19′N   LONG   4°37′W

TIMES AND HEIGHTS OF HIGH AND LOW WATERS   YEAR **1999**

TIME ZONE (UT) — For Summer Time add ONE hour in non-shaded areas

Chart Datum: 3·05 metres below Ordnance Datum (Newlyn)

SEPTEMBER

Day	Time	m	Time	m	Day	Time	m	Time	m
1 W	0123 / 0735 / 1349 / 1956	5.6 / 0.9 / 5.2 / 1.1			16 TH	0142 / 0806 / 1405 / 2012	4.9 / 1.7 / 4.8 / 1.9		
2 TH	0213 / 0826 / 1442 / 2054	5.3 / 1.2 / 5.0 / 1.4			17 F	0224 / 0841 / 1454 / 2106	4.6 / 2.0 / 4.6 / 2.2		
3 F	0312 / 0928 / 1549 / 2207	5.1 / 1.5 / 4.8 / 1.7			18 SA	0320 / 0941 / 1600 / 2219	4.4 / 2.3 / 4.4 / 2.4		
4 SA	0428 / 1046 / 1714 / 2334	4.8 / 1.7 / 4.7 / 1.7			19 SU	0445 / 1104 / 1727 / 2349	4.2 / 2.5 / 4.3 / 2.4		
5 SU	0557 / 1210 / 1838	4.7 / 1.8 / 4.8			20 M	0623 / 1227 / 1846	4.2 / 2.4 / 4.5		
6 M	0054 / 0717 / 1324 / 1946	1.5 / 4.9 / 1.6 / 5.1			21 TU	0104 / 0733 / 1331 / 1943	2.1 / 4.5 / 2.1 / 4.8		
7 TU	0201 / 0821 / 1423 / 2041	1.2 / 5.1 / 1.4 / 5.4			22 W	0158 / 0820 / 1417 / 2027	1.7 / 4.8 / 1.7 / 5.1		
8 W	0255 / 0911 / 1511 / 2126	0.9 / 5.3 / 1.1 / 5.6			23 TH	0240 / 0858 / 1456 / 2105	1.3 / 5.1 / 1.4 / 5.4		
9 TH	0340 / 0952 / 1552 / 2206 ●	0.7 / 5.5 / 0.9 / 5.8			24 F	0317 / 0931 / 1531 / 2140	1.0 / 5.3 / 1.0 / 5.7		
10 F	0420 / 1030 / 1630 / 2244	0.6 / 5.5 / 0.8 / 5.8			25 SA	0352 / 1005 / 1607 / 2217 O	0.7 / 5.5 / 0.8 / 5.9		
11 SA	0457 / 1106 / 1706 / 2321	0.6 / 5.5 / 0.8 / 5.8			26 SU	0428 / 1040 / 1643 / 2254	0.5 / 5.7 / 0.6 / 6.0		
12 SU	0534 / 1142 / 1742 / 2357	0.7 / 5.5 / 0.9 / 5.7			27 M	0505 / 1117 / 1722 / 2335	0.4 / 5.8 / 0.5 / 6.0		
13 M	0609 / 1216 / 1817	0.8 / 5.4 / 1.0			28 TU	0545 / 1157 / 1803	0.4 / 5.7 / 0.6		
14 TU	0031 / 0643 / 1251 / 1852	5.5 / 1.1 / 5.2 / 1.3			29 W	0017 / 0627 / 1240 / 1848	5.9 / 0.6 / 5.6 / 0.8		
15 W	0106 / 0718 / 1326 / 1929	5.2 / 1.4 / 5.0 / 1.6			30 TH	0104 / 0713 / 1327 / 1939	5.7 / 0.9 / 5.4 / 1.1		

OCTOBER

Day	Time	m	Day	Time	m
1 F	0156 / 0806 / 1422 / 2040	5.4 / 1.3 / 5.1 / 1.4	16 SA	0148 / 0759 / 1412 / 2026	4.7 / 2.0 / 4.7 / 2.1
2 SA	0259 / 0910 / 1533 / 2157	5.0 / 1.7 / 4.8 / 1.7	17 SU	0240 / 0853 / 1511 / 2132	4.4 / 2.3 / 4.5 / 2.3
3 SU	0422 / 1033 / 1701 / 2326	4.7 / 1.9 / 4.7 / 1.7	18 M	0354 / 1008 / 1630 / 2257	4.2 / 2.5 / 4.4 / 2.3
4 M	0555 / 1200 / 1827	4.7 / 2.0 / 4.9	19 TU	0534 / 1137 / 1756	4.2 / 2.5 / 4.5
5 TU	0046 / 0714 / 1314 / 1935	1.5 / 4.9 / 1.8 / 5.1	20 W	0017 / 0651 / 1248 / 1900	2.1 / 4.5 / 2.2 / 4.8
6 W	0151 / 0813 / 1411 / 2027	1.3 / 5.1 / 1.5 / 5.4	21 TH	0116 / 0743 / 1339 / 1950	1.7 / 4.8 / 1.8 / 5.1
7 TH	0241 / 0858 / 1456 / 2109	1.0 / 5.3 / 1.2 / 5.6	22 F	0203 / 0824 / 1422 / 2031	1.3 / 5.1 / 1.4 / 5.5
8 F	0323 / 0935 / 1534 / 2146	0.8 / 5.4 / 1.0 / 5.7	23 SA	0243 / 0901 / 1501 / 2110	0.9 / 5.4 / 1.0 / 5.7
9 SA	0359 / 1005 / 1608 / 2220 ●	0.7 / 5.5 / 0.9 / 5.7	24 SU	0322 / 0937 / 1540 / 2149 O	0.6 / 5.7 / 0.7 / 6.0
10 SU	0432 / 1040 / 1642 / 2254	0.7 / 5.6 / 0.9 / 5.7	25 M	0401 / 1014 / 1619 / 2230	0.4 / 5.9 / 0.5 / 6.1
11 M	0505 / 1113 / 1715 / 2328	0.8 / 5.5 / 0.9 / 5.6	26 TU	0441 / 1054 / 1701 / 2313	0.3 / 5.9 / 0.5 / 6.1
12 TU	0537 / 1145 / 1748	1.0 / 5.4 / 1.1	27 W	0523 / 1136 / 1745 / 2359	0.4 / 5.9 / 0.5 / 6.0
13 W	0001 / 0609 / 1218 / 1821	5.4 / 1.2 / 5.3 / 1.3	28 TH	0608 / 1222 / 1834	0.6 / 5.7 / 0.7
14 TH	0034 / 0642 / 1251 / 1857	5.3 / 1.4 / 5.2 / 1.5	29 F	0049 / 0656 / 1312 / 1927	5.7 / 0.9 / 5.5 / 1.0
15 F	0108 / 0718 / 1328 / 1937	5.0 / 1.7 / 5.0 / 1.8	30 SA	0145 / 0751 / 1409 / 2031	5.4 / 1.3 / 5.0 / 1.3
			31 SU	0252 / 0857 / 1519 / 2148	5.0 / 1.7 / 5.0 / 1.6

NOVEMBER

Day	Time	m	Day	Time	m
1 M	0413 / 1017 / 1643 / 2311	4.7 / 2.0 / 4.9 / 1.6	16 TU	0315 / 0922 / 1542 / 2207	4.4 / 2.4 / 4.6 / 2.1
2 TU	0541 / 1140 / 1805	4.7 / 2.1 / 4.9	17 W	0437 / 1041 / 1700 / 2324	4.3 / 2.4 / 4.6 / 2.0
3 W	0026 / 0656 / 1253 / 1912	1.5 / 4.8 / 1.9 / 5.1	18 TH	0557 / 1156 / 1811	4.5 / 2.2 / 4.8
4 TH	0129 / 0753 / 1349 / 2005	1.3 / 5.0 / 1.7 / 5.3	19 F	0029 / 0658 / 1256 / 1908	1.7 / 4.8 / 1.8 / 5.1
5 F	0219 / 0836 / 1435 / 2047	1.2 / 5.2 / 1.4 / 5.4	20 SA	0122 / 0747 / 1346 / 1956	1.3 / 5.1 / 1.5 / 5.4
6 SA	0259 / 0912 / 1513 / 2123	1.1 / 5.3 / 1.2 / 5.5	21 SU	0209 / 0830 / 1431 / 2041	1.0 / 5.4 / 1.1 / 5.7
7 SU	0335 / 0944 / 1547 / 2157	1.0 / 5.4 / 1.1 / 5.5	22 M	0253 / 0911 / 1515 / 2125	0.7 / 5.7 / 0.8 / 5.9
8 M	0407 / 1015 / 1619 / 2230 ●	1.0 / 5.5 / 1.1 / 5.5	23 TU	0336 / 0952 / 1559 / 2210 O	0.5 / 5.8 / 0.5 / 6.1
9 TU	0439 / 1047 / 1652 / 2303	1.0 / 5.5 / 1.1 / 5.4	24 W	0420 / 1035 / 1645 / 2257	0.4 / 6.0 / 0.4 / 6.1
10 W	0510 / 1119 / 1724 / 2335	1.1 / 5.5 / 1.2 / 5.3	25 TH	0506 / 1121 / 1733 / 2347	0.4 / 6.0 / 0.4 / 5.9
11 TH	0541 / 1151 / 1758	1.2 / 5.4 / 1.3	26 F	0553 / 1209 / 1824	0.6 / 5.9 / 0.6
12 F	0008 / 0614 / 1225 / 1833	5.2 / 1.4 / 5.3 / 1.5	27 SA	0039 / 0643 / 1301 / 1919	5.7 / 0.9 / 5.7 / 0.8
13 SA	0044 / 0650 / 1302 / 1913	5.0 / 1.7 / 5.1 / 1.7	28 SU	0136 / 0738 / 1357 / 2020	5.4 / 1.3 / 5.4 / 1.1
14 SU	0124 / 0730 / 1344 / 1959	4.8 / 1.9 / 4.9 / 1.9	29 M	0239 / 0839 / 1501 / 2128	5.0 / 1.7 / 5.2 / 1.4
15 M	0212 / 0819 / 1436 / 2056	4.6 / 2.2 / 4.7 / 2.0	30 TU	0351 / 0950 / 1613 / 2242	4.8 / 1.9 / 5.0 / 1.6

DECEMBER

Day	Time	m	Day	Time	m
1 W	0508 / 1105 / 1728 / 2353	4.7 / 2.1 / 4.9 / 1.6	16 TH	0345 / 0950 / 1609 / 2232	4.5 / 2.1 / 4.8 / 1.8
2 TH	0621 / 1217 / 1837	4.7 / 2.0 / 5.0	17 F	0459 / 1102 / 1719 / 2340	4.6 / 2.1 / 4.9 / 1.6
3 F	0056 / 0721 / 1318 / 1934	1.5 / 4.8 / 1.9 / 5.1	18 SA	0610 / 1211 / 1825	4.7 / 1.9 / 5.0
4 SA	0149 / 0808 / 1408 / 2021	1.4 / 5.0 / 1.7 / 5.2	19 SU	0042 / 0709 / 1311 / 1923	1.4 / 5.0 / 1.5 / 5.3
5 SU	0233 / 0847 / 1450 / 2100	1.3 / 5.2 / 1.5 / 5.2	20 M	0138 / 0801 / 1405 / 2016	1.1 / 5.3 / 1.2 / 5.5
6 M	0310 / 0921 / 1527 / 2136	1.3 / 5.3 / 1.4 / 5.3	21 TU	0229 / 0849 / 1455 / 2107	0.8 / 5.5 / 0.9 / 5.8
7 TU	0344 / 0954 / 1601 / 2210 ●	1.2 / 5.4 / 1.3 / 5.3	22 W	0318 / 0935 / 1545 / 2157 O	0.6 / 5.8 / 0.6 / 5.9
8 W	0417 / 1026 / 1634 / 2243	1.2 / 5.5 / 1.2 / 5.3	23 TH	0406 / 1022 / 1634 / 2247	0.5 / 5.9 / 0.4 / 5.9
9 TH	0448 / 1058 / 1707 / 2317	1.2 / 5.5 / 1.2 / 5.3	24 F	0453 / 1109 / 1724 / 2338	0.5 / 6.0 / 0.4 / 5.9
10 F	0521 / 1131 / 1741 / 2350	1.3 / 5.5 / 1.3 / 5.2	25 SA	0541 / 1158 / 1814	0.6 / 6.0 / 0.5
11 SA	0554 / 1205 / 1816	1.4 / 5.4 / 1.4	26 SU	0029 / 0630 / 1248 / 1906	5.7 / 0.9 / 5.8 / 0.7
12 SU	0026 / 0630 / 1243 / 1854	5.1 / 1.5 / 5.3 / 1.5	27 M	0122 / 0720 / 1340 / 2000	5.4 / 1.1 / 5.6 / 0.9
13 M	0106 / 0709 / 1323 / 1937	4.9 / 1.7 / 5.1 / 1.6	28 TU	0216 / 0813 / 1434 / 2058	5.1 / 1.4 / 5.4 / 1.2
14 TU	0150 / 0753 / 1409 / 2026	4.8 / 1.9 / 5.0 / 1.7	29 W	0315 / 0912 / 1534 / 2201	4.8 / 1.8 / 5.1 / 1.5
15 W	0242 / 0846 / 1504 / 2125	4.6 / 2.0 / 4.9 / 1.8	30 TH	0420 / 1018 / 1640 / 2307	4.6 / 2.0 / 4.9 / 1.7
			31 F	0529 / 1128 / 1749	4.5 / 2.1 / 4.7

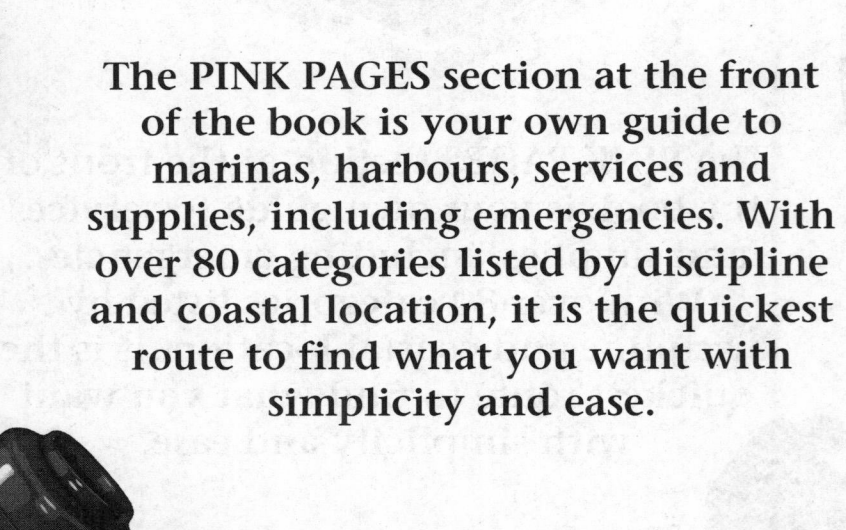

VOLVO PENTA SERVICE

Sales and service centres in area 11
DYFED *Dale Sailing Co Ltd*, Brunel Quay, Neyland, Milford Haven SA73 1PY
Tel (01646) 601636 **SOUTH GLAMORGAN** *John A. Sparks & Co. Ltd*, Ipswich
Road, Cardiff, CF3 7AQ Tel (01222) 492788 *Wigmore - Wright Marine Services*,
The Boatyard, Portway Marina, Penarth CF64 1BW (01222) 709983 **WEST
MIDLANDS** *Marine Performance*, Upton Marina, Upton-on-Severn, Worcester
WR8 0PB Tel (01684) 594540

**VOLVO
PENTA**

Area 11

South Wales and Bristol Channel
Bardsey Island to Lands End

8.11.1	Index	**Page 509**
8.11.2	Diagram of ports, lights, RDF bns, Coast radio and weather stns	**510**
8.11.3	Tidal stream charts	**512**
8.11.4	List of coastal lights, fog signals and waypoints	**514**
8.11.5	Passage information	**518**
8.11.6	Distance table	**519**
8.11.7	Abersoch	**520**
8.11.8	Pwllheli Mochras	**520**
8.11.9	Porthmadog	**521**
8.11.10	Barmouth	**521**
8.11.11	Aberdovey Aberaeron New Quay	**522**
8.11.12	Aberystwyth	**522**
8.11.13	Fishguard Port Cardigan Solva St Brides Bay Skomer	**523**
8.11.14	Milford Haven, Standard Port, tidal curves Off Smalls TSS	**524**
8.11.15	Tenby Caldey Island Saundersfoot	**529**
8.11.16	Burry Inlet Firing ranges Carmarthen	**530**
8.11.17	Swansea Mumbles River Neath Porthcawl	**531**
8.11.18	Barry	**532**
8.11.19	Cardiff Newport	**533**
8.11.20	Sharpness The Severn Bridges	**534**
8.11.21	Bristol (City Docks). (Avonmouth, Standard Port, tidal curves)	**538**
8.11.22	Portishead Weston-super-Mare	**540**
8.11.23	Burnham-on-Sea	**540**
8.11.24	Watchet Minehead Porlock Weir Lynmouth Watermouth	**541**
8.11.25	Ilfracombe Lundy Island	**542**
8.11.26	Rivers Taw and Torridge Clovelly	**542**
8.11.27	Padstow Bude Boscastle Newquay Hayle St Ives	**544**

11

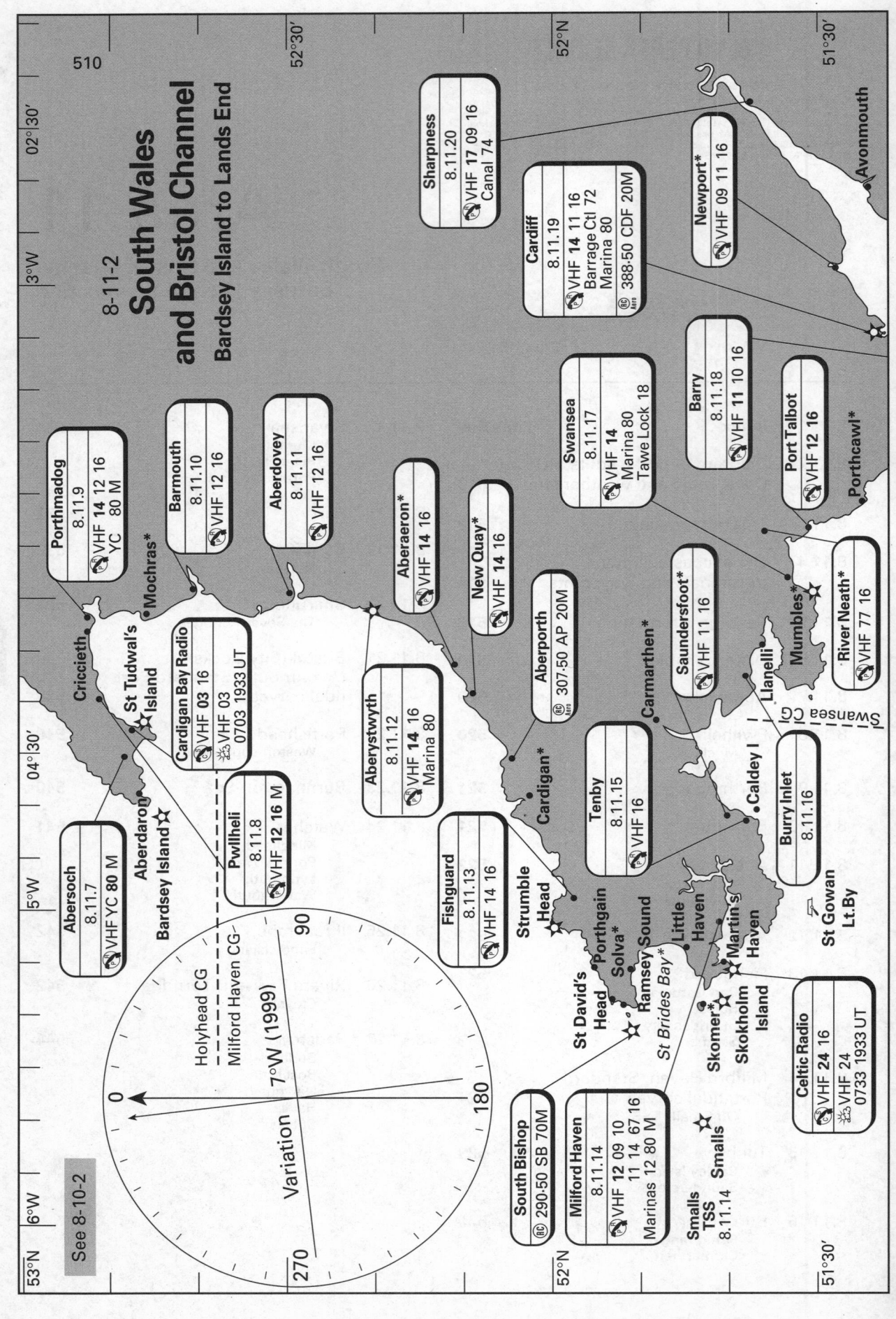

8-11-2
**South Wales
and Bristol Channel**
Bardsey Island to Lands End

See 8-10-2

Abersoch
8.11.7
📻 VHF YC 80 M

Porthmadog
8.11.9
📻 VHF **14** 12 16
YC 80 M

Barmouth
8.11.10
📻 VHF 12 16

Aberdovey
8.11.11
📻 VHF 12 16

Cardigan Bay Radio
📻 VHF 03 16
📡 VHF 03
0703 1933 UT

Pwllheli
8.11.8
📻 VHF **12** 16 M

Aberystwyth
8.11.12
📻 VHF **14** 16
Marina 80

Fishguard
8.11.13
📻 VHF 14 16

Aberaeron*
📻 VHF **14** 16

New Quay*
📻 VHF **14** 16

Aberporth
📻 307·50 AP 20M

Tenby
8.11.15
📻 VHF 16

Burry Inlet
8.11.16

South Bishop
📻 290·50 SB 70M

Milford Haven
8.11.14
📻 VHF **12** 09 10
11 14 67 16
Marinas 12 80 M

Celtic Radio
📻 VHF 24 16
📡 VHF 24
0733 1933 UT

Sharpness
8.11.20
📻 VHF **17** 09 16
Canal 74

Cardiff
8.11.19
📻 VHF **14** 11 16
Barrage Ctl 72
Marina 80
📻 388·50 CDF 20M

Newport*
📻 VHF 09 11 16

Swansea
8.11.17
📻 VHF **14**
Marina 80
Tawe Lock 18

Barry
8.11.18
📻 VHF **11** 10 16

Port Talbot
📻 VHF 12 16

Saundersfoot*
📻 VHF 11 16

River Neath*
📻 VHF 77 16

Variation
7°W (1999)

Holyhead CG
Milford Haven CG

Bardsey Island ☆
Aberdaron ☆
St Tudwal's Island ☆
Criccieth
Mochras*

St David's Head
Strumble Head ☆
Porthgain ☆
Solva*
Ramsey Sound
St Brides Bay*
Little Haven
Martin's Haven
Skomer* ☆
Skokholm Island ☆
Smalls ☆
Smalls TSS
8.11.14
Caldey I
Carmarthen*
Cardigan*
Llanelli
Mumbles* ☆
Porthcawl*
Swansea CG
St Gowan Lt.By ⚓
Avonmouth
Newport

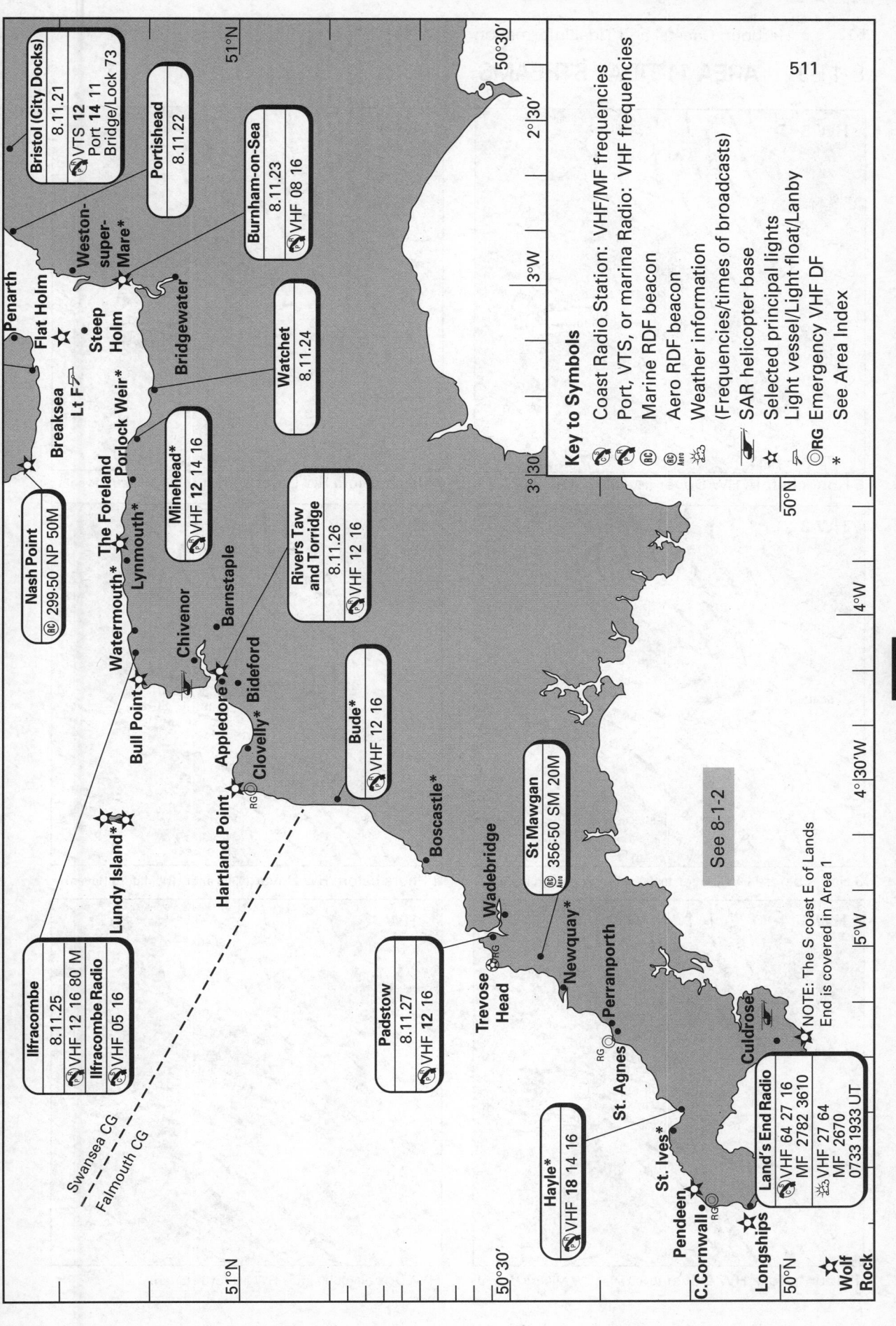

511

11

Key to Symbols

	Coast Radio Station: VHF/MF frequencies
	Port, VTS, or marina Radio: VHF frequencies
RC	Marine RDF beacon
RC Aero	Aero RDF beacon
	Weather information (Frequencies/times of broadcasts)
	SAR helicopter base
☆	Selected principal lights
	Light vessel/Light float/Lanby
◎RG	Emergency VHF DF
*	See Area Index

Bristol (City Docks)
8.11.21
VTS **12**
Port **14** 11
Bridge/Lock 73

Portishead
8.11.22

Burnham-on-Sea
8.11.23
VHF 08 16

Watchet
8.11.24

Nash Point
RC 299·50 NP 50M

Minehead*
VHF 12 14 16

Rivers Taw and Torridge
8.11.26
VHF 12 16

Ilfracombe
8.11.25
VHF 12 16 80 M
Ilfracombe Radio
VHF 05 16

Bude*
VHF 12 16

St Mawgan
RC 356·50 SM 20M
Aero

Padstow
8.11.27
VHF 12 16

Hayle*
VHF 18 14 16

Land's End Radio
VHF 64 27 16
MF 2782 3610
VHF 27 64
MF 2670
0733 1933 UT

NOTE: The S coast E of Lands End is covered in Area 1

See 8-1-2

Penarth
Flat Holm
Breaksea Lt F
Steep Holm
Weston-super-Mare*
Bridgewater
The Foreland
Porlock Weir*
Watermouth*
Lynmouth*
Bull Point
Chivenor
Barnstaple
Appledore
Bideford
Clovelly*
Hartland Point
Lundy Island*
Boscastle*
Wadebridge
Trevose Head
Newquay*
Perranporth
St. Agnes
St. Ives*
Pendeen
C. Cornwall
Longships
Wolf Rock
Culdrose

Swansea CG
Falmouth CG

8-11-3   AREA 11 TIDAL STREAMS

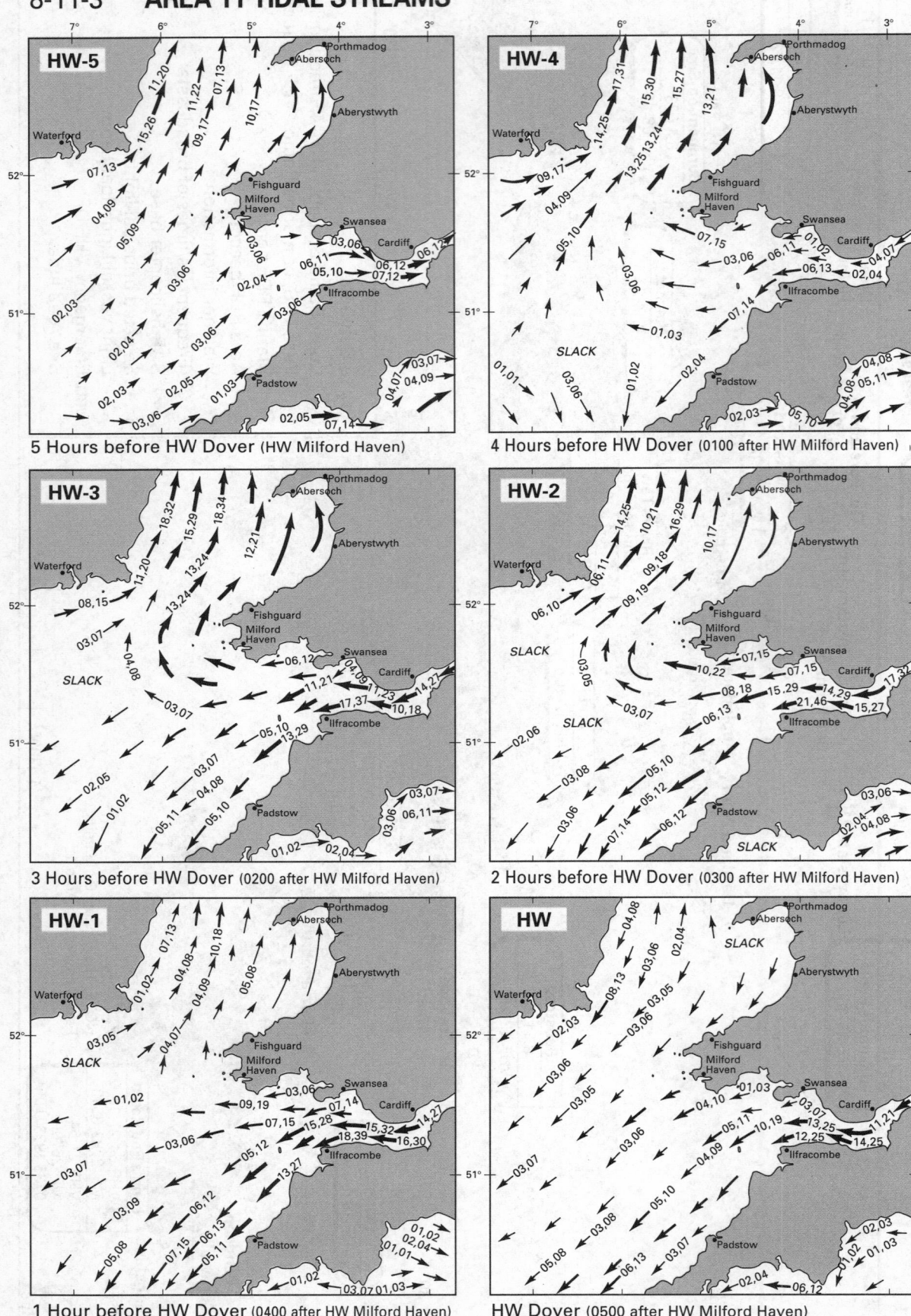

5 Hours before HW Dover (HW Milford Haven)

4 Hours before HW Dover (0100 after HW Milford Haven)

3 Hours before HW Dover (0200 after HW Milford Haven)

2 Hours before HW Dover (0300 after HW Milford Haven)

1 Hour before HW Dover (0400 after HW Milford Haven)

HW Dover (0500 after HW Milford Haven)

Southward 8.1.3   Northward 8.10.3   South Ireland 8.12.3

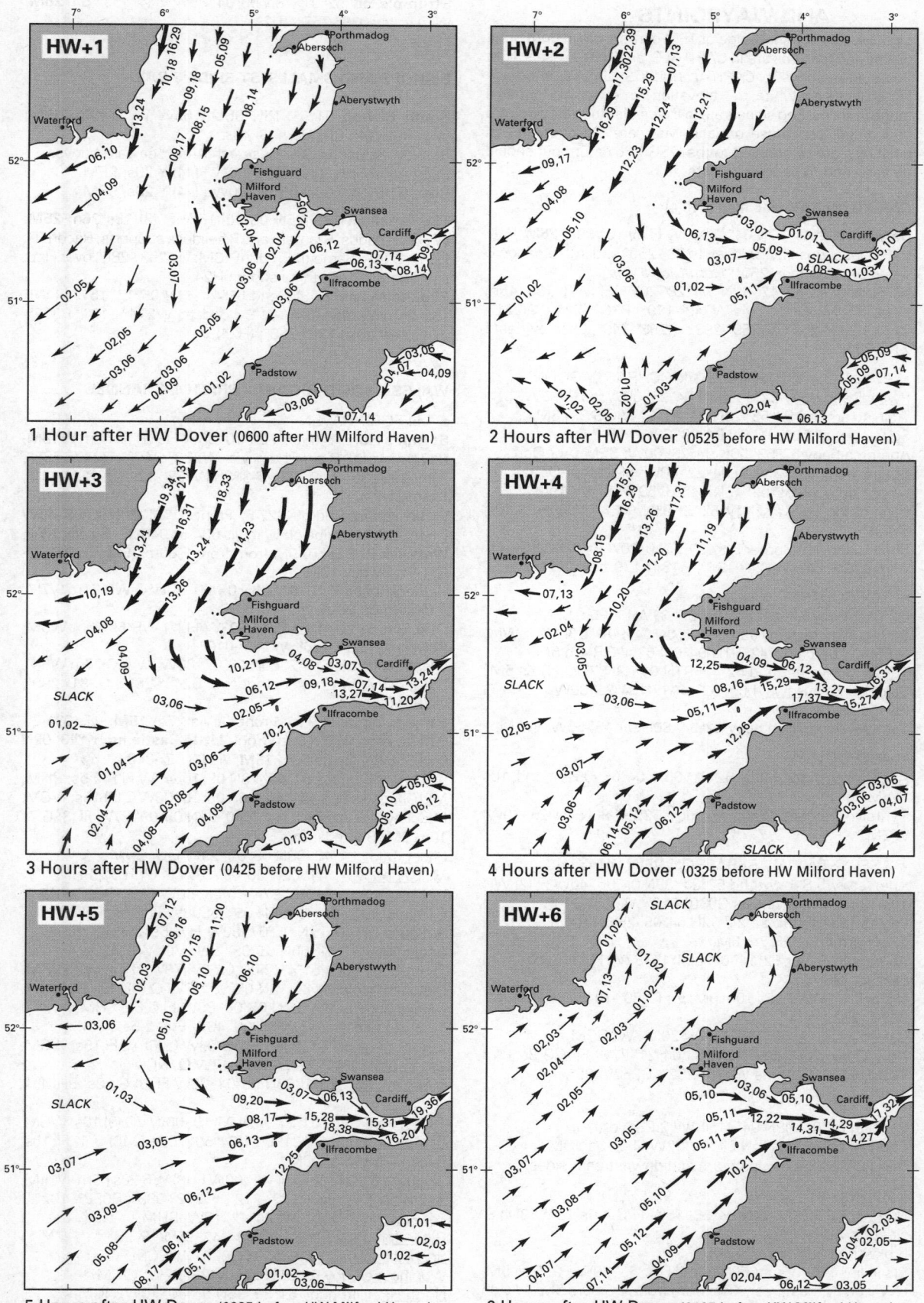

1 Hour after HW Dover (0600 after HW Milford Haven)

2 Hours after HW Dover (0525 before HW Milford Haven)

3 Hours after HW Dover (0425 before HW Milford Haven)

4 Hours after HW Dover (0325 before HW Milford Haven)

5 Hours after HW Dover (0225 before HW Milford Haven)

6 Hours after HW Dover (0125 before HW Milford Haven)

11

8.11.4 COASTAL LIGHTS, FOG SIGNALS AND WAYPOINTS

Lights with a nominal range of 15M or more are in **bold** print, places and features are in CAPITALS, and light-vessels, light floats and Lanbys in *CAPITAL ITALICS*. Unless otherwise stated lights are white. m = elevation in metres; M = nominal range in miles. Fog signals are in *italics*. Useful waypoints are underlined; use those on land with care. All geographical positions are referenced to the OSGB 36 datum but should be assumed to be approximate.

CARDIGAN BAY (see also 8.10.4)

Bardsey I 52°44'·97N 04°47'·93W Fl (5) 15s 39m **26M**; W ☐ tr, R bands; obsc by Bardsey I 198°-250° and in Tremadoc B when brg less than 260°; *Horn Mo(N) 45s.*

St Tudwal's, 52°47'·89N 04°28'·20W Fl WR 15s 46m W14, R10M; W ○ tr; vis W349°-169°, R169°-221°, W221°-243°, R243°-259°, W259°-293°, R293°-349°; obsc by East I 211°-231°.

• PWLLHELI/PORTHMADOG/MOCHRAS LAGOON

Pwllheli app buoy 52°53'·00N 04°23'·00W Iso 2s; SWM.
Training arm hd 52°53'·23N 04°23'·67W QG 3m 3M.
Sewer outfall 52°53'·18N 04°23'·69W Fl R 2·5s.
Abererch buoy 52°53'·50N 04°23'·00W; SPM (Apr-Oct).
Butlins buoy 52°53'·00N 04°22'·00W; SPM (Apr-Oct).
West End buoy 52°52'·40N 04°25'·50W; SPM (Apr-Oct).
Porthmadog Fairway buoy 52°52'·95N 04°11'·11W L Fl 10s; SWM.
Shell Island, NE Corner 52°49'·53N 04°07'·64W Fl WRG 4s; vis G079°-124°, W124°-134°, R134°-179°; (Mar- Nov).

• BARMOUTH

Diffuser buoy 52°43'·17N 04°05'·31W Fl Y 5s; SPM.
Barmouth outer buoy 52°42'·90N 04°04'·90W L Fl 10s; SWM.
N Bank Y perch 52°42'·81N 04°03'·67W QR 4m 5M.
Ynys y Brawd, SE end 52°42'·97N 04°03'·07W Fl R 5s 5M.
Sarn Badrig causeway buoy 52°41'·17N 04°25'·30W   Q (9) 15s; WCM; *Bell*.
Sarn-y-Bwch. Bwch buoy 52°34'·80N 04°13'·50W; WCM.

• ABERDOVEY

Aberdovey outer buoy 52°31'·30N 04°05'·05W; L Fl 10s SWM.
Cynfelyn Patches, Patches buoy 52°25'·80N 04°16'·30W; WCM.

• ABERYSTWYTH/ABERAERON/NEW QUAY

Aberystwyth S bkwtr hd 52°24'·39N 04°05'·46W Fl (2) WG 10s 12m 10M; B col; vis G030°-053°, W053°-210°.
Ldg lts 133°: Front, 52°24'·32N 04°05'·28W FR 4m 5M; rear, 52m from front, FR 7m 6M.
Aberaeron S pier 52°14'·60N 04°15'·87W Fl (3) G 10s 11m 6M; vis 125°-200°.
N pier Fl (4) WRG 15s 10m 6M; vis G050°-104°, W104°-178°, R178°-232°.
Carreg Ina buoy 52°13'·27N 04°20'·47W; NCM.
New Quay pier hd 52°12'·94N 04°21'·27W Fl WG 3s 12m W8M, G5M; G △; vis W135°-252°, G252°-295°.

• CARDIGAN

CG bldg 52°06'·98N 04°41'·14W 2 FR (vert).
Channel bn 52°06'·44N 04°41'·32W Fl (2) 5s; IDM.
Bridge, Iso Y 2s on upstream and downstream sides.

• FISHGUARD

N bkwtr hd 52°00'·74N 04°58'·15W Fl G 4·5s 18m 13M; 8-sided tr; *Bell (1) 8s*.
E bkwtr hd Fl R 3s 10m 5M.
Lts in line 282°. Front 52°00'·65N 04°59'·20W FG 77m 5M; HW ◊ on W mast; rear, 46m from front, FG 89m 5M; W ◊ on W mast.

Penanglas, 152m S of Pt, *Dia (2) 60s*; W obelisk.
Strumble Hd 52°01'·78N 05°04'·35W Fl (4) 15s 45m **26M**; W ○ tr; vis 038°-257°; (H24).

BISHOPS AND SMALLS/ST BRIDE'S BAY

South Bishop 51°51'·15N 05°24'·65W Fl 5s 44m **19M**; W ○ tr; (H24); RC; *Horn (3) 45s*.
Brawdy. St Brides Bay. Research Area, seaward buoys.
Buoy A1 51°49'·30N 05°20'·00W Fl (4) Y 20s; SPM.
Buoy B1 51°48'·30N 05°20'·00W Fl (4) Y 20s; SPM.

The Smalls 51°43'·25N 05°40'·15W Fl (3) 15s 36m **25M**; W ○ tr, R bands, R lantern and R helideck supports; Racon (T); *Horn (2) 60s*. Same tr, FR 33m 13M; vis 253°-285° over Hats and Barrels Rk; both lts shown H24.
Skokholm Island, SW end 51°41'·61N 05°17'·15W Fl WR 10s 54m **W20/R16M**; W 8-sided tr; W274°-212°, R212°-274°; part obsc 226°-258°; (H24).

WALES – SOUTH COAST – BRISTOL CHANNEL

• MILFORD HAVEN

St Ann's Hd 51°40'·85N 05°10'·35W Fl WR 5s 48m **W18M**, **R17**/14M; W 8-sided tr; vis W233°-247°, R247°-285°, R (intens) 285°-314°, R314°-332°, W332°-124°, W129°-131°; *Horn (2) 60s*.
W Blockhouse Pt ldg lts 022·5°. Front, 51°41'·30N 05°09'·40W F 54m 13M; B stripe on W tr; vis 004·5°-040·5°. By day 10M.
Watwick Pt Rear, 0·5M from front F 80m **15M**; vis 013·5°-031·5°. By day 10M.
W Blockhouse Pt 51°41'·26N 05°09'·40W Q WR 21m 9/7M; R lantern on W base.
Dale Fort 51°42'·13N 05°08'·93W Fl (2) WR 5s 20m W5M, R3M; vis R222°-276°, W276°-019°.
Great Castle hd 51°42'·60N 05°07'·00W F WRG 27m W5M, R3M, G3M; W ☐ tr, B stripe; vis R243°-281°, G281°-299°, W299°-029°.
Same tr ldg lts 039·8°: Front Oc 4s 27m **15M**; vis 031·2°-048·2°; **rear**, 890m from front, **Little Castle hd** 51°43'·02N 05°06'·52W Oc 8s 53m **15M**; vis 031·2°-048·2°.
St Anne's hd buoy 51°40'·23N 05°10'·43W Fl R 2·5s; PHM.
Mid Chan Rks buoy 51°40'·16N 05°10'·08W Q (9) 15s; WCM.
Middle Channel Rks lt tr 51°40'·29N 05°09'·77W Fl (3) G 7s 18m 8M; B ● tr, lantern.
Sheep buoy 51°40'·03N 05°08'·23W QG; SHM.
Millbay buoy 51°41'·02N 05°09'·38W Fl (2) R 5s; PHM.
W Chapel buoy 51°40'·97N 05°08'·60W Fl G 10s; SHM.
E Chapel buoy 51°40'·85N 05°08'·08W Fl R 5s; PHM.
Rat buoy 51°40'·77N 05°07'·80W Fl G 5s; SHM.
Angle buoy 51°41'·60N 05°08'·20W VQ; WCM.
Thorn Rock buoy 51°41'·50N 05°07'·70W Q (9) 15s; WCM.
Dakotian buoy 51°42'·13N 05°08'·22W Q (3) 10s; ECM.
Chapel buoy 51°41'·63N 05°06'·80W Fl G 5s; SHM.
Stack buoy 51°42'·00N 05°06'·46W Fl R 2·5s; PHM.
S Hook buoy 51°41'·80N 05°06'·03W Q (6) +L Fl 15s; WCM.
Esso buoy 51°41'·72N 05°05'·17W Q; NCM.
E Angle buoy 51°41'·68N 05°04'·20W Fl (3) G 10s; SHM.

Turbot Bank buoy 51°37'·40N 05°10'·00W VQ (9) 10s; WCM.
St Gowan buoy 51°31'·90N 04°59'·70W Q (6) + L Fl 15s; Racon (T); *Whis*; SCM.
Caldey Is 51°37'·86N 04°41'·00W Fl (3) WR 20s 65m W14M, R12M; W ○ tr; vis R173°-212°, W212°-088°, R088°- 102°.
Eel Pt buoy 51°38'·83N 04°42'·17W; SHM.
Giltar Spit buoy 51°39'·00N 04°42'·05W; PHM.
Spaniel buoy 51°38'·03N 04°39'·67W; ECM.
Woolhouse buoy 51°39'·32N 04°39'·62W; WCM.
North Highcliff buoy 51°39'·35N 04°40'·70W; NCM.

● TENBY/SAUNDERSFOOT/CARMARTHEN BAY/BURRY
Tenby pier hd 51°40'·37N 04°41'·81W FR 7m 7M.
Saundersfoot pier hd 51°42'·55N 04°41'·68W Fl R 5s 6m 7M.
DZ1 buoy 51°42'·02N 04°35'·90; SPM.
DZ2 buoy 51°39'·95N 04°37'·50W Fl Y 2·5s; SPM.
DZ3 buoy 51°37'·35N 04°37'·75W; SPM.
DZ7 buoy 51°38'·05N 04°30'·05W Fl Y 10s; SPM.
DZ4 buoy 51°35'·70N 04°30'·00W Fl Y 5s; SPM.
DZ8 buoy 51°41'·50N 04°24'·30W; SPM.
DZ6 buoy 51°38'·00N 04°24'·17W; SPM.
DZ5 buoy 51°36'·30N 04°24'·17W Fl Y 2·5s; SPM.
Burry Port barrel post 51°40'·47N 04°14'·94W Fl R 3s 5M.
Burry Port Inlet 51°40'·60N 04°14'·98W Fl 5s 7m **15M**.
Llanelli ent N side Fl R 5s 2M
West Helwick (W HWK) buoy 51°31'·37N 04°23'·58W
Q (9) 15s; Racon (T); *Whis*; WCM .
E Helwick buoy 51°31'·77N 04°12'·60W VQ (3) 5s; *Bell*; ECM.

● SWANSEA BAY/SWANSEA
Ledge buoy 51°29'·90N 03°58'·70W VQ (6) + L Fl 10s; SCM.
Mixon buoy 51°33'·10N 03°58'·70W Fl (2) R 5s; *Bell;* PHM.
Outer spoil ground buoy 51°32'·08N 03°55'·67W Fl Y 2·5s;
SPM.
Grounds buoy 51°32'·78N 03°53'·40W VQ (3) 5s; ECM.

Mumbles 51°34'·00N 03°58'·20W Fl (4) 20s 35m **16M**; W tr;
vis 331·5°-336·5°; *Horn (3) 60s.*
Railway pier hd 51°34'·19N 03°58'·36W 2 FR (vert) 11m 9M.
SW Inner Green Grounds buoy 51°34'·04N 03°56'·95W   Q
(6) + L Fl 15s; *Bell*; SCM.
Outer fairway buoy 51°35'·50N 03°56'·01W QG; *Bell*; SHM.
W pier hd 51°36'·47N 03°55'·67W Fl (2) R 10s 11m 9M; FR
lts on radio mast 014° 1·3M.
Swansea inner fairway buoy 51°36'·20N 03°55'·60W Fl G
2·5s; *Bell*; SHM.
E bkwtr hd 51°36'·35N 03°55'·55W 2 FG (vert) 10m 6M; W
tr; *Siren 30s.*
Lts in line 020°: Front, jetty hd   51°36'·51N 03°55'·43W
Oc G 4s 5m 2M; rear, 260m from front, FG 6M.

● SWANSEA BAY/RIVER NEATH/PORT TALBOT
Neath app chan buoy 51°35'·70N 03°52'·75W Fl G 5s; SHM.
Neath SE training wall, near S end 51°36'·30N 03°51'·89W
2 FG (vert) 6m 5M R mast.
Neath SE training wall Middle 51°36'·68N 03°51'·33W FG 6m
5M; R mast.
Neath SE training wall N End 51°37'·07N 03°50'·77W 3 FG
(vert) 6m 5M; R mast.
Cabenda buoy 51°33'·30N 03°52'·15W VQ (6) + L Fl 10s; SCM,
Racon.
P Talbot S outer buoy 51°33'·66N 03°51'·20W Fl G 5s; SHM.
P Talbot N outer buoy 51°33'·76N 03°51'·304W Fl R 5s; PHM.
P Talbot N inner buoy 51°34'·20N 03°50'·18W Fl R 3s; PHM; *Horn.*
Ldg lts 059·8° (occas): Front 51°34'·89N 03°48'·02W, Oc R 3s
12m 6M; Y & Or ◆ on tr; rear, 400m from front, Oc R 6s 32m
6M; Y & Or ◆ on tr.
N bkwtr hd 51°34'·73N 03°48'·93W Fl (4) R 10s 11m 3M.
S bkwtr hd 51°34'·43N 03°48'·95W Fl G 3s 11m 3M.

BRISTOL CHANNEL – EASTERN PART (NORTH SHORE)

Kenfig buoy 51°29'·71N 03°46'·43W, Q (3) 10s; ECM.
W Scarweather (W SCAR) buoy 51°28'·28N 03°55'·50W, Q
(9) 15s; Racon (T); *Bell*; WCM.
S Scarweather (S SCAR) buoy 51°27'·58N 03°51'·50W, Q (6)
+ L Fl 15s; SCM.
Hugo buoy 51°28'·72N 03°48'·30W; PHM.
E Scarweather buoy 51°28'·12N 03°46'·23W; ECM.

● PORTHCAWL
Fairy buoy 51°27'·83N 03°42'·00W; WCM.
Tusker buoy 51°26'·82N 03°40'·67W Fl (2) R 5s; PHM.
Porthcawl bkwtr hd 51°28'·33N 03°41'·95W F WRG 10m
W6M, R4M, G4M; W 6-sided tr, B base; vis G302°-036°,
W036°-082°, R082°-122°.
W Nash buoy 51°25'·95N 03°45'·88W VQ(9) 10s; WCM.
Middle Nash buoy 51°24'·80N 03°39'·34W; WCM.
E Nash buoy 51°24'·03N 03°34'·03W Q (3) 10s; ECM, *Bell.*

Nash 51°24'·00N 03°33'·05W Fl (2) WR 10s 56m **W21M, R20/
17M**; W ○ tr; vis R280°-290°, W290°-097°, R097°-100°, R (intens)
100°-104°, R104°-120°, W120°-128°.

Saint Hilary 51° 27'·40N 03°24'·10W Aero QR 346m 11M;
radio mast; 4 FR (vert) on same mast 6M.
Breaksea Pt intake 51°22'·50N 03°24'·45W Fl R 11m; tr.

Breaksea buoy   51°19'·85N 03°19'·00W Fl 15s; Racon (T);
Horn (2) 30s;
Wenvoe 51°27'·50N 03°16'·80W Aero Q 365m 12M; radio
mast (H24).
Merkur buoy 51°21'·85N 03°15'·90W Fl R 2·5s; PHM.
Welsh Water Barry W buoy 51°22'·23N 03°16'·84W Fl R 5s;
PHM.

● BARRY
W bkwtr hd 51°23'·43N 03°15'·43W Fl 2·5s 12m 10M.
E bkwtr hd 51°23'·50N 03°15'·37W QG 7m 8M.
Lavernock Spit buoy 51°22'·99N 03°10'·74W VQ (6) + L Fl
10s; SCM.
One Fathom N buoy 51°20'·91N 03°12'·08W Q; NCM.
Mackenzie buoy 51°21'·72N 03°08'·15W QR; PHM.
Holm Middle buoy 51°21'·69N 03°06'·64W Fl G 2·5s; SHM.
Wolves buoy 51°23'·10N 03°08'·80W VQ; NCM.

Flat Holm, SE Pt 51°22'·52N 03°07'·05W Fl (3) WR 10s 50m
W15M, R12M; W ○ tr; vis R106°-140°, W140°-151°, R151°-
203°, W203°-106°; H24.
Weston buoy 51°22'·58N 03°05'·66W Fl (2) R 5s; PHM.
Monkstone Rock lt 51°24'·87N 03°05'·92W Fl 5s 13m 12M;
R col on ○ tr.

● CARDIFF AND PENARTH ROADS
Lavernock outfall buoy 51°23'·91N 03°09'·40W Fl Y 5s; SPM.
Ranie buoy 51°24'·22N 03°09'·30W Fl (2) R 5s; PHM.
S Cardiff buoy 51°24'·15N 03°08'·48W Q (6) + L Fl 15s; SCM;
Bell.
Mid Cardiff buoy 51°25'·57N 03°08'·00W Fl (3) G 10s; SHM.
Cardiff Spit buoy 51°25'·53N 03°06'·42W; PHM.
N Cardiff buoy 51°27'·77N 03°05'·28W QG; SHM.

● PENARTH/CARDIFF
Penarth promenade pier near hd 51°26'·06N 03°09'·82W, 2
FR (vert) 8/6m 3M; *Reed Mo(BA) 60s*, sounded 10 min before
a steamer expected.
Penarth Sailing Club pontoon 51°26'·80N 03°10'·50W Q.
Ldg lts 349°: **Front**, 51°27'·67N 03°09'·55W F 4m **17M**; **rear**,
520m from front, F 24m **17M**.
Outer Wrach buoy 51°26'·13N 03°09'·40W Q (9) 15s; WCM.
Inner Wrach buoy 51°26'·67N 03°09'·55W Fl G 2·5s; SHM.
Queen Alexandra Dock ent S jetty hd 51°27'·06N 03°09'·50W
2 FG (vert); tfc sigs; *Dia 60s.*
Tail Patch buoy 51°23'·50N 03°03'·59W QG; SHM.
Hope buoy 51°24'·82N 03°02'·60W Q (3) 10s; ECM.
NW Elbow buoy 51°26'·48N 02°59'·61W VQ (9) 10s; WCM; *Bell.*
English and Welsh Grounds buoy 51°26'·90N 03°00'·10W
L Fl 10s 7M; Racon (O); SWM; *Whis.*

● NEWPORT DEEP
Newport Deep buoy 51°29'·33N 02°59'·03W Fl (3) G 10s;
Bell; SHM.

11

• RIVER USK/NEWPORT
East Usk 51°32'·38N 02°57'·93W Fl (2) WRG 10s 11m
W15M, R11M, G11M; W ○ tr; vis W284°-290°, R290°-017°,
W017°-037°, G037°-115°, W115°-120°. Also Oc WRG 10s
10m W11M, R9M, G9M; vis G018°-022°, W022°-024°, R024°-
028°.
Alexandra Dock, S lock W pier hd 51°32'·84N 02°59'·18W 2 FR
(vert) 9m 6M; *Horn 60s.*
E pier hd 51°32'·93N 02°59'·03W 2 FG (vert) 9m 6M.
Julians Pill ldg lts about 057°: Common Front, 51°33'·28N
02°57'·85W FG 5m 4M; rear, 61m from front, FG 8m 4M.
Ldg lts 149°; rear, 137m from common front, FG 9m 4M.
Birdport jetty 51°33'·64N 02°58'·01W 2 FG (vert) 6m.
Dallimores Wharf 51°33'·85N 02°58'·51W 2 FG (vert).
Transporter bridge, W side 2 FR (vert); 2 FY (vert) shown on
transporter car.
E side 2 FG (vert). Centres of George Street and Newport
bridges marked by FY lts.

SEVERN ESTUARY

• THE SHOOTS
Redcliffe ldg lts 012·9°: Front 51°36'·35N 02°41'·23W F Bu
16m; vis 358°-028°; rear, 320m from front, F Bu 33m 10M.
Lower Shoots bn 51°33'·83N 02°41'·98W Q (9) 15s 6m 7M;
WCM.
North Mixoms 51°34'·03N 02°42'·57W Fl (3) R 10s 6M; PHM.
Upper Shoots bn 51°34'·20N 02°41'·79W (unlit); WCM.

• SECOND SEVERN CROSSING
NW side on caisson, 2FR (vert) 4M, shown up/down stream.
Centre span, Q Bu 5M; Racon.
SE side on caisson, 2FG (vert) 4M, shown up/down stream.
Old Man's Hd 51°34'·72N 02°41'·62W VQ (9) 10s; WCM.
Lady Bench 51°34'·83N 02°42'·13W QR 6m 6M; PHM.
Charston Rk 51°35'·32N 02°41'·60W Fl 3s 5m 13/8M; W ○ tr,
B stripe; (13M) 343°-043°, (8M) 043°-343°.
Chapel Rk 51°36'·40N 02°39'·13W Fl WRG 2·6s 6m W8M,
R5M, G5M; B tr, W lantern; vis W213°-284°, R284°-049°,
W049°-051·5°, G051·5°-160°.
Wye bridge 51°37'·03N 02°39'·54W 2F Bu (hor); centre of
span.

• SEVERN BRIDGE
West tr 3 QR (hor) on upstream and downstream sides;
obscured 040°-065°; *Siren (3) 30s.*
Centre of span 51°36'·57N 02°38'·32W Q Bu, each side.
E tr 3 QG (hor) on upstream and downstream sides.
Aust 51°36'·13N 02°37'·91W 2 QG (vert) 11/5m 6M; power
cable pylon.
Lyde Rk 51°36'·85N 02°38'·58W QR 5m 5M; B tr, W lantern.

• RIVER SEVERN
Sedbury 51°37'·75N 02°38'·93W 2 FR (vert) 10m 3M.
Slime Road ldg lts 210·4°: Front, 51°37'·21N 02°39'·00W
F Bu 9m 5M; rear, 91 m from front, F Bu 16m 5M; B tr,
Inward Rocks ldg lts 252·5°: Front, 51°39'·23N 02°37'·37W F
6m 6M; B tr; rear, 183m from front, F 13m 2M.
Counts buoy 51°39'·45N 02°35'·74W Q; NCM.
Sheperdine ldg lts 070·4°: Front, 51°40'·03N 02°33'·22W
F 8m 5M; B tr, W lantern; rear, 168m from front, F 13m 5M;
B tr, W lantern; *Bell (26) 60s.*
Ledges buoy 51°39'·75N 02°34'·06W Fl (3) G 10s; SHM.
Narlwood Rks ldg lts 224·9°: Front, 51°39'·54N 02°34'·68W
Fl 2s 5m 8M; Y bn, B lantern; rear, 198m from front Fl 2s 9m
8M; Y bn, B lantern.
Hills Flats buoy 51°40'·66N 02°32'·59W Fl G 4s; SHM.
Hayward Rock buoy 51°41'·24N 02°31'·00W Q; NCM.
Conigre ldg lts 077·5°: Front, 51°41'·43N 02°29'·92W F Bu
21m 8M; rear, 213m from front, F Bu 29m 8M.

Fishing House ldg lts 217·7°: Front, 51°40'·95N 02°30'·91W
F 5m 2M: W hut and post; rear, F 11m 2M: W hut and mast.

• BERKELEY
Power station centre 51°41'·62N 02°29'·97W 3x2 FG (vert);
Siren (2) 30s.
Bull Rk 51°41'·78N 02°29'·80W Oc (2) 6m 8M.
Berkeley Pill ldg lts 187·8°. Front, 51°41'·95N 02°29'·32W FG
5m 2M; rear, 152m from front, FG 11m 2M; both B trs, W
lanterns.
Panthurst Pill 51°42'·56N 02°28'·93W F Bu 6m 1M; Y pillar.
Lydney Docks pier hd 51°42'·60N 02°30'·27W FW or R (tidal);
Gong (tidal).

• SHARPNESS DOCKS
S pier hd 51°42'·93N 02°29'·01W 2 FG (vert) 6m 3M; *Siren 20s.*
N pier 2 FR (vert) 6m 3M.
Old ent, S side, 51°43'·49N 02°28'·82W; S*iren 5s* (tidal).

BRISTOL CHANNEL – EASTERN PART (SOUTH SHORE)

• BRISTOL DEEP
N Elbow buoy 51°27'·12N 02°58'·10W QG; *Bell;* SHM.
S Mid Grounds buoy 51°27'·66N 02°58'·34W VQ (6) + L Fl 10s;
SCM.
E Mid Grounds buoy 51°27'·95N 02°54'·00W Fl R 5s; PHM.
Clevedon buoy 51°27'·40N 02°54'·84W VQ; NCM.
Welsh Hook buoy 51°28'·49N 02°51'·78W Q (6) + L Fl 15s;
Bell; SCM.
Avon buoy 51°27'·90N 02°51'·65W Fl G 2·5s; SHM.
Clevedon Pier 51°26'·61N 02°51'·82W 2 FG (vert) 7m 3M.
Walton Bay, old signal station 51°27'·86N 02°49'·71W, Fl
2·5s 35m 2M.
Black Nore Pt 51°29'·05N 02°47'·95W Fl (2) 10s 11m **15M**; W ○
tr; obsc by Sand Pt when brg less than 049°; vis 044°-243°.
Newcome buoy 51°29'·98N 02°46'·63W Fl (3) R 10s; PHM.
Firefly buoy 51°29'·93N 02°45'·27W Fl (2) G 5s; SHM.
Outer buoy 51°29'·97N 02°44'·71W IQ G 12s; SHM.
Middle buoy 51°29'·90N 02°44'·13W Fl G 5s; SHM.
Inner buoy 51°29'·83N 02°43'·78W Fl (3) G 15s; SHM.
Cockburn buoy 51°30'·43N 02°44'·00W Fl R 2·5s; PHM.

Portishead Pt 51°29'·64N 02°46'·34W Q (3) 10s 9m **16M**;
B tr, W base; vis 060°-262°; *Horn 20s.*

• PORTISHEAD
Pier hd 51°29'·66N 02°45'·18W Iso G 2s 5m 3M; W col.
Lock E side 51°29'·54N 02°45'·33W 2 FR (vert) 7m 1M;
Gy col; (occas.)
Lock W side 2 FG (vert) 7m 1M; Gy col; (occas.)

Seabank. Lts in line 086·8°: Front, 51°29'·99N 02°43'·66W
IQ 13m 5M; vis 070·3°-103·3°, 076·8°-096·8°; rear, 500m
from front, IQ W 16m 5M; vis 070·3°-103·3°, 076·8°-096·8°.
By day, both 1M.
Royal Portbury Dock Pier end 51°30'·13N 02°43'·64W L Fl G
15s 5m 6M; Gy pillar.
Pier corner 51°30'·10N 02°43'·77W Fl G 2s 7m 7M; Gy pillar;
Dia 30s, sounded HW-4 to HW+3.
Knuckle lts in line 099·6° 51°29'·92N 02°43'·60W Oc G 5s 6m
6M, rear, 165m from front, FG 13m 6M; vis 044°-134°.

• AVONMOUTH
Royal Edward Dock N pier hd 51°30'·47N 02°43'·00W Fl 10s 15m
10M; ○ tr; vis 060°-228·5°.
S pier hd Oc RG 30s 9m 10M, ○ stone tr; R294°-036°, G036°-
194°; *Bell 10s;* 51°30'·34N 02°43'·02W.
King Road ldg lts 072·4°: N pier hd Front, 51°30'·47N
02°43'·00W Oc R 5s 5m 9M; W obelisk, R bands; vis 062°-
082°; rear, 546m from front, QR 15m 10M; B & W striped ○
on framework tr, Or bands; vis 066°-078°.
Oil jetty hd 51°30'·62N 02°42'·85W 2 FG (vert) 6m 2M.

• RIVER AVON
Ldg lts 127·2°. <u>Front</u>, 51°30'·05N 02°42'·47W FR 7m 3M; W □, R stripes; vis 010°-160°; rear, 142m from front FR 17m 3M; W ○, vis 048°-138°.
Monoliths 51°30'·23N 02°42'·68W Fl R 5s 5m 3M; W □, B stripes on W col; vis 317°-137°.
Saint George ldg lts 173·3°, 51°29'·73N 02°42'·58W both Oc G 5s 6/9m 1M, on Or cols; vis 158°-305°; synch.
Nelson Pt 51°29'·82N 02°42'·43W Fl R 3s 9m 3M; W mast.
Broad Pill 51°29'·6N 02°41'·8W QY 11m 1M; W tr.
Avonmouth Bridge, NE end 51°29'·36N 02°41'·45W L Fl R 10s 5m 3M; SW end L Fl G 10s 5m 3M, showing up and downstream. From here to City Docks, Oc G lts are shown on S bank, and R or Y lts on N bank.

• CUMBERLAND BASIN
Ent N side 51°26'·95N 02°37'·36W 2 FR (vert) 6m 1M; S side W end 2 FG (vert) 7m 1M;

• AVON BRIDGE
N side 51°26'·79N 02°37'·34W FR 6m 1M on bridge pier.
Centre of span Iso 5s 6m 1M.
S side FG 6m 1M on bridge pier.

BRISTOL CHANNEL (SOUTH SHORE/SOMERSET)

• WESTON-SUPER-MARE
<u>Pier hd</u> 51°20'·85N 02°59'·17W 2 FG (vert) 6m.
<u>E Culver buoy</u> 51°17'·70N 03°14'·50W Q (3) 10s; ECM.
<u>W Culver buoy</u> 51°16'·85N 03°19'·20W VQ (9) 10s; WCM.
<u>Gore buoy</u> 51°13'·93N 03°09'·70W Iso 5s; *Bell;* SWM.

• BURNHAM-ON-SEA/RIVER PARRETT
Ent 51°14'·86N 03°00'·26W Fl 7·5s 7m 12M; vis 074°-164°. Dir lt 076°. Dir F WRG 4m W12M, R10M, G10M; same tr; vis G071°-075°, W075°-077°, R077°-081°.
Seafront lts in line 112° (moved for changing chan): Front, 51°14'·38N 02°59'·86W FR 6m 3M W □, Or stripe on sea wall; rear, FR 12m 3M; church tr.
Brue bn 51°13'·50N 03°00'·20W QR 4m 3M; W mast,R bands. (TE 1992).
Stert Reach 51°11'·32N 03°01'·90W Fl 3s 4m 7M; vis 187°-217°.
DZ No 1 buoy 51°15'·25N 03°09'·40W Fl Y 2·5s; SPM.

Hinkley Pt,intake 51°12'·90N 03°07'·96W 2 FG (vert) 7m 3M.
DZ No 2 buoy 51°13'·75N 03°17'·10W Fl Y 10s; SPM.
DZ No 3 buoy 51°15'·50N 03°14'·90W Fl Y 5s; SPM.

• WATCHET
<u>W bkwtr hd</u> FG 9m 9M, R twr, 51°11'·03N 03°19'·67W.
E Pier 51°10'·97N 03°19'·63W 2 FR (vert) 3M.

• MINEHEAD/PORLOCK WEIR
Bkwtr hd 51°12'·78N 03°28'·28W Fl (2) G 5s 4M; vis 127°-262°.
Sewer outfall 51°12'·95N 03°28'·22W QG 6m 7M; SHM bn.

NORTH DEVON

Lynmouth Foreland 51°14'·70N 03°47'·15W Fl (4) 15s 67m **18M**; W ○ tr; vis 083°-275°; (H24).

• LYNMOUTH/WATERMOUTH
River training arm 51°13'·88N 03°49'·77W 2 FR (vert) 6m 5M.
Harbour arm 51°13'·89N 03°49'·78W 2 FG (vert) 6m 5M.

<u>Sand Ridge buoy</u> 51°14'·98N 03°49'·70W; SHM.
<u>Copperas Rock buoy</u> 51°13'·77N 04°00'·50W; SHM.
Watermouth 51°12'·90N 04°04'·50W Oc WRG 5s 1m; W △; vis G149·5°-151·5°, W151·5°-154·5°, R154·5°-156·5°.

• ILFRACOMBE
<u>Lantern Hill</u> 51°12'·63N 04°06'·72W Fl G 2·5s 39m 6M.
Promenade Pier N end 51°12'·66N 04°06'·60W 2 FG (vert).
<u>Horseshoe buoy</u> 51°15'·00N 04°12'·85W Q; NCM.

Bull Point 51°11'·95N 04°12'·05W Fl (3) 10s 54m **25M**; W ○ tr, obscd shore-056°. Same tr; FR 48m 12M; vis 058°-096°.
<u>Morte Stone buoy</u> 51°11'·30N 04°14'·85W; SHM.
<u>Baggy Leap buoy</u> 51°08'·90N 04°16'·90W; SHM.

• BIDEFORD, RIVERS TAW AND TORRIDGE
<u>Bideford fairway buoy</u> 51°05'·23N 04°16'·17W L Fl 10s; *Bell;* SWM.
Bideford Bar buoy 51°04'·93N 04°14'·76W; SHM.
Instow ldg lts 118°: **Front**, 51°03'·59N 04°10'·60W Oc 6s 22m **15M**; vis 104·5°-131·5°; **rear**, 427m from front, Oc 10s 38m **15M**; vis 103°-133°; (H24).
Crow Pt 51°03'·93N 04°11'·32W Fl R 5s 8m 4M; W tr; vis 225°-045°..
Clovelly hbr quay hd 50°59'·85N 04°23'·75W Fl G 5s 5m 5M.

• LUNDY
Near North Pt 51°12'·07N 04°40'·57W Fl 15s 48m **17M**; W ○ tr; vis 009°-285°.
SE Pt 51°09'·70N 04°39'·30W Fl 5s 53m **15M**; W ○ tr; vis 170°-073°; *Horn 25s.*

Hartland Pt 51°01'·27N 04°31'·50W Fl (6) 15s 37m **25M**; (H24); W ○ tr; *Horn 60s.*

NORTH CORNWALL

• BUDE
Compass Pt tr 50°49'·70N 04°33'·35W.

• PADSTOW
Stepper Pt 50°34'·11N 04°56'·63W L Fl 10s 12m 4M.
St Saviour's Pt 50°32'·72N 04°56'·00W L Fl G 10s 1M; G △.
N Quay hd 50°32'·48N 04°56'·10W 2 FG (vert) 6m 2M.
Trevose Hd 50°32'·93N 05°02'·05W Fl R 7·5s 62m **21M**; W ○ tr. *Horn (2) 30s.*

• NEWQUAY
N pier hd 50°25'·04N 05°05'·12W 2 FG (vert) 5m 2M.
S pier hd 50°25'·02N 05°05'·13W 2 FR (vert) 4m 2M; ○ tr.

<u>The Stones buoy</u> 50°15'·60N 05°25'·40W Q; NCM.
Godrevy Is 50°14'·50N 05°23'·95W Fl WR 10s 37m W12M, R9M; W 8-sided tr; vis W022°-101°, R101°-145°, W145°-272°.

• HAYLE
<u>App buoy</u> 50°12'·25N 05°26'·45W Iso G 2s; SHM.
Lts in line 180°; <u>Front</u>, 50°11'·55N 05°26'·14W F 17m 4M; rear, 110m from front, F 23m 4M.
Carnew Weir 50°11'·40N 05°25'·97W Q.

• ST IVES
E pier hd 50°12'·77N 05°28'·53W 2 FG (vert) 8m 5M; W ○ tr.
W pier hd 50°12'·74N 05°28'·67W 2 FR (vert) 5m 3M Gy col.

Pendeen 50°09'·80N 05°40'·20W Fl (4) 15s 59m **16M**; W ○ tr; vis 042°-240°; in bay between Gurnard Hd and Pendeen it shows to coast; *Horn 20s.*

For lights further SW see 8.1.4.

11

8.11.5   PASSAGE INFORMATION

For directions on this coast refer to the Admiralty *W Coasts of England and Wales Pilot. A Cruising Guide to NW England & Wales* (Imray/Griffiths) covers as far S as Tenby; *Lundy and Irish Sea Pilot* (Imray/Taylor) continues to Land's End.

It is useful to know some Welsh words with navigational significance. *Aber:* estuary. *Afon:* river. *Bach, bychan, fach:* little. *Borth:* cove. *Bryn:* hill. *Careg, craig:* rock. *Coch, goch:* red. *Dinas:* fort. *Ddu:* black. *Fawr, Mawr:* big. *Ffrydiau:* tiderip. *Llwyd:* grey. *Moel:* bare conical hill. *Mor:* sea. *Morfa:* sandy shore. *Mynydd:* mountain. *Penrhyn:* headland. *Porth:* cove. *Ynys, Ynysoedd:* island(s).

CARDIGAN BAY (charts 1971, 1972, 1973)

Hbrs are mostly on a lee shore, and/or have bars which make them dangerous to approach in bad weather. Abersoch (8.11.7) and Pwllheli (8.11.8) offer best shelter from prevailing W'lies. There may be overfalls off Trwyn Cilan, SW of St Tudwal's Is (lit). In N part of bay there are three major dangers to coasting yachts, as described briefly below: St Patrick's Causeway (Sarn Badrig) runs 12M SW from Mochras Pt. It is mostly large loose stones, and dries (up to 1.5m) for much of its length. In strong winds the sea breaks heavily at all states of tide. The outer end is marked by a WCM lt buoy. At the inner end there is a chan about 5ca offshore, which can be taken with care at half tide.

Sarn-y-Bwch runs 4M WSW from Pen Bwch Pt. It is composed of rky boulders, drying in places close inshore and with least depth 0.3m over 1M offshore. There is a WCM buoy off W end. NW of Aberystwyth (8.11.12), Sarn Cynfelyn and Cynfelyn Patches extend a total of 6.5M offshore, with depths of 1.5m in places. A WCM buoy is at the outer end. Almost halfway along the bank is Main Channel, 3ca wide, running roughly N/S, but not marked.

A military firing area occupies much of Cardigan B. Beware targets and buoys, some unlit. Range activity is broadcast on VHF Ch 16, 0800-1600LT Mon-Fri or ☎ (01239) 813462.

If on passage N/S through St George's Chan (i.e. not bound for Cardigan B or Milford Haven) the easiest route, and always by night, is W of the Bishops and the Smalls, noting the TSS, 8.11.14. If bound to/from Milford Haven or Cardigan Bay, passage inside both the Smalls and Grassholm is possible.

RAMSEY SOUND AND THE BISHOPS (chart 1482)

The Bishops and the Clerks are islets and rks 2.5M W and NW of Ramsey Is, a bird sanctuary SSW of St David's Hd. N Bishop is the N'ly of the group, 3ca ENE of which is Bell Rk (depth 1.9m). S Bishop (Lt, fog sig, RC) is 3M to the SSW.

Between S Bishop and Ramsey Is the dangers include Daufraich with offliers to the E and heavy overfalls; Llech Isaf and Llech Uchaf drying rks are further ENE. Carreg Rhoson and offliers are between Daufraich and N Bishop. There are navigable routes between most of these islets and rocks, but only by day in good vis and with local knowledge. The N/S route close W of Ramsey Island is said to be easier than Ramsey Sound (see below).

2M W of The Bishops the S-going stream begins at HW Milford Haven + 0400, and the N-going at HW Milford Haven – 0225, sp rates 2kn. Between The Bishops and Ramsey Is the SW-going stream begins at HW Milford Haven + 0330, and the NE-going at HW Milford Haven – 0255, sp rates 5kn.

Ramsey Sound should be taken at slack water. The S-going stream begins at HW Milford Haven + 0300, and the N-going at HW Milford Haven – 0325, sp rates 6kn at The Bitches, where chan is narrowest (2ca), decreasing N and S. The Bitches are rks extending 2ca from E side of Ramsey Is. Other dangers are: Gwahan and Carreg-gafeiliog, at N end of Sound, to W and E; Horse Rk (dries 0.9m) almost in mid-chan about 5ca NNE of The Bitches, with associated overfalls; Shoe Rk (dries 3m) at SE end of chan; and rks extending 5ca SSE from S end of Ramsey Is.

THE SMALLS TO MILFORD HAVEN (chart 1478)

St Brides B (8.11.13) provides anch in settled weather or offshore winds, but is a trap in westerlies. Solva is a little hbr with shelter for boats able to take the ground, or anch behind Black Rk (dries 3.6m) in the middle of the entrance.

The Smalls Lt, where there is a Historic Wreck (see 8.0.3h) is 13M W of the Welsh mainland (Wooltack Pt). 2M and 4M E of The Smalls are the Hats and Barrels, rky patches on which the sea breaks. 7M E of The Smalls is Grassholm Island with a race either end and strong tidal eddies so that it is advisable to pass about 1M off. The chan between Barrels and Grassholm is 2.5M wide, and here the S-going stream begins at HW Milford Haven + 0440, and the N-going at HW Milford Haven – 0135, sp rates 5kn. 5M of clear water lie between Grassholm and Skomer Is/Skokholm Is to the E. But Wildgoose Race, which forms W of Skomer and Skokholm is very dangerous, so keep 2M W of these two Islands.

To E of Skomer is Midland Is, and between here and Wooltack Pt is Jack Sound which is only 2ca wide and should not be attempted without chart 1482, detailed pilotage directions, and only at slack water nps; it is a testing passage. Dangers which must be identified include: The Crab Stones, E from Midland Is; The Cable, a drying rk on E side of chan; Tusker Rk, steep-to on its W side, off Wooltack Pt; the Black Stones; and The Anvil and other rks off Anvil Pt. In Jack Sound the S-going stream begins at HW Milford Haven + 0200, and the N-going at HW Milford Haven – 0425, sp rates 6kn.

MILFORD HAVEN TO MUMBLES HD (charts 1179, 1076)

Milford Haven (8.11.14) is a long natural, all-weather hbr with marinas beyond the oil terminals. 3M S of the ent, beware Turbot Bank (WCM lt buoy). Crow Rk (dries 5.5m) is 5ca SSE of Linney Hd, and The Toes are dangerous submerged rks close W and SE of Crow Rk. There is a passage inshore of these dangers. There are overfalls on St Gowan Shoals which extend 4M SW of St Govan's Hd, and the sea breaks on the shallow patches in bad weather. For firing areas from Linney Hd to Carmarthen Bay, see 8.11.16.

Caldey Is (Lt) lies S of Tenby (8.11.15). Off its NW pt is St Margaret's Is connected by a rky reef. Caldey Sound, between St Margaret's Is and Giltar Pt (chart 1482), is buoyed, but beware Eel Spit near W end of Caldey Is where there can be a nasty sea with wind against tide, and Woolhouse Rks (dry 3.6m) 1ca NE of Caldey Is. Saundersfoot hbr (dries) is 2M N of Tenby, with anch well sheltered from N and W but subject to swell. Streams are weak here. Carmarthen Bay has no offshore dangers for yachts, other than the extensive drying sands at head of B and on its E side off Burry Inlet (8.11.16).

S of Worms Head, Helwick Sands (buoyed at each end) extend 7M W from Port Eynon Pt; least depth of 1.3m is near their W end. Stream sets NE/SW across the sands. There is a narrow chan inshore, close to Port Eynon Pt. Between here and Mumbles Hd the stream runs roughly along coast, sp rates 3kn off Pts, but there are eddies in Port Eynon B and Oxwich B (both yacht anchs), and overfalls SSE of Oxwich Pt.

MUMBLES HEAD TO CARDIFF (charts 1165, 1182)

Off Mumbles Hd (Lt, fog sig) beware Mixon Shoal (dries 0.3m), marked by PHM buoy. In good conditions pass N of shoal, 1ca off Mumbles Hd. Anch N of Mumbles Hd, good holding but exposed to swell. At W side of Swansea Bay, Green Grounds, rky shoals, lie in appr's to Swansea (8.11.17).

Scarweather Sands, much of which dry (up to 3.3m) and where sea breaks heavily, extend 7M W from Porthcawl (8.11.17) and are well buoyed (chart 1161). There is a chan between the sands and coast to E, but beware Hugo Bank (dries 2.6m) and Kenfig Patches (0.5m) with overfalls up to 7ca offshore between Sker Pt and Porthcawl.

Nash Sands extend 7.5M WNW from Nash Pt. Depths vary and are least at inshore end (dries 3m), but Nash Passage, 1ca wide, runs close inshore between E Nash ECM buoy and rky ledge off Nash Pt. On E-going stream there are heavy overfalls off Nash Pt and at W end of Nash Sands. Between Nash Pt and Breaksea Pt the E-going stream begins at HW Avonmouth + 0535, and the W-going at HW Avonmouth – 0035, sp rates 3kn. Off Breaksea Pt there may be overfalls.

From Rhoose Pt to Lavernock Pt the coast is fringed with foul ground. Lavernock Spit extends 1·75M S of Lavernock Pt, and E of the spit is main chan to Cardiff (8.11.19); the other side of the chan being Cardiff Grounds, a bank drying 5·4m which lies parallel with the shore and about 1·5M from it.

SEVERN ESTUARY (charts 1176, 1166)

Near the centre of Bristol Chan, either side of the buoyed fairway are the islands of Flat Holm (Lt, fog sig) and Steep Holm. 7M SW of Flat Holm lies Culver Sand (0·9m), 3M in length, with W & ECM bys. Monkstone Rk (Lt, dries) is 2M NW of the buoyed chan to Avonmouth and Bristol (8.11.21). Extensive drying banks cover the N shore of the estuary, beyond Newport and the Severn bridges (chart 1176).

The range of tide in the Bristol Chan is exceptionally large, 12·2m sp and 6·0m np, and tidal streams are very powerful, particularly above Avonmouth. Between Flat Holm and Steep Holm the E-going stream begins at HW Avonmouth – 0610, sp 3kn, and the W-going at HW Avonmouth + 0015, sp 4kn.

The ent to the R. Avon is just to the S of Avonmouth S Pier Hd. Bristol City Docks lie some 6M up river. Approach the ent via King Road and the Newcombe and Cockburn It buoys and thence via the Swash chan into the Avon. The ent dries at LW but the river is navigable at about half tide. Tidal streams are strong in the approaches to Avonmouth, up to 5kn at sp. The tide is also strong in the R. Avon which is best entered no earlier than HW Avonmouth – 0200.

From Avonmouth it is 16M to Sharpness which yachts should aim to reach at about HW Avonmouth. Spring streams can run 8kn at the Shoots, and 6kn at the Severn bridges (8.11.20). At the Shoots the flood begins at HW Avonmouth –0430 and the ebb at HW Avonmouth + 0045. The Severn Bore can usually be seen if Avonmouth range is 13·5m or more.

AVONMOUTH TO HARTLAND POINT (AC 1152, 1165)

From Avonmouth to Sand Pt, the part-drying English Grounds extend 3M off the S shore. Portishead Dock (8.11.22) is being developed as a marina. Extensive mud flats fill the bays S to Burnham-on-Sea (8.11.23). Westward, the S shore of Bristol Chan is cleaner than N shore. But there is less shelter since hbrs such as Watchet (8.11.24), Minehead, Porlock Weir and Watermouth dry out, see 8.11.24. In bad weather dangerous overfalls occur NW and NE of Foreland Pt. 5M to W there is a race off Highveer Pt. Between Ilfracombe (8.11.25) and Bull Pt the E-going stream begins at HW Milford Haven + 0540, and the W-going at HW Milford Haven – 0025, sp rates 3kn. Overfalls occur up to 1·5M N of Bull Pt and over Horseshoe Rks, which lie 3M N. There is a dangerous race off Morte Pt, 1·5M to W of Bull Pt.

Shelter is available under lee of Lundy Is (8.11.25); but avoid bad races to NE (White Horses), the NW (Hen and Chickens), and to SE; also overfalls over NW Bank. W of Lundy streams are moderate, but strong around the Is and much stronger towards Bristol Chan proper.

Proceeding WSW from Rivers Taw/Torridge (8.11.26), keep 3M off to avoid the race N of Hartland Pt (Lt, fog sig, conspic radome). There is shelter off Clovelly in S/SW winds.

HARTLAND POINT TO LAND'S END (charts 1156, 1149)

The N coast of Cornwall and SW approaches to Bristol Chan are very exposed. Yachts need to be sturdy and well equipped, since if bad weather develops no shelter may be at hand. Bude (8.11.27) dries, and is not approachable in W winds; only accessible in calm weather or offshore winds. Boscastle is a tiny hbr (dries) 3M NE of Tintagel Hd. Only approach in good weather or offshore winds; anch off or dry out alongside.

Padstow is a refuge, but in strong NW winds the sea breaks on bar and prevents entry. Off Trevose Hd (Lt) beware Quies Rks which extend 1M to W. From here S the coast is relatively clear to Godrevy Is, apart from Bawden Rks 1M N of St Agnes Hd. Newquay B (8.11.25) is good anch in offshore winds, and the hbr (dries) is sheltered but uncomfortable in N winds. Off Godrevy Is (Lt) are The Stones, drying rky shoals extending 1·5M offshore and marked by NCM lt buoy.

In St Ives Bay (chart 1168), Hayle (8.11.27) is a commercial port (dries); seas break heavily on bar at times, especially with a ground swell. Stream is strong, so enter just before HW. The bottom is mostly sand. St Ives (dries, 8.11.27) gives shelter from winds E to SW, but is very exposed to N; there is sometimes a heavy breaking sea if there is ground swell.

From St Ives to Land's End coast is rugged and exposed. There are overfalls SW of Pendeen Pt (lt, fog sig). Vyneck Rks lie awash about 3ca NW of C Cornwall. The Brisons are two high rky islets 5ca SW of C Cornwall, with rky ledges inshore and to the S. The Longships (lt, fog sig) group of rks is about 1M W of Land's End. The inshore passage (001° on Brisons) is about 4ca wide with unmarked drying rks on the W side; only to be considered in calm weather. See 8.1.5 for tides. **For Isles of Scilly and South Cornwall, see 8.1.5.**

11

8.11.6   DISTANCE TABLE

Approximate distances in nautical miles are by the most direct route, whilst avoiding dangers and allowing for Traffic Separation Schemes. Places in *italics* are in adjoining areas; places in **bold** are in 8.0.9, Distances across the Irish Sea.

	1	2	3	4	5	6	7	8	9	10	11	12	13	14	15	16	17	18	19	20
1. *Bardsey Island*	1																			
2. Abersoch	14	2																		
3. **Pwllheli**	18	5	3																	
4. Barmouth	27	18	18	4																
5. Aberdovey	31	26	25	14	5															
6. Aberystwyth	33	30	30	20	10	6														
7. **Fishguard**	45	54	58	56	47	40	7													
8. South Bishop	60	70	74	74	67	61	25	8												
9. **Milford Haven**	83	93	97	97	90	84	48	23	9											
8. Tenby	106	116	120	120	113	107	71	46	28	10										
11. Swansea	129	139	143	143	136	130	94	69	55	36	11									
12. Barry	151	161	165	165	158	152	116	91	77	57	37	12								
13. Cardiff	160	170	174	174	167	161	125	100	86	66	46	9	13							
14. Sharpness	191	201	205	205	198	192	156	131	117	106	75	39	33	14						
15. **Avonmouth**	174	184	188	188	181	175	139	114	100	89	58	22	20	18	15					
16. Burnham-on-Sea	168	178	182	182	175	169	133	108	94	70	48	18	53	50	33	16				
17. Ilfracombe	127	137	141	141	134	128	92	67	53	35	25	35	44	74	57	45	17			
18. Lundy Island	110	120	124	124	117	111	75	50	38	30	37	54	63	95	78	66	22	18		
19. **Padstow**	141	151	155	155	148	142	106	81	70	70	76	88	97	127	110	98	55	39	19	
20. *Longships*	168	178	182	182	175	169	133	108	105	110	120	130	139	169	152	140	95	82	50	20

ABERSOCH   8-11-7

Gwynedd 52°49'.29N 04°29'.20W (⚓) Rtg 3-3-2

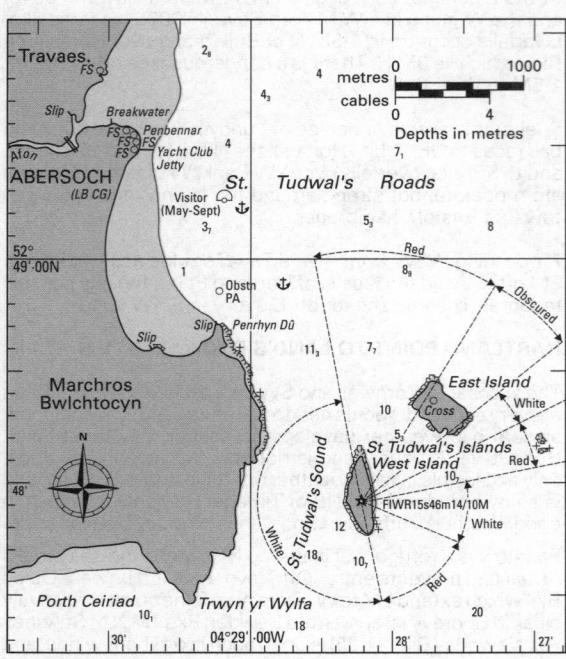

CHARTS
AC 1512, 1971, *1410*; Imray C61; OS 123
TIDES
–0315 Dover; ML 2·5; Duration 0520; Zone 0 (UT)

Standard Port MILFORD HAVEN (→)

Times				Height (metres)			
High Water		Low Water		MHWS	MHWN	MLWN	MLWS
0100	0800	0100	0700	7·0	5·2	2·5	0·7
1300	2000	1300	1900				
Differences ST TUDWAL'S ROADS							
+0155	+0145	+0240	+0310	–2·2	–1·9	–0·7	–0·2
ABERDARON							
+0210	+0200	+0240	+0310	–2·4	–1·9	–0·6	–0·2

SHELTER
There are few moorings for visitors. Apply to Hr Mr or SC. ⚓ in St Tudwal's Roads clear of moored yachts; sheltered from SSE through S to NE.
NAVIGATION
WPT 52°48'.50N 04°26'.06W, 113°/293° from/to YC jetty, 2·4M. There are no navigational dangers, but steer well clear of the drying rks to the E of East Island; a PHM buoy is 2ca E of these rks (just off chartlet). St Tudwal's islands themselves are fairly steep-to, except at N ends. St Tudwal's Sound is clear of dangers.
LIGHTS AND MARKS
The only lt is on St Tudwal's West Island, Fl WR 15s 46m 14/10M (see chartlet and 8.11.4).
RADIO TELEPHONE
S Caernarfon YC Ch **80** M.
TELEPHONE (Dial code 01758)
Hr Mr 812684; MRSC (01407) 762051; ⊞ (01407) 762714; Marinecall 0891 500 460; Police 2022; Dr 612535.
FACILITIES
S. Caernarvonshire YC ☎ 812338, Slip, M, L, FW, R, Bar (May-Sept), D; **Abersoch Power Boat Club** ☎ 812027.
Services: BY, Slip, ME, El, Sh, ACA, CH, P, C (12 ton).
Town EC Wed; CH, V, R, Bar, ✉, ⑧, ⇌ (Pwllheli), ✈ (Chester).

PWLLHELI   8-11-8

Gwynedd 52°53'.21N 04°23'.68W Rtg 1-1-1

CHARTS
AC 1512, 1971, *1410*; Imray C61; OS 123
TIDES
–0315 Dover; ML 2·6; Duration 0510; Zone 0 (UT)

Standard Port MILFORD HAVEN (→)

Times				Height (metres)			
High Water		Low Water		MHWS	MHWN	MLWN	MLWS
0100	0800	0100	0700	7·0	5·2	2·5	0·7
1300	2000	1300	1900				
Differences PWLLHELI							
+0210	+0150	+0245	+0320	–2·0	–1·8	–0·6	–0·2
CRICCIETH							
+0210	+0155	+0255	+0320	–2·0	–1·8	–0·7	–0·3

SHELTER
Good in hbr & marina. Visitors must first report to marina. Pile berths on S side of chan. No ⚓ in hbr; 4kn speed limit. Drying moorings in inner hbr (SW and NW bights).
NAVIGATION
WPT 52°53'.00N 04°23'.00W, SWM lt buoy, Iso 2s, 119°/299° from/to QG lt at head of Training Arm, 0·47M. Ent is safe in most winds, but in strong E to SW winds sea breaks on offshore shoals. Bar and hbr chan are dredged to at least 1·0m; 3 tide gauges. Max tidal stream 2kn.
LIGHTS AND MARKS
No ldg lts/marks, but ent chan well marked (see chartlet). Gimblet Rock (30m) is conspic conical rock 3ca SW of ent.
RADIO TELEPHONE
Hr Mr: VHF Ch **12** 16 (0900-1715). Marina: Ch **80** M H24.
TELEPHONE (Dial code 01758)
Hr Mr 704081; MRSC (01407) 762051; CG 701589; ⊞ (01407) 762714; Marinecall 0891 500 460; Police 701177; Dr 612535.

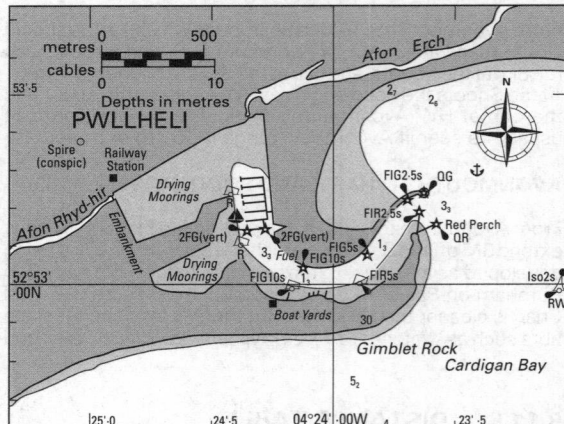

FACILITIES
Marina (400) ☎ 701219 (H24), ⛟ 701443, £8.74, FW, P, D, AC, BH (40 ton), C, Slip, ⊡; **Marina Club** ☎ 612271, Slip, FW; **Hbr Authority** Slip, M, L, FW, AB; **South Caernarvonshire YC** ☎ 812338; **Pwllheli SC** ☎ 612219; **Services:** BY, Slip, L, FW, ME, Gas, Sh, CH, ACA, D, C (14 ton), El, Ⓔ, SM.
Town EC Thurs; V, R, Bar, ✉, ⑧, ⇌, ✈ (Chester).

ADJACENT HARBOUR

MOCHRAS, Gwynedd, 52°49'.55N 04°07'.70W. AC 1512, 1971. HW –0245 on Dover. Small yacht hbr on SE side of Shell Is. Mochras lagoon dries. Bar, about 2ca seaward. Entry advised HW±2. Tide runs strongly in the narrows on the ebb; at sp beware severe eddies inside ent. Ent between Shell Is (lt Fl WRG 4s; G079°-124°, W124°-134°, R134°-179°; shown mid Mar-Nov) and sea wall. 3 grey posts, R topmarks, mark N side of chan. Shifting chan, marked by posts & buoys, runs NE to Pensarn, where permanent moorings limit space. To S, buoyed chan runs to Shell Is Yacht Hbr ☎ (0134123) 453 with facilities: M, FW, Slip, R, Bar, shwrs. Pensarn: drying AB, ⇌.

PORTHMADOG   8-11-9

Gwynedd 52°55'·30N 04°07'·70W   Rtg 5-2-1

CHARTS
AC 1512, 1971, *1410*; Imray C61; OS 124

TIDES
–0247 Dover; ML no data; Duration 0455; Zone 0 (UT)

Standard Port MILFORD HAVEN (→)

Times				Height (metres)			
High Water		Low Water		MHWS	MHWN	MLWN	MLWS
0100	0800	0100	0700	7·0	5·2	2·5	0·7
1300	2000	1300	1900				
Differences PORTHMADOG							
+0235	+0210	No data		–1·9	–1·8		No data

SHELTER
Inner hbr (N of Cei Ballast): Good all year round; visitors' drying AB adjacent Madoc YC or afloat rafted on moored yachts off YC. (Greaves Wharf is obstructed by dinghies and salmon nets). Outer hbr: Summer only and exposed to S winds. Speed limit 6kn in hbr upstream of No 11 By.

NAVIGATION
WPT Fairway SWM buoy, 52°53'·10N 04°10'·94W, 222°/ 042° from/to conspic white Ho at W side of ent, 1·75M; chan shifts and may divide. Bar changes frequently, but is near to No 3 and 4 buoys; dries approx 0·3m. Latest info from Hr Mr on request. Advise entering HW±1½. In SW'lies, waves are steep-sided and close, especially on the ebb.

LIGHTS AND MARKS
Fairway buoy RW, L Fl 10s. Chan marker buoys (14) have R/G reflective top marks and numbers in W reflective tape. Moel-y-Gest is conspic hill (259m) approx 1M WNW of hbr. Harlech Castle (ru) is about 3M SE of appr chan.

RADIO TELEPHONE
Hr Mr Ch 14 12 16 (0900-1715 and when vessel due). Madoc YC: Ch M.

TELEPHONE (Dial code 01766)
Hr Mr 512927, mobile (0402) 719023; MRSC (01407) 762051; Pilot 514939, Home 75684; Hbr Authority Gwynedd Council (01758) 613131; ⌗ (01407) 762714; Marinecall 0891 500 460; Police 512226; Dr 512239.

FACILITIES
Hbr (265 berths) ☎ 512927, £5.70, D, FW, C, Slip; **Madoc YC** ☎ 512976, AB, M, FW, Bar; **Porthmadog SC** ☎ 513546, AB, M, FW, Slip;
Services: CH, ACA, Sh, D, P (cans), C (3½ ton), M, BY, El, Pilot.
Town EC Wed; ⌧, Ⓑ, ⇌, ✈ (Chester).

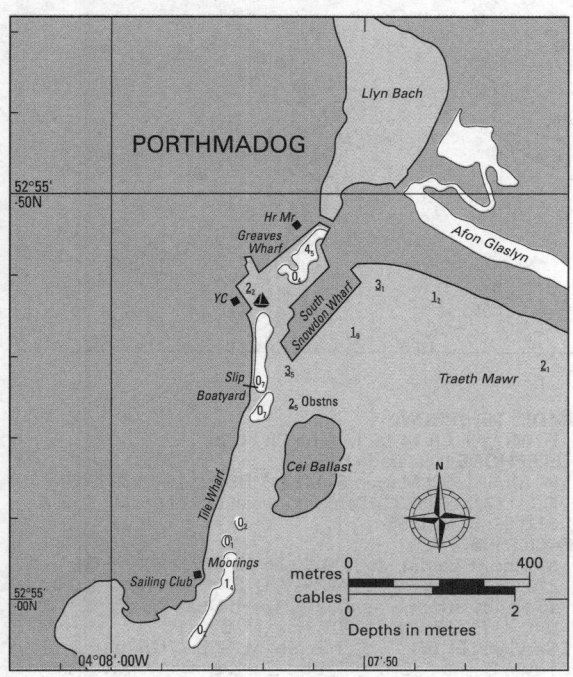

BARMOUTH   8-11-10

Gwynedd 52°42'·95N 04°03'·00W   Rtg 4-4-1

CHARTS
AC 1484, 1971, *1410*; Imray C61; OS 124

TIDES
–0305 Dover; ML 2·6; Duration 0515; Zone 0 (UT)

Standard Port MILFORD HAVEN (→)

Times				Height (metres)			
High Water		Low Water		MHWS	MHWN	MLWN	MLWS
0100	0800	0100	0700	7·0	5·2	2·5	0·7
1300	2000	1300	1900				
Differences BARMOUTH							
+0215	+0205	+0310	+0320	–2·0	–1·7	–0·7	0·0

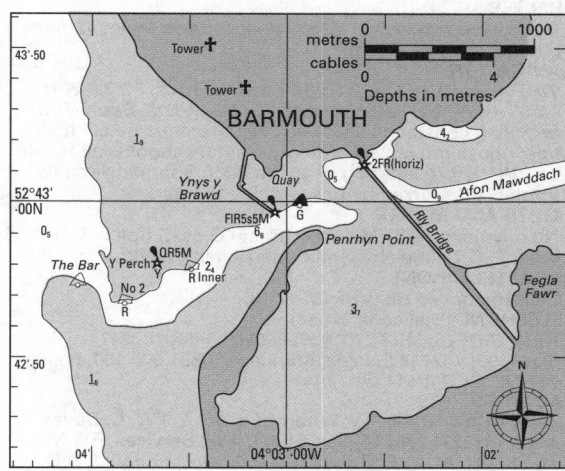

SHELTER
Good. Entry HW±2½ safe, but impossible with strong SW'lies. Exposed ⚓ W of Barmouth Outer buoy in 6 to 10m. In hbr there are 3 Ⓥs; secure as directed by Hr Mr, because of submarine cables and strong tidal streams. A Ⓥ berth is marked at W end of quay, dries at half-tide. The estuary and river (Afon Mawddach) are tidal and can be navigated for about 7M above railway bridge (clearance approx 5·5m); but chan is not buoyed, and sandbanks move constantly - local knowledge essential.

NAVIGATION
WPT, Barmouth Outer SWM buoy, L Fl 10s, 52°42'·90N 04°04'·90W, 277°/097° from/to Y perch lt, QR, 0·75M. Appr from SW between St Patrick's Causeway (Sarn Badrig) and Sarn-y-Bwch (see 8.11.5). Barmouth can be identified by Cader Idris, a mountain 890m high, 5M ESE. Fegla Fawr, a rounded hill, lies on S side of hbr. The Bar, 0·75M W of Penrhyn Pt, with min depth 0·3m is subject to considerable change. Chan is marked by the Bar SHM buoy and 2 PHM buoys, all unlit and moved as required; fitted with radar reflectors and reflective tape. Spring ebb runs 3 - 5kn.
Note: A Historic Wreck (see 8.0.3h) is at 52°46'·73N 04°07'·53W, 4·5M NNW of Barmouth Outer SWM buoy.

LIGHTS AND MARKS
Y perch, QR 4m 5M, R framework tr, marks S end of stony ledge extending 3ca SW from Ynys y Brawd across N Bank. Ynys y Brawd groyne, SE end, marked by bn with lt, Fl R 5s 5M. NW end of rly bridge 2 FR (hor).

RADIO TELEPHONE
Call *Barmouth Hbr* VHF Ch **12** 16 (Apl-Sept 0900-2200LT; Oct-Mar 0900-1600LT); wind and sea state are available.

TELEPHONE (Dial code 01341)
Hr Mr 280671; MRSC (01407) 762051; ⌗ (01407) 762714; Marinecall 0891 500460; Police 280222; Dr 280521.

FACILITIES
Quay £5.60, M (contact Hr Mr in advance if deep water Ⓥ required), D, FW, El, AC, Slip; **Merioneth YC** ☎ 280000;
Services: CH, ACA.
Town EC Wed; P, D, V, R, Bar, ⌧, Ⓑ, ⇌, ✈ (Chester), Ferry across to Penrhyn Pt.

11

ABERDOVEY   8-11-11

Gwynedd 52°32'·55N 04°02'·65W (Jetty)   Rtg 4-4-1

CHARTS
AC 1484, 1972, *1410*; Imray C61; OS 135

TIDES
–0320 Dover; ML 2·6; Duration 0535; Zone 0 (UT)

Standard Port MILFORD HAVEN (→)

Times				Height (metres)			
High Water		Low Water		MHWS	MHWN	MLWN	MLWS
0100	0800	0100	0700	7·0	5·2	2·5	0·7
1300	2000	1300	1900				
Differences ABERDOVEY							
+0215	+0200	+0230	+0305	–2·0	–1·7	–0·5	0·0

SHELTER
Good except in strong W/SW winds. Berth on jetty; to the
E there is heavy silting.

NAVIGATION
WPT Aberdovey Outer SWM buoy, L Fl 10s, 52°31'·30N
04°05'·05W, 230°/050° from/to Bar buoy, 6ca. Bar (0·7m)
and chan constantly shift and are hazardous below half-
tide; buoys moved accordingly. Visitors should call Hr Mr
on VHF before entering or ☎ the Pilot. Submarine cables
(prohib ⚓s) marked by bns with R ◇ topmarks.

LIGHTS AND MARKS
No daymarks. 4 SHM buoys (Bar Fl G 5s, S Spit Fl G 9s,
Inner Fl G 7s and No 4 unlit) mark chan to jetty.

RADIO TELEPHONE
Call *Aberdovey Hbr* VHF Ch 12 16.

TELEPHONE (Dial code 01654)
Hr Mr 767626; MRSC (01646) 690909; Pilot 767247;
⊞ (01407) 762714 Ext 262; Marinecall 0891 500 460; Police
767222; Dr 710414; Ⓗ 710411.

FACILITIES
Jetty AB £6.50, M, FW; **Wharf** Slip, AB, L, FW, C; **Dovey
YC** ☎ (01827) 286514, Bar, Slip, L, FW; **Services:** BY, ME,
EI, Sh, CH, ACA, Ⓔ. **Town** EC Wed (winter only); P & D
(cans), ME, EI, CH, V, R, Bar, ✉, Ⓑ, ⇌, ✈ (Chester).

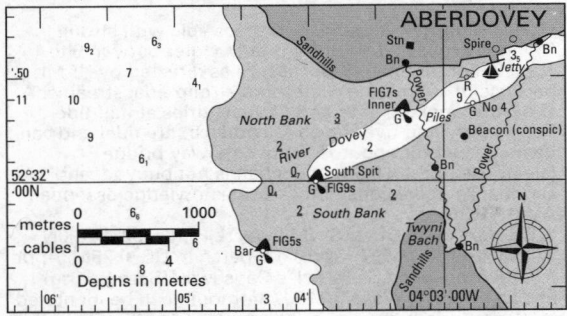

OTHER HARBOURS IN SOUTH CARDIGAN BAY

ABERAERON, Ceredigion, 52°14'·60N 04°15'·87W. AC 1484,
1972, *148*. HW –0325 on Dover; +0140 and –1·9m on
Milford Haven; ML 2·7m; Duration 0540. A small, popular
drying hbr at the mouth of the R Aeron; access HW±1½.
Short drying piers extend each side of river ent. In strong
NW'lies there is little shelter. AB £2.50 on NW wall. Foul
ground with depths of 1·5m extend 3ca offshore to SW of
Aberaeron. Beware Carreg Gloyn (0·3m) 4ca WSW of hbr,
and Sarn Cadwgan (1·8m) shoals 5ca N of the hbr ent.
Lts: N pier Fl (4) WRG 15s 10m 6M, G050°-104°, W104°-
178°, R178°-232°. S pier Fl (3) G 10s 11m 6M, vis 050°-
243°. VHF 14 16. Hr Mr ☎ (01545) 571645; **YC** ☎ 570077.

NEW QUAY, Ceredigion, 52°12'·90N 04°21'·15W. AC 1484,
1972, *148*. HW –0335 on Dover; Duration 0540; see
8.11.12. Good shelter in offshore winds, but untenable in
NW'lies. On E side of bay Carreg Ina, rks drying 1·3m, are
marked by NCM buoy. 2 Y bns indicate a sewer outfall
extending 7ca NNW from Ina Pt. The hbr (dries 1·6m) is
protected by a pier with lt, Fl WG 3s 12m 8/5M; W135°-
252°, G252°-295°. Groyne extends 80m SSE of pierhd to a
SHM bn; close ENE of which is a ECM bn, Q (3) 10s. ⚓s
are 1ca E of pier; £2.50. VHF Ch 12 16 80. Hr Mr ☎ (01545)
560368. CG ☎ 560212; Dr ☎ 560203; YC ☎ 560516.
Facilities: D (from fishermen). **Town** FW, P (3M), ✉, R, Bar.

ABERYSTWYTH   8-11-12

Ceredigion 52°24'·40N 04°05'·40W   Rtg 3-2-1

CHARTS
AC 1484, 1972, *1410*; Imray C61; OS 135

TIDES
–0330 Dover; ML 2·7; Duration 0540; Zone 0 (UT)

Standard Port MILFORD HAVEN (→)

Times				Height (metres)			
High Water		Low Water		MHWS	MHWN	MLWN	MLWS
0100	0800	0100	0700	7·0	5·2	2·5	0·7
1300	2000	1300	1900				
Differences ABERYSTWYTH							
+0145	+0130	+0210	+0245	–2·0	–1·7	–0·7	0·0
NEW QUAY							
+0150	+0125	+0155	+0230	–2·1	–1·8	–0·6	–0·1
ABERPORTH							
+0135	+0120	+0150	+0220	–2·1	–1·8	–0·6	–0·1

SHELTER
Good, in marina (2·3m) on E side of chan; or dry against
Town Quay. Access approx HW±3 (HW±2 for strangers).
The Bar, close off S pier hd, has 0·7m least depth. E edge
of inner hbr chan 0·3m is defined by WCM beacon.

NAVIGATION
WPT 52°24'·81N 04°06'·15W, 313°/133° from/to ent, 0·6M.
Approach dangerous in strong on-shore winds. From N,
beware Castle Rks, within R sector 141°-175° of N bkwtr
lt, QWR 9m 2M; also rks drying 0·5m W of N bkwtr and
boulders below S pier hd. Turn 90° port inside narrow ent.

LIGHTS AND MARKS
N bkwtr hd ≠ 140° Wellington Mon't (on top Pendinas,
conspic hill 120m high) clears to S of Castle Rks. Ldg lts
133°, both FR on Ystwyth Bridge, white daymarks. WCM
bn on with Y daymark leads 100° across bar into hbr ent.

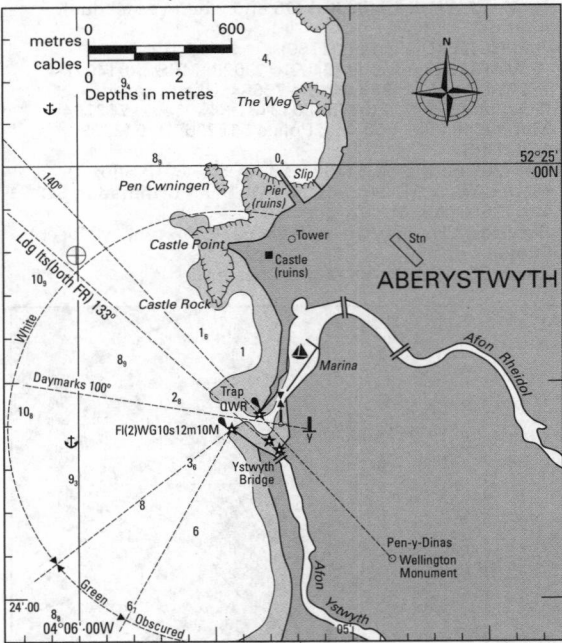

RADIO TELEPHONE
Hr Mr VHF Ch 14 16. Marina Ch 80 16.

TELEPHONE (Dial code 01970)
Hr Mr 611433; Marina 611422; MRSC (01646) 690909;
⊞ (01222) 763880 (H24); Marinecall 0891 500460; Police
612791; Dr 624855.

FACILITIES
Marina (Y Lanfa), ☎ 611422, ⌧ 624122, (88 + 15 Ⓥ),
£10.05, access HW±2, AC, FW, D, Slip, BH (10 ton), C (max
15 ton by arrangement), ⛽; **Town Quay** AB £3.75, C (3
ton), L, FW; **YC** ☎ 612907, Slip, M, Bar;
Services: EI, CH, D, Ⓔ, ME, Sh, M, Slip, C (25 ton), Gas.
Town P (cans), CH, V, R, Bar, ▣, ✉, Ⓑ, ⇌, ✈ (Swansea).

FISHGUARD   8-11-13

Pembrokeshire 52°00'·10N 04°58'·33W
Commercial Hbr Rtg 1-3-3; Lower Hbr Rtg 4-5-1

CHARTS
AC 1484, 1973, *1410, 1178*; Imray C61/60; OS 157

TIDES
−0400 Dover; ML 2·6; Duration 0550; Zone 0 (UT)

Standard Port MILFORD HAVEN (⟶)

Times				Height (metres)			
High Water		Low Water		MHWS	MHWN	MLWN	MLWS
0100	0800	0100	0700	7·0	5·2	2·5	0·7
1300	2000	1300	1900				
Differences FISHGUARD							
+0115	+0100	+0110	+0135	−2·2	−1·8	−0·5	+0·1
PORT CARDIGAN							
+0140	+0120	+0220	+0130	−2·3	−1·8	−0·5	0·0
CARDIGAN (Town)							
+0220	+0150	No data		−2·2	−1·6	No data	
PORTHGAIN							
+0055	+0045	+0045	+0100	−2·5	−1·8	−0·6	0·0
RAMSEY SOUND							
+0030	+0030	+0030	+0030	−1·9	−1·3	−0·3	0·0
SOLVA							
+0015	+0010	+0035	+0015	−1·5	−1·0	−0·2	0·0
LITTLE HAVEN							
+0010	+0010	+0025	+0015	−1·1	−0·8	−0·2	0·0
MARTIN'S HAVEN							
+0010	+0010	+0015	+0015	−0·8	−0·5	+0·1	+0·1
SKOMER IS							
−0005	−0005	+0005	+0005	−0·4	−0·1	0·0	0·0

SHELTER
Good, except in strong NW/NE winds. Access H24 to Goodwick (upper, commercial) hbr with only 2 ♥ berths; no ⏏, except SW of ferry quay. Lower Town (Fishguard) dries 3·2m; access HW±1, limited AB. Good holding in most of the bay; ⏏ off Saddle Pt in 2m or as shown. Strong S'lies funnel down the hbr.

NAVIGATION
WPT 52°01'·00N 04°57'·50W, 057°/237° from/to N bkwtr lt, 0·48m. Beware large swell, especially in N winds. Keep clear of ferries and high-speed SeaCat manoeuvring.

LIGHTS AND MARKS
Strumble Hd lt, Fl (4) 15s 45m 26M, is approx 4M WNW of hbr. N bkwtr Fl G 4·5s 18m 13M, Bell 8s. E bkwtr Fl R 3s 10m 5M. Ldg lts 282° (to ferry berths), both FG; W ◇ on masts.

RADIO TELEPHONE
Hr Mr Ch 14 16. Goodwick Marine Ch M (occas).

TELEPHONE (Dial code 01348)
Commercial Hbr Supervisor 872881; Hr Mr (Lower hbr) 874616/873231; MRSC (01646) 690909; ⌗ (01222) 763880 (H24); Marinecall 0891 500 460; Police 873073; Dr 872802.

FACILITIES
Goodwick Hbr AB £10; **Lower Town, Fishguard**, M (free o'night) via Hr Mr; **Fishguard Bay YC** ☎ 872866, FW, Bar;
Services: BY, Sh, ME, ACA, Slip, CH, El.
Town EC Wed; P & D (cans), V, R, Gas, Bar, ✉, ▢, Ⓑ, ⇌, ✈ (Cardiff), Ferry–Rosslare.

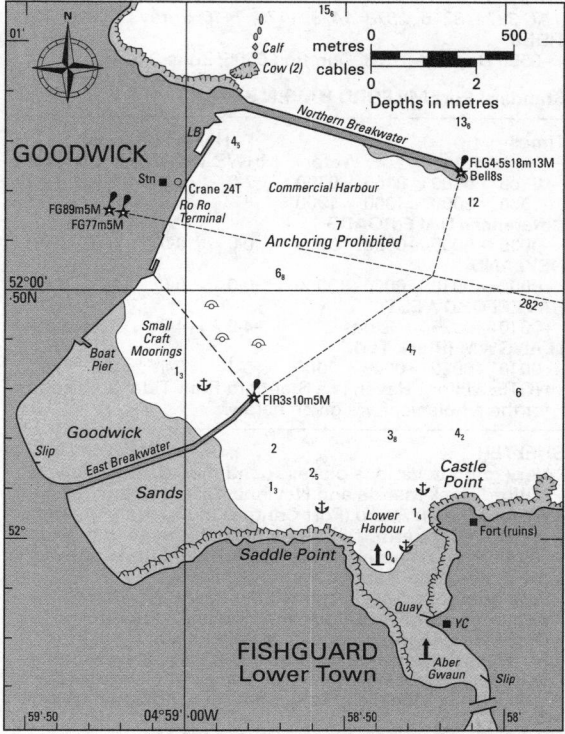

MINOR HARBOUR, 12M NE of Fishguard

PORT CARDIGAN, Ceredigion, 52°07'·00N 04°42'·00W. AC 1484, 1973. HW −0405 on Dover; ML 2·4m; Duration 0550; See above. Shelter is good, but ent dangerous in strong N/NW winds. Large scale chart (1484) and local advice essential. Bar has 0·3m or less; breakers form esp on sp ebb. ⏏ near Hotel (conspic) on E side of ent by 2 FR (vert). Chan is close to E side; IDM bn, Fl (2) 5s, should be left to stbd. From Pen-yr-Ergyd to Bryn-Du chan is unmarked and shifts constantly. ⏏ in pools off Pen-yr-Ergyd or near St Dogmaels. Possible ♘s off Teifi Boating Club. Hr Mr ☎ as Aberaeron or New Quay. Facilities: **Moorings**: at Gwbert (drying) ☎ (01239) 612832, at Netpool (afloat) ☎ 612166; **Teifi BC** Hon Sec ☎ 612361 FW, Bar; **Services**: ME, Sh.
Town EC Wed; Ⓑ, V, CH, P, D, FW, ME, Bar, R, ⇌.

ADJACENT HARBOURS IN ST BRIDES BAY

SOLVA, Pembrokeshire, 51°52'·00N 05°11'·60W. AC *1478*. HW −0450 on Dover; ML 3·2m; Duration 0555. See 8.11.13. Good shelter for small boats that can take the ground; access HW±3. Avoid in strong S winds. Black Scar, Green Scar and The Mare are rks 5ca S. Ent via SSE side; best water near Black Rk in centre of ent. Beware stone spit at Trwyn Caws on W just inside ent. There are 9 R ♘s and some drying moorings available; or ⏏ behind the rk in approx 3m. Small craft can go up to the quay. Facilities limited; stores in village. FW on quay. Hr Mr (01437) 720153, M, CH. **Solva Boat Owners Assn** ☎ 721489.

ST BRIDES BAY, Pembrokeshire, 51°49'·00N 05°10'·00W. AC *1478*. HW (Little Haven) −0450 on Dover; ML 3·2m; Duration 0555. See 8.11.13. A SPM buoy, Fl (5) Y 20s, is midway between Ramsey and Skomer islands at 51°48'·2N 05°20'·0W. Keep at least 100m offshore 1/9-28/2 to avoid disturbing seals, and ditto nesting sea birds 1/3-31/7. Many good ⏏s, especially between Little Haven and Borough Head in S or E winds or between Solva and Dinas Fawr in N or E winds. In W'lies boats should shelter in Solva (above), Skomer (below) or Pendinas Bach. For apprs from the N or S see 8.11.5. Facilities: (Little Haven) CH, V, R, Bar, FW (cans).

SKOMER, Pembrokeshire, 51°44'·40N 05°16'·70W. AC 2878, *1478*. HW −0455 Dover. See 8.11.13. The island is a National Nature Reserve (fee payable to Warden on landing) and also a Marine Nature Reserve, extending to Marloes Peninsula. Keep at least 100m offshore 1/9-28/2 to avoid disturbing seals and ditto nesting sea birds 1/3-31/7. There is a 5kn speed limit within 100m of the island. ⏏ in N or S Haven. Enter N Haven close to W shore, and land on W side of bay on beach or at steps. In N Haven pick up ♘s provided or ⏏ to seaward of them. No access to the island from S Haven. For Jack Sound see 8.11.5. There are no lts, marks or facilities. For info, Marine Conservation Officer ☎ (01646) 636736.

11

MILFORD HAVEN   8-11-14

Pembrokeshire 51°40'·10N 05°08'·10W. Rtg 1-1-2

CHARTS
AC 3274, 3275, *2878, 1478, 1178, 1410*; Imray C60; OS 157
TIDES
–0500 Dover; ML 3·8; Duration 0605; Zone 0 (UT)

Standard Port MILFORD HAVEN (→)

Times				Height (metres)			
High Water		Low Water		MHWS	MHWN	MLWN	MLWS
0100	0800	0100	0700	7·0	5·2	2·5	0·7
1300	2000	1300	1900				
Differences DALE ROADS							
–0005	–0005	–0008	–0008	0·0	0·0	0·0	–0·1
NEYLAND							
+0002	+0010	0000	0000	0·0	0·0	0·0	0·0
HAVERFORDWEST							
+0010	+0025	Dries		–4·8	–4·9	Dries out	
LLANGWM (Black Tar)							
+0010	+0020	+0005	0000	+0·1	+0·1	0·0	–0·1

NOTE: Milford Haven is a Standard Port. Tidal predictions for the whole year are given below.

SHELTER
Very good in various places round the hbr, especially in Milford Dock Marina and Neyland Yacht Haven. Call *Milford Haven Radio* (Port Control) to ascertain the most suitable ⚓ or berth. ⚓s in Dale Bay; off Chapel Bay and Angle Pt on S shore; off Scotch Bay by Milford, above the town; and others above Pembroke Dock.
Free pontoons (May-Oct) include: Dale Bay; waiting pontoons off Milford Dock and Hobbs Pt (Pembroke Dock); and drying pontoons at Dale Beach, Gelliswick, Hazelbeach, Neyland and Burton; mainly intended for tenders. It is possible to dry out safely at inshore areas of Dale, Sandy Haven and Angle Bay, depending on weather.

NAVIGATION
WPT 51°40'·18N, 05°10'·22W, 040°/220° from/to Great Castle Hd ldg lt, 3·18M. The tide sets strongly across the ent to the Haven particularly at sp. In bad weather avoid passing over Mid Chan Rks and St Ann's Hd shoal, where a confused sea and swell will be found. Give St Ann's Head a wide berth especially on the ebb, when East Chan by Sheep Island is better. Beware large tankers entering and leaving the haven and ferries moving at high speed in the lower Haven. Caution: Only 15m clearance below cables between Thorn Island and Thorn Pt.
NB: Milford Haven Port Authority has a jetty, Port Control and offices near Hubberston Pt. Their launches have G hulls and W upperworks with 'PILOT' in black letters and fly a Pilot flag (HOTEL) while on patrol; Fl Bu lt at night. Their instructions must be obeyed. No vessel may pass within 100m of any terminal or any tanker, whether at ⚓ or under way.
River Cleddau is navigable 6M to Picton Pt, at junction of West and East arms, at all tides for boats of moderate draught. Clearance under Cleddau Bridge above Neyland is 37m; and 25m under power cable 1M upstream. Chan to Haverfordwest has 2m at HW and clearances of only 6m below cables and bridge; only feasible for shoal draft/lifting keel and unmasted craft.
Firing Ranges to the S and SE, see 8.11.16 and AC 1076.

LIGHTS AND MARKS
St Ann's Hd Fl WR 5s 48m 18/14M, Horn (2) 60s. Middle Chan Rks Fl (3) G 7s 18m 8M; B tr, steel lantern. Ldg lts (for W chan) 040°: Front Oc 4s 27m 15M; rear Oc 8s 53m 15M; both vis 031°-048° (H24).
Milford Dock ldg lts 348°, both FG, with W ○ daymarks. Dock entry sigs on E side of lock: 2 FG (vert) = gates open, vessels may enter. Exit sigs are given via VHF Ch 12. VHF is normally used for ent/exit by day and night.
RADIO TELEPHONE
Port Authority call: *Milford Haven Radio* (Port Control), VHF Ch **12** 11 14 16 (H24); 09 10 67. *Milford Haven Patrol* launches, Ch 11 12 (H24). To enter Milford Dock call *Milford Pierhead* Ch **12** 16 (HW–4 to HW+3¼); then call *Milford Marina* Ch M. Neyland Yacht Haven Ch **80**, M. Lawrenny Yacht Stn Ch M.
Broadcasts: Local forecasts on Ch 12 14 at 0300UT, 0900, 1500 and 2100UT. Nav warnings follow on Ch14. Gale warnings issued on receipt Ch 12 14. Expected shipping movements for next 24 hours on Ch 12, 0800–0830, 2000–2030LT and on request. Tide hts and winds on request.
TELEPHONE (Dial code 01646)
Port Authority 693091, 🕿 690179; Lock 692275/1; Port Control 692342; MRSC 690909; ☎ (01222) 763880 (H24); Marinecall 0891 500 459; Police (Milford Haven) 692351, (Pembroke) 682121, (Neyland) 600221; ⊞ Haverfordwest (01437) 764545; Dr 600314.
FACILITIES
Marinas/ Berthing (from seaward):
Dale YC 🕿 636362, CH, V, FW, M, P (cans), R, Slip, Gas, Gaz.
Milford Haven Port Authority jetty 🕿 692342 (occas use by visitors with approval from Hr Mr), AB, FW.
Milford Dock Marina (230) 🕿 692272, 🚤 692274; £9.14. VHF Ch 12. Lock hrs: ent HW–4, exit –3½, free flow HW –2 to HW, ent +1¼, exit +1¾, ent +2¾, exit +3¼; FW, D, AC, C, BH (10 ton), CH, El, ME, Sh, SM, Ⓔ, Gas, Gaz, V, R, 🅾, 🅱.
Neyland Yacht Haven (380 inc visitors) 🕿 601601, 🚤 600713, £10.00, FW, D, AC, CH, Ⓔ, Gas, Gaz, 🅾, C (20 ton), SM, SC, ME, El, Sh, R, V; Access lower basin H24, upper basin HW±3½ (sill + gauge);
Lawrenny Yacht Station (100) 🕿 651367, ⚓ £5, L, FW, BY, CH, D, P, Sh, C (15 ton), ME, Slip, 🅾, Bar, R, V, ✉.
Services: All marine services available; check with Hr Mr, marinas or YC/SC. Dale Sailing Co (@ Neyland), BY, CH, ME, Sh, C (20 ton). East Llannion Marine: access HW±3, Slip, scrubbing piles, BH (30 ton), fuel. Rudder's BY, small but useful, is just upstream of Burton Pt.
Yacht Clubs: Dale YC 🕿 636362; Pembrokeshire YC 🕿 692799; Neyland YC 🕿 600267; Pembroke Haven YC 🕿 684403; Lawrenny YC 🕿 651212.
Towns: Milford Haven, EC Thurs; ✉, Ⓑ, 🚆. Pembroke Dock, EC Wed; ✉, Ⓑ, 🚆, ⊞. Neyland, EC Wed; ✉, Ⓑ. Haverfordwest, EC Thurs; ✉, ⊞, Ⓑ, 🚆, ✈ (Swansea or Cardiff); also a small airfield (Withybush) near Haverfordwest. Ferry: Pembroke Dock–Rosslare.

OFF SMALLS TRAFFIC SEPARATION SCHEME

Centred on 51°46'N 05°52'W. The N and S-bound lanes are 3M wide and orientated 016°/196°. The separation zone is 2M wide. Monitor Ch 16 whilst crossing. TheTSS is 4M W of Smalls lt ho which stands in an area of very strong tidal streams. The Hats and Barrels (rky shoals) lie beween the lt ho and Grassholm Is, 8M to the E. See AC 1478, 1.1.3 (Rule 10) and 8.11.5 Passage information.

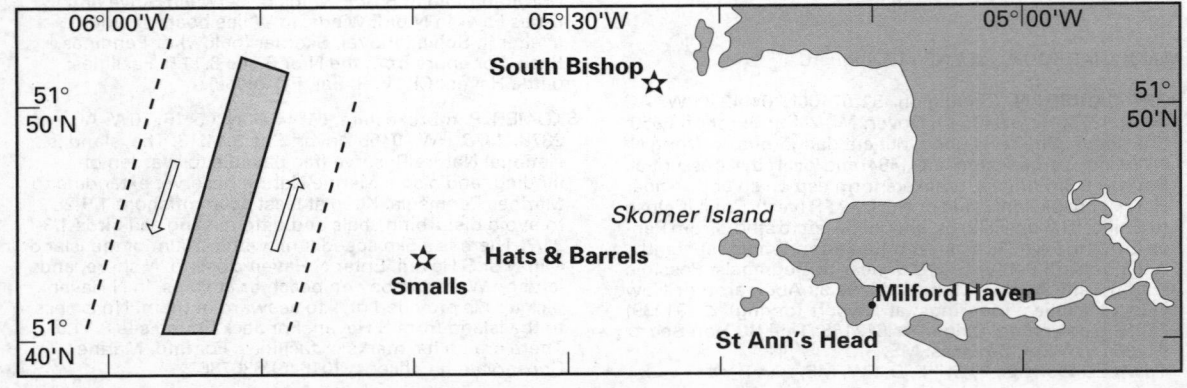

MILFORD HAVEN *continued*

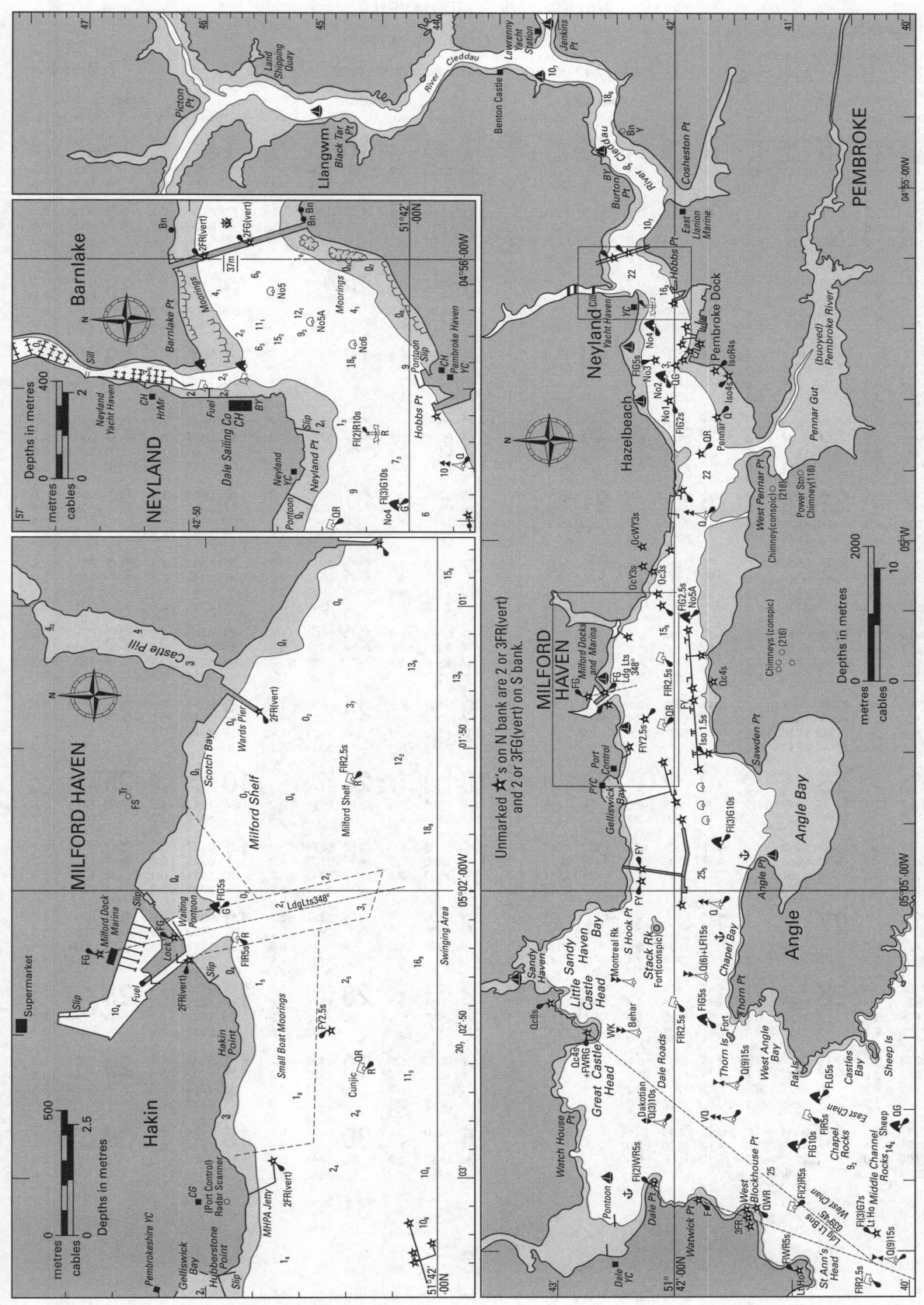

WALES – MILFORD HAVEN

LAT 51°42'N   LONG   5°03'W

TIMES AND HEIGHTS OF HIGH AND LOW WATERS

YEAR **1999**

TIME ZONE (UT)
For Summer Time add ONE hour in non-shaded areas

Chart Datum: 3·71 metres below Ordnance Datum (Newlyn)

JANUARY

Time	m	Time	m
1 F 0512 1138 1739 2359	6.9 0.8 6.9 0.7	**16** SA 0525 1142 1743	6.3 1.4 6.3
2 SA 0603 1228 1828 ○	7.1 0.6 7.0	**17** SU 0000 0602 1221 1820 ●	1.3 6.6 1.1 6.5
3 SU 0046 0649 1315 1914	0.6 7.2 0.5 7.0	**18** M 0037 0639 1258 1857	1.1 6.8 0.9 6.7
4 M 0131 0733 1359 1957	0.6 7.1 0.6 6.9	**19** TU 0114 0716 1336 1935	0.9 6.9 0.9 6.8
5 TU 0213 0815 1441 2039	0.8 7.0 0.9 6.6	**20** W 0152 0754 1414 2013	0.9 7.0 0.8 6.8
6 W 0253 0856 1521 2119	1.1 6.7 1.2 6.3	**21** TH 0230 0833 1454 2053	0.9 7.0 0.8 6.7
7 TH 0331 0936 1600 2159	1.4 6.4 1.5 6.0	**22** F 0309 0914 1535 2135	1.0 6.8 1.0 6.5
8 F 0410 1017 1640 2243	1.8 6.0 1.9 5.6	**23** SA 0351 0959 1619 2222	1.2 6.6 1.2 6.3
9 SA 0452 1103 1727 2333	2.1 5.7 2.2 5.3	**24** SU 0439 1050 1710 2317	1.5 6.3 1.5 6.0
10 SU 0545 1159 1827	2.4 5.4 2.4	**25** M 0536 1150 1812	1.7 6.0 1.8
11 M 0037 0655 1307 1942	5.1 2.6 5.2 2.5	**26** TU 0023 0646 1301 1928	5.7 2.0 5.8 1.9
12 TU 0151 0813 1422 2053	5.1 2.5 5.3 2.4	**27** W 0140 0810 1419 2048	5.7 2.0 5.8 1.8
13 W 0302 0920 1527 2152	5.3 2.3 5.5 2.1	**28** TH 0258 0928 1533 2158	5.8 1.7 6.0 1.6
14 TH 0358 1015 1620 2240	5.7 2.0 5.8 1.8	**29** F 0407 1034 1637 2258	6.2 1.4 6.3 1.2
15 F 0444 1101 1704 2321	6.0 1.7 6.0 1.5	**30** SA 0504 1131 1731 2349	6.5 1.0 6.6 0.9
		31 SU 0553 1220 1818 ○	6.8 0.7 6.8

FEBRUARY

Time	m	Time	m
1 M 0035 0637 1304 1900	0.7 7.0 0.6 6.9	**16** TU 0017 0618 1240 1838 ●	0.9 6.9 0.7 6.9
2 TU 0116 0718 1343 1940	0.6 7.0 0.6 6.9	**17** W 0056 0657 1319 1917	0.6 7.2 0.5 7.1
3 W 0154 0756 1420 2016	0.7 7.0 0.7 6.7	**18** TH 0135 0736 1358 1956	0.4 7.3 0.3 7.1
4 TH 0230 0832 1454 2051	0.9 6.8 0.9 6.5	**19** F 0214 0815 1437 2036	0.4 7.3 0.4 7.1
5 F 0303 0906 1526 2125	1.1 6.5 1.2 6.2	**20** SA 0253 0857 1516 2117	0.5 7.2 0.6 6.9
6 SA 0335 0941 1558 2201	1.4 6.2 1.6 5.9	**21** SU 0334 0940 1558 2201	0.8 6.9 0.9 6.5
7 SU 0409 1017 1633 2240	1.8 5.9 1.9 5.5	**22** M 0418 1028 1645 2252	1.2 6.5 1.3 6.1
8 M 0449 1100 1717 2330	2.1 5.5 2.3 5.2	**23** TU 0511 1124 1743 2355	1.6 6.0 1.8 5.7
9 TU 0543 1156 1821	2.5 5.1 2.6	**24** W 0620 1235 1900	2.0 5.6 2.1
10 W 0039 0702 1315 1952	5.0 2.7 5.0 2.7	**25** TH 0115 0751 1400 2030	5.5 2.1 5.2 2.1
11 TH 0207 0833 1441 2112	5.0 2.6 5.0 2.4	**26** F 0243 0918 1524 2148	5.6 1.9 5.7 1.8
12 F 0322 0943 1549 2211	5.3 2.3 5.4 2.1	**27** SA 0357 1028 1628 2249	5.9 1.5 6.0 1.4
13 SA 0417 1035 1639 2257	5.7 1.8 5.8 1.6	**28** SU 0454 1122 1720 2338	6.3 1.1 6.4 1.0
14 SU 0501 1119 1721 2338	6.2 1.4 6.2 1.3		
15 M 0540 1200 1800	6.6 1.0 6.6		

MARCH

Time	m	Time	m
1 M 0541 1207 1803	6.7 0.8 6.7	**16** TU 0512 1133 1734 2352	6.6 0.9 6.7 0.8
2 TU 0019 0621 1246 1841 ○	0.8 6.9 0.7 6.8	**17** W 0553 1215 1815 ●	7.0 0.5 7.1
3 W 0057 0658 1321 1917	0.7 7.0 0.6 7.0	**18** TH 0033 0634 1256 1855	0.4 7.4 0.2 7.3
4 TH 0131 0733 1353 1950	0.6 6.9 0.6 6.8	**19** F 0114 0715 1337 1935	0.2 7.6 0.1 7.4
5 F 0203 0805 1424 2022	0.7 6.8 0.8 6.6	**20** SA 0155 0756 1417 2016	0.1 7.6 0.1 7.3
6 SA 0233 0836 1452 2052	0.9 6.6 1.1 6.4	**21** SU 0235 0838 1457 2058	0.3 7.4 0.4 7.1
7 SU 0303 0907 1521 2123	1.2 6.4 1.4 6.1	**22** M 0317 0922 1539 2142	0.6 7.0 0.8 6.7
8 M 0333 0938 1552 2157	1.5 6.0 1.7 5.7	**23** TU 0401 1009 1625 2231	1.0 6.5 1.3 6.2
9 TU 0408 1014 1628 2237	1.9 5.6 2.1 5.4	**24** W 0453 1105 1721 2333	1.5 5.9 1.8 5.7
10 W 0453 1059 1718 2333	2.3 5.2 2.5 5.0	**25** TH 0603 1215 1840	2.0 5.4 2.4
11 TH 0558 1206 1839	2.6 4.9 2.8	**26** F 0054 0737 1345 2014	5.4 2.2 5.3 2.2
12 F 0100 0738 1344 2024	5.0 2.7 4.8 2.7	**27** SA 0227 0907 1510 2134	5.4 2.0 5.5 1.9
13 SA 0236 0904 1510 2135	5.0 2.4 5.1 2.3	**28** SU 0341 1014 1613 2233	5.8 1.6 5.9 1.5
14 SU 0342 1003 1607 2227	5.5 1.9 5.6 1.7	**29** M 0436 1105 1701 2319	6.2 1.2 6.3 1.2
15 M 0430 1050 1652 2311	6.1 1.4 6.2 1.2	**30** TU 0520 1145 1741 2357	6.5 0.9 6.5 0.9
		31 W 0559 1221 1818 ○	6.7 0.8 6.7

APRIL

Time	m	Time	m
1 TH 0032 0633 1254 1851	0.8 6.8 0.7 6.8	**16** F 0008 0608 1231 1830 ●	0.3 7.5 0.1 7.5
2 F 0104 0706 1324 1922	0.7 6.8 0.7 6.7	**17** SA 0052 0652 1314 1913	0.1 7.6 0.0 7.5
3 SA 0135 0737 1353 1952	0.7 6.8 0.8 6.6	**18** SU 0135 0736 1357 1956	0.1 7.6 0.1 7.4
4 SU 0205 0807 1422 2022	0.9 6.6 1.0 6.5	**19** M 0218 0820 1439 2040	0.2 7.4 0.4 7.1
5 M 0234 0836 1450 2052	1.1 6.4 1.3 6.2	**20** TU 0302 0905 1522 2125	0.5 6.9 0.8 6.7
6 TU 0305 0907 1520 2124	1.4 6.1 1.6 5.9	**21** W 0348 0954 1609 2216	1.0 6.4 1.3 6.2
7 W 0339 0940 1554 2200	1.8 5.7 2.0 5.5	**22** TH 0442 1050 1705 2317	1.5 5.8 1.9 5.7
8 TH 0420 1021 1637 2249	2.2 5.3 2.4 5.2	**23** F 0550 1158 1820	2.0 5.4 2.2
9 F 0517 1119 1744	2.5 5.0 2.7	**24** SA 0033 0717 1322 1949	5.4 2.1 5.2 2.3
10 SA 0003 0642 1247 1926	5.0 2.6 4.8 2.7	**25** SU 0200 0842 1444 2106	5.4 2.0 5.4 2.0
11 SU 0139 0815 1421 2050	5.1 2.4 5.1 2.3	**26** M 0313 0947 1545 2205	5.7 1.7 5.8 1.7
12 M 0256 0922 1527 2148	5.5 1.9 5.6 1.8	**27** TU 0408 1036 1633 2250	6.1 1.4 6.1 1.4
13 TU 0351 1014 1618 2238	6.1 1.3 6.2 1.2	**28** W 0452 1116 1714 2329	6.3 1.1 6.4 1.1
14 W 0439 1102 1704 2323	6.6 0.8 6.8 0.7	**29** TH 0531 1151 1750	6.5 1.0 6.5
15 TH 0524 1147 1748	7.1 0.4 7.2	**30** F 0003 0605 1224 1823 ○	1.0 6.6 0.9 6.6

WALES – MILFORD HAVEN

LAT 51°42′N   LONG 5°03′W

TIMES AND HEIGHTS OF HIGH AND LOW WATERS

YEAR **1999**

TIME ZONE (UT)
For Summer Time add ONE hour in non-shaded areas

11

MAY

Day	Time	m	Day	Time	m
1 SA	0036 / 0638 / 1255 / 1855	0.9 / 6.6 / 0.9 / 6.6	**16** SU	0029 / 0631 / 1252 / 1853	0.2 / 7.5 / 0.1 / 7.5
2 SU	0108 / 0710 / 1325 / 1925	0.9 / 6.6 / 1.0 / 6.6	**17** M	0117 / 0718 / 1338 / 1939	0.1 / 7.4 / 0.2 / 7.4
3 M	0140 / 0740 / 1355 / 1956	1.0 / 6.5 / 1.1 / 6.5	**18** TU	0203 / 0804 / 1423 / 2025	0.3 / 7.2 / 0.5 / 7.1
4 TU	0211 / 0811 / 1425 / 2027	1.1 / 6.3 / 1.3 / 6.3	**19** W	0250 / 0852 / 1508 / 2112	0.6 / 6.8 / 0.9 / 6.7
5 W	0244 / 0842 / 1457 / 2100	1.4 / 6.1 / 1.6 / 6.0	**20** TH	0338 / 0941 / 1556 / 2202	1.0 / 6.3 / 1.3 / 6.3
6 TH	0319 / 0917 / 1531 / 2137	1.7 / 5.8 / 1.9 / 5.8	**21** F	0431 / 1034 / 1650 / 2259	1.4 / 5.9 / 1.8 / 5.9
7 F	0359 / 0958 / 1613 / 2224	2.0 / 5.5 / 2.2 / 5.5	**22** SA	0532 / 1135 / 1755	1.8 / 5.5 / 2.1
8 SA	0451 / 1052 / 1713 / 2328	2.2 / 5.2 / 2.4 / 5.3	**23** SU	0004 / 0645 / 1247 / 1911	5.6 / 2.1 / 5.3 / 2.2
9 SU	0601 / 1205 / 1834	2.4 / 5.1 / 2.5	**24** M	0119 / 0800 / 1402 / 2024	5.5 / 2.1 / 5.3 / 2.1
10 M	0049 / 0723 / 1330 / 1958	5.3 / 2.2 / 5.3 / 2.2	**25** TU	0231 / 0905 / 1507 / 2125	5.6 / 1.9 / 5.6 / 1.9
11 TU	0207 / 0835 / 1442 / 2105	5.6 / 1.8 / 5.7 / 1.8	**26** W	0330 / 0957 / 1558 / 2214	5.8 / 1.7 / 5.9 / 1.7
12 W	0310 / 0935 / 1541 / 2201	6.1 / 1.3 / 6.2 / 1.3	**27** TH	0418 / 1041 / 1642 / 2256	6.0 / 1.4 / 6.1 / 1.4
13 TH	0405 / 1028 / 1632 / 2253	6.6 / 0.9 / 6.7 / 0.8	**28** F	0500 / 1119 / 1721 / 2334	6.2 / 1.3 / 6.3 / 1.3
14 F	0455 / 1118 / 1721 / 2342	7.0 / 0.5 / 7.1 / 0.4	**29** SA	0538 / 1154 / 1756	6.3 / 1.2 / 6.4
15 SA ●	0543 / 1205 / 1807	7.3 / 0.2 / 7.4	**30** SU O	0010 / 0612 / 1228 / 1830	1.1 / 6.4 / 1.1 / 6.5
			31 M	0045 / 0646 / 1301 / 1903	1.1 / 6.4 / 1.1 / 6.5

JUNE

Day	Time	m	Day	Time	m
1 TU	0119 / 0719 / 1334 / 1935	1.1 / 6.4 / 1.2 / 6.5	**16** W	0151 / 0751 / 1409 / 2011	0.4 / 7.0 / 0.6 / 7.1
2 W	0153 / 0751 / 1406 / 2008	1.2 / 6.3 / 1.3 / 6.3	**17** TH	0239 / 0838 / 1455 / 2058	0.6 / 6.8 / 0.7 / 6.8
3 TH	0227 / 0825 / 1440 / 2043	1.3 / 6.1 / 1.5 / 6.2	**18** F	0326 / 0925 / 1540 / 2145	0.9 / 6.4 / 1.2 / 6.4
4 F	0304 / 0901 / 1517 / 2122	1.5 / 5.9 / 1.7 / 6.0	**19** SA	0413 / 1013 / 1628 / 2234	1.3 / 6.0 / 1.6 / 6.1
5 SA	0345 / 0943 / 1559 / 2208	1.7 / 5.7 / 1.9 / 5.8	**20** SU	0504 / 1105 / 1720 / 2328	1.7 / 5.6 / 2.0 / 5.7
6 SU	0433 / 1033 / 1651 / 2304	1.9 / 5.6 / 2.1 / 5.7	**21** M	0601 / 1203 / 1822	2.0 / 5.4 / 2.2
7 M	0531 / 1135 / 1757	2.0 / 5.5 / 2.2	**22** TU	0030 / 0706 / 1309 / 1930	5.5 / 2.2 / 5.3 / 2.3
8 TU	0011 / 0639 / 1248 / 1911	5.7 / 2.0 / 5.5 / 2.1	**23** W	0138 / 0812 / 1417 / 2036	5.4 / 2.2 / 5.3 / 2.2
9 W	0124 / 0751 / 1400 / 2023	5.8 / 1.8 / 5.8 / 1.8	**24** TH	0244 / 0912 / 1518 / 2134	5.5 / 2.0 / 5.6 / 2.0
10 TH	0231 / 0857 / 1505 / 2127	6.1 / 1.4 / 6.1 / 1.4	**25** F	0341 / 1003 / 1609 / 2224	5.7 / 1.8 / 5.8 / 1.8
11 F	0332 / 0957 / 1603 / 2225	6.5 / 1.1 / 6.6 / 1.0	**26** SA	0429 / 1048 / 1653 / 2307	5.9 / 1.6 / 6.1 / 1.5
12 SA	0429 / 1052 / 1657 / 2320	6.8 / 0.7 / 6.9 / 0.7	**27** SU	0512 / 1128 / 1732 / 2347	6.1 / 1.4 / 6.3 / 1.4
13 SU ●	0523 / 1144 / 1748	7.1 / 0.5 / 7.2	**28** M O	0550 / 1205 / 1809	6.2 / 1.3 / 6.4
14 M	0012 / 0613 / 1234 / 1837	0.4 / 7.2 / 0.4 / 7.3	**29** TU	0024 / 0626 / 1241 / 1844	1.2 / 6.3 / 1.2 / 6.5
15 TU	0103 / 0703 / 1323 / 1924	0.3 / 7.2 / 0.4 / 7.3	**30** W	0101 / 0701 / 1316 / 1918	1.2 / 6.3 / 1.2 / 6.5

JULY

Day	Time	m	Day	Time	m
1 TH	0137 / 0735 / 1351 / 1953	1.2 / 6.4 / 1.2 / 6.5	**16** F	0224 / 0822 / 1437 / 2040	0.6 / 6.8 / 0.8 / 6.9
2 F	0213 / 0811 / 1426 / 2030	1.2 / 6.3 / 1.3 / 6.5	**17** SA	0307 / 0904 / 1518 / 2121	0.9 / 6.5 / 1.1 / 6.6
3 SA	0250 / 0848 / 1504 / 2109	1.3 / 6.2 / 1.4 / 6.4	**18** SU	0347 / 0945 / 1558 / 2203	1.2 / 6.2 / 1.5 / 6.2
4 SU	0330 / 0929 / 1545 / 2152	1.4 / 6.1 / 1.6 / 6.3	**19** M	0427 / 1028 / 1639 / 2247	1.6 / 5.8 / 1.8 / 5.9
5 M	0414 / 1015 / 1631 / 2242	1.5 / 6.0 / 1.7 / 6.1	**20** TU	0510 / 1115 / 1726 / 2337	1.9 / 5.5 / 2.2 / 5.6
6 TU	0504 / 1109 / 1727 / 2340	1.7 / 5.8 / 1.9 / 5.8	**21** W	0602 / 1211 / 1827	2.2 / 5.3 / 2.4
7 W	0604 / 1213 / 1833	1.8 / 5.7 / 1.9	**22** TH	0038 / 0709 / 1320 / 1940	5.3 / 2.4 / 5.1 / 2.5
8 TH	0047 / 0712 / 1324 / 1947	5.9 / 1.8 / 5.8 / 1.8	**23** F	0150 / 0822 / 1433 / 2053	5.2 / 2.4 / 5.2 / 2.4
9 F	0158 / 0824 / 1435 / 2100	6.0 / 1.6 / 6.0 / 1.6	**24** SA	0302 / 0927 / 1537 / 2153	5.3 / 2.2 / 5.5 / 2.1
10 SA	0307 / 0932 / 1541 / 2206	6.2 / 1.4 / 6.3 / 1.3	**25** SU	0401 / 1020 / 1628 / 2243	5.6 / 1.8 / 5.8 / 1.8
11 SU	0411 / 1033 / 1640 / 2305	6.5 / 1.1 / 6.6 / 1.0	**26** M	0449 / 1105 / 1711 / 2326	5.9 / 1.7 / 6.1 / 1.5
12 M	0509 / 1129 / 1735	6.7 / 0.8 / 6.9	**27** TU	0530 / 1144 / 1749	6.1 / 1.4 / 6.4
13 TU ●	0000 / 0602 / 1221 / 1824	0.7 / 6.9 / 0.6 / 7.1	**28** W O	0005 / 0606 / 1222 / 1825	1.3 / 6.3 / 1.2 / 6.6
14 W	0052 / 0651 / 1309 / 1912	0.5 / 7.0 / 0.6 / 7.2	**29** TH	0043 / 0642 / 1258 / 1900	1.1 / 6.5 / 1.1 / 6.7
15 TH	0139 / 0738 / 1354 / 1957	0.6 / 7.0 / 0.6 / 7.1	**30** F	0120 / 0718 / 1334 / 1936	1.0 / 6.6 / 1.0 / 6.8
			31 SA	0156 / 0755 / 1411 / 2014	0.9 / 6.6 / 1.0 / 6.8

AUGUST

Day	Time	m	Day	Time	m
1 SU	0234 / 0832 / 1448 / 2052	0.9 / 6.6 / 1.0 / 6.8	**16** M	0314 / 0912 / 1524 / 2128	1.1 / 6.3 / 1.3 / 6.4
2 M	0312 / 0911 / 1527 / 2133	1.0 / 6.5 / 1.2 / 6.6	**17** TU	0347 / 0948 / 1557 / 2204	1.5 / 6.0 / 1.7 / 6.0
3 TU	0353 / 0954 / 1610 / 2219	1.2 / 6.3 / 1.4 / 6.4	**18** W	0421 / 1027 / 1635 / 2245	1.9 / 5.7 / 2.1 / 5.6
4 W	0439 / 1043 / 1701 / 2313	1.4 / 6.1 / 1.7 / 6.1	**19** TH	0502 / 1113 / 1725 / 2338	2.3 / 5.3 / 2.4 / 5.2
5 TH	0533 / 1142 / 1803	1.7 / 5.8 / 1.9	**20** F	0559 / 1217 / 1838	2.6 / 5.0 / 2.7
6 F	0018 / 0641 / 1255 / 1921	5.9 / 1.9 / 5.7 / 2.0	**21** SA	0051 / 0725 / 1343 / 2011	5.0 / 2.7 / 5.0 / 2.7
7 SA	0134 / 0801 / 1414 / 2044	5.8 / 1.9 / 5.8 / 1.9	**22** SU	0220 / 0852 / 1505 / 2125	5.0 / 2.6 / 5.3 / 2.4
8 SU	0252 / 0918 / 1528 / 2157	5.9 / 1.7 / 6.0 / 1.6	**23** M	0334 / 0954 / 1603 / 2220	5.3 / 2.2 / 5.7 / 2.0
9 M	0402 / 1023 / 1632 / 2259	6.2 / 1.4 / 6.4 / 1.2	**24** TU	0425 / 1041 / 1647 / 2304	5.7 / 1.8 / 6.1 / 1.6
10 TU	0501 / 1120 / 1726 / 2352	6.5 / 1.1 / 6.8 / 0.8	**25** W	0507 / 1122 / 1726 / 2343	6.1 / 1.5 / 6.5 / 1.2
11 W ●	0553 / 1209 / 1814	6.8 / 0.8 / 7.0	**26** TH O	0544 / 1159 / 1802	6.4 / 1.2 / 6.8
12 TH	0040 / 0638 / 1255 / 1857	0.6 / 6.9 / 0.7 / 7.1	**27** F	0021 / 0620 / 1237 / 1838	0.9 / 6.7 / 0.9 / 7.0
13 F	0124 / 0720 / 1336 / 1938	0.6 / 6.9 / 0.6 / 7.1	**28** SA	0058 / 0657 / 1314 / 1915	0.7 / 6.9 / 0.7 / 7.2
14 SA	0203 / 0759 / 1418 / 2016	0.6 / 6.8 / 0.8 / 7.0	**29** SU	0136 / 0734 / 1351 / 1953	0.6 / 7.0 / 0.7 / 7.2
15 SU	0240 / 0837 / 1450 / 2052	0.6 / 6.6 / 1.0 / 6.7	**30** M	0214 / 0812 / 1429 / 2032	0.6 / 7.0 / 0.7 / 7.2
			31 TU	0252 / 0852 / 1508 / 2113	0.7 / 6.9 / 0.9 / 6.9

Chart Datum: 3·71 metres below Ordnance Datum (Newlyn)

WALES – MILFORD HAVEN

LAT 51°42′N LONG 5°03′W

TIMES AND HEIGHTS OF HIGH AND LOW WATERS

YEAR **1999**

TIME ZONE (UT)
For Summer Time add ONE hour in non-shaded areas

SEPTEMBER

Day	Time	m	Day	Time	m
1 W	0332 / 0933 / 1550 / 2158	1.0 / 6.6 / 1.2 / 6.6	**16** TH	0338 / 0944 / 1554 / 2200	1.8 / 5.8 / 2.0 / 5.7
2 TH	0415 / 1020 / 1639 / 2250	1.4 / 6.2 / 1.6 / 6.2	**17** F	0413 / 1023 / 1637 / 2244	2.2 / 5.4 / 2.4 / 5.3
3 F	0508 / 1118 / 1741 / 2356	1.8 / 5.8 / 2.0 / 5.7	**18** SA	0502 / 1118 / 1742 / 2350	2.6 / 5.1 / 2.8 / 4.9
4 SA	0619 / 1233 / 1907	2.1 / 5.6 / 2.2	**19** SU	0621 / 1245 / 1924	2.9 / 4.9 / 2.9
5 SU	0118 / 0748 / 1402 / 2039	5.5 / 2.2 / 5.6 / 2.1	**20** M	0130 / 0903 / 1425 / 2052	4.8 / 2.8 / 5.1 / 2.6
6 M	0246 / 0912 / 1523 / 2155	5.6 / 2.0 / 5.9 / 1.7	**21** TU	0301 / 0922 / 1531 / 2150	5.1 / 2.5 / 5.5 / 2.1
7 TU	0358 / 1018 / 1625 / 2254	6.0 / 1.6 / 6.4 / 1.3	**22** W	0356 / 1012 / 1617 / 2235	5.6 / 2.0 / 6.1 / 1.6
8 W	0453 / 1111 / 1715 / 2342	6.4 / 1.2 / 6.7 / 0.9	**23** TH	0438 / 1054 / 1656 / 2316	6.1 / 1.5 / 6.5 / 1.2
9 TH ●	0540 / 1156 / 1759	6.7 / 0.9 / 7.0	**24** F	0517 / 1133 / 1734 / 2354	6.6 / 1.1 / 7.0 / 0.8
10 F	0024 / 0620 / 1236 / 1838	0.7 / 6.9 / 0.7 / 7.1	**25** SA O	0555 / 1211 / 1813	7.0 / 0.7 / 7.3
11 SA	0102 / 0658 / 1313 / 1914	0.6 / 7.0 / 0.7 / 7.1	**26** SU	0033 / 0632 / 1251 / 1851	0.5 / 7.2 / 0.5 / 7.5
12 SU	0136 / 0733 / 1347 / 1948	0.7 / 6.9 / 0.8 / 7.0	**27** M	0113 / 0711 / 1330 / 1931	0.3 / 7.4 / 0.4 / 7.5
13 M	0209 / 0806 / 1419 / 2021	0.9 / 6.7 / 1.0 / 6.7	**28** TU	0152 / 0751 / 1409 / 2012	0.4 / 7.3 / 0.5 / 7.4
14 TU	0239 / 0838 / 1449 / 2053	1.1 / 6.5 / 1.3 / 6.5	**29** W	0231 / 0831 / 1450 / 2054	0.6 / 7.1 / 0.8 / 7.1
15 W	0308 / 0910 / 1520 / 2125	1.5 / 6.2 / 1.6 / 6.1	**30** TH	0312 / 0914 / 1533 / 2140	0.9 / 6.8 / 1.2 / 6.6

OCTOBER

Day	Time	m	Day	Time	m
1 F	0357 / 1002 / 1624 / 2233	1.4 / 6.3 / 1.6 / 6.1	**16** SA	0338 / 0946 / 1604 / 2205	2.2 / 5.6 / 2.4 / 5.3
2 SA	0450 / 1101 / 1729 / 2341	1.9 / 5.9 / 2.1 / 5.6	**17** SU	0421 / 1034 / 1701 / 2301	2.6 / 5.2 / 2.7 / 5.0
3 SU	0604 / 1219 / 1902	2.3 / 5.5 / 2.3	**18** M	0527 / 1147 / 1829	2.9 / 5.0 / 2.9
4 M	0108 / 0739 / 1352 / 2035	5.4 / 2.4 / 5.5 / 2.1	**19** TU	0030 / 0712 / 1328 / 2005	4.8 / 2.9 / 5.1 / 2.7
5 TU	0238 / 0903 / 1512 / 2147	5.5 / 2.1 / 5.9 / 1.7	**20** W	0210 / 0837 / 1444 / 2110	5.0 / 2.6 / 5.5 / 2.2
6 W	0346 / 1006 / 1611 / 2241	6.0 / 1.7 / 6.3 / 1.3	**21** TH	0314 / 0934 / 1537 / 2159	5.5 / 2.1 / 5.6 / 1.7
7 TH	0438 / 1055 / 1658 / 2324	6.4 / 1.3 / 6.7 / 1.0	**22** F	0402 / 1020 / 1621 / 2243	6.1 / 1.5 / 6.6 / 1.1
8 F	0520 / 1136 / 1738	6.7 / 1.0 / 6.9	**23** SA	0445 / 1103 / 1704 / 2325	6.7 / 1.0 / 7.1 / 0.7
9 SA ●	0002 / 0558 / 1213 / 1814	0.8 / 6.8 / 0.9 / 7.0	**24** SU O	0526 / 1145 / 1746	7.1 / 0.7 / 7.4
10 SU	0036 / 0633 / 1247 / 1848	0.8 / 6.9 / 0.8 / 7.0	**25** M	0007 / 0607 / 1227 / 1827	0.4 / 7.4 / 0.4 / 7.6
11 M	0107 / 0706 / 1318 / 1920	0.9 / 6.9 / 0.9 / 6.9	**26** TU	0049 / 0649 / 1309 / 1910	0.2 / 7.6 / 0.3 / 7.6
12 TU	0138 / 0737 / 1349 / 1951	0.9 / 6.8 / 1.0 / 6.7	**27** W	0131 / 0731 / 1352 / 1954	0.3 / 7.5 / 0.4 / 7.4
13 W	0207 / 0807 / 1419 / 2021	1.2 / 6.6 / 1.3 / 6.5	**28** TH	0213 / 0814 / 1436 / 2039	0.5 / 7.1 / 0.7 / 7.1
14 TH	0235 / 0838 / 1450 / 2052	1.4 / 6.3 / 1.6 / 6.1	**29** F	0257 / 0859 / 1522 / 2127	0.9 / 6.9 / 1.1 / 6.6
15 F	0305 / 0910 / 1524 / 2125	1.8 / 6.0 / 2.0 / 5.8	**30** SA	0343 / 0949 / 1615 / 2222	1.4 / 6.4 / 1.6 / 6.0
			31 SU	0439 / 1049 / 1722 / 2329	1.9 / 6.0 / 2.0 / 5.6

NOVEMBER

Day	Time	m	Day	Time	m
1 M	0551 / 1203 / 1849	2.3 / 5.6 / 2.2	**16** TU	0451 / 1107 / 1741 / 2341	2.7 / 5.3 / 2.6 / 5.0
2 TU	0051 / 0721 / 1330 / 2016	5.4 / 2.4 / 5.6 / 2.1	**17** W	0612 / 1227 / 1905	2.8 / 5.3 / 2.5
3 W	0216 / 0841 / 1447 / 2124	5.5 / 2.2 / 5.8 / 1.8	**18** TH	0108 / 0739 / 1347 / 2018	5.1 / 2.6 / 5.5 / 2.2
4 TH	0323 / 0943 / 1546 / 2217	5.9 / 1.8 / 6.2 / 1.5	**19** F	0223 / 0847 / 1450 / 2117	5.5 / 2.1 / 6.0 / 1.7
5 F	0413 / 1031 / 1633 / 2259	6.2 / 1.5 / 6.5 / 1.2	**20** SA	0321 / 0942 / 1544 / 2208	6.1 / 1.6 / 6.5 / 1.2
6 SA	0456 / 1112 / 1713 / 2335	6.5 / 1.2 / 6.7 / 1.1	**21** SU	0411 / 1031 / 1633 / 2256	6.6 / 1.1 / 7.0 / 0.8
7 SU	0533 / 1147 / 1750	6.7 / 1.1 / 6.8	**22** M	0458 / 1119 / 1720 / 2342	7.0 / 0.7 / 7.3 / 0.5
8 M ●	0008 / 0607 / 1221 / 1823	1.0 / 6.8 / 1.0 / 6.8	**23** TU O	0544 / 1206 / 1807	7.4 / 0.4 / 7.5
9 TU	0040 / 0640 / 1253 / 1855	1.0 / 6.8 / 1.0 / 6.7	**24** W	0028 / 0629 / 1253 / 1853	0.3 / 7.5 / 0.3 / 7.5
10 W	0111 / 0711 / 1325 / 1926	1.1 / 6.7 / 1.1 / 6.6	**25** TH	0114 / 0715 / 1339 / 1940	0.3 / 7.5 / 0.3 / 7.4
11 TH	0141 / 0742 / 1356 / 1957	1.2 / 6.6 / 1.3 / 6.4	**26** F	0159 / 0801 / 1426 / 2028	0.5 / 7.3 / 0.6 / 7.0
12 F	0211 / 0813 / 1429 / 2029	1.4 / 6.4 / 1.5 / 6.2	**27** SA	0245 / 0848 / 1515 / 2117	0.9 / 7.0 / 1.0 / 6.6
13 SA	0242 / 0846 / 1503 / 2102	1.7 / 6.1 / 1.8 / 5.8	**28** SU	0333 / 0939 / 1607 / 2210	1.3 / 6.6 / 1.4 / 6.1
14 SU	0315 / 0922 / 1543 / 2141	2.1 / 5.8 / 2.2 / 5.5	**29** M	0426 / 1034 / 1708 / 2310	1.7 / 6.2 / 1.8 / 5.7
15 M	0356 / 1007 / 1633 / 2231	2.4 / 5.5 / 2.5 / 5.2	**30** TU	0530 / 1138 / 1820	2.1 / 5.8 / 2.1

DECEMBER

Day	Time	m	Day	Time	m
1 W	0019 / 0645 / 1252 / 1936	5.4 / 2.3 / 5.6 / 2.1	**16** TH	0527 / 1141 / 1810	2.4 / 5.6 / 2.2
2 TH	0136 / 0801 / 1407 / 2046	5.4 / 2.3 / 5.7 / 2.0	**17** F	0015 / 0640 / 1253 / 1922	5.4 / 2.4 / 5.7 / 2.1
3 F	0245 / 0907 / 1510 / 2142	5.6 / 2.0 / 5.9 / 1.8	**18** SA	0130 / 0755 / 1403 / 2031	5.4 / 2.1 / 5.9 / 1.8
4 SA	0341 / 1000 / 1602 / 2228	5.9 / 1.8 / 6.1 / 1.6	**19** SU	0238 / 0902 / 1507 / 2133	5.9 / 1.8 / 6.3 / 1.4
5 SU	0427 / 1044 / 1646 / 2307	6.2 / 1.6 / 6.3 / 1.4	**20** M	0339 / 1002 / 1605 / 2229	6.4 / 1.3 / 6.7 / 1.0
6 M	0508 / 1122 / 1725 / 2343	6.4 / 1.4 / 6.4 / 1.3	**21** TU	0434 / 1057 / 1659 / 2322	6.8 / 0.9 / 7.1 / 0.7
7 TU	0545 / 1158 / 1801	6.5 / 1.3 / 6.5	**22** W O	0525 / 1149 / 1751	7.1 / 0.6 / 7.2
8 W	0016 / 0619 / 1233 / 1835	1.2 / 6.6 / 1.2 / 6.5	**23** TH	0012 / 0614 / 1240 / 1841	0.5 / 7.3 / 0.4 / 7.3
9 TH	0050 / 0652 / 1307 / 1908	1.2 / 6.6 / 1.2 / 6.5	**24** F	0101 / 0703 / 1330 / 1930	0.4 / 7.4 / 0.4 / 7.3
10 F	0122 / 0724 / 1340 / 1940	1.3 / 6.6 / 1.3 / 6.4	**25** SA	0148 / 0750 / 1418 / 2017	0.5 / 7.3 / 0.5 / 7.0
11 SA	0154 / 0757 / 1414 / 2013	1.4 / 6.4 / 1.4 / 6.2	**26** SU	0234 / 0837 / 1505 / 2105	0.7 / 7.1 / 0.8 / 6.7
12 SU	0226 / 0830 / 1449 / 2047	1.6 / 6.3 / 1.6 / 6.0	**27** M	0321 / 0924 / 1553 / 2152	1.1 / 6.8 / 1.1 / 6.3
13 M	0301 / 0907 / 1528 / 2125	1.8 / 6.1 / 1.8 / 5.8	**28** TU	0408 / 1013 / 1643 / 2242	1.4 / 6.4 / 1.5 / 5.9
14 TU	0340 / 0948 / 1612 / 2210	2.0 / 5.9 / 2.0 / 5.6	**29** W	0459 / 1105 / 1738 / 2338	1.8 / 6.0 / 1.9 / 5.6
15 W	0427 / 1038 / 1705 / 2306	2.2 / 5.7 / 2.2 / 5.4	**30** TH	0557 / 1204 / 1841	2.2 / 5.7 / 2.2
			31 F	0042 / 0705 / 1312 / 1950	5.4 / 2.3 / 5.5 / 2.3

Chart Datum: 3·71 metres below Ordnance Datum (Newlyn)

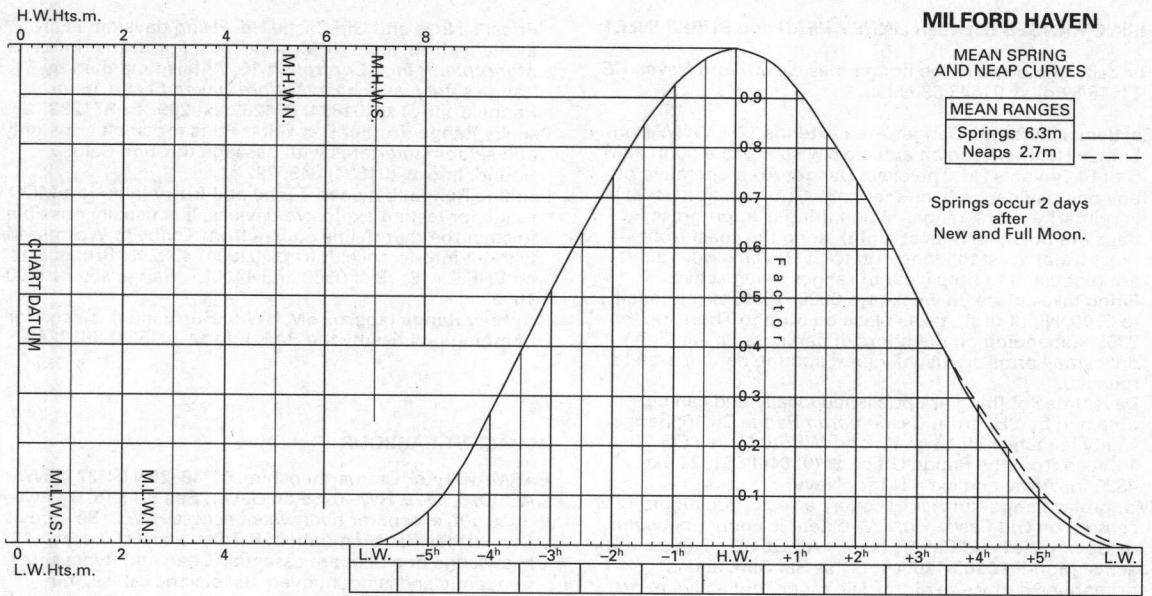

MILFORD HAVEN

MEAN SPRING
AND NEAP CURVES

MEAN RANGES
Springs 6.3m
Neaps   2.7m

Springs occur 2 days
after
New and Full Moon.

TENBY   8-11-15

Pembrokeshire 51·40'·40N 04°41'·85W   Rtg 3-4-1

CHARTS
AC 1482, 1076, *1179*; Imray C60; Stanfords 14; OS 158

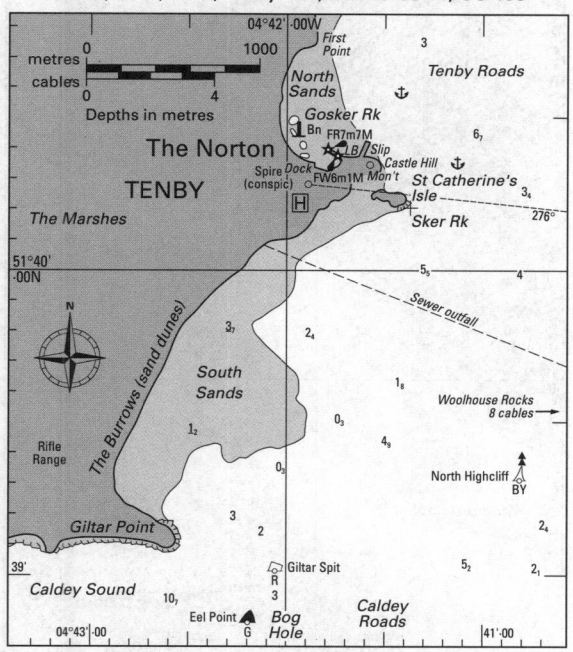

TIDES
−0510 Dover; ML 4·5; Duration 0610; Zone 0 (UT)

Standard Port MILFORD HAVEN (←—)

Times				Height (metres)			
High Water		Low Water		MHWS	MHWN	MLWN	MLWS
0100	0800	0100	0700	7·0	5·2	2·5	0·7
1300	2000	1300	1900				
Differences TENBY							
−0015	−0010	−0015	−0020	+1·4	+1·1	+0·5	+0·2
STACKPOLE QUAY (7M W of Caldey Island)							
−0005	+0025	−0010	−0010	+0·9	+0·7	+0·2	+0·3

SHELTER
Good, but hbr dries up to <u>5</u>m; access HW±2½. Sheltered
⚓s, depending on wind direction, to NE in Tenby Roads, in
Lydstep Haven (2·5M SW), and around Caldey Island as
follows: Priory Bay (shallow, to the N), Jone's Bay (NE),
Drinkim Bay (E) or Sandtop Bay (W). Also at Saundersfoot
about 2M to the N; see below.

NAVIGATION
WPT 51°40'·00N 04°38'·00W, 099°/279° from/to monument
on Castle Hill, 2·2M. The ⊕ WPT (off chartlet) is 2ca W of
DZ2 SPM buoy, Fl Y 2·5s. Beware Woolhouse Rks (<u>3·6m</u>)
1·5M SExE of the hbr, marked by unlit SCM buoy; and
Sker Rk (1m high) closer in off St Catherine's Island (28m).
From the W, Caldey Sound is navigable with care by day
between Eel Pt SHM and Giltar Spit PHM unlit buoys.
Approaching Tenby Roads, keep outside the line of
mooring buoys. For adjacent Firing ranges, see overleaf.

LIGHTS AND MARKS
Church spire and N side of St Catherine's Is in line at 276°. FR
7m 7M on pier hd. Inside hbr, FW 6m 1M marks landing ⬎.
PHM beacon (unlit) marks outcrop from Gosker Rk on beach
close N of hbr ent. Hbr is floodlit.

RADIO TELEPHONE
VHF Ch 16 80 (listening during HO).

TELEPHONE (Dial code 01834)
Hr Mr 842717 (end May-end Sept), Mobile 0831 185917;
MRSC (01646) 690909; ⌗ (01222) 763880 (H24); Marinecall
0891 500459; Police 842303; Dr 844161; ⊞ 842040.

FACILITIES
Hbr ☎/🕾 842717, Slip (up to 4·2m), L, AB, Sh, FW; **Tenby
YC** ☎ 842762;
Town EC Wed; P & D (cans), Ⓞ, CH, V, R, Bar, Gas, ✉, Ⓑ,
≈, ✈ (Swansea; and a small airfield at Haverfordwest).

ADJACENT HARBOUR

SAUNDERSFOOT, Pembrokeshire, 51°42'·58N 04°41'·68W.
AC 1482, 1076, *1179*. HW −0510 on Dover; ML 4·4m;
Duration 0605. See 8.11.15. A half-tide hbr with good
shelter, but there may be a surge in prolonged E winds.
On appr, beware buoys marking restricted area (power
boats, etc) between Coppett Hall Pt and Perry's Pt. AB
may be available (see Hr Mr), or moorings in the middle.
Pier hd lt Fl R 5s 6m 7M on stone cupola. VHF: Hr Mr 11
16. Hr Mr ☎/🕾 (01834) 812094/(Home 813782). Facilities:
CH, FW (on SW wall), Slip, P & D (cans), ME, BH.
Town EC Wed; V, R, Bar, ✉, Ⓑ, ≈ (Tenby/Saundersfoot).

11

FIRING RANGES between LINNEY HEAD and BURRY INLET

For daily info on all range firing times call *Milford Haven CG* Ch 16/67 or ☎ 01646 690909.

Castlemartin Range Danger Area extends 12M WNW from Linney Hd, thence in an anti-clockwise arc to a point 12M S of St Govan's Hd. The exact Danger Area operative on any one day depends on the ranges/ammunition used; it is primarily a tank range. When firing is in progress R flags are flown (Fl R lts at night) along the coast from Freshwater West to Linney Hd to St Govan's Hd. Yachts are requested to keep clear of ranges when active. Firing takes place on weekdays 0900 -1630, exceptionally to 1700. Night firing takes place on Mon to Thurs, up to 2359, depending on the hours of darkness. In Jan/Feb only small arms are usually fired and the danger area is reduced.
Days/times of firing are published locally and can be obtained by VHF from *Castlemartin Range* Ch 16; Range safety launches Ch 16 or 12; and Milford Haven CG Ch 16. Also from the Range Office ☎ (01646) 661321 ext 4336 for Army and ext 4241 for Navy.

Manorbier Range (further E) covers a sector arc radius 12M centred on Old Castle Hd; E/W extent is approx between St Govan's Hd and Caldey Is (see AC Q6402). It is usually active Mon-Fri 0900-1700LT, occas Sat/Sun, and is primarily a surface to air missile range, but active parts depend on the weapons in use on any given day. On firing days warnings are broadcast on Ch 16, 73 at 0830, 1430 and on completion; R flags are flown either side of Old Castle Hd. Yachts on passage should either stay 12M offshore or close inshore via Stackpole Hd, Trewent Pt,

Priest's Nose and Old Castle Hd. Firing days/times are available from local Hr Mrs and YCs. For further info call: *Manorbier Range Control* Ch 16, 73 (also manned by Range safety launches); *Milford Haven CG* Ch 16; or Range Control ☎ (01834) 871282 ext 209, ⚓ 871283.

Penally Range (further E at Giltar Pt) is for small arms only and seldom interferes with passage through Caldey Sound. Info ☎ (01834) 843522.

Pendine Range (between Tenby and Burry Inlet) is a MOD range for testing explosive devices. It is usually possible to steer the rhumb line course from Tenby to Worms Hd without interference. Info ☎ (01994) 453243. Broadcasts on VHF Ch 16, 73 at 0900 and 1400LT. Range active 0800-1615.

Pembrey Range (approx 5M NW of Burry Inlet) is used for bombing practice by the RAF. Info ☎ (01554) 891224.

ADJACENT HARBOUR

CARMARTHEN, Carmarthenshire, 51°46´·25N 04°22´·45W. AC 1076, *1179*. HW −0455 on Dover. See 8.11.16. R Towy dries out, except for river water; access HW±2. Beware Carmarthen Bar off mouth of R Towy and Taf. Local knowledge or a pilot are essential. Chan into rivers shifts frequently and is not buoyed. Six electric cables, min clearance 15m, cross between the mouth and the fixed rly bridge in Carmarthen. Visitors berths at R Towy YC at Ferryside (9M below Carmarthen), access HW±3 (liable to dry). Facilities: **R Towy YC** ☎ (01267) 267366, Bar, FW, M. **Town** Usual facilities, ⒷB, Bar, Gas, ⊠, V, ⇌, ✈ (Cardiff).

BURRY INLET   8-11-16

Carmarthenshire 51°40'·50N 04°14'·85W (Burry Port)
Rtg 4-4-3

CHARTS
AC 1167, 1076, *1179*; Imray C59, C60; Stanfords 14; OS 159
TIDES
−0500 Dover; ML 4·7; Duration 0555; Zone 0 (UT)

Standard Port MILFORD HAVEN (←)

Times				Height (metres)			
High Water		Low Water		MHWS	MHWN	MLWN	MLWS
0100	0800	0100	0700	7·0	5·2	2·5	0·7
1300	2000	1300	1900				
Differences BURRY PORT							
+0003	+0003	+0007	+0007	+1·6	+1·4	+0·5	+0·4
LLANELLI							
−0003	−0003	+0150	+0020	+0·8	+0·6	No data	
FERRYSIDE							
0000	−0010	+0220	0000	−0·3	−0·7	−1·7	−0·6
CARMARTHEN							
+0010	0000	Dries out		−4·4	−4·8	Dries out	

SHELTER
Good in Burry Port hbr (dries); access HW±2. Inspect before entry as it is entirely filled with moorings, none for visitors. ‡ 1 to 2ca E of barrel post. Sp tides run hard. Note: If bad weather precludes access to Burry Inlet, see 8.11.15 for ‡s around Caldey Island, especially in W'lies.
NAVIGATION
WPT 51°36´·35N 04°24´·30W, 267°/087° from/to Burry Holms 3·3M; thence 4·5M to Burry Port. Carmarthen Bar, extending from the R Towy ent SE to Burry Holms, should not be attempted in W winds >F5 nor at night. Best entry is close NW of Burry Holms at HW−2; thence track 018° with Worms Hd on a stern transit (198°) between Burry Holms and Limekiln Pt. When Whiteford lt ho (disused) bears about 082°, alter to approx 050° into deeper water and steer to leave the barrel post about 1½ ca to port. Continue on this line to ‡ in deep water beyond hbr ent, as shown. Chan is not buoyed/lit and is liable to shift. Before appr, check Firing range activity (above).
LIGHTS AND MARKS
Whiteford lt ho is conspic, but no longer lit. Barrel post, Fl R 3s 5M, is 1½ca S of conspic Old lt ho, W tr, R top, Fl 5s 7m 15M, and FS on W bkwtr.

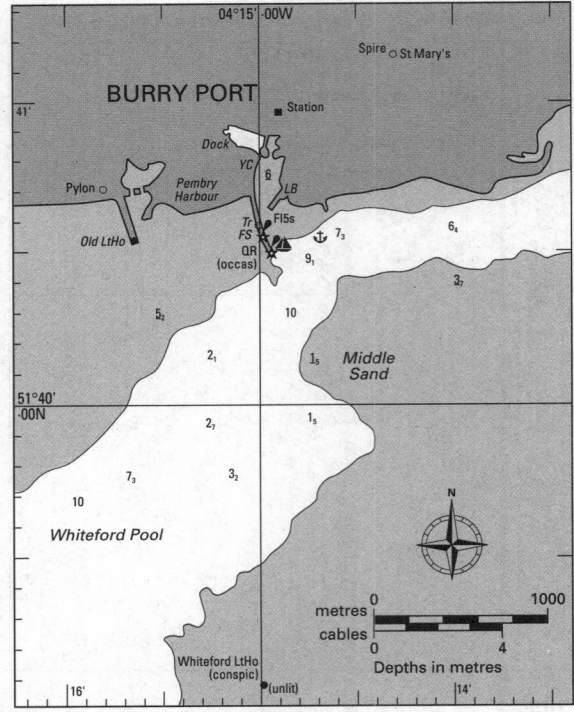

▲ Report to Burry Port Yacht Services

RADIO TELEPHONE
None.
TELEPHONE (Dial code 01554)
Superintendent 758181; MRCC (01792) 366534; ⌗ (01222) 763880 (H24); Pendine Range (01994) 453243 Ext 240; Marinecall 0891 500459; Police 772222; Dr 832240.
FACILITIES
Outer Hbr W pier and Basin ☎ 833342, Slip, M, L, CH; Note: marina planned by 2002. **E Pier** Slip;
Burry Port YC Bar; **Services**: D, ME, El, Sh, C, Gas.
Town EC Tues; P, D, V, R, Bar, ⊠, Ⓑ, ⇌, ✈ (Cardiff).

SWANSEA   8-11-17

Swansea 51°36'·40N 03°55'·60W. Rtg 2-1-1

CHARTS
AC 1161, *1165, 1179*; Imray C59; Stanfords 14; OS 159
TIDES
−0500 Dover; ML 5·2; Duration 0620; Zone 0 (UT)

Standard Port MILFORD HAVEN (←)

Times				Height (metres)			
High Water		Low Water		MHWS	MHWN	MLWN	MLWS
0100	0800	0100	0700	7·0	5·2	2·5	0·7
1300	2000	1300	1900				
Differences SWANSEA							
+0004	+0006	−0006	−0003	+2·6	+2·1	+0·7	+0·3
MUMBLES							
+0005	+0010	−0020	−0015	+2·3	+1·7	+0·6	+0·2
PORT TALBOT							
+0003	+0003	−0013	−0007	+2·7	+2·2	+1·0	+0·3
PORTHCAWL							
0000	0000	0000	−0015	+2·9	+2·3	+0·8	+0·3

SHELTER
Very good in marina; enter via R Tawe Barrage lock, which operates on request HW±4½ (co-ordinated with the marina lock), 0700-2200BST; out of season, 0700-1900UT, but to 2200 at w/ends. Yachts normally lock out of Tawe barrage lock on the Hour, and inwards at H+30. Marina lock operates in unison. Locks are closed when ht of tide falls to 1·5m above CD, usually at MLWS. At sp, yachts should not enter river until LW+2. Two large Or holding buoys below barrage in mid-stream; also, at W side of barrage lock, a landing pontoon (dries, foul ground). No ⓥ berths at SY & SAC pontoons close N of marina ent.
NAVIGATION
WPT SHM By, QG, Bell, 51°35'·50N 03°56'·06W, 200°/020° from/to E bkwtr lt, 0·92M. In Swansea Bay tidal streams flow anti-clockwise for 9½ hrs (Swansea HW −3½ to +6), with at times a race off Mumbles Hd. From HW−6 to −3 the stream reverses, setting N past Mumbles Hd towards Swansea. Keep seaward of Mixon Shoal. When N of SW Inner Green Grounds (SWIGG) SCM lt buoy, Q (6)+L Fl 15s, keep to W of dredged chan and clear of commercial ships. Yachts must motor in hbr and appr, max speed 4kn.
LIGHTS AND MARKS
Mumbles Hd, Fl (4) 20s 35m 16M, is 3M SSW of hbr ent. A conspic TV mast (R lts) NNE of hbr is almost aligned with the fairway. Ldg lts 020°: front Oc G 4s 5m 2M; rear FG 6M; these mark E side of chan dredged 3m. From E, keep well seaward of the inner fairway buoy (SHM, Fl G 2·5s).
Port Traffic sigs are conspic at W side of ent to King's Dock; there are 9 lts, Ⓡ or Ⓖ, arranged in a 3 x 3 frame. Yachts arriving must obey the middle lt in left column:
Ⓡ = Do not enter the river; hold SW of W Pier.
Ⓖ = Yachts may enter the river, keeping to mid-chan, then to W of holding buoys.
Lock Master will advise on tfc movements Ch 18.
Lock sigs for barrage and marina locks alike are:

2 Ⓡ	= Lock closed. Do not proceed
Ⓡ	= Wait
Ⓖ	= Enter with caution
Ⓡ Ⓖ }	= Free flow operating; proceed with caution

Barrage lock lit by 2FR/FG (vert) to seaward.
RADIO TELEPHONE
For barrage, call *Tawe Lock* Ch 18. For marina call *Swansea Marina* Ch 80. For commercial docks call *Swansea Docks Radio* VHF Ch14 (H24).
TELEPHONE (Dial code 01792)
Hr Mr 650855 Ext 260; Barrage 456014; MRCC 366534; Police 456999; ∰ 652373/4 and (01222) 763880 (H24); Marinecall 0891 500 459; Ⓗ 205666; Dr 653452; DVLA (for SSR) 783355.
FACILITIES
Swansea Marina (350+50 visitors) ☎ 470310, 🖢 463948, £13.23, D (no P), AC, FW, C (1 ton), BH (18 ton), Gas, Gaz, CH, ME, El, Ⓔ, Sh, Ⓞ, Ⓖ, Bar, R;
Swansea Yacht & Sub Aqua Club ☎ 654863, M, L, (no visitors' berths) FW, C (5 ton static), R, Bar;
Services: ME, SM, ACA, CH, El, Ⓔ, Sh.
City ME, El, Sh, CH, V, R, Bar, ✉, Ⓑ, ⇌, ✈.

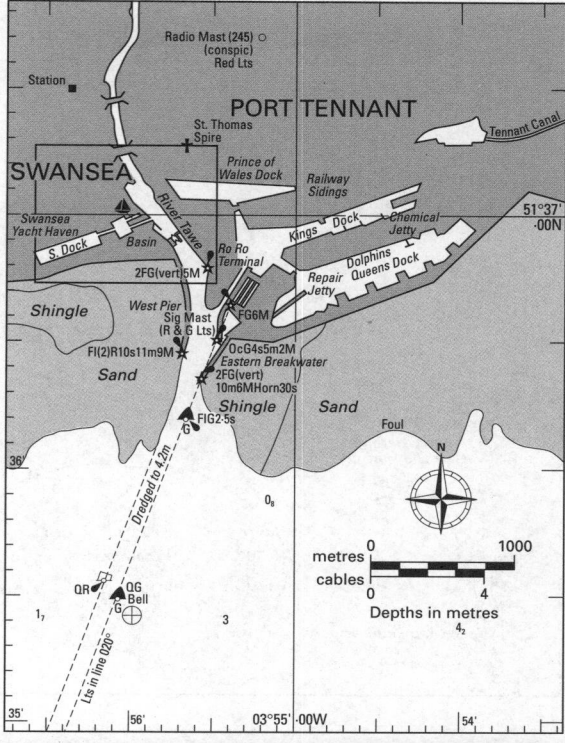

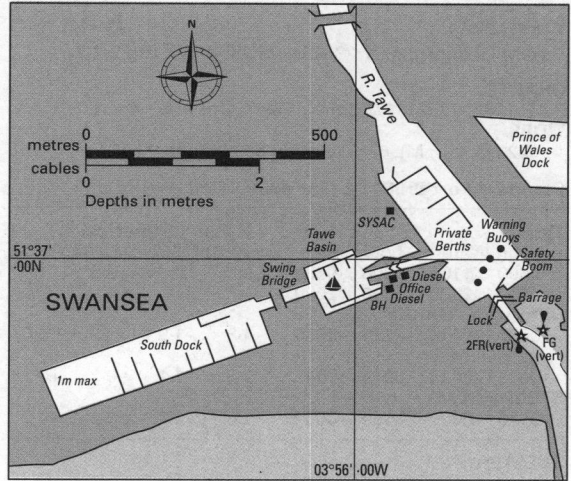

ADJACENT HARBOURS AND ANCHORAGES

MUMBLES, 51°34'·2N 03°58'·2W. Good ⚓ in W'lies 5ca N of Mumbles Hd lt ho. **Bristol Chan YC** ☎ (01792) 366000, Slip, M; **Mumbles YC** ☎ 369321, Slip, M, L, FW, C (hire).

R NEATH, 51°37'·85N 03°49'·9W. **Monkstone Marina**, on W bank just S of bridge, has about 1m. Ent over bar HW±2½ via 1·5M chan, marked/lit training wall. Facilities: AB, M, D, FW, Slip, BH (15 ton), R, Bar, Visitors welcome; **Monkstone C & SC,** ☎ (01792) 812229; VHF Ch M (occas).

PORTHCAWL, Bridgend, 51°28'·45N 03°41'·95W. AC 1169, *1165*. HW −0500 on Dover; ML 5·3m. See 8.11.17. A tiny drying hbr (access HW±2) protected by bkwtr running SE from Porthcawl Pt. Beware rk ledge (dries) W of bkwtr. Porthcawl lt ho, W 6-sided tr with B base, F WRG 10m 6/4M, vis G302°-036°, W036°-082°, R082°-122°; in line 094° with St Hilary radio mast (QR & FR) leads through Shord chan. Tidal streams can reach 6kn at sp off end of bkwtr. ⚓ approx 3ca SSE of lt ho. Hr Mr ☎ (01656) 782756, 3 ⚓s; Facilities: **Porthcawl Hbr B C** ☎ 782342. **Town** EC Wed; P & D (cans), CH, V, R, Bar, ✉, Ⓑ, ⇌ (Bridgend), ✈ (Cardiff).

11

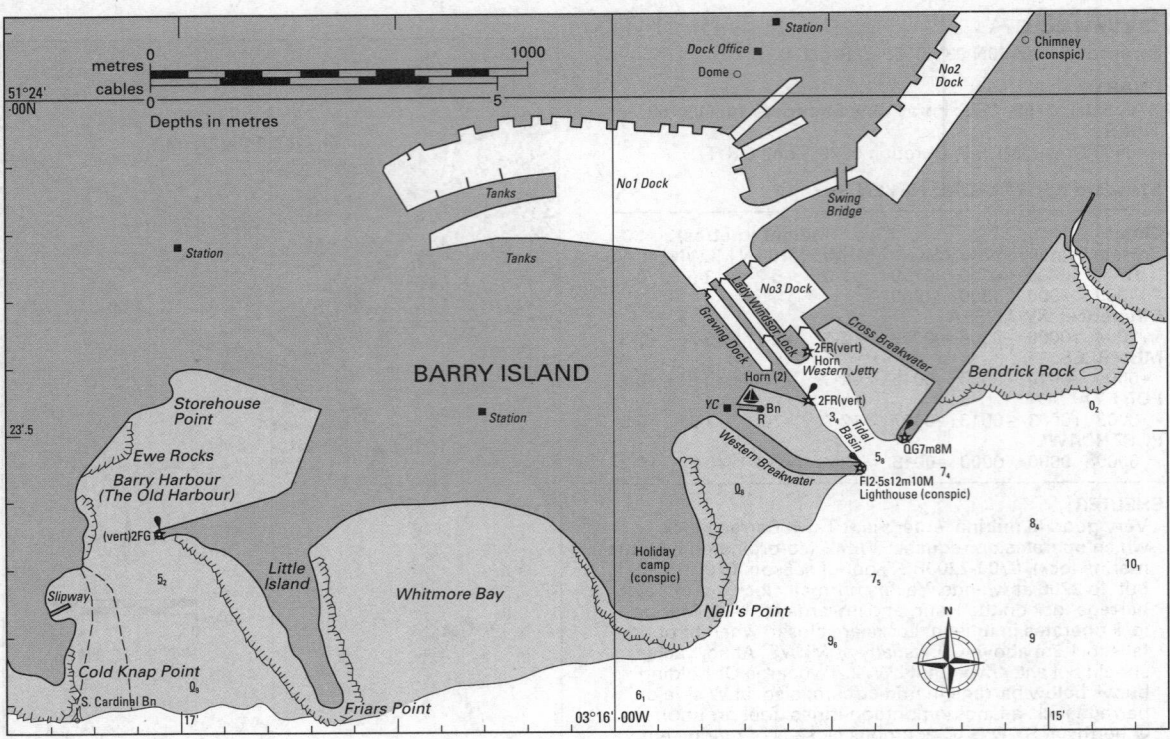

BARRY   8-11-18

Vale of Glamorgan 51°23'·45N 03°15'·37W   Rtg 2-2-2

CHARTS
AC 1182, *1152, 1179*; Imray C59; Stanfords 14; OS 171
TIDES
–0423 Dover; ML 6·1; Duration 0630; Zone 0 (UT)

Standard Port BRISTOL (AVONMOUTH) (→)

Times				Height (metres)			
High Water		Low Water		MHWS	MHWN	MLWN	MLWS
0600	1100	0300	0800	13·2	9·8	3·8	1·0
1800	2300	1500	2000				
Differences BARRY							
–0030	–0015	–0125	–0030	–1·8	–1·3	+0·2	0·0
FLAT HOLM							
–0015	–0015	–0045	–0045	–1·3	–1·1	–0·2	+0·2
STEEP HOLM							
–0020	–0020	–0050	–0050	–1·6	–1·2	–0·2	–0·2

SHELTER
Good, but in strong E/SE winds avoid Barry; No 1 Dock is
no longer available to pleasure craft. Access HW±3 to the
Outer hbr. No AB; pick up a mooring (free) and see YC.
The Old Hbr to W of Barry Island dries and is not used.
NAVIGATION
WPT 51°23'·00N 03°15'·00W, 152°/332° from/to ent, 0·53M.
Beware heavy merchant traffic. Approaching from E keep
well out from the shore. Strong tidal stream across ent.
LIGHTS AND MARKS
Welsh Water Barry West PHM buoy, Fl R 5s, and Merkur
PHM buoy, Fl R 2·5s, lie respectively 217°/1·5M and 191°/
1·65M from hbr ent. A SPM buoy, Fl Y 5s, 6ca E of hbr ent
marks sewer outfall. W bkwtr Fl 2·5s 10M. E bkwtr QG 8M.
RADIO TELEPHONE
Call: *Barry Radio* VHF Ch **11** 10 16 (HW–4 to HW+3). Tidal
info available on request.
TELEPHONE (Dial code 01446)
Hr Mr 700754; MRCC (01792) 366534; ⌗ (01222) 763880
(H24); Marinecall 0891 500 459; Police 734451; Dr 739543.
FACILITIES
Barry YC (130) ☎ 735511, access HW±3½, Slip, M, Bar, FW;
Services: Slip, D, FW, Gas, ME, El, Sh, CH, SM.
Town EC Wed; P (cans, 1M away), D, CH, V, R, Bar, ⊠, Ⓑ,
⇌, ✈ (Cardiff).

CARDIFF (Penarth)   8-11-19

Vale of Glamorgan 51°27'·10N 03°09'·55W   Rtg 3-2-1

CHARTS
AC 1182, *1176, 1179*; Imray C59; Stanfords 14; OS 171
TIDES
–0425 Dover; ML 6·4; Duration 0610; Zone 0 (UT)

Standard Port BRISTOL (AVONMOUTH) (→)

Times				Height (metres)			
High Water		Low Water		MHWS	MHWN	MLWN	MLWS
0600	1100	0300	0800	13·2	9·8	3·8	1·0
1800	2300	1500	2000				
Differences CARDIFF							
–0015	–0015	–0100	–0030	–1·0	–0·6	+0·1	0·0
NEWPORT							
–0020	–0010	0000	–0020	–1·1	–1·0	–0·6	–0·7
CHEPSTOW (River Wye)							
+0020	+0020	No data		No data		No data	

Note: At Newport the ht of LW does not normally fall below
MLWS. Tidal hts are based on a minimum river flow; max
flow may raise ht of LW by as much as 0·3m.

SHELTER
Very good in marina. Access H24, via marina lock which
is permanently open. Depth gauge on outer wall shows
ht of water above sill (3·5m above CD). See below for
details of the barrage locks. Waiting space in the hbr
outside the locks; or ‡ off Penarth seafront in W'lies; in
E'lies cramped ‡ off Alexandra Dock ent in 2m.
NAVIGATION
WPT 51°24'·00N 03°08'·73W (2½ca SW of S Cardiff SCM lt
buoy), 169°/349° from/to barrage locks, 2·9M. The outer
appr's from W or SW are via Breaksea lt float and N of
One Fathom Bank. Keep S of Lavernock Spit (SCM lt buoy)
and NW of Flat Holm and Wolves drying rk (NCM lt buoy).
From NE, drying ledges and shoals extend >1M offshore.
From E, appr via Monkstone lt ho and S Cardiff SCM lt
buoy. On the ldg line 349°, Ranny Spit (dries) is 3½ca to
the W, and Cardiff Grounds same distance to the E. The
Wrach Chan is buoyed/lit and dredged 1·2m; it passes
1½ca off Penarth Head. Do not impede merchant
shipping, which can be heavy.

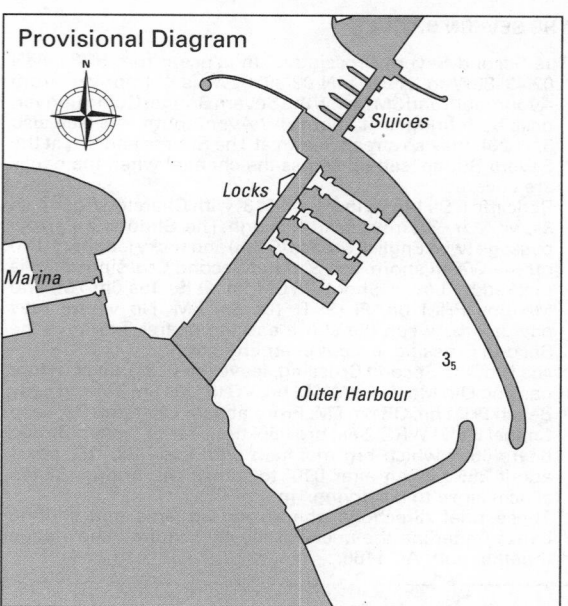

Provisional Diagram

CARDIFF *continued*

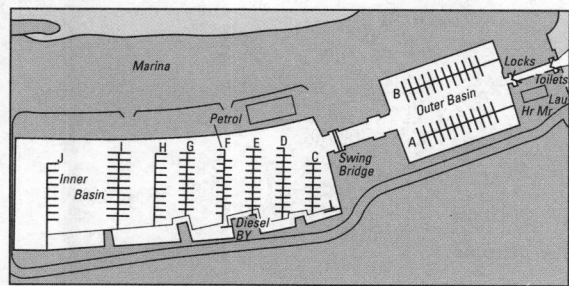

CARDIFF BAY BARRAGE
Construction of the barrage was completed at the end of
1998. Cardiff Bay, Penarth marina and some commercial
docks are entered by 3 barrage locks which are in use
H24; a toll is levied. The marina lock is permanently open.
The appr chan to the locks is dredged 2·5m; the outer hbr
adjacent to the locks is dredged 3·5m.
Note: Some of the above information is provisional, as is
the chartlet at upper right, showing the outer harbour,
barrage locks and approach to Penarth marina.
*When known, details of procedures at the new locks will
be published in the Supplement(s). A further chartlet will
be published when a hydrographic survey is available.*
LIGHTS AND MARKS
Ldg lts 349°, both FW 4/24m 17M, hard to identify due to
other adjacent lts; front ldg lt is obscured by the Barrage
at certain states of the tide.
RADIO TELEPHONE
Port VHF Ch **14** 11 16 (HW–4 to HW+3). *Barrage Control*
Ch 72. Penarth marina Ch 80.
TELEPHONE (Dial code 01222)
Hr Mr 471311; Marina 705021; MRCC (01792) 366534;
⌗ (01222) 763880 (H24); Marinecall 0891 500 459; Weather
Centre 397020; Police 373934; Dr 415258.
FACILITIES
Penarth Marina (350 + 50 visitors; max draft 3m),
☎ 705021, ⚓ 712170, £13.71, FW, AC, P (0930-1630), D
(Mon-Fri 0800-1700; Sat/Sun 1000-1400), El, ME, Sh, C,
CH, BY, Gas, ▣, R;
Penarth YC ☎ 708196, Slip, FW, Bar; **Cardiff YC**
☎ 387697, Slip, M, FW, L (floating pontoon), Bar;
Penarth MB & SC ☎ 226575, M, L, C, FW, Bar, Slip;
Services: D, SM, Sh, C (20 ton), CH, ACA, ME, El, Ⓔ, BY,
Slip, BH (10 ton), Gas.
City EC Wed; P, D, ME, El, V, R, Bar, ✉, Ⓑ, ≈, ✈.

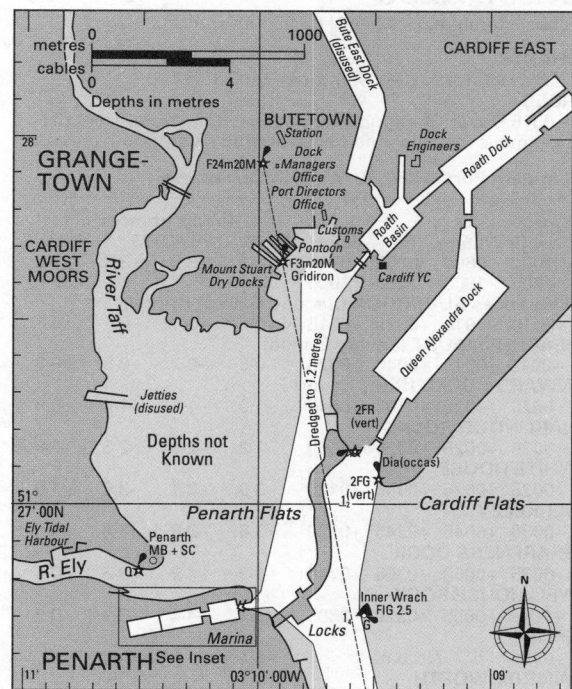

> ## NEW CARDIFF DIALLING CODE
> A new **Cardiff** dialling code will be intro-
> duced in 1999. It can be used in parallel
> with the existing code for at least a year.
> The new code 029 20 replaces the present
> dialling code. Thus existing 01222 926222
> becomes 029 20 926222.

ADJACENT HARBOUR
NEWPORT, Newport, 51°32′·95N 02°59′·13W. AC *1176,
1152, 1179*. HW –0425 on Dover; ML 6·0m; Duration 0620.
See 8.11.19. A commercial port controlled by ABP, but a
safe shelter for yachts. Enter R Usk over bar (approx
0·5m) E of West Usk buoy, QR Bell) and follow buoyed
and lit chan to S Lock ent; turn NE (ldg lts 057°) for yacht
moorings on S side between power stn pier and YC.
Beware overhead cables in Julian's Pill, clearance 3·8m.
East Usk lt ho Fl (2) WRG 10s 11m 15/11M, W284°-290°,
R290°-017°, W017°-037°, G037°-115°, W115°-120°. Ldg lts
057°, both FG. Alexandra Dock, S lock W pier head 2 FR
(vert) 9/7m 6M. E pier head 2 FG (vert) 9/7m 6M. Port VHF
Ch 16 09 69 **71** (HW ±4). VTS, not compulsory for yachts,
is on same chans/times, call *Newport Radio*. Hr Mr (ABP)
☎ (01633) 244411, ⚓ 221285. ⌗ ☎ 273709; Facilities:
Newport and Uskmouth SC Bar, M; **Services:** CH, El, ME,
Sh, Ⓔ. **Town** EC Thurs; all facilities.

THE SEVERN BRIDGES

The Second Severn Crossing (37m cl'nce), from 51°34'·88N 02°43'·80W to 51°34'·14N 02°39'·82W, is 4M upriver from Avonmouth and 3M below the Severn Bridge. Going upriver, pass both bridges at about HW Avonmouth −1¾ (see also 8.11.20); max sp stream is 8kn at The Shoots and 6kn at the Severn Bridge, setting across the channel when the banks are covered.

Redcliffe F Bu ldg lts in transit 013° with Charston Rock lt, Fl 3s, W ○ tr, B stripe, lead through The Shoots, a narrow passage twixt English Stones (6.2m) and rocky ledges (5·1m) off the Welsh shore. 5ca S of the Second Crossing, chan is marked by Lower Shoots WCM bn, Q (9) 15s 6m 7M, and Mixoms PHM bn, Fl (3) R 10s 6m 6M. No vessel may navigate between the shore and the nearer Tower of the Second Crossing, except in emergency.

4ca N of the Second Crossing, leave the 013° transit before passing Old Man's Hd WCM bn, VQ (9) 10s 6m 7M and Lady Bench PHM bn, QR 6m 6M. From abeam Charston Rk, keep Chapel Rk, Fl WRG 2·6s, brg 050° until E tr of Severn Bridge bears 068°; which brg maintain until Lyde Rk, QR, bears about 355°, when alter 010° to transit the bridge (36·6m cl'nce) close to rks drying 1m.

These brief directions, the strong streams and shifting banks underline the need for locally acquired knowledge together with AC 1166.

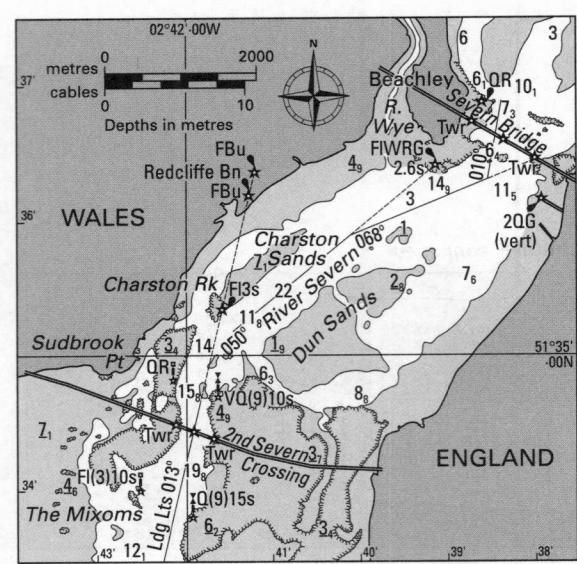

SHARPNESS   8-11-20

Gloucestershire 51°43'·00N 02°29'·00W   Rtg 3-3-2

CHARTS
AC 1166, Imray C59; Stanfords 14; OS 162
TIDES
−0315 Dover; Duration 0415; Zone 0 (UT). Note: The tidal regime is irregular and deviates from Avonmouth curve.

Standard Port BRISTOL (AVONMOUTH) (→)

Times				Height (metres)			
High Water		Low Water		MHWS	MHWN	MLWN	MLWS
0000	0600	0000	0700	13·2	9·8	3·8	1·0
1200	1800	1200	1900				
Differences SUDBROOK (Second Severn Bridge)							
+0010	+0010	+0025	+0015	+0·2	+0·1	−0·1	+0·1
BEACHLEY/AUST (Severn Bridge)							
+0010	+0015	+0040	+0025	−0·2	−0·2	−0·5	−0·3
INWARD ROCKS (River Severn)							
+0020	+0020	+0105	+0045	−1·0	−1·1	−1·4	−0·6
NARLWOOD ROCKS							
+0025	+0025	+0120	+0100	−1·9	−2·0	−2·3	−0·8
WHITE HOUSE							
+0025	+0025	+0145	+0120	−3·0	−3·1	−3·6	−1·0
BERKELEY							
+0030	+0045	+0245	+0220	−3·8	−3·9	−3·4	−0·5
SHARPNESS DOCK							
+0035	+0050	+0305	+0245	−3·9	−4·2	−3·3	−0·4
WELLHOUSE ROCK							
+0040	+0055	+0320	+0305	−4·1	−4·4	−3·1	−0·2
EPNEY							
+0130	No data			−9·4	No data		
MINSTERWORTH							
+0140	No data			−10·1	No data		
LLANTHONY							
+0215	No data			−10·7	No data		

SHELTER
Very good. The lock into Commercial Docks opens HW −2 to HW, but prompt arrival is not advised due to lack of water; the flood starts to make much later in the upper river. Pass 2 swing bridges for marina or Gloucester & Sharpness Canal.
NAVIGATION
WPT 51°42'·80N 02°29'·20W, 208°/028° from/to ent, 2ca. Leave King Road, Avonmouth (17M downriver) not before HW Sharpness −3, to be off hbr ent about HW −½. Stem strong flood S of F Bu lt; beware cross tide. Low-powered craft arriving any earlier may be unable to stem the tide. The fairway between King Road and Sharpness ent is defined as a narrow chan (Rule 9 of IRPCS). Small craft shall not impede the passage of commercial vessels.
LIGHTS AND MARKS
Berkeley Power Stn is conspic 1·5M S of lock. Lts as chartlet, but night passage not advised without local knowledge/pilot.

RADIO TELEPHONE
Call: *Sharpness Pierhead* VHF Ch **17** 16 (HW −6 to +2) for lock. Gloucester & Sharpness Canal Ch 74 for bridges; no locks.
TELEPHONE (Dial code 01453)
Pierhead 511968 (HW−6 to HW+2); Hr Mr 811862/64 (HO); ⌗ (01222) 763880 (H24); Marinecall 0891 500 459; MRCC (01792) 366534; Police 810477; Ⓗ 810777.
FACILITIES
Sharpness Marine (100+15) ☎ 811476, £4, AC, FW, Sh, CH, Gas; **Services:** ME, El, C. **Town** EC Sat; V, R, Bar, ✉, Ⓑ (Berkeley), ⇌ (Stonehouse), ✈ (Bristol). ACA, Gloucester.

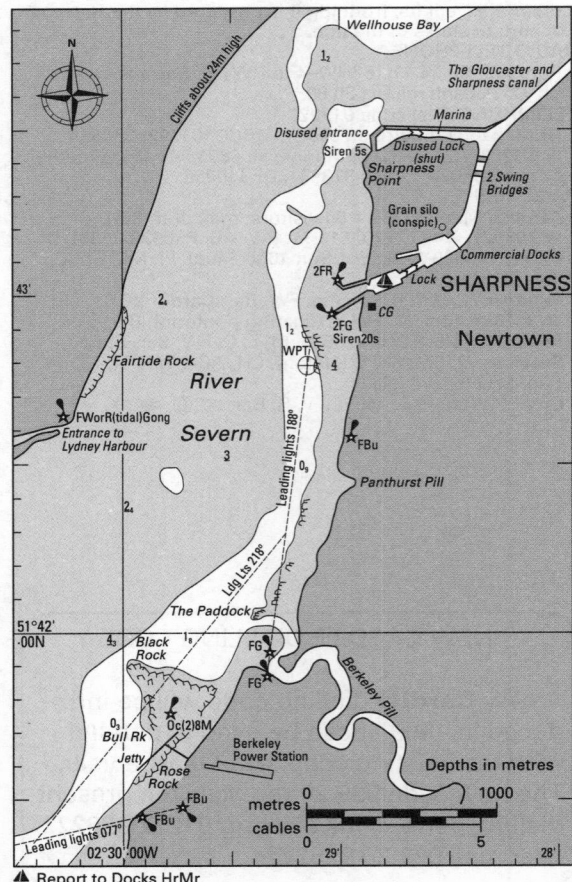

⚑ Report to Docks HrMr

TIME ZONE (UT)
For Summer Time add ONE hour in non-shaded areas

ENGLAND – PORT OF BRISTOL (AVONMOUTH)

LAT 51°30′N LONG 2°44′W

TIMES AND HEIGHTS OF HIGH AND LOW WATERS

YEAR **1999**

JANUARY

Day	Time	m		Day	Time	m
1 F	0031 / 0611 / 1300 / 1838	1.4 / 13.1 / 1.3 / 13.4		**16** SA	0024 / 0611 / 1248 / 1833	2.1 / 12.2 / 1.8 / 12.2
2 SA O	0125 / 0700 / 1353 / 1928	1.0 / 13.6 / 1.0 / 13.6		**17** SU ●	0114 / 0654 / 1338 / 1916	1.8 / 12.6 / 1.6 / 12.5
3 SU	0215 / 0748 / 1442 / 2015	0.8 / 13.8 / 0.9 / 13.7		**18** M	0201 / 0735 / 1424 / 1958	1.6 / 12.9 / 1.5 / 12.7
4 M	0302 / 0833 / 1527 / 2100	0.8 / 13.8 / 1.0 / 13.5		**19** TU	0244 / 0815 / 1507 / 2037	1.6 / 13.0 / 1.5 / 12.8
5 TU	0342 / 0916 / 1606 / 2141	1.1 / 13.5 / 1.4 / 13.0		**20** W	0322 / 0854 / 1544 / 2116	1.7 / 13.0 / 1.5 / 12.8
6 W	0415 / 0955 / 1635 / 2218	1.5 / 13.0 / 1.9 / 12.4		**21** TH	0353 / 0932 / 1615 / 2154	1.7 / 13.0 / 1.5 / 12.8
7 TH	0441 / 1031 / 1700 / 2251	1.9 / 12.3 / 2.3 / 11.8		**22** F	0423 / 1011 / 1647 / 2233	1.7 / 12.9 / 1.6 / 12.6
8 F	0509 / 1106 / 1729 / 2326	2.3 / 11.6 / 2.6 / 11.1		**23** SA	0457 / 1053 / 1723 / 2316	1.8 / 12.6 / 1.8 / 12.2
9 SA	0543 / 1146 / 1807	2.7 / 10.9 / 3.0		**24** SU	0535 / 1140 / 1805	2.0 / 12.1 / 2.2
10 SU	0009 / 0627 / 1238 / 1856	10.4 / 3.2 / 10.3 / 3.4		**25** M	0005 / 0620 / 1236 / 1855	11.6 / 2.5 / 11.4 / 2.7
11 M	0108 / 0725 / 1347 / 1957	10.0 / 3.6 / 10.0 / 3.7		**26** TU	0105 / 0719 / 1348 / 2006	11.0 / 3.2 / 10.9 / 3.2
12 TU	0224 / 0832 / 1501 / 2108	9.9 / 3.7 / 10.1 / 3.6		**27** W	0225 / 0859 / 1514 / 2156	10.7 / 3.5 / 10.9 / 3.2
13 W	0336 / 0945 / 1604 / 2222	10.2 / 3.4 / 10.5 / 3.2		**28** TH	0351 / 1039 / 1630 / 2311	10.9 / 3.1 / 11.4 / 2.6
14 TH	0435 / 1056 / 1659 / 2329	10.9 / 2.8 / 11.1 / 2.6		**29** F	0500 / 1146 / 1732	11.7 / 2.3 / 12.1
15 F	0526 / 1155 / 1748	11.6 / 2.2 / 11.7		**30** SA	0012 / 0557 / 1244 / 1826	1.9 / 12.5 / 1.6 / 12.8
				31 SU O	0108 / 0648 / 1338 / 1915	1.3 / 13.2 / 1.1 / 13.3

FEBRUARY

Day	Time	m		Day	Time	m
1 M	0159 / 0734 / 1428 / 2001	0.9 / 13.6 / 0.9 / 13.5		**16** TU ●	0142 / 0716 / 1408 / 1940	1.6 / 13.1 / 1.3 / 13.1
2 TU	0247 / 0818 / 1513 / 2043	0.7 / 13.7 / 0.8 / 13.5		**17** W	0231 / 0759 / 1455 / 2021	1.4 / 13.4 / 1.1 / 13.4
3 W	0328 / 0859 / 1551 / 2121	0.8 / 13.6 / 1.1 / 13.2		**18** TH	0313 / 0839 / 1535 / 2101	1.2 / 13.6 / 1.0 / 13.5
4 TH	0401 / 0934 / 1620 / 2153	1.2 / 13.2 / 1.5 / 12.8		**19** F	0349 / 0919 / 1609 / 2139	1.1 / 13.7 / 1.0 / 13.5
5 F	0425 / 1005 / 1639 / 2221	1.6 / 12.7 / 1.9 / 12.2		**20** SA	0419 / 0958 / 1638 / 2218	1.2 / 13.6 / 1.1 / 13.3
6 SA	0444 / 1034 / 1659 / 2250	1.9 / 12.1 / 2.2 / 11.6		**21** SU	0447 / 1038 / 1708 / 2257	1.3 / 13.2 / 1.4 / 12.7
7 SU	0510 / 1104 / 1726 / 2322	2.2 / 11.4 / 2.5 / 11.0		**22** M	0519 / 1120 / 1743 / 2341	1.7 / 12.4 / 1.9 / 11.9
8 M	0544 / 1140 / 1803	2.6 / 10.7 / 3.0		**23** TU	0558 / 1210 / 1826	2.3 / 11.5 / 2.7
9 TU	0003 / 0628 / 1230 / 1854	10.3 / 3.2 / 10.0 / 3.6		**24** W	0035 / 0648 / 1319 / 1926	11.0 / 3.1 / 10.6 / 3.5
10 W	0102 / 0733 / 1345 / 2009	9.8 / 3.8 / 9.6 / 3.9		**25** TH	0156 / 0813 / 1455 / 2131	10.3 / 3.8 / 10.3 / 3.7
11 TH	0230 / 0853 / 1512 / 2131	9.6 / 3.8 / 9.8 / 3.8		**26** F	0332 / 1022 / 1616 / 2253	10.4 / 3.5 / 10.7 / 3.0
12 F	0352 / 1010 / 1624 / 2247	10.1 / 3.4 / 10.5 / 3.1		**27** SA	0445 / 1130 / 1719 / 2354	11.1 / 2.6 / 11.6 / 2.1
13 SA	0455 / 1120 / 1721 / 2353	11.0 / 2.6 / 11.3 / 2.4		**28** SU	0544 / 1226 / 1813	12.1 / 1.7 / 12.5
14 SU	0547 / 1221 / 1811	11.9 / 2.0 / 12.1				
15 M	0049 / 0633 / 1316 / 1856	1.9 / 12.6 / 1.6 / 12.7				

MARCH

Day	Time	m		Day	Time	m
1 M	0048 / 0633 / 1319 / 1859	1.3 / 12.9 / 1.1 / 13.1		**16** TU	0024 / 0608 / 1253 / 1833	2.0 / 12.6 / 1.5 / 12.9
2 TU O	0139 / 0718 / 1407 / 1942	0.8 / 13.5 / 0.7 / 13.4		**17** W ●	0119 / 0654 / 1346 / 1918	1.5 / 13.3 / 1.1 / 13.5
3 W	0226 / 0759 / 1452 / 2021	0.6 / 13.6 / 0.7 / 13.5		**18** TH	0210 / 0737 / 1435 / 2000	1.1 / 13.8 / 0.8 / 13.9
4 TH	0307 / 0836 / 1529 / 2056	0.6 / 13.5 / 0.9 / 13.2		**19** F	0255 / 0820 / 1517 / 2041	0.8 / 14.1 / 0.6 / 14.0
5 F	0341 / 0908 / 1558 / 2125	0.9 / 13.2 / 1.4 / 12.9		**20** SA	0334 / 0901 / 1553 / 2121	0.7 / 14.2 / 0.6 / 14.0
6 SA	0404 / 0937 / 1614 / 2151	1.4 / 12.8 / 1.8 / 12.4		**21** SU	0406 / 0941 / 1623 / 2159	0.8 / 14.0 / 0.8 / 13.6
7 SU	0419 / 1003 / 1627 / 2216	1.7 / 12.3 / 2.0 / 11.9		**22** M	0435 / 1021 / 1651 / 2239	1.0 / 13.4 / 1.2 / 13.0
8 M	0438 / 1029 / 1648 / 2243	1.9 / 11.7 / 2.2 / 11.4		**23** TU	0504 / 1103 / 1722 / 2321	1.5 / 12.5 / 1.9 / 12.0
9 TU	0506 / 1057 / 1718 / 2315	2.2 / 11.0 / 2.6 / 10.7		**24** W	0540 / 1150 / 1802	2.3 / 11.4 / 2.8
10 W	0542 / 1136 / 1759	2.8 / 10.3 / 3.2		**25** TH	0013 / 0627 / 1259 / 1900	10.9 / 3.2 / 10.3 / 3.7
11 TH	0001 / 0634 / 1235 / 1901	10.0 / 3.5 / 9.6 / 3.9		**26** F	0137 / 0751 / 1441 / 2110	10.0 / 4.0 / 9.9 / 4.0
12 F	0114 / 0759 / 1408 / 2041	9.5 / 4.0 / 9.4 / 4.1		**27** SA	0316 / 1004 / 1558 / 2232	10.1 / 3.6 / 10.5 / 3.2
13 SA	0302 / 0930 / 1547 / 2210	9.7 / 3.7 / 10.0 / 3.5		**28** SU	0426 / 1109 / 1700 / 2332	10.9 / 2.6 / 11.4 / 2.2
14 SU	0421 / 1047 / 1653 / 2322	10.6 / 2.9 / 11.0 / 2.7		**29** M	0523 / 1203 / 1751	11.9 / 1.7 / 12.3
15 M	0519 / 1154 / 1746	11.6 / 2.1 / 12.0		**30** TU	0023 / 0611 / 1253 / 1836	1.4 / 12.7 / 1.1 / 12.9
				31 W O	0112 / 0654 / 1340 / 1917	0.8 / 13.2 / 0.7 / 13.3

APRIL

Day	Time	m		Day	Time	m
1 TH	0158 / 0733 / 1423 / 1954	0.6 / 13.4 / 0.7 / 13.3		**16** F ●	0143 / 0713 / 1408 / 1936	0.9 / 14.0 / 0.5 / 14.1
2 F	0240 / 0809 / 1501 / 2026	0.6 / 13.3 / 0.9 / 13.1		**17** SA	0230 / 0757 / 1453 / 2019	0.6 / 14.3 / 0.3 / 14.3
3 SA	0315 / 0840 / 1531 / 2055	0.9 / 13.0 / 1.4 / 12.8		**18** SU	0313 / 0841 / 1532 / 2101	0.4 / 14.3 / 0.4 / 14.2
4 SU	0340 / 0908 / 1549 / 2121	1.3 / 12.6 / 1.8 / 12.4		**19** M	0349 / 0924 / 1606 / 2142	0.5 / 14.0 / 0.7 / 13.8
5 M	0354 / 0934 / 1557 / 2146	1.6 / 12.2 / 2.0 / 12.0		**20** TU	0422 / 1006 / 1636 / 2222	0.9 / 13.4 / 1.2 / 13.0
6 TU	0410 / 0959 / 1617 / 2211	1.8 / 11.7 / 2.2 / 11.5		**21** W	0453 / 1048 / 1708 / 2305	1.5 / 12.4 / 1.9 / 12.0
7 W	0436 / 1027 / 1646 / 2243	2.0 / 11.2 / 2.3 / 11.0		**22** TH	0529 / 1137 / 1747 / 2358	2.3 / 11.3 / 2.8 / 10.9
8 TH	0510 / 1105 / 1724 / 2327	2.5 / 10.6 / 2.9 / 10.3		**23** F	0617 / 1244 / 1845	3.2 / 10.3 / 3.6
9 F	0556 / 1158 / 1815	3.1 / 9.9 / 3.6		**24** SA	0123 / 0735 / 1419 / 2033	10.1 / 3.8 / 9.9 / 4.0
10 SA	0029 / 0705 / 1314 / 1940	9.7 / 3.8 / 9.5 / 4.1		**25** SU	0252 / 0934 / 1531 / 2202	10.2 / 3.5 / 10.4 / 3.3
11 SU	0200 / 0847 / 1458 / 2130	9.7 / 3.7 / 9.9 / 3.7		**26** M	0357 / 1038 / 1630 / 2301	10.8 / 2.7 / 11.1 / 2.4
12 M	0340 / 1012 / 1618 / 2248	10.4 / 3.0 / 10.9 / 2.9		**27** TU	0453 / 1132 / 1721 / 2352	11.6 / 1.9 / 11.9 / 1.6
13 TU	0446 / 1123 / 1716 / 2353	11.5 / 2.1 / 12.0 / 2.0		**28** W	0541 / 1220 / 1806	12.3 / 1.3 / 12.6
14 W	0539 / 1223 / 1806	12.5 / 1.4 / 13.0		**29** TH	0040 / 0624 / 1307 / 1846	1.0 / 12.8 / 1.0 / 12.9
15 TH	0050 / 0627 / 1318 / 1852	1.4 / 13.4 / 0.9 / 13.7		**30** F O	0126 / 0703 / 1350 / 1922	0.8 / 13.0 / 0.9 / 13.0

11

Chart Datum: 6·50 metres below Ordnance Datum (Newlyn)

TIME ZONE (UT)
For Summer Time add ONE hour in non-shaded areas

ENGLAND – PORT OF BRISTOL (AVONMOUTH)

LAT 51°30'N   LONG   2°44'W

TIMES AND HEIGHTS OF HIGH AND LOW WATERS

YEAR 1999

MAY

Date	Time	m	Date	Time	m
1 SA	0208	0.8	**16** SU	0204	0.6
	0738	12.9		0736	14.2
	1429	1.1		1428	0.3
	1955	12.9		1957	14.3
2 SU	0245	1.1	**17** M	0251	0.4
	0811	12.6		0822	14.2
	1502	1.4		1512	0.4
	2026	12.6		2042	14.1
3 M	0314	1.4	**18** TU	0333	0.6
	0842	12.3		0908	13.9
	1524	1.8		1550	0.7
	2055	12.3		2126	13.7
4 TU	0333	1.7	**19** W	0411	0.9
	0910	12.0		0953	13.3
	1535	2.0		1625	1.2
	2121	11.9		2209	13.0
5 W	0349	1.8	**20** TH	0446	1.5
	0937	11.7		1037	12.4
	1555	2.0		1659	1.9
	2148	11.6		2254	12.1
6 TH	0416	1.9	**21** F	0523	2.2
	1007	11.3		1125	11.5
	1626	2.2		1738	2.6
	2223	11.2		2346	11.1
7 F	0451	2.2	**22** SA	0608	2.9
	1047	10.9		1225	10.6
	1704	2.6		1829	3.3
	2307	10.7			
8 SA	0535	2.7	**23** SU	0058	10.4
	1137	10.4		0708	3.4
	1752	3.2		1344	10.1
				1939	3.7
9 SU	0005	10.2	**24** M	0217	10.3
	0635	3.3		0831	3.5
	1244	10.0		1453	10.3
	1900	3.6		2109	3.4
10 M	0121	10.1	**25** TU	0320	10.7
	0802	3.4		0952	3.1
	1407	10.1		1552	10.8
	2041	3.6		2219	2.8
11 TU	0250	10.5	**26** W	0416	11.2
	0931	2.9		1051	2.4
	1534	10.9		1644	11.4
	2209	2.9		2314	2.1
12 W	0406	11.4	**27** TH	0505	11.8
	1047	2.2		1142	1.9
	1641	11.9		1731	12.0
	2319	2.1			
13 TH	0506	12.4	**28** F	0003	1.6
	1151	1.5		0549	12.2
	1736	12.8		1230	1.5
				1812	12.4
14 F	0019	1.4	**29** SA	0050	1.3
	0559	13.3		0630	12.4
	1248	0.9		1314	1.3
	1825	13.6		1850	12.6
15 SA	0114	0.9	**30** SU	0134	1.3
	0648	13.9		0708	12.4
	1340	0.5		1356	1.3
●	1912	14.1	O	1926	12.6
			31 M	0214	1.3
				0744	12.3
				1433	1.5
				2001	12.4

JUNE

Date	Time	m	Date	Time	m
1 TU	0249	1.5	**16** W	0321	0.7
	0819	12.1		0854	13.6
	1503	1.8		1539	0.7
	2034	12.2		2113	13.6
2 W	0317	1.8	**17** TH	0403	1.0
	0852	11.9		0941	13.2
	1523	2.0		1617	1.2
	2104	12.0		2158	13.1
3 TH	0338	1.9	**18** F	0441	1.4
	0923	11.7		1025	12.6
	1544	2.0		1651	1.7
	2135	11.8		2241	12.4
4 F	0406	2.0	**19** SA	0515	2.0
	0957	11.5		1109	11.8
	1615	2.1		1725	2.3
	2211	11.5		2327	11.6
5 SA	0441	2.1	**20** SU	0551	2.5
	1037	11.3		1156	11.0
	1653	2.3		1805	2.8
	2255	11.2			
6 SU	0524	2.4	**21** M	0020	10.9
	1124	11.0		0635	3.0
	1739	2.7		1253	10.4
	2348	10.9		1855	3.2
7 M	0618	2.7	**22** TU	0126	10.4
	1221	10.7		0728	3.3
	1838	3.1		1401	10.2
				1956	3.4
8 TU	0053	10.7	**23** W	0232	10.4
	0726	2.9		0831	3.3
	1331	10.6		1504	10.3
	1954	3.2		2105	3.3
9 W	0209	10.9	**24** TH	0331	10.6
	0848	2.8		0943	3.1
	1449	10.9		1601	10.7
	2127	2.9		2219	2.9
10 TH	0326	11.4	**25** F	0424	11.0
	1010	2.4		1052	2.6
	1604	11.6		1652	11.3
	2246	2.3		2320	2.3
11 F	0434	12.1	**26** SA	0513	11.5
	1120	1.8		1148	2.1
	1706	12.5		1738	11.8
	2350	1.7			
12 SA	0533	12.9	**27** SU	0012	1.8
	1220	1.2		0558	11.8
	1801	13.2		1238	1.7
				1820	12.2
13 SU	0048	1.1	**28** M	0100	1.5
	0626	13.4		0639	12.1
	1316	0.8		1324	1.6
●	1851	13.7	O	1901	12.4
14 M	0143	0.8	**29** TU	0145	1.5
	0717	13.8		0720	12.1
	1408	0.6		1407	1.6
	1939	14.0		1940	12.4
15 TU	0234	0.6	**30** W	0228	1.6
	0806	13.8		0800	12.1
	1456	0.5		1446	1.7
	2027	13.9		2017	12.3

JULY

Date	Time	m	Date	Time	m
1 TH	0305	1.7	**16** F	0355	0.9
	0838	12.0		0926	13.3
	1518	1.9		1608	1.0
	2052	12.2		2142	13.3
2 F	0337	1.8	**17** SA	0432	1.3
	0913	12.0		1007	12.8
	1543	2.0		1640	1.5
	2127	12.1		2222	12.7
3 SA	0405	1.9	**18** SU	0501	1.7
	0949	11.9		1045	12.2
	1612	2.0		1707	1.9
	2203	12.0		2259	12.0
4 SU	0437	1.9	**19** M	0527	2.2
	1027	11.8		1121	11.5
	1647	2.0		1737	2.4
	2244	11.8		2336	11.3
5 M	0516	2.0	**20** TU	0559	2.6
	1111	11.6		1200	10.8
	1728	2.2		1815	2.8
	2332	11.5			
6 TU	0602	2.2	**21** W	0021	10.6
	1201	11.3		0641	3.0
	1818	2.6		1250	10.2
				1904	3.3
7 W	0028	11.2	**22** TH	0122	10.1
	0656	2.5		0735	3.4
	1301	11.0		1358	9.9
	1918	2.4		2007	3.6
8 TH	0136	11.0	**23** F	0234	10.0
	0805	2.8		0839	3.5
	1412	10.9		1510	10.1
	2042	3.1		2117	3.4
9 F	0254	11.1	**24** SA	0340	10.3
	0935	2.7		0952	3.2
	1532	11.2		1612	10.6
	2217	2.8		2231	3.0
10 SA	0408	11.6	**25** SU	0438	10.8
	1054	2.3		1104	2.7
	1642	11.9		1707	11.3
	2329	2.1		2335	2.3
11 SU	0513	12.2	**26** M	0529	11.4
	1159	1.7		1204	2.2
	1742	12.6		1755	11.9
12 M	0030	1.5	**27** TU	0030	1.8
	0610	12.9		0616	11.8
	1257	1.2		1256	1.8
	1835	13.3		1839	12.3
13 TU	0127	1.1	**28** W	0121	1.6
	0703	13.3		0700	12.2
	1352	0.8		1346	1.7
●	1925	13.7	O	1921	12.6
14 W	0221	0.8	**29** TH	0210	1.5
	0753	13.5		0742	12.3
	1443	0.7		1432	1.7
	2013	13.8		2001	12.4
15 TH	0311	0.7	**30** F	0254	1.5
	0841	13.5		0823	12.4
	1529	0.7		1512	1.7
	2059	13.7		2039	12.7
			31 SA	0333	1.6
				0901	12.4
				1544	1.8
				2116	12.7

AUGUST

Date	Time	m	Date	Time	m
1 SU	0405	1.6	**16** M	0439	1.6
	0937	12.5		1015	12.4
	1611	1.8		1644	1.8
	2152	12.6		2226	12.3
2 M	0433	1.6	**17** TU	0457	2.1
	1014	12.4		1043	11.8
	1640	1.8		1705	2.1
	2231	12.4		2255	11.5
3 TU	0505	1.7	**18** W	0521	2.4
	1054	12.2		1114	11.1
	1715	1.9		1735	2.6
	2314	12.1		2329	10.8
4 W	0542	2.0	**19** TH	0553	2.9
	1139	11.7		1153	10.4
	1756	2.3		1815	3.2
5 TH	0004	11.5	**20** F	0014	10.0
	0627	2.4		0639	3.4
	1233	11.2		1249	9.7
	1847	2.9		1913	3.8
6 F	0107	10.9	**21** SA	0126	9.5
	0726	3.0		0746	3.9
	1342	10.7		1414	9.5
	2000	3.4		2030	4.0
7 SA	0229	10.6	**22** SU	0256	9.5
	0904	3.3		0907	3.8
	1508	10.7		1536	10.0
	2159	3.3		2150	3.5
8 SU	0352	10.9	**23** M	0407	10.2
	1036	2.8		1026	3.3
	1625	11.3		1638	10.8
	2316	2.6		2304	2.8
9 M	0501	11.6	**24** TU	0504	11.0
	1144	2.1		1135	2.5
	1729	12.1		1731	11.7
10 TU	0018	1.8	**25** W	0005	2.0
	0559	12.4		0553	11.8
	1243	1.4		1232	2.0
	1823	12.9		1817	12.4
11 W	0115	1.1	**26** TH	0100	1.6
	0651	13.0		0639	12.4
	1338	0.9		1325	1.7
●	1913	13.5	O	1900	12.8
12 TH	0208	0.7	**27** F	0151	1.3
	0740	13.4		0722	12.7
	1428	0.6		1415	1.5
	1959	13.8		1942	13.1
13 F	0256	0.6	**28** SA	0239	1.2
	0825	13.5		0803	12.9
	1514	0.6		1459	1.4
	2042	13.8		2021	13.2
14 SA	0339	0.7	**29** SU	0321	1.2
	0907	13.4		0842	13.0
	1553	0.8		1536	1.5
	2122	13.5		2059	13.3
15 SU	0415	1.1	**30** M	0355	1.3
	0943	13.0		0920	13.0
	1623	1.3		1604	1.5
	2156	12.9		2136	13.2
			31 TU	0423	1.4
				0956	12.9
				1630	1.6
				2214	12.9

Chart Datum: 6·50 metres below Ordnance Datum (Newlyn)

TIME ZONE (UT)
For Summer Time add ONE hour in non-shaded areas

ENGLAND – PORT OF BRISTOL (AVONMOUTH)

LAT 51°30′N   LONG 2°44′W

TIMES AND HEIGHTS OF HIGH AND LOW WATERS   YEAR **1999**

SEPTEMBER

Day	Time m	Time m	Time m	Time m
1 W	0450 1.6	1035 12.6	1659 1.8	2255 12.3
2 TH	0521 1.9	1117 11.9	1735 2.3	2341 11.5
3 F	0600 2.6	1207 11.1	1820 3.1	
4 SA	0042 10.6	0653 3.3	1317 10.3	1927 3.8
5 SU	0214 10.1	0847 3.8	1456 10.2	2152 3.7
6 M	0343 10.5	1025 3.2	1615 10.9	2306 2.8
7 TU	0452 11.3	1130 2.3	1718 11.9	2339 2.2
8 W	0004 1.8	0547 12.3	1227 1.4	1810 12.9
9 TH ●	0058 1.0	0637 13.0	1319 0.8	1857 13.5
10 F	0148 0.6	0721 13.5	1407 0.5	1940 13.8
11 SA	0234 0.4	0803 13.6	1452 0.4	2020 13.8
12 SU	0316 0.6	0841 13.4	1530 0.7	2056 13.5
13 M	0350 1.1	0914 13.0	1559 1.2	2126 12.9
14 TU	0413 1.7	0942 12.5	1617 1.8	2153 12.3
15 W	0425 2.1	1007 11.9	1633 2.1	2218 11.7
16 TH	0441 2.4	1034 11.3	1656 2.5	2245 10.9
17 F	0507 2.8	1104 10.6	1728 3.0	2319 10.2
18 SA	0543 3.4	1146 9.8	1815 3.8	
19 SU	0013 9.4	0639 4.1	1301 9.2	1938 4.3
20 M	0201 9.1	0821 4.4	1500 9.5	2113 4.0
21 TU	0337 9.7	0952 3.8	1610 10.4	2234 3.2
22 W	0438 10.7	1107 2.9	1704 11.4	2339 2.2
23 TH	0529 11.8	1206 2.1	1752 12.4	
24 F	0035 1.6	0614 12.6	1300 1.6	1835 13.1
25 SA O	0127 1.2	0657 13.1	1351 1.4	1917 13.5
26 SU	0215 1.0	0739 13.5	1436 1.2	1958 13.7
27 M	0258 0.9	0819 13.6	1516 1.1	2038 13.8
28 TU	0335 1.0	0858 13.6	1549 1.2	2117 13.7
29 W	0405 1.2	0936 13.3	1617 1.4	2157 13.2
30 TH	0433 1.5	1016 12.8	1645 1.8	2238 12.5

OCTOBER

Day	Time m	Time m	Time m	Time m
1 F	0502 2.0	1057 12.0	1718 2.4	2323 11.5
2 SA	0538 2.8	1147 11.0	1801 3.3	
3 SU	0024 10.4	0630 3.6	1303 10.1	1913 4.1
4 M	0207 9.8	0839 4.1	1447 10.1	2141 3.8
5 TU	0332 10.3	1009 3.4	1600 10.9	2248 2.8
6 W	0435 11.2	1110 2.3	1659 11.9	2343 1.8
7 TH	0529 12.2	1203 1.4	1750 12.8	
8 F	0033 1.0	0615 13.0	1253 0.8	1834 13.4
9 SA ●	0121 0.6	0657 13.4	1340 0.5	1915 13.7
10 SU	0206 0.5	0736 13.5	1423 0.5	1953 13.6
11 M	0246 0.7	0812 13.3	1502 0.8	2027 13.3
12 TU	0320 1.2	0843 12.9	1532 1.3	2056 12.8
13 W	0344 1.8	0910 12.5	1551 1.8	2123 12.3
14 TH	0354 2.2	0935 11.9	1603 2.1	2147 11.7
15 F	0408 2.3	1000 11.4	1624 2.4	2213 11.1
16 SA	0432 2.6	1028 10.8	1655 2.8	2245 10.4
17 SU	0506 3.1	1107 10.1	1735 3.5	2332 9.7
18 M	0552 3.9	1206 9.4	1839 4.2	
19 TU	0048 9.1	0711 4.5	1354 9.3	2027 4.2
20 W	0252 9.5	0909 4.2	1532 10.1	2155 3.5
21 TH	0404 10.5	1030 3.3	1631 11.2	2305 2.5
22 F	0458 11.6	1133 2.4	1721 12.3	
23 SA	0003 1.7	0545 12.6	1229 1.7	1807 13.1
24 SU O	0056 1.2	0630 13.3	1320 1.3	1851 13.7
25 M	0145 0.9	0713 13.8	1407 1.0	1934 14.0
26 TU	0231 0.7	0755 14.0	1450 0.9	2017 14.1
27 W	0311 0.7	0836 14.0	1529 1.0	2059 13.9
28 TH	0346 1.0	0918 13.7	1603 1.2	2142 13.4
29 F	0418 1.4	1000 13.0	1635 1.7	2225 12.6
30 SA	0450 2.0	1043 12.2	1710 2.4	2312 11.5
31 SU	0527 2.8	1135 11.1	1755 3.3	

NOVEMBER

Day	Time m	Time m	Time m	Time m
1 M	0014 10.5	0620 3.7	1253 10.3	1909 4.0
2 TU	0150 10.0	0808 4.1	1428 10.3	2114 3.8
3 W	0307 10.3	0941 3.5	1535 10.9	2219 2.9
4 TH	0408 11.1	1041 2.6	1632 11.7	2313 2.0
5 F	0501 12.0	1133 1.7	1722 12.5	
6 SA	0002 1.3	0547 12.7	1222 1.1	1806 13.0
7 SU	0049 1.0	0629 13.1	1308 0.8	1847 13.4
8 M ●	0133 0.9	0707 13.2	1351 0.8	1924 13.2
9 TU	0214 1.0	0742 13.1	1430 1.1	1958 12.9
10 W	0249 1.3	0814 12.8	1503 1.5	2030 12.6
11 TH	0316 1.8	0843 12.4	1527 1.9	2058 12.1
12 F	0331 2.2	0911 12.0	1542 2.2	2125 11.7
13 SA	0345 2.3	0936 11.5	1603 2.4	2152 11.3
14 SU	0411 2.5	1006 11.1	1634 2.6	2226 10.8
15 M	0445 2.8	1046 10.6	1714 3.1	2312 10.2
16 TU	0528 3.4	1138 10.0	1808 3.6	
17 W	0013 9.8	0628 4.0	1251 9.7	1928 3.9
18 TH	0136 9.7	0804 4.1	1428 10.1	2103 3.6
19 F	0311 10.3	0940 3.5	1546 11.0	2221 2.8
20 SA	0418 11.4	1052 2.7	1645 12.0	2326 2.0
21 SU	0513 12.4	1153 2.0	1736 12.9	
22 M	0023 1.4	0601 13.2	1248 1.4	1824 13.6
23 TU O	0115 0.9	0647 13.8	1339 1.0	1911 14.0
24 W	0204 0.7	0733 14.1	1427 0.8	1958 14.2
25 TH	0249 0.6	0818 14.2	1511 0.8	2044 14.0
26 F	0330 0.8	0903 13.9	1552 1.1	2130 13.5
27 SA	0407 1.2	0948 13.3	1630 1.6	2215 12.8
28 SU	0443 1.8	1034 12.5	1708 2.2	2303 11.9
29 M	0521 2.5	1125 11.6	1751 2.9	2359 11.0
30 TU	0609 3.2	1231 10.8	1847 3.5	

DECEMBER

Day	Time m	Time m	Time m	Time m
1 W	0115 10.4	0715 3.7	1353 10.6	2011 3.7
2 TH	0230 10.3	0848 3.7	1500 10.8	2135 3.4
3 F	0332 10.8	1000 3.1	1557 11.3	2234 2.8
4 SA	0426 11.4	1056 2.5	1649 11.8	2326 2.1
5 SU	0515 12.0	1147 1.9	1735 12.3	
6 M	0014 1.7	0558 12.5	1234 1.5	1817 12.6
7 TU ●	0059 1.4	0637 12.8	1318 1.3	1856 12.7
8 W	0141 1.3	0714 12.8	1400 1.4	1933 12.6
9 TH	0219 1.5	0749 12.7	1437 1.6	2008 12.4
10 F	0252 1.8	0823 12.4	1508 1.9	2041 12.1
11 SA	0316 2.1	0854 12.1	1531 2.1	2111 11.8
12 SU	0334 2.3	0923 11.8	1553 2.3	2142 11.5
13 M	0400 2.3	0955 11.5	1624 2.4	2216 11.3
14 TU	0434 2.5	1033 11.2	1702 2.6	2258 11.0
15 W	0515 2.8	1120 10.8	1749 2.9	2349 10.6
16 TH	0606 3.2	1219 10.5	1848 3.3	
17 F	0052 10.4	0711 3.6	1330 10.5	2003 3.4
18 SA	0208 10.5	0838 3.5	1451 10.9	2131 3.1
19 SU	0330 11.1	1007 3.0	1605 11.6	2248 2.5
20 M	0438 11.9	1119 2.3	1707 12.4	2352 1.8
21 TU	0535 12.8	1220 1.7	1802 13.2	
22 W O	0049 1.2	0626 13.5	1316 1.2	1853 13.7
23 TH	0142 0.9	0716 14.0	1409 0.9	1943 14.0
24 F	0232 0.7	0804 14.1	1459 0.8	2032 13.9
25 SA	0318 0.7	0851 14.0	1544 0.9	2119 13.7
26 SU	0400 1.0	0937 13.6	1625 1.3	2205 13.2
27 M	0437 1.5	1022 13.0	1702 1.8	2249 12.4
28 TU	0512 2.0	1108 12.3	1737 2.3	2334 11.6
29 W	0549 2.6	1157 11.5	1816 2.9	
30 TH	0027 10.9	0633 3.1	1259 10.8	1903 3.3
31 F	0134 10.3	0728 3.5	1410 10.5	2003 3.6

11

Chart Datum: 6·50 metres below Ordnance Datum (Newlyn)

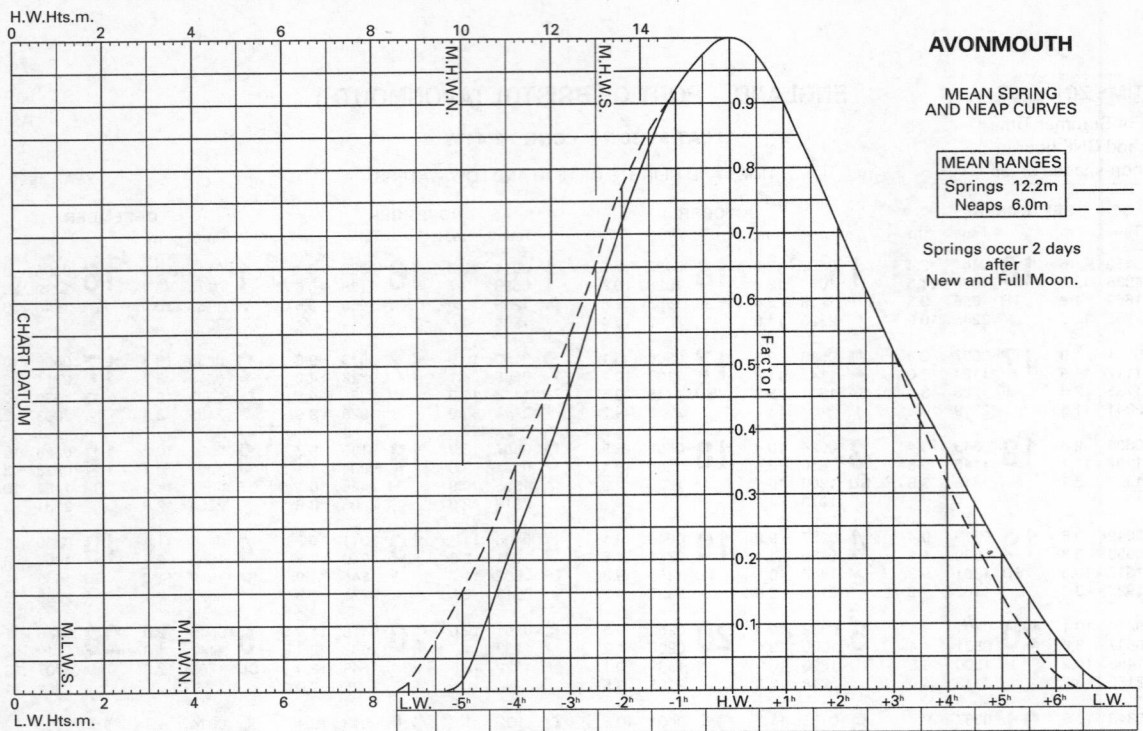

AVONMOUTH

MEAN SPRING
AND NEAP CURVES

| MEAN RANGES |
| Springs 12.2m ——— |
| Neaps 6.0m - - - - |

Springs occur 2 days
after
New and Full Moon.

BRISTOL (CITY DOCKS)   8-11-21

City of Bristol 51°26'·92N 02°37'·36W   Rtg 3-1-1

CHARTS
AC 1859, *1176, 1179*; Imray C59; Stanfords 14; OS 172
TIDES
−0410 on Dover; ML 7·0; Duration 0620; Zone 0 (UT)

Standard Port BRISTOL (AVONMOUTH) (←—)

Times				Height (metres)			
High Water		Low Water		MHWS	MHWN	MLWN	MLWS
0200	0800	0300	0800	13·2	9·8	3·8	1·0
1400	2000	1500	2000				
Differences SHIREHAMPTON (River Avon)							
+0000	−0000	+0035	+0010	−0·7	−0·7	−0·8	0·0
SEA MILLS							
+0005	+0005	+0105	+0030	−1·4	−1·5	−1·7	−0·1
CUMBERLAND BASIN (Ent)							
+0010	+0010	Dries out		−2·9	−3·0	Dries out	

NOTE: The Port of Bristol (Avonmouth) is a Standard Port and predictions for each day are given above. Predictions are for the ent to Royal Portisbury Dock.
SHELTER
Excellent in Harbour and marina. For R Avon, Cumberland Basin & Bristol Hbr refer to *Bristol Harbour: Info for Boat Owners*, (from Hr Mr). Pill Creek has drying moorings.
NAVIGATION
Avonmouth WPT 51°30'·42N 02°43'·25W, 307°/127° from/ to front ldg lt, 0·61M. The chan from Flatholm is buoyed. See R/T below for compliance with VTS and reporting. Avonmouth, Royal Portbury and Portishead Docks are prohib to yachts, except in emergency. Tidal stream across ent can run at >5kn. Best to reach ent lock into Cumberland Basin by HW (approx 7M upriver from WPT); waiting pontoon (dries). Ent lock opens at HW−2½, −1½ and −¼hr for arrivals; departing craft lock out approx 15 mins after these times. Swing bridge opens in unison with lock, but not during road tfc rush hrs 0800-0900 and 1700-1800 Mon-Fri. Inner (Junction) lock is always open, except if ht of HW >9·5m ('stopgate' tide) when it closes.

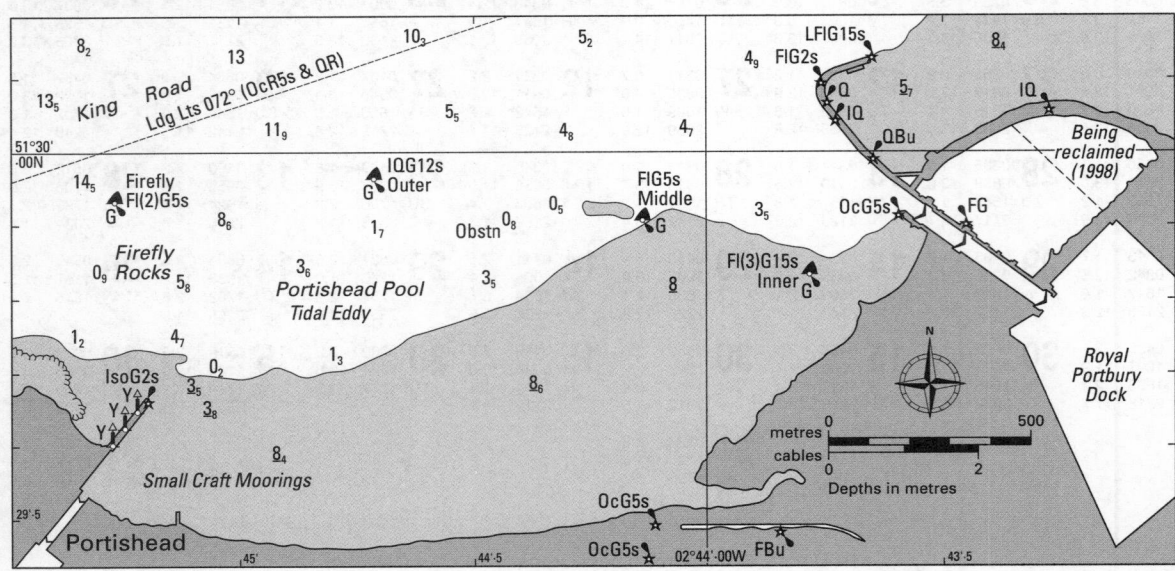

LIGHTS AND MARKS

R Avon ent is abeam S pier lt Oc RG 30s, vis R294°-036°, G036°-194°. Ldg lts 127° both FR. St George ldg lts 173°, both Oc G 5s synch, Or daymarks. Above Pill Creek SHM lts are Oc G 5s, and PHM are mostly FY.

Ent sigs to Bristol Hbr are on E bank, 1½ and 2½ca beyond Clifton Suspension Bridge: ⑤ = continue with caution; ⑧ = stop and await orders.

Bridges: Prince St and Redcliffe bridges are manned 0600-2230 summer, 0900-1645 winter. Other bridges HW–3 to +1. Pre-notify Bridgemaster ☎ 9299338, or sound ·—·(R).

RADIO TELEPHONE

Yachts bound to/from Bristol should call *Avonmouth Radio* VHF Ch **12** 09 at English and Welsh Grounds SWM buoy and at Welsh Hook PHM buoy; comply with any VTS orders. On entering R Avon call again, low power, stating that you are bound for City Docks. (If no radio fitted, sig Avonmouth Sig Stn with Flag R or flash morse R (·—·). The sig stn will reply by light or loud hailer). Keep well clear of large vessels.

At Black Rks (0·8M to run) call *City Docks Radio* Ch **14** 11 (HW–3 to HW+1) for locking instructions.

For berths, call *Bristol Hbr* Ch 73 16 (HO), and/or Bristol Marina Ch **80** M. Prince St bridge, Netham lock Ch 73.

TELEPHONE (Dial code 0117)

Hr Mr 9264797; Dock Master, Cumberland Basin 9273633; Prince St & Redcliffe Bridges 9299338; Netham Lock 9776590; ⌗ (01222) 763880 (H24); MRCC (01792) 366534; Weather 9279298; Marinecall 0891 500 459; Police 9277777; Ⓗ 9230000.

FACILITIES

Portishead CC (Pill Creek), M; **Bristol Hbr** ☎ 9264797, AB £7.00; gridiron outside Cumberland Basin;
Bristol Marina (150, inc Ⓥ) ☎ 9265730, £7.74, AC, D, FW, access HW–3 to +1, El, ME, Sh, SM, Slip, C, BH (30 ton), Ⓚ;
Baltic Wharf Leisure Centre ☎ 9297608, Slip, L, Bar;
Cabot Cruising Club ☎ 9268318, M, L, FW, AB, Bar;
Portavon Marina ☎ 9861626, Slip, M, FW, ME, Sh, CH, R;
Services: C (8 ton), FW, ME, El, Sh, CH, Ⓔ, ACA, P, D.
City EC Wed/Sat; all facilities, ✉, Ⓑ, ⇌, ✈.

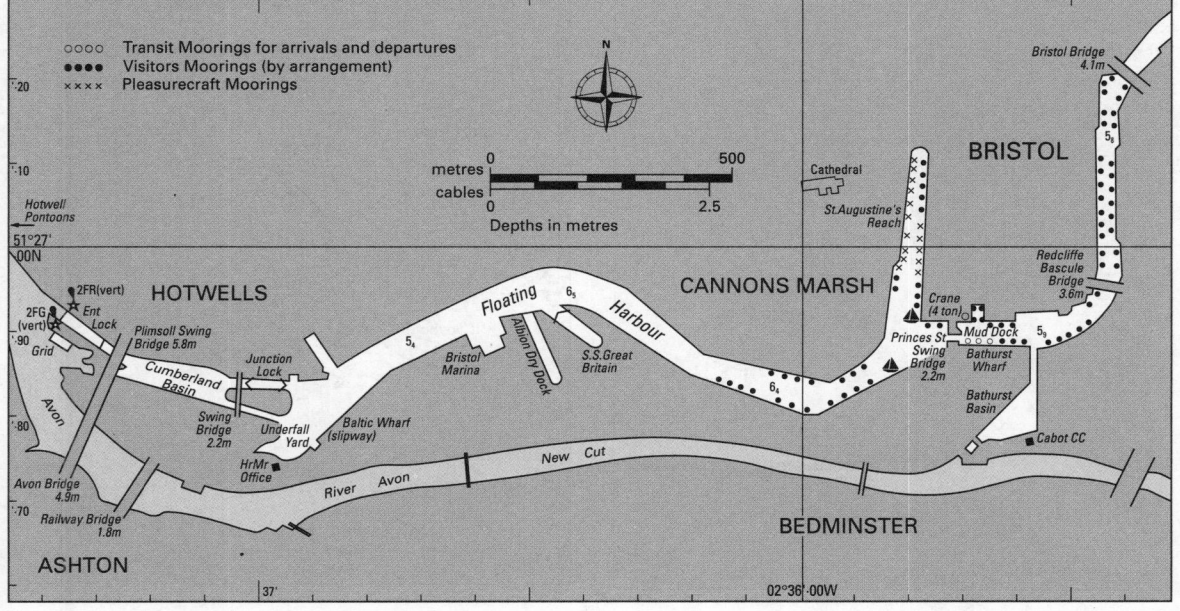

AGENTS WANTED

If you are interested in becoming our agent for any of the following ports, please write to: The Editor, Edington House, Trent, Sherborne, Dorset DT9 4SR, England – and get your free copy of the Almanac annually. You do not have to live in a port to be the agent, but should at least be a fairly regular visitor.

Plymouth	Port Haliguen
Walton-on-the-Naze	La Trinité-sur-Mer
Hopeman	Piriac
Burghead	St Nazaire/Loire
Findhorn	Pornic
Nairn	St Gilles-Croix-de-Vie
Inverness	Les Sables d'Olonne
Loch Aline	River Seudre
Craobh	Port Bloc/Gironde
Workington	Anglet/Bayonne
Lough Swilly	St Jean-de-Luz
Portbail	Hendaye
St Malo/Dinard	Grandcamp-Maisy
Le Légué/St Brieuc	Port-en-Bessin
Lampaul	Ouistreham/Caen
L'Aberildut	Dives
Douarnenez	St Valéry-en-Caux
Lorient	Dunkerque
River Étel	Emden
Le Palais (Belle Ile)	Langeoog

11

PORTISHEAD   8-11-22
Somerset 51°29'·53N 02°45'·33W

CHARTS
AC 1859, *1176*; Imray C59; Stanfords 14; OS 171/2
TIDES
−0405 Dover; ML 6·8; Zone 0 (UT)

Standard Port BRISTOL (AVONMOUTH) (←)

Times				Height (metres)			
High Water		Low Water		MHWS	MHWN	MLWN	MLWS
0200	0800	0300	0800	13·2	9·8	3·8	1·0
1400	2000	1500	2000				
Differences PORTISHEAD							
−0002	0000	No data		−0·1	−0·1	No data	
CLEVEDON							
−0010	−0020	−0025	−0015	−0·4	−0·2	+0·2	0·0
ST THOMAS HEAD							
0000	0000	−0030	−0030	−0·4	−0·2	+0·1	+0·1
ENGLISH AND WELSH GROUNDS							
−0008	−0008	−0030	−0030	−0·5	−0·8	−0·3	0·0
WESTON-SUPER-MARE							
−0020	−0030	−0130	−0030	−1·2	−1·0	−0·8	−0·2

SHELTER
Good in marina which is due to open spring 1999. Latest info from Crest Nicholson ☎ 0117 9236466. Phase I = six pontoons and 120 berths. Access HW±3½, via lock 134m x 20m. Dock is 550m x 106m. *Details will be in the Supplements, as available.*
NAVIGATION
WPT 51°29'·93N 02°45'·27W, Firefly SHM buoy, Fl (2) G 5s, 348°/168° from/to pier hd, 500m. Firefly Rks (0·9m) are close W of the 168° appr track. Appr's dry to mud and are exposed to N/NE winds. Close inshore a W-going eddy begins at HW −3 whilst the flood is still making E.
LIGHTS AND MARKS
Portishead Pt, Q (3) 10s9m 16M, is 7ca W of Portishead pierhd, Iso G 2s 5m 3M. Lock ent has 2FG and 2FR (vert).
RADIO TELEPHONE
Monitor *Avonmouth Radio* Ch 12 for VTS. Marina VHF tba.
TELEPHONE (Dial code 01275)
Marina tba; MRCC (01792) 366534; ⌗ (01446) 420241; Marinecall 0891 500 459.
FACILITIES
Marina 120 berths, FW, AC, BH (35 ton).
Portishead Cruising Club;
Town ⌧, Ⓑ, ≋, ✈ (Bristol).

ADJACENT HARBOUR
WESTON-SUPER-MARE, Somerset, 51°21'·00N 02°59'·20W. AC 1152, 1176, *1179*. HW −0435 on Dover; ML 6·1m; Duration 0655. See 8.11.22. Good shelter, except in S'lies, in Knightstone Hbr (dries) at N end of bay; access HW±2. Causeway at ent marked by bn. Grand Pier hd 2 FG (vert) 6/5m. Or ⚓ in good weather in R Axe (dries), entry HW±2. Facilities: **Weston Bay YC** ☎ 620772, FW, Bar, VHF Ch **80;** Services: AB, CH, EI, D, BH (10 ton), FW, Slip, ME, Sh. **Town** EC Mon; Bar, Ⓑ, FW, P, ⌧, R, ≋, V.

BURNHAM-ON-SEA   8-11-23
Somerset 51°14'·20N 03°00'·25W

CHARTS
AC 1152, *1179*; Imray C59; Stanfords 14; OS 182
TIDES
−0435 Dover; ML 5·4; Duration 0620; Zone 0 (UT)

Standard Port BRISTOL (AVONMOUTH) (←)

Times				Height (metres)			
High Water		Low Water		MHWS	MHWN	MLWN	MLWS
0200	0800	0300	0800	13·2	9·8	3·8	1·0
1400	2000	1500	2000				
Differences BURNHAM-ON-SEA							
−0020	−0025	−0030	0000	−2·3	−1·9	−1·4	−1·1
BRIDGWATER							
−0015	−0030	+0305	+0455	−8·6	−8·1	Dries out	

SHELTER
Ent is very choppy in strong winds, especially from SW to W and from N to NE. ⚓ in 4m about 40m E of No 1 buoy or S of town jetty or for best shelter ⚓ in R. Brue (dries).
NAVIGATION
WPT 51°13'·35N 03°10'·00W, 256°/076° from/to Low lt, 6·2M. Enter HW −3 to HW; not advised at night. From 0·5M S of Gore SWM buoy pick up 076° transit of Low lt ho with High lt ho (disused). Approx 1·3M past No 1 buoy, steer on ldg line/lts 112°; thence alter 180° into the river chan. Beware unmarked fishing stakes outside appr chan.

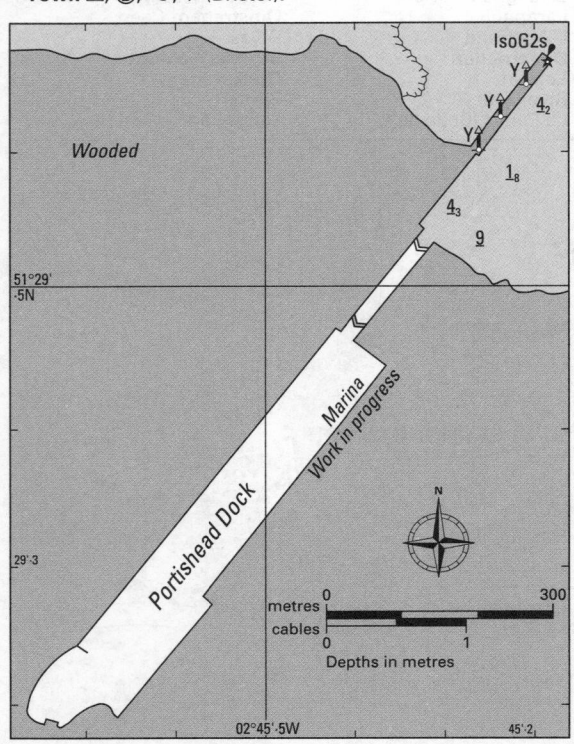

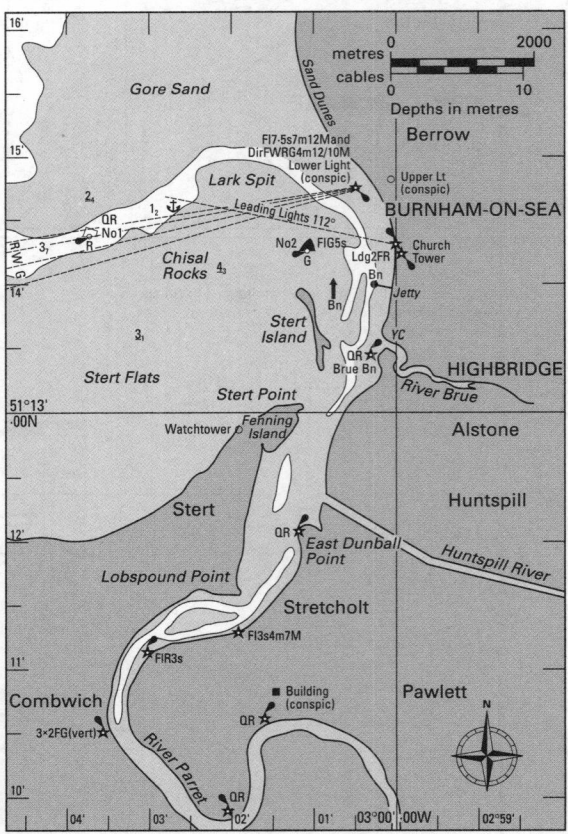

BURNHAM *continued*

LIGHTS AND MARKS
Low lt ho Dir 076° as chartlet and 10.11.4. Ldg lts/marks 112° (moved as chan shifts): front FR 6m 3M, Or stripe on ☐ W background on sea wall; rear FR 12m 3M, church tr.

RADIO TELEPHONE
Hr Mr and Pilot VHF Ch 08 16 (when vessel expected).

TELEPHONE (Dial code 01278)
Hr Mr and Pilot 782180; MRCC (01792) 366534; ⌗ (01446) 420241; Marinecall 0891 500 459; Police 782288; Ⓗ 782262.

FACILITIES
Burnham-on-Sea YC ☎ 792911, M, few drying ⚓s in River Brue, L, Slip, Bar; **Services**: ME, El, Sh, ACA (Bridgwater). **Town** EC Wed; Gas, ✉, Ⓑ, ⇌ (Highbridge), ✈ (Bristol). Note: No access to Bridgwater marina from sea/R Parrett.

WATCHET   8-11-24

Somerset 51°11′·00N 03°19′·64W

CHARTS
AC 1160, 1152, *1179*; Imray C59; Stanfords 14; OS 181

TIDES
−0450 Dover; ML 5·9; Duration 0655; Zone 0 (UT)

Standard Port BRISTOL (AVONMOUTH) (←)

Times				Height (metres)			
High Water		Low Water		MHWS	MHWN	MLWN	MLWS
0200	0800	0300	0800	13·2	9·8	3·8	1·0
1400	2000	1500	2000				
Differences HINKLEY POINT							
−0020	−0025	−0100	−0040	−1·7	−1·4	−0·2	−0·2
WATCHET							
−0035	−0050	−0145	−0040	−1·9	−1·5	+0·1	+0·1
MINEHEAD							
−0037	−0052	−0155	−0045	−2·6	−1·9	−0·2	0·0
PORLOCK BAY							
−0045	−0055	−0205	−0050	−3·0	−2·2	−0·1	−0·1
LYNMOUTH							
−0055	−0115	No data		−3·6	−2·7	No data	

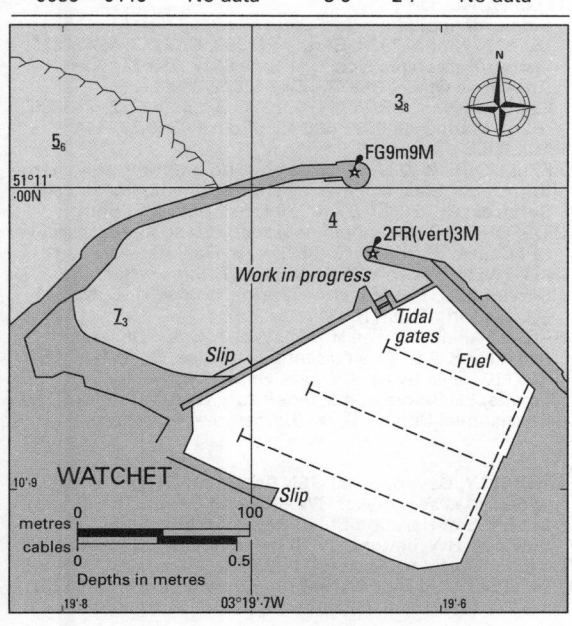

FG9m9M

51°11′·00N

2FR(vert)3M

Work in progress

4

3₈

5₆

7₃

Tidal gates

Slip

Fuel

WATCHET

Slip

metres 0   100
cables 0   0·5
Depths in metres
19′·8   03°19′·7W   19′·6

SHELTER
Good, but open to N and E winds. The outer hbr ent dries 6·5m, but has about 6m depth at MHWS; access approx HW±2½. Visitors dry out against walls or contact Boat Owners' Ass'n for tempy fore-and-aft moorings. Note: Work is in progress on a marina in the SE part of the former commercial port, entered over a drying sill. The chartlet is based on a drawing copyright of Posford Duvivier Ltd, courtesy of West Somerset District Council.

NAVIGATION
WPT 51°12′·00N 03°18′·80W, 028°/208° from/to hbr ent, 1·1M. Rks/mud dry 5ca to seaward. Beware tidal streams 4-5kn at sp offshore and around W pier hd. Culver Sand (0·9m) is approx 6M NNE, marked by ECM and WCM lt buoys. 5M E of hbr are Lilstock range target buoys. DZ No 2 SPM buoy, Fl Y 10s, bears 030°/3·2M from Watchet.

LIGHTS AND MARKS
Two unlit radio masts (206m) bearing 208°/1·6M from hbr ent are conspic approach marks. Hinkley Pt nuclear power stn is conspic 7·5M to the E. W pier hd FG 9m 9M on Red (R) tr. E pier hd 2 FR (vert) 3M.

RADIO TELEPHONE
VHF Ch 09 12 14 16 (from HW−2, but occas).

TELEPHONE (Dial code 01984)
Hr Mr 631264; Watchet Boat Owners Association 634242; ⌗ (01446) 420241; MRCC (01792) 366534; Marinecall 0891 500 459; Police (01643) 703361 (Minehead).

FACILITIES
Work on a 288 berth marina was planned to start in spring 1999, subject to completion of a Harbour Revision Order. **Services**: FW, Slip, ACA (Bridgwater). **Town** EC Wed; ✉, Ⓑ, V, R, Bar. At Williton (2M): Gas, D & P (cans); Ⓗ (Minehead 8M), ⇌ (Taunton 18M), ✈ (Bristol).

OTHER HARBOURS ON S SHORE OF BRISTOL CHANNEL

11

MINEHEAD, Somerset, 51°12′·76N 03°28′·29W. AC 1160, 1165, *1179*. HW −0450 on Dover. ML 5·7m. See 8.11.24. Small hbr, dries 7·5m; access HW±2. Good shelter within pier curving E and then SE, over which seas may break in gales at MHWS; exposed to E'lies. Best appr from N or NW; beware The Gables, shingle bank (dries 3·7m) about 5ca ENE of pier. Keep E of a sewer outfall which passes ½ca E of pierhd and extends 1¾ca NNE of it; outfall is protected by rk covering, drying 2·8m and N end marked by SHM bn QG 6m 7M. There are 8 R ⚓s at hbr ent just seaward of 3 posts or dry out against pier. Hbr gets very crowded. Holiday camp is conspic 6ca SE. Pierhd lt Fl (2) G 5s 4M, vis 127°-262°. VHF Ch 16 12 14 (occas). Hr Mr ☎ (01643) 702566; Facilities: Hbr FW, Slip. **Town** EC Wed; D, P, El, Gas, ME, Sh, R, Bar, V, ✉, Ⓑ, ⇌ (Taunton).

PORLOCK WEIR, Somerset, 51°13′·14N 03°37′·57W. AC 1160, 1165, *1179*. HW −0500 on Dover; ML 5·6m. See 8.11.24. Access HW±1½. Ent chan (250°), about 15m wide marked by withies (3 PHM and 1 SHM), between shingle bank/wood pilings to stbd and sunken wooden wall to port is difficult in any seas. A small pool (1m) just inside ent is for shoal draft boats; others dry out on pebble banks. Or turn 90° stbd, via gates (usually open), into inner drying dock with good shelter. No lts. Hr Mr ☎ (01643) 863277. **Porlock Weir SC** ☎ 862028. Facilities: FW and limited V.

LYNMOUTH, Devon, 51°14′·13N 03°49′·72W. AC 1160,1165. HW−0515 on Dover. See 8.11.24. Tiny hbr, dries approx 5m; access HW±1, but only in settled offshore weather. Appr from Sand Ridge SHM buoy, 1·6M W of Foreland Pt and 9ca N of hbr ent. The narrow appr chan between drying boulder ledges is marked by 7 unlit posts. Hbr ent is between piers, 2FR/FG lts, on W side of river course. Berth on E pier, which covers at MHWS. Resort facilities.

WATERMOUTH, Devon, 51°13′·00N 04°04′·60W. AC 1165, *1179*. HW −0525 on Dover; ML 4·9m; Duration 0625. Use 8.11.25. Good shelter in drying hbr, but heavy surge runs in strong NW winds. Access HW±3 at sp; only as far as inner bkwtr at np. Dir lt 153° Oc WRG 5s 1m, vis W151·5°-154·5°, W △ on structure, 1½ca inside ent on S shore. Bkwtr, covered at half tide, has Fl G 5s 2M. Eight Y ⚓s with B handles. Hr Mr ☎ (01271) 865422. Facilities: **Hbr** D (cans), FW (cans), CH, C (12 ton), Slip; **YC** ☎ 865048, Bar.

ILFRACOMBE   8-11-25

Devon 51°12'·62N 04°06'·58W   Rtg 3-4-2

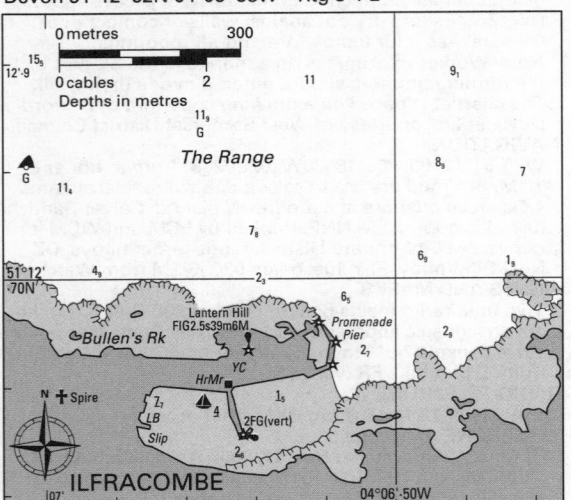

CHARTS
AC 1160, *1165, 1179;* Imray C59; Stanfords 14; OS 180
TIDES
−0525 Dover; ML 5·0; Duration 0625; Zone 0 (UT)

Standard Port MILFORD HAVEN (←)

Times				Height (metres)			
High Water		Low Water		MHWS	MHWN	MLWN	MLWS
0100	0700	0100	0700	7·0	5·2	2·5	0·7
1300	1900	1300	1900				
Differences ILFRACOMBE							
−0030	−0015	−0035	−0055	+2·2	+1·7	+0·5	0·0
LUNDY ISLAND							
−0030	−0030	−0020	−0040	+1·0	+0·7	+0·2	+0·1

SHELTER
Good except in NE/E winds. SW gales can cause surge in hbrs, which dry. 12 ⚓s in outer hbr; or ⚓ clear of pier and LB Slip. Possible AB on quays in inner hbr, access HW±3.
NAVIGATION
WPT 51°13'·20N 04°06'·60W, 000°/180° from/to pier hd, 0·55M. From E, beware Copperas Rks (4M to E), (SHM buoy) and tiderips on Buggy Pit, 7ca NE of ent. On entry keep toward Promenade Pier to clear drying ledges and lobster keep-pots obstructing hbr ent on SE side.
LIGHTS AND MARKS
No ldg marks/lts. Lantern Hill lt, Fl G 2·5s 39m 6M, on small conspic chapel. Promenade Pier has three 2FG (vert), shown 1/9-30/4. Inner bkwtr 2 FG (vert).
RADIO TELEPHONE
Call: *Ilfracombe Hbr* VHF Ch 12 16 (Apl-Oct 0800-2000 when manned; Nov-Mar occas). Ch **80** M (occas).
TELEPHONE (Dial code 01271)
Hr Mr 862108; MRCC (01792) 366534; ✠ (01222) 763880 (H24); Marinecall 0891 500 459; Police 863633; Dr 863119.
FACILITIES
Hbr M, D (cans), FW, CH, Slip, ME, El, Sh; **Ilfracombe YC** ☎ 863969, M, ◎, Bar, C (35 ton, as arranged); **Town** EC Thurs, V, R, Bar, ✉, Ⓑ, ⇌ (bus to Barnstaple), ✈ (Exeter).

LUNDY ISLAND, Devon, 51°09'·80N 04°39'·20W. AC *1164, 1179.* HW −0530 on Dover; ML 4·3m; Duration 0605. See above. Shelter good in lee of island's high ground (145m). In SSW to NW winds, usual ⚓ is close inshore to NW of SE Pt and Rat Is, clear of ferry. In N'lies ⚓ in The Rattles, small bay on S side. In E'lies Jenny's Cove is safe if no W'ly swell. Beware bad tide races, esp on E-going flood, off the N and SE tips of the Is; and to the SW on the W-going ebb. A violent race forms over Stanley Bank 3M NE of the N tip. Waters off the Is are a Marine Nature Reserve. Lts: NW Pt, Fl 15s 48m 17M, vis 009°-285°, W ○ tr. On SE Pt, Fl 5s 53m 15M, vis 170°-073°, W ○ tr, horn 25s. Two Historic Wrecks (see 8.0.3h) lie on the E side of the island, at 51°11'N 04°39'·4W, and 4ca further E. Facilities: Landing by the ⚓ off SE end of Island; £2 per head landing fee. **Lundy Co Landmark Trust** ☎ (01271) 870870, CH, Gas, bar and hotel.

RIVERS TAW & TORRIDGE
Devon 51°04'·34N 04°12'·81W   Rtg 3-5-1   **8-11-26**
CHARTS
AC 1160, *1164,* 1179; Imray C58; Stanfords 14; OS 180
TIDES
−0525 (Appledore) Dover; ML 3·6; Duration 0600; Zone 0 (UT)

Standard Port MILFORD HAVEN (←)

Times				Height (metres)			
High Water		Low Water		MHWS	MHWN	MLWN	MLWS
0100	0700	0100	0700	7·0	5·2	2·5	0·7
1300	1900	1300	1900				
Differences APPLEDORE							
−0020	−0025	+0015	−0045	+0·5	0·0	−0·9	−0·5
YELLAND MARSH (R Taw)							
−0010	−0015	+0100	−0015	+0·1	−0·4	−1·2	−0·6
FREMINGTON (R Taw)							
−0010	−0015	+0030	−0030	−1·1	−1·8	−2·2	−0·5
BARNSTAPLE (R Taw)							
0000	−0015	−0155	−0245	−2·9	−3·8	−2·2	−0·4
BIDEFORD (R Torridge)							
−0020	−0025	0000	0000	−1·1	−1·6	−2·5	−0·7
CLOVELLY							
−0030	−0030	−0020	−0040	+1·3	+1·1	+0·2	+0·2

SHELTER
Very well protected, but ent in strong on-shore winds is dangerous. Yachts can ⚓ or pick up buoy in Appledore Pool, N of Skern Pt where sp stream can reach 5kn. The quay at Bideford dries to soft mud; used by coasters.
NAVIGATION
WPT 51°05'·40N 04°16'·04W (abeam Fairway buoy, off chartlet), 298°/118° from/to Bar buoy, 0·9M. Bar and sands constantly shift and buoys are moved occasionally to comply. Advice on bar, where there are depths of 0·1 and 0·4m, from Pilot VHF Ch 12 or Swansea CG. Estuary dries; access is only feasible from HW−2 to HW. Once tide is ebbing, breakers quickly form between Bar buoy (unlit NCM) and Middle Ridge SHM buoy. 2M passage to Bideford is not difficult. If going 7M up to Barnstaple, take a pilot (from Appledore) or seek local knowledge.
LIGHTS AND MARKS
Entry at night is NOT advised. Apart from jetties etc, only lts are Bideford Fairway buoy L Fl 10s, Outer Pulley buoy Fl G 2·5s, Crow Pt Fl R 5s, and the two ldg marks; these are W trs, lit H24; front Oc 6s, rear Oc 10s. The ldg line 118° is only valid as far as Outer Pulley buoy after which the chan deviates to stbd toward Pulley unlit SHM buoy, Grey Sand Hill and Appledore. The Torridge is unlit, other than a QY on Bideford bridge showing the preferred chan.
RADIO TELEPHONE
Two Rivers Port/Pilots VHF Ch 12 16 (From HW−2).
TELEPHONE
Bideford/Appledore Nos: Dial code 01237. Hr Mr 476711 Ext 317; Pilot 477928; Berths 474569; Dr 474994, 471071.
Instow/Barnstaple Nos: Dial code 01271. Hr Mr via Amenities Officer 388327; Dr 372672/329004.
Common Nos: MRCC (01792) 366534; ✠ (01222) 763880 (H24); Marinecall 0891 500 459; Police 0990 777444.
FACILITIES
APPLEDORE: (01237) is a free port; no authority can charge for use of public facilities eg slips at town quay and AB.
    Services: CH, El, Ⓔ, BY, C (70 tons), Slip, ME, Sh.
BIDEFORD: AB (few/not encouraged due to increase in FVs; call Capt V. Harris ☎ 474569), V, R, Gas, Bar.
INSTOW: **N. Devon YC** FW ☎ 860367, Slip, R, Bar;
    Services: AB £5 via Instow Marine ☎ 861081, D, ME, M, Ⓔ, C (4 ton). **Town** R, FW, Bar.
BARNSTAPLE: AB (see Hr Mr), V, Bar, Gas. FW: limited facilities; P & D: small quantities in cans. Bulk D (min 500 ltrs/110 galls) by bowser, see Hr Mr.
    Towns: EC Barnstaple & Bideford = Wed; ✉ (all four), Ⓑ (Barnstaple, Bideford), ⇌ (Barnstaple, ✈ (Exeter).

CLOVELLY, Devon, 51°00'·15N 04°23'·70W. Rtg 5-4-1. AC *1164.* Tides see above. HW −0524 on Dover. Tiny drying hbr 5M E of Hartland Pt has some AB £5 on pier, access only near HW; better to ⚓ off in 5m, sheltered from S/SW winds. Useful to await the tide around Hartland Pt or into Bideford. Lt Fl G 5s 5m 5M on hbr wall. Hr Mr ☎ (01237) 431237 (Red Lion). Facilities: Slip, FW, ✉, limited V.

RIVERS TAW & TORRIDGE *continued*

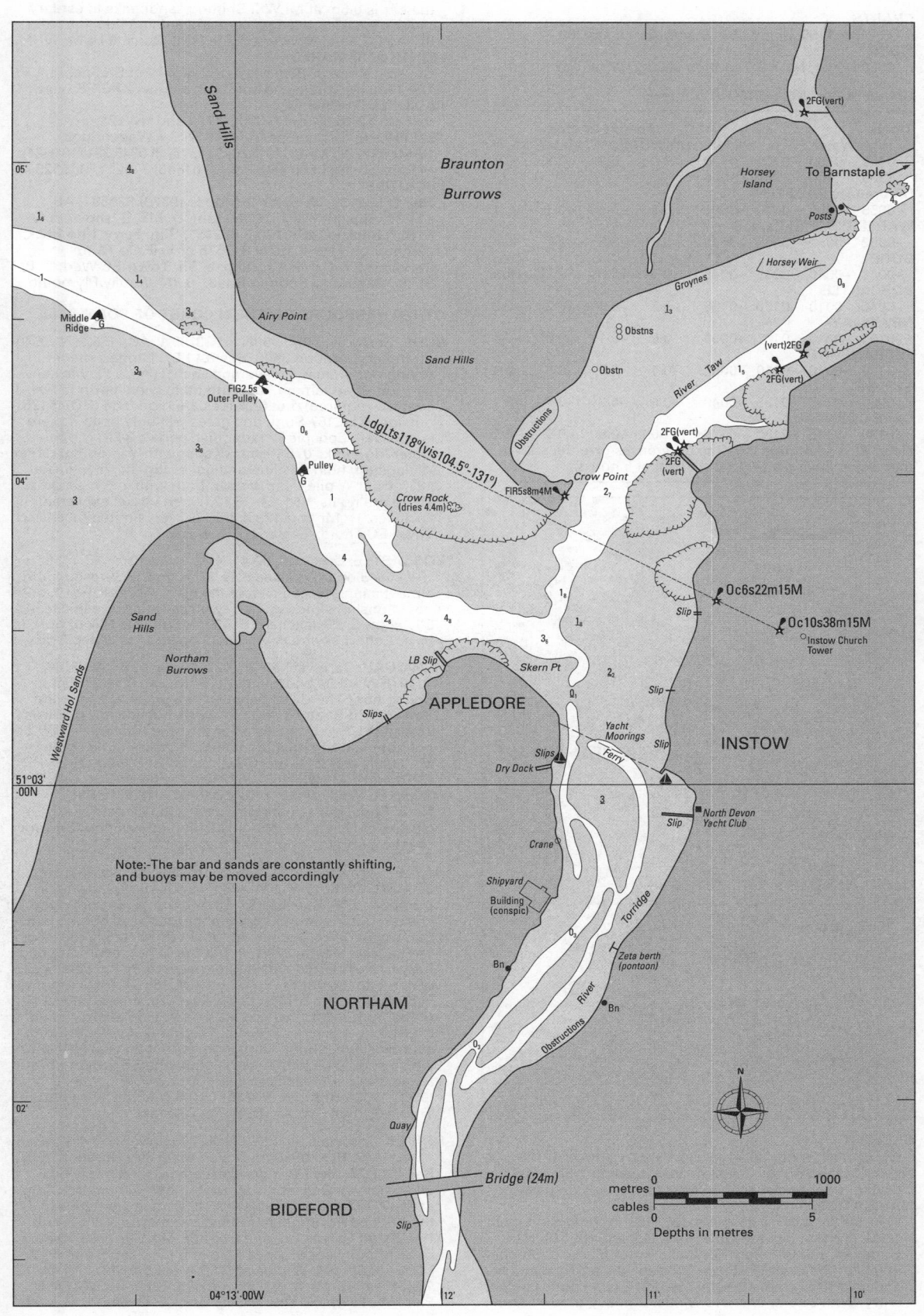

Note:-The bar and sands are constantly shifting, and buoys may be moved accordingly

PADSTOW   8-11-27

Cornwall 50°32'·48N 04°56'·10W. Rtg 3-3-1

CHARTS
AC 1168, 1156; Imray C58; Stanfords 13; OS 200
TIDES
–0550 Dover; ML 4·0; Duration 0600; Zone 0 (UT)

Standard Port MILFORD HAVEN (←—)

Times				Height (metres)			
High Water		Low Water		MHWS	MHWN	MLWN	MLWS
0100	0700	0100	0700	7·0	5·2	2·5	0·7
1300	1900	1300	1900				
Differences PADSTOW							
–0055	–0050	–0040	–0050	+0·3	+0·4	+0·1	+0·1
WADEBRIDGE (R Camel)							
–0052	–0052	+0235	+0245	–3·8	–3·8	–2·5	–0·4
BUDE							
–0040	–0040	–0035	–0045	+0·7	+0·6		No data
BOSCASTLE							
–0045	–0010	–0110	–0100	+0·3	+0·4	+0·2	+0·2
NEWQUAY							
–0100	–0110	–0105	–0050	0·0	+0·1	0·0	–0·1
PERRANPORTH							
–0100	–0110	–0105	–0050	–0·1	0·0	0·0	+0·1
ST IVES							
–0050	–0115	–0105	–0040	–0·4	–0·3	–0·1	+0·1
CAPE CORNWALL							
–0130	–0145	–0120	–0120	–1·0	–0·9	–0·5	–0·1

Note: At Wadebridge LW time differences give the start of
the rise, following a LW stand of about 5 hours.

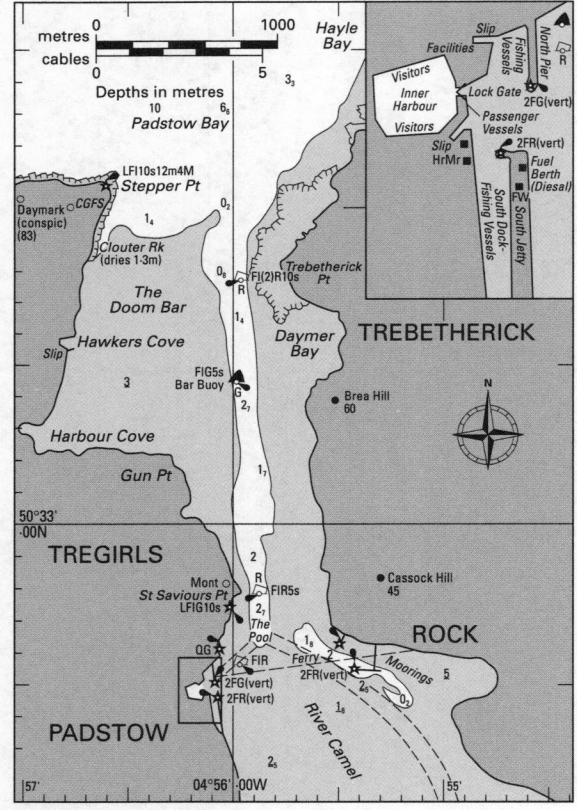

SHELTER
Good in inner hbr 3m+, access HW±2 via lock; or HW±4½
moor in the Pool or ‡ just down-stream in 1·5m LWS.
Drying moorings available for small vessels on passage.
NAVIGATION
WPT 50°35'·00N 04°58'·50W, 305°/125° from/to Stepper Pt,
1·5M. From S, beware Quies Rks, Gulland Rk, The Hen,
Gurley Rk and Chimney Rks and a wreck 5ca W of Stepper
Pt (all off the chartlet). From N, keep well off Newland Is
and its offlying reef. Identify the first 2 chan buoys before
entry. With strong onshore winds or heavy ground swell,

seas can break on Doom Bar and in adjacent chan. Final
appr S of St Saviour's Pt runs close to W shore. Allow
ample rise of tide. Do not enter LW±1½; least depth on
the bar is 0·5m at MLWS. Shifting sandbanks in estuary
require local knowledge, care and a rising tide; ditto the
drying R Camel to Wadebridge (4M). Consult Hr Mr (VHF).
LIGHTS AND MARKS
Conspic stone tr (83m daymark), 3ca W of Stepper Pt, L Fl
10s 12m 4M, marks the ent. Lock ent has 2 FG/FR (vert).
RADIO TELEPHONE
VHF Ch 12 16 (Mon-Fri 0800–1700 and HW±2).
TELEPHONE (Dial codes 01841; 01208 = Wadebridge)
Hr Mr 532239; MRCC (01326) 317575; ⌘ 0345 231110 (H24);
Marinecall 0891 500 458; Police (01566) 774211; Dr 532346.
FACILITIES
Hbr ☎ 532239, ⛽ 533346, Mobile (0379) 338531, AB
£11.30, Slip, M, FW, El, C (60 ton), D, ME, ⬚, showers, V,
R, Bar; **Rock SC** ☎ (01208) 862431, Slip; **Ferry 1** (to Rock,
summer only) ☎ (01326) 317575 or VHF Ch 12 16;
Services: BY, C, ME, CH, Slip, L, Sh. **Town** EC Wed; ⬚, P,
✉, Ⓑ, ⇌ (bus to Bodmin Road), ✈ (Newquay/Plymouth).

OTHER HARBOURS ON THE N COAST OF CORNWALL

BUDE, Cornwall, 50°49'·90N 04°33'·30W. AC 1156. HW –0540
on Dover. Duration 0605. See 8.11.27. Limited shelter in
drying hbr, access for average yacht HW±2. Yachts can,
by prior arrangement, lock into quiet canal berth (5·5m
over CD required), but lock fees are high (£86 (HO); £125
outside HO; £167 Sun), and gates will only open if there
is no swell. Conspic W radar dish aerials 3·3M N of hbr.
Outer ldg marks 075°, front W spar with Y ◇ topmark, rear
W flagstaff; hold this line until inner ldg marks in line at
131°, front W pile, rear W spar, both with Y △ topmarks.
There are no lts. VHF Ch 16 12 (when vessel expected).
Facilities: Hr Mr ☎ (01288) 353111; very limited facilities;
Town EC Thurs; Ⓑ, Bar, ✉, R, V, Gas.

BOSCASTLE, Cornwall, 50°41'·45N 04°42·10W. AC 1156.
HW –0543 on Dover; see 8.11.27. A tiny, picturesque hbr,
almost a land-locked cleft in the cliffs. Access HW±2, but
not in onshore winds when swell causes surge inside. An
E'ly appr, S of Meachard Rk (37m high, 2ca NW of hbr), is
best. 2 short bkwtrs at ent; moor bows-on to drying S quay.

NEWQUAY, Cornwall, 50°25'·03N 05°05'·12W. AC 1168,
1149. HW –0604 on Dover; ML 3·7m; see 8.11.27. Ent to
drying hbr ('The Gap') between two walls, is 23m wide.
Beware Old Dane Rk and Listrey Rk outside hbr towards
Towan Hd. Swell causes a surge in the hbr. Enter HW±2
but not in strong onshore winds. Berth as directed by Hr
Mr. Lts: N pier 2 FG (vert) 2M; S pier 2 FR (vert) 2M. VHF
Ch16 14. Hr Mr ☎ (01637) 872809. Facilities: Gas, Gaz, CH.
Town EC Wed (winter only); FW, Slip, D, V, R, Bar.
Note: Shoal draft boats can dry out in Gannel Creek,
close S of Newquay, but only in settled weather. Beware
causeway bridge about half way up the creek.

HAYLE, Cornwall, 50°11'·74N 05°26'·10W (Chan ent). Rtg
5.5.3. AC 1168, 1149. HW –0605 on Dover; ML 3·6m;
Duration 0555. See 8.11.27. Drying hbr gives very good
shelter, but in ground swell dangerous seas break on the
bar, drying 2·7m; approx 4m at ent @ MHWS. Cross the
bar in good weather HW±1, but hbr is not recommended
for yachts. Charted aids do not necessarily indicate best
water. Ldg lts, both FW 17/23m 4M, 180°. A PHM lt buoy,
Fl (2) R 5s, and a SHM lt buoy, Iso G 2s, are about 8ca N
of the front ldg lt. Training wall on W side of ent chan is
marked by 4 perches (FG lts). The hbr is divided by long
central island (about 700m long, with lt bn Q at NW end)
which should be left to stbd. Follow the SE arm of hbr to
Hayle; the S arm leads to Lelant Quay. VHF Ch 18 16
(0900-1700). Hr Mr ☎ (01736) 754043, AB £6. Facilities: EC
Thurs; Ⓑ, Bar, FW, ⇌, R, V, P & D (cans).

ST IVES, Cornwall, 50°12'·76N 05°28'·60W. Rtg 3-4-1. AC
1168, 1149. HW –0610 on Dover; ML 3·6m; Duration 0555.
See 8.11.27. Shelter is good except in on-shore winds
when heavy swell works in. Drying hbr with approx 4·5m
at MHWS; 7 ⚓s accessible HW±2. Or ‡ in 3m between
the hbr and Porthminster Pt to S. From the NW beware
Hoe Rk off St Ives Hd, and from SE The Carracks. Keep E
of SHM buoy about 1½ ca ENE of E pier. Lts: E pier hd 2
FG (vert) 8m 5M. W pier hd 2 FR (vert) 5m 3M. VHF Ch 12
16 (occas). Hr Mr ☎ (01736) 795018. Facilities: ⚓s £8; **E
Pier** FW. **Town** EC Thurs; Gas, Gaz, Ⓑ, ⬚, Bar, ✉, R, V, ⇌.

VOLVO PENTA SERVICE

Sales and service centres in area 12

Republic of Ireland COUNTY DUBLIN *Western Marine Ltd*, Bulloch Harbour, Dalkey, Dublin Tel 00 353 1 2800321 **COUNTY CORK** *Kilmacsimon Boatyard Ltd*, Kilmacsimon Quay, Bandon Tel 00 353 21 775134 **COUNTY CLARE** *Derg Marine*, Kilaloe Tel 00 353 61 376364

VOLVO PENTA

Area 12

South Ireland
Malahide clockwise to Liscanor Bay

8.12.1	Index	**Page 545**
8.12.2	Diagram of ports, lights, RDF bns, Coast radio and weather stns	**546**
8.12.3	Tidal stream charts	**548**
8.12.4	List of coastal lights, fog signals and waypoints	**550**
8.12.5	Passage information	**553**
8.12.6	Distance table	**554**
8.12.7	Special notes for Ireland	**555**
8.12.8	Malahide	**556**
8.12.9	Howth	**557**
8.12.10	Dublin, Standard Port, tidal curves. Dun Laoghaire	**558**
8.12.11	Wicklow	**563**
8.12.12	Arklow	**563**
8.12.13	Wexford	**564**
8.12.14	Rosslare Harbour Tuskar Rock TSS	**565**
8.12.15	Kilmore Quay	**566**
8.12.16	Waterford	**567**
8.12.17	Dunmore East	**568**
8.12.18	Youghal	**568**
8.12.19	Cork Harbour, (Cobh, Standard Port, tidal curves) Dungarvan Bay Ballycotton	**572**
8.12.20	Kinsale Oysterhaven	**574**
8.12.21	Courtmacsherry	**574**
8.12.22	Glandore	**575**
8.12.23	Castle Haven Barloge Creek	**575**
8.12.24	Baltimore Horseshoe Harbour Cape Clear, North Harbour Roaring Water Bay Fastnet Rock TSS	**576**
8.12.25	Schull	**577**
8.12.26	Crookhaven Goleen Dunmanus Bay	**577**
8.12.27	Bantry Bay Castletown Lawrence's Cove Lonehort Harbour Adrigole Bantry Glengariff	**578**
8.12.28	Kenmare River	**579**
8.12.29	Dingle Portmagee Valentia Ventry Smerwick Harbour Brandon Bay Tralee Bay (Fenit)	**580**
8.12.30	Shannon Estuary	**581**
8.12.31	Kilrush	**582**

12

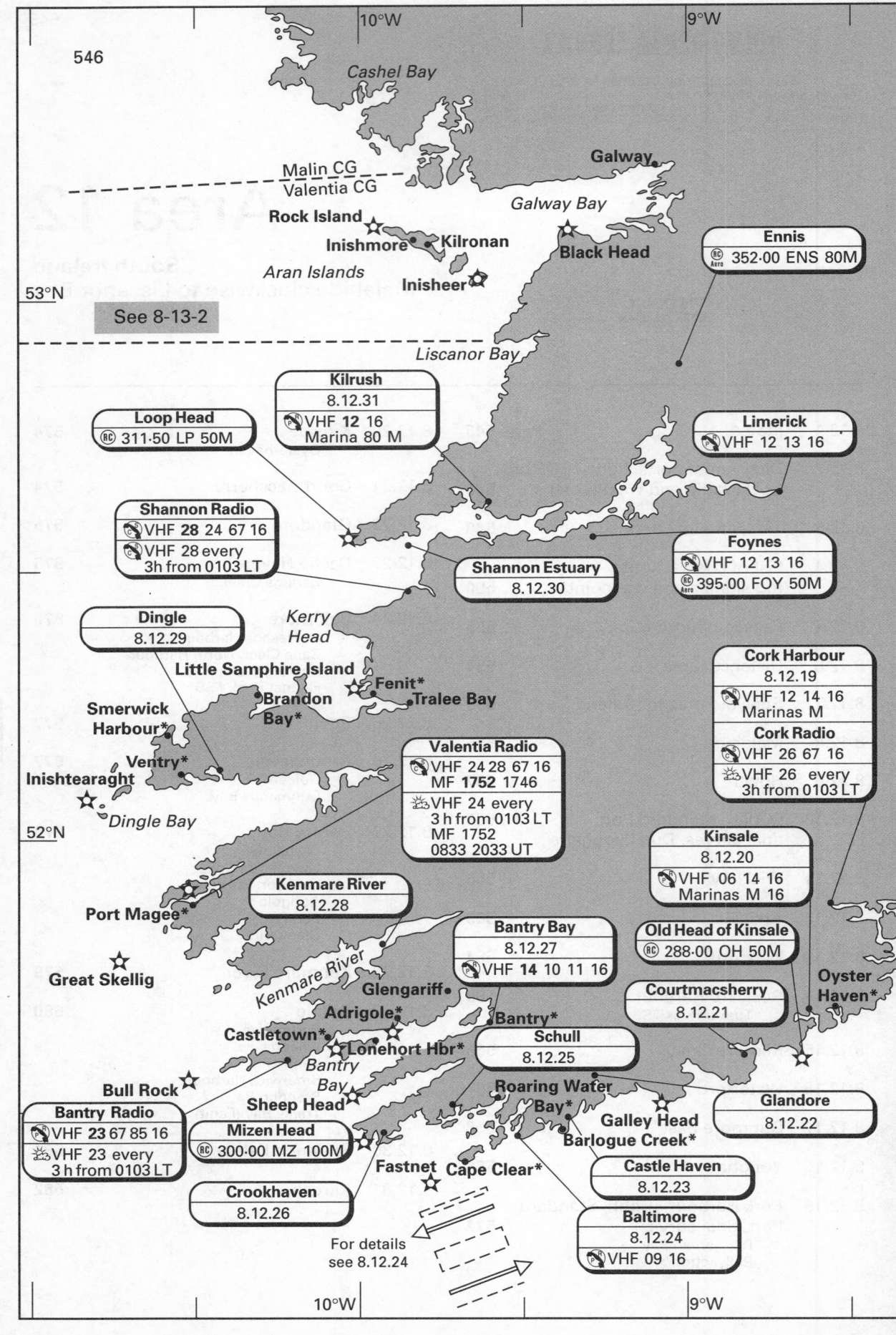

546

Cashel Bay

Malin CG
Valentia CG

Galway

Galway Bay

Rock Island

Inishmore   Kilronan

Aran Islands

Black Head

Ennis
RC Aero 352·00 ENS 80M

Inisheer

53°N

See 8-13-2

Liscanor Bay

Kilrush
8.12.31
VHF **12** 16
Marina 80 M

Loop Head
RC 311·50 LP 50M

Limerick
VHF 12 13 16

Shannon Radio
VHF **28** 24 67 16
VHF 28 every
3h from 0103 LT

Shannon Estuary
8.12.30

Foynes
VHF 12 13 16
RC Aero 395·00 FOY 50M

Dingle
8.12.29

Kerry
Head

Little Samphire Island

Fenit*

Brandon
Bay*   Tralee Bay

**Smerwick
Harbour***

Ventry*

Inishtearaght

52°N   Dingle Bay

Valentia Radio
VHF 24 28 67 16
MF **1752** 1746
VHF 24 every
3 h from 0103 LT
MF 1752
0833 2033 UT

Cork Harbour
8.12.19
VHF 12 14 16
Marinas M
Cork Radio
VHF 26 67 16
VHF 26 every
3h from 0103 LT

Kinsale
8.12.20
VHF 06 14 16
Marinas M 16

Port Magee*

Great Skellig

Kenmare River

Kenmare River
8.12.28

Old Head of Kinsale
RC 288·00 OH 50M

Bantry Bay
8.12.27
VHF **14** 10 11 16

Glengariff

Adrigole*

Castletown*

Lonehort Hbr*

Bantry
Bay

Bull Rock

Sheep Head

Bantry Radio
VHF **23** 67 85 16
VHF 23 every
3 h from 0103 LT

Mizen Head
RC 300·00 MZ 100M

Crookhaven
8.12.26

Bantry*

Schull
8.12.25

Roaring Water
Bay*

Courtmacsherry
8.12.21

Oyster
Haven*

Galley Head

Glandore
8.12.22

Barlogue Creek*

Fastnet   Cape Clear*

For details
see 8.12.24

Castle Haven
8.12.23

Baltimore
8.12.24
VHF 09 16

10°W   9°W

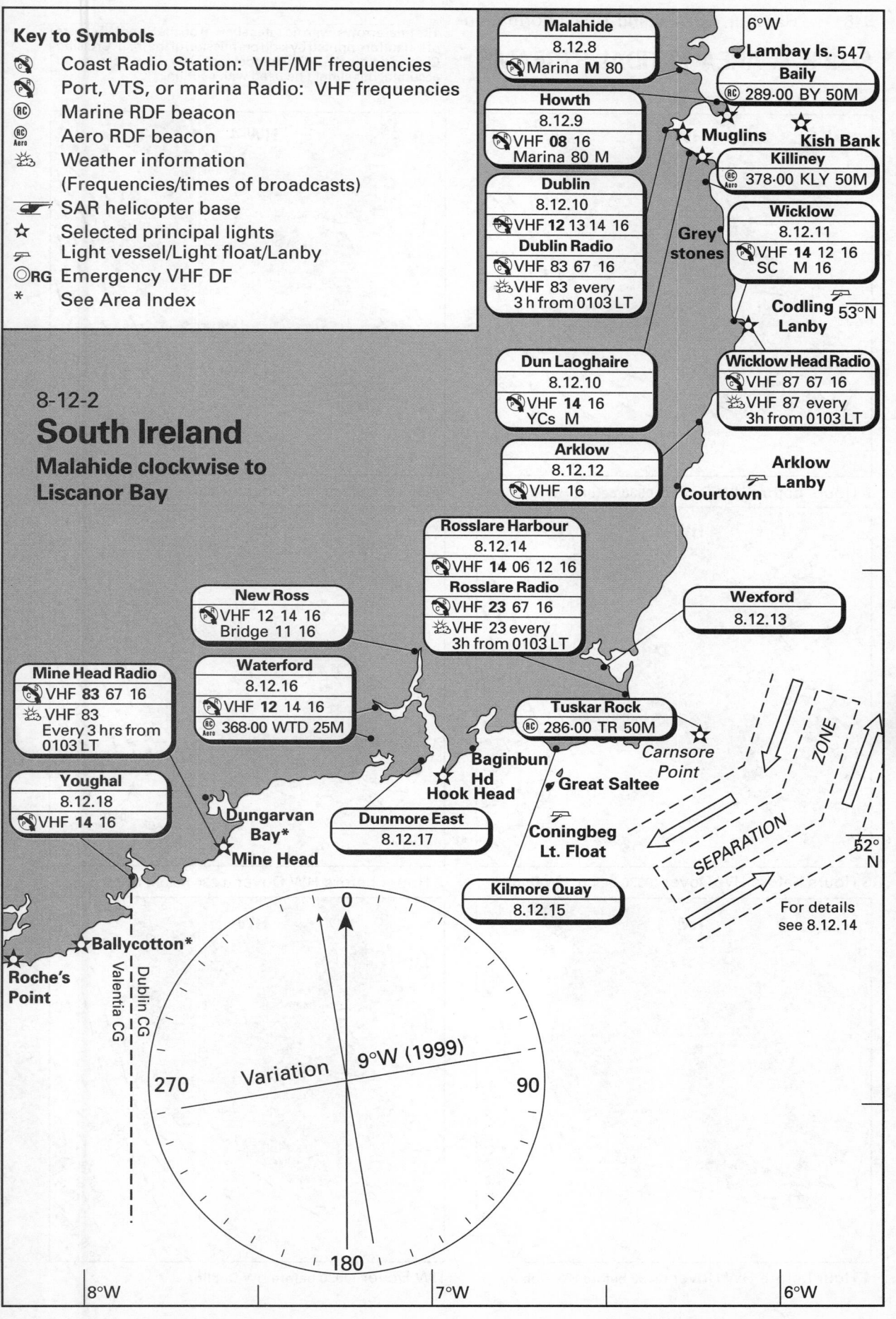

Key to Symbols

📻 Coast Radio Station: VHF/MF frequencies
📻ᴾᴿ Port, VTS, or marina Radio: VHF frequencies
ⓇC Marine RDF beacon
ⓇCₐₑᵣₒ Aero RDF beacon
🌊 Weather information
   (Frequencies/times of broadcasts)
🚁 SAR helicopter base
☆ Selected principal lights
⊂⊃ Light vessel/Light float/Lanby
Ⓡ RG Emergency VHF DF
* See Area Index

8-12-2
South Ireland
Malahide clockwise to Liscanor Bay

Malahide
8.12.8
📻ᴾᴿ Marina **M** 80

Howth
8.12.9
📻 VHF **08** 16
Marina 80 M

Dublin
8.12.10
📻 VHF **12** 13 14 16

Dublin Radio
📻 VHF 83 67 16
🌊 VHF 83 every 3 h from 0103 LT

Dun Laoghaire
8.12.10
📻 VHF **14** 16
YCs M

Arklow
8.12.12
📻 VHF 16

New Ross
📻ᴾᴿ VHF 12 14 16
Bridge 11 16

Rosslare Harbour
8.12.14
📻 VHF **14** 06 12 16

Rosslare Radio
📻 VHF 23 67 16
🌊 VHF 23 every 3 h from 0103 LT

Wexford
8.12.13

Mine Head Radio
📻 VHF **83** 67 16
🌊 VHF 83 Every 3 hrs from 0103 LT

Waterford
8.12.16
📻 VHF **12** 14 16
ⓇCₐₑᵣₒ 368·00 WTD 25M

Tuskar Rock
ⓇC 286·00 TR 50M

Youghal
8.12.18
📻 VHF **14** 16

Dunmore East
8.12.17

Kilmore Quay
8.12.15

Lambay Is. 547

Baily
ⓇC 289·00 BY 50M

Muglins   ☆ Kish Bank

Killiney
ⓇCₐₑᵣₒ 378·00 KLY 50M

Wicklow
8.12.11
📻 VHF **14** 12 16
SC   M 16

Grey stones

Codling 53°N
Lanby

Wicklow Head Radio
📻 VHF 87 67 16
🌊 VHF 87 every 3h from 0103 LT

Arklow
Lanby

Courtown

Baginbun
Hd
☆ Hook Head

Great Saltee

Carnsore
Point

SEPARATION ZONE

For details
see 8.12.14

Coningbeg
Lt. Float

☆ Ballycotton*

☆ Roche's
Point

Dublin CG
Valentia CG

Dungarvan
Bay*
☆ Mine Head

52°N

12

Variation
9°W (1999)
0
90
180
270

8°W   7°W   6°W   6°W

8-12-3   AREA 12 TIDAL STREAMS

The tidal arrows (with no rates shown) off the S and W coasts of Ireland are printed by kind permission of the Irish Cruising Club, to whom the Editor is indebted. They have been found accurate, but should be used with caution.

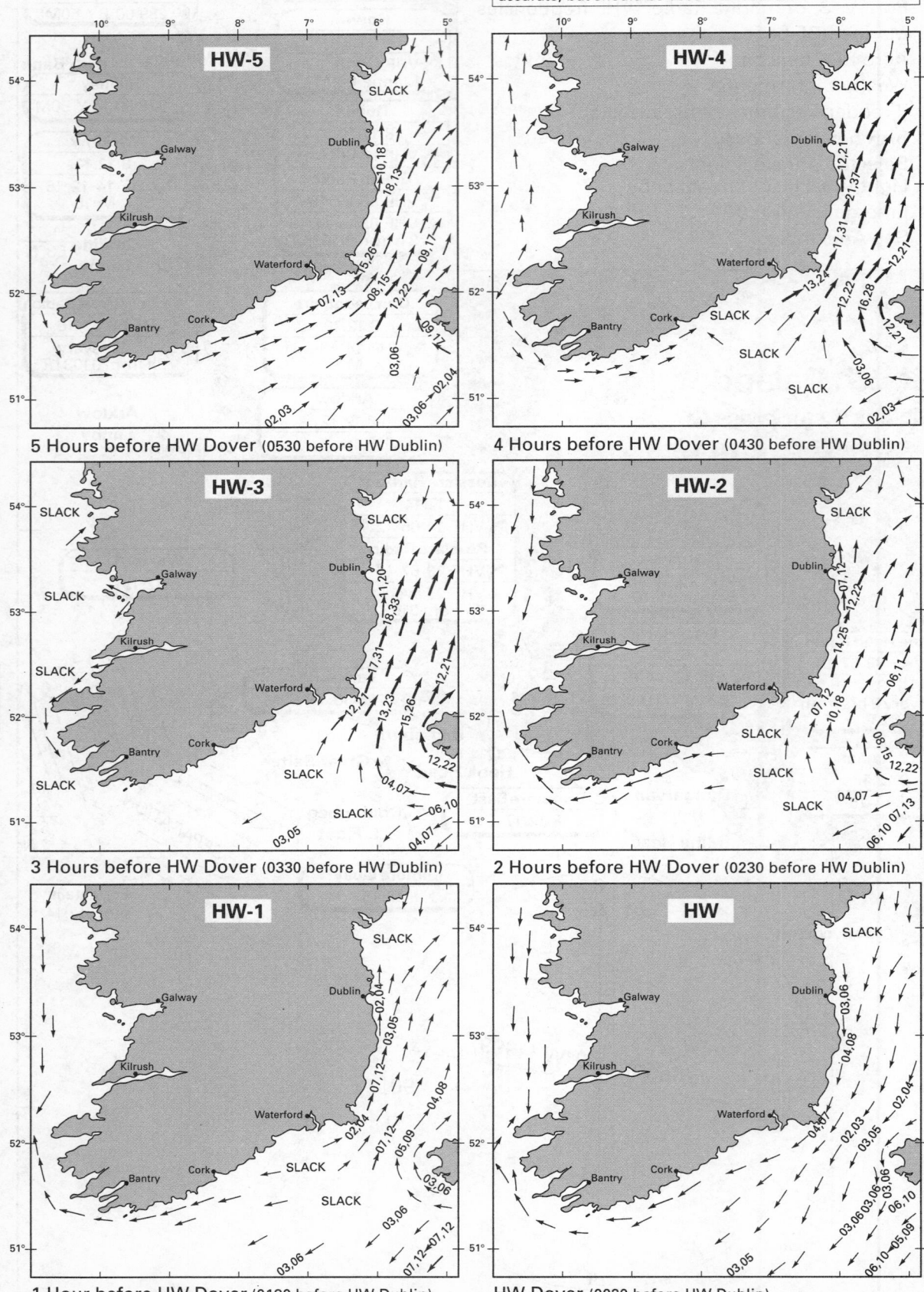

5 Hours before HW Dover (0530 before HW Dublin)

4 Hours before HW Dover (0430 before HW Dublin)

3 Hours before HW Dover (0330 before HW Dublin)

2 Hours before HW Dover (0230 before HW Dublin)

1 Hour before HW Dover (0130 before HW Dublin)

HW Dover (0030 before HW Dublin)

The tidal arrows (with no rates shown) off the S and W coasts of Ireland are printed by kind permission of the Irish Cruising Club, to whom the Editor is indebted. They have been found accurate, but should be used with caution.

Northward 8.13.3   South Irish Sea 8.11.3

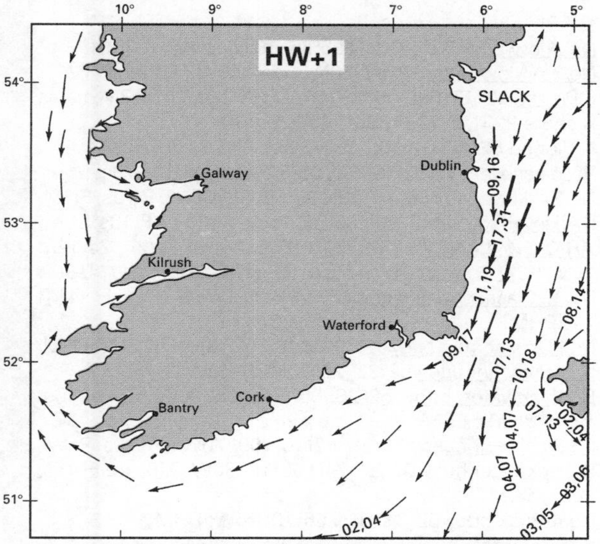

HW+1

1 Hour after HW Dover (0030 after HW Dublin)

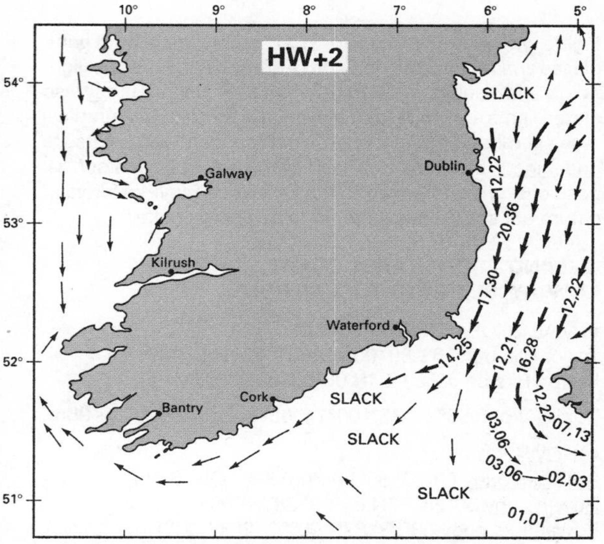

HW+2

2 Hours after HW Dover (0130 after HW Dublin)

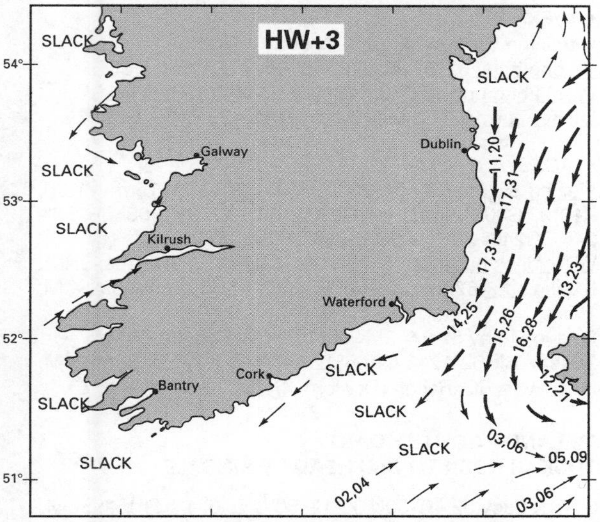

HW+3

3 Hours after HW Dover (0230 after HW Dublin)

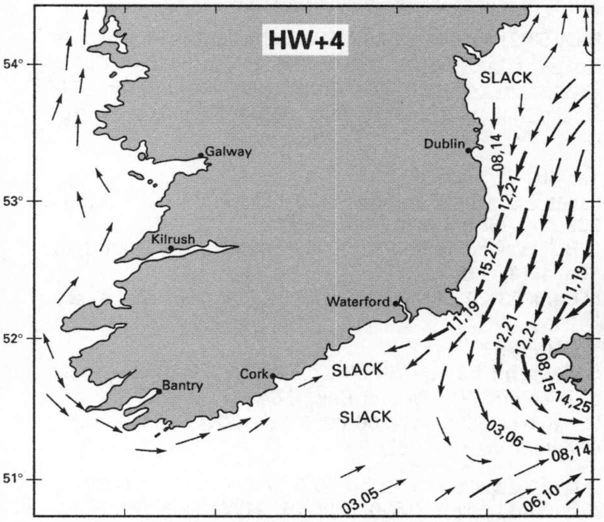

HW+4

4 Hours after HW Dover (0330 after HW Dublin)

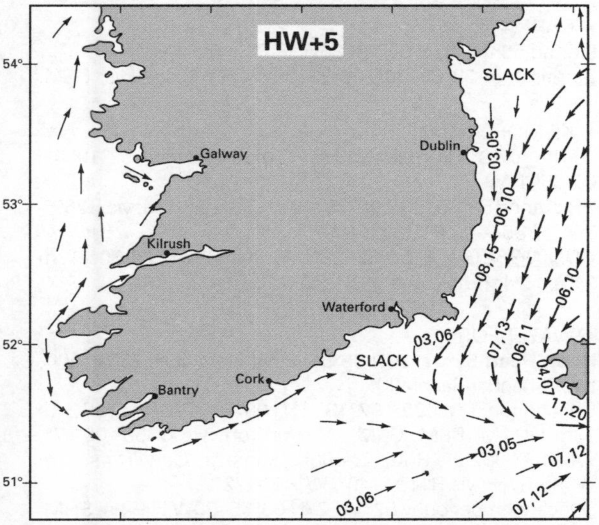

HW+5

5 Hours after HW Dover (0430 after HW Dublin)

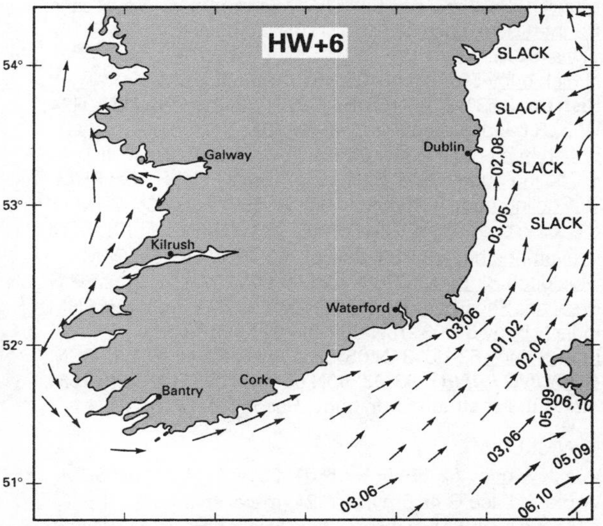

HW+6

6 Hours after HW Dover (0530 after HW Dublin)

12

8.12.4 COASTAL LIGHTS, FOG SIGNALS AND WAYPOINTS

Lights with a nominal range of 15M or more are in **bold** print, places and features are in CAPITALS, and light-vessels, light floats and Lanbys in *CAPITAL ITALICS*. Unless otherwise stated lights are white. m = elevation in metres; M = nominal range in miles. Fog signals are in *italics*. Useful waypoints are underlined; use those on land with care. All geographical positions are referenced to the Ordnance Survey of Ireland datum but should be assumed to be approximate.

IRELAND – SOUTH EAST COAST
LAMBAY ISLAND TO TUSKAR ROCK

• MALAHIDE/LAMBAY ISLAND
Taylor Rks buoy 53°30'·00N 06°01'·75W; SHM.
Burren Rks bn 53°29'·34N 06°02'·40W; SHM.

Dublin Airport 53°25'·75N 06°14'·65W Aero Al Fl WG 4s 95m.

• HOWTH
S Rowan buoy 53°23'·80N 06°03'·89W QG; SHM.
Howth buoy 53°23'·72N 06°03'·58W Fl G 5s; SHM.
Rowan Rks buoy 53°23'·87N 06°03'·20W Q (3) 10s; ECM.
E Pier hd 53°23'·64N 06°03'·97W Fl (2) WR 7·5s 13m W12M, R9M; W tr; vis W256°-295°, R295°-256°.

Baily 53°21'·68N 06°03'·08W Fl 15s 41m **26M**; tr; RC; Racon (K).
Rosbeg E buoy 53°21'·00N 06°03'·39W Q (3) 10s; ECM.
Rosbeg S buoy 53°20'·37N 06°04'·27W Q (6) + L Fl 15s; SCM.
Dublin Bay buoy 53°19'·90N 06°04'·58W Mo (A) 10s; Racon (M); SWM.

• PORT OF DUBLIN
Great S Wall hd, **Poolbeg** 53°20'·52N 06°09'·02W Oc (2) R 20s 20m **15M**; R ● tr; *Horn (2) 60s.*
N Bull Wall hd, **N Bull** 53°20'·67N 06°08'·92W Fl (3) G 10s 15m **15M**; G ● tr.
N Bank 53°20'·68N 06°10'·53W Oc G 8s 10m **16M**; G ■ tr.

• DUN LAOGHAIRE
E bkwtr hd 53°18'·13N 06°07'·57W Fl (2) R 10s 16m **17M**; tr, R lantern; *Horn 30s (or Bell (1) 6s).*
W bkwtr hd 53°18'·17N 06°07'·82W Fl (3) G 7·5s 11m 7M; tr, G lantern; vis 188°-062°.

N Burford buoy 53°20'·05N 06°01'·44W Q; *Whis;* NCM.
S Burford buoy 53°18'·05N 06°01'·21W VQ (6) + L Fl 10s; *Whis;* SCM.
Muglins 53°16'·53N 06°04'·52W Fl 5s 14m 11M; W tr, R band.
Bennett Bank buoy 53°20'·15N 05°55'·05W Q (6) + L Fl 15s; *Whis;* SCM.
N Kish buoy 53°18'·54N 05°56'·38W VQ; NCM.
Kish Bank 53°18'·68N 05°55'·38W Fl (2) 20s 29m **22M**, H24; W tr, R band; Racon (T); *Horn (2) 30s.*
E Kish buoy 53°14'·33N 05°53'·50W Fl (2) R 10s; PHM.
E Codling buoy 53°08'·52N 05°47'·05W Fl (4) R 10s; PHM.
W Codling buoy 53°06'·95N 05°54'·45W Fl G 10s; SHM.
S Codling buoy 53°04'·72N 05°49'·70W VQ (6) + L Fl 10s; SCM.
Greystones buoy 53°08'·38N 06°02'·44W Fl Y 5s; SPM.
Moulditch Bk buoy 53°08'·40N 06°01'·16W Fl R 10s; PHM.
Breaches Shoal buoy 53°05'·65N 05°59'·75W Fl (2) R 6s; PHM.
India N buoy 53°03'·15N 05°53'·40W VQ; NCM.
India S buoy 53°00'·34N 05°53'·25W Q (6) + L Fl 15s; SCM.
CODLING LANBY 53°03'·00N 05°40'·70W Fl 4s 12m **15M**, H24; tubular structure on buoy; Racon (G); *Horn 20s.*

• WICKLOW
Wicklow buoy 52°59'·55N 06°01'·23W; Fl (4) Y 10s; SPM.
W pier hd, Iso G 4s 5m 6M, H24, metal column.
E Pier hd 52°58'·98N 06°02'·01W Fl WR 5s 11m 6M; W tr, R base and cupola; vis R136°-293°, W293°-136°

Wicklow Hd 52°57'·93N 05°59'·83W Fl (3) 15s 37m **23M**; W tr.
Horseshoe buoy 52°56'·60N 05°59'·25W Fl R 3s; PHM.

• ARKLOW
N Arklow buoy 52°53'·84N 05°55'·15W Q; *Whis;* NCM.
No 2 Arklow buoy 52°50'·20N 05°54'·50W Fl R 6s; PHM.
S Pier hd 52°47'·59N 06°08'·16W Fl WR 6s 11m 13M; tr; vis R shore-223°, W223°-350°; R350°-shore.
N Pier hd 52°47'·61N 06°08'·23W L Fl G 7s 7m 10M.
Roadstone jetty hd 52°46'·68N 05°59'·30W Oc R 10s 9m 9M.
No 1 Arklow buoy 52°44'·30N 05°55'·96W Fl (3) R 10s; PHM.
S Arklow buoy 52°40'·80N 05°59'·15W VQ (6) + L Fl 10s; SCM.
ARKLOW LANBY 52°39'·50N 05°58'·10W Fl (2) 12s 12m **15M**, H24; ○ structure on buoy; Racon (O); *Horn Mo (A) 30s.*
No 2 Glassgorman buoy 52°44'·50N 06°05'·30W Fl (4) R 10s; PHM.
No 1 Glassgorman buoy 52°39'·06N 06°07'·40W Fl (2) R 6s; PHM.
N Blackwater buoy 52°32'·20N 06°09'·50W Q; NCM.
E Blackwater buoy 52°28'·00N 06°08'·00W Q (3) 10s; *Horn (3) 20s;* ECM.
SE Blackwater buoy 52°25'·62N 06°09'·70W Fl R 10s; PHM.
S Blackwater buoy 52°22'·74N 06°12'·80W Q (6) + L Fl 15s; *Whis;* SCM.
No 4 Rusk buoy 52°31'·05N 06°10'·75W; PHM.
W Blackwater buoy 52°25'·83N 06°13'·20W; SHM.

• WEXFORD
N training Wall bn 52°20'·18N 06°26'·78W.
N Long buoy 52°21'·42N 06°16'·90W Q; *Whis;* NCM.
West Long buoy 52°18'·16N 06°17'·90W QG; SHM.
Lucifer buoy 52°17'·00N 06°12'·61W VQ (3) 5s; ECM.

• ROSSLARE
Pier hd 52°15'·42N 06°20'·23W Oc WRG 5s 15m W13M, R10M, G10M; R tr; vis G098°-188°, W188°-208°, R208°-246°, G246°-283°, W283°-286°, R286°-320°.
W Holdens buoy 52°15'·75N 06°18'·68W Fl (3) G 10s; SHM.
S Long buoy 52°14'·82N 06°15'·58W VQ (6) + L Fl 10s; SCM; *Whis.*
Splaugh buoy 52°14'·35N 06°16'·70W Fl R 6s; PHM.
Tuskar Rk 52°12'·17N 06°12'·40W Q (2) 7·5s 33m **24M**, H24; W tr; RC; Racon (T); *Horn (4) 45s.*

IRELAND – SOUTH COAST
TUSKAR ROCK TO OLD HEAD OF KINSALE

S Rock buoy 52°10'·80N 06°12'·80W Q (6) + L Fl 15s; SCM.
Fundale buoy 52°10'·66N 06°20'·20W Fl (2) R 10s; PHM.

• CARNA
Pier hd 52°11'·89N 06°20'·80W Fl R 3s 6m 4M.
Barrels buoy 52°08'·30N 06°22'·00W Q (3) 10s; *Whis;* ECM.

• KILMORE QUAY
Ldg lts 007·9°: Both Oc 4s 20m, W pylons, R stripe. 52°10'·4N 06°35'·1W.
N Bkwtr hd 52°10'·25N 06°35'·10W Q RG 6m 5M; vis R269°-354°, G354°-003°, R003°-077°.
CONINGBEG lt F 52°02'·38N 06°39'·44W Fl (3) 30s 12m **24M**, H24; R hull, and tr, Racon (M); *Horn (3) 60s.*

• WATERFORD
Hook Head 52°07'·30N 06°55'·80W Fl 3s 46m **23M**; W tr, two B bands; Racon (K).
Duncannon dir lt 002°. 52°13'·21N 06°56'·19W Oc WRG 4s 13m W11M, R8M, G8M; W tr on fort; vis G358°-001·7°, W001·7°-002·2°, R002·2°-006°. Same tr, Oc WR 4s 13m W9M, R7M; vis R119°-149°, W149°-172°.
Duncannon Bar buoy 52°11'·27N 06°55'·90W Fl G 2s; SHM.
Duncannon Bar buoy 52°11'·27N 06°56'·23W Fl R 2s; PHM.

Duncannon Spit buoy 52°12'·67N 06°56'·00W Fl (2) G 5s; SHM.

Passage Pt 52°14'·23N 06°57'·70W Fl WR 5s 7m W6M, R5M; R pile structure; vis W shore-127°, R127°-302°.

Cheek Pt 52°16'·11N 06°59'·30W Q WR 6m 5M; W mast; vis W007°-289°, R289°-007°.

Sheagh 52°16'·29N 06°59'·38W Fl R 3s 29m 3M; Gy tr; vis 090°-318°.

Kilmokea 52°16'·48N 06°58'·85W Fl 5s.

R. Barrow railway bridge 2 FR (Hor); tfc sigs.

Snowhill Pt ldg lts 255°. Front, 52°16'·37N 07°00'·85W Fl WR 2·5s 5m 3M; vis W222°-020°, R020°-057°, W057°-107°; rear, Flour Mill, 750m from front, Q 12m 5M.

Queen's Chan ldg lts 098°. Front, 52°15'·30N 07°02'·32W QR 8m 5M; B tr, W band; vis 030°-210°; rear, 550m from front, Q 15m 5M; W mast.

Giles Quay 52°15'·47N 07°04'·15W Fl 3s 9m; vis 255°-086°.

Cove 52°15'·02N 07°05'·10W Fl WRG 6s 6m 2M; W tr; vis R111°-161°, G161°-234°, W234°-111°.

Smelting Ho Pt 52°15'·13N 07°05'·20W Q 8m 3M; W mast.

Ballycar 52°15'·06N 07°05'·42W Fl RG 3s 5m; vis G127°-212°, R212°-284°.

• DUNMORE EAST

Dunmore East,E Pier hd 52°08'·91N 06°59'·32W Fl WR 8s 13m **W17M**, R13M; Gy tr, vis W225°-310°, R310°-004°.

E bkwtr extn 52°08'·96N 06°59'·32W Fl R 2s 6m 4M; vis 000°-310°.

• DUNGARVAN

Ballinacourty Pt 52°04'·67N 07°33'·13W Fl (2) WRG 10s 16m W10M, R8M, G8M; W tr; vis G245°-274°, W274°-302°, R302°-325°, W325°-117°.

Helvick buoy 52°03'·59N 07°32'·20W Q (3) 10s; ECM.

Mine Head 51°59'·50N 07°35'·20W Fl (4) 20s 87m **28M**; W tr, B band; vis 228°-052°.

• YOUGHAL

Bar Rocks buoy 51°54'·83N 07°50'·00W; SCM.

Blackball Ledge buoy 51°55'·32N 07°48'·48W; PHM.

W side of ent 51°56'·55N 07°50'·48W Fl WR 2·5s 24m **W17M**, R13M; W tr; vis W183°-273°, R273°-295°, W295°-307°, R307°-351°, W351°-003°.

• BALLYCOTTON

Ballycotton 51°49'·50N 07°59'·10W Fl WR 10s 59m **W21M, R17M**; B tr, within W walls, B lantern; vis W238°-048°, R048°-238°; *Horn (4) 90s.*

Smiths buoy 51°48'·60N 08°00'·66W Fl (3) R 10s; PHM.

Pollock Rk buoy 51°46'·20N 08°07'·80W Fl R 6s; PHM.

• CORK

Daunt Rk buoy 51°43'·50N 08°17'·60W Fl (2) R 6s; PHM.

Cork buoy 51°42'·90N 08°15'·55W L Fl 10s; *Whis;* Racon (T); SWM.

Fort Davis ldg lts 354·1°. Front, 51°48'·79N 08°15'·77W Oc 5s 29m 10M; Or □ . Dir lt WRG; vis FG351·5°-352·25°, AlWG352·25°-353°, FW353°-355°, AlWR355°-355·75°, FR355·75°-356·5°; rear, Dognose Quay, 203m from front, Oc 5s 37m 10M; Or □, synch with front.

Roche's Pt 51°47'·57N 08°15'·24W Fl WR 3s 30m **W20M, R16M**; vis Rshore-292°, W292°-016°, R016°-033°, W(unintens) 033°-159°, R159°-shore.

Outer Hbr buoy E2 51°47'·50N 08°15'·62W Fl R 2·5s; PHM.

Chicago Knoll buoy E1 51°47'·66N 08°15'·50W Fl G 5s; SHM.

The Sound buoy E4 51°47'·91N 08°15'·72W Q; NCM.

White Bay ldg lts 034·6°. Front, 51°48'·51N 08°15'·18W Oc R 5s 11m 5M; W hut. Rear, 113m from front, Oc R 5s 21m 5M; W hut; synch with front.

Curraghbinney ldg lts 252°. Front, 51°48'·63N 08°17'·56W F 10m 3M; W ◊ on col. Rear, 61m from front, F 15m 3M; W ◊ on col; vis 229·5°-274·5°.

Spit Bank Pile 51°50'·70N 08°16'·41W Iso WR 4s 10m W10M, R7M; W house on R piles; vis R087°-196°, W196°-221°, R221°-358°.

East Ferry Marina, E Passage 51°51'·90N 08°12'·75W 2 FR (vert) at N and S ends.

Power buoy 51°45'·57N 08°06'·62W Q (6) + L Fl 15s; SCM.

• KINSALE/OYSTER HAVEN

Bulman buoy 51°40'·11N 08°29'·70W Q (6) + L Fl 15s; SCM; *Bell.*

Charle's Fort 51°41'·72N 08°29'·94W Fl WRG 5s 18m W8M, R5M, G6M; vis G348°-358°, W358°-004°, R004°-168°; H24.

OLD HEAD OF KINSALE TO MIZEN HEAD

Old Head of Kinsale, S point 51°36'·26N 08°31'·98W Fl (2) 10s 72m **25M**; B tr, two W bands; RC; *Horn (3) 45s.*

• COURTMACSHERRY

Black Tom buoy 51°36'·39N 08°37'·00W; SHM.

Wood Pt (Land Pt) 51°38'·3N 08°41'·0W Fl (2) WR 5s 15m 5M; vis W315°-332°, R332°-315°.

Galley Head summit 51°31'·78N 08°57'·14W Fl (5) 20s 53m **23M**; W tr; vis 256°-065°.

• GLANDORE

Glandore Harbour SW lt bn 51°33'·12N 09°06'·60W Fl (2+1) G 10s 4M; GRG.

Sunk Rk buoy 51°33'·50N 09°06'·80W Q; NCM.

• CASTLE HAVEN

Reen Pt 51°30'·95N 09°10'·46W Fl WRG 10s 9m W5M, R3M, G3M; W tr; vis Gshore-338°, W338°-001°, R001°-shore.

Kowloon Bridge buoy 51°27'·55N 09°13'·71W Q (6) + L Fl 15s; SCM.

• BALTIMORE

Barrack Pt 51°28'·33N 09°23'·65W Fl (2) WR 6s 40m W6M, R3M; vis R168°-294°, W294°-038°.

Loo Rk buoy 51°28'·42N 09°23'·42W Fl G 3s; SHM.

Fastnet, W end 51°23'·33N 09°36'·14W Fl 5s 49m **27M**; Gy tr; Racon (G); *Horn (4) 60s.*

Copper Pt Long Island, E end 51°30'·22N 09°32'·02W Q (3) 10s 16m 8M; W ● tr.

Amelia Rk buoy 51°29'·95N 09°31'·42W Fl G 3s; SHM.

• SCHULL

Ldg lts 346° Front, 51°31'·64N 09°32'·39W Oc 5s 5m 11M, W mast; rear, 91m from front, Oc 5s 8m 11M; W mast.

• CROOKHAVEN

Rock Island Pt 51°28'·57N 09°42'·23W L Fl WR 8s 20m W13M, R11M; W tr; vis W over Long Island B to 281°, R281°-340°; inside harbour R281°-348°, W348° towards N shore.

Mizen Head 51°26'·97N 09°49'·18W Iso 4s 55m **15M**; vis 313°-133°; RC.

IRELAND – SOUTH WEST COAST
MIZEN HEAD TO DINGLE BAY

Sheep's Head 51°32'·57N 09°50'·89W Fl (3) WR 15s 83m **W18M, R15M**; W bldg; vis R007°-017°, W017°-212°.

• BANTRY BAY/CASTLETOWN BEARHAVEN/WHIDDY ISLAND/BANTRY/GLENGARIFF

Roancarrigmore 51°39'·17N 09°44'·79W Fl WR 3s 18m **W18M**, R14M; W ● tr, B band; vis W312°-050°, R050°-122°, R(unintens) 122°-242°, R242°-312°. Reserve lt W8M, R6M obsc 140°-220°.

Whiddy Island W clearing lt 51°41'·01N 09°31'·81W Oc 2s 22m 3M; vis 073°-106°.
W ent, **Ardnakinna Pt** 51°37'·08N 09°55'·06W Fl (2) WR 10s 62m **W17M**, R14M, H24; W ○ tr; vis R319°-348°, W348°-066°, R066°-shore.
FR on radio mast 3·45M 295°.
Castletown dir lt 024° 51°38'·78N 09°54'·05W Dir Oc WRG 5s 4m W14M, R11M, G11M; W hut, R stripe; vis G020·5°-024°, W024°-024·5°, R024·5°-027·5°.
Perch Rk 51°38'·82N 09°54'·43W QG 4m 1M; G col.
Castletown ldg lts 010°. Front, 51°39'·14N 09°54'·37W Oc 3s 4m 1M; W col, R stripe; vis 005°-015°. Rear, 80m from front, Oc 3s 7m 1M; W with R stripe; vis 005°-015°.

Bull Rock, Fl 15s 83m **21M**, vis 220°-186°; W tr; Racon (N), 51°35'·50N 10°18'·02W.

● KENMARE RIVER/DARRYNANE/BALLYCROVANE
Ballycrovane Hbr 51°42'·63N 09° 57'·53W Fl R 3s.
Bunaw, ldg lts 041°: Front Oc R3s 9m; rear Iso R 2s 11m; both B poles, Y bands.
Darrynane ldg lts 034°. Front, 51°45'·90N 10°09'·20W, Oc 3s 10m 4M; rear, Oc 3s 16m 4M.

Skelligs Rk 51°46'·09N 10°32'·45W Fl (3) 10s 53m **27M**; W tr; vis 262°-115°; partly obsc'd by land within 6M 110°-115°.

● VALENTIA/PORTMAGEE
Fort (Cromwell) Pt 51°56'·00N 10°19'·25W Fl WR 2s 16m **W17M**, **R15M**; W tr; vis R304°-351°, W102°-304°; obsc from seaward by Doulus hd when brg more than 180°.
FR lts on radio masts on Geokaun hill 1·20M WSW.
Harbour Rk lt 51°55'·79N 10°18'·91W Q (3) 10s 4m 5M; vis 080°-040°; ECM.
ldg lts 141°. Front, 51°55'·49N 10°18'·39W Oc WRG 4s 25m W11M, R8M, G8M; W tr, R stripe; vis G134°-140°, W140°-142°, R142°-148°. Rear, 122m from front, Oc 4s 43m 5M; vis 133°-233° synch with front.

DINGLE BAY TO LOOP HEAD

● DINGLE BAY/VENTRY/DINGLE
Dingle, NE side of ent 52°07'·28N 10°15'·48W Fl G 3s 20m 6M.
Pier hd 52°08'·21N 10°16'·49W.
Ldg lts 182°: Front 52°07'·40N 10°16'·53W; rear 100m from front, both Oc 3s.

Inishtearaght, W end Blasket Islands 52°04'·51N 10°39'·66W Fl (2) 20s 84m **27M**; W tr; vis 318°-221°; Racon (O).

● BRANDON BAY
Brandon Pier hd 52°16'·05N 10°09'·58W 2 FG (vert) 5m 4M.

● TRALEE BAY
Little Samphire Island 52°16'·23N 09°52'·88W Fl WRG 5s 27m **W16M**, R13M; G13M; Bu ● tr; vis R262°-275°, R280°-090°, G090°-140°, W140°-152°, R152°-172°.
Gt Samphire Island 52°16'·13N 09°51'·78W QR 15m 3M; vis 242°-097°.
Fenit Hbr Pier hd 52°16'·22N 09°51'·51W 2 FR (vert) 12m 3M; vis 148°-058°.

SHANNON ESTUARY

Loop Head 52°33'·65N 09°55'·90W Fl (4) 20s 84m **23M**; RC.
Ballybunnion buoy 52°32'·50N 09°46'·90W Q; NCM: Racon.
Kilcredaune Head 52°34'·79N 09°42'·58W Fl 6s 41m 13M; W tr; obsc 224°-247° by hill within 1M.
Kilcredaune buoy 52°34'·42N 09°41'·17W Fl (2+1) R 10s; PHM.
Tail of Beal buoy 52°34'·37N 09°40'·71W Q (9) 15s; WCM.
Carrigaholt buoy 52°34'·90N 09°40'·47W Fl (2) R 6s; PHM.

Beal Spit buoy 52°34'·80N 09°39'·94W VQ (9) 10s; WCM.
Beal Bar buoy 52°35'·16N 09°39'·19W Q; NCM.
Doonaha buoy 52°35'·47N 09°38'·46W Fl (3) R 10s; PHM.
Letter Pt buoy 52°35'·42N 09°35'·85W Fl R 7s; PHM.
Asdee buoy 52°35'·07N 09°34'·51W Fl R 5s; PHM.
Rineanna buoy 52°35'·57N 09°31'·20W QR; PHM.
Carrig buoy 52°35'·59N 09°29'·72W Fl G 3s; SHM.
Scattery Island, Rineana Pt 52°36'·32N 09°31'·03W Fl (2) 7·5s 15m 10M; W tr; vis 208°-092° (H24).

● KILRUSH
Marina ent chan ldg lts 355°: Front, 52°37'·93N 09°30'·26W Oc 3s; rear, 75m from front, Oc 3s.
Tarbert I N Pt 52°35'·50N 09°21'·79W Iso WR 4s 18m W14M, R10M; W ○ tr; vis W069°-277°, R277°-287°, W287°-339°.
Tarbert (Ballyhoolahan Pt) ldg lts 128·2°: Front, 52°34'·32N 09°18'·75W Iso 2s 13m 3M; △ on W tr; vis 123·2°-133·2°. Rear, 400m from front, Iso 5s 18m 3M; G stripe on W bn.
Garraunbaun Pt 51°35'·59N 09°13'·90W Fl (3) WR 10s 16m W8M, R5M; W □ col, vis R shore-072°, W072°-242°, R242°-shore.
Rinealon Pt 52°37'·10N 09°09'·77W Fl 2·5s 4m 7M; B col, W bands; vis 234°-088°.

● FOYNES
W Chan ldg lts 107·6° (may be moved for changes in chan):
Front, Barneen Pt 52°36'·89N 09°06'·55W Iso WRG 4s 3m W4M, R3M, G3M; B △ with W stripe on W col with B bands; vis W273·2°-038·2°, R038·2°-094·2°, G094·2°-104·2°, W104·2°-108·2°, R108·2°-114·2°. Rear, E jetty, 540m from front, Oc 4s 16m 10M; Or △ on post.
Colleen Pt No. 3 52°36'·89N 09°06'·81W QG 2m 2M; W col, B bands.
Hunts (Weir) Pt No. 4 52°37'·01N 09°06'·96W VQ (4) R 10s 2m 2M; W col, B bands.

RIVER SHANNON

Beeves Rk 52°39'·00N 09°01'·30W Fl WR 5s 12m W12M, R9M; vis W064·5°-091°, R091°-238°, W238°-265°, W(unintens) 265°-064·5°.
Shannon Airport 52°41'·71N 08°55'·66W Aero Al Fl WG 7·5s 40m.
Dernish Island Pier hd, 2 FR (vert) 4m 2M each end.
E bkwtr hd 52°40'·82N 08°54'·80W QR 3m 1M.
Conor Rock 52°40'·91N 08°54'·20W Fl R 4s 6m 6M; W tr; vis 228°-093°.
N Channel ldg lts 093°. Front, Tradree Rk 52°40'·99N 08°49'·82W Fl R 2s 6m 5M; W trs; vis 246°-110°. Rear 0·65M from front, Iso 6s 14m 5M; W tr, R bands; vis 327°-190°.
Bird Rock 52°40'·93N 08°50'·22W QG 6m 5M; W tr.
Grass I 52°40'·41N 08°48'·40W Fl G 2s 6m 4M; W col, B bands.
Laheen's Rk 52°40'·32N 08°48'·10W QR 4m 5M.
S side Spilling Rk 52°40'·0N 08°47'·1W Fl G 5s 5m 5M.
N side, ldg lts 061°. Front, 52°40'·69N 08°45'·23W, Crawford Rk 490m from rear, Fl R 3s 6m 5M. Crawford No. 2, Common Rear, 52°40'·83N 08°44'·84W Iso 6s 10m 5M.
Ldg lts 302·1°. Flagstaff Rk, 670m from rear, Fl R 2s 7m 5M.
The Whelps 52°40'·67N 08°45'·05W Fl G 3s 5m 5M; W pile.
Ldg lts 106·5°. Meelick Rk, Front 52°40'·23N 08°42'·31W Iso 4s 6m 3M. Meelick No. 2, rear 275m from front Iso 6s 9m 5M; both W pile structures.
Ldg lts 146°, Braemar Pt, Front 52°39'·16N 08°41'·89W Iso 4s 5m 5M. Rear, Braemar No. 2, 122m from front, Iso 6s 6m 4M; both W pile structures.
N side Clonmacken Pt 52°39'·50N 08°40'·64W Fl R 3s 7m 4M.
E side Spillane's tr 52°39'·33N 08°39'·67W Fl 3s 11m 6M; turret on tr.

● LIMERICK DOCK
Lts in line 098·5°. Front, 52°39'·48N 08°38'·76W. Rear, 100m from front; both F; R ◇ on cols; occas.

8.12.5 PASSAGE INFORMATION

For all Irish waters the Sailing Directions published by the Irish Cruising Club are strongly recommended, and particularly on the W coast, where other information is scarce. They are published in two volumes: *E and N coasts of Ireland* which runs anti-clockwise from Carnsore Pt to Bloody Foreland, and *S and W coasts of Ireland* which goes clockwise. For notes on crossing the Irish Sea, see 8.13.5; and for Distances across it see 8.0.9.

MALAHIDE TO TUSKAR ROCK (charts 1468, 1787)

Malahide (8.12.8), 4M from both Lambay Is and Howth, can be entered in most weather via a chan dredged (allegedly in 1996) through drying sandbanks. Ireland's Eye, a rky island which rises steeply to a height of 99m, lies about 7½ca N of Howth (8.12.9) with reefs running SE and SW from Thulla Rk at its SE end. Ben of Howth, on N side of Dublin Bay, is steep-to, with no dangers more than 1ca offshore.

Rosbeg Bank lies on the N side of Dublin Bay. Burford Bank, on which the sea breaks in E gales, and Kish Bank lie offshore in the approaches. The N-going stream begins at HW Dublin – 0600, and the S-going at HW Dublin, sp rates 3kn.

From Dublin (8.12.10) to Carnsore Pt the shallow offshore banks cause dangerous overfalls and dictate the route which is sheltered from the W winds. Tidal streams run mainly N and S, but the N-going flood sets across the banks on the inside, and the S-going ebb sets across them on the outside. As a cruising area, hbr facilities are starting to improve (1999).

Leaving Dublin Bay, yachts normally use Dalkey Sound, but with a foul tide or light wind it is better to use Muglins Sound. Muglins (lt) is steep-to except for a rk about 1ca WSW of the lt. Beware Leac Buidhe (dries) 1ca E of Clare Rk. The inshore passage is best as far as Wicklow (8.12.11).

Thereafter yachts may either route offshore, passing east of Arklow Bank and its Lanby to fetch Tuskar Rock or Greenore Pt. Or keep inshore of Arklow Bank, avoiding Glassgorman Banks; through the Rusk Channel, inside Blackwater and Lucifer Banks, to round Carnsore Pt NW of Tuskar Rock. Arklow (8.12.12) is safe in offshore winds; Wexford (8.12.13) has a difficult entrance. Rosslare (8.12.14) lacks yacht facilities, but provides good shelter to wait out a SW'ly blow.

TUSKAR ROCK TO OLD HEAD OF KINSALE (chart 2049)

Dangerous rks lie up to 2ca NW and 6½ca SSW of Tuskar Rk and there can be a dangerous race off Carnsore Pt. In bad weather or poor visibility, use the Inshore Traffic Zone of the Tuskar Rock TSS (8.12.14), passing to seaward of Tuskar Rk (lt, RC), the Barrels ECM lt buoy and Coningbeg lt float.

If taking the inshore passage from Greenore Pt, stay inside The Bailies to pass 2ca off Carnsore Pt. Watch for lobster pots in this area. Steer WSW to pass N of Black Rk and the Bohurs, S of which are extensive overfalls. The little hbr of Kilmore Quay (8.12.15) has been rebuilt with a new marina, but beware rks and shoals in the approaches.

Saltee Sound (chart 2740) is a safe passage, least width 3ca, between Great and Little Saltee, conspic islands to S and N. Sebber Bridge extends 7½ca N from the NE point of Great Saltee and Jackeen Rk is 1M NW of the S end of Little Saltee, so care is needed through the sound, where the stream runs 3·5 kn at sp. There are several rks S of the Saltees, but yachts may pass between Coningbeg Rk and the lt float. There are no obstructions on a direct course for a point 1M S of Hook Head, to avoid the overfalls and Tower Race, which at times extend about 1M S of the Head.

Dunmore East (8.12.17 and chart 2046) is a useful passage port at the mouth of Waterford Hbr (8.12.16). To the W, beware salmon nets and Falskirt, a dangerous rk off Swines Pt. There are few offlying rks from Tramore Bay to Ballinacourty

Pt on the N side of Dungarvan Bay (8.12.19 and chart 2017). Helvick is a small sheltered hbr approached along the S shore of the bay, keeping S of Helvick Rk (ECM lt buoy) and other dangers to the N.

Mine Hd (lt) has two dangerous rks, The Rogue about 2½ca E and The Longship 1M SW. To the W, there is a submerged rk 100m SE of Ram Hd. Here the W-going stream starts at HW Cobh + 0230, and the E-going at HW Cobh –0215, sp rates 1·5 kn. For Youghal, see 8.12.18. Pass 1ca S of Capel Island. The sound is not recommended.

The N side of Ballycotton B is foul up to 5ca offshore. Ballycotton Hbr (8.12.19) is small and crowded, but usually there is sheltered anch outside. Sound Rk and Small Is lie between the mainland and Ballycotton Is (lt, fog sig). From Ballycotton to Cork keep at least 5ca off for dangers including The Smiths (PHM lt buoy) 1·5M WSW of Ballycotton Island. Pass between Hawk Rk, close off Power Hd, and Pollock Rk (PHM lt buoy) 1.25M SE.

Near the easy entrance and excellent shelter of Cork Harbour (8.12.19 and chart 1777), Ringabella Bay offers temp anch in good weather. 7ca SE of Robert's Hd is Daunt Rk (3·5m) on which seas break in bad weather; marked by PHM lt buoy. Little Sovereign on with Reanies Hd 241° leads inshore of it. The Sovereigns are large rks off Oyster Haven, a good hbr but prone to swell in S'lies. The ent is clear except for Harbour Rk which must be passed on its W side, see 8.12.20. Bulman Rk (SCM lt buoy) is 4ca S of Preghane Pt at the ent to Kinsale's fine harbour (8.12.20).

Old Head of Kinsale (lt, fog sig, RC) is quite steep-to, but a race extends 1M to SW on W-going stream, and to SE on E-going stream. There is an inshore passage in light weather, but in strong winds keep 2M off.

OLD HEAD OF KINSALE TO MIZEN HEAD (chart 2424)

From Cork to Mizen Hd there are many natural hbrs. Only the best are mentioned here. Offshore the stream seldom exceeds 1·5kn, but it is stronger off headlands causing races and overfalls with wind against tide. Prolonged W winds increase the rate/duration of the E-going stream, and strong E winds have a similar effect on the W-going stream.

In the middle of Courtmacsherry Bay are several dangers, from E to W: Blueboy Rk, Barrel Rk (with Inner Barrels closer inshore), and Black Tom; Horse Rk is off Barry's Pt at the W side of the bay. These must be avoided going to or from Courtmacsherry, where the bar breaks in strong S/SE winds, but the river carries 2·5m; see 8.12.21. Beware Cotton Rk and Shoonta Rk close E of Seven Heads, off which rks extend 50m. Clonakilty B has little to offer. Keep at least 5ca off Galley Hd to clear Dhulic Rk, and further off in fresh winds. Offshore the W-going stream makes at HW Cobh + 0200, and the E-going at HW Cobh – 0420, sp rates 1·5 kn.

Across Glandore Bay there are good anchs off Glandore (8.12.22), or off Union Hall. Sailing W from Glandore, pass outside or inside High Is and Low Is, but if inside beware Belly Rk (awash) about 3ca S of Rabbit Is. On passage Toe Head has foul ground 100m S, and 7½ca S is a group of rks called the Stags. Castle Haven (8.12.23), a sheltered and attractive hbr, is entered between Reen Pt (lt) and Battery Pt. Baltimore (8.12.24) is 10M further W.

Fastnet Rk (lt, fog sig) is nearly 4M WSW of C Clear; 2½ca NE of it is an outlying rk. An E/W TSS (8.12.24) lies between 2 and 8M SSE of the Fastnet. Long Island Bay can be entered from C Clear or through Gascanane Sound, between Clear Is and Sherkin Is. Carrigmore Rks lie in the middle of this chan, with Gascanane Rk 1ca W of them. The chan between Carrigmore Rks and Badger Island is best. If bound for Crookhaven, beware Bullig Reef, N of Clear Is.

Schull (8.12.25) is N of Long Island, inside which passage can be made W'ward to Crookhaven (8.12.26). This is a well sheltered hbr, accessible at all states of tide, entered between

Rock Is lt Ho and Alderman Rks, ENE of Streek Hd. Anch off the village.

Off Mizen Hd (lt ho) the W-going stream starts at HW Cobh + 0120, and the E-going at HW Cobh − 0500. The sp rate is 4 kn, which with wind against tide forms a dangerous race, sometimes reaching to Brow Hd or Three Castle Hd , with broken water right to the shore.

THE WEST COAST

This coast offers wonderful cruising, although exposed to the Atlantic and any swell offshore; but this diminishes mid-summer. In bad weather however the sea breaks dangerously on shoals with quite substantial depths. There is usually a refuge close by, but if caught out in deteriorating weather and poor vis, a stranger may need to make an offing until conditions improve, so a stout yacht and good crew are required. Even in mid-summer at least one gale may be meet in a two-week cruise. Fog is less frequent than in the Irish Sea. Listen regularly to the Radio Telefis Eireann forecasts; see 5.9.1.

Tidal streams are weak, except round headlands. There are few lights, so inshore navigation is unwise after dark. Coastal navigation is feasible at night in good visibility. Keep a good watch for drift nets off the coast, and for lobster pots in inshore waters. Stores, fuel and water are not readily available.

MIZZEN HEAD TO DINGLE BAY (chart 2423)

At S end of Dunmanus Bay Three Castle Hd has rks 1ca W, and sea can break on S Bullig 4ca off Hd. Dunmanus B (chart 2552) has three hbrs: Dunmanus, Kitchen Cove and Dunbeacon. Carbery, Cold and Furze Is lie in middle of B, and it is best to keep N of them. Sheep's Hd (lt) is at the S end of Bantry Bay (8.12.27; charts 1838, 1840) which has excellent hbrs, notably Glengariff and Castletown. There are few dangers offshore, except around Bear and Whiddy Islands. Off Blackball Hd at W entrance to Bantry B there can be a nasty race, particularly on W-going stream against the wind. Keep 3ca off Crow Is to clear dangers.

Dursey Island is steep-to except for rk 7½ca NE of Dursey Hd and Lea Rk (1·4m)1½ca SW . The Bull (lt, fog sig, Racon) and two rks W of it lie 2·5M WNW of Dursey Hd. The Cow is midway between The Bull and Dursey Hd, with clear water each side. Calf and Heifer Rks are 7½ca SW of Dursey Hd, where there is often broken water. 2M W of The Bull the stream turns NW at HW Cobh + 0150, and SE at HW Cobh − 0420. Dursey Sound (chart 2495) is a good short cut, but the stream runs 4kn at sp; W-going starts at HW Cobh + 0135, and E-going at HW Cobh − 0450. Flag Rk lies almost awash in mid-chan at the narrows, which are crossed by cables 25m above MHWS. Hold very close to the Island shore. Beware wind changes in the sound, and broken water at N entrance.

Kenmare R. (chart 2495 and 8.12.28) has attractive hbrs and anchs, but its shores are rky, with no lights. The best places are Sneem, Kilmakilloge and Ardgroom. Off Lamb's Head, Two Headed Island is steep-to; further W is Moylaun Is with a rk 300m SW of it. Little Hog (or Deenish) Island is rky 1·5M to W, followed by Great Hog (or Scariff) Is which has a rk close N, and a reef extending 2ca W.

Darrynane is an attractive, sheltered hbr NNW of Lamb Hd. The entrance has ldg lts and marks, but is narrow and dangerous in bad weather. Ballinskelligs Bay has an anch N of Horse Is, which has two rks close off E end. Centre of bay is a prohib anch (cables reported).

Rough water is met between Bolus Hd and Bray Hd with fresh onshore winds or swell. The SW end of Puffin Island is steep-to, but the sound to the E is rky and not advised. Great Skellig (lit) is 6M, and Little Skellig 5M WSW of Puffin Is. Lemon Rk lies between Puffin Is and Little Skellig. Here the stream turns N at HW Cobh + 0500, and S at HW Cobh − 018. There is a rk 3ca SW of Great Skellig. When very calm it is possible to go alongside at Blind Man's Cove on NE side of Great Skellig, where there are interesting ruins.

DINGLE BAY TO LISCANOR BAY (chart 2254)

Dingle Bay (charts 2789, 2790) is wide and deep, with few dangers around its shores. Dingle (8.12.29) has a small marina. The best anchs are at Portmagee and Ventry. At the NW ent to the bay, 2·5M SSW of Slea Hd, is Wild Bank (or Three Fathom Pinnacle), a shallow patch with overfalls. 3M SW of Wild Bank is Barrack Rk, which breaks in strong winds.

The Blasket Islands are very exposed, with strong tides and overfalls, but worth a visit in settled weather (chart 2790). Great Blasket and Inishvickillane each have anch and landing on their NE side. Inishtearaght is the most W'ly Is (lt), but further W lie Tearaght Rks, and 3M S are Little Foze and Gt Foze Rks. Blasket Sound is the most convenient N-S route, 1M wide, and easy in daylight and reasonable weather with fair wind or tide; extensive rks and shoals form its W side. The N-going stream starts at HW Galway + 0430, and the S-going at HW Galway − 0155, with sp rate 3 kn.

Between Blasket Sound and Sybil Pt there is a race in W or NW winds with N-going tide, and often a nasty sea. Sybil Pt has steep cliffs, and offlying rks extend 3½ca.

Smerwick hbr, entered between Duncapple Is and the E Sister is sheltered, except from NW or N winds. From here the scenery is spectacular to Brandon Bay on the W side of which there is an anch, but exposed to N winds and to swell.

There is no lt from Inishtearaght to Loop Hd, apart from Little Samphire Is in Tralee B, where Fenit hbr provides the only secure refuge until entering the Shannon Estuary. The coast from Loop Hd to Liscanor Bay has no safe anchs, and no lts. Take care not to be set inshore, although there are few offlying dangers except near Mutton Is and in Liscanor Bay.

THE SHANNON ESTUARY (charts 1819, 1547, 1548, 1549)

The estuary and lower reaches of the Shannon (8.12.30), are tidal for 50M, from its mouth between Loop Hd and Kerry Hd up to Limerick Dock, some 15M beyond the junction with R. Fergus. The tides and streams are those of a deep-water inlet, with roughly equal durations of rise and fall, and equal rates of flood and ebb streams. In the entrance the flood stream begins at HW Galway − 0555, and the ebb at HW Galway + 0015.

There are several anchs available for yachts on passage up or down the coast. Kilbaha Bay (chart 1819) is about 3M E of Loop Hd, and is convenient in good weather or in N winds, but exposed to SE and any swell. Carrigaholt B (chart 1547), entered about 1M N of Kilcredaun Pt, is well sheltered from W winds and has little tidal stream. In N winds there is anch SE of Querrin Pt (chart 1547), 4·5M further up river on N shore. At Kilrush (8.12.31) there is a marina and anchs E of Scattery Is and N of Hog Is. Note that there are overfalls 0·75M S of Scattery Is with W winds and ebb tide.

Off Kilcredaun Pt the ebb reaches 4kn at sp, and in strong winds between S and NW a bad race forms. This can be mostly avoided by keeping near the N shore, which is free from offlying dangers, thereby cheating the worst of the tide. When leaving the Shannon in strong W winds, aim to pass Kilcredaun Pt at slack water, and again keep near the N shore. Loop Hd (lt, RC) marks the N side of Shannon est, and should be passed 3ca off. Here the stream runs SW from HW Galway + 0300, and NE from HW Galway − 0300.

Above the junction with R. Fergus (chart 1540) the tidal characteristics become more like those of most rivers, ie the flood stream is stronger than the ebb, but it runs for a shorter time. In the Shannon the stream is much affected by the wind. S and W winds increase the rate and duration of the flood stream, and reduce the ebb. Strong N or E winds have the opposite effect. Prolonged or heavy rain increases the rate and duration of the ebb. The Shannon is the longest river in Ireland, rising at Lough Allen 100M above Limerick, thence 50M to the sea.

8.12.6 DISTANCE TABLE

Approximate distances in nautical miles are by the most direct route, whilst avoiding dangers and allowing for Traffic Separation Schemes. Places in *italics* are in adjoining areas; places in **bold** are in 8.0.9, Distances across the Irish Sea.

	1	2	3	4	5	6	7	8	9	10	11	12	13	14	15	16	17	18	19	20
1. *Carlingford Lough*	**1**																			
2. Howth	39	**2**																		
3. **Dun Laoghaire**	48	8	**3**																	
4. **Wicklow**	63	25	21	**4**																
5. **Arklow**	75	37	36	15	**5**															
6. **Tuskar Rock**	113	73	70	52	37	**6**														
7. **Rosslare**	108	70	66	47	34	8	**7**													
8. **Dunmore East**	139	101	102	84	69	32	32	**8**												
9. **Youghal**	172	134	133	115	100	63	65	34	**9**											
8. **Crosshaven**	192	154	155	137	122	85	85	59	25	**10**										
11. Kinsale	202	164	168	150	135	98	95	69	35	17	**11**									
12. **Baltimore**	239	201	196	177	164	128	132	102	70	54	42	**12**								
13. **Fastnet Rock**	250	212	207	189	174	137	144	112	78	60	49	10	**13**							
14. Bantry	281	243	241	223	208	171	174	146	112	94	83	42	34	**14**						
15. Darrynane	283	245	240	221	208	172	176	146	114	98	86	44	39	38	**15**					
16. Valentia	295	257	252	242	227	184	188	165	131	113	102	56	48	55	16	**16**				
17. Dingle	308	270	265	246	233	197	201	171	139	123	111	69	61	63	29	13	**17**			
18. Kilrush	361	323	318	299	286	250	254	224	192	176	164	122	114	116	82	66	64	**18**		
19. *Galway*	366	362	357	339	324	287	291	262	228	210	199	159	150	155	119	103	101	76	**19**	
20. *Slyne Head*	317	351	346	328	313	276	283	251	217	199	188	153	139	144	113	97	95	75	49	**20**

SPECIAL NOTES FOR IRELAND

8.12.7

Céad Míle Fáilte! One hundred thousand Welcomes!

ORDNANCE SURVEY map numbers refer to the Irish OS maps, scale 1:50,000 or 1¼ inch to 1 mile, which cover the whole island, including Ulster, in 89 sheets.

IRISH CUSTOMS: First port of call should preferably be at Customs posts in one of the following hbrs: Dublin, Dun Laoghaire, Waterford, New Ross, Cork, Ringaskiddy, Bantry, Foynes, Limerick, Galway, Sligo and Killybegs. Yachts may, in fact, make their first call anywhere and if no Customs officer arrives within a reasonable time, the skipper should inform the nearest Garda (Police) station of the yacht's arrival. Only non-EC members should fly flag Q or show Ⓡ over Ⓦ lts on arrival. Passports are not required by UK citizens.

IRISH MARINE EMERGENCY SERVICE (IMES): SAR ops in the Republic are controlled by MRSCs at Dublin, Malin Head and Valentia; and coordinated by Dublin MRCC, ☎ (01) 6620922/3. See 6.11.1. MRSC ☎ No(s), as shown in each port, should normally be used, but in emergency dial 999 and ask for *Marine Rescue*.

Dublin MRCC communicates/relays to vessels via the Coast Radio Stns at Dublin, Wicklow, Rosslare, Minehead, Cork, Bantry, Valentia, Shannon, Glenhead, Clifden, Belmullet and Malin Head (see 4.10.2 for VHF channels). The IMES can call on IMES helicopters, based at Dublin, Shannon and Finner (Donegal), the RNLI, Coast & Cliff Rescue Service, Irish Air Corps helicopters and search aircraft, Irish naval vessels, civil aircraft, the Irish lighthouse service and the Garda Siochana. The IMES liaises with UK and France and acts as a clearing house for all messages received during any rescue operation within 100M of the Irish coast.

COAST AND CLIFF RESCUE SERVICE: This is part of the IMES and comprises about 50 stations manned by volunteers, who are trained in first aid and equipped with inflatables, breeches buoys, cliff ladders etc. Their ☎ numbers (the Leader's residence) are given, where appropriate under each port.

WEATHER: Weather bulletins (comprising gale warnings and a 24 hrs forecast for the Irish Sea and Irish waters up to 30M offshore) are broadcast by RTE Radio 1 at: 0602, 1253, 1834 (Sat, Sun, Hols), 1902 (Mon-Fri) and 2355LT. See also 5.8.1 and 5.8.2 for other weather services.

TELEPHONE: To call the Irish Republic from the UK, dial 00 -353, then the area code (given in UK ☎ directories and below) minus the initial 0, followed by the ☎ number. To call UK from the Irish Republic: dial 00-44, followed by the area code minus the initial 0, then the number.

SALMON DRIFT NETS are everywhere along the S and W coasts, off headlands and islands during the summer and especially May-Jul. They may be 1½ to 3M long and are hard to see. FVs may give warnings on VHF Ch 16, 06, 08.

LIQUIFIED PETROLEUM GAS: In Eire LPG is supplied by Kosan, a sister company of Calor Gas Ltd, but the bottles have different connections, and the smallest bottle is taller than the normal Calor one fitted in most yachts. Calor Gas bottles can be filled in most larger towns. Camping Gaz is widely available. The abbreviation Kos indicates where Kosan gas is available.

INFORMATION: The Irish Cruising Club publishes 2 highly recommended books of Sailing Directions, one for the S and W coasts of Ireland, the other for the N and E coasts. They are distributed by Imray and are available in good UK bookshops and chandleries. For further info about the Republic of Ireland, write to: Irish Yachting Association, 3 Park Road, Dun Laoghaire, Co Dublin ☎ (01) 2800239 or to Irish Tourist Board, 150 New Bond Street, London W1Y 0AQ ☎ (0171) 493 3201.

CURRENCY in the Republic of Ireland is the Punt (£IR), divided into 100p. Cash is most readily obtained via Euro or Travellers' cheques.

ACCESS BY AIR: There are airports in Eire at Dublin, Waterford, Cork, Kerry, Shannon, Galway, Connaught, Sligo and Donegal/Carrickfin. See also Ferries in 8.0.4.

GAELIC: As in Scotland (see 8.8.5), it helps to understand some of the commoner words for navigational features (courtesy of the Irish Cruising Club):

Ail, alt: cliff, height. *Ath:* ford. *Bal, Bally:* town. *Barra:* sandbank. *Bel, beal:* river mouth, strait. *Beg:* little. *Ben, bin, binna:* hill. *Bo:* (Cow), sunken rock. *Boy, bwee:* yellow. *Bullig:* shoal, rounded rock, breaker. *Bun:* end, river mouth. *Caher:* fort. *Camus:* bay, river bend. *Carrick, carrig:* rock. *Cuan, coon:* harbour. *Derg, dearg:* red. *Drum:* hill, ridge. *Duff, dubh:* black. *Dun, doon:* fort. *Ennis:* island. *Fad, fadda:* long. *Fan:* slope. *Fin:* white. *Freagh, free:* heather. *Glas, glass:* green. *Gorm:* blue. *Gub:* point of land. *Hassans:* swift current. *Inish, innis, illaun:* island. *Inver:* river mouth. *Keal, keel:* narrow place, sound. *Kill:* church. *Kin, ken:* head, promontory. *Knock:* hill. *Lahan:* broad. *Lea:* grey. *Lenan:* weed-covered rock. *Long, luing:* ship. *Maan:* middle. *Maol, mwee:* bare. *More, mor:* big. *Rannagh, rin, rush:* point. *Roan:* seal. *Roe, ruadh:* red. *Scrow, scrah, scraw:* boggy, grass sward. *Slieve:* mountain. *Stag, stac:* high rock. *Togher:* causeway. *Tra, traw:* strand. *Turlin:* boulder beach. *Vad, bad:* boat.

NORTHERN IRELAND:
Belfast CG (MRSC) is at Bangor, Co Down, ☎ (01247) 463933, 📠 465886.
HM Customs (#) should be contacted on ☎ (01232) 358250 at the following ports, if a local Customs Officer is not available: Belfast, Warrenpoint, Kilkeel, Ardglass, Portavogie, Larne, Londonderry, Coleraine.
Northern Ireland's main airport is Belfast (Aldergrove).

12

MALAHIDE   8-12-8
Dublin 53°27'·20N 06°08'·90W   Rtg 3-2-2

CHARTS
AC 633, 1468; Imray C61, C62; Irish OS 50
TIDES
+0030 Dover; ML 2·4; Duration 0615; Zone 0 (UT)

Standard Port DUBLIN (NORTH WALL) (→)

Times				Height (metres)			
High Water		Low Water		MHWS	MHWN	MLWN	MLWS
0000	0700	0000	0500	4·1	3·4	1·5	0·7
1200	1900	1200	1700				
Differences MALAHIDE							
–0019	–0013	+0014	+0006	+0·1	+0·1	0·0	0·0

SHELTER
Good in the marina, dredged approx 2·3m. Or safe ⚓
about 3ca E of conspic Grand Hotel. Caution: crowded
moorings.
*Note: Consult the marina or the Supplement(s) to this
Almanac for latest details of buoys/lts and the alignment
and depths of the dredged chan from the bar to the
marina (see also under NAVIGATION).*

LIGHTS AND MARKS
Outer appr with ch spire on 266° just open N of conspic
Grand Hotel. The chan across the bar to the marina is
planned to be marked by piles, all lit. Temporary buoys
may be laid by the YC in season.
RADIO TELEPHONE
Marina Ch **M** (H24) 80. MYC, call *Yacht Base* Ch M (occas).
TELEPHONE (Dial code 01)
Marina 8454129, 🖶 8454255; MRCC 6620922/3;
⌗ 8746571; Police 845 0216; Dr 845 1953; Ⓗ 837 7755.
FACILITIES
Marina (150, increasing to 348 berths) ☎ 8454129, 🖶
8454255, £IR 12.80, FW, AC, D, P, Gas, BH (30 ton), BY, R,
Bar, Ice, Ⓒ;
Malahide YC ☎ 8450216, Slip, Scrubbing posts for <10m
LOA; **Services:** Ⓔ, Sh, Kos.
Town Ⓞ, ✉, Ⓑ, ⇌, ✈ (Dublin).

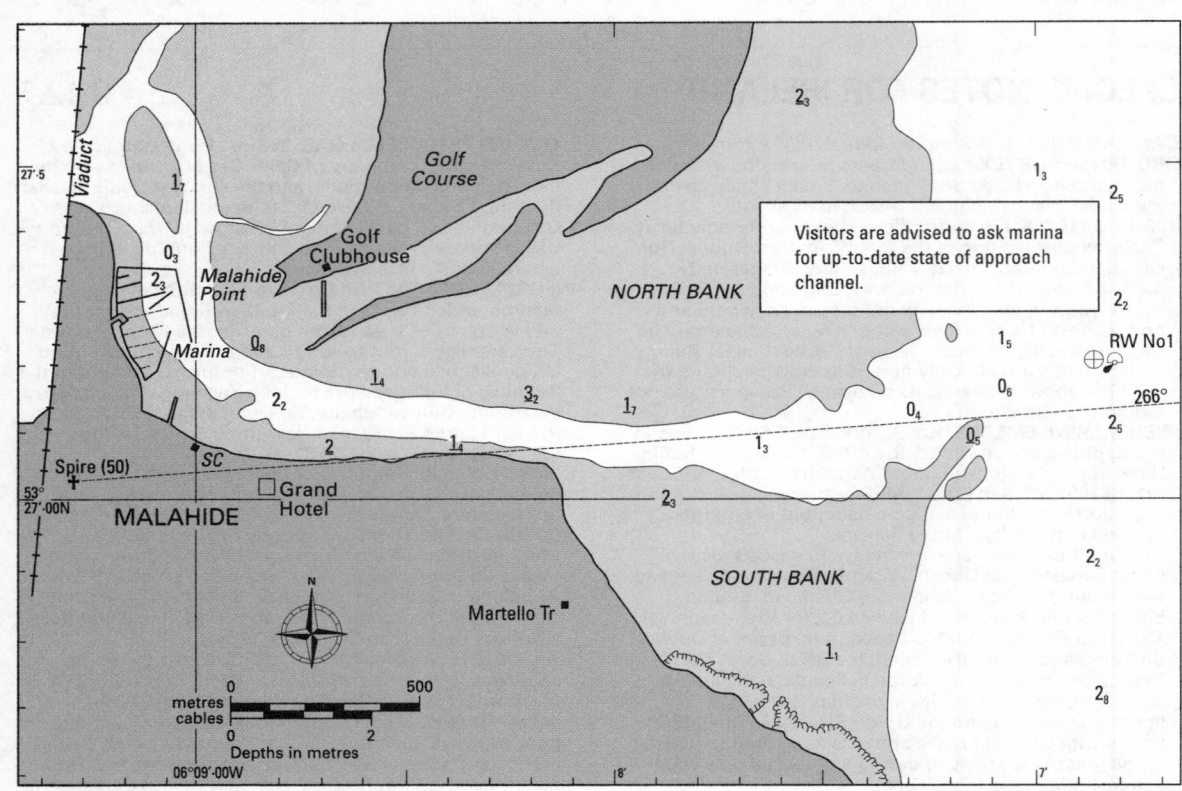

NAVIGATION
WPT 53°27'·20N 06°06'·80W, SWM lt buoy, 082°/262°
from/to abeam Grand Hotel, 1·2M. Caution: The lat/long
of the SWM is last known position and may have
changed. WPT is approx 2ca E of the Bar, which was
planned to be dredged to 2·9m. The appr chan across
drying sandbanks was planned to be dredged to 2·3m. Do
not attempt entry in thick weather or HN, nor in strong
onshore winds. The flood reaches 3kn sp, and the ebb
3½kn. Speed limit 4kn in fairway and marina.

*The 1996, 1997 & 1998 Almanacs and their Supplements
have repeatedly stressed the need to obtain up-to-date
information by ☎ or VHF from the marina as to the latest
state of dredging, depths and buoyage BEFORE even
considering an approach.
Dredging of the bar and approach channel up to the
marina has been much delayed, although it is believed to
have been completed in 1998. The final alignment,
depths and buoyage of this chan have been deleted from
the chartlet, until accurate and reliable information is
available.*

HOWTH   8-12-9

Dublin 53°23'·60N 06°04'·00W   Rtg 1-2-1

CHARTS
AC 1415, 1468; Imray C61, C62; Irish OS 50

TIDES
+0025 Dover; ML 2·4; Duration 0625; Zone 0 (UT)

Standard Port DUBLIN (NORTH WALL) (→)

Times				Height (metres)			
High Water		Low Water		MHWS	MHWN	MLWN	MLWS
0000	0700	0000	0500	4·1	3·4	1·5	0·7
1200	1900	1200	1700				
Differences HOWTH							
−0005	−0015	−0005	+0005	0·0	0·0	−0·3	0·0

SHELTER
Good, available at all tides and in almost any conditions. After a severe ENE'ly storm, expect a dangerous scend in the app chan. Marina dredged to 3m. No ent to FV basin for yachts. Caution: many moorings in E part of outer hbr. Inside the inner hbr keep strictly to chan to avoid drying shoals on either side and a substantial wavebreak. 4kn speed limit. There is a fair weather ‡ in 2-3m at Carrigeen Bay, SW side of Irelnd's Eye.

NAVIGATION
WPT Howth SHM buoy, Fl G 5s, 53°23'·72N 06°03'·53W, 071°/251° from/to E pier lt, 0·27M. Beware Casana Rk 4ca S of the Nose of Howth, where Puck's Rks extend about 50m off it. Ireland's Eye is 0·6M N of hbr, with the Rowan Rks SE and SW from Thulla, marked by Rowan Rks ECM, and S Rowan SHM lt buoys.

The usual appr is S of Ireland's Eye; to the W of which Howth Sound has 2·4m min depth. Between the Nose and the hbr, watch out for lobster pots. Beware rks off both pier hds. Give way to FVs (constrained by draft) in the Sound and hbr entrance.

LIGHTS AND MARKS
E pier lt, Fl (2) WR 7·5s 13m 12/9M; W 256°–295°, R elsewhere. W sector leads safely to NE pierhead which should be rounded 50m off. Ent to FV Basin has QR and Fl G 3s. The chan to marina is unlit, but marked by R and G floating perches with W reflective tops; these are reported to be difficult to discern at night. Baily Lt Ho, Fl 15s 41m 26M, is 1·5M S of Nose of Howth.

RADIO TELEPHONE
Hr Mr VHF Ch 16 08 (Mon-Fri 0700–2300LT; Sat/Sun occas). Marina Ch M 80 (H24).

TELEPHONE (Dial code 01)
Hr Mr 832 2252; MRCC 6620922/3; ⌗ 8746571; Police 832 2806; Dr 832 3191; Ⓗ 837 7755.

FACILITIES
Howth YC Marina (300 inc Ⓥ) ☎ 839 2777, ⬎ 839 2430, £IR8.50, M, D (H24), P (cans), FW, Slip, C (7 ton), AC, Ⓞ, &;
Howth YC ☎ 832 2141, Scrubbing posts <20m LOA, R (☎ 839 2100), Bar (☎ 832 0606), Ⓞ, &;
Services: LB, Gas, Kos, ME, SM, CH, El, Ⓔ.
Town EC Sat; P & D (cans), ✉, Ⓑ, Ⓞ, ⇌, ✈ (Dublin).

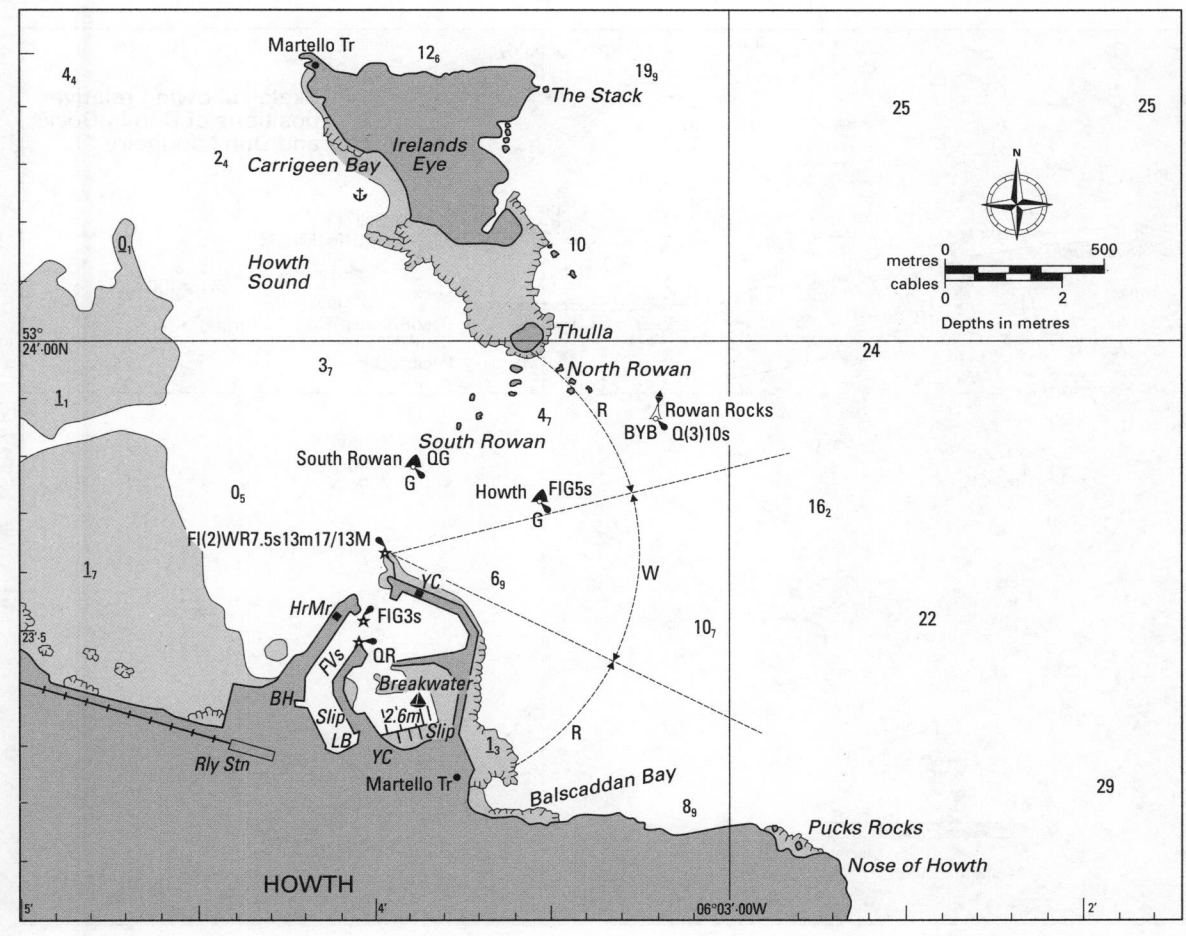

DUBLIN/DUN LAOGHAIRE   8-12-10

Dun Laoghaire (Port ent) 53°18'·16N 06°07'·68W
Rtgs: 1-2-1 (Dun Laoghaire); 1-4-3 (Dublin)

CHARTS

AC 1447, 1415, 1468; Imray C61, C62; Irish OS 50

TIDES

+0042 Dover; ML 2·4; Duration 0640; Zone 0 (UT)

Standard Port DUBLIN (NORTH WALL) (→)

Times				Height (metres)			
High Water		Low Water		MHWS	MHWN	MLWN	MLWS
0000	0700	0000	0500	4·1	3·4	1·5	0·7
1200	1900	1200	1700				

Differences DUBLIN BAR and DUN LAOGHAIRE

–0006 –0001 –0002 –0003   0·0   0·0   0·0   +0·1

GREYSTONES (53°09'N 06°04'W)

–0008 –0008 –0008 –0008   –0·5   –0·4   No data

Dublin is a Standard Port; daily predictions are overleaf.

SHELTER

Dun Laoghaire, one of the main yachting centres for Dublin, is accessible H24, but is open to NE swell and ⚓ holding is poor. No ⚓ in areas marked 'moorings' and in fairways. All YCs advertise ⚓s and have pontoons, but only for fuel/stores/FW. Yachts may find AB inshore of Traders Wharf (priority to FVs). In bad conditions, unless YCs can offer sheltered ⚓s (the best option), yachts should go to **Howth** (7·5M NNE). A marina is planned to the NNE of Royal Irish YC.
Dublin Port is a commercial port which, due to security risks and lift-bridge/road tfc delays, does not encourage yachts, unless too big for Dun Laoghaire. For clearance to enter call *Dublin Port Radio* Ch 12. Expect to berth at the inner end of S Quay, near Poolbeg YC.

NAVIGATION

WPT 53°18'·40N 06°07'·00W, 060°/240° from/to ent to Dun Laoghaire, 0·47M. Keep clear of the many coasters and ferries, not least the HSS catamarans (41kn), which turn off St Michael's Pier. Beware drying rks approx 10m off the E Pierhead.
TSS: Dublin Bay SWM buoy, Mo (A) 10s, (53°19'·90N 06°04'·58W, 2·5M NE of Dun Laoghaire and 2·75M ESE of Dublin Port) is the centre of a circular TSS, radius 2·3ca. Ships bound to/from Dublin Port follow this TSS in an anti-clockwise direction. Yachts must not impede large vessels and should keep clear of the TSS and fairway.

LIGHTS AND MARKS

There are no ldg lts/marks. On W Pier 2 △ bns in transit define the E edge of the triangular anchorage. Close to ☆ Q on St Michael's Pier, a ☆ QY = Ferries under way; small craft keep clear of No 1 Fairway (which extends 600m to seaward of the pier heads). Other lts as chartlet.

RADIO TELEPHONE

Call *Dun Laoghaire Hbr* VHF Ch **14** 16 (H24). YCs Ch M. At Dublin: call *Dublin Port Radio* Ch **12** 13 14 16 (H24). Lifting bridge (call *Eastlink*) Ch 12 13. Poolbeg YC Ch 12 16. Dublin Coast Radio Stn 16 67 83.

TELEPHONE (Dial code 01)

Hr Mr Dun Laoghaire 2801130; Hr Mr Dublin 8550888 (H24); MRCC 6620922/3; Coast/Cliff Rescue Service 2803900; ⌗ 2803992; Weather 1550 123855; Police (Dun Laoghaire) 2801285, (Dublin) 6778141; Dr 2859244; Ⓗ 2806901.

FACILITIES

No Ⓥ fees at Dun Laoghaire. V within ½M of all YCs.
Yacht Clubs (E toW): **National YC** ☎ 2805725, 📞 2807837, Slip, M, L, C (7 ton), FW, D, R, Bar;
Royal St. George YC ☎ 2801811, 📞 2843002, Slip, M, D, L, FW, C (5 ton), R, Bar;
Royal Irish YC ☎ 2809452, 📞 2809723, Slip, M, D, L, FW, C (5 ton), R, Bar;
Dun Laoghaire Motor YC ☎ 2801371, 📞 2800870, Slip, FW, AB, Bar.
At Dublin Port: **Poolbeg YC** ☎ 6604681, M, AB only for 20ft max LOA, Slip, Bar, FW.
Services FW, C (5 ton), AB, SM, CH, ACA, Sh, Ⓔ, El, Gas.
City of Dublin All needs, ⇌, ✈.

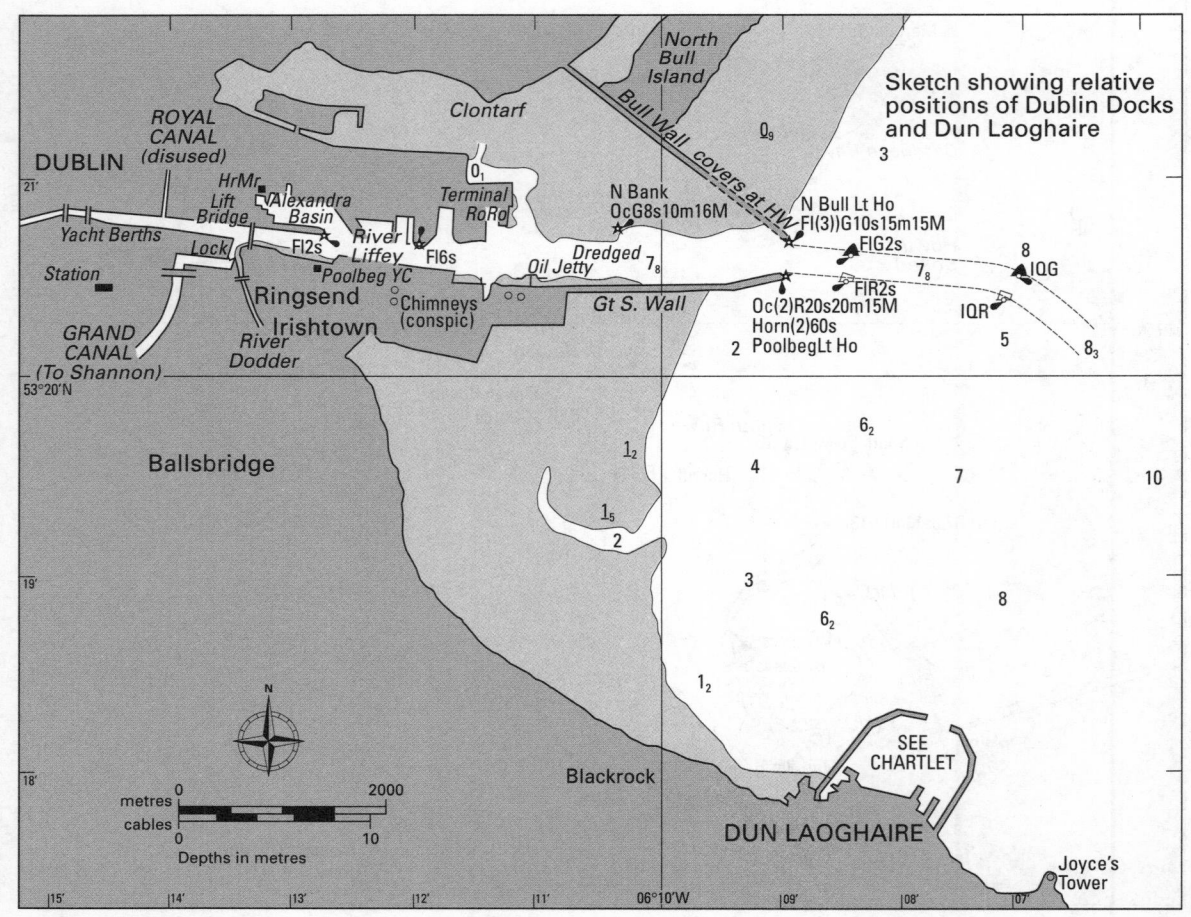

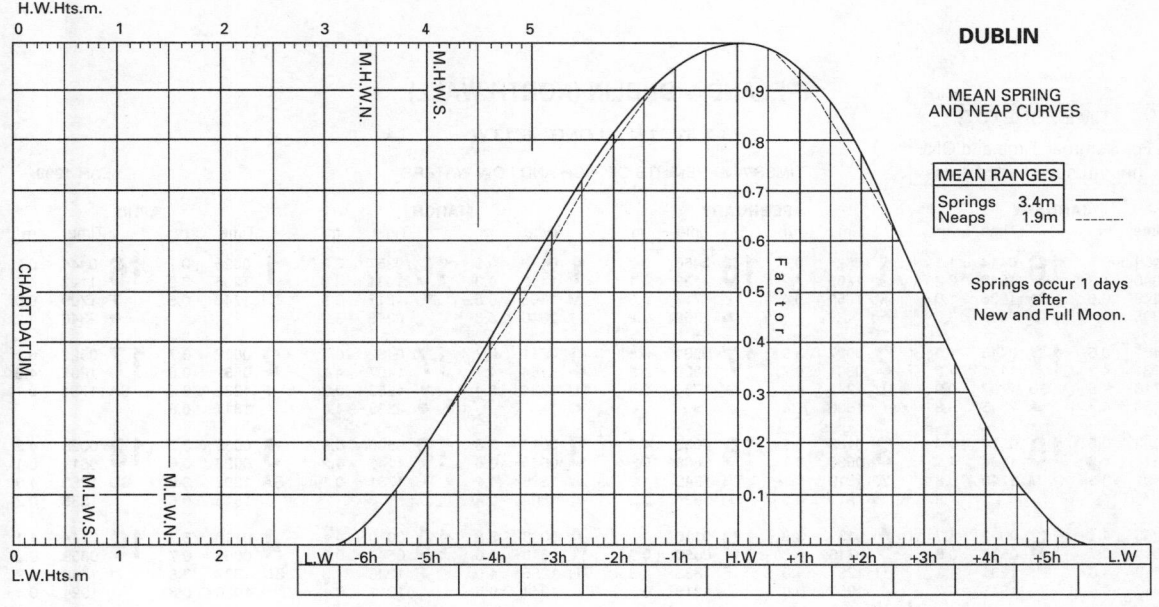

DUBLIN

**MEAN SPRING
AND NEAP CURVES**

MEAN RANGES	
Springs	3.4m
Neaps	1.9m

Springs occur 1 days
after
New and Full Moon.

WEATHER BROADCASTS BY LOCAL RADIO STATIONS

East Coast Radio   *Daily:* Every H+06 (0700-1800LT)
after the news, broadcasts a general forecast for coastal
(and inland) areas from Dublin Head to Arklow Head.
There are transmitters at:
Kippure 94·9MHz, Bray Head 96·2, Wicklow Head 102·9 and
Arklow 104·4.

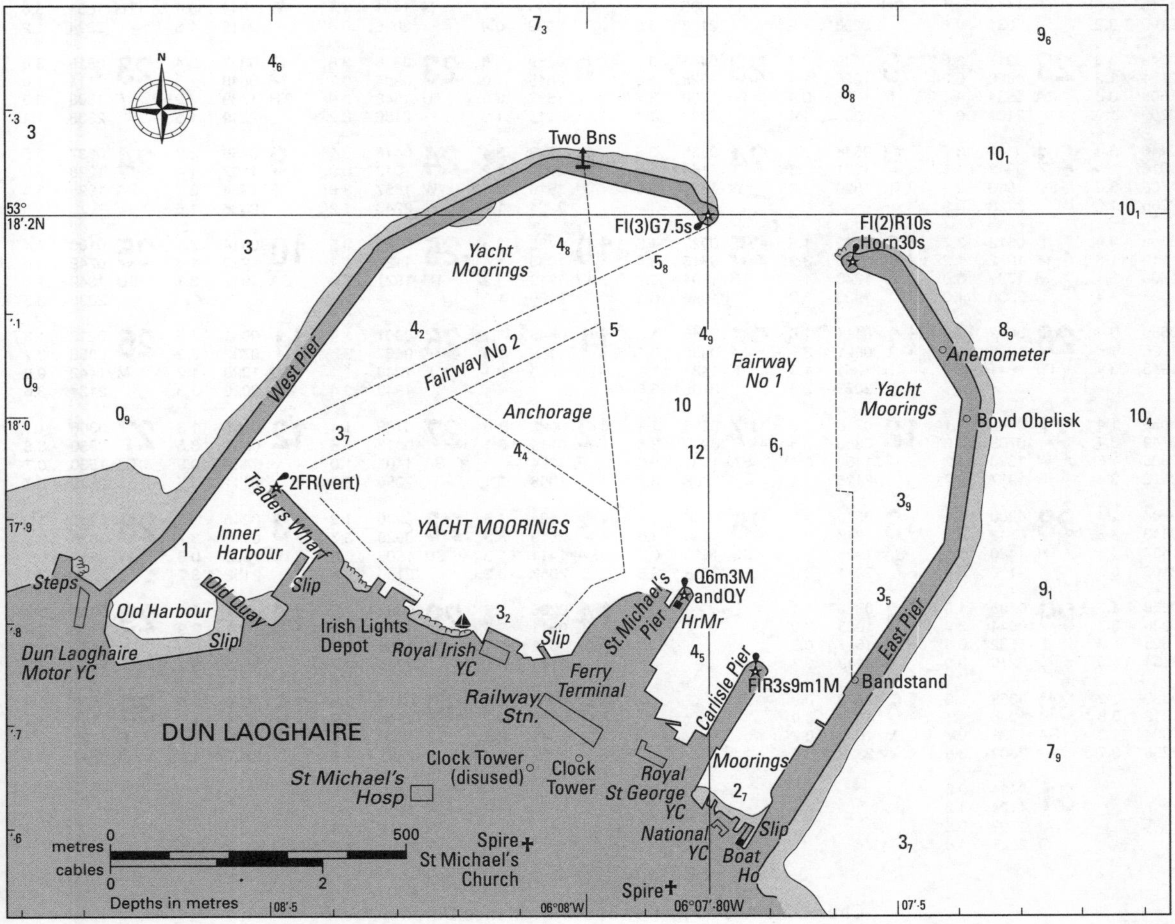

12

(Chart of Dun Laoghaire harbour)

IRELAND – DUBLIN (NORTH WALL)

LAT 53°21′N   LONG   6°13′W

TIMES AND HEIGHTS OF HIGH AND LOW WATERS

YEAR **1999**

TIME ZONE (UT)
For Summer Time add ONE hour in non-shaded areas

JANUARY

Day	Time	m	Day	Time	m
1 F	0404 / 1045 / 1629 / 2305	0.7 / 4.2 / 0.6 / 4.1	**16** SA	0414 / 1049 / 1636 / 2312	1.1 / 3.9 / 1.0 / 3.8
2 SA O	0451 / 1131 / 1716 / 2353	0.6 / 4.3 / 0.5 / 4.1	**17** SU ●	0446 / 1121 / 1707 / 2345	1.0 / 4.0 / 0.9 / 3.8
3 SU	0533 / 1214 / 1801	0.6 / 4.3 / 0.5	**18** M	0517 / 1154 / 1740	0.9 / 4.1 / 0.8
4 M	0038 / 0614 / 1258 / 1846	4.1 / 0.7 / 4.3 / 0.5	**19** TU	0020 / 0551 / 1231 / 1815	3.9 / 0.8 / 4.1 / 0.7
5 TU	0124 / 0657 / 1342 / 1932	4.0 / 0.8 / 4.2 / 0.6	**20** W	0059 / 0629 / 1312 / 1856	3.9 / 0.8 / 4.2 / 0.6
6 W	0209 / 0741 / 1427 / 2019	3.9 / 0.9 / 4.1 / 0.7	**21** TH	0141 / 0711 / 1356 / 1941	3.9 / 0.8 / 4.2 / 0.6
7 TH	0258 / 0829 / 1516 / 2109	3.7 / 1.1 / 4.0 / 0.9	**22** F	0227 / 0758 / 1444 / 2031	3.9 / 0.8 / 4.1 / 0.6
8 F	0349 / 0921 / 1608 / 2200	3.6 / 1.3 / 3.8 / 1.0	**23** SA	0317 / 0850 / 1534 / 2124	3.8 / 0.9 / 4.1 / 0.7
9 SA	0446 / 1018 / 1706 / 2255	3.4 / 1.4 / 3.6 / 1.2	**24** SU	0411 / 0948 / 1628 / 2223	3.7 / 1.1 / 3.9 / 0.9
10 SU	0548 / 1119 / 1809 / 2355	3.4 / 1.6 / 3.5 / 1.4	**25** M	0512 / 1052 / 1729 / 2330	3.7 / 1.2 / 3.8 / 1.0
11 M	0650 / 1225 / 1913	3.4 / 1.6 / 3.4	**26** TU	0622 / 1205 / 1841	3.6 / 1.3 / 3.7
12 TU	0059 / 0749 / 1335 / 2012	1.4 / 3.4 / 1.6 / 3.4	**27** W	0045 / 0735 / 1320 / 1957	1.1 / 3.6 / 1.2 / 3.7
13 W	0204 / 0843 / 1437 / 2106	1.4 / 3.5 / 1.5 / 3.5	**28** TH	0200 / 0843 / 1430 / 2108	1.1 / 3.8 / 1.1 / 3.8
14 TH	0258 / 0930 / 1525 / 2154	1.3 / 3.7 / 1.3 / 3.6	**29** F	0305 / 0944 / 1532 / 2210	1.0 / 3.9 / 0.9 / 3.9
15 F	0339 / 1012 / 1604 / 2236	1.2 / 3.8 / 1.2 / 3.7	**30** SA	0359 / 1038 / 1623 / 2303	0.9 / 4.1 / 0.7 / 3.9
			31 SU O	0444 / 1124 / 1709 / 2348	0.8 / 4.2 / 0.5 / 4.0

FEBRUARY

Day	Time	m	Day	Time	m
1 M	0524 / 1205 / 1750	0.7 / 4.2 / 0.4	**16** TU ●	0456 / 1132 / 1717 / 2358	0.7 / 4.1 / 0.5 / 3.9
2 TU	0027 / 0601 / 1242 / 1830	3.9 / 0.7 / 4.2 / 0.4	**17** W	0531 / 1208 / 1754	0.5 / 4.2 / 0.4
3 W	0103 / 0638 / 1319 / 1910	3.9 / 0.7 / 4.1 / 0.5	**18** TH	0035 / 0608 / 1249 / 1834	4.0 / 0.5 / 4.3 / 0.3
4 TH	0139 / 0716 / 1357 / 1950	3.8 / 0.8 / 4.0 / 0.8	**19** F	0116 / 0650 / 1333 / 1918	4.0 / 0.5 / 4.3 / 0.3
5 F	0219 / 0757 / 1439 / 2032	3.7 / 0.9 / 3.9 / 0.8	**20** SA	0200 / 0735 / 1420 / 2006	4.0 / 0.5 / 4.2 / 0.4
6 SA	0301 / 0841 / 1522 / 2117	3.6 / 1.0 / 3.8 / 1.0	**21** SU	0249 / 0826 / 1510 / 2059	3.9 / 0.7 / 4.1 / 0.6
7 SU	0347 / 0931 / 1610 / 2206	3.5 / 1.2 / 3.6 / 1.2	**22** M	0341 / 0923 / 1605 / 2156	3.8 / 0.8 / 3.9 / 0.9
8 M	0440 / 1028 / 1708 / 2300	3.3 / 1.4 / 3.4 / 1.4	**23** TU	0441 / 1028 / 1708 / 2303	3.6 / 1.0 / 3.7 / 1.1
9 TU	0546 / 1131 / 1820	3.2 / 1.6 / 3.2	**24** W	0555 / 1143 / 1827	3.5 / 1.2 / 3.6
10 W	0002 / 0658 / 1240 / 1930	1.5 / 3.2 / 1.6 / 3.2	**25** TH	0022 / 0715 / 1304 / 1950	1.3 / 3.5 / 1.2 / 3.5
11 TH	0111 / 0801 / 1351 / 2033	1.6 / 3.3 / 1.6 / 3.3	**26** F	0146 / 0830 / 1421 / 2105	1.3 / 3.6 / 1.1 / 3.6
12 F	0218 / 0856 / 1452 / 2126	1.5 / 3.5 / 1.4 / 3.4	**27** SA	0256 / 0935 / 1524 / 2208	1.1 / 3.8 / 0.9 / 3.7
13 SA	0310 / 0943 / 1536 / 2211	1.3 / 3.6 / 1.2 / 3.6	**28** SU	0350 / 1030 / 1613 / 2258	1.0 / 3.9 / 0.7 / 3.8
14 SU	0349 / 1023 / 1611 / 2249	1.1 / 3.8 / 0.9 / 3.8			
15 M	0423 / 1058 / 1643 / 2323	0.9 / 4.0 / 0.7 / 3.8			

MARCH

Day	Time	m	Day	Time	m
1 M	0433 / 1116 / 1656 / 2340	0.8 / 4.0 / 0.5 / 3.8	**16** TU ●	0357 / 1031 / 1617 / 2258	0.8 / 3.9 / 0.5 / 3.9
2 TU O	0511 / 1154 / 1734	0.7 / 4.1 / 0.4	**17** W ●	0432 / 1107 / 1653 / 2333	0.5 / 4.1 / 0.2 / 4.0
3 W	0012 / 0545 / 1225 / 1809	3.8 / 0.6 / 4.1 / 0.4	**18** TH	0509 / 1145 / 1731	0.3 / 4.2 / 0.1
4 TH	0038 / 0618 / 1255 / 1844	3.8 / 0.6 / 4.0 / 0.4	**19** F	0010 / 0547 / 1226 / 1811	4.1 / 0.2 / 4.3 / 0.1
5 F	0108 / 0651 / 1328 / 1919	3.8 / 0.7 / 4.0 / 0.6	**20** SA	0050 / 0629 / 1310 / 1855	4.1 / 0.2 / 4.3 / 0.2
6 SA	0142 / 0726 / 1405 / 1955	3.7 / 0.7 / 3.9 / 0.7	**21** SU	0135 / 0715 / 1359 / 1943	4.1 / 0.3 / 4.2 / 0.4
7 SU	0219 / 0804 / 1445 / 2033	3.6 / 0.9 / 3.7 / 0.9	**22** M	0223 / 0807 / 1451 / 2036	4.0 / 0.5 / 4.1 / 0.6
8 M	0259 / 0845 / 1527 / 2115	3.6 / 1.0 / 3.5 / 1.1	**23** TU	0316 / 0906 / 1548 / 2136	3.8 / 0.7 / 3.9 / 0.9
9 TU	0343 / 0932 / 1616 / 2204	3.4 / 1.2 / 3.3 / 1.3	**24** W	0418 / 1013 / 1657 / 2243	3.7 / 0.9 / 3.6 / 1.2
10 W	0436 / 1035 / 1719 / 2309	3.3 / 1.4 / 3.2 / 1.5	**25** TH	0535 / 1127 / 1821	3.5 / 1.1 / 3.5
11 TH	0548 / 1150 / 1845	3.1 / 1.5 / 3.1	**26** F	0001 / 0657 / 1249 / 1942	1.4 / 3.5 / 1.1 / 3.4
12 F	0022 / 0714 / 1304 / 1958	1.6 / 3.1 / 1.5 / 3.1	**27** SA	0129 / 0813 / 1407 / 2056	1.4 / 3.6 / 1.0 / 3.6
13 SA	0134 / 0819 / 1411 / 2057	1.5 / 3.3 / 1.3 / 3.3	**28** SU	0240 / 0918 / 1508 / 2156	1.2 / 3.7 / 0.8 / 3.6
14 SU	0236 / 0911 / 1502 / 2144	1.3 / 3.5 / 1.1 / 3.5	**29** M	0332 / 1015 / 1555 / 2245	1.0 / 3.9 / 0.7 / 3.7
15 M	0320 / 0953 / 1541 / 2223	1.1 / 3.7 / 0.8 / 3.7	**30** TU	0415 / 1100 / 1636 / 2323	0.9 / 3.9 / 0.6 / 3.7
			31 W O	0452 / 1136 / 1712 / 2351	0.7 / 4.0 / 0.5 / 3.7

APRIL

Day	Time	m	Day	Time	m
1 TH	0526 / 1205 / 1746	0.7 / 3.9 / 0.5	**16** F ●	0446 / 1122 / 1709 / 2346	0.2 / 4.3 / 0.0 / 4.2
2 F	0012 / 0557 / 1232 / 1817	3.7 / 0.6 / 3.9 / 0.6	**17** SA	0527 / 1206 / 1751	0.1 / 4.3 / 0.1
3 SA	0039 / 0628 / 1302 / 1848	3.7 / 0.6 / 3.8 / 0.6	**18** SU	0028 / 0611 / 1253 / 1835	4.2 / 0.1 / 4.3 / 0.2
4 SU	0110 / 0659 / 1337 / 1920	3.7 / 0.7 / 3.8 / 0.8	**19** M	0114 / 0659 / 1343 / 1924	4.1 / 0.2 / 4.2 / 0.4
5 M	0146 / 0732 / 1415 / 1954	3.7 / 0.8 / 3.7 / 0.9	**20** TU	0204 / 0754 / 1438 / 2018	4.0 / 0.4 / 4.0 / 0.7
6 TU	0225 / 0810 / 1457 / 2033	3.6 / 0.9 / 3.5 / 1.1	**21** W	0259 / 0855 / 1539 / 2118	3.9 / 0.6 / 3.8 / 1.0
7 W	0308 / 0853 / 1544 / 2119	3.5 / 1.1 / 3.4 / 1.3	**22** TH	0402 / 1000 / 1651 / 2224	3.7 / 0.8 / 3.6 / 1.2
8 TH	0357 / 0948 / 1639 / 2219	3.4 / 1.3 / 3.2 / 1.5	**23** F	0518 / 1111 / 1808 / 2338	3.6 / 1.0 / 3.5 / 1.4
9 F	0456 / 1102 / 1754 / 2336	3.2 / 1.4 / 3.1 / 1.6	**24** SA	0637 / 1228 / 1925	3.5 / 1.0 / 3.4
10 SA	0614 / 1220 / 1917	3.1 / 1.4 / 3.1	**25** SU	0100 / 0749 / 1342 / 2035	1.4 / 3.6 / 1.0 / 3.5
11 SU	0051 / 0732 / 1328 / 2020	1.5 / 3.2 / 1.2 / 3.3	**26** M	0212 / 0855 / 1442 / 2134	1.3 / 3.7 / 0.9 / 3.6
12 M	0155 / 0831 / 1423 / 2111	1.3 / 3.5 / 0.9 / 3.5	**27** TU	0306 / 0950 / 1530 / 2220	1.1 / 3.8 / 0.7 / 3.7
13 TU	0245 / 0918 / 1509 / 2152	1.0 / 3.7 / 0.6 / 3.7	**28** W	0350 / 1035 / 1611 / 2257	1.0 / 3.9 / 0.7 / 3.7
14 W	0327 / 1001 / 1549 / 2230	0.7 / 3.9 / 0.3 / 3.9	**29** TH	0428 / 1112 / 1647 / 2325	0.9 / 3.9 / 0.6 / 3.7
15 TH	0406 / 1041 / 1629 / 2307	0.5 / 4.1 / 0.1 / 4.1	**30** F O	0503 / 1141 / 1721 / 2347	0.8 / 3.8 / 0.7 / 3.7

Chart Datum: 0·20 metres above Ordnance Datum (Dublin)

IRELAND – DUBLIN (NORTH WALL)

LAT 53°21′N   LONG   6°13′W

TIMES AND HEIGHTS OF HIGH AND LOW WATERS

YEAR **1999**

TIME ZONE (UT)
For Summer Time add ONE hour in non-shaded areas

MAY

Day	Time	m	Day	Time	m
1 SA	0535 / 1209 / 1751	0.7 / 3.8 / 0.7	16 SU	0510 / 1150 / 1733	0.2 / 4.3 / 0.2
2 SU	0013 / 0606 / 1240 / 1820	3.8 / 0.7 / 3.8 / 0.8	17 M	0011 / 0556 / 1240 / 1819	4.2 / 0.2 / 4.3 / 0.3
3 M	0044 / 0635 / 1314 / 1850	3.8 / 0.8 / 3.7 / 0.8	18 TU	0058 / 0647 / 1332 / 1908	4.2 / 0.3 / 4.1 / 0.5
4 TU	0119 / 0707 / 1352 / 1924	3.8 / 0.8 / 3.6 / 0.9	19 W	0149 / 0743 / 1428 / 2002	4.1 / 0.4 / 4.0 / 0.8
5 W	0159 / 0744 / 1433 / 2004	3.7 / 0.9 / 3.6 / 1.1	20 TH	0245 / 0842 / 1530 / 2100	4.0 / 0.6 / 3.8 / 1.0
6 TH	0242 / 0829 / 1520 / 2050	3.6 / 1.0 / 3.4 / 1.2	21 F	0348 / 0945 / 1636 / 2202	3.8 / 0.7 / 3.6 / 1.2
7 F	0331 / 0921 / 1612 / 2146	3.5 / 1.1 / 3.3 / 1.4	22 SA	0458 / 1050 / 1745 / 2308	3.7 / 0.9 / 3.5 / 1.4
8 SA	0425 / 1025 / 1715 / 2254	3.4 / 1.2 / 3.2 / 1.5	23 SU	0609 / 1158 / 1855	3.7 / 1.0 / 3.4
9 SU	0530 / 1138 / 1828	3.3 / 1.2 / 3.2	24 M	0020 / 0717 / 1307 / 2000	1.5 / 3.6 / 1.0 / 3.5
10 M	0007 / 0640 / 1246 / 1935	1.4 / 3.4 / 1.1 / 3.4	25 TU	0132 / 0820 / 1408 / 2058	1.4 / 3.7 / 1.0 / 3.5
11 TU	0112 / 0745 / 1345 / 2031	1.3 / 3.5 / 0.9 / 3.6	26 W	0232 / 0916 / 1459 / 2145	1.3 / 3.7 / 0.9 / 3.6
12 W	0207 / 0840 / 1436 / 2118	1.0 / 3.8 / 0.6 / 3.8	27 TH	0320 / 1003 / 1542 / 2223	1.2 / 3.8 / 0.9 / 3.7
13 TH	0256 / 0930 / 1522 / 2202	0.8 / 4.0 / 0.4 / 4.0	28 F	0402 / 1042 / 1620 / 2254	1.0 / 3.8 / 0.9 / 3.7
14 F	0341 / 1017 / 1606 / 2244	0.5 / 4.2 / 0.2 / 4.1	29 SA	0439 / 1115 / 1654 / 2322	1.0 / 3.8 / 0.8 / 3.8
15 SA	0425 / 1103 / 1649 / ● 2327	0.3 / 4.3 / 0.1 / 4.2	30 SU	0513 / 1147 / 1725 / O 2351	0.9 / 3.7 / 0.9 / 3.8
			31 M	0545 / 1218 / 1755	0.9 / 3.7 / 0.9

JUNE

Day	Time	m	Day	Time	m
1 TU	0021 / 0614 / 1253 / 1824	3.8 / 0.9 / 3.7 / 0.9	16 W	0045 / 0637 / 1321 / 1853	4.2 / 0.3 / 4.1 / 0.6
2 W	0057 / 0645 / 1330 / 1859	3.8 / 0.9 / 3.7 / 1.0	17 TH	0136 / 0730 / 1414 / 1943	4.2 / 0.4 / 3.9 / 0.8
3 TH	0137 / 0723 / 1412 / 1940	3.8 / 0.9 / 3.6 / 1.1	18 F	0229 / 0825 / 1510 / 2037	4.1 / 0.6 / 3.8 / 1.0
4 F	0221 / 0808 / 1458 / 2027	3.8 / 1.0 / 3.5 / 1.1	19 SA	0326 / 0922 / 1609 / 2133	3.9 / 0.7 / 3.6 / 1.2
5 SA	0308 / 0859 / 1548 / 2119	3.7 / 1.0 / 3.5 / 1.2	20 SU	0427 / 1021 / 1710 / 2232	3.8 / 0.9 / 3.5 / 1.3
6 SU	0400 / 0957 / 1644 / 2219	3.6 / 1.0 / 3.4 / 1.3	21 M	0532 / 1120 / 1813 / 2335	3.7 / 1.0 / 3.4 / 1.3
7 M	0457 / 1100 / 1746 / 2324	3.6 / 1.0 / 3.4 / 1.3	22 TU	0636 / 1223 / 1915	3.6 / 1.1 / 3.4
8 TU	0600 / 1205 / 1851	3.6 / 1.0 / 3.5	23 W	0043 / 0737 / 1326 / 2011	1.5 / 3.6 / 1.2 / 3.5
9 W	0029 / 0704 / 1308 / 1951	1.2 / 3.7 / 0.9 / 3.6	24 TH	0150 / 0835 / 1423 / 2102	1.4 / 3.6 / 1.1 / 3.5
10 TH	0130 / 0805 / 1405 / 2047	1.1 / 3.8 / 0.7 / 3.8	25 F	0247 / 0925 / 1511 / 2145	1.3 / 3.6 / 1.1 / 3.6
11 F	0226 / 0903 / 1458 / 2138	0.9 / 4.0 / 0.5 / 4.0	26 SA	0335 / 1010 / 1552 / 2223	1.2 / 3.7 / 1.1 / 3.6
12 SA	0318 / 0957 / 1547 / 2225	0.7 / 4.1 / 0.4 / 4.1	27 SU	0415 / 1049 / 1628 / 2257	1.1 / 3.7 / 1.0 / 3.8
13 SU	0408 / 1049 / 1634 / ● 2312	0.5 / 4.2 / 0.4 / 4.2	28 M	0450 / 1124 / 1700 / O 2329	1.1 / 3.7 / 1.0 / 3.9
14 M	0457 / 1139 / 1720 / 2358	0.4 / 4.2 / 0.4 / 4.2	29 TU	0522 / 1158 / 1731	1.0 / 3.7 / 1.0
15 TU	0546 / 1229 / 1806	0.3 / 4.2 / 0.5	30 W	0000 / 0552 / 1232 / 1801	3.9 / 0.9 / 3.7 / 0.9

JULY

Day	Time	m	Day	Time	m
1 TH	0035 / 0624 / 1309 / 1836	3.9 / 0.9 / 3.7 / 0.9	16 F	0117 / 0713 / 1353 / 1921	4.2 / 0.4 / 3.9 / 0.6
2 F	0115 / 0702 / 1350 / 1917	3.9 / 0.9 / 3.7 / 1.0	17 SA	0204 / 0802 / 1441 / 2008	4.1 / 0.5 / 3.8 / 0.9
3 SA	0158 / 0746 / 1434 / 2002	3.9 / 0.8 / 3.7 / 1.0	18 SU	0253 / 0853 / 1530 / 2059	4.0 / 0.7 / 3.6 / 1.1
4 SU	0245 / 0835 / 1522 / 2052	3.9 / 0.8 / 3.7 / 1.1	19 M	0346 / 0944 / 1624 / 2153	3.8 / 0.9 / 3.5 / 1.3
5 M	0334 / 0928 / 1614 / 2147	3.9 / 0.9 / 3.6 / 1.1	20 TU	0444 / 1038 / 1722 / 2251	3.7 / 1.1 / 3.4 / 1.4
6 TU	0427 / 1026 / 1710 / 2246	3.8 / 0.9 / 3.6 / 1.2	21 W	0548 / 1134 / 1823 / 2353	3.5 / 1.2 / 3.3 / 1.5
7 W	0526 / 1129 / 1813 / 2352	3.8 / 0.9 / 3.6 / 1.2	22 TH	0652 / 1235 / 1923	3.5 / 1.3 / 3.4
8 TH	0630 / 1234 / 1919	3.8 / 0.9 / 3.6	23 F	0101 / 0753 / 1339 / 2019	1.6 / 3.4 / 1.4 / 3.5
9 F	0058 / 0738 / 1339 / 2021	1.1 / 3.8 / 0.9 / 3.7	24 SA	0210 / 0850 / 1437 / 2109	1.5 / 3.5 / 1.3 / 3.6
10 SA	0203 / 0844 / 1439 / 2119	1.0 / 3.9 / 0.8 / 3.9	25 SU	0308 / 0940 / 1524 / 2154	1.4 / 3.5 / 1.2 / 3.7
11 SU	0303 / 0944 / 1534 / 2212	0.8 / 4.0 / 0.7 / 4.0	26 M	0352 / 1024 / 1602 / 2233	1.2 / 3.6 / 1.1 / 3.8
12 M	0359 / 1040 / 1624 / 2301	0.6 / 4.1 / 0.6 / 4.2	27 TU	0427 / 1102 / 1636 / 2306	1.1 / 3.7 / 1.0 / 3.9
13 TU	0450 / 1131 / 1707 / ● 2347	0.5 / 4.1 / 0.6 / 4.2	28 W	0458 / 1137 / 1707 / O 2338	1.0 / 3.7 / 0.9 / 4.0
14 W	0538 / 1219 / 1753	0.4 / 4.1 / 0.6	29 TH	0528 / 1210 / 1738	0.8 / 3.8 / 0.8
15 TH	0031 / 0625 / 1306 / 1836	4.2 / 0.4 / 4.0 / 0.7	30 F	0012 / 0600 / 1245 / 1813	4.1 / 0.7 / 3.8 / 0.8
			31 SA	0051 / 0638 / 1325 / 1852	4.1 / 0.7 / 3.8 / 0.8

AUGUST

Day	Time	m	Day	Time	m
1 SU	0133 / 0720 / 1408 / 1935	4.1 / 0.6 / 3.8 / 0.8	16 M	0216 / 0817 / 1446 / 2022	4.0 / 0.7 / 3.6 / 1.0
2 M	0218 / 0807 / 1454 / 2024	4.1 / 0.7 / 3.8 / 0.9	17 TU	0301 / 0904 / 1532 / 2112	3.8 / 0.9 / 3.5 / 1.2
3 TU	0306 / 0859 / 1543 / 2117	4.0 / 0.7 / 3.7 / 1.0	18 W	0352 / 0953 / 1623 / 2207	3.6 / 1.1 / 3.4 / 1.4
4 W	0359 / 0955 / 1638 / 2216	3.9 / 0.8 / 3.7 / 1.1	19 TH	0451 / 1047 / 1725 / 2308	3.4 / 1.3 / 3.3 / 1.5
5 TH	0457 / 1057 / 1741 / 2322	3.8 / 1.0 / 3.6 / 1.2	20 F	0604 / 1146 / 1835	3.3 / 1.5 / 3.3
6 F	0605 / 1207 / 1853	3.7 / 1.1 / 3.6	21 SA	0016 / 0715 / 1252 / 1939	1.6 / 3.3 / 1.5 / 3.3
7 SA	0036 / 0721 / 1320 / 2004	1.2 / 3.7 / 1.1 / 3.7	22 SU	0130 / 0818 / 1400 / 2037	1.6 / 3.3 / 1.5 / 3.5
8 SU	0150 / 0835 / 1428 / 2108	1.1 / 3.7 / 1.0 / 3.8	23 M	0240 / 0914 / 1456 / 2126	1.4 / 3.4 / 1.4 / 3.6
9 M	0257 / 0940 / 1527 / 2204	0.9 / 3.8 / 0.9 / 4.0	24 TU	0327 / 1000 / 1537 / 2207	1.2 / 3.6 / 1.2 / 3.8
10 TU	0355 / 1036 / 1617 / 2253	0.7 / 3.9 / 0.8 / 4.1	25 W	0402 / 1040 / 1611 / 2242	1.0 / 3.7 / 1.0 / 4.0
11 W	0444 / 1125 / 1700 / ● 2336	0.5 / 4.0 / 0.7 / 4.2	26 TH	0433 / 1114 / 1643 / O 2314	0.8 / 3.8 / 0.8 / 4.1
12 TH	0528 / 1208 / 1739	0.4 / 4.0 / 0.7	27 F	0503 / 1146 / 1714 / 2347	0.6 / 3.9 / 0.7 / 4.2
13 F	0015 / 0609 / 1247 / 1817	4.2 / 0.4 / 3.9 / 0.7	28 SA	0535 / 1219 / 1749	0.5 / 4.0 / 0.6
14 SA	0054 / 0651 / 1325 / 1856	4.2 / 0.4 / 3.9 / 0.7	29 SU	0024 / 0612 / 1258 / 1827	4.2 / 0.4 / 4.0 / 0.6
15 SU	0133 / 0733 / 1404 / 1937	4.1 / 0.6 / 3.8 / 0.8	30 M	0106 / 0653 / 1339 / 1910	4.3 / 0.4 / 4.0 / 0.6
			31 TU	0151 / 0739 / 1425 / 1957	4.2 / 0.5 / 3.9 / 0.7

12

Chart Datum: 0·20 metres above Ordnance Datum (Dublin)

IRELAND – DUBLIN (NORTH WALL)

LAT 53°21′N   LONG 6°13′W

TIMES AND HEIGHTS OF HIGH AND LOW WATERS   YEAR **1999**

TIME ZONE (UT)
For Summer Time add ONE hour in non-shaded areas

Chart Datum: 0·20 metres above Ordnance Datum (Dublin)

SEPTEMBER

Day	Time	m		Day	Time	m
1 W	0239 / 0830 / 1515 / 2051	4.1 / 0.7 / 3.8 / 0.9		**16** TH	0309 / 0907 / 1532 / 2122	3.6 / 1.2 / 3.5 / 1.3
2 TH	0333 / 0927 / 1610 / 2152	4.0 / 0.9 / 3.7 / 1.0		**17** F	0400 / 1000 / 1625 / 2224	3.4 / 1.4 / 3.4 / 1.5
3 F	0434 / 1032 / 1715 / 2303	3.8 / 1.1 / 3.6 / 1.2		**18** SA	0510 / 1102 / 1737 / 2335	3.2 / 1.6 / 3.3 / 1.6
4 SA	0549 / 1146 / 1834	3.6 / 1.3 / 3.6		**19** SU	0636 / 1210 / 1858	3.1 / 1.7 / 3.3
5 SU	0023 / 0715 / 1307 / 1951	1.3 / 3.6 / 1.3 / 3.6		**20** M	0050 / 0747 / 1322 / 2002	1.6 / 3.2 / 1.6 / 3.4
6 M	0144 / 0833 / 1420 / 2059	1.2 / 3.6 / 1.2 / 3.8		**21** TU	0204 / 0847 / 1424 / 2055	1.4 / 3.4 / 1.4 / 3.6
7 TU	0253 / 0939 / 1519 / 2157	1.0 / 3.8 / 1.1 / 4.0		**22** W	0255 / 0935 / 1509 / 2138	1.2 / 3.6 / 1.2 / 3.8
8 W	0348 / 1033 / 1606 / 2245	0.7 / 3.9 / 0.9 / 4.1		**23** TH	0332 / 1014 / 1544 / 2214	0.9 / 3.8 / 1.0 / 4.0
9 TH ●	0433 / 1118 / 1647 / 2325	0.5 / 3.9 / 0.8 / 4.2		**24** F	0404 / 1048 / 1617 / 2248	0.7 / 3.9 / 0.7 / 4.2
10 F	0513 / 1155 / 1723 / 2358	0.4 / 3.9 / 0.7 / 4.2		**25** SA O	0436 / 1120 / 1650 / 2322	0.4 / 4.0 / 0.6 / 4.3
11 SA	0550 / 1225 / 1757	0.4 / 3.9 / 0.7		**26** SU	0510 / 1153 / 1726 / 2359	0.3 / 4.1 / 0.4 / 4.4
12 SU	0029 / 0626 / 1255 / 1831	4.1 / 0.5 / 3.8 / 0.7		**27** M	0548 / 1230 / 1805	0.2 / 4.1 / 0.4
13 M	0104 / 0702 / 1329 / 1908	4.1 / 0.6 / 3.8 / 0.8		**28** TU	0040 / 0628 / 1313 / 1848	4.4 / 0.3 / 4.1 / 0.5
14 TU	0143 / 0740 / 1407 / 1947	4.0 / 0.8 / 3.7 / 0.9		**29** W	0127 / 0714 / 1359 / 1936	4.3 / 0.5 / 4.1 / 0.6
15 W	0224 / 0821 / 1447 / 2031	3.8 / 0.9 / 3.6 / 1.1		**30** TH	0217 / 0806 / 1450 / 2032	4.1 / 0.7 / 3.9 / 0.8

OCTOBER

Day	Time	m		Day	Time	m
1 F	0314 / 0905 / 1547 / 2137	3.9 / 1.0 / 3.8 / 1.0		**16** SA	0326 / 0913 / 1544 / 2140	3.4 / 1.4 / 3.5 / 1.4
2 SA	0420 / 1013 / 1656 / 2251	3.7 / 1.2 / 3.7 / 1.2		**17** SU	0426 / 1017 / 1643 / 2253	3.3 / 1.6 / 3.4 / 1.6
3 SU	0545 / 1130 / 1819	3.6 / 1.4 / 3.6		**18** M	0550 / 1130 / 1801	3.1 / 1.7 / 3.3
4 M	0013 / 0710 / 1253 / 1937	1.2 / 3.5 / 1.5 / 3.7		**19** TU	0008 / 0710 / 1242 / 1917	1.6 / 3.2 / 1.7 / 3.4
5 TU	0135 / 0827 / 1407 / 2046	1.1 / 3.6 / 1.3 / 3.8		**20** W	0118 / 0813 / 1344 / 2016	1.4 / 3.4 / 1.5 / 3.5
6 W	0241 / 0930 / 1504 / 2144	0.9 / 3.8 / 1.2 / 4.0		**21** TH	0214 / 0903 / 1433 / 2102	1.2 / 3.6 / 1.3 / 3.8
7 TH	0332 / 1021 / 1549 / 2232	0.6 / 3.9 / 1.0 / 4.1		**22** F	0257 / 0943 / 1513 / 2142	0.9 / 3.8 / 1.0 / 4.0
8 F	0415 / 1104 / 1629 / 2311	0.6 / 3.9 / 0.9 / 4.1		**23** SA	0333 / 1018 / 1549 / 2220	0.6 / 3.9 / 0.7 / 4.2
9 SA ●	0453 / 1138 / 1705 / 2341	0.5 / 3.9 / 0.8 / 4.1		**24** SU O	0409 / 1052 / 1626 / 2257	0.4 / 4.1 / 0.5 / 4.3
10 SU	0528 / 1203 / 1738	0.5 / 3.9 / 0.7		**25** M	0446 / 1128 / 1704 / 2338	0.2 / 4.2 / 0.4 / 4.4
11 M	0009 / 0601 / 1229 / 1810	4.1 / 0.6 / 3.9 / 0.8		**26** TU	0526 / 1207 / 1746	0.2 / 4.3 / 0.3
12 TU	0041 / 0633 / 1300 / 1844	4.0 / 0.7 / 3.9 / 0.8		**27** W	0021 / 0607 / 1251 / 1831	4.4 / 0.3 / 4.3 / 0.4
13 W	0116 / 0706 / 1335 / 1919	3.9 / 0.8 / 3.8 / 0.9		**28** TH	0110 / 0654 / 1339 / 1922	4.3 / 0.5 / 4.2 / 0.5
14 TH	0155 / 0742 / 1414 / 1959	3.8 / 1.0 / 3.8 / 1.0		**29** F	0203 / 0746 / 1432 / 2021	4.1 / 0.8 / 4.1 / 0.7
15 F	0238 / 0823 / 1456 / 2044	3.6 / 1.2 / 3.6 / 1.2		**30** SA	0304 / 0847 / 1532 / 2126	3.9 / 1.1 / 3.9 / 0.9
				31 SU	0415 / 0955 / 1643 / 2237	3.7 / 1.3 / 3.8 / 1.1

NOVEMBER

Day	Time	m		Day	Time	m
1 M	0536 / 1109 / 1801 / 2355	3.6 / 1.5 / 3.7 / 1.2		**16** TU	0500 / 1042 / 1709 / 2319	3.3 / 1.7 / 3.4 / 1.4
2 TU	0656 / 1230 / 1915	3.6 / 1.5 / 3.8		**17** W	0617 / 1154 / 1818	3.3 / 1.7 / 3.4
3 W	0113 / 0808 / 1343 / 2023	1.1 / 3.7 / 1.5 / 3.9		**18** TH	0027 / 0725 / 1258 / 1923	1.3 / 3.4 / 1.6 / 3.6
4 TH	0218 / 0909 / 1440 / 2122	1.0 / 3.8 / 1.3 / 4.0		**19** F	0127 / 0819 / 1352 / 2018	1.1 / 3.6 / 1.3 / 3.8
5 F	0309 / 1000 / 1528 / 2211	0.8 / 3.9 / 1.1 / 4.0		**20** SA	0218 / 0905 / 1438 / 2107	0.9 / 3.8 / 1.1 / 4.0
6 SA	0353 / 1041 / 1609 / 2251	0.7 / 3.9 / 1.0 / 4.0		**21** SU	0302 / 0947 / 1522 / 2152	0.6 / 4.0 / 0.8 / 4.2
7 SU	0431 / 1115 / 1645 / 2323	0.7 / 3.9 / 0.9 / 4.0		**22** M	0344 / 1027 / 1604 / 2237	0.4 / 4.2 / 0.6 / 4.3
8 M ●	0505 / 1141 / 1720 / 2351	0.7 / 3.9 / 0.9 / 4.0		**23** TU O	0426 / 1107 / 1647 / 2322	0.3 / 4.3 / 0.4 / 4.4
9 TU	0538 / 1206 / 1753	0.8 / 3.9 / 0.9		**24** W	0508 / 1150 / 1732	0.3 / 4.4 / 0.4
10 W	0022 / 0608 / 1237 / 1825	3.9 / 0.9 / 3.9 / 0.9		**25** TH	0009 / 0552 / 1236 / 1820	4.4 / 0.4 / 4.4 / 0.4
11 TH	0056 / 0639 / 1310 / 1858	3.9 / 1.0 / 3.9 / 1.0		**26** F	0100 / 0639 / 1325 / 1912	4.3 / 0.6 / 4.3 / 0.5
12 F	0133 / 0712 / 1348 / 1934	3.8 / 1.1 / 3.9 / 1.1		**27** SA	0155 / 0731 / 1419 / 2010	4.1 / 0.8 / 4.2 / 0.6
13 SA	0215 / 0750 / 1430 / 2016	3.6 / 1.2 / 3.8 / 1.2		**28** SU	0256 / 0829 / 1519 / 2112	3.9 / 1.1 / 4.1 / 0.8
14 SU	0301 / 0835 / 1516 / 2105	3.5 / 1.4 / 3.7 / 1.3		**29** M	0404 / 0933 / 1625 / 2217	3.8 / 1.3 / 3.9 / 1.0
15 M	0355 / 0932 / 1608 / 2207	3.4 / 1.6 / 3.5 / 1.4		**30** TU	0515 / 1041 / 1735 / 2326	3.6 / 1.5 / 3.8 / 1.1

DECEMBER

Day	Time	m		Day	Time	m
1 W	0627 / 1154 / 1844	3.6 / 1.6 / 3.8		**16** TH	0521 / 1058 / 1729 / 2332	3.4 / 1.6 / 3.6 / 1.2
2 TH	0038 / 0735 / 1307 / 1950	1.1 / 3.6 / 1.5 / 3.8		**17** F	0627 / 1205 / 1832	3.5 / 1.5 / 3.6
3 F	0145 / 0836 / 1410 / 2050	1.1 / 3.7 / 1.4 / 3.8		**18** SA	0038 / 0729 / 1308 / 1934	1.1 / 3.6 / 1.4 / 3.7
4 SA	0241 / 0929 / 1502 / 2143	1.0 / 3.8 / 1.3 / 3.9		**19** SU	0139 / 0826 / 1404 / 2033	1.0 / 3.8 / 1.2 / 3.9
5 SU	0328 / 1012 / 1547 / 2226	1.0 / 3.9 / 1.2 / 3.9		**20** M	0233 / 0917 / 1457 / 2129	0.8 / 4.0 / 0.9 / 4.1
6 M	0408 / 1047 / 1627 / 2302	0.9 / 3.9 / 1.1 / 3.9		**21** TU	0323 / 1005 / 1546 / 2221	0.6 / 4.1 / 0.7 / 4.2
7 TU ●	0443 / 1118 / 1703 / 2334	0.9 / 3.9 / 1.0 / 3.9		**22** W O	0410 / 1051 / 1635 / 2312	0.5 / 4.3 / 0.5 / 4.3
8 W	0516 / 1147 / 1737	0.9 / 4.0 / 1.0		**23** TH	0456 / 1137 / 1723	0.5 / 4.4 / 0.4
9 TH	0006 / 0546 / 1217 / 1809	3.8 / 1.0 / 4.0 / 1.0		**24** F	0002 / 0541 / 1225 / 1811	4.3 / 0.5 / 4.4 / 0.3
10 F	0039 / 0616 / 1250 / 1840	3.8 / 1.0 / 4.0 / 1.0		**25** SA	0052 / 0627 / 1313 / 1902	4.2 / 0.6 / 4.4 / 0.4
11 SA	0114 / 0648 / 1326 / 1913	3.7 / 1.1 / 3.9 / 1.1		**26** SU	0145 / 0716 / 1405 / 1955	4.0 / 0.8 / 4.3 / 0.5
12 SU	0154 / 0724 / 1407 / 1952	3.7 / 1.2 / 3.9 / 1.1		**27** M	0241 / 0809 / 1500 / 2051	3.9 / 1.0 / 4.2 / 0.7
13 M	0238 / 0807 / 1451 / 2037	3.6 / 1.3 / 3.8 / 1.1		**28** TU	0340 / 0906 / 1558 / 2148	3.8 / 1.2 / 4.0 / 0.8
14 TU	0326 / 0856 / 1539 / 2128	3.5 / 1.4 / 3.7 / 1.2		**29** W	0442 / 1006 / 1701 / 2249	3.6 / 1.4 / 3.9 / 1.0
15 W	0420 / 0953 / 1632 / 2226	3.4 / 1.5 / 3.6 / 1.2		**30** TH	0547 / 1111 / 1805 / 2353	3.5 / 1.5 / 3.7 / 1.2
				31 F	0651 / 1220 / 1909	3.5 / 1.6 / 3.7

Chart Datum: 0·20 metres above Ordnance Datum (Dublin)

WICKLOW   8-12-11

Wicklow 52°58'·98N 06°02'·70W   Rtg 1-4-2

CHARTS
AC 633, 1468; Imray C61; Irish OS 56
TIDES
–0010 Dover; ML 1·7; Duration 0640; Zone 0 (UT)

Standard Port DUBLIN (NORTH WALL) (←)

Times				Height (metres)			
High Water		Low Water		MHWS	MHWN	MLWN	MLWS
0000	0700	0000	0500	4·1	3·4	1·5	0·7
1200	1900	1200	1700				
Differences WICKLOW							
–0019	–0019	–0024	–0026	–1·4	–1·1	–0·4	0·0

SHELTER
Very safe, and access H24. Outer hbr is open to NE winds
which cause a swell. Moorings in NW of hbr belong to
YC. Berths on E Pier (2·5m) are convenient and now well
fendered; W pier is not recommended. Inner hbr (river)
gives excellent shelter in 2·5m on New Quay (S), which is
used by FVs. Packet Quay (N) is for ships (2·5m), but may
be used if none due. ⚓ in hbr is restricted by ships'
turning circle and foul ground. A rk, 5m NNW of Packet
Quay point, should be avoided by at least 10m at LWS.
NAVIGATION
WPT 52°59'·20N 06°01'·80W, 040°/220° from/to ent, 0·27M.
Appr presents no difficulty; keep in the R sector of the E
pier lt to avoid Planet Rk and Pogeen Rk.
LIGHTS AND MARKS
No ldg marks/lts; lts are as on the chartlet. W pier head lt,
Iso G 4s, is shown H24. ☆ Fl WG 10s on W Packet Quay
head is vis G076°-256°, W256°-076°.

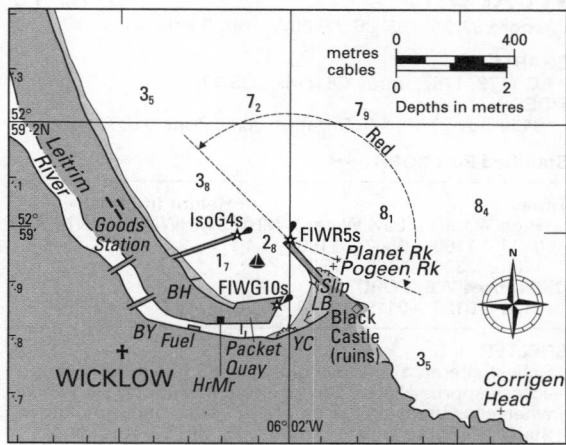

RADIO TELEPHONE
VHF Ch 12, 14, 16. Wicklow SC Ch M 16.
TELEPHONE (Dial code 0404)
Hr Mr 67455; MRCC (01) 6620922; Coast/Cliff Rescue
Service 67310; ⌗ 67222; Police 67107; Dr 67381.
FACILITIES
East Pier L, AB £IR5.50, plus good deals for longer stay;
New (S) Quay, P & D (cans; bulk: see Hr Mr), L, FW, AB;
Wicklow SC ☎ 67526, Slip (HW), M, L, FW, Bar; **Services:**
M, ME, El, C, Sh, AB, Kos, Gaz.
Town EC Thurs; CH, V, R, Bar, ✉, Ⓑ, ≈, ✈ (Dublin).

ARKLOW   8-12-12

Wicklow 52°47'·60N 06°08'·20W   Rtg 2-2-2

CHARTS
AC 633, 1468; Imray C61; Irish OS 62

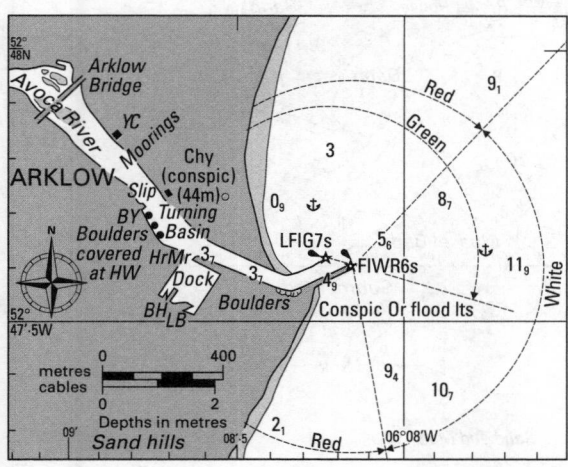

TIDES
–0150 Dover; ML 1·0; Duration 0640; Zone 0 (UT)

Standard Port DUBLIN (NORTH WALL) (←)

Times				Height (metres)			
High Water		Low Water		MHWS	MHWN	MLWN	MLWS
0000	0700	0000	0500	4·1	3·4	1·5	0·7
1200	1900	1200	1700				
Differences ARKLOW (Note small Range)							
–0315	–0201	–0140	–0134	–2·7	–2·2	–0·6	–0·1
COURTOWN							
–0328	–0242	–0158	–0138	–2·8	–2·4	–0·5	0·0

SHELTER
Good, access H24; but ent unsafe in strong NE to SE
onshore winds, when seas break across the bar. Ent is
difficult without power, due to blanking by piers. Night
entry, see below. Once in Dock (3m), berth on SE wall in
perfect shelter, but amidst FVs. One ⚓ in river off slipway
and one AB for Ⓥ (1.4m) at YC quay, but Caution: keep to
N side of river, due to obstructions up-river of Dock ent;
take local advice. Good ⚓ in bay; avoid whelk pots.
Arklow Rock Hbr, 1M S of Arklow, offers emergency ⚓
during SE winds off Roadstone Jetty (Oc R 10s 9m 9M).
2ca S of jetty a mole (QY) extends ENE for 3ca. Best ⚓ in
4m between jetty and mole, neither suitable for AB.
Courtown, 10M S of Arklow at 52°38'·55N 06°13'·50W, is
not advised for visitors due to silting and very narrow ent.
NAVIGATION
WPT 52°47'·60N 06°07'·50W, 090°/270° from/to ent,
0·40M. No navigational dangers, but beware ebb setting
SE across hbr ent. The ent to the dock is 13·5m wide.
LIGHTS AND MARKS
No ldg lts/marks. 2 conspic factory chy's 2·5ca NW of
piers. N pier L Fl G 7s 7m 10M, vis shore-287°. S pier Fl
WR 6s 11m 13M; vis R shore–223°, W223°–350°, R350°–
shore. **Caution:** The pier head lts are very difficult to see
due to powerful orange flood lts near the root of both
piers shining E/ENE onto the piers (to assist pilotage of
departing commercial vessels). Best advice to visitors is
to approach from the N in the R sector of the S pier lt, or
enter by day.
RADIO TELEPHONE
VHF Ch 16 (HJ).
TELEPHONE (Dial code 0402)
Hr Mr 32426; MRCC (01) 6620922/3; Coast/Cliff Rescue
Service 32430; RNLI 32001; ⌗ 32497; Police 2101;
Dr 32421.
FACILITIES
Dock ☎ 32426, AB £9.75 for 1 week, FW, ME, El, C (1 ton),
D (hose, as arranged), BH, Slip; showers in LB stn. **Arklow
YC** (on NE bank, 500m up-river from Dock) quay/jetty, M;
Services: BY, M, FW, ME, El, Sh, C (5 ton mobile), Kos.
Town EC Wed; CH, V, R, P & D (cans), Bar, ✉, Ⓑ, ≈, ✈
(Dublin).

12

WEXFORD   8-12-13

Wexford 52°20'·10N 06°27'·00W   Rtg 3-3-1

CHARTS
AC 1772, 1787; Imray C61; Irish OS 77

TIDES
−0450 Dover; ML 1·3; Duration 0630; Zone 0 (UT)

Standard Port COBH (→)

Times				Height (metres)			
High Water		Low Water		MHWS	MHWN	MLWN	MLWS
0500	1100	0500	1100	4·1	3·2	1·3	0·4
1700	2300	1700	2300				
Differences WEXFORD							
+0126	+0126	+0118	+0108	−2·1	−1·7	−0·3	+0·1

SHELTER
Safe sheltered ⚓ off town quays in 2·3m, but difficult ent; access approx HW±2. Do not attempt in strong E/S winds, when seas break on the bar. No commercial users, other than FVs. Some ⚓s are provided by WHBC, close N of Ballast Bank. It may also be possible to berth alongside mussel dredgers on E side of river just below the bridge. On W side of river work continues on new waterfront: 250m of AB just below the bridge should be completed by June 1999. A decision is pending on a small marina.

NAVIGATION
WPT 52°20'·55N 06°20'·15W, Bar buoy, Iso Y, (pillar-shape, dayglow orange) about 8ca ESE of The Raven Pt. The Bar partly dries and shifts. Hbr Board does not function, so in summer about 20 dayglow orange buoys are locally laid to mark the chan which has only 1m in places.
The following directions are liable to change annually: After 3rd PHM buoy, N of *Submerged Ruins* (awash at HW), head NW. About ¼M off, parallel the shore for about 1M. After passing 2 W posts, head SW towards conspic chy, near SE end of town. Turn stbd when 1ca off training wall. Within the trng walls, Ballast Bank (small islet) can be passed either side.
There are no pilots; it is recommended that first-time visitors should seek local advice from Mr J Sherwood ☎ 22875 (home 22713).

LIGHTS AND MARKS
Ldg marks and tracks on chartlet should be treated with great caution. Channel buoys are re-laid annually using a depth sounder to find best water.

RADIO TELEPHONE
Wexford Hbr BC VHF Ch 16 occas.

TELEPHONE (Dial code 053)
Hr Mr 33114; MRSC (01) 6620922/3; ⌗ 33116; Police 22333; Dr 31154; Ⓗ 42233.

FACILITIES
Wexford Quays AB (free), Slip, P, D, FW, ME, EI, V, CH; **Wexford Hbr Boat Club** ☎ 22039, Slip, C (5 ton), Bar; **Town** ✉, Ⓑ, ≋, ✈ (Waterford).

WEATHER BROADCASTS BY LOCAL RADIO STATIONS

South East Radio   *Mon-Fri:* 0712LT and every H+30 (H24) after the commercial break, broadcasts a detailed general forecast, synopsis for coastal (and inland) areas along the Wexford coast. There are transmitters at: Mount Leinster 95·6MHz, Gorey 96·2 and Wexford 96·4.

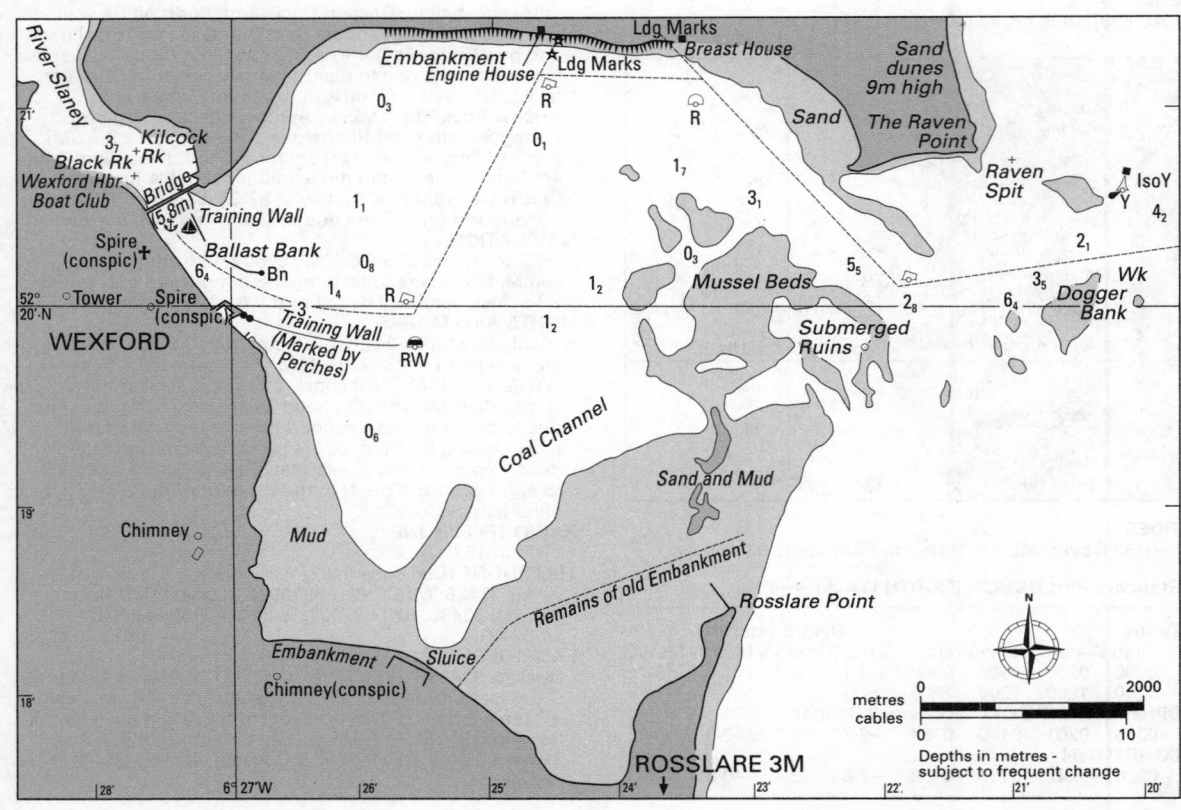

ROSSLARE HARBOUR   8-12-14

Dublin 52°15'·30N 06°20'·90W   Rtg 2-4-3

CHARTS
AC 1772, 1787; Imray C61; Irish OS 77
TIDES
−0510 Dover; ML 1·1; Duration 0640; Zone 0 (UT)

Standard Port COBH (→)

Times				Height (metres)			
High Water		Low Water		MHWS	MHWN	MLWN	MLWS
0500	1100	0500	1100	4·1	3·2	1·3	0·4
1700	2300	1700	2300				
Differences ROSSLARE HARBOUR							
+0055	+0043	+0022	+0002	−2·2	−1·8	−0·5	−0·1

SHELTER
Useful passage shelter from SW'lies, but few facilities for yachts which may berth on E wall of marshalling area (⏚ on the chartlet, 3·7m), or ⚓ about 0·5M W of hbr. In winds from WNW-NNE it is often uncomfortable and, if these winds freshen, dangerous; leave at once, via S Shear. Rosslare has 160 ferry/high-speed catamaran (41kn) movements per week. Small craft hbr has 1m max at LW, bottom is reported foul; mainly used by locals.
NAVIGATION
WPT 52°14'·70N 06°15·60W, (abeam S Long SCM buoy, VQ (6)+L Fl 10s), 105°/285° from/to bkwtr lt, 2·92M. Main appr from E, S and W is via S Shear, buoyed/lit chan to S of Holden's Bed, a shoal of varying depth; the tide sets across the chan. From S, beware rks off Greenore Pt, and overfalls here and over The Baillies. From the N, appr via N Shear. Tuskar TSS (next col) is approx 8M ESE of hbr.
LIGHTS AND MARKS
Water tr (R lt, 35m) is conspic 0·8M SSE of hbr ent. Tuskar Rk, Q (2) 7·5s 33m 28M, is 5·8M SE of hbr ent. Bkwtr lt, Oc WRG 5s 15m 13/10M, see 8.12.4. The two W sectors (188°-208° and 283°–286°) cover N Shear and S Shear respectively. Note: powerful floodlights in the hbr make identification of navigational lights difficult.
RADIO TELEPHONE
Call: *Rosslare Hbr* VHF Ch **12** (H24) before entering hbr.
TELEPHONE (Dial code 053)
Hr Mr 33864/33162; MRCC (01) 6620922/3; LB Lookout Stn 33205; ≢ 33116; Police 22333; Dr 31154; ⊞ 42233.

FACILITIES
Pier ☎ 33114, No fee, M, P, D, L, FW, ME, C, Divers; **Services:** Kos, BY, ME, Sh, El, Slip, C. (Marina planned) **Town** EC Thurs; V, R, Bar, ✉, Ⓑ, ⇌, ✈ (Dublin). Ferries to Fishguard, Pembroke Dock, Cherbourg, Le Havre and Roscoff.

OFF TUSKAR ROCK TRAFFIC SEPARATION SCHEME
Centred on 52°08'·5N 06°03'·8W. The 3M wide lanes are orientated 199°/011° and 232°/052° and the separation zone is 2M wide. Monitor Ch 16 whilst crossing. The ITZ lies between Tuskar Rk and the NW boundary of the TSS. Yachts, bound N/S, will usually navigate to the W of Tuskar Rk where the 3·5M wide chan lies to seaward of The Bailies. A passage inshore of The Bailies requires local knowledge and should not be attempted at night. In heavy weather or poor vis, passage E of Tuskar Rk is advised. See AC 1772, 1.1.3 (Rule 10) and 8.12.5.

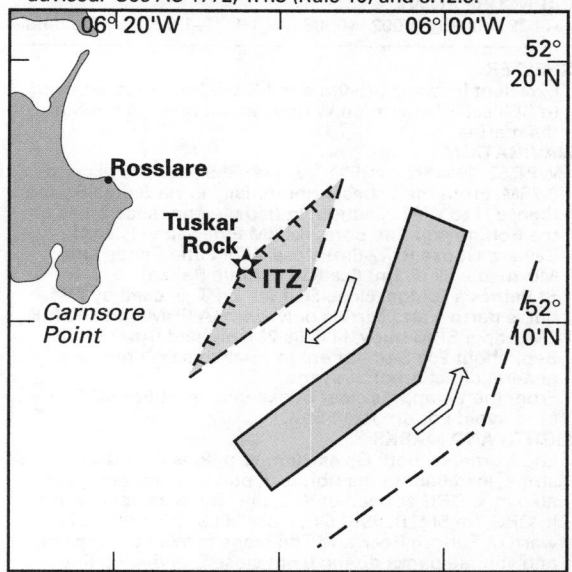

12

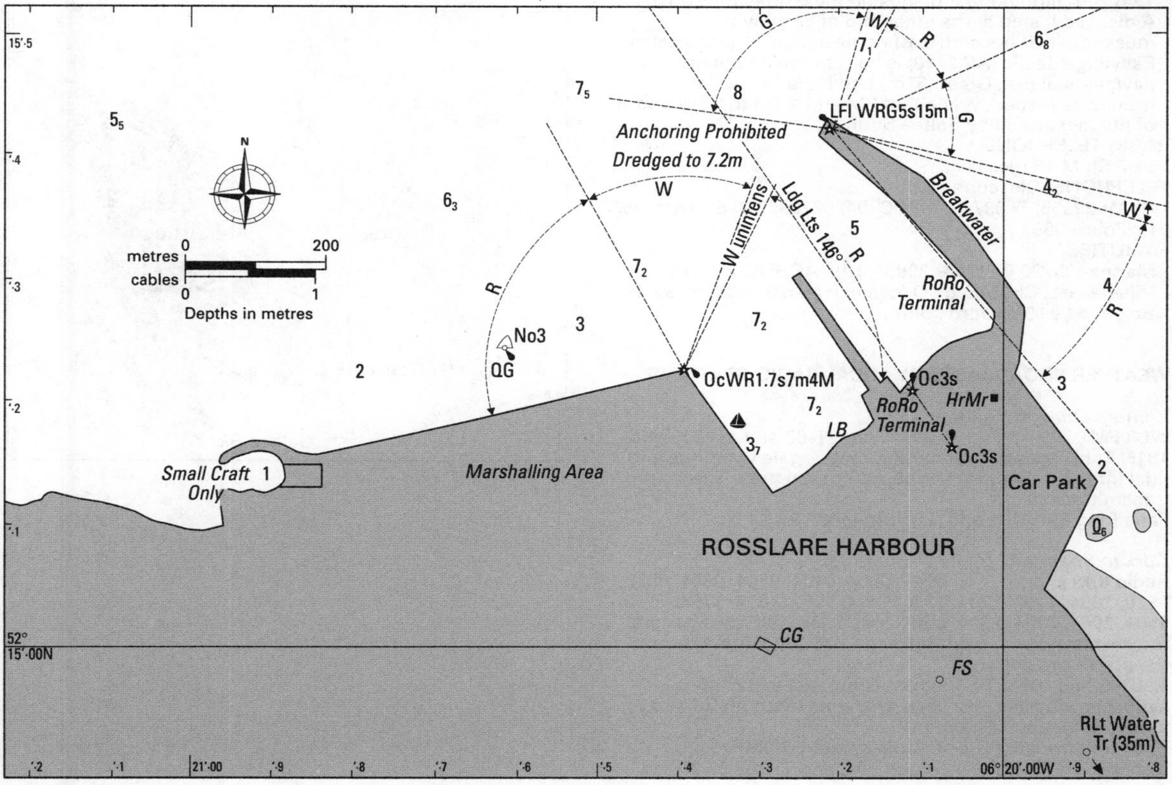

Small Craft 1 Only

Marshalling Area

ROSSLARE HARBOUR

Car Park

RLt Water Tr (35m)

KILMORE QUAY   8-12-15

Wexford 52°10'·25N 06°35'·15W   Rtg 2-3-1

CHARTS
AC 2740, 2049; Imray C61, C57; Irish OS 77

TIDES
−0535 Dover; ML No data; Duration 0605; Zone 0 (UT)

Standard Port COBH (→)

Times				Height (metres)			
High Water		Low Water		MHWS	MHWN	MLWN	MLWS
0500	1100	0500	1100	4·1	3·2	1·3	0·4
1700	2300	1700	2300				
Differences BAGINBUN HEAD							
+0003	+0003	−0008	−0008	−0·2	−0·1	+0·2	+0·2
GREAT SALTEE							
+0019	+0009	−0004	+0006	−0·3	−0·4	No data	
CARNSORE POINT							
+0029	+0019	−0002	+0008	−1·1	−1·0	No data	

SHELTER
Excellent in marina (3·0m depth), but hbr ent is exposed to SE'lies. FVs berth on W quay and E quay to the S of the marina.

NAVIGATION
WPT 52°09'·46N 06°35'·10W, 179°/359° from/to bkwtr lt, 0·75M. From the E, best appr initially is via Saltee Sound, thence N to WPT. Caution: In bad weather seas break on the Bohurs and The Bore, rks 2M E of Saltee Islands. Beware Goose Rk (2·6m) close W of Little Saltee and Murroch's Rk (2·1m) 6ca NW of Little Saltee.
St Patrick's Bridge, close S of the WPT, is used by FVs, but is narrow and carries only 2·4m. A PHM buoy, Fl R 6s 2M, and a SHM buoy, Fl G 6s 2M, are laid (Apr to mid-Sep) about 9ca S of hbr ent to mark this E/W passage; general direction of buoyage is E.
From the W, appr is clear but keep at least 5ca off Forlorn Pt to avoid Forlorn Rk (1·5m).

LIGHTS AND MARKS
Ldg lts/marks, both Oc 4s 20m, W pylons with R vert stripe, lead 008° to the hbr; turn port into hbr ent when abeam ☆ QRG at head of W Quay. The R sectors of this lt, QRG 7m 5M, R269°-354°, G354°-003°(9°), R003°-077°, warn of Forlorn Rock and The Lings to W of the ldg line and shingle banks drying 0·6m close E of the ldg line.
Two 20m high flood lt pylons on the E quay are conspic. A disued lt ship at the inner end of W quay is a museum; its lt housing is of no navigational significance. Ballyteige Castle (AC 2740) is hard to see and of no navigational use. Great (57m) and Little (35m) Saltee Islands lie respectively about 3M and 1·7M to SSW and S of hbr, separated by Saltee Sound.

RADIO TELEPHONE
VHF Ch M 16 (occas).

TELEPHONE (Dial code 053)
Hr Mr 29955; ⌗ 33741; MRCC (01) 6620922/3; Emergency/ Dr/Police 999.

FACILITIES
Marina (35+20 Ⓥ) ☎/🐟 29955, £10, AC, FW, Slip, LB; **Village** Gaz, CH, ME, El, D (cans), P (cans) is 3M away, R, Bar, V, ✉, Ⓗ (Wexford 15M).

WEATHER BROADCASTS BY LOCAL RADIO STATIONS

Kilmore Quay to Youghal
WLR FM   *Daily:* Every H+03 and at 1315 and 1815LT, broadcasts a general forecast, gale warnings and tidal info (Jun-Sep) for the above coastal area. There are transmitters at:
Faha Ring 95·1MHz and Carrickpherish 97·5.

Cork to Shannon
Radio Kerry   *Daily:* 0004, 0104, 0704, 0804, 0835, 0910, 1004, 1107, 1204, 1330, 1404, 1507, 1607, 1704, 1740, 1904, 2004, 2104, 2204, and 2304UT, broadcasts a general forecast, synopsis, gale warnings and wind strength for the above coastal area.
At 0755 and 1155LT a forecast is broadcast including synopsis, visibility, sea state and wind strength for sea areas Fastnet and Shannon.
There are transmitters at: Mullaganish 97·0MHz, Knockanure 97·6, Kilkieveragh 96·2 and Tralee 96·2.

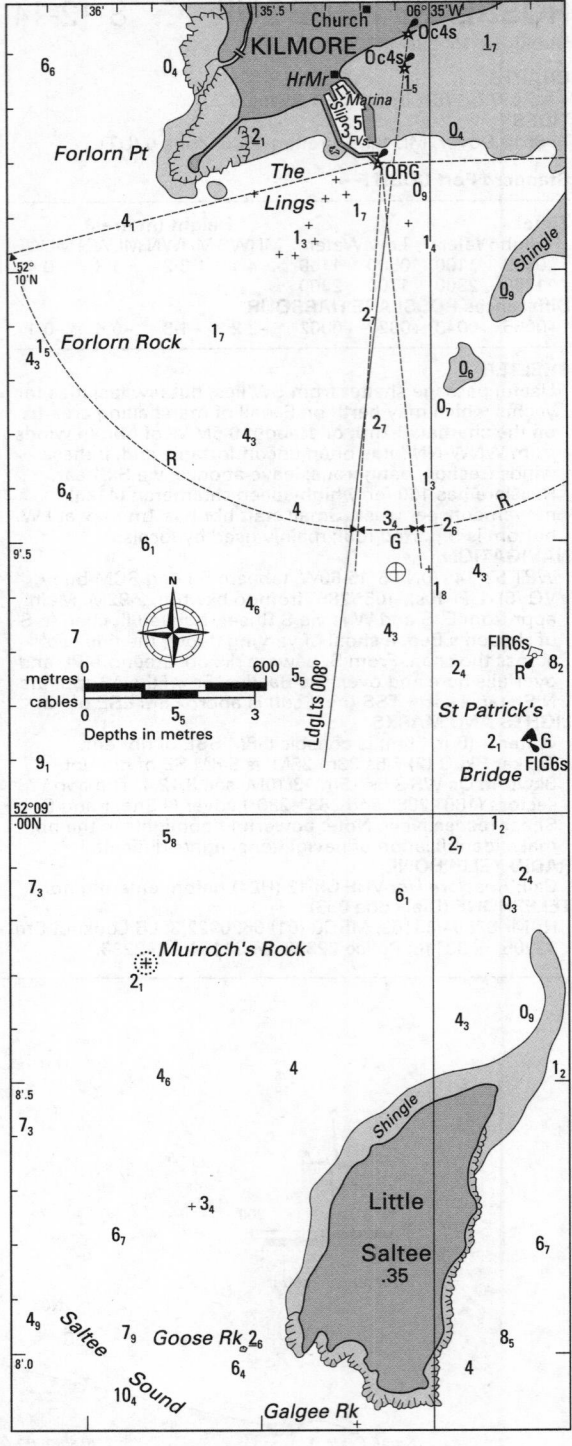

WATERFORD   8-12-16

Waterford 52°15'·50N 07°06'·00W   Rtg 1-3-1

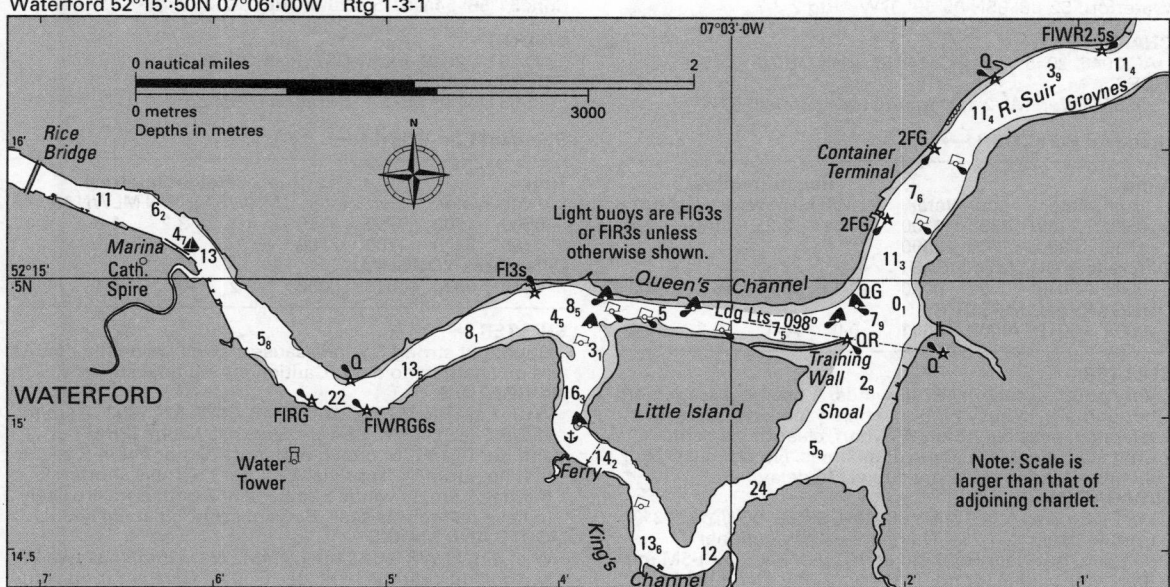

CHARTS
AC 2046, 2049; Imray C57; Irish OS 76

TIDES
–0520 Dover; ML 2·4; Duration 0605; Zone 0 (UT)

Standard Port COBH (→)

Times				Height (metres)			
High Water		Low Water		MHWS	MHWN	MLWN	MLWS
0500	1100	0500	1100	4·1	3·2	1·3	0·4
1700	2300	1700	2300				
Differences WATERFORD							
+0057	+0057	+0046	+0046	+0·4	+0·3	–0·1	+0·1
CHEEK POINT							
+0022	+0020	+0020	+0020	+0·3	+0·2	+0·2	+0·1
KILMOKEA POINT							
+0026	+0022	+0020	+0020	+0·2	+0·1	+0·1	+0·1
NEW ROSS							
+0100	+0030	+0055	+0130	+0·3	+0·4	+0·3	+0·4

SHELTER
Very good in Waterford on a 170m long yacht pontoon S bank, near to cathedral spire. Caution: strong tidal stream. Many excellent ⚓s: 9M up the estuary, off the quays just W of Cheek Pt where 4 groynes marked by SPM buoys, FY and Fl Y 2s, extend into the river; about 3M further W, off S side of R Suir in King's Chan (only to be entered W of Little Is); up the R Barrow near Marsh Pt (about 2M S of New Ross) and 0·5M S of New Ross fixed bridge.

NAVIGATION
WPT 52°06'·50N 06°56'·50W, 182°/002° from/to Dir lt at Duncannon, 6·7M. From the E, keep clear of Brecaun reef (2M NE of Hook Hd). Give Tower Race a wide berth, especially HW Dover ±2; overfalls extend about 1·5M S of Hook Hd. From the W do not confuse Waterford ent with Tramore Bay; beware Falskirt Rk (2ca off Swine Hd).

LIGHTS AND MARKS
The ent to R Suir lies between Dunmore East L Fl WR 8s 13m 16/12M; vis W225°–310°, R310°–004°; and Hook Hd, Fl 3s 46m 23M, W tr with 2 B bands. Duncannon Dir lt Oc WRG 4s 13m 11/8M, G358°–001·7°, W001·7°–002·2°, R002·2°–006°, leads 002° up-river via well-buoyed lit chan. On same structure is lt, Oc WR 4s 13m 9/7M, R119°-149°, W149°-172°. The R Suir from Cheek Pt to Waterford is lit and buoyed. The R Barrow is also well lit/marked up to New Ross. The rly swing bridge at the river ent opens at its W end. Call bridge-keeper VHF Ch 16 or ☎ 88137.

RADIO TELEPHONE
Waterford and New Ross VHF Ch 12 14 16.

TELEPHONE (Dial code 051)
Hr Mrs Waterford 874499/New Ross 21303; MRCC (01) 6620922; ⌗ 875391; Police 874888; Dr 883194; Ⓗ 875429.

FACILITIES
Yacht pontoon FW, AC, 2m at all tides on outside berths; showers at Viking House (300m). **Services:** ME, El, Sh, C, BY (Ballyhack). **City** EC Thurs; P, D, Gaz, V, R, Bar, ✉, ⓞ, Ⓑ, ⇌ to Dublin, ✈ to Stansted, bus/ferry to London.

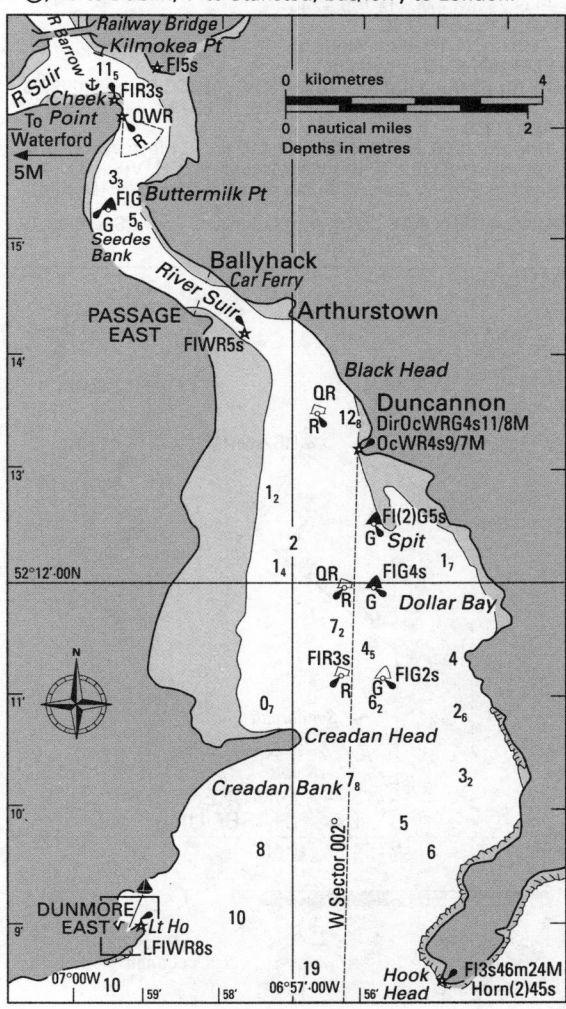

DUNMORE EAST   8-12-17

Waterford 52°08'·95N 06°59'·37W   Rtg 2-3-3

CHARTS
AC 2046, 2049; Imray C61, C57; Irish OS 76
TIDES
−0535 Dover; ML 2·4; Duration 0605; Zone 0 (UT)

Standard Port COBH (→)

Times				Height (metres)			
High Water		Low Water		MHWS	MHWN	MLWN	MLWS
0500	1100	0500	1100	4·1	3·2	1·3	0·4
1700	2300	1700	2300				
Differences DUNMORE EAST							
+0008	+0003	0000	0000	+0·1	+0·1	+0·2	0·0
DUNGARVAN HARBOUR							
+0004	+0012	+0007	−0001	0·0	+0·1	−0·2	0·0

SHELTER
Very good, except in NE/SE winds. A useful passage port, but primarily a busy FV hbr, where yachts are scarcely tolerated; possible AB on W Wharf, clear of ice berth. Craft stay afloat in 2 - 3·4m at all times. No ⌀s, but ⌁ N of the hbr. (Marina plans are subject to delay).
NAVIGATION
WPT (see also 8.12.17) 52°08'·00N, 06°58'·00W, 137°/317° from/to bkwtr lt, 1·2M. There are no navigational dangers, but clear Hook Hd and Tower Race by 1·5M min; then alter course for hbr in R sector of E pier lt ho. From W, beware Falskirt Rk; by night steer for Hook Hd until in R sector of E pier lt, then alter to N. Enter under power.
LIGHTS AND MARKS
E Pier lt ho Fl WR8s 13m 17/13M, W225°-310°, R310°-004°. E bkwtr hd Fl R2s 6m 4M, vis 000°-310°. W wharf Fl G 2s 6m 4M, vis 165°−246°.
RADIO TELEPHONE
VHF Ch 14 16 (Pilot Station).
TELEPHONE (Dial code 051)
Hr Mr 83166; Pilot 83119; ⌗ 75391; MRCC (01) 6620922/3; Coast Life Saving Service 83115; Dr 83194.
FACILITIES
Hbr ☎ 83166, BH (230 ton), D, FW (on E pier); Waterford Hbr SC ☎ 83389, R, Bar; Services: Kos, CH. Village D, P (cans), Slip, R, Bar, V, Ⓑ, ✉, ⇌ (Waterford), ✈ (Dublin).

DUNGARVAN BAY (22M W of Dunmore East): See 8.12.19.

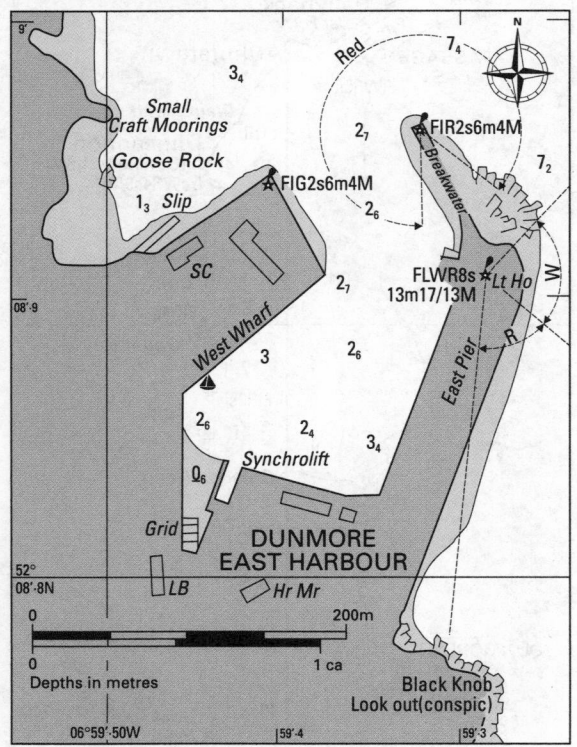

YOUGHAL   8-12-18

Cork 51°56'·54N 07°50'·20W   Rtg 3-2-2

CHARTS
AC 2071, 2049; Imray C57; Irish OS 81, 82
TIDES
−0556 Dover; ML 2·1; Duration 0555; Zone 0 (UT)

Standard Port COBH (→)

Times				Height (metres)			
High Water		Low Water		MHWS	MHWN	MLWN	MLWS
0500	1100	0500	1100	4·1	3·2	1·3	0·4
1700	2300	1700	2300				
Differences YOUGHAL							
0000	+0010	+0010	0000	−0·2	−0·1	−0·1	−0·1

SHELTER
Good, but strong S winds cause a swell inside the hbr. ⌁s as on chartlet; no dues. Caution strong tidal streams.
NAVIGATION
WPT, East Bar, 51°55'·62N 07°48'·00W, 122°/302° from/to Fl WR 2·5s lt, 1·8M. Beware Blackball Ledge (PHM buoy) and Bar Rks (SCM buoy), both outside hbr ent in R sector of lt ho. From W, appr via West Bar (1·7m) is shorter; E Bar has 2·0m. In winds E to SSW >F6 both Bars are likely to have dangerous seas. Beware salmon nets May-July.
LIGHTS AND MARKS
W of ent, Fl WR 2·5s 24m 17/14M, W tr (15m), has two W sectors ldg over the bars (see 8.12.4). Convent tr on with the town hall at 175° leads clear W of Red Bank up-river. Conspic water tr approx 0·65M WNW of clock tr.
RADIO TELEPHONE
VHF Ch 14 16 HW±3.
TELEPHONE (Dial code 024)
Hr Mr 92820; MRCC (01) 6620922/3; Coast/Cliff Rescue Service 93252; ⌗ (021) 968783; Police 92200; Dr 92702.
FACILITIES
Services: ME, El, Sh, CH, L, FW (see Hr Mr), Slip. **Town** P & D (cans), V, R, Bar, ✉, Ⓑ, ⇌ (Cork/Waterford), ✈ (Cork).

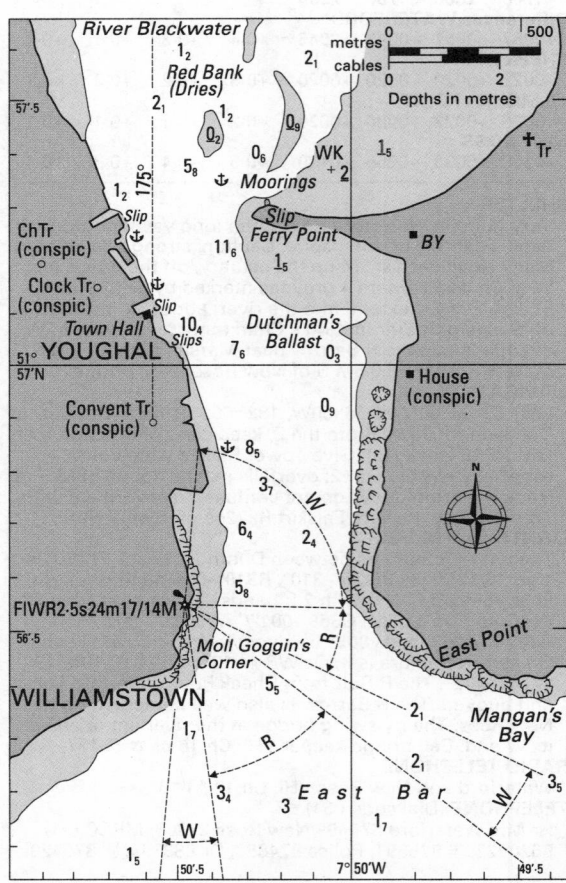

IRELAND – COBH

LAT 51°51′N   LONG 8°18′W

TIMES AND HEIGHTS OF HIGH AND LOW WATERS

YEAR **1999**

TIME ZONE (UT)
For Summer Time add ONE hour in non-shaded areas

JANUARY

Day	Time m	Time m	Time m	Time m		Day	Time m	Time m	Time m	Time m
1 F	0422 4.1	1100 0.5	1649 4.2	2321 0.4		**16** SA	0433 3.9	1057 0.8	1654 3.9	2316 0.8
2 SA O	0515 4.3	1150 0.4	1738 4.2			**17** SU ●	0515 4.0	1136 0.7	1732 4.0	2353 0.7
3 SU	0008 0.3	0602 4.3	1237 0.4	1823 4.2		**18** M	0553 4.1	1213 0.7	1807 4.0	
4 M	0053 0.3	0647 4.3	1321 0.4	1905 4.2		**19** TU	0030 0.6	0629 4.2	1251 0.6	1842 4.1
5 TU	0136 0.4	0729 4.2	1403 0.5	1946 4.0		**20** W	0108 0.6	0707 4.2	1330 0.6	1920 4.0
6 W	0218 0.6	0811 4.1	1446 0.7	2026 3.9		**21** TH	0148 0.6	0747 4.1	1411 0.7	2001 4.0
7 TH	0301 0.7	0853 3.9	1528 0.9	2107 3.7		**22** F	0231 0.7	0830 4.1	1454 0.8	2044 3.9
8 F	0346 0.9	0936 3.7	1613 1.1	2150 3.6		**23** SA	0317 0.7	0916 4.0	1540 0.9	2132 3.8
9 SA	0433 1.1	1022 3.6	1702 1.2	2238 3.4		**24** SU	0407 0.9	1006 3.9	1631 1.0	2225 3.7
10 SU	0526 1.2	1115 3.4	1758 1.3	2336 3.3		**25** M	0504 1.0	1103 3.7	1731 1.1	2327 3.6
11 M	0625 1.3	1218 3.4	1859 1.4			**26** TU	0610 1.1	1208 3.6	1842 1.2	
12 TU	0045 3.3	0727 1.3	1326 3.4	2000 1.3		**27** W	0037 3.5	0725 1.1	1322 3.6	1959 1.1
13 W	0155 3.4	0827 1.3	1429 3.5	2058 1.2		**28** TH	0155 3.6	0843 1.0	1436 3.6	2114 0.9
14 TH	0255 3.6	0923 1.1	1523 3.6	2150 1.1		**29** F	0310 3.7	0953 0.8	1542 3.8	2218 0.7
15 F	0347 3.7	1013 1.0	1612 3.8	2236 0.9		**30** SA	0413 4.0	1051 0.6	1639 4.0	2311 0.5
						31 SU O	0506 4.1	1141 0.4	1727 4.1	2357 0.4

FEBRUARY

Day	Time m	Time m	Time m	Time m		Day	Time m	Time m	Time m	Time m
1 M	0551 4.2	1224 0.4	1810 4.2			**16** TU ●	0533 4.1	1156 0.5	1751 4.1	
2 TU	0038 0.3	0631 4.3	1304 0.4	1848 4.1		**17** W	0012 0.4	0611 4.2	1234 0.4	1827 4.1
3 W	0117 0.4	0709 4.2	1342 0.5	1924 4.1		**18** TH	0050 0.3	0649 4.2	1312 0.4	1904 4.1
4 TH	0154 0.5	0746 4.1	1418 0.6	1959 3.9		**19** F	0130 0.3	0728 4.2	1352 0.4	1944 4.1
5 F	0230 0.6	0822 4.0	1454 0.8	2034 3.8		**20** SA	0212 0.4	0810 4.1	1434 0.5	2025 4.0
6 SA	0307 0.8	0858 3.8	1530 0.9	2111 3.7		**21** SU	0256 0.5	0854 4.0	1518 0.6	2110 3.9
7 SU	0345 1.0	0936 3.7	1609 1.1	2151 3.6		**22** M	0344 0.6	0942 3.8	1606 0.8	2200 3.7
8 M	0429 1.1	1019 3.5	1657 1.3	2239 3.4		**23** TU	0438 0.8	1036 3.6	1703 1.0	2258 3.5
9 TU	0524 1.3	1110 3.3	1757 1.4	2339 3.3		**24** W	0542 1.0	1141 3.4	1812 1.1	
10 W	0629 1.4	1217 3.2	1906 1.4			**25** TH	0011 3.4	0659 1.1	1301 3.3	1936 1.2
11 TH	0054 3.2	0738 1.4	1338 3.2	2014 1.3		**26** F	0139 3.4	0828 1.0	1423 3.4	2102 1.0
12 F	0214 3.3	0844 1.2	1450 3.4	2117 1.2		**27** SA	0300 3.6	0944 0.8	1532 3.6	2209 0.7
13 SA	0317 3.6	0944 1.0	1546 3.6	2210 0.9		**28** SU	0403 3.8	1042 0.6	1627 3.8	2301 0.5
14 SU	0409 3.8	1024 0.8	1633 3.8	2255 0.7						
15 M	0453 4.0	1117 0.6	1713 4.0	2334 0.5						

MARCH

Day	Time m	Time m	Time m	Time m		Day	Time m	Time m	Time m	Time m
1 M	0452 4.0	1128 0.4	1713 4.0	2344 0.3		**16** TU	0424 3.9	1051 0.5	1647 3.9	2309 0.4
2 TU O	0535 4.1	1208 0.3	1753 4.1			**17** W ●	0506 4.1	1132 0.3	1727 4.1	2349 0.2
3 W	0021 0.3	0611 4.2	1244 0.3	1828 4.1		**18** TH	0547 4.2	1212 0.2	1806 4.2	
4 TH	0055 0.3	0646 4.1	1316 0.4	1900 4.0		**19** F	0029 0.1	0626 4.3	1252 0.1	1844 4.2
5 F	0126 0.4	0718 4.1	1347 0.5	1930 4.0		**20** SA	0110 0.1	0707 4.2	1332 0.2	1924 4.2
6 SA	0157 0.5	0822 3.9	1418 0.7	2002 3.9		**21** SU	0153 0.2	0750 4.2	1414 0.3	2007 4.1
7 SU	0229 0.7	0822 3.8	1449 0.8	2035 3.8		**22** M	0238 0.3	0834 4.0	1459 0.4	2051 3.9
8 M	0303 0.9	0856 3.7	1524 1.0	2113 3.6		**23** TU	0326 0.5	0922 3.8	1548 0.6	2141 3.7
9 TU	0343 1.0	0934 3.5	1605 1.2	2156 3.5		**24** W	0420 0.7	1015 3.5	1644 0.9	2239 3.5
10 W	0432 1.2	1020 3.3	1700 1.3	2249 3.3		**25** TH	0523 0.9	1121 3.3	1753 1.1	2354 3.3
11 TH	0537 1.4	1120 3.2	1813 1.5	2359 3.2		**26** F	0643 1.1	1244 3.2	1921 1.1	
12 F	0652 1.4	1238 3.1	1930 1.4			**27** SA	0127 3.3	0815 1.0	1408 3.3	2049 1.0
13 SA	0125 3.2	0804 1.3	1407 3.2	2039 1.2		**28** SU	0246 3.5	0929 0.8	1515 3.5	2155 0.7
14 SU	0241 3.4	0909 1.0	1514 3.4	2138 0.9		**29** M	0345 3.7	1019 0.5	1608 3.7	2245 0.5
15 M	0338 3.7	1004 0.8	1604 3.7	2227 0.6		**30** TU	0432 3.9	1109 0.4	1653 3.9	2325 0.4
						31 W O	0512 4.0	1147 0.3	1731 4.0	

APRIL

Day	Time m	Time m	Time m	Time m		Day	Time m	Time m	Time m	Time m
1 TH	0000 0.3	0548 4.1	1220 0.3	1804 4.0		**16** F ●	0520 4.2	1148 0.1	1742 4.2	
2 F	0030 0.4	0620 4.0	1249 0.4	1834 4.0		**17** SA	0008 0.0	0603 4.3	1232 0.0	1823 4.3
3 SA	0057 0.5	0650 4.0	1317 0.5	1903 4.0		**18** SU	0052 0.0	0647 4.2	1315 0.1	1906 4.2
4 SU	0125 0.6	0719 3.9	1345 0.6	1932 3.9		**19** M	0137 0.1	0732 4.2	1359 0.2	1951 4.1
5 M	0155 0.7	0749 3.8	1415 0.8	2005 3.8		**20** TU	0224 0.2	0818 4.0	1446 0.3	2037 4.0
6 TU	0229 0.8	0822 3.7	1448 0.9	2041 3.7		**21** W	0314 0.4	0907 3.8	1536 0.5	2128 3.7
7 W	0307 1.0	0859 3.6	1528 1.1	2123 3.5		**22** TH	0408 0.6	1001 3.5	1633 0.8	2227 3.5
8 TH	0354 1.2	0944 3.4	1619 1.3	2213 3.4		**23** F	0511 0.9	1106 3.3	1741 1.0	2341 3.3
9 F	0455 1.3	1040 3.2	1728 1.4	2317 3.2		**24** SA	0628 1.0	1225 3.2	1904 1.0	
10 SA	0609 1.4	1152 3.1	1847 1.4			**25** SU	0107 3.3	0752 1.0	1344 3.3	2025 0.9
11 SU	0037 3.2	0724 1.3	1316 3.2	1958 1.2		**26** M	0220 3.4	0902 0.8	1449 3.4	2128 0.7
12 M	0156 3.4	0830 1.0	1430 3.4	2059 0.9		**27** TU	0316 3.6	0956 0.6	1541 3.7	2218 0.6
13 TU	0258 3.6	0928 0.7	1527 3.7	2153 0.6		**28** W	0404 3.8	1041 0.5	1625 3.8	2259 0.5
14 W	0349 3.9	1019 0.5	1615 3.9	2240 0.4		**29** TH	0444 3.9	1119 0.4	1704 3.9	2333 0.5
15 TH	0436 4.1	1105 0.2	1659 4.1	2325 0.2		**30** F O	0521 3.9	1152 0.5	1738 4.0	

12

Chart Datum: 0·13 metres above Ordnance Datum (Dublin)

IRELAND – COBH

LAT 51°51′N   LONG 8°18′W

TIMES AND HEIGHTS OF HIGH AND LOW WATERS

YEAR 1999

TIME ZONE (UT)
For Summer Time add ONE hour in non-shaded areas

MAY

Day	Time	m	Time	m	Time	m	Time	m
1 SA	0002	0.5	0553	3.9	1221	0.5	1808	3.9
2 SU	0029	0.6	0623	3.9	1248	0.6	1837	3.9
3 M	0056	0.6	0651	3.9	1316	0.7	1907	3.9
4 TU	0128	0.7	0721	3.8	1348	0.8	1940	3.8
5 W	0203	0.8	0755	3.7	1423	0.9	2017	3.7
6 TH	0243	1.0	0834	3.6	1505	1.0	2059	3.6
7 F	0329	1.1	0919	3.5	1554	1.2	2148	3.5
8 SA	0425	1.2	1013	3.4	1656	1.3	2248	3.4
9 SU	0532	1.2	1118	3.3	1808	1.3	2358	3.4
10 M	0644	1.2	1232	3.3	1918	1.1		
11 TU	0111	3.5	0751	1.0	1344	3.5	2021	0.9
12 W	0217	3.7	0851	0.7	1445	3.7	2118	0.6
13 TH	0313	3.9	0946	0.5	1540	3.9	2211	0.4
14 F	0405	4.1	1038	0.3	1630	4.1	2301	0.2
15 SA	0455	4.2	1126	0.1	1719	4.2	2349 ●	0.1
16 SU	0543	4.2	1214	0.1	1805	4.3		
17 M	0037	0.0	0630	4.2	1301	0.1	1851	4.2
18 TU	0125	0.1	0717	4.1	1348	0.2	1938	4.1
19 W	0213	0.2	0805	4.0	1436	0.3	2026	4.0
20 TH	0304	0.4	0855	3.8	1527	0.5	2118	3.8
21 F	0358	0.6	0948	3.6	1623	0.7	2214	3.5
22 SA	0457	0.8	1047	3.4	1725	0.9	2320	3.4
23 SU	0605	0.9	1156	3.3	1836	0.9		
24 M	0034	3.3	0716	1.0	1308	3.3	1947	0.9
25 TU	0142	3.4	0821	0.9	1411	3.4	2048	0.8
26 W	0239	3.5	0916	0.8	1504	3.5	2140	0.7
27 TH	0328	3.6	1004	0.7	1551	3.7	2224	0.7
28 F	0411	3.8	1045	0.6	1632	3.8	2301	0.6
29 SA	0451	3.8	1121	0.6	1710	3.9	2332	0.6
30 SU	0527	3.9	1153	0.6	1744 O	3.9		
31 M	0001	0.7	0558	3.8	1223	0.7	1815	3.9

JUNE

Day	Time	m	Time	m	Time	m	Time	m
1 TU	0032	0.7	0629	3.8	1254	0.7	1847	3.9
2 W	0106	0.7	0701	3.8	1328	0.8	1921	3.9
3 TH	0143	0.8	0736	3.8	1406	0.9	1959	3.8
4 F	0225	0.9	0816	3.7	1448	0.9	2041	3.7
5 SA	0310	1.0	0901	3.6	1536	1.0	2129	3.7
6 SU	0402	1.1	0953	3.5	1631	1.1	2224	3.6
7 M	0501	1.1	1051	3.5	1733	1.1	2326	3.6
8 TU	0606	1.1	1156	3.5	1840	1.0		
9 W	0034	3.6	0712	1.0	1304	3.6	1945	0.9
10 TH	0140	3.7	0816	0.8	1408	3.7	2046	0.7
11 F	0241	3.9	0916	0.6	1508	3.9	2146	0.6
12 SA	0339	4.0	1014	0.4	1606	4.0	2242	0.3
13 SU	0434	4.1	1108	0.3	1700	4.2	2334 ●	0.2
14 M	0526	4.2	1159	0.2	1750	4.2		
15 TU	0024	0.1	0616	4.2	1248	0.1	1838	4.2
16 W	0113	0.1	0704	4.1	1336	0.2	1926	4.1
17 TH	0202	0.2	0751	4.0	1424	0.3	2013	4.0
18 F	0251	0.4	0839	3.8	1513	0.5	2102	3.8
19 SA	0341	0.6	0928	3.7	1604	0.6	2152	3.6
20 SU	0434	0.8	1019	3.5	1658	0.8	2247	3.5
21 M	0531	0.9	1116	3.4	1757	0.9	2348	3.4
22 TU	0632	1.0	1218	3.3	1859	1.0		
23 W	0053	3.3	0732	1.0	1322	3.3	1958	1.0
24 TH	0153	3.4	0828	1.0	1420	3.4	2053	0.9
25 F	0247	3.5	0921	0.8	1512	3.5	2142	0.9
26 SA	0336	3.6	1008	0.7	1559	3.7	2226	0.8
27 SU	0421	3.7	1050	0.6	1642	3.8	2304	0.7
28 M	0501	3.8	1127	0.7	1721	3.9	2338 O	0.7
29 TU	0538	3.8	1201	0.7	1756	3.9		
30 W	0012	0.7	0611	3.8	1235	0.7	1831	3.9

JULY

Day	Time	m	Time	m	Time	m	Time	m
1 TH	0049	0.7	0645	3.8	1311	0.7	1906	3.9
2 F	0127	0.7	0721	3.8	1349	0.7	1944	3.9
3 SA	0208	0.8	0800	3.8	1431	0.8	2025	3.9
4 SU	0251	0.8	0844	3.7	1516	0.8	2111	3.8
5 M	0339	0.9	0932	3.7	1605	0.8	2201	3.8
6 TU	0431	1.0	1025	3.6	1700	1.0	2257	3.7
7 W	0529	1.0	1124	3.6	1803	1.0		
8 TH	0000	3.7	0635	1.0	1229	3.6	1910	0.9
9 F	0107	3.7	0744	0.9	1337	3.7	2019	0.8
10 SA	0213	3.7	0851	0.8	1444	3.8	2125	0.7
11 SU	0318	3.8	0955	0.6	1548	3.9	2227	0.5
12 M	0418	4.0	1053	0.4	1646	4.1	2322	0.3
13 TU	0513	4.1	1146	0.3	1738 ●	4.2		
14 W	0012	0.2	0602	4.1	1235	0.2	1825	4.2
15 TH	0100	0.2	0649	4.1	1321	0.2	1911	4.2
16 F	0145	0.3	0733	4.0	1406	0.3	1954	4.0
17 SA	0230	0.4	0817	3.9	1450	0.4	2038	3.9
18 SU	0315	0.6	0900	3.7	1535	0.6	2121	3.7
19 M	0400	0.8	0943	3.6	1620	0.8	2206	3.6
20 TU	0448	0.9	1029	3.4	1709	1.0	2255	3.4
21 W	0540	1.1	1121	3.3	1803	1.1	2353	3.3
22 TH	0637	1.2	1223	3.3	1902	1.2		
23 F	0059	3.3	0737	1.2	1331	3.3	2002	1.2
24 SA	0204	3.3	0836	1.1	1433	3.4	2059	1.1
25 SU	0302	3.5	0932	1.0	1528	3.6	2152	1.0
26 M	0353	3.6	1021	0.8	1616	3.7	2237	0.8
27 TU	0438	3.7	1103	0.7	1659	3.9	2317	0.7
28 W	0518	3.8	1140	0.7	1738	4.0	2354 O	0.7
29 TH	0555	3.9	1215	0.7	1814	4.0		
30 F	0030	0.6	0629	3.9	1251	0.6	1849	4.0
31 SA	0108	0.6	0704	3.9	1329	0.6	1926	4.0

AUGUST

Day	Time	m	Time	m	Time	m	Time	m
1 SU	0148	0.6	0743	3.9	1410	0.6	2006	4.0
2 M	0230	0.7	0824	3.8	1453	0.7	2049	3.9
3 TU	0314	0.7	0909	3.8	1539	0.7	2136	3.9
4 W	0402	0.8	0958	3.7	1630	0.8	2228	3.7
5 TH	0457	0.9	1054	3.6	1730	1.0	2329	3.6
6 F	0602	1.0	1159	3.5	1840	1.0		
7 SA	0039	3.5	0716	1.0	1313	3.5	1956	1.0
8 SU	0154	3.5	0832	0.9	1429	3.6	2111	0.8
9 M	0305	3.7	0943	0.7	1538	3.8	2217	0.6
10 TU	0407	3.9	1043	0.5	1637	4.0	2312	0.4
11 W	0501	4.0	1134	0.3	1726	4.1	2359 ●	0.3
12 TH	0548	4.1	1219	0.2	1811	4.2		
13 F	0042	0.2	0630	4.1	1301	0.2	1851	4.2
14 SA	0123	0.3	0710	4.0	1341	0.3	1929	4.1
15 SU	0202	0.4	0748	3.9	1419	0.4	2007	3.9
16 M	0241	0.6	0825	3.8	1457	0.6	2044	3.8
17 TU	0319	0.8	0903	3.7	1535	0.8	2122	3.6
18 W	0359	1.0	0942	3.5	1617	1.0	2203	3.5
19 TH	0444	1.1	1028	3.4	1705	1.2	2252	3.3
20 F	0540	1.3	1123	3.2	1806	1.3	2354	3.2
21 SA	0646	1.3	1236	3.2	1913	1.3		
22 SU	0114	3.2	0754	1.3	1355	3.3	2019	1.3
23 M	0228	3.3	0857	1.1	1500	3.4	2120	1.1
24 TU	0326	3.5	0952	0.9	1551	3.7	2211	0.9
25 W	0414	3.7	1038	0.7	1635	3.9	2254	0.7
26 TH	0455	3.8	1117	0.6	1715	4.0	2332	0.5
27 F	0533	3.9	1152	0.5	1751	4.1		
28 SA	0009	0.5	0607	4.0	1229	0.4	1826	4.1
29 SU	0046	0.4	0643	4.0	1306	0.4	1903	4.1
30 M	0125	0.4	0721	4.0	1347	0.4	1943	4.1
31 TU	0206	0.5	0801	4.0	1429	0.5	2025	4.0

Chart Datum: 0·13 metres above Ordnance Datum (Dublin)

IRELAND – COBH

LAT 51°51'N LONG 8°18'W

TIMES AND HEIGHTS OF HIGH AND LOW WATERS

YEAR **1999**

TIME ZONE (UT)
For Summer Time add ONE hour in non-shaded areas

SEPTEMBER

Day	Time	m	Day	Time	m
1 W	0250	0.6	**16** TH	0311	1.0
	0845	3.9		0901	3.6
	1515	0.6		1528	1.1
	2111	3.9		2118	3.5
2 TH	0337	0.7	**17** F	0351	1.2
	0934	3.8		0943	3.4
	1605	0.8		1613	1.3
	2202	3.7		2202	3.4
3 F	0431	0.9	**18** SA	0444	1.3
	1029	3.6		1035	3.3
	1704	1.0		1713	1.4
	2303	3.5		2257	3.2
4 SA	0536	1.1	**19** SU	0555	1.5
	1137	3.4		1142	3.1
	1817	1.1		1827	1.5
5 SU	0018	3.4	**20** M	0014	3.1
	0656	1.1		0712	1.4
	1300	3.4		1311	3.2
	1942	1.1		1941	1.4
6 M	0142	3.4	**21** TU	0149	3.2
	0822	1.0		0821	1.3
	1424	3.5		1427	3.4
	2105	0.9		2046	1.2
7 TU	0257	3.6	**22** W	0255	3.4
	0936	0.8		0919	1.0
	1532	3.8		1522	3.6
	2209	0.6		2140	0.9
8 W	0357	3.8	**23** TH	0345	3.7
	1034	0.5		1007	0.8
	1626	4.0		1606	3.9
	2300	0.4		2226	0.7
9 TH	0447	4.0	**24** F	0427	3.9
	1121	0.3		1048	0.5
	1712	4.1		1646	4.1
●	2344	0.3		2306	0.5
10 F	0531	4.1	**25** SA	0505	4.0
	1202	0.3		1127	0.4
	1751	4.2		1724	4.2
			O	2344	0.4
11 SA	0022	0.3	**26** SU	0542	4.1
	0609	4.1		1204	0.3
	1239	0.3		1802	4.3
	1827	4.2			
12 SU	0057	0.4	**27** M	0023	0.3
	0645	4.1		0619	4.2
	1312	0.4		1244	0.3
	1901	4.1		1840	4.3
13 M	0131	0.5	**28** TU	0103	0.3
	0718	4.0		0659	4.1
	1345	0.5		1325	0.3
	1933	4.0		1921	4.2
14 TU	0203	0.6	**29** W	0145	0.4
	0750	3.9		0740	4.1
	1417	0.7		1409	0.4
	2006	3.8		2004	4.1
15 W	0236	0.8	**30** TH	0230	0.5
	0824	3.7		0825	4.0
	1450	0.9		1456	0.6
	2040	3.7		2051	3.9

OCTOBER

Day	Time	m	Day	Time	m
1 F	0318	0.7	**16** SA	0309	1.2
	0915	3.8		0908	3.5
	1548	0.8		1533	1.3
	2143	3.7		2123	3.5
2 SA	0414	0.9	**17** SU	0400	1.4
	1012	3.6		0958	3.4
	1648	1.0		1631	1.5
	2246	3.4		2217	3.3
3 SU	0521	1.1	**18** M	0508	1.5
	1124	3.4		1100	3.2
	1803	1.2		1744	1.5
				2326	3.2
4 M	0005	3.3	**19** TU	0628	1.5
	0645	1.2		1219	3.2
	1254	3.3		1901	1.5
	1935	1.1			
5 TU	0133	3.3	**20** W	0052	3.2
	0815	1.0		0740	1.3
	1417	3.5		1341	3.4
	2057	0.9		2008	1.2
6 W	0246	3.6	**21** TH	0211	3.4
	0926	0.8		0840	1.1
	1519	3.8		1442	3.7
	2156	0.7		2105	1.0
7 TH	0342	3.8	**22** F	0306	3.7
	1019	0.5		0932	0.8
	1609	4.0		1530	3.9
	2243	0.5		2154	0.7
8 F	0429	4.0	**23** SA	0352	3.9
	1103	0.4		1018	0.6
	1652	4.1		1614	4.1
	2323	0.4		2238	0.5
9 SA	0510	4.1	**24** SU	0435	4.1
	1141	0.4		1101	0.4
	1729	4.2		1656	4.3
●	2358	0.4	O	2320	0.3
10 SU	0546	4.1	**25** M	0516	4.2
	1214	0.4		1143	0.3
	1802	4.1		1738	4.3
11 M	0029	0.5	**26** TU	0002	0.3
	0618	4.1		0557	4.3
	1243	0.5		1226	0.2
	1832	4.1		1819	4.3
12 TU	0059	0.6	**27** W	0045	0.3
	0648	4.0		0640	4.3
	1311	0.6		1309	0.3
	1902	4.0		1903	4.3
13 W	0127	0.9	**28** TH	0129	0.3
	0718	3.9		0725	4.2
	1340	0.8		1355	0.4
	1931	3.9		1948	4.1
14 TH	0157	0.9	**29** F	0216	0.5
	0751	3.8		0812	4.0
	1412	0.9		1445	0.6
	2004	3.8		2037	3.9
15 F	0230	1.0	**30** SA	0307	0.7
	0827	3.7		0904	3.8
	1449	1.1		1538	0.8
	2040	3.7		2131	3.7
			31 SU	0404	0.9
				1002	3.6
				1639	1.0
				2233	3.4

NOVEMBER

Day	Time	m	Day	Time	m
1 M	0511	1.1	**16** TU	0432	1.4
	1114	3.4		1028	3.5
	1754	1.2		1706	1.5
	2350	3.3		2250	3.4
2 TU	0634	1.1	**17** W	0543	1.5
	1239	3.4		1136	3.4
	1922	1.1		1818	1.5
3 W	0114	3.4	**18** TH	0003	3.4
	0758	1.0		0655	1.4
	1356	3.5		1249	3.5
	2035	1.0		1927	1.3
4 TH	0224	3.5	**19** F	0118	3.5
	0904	0.8		0759	1.1
	1455	3.8		1355	3.7
	2132	0.8		2027	0.8
5 F	0318	3.8	**20** SA	0221	3.7
	0956	0.7		0856	0.9
	1544	3.9		1451	3.9
	2218	0.6		2121	0.8
6 SA	0405	3.9	**21** SU	0315	4.0
	1039	0.6		0948	0.7
	1626	4.1		1541	4.1
	2258	0.6		2211	0.6
7 SU	0445	4.1	**22** M	0405	4.2
	1117	0.5		1038	0.5
	1704	4.1		1630	4.3
	2333	0.6		2259	0.4
8 M	0522	4.1	**23** TU	0453	4.3
	1148	0.6		1125	0.5
	1737	4.1		1717	4.4
●			O	2346	0.3
9 TU	0003	0.6	**24** W	0540	4.4
	0553	4.1		1212	0.3
	1217	0.7		1803	4.4
	1806	4.1			
10 W	0031	0.7	**25** TH	0031	0.3
	0623	4.0		0626	4.4
	1243	0.8		1259	0.3
	1835	4.0		1849	4.3
11 TH	0058	0.8	**26** F	0118	0.3
	0653	4.0		0714	4.3
	1312	0.9		1347	0.4
	1904	3.9		1937	4.2
12 F	0128	0.9	**27** SA	0207	0.5
	0725	3.9		0803	4.1
	1345	1.0		1437	0.6
	1936	3.9		2026	4.0
13 SA	0202	1.0	**28** SU	0258	0.6
	0801	3.8		0855	3.9
	1423	1.1		1530	0.8
	2012	3.7		2119	3.7
14 SU	0242	1.2	**29** M	0354	0.8
	0842	3.7		0952	3.7
	1507	1.3		1628	1.0
	2055	3.6		2217	3.5
15 M	0331	1.3	**30** TU	0456	1.0
	0930	3.6		1055	3.6
	1601	1.4		1735	1.1
	2147	3.5		2324	3.4

DECEMBER

Day	Time	m	Day	Time	m
1 W	0608	1.1	**16** TH	0503	1.3
	1207	3.5		1059	3.6
	1850	1.2		1735	1.4
				2323	3.5
2 TH	0038	3.4	**17** F	0610	1.3
	0723	1.1		1204	3.6
	1319	3.5		1843	1.3
	1959	1.1			
3 F	0147	3.5	**18** SA	0031	3.6
	0828	1.0		0717	1.2
	1419	3.6		1310	3.7
	2057	1.0		1948	1.1
4 SA	0244	3.6	**19** SU	0138	3.7
	0923	0.9		0821	1.0
	1511	3.8		1413	3.9
	2146	0.9		2050	0.9
5 SU	0333	3.8	**20** M	0240	3.9
	1009	0.8		0921	0.8
	1556	3.9		1512	4.0
	2229	0.8		2148	0.7
6 M	0417	3.9	**21** TU	0339	4.1
	1049	0.8		1018	0.6
	1636	4.0		1608	4.2
	2306	0.8		2242	0.5
7 TU	0456	4.0	**22** W	0435	4.2
	1123	0.8		1112	0.4
	1712	4.0		1701	4.3
	2338	0.8	O	2333	0.4
8 W	0531	4.1	**23** TH	0527	4.3
	1153	0.8		1202	0.3
	1745	4.0		1751	4.3
9 TH	0007	0.8	**24** F	0021	0.3
	0604	4.1		0616	4.4
	1222	0.9		1251	0.3
	1815	4.0		1839	4.3
10 F	0037	0.8	**25** SA	0109	0.3
	0635	4.0		0704	4.3
	1253	0.9		1339	0.4
	1845	4.0		1926	4.2
11 SA	0108	0.9	**26** SU	0157	0.4
	0708	4.0		0753	4.2
	1328	1.0		1427	0.5
	1917	3.9		2013	4.0
12 SU	0144	1.0	**27** M	0246	0.5
	0744	3.9		0841	4.1
	1406	1.1		1516	0.7
	1954	3.8		2102	3.9
13 M	0224	1.1	**28** TU	0337	0.7
	0824	3.9		0931	3.9
	1449	1.2		1608	0.8
	2035	3.7		2152	3.7
14 TU	0310	1.2	**29** W	0430	0.9
	0909	3.8		1024	3.7
	1537	1.3		1703	1.0
	2124	3.6		2246	3.5
15 W	0403	1.3	**30** TH	0529	1.0
	1001	3.7		1123	3.5
	1632	1.3		1804	1.2
	2219	3.6		2347	3.4
			31 F	0633	1.1
				1227	3.4
				1908	1.2

Chart Datum: 0·13 metres above Ordnance Datum (Dublin)

12

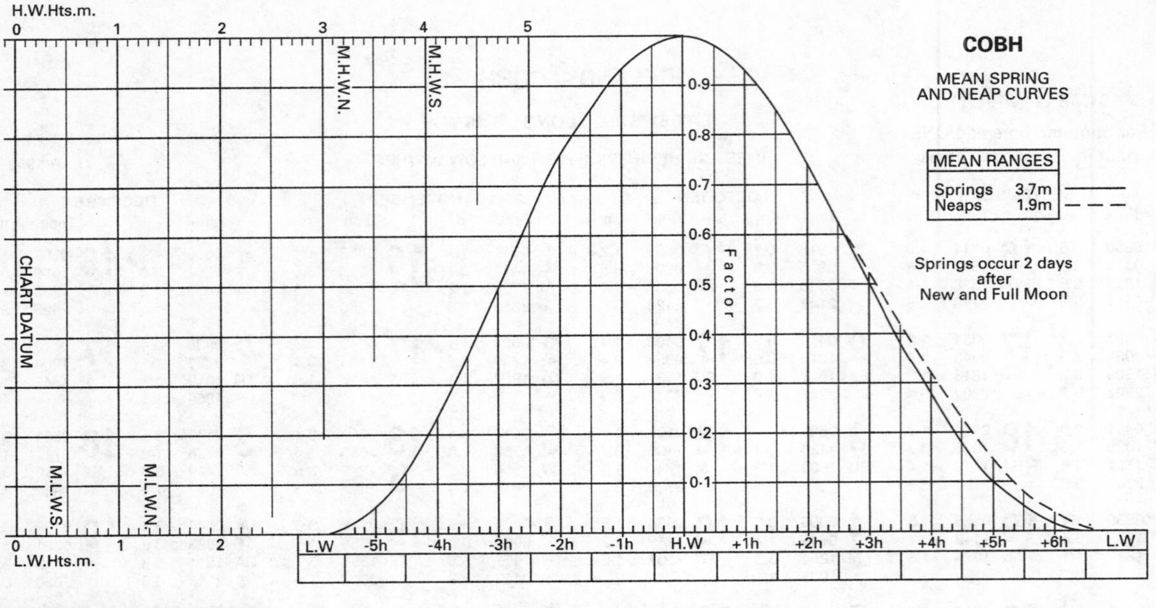

H.W.Hts.m.
0 1 2 3 4 5
M.H.W.N.
M.H.W.S.
CHART DATUM
M.L.W.S.
M.L.W.N.
0 1 2
L.W.Hts.m.
0.9
0.8
0.7
0.6
0.5
0.4
0.3
0.2
0.1
Factor
L.W -5h -4h -3h -2h -1h H.W +1h +2h +3h +4h +5h +6h L.W
COBH
MEAN SPRING AND NEAP CURVES
MEAN RANGES
Springs 3.7m
Neaps 1.9m
Springs occur 2 days after New and Full Moon

CORK HARBOUR 8-12-19

Cork 51°47'·50N 08°15'·54W Rtg 1-1-1

CHARTS
AC 1773, 1777, 1765; Imray C56, C57; Irish OS 81, 87

TIDES
–0523 Dover; ML 2·3; Duration 0555; Zone 0 (UT)

Standard Port COBH (⟵)

Times				Height (metres)			
High Water		Low Water		MHWS	MHWN	MLWN	MLWS
0500	1100	0500	1100	4·1	3·2	1·3	0·4
1700	2300	1700	2300				
Differences BALLYCOTTON (15M ENE of Roche's Point)							
–0011	+0001	+0003	–0009	0·0	0·0	–0·1	0·0
RINGASKIDDY							
+0005	+0020	+0007	+0013	+0·1	+0·1	+0·1	+0·1
MARINO POINT							
0000	+0010	0000	+0010	+0·1	+0·1	0·0	0·0
CORK CITY							
+0005	+0010	+0020	+0010	+0·4	+0·4	+0·3	+0·2
ROBERTS COVE (approx 4M SW of Roche's Point)							
–0005	–0005	–0005	–0005	–0·1	0·0	0·0	+0·1

NOTE: Cobh is a Standard Port. Daily predictions are above.

SHELTER
Very good in all conditions, esp in Crosshaven and East Passage. There are 3 main marinas at Crosshaven (see Facilities), plus a small private marina and several ⚓s further up the Owenboy River, in particular at Drake's Pool. There is also a marina at E Ferry in E Passage at the E end of Great Island. Cork City and Cobh are commercial and ferry ports; before proceeding up river contact Port Operations for advice on possible yacht berths.

NAVIGATION
WPT 51°46'·00N, 08°15'·30W, 174°/354° from/to front ldg lt, 2·8M. There are no navigational dangers for yachts. It is one of the safest hbrs to enter in the world, being deep and well marked. Tidal rate is about 1½kn in ent at sp, but more between the forts. Main chan up to Cork is buoyed. Ent to Owenboy River carries at least of 2·5m at LWS, and the chan is buoyed. Head for Cage buoy (C1), Fl G 10s to pick up the ldg lts 252°.

LIGHTS AND MARKS
The hammerhead water tr S of Crosshaven is a very conspic mark, 24·5m high. There are two sets of ldg lts, both below Fort Davis on E shore:
(a) Both Oc 5s, lead 354° E of Hbr Rk. At the front ldg lt is also a Dir lt WRG 354°; see 8.12.4 for details.
(b) Both Oc R 5s, lead 034·6° W of Hbr Rk.
Ldg lts, FW 10/15m 3M, with W ◇ day marks, lead 252° to Crosshaven; lts are now easier to see and chan carries 3m LWS. 6 extra buoys are laid during Race weeks.

RADIO TELEPHONE
Call: *Cork Hbr Radio* (Port Ops) VHF Ch 12 14 16 (H24); Crosshaven BY Ch M (Mon– Fri: 0830– 1700LT). Royal Cork YC Marina Ch M (1000– 2359LT). East Ferry Marina Ch M 80 (0800– 2200LT).

TELEPHONE (Dial code 021)
Hr Mr 273125; Port Operations 811380; MRCC (01) 6620922/3; Coast/Cliff Rescue Service 831448; # 311024; Police 831222; Dr 831716; Ⓗ + Emergency 546400.

FACILITIES
Crosshaven BY Marina (100 + 20 visitors) ☎ 831161, 📠 831603, £10, FW, AC, BH (40 ton), C (1.5 tons), M, Ⓔ, CH, D, P (cans), El, Gas, Gaz, Kos, SM, ME, Sh, Slip (100 tons);
Salve Marine (45 + 12 visitors) ☎ 831145, 📠 831747, AB £10, M, FW, AC, BY, El, ME, C, CH, D, P (cans), Slip;
Royal Cork YC Marina (100 + 15 visitors) ☎ 831023, 📠 831586, £12, AC, FW, P (cans), Bar, R, Slip, ♿;
East Ferry Marina (85 + 15 visitors) ☎ 811342, £10, D, AC, FW, Bar, R, Slip; access all tides, max draft 5·5m.
Crosshaven Village FV pier in 3·5m at Town quay, L, Slip, Grid, SM, ACA, Bar, Dr, ✉, R, V, ▣.
Cork City All facilities. Ferries (to UK and France), ⇌, ✈.

MINOR HARBOUR 16M ENE of YOUGHAL

DUNGARVAN BAY, Waterford, 52°05'·15N 07°36'·70W. Rtg 3-4-3. AC 2017. HW –0540 on Dover; Duration 0600. See 8.12.17. A large bay, drying to the W, entered between Helvick Hd to the S and Ballinacourty Pt to the N. Appr in W sector (274°–302°) of Ballinacourty Pt Dir lt, Fl (2) WRG 10s; see 8.12.4 for details. This clears Carricknamoan islet to the N, and Carrickapane Rk and Helvick Rk (ECM buoy Q (3) 10s) to the SW. The Gainers, a large unmarked rky patch (dries 0·8m), are 2 to 5ca NNW of Helvick New Pier. ⚓ in approx 4m off Helvick hbr, or head W to Dungarvan town hbr not later than HW+3½, via buoyed chan. The chan has shifted N'ward and both sets of ldg lts have been discontinued, but may be re-instated. Beware salmon nets. Facilities at Dungarvan: EC Thurs; AB, no dues, Bar, Ⓑ, D (cans), P (on quay), ✉, R, V, Kos.

MINOR HARBOUR 15M ENE of ROCHE'S POINT

BALLYCOTTON, Cork, 51°49'·70N 08°00·19W. AC 2424. HW –0555 on Dover; ML no data; Duration 0550. See above. Small, NE-facing hbr at W end of bay; suffers from scend in strong SE winds. 3m in ent and about 1·5m against piers. Many FVs alongside piers, on which yachts should berth, rather than ⚓ in hbr, which is foul with old ground tackle. Outside hbr, good ⚓ in offshore winds in 6m NE of pier, protected by Ballycotton Is. Lt ho Fl WR 10s 59m 21/17M, B tr in W walls; W238°–048°, R048°–238°; Horn (4) 90s. Facilities: FW on pier. **Village** Hotel, R, ✉, V, LB, Kos.

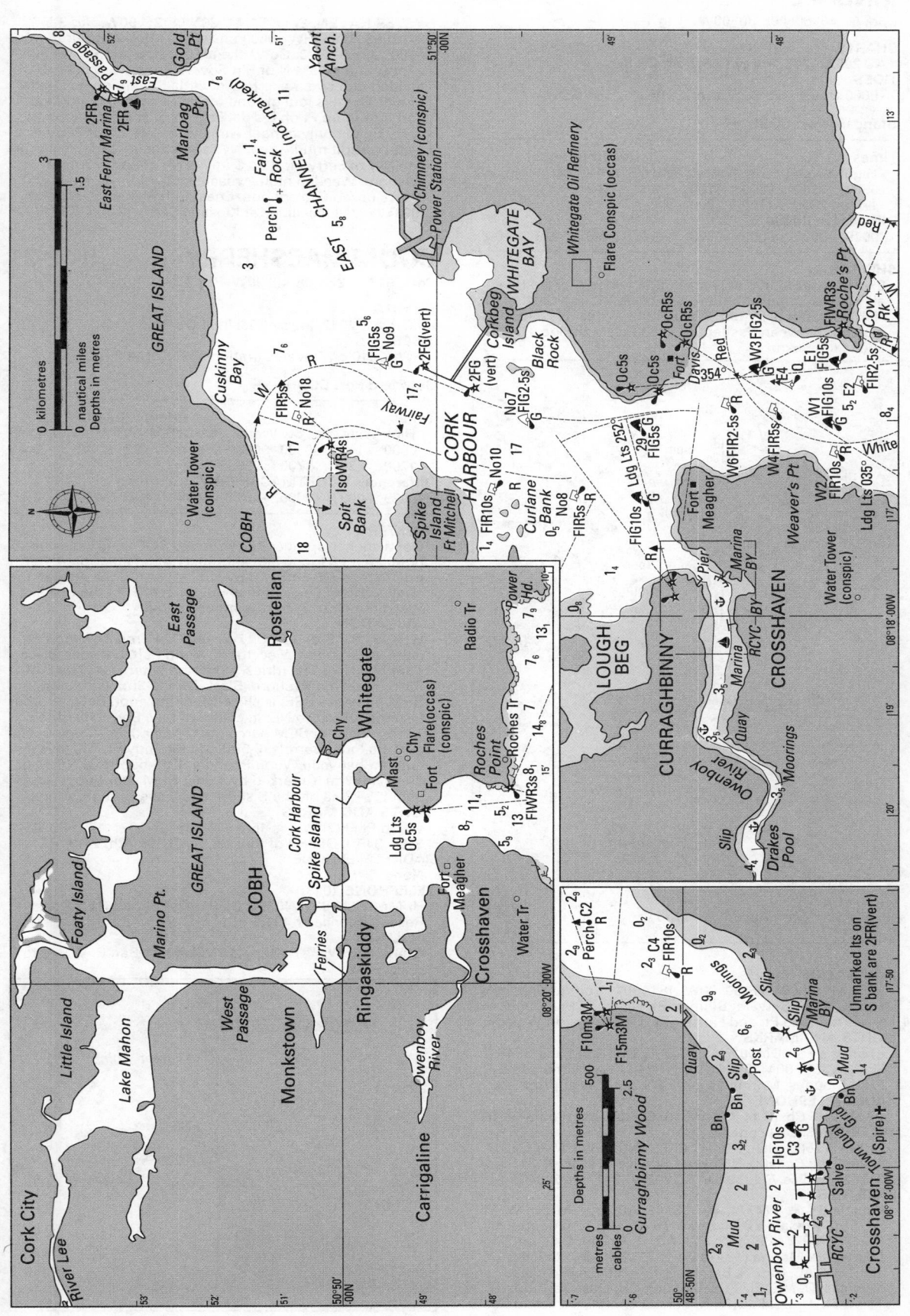

12

KINSALE   8-12-20

Cork 51°40'·80N 08°30'·00W   Rtg 1-1-1

CHARTS
AC 2053, 1765; Imray C56; Irish OS 87

TIDES
–0600 Dover; ML 2·2; Duration 0600; Zone 0 (UT)

Standard Port COBH (←)

Times				Height (metres)			
High Water		Low Water		MHWS	MHWN	MLWN	MLWS
0500	1100	0500	1100	4·1	3·2	1·3	0·4
1700	2300	1700	2300				
Differences KINSALE							
–0019	–0005	–0009	–0023	–0·2	0·0	+0·1	+0·2

SHELTER
Excellent, except in very strong SE winds. Access H24 in all weathers/tides. Marinas at Kinsale YC and Castlepark; NNW of latter is FV pontoon and no ⚓ area. New marina planned between Castlepark and Kinsale Bridge. Hbr speed limit 6kn.

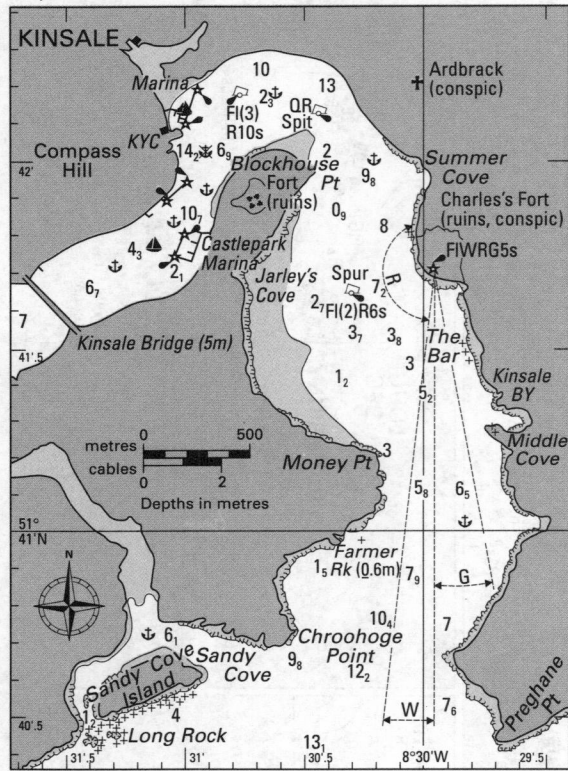

NAVIGATION
WPT 51°40'·00N 08°30'·00W, 181°/001° from/to Charles's Fort lt, 1·7M. Beware: Bulman Rk (0·9m; SCM lt buoy) 4ca S of Preghane Pt; and Farmer Rk (0·6m) ¾ca off W bank.

LIGHTS AND MARKS
Charles's Fort Dir 001°, Fl WRG 5s 18m 9/6M, vis G348°-358°, W358°-004°, R004°-168° (H24). Chan is marked by PHM lt buoys. Marina lts are 2 FG or FR as appropriate.

RADIO TELEPHONE
Hr Mr VHF Ch 16 **14**. KYC M 16. Castlepark marina 06 16.

TELEPHONE (Dial code 021)
Hr Mr 772503 (HO), 773047 (OT), ⚓ 774695; MRCC (01) 6620922/3; Coast/Cliff Rescue Service 772346; ≡ 311044/315426; Police 772302; Dr 772253, 772717; Ⓗ 546400.

FACILITIES
Kinsale BY, ☎ 774774, ⚓ 775405. AB (3m), M, D, FW, ME, Sh, El, C. **Kinsale YC Marina** (170 + 50 Ⓥ; 10m depth), ☎ 772196, ⚓ 774455, £13, FW, AC, D, P, Slip, C, R, Bar, Ⓢ; **Castlepark Marina** (70+20 Ⓥ) ☎ 774959, ⚓ 774958, £14, 10m, FW, AC, Slip, R, Bar, El, Ⓒ; ferry (3 mins) to town. **Services:** D, ME, El, Ⓔ, C (35 ton), CH, Gas, Gaz, SM. **Town** EC Thurs; P, D, V, R, Bar, ⊠, Ⓑ, ≈, ✈ (bus to Cork).

MINOR HARBOUR 2M EAST OF KINSALE

OYSTER HAVEN, Cork, 51°41'·20N 08°26'·90W. Rtg 3-5-2. AC 2053, 1765. HW –0600 on Dover; ML 2·2m; Duration 0600. Use 8.12.20. Good shelter but subject to swell in S winds. Enter 0·5M N of Big Sovereign, a steep islet divided into two. Keep to S of Little Sovereign on E side of ent. There is foul ground off Ballymacus Pt on W side, and off Kinure Pt on E side. Pass W of Hbr Rk (0·9m) off Ferry Pt, the only danger within hbr. ⚓ NNW of Ferry Pt in 4–6m on soft mud/weed. NW arm shoals suddenly about 5ca NW of Ferry Pt. Also ⚓ up N arm of hbr in 3m off the W shore. Weed in higher reaches may foul ⚓. No lts, marks or radio telephone. Coast/Cliff Rescue Service ☎ (021) 770711. Facilities at Kinsale. See 8.12.20.

COURTMACSHERRY   8-12-21

Cork 51°38'·22N 08°40'·90W Rtg 3-3-1

CHARTS
AC 2081, 2092; Imray C56; Irish OS 87

TIDES
HW –0610 on Dover; Duration 0545; Zone 0 (UT)

Standard Port COBH (←)

Times				Height (metres)			
High Water		Low Water		MHWS	MHWN	MLWN	MLWS
0500	1100	0500	1100	4·1	3·2	1·3	0·4
1700	2300	1700	2300				
Differences COURTMACSHERRY							
–0029	–0007	+0005	–0017	–0·4	–0·3	–0·2	–0·1

SHELTER
Good shelter up-river, but in strong S/SE winds seas break on the bar (2·3m), when ent must not be attempted. Berth on pontoon (18·5m) or jetty (16·3m) or dry out against the quay. ⚓ NE of Ferry Pt in about 2·5m or N of the quay. Weed may foul ⚓; best to moor fore/aft.

NAVIGATION
WPT, 51°37'·50N 08°40'·17W, 144°/324° from/to Wood Pt, 0·8M. Appr in the W sector of Wood Pt lt, between Black Tom and Horse Rk (dries 3·6m); the latter is 3-4½ca E of Barry Pt on the W shore. Black Tom (2·3m), with unlit SHM buoy 5ca SSE, is close NE of the appr. Beware other hazards further to NE: In centre of bay, Barrel Rk (dries 2·6m), has unlit SCM perch (no topmark). To NNW and E of it are Inner Barrels (0·5m) and Blueboy Rk. The river is entered between Wood Pt and a SHM buoy 2ca NE, Fl G 3s. Chan (2m) is marked by 4 unlit SHM spar buoys; keep about ½ – ¾ca off the S shore and close N of moorings.

LIGHTS AND MARKS
Wood Pt Fl (2) WR 5s 15m 5M, W315°-332° (17°), R332°-315° (343°). Old Hd of Kinsale, Fl (2) 10s 72m 25M, RC.

RADIO TELEPHONE
None.

TELEPHONE (023)
Hr Mr/RNLI 46311/40394; Dr 46142; Police 46122; Coast Rescue Service ☎ 4018.

FACILITIES
Quay AC, FW, Ⓢ, D, Slip, LB. **Village** ⊠, Bar, R, V, Bus to Cork, ✈, ≈.

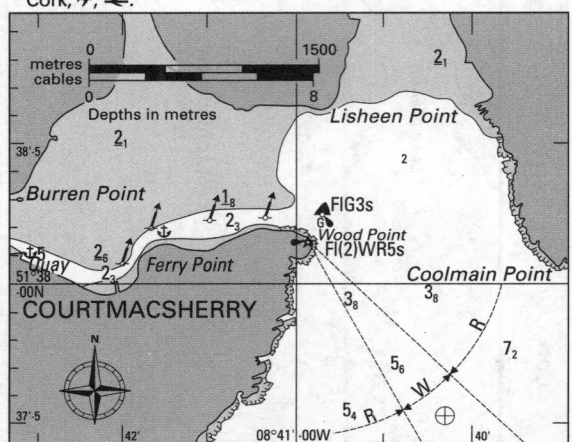

GLANDORE   8-12-22

Cork, 51°33'·70N 09°07'·20W   Rtg 3-4-1

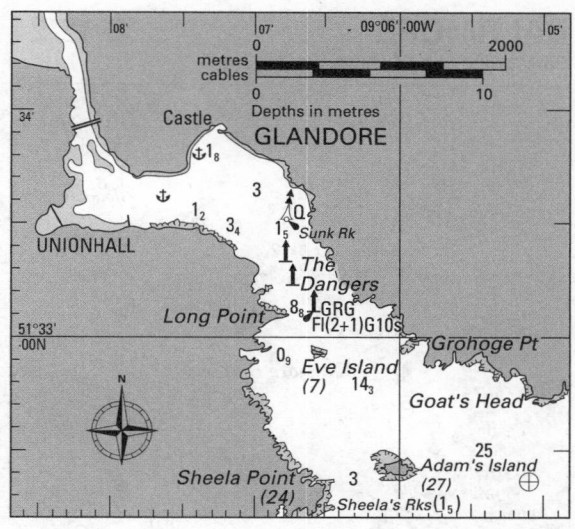

CHARTS
AC 2092; Imray C56; Irish OS 89

TIDES
Approx as for 10·12·23 Castletownshend. Zone 0 (UT)

SHELTER
Excellent. ⚓ 1½ca SW of Glandore Pier in 2m or 1ca NE of the New pier at Unionhall in 3m.

NAVIGATION
WPT 51°32'·35N 09°05'·10W, 309°/129° from/to Outer Dangers 1·2M. Approach between Adam Is and Goat's Hd, thence keep E of Eve Is and W of the chain of rks: Outer, Middle and Inner Dangers and Sunk Rk. Before altering W for Unionhall, stand on to clear mudbank 1ca off S shore.

LIGHTS AND MARKS
Galley Hd, Fl (5) 20s, is 5M E of the ent. Outer Dangers are marked by a preferred-chan-to-port bn (GRG), Fl (2+1) G 10s, and a PHM bn (not on chartlet); Middle and Inner Dangers by 2 SHM bns; and Sunk Rk by a NCM lt buoy, Q.

RADIO TELEPHONE
None.

TELEPHONE (Dial code 028)
No Hr Mr; Police 48162; Dr 21488; Coast Rescue ☎ 33115.

FACILITIES
FW at both piers; **Glandore** CH, YC, ✉, R, V, Bar, Kos.
Unionhall D, P, ME, Gas, ✉, R, Bar, V.

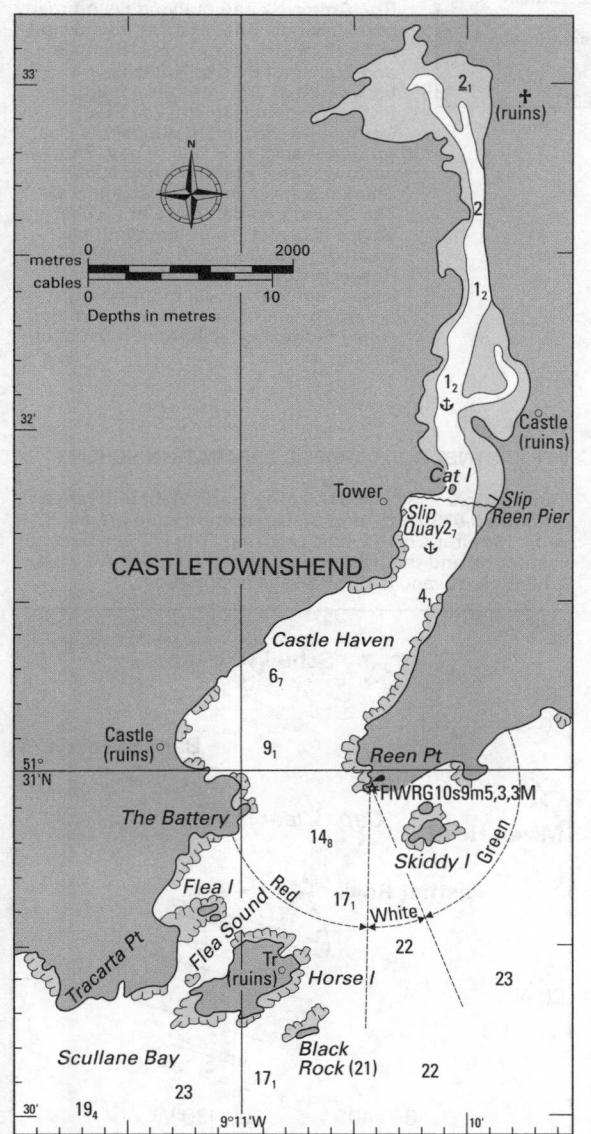

CASTLE HAVEN   8-12-23

Cork 51°30'·90N 09°10'·70W   Rtg 3-4-1

CHARTS
AC 2129, 2092; Imray C56; Irish OS 88, 89

TIDES
+0605 Dover; ML 2·2; Duration 0605; Zone 0 (UT)

Standard Port COBH (←)

Times				Height (metres)			
High Water		Low Water		MHWS	MHWN	MLWN	MLWS
0500	1100	0500	1100	4·1	3·2	1·3	0·4
1700	2300	1700	2300				
Differences CASTLETOWNSHEND							
−0020	−0030	−0020	−0050	−0·4	−0·2	+0·1	+0·3
CLONAKILTY BAY							
−0033	−0011	−0019	−0041	−0·3	−0·2	No data	

SHELTER
Excellent ⚓ protected from all weathers and available at all tides, H24, although the outer part of hbr is subject to swell in S winds. ⚓ in midstream SE of Castletownshend slip; N of Cat Island, or upstream as depth permits.

NAVIGATION
WPT 51°29'·00N, 09°10'·00W, 171°/351° from/to Reen Pt lt, 2M. Enter between Horse Is and Skiddy Is both of which have foul ground all round. Black Rk lies off the SE side of Horse Is and is steep-to along its S side. Inside Horse Is, Flea Sound is a narrow boat chan, obstructed by rks. Colonel Rk (0·5m) lies close to the E shore, 2ca N of Reen Pt. A submarine cable runs E/W across the hbr from the slip close N of Reen Pier to the slip at Castletownshend.

LIGHTS AND MARKS
Reen Pt lt, Fl WRG 10s 9m 5/3M; W tr; vis G shore– 338°, W338°– 001°, R001°– shore. A ruined tr stands on E end of Horse Is.

RADIO TELEPHONE
None.

TELEPHONE (Dial code 028)
MRCC (01) 6620922/3; Coast/Cliff Rescue Service 21039; ⌗ Bantry (027) 50061; Police 36144; Dr 21488; Ⓗ 21677.

FACILITIES
Reen Pier L, FW; **SC** ☎ 36100. **Castletownshend Village** Slip, Bar, R, V, FW, ✉, Ⓑ (Skibbereen), ⇌, ✈ (Cork).

ANCHORAGE W OF TOE HEAD

BARLOGE CREEK, Cork, 51°29'·57N 09°17'·58W. AC 2129. Tides approx as Castletownshend. A narrow creek, well-sheltered except from S/SE winds. Appr with Gokane Pt brg 120°. Enter W of Bullock Is, keeping to the W side to clear rks S of the island. ⚓ W of the Is in 3m. No facilities.

12

BALTIMORE   8-12-24

Cork 51°28'·30N 09°23'·40W   Rtg 2-4-1

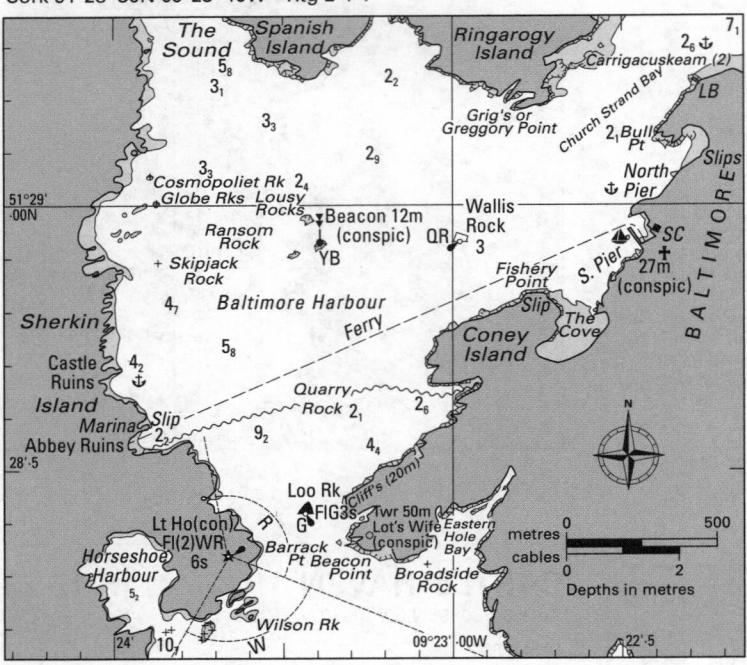

ADJACENT ANCHORAGES

HORSESHOE HARBOUR, 51°28'·20N 09°23'·86W. Small unlit hbr on Sherkin Is, 3ca WSW of ent to Baltimore. Keep to the W at narrow ent. ⚓ in about 5m in centre of cove.

CLEAR ISLAND, NORTH HARBOUR, 51°26'·60N 09°30'·20W. AC 2129. Tides approx as Schull, 8.12.25. A tiny, partly drying inlet on N coast of Clear Is, exposed to N'ly swell. There are rks either side of the outer appr 196°. Inside the narrow (30m), rky ent keep to the E. ⚓ fore & aft on E side in about 1·5m or berth at inner end of pier. Few facilities.

ROARING WATER BAY

Long Island Bay, entered between Cape Clear and Mizen Hd, extends NE into Roaring Water Bay (AC 2129). The Fastnet Rk, Fl 5s 49m 28M, Horn (4) 60s, is 4M to seaward. Safest appr, S of Schull, is via Carthy's Sound (51°30'N 09°30'W). From the SE appr via Gascanane Sound, but beware Toorane Rks, Anima Rk and outlying rks off many of the islands. Shelter in various winds at ⚓s clockwise from Horse Island: 3ca E and 7ca NE of E tip of Horse Is; in Ballydehob B 2m; Poulgorm B 2m; 5ca ENE of Mannin Is in 4m; 2ca SE of Carrigvalish Rks in 6m. Rincolisky Cas (ru) is conspic on S side of bay. The narrow chan E of Hare Is and N of Sherkin Is has two ⚓s; it also leads via The Sound into Baltimore hbr. Local advice is useful. There are temp fair weather ⚓s in the Carthy's Islands. Rossbrin Cove, 2·5M E of Schull, is a safe ⚓, but many local moorings; no access from E of Horse Is due to drying Horse Ridge. No facilities at most of the above ⚓s.

CHARTS
AC 3725, 2129; Imray C56; Irish OS 88

TIDES
−0605 Dover; ML 2·1; Duration 0610; Zone 0 (UT)

Standard Port COBH (←—)

Times				Height (metres)			
High Water		Low Water		MHWS	MHWN	MLWN	MLWS
0500	1100	0500	1100	4·1	3·2	1·3	0·4
1700	2300	1700	2300				
Differences BALTIMORE							
−0025	−0005	−0010	−0050	−0·6	−0·3	+0·1	+0·2

SHELTER
Excellent; access H24. Hbr, partly drying, is between N and S piers. The marina (20 berths) is a large water barge at the end of the S pier. Possible AB on N side of N pier for FW. ⚓ N or W of N pier, or in Church Strand Bay beyond LB slip in 2 to 3m. In strong W'ly winds ⚓ off ruined castle on Sherkin Is (off chartlet), 1ca N of ferry and submarine cable. A similar water barge/marina is close S on Sherkin Is at the jetty below ruined abbey.

NAVIGATION
WPT 51°27'·80N 09°23'·42W, 180°/000° from/to Loo Rk SHM Fl G 3s, 0·62M. Beware Lousy Rks (SCM bn) and Wallis Rk (PHM buoy, QR) in the middle of the bay. Hbr can also be entered from the N via The Sound, but this is tricky and not recommended; ICC SDs essential. R Ilen is navigable on the flood for at least 4M above The Sound.

LIGHTS AND MARKS
Ent easily identified by conspic W tr (Lot's Wife) to stbd on Beacon Pt and Barrack Pt lt ho, Fl (2) WR 6s, to port.

RADIO TELEPHONE
VHF Ch 09 16.

TELEPHONE (Dial code 028)
Hr Mr 20132; MRCC (01) 6620922/3; Coast/Cliff Rescue Service 20125; ⌗ (027) 50061; Police 20102; Dr 21488; Ⓗ 21677.

FACILITIES
Marina (20 inc visitors) ☎ (021) 774959, 🛥 (021) 774958, (May-Sept), Slip, AB, FW; **Baltimore SC** ☎/🛥 20426, Bar, showers, visitors welcome; **Glenans Irish Sailing School** ☎ (01) 6611481. **Services:** P & D, BY, ME, EI, CH, V, Gas, Gaz, Kos, Sh, ACA;
Village EC None; P, Bar, ✉, ⇌ (bus to Cork), ✈ (Cork).

OFF FASTNET ROCK TRAFFIC SEPARATION SCHEME

Centred on 51°19'N 09°31'W. The E and W-bound lanes, orientated 073°/253°, and the separation zone are all 2M wide. Monitor Ch 16 whilst crossing. The ITZ lies between Fastnet Rk and the N boundary of the TSS. See AC 2424, 1.1.2 (Rule 10) and 8.12.5 Passage information.

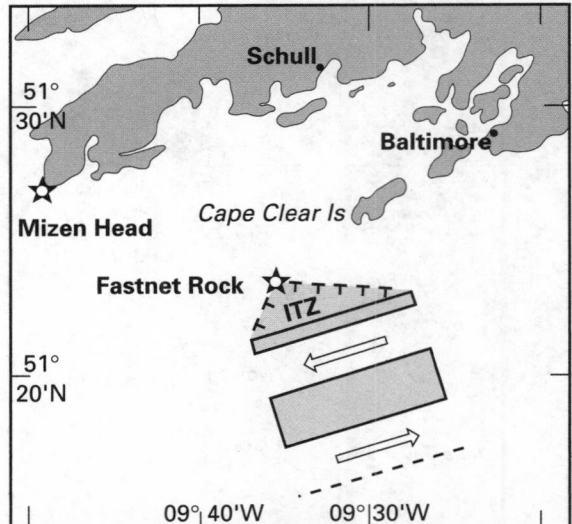

SCHULL   8-12-25

Cork 51°30'·80N 09°32'·00W   Rtg 2-3-1

CHARTS
AC 2129, 2184; Imray C56; Irish OS 88

TIDES
+0610 Dover; ML 1·8; Duration 0610; Zone 0 (UT)

Standard Port COBH (←)

Times				Height (metres)			
High Water		Low Water		MHWS	MHWN	MLWN	MLWS
0500	1100	0500	1100	4·1	3·2	1·3	0·4
1700	2300	1700	2300				
Differences SCHULL							
−0040	−0015	−0015	−0110	−0.9	−0.6	−0.2	0.0

SHELTER
Good, except in strong S/SE winds when best shelter is N of Long Island. Schull Hbr access H24. ⚓ in 3m clear of fairway, 1ca SE of pier, usually lit by street lts all night.

NAVIGATION
WPT 51°29'·60N 09°31'·60W, 166°/346° from/to front ldg lt, 2·1M. In mid-chan between Schull Pt and Coosheen Pt, keep E of Bull Rk (dries 1·8m) marked by a R iron perch.

LIGHTS AND MARKS
Ldg lts, Oc 5s 5/8m 11M, lead 346° between Long Is Pt, Q (3) 10s 16m 8M, W ○ tr, and Amelia Rk SHM buoy Fl G 3s; thence E of Bull Rk and toward head of bay. By day 2 W radomes conspic on Mt Gabriel (2M N of Schull) lead 355° with Long Is Pt lt ho in transit.

RADIO TELEPHONE
None.

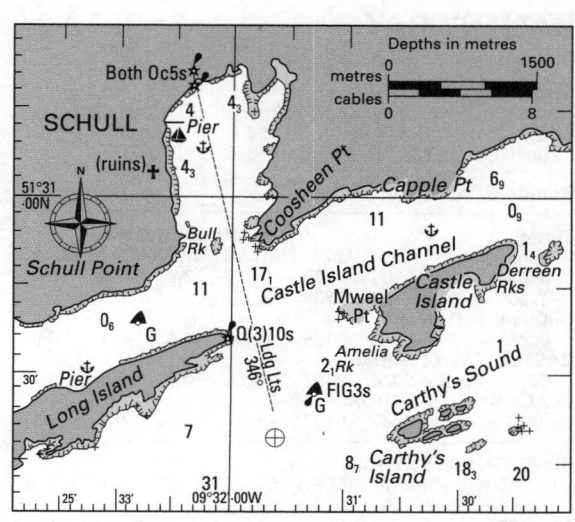

TELEPHONE (Dial code 028)
Hr Mr 28136; MRCC (01) 6620922/3; Coast/Cliff Rescue Service 35117; ℍ (027) 50061; Police 28111; Dr 28311; Ⓗ (027) 50133.

FACILITIES
Schull Pier Slip, M, D, L, FW, AC, AB; **Sailing Club** ☎ 37532; **Services:** Kos, BY, M, Sh, Slip, CH.
Village EC Tues; P, Dr, ME, El, Sh, V, R, Bar, ✉, Ⓑ, bus to Cork for ⇌, ✈, car ferry.

CROOKHAVEN   8-12-26

Cork 51°28'·50N 09°42'·00W   Rtg 3-4-1

CHARTS
AC 2184; Imray C56; Irish OS 88

TIDES
+0550 Dover; ML 1·8; Duration 0610; Zone 0 (UT)

Standard Port COBH (←)

Times				Height (metres)			
High Water		Low Water		MHWS	MHWN	MLWN	MLWS
0500	1100	0500	1100	4·1	3·2	1·3	0·4
1700	2300	1700	2300				
Differences CROOKHAVEN							
−0057	−0033	−0048	−0112	−0.8	−0.6	−0.4	−0.1
DUNMANUS HARBOUR							
−0107	−0031	−0044	−0120	−0.7	−0.6	−0.2	0.0
DUNBEACON HARBOUR							
−0057	−0025	−0032	−0104	−0.8	−0.7	−0.3	−0.1

SHELTER
Excellent, but holding is poor, especially in strong SW'lies. ⚓s in middle of bay in 3m; off W tip of Rock Is; and E of Granny Is; last two are far from the village. Beware weed. A pontoon for 8-12 yachts was intended for summer 97.

NAVIGATION
WPT 51°28'·50N 09°40'·50W, 094°/274° from/to Rock Is lt ho, 1M. Ent between this lt and NCM bn on Black Horse Rks (3½ca ESE). From S, keep 1ca E of Alderman Rks and ½ca off Black Horse Rks bn. Passage between Streek Hd and Alderman Rks is not advised. Inside the bay the shores are steep to.

LIGHTS AND MARKS
Lt ho on Rock Is (conspic W tr) L Fl WR 8s 20m 13/11M; vis outside hbr: W over Long Is Bay–281°, R281°–340°; vis inside hbr: R 281°–348°, W348°–N shore.

RADIO TELEPHONE
None.

TELEPHONE (Dial code 028)
MRCC (01) 6620922/3; Coast/Cliff Rescue Service Goleen 35318; ℍ (027) 50061; Dr 35148.

FACILITIES
Village Sh, ME, V, Kos, Ⓑ (Bantry), ✉, ⇌ and ✈ (Cork).

ADJACENT HARBOURS

GOLEEN (Kireal-coegea), Cork, 51°29'·65N 09°42'·21W. AC 2184. Tides as Crookhaven. A narrow inlet 6ca N of Spanish Pt; good shelter in fair weather, except from SE. 2 churches are easily seen, but ent not visible until close. Keep to S side of ent and ⚓ fore-and-aft just below quay, where AB also possible. Facilities: P, V, Bar.

DUNMANUS BAY, Cork. AC 2552. Tides see 8.12.26. Appr between Three Castle Hd and Sheep's Hd, Fl (3) WR 15s 83m 18/15M; no other lts. Ent to **Dunmanus Hbr**, 51°32'·70N 09°39'·86W, is 1ca wide; breakers both sides. ⚓ in 4m centre of B. **Kitchen Cove**, 51°35'·50N 09°38'·05W, is the best of the 3 hbrs; enter W of Owens Is and ⚓ 1ca NNW of it or 2ca further N in 3m. Exposed to S, but good holding. Quay at Ahakista village: V, R, Bar. **Dunbeacon Hbr**, 51°36'·35N 09°33'·60W, is shallow and rock-girt. ⚓ E or SE of Mannion Is. At Durrus (1¼M): Fuel (cans), R, Bar.

12

BANTRY BAY   8-12-27

Cork 51°34'N 09°57'W   Rtg 2-3-1

CHARTS
AC 1838, 1840, 2552; Imray C56; Irish OS 84, 85, 88
TIDES
+0600 Dover; ML 1·8; Duration 0610; Zone 0 (UT)

Standard Port COBH (◄—)

Times				Height (metres)			
High Water		Low Water		MHWS	MHWN	MLWN	MLWS
0500	1100	0500	1100	4·1	3·2	1·3	0·4
1700	2300	1700	2300				
Differences BANTRY							
−0045	−0025	−0040	−0105	−0·9	−0·8	−0·2	0·0
CASTLETOWN (Bearhaven)							
−0048	−0012	−0025	−0101	−0·9	−0·6	−0·1	0·0
BLACK BALL HARBOUR							
−0115	−0035	−0047	−0127	−0·7	−0·6	−0·1	+0·1

SHELTER/NAVIGATION
Bantry Bay extends 20M ENE from Sheep's Hd, Fl (3) WR 15s 83m 18/15M. Access is easy, but the Bay is exposed to W'lies. The shore is clean everywhere except off Bear Is and Whiddy Is. Some of the many well sheltered ⚓s on the N shore are detailed on this page. The S shore has few ⚓s. See also chartlet 8.12.28.

CASTLETOWN, 51°38'·80N 09°54'·45W. AC 1840. Sheltered ⚓ in 2·4m NW of Dinish Is, to E of 010° ldg line; also at **Dunboy Bay**, W of Piper Sound (open to E). Lts: At W ent, Ardnakinna Pt, Fl (2) WR 10s 62m 17/14M, H24. At E ent to Bearhaven: Roancarrigmore, Fl WR 3s 18m 18/14M. Appr W of Bear Is on 024° Dir lt, Oc WRG 5s 4m 14/11M (W024°–024·5°); thence inner ldg lts 010°, both Oc 3s 4/7m 1M, vis 005°-015°, via ent chan which narrows to 50m abeam Perch Rk lt bn, QG. Beware Walter Scott Rk (2·7m), SCM buoy, Q (6) + L Fl 15s, and Carrigaglos (0·6m high) S of Dinish Is. VHF Ch 08 16. Hr Mr ☎ (027) 70220, 📠 70329. Facilities: FW & D on quay; BH on Dinish Is.
Town El, ME, Sh, P (cans), Bar, Ⓑ, ✉, V, R, Kos.

HARBOURS AT EAST END OF BEAR ISLAND

LAWRENCE'S COVE, 51°38'·28N 09°49'·28W AC 1840. Good shelter on N side of Bear Island, open only to the N. ⚓ in 4m to W of Turk Is or, closer in, to NW of rky ridge off E shore. New marina on S side of cove has E/W pontoon 50m long (about 2.4m at LW). ☎/📠 027 75044, mobile ☎ 087 506429; VHF Ch 16. AB (£10), FW, AC, D, R. At Rerrin village: BY, Slip, V, R, Bar, ✉; Glenans sailing school.

LONEHORT HARBOUR, 51°38'·12N 09°47'·80W. AC 1840. At E tip of Bear Is, good shelter but keep S at ent to clear unmarked rks; then turn ENE to ⚓ in 2·7m at E end of cove.

ADRIGOLE, 51°40'·51N 09°43'·22W. AC 1840.1M SSW of ent beware Doucallia Rk, dries 1·2m. Beyond the 2ca wide ent, keep E of Orthons Is (rks on W side). ⚓s to suit wind direction: off pier on E shore 4m; N or NW of Orthons Is. Good shelter, but squally in W/N gales. Drumlave (½M E): V.

HARBOURS AT THE HEAD OF THE BAY

GLENGARIFF, 51°44'·20N 09°31'·90W. AC 1838. Tides as Bantry. Beautiful ⚓ S of Bark Is in 7-10m; or to NE in 3m. Better for yachts than Bantry hbr. Ent between Big Pt and Gun Pt. No lts/marks. Keep 1ca E of rks off Garinish Island (Illnacullen) and Ship Is; beware marine farms. Rky chan W of Garinish, with HT cable 15m clearance, should not be attempted. Facilities: **Village** FW, Bar, D, P, ✉, R, V, Kos.

BANTRY, 51°40'·85N 09°27'·85W. AC 1838. Beware Gerane Rks 1M W of Whiddy Is lt, Oc 2s 22m 3M, vis 073°-106°. Appr via the buoyed/lit N chan (10m) to E of Horse and Chapel Is; keep 2ca off all islands to clear unlit mussel rafts. The S chan, fair weather only, has a bar 2m; ldg marks 091°, front RW post, FW lt; rear W post, FR lt. VHF Ch 14 11 16 (H24). Hr Mr (027) 505205; ⌗ 50061; Police 50045; Dr 50405; Ⓗ 50133. MRCC (01) 6620922. Facilities: **Pier** L, FW; **Bantry Bay SC** ☎ 50081 Slip, L; **Town** EC Wed; P & D (cans), Kos, ME, CH, V, R, Bar, ✉, Ⓑ, bus to Cork.

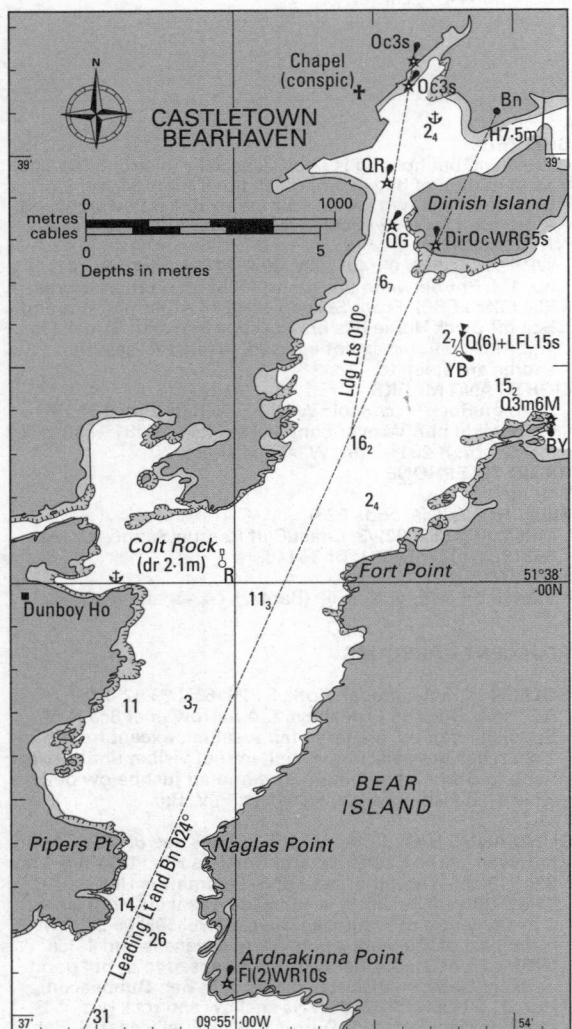

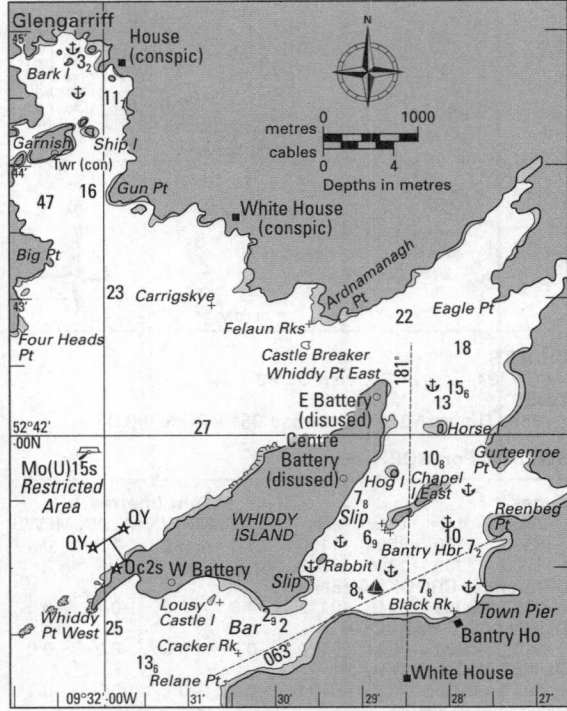

KENMARE RIVER   8-12-28

Kerry 51°45'·00N 10°00'·00W   Rtg 1-5-2

CHARTS
AC 2495; Imray C56; Irish OS 84

TIDES
+0515 Dover; Duration Dunkerron 0620; West Cove 068.
Zone 0 (UT)

Standard Port COBH (←)

Times				Height (metres)			
High Water		Low Water		MHWS	MHWN	MLWN	MLWS
0500	1100	0500	1100	4·1	3·2	1·3	0·4
1700	2300	1700	2300				
Differences BALLYCROVANE HARBOUR (Coulagh Bay)							
–0116	–0036	–0053	–0133	–0·6	–0·5	–0·1	0·0
DUNKERRON HARBOUR							
–0117	–0027	–0050	–0140	–0·2	–0·3	+0·1	0·0
WEST COVE (51°46'N 10°03'W)							
–0113	–0033	–0049	–0129	–0·6	–0·5	–0·1	0·0
BALLINSKELLIGS BAY							
–0119	–0039	–0054	–0134	–0·5	–0·5	–0·1	0·0
VALENTIA HARBOUR (Knights Town)							
–0118	–0038	–0056	–0136	–0·4	–0·4	–0·1	0·0

SHELTER
Garnish Bay: is only good in settled weather and W'ly winds. ‡ either W or 1ca S of the Carrigduff concrete bn.
Ballycrovane: in NE of Coulagh B is a good ‡, but open to W'ly swell which breaks on submerged rks in SE. N and E shores are foul. ‡ ½ca NE of Bird Is.
Cleanderry: Ent NE of Illaunbweeheen (Yellow Is) is only 7m wide and rky. ‡ ENE of inner hbr.
Ardgroom: excellent shelter, but intricate ent over rky bar. Appr with B bn brg 135°; then 2 W bns (front on Black Rk, rear ashore) lead 099° through bar. Alter 206° as two bns astern come in transit. When clear, steer WNW to ‡ ½ca E of Reenavade pier; power needed. Beware fish farms.
Kilmakilloge: is a safe ‡ in all winds. Beware mussel beds and rky shoals. On appr steer W of Spanish Is, but pass N of it. Bunaw Hbr ldg lts 041°, front Oc R 3s, rear Iso R 2s, (access only near HW; AB for shoal draft). ‡ 2ca E of Spanish Is; 2ca W of Carrigwee bn; S of Eskadawer Pt; or Collorus Hbr. **Ormond's Hbr:** gives good shelter, but beware rk 2½ca ENE of Hog Is. ‡ in S half of bay.

Kenmare: Good shelter. Access only near HW. 2 W piles in line astern mark max depth to the quay (AB) on N side of river, just below town.
Dunkerron Hbr: Ent between Cod Rks and The Boar to ‡ 1ca NW of Fox Is in 3·2m; land at Templenoe pier. 4ca E of Reen Pt behind pier, AB (£IR7) at floating jetty in 1·8m.
Sneem: enter between Sherky Is and Rossdohan Is. Hotel conspic NE of hbr. ‡ NE of Garinish Is, but uncomfortable when considerable swell passes each side of Sherky Is.
Darrynane: 1½M NW of Lamb's Hd, is appr'd from the S between Deenish and Moylaun Islands, but not with high SW swell. Enter with care on the ldg marks/lts 034°, 2 W bns, both Oc 3s 10/16m 4M. Safe ‡ (3m) NE of Lamb's Is. Other ‡s include Lehid Hbr, R Blackwater, Coongar Hbr and W Cove.

NAVIGATION
WPT 51°40'·00N 10°17'·20W, 245°/065° from/to 0.5M S of Sherky Island 15·6M. At night, an appr into the river is possible, but close appr to hbrs or ‡s is not advised. From SW, keep NW of The Bull and Dursey Is. From SE, Dursey Sound is possible in fair wx but narrow (beware Flag Rk 0·3m) and with cable car, 21m clearance. To clear dangerous rks off Coulagh Bay, keep twr on Dursey Is well open of Cod's Head 220°. From NW, there are 3 deep chans off Lamb's Head: between Scarriff Is and Deenish Is which is clear; between Deenish and Moylaun Is which has rky shoals; and between Moylaun and Two Headed Is which is clear and 4½ca wide. Up-river from Sneem Hbr, keep N of Maiden Rk, dries 0·5m, and Church Rks; also Lackeen Rks. Beware salmon nets Jun -Sep. See 8.12.5.

LIGHTS AND MARKS
On Dursey Is: Old Watch Twr (conspic) 250m. Eagle Hill (Cod's Hd) 216m. The few lights are as on chartlet.

RADIO TELEPHONE
None.

TELEPHONE (Dial code 064)
MRCC (01) 6620922/3; Coast/Cliff Rescue Service (Waterville) (066) 74320; ⊞ Bantry (027) 50061; Ⓗ 41088.

FACILITIES
ARDGROOM (Pallas Hbr): D & P (cans), V, R, Bar, Kos, ✉ at Ardgroom village (2M SSW of Reenavade pier), .
KILMAKILLOGE: Bunaw Pier, AB, V, Bar; 2M to D, Kos, ✉.
KENMARE: AB. **Town** D & P (cans), Kos, Gaz, R, V, Bar, Ⓗ, ✉, Ⓑ, ⇌ (bus to Killarney), ✈ (Cork or Killarney).
SNEEM: L at Hotel Parknasilla & Oysterbed Ho pier (FW).
Town (2M from hbr), P & D (cans), R, Bar, ✉, Slip, V, Kos.

12

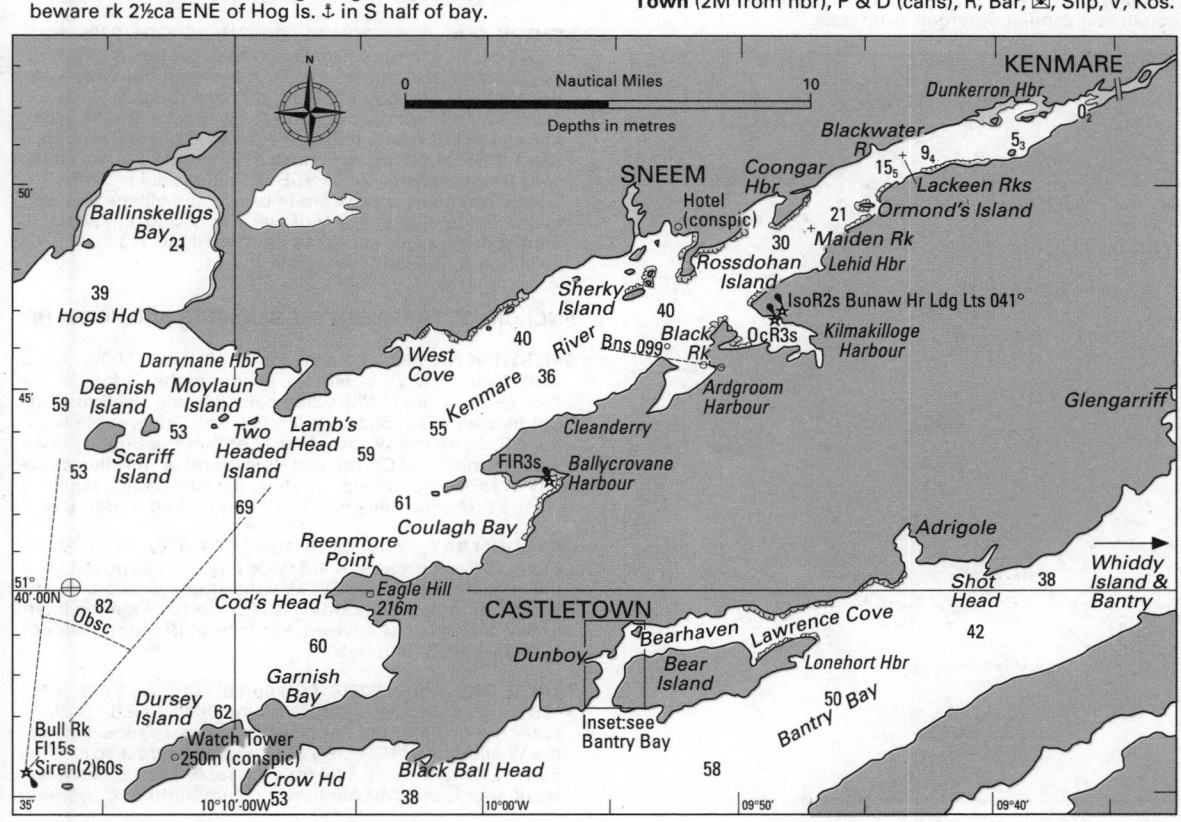

ANCHORAGES ON S SIDE OF ENTRANCE TO DINGLE BAY

PORTMAGEE, Kerry, 51°53'·20N 10°22'·29W. AC 2125. HW +0550 on Dover; ML 2·0m; Duration 0610; See 10·12·28 under VALENTIA HBR. A safe ⚓ 2·5M E of Bray Hd in Portmagee Sound between the mainland and Valentia Is. The ent to the Sound often has bad seas, but dangers are visible. Care required E of Reencaheragh Pt (S side) due to rks either side. Deepest water is N of mid-chan. ⚓ off the pier in 5m, opposite Skelling Heritage Centre (well worth a visit). AB on pier is not recommended due to strong tides. Facilities: ⚓, FW, V, R, Bar, Kos. 1ca E of pier, road bridge centre span opens, as pre-arranged with ☎ (066) 77174 or call *Valentia Radio* VHF Ch 24, 28; giving access to Valentia Hbr (Knight's Town) via intricate chan with 1·5m.

VALENTIA HARBOUR, Kerry, 51°56'·20N 10°19'·31W. AC 2125. Tides at 8.12.28. Main ent is at NE end of Valentia Is, between Fort Pt and Beginish Is. Easy access except in strong NW winds. Fort Pt lt, Fl WR 2s 16m 17/15M, W102°-304°, R304°-351°, obsc'd from seaward when E of Doulus Head. Ldg lts 141°: Front Dir Oc WRG 4s 25m 11/8M, W sector 140°-142°; rear, Oc 4s 43m 5M, synch. Beware Hbr Rk, 2·6m, 3ca SE of Fort Pt and 100m SW of ldg line; marked by ECM bn Q (3) 10s. Good shelter in ⚓s at: Glanleam B, 6ca S of Fort Pt in 4m; 1ca NW of LB slip in 2·5m (beware The Foot, spit drying 1·2m, marked by ECM buoy, Q (3) 5s); off the ferry pier at Knight's Town (E end of the island) in 4m; in bay on the S side of Beginish Is in 3m. Moorings via Hr Mr ☎ (066) 76124. Facilities (Knightstown): BY, Sh, ME, Gas, Fuel (cans), Kos, some V, R, Bar, ⊡. Ferry/bus to Cahersiveen (2½M) for all normal shops; EC Thurs.

DINGLE   8-12-29

Kerry 52°07'·14N 10°15'·48W   Rtg 1-1-1

CHARTS
AC 2790, 2789; Imray C55, 56; Irish OS 70

TIDES
+0540 Dover; ML 2·1m; Duration 0605; Zone 0 (UT)

Standard Port COBH (←—)

Times				Height (metres)			
High Water		Low Water		MHWS	MHWN	MLWN	MLWS
0500	1100	0500	1100	4·1	3·2	1·3	0·4
1700	2300	1700	2300				
Differences DINGLE							
–0111	–0041	–0049	–0119	–0·1	0·0	+0·3	+0·4
SMERWICK HARBOUR							
–0107	–0027	–0041	–0121	–0·3	–0·4	No data	
FENIT PIER (Tralee Bay)							
–0057	–0017	–0029	–0109	+0·5	+0·2	+0·3	+0·1

SHELTER
Excellent at marina (5m depth) in landlocked hbr. A busy fishing port. There is ⚓ 7ca S of pier, clear of dredged chan and semi-submerged store pots.

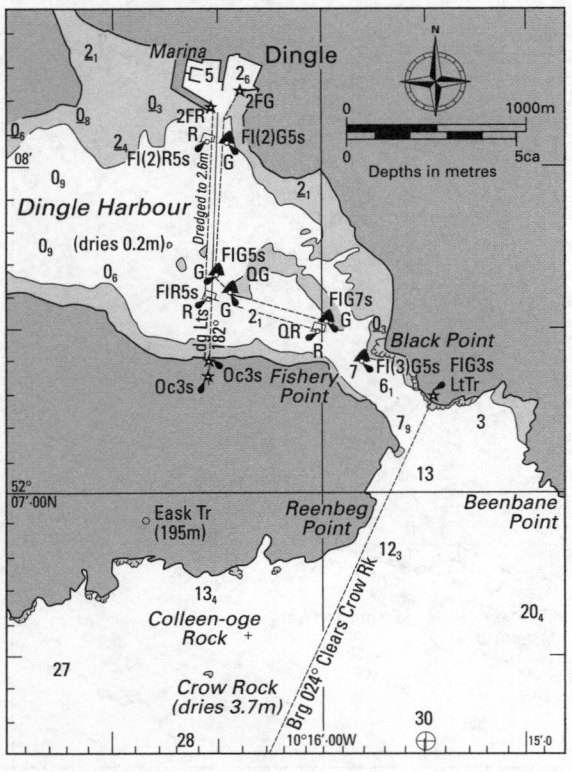

Depths in metres

NAVIGATION
WPT 52°06'·20N 10° 15'·48W, 180°/360° from/to lt Fl G 3s, 1·06M. Easy ent H24. Beware Crow Rk (dries 3·7m), 0·8M SW of Reenbeg Pt; and rky ledge SW of Black Pt. Note: Castlemaine Hbr, approx 15M E at the head of Dingle Bay, largely dries and should not be attempted.

LIGHTS AND MARKS
Eask Twr (195m, with fingerpost pointing E) is conspic 0·85M WSW of ent. Lt tr, Fl G 3s 20m 6M, on NE side of ent. Ent chan, dredged 2·6m, is marked by 5 SHM lt buoys and 3 PHM lt buoys, as chartlet. Ldg lts, both Oc 3s, (◊ daymarks) lead from astern 182° to hbr bkwtrs.

RADIO TELEPHONE
Ch M, 14 (occas). Valentia Radio (Ch 24 28) has good VHF cover and will relay urgent messages to Dingle.

TELEPHONE (Dial code 066)
Hr Mr 51629; MRCC (01) 6620922/3; ⊞ 21480; Dr 51341; Ⓗ 51455; Police 51522. All emergencies: 999 or 112.

FACILITIES
Marina (60 + 20 Ⓥ) ☎/⇆ 51629, £10, AC, FW, D, ⛽, C (hire). **Town** EC Thurs; P (cans), Kos, ME, Ⓔ, SM, ⊠, R, Bar, V, Ⓑ, ⇌ Tralee (by bus), ✈ (Kerry/Farranfore 30M).

ANCHORAGE CLOSE WEST OF DINGLE BAY

VENTRY Kerry, 52°06'·70N 10°20'·30W. AC 2790, 2789. HW +0540 on Dover; ML 2·1m; Duration 0605; Use 8·12·29. Ent is 2M W of conspic Eask Tr. A pleasant hbr with easy ent 1M wide and good holding on hard sand; sheltered from SW to N winds, but open to swell from the SE, and in fresh W'lies prone to sharp squalls. Beware Reenvare Rks 1ca SE of Parkmore Pt; also a rky ridge 2·9m, on which seas break, extends 2·5ca SSE of Ballymore Pt. ⚓ off Ventry Strand in approx 4m (⊕ brg W, the village NE) or in 3m S side of bay, 1ca N of pier. On N side a new pier, almost dries, gives access to Ventry village. No lts. Facilities: L, P, Slip, V, Kos, Bar, R, ⊠.

ANCHORAGES BETWEEN THE BLASKETS AND KERRY HD

SMERWICK HARBOUR, Kerry, 52°13'·00N 10°24'·00W. AC 2789. Tides 8.12.29. Adequate shelter in this 1M wide bay, except from NW'ly when considerable swell runs in. Ent between East Sister (150m hill) and Dunacapple Is to the NE. ⚓s at: the W side close N or S of the Boat Hr in 3-10m; to the S, off Carrigveen Pt in 2·5m; or in N'lies at the bay in NE corner inside 10m line. Facilities: Ballynagall village on E side has pier (0·5m) and limited V, Bar, Bus.

BRANDON BAY, Kerry, 52°16'·10N 10°09'·92W. AC 2739. Tides as Fenit 8.12.29. A 4M wide bay, very exposed to the N, but in moderate SW-W winds there is safe ⚓ in 6m close E of drying Brandon Pier, 2FG (vert). Cloghane Inlet in SW of Bay is not advised. Facilities at Brandon: limited V, P (1M), ⊠, R, Bar, bus.

TRALEE BAY, Kerry, 52°18'·00N 09°56'·00W. AC 2739. HW –0612 on Dover; ML 2·6m; Duration 0605. See 8·12·29. Enter the bay passing 3M N of Magharee Islands. Pick up the W sector (W140°–152°) of Little Samphire Is lt, Fl WRG 5s 17m 16/13M; see 8.12.4 for sectors. Approach between Magharee Is and Mucklaghmore (30m high).   *Continued*

FENIT HARBOUR, 52°16'·20N 09°51'·61W, is in SE corner of Tralee Bay. Appr on 146° to Little Samphire Is, conspic lt ho, Fl WRG 5s 17m 16/13M, thence 7ca E to Samphire Is; 3 conspic fuel tanks and lt QR 15m 3M vis 242°–097°. Good shelter in marina, but a few berths exposed to SE winds. Fenit Pier head 2 FR (vert) 12m 3M, vis 148°–058°. For ⚓s call *Neptune* (Tralee SC) VHF Ch 14 16, or ⚓ N of the pier hd in 4m on good holding. Hr Mr: VHF Ch M (0900-2100UT), ☎/🖷 (066) 36231, mobile ☎ 087 460516; ⌗ ☎ 36115. **Marina** (114 inc Ⓥ; max LOA 15m), £10, FW, AC, D, 🖾, ♿; **Village** Slip, C, P (cans), ME, V, Bar, R, ✉.

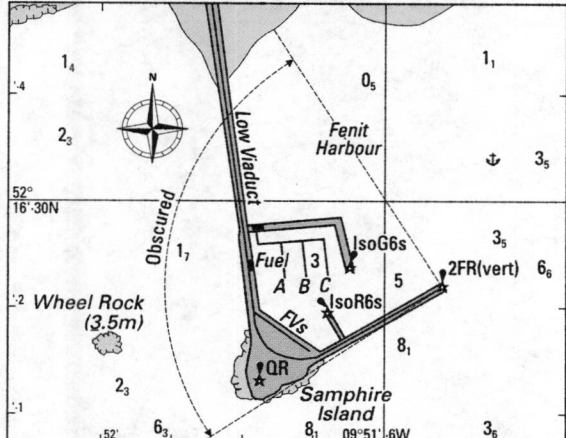

SHANNON ESTUARY   8-12-30

Clare (N); Kerry and Limerick (S) 52°35'·00N 09°40'·00W

CHARTS
AC 1819, 1547, 1548, 1549, 1540; L. Derg 5080; L. Ree 5078. Imray C55. OS 63, 64. The ICC's *Sailing Directions for S & W Ireland* and/or Admiralty *Irish Coast Pilot* are essential.

TIDES

HW at	HW Galway	HW Dover
Kilbaha & Carrigaholt	−0015	+0605
Tarbert	+0035	−0530
Foynes	+0050	−0515
Limerick	+0130	−0435

At Limerick strong S-W winds increase the height and delay the times of HW; strong N-E winds do the opposite.

SHELTER
The Shannon Estuary is 50M long, (Loop Hd to Limerick). For boats on passage N/S the nearest ⚓ is Kilbaha Bay, 3M inside Loop Hd; it has ⚓s sheltered in winds from W to NE, but is exposed to swell and holding is poor.
6M further E, Carrigaholt Bay has ⚓s and good shelter

from W'lies; ⚓ just N of the new quay, out of the tide. Kilrush marina (8.12.31) with all facilities is 7M further E. From Kilconly and Kilcredaun Pts in the W to the R Fergus ent (about 25M) there are ⚓s or ⚓s, protected from all but E winds, at Tarbert Is, Glin, Labashadee, Killadysert and among the islands in the Fergus mouth. The best ⚓ in the estuary is at Foynes on the S bank, with also a pontoon off the YC. There are drying quays at Ballylongford Creek (Saleen), Knock and Clarecastle (S of Ennis, off chartlet). Yachts may enter Limerick Dock, but this is a commercial port with usual problems; major improvements planned.

NAVIGATION
WPT 52°32'·50N 09°46'·90W, Ballybunnion NCM By VQ, 244°/064° from/to Tail of Beal Bar buoy WCM, Q (9) 15s, 4·2M. For notes on ent and tidal streams see 8·12·5. The ebb can reach 4kn. The lower estuary between Kerry and Loop Heads is 9M wide, narrowing to 2M off Kilcredaun Pt. Here the chan is well buoyed in mid-stream and then follows the Kerry shore, S of Scattery Is. From Tarbert Is to Foynes Is the river narrows to less than 1M in places, before widening where the R Fergus joins from the N, abeam Shannon airport.
Above this point the buoyed chan narrows and becomes shallower although there is a minimum of 2m at LWS.
AC 1540 is essential for the final 15M stretch to Limerick.

RIVER SHANNON
The Shannon, the longest navigable river in the UK or Ireland, is managed by Limerick Hbr Commissioners up to Limerick. Up-stream it effectively becomes an inland waterway; progress is restricted by locks and bridges. Info on navigation and facilities can be obtained from the Waterways Service, Dept of Art, Culture & the Gaeltacht, 51 St Stephen's Green, Dublin 2, ☎ 01-6613111; or from the Inland Waterways Association of Ireland, Kingston House, Ballinteer, Dublin 4, ☎ 01-983392; also from Tourist Offices and inland marinas.

LIGHTS AND MARKS
Principal lts are listed in 8·12·4. There are QW (vert) aero hazard lts on tall chimneys at Money Pt power station 3M ESE of Kilrush. 2 chys at Tarbert Is are conspic (R lts).

RADIO TELEPHONE
Foynes Ch 12 13 16 (occas). Limerick Ch 12 13 16 (HO).

FACILITIES
Marine facilities are available at several communities on the Shannon; P & D (cans), FW, V, M can be found at many villages. ⚓s are being laid at Labasheeda, Glin Pier (pontoon) and Foynes. E of Aughanish Is on S shore, R Deal is navigable 3M to Askeaton. Ent, marked by RW bn, is 8ca SE of Beeves Rk with 1m in buoyed chan. BY at Massey's Pier ☎ 061-392198, 🖷 392344, ⚓s, FW, C, CH, AC, D, Slip. At the two major hbrs facilities include:
Foynes Slip, L, AB, P & D (cans), FW, ✉, Ⓑ, Dr, V, R, Bar; **Foynes YC** ☎ (069) 65261, Bar, R.
Limerick: Hbr Commission ☎ (061) 315377; ⌗ ☎ 415366. **City** Slip, AB, L, FW, P & D (cans), Kos, Gas, Gaz, ME, El, Dr, Ⓗ, ✉, all usual city amenities, ⇌, ✈ (Shannon).

12

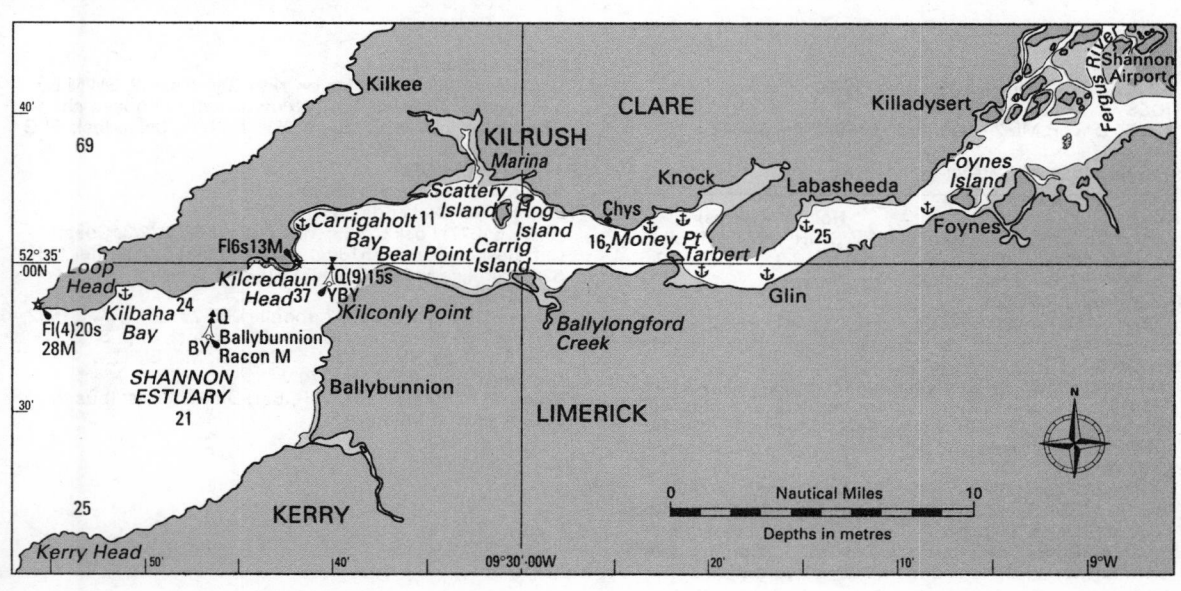

KILRUSH   8-12-31

Clare 52°37'·90N 09°29'·70W   Rtg 1-1-1

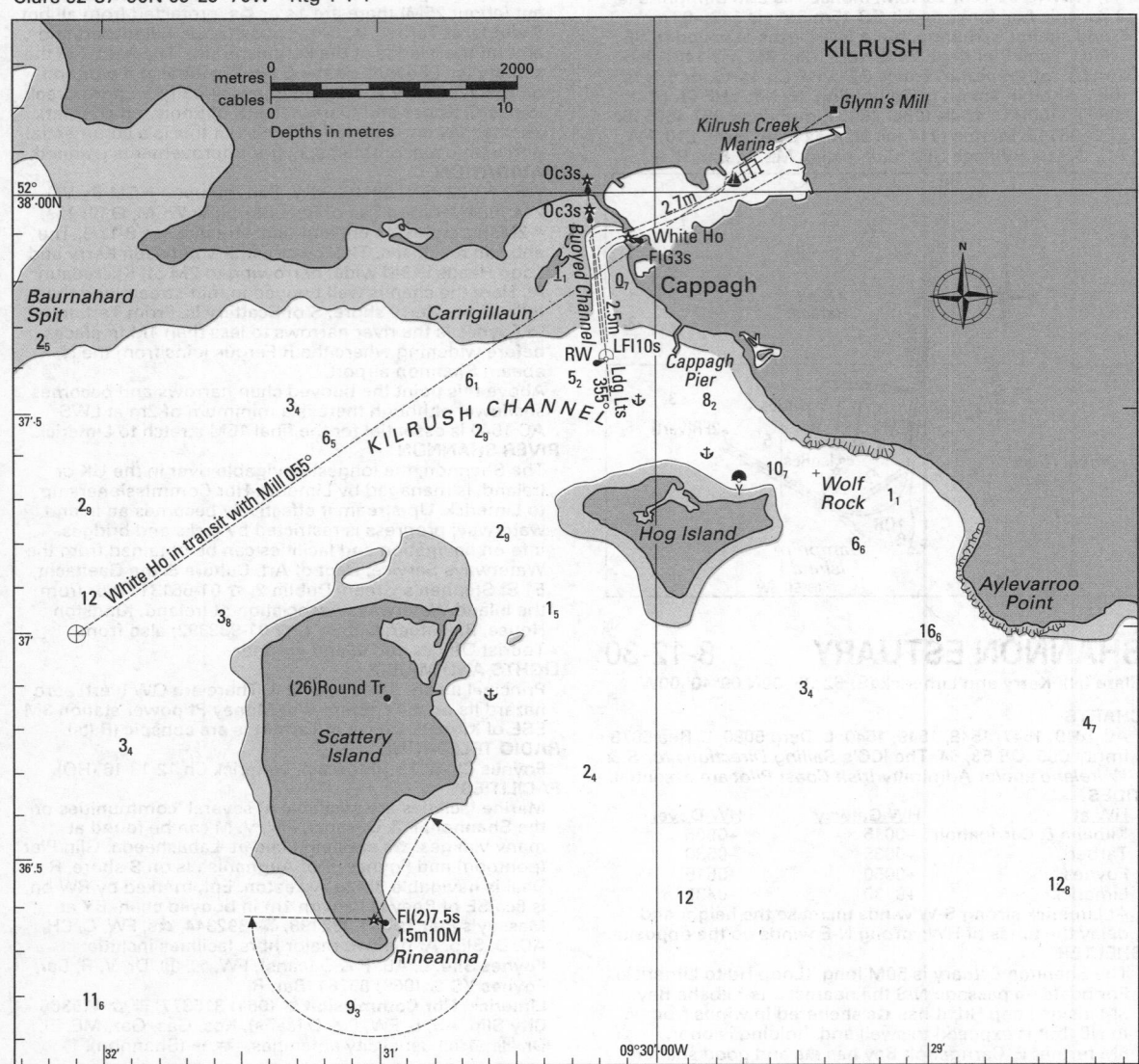

CHARTS
AC 1547, 1819; Imray C55; Irish OS 63
TIDES
−0555 Dover; ML 2·6; Duration 0610; Zone 0 (UT)

Standard Port GALWAY (→)

Times				Height (metres)			
High Water		Low Water		MHWS	MHWN	MLWN	MLWS
1000	0500	0000	0600	5·1	3·9	2·0	0·6
2200	1700	1200	1800				
Differences KILRUSH							
−0006	+0027	+0057	−0016	−0·1	−0·2	−0·3	−0·1

SHELTER
Excellent in Kilrush Creek Marina (2·7m), access via lock H24. Close to the E, Cappagh hbr partly dries, but is well sheltered except in SE winds; pier is constantly used by Shannon pilot boats and tugs. Day ⚓ in lee of Scattery Is.
NAVIGATION
WPT 52°37'·00N 09°32'·10W, 242°/062° from/to SWM buoy, 1·33M. See also 10·12·30. From seaward usual appr is N of Scattery Is (conspic Round Twr, 26m); beware Baurnahard Spit and Carrigillaun to the N. Coming down-river between Hog Is and mainland, beware Wolf Rk.

LIGHTS AND MARKS
Ldg marks 055° White Ho on with Glynn's Mill. SWM By L Fl 10s (52°37'·6N 09°30'·2W) marks ent to buoyed chan (dredged 2·5m), with ldg lts 355°, both Oc 3s, to lock. Fl G 3s 2M, S side of lock.
RADIO TELEPHONE
VHF Ch 12 16. Marina Ch 80.
TELEPHONE (Dial code 065)
Hr Mr 51327; Lock 52155; MRCC (01) 6620922/3; Coast/ Cliff Rescue Service 51004; ⌗ (061) 415366; Weather (061) 62677; Police 51017; Dr (065) 51581.
FACILITIES
Marina (120+50) ☎ 52072, mobile 087-2313870, 🛥 51692, £9.10, £2.50 for <6hrs, AC, FW, D, P (cans), Slip, BY, CH, Gas, Gaz, Kos, BH (45 ton), C (26 ton), ME, El, 🗓, V;
Cappagh, Slip, AB, L, FW, P, V.
Town EC Thurs; El, CH, V, R, Bar, Dr, ✉, Ⓑ, 🚌 (bus to Limerick), ✈ (Shannon).

VOLVO PENTA SERVICE

Sales and service centres in area 13
Northern Ireland *Robert Craig & Sons Ltd*, 15-21 Great Georges Street,
Belfast BT15 1BW Tel (01232) 232971

Area 13

North Ireland
Lambay Island anti-clockwise
to Liscanor Bay

**VOLVO
PENTA**

8.13.1	Index	**Page 583**
8.13.2	Diagram of ports, lights, RDF bns, Coast radio and weather stns	**584**
8.13.3	Tidal stream charts	**586**
8.13.4	List of coastal lights, fog signals and waypoints	**588**
8.13.5	Passage information	**592**
8.13.6	Distance table	**594**
8.13.7	Special notes for Ireland	**See 8.12.7**
8.13.8	Carlingford Lough Skerries Balbriggan Kilkeel Annalong Dundrum Bay	**594**
8.13.9	Ardglass	**596**
8.13.10	Strangford Lough Portavogie	**596**
8.13.11	Belfast Lough, Standard Port, tidal curves Donaghadee	**598**
8.13.12	Larne Carnlough Red Bay Rathlin Island Ballycastle North Channel TSS	**603**
8.13.13	Tidal streams off Rathlin Island	**605**
8.13.14	Portrush Portstewart	**606**
8.13.15	River Bann and Coleraine	**606**
8.13.16	Lough Foyle	**607**
8.13.17	Lough Swilly Mulroy Bay Sheep Haven Gweedore/Bunbeg Burtonport Teelin Harbour	**608**
8.13.18	Killybegs	**609**
8.13.19	Sligo Mullaghmore Killala Bay	**610**
8.13.20	Westport and Clew Bay Broadhaven Portnafrankagh Blacksod Bay Inishbofin Killary Ballynakill Clifden Bay	**611**
8.13.21	Galway Bay, Standard Port, tidal curves Galway Harbour	**612**

13

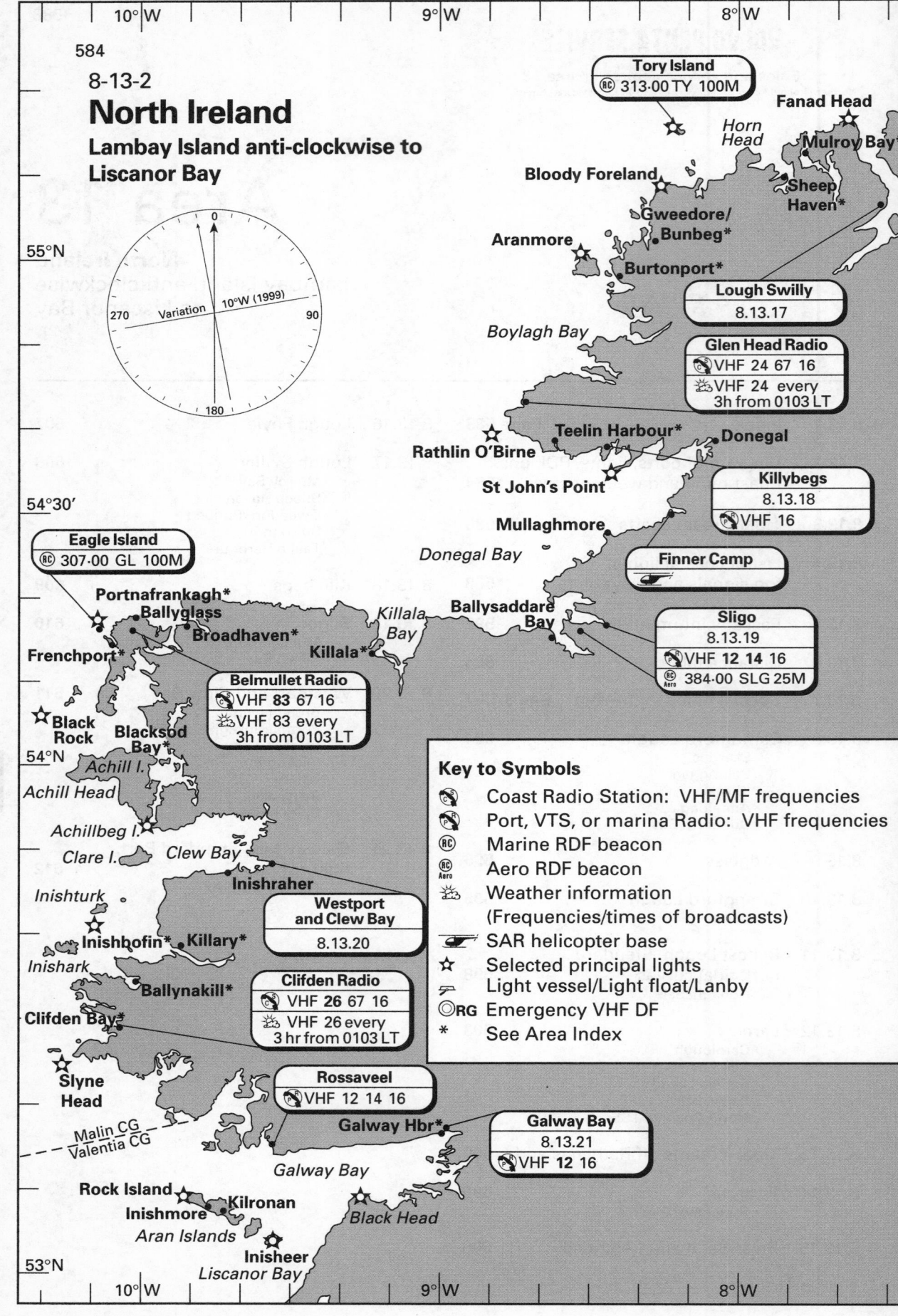

584

8-13-2

North Ireland

Lambay Island anti-clockwise to Liscanor Bay

Variation 10°W (1999)

Tory Island
(RC) 313·00 TY 100M

Horn Head

Fanad Head

Mulroy Bay*

Bloody Foreland

Sheep Haven*

Gweedore/ Bunbeg*

Aranmore

Burtonport*

Lough Swilly
8.13.17

Boylagh Bay

Glen Head Radio
📻 VHF 24 67 16
🌀 VHF 24 every 3h from 0103 LT

Rathlin O'Birne

Teelin Harbour*

Donegal

St John's Point

Killybegs
8.13.18
📻 VHF 16

Mullaghmore

Donegal Bay

Finner Camp

Eagle Island
(RC) 307·00 GL 100M

Ballysaddare Bay

Killala Bay

Sligo
8.13.19
📻 VHF 12 14 16
(RC Aero) 384·00 SLG 25M

Portnafrankagh*
Ballyglass

Broadhaven*

Frenchport*

Killala*

Belmullet Radio
📻 VHF 83 67 16
🌀 VHF 83 every 3h from 0103 LT

⭐ **Black Rock**

Blacksod Bay*

Achill I.

Achill Head

Achillbeg I.

Clare I.

Clew Bay

Inishturk

Inishraher

Westport and Clew Bay
8.13.20

*Inishbofin*** **Killary***

Inishark

Ballynakill*

Clifden Radio
📻 VHF 26 67 16
🌀 VHF 26 every 3 hr from 0103 LT

Clifden Bay*

⭐ **Slyne Head**

Rossaveel
📻 VHF 12 14 16

Galway Hbr*

Galway Bay
8.13.21
📻 VHF 12 16

Malin CG Valentia CG

Galway Bay

Rock Island

Kilronan

Inishmore

Black Head

Aran Islands

Inisheer

Liscanor Bay

Key to Symbols

📻 Coast Radio Station: VHF/MF frequencies
📻 Port, VTS, or marina Radio: VHF frequencies
(RC) Marine RDF beacon
(RC Aero) Aero RDF beacon
🌀 Weather information (Frequencies/times of broadcasts)
🚁 SAR helicopter base
☆ Selected principal lights
⚓ Light vessel/Light float/Lanby
◯RG Emergency VHF DF
* See Area Index

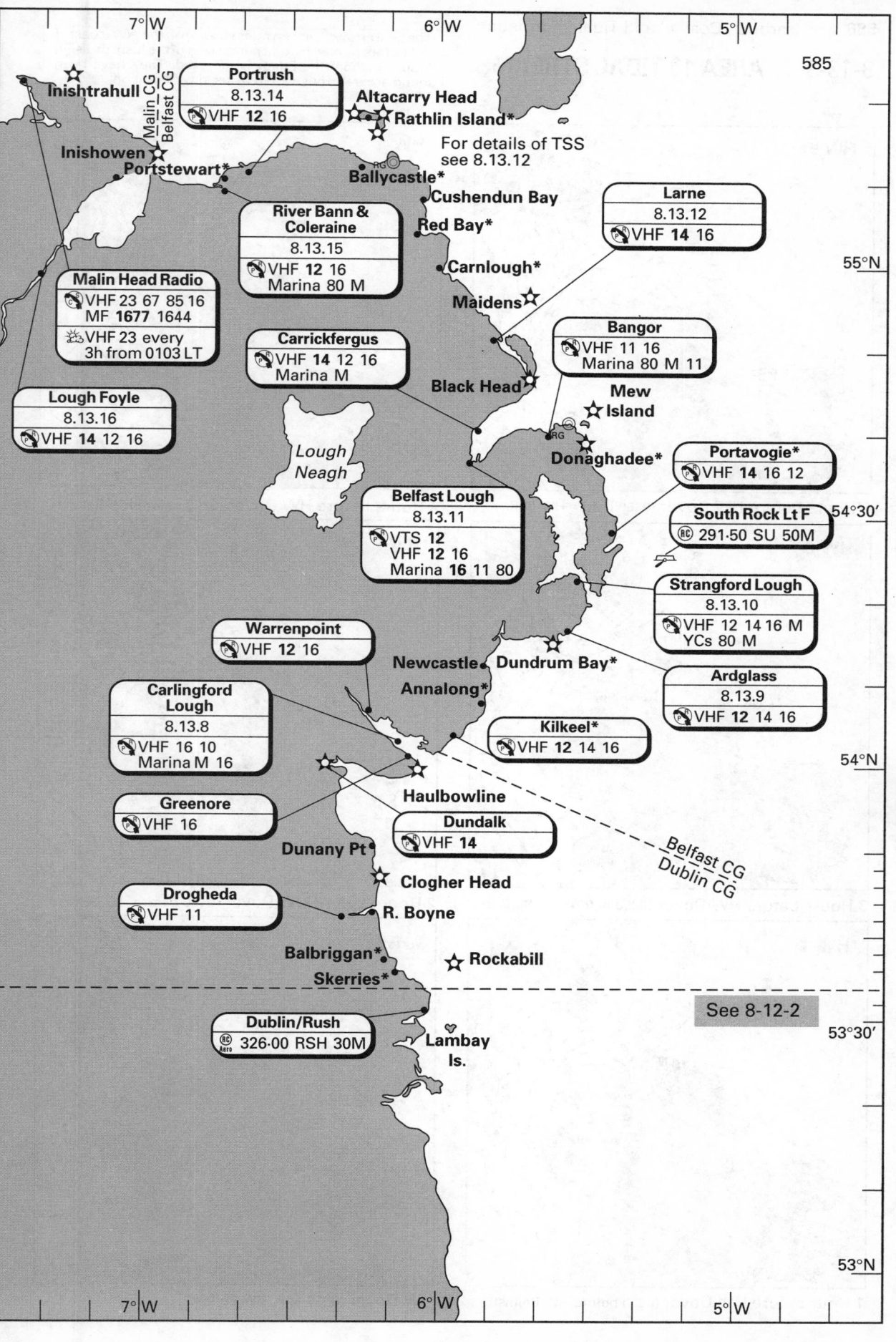

Inishtrahull ☆

Malin CG
Belfast CG

Portrush
8.13.14
📞 VHF **12** 16

Altacarry Head ☆☆
☆ Rathlin Island*

Inishowen ☆
Portstewart*

Ballycastle*

For details of TSS
see 8.13.12

Cushendun Bay

**River Bann &
Coleraine**
8.13.15
📞 VHF **12** 16
Marina 80 M

Red Bay*

Larne
8.13.12
📞 VHF **14** 16

55°N

Carnlough*

Malin Head Radio
📞 VHF 23 67 85 16
MF **1677** 1644
☼ VHF 23 every
3h from 0103 LT

Maidens ☆

Carrickfergus
📞 VHF **14** 12 16
Marina M

Bangor
📞 VHF 11 16
Marina 80 M 11

Lough Foyle
8.13.16
📞 VHF **14** 12 16

Black Head

Mew
☆ Island

*Lough
Neagh*

Donaghadee*

Portavogie*
📞 VHF **14** 16 12

South Rock Lt F
Ⓡ 291·50 SU 50M

54°30'

Belfast Lough
8.13.11
📞 VTS **12**
VHF **12** 16
Marina **16** 11 80

Strangford Lough
8.13.10
📞 VHF 12 14 16 M
YCs 80 M

Warrenpoint
📞 VHF **12** 16

Newcastle
Annalong*

Dundrum Bay*

Ardglass
8.13.9
📞 VHF **12** 14 16

54°N

**Carlingford
Lough**
8.13.8
📞 VHF 16 10
Marina M 16

Kilkeel*
📞 VHF **12** 14 16

Belfast CG
Dublin CG

13

Greenore
📞 VHF 16

Haulbowline
Dundalk
📞 VHF **14**

Dunany Pt

Drogheda
📞 VHF 11

Clogher Head ☆

R. Boyne

Balbriggan*

☆ Rockabill

Skerries*

See 8-12-2

Dublin/Rush
Ⓡ Aero 326·00 RSH 30M

Lambay
Is.

53°30'

53°N

8-13-3   AREA 13 TIDAL STREAMS

The tidal arrows (with no rates shown) off the NW coast of Ireland are printed by kind permission of the Irish Cruising Club, to whom the Editor is indebted. They have been found accurate, but should be used with caution.

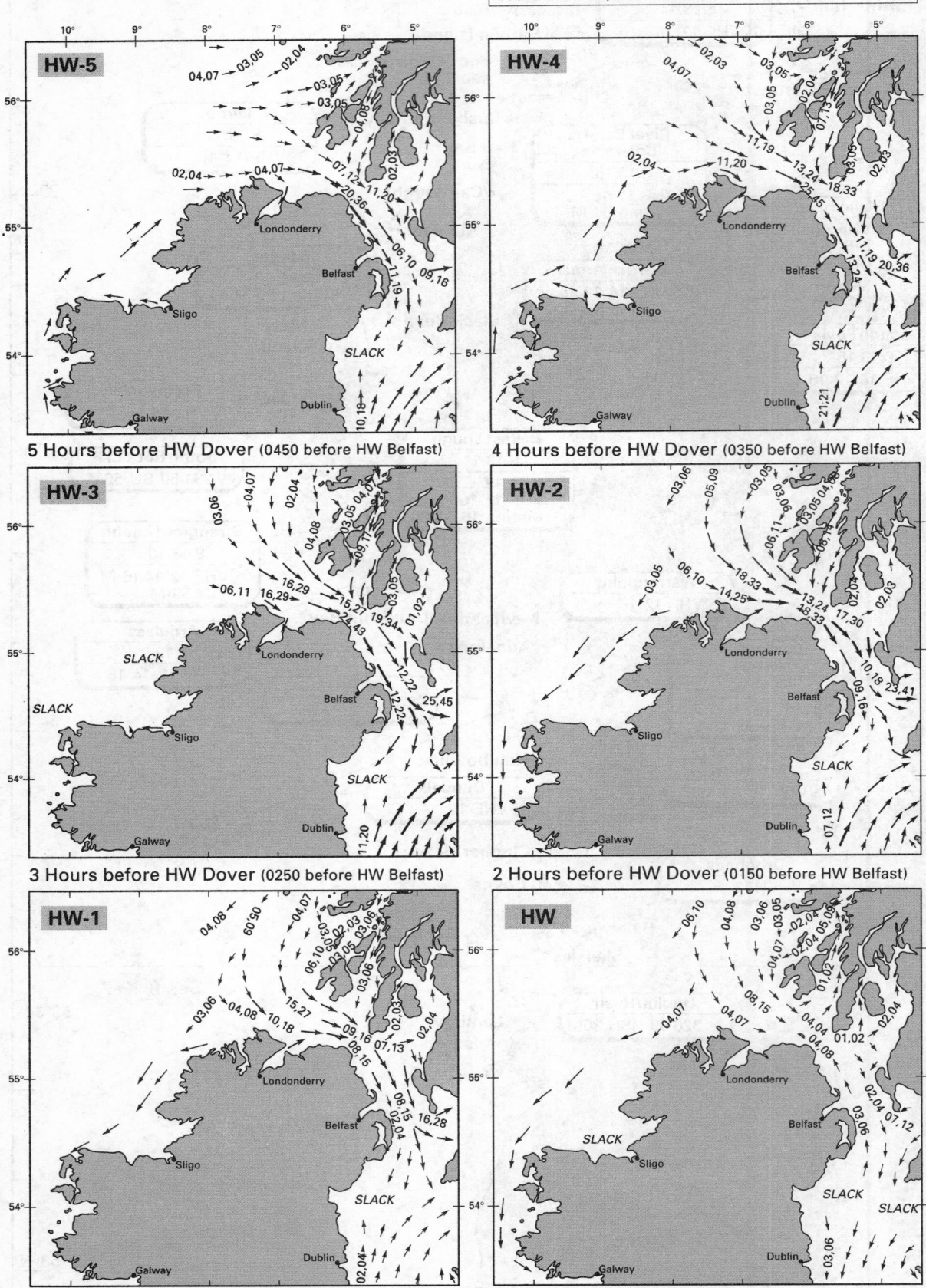

5 Hours before HW Dover (0450 before HW Belfast)

4 Hours before HW Dover (0350 before HW Belfast)

3 Hours before HW Dover (0250 before HW Belfast)

2 Hours before HW Dover (0150 before HW Belfast)

1 Hour before HW Dover (0050 before HW Belfast)

HW Dover (0010 after HW Belfast)

The tidal arrows (with no rates shown) off the NW coast of Ireland are printed by kind permission of the Irish Cruising Club, to whom the Editor is indebted. They have been found accurate, but should be used with caution.

Rathlin Island 8.13.13
Mull of Kintyre 8.9.12
North Irish Sea 8.10.3

SW Scotland 8.9.3
South Ireland 8.12.3

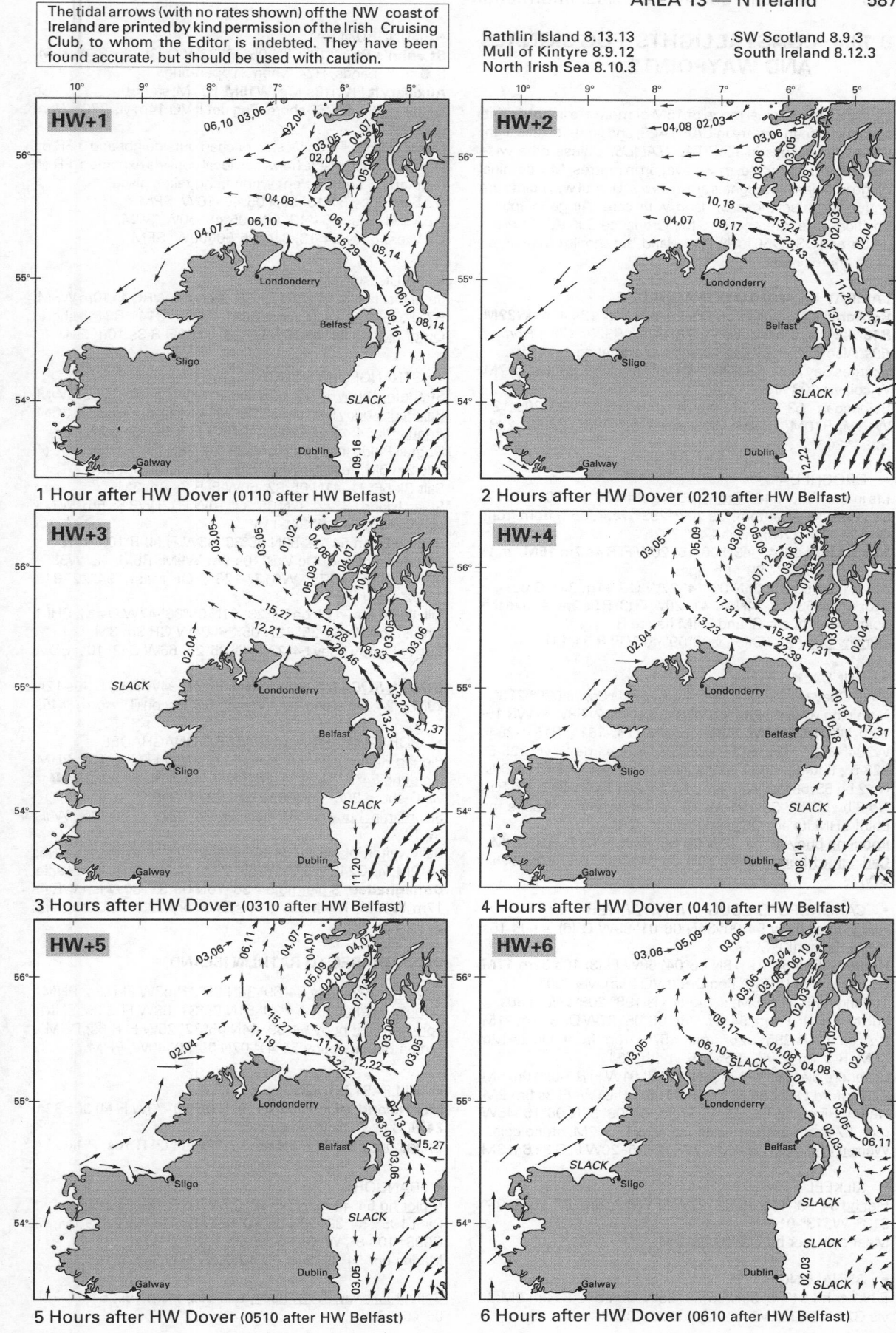

HW+1

1 Hour after HW Dover (0110 after HW Belfast)

HW+2

2 Hours after HW Dover (0210 after HW Belfast)

HW+3

3 Hours after HW Dover (0310 after HW Belfast)

HW+4

4 Hours after HW Dover (0410 after HW Belfast)

HW+5

5 Hours after HW Dover (0510 after HW Belfast)

HW+6

6 Hours after HW Dover (0610 after HW Belfast)

13

8.13.4 COASTAL LIGHTS, FOG SIGNALS AND WAYPOINTS

Lights with a nominal range of 15M or more are in **bold** print, places and features are in CAPITALS, and light-vessels, light floats and Lanbys in *CAPITAL ITALICS*. Unless otherwise stated lights are white. m = elevation in metres; M = nominal range in miles. Fog signals are in *italics*. Useful waypoints are underlined; use those on land with care. All geographical positions are referenced to the Ordnance Survey of Ireland datum and OSGB 36 for North Ireland, but should be assumed to be approximate.

LAMBAY ISLAND TO DONAGHADEE

Rockabill 53°35'·80N 06°00'·20W Fl WR 12s 45m **W22M, R18M**; W tr, B band; vis W178°-329°, R329°-178°; *Horn (4) 60s*. Also shown by day when))) is operating.
Skerries Bay pier hd 53°35'·08N 06°06'·43W Oc R 6s 7m 7M; W col; vis 103°-154°.
Balbriggan 53°36'·75N 06°10'·75W Fl (3) WRG 20s 12m W13M, R10M, G10M; W tr; vis G159°-193°, W193°-288°, R288°-305°.

* DROGHEDA
Lts in line about 248°: **Front**, 53°43'·14N 06°14'·80W Oc 12s 8m **15M**; tr, W lantern; vis 203°-293°; **rear**, 85m from front, Oc 12s 12m **17M**; tr; vis 246°-252°.
North Light 53°43'·43N 06°15'·20W Fl R 4s 7m **15M**; tr, W lantern; vis 282°-288°; tfc sigs.
Aleria lt bn 53°43'·34N 06°14'·27W QG 11m 3M; G bn.
Lyons lt bn 53°43'·24N 06°41'·20W Fl (3) R 5s 2m. Above this point SHM lts are G, and PHM lts are R.
Dunany buoy 53°53'·55N 06°09'·40W Fl R 3s; PHM.

* DUNDALK
Giles Quay 53°59'·04N 06°14'·35W Fl G 3s;vis 030°-210°.
N training wall hd, **Pile lt** 53°58'·54N 06°17'·68W Fl WR 15s 10m **W21M, R18M**; W Ho; vis W124°-151°, R151°-284°, W284°-313°, R313°-124°. Oc G 5s 8m; same tr; vis 325·5°-328·5°; Fog det lt VQ 7m, vis when brg 358°; *Horn (3) 60s*.
No 2 bn 53°58'·33N 06°17'·73W Fl (2) R 5s 4m 3M; 2 in R □.
No 8 bn 53°59'·30N 06°18'·91W Fl R 3s; R pile. Above this point SHM lts are QG, and PHM lts QR.
Imogene buoy 53°57'·02N 06°06'·95W Fl (2) R 10s; PHM.
Carlingford buoy 53°58'·75N 06°01'·06W L Fl 10s; *Whis*; SWM.

* CARLINGFORD LOUGH/NEWRY RIVER
Hellyhunter buoy 54°00'·34N 06°01'·99W Q (6) + L Fl 15s; *Whis;* Racon (K); SCM.
Haulbowline 54°01'·18N 06°04'·68W Fl (3) 10s 32m **17M**; Gy tr; reserve lt 15M; Fog Det lt VQ 26m; vis 330°.
Turning lt FR 21m 9M; same tr; vis 196°-208°; *Horn 30s*.
Ldg lts 310·4° Front, 54°01'·78N 06°05'·37W Oc 3s 7m 11M; R △ on tr; vis 295°-325°; rear, 457m from front, Oc 3s 12m 11M; R ▽ on tr; vis 295°-325°; both H24.
Greenore pier hd 54°02'·06N 06°07'·91W Fl R 7·5s 10m 5M.
Carlingford Quay hd 54°02'·59N 06°11'·01W Fl 3s 5m 2M.
Newry River ldg lts 310·4°: Front, 54°06'·37N 06°16'·46W; rear, 274m from front. Both Iso 4s 5/15m 2M; stone cols.
Warren Pt bkwtr hd 54°05'·78N 06°15'·20W Fl G 3s 6m 3M.

* KILKEEL
Pier hd 54°03'·45N 05°59'·27W Fl WR 2s 8m 8M; vis R296°-313°, W313°-017°.
Meeney's pier hd Fl G 3s 6m 2M.

* ANNALONG
E bkwtr hd 54°06'·50N 05°53'·65W Oc WRG 5s 8m 9M; tr; vis G204°-249°, W249°-309°, R309°-024°.

* DUNDRUM BAY
St John's Pt 54°13'·60N 05°39'·23W Q (2) 7·5s 37m **25M**; B ● tr, Y bands; H24 when))) operating.
Auxiliary lt Fl WR 3s 14m **W15M**, R11M; same tr,   vis W064°-078°, R078°-shore; Fog det lt VQ 14m vis 270°; *Horn (2) 60s.*
Dundrum Hbr FR on W side of chan outside hbr and 3 FR on W side of chan inside hbr when local vessels expected. FR on flagstaffs S and E of ent when firing takes place.
DZ East buoy 54°13'·50N 05°46'·16W; SPM.
DZ Middle buoy 54°13'·00N 05°48'·50W; SPM.
DZ West buoy 54°13'·34N 05°50'·00W; SPM.

* ARDGLASS
Inner pier hd 54°15'·78N 05°36'·28W Iso WRG 4s 10m W8M, R7M, G5M; tr; vis G shore-308°, W308°-314°, R314°-shore.
Outer pier hd 54°15'·62N 05°36'·07W Fl R 3s 10m 5M.

* STRANGFORD LOUGH
Strangford buoy 54°18'·63N 05°28'·62W L Fl 10s;*Whis;* SWM.
Bar Pladdy buoy 54°19'·33N 05°30'·43W Q (6) + L Fl 15s; SCM.
Angus Rk 54°19'·83N 05°31'·48W Fl R 5s 15m 6M; H24.
Dogtail Pt ldg lts 341°: Front, 54°20'·78N 05°31'·78W Oc (4) 10s 2m 5M; rear, Gowlands Rk, Oc (2) 10s 6m 5M.
Salt Rk 56°21'·41N 05°32'·60W Fl R 3s 8m 3M.
Swan Island 54°22'·37N 05°33'·10W Fl (2) WR 6s 5m; W col; vis W115°-334°, R334°-115°.
Church Pt bn 54°22'·59N 05°33'·35W Fl (4) R 10s.
Portaferry pierhd, Oc WR 10s 9m W9M, R6M; vis W335°-005°, R005°-017°, W017°-128°; Or mast; 54°22'·81N 05°32'·94W.
Killyleagh Town Rk bn 54°23'·61N 05°38'·47W Q 4M; PHM.
Limestone Rk 54°25'·13N 05°36'·04W QR 3m 3M.
Butter Pladdy buoy 54°22'·44N 05°25'·66W Q (3) 10s; ECM.

SOUTH ROCK lt F 54°24'·48N 05°21'·94W Fl (3) R 30s 12m **20M**, H24; R hull and lt tr, W mast; RC; Racon (T); *Horn (3) 45s.*

* PORTAVOGIE/BALLYWATER/DONAGHADEE
Plough Rk buoy 54°27'·39N 05°25'·04W Fl (2) R 10s; PHM.
S pier hd 54°27'·44N 05°26'·08W, Iso WRG 5s 9m 9M; ■ tr; vis G shore-258°, W258°-275°, R275°-348°.
Skulmartin buoy 54°31'·83N 05°24'·83W L Fl 10s; *Whis;* SWM.
Ballywalter, bkwtr hd 54°32'·67N 05°28'·75W Fl WRG 1·5s 5m 9M; vis G240°-267°, W267°-277°, R277°-314°. Unreliable.
Donaghadee, S pier hd 54°38'·70N 05°31'·80W Iso WR 4s 17m **W18M**, R14M; W tr; vis W shore-326°, R326°-shore; *Siren 12s.*

DONAGHADEE TO RATHLIN ISLAND

Governor Rks buoy 54°39'·36N 05°31'·93W Fl R 3s; PHM.
Deputy Reefs buoy 54°39'·51N 05°31'·88W Fl G 2s; SHM.
Foreland Spit buoy 54°39'·64N 05°32'·25W Fl R 6s; PHM.
Ninion Bushes buoy 54°41'·07N 05°30'·40W; PHM.

* BELFAST LOUGH
Mew Island NE end 54°41'·91N 05°30'·73W Fl (4) 30s 37m **24M**; B tr, W band; Racon (O).
Briggs buoy 54°41'·19N 05°35'·66W Fl (2) R 10s; PHM.

* BANGOR
N pier hd 54°40'·02N 05°40'·30W Iso R 12s 9m14M.
Dir lt 105°. 54°39'·98N 05°40'·09W Dir Oc 10s WRG 1M; vis G093°-104·8°, W104·8°-105·2°, R105·2°-117°.
Marina ent 54°39'·97N 05°40'·22W Fl G 3s 5m 1M.

Belfast Fairway SWM buoy, L Fl 10s, Horn 16s; 54°41'·71N 05°46'·16W.

• CARRICKFERGUS
E pier hd 54°42'·63N 05°48'·30W Fl G 7·5s 5m 4M; G col.
Marina E bkwtr 54°42'·71N 05°48'·63W QG 8m 3M; G ● pillar.
W bkwtr QR 7m 3M; R ● pillar.
W bkwtr dir lt 320°, F WRG 5m 3M, vis G308°-317·5°,
W317·5°-322·5°, R322·5°-332°; 54°42'·58N 05°48'·71W.
Kilroot Pt jetty hd, Oc G 10s 6m 9M, 54°43'·47N 05°44'·53W.
Cloghan jetty SHM buoy, QG; 54°44'·10N 05°41'·52W.

Black Hd 54°45'·99N 05°41'·27W Fl 3s 45m **27M**; W tr; RC.
N Hunter Rk buoy 54°53'·04N 05°45'·05W Q; NCM.
S Hunter Rk buoy 54°52'·69N 05°45'·22W Q (6) + L Fl 15s.

• LARNE
Barr Pt 54°51'·50N 05°46'·73W; *Horn 30s.* Fog Det lt VQ.
No 1 buoy 54°51'·62N 05°47'·53W Q (3) 10s; ECM.
No 3 buoy 54°51'·27N 05°47'·56W Fl (2) G 6s; SHM.
Chaine Tr 54°51'·27N 05°47'·82W Iso WR 5s 23m **16M**; Gy
tr; vis W230°-240°, R240°-shore.
Larne No 2 lt bn 54°51'·07N 05°47'·47W Fl R 3s.
Ent ldg lts 184°: No 11 Front, 54°49'·59N 05°47'·74W Oc 4s
6m 12M; W ◊ with R stripe on R pile structure; vis 179°-189°.
No 12 Rear, 610m from front, Oc 4s 14m 12M; W ◊ with R
stripe on R ● tr; synch with front, vis 179°-189°.
Maidens 54°55'·73N 05°43'·60W Fl (3) 20s 29m **24M**, H24;
W tr, B band; Racon (M). Auxiliary lt Fl R 5s 15m 8M; same
tr; vis 142°-182° over Russel and Highland Rks.

• CARNLOUGH/RED BAY
Carnlough hbr N pier 54°59'·58N 05°59'·20W Fl G 3s 4m 5M;
W col, B bands.
Red Bay pier 55°03'·92N 06°03'·12W Fl 3s 10m 5M.

RATHLIN ISLAND TO INISHTRAHULL

• RATHLIN ISLAND
Rue Pt 55°15'·53N 06°11'·40W Fl (2) 5s 16m 14M; W 8-sided
tr, B bands.
Drake buoy 55°17'·00N 06°12'·41W Q (6) + L Fl 15s; SCM.
Altacarry Head (Rathlin Island E) 55°18'·06N 06°10'·23W
Fl (4) 20s 74m **26M**, H24; W tr, B band; vis 110°-006° and
036°-058°; Racon (O).
Rathlin W (0·5M NE of Bull Pt) 55°18'·05N 06°16'·75W Fl R
5s 62m **22M**; W tr, lantern at base; vis 015°-225°; H24.
Manor House Dir lt, Oc WRG 4s 5M, vis G020°-023°, W023°-
026°, R026°-029°; 55°17'·56N 06°11'·64W.
Church Bay Hbr, W pier Fl R 2s 5·3m 3M.

• BALLYCASTLE
N pier Fl (3) G 6s 6·5m 6M; 55°12'·48N 06°14'·16W.
S pier Fl (2) R 4s 4·6m 1M, obsc'd N of brg 261° by N pier.

• PORTRUSH
N pier 55°12'·35N 06°39'·52W Fl R 3s 6m 3M; vis 220°-160°.
Portstewart Pt 55°11'·32N 06°43'·20W Oc R 10s 21m 5M;
R ■ hut; vis 040°-220°.

• RIVER BANN/COLERAINE
Ldg lts 165°: Front, 55°09'·95N 06°46'·17W Oc 5s 6m 2M;
W tr; rear, 245m from front, Oc 5s 14m 2M; W □ tr. River
marked by Fl G on stbd hand, and Fl R on port.
W mole 56°10'·32N 06°46'·40W Fl G 5s 4m 2M; Gy mast;
vis 170°-000°.
Lough Foyle buoy 55°15'·32N 06°52'·55W L Fl 10s; *Whis;*
SWM;
Tuns buoy 55°14'·00N 06°53'·49W Fl R 3s; PHM.
Inishowen 55°13'·56N 06°55'·69W Fl (2) WRG 10s 28m
W18M, R14M, G14M; W tr, 2 B bands; vis G197°-211°,
W211°-249°, R249°-000°; *Horn (2) 30s.* Fog det lt VQ 16m.

• LOUGH FOYLE
Greencastle ldg lts 032°: Front, 55°12'·20N 06°58'·90W
Fl 3s 11m 2M; Or ◊ on mast; rear, 50m from front, Fl 3s 13m
2M; Or ◊ on mast. F WR 10m; vis R072°-082°, W082°-072°.
F WR 5m; vis R037°-052°, W052°-037°.
Warren Pt lt bn 55°12'·58N 06°57'·06W Fl 1·5s 9m 10M; W
○ tr, G abutment; vis 232°-061°.
Magilligan Pt 55°11'·74N 06°57'·97W QR 7m 4M; R structure.
FR lts shown from 700m-3M SSE when firing taking place.
McKinney's Bank 55°10'·92N 07°00'·50W Fl R 5s 6m 4M; R
pile structure.
Moville 55°11'·00N 07°02'·06W Fl WR 2·5s 11m 4M; W
house on G piles vis W240°-064°, R064°-240°.
Above this point the chan to R.Foyle is marked by SHM lts Fl
G, shown from W structures on G or B piles; and by PHM Fl
R, shown from W structures on R piles.
Kilderry 55°04'·09N 07°13'·95W Fl G 2s 6m 3M; W structure.
Muff 55°03'·63N 07°14'·21W Fl G 2s 5m 3M; G structure.
Coneyburrow 55°03'·32N 07°14'·42W Fl G 2·5s 5m 3M.
Faughan 55°03'·12N 07°14'·42W Fl R 4s 5m 3M.
Culmore Pt 55°02'·78N 07°15'·20W Q 6m 3M; G ● tr.
Culmore Bay 55°02'·72N 07°15'·65W Fl G 5s 4m 2M.
Ballynagard 55°02'·28N 07°16'·37W Fl 3s 6m 3M; W lantern
on G ● house.
Otter Bank 55°01'·95N 07°16'·65W Fl R 4s 6m 3M; W
structure on R ● tr.
Brook Hall 55°01'·70N 07°17'·07W QG 6m 3M; W structure
on G base.
Mountjoy 55°01'·25N 07°17'·49W QR 5m 3M; W lantern on
R piles.

Inishtrahull 55°25'·85N 07°14'·58W Fl (3) 15s 59m **25M**; W
tr; Racon (T).

INISHTRAHULL TO BLOODY FORELAND

• LOUGH SWILLY/BUNCRANA/RATHMULLAN
Fanad Hd 55°16'·57N 07°37'·86W Fl (5) WR 20s 39m **W18M**,
R14M; W tr; vis R100°-110°, W110°-313°, R313°-345°, W345°-
100°. FR on radio mast 3·08M 200°.
Swilly More buoy 55°15'·11N 07°35'·74W Fl G 3s; SHM.
Dunree 55°11'·88N 07°33'·20W Fl (2) WR 5s 46m W12M,
R9M; vis R320°-328°, W328°-183°, R183°-196°.
Colpagh buoy 55°10'·42N 07°31'·50W; Fl R 6s; PHM.
White Strand Rks buoy 55°09'·06N 07°29'·90W Fl R 10s; PHM.
Buncrana pier near hd 55°07'·61N 07°29'·82W Iso WR 4s 8m
W14M, R11M; vis R shore-052° over Inch spit, W052°-139°,
R139°-shore over White Strand Rk.
Rathmullan pier hd 55°05'·70N 07°31'·66W Fl G 3s 5M;   vis
206°-345°.

• MULROY BAY
Limeburner buoy 55°18'·54N 07°48'·35W Q Fl; NCM; *Whis.*
Ravedy Is 55°15'·15N 07°46'·80W Fl 3s 9m 3M; tr; vis 177°-357°.
Dundooan Rks 55°13'·14N 07°47'·91W QG 4m 1M; G tr.
Crannoge Pt 55°12'·29N 07°48'·37W Fl G 5s 5m 2M; G tr.

• SHEEPHAVEN
Downies Bay pier hd 55°11'·36N 07°50'·42W Fl R 3s 5m 2M;
vis 283° through N till obsc by Downies Pt.
Portnablahy ldg lts 125·3°: Front 55°10'·80N 07°55'·60W Oc
6s 7m 2M; B col, W bands; rear, 81m from front, Oc 6s 12m
2M; B col, W bands.
Tory Island NW Pt 55°16'·35N 08°14'·92W Fl (4) 30s 40m
27M, H24; B tr, W band; vis 302°-277°; RC; Racon (M); H24.
Inishbofin Pier 55°10'·1N 08°10·5W Fl 8s 3m 3M; part obsc.
Ballyness Hbr, ldg lts 119·5°: Front, 55°09'·0N 08°06'·9W Iso
4s 25m 1M; rear, 61m from front, Iso 4s 26m 1M.
Bloody Foreland 55°09'·51N 08°16'·98W Fl WG 7·5s 14m
W6M, G4M; vis W062°-232°, G232°-062°.

13

BLOODY FORELAND TO RATHLIN O'BIRNE

Glassagh, ldg lts 137·4°: Front, 55°06'·85N 08°18'·90W Oc 8s 12m 3M; rear, 46m from front, Oc 8s 17m 3M, synch with front.
Inishsirrer, NW end 55°07'·41N 08°20'·89W Fl 3·7s 20m 4M; W □ tr vis 083°-263°.

- BUNBEG/MULLAGHDOO/OWEY SOUND

Gola Is ldg lts 171·2°: Front, 55°05'·12N 08°21'·02W Oc 3s 9m 2M; W bn, B band; rear, 86m from front, Oc 3s 13m 2M; B bn, W band; synch with front.
Bo Island E Pt 55°04'·78N 08°20'·08W Fl G 3s 3m; G bn.
Inishinny No 1 55°04'·48N 08°19'·78W QG 3m 1M; ■ col.
Inishcoole No 4 55°03'·98N 08°18'·88W QR 4m 2M; R ■ col on base.
Yellow Rks No 6 55°03'·67N 08°18'·90W QR 3m 1M; ■ col with steps; Neon.
Cruit Is. Owey Sound ldg lts 068·3°: Front, 55°03'·07N 08°25'·79W Oc 10s; rear, 107m from front, Oc 10s.
Rinnalea Pt 55°02'·60N 08°23'·67W Fl 7·5s 19m 9M; ■ tr; vis 132°-167°.

Aranmore, Rinrawros Pt 55°00'·90N 08°33'·60W Fl (2) 20s 71m **29M**; W tr; obsc by land about 234°-007° and about 013°.
Auxiliary lt Fl R 3s 61m 13M, same tr; vis 203°-234°.

- NORTH SOUND OF ARAN/RUTLAND NORTH CHAN

Ldg lts 186°: Front, 54°58'·94N 08°29'·22W Oc 8s 8m 3M; B bn, W band; rear, 395m from front, Oc 8s 17m 3M; B bn.
Ballagh Rks 54°59'·96N 08°28'·80W Fl 2·5s 13m 5M; W structure, B band.
Black Rks 54°59'·43N 08°29'·59W Fl R 3s 3m 1M; R col.
Inishcoo ldg lts 119·3°: Front, 54°59'·12N 08°27'·70W Iso 6s 6m 1M; W bn, B band; rear, 248m from front, Iso 6s 11m 1M; B bn, Y band.
Carrickatine No 2 bn 54°59'·26N 08°28'·06W QR 6m 1M;   R bn with steps; Neon.
Rutland Is ldg lts 137·6°: Front, 54°58'·97N 08°27'·63W Oc 6s 8m 1M; W bn, B band; rear, 330m from front, Oc 6s 14m 1M; B bn, Y band.

- BURTONPORT

Ldg lts 068·1°: Front 54°58'·96N 08°26'·36W FG 17m 1M; Gy bn, W band; rear, 355m from front, FG 23m 1M; Gy bn, Y band.

- SOUTH SOUND OF ARAN/RUTLAND SOUTH CHANNEL

Illancrone Is 54°56'·28N 08°28'·53W Fl 5s 7m 6M; W □ tr.
Wyon Pt 54°56'·50N 08°27'·50W Fl (2) WRG 10s 8m W6M, R3M; W □ tr; vis G shore-021°, W021°-042°, R042°-121°, W121°-150°, R 150°-shore.
Turk Rks 54°57'·30N 08°28'·15W Fl G 5s 6m 2M; G ■ tr.
Aileen Reef 54°58'·18N 08°28'·78W QR 6m 1M. R ■ bn.
Leac na bhFear 54°82'·1N 08°29'·2W Q (2) 5s 4m 2M.
Carrickbealatroha, Upper 54°58'·64N 08°28'·58W Fl 5s 3m 2M; W □ brickwork tr.
Corren's Rk 54°58'·12N 08°26'·68W Fl R 3s 4m 2M; R ■ tr.
Teige's Rk 54°58'·61N 08°26'·75W Fl 3s 4m 2M; W ○ tr, □ base.
Dawros Hd 54°49'·60N 08°33'·60W L Fl 10s 39m 4M; W □ col.
Dawros Bay 54°49'·3N 08°32'W Fl (2) 10s 5m 3M.
Rathlin O'Birne, W side 54°39'·80N 08°49'·90W Fl WR 15s 35m **W18M, R14M**; W tr; vis R195°-307°, W307°-195°; Racon (O).

RATHLIN O'BIRNE TO EAGLE ISLAND

- DONEGAL BAY, TEELIN/KILLYBEGS

Teelin Hbr 54°37'·32N 08°37'·72W Fl R 10s; R structure.
St John's Pt 54°34'·15N 08°27'·60W Fl 6s 30m 14M; W tr.
Bullockmore buoy 54°33'·98N 08°30'·10W Qk Fl (9) 15s; WCM.

Rotten Is 54°36'·87N 08°26'·39W Fl WR 4s 20m **W15M**, R11M; W tr; vis W255°-008°, R008°-039°, W039°-208°.
New Landing dir lt 338°. 54°38'·13N 08°26'·33W Dir WRG; vis G328°°-334°, Al WG334°-336°, W336°-340°, Al WR340°-342°, R342°-348°.
Killybegs Outer buoy 54°37'·92N 08°26'·09W VQ (6) + L Fl 10s; SCM.
Black Rk jetty 54°38'·03N 08°26'·55W Fl RG 5s; Gy col; vis R254°-204°, G204°-254°.
Finner Camp 54°29'·70N 08°13'·90W Aero Q WRG 67m.

- SLIGO

Wheat Rk buoy 54°18'·82N 08°39'·02W Q (6) + L Fl 15s; SCM.
Black Rock 54°18'·45N 08°37'·03W Fl 5s 24m 13M; W tr, B band. Auxiliary lt Fl R 3s 12m 5M; same tr; vis 107°-130° over Wheat and Seal rks.
Lower Rosses, N of Pt (Cullaun Bwee) 54°19'·71N 08°34'·36W Fl (2) WRG 10s 8m W10M, R8M, G8M; W hut on piles; vis G over Bungar bank-066°, W066°-070°, R070° over Drumcliff bar; shown H24.
Ldg lts 125°: Front, Metal Man 54°18'·23N 08°34'·51W Fl 4s 3m 7M; rear, Oyster I, 365m from front, Oc 4s 13m 10M. Both shown H24.

- KILLALA

Inishcrone Pier Root 54°13'·20N 09°05'·74W Fl WRG 1·5s 8m 2M; vis W098°-116°, G116°-136°, R136°-187°.
Ldg lts 230°: Rinnaun Pt, Front No 1, 54°13'·53N 09°12'·21W Oc 10s 7m 5M; ■ tr; rear, 150m from front, No 2 Oc 10s 12m 5M; ■ tr.
Dir lt 215°, Inch I, 54°13'·29N 09°12'·25W Fl WRG 2s 6m 3M; ■ tr; vis G205°-213°, W213°-217°, R217°-225°.
Ldg lts 196°: Kilroe, Front, 54°12'·62N 09°12'·28W Oc 4s 5m 2M; ■ tr; rear, 120m from front, Oc 4s 10m 2M; ■ tr.
Ldg lts 236°: Pier, Front, 54°13'·01N 09°12'·80W Iso 2s 5m 2M; W ◊ on tr; rear, 200m from front, Iso 2s 7m 2M; W ◊ on pole.
Killala Bay. Bone Rk, NE end 54°15'·80N 09°11'·20W Q 7m; NCM.

- BROAD HAVEN BAY

Gubacashel Pt 54°16'·05N 09°53'·28W Iso WR 4s 27m W12M, R9M; W tr; vis W shore (S side of bay)-355°, R355°-shore.
Ballyglass 54°15'·28N 09°53'·38W Fl G 3s.
Eagle Is, W end 54°17'·02N 10°05'·51W Fl (3) 10s 67m **23M**; W tr; RC. Shown H24.

EAGLE ISLAND TO SLYNE HEAD

Black Rk 54°04'·00N 10°19'·20W Fl WR 12s 86m **W22M, R16M**, H24; W tr; vis W276°-212°, R212°-276°.

- BLACKSOD BAY

Blacksod buoy 54°05'·88N 10°02'·96W Q (3) 10s, ECM.
Blacksod pier root 54°05'·91N 10°03'·60W Fl (2) WR 7·5s 13m W12M, R9M; W tr on dwelling; vis R189°-210°, W210°-018°.
Achill Is Ridge Pt 54°01'·80N 09°58'·50W Fl 5s 21m 5M.

- ACHILL SOUND

Achill Sound 53°56'·06N 09°55'·21W QR; R bn.
Ldg lts 330° Whitestone Pt, Front and rear both Oc 4s 5/6m; W ◊, B stripe.
Saulia Pier 53°57'·03N 09°55'·53W Fl G 3s 12m.
Achillbeg E lt bn 53°52'·12N 09°56'·50W Fl R 2s 5m; R ■ tr.
Carrigin-a-tShrutha 53°52'·29N 09°56'·70W Q (2) R 5s; R bn.

Achill Is ldg lts 310° Purteen 53°57'·79N 10°05'·92W (PA) Oc 8s 5m; rear, 46m from front Oc 8s 6m.

- CLEW BAY/WESTPORT

Achillbeg I S Pt 53°51'·50N 09°56'·80W Fl WR 5s 56m

W18M, **R18M**, **R15M**; W ○ tr on □ building; vis R262°-281°, W281°-342°, R342°-060°, W060°-092°, R(intens) 092°-099°, W099°-118°.

Clare I, E pier 53°48'·00N 09°57'·00W Fl R 3s 5m 3M.

Cloghcormick buoy 53°50'·55N 09°43'·15W; WCM.

Dorinish buoy 53°49'·47N 09°40'·45W Fl G 3s; SHM.

Inishgort S Pt 53°49'·60N 09°40'·20W L Fl 10s 11m 10M; W tr. Shown H24.

Westport appr 53°47'·97N 09°34'·30W Fl 3s; G box on conical bn.

Roonagh Quay ldg lts 144°: Front 53°45'·80N 09°54'·20W; rear, 54m from front, both Iso 10s 9/15m.

• INISHBOFIN/CLIFDEN BAY

Inishlyon Lyon Hd 53°36'·70N 10°09'·50W Fl WR 7·5s 13m W7M, R4M; W post; vis W036°-058°, R058°-184°, W184°-325°, R325°-036°.

Gun Rk 53°36'·58N 10°13'·18W Fl (2) 6s 8m 4M; W col; vis 296°-253°.

Cleggan Pt 53°34'·50N 10°07'·70W Fl (3) WRG 15s 20m W6M, R3M, G3M; W col on W hut; vis W shore-091°, R091°-124°, G124°-221°.

Carrickrana Rks bn 53°29'·20N 10°09'·50W; large W bn.

Slyne Hd, N tr, Illaunamid 53°23'·98N 10°14'·02W Fl (2) 15s 35m **24M**; B tr; Racon (T).

SLYNE HEAD TO BLACK HEAD

Inishnee 53°22'·75N 09°54'·40W Fl (2) WRG 10s 9m W5M, R3M, G3M; W col on W □ base; vis G314°-017°, W017°-030°, R030°-080°, W080°-194°.

Croaghnakeela Is 53°19'·40N 09°58'·11W Fl 3·7s 7m 5M; W col; vis 034°-045°, 218°-286°, 311°-325°.

• GALWAY BAY/ARAN ISLANDS

Eeragh, Rock Is 53°08'·90N 09°51'·34W Fl 15s 35m **23M**; W tr, two B bands; vis 297°-262°.

Straw Is 53°07'·05N 09°37'·80W Fl (2) 5s 11m **15M**; W tr. Ldg lts 192°: Front, 53°06'·25N 09°39'·70W Oc 5s 6m 3M; W col on W □ base; vis 142°-197°; rear, 43m from front, Oc 5s 8m 2M; W col on W □ base; vis 142°-197°.

Killeany buoy 53°07'·25N 09°38'·19W Fl G 3s; SHM.

Kilronan pier hd 53°07'·10N 09°39'·95W Fl WG 1·5s 5m 3M; W col; vis G240°-326°, W326°-000°.

Inisheer 53°02'·77N 09°31'·59W Iso WR 12s 34m **W20M, R16M**; vis 225°-231°, W231°-245°, R245°-269°, W280°-218°; Racon (K).

• KIGGAUL BAY

Kiggaul Bay 53°14'·01N 09°43'·00W Fl WR 3s 5m W5M, R3M; vis W329°-359°, R359°-059°, part obsc by W shore of bay.

• CASHLA BAY/SPIDDLE

Ent W side 53°14'·23N 09°35'·14W Fl (3) WR 10s 8m W6M, R3M; W col on concrete structure; vis W216°-000°, R000°-069°.

Cannon Rk buoy 53°14'·05N 09°34'·29W Fl G 5s; SHM.

Lion Pt dir lt 53°15'·83N 09°33'·93W Dir Iso WRG 4s 6m W8M, R6M, G6M; W □ tr on col; vis G357·5°-008·5°, W008·5°-011·5°, R011·5°-017·5°.

Rossaveel pier ldg lts 116°: Front, 53°15'·98N 09°33'·36W Oc 3s 7m 3M; W mast; rear, 90m from front, Oc 3s 8m 3M; W mast.

Spiddle pier hd 53°14'·42N 09°18'·50W Fl WRG 3·5s 11m W6M, R4M, G4M; Y col; vis G102°-282°, W282°-024°, R024°-066°.

• GALWAY

Margaretta Shoal buoy 53°13'·67N 09°05'·95W Fl G 3s; SHM.

Black Rock buoy 53°13'·99N 09°06'·51W Fl R 3s; PHM.

Tawin Shoals buoy 53°14'·29N 09°04'·22W Fl (3) G 10s; SHM.

Mutton Is buoy 53°15'·06N 09°02'·89W Fl (2)R 6s; PHM.

Peter Rk buoy 53°15'·15N 09°01'·07W; SCM.

Leverets 53°15'·32N 09°01'·87W Q WRG 9m 10M; B ● tr, W bands; vis G015°-058°, W058°-065°, R065°-103°, G103°-143·5°, W143·5°-146·5°, R146·5°-015°.

Rinmore 53°16'·11N 09°01'·93W Iso WRG 4s 7m 5M; W □ tr; vis G359°-008°, W008°-018°, R018°-027°.

Approach chan dir lt 325°, GWR, vis: FG 322¼°-323¾°, Al GW 3s 323¾°-324¾°, FW 324¾°-325¼°, Al RW 3s 325¼°-326¼°, FR 326¼°-331¼°, Fl R 3s 331¼°-332¼°.

Nimmo's pier hd 53°15'·99N 09°02'·77W Fl Y 2s 7m 7·2M.

Black Hd 53°09'·25N 09°15'·78W Fl WR 5s 20m W11M, R8M, W □ tr; vis 045°-268°, R268°-276°.

13

8.13.5   PASSAGE INFORMATION

For all Irish waters the Sailing Directions published by the Irish Cruising Club are strongly recommended, and particularly on the N and W coasts, where other information is scarce. They are published in 2 volumes: *E and N coasts of Ireland* which runs anti-clockwise from Carnsore Pt to Bloody Foreland, and *S and W coasts of Ireland* which goes clockwise.

CROSSING THE IRISH SEA (charts 1123, 1121, 1411)

Passages across the Irish Sea can range from the fairly long haul from Land's End to Cork (140M), to the relatively short hop from Mull of Kintyre to Torr Pt (11M). But such distances are deceptive, because the average cruising yacht needs to depart from and arrive at a reasonably secure hbr; also in the North Chan strong tidal streams can cause heavy overfalls. So each passage needs to be treated on its merits. See 8.0.9 for distances across the Irish Sea.

Many yachts use the Land's End/Cork route on their way to (and from) the delightful cruising ground along the S coast of Ireland, see 8.12.5. Penzance Bay, or one of the Scilly Is anchs, make a convenient place from which to leave, with good lights to assist departure.

Although the Celtic Sea is exposed to the Atlantic, there are no dangers on passage and the tidal streams are weak. A landfall between Ballycotton and Old Hd of Kinsale (RC) (both have good lights) presents no offlying dangers, and in poor vis decreasing soundings indicate approach to land. There is a likelihood, outward bound under sail, that the boat will be on the wind – a possible benefit on the return passage. If however the wind serves, and if it is intended to cruise along the southern coast, a landfall at the Fastnet with arrival at (say) Baltimore will place the yacht more to windward, for little extra distance.

From Land's End the other likely destination is Dun Laoghaire. A stop at (say) Milford Haven enables the skipper to select the best time for passing the Smalls or Bishops (see 8.11.5) and roughly divides the total passage into two equal parts. From S Bishop onwards there are the options of making the short crossing to Tuskar Rk and going N inside the banks (theoretically a good idea in strong W winds), or of keeping to seaward. But in bad weather the area off Tuskar is best avoided; apart from the Traffic Separation Scheme (8.12.14), the tide is strong at sp and the sea can be very rough.

The ferry route Holyhead/Dun Laoghaire is another typical crossing, and is relatively straightforward with easy landfalls either end. The tide runs hard round Anglesey at sp, so departure just before slack water minimises the set N or S. Beware also the TSS off The Skerries, see 8.10.22.

The Isle of Man (8.10.5) is a good centre for cruising in the Irish Sea, and its hbrs provide convenient staging points whether bound N/S or E/W.

CROSSING TO SCOTLAND (charts 2198, 2199, 2724)

Between Scotland and Northern Ireland there are several possible routes, but much depends on weather and tide. Time of departure must take full advantage of the stream, and avoid tide races and overfalls (see 8.9.5). Conditions can change quickly, so a flexible plan is needed.

From Belfast Lough ent, the passage distance to Mull of Kintyre is about 35M and, with a departure at HW Dover (also local HW) providing at least 6hrs of N-going tides, fair winds make it possible to get past the Mull or Sanda Is on one tide. But to be more confident of reaching Port Ellen or Gigha Is a departure from Carnlough or Red Bay at HW makes a shorter passage with better stream advantage. The inshore side of the TSS (8.13.12) coincides with the outer limit of the race S and SW off the Mull of Kintyre; this occurs between HW Dover + 0430 and + 0610 when a local S-going stream opposes the main N-going stream (8.9.12).
For information on submarine hazards see 6.9.1.

LAMBAY ISLAND TO FAIR HEAD (AC 44, 2093, 2198/9)

The coast is fairly steep-to except in larger bays, particularly Dundalk. Streams offshore run up to 2·5kn as far as Rockabill, but are weaker further N until approaching Belfast Lough. Lambay Island is private, and steep-to except on W side, where there can be overfalls. Skerries Islands (Colt, Shenick's and St Patrick's) are 1M E and SE of Red Island, to E of Skerries hbr. Shenick's Island is connected to shore at LW. Pass between Colt and St Patrick's Islands, but the latter has offliers 3ca to S. Rockabill, two steep-to rks with lt ho, is 2·5M E of St Patrick's Island.

Going NE from Carlingford Lough (8.13.8), after rounding Hellyhunter By, there are no offshore dangers until Strangford Lough (8.13.10). For Ardglass, see 8.13.9. N of Strangford keep 5ca off Ballyquintin Pt. 3M to NE are Butter Pladdy Rks; keep to E of these. 2M further N is South Rk, with disused lt ho, part of group of rks to be avoided in poor vis or bad weather by closing South Rk lt float. In good vis pass inshore of South Rk, between it and North Rks (chart 2156).

Three routes lead into Belfast Lough (8.13.11): **a**. E of Mew Is, but beware Ram Race (to the N on the ebb, and the S on the flood); **b**. Copeland Sound, between Mew Is and Copeland Is, is passable but not recommended; **c**. Donaghadee Sound is buoyed and a good short cut for yachts. Here the stream runs SSE from HW Belfast + 0530 and NW from HW Belfast – 0030, 4·5kn max. An eddy extends S to Ballyferris Pt, and about 1M offshore. For Donaghadee, see chart 3709.

N from Belfast Lough, Black Hd is clean. Pass E of Muck Is, which is steep-to. Hunter Rk (0·8m), 2·5M NE of Larne, is marked by N & S cardinals. 2M further N are the Maidens, two dangerous groups of rks extending 2·5M N/S; E Maiden is lit.

The very small hbr of Carnlough (8.13.12) provides shelter for small yachts, but should not be approached in strong onshore winds. Other anchs in offshore winds are at Red Bay (8.13.12) 5M further N, and in Cushendun B, 5M NNW of Garron Pt. All provide useful anch on passage to/from the Clyde or Western Is. Fair Hd is a bold 190m headland, steep-to all round, but with extensive overfalls in Rathlin Sound.

FAIR HEAD TO BLOODY FORELAND (chart 2723)

This is a good cruising area, under the lee of land in SW'lies, but very exposed to NW or N. Beware fishing boats and nets in many places and the North Channel TSS, see 8.13.12.

A fair tide is essential through Rathlin Sound (8.13.13), as sp rates reach 6kn, with dangerous overfalls. The main stream sets W from HW Dover +½ for 5 hrs, and E from HW Dover –5½ for 5 hrs. The worst overfalls are S of Rue Pt (Slough-na-more) from HW Dover +1½ to +2½, and it is best to enter W-bound at the end of this period, on the last of fair tide. E-bound enter the Sound at HW Dover –5. Close inshore between Fair Hd and Carrickmannanon Rk a counter eddy runs W from HW Dover –3, and an E-going eddy runs from HW Dover +2 to +3. Pass outside Carrickmannanon Rk (0·3m) and Sheep Is. There are small hbrs in Church Bay (Rathlin Is) and at Ballycastle.

Proceeding to Portrush (8.13.14), use Skerries Sound in good weather. Enter Lough Foyle by either the North Chan W of The Tuns, or S chan passing 2ca N of Magilligan Pt and allowing for set towards The Tuns on the ebb (up to 3·5kn).

Tor Rks, Inishtrahull and Garvan Isles lie NE and E of Malin Hd. In bad weather it is best to pass at least 3M N of Tor Rks. Inishtrahull is lit and about 1M long; rks extend N about 3ca into Tor Sound. Inishtrahull Sound, between Inishtrahull and Garvan Isles, is exposed; tidal streams up to 4kn sp can raise a dangerous sea with no warning. Stream also sets hard through Garvan Isles, S of which Garvan Sound can be passed safely in daylight avoiding two sunken rks, one 1½ca NE of Rossnabarton, and the other 5ca NW. The main stream runs W for only 3hrs, from HW Galway – 0500 to – 0200. W of Malin Hd a W-going eddy starts at HW Galway + 0400, and an E-going one at HW Galway – 0300.

W of Malin Head the direction of buoyage changes to E.

From Malin Head SW to Dunaff Head, at ent to Lough Swilly (8.13.17), keep 5ca offshore. Trawbreaga Lough (AC 2697) gives shelter, but is shallow, and sea can break on bar; only approach when no swell, and at half flood. Ent to L Swilly is clear except for Swilly Rks off the W shore, SSE of Fanad Hd.

W from Lough Swilly the coast is very foul. Beware Limeburner Rk (2m), 6·8M WNW of Fanad Hd. Mulroy Bay (8.13.17) has good anchs but needs accurate pilotage, as in *ICC SDs*.

Between Mulroy B and Sheephaven there is inshore passage S of Frenchman's Rk, and between Guill Rks and Carnabollion, safe in good weather; otherwise keep 1M offshore. Sheep Haven B (8.13.17) is easy to enter between Rinnafaghla Pt and Horn Hd, and has good anchs except in strong NW or N winds. Beware Wherryman Rks, dry 1·5m, 1ca off E shore.

Between Horn Hd and Bloody Foreland (chart 2752) are three low-lying islands: Inishbeg, Inishdooey and Inishbofin. The latter is almost part of the mainland; it has a temp anch on S side and a more sheltered anch on NE side in Toberglassan B. 6M offshore is Tory Is (lt, fog sig, RC) with rks for 5ca off SW side. Temp anch in good weather in Camusmore B. In Tory Sound the stream runs W from HW Galway + 0230, and E from HW Galway – 0530, sp rates 2kn.

BLOODY FORELAND TO EAGLE ISLAND (chart 2725)

Off low-lying Bloody Foreland (lt) there is often heavy swell. The coast and islands 15M SW to Aran Is give good cruising (chart 1883). An inshore passage avoids offlying dangers: Buniver and Brinlack shoals, which can break; Bullogconnell 1M NW of Gola Is; and Stag Rks 2M NNW of Owey Is. Anchs include Bunbeg and Gweedore hbr, and Cruit B which has easier access. Behind Aran Is are several good anchs. Use N ent, since S one is shallow (chart 2792). Rutland N Chan is main appr to Burtonport (8.13.17).

Boylagh B has shoals and rks N of Roaninish Is. Connell Rk (0·3m) is 1M N of Church Pool, a good anch, best approached from Dawros Hd 4·5M to W. On S side of Glen B a temp anch (but not in W or NW winds) is just E of Rinmeasa Pt. Rathlin O'Birne Is has steps E side; anch SE of them 100m offshore. Sound is 5ca wide; hold Is side to clear rks off Malin Beg Hd.

In Donegal B (chart 2702) beware uncharted rks W of Teelin, a good natural hbr but exposed to S/SW swell. Killybegs (8.13.18) has better shelter and is always accessible. Good shelter with fair access in Donegal Hbr (chart 2715). Good anch or ⚓ via YC at Mullaghmore in fair weather; sea state is calm with winds from SE through S to NW. Inishmurray is worth a visit in good weather, anch off S side. There are shoals close E and NE of the Is, and Bomore Rks 1·5M to N. Keep well clear of coast S to Sligo (8.13.19) in onshore winds, and watch for lobster pots.

Killala B has temp anch 1M S of Kilcummin Hd, on W side. Proceeding to Killala beware St Patrick's Rks. Ent has ldg lts and marks, but bar is dangerous in strong NE winds.

The coast W to Broadhaven is inhospitable. Only Belderg and Portacloy give a little shelter. Stag Rks are steep-to and high. Broadhaven (chart 2703) is good anch and refuge, but in N/NW gales sea can break in ent. In approaches beware Slugga Rk on E side with offlier, and Monastery Rk (0·3m) on S side.

EAGLE ISLAND TO SLYNE HEAD (chart 2420)

This coast has many inlets, some sheltered. Streams are weak offshore. There are few lights. Keep 5ca off Erris Hd, and further in bad weather. Unless calm, keep seaward of Eagle Is (lt, RC) where there is race to N. Frenchport (chart 2703) is good temp anch except in strong W winds. Inishkea Is (chart 2704) can be visited in good weather; anch N or S of Rusheen Is. On passage keep 5ca W of Inishkea to avoid bad seas if wind over tide. The sound off Mullett Peninsula is clear, but for Pluddany Rk 6ca E of Inishkea N.

Blacksod B (chart 2704 and 8.13.20) has easy ent (possible at night) and good shelter. In the approaches Black Rk (lt) has rks up to 1·25M SW. From N, in good weather, there is chan between Duvillaun Beg and Gaghta Is, but in W gales beware breakers 1M SE of Duvillaun More.

Rough water is likely off impressive Achill Hd. Achill Sound (chart 2667) is restricted by cables 11m high at swing bridge. Anchs each end of Sound, but the stream runs strongly.

Clare Is has Two Fathom Rk (3·4m) 5ca off NW coast, and Calliaghcrom Rk 5ca to the N; anch on NE side. In Clew Bay Newport and Westport (AC 2667, 2057 and 8.13.19) need detailed pilotage directions. S of Clare Is beware Meemore Shoal 1·5M W of Roonagh Hd. 2M further W is the isolated rk Mweelaun. The islands of Caher, Ballybeg, Inishturk (with anch on E side) and Inishdalla have few hidden dangers, but the coast to the E must be given a berth of 1·5M even in calm weather; in strong winds seas break much further offshore.

Killary B (chart 2706) and Little Killary both have good anchs in magnificent scenery. Consult sailing directions, and only approach in reasonable weather and good vis.

Ballynakill Hbr (chart 2706), easily entered either side of Freaghillaun South, has excellent shelter; Tully mountain is conspic to N. Beware Mullaghadrina and Ship Rk in N chan. Anch in Fahy, Derryinver or Barnaderg B. There is anch on S side of Inishbofin (lt), but difficult access/exit in strong SW wind or swell (8.13.20). Rks and breakers exist E of Inishbofin and S of Inishshark; see chart 2707 for clearing lines. Lecky Rks lie 1M SSE of Davillaun. Carrickmahoy is a very dangerous rk (1·9m) between Inishbofin and Cleggan Pt.

Cleggan B is moderate anch, open to NW but easy access. High Is Sound is usual coasting route, not Friar Is Sound or Aughrus Passage. Clifden B (chart 2708) has offlying dangers with breakers; enter 3ca S of Carrickrana Bn and anch off Drinagh Pt, in Clifden Hbr or Ardbear B; see 8.13.20.

Slyne Hd (lt, Racon) marks SW end of the rocks and islets stretching 2M WSW from coast. Here the stream turns N at HW Galway – 0320, and S at HW Galway + 0300. It runs 3kn at sp, and in bad weather causes a dangerous race; keep 2M offshore. Seas break on Barret Shoals, 3M NW of Slyne Hd.

SLYNE HEAD TO LISCANNOR BAY (chart 2173)

In good visibility the Connemara coast (charts 2709, 2096) and Aran Islands (chart 3339) give excellent cruising. But there are many rks, and few navigational marks. Between Slyne Head and Roundstone B are many offlying dangers. If coasting, keep well seaward of Skerd Rks. A conspic twr (24m) on Golan Head is a key feature. Going E the better hbrs are Roundstone B, Cashel B, Killeany B, Greatman B and Cashla B. Kilronan (Killeany B) on Inishmore is only reasonable hbr in Aran Islands, but is exposed in E winds. Disused lt ho on centre of island is conspic.

Normal approach to Galway B is through N Sound or S Sound. N Sound is 4M wide from Eagle Rk and other dangers off Lettermullan shore, to banks on S side which break in strong winds. S Sound is 3M wide, with no dangers except Finnis Rk (0·4m) 5ca SE of Inisheer. The other channels are Gregory Sound, 1M wide between Inishmore and Inishmaan, and Foul Sound between Inishmaan and Inisheer. The latter has one danger, Pipe Rk and the reef inshore of it, extending 3ca NW of Inisheer.

The N side of Galway Bay is exposed, with no shelter. Galway (8.13.21) is a commercial port, with possible marina plans. 3M SE, New Hbr (chart 1984) is a more pleasant anch with moorings off Galway Bay SC. Westward to Black Hd there are many bays and inlets, often poorly marked, but providing shelter and exploration. The coast SW to Liscannor Bay is devoid of shelter. O'Brien's Twr is conspic just N of the 199m high Cliffs of Moher.

13

8.13.6   DISTANCE TABLE

Approximate distances in nautical miles are by the most direct route, whilst avoiding dangers and allowing for Traffic Separation Schemes. Places in *italics* are in adjoining areas; places in **bold** are in 8.0.9, Distances across the Irish Sea.

1.	*Dun Laoghaire*	**1**																		
2.	**Carlingford Lough**	50	**2**																	
3.	**Strangford Lough**	71	36	**3**																
4.	**Bangor**	96	61	34	**4**															
5.	**Carrickfergus**	101	66	39	6	**5**														
6.	**Larne**	108	73	45	16	16	**6**													
7.	**Carnlough**	118	78	50	25	26	11	**7**												
8.	Altacarry Head	135	102	74	45	45	31	21	**8**											
9.	**Portrush**	150	115	87	58	60	48	35	19	**9**										
8.	**Lough Foyle**	157	121	92	72	73	55	47	30	11	**10**									
11.	L Swilly (Fahan)	200	166	138	109	104	96	81	65	48	42	**11**								
12.	**Tory Island**	209	174	146	117	113	105	90	74	57	51	35	**12**							
13.	Burtonport	218	182	153	130	130	116	108	90	74	68	49	18	**13**						
14.	Killybegs	267	232	204	175	171	163	148	132	115	109	93	58	43	**14**					
15.	Sligo	281	246	218	189	179	177	156	146	123	117	107	72	51	30	**15**				
16.	Eagle Island	297	262	234	205	198	193	175	162	147	136	123	88	72	62	59	**16**			
17.	Westport	337	323	295	266	249	240	226	207	193	187	168	137	120	108	100	57	**17**		
18.	Slyne Head	352	317	289	260	257	248	234	217	201	195	178	143	128	117	114	55	44	**18**	
19.	*Galway*	348	366	338	309	307	297	284	266	253	245	227	192	178	166	163	104	94	49	**19**
20.	*Kilrush*	318	361	364	335	332	323	309	291	276	270	251	220	203	191	183	142	119	75	76	**20**

8.13.7   Special Notes for Ireland: see 8.12.7

MINOR HARBOURS AND ANCHORAGES TO THE NORTH WEST OF LAMBAY ISLAND

SKERRIES, Dublin, 53°35'·1N 06°06'·66W. AC 633. Tides as Balbriggan, 8.13.8. E & SE of Red Island (a peninsula) lie Colt, Shenick's and St Patrick's Islands, the latter foul to S and SW. Inshore passage between Colt and St Patrick's Is uses transit/brg as on chart to clear dangers. Good shelter and holding in 3m at Skerries Bay, W of Red Is. Appr from E or NE outside PHM buoy, Fl R 10s, off Red Is. ‡ WNW of pier, Oc R 6s 7m 7M, vis 103°-154°; clear of moorings. Most facilities; Skerries SC ☎ 1-849 1233. Rockabill Lt, Fl WR 12s 45m 23/19M, is conspic 2·4M ExN of St Patrick's Is.

BALBRIGGAN, Dublin, 53°36'·8N 06°10'·7W. AC 1468, 44. Tides see 8.13.8. Good shelter in small hbr, dries about 0·9m, access approx HW ±2. Appr on SW, to open the outer hbr which is entered on SE; thence to inner hbr and AB on SE quay. Beware shoaling on both sides of outer hbr. Lt, Fl (3) WRG 20s 12m 13/10M, conspic W tr on E bkwtr head, vis G159°-193°, W193°-288°, R288°-305°. Facilities: FW, D, Gas, Slip, BH (9 ton), R, Bar, V. EC Thurs.

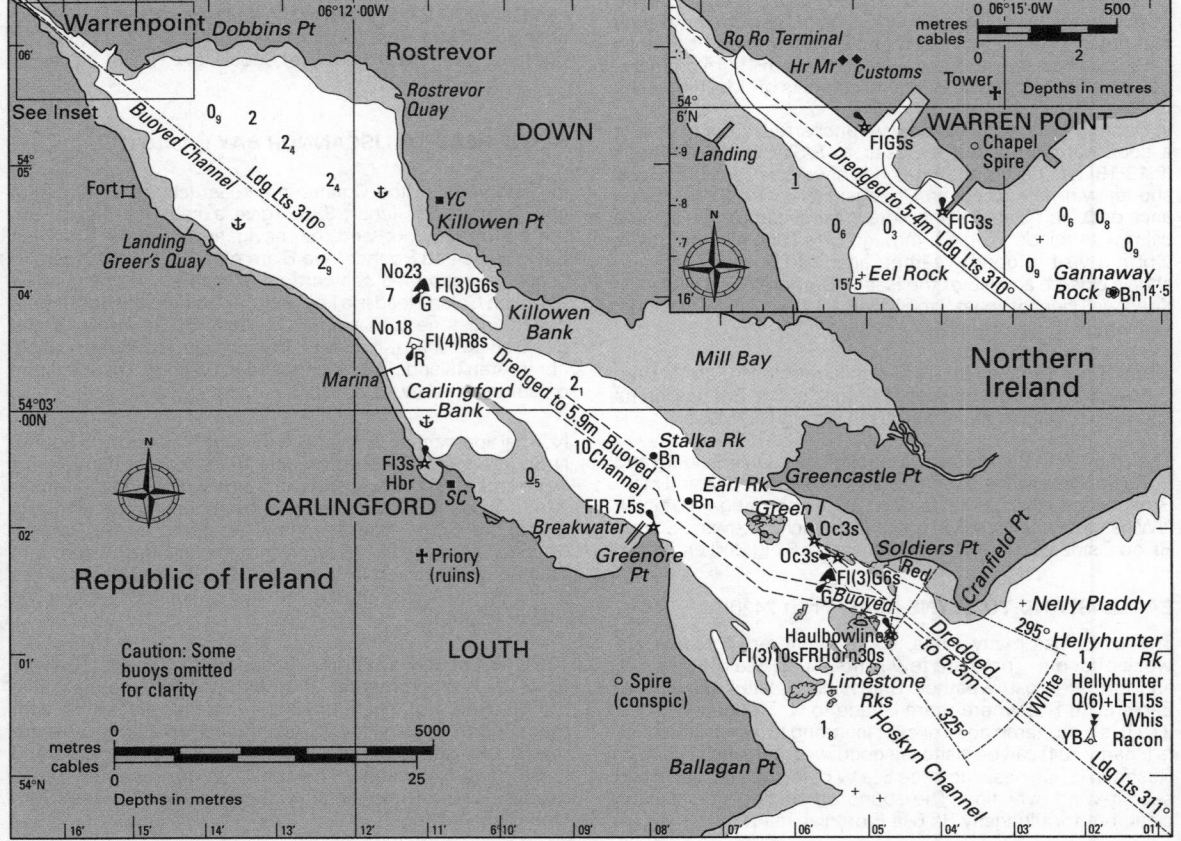

CARLINGFORD LOUGH   8-13-8

Louth/Down 54°01'·25N 06°04'·30W. Rtg (Warrenpoint) 2-3-2

CHARTS
AC 2800, 44; Imray C62; Irish OS 29, 36

TIDES
Cranfield Pt +0025 and Warrenpoint +0035 Dover; ML 2·9;
Duration Cranfield Pt 0615, Warrenpoint 0540; Zone 0 (UT)

Standard Port DUBLIN (NORTH WALL) (←—)

Times				Height (metres)			
High Water		Low Water		MHWS	MHWN	MLWN	MLWS
0000	0700	0000	0500	4·1	3·4	1·5	0·7
1200	1900	1200	1700				
Differences CRANFIELD POINT							
–0027	–0011	+0017	–0007	+0·7	+0·9	+0·3	+0·2
WARRENPOINT							
–0020	–0010	+0040	+0040	+1·0	+0·9	+0·1	+0·2
NEWRY (VICTORIA LOCK)							
–0010	–0010	+0040	Dries	+1·1	+1·0	+0·1	Dries
DUNDALK (SOLDIERS POINT)							
–0010	–0010	0000	+0045	+1·0	+0·8	+0·1	–0·1
DUNANY POINT							
–0028	–0018	–0008	–0006	+0·7	+0·9		No data
RIVER BOYNE BAR							
–0025	–0015	+0110	0000	+0·4	+0·3		No data
BALBRIGGAN							
–0021	–0015	+0010	+0002	+0·3	+0·2		No data

SHELTER
Good. Options clockwise from ent include: ‡ at Greenore Pt, between SW end of quay and bkwtr, in 3m clear of commercial tfc. Carlingford Hbr (dries 2·2m), AB at piers. Carlingford Marina (pontoons: 1·4m; max depth 3·5m), protected on S side by sunken barges; appr from NE to clear the tail of Carlingford Bank (dries). Nos 18 and 23 buoys, on 012° astern, lead to marina. ‡ off Greer's Quay in 2m. Warrenpoint has pontoons on NW side of bkwtr (Fl G 3s); access dredged 1·1m. Caution: much shipping in narrow chan dredged 5·4m, outside which the head of the lough is shallow. ‡s off Rostrevor Quay, Killowen Pt (YC) and off derelict pier at Greencastle Pt (beware rks).

NAVIGATION
WPT 54°00'·23N 06°02'·20W, (abeam Hellyhunter SCM lt buoy) 131°/311° from/to first chan buoys, 1·1M. The main chan is Carlingford Cut (6·3m), about 3ca SW of Cranfield Pt, and passing 2ca NE of Haulbowline lt ho. Drying rks and shoals obstruct most of the ent. The lough becomes choppy in S winds and the ent is impassable in on-shore winds. Tides run up to 5kn off Greenore Pt and entry is impracticable against the ebb. Beware sudden squalls and waterspouts. Note: The NE bank is Ulster, SW bank is the Republic of Ireland. Yachts may be stopped by Naval vessels.

LIGHTS AND MARKS
Haulbowline Fl (3) 10s 32m 17M; granite tr; also turning lt FR 21m 9M, vis 196°-208°, horn 30s. Ldg lts 310°26': both Oc 3s 7/12m 11M, vis 295°-325°; R △ front, ▽ rear, on framework trs. Greenore Pier Fl R 7·5s 10m 5M. Newry R: Ldg lts 310°, both Iso 4s 5/15m 2M, stone columns.

RADIO TELEPHONE
Greenore (*Ferry Greenore*) Ch 12 16 (HJ). Carlingford marina Ch M 16. Warrenpoint Ch 12 16 (H24); call Ch 12 at By No. 23 to enter dredged chan. Dundalk Ch 14 16 (HW±3).

TELEPHONE
(Dial code Greenore/Carlingford 042; Warrenpoint 016937). Hr Mr Warrenpoint 73381, ⛴ 73962; MRCC (01) 6620922/3 or (01247) 463933; ✉ (01232) 358250; Irish ✉, Dundalk (042) 34114; Marinecall 0891 500 465; Dr (042) 73110; Ⓗ Newry 65511, (042) 34701; Police (042) 73102, (016937) 722222.

FACILITIES
Carlingford Marina (50 + 30 ⚓s), ☎/⛴ 73492, £9.10, AC, D, FW, P, C, CH, Divers, Slip. **Hbr** AB, Slip; **Village** V, R, Bar, ✉. **Carlingford YC** ☎ 38604, Slip, Bar, M, V, FW; **Dundalk SC** FW, Slip; **Services:** ME, El, Sh, Kos, Gas. **Warrenpoint** EC Wed; AB, M (but no access at LW), FW, P, D, ✉ (also at Rostrevor, Carlingford), Ⓑ (also Dundalk), ⇌ (Dundalk, Newry), ✈ (Dublin).

MINOR HARBOURS BETWEEN CARLINGFORD LOUGH AND ST. JOHN'S POINT

KILKEEL, Down, 54°03'·47N 05°59'·26W. AC 2800, 44. HW +0015 on Dover; ML 2·9m; Duration 0620. See 8.13.9. Inner basin is completely sheltered, but gets crowded by FVs; depth off quays approx 1m. Secure in inner basin and see Hr Mr. There are drying banks both sides of ent chan and SW gales cause a sandbank right across ent. This is dredged or slowly eroded in E winds. S bkwtr lt Fl WR 2s 8m 8M, R296°-313°, W313°-017°, storm sigs. Meeney's pier (N bkwtr) Fl G 3s 6m 2M. VHF Ch 12 14 16 (Mon-Fri: 0900-2000). Hr Mr ☎ (016937) 62287; ✉ (01232) 358250 or 62158; Facilities: FW on quay, BY (between fish market and dock), El, ME, Sh, Slip. **Town** (¾M) EC Thurs; Bar, ✉, R, V, Gas, Ⓖ.

ANNALONG HBR, Down, 54°06'·50N 05°53'·65W. AC 44. Tides as Kilkeel, see 8.13.9. Excellent shelter in small drying hbr, approx 2m from HW±3. Appr in W sector of S bkwtr lt, Oc WRG 5s 8m 9M, vis G204°-249°, W249°-309°, R309°-024°. Hug N side of the bkwtr to avoid rky shore to stbd. 40m beyond a spur on N side, turn hard port into the basin; berth as available. Caution: many warps are rigged across hbr. Surge gate at hbr ent may be closed in SE winds. Facilities: V, Bar, ✉.

DUNDRUM BAY, Down. AC 44. Tides see 8.13.9. This 8M wide bay to the W of St John's Pt is shoal to 5ca offshore and unsafe in onshore winds. The small drying hbr at **Newcastle** (54°11'·8N 05°53'·0W) is for occas use in fair weather. Hr Mr ☎ (013967) 22106.
Dundrum Hbr (54°14'·2N 05°49'·4W) provides ‡ in 2m for shoal draft; the bar carries about 0·3m. A steep sea can run at the bar in onshore winds. HW Dundrum is approx that of HW Liverpool; see also 8.13.9 Newcastle. ICC SDs are essential for the 1M long, buoyed appr chan. 3 unlit DZ buoys offshore are part of the Ballykinler firing range, 2M E of hbr; R flag/lts indicate range active.

13

NEW BELFAST AND N IRELAND DIALLING CODES

New dialling codes for **Belfast** and **N Ireland** will be introduced from summer 1999 and can be fully used from 22 April 2000. A single new code 028, plus 2 or 3 digits, replaces the present codes. The present codes can however be used in parallel with the new until April 2001. From April 2001 it will be optional to use 028 for calls within N Ireland. Local numbers will all become 8 digits instead of the present mix of 5 and 6 digit numbers. Thus in Belfast, for example, existing 01232 926222 will become 028 **9092** 6222.

Old and new codes/numbers for harbours in this Almanac, are given below, anti-clockwise from the S.

Area	Old Code & No.	New Code & No.	
Warrenpoint	016937 73381	028	**4177** 3381
Newcastle	013967 22106	028	**4372** 2106
Downpatrick	01396 841292	028	**4484** 1292
Portavogie	012477 71470	028	**4277** 1470
Belfast City	01232 428041	028	**9042** 8041
Bangor	01247 453450	028	**9145** 3450
Carrickfergus	01960 366666	028	**9336** 6666
Larne	01574 279221	028	**2827** 9221
Ballycastle	012657 62226	028	**2076** 2226
Portrush	01265 822307	028	**7082** 2307
Coleraine	01265 42012	028	**7034** 2012
Londonderry	01504 860555	028	**7186** 0555

ARDGLASS   8-13-9

Down 54°15'·63N 05°35'·96W   Rtg 1-3-2

CHARTS
AC 633, 2093; Imray C62; Irish OS 21
TIDES
HW +0025 Dover; ML 3·0; Duration 0620; Zone 0 (UT)

Standard Port BELFAST (→)

Times				Height (metres)			
High Water		Low Water		MHWS	MHWN	MLWN	MLWS
0100	0700	0000	0600	3·5	3·0	1·1	0·4
1300	1900	1200	1800				
Differences KILKEEL							
+0040	+0030	+0010	+0010	+1·2	+1·1	+0·4	+0·4
NEWCASTLE							
+0025	+0035	+0020	+0040	+1·6	+1·1	+0·4	+0·1
KILLOUGH HARBOUR							
0000	+0020	No data		+1·8	+1·6	No data	
ARDGLASS							
+0010	+0015	+0005	+0010	+1·7	+1·2	+0·6	+0·3

SHELTER
Good, except in strong E/S winds. Phennick Cove marina is on W side of hbr, with depths 1·0m to 2·8m. The busy fishing port is in South Hbr, with quays (2·1m) on inside of extended S pier. At NW end of hbr, old drying N Dock is also used by FVs. If marina full, ⌱ clear of FVs in S Hbr.
NAVIGATION
WPT 54°15'·30N 05°35'·32W, 311°/131° from/to hbr ent, 5ca. Appr 311° in W sector of WRG Dir lt. Depth in chan 2·4m. The inner bkwtr is marked by an ECM buoy, VQ (3) 5s. The chan into the marina is marked by Nos 2 & 4 PHM buoys, QR & Fl R 4s; and by Nos 3 & 5 SHM buoys, QG and Fl G 3s. The drying SW part of inner bkwtr, marked by two unlit perches, should not be crossed.
LIGHTS AND MARKS
Dir lt, 311°, conspic W tr at inner hbr, Iso WRG 4s 10m 8/7/5M, G shore-308°, W308°-314°, R314° -shore. S bkwtr Fl R 3s 10m 5M. W roof of shed on S bkwtr is conspic. If entering S Hbr, avoid Churn Rk, unlit SCM bn.
RADIO TELEPHONE
Hbr VHF Ch 12 14 16. Marina Ch M, 80.
TELEPHONE (Dial code 01396)
Hr Mr 841291; MRSC (01247) 463933; ⌗ (01232) 358250; Marinecall 0891 500 465; Police 841202; Dr 841242.
FACILITIES
Marina (55, inc 20 Ⓥ), ☎/🛢 842332, £12, AC, FW.
Town P & D (cans), Bar, ✉, R, V, Gas.

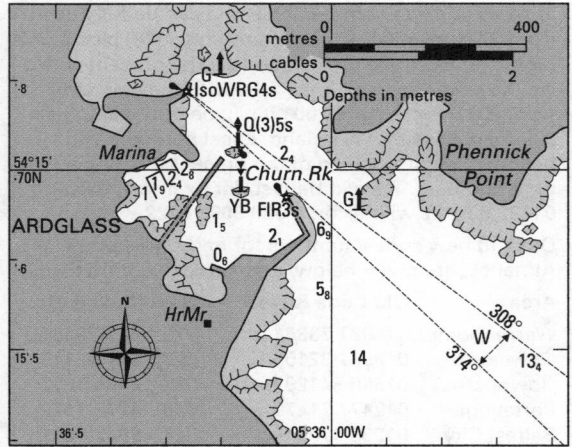

STRANGFORD LOUGH   8-13-10

Down 54°19'·33N 05°30'·85W   Rtg (Narrows) 3-4-1

CHARTS
AC 2159, 2156; Imray C62; Irish OS 21
TIDES
Killard Pt 0000, Strangford Quay +0200 Dover; ML 2·0; Duration 0610; Zone 0 (UT)

Standard Port BELFAST (→)

Times				Height (metres)			
High Water		Low Water		MHWS	MHWN	MLWN	MLWS
0100	0700	0000	0600	3·5	3·0	1·1	0·4
1300	1900	1200	1800				
Differences STRANGFORD							
+0147	+0157	+0148	+0208	+0·1	+0·1	−0·2	0·0
KILLARD POINT							
+0011	+0021	+0005	+0025	+1·0	+0·8	+0·1	+0·1
QUOILE BARRIER							
+0150	+0200	+0150	+0300	+0·2	+0·2	−0·3	−0·1
KILLYLEAGH							
+0157	+0207	+0211	+0231	+0·3	+0·3	No data	
SOUTH ROCK							
+0023	+0023	+0025	+0025	+1·0	+0·8	+0·1	+0·1
PORTAVOGIE							
+0010	+0020	+0010	+0020	+1·2	+0·9	+0·3	+0·2

SHELTER
Excellent, largest inlet on E coast. Good ⌱s in the Narrows at Cross Roads; in Strangford Creek (NW of Swan Island, which is marked by 3 lt bns to S, E and N); in Audley Rds and Ballyhenry Bay. 3 🅐s at Strangford; AB on piers depends on state of tide. Portaferry has a small marina. Many good ⌱s and some 🅐s up the lough, by villages and YCs; dues, if applicable, are seldom collected.
NAVIGATION
WPT Strangford Fairway SWM buoy, L Fl 10s, Whis, 54°18'·62N 05°28'·62W, 126°/306° from/to Angus Rk lt tr, 2·05M. Strangers should use the E Chan. Beware St Patricks Rk, Bar Pladdy and Pladdy Lug; also overfalls in the SE apprs and at the bar, which can be dangerous when ebb from narrows is running against strong E to SSW winds. During flood the bar presents no special problem, but preferably enter on the young flood or when tide in the Narrows is slack. Strong (up to 7kn at sp) tidal streams flow through the Narrows. Tidal flow in Narrows, and hence the overfalls, relates to HW Strangford Quay (+0200 Dover) not to Killard Pt (0000). Beware car ferry plying from Strangford, S and E of Swan Is, to Portaferry. Swan Island, seen as agrassy mound at HW, is edged with rks and a reef extends 32m E ending at W bn, Fl (2) WR 6s.
Further up the lough, AC 2156 is essential; pladdies are drying patches, often un-marked.
LIGHTS AND MARKS
See chartlet. Ent identified by Fairway buoy (SWM), W tr on Angus Rk, Pladdy Lug bn (W), Bar Pladdy SCM lt buoy and St Patrick's Rock perch. From NE, St Patrick's Rock perch on with Guns Island obelisk 224° clears Quintin Rk.
RADIO TELEPHONE
Strangford FerryTerminal Ch 12 14 16 M (Mon-Fri 0900-1700LT). In Strangford Lough most YCs and Riordan Marine: Ch 80 M.
TELEPHONE (Dial code 01396, or as shown)
Hr Mr 881637; MRSC (01247) 463933; ⌗ (01232) 358250; Marinecall 0891 500 465; Police 615011; Medical Clinic 313016; Casualty 613311.
FACILITIES
STRANGFORD: AB £10, 3 🅐s SE of Swan Is, FW, EI, Ⓔ, Sh, D (cans), V, R, Bar, ✉.
PORTAFERRY: **Boatpark** £10, Gas, Gaz, P & D (cans), V, R, Bar, ✉, Ⓑ. **Cook St Pier** (2½ca S) has limited AB, FW.
QUOILE RIVER: **Quoile YC** ☎ 612266. AB, M, Slip, FW.
KILLYLEAGH: M, P & D (cans), L, CH, V, Gas, Gaz, Kos, R, Ⓑ, Bar, ✉; **Killyleagh YC** marina planned; N of village, **East Down YC** ☎ 828375, AB.
RINGHADDY QUAY: CC, M, AB drying, FW, Slip.
SKETRICK ISLAND: To the SW in White Rk B, **Strangford Lough YC**, ☎ (01238) 541202, L, AB, FW, BY, CH, R, Bar. To the NW, **Down CC**, FW, D, Bar, SM (Irish Spars & Rigging ☎ 01238 541727).
KIRCUBBIN: Gas, P & D (cans), Ⓑ, R, Bar, V, ✉.

STRANGFORD LOUGH *continued*

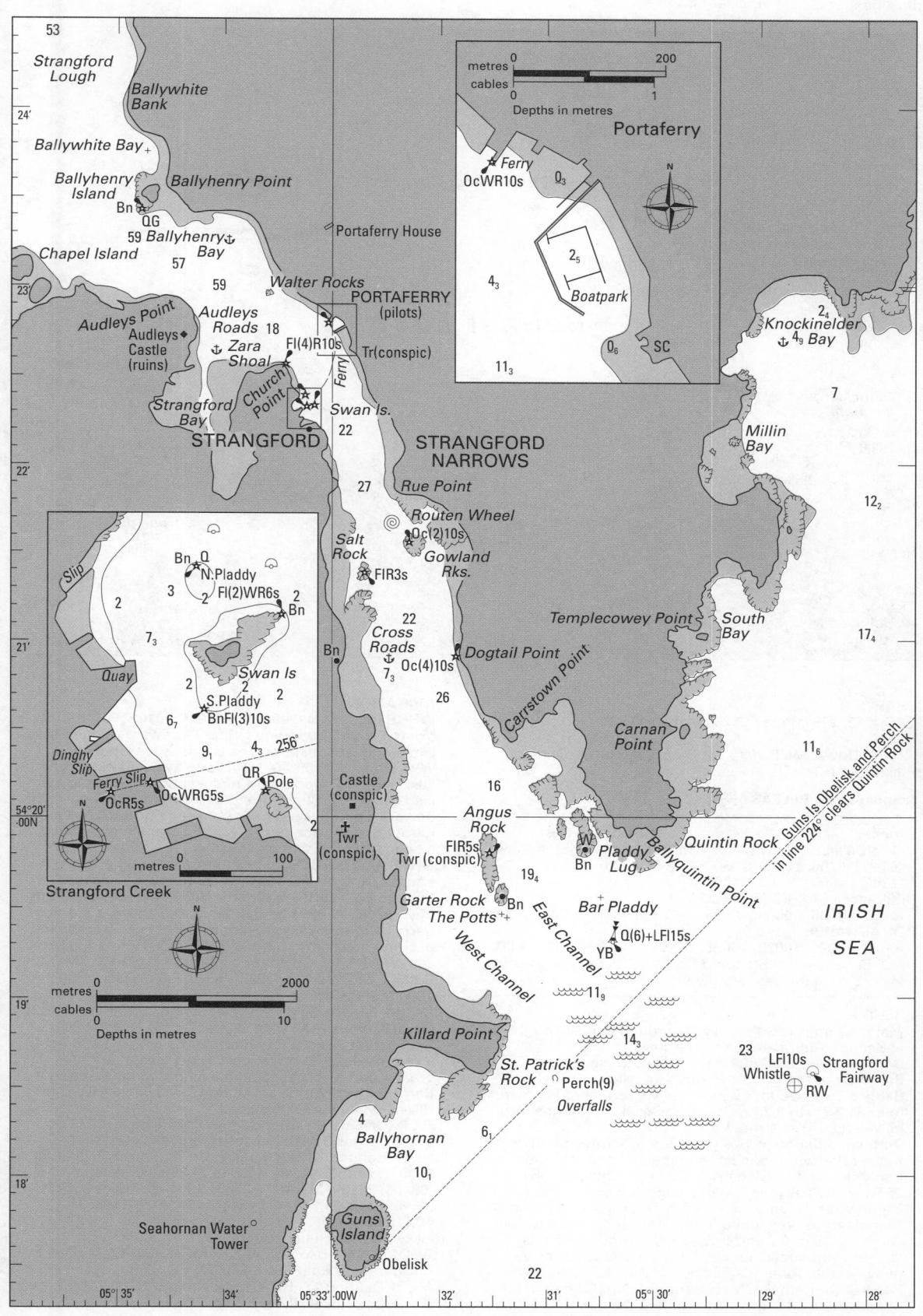

53

Strangford
Lough

Ballywhite
Bank

24'

Ballywhite Bay +

Ballyhenry
Island

Bn

QG

Ballyhenry Point

59 Ballyhenry
Bay

Chapel Island

57

23'

59

Audleys Point

Audleys
Roads

Audleys ◆
Castle
(ruins)

Zara
Shoal

Walter Rocks

PORTAFERRY
(pilots)

Fl(4)R10s

Tr(conspic)

Strangford
Bay

Church
Point

STRANGFORD

Swan Is.

22'

18

22

STRANGFORD
NARROWS

27

Rue Point

Routen Wheel

Oc(2)10s

Salt
Rock

FlR3s

Gowland
Rks.

Bn Q

N.Pladdy

Fl(2)WR6s

Bn

2

3

2

7₃

Slip

2

Quay

2

Swan Is

2

S.Pladdy

2

BnFl(3)10s

6₇

9₁

Dinghy
Slip

Ferry Slip

OcR5s

OcWRG5s

QR

Pole

4₃ 256°

Strangford Creek

metres 0   100

Cross
Roads

Oc(4)10s

Bn

22

7₃

Dogtail Point

26

Carrstown Point

Templecowey Point

South
Bay

16

Castle
(conspic)

Twr
(conspic)

Angus
Rock

FlR5s

Twr (conspic)

Garter Rock
The Potts ++

West Channel

East Channel

19₄

W
Bn

Pladdy
Lug

Bar Pladdy

YB Q(6)+LFl15s

Carnan
Point

Quintin Rock

Ballyquintin Point

IRISH
SEA

Killard Point

11₉

14₃

metres 0   2000

cables 0   10

Depths in metres

19'

St. Patrick's
Rock

Perch(9)

Overfalls

4

Ballyhornan
Bay

10₁

6₁

23 LFl10s
Whistle Strangford
RW Fairway

Seahornan Water °
Tower

18'

Guns
Island

Obelisk

22

05° 35'   34'   05°33'·00W   32'   31'   05° 30'   29'   28'

54°20'
·00N

Portaferry inset:

metres 0   200

cables 0   1

Depths in metres

Portaferry

Ferry
OcWR10s

Q₃

N

2₅

Boatpark

4₃

11₃

Q₆

SC

Knockinelder
4₉ Bay

Millin
Bay

12₂

7

17₄

11₆

Guns Is Obelisk and Perch
in line 224° clears Quintin Rock

13

BELFAST LOUGH   8-13-11
County Down and County Antrim 54°42'N 05°45'W
Rtgs: Bangor 2-2-2; Carrickfergus 2-2-2

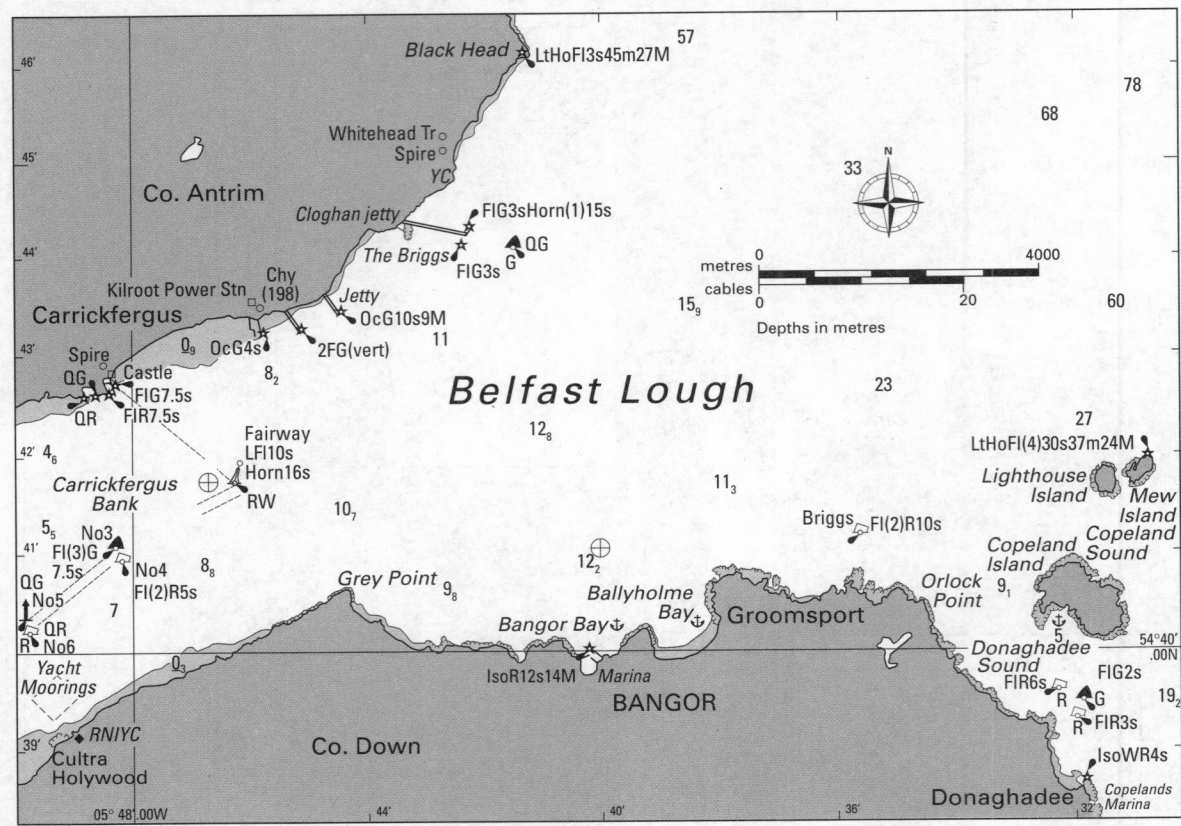

CHARTS
AC 1753, 2198; Imray C62, C64; Irish OS 15

TIDES
+0007 Dover; ML Belfast 2·0, Carrickfergus 1·8; Duration 0620; Zone 0 (UT)

Standard Port BELFAST (→)

Times				Height (metres)			
High Water		Low Water		MHWS	MHWN	MLWN	MLWS
0100	0700	0000	0600	3·5	3·0	1·1	0·4
1300	900	1200	1800				
Differences CARRICKFERGUS							
+0005	+0005	+0005	+0005	–0·3	–0·3	–0·2	–0·1
DONAGHADEE							
+0020	+0020	+0023	+0023	+0·5	+0·4	0·0	+0·1

NOTE: Belfast is a Standard Port and tidal predictions for every day of the year are given below.

SHELTER
Main sailing centres, clockwise around Belfast Lough, are at Bangor, Cultra and Carrickfergus.
Donaghadee: small marina at SE ent to the Lough.
Ballyholme Bay: good ‡ in offshore winds.
Bangor: exposed to N winds, but well sheltered in marina (depths 2·9m to 2·2m). Speed limits: 4kn in marina, 8kn between Luke's Pt and Wilson's Pt.
Cultra: in offshore winds good ‡ & moorings off RNoIYC.
Belfast Harbour is a major commercial port, but there are pontoons on the NW bank at Donegall Quay (54°36'·16N 05°55'·20W) between Lagan Bridge, 8m clearance, and Lagan Weir. To enter call *Belfast Port Control* VHF Ch **12**.
Carrickfergus: very good in marina, depths 1·9m to 2·4m. Good ‡ SSE of Carrickfergus Pier, except in E winds. The former commercial hbr has 10 yacht berths on the W quay. A stub bkwtr, marked by 2 PHM bns, extends NNE into the hbr from the W pier. The ent and SW part of the hbr are dredged 2·4m; the NE part of the hbr dries 0·7m.

NAVIGATION
WPT Bangor 54°41'·00N 05°40'·00W, 010°/190° from/to bkwtr lt, 1·0M. Rounding Orlock Pt beware Briggs Rocks extending ¾M offshore. The Lough is well marked.
WPT 54°41'·71N 05°46'·16W, Fairway SWM buoy, L Fl 10s, Horn 16s, marks start of the chan to Belfast Hbr. It also bears 121°/301° from/to Carrickfergus marina, 1.7M. Beware a drying sand bank between Carrickfergus and Kilroot Pt up to 4ca offshore; and Carrickfergus Bank extends 1·5M SSW from the hbr.

LIGHTS AND MARKS
Bangor Dir Oc WRG 10s lt; W sector 105° leads into ent. Chan to Belfast Hbr is well marked/lit by buoys and bns. Beyond No 12 PHM bn it is dangerous to leave the chan. Carrickfergus is easily recognised by conspic castle to E of commercial port; marina is close W. On marina bkwtr, 30m W of the ☆ QR 7m 3M, a Dir lt, F WRG 5m 3M, (H24), G308°-317½°, W317½°-322½°, R322½°-332°, leads 320°.

RADIO TELEPHONE
Bangor Marina Ch **80** M (H24); Bangor Hr Mr Ch 11 (H24). Royal N of Ireland YC (at Cultra) Ch **16**; 11 (H24) 80. *Belfast Port Control* (at Milewater Basin) Ch **12** 16 (H24); VTS provides info on request to vessels in port area. The greater part of Belfast Lough is under radar surveillance. Carrickfergus Marina Ch M. Hbr Ch 12 14 16 (HW–3 to HW+1, when vessel expected).

TELEPHONE (Dial codes: Bangor 01247; Belfast 01232; Carrickfergus 01960; but see new codes opposite)
Hr Mr Bangor (01247) 453297; Hr Mr Belfast 553011/☎ 553017; MRSC (01247) 463933; ⌗ 358250; Weather (08494) 22339; Marinecall 0891 500 465; Police 558411, (01960) 362021, (01247) 454444; Dr (01247)468521.

FACILITIES
Clockwise around the Lough:
GROOMSPORT BAY (01247): Hr Mr ☎ 464733, M, Slip, FW; **Cockle Island Boat Club**, Slip, M, FW, L, R.
BALLYHOLME BAY (01247): **Ballyholme YC** ☎ 271467, two ⚓s, R, Bar; **Royal Ulster YC** ☎ 270568, M, R, Bar.

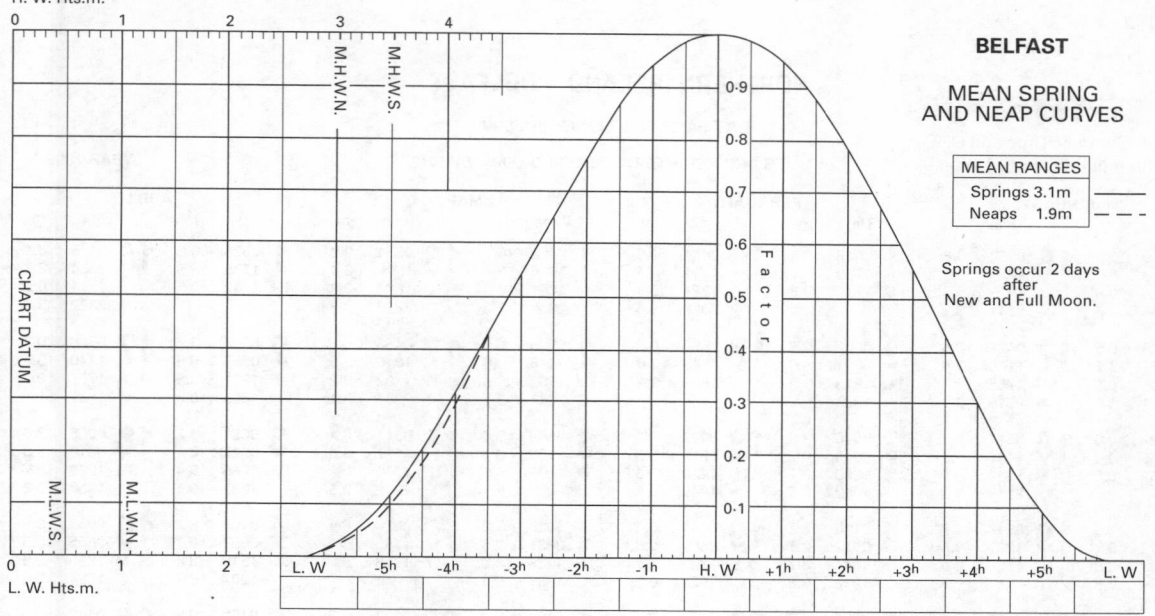

H. W. Hts.m.

BELFAST

MEAN SPRING
AND NEAP CURVES

MEAN RANGES	
Springs 3.1m	—
Neaps 1.9m	- - -

Springs occur 2 days
after
New and Full Moon.

CHART DATUM

M.H.W.N.   M.H.W.S.

Factor

M.L.W.S.   M.L.W.N.

L. W   -5h -4h -3h -2h -1h H. W +1h +2h +3h +4h +5h L. W

L. W. Hts.m.

NEW BELFAST AND N IRELAND DIALLING CODES

New **Belfast** and **N Ireland** dialling codes will be introduced in 1999. They can be used in parallel with the existing code for at least a year. The new code 028, plus 2 or 3 digits, replaces the present codes. Thus in Belfast, for example, existing 01232 926222 becomes 028 90 926222. For codes which affect other ports and harbours in this Almanac, see page 595.

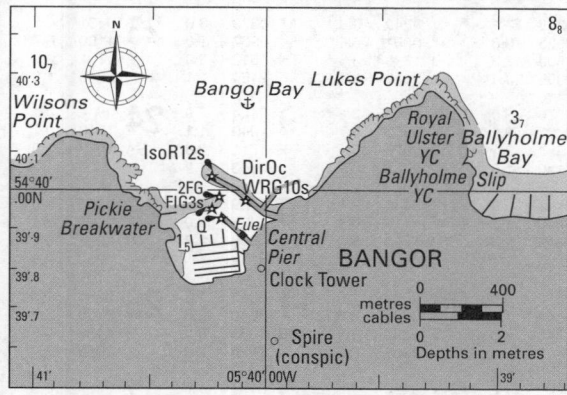

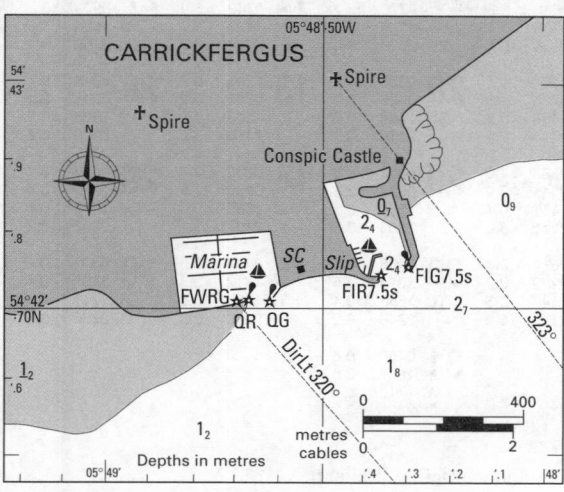

BANGOR (01247): **Bangor Marina** (560 + 40 Ⓥ) ☎ 453297, 📠 453450, £12.74 (£3 for 4 hrs), FW, AC, P, D, C, CH, BH (40 ton), ME, EI, Ⓔ, Sh, Gas, Gaz, Slip, SM, V, ◻; **Todd Chart Agency** ☎ 466640, 📠 471070 ACA, CH. **Services:** BY, Diving, Gas, ME, EI, Sh. **Town** EC Thurs; V, R, Bar, ✉, Ⓑ, ⇌, ✈ (Belfast).

CULTRA (01232): **Royal North of Ireland YC**, ☎ 428041, M, L, AB, FW, Slip, P (½M), D, R, Bar. **Services:** ME, EI, Sh; **Town** P, CH, V, R, Bar, ✉, Ⓑ, ⇌, ✈.

BELFAST (01232): River manager ☎ 315304, AB, P, D, FW, ME, EI, Sh, CH, C (200 ton), SM, Gas. **City** EC Wed; all facilities, ⇌, ✈.

CARRICKFERGUS (01960): **Marina** (270+30 Ⓥ) ☎ 366666, £16.10, AC, FW, EI, Sh; **Hbr** (marina extension) 10 AB, D, BH (45 ton). **Carrick SC** ☎ 351402, M, L, FW, C, AB; **Services:** Gas, Rigging, ME, EI, Sh, Ⓔ. **Town** EC Wed; V, R, Ⓑ, ✉, ⇌, ✈ (Belfast).

MINOR HARBOURS BETWEEN STRANGFORD AND BELFAST LOUGHS

PORTAVOGIE, Down, 54°27′·45N 05°26′·08W. Rtg 3-4-3. AC 2156. HW +0016 on Dover; ML 2·6m; Duration 0620. See 8.13.10. Good shelter, but hbr so full of FVs as to risk damage; best only for overnight or emergency. Entrance dangerous in strong onshore winds. Beware Plough Rks to SE marked by PHM buoy, Fl (2) R 10s, and McCammon Rks to NE of ent. Keep in W sector of outer bkwtr lt, Iso WRG 5s 9m 9M, G shore–258°, W258°–275°, R275°–348°. Inner bkwtr 2 FG (vert) 6m 4M. VHF Ch 12 14 16 (Mon-Fri: 0900-1700LT). Hr Mr ☎ (012477) 71470. Facilities: Slip, FW (on central quay) Sh, ME, EI. **Town** EC Thurs; CH, D & P (cans), ✉, R, Gas, V. No licensed premises.

DONAGHADEE, Down, 54°38′·71N 05°31′·85W. Rtg 4-4-1. AC 3709, 1753. HW +0025 on Dover; see 8.13.11; ML no data; Duration 0615. Excellent shelter and basic facilities in tiny marina, access HW±4 over sill; covers approx 1.1m at half tide. Appr on about 275° on ldg marks, orange △s to tricky ent with sharp 90° port turn into marina (pilots available). Appr in strong winds or at night not advised. 3ca to the N, the Old Hbr is small and very full; scend often sets in. Beware rky reef with less than 2m extends 1·5ca ENE from S pier hd. Max depth in hbr is approx 2·5m, dries at SW end; best berth alongside SE quay. S pier lt, Iso WR 4s 17m 18/14M, W shore–326°, R326°–shore. Hr Mr ☎ (01247) 882377. Police 882526. Facilities: **Copelands Marina** ☎ 882184; VHF Ch **16** 11 80; AB for 6 Ⓥ, FW, D, AC, C (20 ton). **Old Hbr** AB £4. **Town** Bar, D, P, Gas, ✉, R, V, Ⓑ, ⇌ (Bangor), ✈ (Belfast).

13

TIME ZONE (UT)
For Summer Time add ONE hour in non-shaded areas

NORTHERN IRELAND – BELFAST

LAT 54°36′N   LONG 5°55′W

TIMES AND HEIGHTS OF HIGH AND LOW WATERS   YEAR **1999**

JANUARY

Day	Time	m	Day	Time	m
1 F	0350 / 1008 / 1616 / 2233	0.6 / 3.6 / 0.6 / 3.5	16 SA	0353 / 1029 / 1627 / 2241	0.8 / 3.3 / 0.6 / 3.2
2 SA O	0440 / 1057 / 1705 / 2324	0.6 / 3.7 / 0.5 / 3.5	17 SU ●	0432 / 1105 / 1705 / 2316	0.8 / 3.4 / 0.7 / 3.3
3 SU	0527 / 1145 / 1752	0.6 / 3.8 / 0.5	18 M	0511 / 1137 / 1742 / 2348	0.7 / 3.5 / 0.6 / 3.3
4 M	0013 / 0612 / 1232 / 1836	3.5 / 0.7 / 3.8 / 0.5	19 TU	0549 / 1207 / 1820	0.7 / 3.5 / 0.6
5 TU	0101 / 0657 / 1318 / 1920	3.4 / 0.7 / 3.8 / 0.5	20 W	0023 / 0627 / 1242 / 1858	3.3 / 0.7 / 3.6 / 0.6
6 W	0148 / 0741 / 1403 / 2003	3.3 / 0.8 / 3.7 / 0.6	21 TH	0104 / 0707 / 1322 / 1938	3.3 / 0.6 / 3.6 / 0.5
7 TH	0235 / 0826 / 1449 / 2048	3.2 / 0.9 / 3.6 / 0.7	22 F	0149 / 0750 / 1406 / 2023	3.3 / 0.7 / 3.6 / 0.5
8 F	0322 / 0914 / 1536 / 2137	3.1 / 1.0 / 3.5 / 0.8	23 SA	0238 / 0838 / 1455 / 2113	3.3 / 0.7 / 3.6 / 0.6
9 SA	0411 / 1007 / 1625 / 2231	3.0 / 1.1 / 3.3 / 0.9	24 SU	0332 / 0930 / 1549 / 2209	3.2 / 0.8 / 3.5 / 0.7
10 SU	0503 / 1108 / 1717 / 2330	2.9 / 1.2 / 3.2 / 1.0	25 M	0430 / 1028 / 1650 / 2315	3.1 / 0.9 / 3.3 / 0.8
11 M	0601 / 1214 / 1815	2.8 / 1.2 / 3.0	26 TU	0534 / 1138 / 1800	3.1 / 1.0 / 3.2
12 TU	0034 / 0707 / 1319 / 1920	1.1 / 2.9 / 1.2 / 3.0	27 W	0033 / 0647 / 1303 / 1919	0.9 / 3.1 / 1.0 / 3.2
13 W	0135 / 0812 / 1417 / 2024	1.1 / 3.0 / 1.0 / 3.0	28 TH	0148 / 0801 / 1416 / 2033	0.9 / 3.2 / 0.9 / 3.2
14 TH	0227 / 0904 / 1505 / 2117	1.0 / 3.1 / 1.0 / 3.0	29 F	0249 / 0903 / 1517 / 2135	0.8 / 3.4 / 0.8 / 3.3
15 F	0312 / 0949 / 1548 / 2201	0.9 / 3.2 / 0.9 / 3.2	30 SA	0343 / 0958 / 1611 / 2228	0.7 / 3.5 / 0.6 / 3.4
			31 SU O	0432 / 1047 / 1700 / 2317	0.6 / 3.7 / 0.5 / 3.4

FEBRUARY

Day	Time	m	Day	Time	m
1 M	0518 / 1133 / 1745	0.6 / 3.7 / 0.5	16 TU ●	0454 / 1111 / 1724 / 2328	0.6 / 3.5 / 0.4 / 3.3
2 TU	0002 / 0601 / 1218 / 1825	3.3 / 0.6 / 3.8 / 0.5	17 W	0532 / 1143 / 1802	0.5 / 3.6 / 0.3
3 W	0046 / 0640 / 1300 / 1902	3.3 / 0.7 / 3.7 / 0.5	18 TH	0003 / 0610 / 1220 / 1840	3.4 / 0.5 / 3.6 / 0.3
4 TH	0126 / 0717 / 1341 / 1936	3.2 / 0.7 / 3.7 / 0.6	19 F	0044 / 0649 / 1302 / 1920	3.4 / 0.5 / 3.7 / 0.3
5 F	0206 / 0754 / 1422 / 2013	3.2 / 0.8 / 3.6 / 0.6	20 SA	0128 / 0732 / 1348 / 2003	3.4 / 0.5 / 3.6 / 0.4
6 SA	0247 / 0834 / 1504 / 2053	3.1 / 0.8 / 3.5 / 0.7	21 SU	0216 / 0818 / 1438 / 2052	3.3 / 0.6 / 3.6 / 0.5
7 SU	0329 / 0917 / 1547 / 2138	3.0 / 0.9 / 3.3 / 0.9	22 M	0308 / 0909 / 1533 / 2147	3.3 / 0.7 / 3.4 / 0.7
8 M	0414 / 1008 / 1634 / 2231	2.9 / 1.1 / 3.1 / 1.0	23 TU	0405 / 1008 / 1635 / 2254	3.2 / 0.8 / 3.3 / 0.9
9 TU	0504 / 1112 / 1727 / 2335	2.9 / 1.2 / 3.0 / 1.1	24 W	0509 / 1123 / 1746	3.1 / 0.9 / 3.1
10 W	0604 / 1230 / 1829	2.8 / 1.2 / 2.8	25 TH	0018 / 0625 / 1253 / 1912	1.0 / 3.0 / 0.9 / 3.0
11 TH	0051 / 0717 / 1339 / 1942	1.2 / 2.8 / 1.2 / 2.8	26 F	0137 / 0747 / 1408 / 2030	0.9 / 3.1 / 0.8 / 3.1
12 F	0156 / 0830 / 1436 / 2050	1.1 / 2.9 / 1.0 / 2.9	27 SA	0240 / 0830 / 1510 / 2129	0.8 / 3.3 / 0.7 / 3.2
13 SA	0248 / 0923 / 1524 / 2140	0.9 / 3.1 / 0.8 / 3.1	28 SU	0334 / 0946 / 1604 / 2220	0.7 / 3.4 / 0.5 / 3.2
14 SU	0333 / 1004 / 1606 / 2220	0.8 / 3.3 / 0.6 / 3.3			
15 M	0414 / 1040 / 1646 / 2255	0.7 / 3.4 / 0.5 / 3.3			

MARCH

Day	Time	m	Day	Time	m
1 M	0422 / 1034 / 1651 / 2305	0.7 / 3.6 / 0.5 / 3.3	16 TU	0354 / 1006 / 1623 / 2228	0.6 / 3.4 / 0.3 / 3.3
2 TU O	0506 / 1118 / 1732 / 2347	0.6 / 3.6 / 0.4 / 3.3	17 W ●	0433 / 1040 / 1702 / 2304	0.5 / 3.5 / 0.2 / 3.4
3 W	0546 / 1159 / 1807	0.6 / 3.7 / 0.5	18 TH	0511 / 1117 / 1740 / 2342	0.4 / 3.6 / 0.2 / 3.5
4 TH	0025 / 0621 / 1238 / 1837	3.2 / 0.6 / 3.6 / 0.5	19 F	0550 / 1158 / 1818	0.4 / 3.7 / 0.2
5 F	0101 / 0652 / 1315 / 1907	3.2 / 0.7 / 3.6 / 0.6	20 SA	0024 / 0630 / 1244 / 1859	3.5 / 0.4 / 3.7 / 0.3
6 SA	0134 / 0724 / 1352 / 1939	3.2 / 0.7 / 3.5 / 0.6	21 SU	0109 / 0713 / 1332 / 1943	3.5 / 0.4 / 3.6 / 0.4
7 SU	0208 / 0759 / 1429 / 2015	3.2 / 0.7 / 3.4 / 0.7	22 M	0157 / 0759 / 1425 / 2032	3.4 / 0.4 / 3.5 / 0.5
8 M	0245 / 0838 / 1509 / 2055	3.1 / 0.8 / 3.3 / 0.8	23 TU	0249 / 0851 / 1523 / 2129	3.3 / 0.6 / 3.3 / 0.7
9 TU	0326 / 0922 / 1554 / 2140	3.0 / 0.9 / 3.1 / 1.0	24 W	0346 / 0953 / 1626 / 2239	3.2 / 0.7 / 3.1 / 0.9
10 W	0413 / 1019 / 1645 / 2238	2.9 / 1.1 / 2.9 / 1.1	25 TH	0449 / 1114 / 1740	3.1 / 0.8 / 3.0
11 TH	0510 / 1144 / 1746	2.8 / 1.2 / 2.8	26 F	0002 / 0606 / 1239 / 1908	1.0 / 3.0 / 0.8 / 2.9
12 F	0003 / 0616 / 1305 / 1855	1.2 / 2.8 / 1.1 / 2.7	27 SA	0120 / 0730 / 1355 / 2020	1.0 / 3.1 / 0.7 / 3.0
13 SA	0124 / 0735 / 1406 / 2014	1.1 / 2.8 / 0.9 / 2.9	28 SU	0226 / 0835 / 1458 / 2116	0.9 / 3.2 / 0.6 / 3.1
14 SU	0223 / 0844 / 1457 / 2111	1.0 / 3.0 / 0.7 / 3.2	29 M	0321 / 0928 / 1550 / 2203	0.8 / 3.4 / 0.5 / 3.2
15 M	0311 / 0929 / 1542 / 2152	0.8 / 3.2 / 0.5 / 3.2	30 TU	0408 / 1014 / 1633 / 2246	0.7 / 3.5 / 0.4 / 3.2
			31 W O	0450 / 1056 / 1710 / 2325	0.6 / 3.5 / 0.5 / 3.2

APRIL

Day	Time	m	Day	Time	m
1 TH	0526 / 1135 / 1742	0.6 / 3.5 / 0.5	16 F ●	0448 / 1054 / 1714 / 2322	0.4 / 3.7 / 0.2 / 3.6
2 F	0000 / 0558 / 1211 / 1809	3.2 / 0.6 / 3.5 / 0.6	17 SA	0528 / 1140 / 1755	0.3 / 3.7 / 0.2
3 SA	0031 / 0627 / 1245 / 1837	3.2 / 0.7 / 3.4 / 0.6	18 SU	0006 / 0610 / 1229 / 1838	3.6 / 0.3 / 3.7 / 0.3
4 SU	0100 / 0657 / 1318 / 1907	3.2 / 0.7 / 3.4 / 0.7	19 M	0053 / 0655 / 1320 / 1924	3.6 / 0.3 / 3.6 / 0.4
5 M	0132 / 0728 / 1354 / 1941	3.2 / 0.7 / 3.3 / 0.7	20 TU	0142 / 0743 / 1415 / 2015	3.5 / 0.4 / 3.5 / 0.6
6 TU	0207 / 0804 / 1434 / 2018	3.2 / 0.7 / 3.2 / 0.8	21 W	0233 / 0837 / 1513 / 2114	3.4 / 0.5 / 3.3 / 0.8
7 W	0245 / 0846 / 1519 / 2101	3.2 / 0.8 / 3.1 / 0.9	22 TH	0329 / 0942 / 1617 / 2223	3.3 / 0.6 / 3.1 / 0.9
8 TH	0329 / 0937 / 1612 / 2154	3.0 / 1.0 / 2.9 / 1.1	23 F	0431 / 1100 / 1731 / 2340	3.2 / 0.7 / 2.9 / 1.0
9 F	0424 / 1049 / 1711 / 2303	2.9 / 1.1 / 2.8 / 1.2	24 SA	0544 / 1218 / 1852	3.1 / 0.7 / 2.9
10 SA	0529 / 1226 / 1816	2.8 / 1.0 / 2.8	25 SU	0053 / 0704 / 1331 / 1959	1.0 / 3.1 / 0.7 / 2.9
11 SU	0043 / 0640 / 1333 / 1926	1.2 / 2.8 / 0.9 / 2.9	26 M	0201 / 0809 / 1435 / 2052	0.9 / 3.2 / 0.6 / 3.0
12 M	0151 / 0749 / 1427 / 2029	1.0 / 3.0 / 0.7 / 3.0	27 TU	0257 / 0902 / 1524 / 2139	0.8 / 3.3 / 0.5 / 3.1
13 TU	0243 / 0845 / 1513 / 2116	0.8 / 3.2 / 0.4 / 3.2	28 W	0345 / 0948 / 1605 / 2220	0.7 / 3.4 / 0.5 / 3.2
14 W	0328 / 0930 / 1555 / 2158	0.7 / 3.4 / 0.3 / 3.4	29 TH	0426 / 1030 / 1640 / 2257	0.7 / 3.4 / 0.6 / 3.2
15 TH	0408 / 1012 / 1635 / 2239	0.5 / 3.5 / 0.2 / 3.5	30 F O	0502 / 1107 / 1711 / 2330	0.7 / 3.4 / 0.6 / 3.2

Chart Datum: 2·01 metres below Ordnance Datum (Belfast)

NORTHERN IRELAND – BELFAST

LAT 54°36′N   LONG 5°55′W

TIMES AND HEIGHTS OF HIGH AND LOW WATERS

YEAR **1999**

TIME ZONE (UT)
For Summer Time add ONE hour in non-shaded areas

MAY

Day	Time	m		Day	Time	m
1 SA	0534 / 1140 / 1739 / 2359	0.7 / 3.4 / 0.7 / 3.3		**16** SU	0508 / 1124 / 1734 / 2349	0.4 / 3.7 / 0.3 / 3.7
2 SU	0604 / 1213 / 1808	0.7 / 3.3 / 0.7		**17** M	0554 / 1215 / 1820	0.3 / 3.6 / 0.4
3 M	0029 / 0632 / 1247 / 1838	3.3 / 0.7 / 3.3 / 0.8		**18** TU	0038 / 0641 / 1308 / 1909	3.7 / 0.3 / 3.5 / 0.5
4 TU	0102 / 0702 / 1324 / 1912	3.3 / 0.7 / 3.3 / 0.8		**19** W	0128 / 0730 / 1402 / 2001	3.6 / 0.3 / 3.4 / 0.6
5 W	0137 / 0737 / 1404 / 1950	3.3 / 0.7 / 3.2 / 0.8		**20** TH	0218 / 0825 / 1500 / 2059	3.6 / 0.4 / 3.2 / 0.8
6 TH	0214 / 0818 / 1450 / 2034	3.3 / 0.8 / 3.1 / 0.9		**21** F	0312 / 0929 / 1602 / 2204	3.4 / 0.5 / 3.1 / 0.9
7 F	0256 / 0907 / 1543 / 2125	3.2 / 0.9 / 3.0 / 1.0		**22** SA	0410 / 1039 / 1711 / 2313	3.3 / 0.6 / 2.9 / 1.0
8 SA	0346 / 1008 / 1641 / 2225	3.1 / 0.9 / 2.9 / 1.1		**23** SU	0515 / 1149 / 1823	3.2 / 0.7 / 2.9
9 SU	0447 / 1129 / 1742 / 2336	3.0 / 0.9 / 2.9 / 1.1		**24** M	0019 / 0627 / 1257 / 1927	1.0 / 3.1 / 0.7 / 2.9
10 M	0555 / 1248 / 1846	3.0 / 0.8 / 3.0		**25** TU	0125 / 0735 / 1358 / 2021	1.0 / 3.2 / 0.6 / 3.0
11 TU	0100 / 0703 / 1348 / 1947	1.1 / 3.1 / 0.6 / 3.1		**26** W	0223 / 0831 / 1449 / 2107	0.9 / 3.2 / 0.6 / 3.1
12 W	0204 / 0805 / 1439 / 2041	0.9 / 3.2 / 0.5 / 3.3		**27** TH	0314 / 0918 / 1530 / 2148	0.8 / 3.3 / 0.6 / 3.2
13 TH	0255 / 0858 / 1524 / 2129	0.7 / 3.4 / 0.3 / 3.4		**28** F	0358 / 0959 / 1605 / 2225	0.8 / 3.3 / 0.7 / 3.2
14 F	0340 / 0947 / 1606 / 2215	0.6 / 3.6 / 0.3 / 3.6		**29** SA	0435 / 1037 / 1638 / 2259	0.8 / 3.3 / 0.7 / 3.3
15 SA ●	0424 / 1035 / 1649 / 2302	0.4 / 3.7 / 0.3 / 3.6		**30** SU O	0509 / 1111 / 1709 / 2331	0.8 / 3.3 / 0.8 / 3.3
				31 M	0539 / 1145 / 1741	0.8 / 3.3 / 0.8

JUNE

Day	Time	m		Day	Time	m
1 TU	0004 / 0610 / 1221 / 1813	3.3 / 0.8 / 3.3 / 0.8		**16** W	0022 / 0630 / 1254 / 1855	3.7 / 0.3 / 3.5 / 0.6
2 W	0038 / 0642 / 1258 / 1849	3.4 / 0.7 / 3.2 / 0.8		**17** TH	0112 / 0719 / 1347 / 1946	3.7 / 0.4 / 3.4 / 0.7
3 TH	0112 / 0718 / 1338 / 1929	3.4 / 0.7 / 3.2 / 0.8		**18** F	0201 / 0811 / 1442 / 2040	3.7 / 0.4 / 3.2 / 0.8
4 F	0149 / 0758 / 1423 / 2013	3.4 / 0.7 / 3.1 / 0.8		**19** SA	0252 / 0908 / 1539 / 2139	3.6 / 0.6 / 3.1 / 0.9
5 SA	0229 / 0844 / 1514 / 2102	3.3 / 0.7 / 3.1 / 0.9		**20** SU	0346 / 1010 / 1638 / 2240	3.4 / 0.6 / 3.0 / 1.0
6 SU	0317 / 0939 / 1610 / 2156	3.3 / 0.8 / 3.0 / 1.0		**21** M	0441 / 1113 / 1739 / 2341	3.3 / 0.7 / 2.9 / 1.0
7 M	0411 / 1041 / 1708 / 2256	3.2 / 0.8 / 3.0 / 1.0		**22** TU	0541 / 1215 / 1842	3.2 / 0.8 / 2.9
8 TU	0514 / 1151 / 1808	3.2 / 0.8 / 3.1		**23** W	0043 / 0646 / 1315 / 1939	1.0 / 3.1 / 0.8 / 2.9
9 W	0002 / 0622 / 1302 / 1910	1.0 / 3.2 / 0.7 / 3.1		**24** TH	0144 / 0750 / 1408 / 2030	1.0 / 3.1 / 0.8 / 3.0
10 TH	0116 / 0730 / 1402 / 2009	1.0 / 3.3 / 0.6 / 3.3		**25** F	0239 / 0843 / 1452 / 2114	0.9 / 3.1 / 0.8 / 3.1
11 F	0220 / 0831 / 1454 / 2103	0.8 / 3.4 / 0.5 / 3.4		**26** SA	0327 / 0929 / 1531 / 2154	0.9 / 3.1 / 0.8 / 3.2
12 SA	0315 / 0926 / 1542 / 2154	0.9 / 3.5 / 0.4 / 3.6		**27** SU	0407 / 1009 / 1606 / 2232	0.8 / 3.2 / 0.8 / 3.6
13 SU ●	0405 / 1018 / 1630 / 2244	0.5 / 3.6 / 0.4 / 3.7		**28** M	0443 / 1047 / 1642 / 2308	0.8 / 3.2 / 0.8 / 3.3
14 M	0454 / 1109 / 1717 / 2333	0.4 / 3.6 / 0.4 / 3.7		**29** TU O	0517 / 1123 / 1717 / 2342	0.8 / 3.2 / 0.8 / 3.4
15 TU	0542 / 1201 / 1806	0.4 / 3.6 / 0.5		**30** W	0551 / 1158 / 1754	0.7 / 3.2 / 0.8

JULY

Day	Time	m		Day	Time	m
1 TH	0014 / 0625 / 1233 / 1831	3.4 / 0.7 / 3.2 / 0.8		**16** F	0054 / 0706 / 1328 / 1927	3.7 / 0.4 / 3.3 / 0.7
2 F	0047 / 0701 / 1312 / 1910	3.4 / 0.7 / 3.2 / 0.8		**17** SA	0141 / 0751 / 1418 / 2014	3.7 / 0.4 / 3.2 / 0.8
3 SA	0124 / 0740 / 1355 / 1953	3.5 / 0.6 / 3.2 / 0.8		**18** SU	0228 / 0837 / 1507 / 2103	3.6 / 0.5 / 3.1 / 0.9
4 SU	0205 / 0823 / 1443 / 2039	3.5 / 0.6 / 3.2 / 0.8		**19** M	0316 / 0926 / 1557 / 2155	3.5 / 0.7 / 3.0 / 0.9
5 M	0251 / 0912 / 1537 / 2129	3.4 / 0.6 / 3.1 / 0.8		**20** TU	0405 / 1020 / 1648 / 2252	3.3 / 0.8 / 2.9 / 1.0
6 TU	0342 / 1008 / 1633 / 2224	3.4 / 0.7 / 3.1 / 0.9		**21** W	0457 / 1119 / 1741 / 2354	3.2 / 0.9 / 2.9 / 1.1
7 W	0440 / 1110 / 1732 / 2326	3.3 / 0.7 / 3.1 / 1.0		**22** TH	0554 / 1221 / 1841	3.0 / 1.0 / 2.9
8 TH	0547 / 1221 / 1836	3.2 / 0.7 / 3.1		**23** F	0059 / 0658 / 1322 / 1944	1.1 / 2.9 / 1.0 / 2.9
9 F	0038 / 0700 / 1332 / 1940	1.0 / 3.2 / 0.7 / 3.2		**24** SA	0201 / 0806 / 1414 / 2039	1.1 / 3.0 / 1.0 / 3.0
10 SA	0155 / 0809 / 1433 / 2041	1.0 / 3.3 / 0.6 / 3.4		**25** SU	0254 / 0902 / 1459 / 2126	1.0 / 3.1 / 0.9 / 3.2
11 SU	0259 / 0911 / 1527 / 2136	0.8 / 3.4 / 0.6 / 3.5		**26** M	0339 / 0947 / 1540 / 2207	0.9 / 3.1 / 0.9 / 3.3
12 M	0354 / 1006 / 1617 / 2227	0.6 / 3.4 / 0.6 / 3.6		**27** TU	0418 / 1027 / 1619 / 2245	0.8 / 3.2 / 0.8 / 3.3
13 TU ●	0445 / 1058 / 1705 / 2317	0.5 / 3.5 / 0.6 / 3.7		**28** W O	0454 / 1104 / 1657 / 2317	0.7 / 3.2 / 0.8 / 3.4
14 W	0534 / 1149 / 1753	0.4 / 3.5 / 0.6		**29** TH	0531 / 1136 / 1734 / 2346	0.6 / 3.2 / 0.7 / 3.4
15 TH	0006 / 0621 / 1239 / 1840	3.7 / 0.4 / 3.4 / 0.6		**30** F	0607 / 1207 / 1812	0.6 / 3.3 / 0.7
				31 SA	0018 / 0642 / 1245 / 1850	3.5 / 0.6 / 3.3 / 0.7

AUGUST

Day	Time	m		Day	Time	m
1 SU	0057 / 0719 / 1327 / 1931	3.5 / 0.5 / 3.3 / 0.7		**16** M	0200 / 0759 / 1430 / 2022	3.6 / 0.6 / 3.1 / 0.9
2 M	0139 / 0800 / 1414 / 2015	3.6 / 0.5 / 3.3 / 0.7		**17** TU	0242 / 0839 / 1513 / 2105	3.5 / 0.7 / 3.1 / 0.9
3 TU	0225 / 0846 / 1505 / 2103	3.6 / 0.6 / 3.2 / 0.8		**18** W	0326 / 0923 / 1559 / 2153	3.3 / 0.9 / 3.0 / 1.0
4 W	0316 / 0938 / 1601 / 2157	3.4 / 0.7 / 3.2 / 0.9		**19** TH	0414 / 1014 / 1647 / 2253	3.1 / 1.0 / 2.9 / 1.2
5 TH	0414 / 1039 / 1700 / 2258	3.3 / 0.8 / 3.1 / 0.9		**20** F	0507 / 1117 / 1743	3.0 / 1.1 / 2.9
6 F	0520 / 1152 / 1806	3.2 / 0.9 / 3.1		**21** SA	0008 / 0607 / 1232 / 1848	1.2 / 2.8 / 1.2 / 2.9
7 SA	0016 / 0637 / 1314 / 1917	1.0 / 3.1 / 0.9 / 3.2		**22** SU	0120 / 0724 / 1338 / 2001	1.2 / 2.8 / 1.1 / 3.0
8 SU	0142 / 0757 / 1421 / 2025	1.0 / 3.2 / 0.8 / 3.3		**23** M	0220 / 0824 / 1431 / 2058	1.0 / 2.9 / 1.0 / 3.1
9 M	0249 / 0904 / 1516 / 2123	0.8 / 3.3 / 0.7 / 3.4		**24** TU	0310 / 0927 / 1516 / 2142	0.9 / 3.1 / 0.9 / 3.2
10 TU	0347 / 1000 / 1607 / 2214	0.6 / 3.3 / 0.7 / 3.6		**25** W	0352 / 1007 / 1557 / 2218	0.7 / 3.2 / 0.8 / 3.4
11 W ●	0438 / 1050 / 1654 / 2303	0.5 / 3.4 / 0.7 / 3.7		**26** TH O	0431 / 1042 / 1636 / 2247	0.6 / 3.3 / 0.7 / 3.4
12 TH	0525 / 1137 / 1740 / 2349	0.4 / 3.4 / 0.7 / 3.7		**27** F	0508 / 1111 / 1713 / 2316	0.5 / 3.3 / 0.7 / 3.5
13 F	0609 / 1222 / 1823	0.4 / 3.3 / 0.7		**28** SA	0544 / 1142 / 1750 / 2350	0.4 / 3.4 / 0.6 / 3.6
14 SA	0033 / 0647 / 1306 / 1903	3.7 / 0.5 / 3.2 / 0.7		**29** SU	0619 / 1218 / 1827	0.4 / 3.4 / 0.6
15 SU	0117 / 0723 / 1348 / 1942	3.6 / 0.5 / 3.2 / 0.8		**30** M	0030 / 0655 / 1300 / 1907	3.6 / 0.4 / 3.4 / 0.6
				31 TU	0115 / 0735 / 1346 / 1950	3.6 / 0.5 / 3.4 / 0.7

Chart Datum: 2·01 metres below Ordnance Datum (Belfast)

13

NORTHERN IRELAND – BELFAST

LAT 54°36′N   LONG 5°55′W

TIMES AND HEIGHTS OF HIGH AND LOW WATERS   YEAR **1999**

TIME ZONE (UT)
For Summer Time add ONE hour in non-shaded areas

SEPTEMBER

Day	Time	m	Day	Time	m
1 W	0202 / 0820 / 1437 / 2038	3.6 / 0.6 / 3.3 / 0.7	**16** TH	0247 / 0836 / 1511 / 2105	3.3 / 0.9 / 3.1 / 1.0
2 TH	0254 / 0911 / 1533 / 2132	3.4 / 0.7 / 3.2 / 0.9	**17** F	0333 / 0921 / 1559 / 2158	3.1 / 1.0 / 3.0 / 1.1
3 F	0354 / 1013 / 1634 / 2236	3.3 / 0.9 / 3.1 / 1.0	**18** SA	0425 / 1016 / 1653 / 2315	3.0 / 1.2 / 2.9 / 1.2
4 SA	0503 / 1132 / 1742	3.1 / 1.0 / 3.1	**19** SU	0525 / 1137 / 1755	2.8 / 1.3 / 2.9
5 SU	0004 / 0626 / 1302 / 1900	1.0 / 3.0 / 1.1 / 3.1	**20** M	0039 / 0635 / 1302 / 1907	1.2 / 2.8 / 1.3 / 2.9
6 M	0132 / 0755 / 1410 / 2013	1.0 / 3.0 / 1.0 / 3.2	**21** TU	0145 / 0803 / 1402 / 2019	1.1 / 2.9 / 1.1 / 3.0
7 TU	0241 / 0901 / 1506 / 2112	0.8 / 3.2 / 0.9 / 3.4	**22** W	0239 / 0900 / 1451 / 2107	0.9 / 3.0 / 1.0 / 3.2
8 W	0338 / 0953 / 1556 / 2202	0.6 / 3.3 / 0.8 / 3.6	**23** TH	0324 / 0940 / 1534 / 2143	0.7 / 3.2 / 0.8 / 3.4
9 TH	0428 / 1039 / 1642 / ● 2247	0.5 / 3.3 / 0.7 / 3.6	**24** F	0404 / 1013 / 1612 / 2215	0.5 / 3.4 / 0.7 / 3.5
10 F	0511 / 1122 / 1724 / 2330	0.5 / 3.3 / 0.7 / 3.6	**25** SA	0441 / 1044 / 1649 / O 2248	0.4 / 3.5 / 0.6 / 3.6
11 SA	0550 / 1202 / 1803	0.5 / 3.3 / 0.7	**26** SU	0517 / 1118 / 1725 / 2326	0.4 / 3.5 / 0.6 / 3.7
12 SU	0011 / 0622 / 1239 / 1837	3.7 / 0.6 / 3.3 / 0.8	**27** M	0552 / 1156 / 1803	0.4 / 3.5 / 0.6
13 M	0050 / 0651 / 1315 / 1909	3.6 / 0.6 / 3.2 / 0.8	**28** TU	0008 / 0629 / 1238 / 1843	3.7 / 0.4 / 3.5 / 0.6
14 TU	0128 / 0722 / 1351 / 1944	3.5 / 0.7 / 3.2 / 0.9	**29** W	0054 / 0711 / 1324 / 1928	3.7 / 0.5 / 3.5 / 0.6
15 W	0206 / 0757 / 1429 / 2022	3.4 / 0.8 / 3.2 / 0.9	**30** TH	0144 / 0757 / 1415 / 2017	3.6 / 0.7 / 3.4 / 0.7

OCTOBER

Day	Time	m	Day	Time	m
1 F	0239 / 0850 / 1510 / 2113	3.4 / 0.8 / 3.3 / 0.8	**16** SA	0258 / 0840 / 1516 / 2115	3.2 / 1.1 / 3.2 / 1.1
2 SA	0343 / 0953 / 1612 / 2222	3.2 / 1.0 / 3.2 / 0.9	**17** SU	0350 / 0932 / 1608 / 2218	3.0 / 1.2 / 3.0 / 1.2
3 SU	0455 / 1117 / 1722 / 2352	3.0 / 1.2 / 3.1 / 1.0	**18** M	0449 / 1037 / 1709 / 2352	2.9 / 1.3 / 2.9 / 1.2
4 M	0624 / 1212 / 1845	2.9 / 1.2 / 3.1	**19** TU	0554 / 1211 / 1816	2.8 / 1.4 / 2.9
5 TU	0116 / 0748 / 1355 / 1958	0.9 / 3.0 / 1.1 / 3.2	**20** W	0105 / 0706 / 1326 / 1923	1.1 / 2.9 / 1.2 / 3.0
6 W	0227 / 0849 / 1452 / 2056	0.8 / 3.1 / 1.0 / 3.4	**21** TH	0202 / 0814 / 1419 / 2020	0.9 / 3.1 / 1.1 / 3.2
7 TH	0324 / 0938 / 1542 / 2145	0.6 / 3.2 / 0.8 / 3.5	**22** F	0250 / 0901 / 1504 / 2106	0.7 / 3.3 / 0.9 / 3.4
8 F	0410 / 1021 / 1625 / 2228	0.6 / 3.3 / 0.7 / 3.6	**23** SA	0332 / 0943 / 1544 / 2146	0.5 / 3.4 / 0.7 / 3.5
9 SA	0450 / 1101 / 1705 / ● 2309	0.6 / 3.3 / 0.6 / 3.6	**24** SU	0409 / 1021 / 1621 / O 2226	0.4 / 3.6 / 0.6 / 3.7
10 SU	0524 / 1138 / 1740 / 2346	0.6 / 3.4 / 0.6 / 3.6	**25** M	0446 / 1056 / 1659 / 2308	0.4 / 3.6 / 0.6 / 3.7
11 M	0552 / 1211 / 1811	0.7 / 3.4 / 0.8	**26** TU	0524 / 1138 / 1740 / 2353	0.4 / 3.7 / 0.5 / 3.7
12 TU	0021 / 0619 / 1243 / 1839	3.5 / 0.8 / 3.4 / 0.8	**27** W	0606 / 1222 / 1824	0.5 / 3.7 / 0.5
13 W	0057 / 0648 / 1316 / 1911	3.5 / 0.8 / 3.4 / 0.9	**28** TH	0042 / 0650 / 1309 / 1910	3.7 / 0.6 / 3.6 / 0.5
14 TH	0134 / 0720 / 1352 / 1946	3.4 / 0.9 / 3.3 / 0.9	**29** F	0135 / 0739 / 1400 / 2001	3.5 / 0.7 / 3.6 / 0.6
15 F	0213 / 0757 / 1431 / 2027	3.3 / 1.0 / 3.3 / 1.0	**30** SA	0233 / 0834 / 1455 / 2059	3.4 / 0.9 / 3.4 / 0.7
			31 SU	0336 / 0939 / 1556 / 2210	3.2 / 1.1 / 3.3 / 0.8

NOVEMBER

Day	Time	m	Day	Time	m
1 M	0448 / 1059 / 1704 / 2332	3.0 / 1.2 / 3.2 / 0.9	**16** TU	0415 / 0959 / 1623 / 2246	3.0 / 1.2 / 3.1 / 1.1
2 TU	0612 / 1218 / 1822	3.0 / 1.2 / 3.2	**17** W	0516 / 1105 / 1727	2.9 / 1.3 / 3.1
3 W	0050 / 0728 / 1329 / 1934	0.9 / 3.0 / 1.1 / 3.3	**18** TH	0005 / 0620 / 1222 / 1833	1.1 / 3.0 / 1.3 / 3.1
4 TH	0202 / 0827 / 1429 / 2033	0.8 / 3.1 / 1.0 / 3.4	**19** F	0114 / 0724 / 1332 / 1936	0.9 / 3.1 / 1.2 / 3.2
5 F	0259 / 0915 / 1520 / 2122	0.7 / 3.2 / 0.9 / 3.5	**20** SA	0208 / 0820 / 1426 / 2031	0.8 / 3.3 / 1.0 / 3.4
6 SA	0344 / 0958 / 1604 / 2206	0.7 / 3.3 / 0.8 / 3.5	**21** SU	0254 / 0909 / 1512 / 2120	0.6 / 3.4 / 0.8 / 3.5
7 SU	0422 / 1037 / 1643 / 2245	0.7 / 3.4 / 0.8 / 3.5	**22** M	0337 / 0953 / 1555 / 2207	0.6 / 3.6 / 0.7 / 3.7
8 M	0453 / 1113 / 1717 / ● 2321	0.6 / 3.4 / 0.8 / 3.5	**23** TU	0419 / 1038 / 1638 / O 2254	0.5 / 3.7 / 0.6 / 3.7
9 TU	0522 / 1145 / 1747 / 2356	0.8 / 3.4 / 0.9 / 3.5	**24** W	0502 / 1123 / 1723 / 2344	0.5 / 3.8 / 0.5 / 3.7
10 W	0549 / 1216 / 1815	0.9 / 3.4 / 0.9	**25** TH	0548 / 1210 / 1810	0.5 / 3.8 / 0.5
11 TH	0030 / 0618 / 1250 / 1845	3.4 / 0.9 / 3.5 / 0.9	**26** F	0035 / 0635 / 1259 / 1858	3.6 / 0.6 / 3.8 / 0.5
12 F	0107 / 0651 / 1325 / 1919	3.4 / 0.9 / 3.4 / 0.9	**27** SA	0129 / 0726 / 1349 / 1950	3.5 / 0.8 / 3.7 / 0.5
13 SA	0146 / 0729 / 1402 / 1959	3.3 / 1.0 / 3.4 / 0.9	**28** SU	0226 / 0821 / 1443 / 2047	3.4 / 0.9 / 3.6 / 0.6
14 SU	0229 / 0812 / 1441 / 2045	3.2 / 1.0 / 3.3 / 1.0	**29** M	0326 / 0924 / 1540 / 2154	3.2 / 1.0 / 3.5 / 0.7
15 M	0319 / 0901 / 1528 / 2139	3.1 / 1.1 / 3.2 / 1.1	**30** TU	0433 / 1035 / 1642 / 2306	3.1 / 1.1 / 3.4 / 0.8

DECEMBER

Day	Time	m	Day	Time	m
1 W	0546 / 1146 / 1751	3.0 / 1.2 / 3.3	**16** TH	0435 / 1025 / 1640 / 2307	3.0 / 1.1 / 3.2 / 0.9
2 TH	0017 / 0656 / 1254 / 1901	0.8 / 3.0 / 1.1 / 3.3	**17** F	0535 / 1127 / 1744	3.0 / 1.2 / 3.2
3 F	0125 / 0757 / 1357 / 2003	0.8 / 3.1 / 1.1 / 3.3	**18** SA	0015 / 0638 / 1237 / 1853	0.9 / 3.1 / 1.2 / 3.2
4 SA	0224 / 0847 / 1452 / 2055	0.8 / 3.2 / 1.0 / 3.4	**19** SU	0122 / 0742 / 1346 / 1959	0.8 / 3.2 / 1.1 / 3.3
5 SU	0311 / 0932 / 1539 / 2141	0.8 / 3.3 / 0.9 / 3.4	**20** M	0221 / 0840 / 1445 / 2057	0.7 / 3.4 / 0.9 / 3.5
6 M	0350 / 1012 / 1620 / 2222	0.8 / 3.3 / 0.9 / 3.4	**21** TU	0313 / 0932 / 1536 / 2151	0.6 / 3.5 / 0.7 / 3.6
7 TU	0424 / 1049 / 1656 / ● 2259	0.9 / 3.4 / 0.9 / 3.4	**22** W	0401 / 1021 / 1625 / O 2243	0.6 / 3.7 / 0.6 / 3.6
8 W	0454 / 1123 / 1727 / 2335	0.9 / 3.4 / 0.9 / 3.4	**23** TH	0448 / 1110 / 1713 / 2335	0.5 / 3.8 / 0.5 / 3.6
9 TH	0525 / 1157 / 1756	0.9 / 3.5 / 0.9	**24** F	0536 / 1159 / 1801	0.6 / 3.8 / 0.4
10 F	0010 / 0556 / 1231 / 1827	3.3 / 0.9 / 3.5 / 0.9	**25** SA	0027 / 0624 / 1248 / 1849	3.6 / 0.6 / 3.8 / 0.4
11 SA	0046 / 0631 / 1305 / 1901	3.3 / 0.9 / 3.5 / 0.9	**26** SU	0120 / 0714 / 1338 / 1939	3.5 / 0.7 / 3.8 / 0.4
12 SU	0123 / 0709 / 1338 / 1939	3.3 / 0.9 / 3.5 / 0.9	**27** M	0213 / 0806 / 1429 / 2032	3.3 / 0.8 / 3.7 / 0.5
13 M	0202 / 0750 / 1414 / 2022	3.2 / 1.0 / 3.4 / 0.8	**28** TU	0309 / 0902 / 1522 / 2130	3.2 / 0.9 / 3.6 / 0.6
14 TU	0247 / 0837 / 1455 / 2110	3.2 / 1.0 / 3.4 / 0.8	**29** W	0407 / 1004 / 1617 / 2233	3.1 / 1.0 / 3.5 / 0.7
15 W	0338 / 0928 / 1544 / 2206	3.1 / 1.1 / 3.3 / 0.9	**30** TH	0508 / 1109 / 1715 / 2338	3.0 / 1.1 / 3.3 / 0.8
			31 F	0614 / 1215 / 1818	2.9 / 1.1 / 3.2

Chart Datum: 2·01 metres below Ordnance Datum (Belfast)

LARNE   8-13-12

Antrim 54°51'·20N 05°47'·50W   Rtg 1-4-2

CHARTS
AC 1237, 2198; Imray C62, C64; Irish OS 9

TIDES
+0005 Dover; ML 1·6; Duration 0620; Zone 0 (UT)

Standard Port BELFAST (←)

Times				Height (metres)			
High Water		Low Water		MHWS	MHWN	MLWN	MLWS
0100	0700	0000	0600	3·5	3·0	1·1	0·4
1300	1900	1200	1800				
Differences LARNE							
+0005	0000	+0010	−0005	−0·7	−0·5	−0·3	0·0
RED BAY							
+0022	−0010	+0007	−0017	−1·9	−1·5	−0·8	−0·2
CUSHENDUN BAY							
+0010	−0030	0000	−0025	−1·7	−1·5	−0·6	−0·2

SHELTER
Secure shelter in Larne Lough or ⚓ overnight outside hbr in Brown's Bay (E of Barr Pt) in 2–4m. Hbr can be entered H24 in any conditions. Larne is a busy commercial and ferry port; W side is commercial until Curran Pt where there are two YCs with congested moorings. ⚓ S of Ballylumford Power Stn. No AB available for visitors. Yachts should not berth on any commercial quays, inc Castle Quay, without Hr Mr's express permission.

Boat Hbr (0·6m) 2ca S of Ferris Pt only for shoal draft craft. Note: Work continues (started 1993) to extend the harbour southward and will eventually result in E Antrim BC moving to Curran Point, with fewer moorings.

NAVIGATION
WPT 54°51'·70N 05°47'·47W, 004°/184° from/to front ldg lt, 2·1M. Beware Hunter Rk 2M NE of hbr ent. Magnetic abnomalies exist near Hunter Rk and between it and the mainland. Inside the narrow ent, the recommended chan is close to the E shore. Tide in the ent runs at up to 3½kn.

LIGHTS AND MARKS
Ldg lts 184°, Oc 4s 6/14m 12M, synch and vis 179°-189°; W ◇ with R stripes. Chaine Tr and fairway lts as chartlet. Note: Many shore lts on W side of ent may be mistaken for nav lts.

RADIO TELEPHONE
VHF Ch 14 16 Larne Harbour. Traffic, weather and tidal info available on Ch 14.

TELEPHONE (Dial code 01574)
Hr Mr 279221; MRSC (01247) 463933; Pilot 273785; ⌗ (01232) 358250; Marinecall 0891 500 465; Police 272266; Dr 275331.

FACILITIES
Pier ☎ 279221, M, L, FW, C (32 ton); **E Antrim Boat Club** ☎ 277204, Visitors should pre-contact Sec'y for advice on moorings; Slip, L, V, FW, Bar; **Services:** D, Gas, Sh, El. **Town** EC Tues; P & D (delivered, tidal), CH, V, R, Bar, ✉, Ⓑ, ⇌, Ferry to Cairnryan, ✈ (Belfast City and Belfast/Aldergrove).

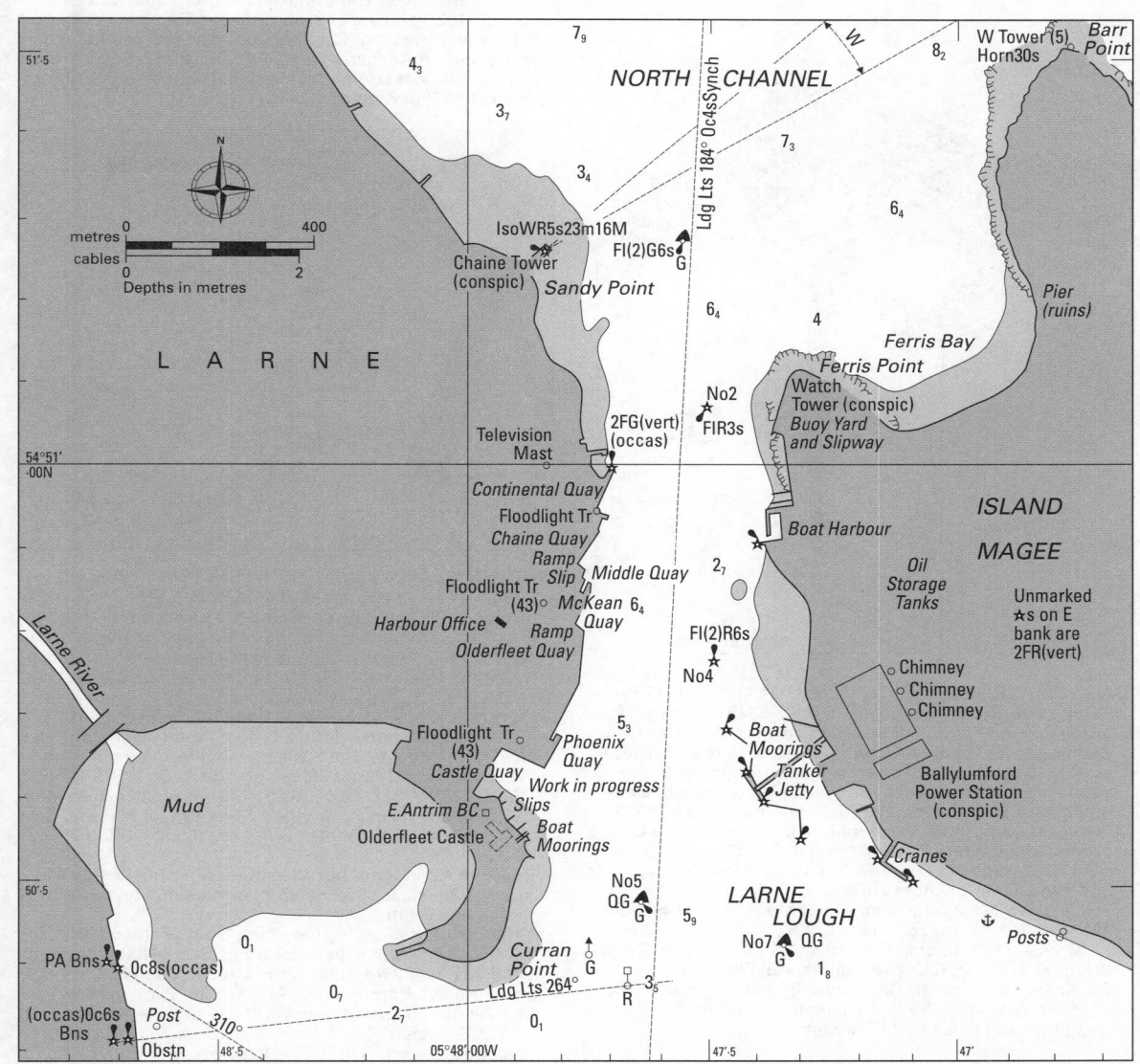

MINOR HARBOURS AND ANCHORAGES BETWEEN LARNE AND PORTRUSH

CARNLOUGH HARBOUR, Antrim, 54°59′·87N 05°59′·20W. AC 2198. HW +0006 on Dover, +0005 on Belfast; HW −1·6m on Belfast; ML no data; Duration 0625. Good shelter except in SE gales; do not ent in onshore winds >F6. Ldg marks 310°, Y ▽s on B/W posts. N pier lt, Fl G 3s 4m 5M; S pier Fl R 3s 6m 5M, both lts on B/W columns. Beware: fish farms in the bay marked by lt buoys (unreliable); and rks which cover at HW on either side of ent. Small hbr used by yachts and small FVs; visitors welcome. Ent and hbr dredged 2m every May. Hr Mr ☎ (01574) 272677. Facilities: **Quay** AB £2.10, AC (see Hr Mr), FW, Slip. **Town** P & D (cans), Gas, Gaz, ⊠, R, V, Bar, ♿.

RED BAY, Antrim, 55°03′·91N 06°03′·13W. AC 2199. HW +0010 on Dover; ML 1·1m; Duration 0625. See 8.13.12. Good holding, but open to E winds. Beware rks, 2 ruined piers W of Garron Pt and fish farms, marked by lt buoys, on S side of bay, approx ½M from shore. Glenariff pier has lt Fl 3s 10m 5M. In S and E winds ⚓ 2ca off W stone arch near hd of bay in approx 3·5m; in N or W winds ⚓ S of small pier in 2 − 5m, ½M NE of Waterfoot village. Facilities: **Cushendall** (1M N of pier) Bar, D & P (cans), ⊠, R, V, Gas; **Services:** CH, El, Slip. **Waterfoot** Bar, R, ⊠.

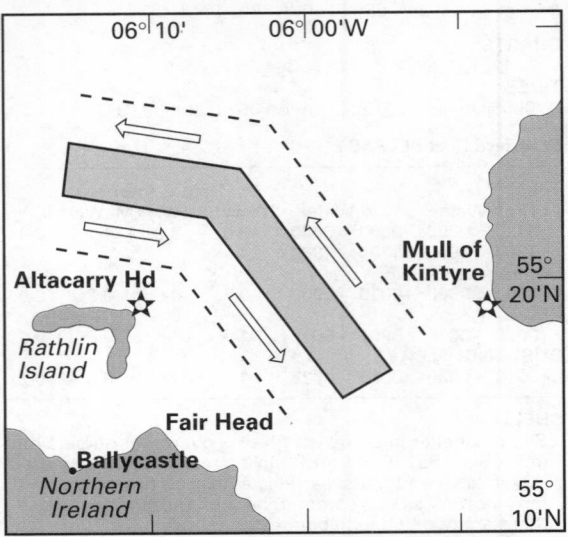

NORTH CHANNEL TRAFFIC SEPARATION SCHEME

Centred on 55°22′·8N 06°04′·6W. See AC 2798, 8.13.5, 8.9.5 and 1.1.3 (Rule 10). The traffic lanes, orientated 325°/145° and 282°/102°, and separation zone are 2M wide. Monitor Ch 16 whilst crossing. Caution: tidal races off Mull of Kintyre and off Altacarry Head, Rathlin Island. See chartlets opposite for tidal streams off Rathlin Island and 8.9.12 for those off Mull of Kintyre.

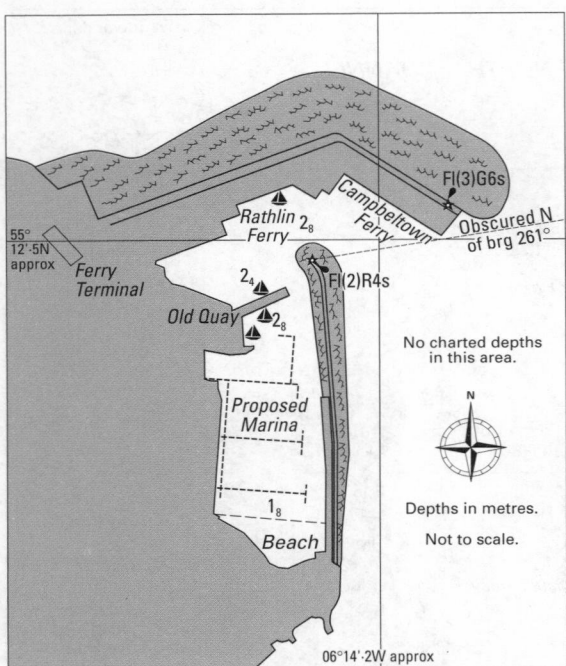

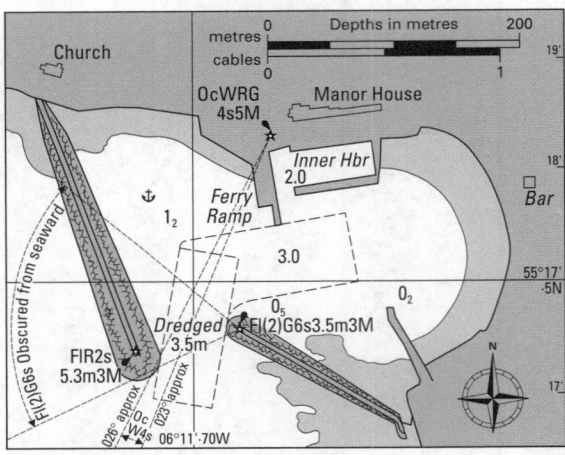

RATHLIN ISLAND, Antrim, 55°17′·52N 06°11′·60W. AC 2798. HW sp −0445, nps −0200 on Dover. Small hbr in NE corner of Church Bay, sheltered from winds NW through E to SSE. New outer piers and ramp have equipped it for ferry service to Ballycastle. Beware sp streams up to 6kn in Rathlin Sound and the North Channel TSS (above), 2M to the N and E of the island.
Pass N or E of a wreck 6ca SW of hbr, marked on its SE side by a SCM buoy, Q(6)+L Fl 15s. When clear, appr on NNE to the new W and S piers which form an outer hbr. White sector of Manor House pier dir lt, Oc WRG 4s 5M, G020°–023°, W023°–026°, R026°–029°, leads 024·5° to inner hbr (2m) ent via chan dredged 3·5m. W pier Fl R 2s 5·3m 3M; S pier Fl (2) G 6s 3·5m 3M, obsc'd 062°–130° (68°) by W pier.
Possible AB in inner hbr. ⚓ in outer hbr on NW side in about 1.2m clear of ferry ramp; or outside hbr, close to W pier in about 5m.
Other lts on Rathlin Is: Rue Point (S tip), Fl (2) 5s 16m 14M, W 8-sided tr, B bands. Rathlin East (Altacarry Head), Fl (4) 20s 74m 26M, H24, vis 110°–006°, 036°–058°, W tr, B band, Racon. Rathlin West, Fl R 5s 62m 22M, vis 015°–225°, shown by day in low vis, W tr, lamp at base; fog det lt VQ, 69m, vis 119°.
Facilities: Church Bay R, Bar, V, ⊠. Ferry to Ballycastle.

BALLYCASTLE, Antrim, 55°12′·50N 06°14′·30W. AC 2798. Tides as for Rathlin Island; ML 0·8m; −0320 on Dover. The original small hbr has been much developed for ferries to Campbeltown (Mull of Kintyre) and Rathlin Island. These berth on the outer and inner parts of a new N bkwtr. Yachts may berth in about 3m each side of the Old Quay; at the new quay joining Old Quay and pier; and at the low-level quay. (A 70 berth marina in the S part of hbr is proposed for 2000). Outside the hbr is a fair weather ⚓, clear of strong tidal streams, but liable to sudden swell and exposed to onshore winds.
Lts: N bkwtr Fl (3) G 6s 6·5m 6M; S bkwtr Fl (2) R 4s 4·6m 1M, obsc'd N of brg 261° by N bkwtr.
Hr Mr via Moyle District Council ☎ (012657) 62225; CG ☎ (012657) 62226; ℍ 62666. **Facilities:** AB, FW, L, Slip.
Services: P & D (cans), Gas. **Town** EC Wed; R, Bar, V, ⊠, ⑧, ♿. Ferry to/from Rathlin Island (next column) and Campbeltown (8.9.11, Mull of Kintyre).

TIDAL STREAMS AROUND RATHLIN ISLAND

8-13-13

North Ireland 8.13.3   Off Mull of Kintyre 8.9.12   South Ireland 8.12.3
North Irish Sea 8.10.3   SW Scotland 8.9.3

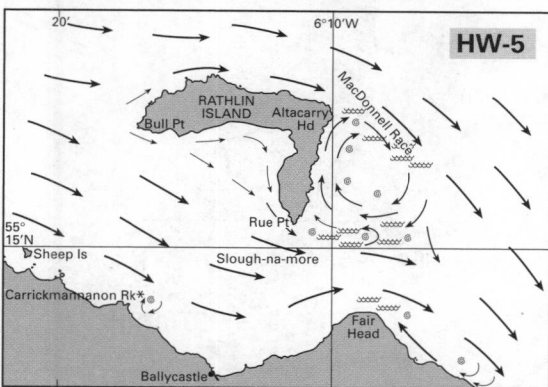

5 Hours before HW Dover (0605 after HW Greenock)

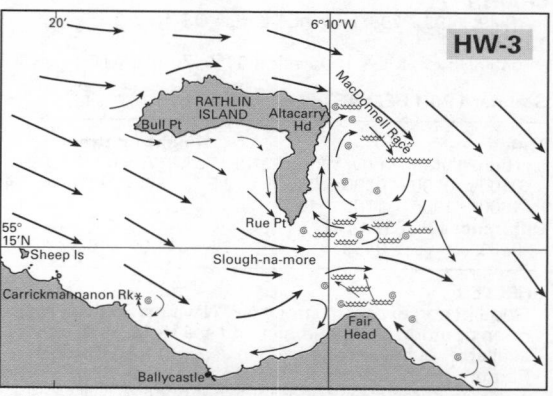

3 Hours before HW Dover (0420 before HW Greenock)

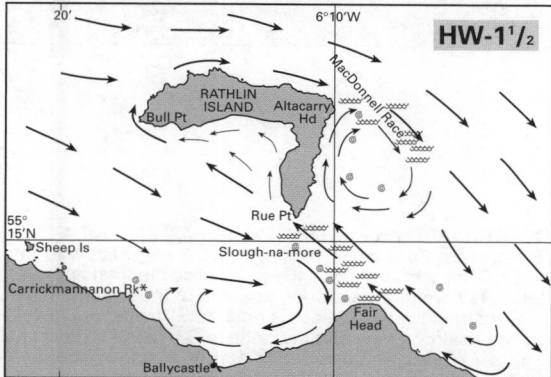

1½ Hours before HW Dover (0250 before HW Greenock)

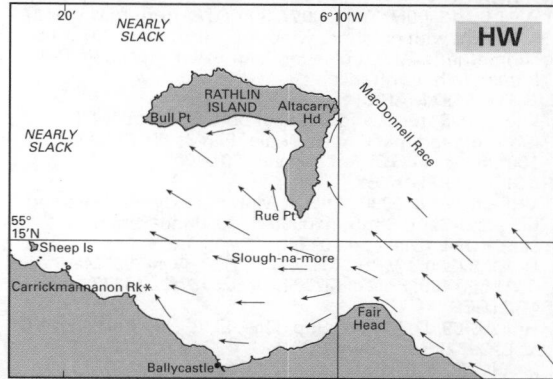

HW Dover (0120 before HW Greenock)

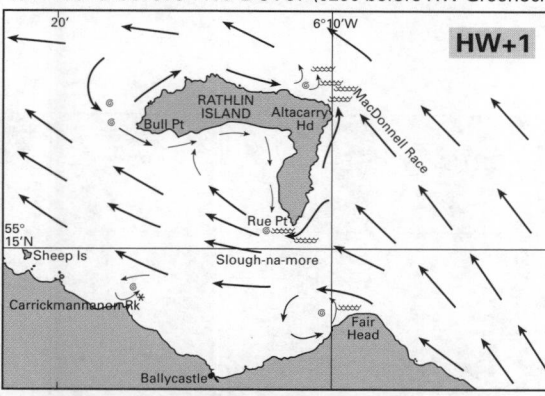

1 Hour after HW Dover (0020 before HW Greenock)

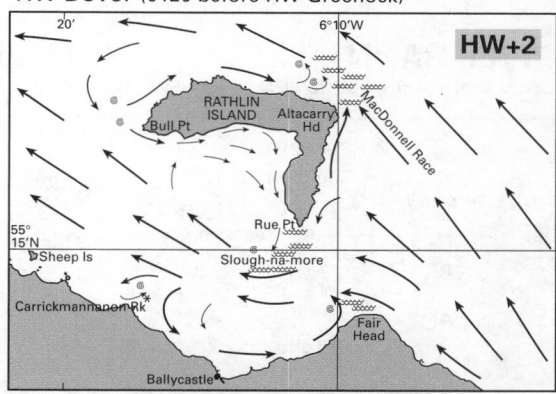

2 Hours after HW Dover (0040 after HW Greenock)

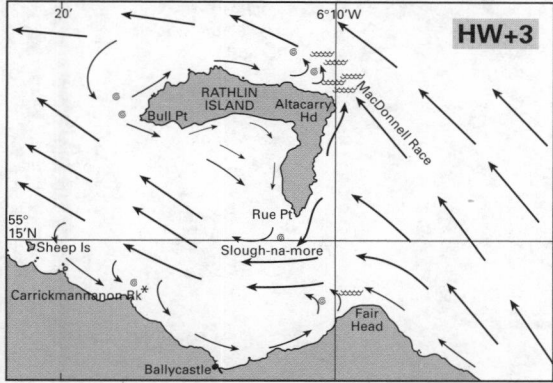

3 Hours after HW Dover (0140 after HW Greenock)

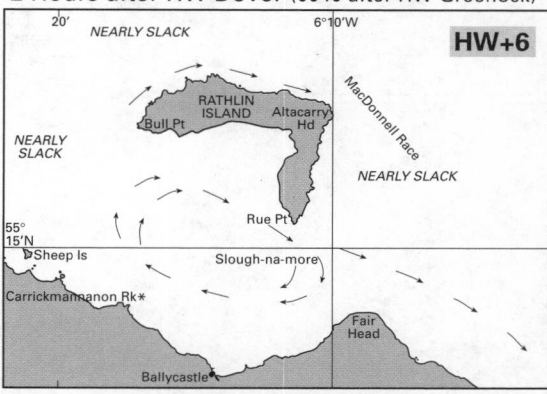

6 Hours after HW Dover (0440 after HW Greenock)

13

PORTRUSH   8-13-14

Antrim 55°12'·34N 06°39'·49W   Rtg 3-2-1

CHARTS
AC 49, 2499, 2798; Imray C64; Irish OS 4
TIDES
–0400 Dover; ML 1·1; Duration 0610; Zone 0 (UT)

Standard Port BELFAST (◄──)

Times				Height (metres)			
High Water		Low Water		MHWS	MHWN	MLWN	MLWS
0100	0700	0000	0600	3·5	3·0	1·1	0·4
1300	1900	1200	1800				
Differences PORTRUSH							
–0433		–0433		–1·6	–1·6	–0·3	0·0

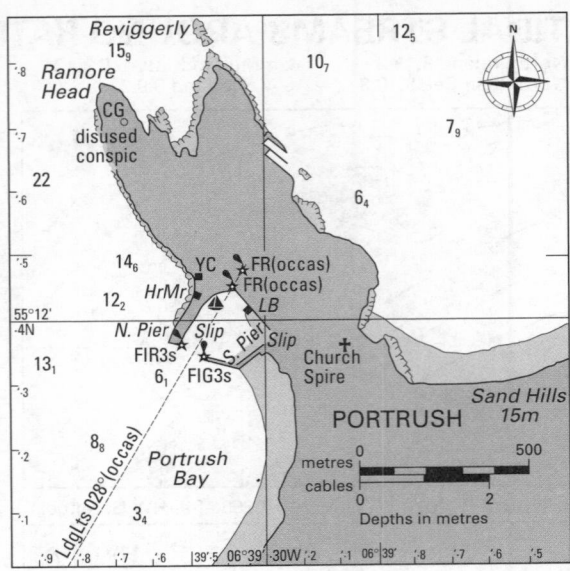

SHELTER
Good in hbr, except in strong NW/N winds. Berth on N pier or on pontoon at NE end of it and see Hr Mr. A ⚓ may be available, but very congested in season. ⚓ on E side of Ramore Hd in Skerries Roads 1ca S of Large Skerrie gives good shelter in most conditions, but open to NW sea/swell.
NAVIGATION
WPT 55°13'·00N 06°41'·00W, 308°/128° from/to N pier lt, 1·1M. Ent with on-shore winds >F 4 is difficult. Beware submerged bkwtr projecting 20m SW from N pier. Depth is 2·8m in hbr entrance.
LIGHTS AND MARKS
Ldg lts 028° (occas, for LB use) both FR 6/8m 1M; R △ on metal bn and metal mast. N pier Fl R 3s 6m 3M; vis 220°-160°. S pier Fl G 3s 6m 3M; vis 220°-100°.
RADIO TELEPHONE
VHF Ch 12 16 (0900-1700LT, Mon-Fri; extended evening hrs June-Sept; Sat-Sun: 0900–1700, June-Sept only).
TELEPHONE (Dial code 01265)
Hr Mr 822307; MRSC (01247) 463933; ⌗ 44803; Marinecall 0891 500 465; Police 822721; Dr 823767; Ⓗ 44177.
FACILITIES
Hbr AB £9, D, FW, M, Slip, Gas, El, Ⓔ, &; **Portrush YC** ☎ 823932, Bar; **Town** EC Wed; V, R, Bar, ◻, D & P (cans), ✉, Ⓑ, ⇌, ✈ (Belfast). Giant's Causeway is 10M ENE.

PORTSTEWART, Antrim, 55°11'·21N 06°43'·21W. AC 49. Tides as for Portrush. A tiny hbr 1·1ca S of Portstewart Pt lt, Oc R 10s 21m 5M, vis 040°–220°, obscd in final appr. A temp, fair weather berth (£9) at S end of inner basin in 0·8 – 1·7m; the very narrow ent is open to SW wind and swell. Beware salmon nets and rks close to S bkwtr. Facilities: EC Thurs; FW, Gas, D (tanker), Slip, Bar, V, R, handy shops.

RIVER BANN   8-13-15

Londonderry/Antrim 55°10'·32N 06°46'·35W   Rtg 3-2-2

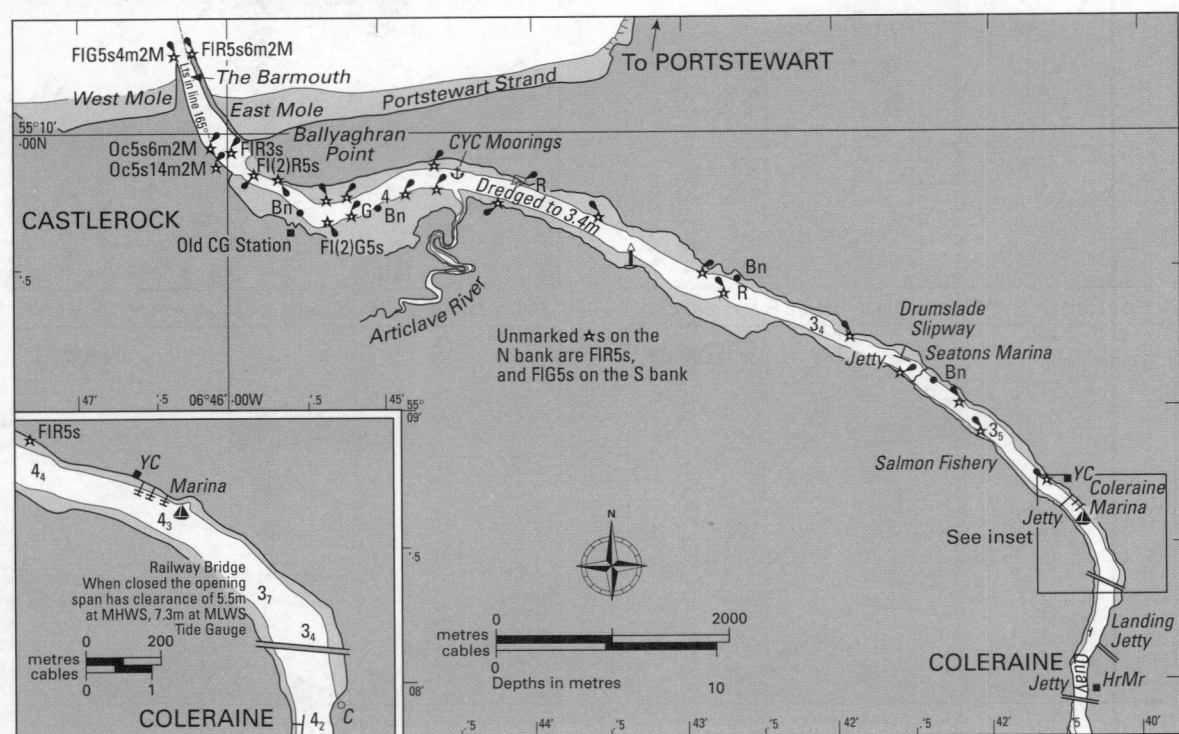

RIVER BANN *continued*

CHARTS
AC 2499, 2798, 2723; Imray C64; Irish OS 4

TIDES
–0345 Dover (Coleraine); ML 1·1; Duration 0540; Zone 0 (UT)

Standard Port BELFAST (←—)

Times				Height (metres)			
High Water		Low Water		MHWS	MHWN	MLWN	MLWS
0100	0700	0000	0600	3·5	3·0	1·1	0·4
1300	1900	1200	1800				
Differences COLERAINE							
–0403		–0403		–1·3	–1·2	–0·2	0·0

SHELTER
Good, once inside the river ent (The Barmouth) between 2 training walls, extending 2ca N from the beaches. Do not try to enter in strong on-shore winds or when swell breaks on the pierheads. If in doubt call *Coleraine Hbr Radio* or ring Hr Mr. ⚓ upstream of old CG stn, or berth at Seaton's or Coleraine marinas, 3½M & 4½M from ent, on NE bank.

NAVIGATION
WPT 55°11'·00N, 06°46'·65W, 345°/165° from/to ent, 0·72M. Appr from E of N to bring ldg lts into line at bkwtr ends. The sand bar is constantly moving but ent is dredged to approx 3·5m. Beware salmon nets across the width of the river at 2M or 4M above ent, May to July. Also beware commercial traffic.

LIGHTS AND MARKS
Ldg lts 165°, both Oc 5s 6/14m 2M, front on W pyramidal metal tr; rear W □ tr. Portstewart Pt, Oc R 10s, is 2M ENE.

RADIO TELEPHONE
Coleraine Hbr Radio Ch 12 (Mon-Fri: HO and when vessel due). Coleraine Marina Ch M.

TELEPHONE (Dial code 01265)
Hr Mr 42012, ☎ 52000; ✉ (01232) 358250 or 44803; MRSC (01247) 463933; Marinecall 0891 500 465; Rly Bridge 42403; Police 44122; Ⓗ 44177; Dr 44831.

FACILITIES
Seatons Marina ☎ 832086, £8.00, BH (12 ton), CH, Slip. **Coleraine Hbr** ☎ 42012, BH (35 ton); **Coleraine (Borough Council) Marina** (45+15 visitors), ☎ 44768, £9, Slip, D, FW, R, BH (15 ton), AC; **Coleraine YC** ☎ 44503, Bar, M; **Services:** Gas, Kos, El, Ⓔ. **Town** EC Thurs; P & D (cans), V, R, ✉, Ⓑ, ⇌, ✈ (Belfast).

LOUGH FOYLE   8-13-16
Londonderry (to SE)/Donegal (to NW) 55°14'N 06°54'W

CHARTS
AC 2499, 2798, 2723; Imray C64; Irish OS 3, 4, 7

TIDES
Warren Point –0430 Dover
Moville) –0350 Dover
Moville) –0055 Londonderry
Moville) –0400 Belfast
Culmore Point –0025 Londonderry
Londonderry –0255 Dover
ML 1·6; Duration 0615; Zone 0 (UT)

Standard Port GALWAY (—→)

Times				Height (metres)			
High Water		Low Water		MHWS	MHWN	MLWN	MLWS
0200	0900	0200	0800	5·1	3·9	2·0	0·6
1400	2100	1400	2000				
Differences LONDONDERRY							
+0254	+0319	+0322	+0321	–2·4	–1·8	–0·8	–0·1
INISHTRAHULL							
+0100	+0100	+0115	+0200	–1·8	–1·4	–0·4	–0·2
PORTMORE							
+0120	+0120	+0135	+0135	–1·3	–1·1	–0·4	–0·1
TRAWBREAGA BAY							
+0115	+0059	+0109	+0125	–1·1	–0·8	No data	

SHELTER
The SE side of the Lough is low lying and shallow. The NW rises steeply and has several village hbrs between the ent and Londonderry (often referred to as Derry).
Greencastle: a busy fishing hbr, open to swell in winds SW to E. Only advised for yachts in emergency.
Moville: the pier, with 1·5m at the end, is near the village (shops closed all day Wed), but is considerably damaged. ⚓ outside hbr is exposed; inside for shoal draft only.
Carrickarory: pier/quay is condemned as unsafe. ⚓ in bay is sheltered in winds from SW to NNW.
Culmore Bay: Complete shelter; ⚓ 1½ca W of Culmore Pt in pleasant cove, 4M from Londonderry.
Londonderry: Rarely used by yachts, although commercial operations have been transferred to new facilities at Lisahally (55°02'·6N 07°15'·6W). AB on non-commercial quay below Guildhall or ⚓ close below Craigavon Bridge clearance 1·7m.

NAVIGATION
WPT Tuns PHM buoy, Fl R 3s, 55°14'·01N 06°53'·38W, 055°/235° from/to Warren Pt lt, 2·5M. The Tuns bank lies 3M NE of Magilligan Pt. The main or N Chan, ¾M wide, runs NW of The Tuns; a lesser chan, min depth 4m, runs 3ca off shore around NE side of Magilligan Pt. Beware commercial traffic. Foyle Bridge at Rosses Pt has 32m clearance. In June and July the chan is at times obstructed by salmon nets at night. N Chan tides reach 3½kn, and up in the river the ebb runs up to 6kn.

LIGHTS AND MARKS
Inishowen Fl (2) WRG 10s 28m 18/14M; W tr, two B bands; vis G197°–211°, W211°–249°, R249°–000°; Horn (2) 30s. Warren Pt Fl 1·5s 9m 10M; W tr, G abutment; vis 232°–061°. Magilligan Pt QR 7m 4M; R structure. The main chan up to Londonderry is very well lit. Foyle Bridge centre FW each side; VQG on W pier; VQR on E pier.

RADIO TELEPHONE
VHF Ch **14** 12 16 (H24). Traffic and nav info Ch 14.

TELEPHONE (Dial code 01504)
Hr Mr (at Lisahally) 860555, ☎ 861168; MRSC (01247) 463933; ✉ 261937 or (01232) 358250; Marinecall 0891 500 465; Police 261893; Dr 264868; Ⓗ 45171.

FACILITIES (Londonderry)
Hbr Mr ☎ 860555, M, FW; **Prehen Boat Club** ☎ 43405. **City** P & D (cans), ME, El, V, R, Bar, ✉, Ⓑ, ⇌, ✈.

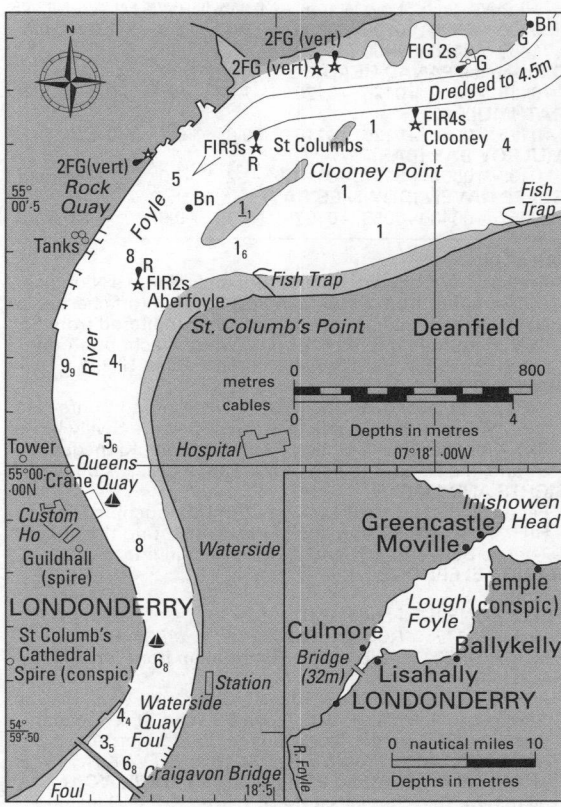

LOUGH SWILLY   8-13-17
Donegal 55°17'N 07°34'W

CHARTS
AC 2697; Irish OS 2, 3, 6

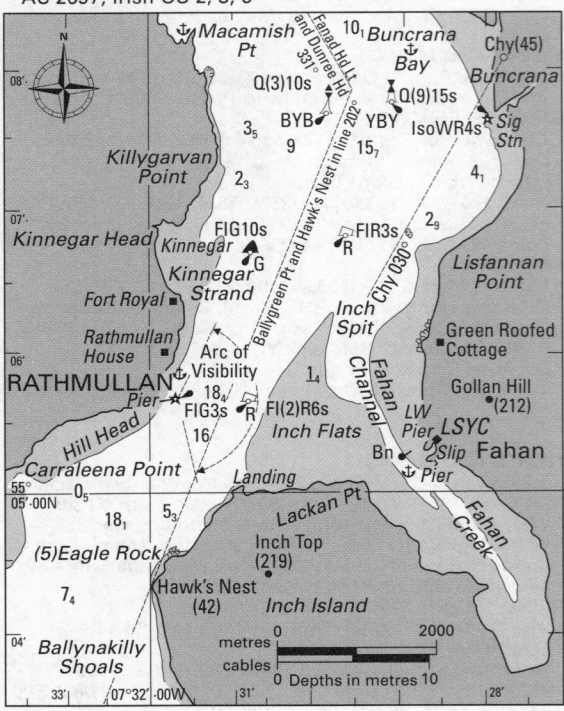

TIDES
−0500 Dover; ML 2·3; Duration 0605; Zone 0 (UT)

Standard Port GALWAY (⟶)

Times				Height (metres)			
High Water		Low Water		MHWS	MHWN	MLWN	MLWS
0200	0900	0200	0800	5·1	3·9	2·0	0·6
1400	2100	1400	2000				
Differences FANAD HEAD							
+0115	+0040	+0125	+0120	−1·1	−0·9	−0·5	−0·1
RATHMULLAN							
+0125	+0050	+0126	+0118	−0·8	−0·7	−0·1	−0·1
MULROY BAY (BAR)							
+0108	+0052	+0102	+0118	−1·2	−1·0	No data	
SHEEP HAVEN (DOWNIES BAY)							
+0057	+0043	+0053	+0107	−1·1	−0·9	No data	

SHELTER
Ent easy, but beware downdrafts on E side. ⚓s N of Inch Is may suffer from swell. ⚓ in Port Salon B (off chartlet to NW), except in E'lies; off Macamish Pt sheltered from SE to N; Rathmullan Road N of pier, where yacht pontoon lies N/S in 3·6m MLWS; Fahan Creek, ent at HW−1.

NAVIGATION
WPT 55°17'·50N 07°34'·50W, 352°/172° from/to Dunree Hd lt, 5·7M. Main chan is well lit/buoyed. Beware Swilly More Rks, Kinnegar Spit, Colpagh Rks off E shore, Kinnegar Strand, Inch Flats and fish farms. Fahan Creek is buoyed.

LIGHTS AND MARKS
Fanad Hd lt, Fl (5) WR 20s 39m 18/14M, touching Dunree Hd lt, Fl (2) WR 5s 46m 12/9M, leads 151° into the Lough. Thence Ballygreen Pt and Hawk's Nest in line at 202°.

RADIO TELEPHONE
None.

TELEPHONE (Dial code 074)
Hr Mr 58177; MRCC (01) 6620922/3; ⌗ 21935; Police 58113; Dr 58135; Pier Hotel, Rathmullan pontoon 58178.

FACILITIES
RATHMULLAN: **Pier** AB (£10), AC, C (5 ton), FW, L, M, Slip; **Services**: CH, M, ⊡, R, Bar. **Town** EC Wed; D & P (cans), Kos, Bar, R, V, ⊠, Ⓑ, ⇌, ✈ (bus to Londonderry).
RAMELTON: AB, L. **Town** Bar, P & D (cans), FW, Kos, R, V, ⊠.
FAHAN: AB on pontoon, Slip, FW, L, R; **L Swilly YC** ☎ 60189, M, Bar; **Services**: (1M SE), Kos, V, P & D (cans).

WEATHER BROADCASTS BY LOCAL RADIO STATIONS

Reception Areas: Malin Head to Downpatrick Hd (54°20'N 09°21'W); and Malin Head to Slyne Head.

MWR FM   *Daily:* 0800, 2000UT, broadcasts a coastal forecast, synopsis, gale warnings and 24 hrs outlook for NW and W Irish coastal waters from Fair Head to Slyne Head; plus visibility reports for all Irish coastal waters and Irish Sea; and heavy swell warnings for SW and N Irish coastal waters.
Storm warnings are broadcast on or about H from 0704 to 2359UT.
There are transmitters at:
Kiltimagh (53°52'N 09°03'W) on 95·8MHz and at Achill Island (53°57'N 10°01'W) on 97·1MHz.

RTE Radio 1 (See 5.8.1)
There are transmitters at:
Maghera, Co Donegal (54°46'N 08°31'W) on 88·8MHz.

AGENTS WANTED

If you are interested in becoming our agent for any of the following ports, please write to: The Editor, Edington House, Trent, Sherborne, Dorset DT9 4SR, England – and get your free copy of the Almanac annually. You do not have to live in a port to be the agent, but should at least be a fairly regular visitor.

Plymouth
Walton-on-the-Naze
Hopeman
Burghead
Findhorn
Nairn
Inverness
Loch Aline
Craobh
Workington
Lough Swilly
Portbail
St Malo/Dinard
Le Légué/St Brieuc
Lampaul
L'Aberildut
Douarnenez
Lorient
River Étel
Le Palais (Belle Ile)

Port Haliguen
La Trinité-sur-Mer
Piriac
St Nazaire/Loire
Pornic
St Gilles-Croix-de-Vie
Les Sables d'Olonne
River Seudre
Port Bloc/Gironde
Anglet/Bayonne
St Jean-de-Luz
Hendaye
Grandcamp-Maisy
Port-en-Bessin
Ouistreham/Caen
Dives
St Valéry-en-Caux
Dunkerque
Emden
Langeoog

OTHER HARBOURS AND ANCHORAGES IN DONEGAL

MULROY BAY, Donegal, 55°15'·30N 07°46'·30W. AC 2699; HW (bar) –0455 on Dover. See 8.13.17. Beware Limeburner Rk, (marked by NCM buoy, Q, whis) 3M N of ent and the bar which is dangerous in swell or onshore winds. Ent at half flood (not HN); chan lies between Bar Rks and Sessiagh Rks, thence through First, Second and Third Narrows (with strong tides) to Broad Water. HW at the head of the lough is 2¼ hrs later than at the bar. ‡s: Close SW of Ravedy Is (Fl 3s 9m 3M); Fanny's Bay (2m), excellent; Rosnakill Bay (3·5m) in SE side; Cranford Bay; Milford Port (3 to 4m). Beware power cable 6m, over Moross chan, barring North Water to masted boats. Facilities: **Milford Port** AB, FW, V; **Fanny's Bay** ✉, Shop at Downings village (1M), hotel at Rosepenna (¾M).

SHEEP HAVEN, Donegal, 55°11'·00N 07°51'·00W. AC 2699. HW –0515 on Dover. See 8.13.17. Bay is 4M wide with many ‡ s, easily accessible in daylight, but exposed to N winds. Beware rks for 3ca off Rinnafaghla Pt; also Wherryman Rks, which dry, 1ca off E shore 2¼M S of Rinnafaghla Pt. ‡ in Downies (or Downings) Bay to SW of pier; in Pollcormick Inlet close W in 3m; in Ards Bay for excellent shelter, but beware the bar in strong winds. Lts: Portnablahy Idg Its 125°, both Oc 6s 7/12m 2M, B col, W bands; Downies pier hd, Fl R 3s 5m 2M, R post. Facilities: (Downies) EC Wed; V, FW, P (cans 300m), R, Bar; (Portnablahy Bay) V, P (cans), R, Bar.

GWEEDORE HBR/BUNBEG, Donegal, 55°03'·75N 08°18'·87W. AC 1883. Tides see 8.13.18. Gweedore hbr, the estuary of the R Gweedore, has sheltered ‡s or temp AB at Bunbeg Quay, usually full of FVs. Apprs via Gola N or S Sounds are not simple especially in poor visibility. N Sound is easier with Idg Its 171°, both Oc 3s 9/13m 2M, B/W bns, on the SE tip of Gola Is. (There are also ‡s on the S and E sides of Gola Is). E of Bo Is the bar 0·4m has a Fl G 3s and the chan, lying E of Inishinny Is and W of Inishcoole, is marked by a QG and 3 QR. A QG marks ent to Bunbeg. Night ent not advised. Facilities: FW, D at quay; V, ✉, Ⓑ, Bar at village ½M.

BURTONPORT, Donegal, 54°58'·93N 08°26'·60W. AC 2792, 1879. HW –0525 on Dover; ML 2·0m; Duration 0605. See 8.13.18. Normal ent via N Chan. Hbr very full, no space to ‡; berth on local boat at pier or go to Rutland Hbr or Aran Is. Ent safe in all weathers except NW gales. Ldg marks/lts: N Chan Idg Its on Inishcoo 119°, both Iso 6s 6/11m 1M; front W bn, B band; rear B bn, Y band. Rutland Is Idg Its 138°, both Oc 6s 8/14m 1M; front W bn, B band; rear B bn, Y band. Burtonport Idg Its 068°, both FG 17/23m 1M; front Gy bn, W band; rear Gy bn, Y band. Hr Mr ☎ (075) 42258 (43170 home), 🛥 (074) 41205; VHF Ch 06, 12, **14**, 16. Facilities: D (just inside pier), FW (root of pier), P (½M inland). **Village** Bar, ✉, R, V, Kos.

TEELIN HARBOUR, Donegal, 54°37'·50N 08°37'·87W. AC 2792. Tides as for Killybegs (below). A possible passage ‡, being mid-way between Rathlin O'Birne and Killybegs. But the hbr is open to S'ly swell and prone to squalls in NW winds. Ent, 1ca wide, is close E of Teelin Pt It, Fl R 10s, which is hard to see by day. ‡ on W side in 3m to N of pier, or on E side near derelict pier. Many moorings and, in the NE, mussel rafts. Facilities: possible FW, D, V at Carrick, 3M inland.

KILLYBEGS   8-13-18

Donegal 54°36'·90N 08°26'·80W   Rtg 1-3-3

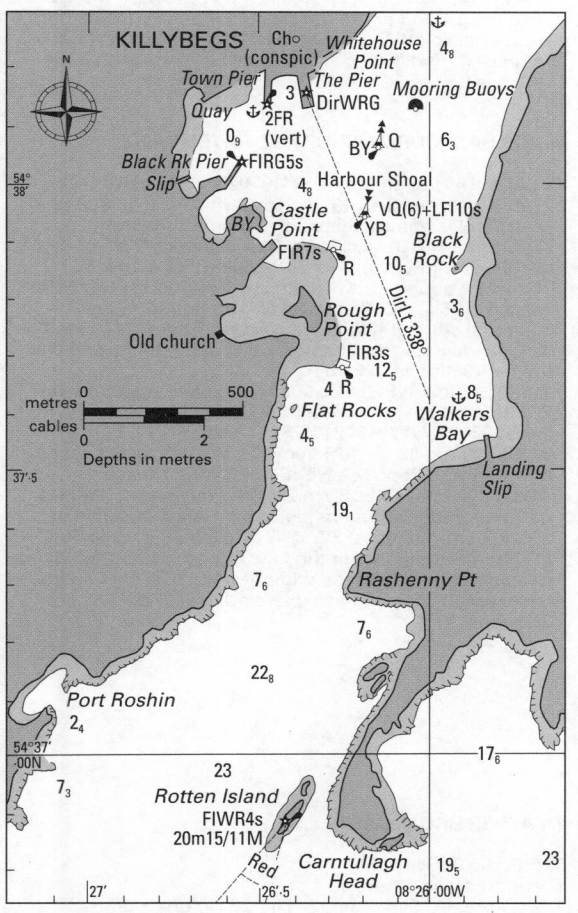

CHARTS
AC 2792, 2702; Irish OS 10
TIDES
–0520 Dover; ML 2·2; Duration 0620; Zone 0 (UT)

Standard Port GALWAY (→)

Times				Height (metres)			
High Water		Low Water		MHWS	MHWN	MLWN	MLWS
0600	1100	0000	0700	5·1	3·9	2·0	0·6
1800	2300	1200	1900				
Differences KILLYBEGS							
+0040	+0050	+0055	+0035	–1·0	–0·9	–0·5	0·0
GWEEDORE HARBOUR							
+0048	+0100	+0055	+0107	–1·3	–1·0	–0·5	–0·1
BURTONPORT							
+0042	+0055	+0115	+0055	–1·2	–1·0	–0·6	–0·1
DONEGAL HARBOUR (SALTHILL QUAY)							
+0038	+0050	+0052	+0104	–1·2	–0·9		No data

SHELTER
Secure natural hbr, but some swell in SSW winds. A busy major FV port, H24 access. ‡ about 2½ca NE of the Pier, off blue shed (Gallagher Bros) in 3m, clear of FV wash. Or **Bruckless Hbr**, about 2M E at the head of McSwyne's Bay, is a pleasant ‡ in 1·8m, sheltered from all except SW winds. Ent on 038° between rks; ICC SDs are essential.
NAVIGATION
WPT 54°36'·00N 08°27'·00W, 202°/022° from/to Rotten Is It, 0·94M. From W, beware Manister Rk (covers at HW; dries at LW) off Fintragh B. Keep mid chan until off Rough Pt, then follow the Dir It or Y ◇ Idg marks 338° into hbr.
LIGHTS AND MARKS
Rotten Is It, Fl WR 4s 20m 15/11M, W tr, vis W255°–008°, R008°–039°, W039°–208°. Dir It 338°, F W and Al WG/WR; W sector 336°-340° (see 8.13.4). Harbour Shoal (2·3m) is marked by a SCM and NCM It buoy.
RADIO TELEPHONE
Hr Mr VHF Ch 16 14; essential to request a berth.
TELEPHONE (Dial code 073)
Hr Mr 31032; MRCC (01) 6620922/3; Bundoran Inshore Rescue ☎ (072) 41713; ⌗ 31070; Police 31002; Dr 31148 (Surgery).
FACILITIES
Town Pier ☎ 31032, AB (free), M, D & P (cans), FW, ME, EI, CH, Slip, V, R, Bar; **Black Rock Pier** AB, M, Slip, D; **Services:** Sh, C (12 ton), ME, EI, Sh, Kos, Ⓔ. **Town** EC Wed; ✉, Ⓑ, ⇌ (bus to Sligo), ✈ (Strandhill).

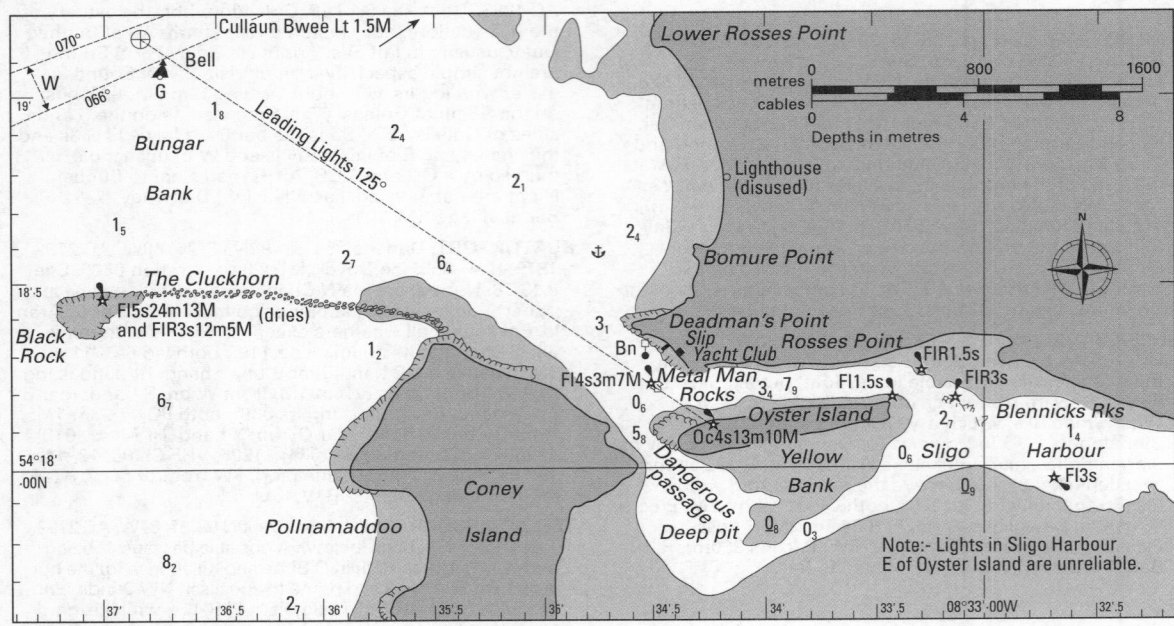

SLIGO 8-13-19

Sligo 54°18'·30N 08°34'·70W Rtg 3-4-1

CHARTS
AC 2852, 2767; Imray C54; Irish OS 16, 25

TIDES
−0511 Dover; ML 2·3; Duration 0620; Zone 0 (UT)

Standard Port GALWAY (⟶)

Times				Height (metres)			
High Water		Low Water		MHWS	MHWN	MLWN	MLWS
0600	1100	0000	0700	5·1	3·9	2·0	0·6
1800	2300	1200	1900				
Differences SLIGO HARBOUR (Oyster Is)							
+0043	+0055	+0042	+0054	−1·0	−0·9	−0·5	−0·1
MULLAGHMORE							
+0036	+0048	+0047	+0059	−1·4	−1·0	−0·4	−0·2
BALLYSADARE BAY (Culleenamore)							
+0059	+0111	+0111	+0123	−1·2	−0·9	No data	
KILLALA BAY (Inishcrone)							
+0035	+0055	+0030	+0050	−1·3	−1·2	−0·7	−0·2

SHELTER
The lower hbr is fairly exposed; ⚓ along N side of Oyster Island, or proceed 4M (not at night) up to the shelter of Sligo town; 2nd berth below bridge for yachts.

NAVIGATION
WPT 54°19'·15N 08°36'·77W, 305°/125° from/to front ldg lt, 1·6M. The passage between Oyster Island and Coney Island is marked 'Dangerous'. Pass N of Oyster Is leaving Blennick Rks to port. Passage up to Sligo town between training walls. Some perches are in bad repair. Pilots at Raghly Pt and Rosses Pt. Chan up to quays dredged 1·6m.

LIGHTS AND MARKS
Cullaun Bwee Dir It (1·5M ENE off chartlet), Fl (2) WRG 10s 8m10/8M (H24), W sector 066°-070°. Ldg lts (H24) lead 125° into ent: front, Fl 4s 3m 7M, Metal Man Rks (statue of a man on a twr); rear, Oyster Is lt ho, Oc 4s 13m 10M. Lts up-channel are unreliable.

RADIO TELEPHONE
Pilots VHF Ch 12 16.

TELEPHONE (Dial code 071)
Hbr Office 61197; MRCC (01) 6620922/3; ≣ 61064; Police 42031; Dr 42886; Ⓗ 71111.

FACILITIES
No 3 berth (next to bridge) AB £10, P & D (in cans), FW, ME, El, Sh, CH, C (15 ton); **Sligo YC** ☎ 77168, ⚓s, FW, Bar, Slip. **Services:** Slip, D, ME, El, Sh, SM, Gas; **Town** V, R, Bar, ✉, Ⓑ, ⇌ Irish Rail ☎ 69888, Bus ☎ 60066, ✈ (Strandhill) ☎ 68280.

MINOR HARBOUR ON S SIDE OF DONEGAL BAY

MULLAGHMORE 54°27'·90N 08°26'·80W. AC 2702. Tides see 8.13.19. Fair weather ⚓ in 2-3m off hbr ent, sheltered by Mullaghmore Head, except from N/NE winds. For ⚓s near hbr ent; call Rodney Lomax at BY, ☎/✆ 071 66124, mobile ☎ 088 2727358. Keep close to N pier to avoid a rk drying 1m, ⅔ of the way across the ent toward the S pier. Take the ground or dry out against the piers inside hbr, access approx HW±2 when least depth is 2m. VHF Ch 16 18 (occas). Facilities: BY, Sh, D (cans), V, R, Bar.

MINOR HARBOUR/ANCHORAGE TO THE WEST

KILLALA BAY, Sligo/Mayo, 54°13'·02N 09°12'·80W. AC 2715. Tides, see 8.13.19 The bay, which is exposed to the N and NE, is entered between Lenadoon Pt and Kilcummin Hd, 6M to the W. Carrickpatrick ECM buoy, Q (3) 10s, in mid-bay marks St Patrick's Rks to the W. Thence, if bound for Killala hbr, make good Killala SHM buoy, Fl G 6s, 7½ca to the SSW. The Round Tr and cathedral spire at Killala are conspic. Four sets of ldg bns/lts lead via a narrow chan between sand dunes and over the bar (0·3m) as follows:
1. 230°, Rinnaun Pt lts Oc 10s 7/12m 5M, ☐ concrete trs.
2. 215°, Inch Is, ☐ concrete trs; the rear has Dir lt Fl WRG 2s, G205°-213°, W213°-217°, R217°-225°.
3. 196°, Kilroe lts Oc 4s 5/10m 2M, W ☐ trs, which lead to ⚓ in Bartragh Pool, 6ca NE of Killala hbr; thence
4. 236°, Pier lts Iso 2s 5/7m 2M, W ◇ daymarks, lead via narrow, dredged chan to pier where AB is possible in about 1·5m. Facilities: FW, P & D (cans), V in town ½M, EC Thurs. Other hbrs in the bay: R Moy leading to Ballina should not be attempted without pilot/local knowledge. Inishcrone in the SE has a pier and lt, Fl WRG 1·5s 8m 2M; see 8.13.4.

WEATHER BROADCASTS

RTE Radio 1 (See 5.8.1)
There are transmitters at:
Truskmore, Co Sligo (54°22'N 08°22'W) on 88·2MHz.

WESTPORT (CLEW BAY)   8-13-20

Mayo 53°47'·85N 09°35'·40W   Rtg 4·4·1

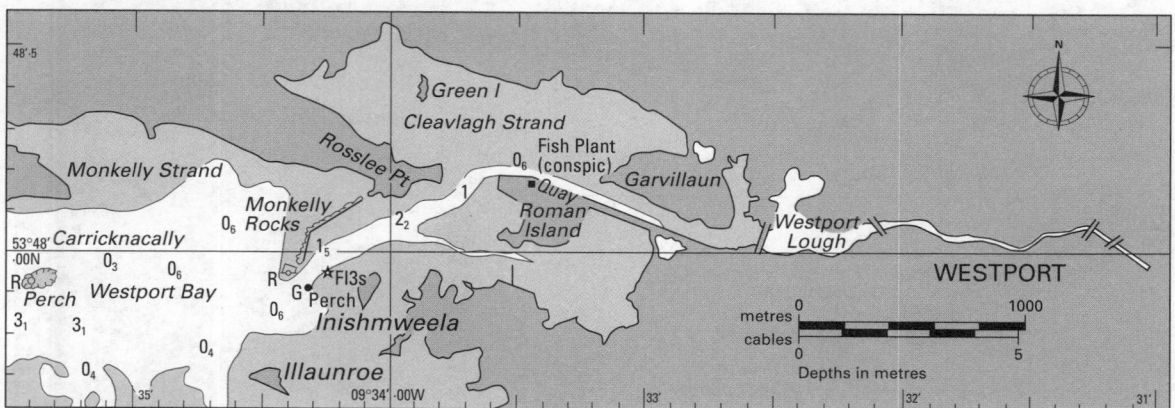

CHARTS
AC 2057, 2667; Imray C54; Irish OS 30, 31
TIDES
–0545 Dover; ML 2·5; Duration 0610; Zone 0 (UT)

Standard Port GALWAY (→)

Times				Height (metres)			
High Water		Low Water		MHWS	MHWN	MLWN	MLWS
0600	1100	0000	0700	5·1	3·9	2·0	0·6
1800	2300	1200	1900				
Differences INISHRAHER							
+0030	+0012	+0058	+0026	–0·6	–0·5	–0·3	–0·1
BROADHAVEN							
+0040	+0050	+0040	+0050	–1·4	–1·1	–0·4	–0·1
BLACKSOD QUAY							
+0025	+0035	+0040	+0040	–1·2	–1·0	–0·6	–0·2
BLACKSOD BAY (BULL'S MOUTH)							
+0101	+0057	+0109	+0105	–1·5	–1·0	–0·6	–0·1
CLARE ISLAND							
+0019	+0013	+0029	+0023	–1·0	–0·7	–0·4	–0·1
KILLARY HARBOUR							
+0021	+0015	+0035	+0029	–1·0	–0·8	–0·4	–0·1
INISHBOFIN HARBOUR							
+0013	+0009	+0021	+0017	–1·0	–0·8	–0·4	–0·1
CLIFDEN BAY							
+0005	+0005	+0016	+0016	–0·7	–0·5		No data
SLYNE HEAD							
+0002	+0002	+0010	+0010	–0·7	–0·5		No data

SHELTER
Secure ⚓s amongst the islands at all tides, as follows: E of Inishlyre in about 2m; E of Collan More via narrow ent off Rosmoney Pt; and 2ca NE of Dorinish More, good holding in lee of Dorinish Bar (dries). Or go up to Westport Quay HW±1½, to dry out on S side. Newport Hbr (dries) can be reached above mid-flood with careful pilotage (AC 2667); dry out against N quay or ⚓ at E end of Rabbit Is.
NAVIGATION
WPT 53°49'·20N 09°42'·10W, 251°/071° from/to Inishgort lt ho, 1·2M. Contact Tom Gibbons (Inishlyre Is) ☎ (098) 26381 for pilotage advice. Beware of Monkellys Rks (PHM buoy) and the Spit (G perch).
LIGHTS AND MARKS
Westport B entered via Inishgort lt, L Fl 10s 11m 10M (H24), and a series of ldg lines, but not advised at night. Final appr line 080° towards lt bn, Fl 3s. Chan from Westport Bay to Westport Quay, 1½M approx, is marked by bns.
RADIO TELEPHONE
None.
TELEPHONE (Dial code 098)
MRCC (01) 6620922/3; ⌗ (094) 21131; Police 25555; Ⓗ (094) 21733.
FACILITIES
Quays M, AB free, Slip, V, R, Bar; **Mayo SC** ☎ 26160 L, Slip, Bar, at Rosmoney (safe for leaving boat); **Glénans Irish SC** ☎ 26046 on Collan More Is; **Services:** Kos, El, Ⓔ; **Town** EC Wed; P & D (cans), ✉, Ⓑ, ⇌, ✈ (Galway/Knock).

OTHER ANCHORAGES FROM EAGLE IS TO SLYNE HEAD

BROAD HAVEN, Mayo, 54°16'·00N 09°53'·20W. AC 2703. See 8.13.20 for tides; ML 1·9m. A safe refuge in all but N'lies. Easy appr across Broad Haven Bay to the ent between Brandy Pt and Gubacashel Pt, Iso WR 4s27m 12/9M, W tr. 7ca S of this lt is Ballyglas Fl G 3s on W side. ⚓ close N or S of Ballyglas which has pier (2m); or in E'lies ⚓ 3ca S of Inver Pt out of the tide. Further S, the inlet narrows off Barrett Pt then turns W to Belmullet. Facilities: V, ✉.

PORTNAFRANKAGH Mayo, 54°14'·95N 10°06'·00W. AC 2703. Tides approx as Broad Haven. A safe passage ⚓, close to the coastal route, but swell enters in all winds. Appr toward Port Pt, thence keep to the N side for better water; middle and S side break in onshore winds. ⚓ in 4–5m on S side, close inshore. L and slip at new pier. Unlit, but Eagle Is lt, Fl (3) 10s 67m 26M H24, W tr, is 2M N. No facilities; Belmullet 4M, V.

BLACKSOD BAY, Mayo, 54°05'·00N 10°02'·00W. AC 2704. HW – 0525 on Dover; ML 2·2m; Duration 068. See 8.13.20. Safe ⚓ with no hidden dangers, access day or night. Good ⚓s NW of Blacksod Quay (3m); at Elly B (1·8m); Elly Hbr; Saleen B; N of Claggan Pt. Beware drying rk 3·5ca SSE of Ardmore Pt. Lts: Blacksod Pt, Fl (2) WR 7·5s 13m 9M, R189°-210°, W210°-018°. ECM buoy Q (3) 10s. Blacksod pier hd, 2 FR (vert) 6m 3M. No facilities, but supplies, inc P & D (cans), at Belmullet 2·5M N.

KILLARY HARBOUR, Mayo/Galway, 53°37'·83N 09°54'·00W. AC 2706. Tides 8.13.20. A spectacular 7M long inlet, narrow and deep. Appr in good vis to identify ldg marks. Doonee Is and Inishbarna bns lead 099° to ent. (Lat/Long above is 4ca W of Doonee Is on the ldg line). Caution fish farms, some with Fl Y lts. ⚓s off Dernasliggaun, Bundorragha and Leenaun at head of inlet. (Village: V, Bar, hotel). Enter Little Killary Bay 4ca S of Doonee. Rks at ent do not cover. Good ⚓ in 3m at hd of bay.

BALLYNAKILL, Galway, 53°34'·95N 10°03'·00W. AC 2706. Tides as Inishbofin/Killary. Easy appr between Cleggan Pt, Fl (3) WRG 15s and Rinvyle Pt. Usual ent N of Freaghillaun South Is, E of which is good passage ⚓ in 7m. Further E, Carrigeen and Ardagh Rks lie in mid-chan. Keep N for ⚓ in Derryinver B. S chan leads to ⚓s off Ross Pt; S of Roeillaun; or, inside bar dries 0·2m, in complete shelter at Fahy B. No facilities.

INISHBOFIN, Mayo, 53°36'·60N 10°13'·20W. AC 2707, 1820. HW –0555 on Dover; ML 1·9m. See 8.13.20. Very safe hbr once inside narrow ent. 2 conspic W trs lead 032°. ⚓ between new pier and Port Is. Old pier to the E dries. Gun Rock, Fl (2) 6s 8m 4M, vis 296°-253°. Facilities: FW, R, Bar, V, Hotel ☎ (095) 45803.

CLIFDEN BAY, Galway, 53°29'·40N 10°05'·90W. AC 2708, 1820. HW –0600 on Dover; Duration 068. Tides see 8.13.20. The high W bn on Carrickrana Rks, 2·8M WSW of Fishing Pt, must be identified before entering. Ldg marks 080°: W bn at Fishing Pt on with Clifden Castle. Beware bar at ent by Fishing Pt and another SE of creek going up to Clifden; also Doolick Rks, Coghan Rks and rks off Errislannon Pt. ⚓ between Larner Rks and Drinagh Pt; dry out against Clifden Quay (beware ruined training wall); or ⚓ in Ardbear Bay SE of Yellow Slate Rks in 3·4m. Keep clear of fish farms. Facilities: **Town** EC Thurs; Bar, Ⓑ, CH, D, P, ✉, R, V, Kos, FW, V, R, Dr, Ⓗ. Bus to Galway.

13

GALWAY BAY   8-13-21

Galway 53°12'N 09°08'W

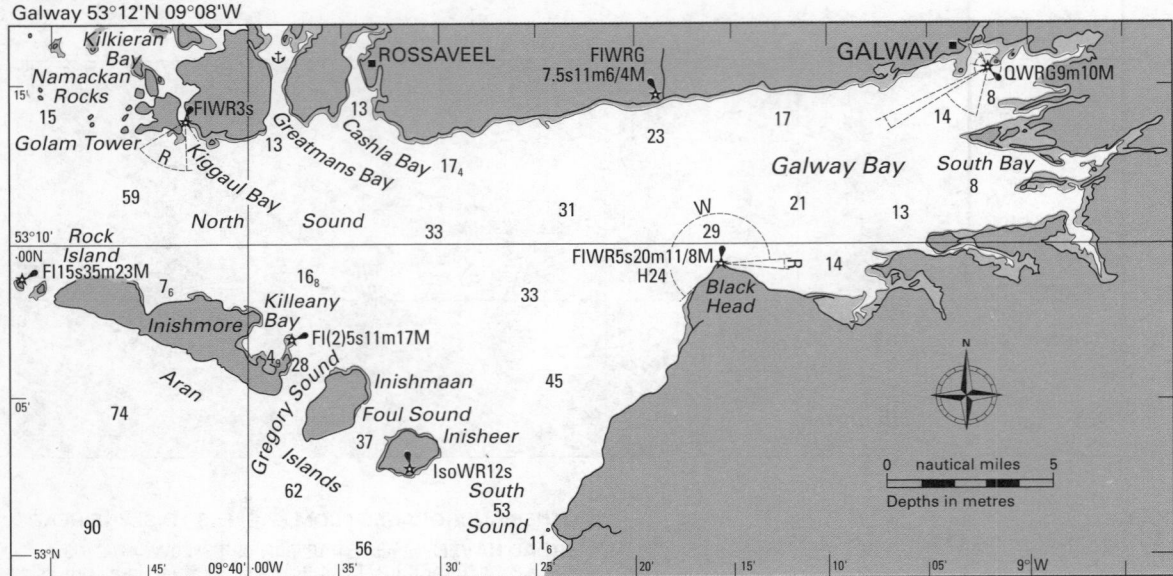

CHARTS
AC 1903, 1984, 3339, 2173; Imray C55; Irish OS 45, 46, 51

TIDES
−0555 Dover; ML 2·9; Duration 0620; Zone 0 (UT)

Standard Port GALWAY (⟶)

Times				Height (metres)			
High Water		Low Water		MHWS	MHWN	MLWN	MLWS
0600	1100	0000	0700	5·1	3·9	2·0	0·6
1800	2300	1200	1900				
Differences KILKIERAN COVE							
+0005	+0005	+0016	+0016	−0·3	−0·2	−0·1	0·0
ROUNDSTONE BAY							
+0003	+0003	+0008	+0008	−0·7	−0·5	−0·3	−0·1
KILLEANY BAY (Aran Islands)							
−0008	−0008	+0003	+0003	−0·4	−0·3	−0·2	−0·1
LISCANNOR							
−0003	−0007	+0006	+0002	−0·4	−0·3		No data

NOTE: Galway is a Standard Port and tidal predictions for each day of the year are given below.

SHELTER
Galway Bay is sheltered from large swells by Aran Is, but seas get up in the 20M from Aran Is to Galway. Beware salmon drift nets in the apps to many bays. The better ⚓s clock-wise from Slyne Head and around Galway Bay are:
Bunowen B: Easy ent NE of Split Rk. ⚓ in 3-4m below conspic Doon Hill. Shelter in W-NE winds; unsafe in S'ly.
Roundstone B: (Off chartlet.) Safe shelter/access, except in SE'ly. ⚓ in 2m off N quay; other ⚓s E'ward in Cashel B.
Kilkieran B: A long (14M), sheltered bay with many ⚓s to suit wind conditions. Easy ent abeam Golam Tr (conspic).
Kiggaul B: Easy ent, H24; ⚓ close W/NW of lt Fl WR 3s 5/3M. Depth 3 to 4m; exposed to S/SE winds.
Greatman B: Beware English Rk (dries 1·2m), Keeraun Shoal (breaks in heavy weather), Arkeena Rk, Trabaan Rk, Rin Rks and Chapel Rks. ⚓ off Natawny Quay or go alongside at Maumeen Quay.
Cashla B: Easiest hbr on this coast; ent in all weather. ⚓ off Sruthan pier. Rossaveel, opposite, is busy fish and ferry hbr.
Note: There is no safe hbr from Cashla to Galway (20M).
Bays between Galway and Black Hd have rks and shoals, but give excellent shelter. Kinvarra B, Aughinish B, South B and Ballyvaghan B are the main ones. Enter Kinvarra B with caution on the flood; beware rks. Berth in small drying hbr. Ballvaghan B, entered either side of Illaunloo Rk, leads to two piers (both dry) or ⚓ close NE in pool (3m). Best access HW±2..
Aran Islands: The only reasonable shelter is on Inishmore at Killeany Bay, but very crowded with FVs and exposed to E/NE winds. ⚓ S of Kilronan pier, or off Trawmore Strand; or in good weather at Portmurvy.

NAVIGATION
Enter the Bay by one of four Sounds:
(1)   N Sound between Inishmore and Golam Tr (conspic), 4½M wide, is easiest but beware Brocklinmore Bank in heavy weather.
(2)   Gregory Sound between Inishmore and Inishmaan, is free of dangers, but give Straw Is a berth of 2 to 3ca.
(3)   Foul Sound between Inishmaan and Inisheer; only danger is Pipe Rk (dries) at end of reef extending 3ca NW of Inisheer.
(4)   S Sound between Inisheer and mainland. Only danger Finnis Rk (dries 0·4m) 4½ca SE of E point of Inisheer (marked by ECM buoy Q (3) 10s). From S, beware Kilstiffin Rks off Liscanor B.

LIGHTS AND MARKS
Roundstone B: Croaghnakeela Is Fl 3·7s 7m 5M. Inishnee lt Fl (2) WRG 10s 9m 5/3M has W sector 017°-030°.
Kiggaul B: Fl WR 3s 5m 5/3M, W329°-359°, R359°-059°.
Cashla B: Killeen Pt Fl (3) WR 10s 6/3M; Lion Pt Dir (010°) Iso WRG 4s 8/6M, W008·5°-011·5°. Rossaveel ldg lts 116°, Oc 3s.
Black Hd lt Fl WR 5s 20m 11/8M H24, vis W045°-268°, R268°-276° covers Illanloo Rk.
Aran Islands:
Inishmore: Eeragh Island (Rk Is) Fl 15s 35m 23M, W tr, B bands. Killeany B: Straw Is, Fl (2) 5s 11m 17M. Kilronan pier Fl WG 1·5s. Ldg lts 192° both Oc 5s for Killeany hbr.
Inisheer: Iso WR 12s 34m 20/16M, Racon, vis W225°-245° (partially obscd 225°-231° beyond 7M), R245°-269° covers Finnis Rk, W269°-115°; obscd 115°-225°.

FACILITIES
BUNOWEN B: No facilities.
ROUNDSTONE B: V, FW, Bar, ✉, Bus to Galway.
KILKIERAN B: Bar, ☎, P, V, Bus to Galway.
KIGGAUL B: Bar (no ☎), shop at Lettermullen (1M).
GREATMAN B: Maumeen V, P (1M), Bar.
CASHLA B: **Carraroe** (1M SW) V, Hotel, ☎; **Rossaveel** Hr Mr ☎ 091-72109, FW, D, ME; **Costelloe** (1½M E), Hotel, ✉, Gge.
KILRONAN: (Killeany B, Inishmore) V, D, FW, ✉, Ferry to Galway, ✈ to Galway from airstrip on beach.

WEATHER BROADCASTS BY LOCAL RADIO STATIONS

Galway Bay FM   *Daily:* Every H+10 and H+31 (0900-1800LT) then every H+04 and H+31 (1900-0300LT), broadcasts a coastal forecast, including gale warnings for Galway Bay. There are transmitters at:
Galway City 95·8MHz and Knock Roe Hill 96·8.

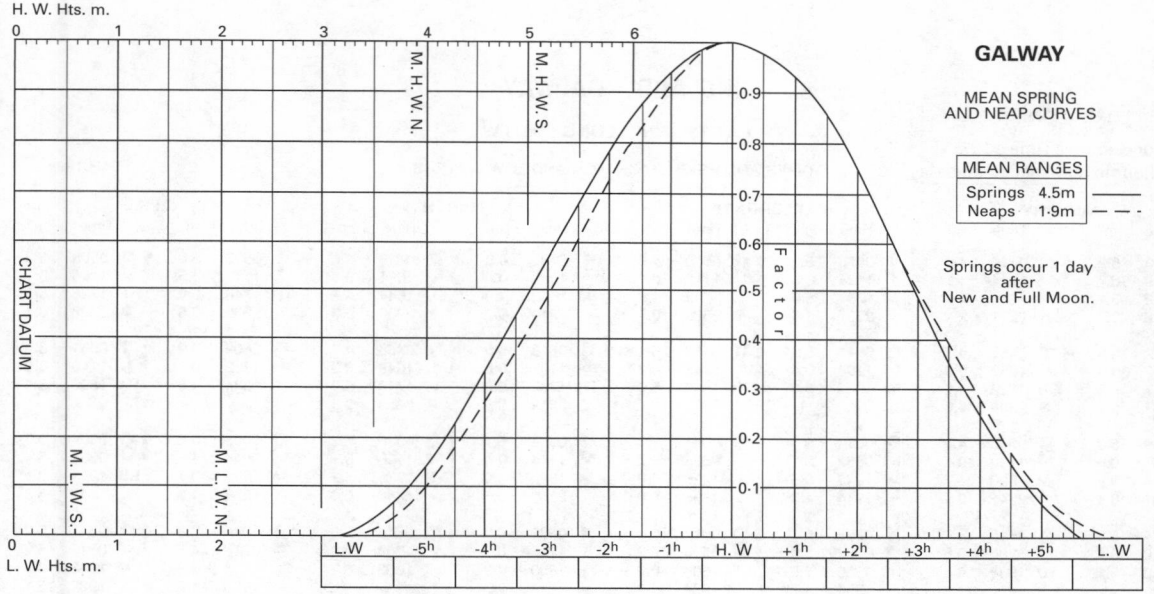

H. W. Hts. m.

GALWAY

MEAN SPRING
AND NEAP CURVES

MEAN RANGES	
Springs	4.5m
Neaps	1.9m

Springs occur 1 day
after
New and Full Moon.

CHART DATUM

L. W. Hts. m.

13

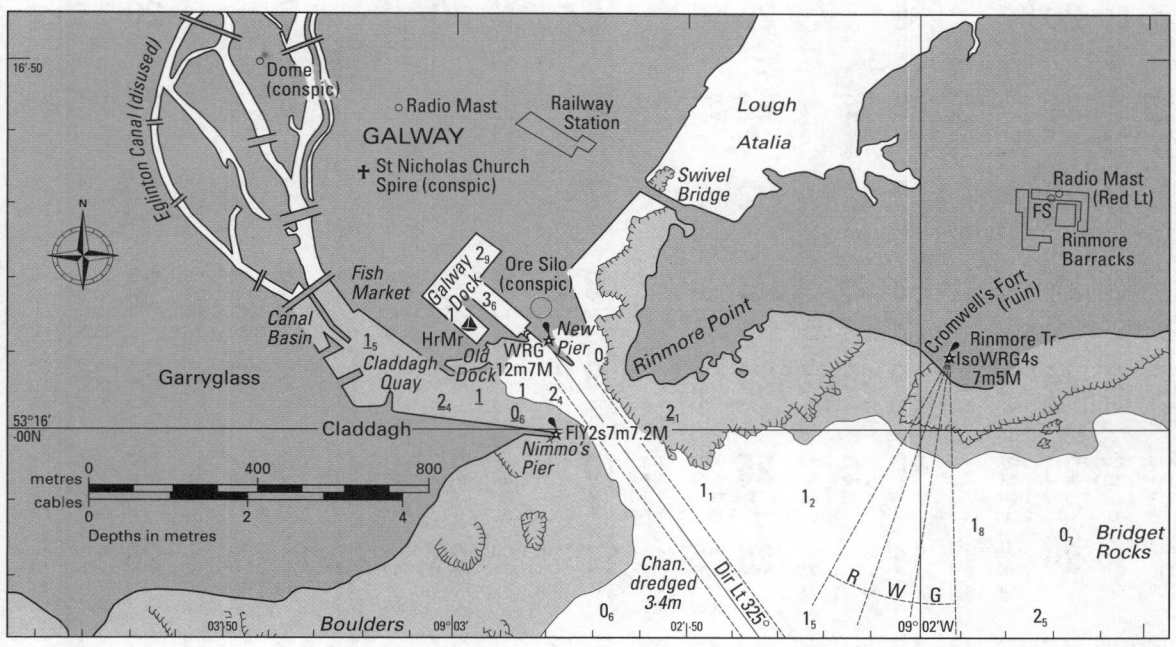

GALWAY HARBOUR 53°16'·07N 09°02'·74W Rtg 2-3-1

SHELTER
Very good in Galway hbr, being protected from SW by
Mutton Island. Dock gates open HW−2 to HW, when min
depth is 6m. Enter Galway dock and secure in SW corner
of basin, or ask Hr Mr for waiting berth on lead-in pier. It
is dangerous to lie in the 'Layby' (a dredged cut NE of
New pier) when wind is SE or S; if strong from these
points, seas sweep round the pierhead.
Note: Marina in Canal basin is under active discussion.
New Harbour (2·5M ESE and home of Galway Bay SC) is
nearest safe ⚓ to Galway.

NAVIGATION
Galway WPT 53°14'·80N 09°03'·40W, 241°/061° from/to
Leverets lt, 1·1M.

LIGHTS AND MARKS
Leverets Q WRG 9m 10M; B tr, W bands; G015°-058°, W058°-
065°, R065°-103°, G103°-143°, W143°-146°, R146°-015°.
Rinmore Iso WRG 4s 7m 5M; W □ tr; G359°-008°, W008°-
018°, R018°-027°.

Appr chan 325° is defined by a Dir lt WRG on New Pier,
sectors: FG 322¼°-323¾°, Al GW 3s 323¾°-324¾°,
FW 324¾°-325¼°, Al RW 3s 325¼°-326¼°, FR 326¼°-331¼°,
Fl R 3s 331¼°-332¼°.

RADIO TELEPHONE
Call Hr Mr Galway VHF Ch 12 16 (HW−2½ to HW+1).

TELEPHONE (Dial code 091)
Hr Mr 561874, ☎ 563738; MRCC (01) 6620922; Coast/Cliff
Rescue Service (099) 61107; Police 563161; Dr 562453.

FACILITIES
Dock AB £IR5 (see Hr Mr), FW, El, ME, Sh, C (35 ton), CH,
LB, PV, SM, V, R, Bar; **Galway YC** M, Slip, FW, C, CH, Bar;
Galway Bay SC ☎ 794527, M, CH, Bar;
Town EC Mon; P, D, ACA, Gas, Gaz, Kos, V, R, Bar, ✉, Ⓑ,
🚄, ✈ Carnmore (6M to the E of Galway City).

IRELAND – GALWAY

LAT 53°16′N   LONG   9°03′W

TIMES AND HEIGHTS OF HIGH AND LOW WATERS

YEAR **1999**

TIME ZONE (UT)
For Summer Time add ONE hour in non-shaded areas

JANUARY

Time	m	Time	m
1 0403 1005 F 1629 2222	5.2 0.7 5.1 0.7	**16** 0419 1014 SA 1644 2231	4.6 1.1 4.4 1.1
2 0452 1052 SA 1717 O 2307	5.3 0.5 5.2 0.7	**17** 0457 1053 SU 1722 ● 2308	4.7 0.9 4.6 1.0
3 0539 1137 SU 1804 2351	5.3 0.5 5.2 0.7	**18** 0536 1130 M 1800 2345	4.9 0.7 4.7 0.9
4 0624 1220 M 1850	5.3 0.5 5.1	**19** 0615 1206 TU 1838	5.0 0.6 4.8
5 0034 0708 TU 1303 1934	0.8 5.2 0.6 4.9	**20** 0022 0653 W 1244 1916	0.8 5.0 0.5 4.8
6 0117 0752 W 1345 2020	1.0 4.9 0.8 4.6	**21** 0101 0732 TH 1322 1956	0.8 5.0 0.6 4.7
7 0201 0836 TH 1428 2108	1.3 4.7 1.1 4.4	**22** 0142 0813 F 1404 2040	1.0 4.9 0.7 4.6
8 0248 0924 F 1516 2201	1.5 4.4 1.4 4.1	**23** 0227 0858 SA 1450 2132	1.2 4.7 1.0 4.4
9 0342 1015 SA 1611 2258	1.8 4.1 1.7 3.9	**24** 0319 0953 SU 1543 2233	1.4 4.5 1.2 4.2
10 0446 1111 SU 1717 2358	2.0 3.9 1.9 3.9	**25** 0420 1056 M 1646 2340	1.6 4.3 1.5 4.2
11 0554 1216 M 1828	2.1 3.8 1.9	**26** 0536 1205 TU 1804	1.7 4.2 1.6
12 0102 0700 TU 1331 1935	3.9 2.0 3.8 1.9	**27** 0053 0703 W 1322 1934	4.2 1.6 4.3 1.5
13 0206 0800 W 1436 2029	4.0 1.9 3.9 1.7	**28** 0206 0813 TH 1432 2037	4.4 1.4 4.4 1.3
14 0257 0850 TH 1525 2113	4.2 1.7 4.1 1.5	**29** 0305 0909 F 1530 2127	4.6 1.1 4.7 1.1
15 0340 0934 F 1606 2153	4.4 1.4 4.3 1.3	**30** 0356 0957 SA 1620 2212	4.9 0.8 4.8 0.9
		31 0443 1042 SU 1706 O 2255	5.0 0.6 5.0 0.7

FEBRUARY

Time	m	Time	m
1 0528 1124 M 1751 2337	5.1 0.5 5.0 0.6	**16** 0518 1112 TU 1742 ● 2329	4.9 0.4 4.8 0.5
2 0611 1204 TU 1833	5.2 0.4 5.0	**17** 0557 1149 W 1819	5.1 0.2 5.0
3 0017 0652 W 1243 1914	0.6 5.1 0.5 4.9	**18** 0006 0635 TH 1226 1856	0.4 5.2 0.2 5.0
4 0056 0732 TH 1320 1954	0.7 5.0 0.6 4.7	**19** 0044 0714 F 1304 1934	0.4 5.2 0.2 4.9
5 0134 0810 F 1357 2035	0.9 4.7 0.9 4.5	**20** 0124 0754 SA 1344 2015	0.5 5.0 0.4 4.7
6 0213 0849 SA 1436 2118	1.2 4.5 1.2 4.2	**21** 0207 0837 SU 1427 2102	0.7 4.8 0.7 4.5
7 0256 0930 SU 1518 2204	1.5 4.2 1.5 4.0	**22** 0256 0928 M 1517 2201	1.1 4.5 1.1 4.2
8 0346 1014 M 1610 2255	1.8 3.9 1.8 3.8	**23** 0354 1033 TU 1618 2313	1.4 4.2 1.5 4.0
9 0453 1104 TU 1724 2354	2.0 3.7 2.0 3.7	**24** 0509 1147 W 1739	1.7 4.0 1.8
10 0613 1209 W 1852	2.1 3.5 2.0	**25** 0034 0644 TH 1310 1921	4.0 1.7 4.0 1.7
11 0111 0725 TH 1357 2001	3.7 2.0 3.6 1.9	**26** 0155 0803 F 1425 2029	4.1 1.5 4.2 1.5
12 0227 0825 F 1504 2052	3.8 1.7 3.8 1.6	**27** 0256 0901 SA 1522 2117	4.4 1.2 4.5 1.2
13 0319 0913 SA 1548 2135	4.1 1.4 4.1 1.3	**28** 0346 0946 SU 1609 2159	4.7 0.9 4.7 0.9
14 0400 0956 SU 1627 2214	4.4 1.1 4.4 1.0		
15 0439 1035 M 1704 2252	4.6 0.7 4.6 0.7		

MARCH

Time	m	Time	m
1 0431 1028 M 1652 2240	4.9 0.6 4.9 0.7	**16** 0416 1011 TU 1641 2230	4.6 0.6 4.7 0.6
2 0513 1107 TU 1733 O 2319	5.0 0.5 5.0 0.6	**17** 0455 1049 W 1718 ● 2308	4.9 0.3 5.0 0.3
3 0554 1144 W 1812 2356	5.1 0.4 5.0 0.5	**18** 0535 1126 TH 1755 2346	5.2 0.1 5.2 0.1
4 0632 1218 TH 1850	5.0 0.4 5.0	**19** 0614 1203 F 1833	5.3 0.0 5.1
5 0031 0709 F 1252 1926	0.6 4.9 0.6 4.8	**20** 0024 0654 SA 1242 1911	0.1 5.3 0.0 5.1
6 0107 0744 SA 1325 2003	0.7 4.7 0.8 4.5	**21** 0105 0735 SU 1322 1951	0.2 5.2 0.3 4.9
7 0142 0819 SU 1359 2040	1.0 4.5 1.1 4.3	**22** 0148 0818 M 1406 2037	0.5 4.9 0.7 4.6
8 0219 0854 M 1435 2120	1.3 4.2 1.4 4.1	**23** 0236 0910 TU 1455 2134	0.9 4.5 1.2 4.3
9 0259 0934 TU 1514 2206	1.6 3.9 1.7 3.9	**24** 0334 1015 W 1556 2250	1.3 4.2 1.6 4.0
10 0348 1023 W 1606 2300	1.9 3.7 2.1 3.7	**25** 0451 1133 TH 1724	1.6 4.0 1.9
11 0520 1121 TH 1810	2.1 3.5 2.2	**26** 0018 0626 F 1257 1905	3.9 1.7 3.9 1.8
12 0003 0651 F 1240 1931	3.6 2.0 3.5 2.0	**27** 0139 0749 SA 1412 2014	4.1 1.5 4.2 1.6
13 0144 0756 SA 1440 2027	3.7 1.8 3.7 1.7	**28** 0240 0846 SU 1507 2101	4.3 1.2 4.4 1.3
14 0252 0847 SU 1526 2111	4.0 1.4 4.0 1.3	**29** 0329 0928 M 1552 2141	4.6 0.9 4.7 1.0
15 0336 0931 M 1604 2152	4.3 1.0 4.4 0.9	**30** 0412 1007 TU 1632 2219	4.8 0.7 4.8 0.8
		31 0453 1044 W 1711 O 2257	4.9 0.6 4.9 0.6

APRIL

Time	m	Time	m
1 0532 1119 TH 1748 2332	5.0 0.5 5.0 0.6	**16** 0508 1100 F 1728 ● 2323	5.3 0.1 5.3 0.1
2 0609 1152 F 1824	4.9 0.6 4.9	**17** 0551 1140 SA 1809	5.4 0.0 5.4
3 0006 0644 SA 1223 1858	0.6 4.9 0.7 4.8	**18** 0004 0634 SU 1221 1849	0.0 5.4 0.1 5.3
4 0040 0718 SU 1254 1933	0.8 4.7 0.9 4.7	**19** 0047 0717 M 1303 1932	0.2 5.3 0.3 5.1
5 0113 0751 M 1326 2008	1.0 4.5 1.1 4.5	**20** 0132 0803 TU 1347 2019	0.4 4.9 0.7 4.8
6 0148 0826 TU 1359 2046	1.2 4.3 1.4 4.2	**21** 0221 0855 W 1437 2116	0.8 4.6 1.2 4.4
7 0225 0905 W 1437 2131	1.5 4.0 1.7 4.0	**22** 0319 1000 TH 1539 2233	1.2 4.2 1.7 4.1
8 0309 0954 TH 1523 2224	1.8 3.8 2.0 3.8	**23** 0435 1116 F 1707 2358	1.5 4.0 1.9 4.0
9 0409 1051 F 1633 2323	2.0 3.6 2.3 3.7	**24** 0602 1236 SA 1838	1.6 4.0 1.9
10 0612 1156 SA 1856	2.0 3.6 2.1	**25** 0114 0720 SU 1349 1947	4.1 1.5 4.1 1.7
11 0032 0720 SU 1349 1954	3.7 1.8 3.7 1.8	**26** 0216 0819 M 1444 2037	4.3 1.3 4.4 1.4
12 0205 0815 M 1451 2042	3.9 1.4 4.1 1.4	**27** 0305 0903 TU 1528 2117	4.5 1.1 4.6 1.2
13 0301 0901 TU 1532 2124	4.3 1.0 4.5 1.0	**28** 0349 0941 W 1608 2155	4.6 0.9 4.8 0.9
14 0344 0942 W 1610 2204	4.7 0.6 4.8 0.6	**29** 0429 1018 TH 1645 2232	4.7 0.8 4.9 0.8
15 0426 1021 TH 1648 2243	5.0 0.3 5.1 0.3	**30** 0507 1052 F 1721 O 2308	4.8 0.8 4.9 0.8

Chart Datum: 0·20 metres below Ordnance Datum (Dublin)

IRELAND – GALWAY

LAT 53°16′N   LONG 9°03′W

TIMES AND HEIGHTS OF HIGH AND LOW WATERS

YEAR **1999**

TIME ZONE (UT)
For Summer Time add ONE hour in non-shaded areas

Heights in metres (m). ● = new moon, O = full moon.

MAY

Day	1	2	3	4
1 SA	0544 4.8	1124 0.8	1756 4.9	2342 0.8
2 SU	0619 4.7	1155 0.9	1830 4.8	
3 M	0015 0.9	0653 4.6	1226 1.1	1905 4.7
4 TU	0049 1.0	0728 4.5	1258 1.2	1941 4.5
5 W	0124 1.2	0803 4.3	1332 1.5	2019 4.4
6 TH	0202 1.4	0843 4.1	1411 1.7	2103 4.2
7 F	0246 1.6	0930 3.9	1458 2.0	2155 4.0
8 SA	0340 1.8	1025 3.8	1600 2.2	2252 3.9
9 SU	0458 1.9	1126 3.8	1807 2.1	2354 3.9
10 M	0635 1.7	1235 3.9	1915 1.9	
11 TU	0103 4.1	0736 1.4	1356 4.2	2007 1.5
12 W	0214 4.4	0826 1.1	1451 4.5	2053 1.1
13 TH	0309 4.7	0911 0.7	1536 4.9	2136 0.7
14 F	0356 5.0	0954 0.4	1618 5.2	2218 0.4
15 SA	0442 5.3	1035 0.2	1702 5.4	● 2301 0.2
16 SU	0529 5.4	1118 0.2	1746 5.4	2346 0.1
17 M	0616 5.4	1201 0.3	1831 5.4	
18 TU	0031 0.5	0702 5.2	1246 0.5	1916 5.2
19 W	0118 0.4	0749 5.0	1332 0.8	2005 4.9
20 TH	0208 0.7	0841 4.6	1421 1.2	2101 4.5
21 F	0304 1.1	0942 4.3	1521 1.6	2211 4.2
22 SA	0412 1.4	1051 4.1	1638 1.9	2328 4.1
23 SU	0529 1.5	1203 4.0	1759 1.9	
24 M	0038 4.1	0639 1.5	1313 4.1	1908 1.8
25 TU	0142 4.1	0741 1.5	1412 4.2	2004 1.6
26 W	0236 4.3	0831 1.3	1459 4.4	2049 1.4
27 TH	0321 4.4	0912 1.2	1540 4.6	2129 1.2
28 F	0402 4.5	0950 1.1	1617 4.7	2207 1.0
29 SA	0441 4.5	1025 1.1	1652 4.7	2243 1.0
30 SU	0518 4.6	1058 1.1	1728 4.8	O 2319 1.0
31 M	0554 4.6	1130 1.1	1804 4.8	2353 1.0

JUNE

Day	1	2	3	4
1 TU	0631 4.5	1202 1.2	1841 4.7	
2 W	0028 1.0	0707 4.5	1237 1.3	1917 4.6
3 TH	0105 1.1	0744 4.4	1313 1.4	1956 4.5
4 F	0144 1.2	0824 4.2	1353 1.6	2039 4.3
5 SA	0227 1.4	0908 4.1	1440 1.7	2129 4.2
6 SU	0318 1.5	1000 4.0	1536 1.9	2224 4.1
7 M	0417 1.6	1057 4.0	1648 2.0	2323 4.1
8 TU	0528 1.6	1158 4.1	1822 1.8	
9 W	0026 4.2	0645 1.4	1306 4.3	1929 1.5
10 TH	0134 4.4	0749 1.2	1411 4.5	2023 1.2
11 F	0236 4.7	0841 0.9	1505 4.8	2111 0.8
12 SA	0330 4.9	0929 0.7	1553 5.1	2157 0.5
13 SU	0421 5.1	1014 0.5	● 2243 0.3	
14 M	0511 5.2	1059 0.4	1728 5.3	2330 0.2
15 TU	0600 5.2	1145 0.4	1815 5.3	
16 W	0017 0.2	0647 5.2	1231 0.6	1902 5.2
17 TH	0104 0.4	0735 5.0	1316 0.8	1951 4.9
18 F	0152 0.6	0824 4.7	1404 1.1	2043 4.6
19 SA	0243 0.9	0918 4.4	1456 1.4	2143 4.3
20 SU	0340 1.2	1017 4.2	1559 1.7	2248 4.1
21 M	0445 1.5	1120 4.0	1712 1.9	2354 4.1
22 TU	0552 1.6	1224 4.0	1822 1.9	
23 W	0058 3.9	0655 1.6	1328 4.0	1925 1.8
24 TH	0159 4.0	0752 1.6	1424 4.1	2018 1.6
25 F	0251 4.1	0841 1.5	1510 4.3	2102 1.4
26 SA	0336 4.2	0922 1.4	1549 4.4	2143 1.2
27 SU	0416 4.3	1000 1.3	1626 4.5	2221 1.1
28 M	0455 4.4	1036 1.2	1703 4.6	O 2259 1.0
29 TU	0533 4.4	1111 1.1	1741 4.7	2336 0.9
30 W	0611 4.5	1146 1.1	1819 4.7	

JULY

Day	1	2	3	4
1 TH	0012 0.9	0648 4.5	1222 1.1	1857 4.7
2 F	0049 0.9	0725 4.5	1258 1.1	1935 4.6
3 SA	0127 0.9	0804 4.4	1338 1.3	2016 4.5
4 SU	0208 1.0	0845 4.3	1421 1.4	2102 4.4
5 M	0254 1.2	0932 4.2	1512 1.6	2156 4.3
6 TU	0347 1.3	1026 4.2	1613 1.7	2255 4.3
7 W	0446 1.4	1126 4.2	1725 1.7	2357 4.2
8 TH	0555 1.4	1230 4.2	1850 1.6	
9 F	0104 4.3	0711 1.4	1341 4.4	1958 1.3
10 SA	0213 4.5	0816 1.2	1443 4.7	2053 1.0
11 SU	0312 4.7	0910 0.9	1536 4.9	2142 0.7
12 M	0406 4.9	0958 0.7	1626 5.1	2230 0.4
13 TU	0456 5.0	1045 0.6	1714 5.2	● 2317 0.3
14 W	0546 5.1	1130 0.5	1802 5.2	
15 TH	0003 0.2	0632 5.1	1215 0.6	1848 5.1
16 F	0047 0.3	0718 4.9	1258 0.7	1933 5.0
17 SA	0131 0.5	0803 4.7	1341 0.9	2020 4.7
18 SU	0215 0.8	0849 4.5	1426 1.2	2109 4.4
19 M	0302 1.1	0939 4.2	1516 1.5	2203 4.1
20 TU	0355 1.4	1032 4.0	1616 1.8	2301 3.9
21 W	0457 1.6	1128 3.9	1729 1.9	
22 TH	0003 3.7	0603 1.8	1232 3.8	1840 1.9
23 F	0112 3.7	0709 1.8	1340 3.8	1944 1.8
24 SA	0219 3.7	0808 1.7	1440 4.0	2037 1.6
25 SU	0312 3.9	0856 1.6	1526 4.2	2121 1.3
26 M	0356 4.1	0938 1.4	1605 4.4	2201 1.1
27 TU	0436 4.2	1017 1.2	1643 4.6	2240 0.9
28 W	0514 4.4	1055 1.0	1721 4.7	O 2318 0.7
29 TH	0552 4.5	1131 0.9	1759 4.8	2354 0.6
30 F	0629 4.6	1206 0.8	1836 4.8	
31 SA	0030 0.5	0705 4.7	1242 0.8	1914 4.8

AUGUST

Day	1	2	3	4
1 SU	0107 0.6	0742 4.6	1319 0.9	1952 4.7
2 M	0146 0.7	0820 4.5	1401 1.0	2034 4.6
3 TU	0229 0.9	0902 4.4	1447 1.3	2125 4.4
4 W	0318 1.1	0953 4.3	1543 1.5	2226 4.3
5 TH	0415 1.4	1054 4.1	1650 1.7	2333 4.2
6 F	0522 1.6	1202 4.1	1818 1.6	
7 SA	0044 4.2	0645 1.6	1321 4.2	1942 1.4
8 SU	0159 4.3	0801 1.2	1432 4.5	2043 1.1
9 M	0302 4.5	0858 1.2	1527 4.7	2133 0.8
10 TU	0355 4.7	0946 0.9	1616 5.0	2219 0.5
11 W	0444 4.9	1031 0.7	1703 5.1	● 2303 0.3
12 TH	0531 5.0	1114 0.6	1748 5.2	2345 0.3
13 F	0615 5.0	1156 0.5	1831 5.1	
14 SA	0025 0.3	0657 5.0	1236 0.6	1912 5.0
15 SU	0105 0.5	0737 4.8	1314 0.8	1952 4.8
16 M	0143 0.7	0818 4.6	1353 1.0	2034 4.5
17 TU	0223 1.0	0900 4.4	1435 1.4	2117 4.2
18 W	0307 1.4	0944 4.1	1523 1.7	2206 3.9
19 TH	0400 1.7	1032 3.9	1629 2.0	2302 3.7
20 F	0511 2.0	1127 3.7	1755 2.1	
21 SA	0013 3.5	0630 2.0	1241 3.7	1911 2.0
22 SU	0146 3.6	0737 1.9	1410 3.8	2011 1.7
23 M	0253 3.8	0831 1.7	1506 4.1	2058 1.4
24 TU	0338 4.0	0916 1.4	1546 4.3	2139 1.1
25 W	0416 4.3	0956 1.2	1624 4.6	2218 0.8
26 TH	0453 4.5	1034 0.9	1700 4.8	O 2255 0.5
27 F	0529 4.7	1110 0.7	1737 5.0	2331 0.4
28 SA	0605 4.8	1146 0.5	1813 5.1	
29 SU	0007 0.3	0640 4.9	1221 0.5	1850 5.1
30 M	0043 0.3	0716 4.9	1259 0.6	1927 5.0
31 TU	0122 0.5	0752 4.8	1339 0.8	2008 4.8

13

Chart Datum: 0·20 metres below Ordnance Datum (Dublin)

IRELAND – GALWAY

LAT 53°16′N   LONG 9°03′W

TIMES AND HEIGHTS OF HIGH AND LOW WATERS

YEAR **1999**

SEPTEMBER

Day	Time / m	Day	Time / m
1 W	0204 0.8 / 0832 4.6 / 1423 1.0 / 2057 4.5	16 TH	0223 1.5 / 0902 4.2 / 1437 1.7 / 2122 4.0
2 TH	0251 1.1 / 0921 4.4 / 1516 1.4 / 2201 4.3	17 F	0306 1.9 / 0946 4.0 / 1526 2.0 / 2214 3.7
3 F	0348 1.5 / 1025 4.1 / 1624 1.7 / 2314 4.1	18 SA	0409 2.2 / 1037 3.8 / 1705 2.2 / 2316 3.5
4 SA	0459 1.7 / 1141 4.0 / 1801 1.8	19 SU	0558 2.3 / 1137 3.7 / 1838 2.1
5 SU	0033 4.1 / 0635 1.8 / 1311 4.1 / 1936 1.5	20 M	0101 3.5 / 0708 2.2 / 1322 3.7 / 1941 1.9
6 M	0151 4.2 / 0752 1.6 / 1425 4.4 / 2036 1.2	21 TU	0230 3.8 / 0804 1.9 / 1439 4.0 / 2031 1.5
7 TU	0254 4.5 / 0847 1.3 / 1519 4.7 / 2123 0.9	22 W	0314 4.1 / 0850 1.6 / 1521 4.3 / 2112 1.1
8 W	0344 4.7 / 0933 1.0 / 1605 5.0 / 2204 0.6	23 TH	0350 4.4 / 0931 1.2 / 1558 4.6 / 2151 0.8
9 TH	0429 4.9 / 1015 0.8 / 1648 5.1 / ● 2244 0.4	24 F	0425 4.7 / 1009 0.9 / 1634 4.9 / 2228 0.5
10 F	0512 5.0 / 1055 0.6 / 1729 5.2 / 2323 0.4	25 SA	0501 4.9 / 1046 0.6 / 1710 5.1 / O 2304 0.3
11 SA	0553 5.1 / 1133 0.6 / 1809 5.2	26 SU	0536 5.1 / 1122 0.4 / 1747 5.3 / 2341 0.2
12 SU	0000 0.4 / 0632 5.0 / 1211 0.6 / 1847 5.0	27 M	0613 5.2 / 1159 0.3 / 1826 5.3
13 M	0036 0.6 / 0709 4.9 / 1246 0.8 / 1924 4.8	28 TU	0018 0.2 / 0649 5.2 / 1237 0.4 / 1905 5.2
14 TU	0111 0.8 / 0746 4.7 / 1322 1.0 / 2001 4.6	29 W	0058 0.4 / 0726 5.0 / 1318 0.6 / 1948 5.0
15 W	0146 1.1 / 0823 4.5 / 1358 1.3 / 2039 4.3	30 TH	0141 0.8 / 0807 4.8 / 1403 0.9 / 2038 4.7

OCTOBER

Day	Time / m	Day	Time / m
1 F	0228 1.2 / 0857 4.5 / 1456 1.4 / 2142 4.3	16 SA	0225 2.0 / 0911 4.2 / 1446 2.0 / 2141 3.8
2 SA	0326 1.7 / 1002 4.2 / 1605 1.7 / 2300 4.1	17 SU	0312 2.3 / 1001 4.0 / 1544 2.2 / 2240 3.7
3 SU	0445 2.0 / 1128 4.1 / 1750 1.8	18 M	0519 2.5 / 1058 3.8 / 1757 2.2 / 2350 3.7
4 M	0022 4.1 / 0626 2.0 / 1300 4.1 / 1926 1.6	19 TU	0636 2.3 / 1201 3.8 / 1904 2.0
5 TU	0141 4.3 / 0738 1.7 / 1411 4.4 / 2024 1.3	20 W	0141 3.8 / 0731 2.1 / 1341 4.0 / 1956 1.7
6 W	0240 4.6 / 0831 1.5 / 1503 4.7 / 2106 1.0	21 TH	0236 4.1 / 0819 1.7 / 1442 4.3 / 2041 1.3
7 TH	0327 4.8 / 0914 1.2 / 1548 5.0 / 2144 0.8	22 F	0315 4.5 / 0902 1.3 / 1523 4.7 / 2121 0.9
8 F	0409 5.0 / 0955 0.9 / 1629 5.1 / 2222 0.6	23 SA	0351 4.8 / 0941 0.9 / 1601 5.0 / 2159 0.6
9 SA	0449 5.1 / 1033 0.8 / 1708 5.2 / ● 2258 0.6	24 SU	0427 5.1 / 1019 0.6 / 1641 5.3 / O 2236 0.3
10 SU	0527 5.1 / 1110 0.7 / 1745 5.1 / 2333 0.7	25 M	0505 5.3 / 1057 0.4 / 1721 5.5 / 2315 0.3
11 M	0605 5.1 / 1145 0.8 / 1822 5.0	26 TU	0544 5.4 / 1137 0.3 / 1804 5.5 / 2355 0.3
12 TU	0005 0.8 / 0640 5.0 / 1219 0.9 / 1857 4.9	27 W	0625 5.4 / 1218 0.3 / 1847 5.4
13 W	0038 1.0 / 0716 4.8 / 1253 1.1 / 1932 4.6	28 TH	0037 0.5 / 0706 5.3 / 1302 0.5 / 1933 5.1
14 TH	0112 1.3 / 0751 4.6 / 1327 1.4 / 2008 4.4	29 F	0122 0.9 / 0750 5.0 / 1348 0.9 / 2024 4.8
15 F	0146 1.6 / 0829 4.4 / 1404 1.6 / 2050 4.1	30 SA	0211 1.3 / 0842 4.7 / 1441 1.3 / 2128 4.4
		31 SU	0310 1.8 / 0947 4.4 / 1550 1.7 / 2244 4.2

NOVEMBER

Day	Time / m	Day	Time / m
1 M	0431 2.0 / 1112 4.2 / 1728 1.8	16 TU	0346 2.4 / 1025 4.1 / 1625 2.1 / 2311 3.9
2 TU	0004 4.2 / 0605 2.0 / 1236 4.2 / 1900 1.7	17 W	0548 2.4 / 1123 4.1 / 1812 2.0
3 W	0119 4.3 / 0715 1.9 / 1346 4.4 / 2001 1.4	18 TH	0018 4.0 / 0651 2.2 / 1226 4.1 / 1914 1.7
4 TH	0218 4.6 / 0808 1.6 / 1440 4.7 / 2044 1.2	19 F	0134 4.2 / 0743 1.8 / 1339 4.4 / 2004 1.4
5 F	0304 4.8 / 0852 1.4 / 1525 4.9 / 2122 1.0	20 SA	0229 4.5 / 0830 1.4 / 1440 4.7 / 2049 1.0
6 SA	0346 5.0 / 0933 1.1 / 1606 5.0 / 2158 0.9	21 SU	0313 4.9 / 0913 1.1 / 1528 5.0 / 2130 0.7
7 SU	0424 5.2 / 1011 1.0 / 1644 5.0 / 2233 0.9	22 M	0355 5.2 / 0954 0.7 / 1613 5.3 / 2210 0.5
8 M	0501 5.1 / 1047 1.0 / 1721 5.0 / ● 2306 1.0	23 TU	0437 5.4 / 1036 0.5 / 1659 5.5 / O 2252 0.4
9 TU	0537 5.1 / 1121 1.0 / 1757 4.9 / 2338 1.1	24 W	0521 5.5 / 1119 0.3 / 1746 5.5 / 2336 0.4
10 W	0613 5.0 / 1155 1.1 / 1832 4.8	25 TH	0606 5.5 / 1203 0.3 / 1833 5.4
11 TH	0009 1.3 / 0648 4.9 / 1229 1.2 / 1908 4.6	26 F	0020 0.6 / 0651 5.4 / 1249 0.5 / 1921 5.2
12 F	0043 1.5 / 0725 4.7 / 1304 1.4 / 1945 4.4	27 SA	0108 0.9 / 0738 5.2 / 1337 0.7 / 2013 4.9
13 SA	0119 1.7 / 0802 4.5 / 1341 1.6 / 2026 4.2	28 SU	0157 1.3 / 0830 4.8 / 1429 1.1 / 2112 4.6
14 SU	0158 2.0 / 0843 4.3 / 1423 1.8 / 2114 4.0	29 M	0254 1.6 / 0932 4.5 / 1530 1.4 / 2221 4.3
15 M	0243 2.2 / 0931 4.2 / 1513 2.0 / 2210 3.9	30 TU	0405 1.9 / 1046 4.3 / 1650 1.7 / 2334 4.2

DECEMBER

Day	Time / m	Day	Time / m
1 W	0528 2.0 / 1200 4.2 / 1816 1.7	16 TH	0419 2.2 / 1048 4.2 / 1647 1.8 / 2335 4.1
2 TH	0044 4.3 / 0639 2.0 / 1310 4.3 / 1925 1.6	17 F	0543 2.1 / 1146 4.3 / 1806 1.7
3 F	0146 4.4 / 0738 1.8 / 1410 4.4 / 2016 1.5	18 SA	0037 4.2 / 0658 1.9 / 1252 4.4 / 1919 1.5
4 SA	0237 4.6 / 0827 1.6 / 1500 4.5 / 2057 1.3	19 SU	0143 4.5 / 0756 1.6 / 1401 4.6 / 2016 1.2
5 SU	0320 4.7 / 0910 1.4 / 1542 4.6 / 2134 1.2	20 M	0239 4.8 / 0846 1.2 / 1500 4.9 / 2104 0.9
6 M	0359 4.8 / 0949 1.3 / 1621 4.7 / 2210 1.2	21 TU	0329 5.1 / 0933 0.9 / 1553 5.1 / 2150 0.7
7 TU	0435 4.9 / 1026 1.2 / 1658 4.7 / 2243 1.2	22 W	0416 5.3 / 1019 0.6 / 1643 5.3 / O 2235 0.6
8 W	0512 4.9 / 1102 1.1 / 1735 4.7 / 2316 1.2	23 TH	0504 5.4 / 1105 0.4 / 1732 5.4 / 2322 0.5
9 TH	0549 4.9 / 1137 1.1 / 1811 4.7 / 2349 1.3	24 F	0553 5.5 / 1152 0.3 / 1821 5.3
10 F	0626 4.9 / 1212 1.2 / 1848 4.6	25 SA	0008 0.6 / 0640 5.4 / 1238 0.4 / 1909 5.2
11 SA	0024 1.4 / 0703 4.8 / 1248 1.2 / 1926 4.5	26 SU	0055 0.8 / 0728 5.2 / 1325 0.5 / 1958 4.9
12 SU	0101 1.6 / 0741 4.7 / 1325 1.3 / 2005 4.4	27 M	0143 1.0 / 0817 5.0 / 1412 0.8 / 2051 4.6
13 M	0140 1.7 / 0820 4.5 / 1405 1.5 / 2049 4.2	28 TU	0233 1.4 / 0911 4.7 / 1504 1.2 / 2151 4.4
14 TU	0223 1.9 / 0903 4.4 / 1450 1.6 / 2140 4.1	29 W	0331 1.7 / 1012 4.4 / 1605 1.5 / 2254 4.2
15 W	0315 2.1 / 0953 4.3 / 1543 1.7 / 2236 4.1	30 TH	0439 1.9 / 1117 4.2 / 1718 1.7 / 2359 4.1
		31 F	0551 2.0 / 1223 4.0 / 1834 1.8

Chart Datum: 0·20 metres below Ordnance Datum (Dublin)

VOLVO PENTA SERVICE

Sales and service centres in area 14
Channel Islands GUERNSEY *Chicks Marine Ltd,* Collings Road, St. Peter Port
GY1 1FL Tel (01481) 723716/724536 **JERSEY** *D. K. Collins Marine Ltd,*
South Pier, St. Helier, JE2 3NB Tel (01534) 32415

Area 14

Channel Islands
Alderney to Jersey

VOLVO PENTA

8.14.1   Index   **Page 617**

8.14.2   Diagram of ports, lts, RDF bns,
          Coast radio and weather stns   **618**

8.14.3   Tidal stream charts   **620**

8.14.4   List of coastal lights,
          fog signals and waypoints   **622**

8.14.5   Passage information   **623**

8.14.6   Distance table   **625**

8.14.7   English Channel waypoints
                                          See 8.1.7

8.14.8   Special notes for
          The Channel Islands   **626**

8.14.9   Braye (Alderney)   **626**
             Saye Bay
             Corblet Bay
             Longy Bay
             La Tchue
             Telegraph Bay
             Hannaine Bay
             Platte Saline Bay
             Burhou

8.14.10   Beaucette (Guernsey)   **628**

8.14.11   The Little Russel Channel   **628**
          Minor harbours and anchorages
          around Guernsey:
             Bordeaux Harbour
             St Sampson
             Havelet Bay
             Soldier's Bay
             Fermain Bay
             Petit Port
             Moulin Huet
             Saints Bay
             Icart Bay

          Jaonnet
          Petit Bôt Bay
          Portelet
          Portelet Harbour
          Lihou Island
          Perelle Bay
          Vazon Bay
          Cobo Bay
          Grande Havre
          L'Ancresse Bay
          Fontenelle Bay

8.14.12   St Peter Port (Guernsey),
          Standard Port, tidal curves   **630**
             Herm Island

8.14.13   Sark   **635**
             Saignie Bay
             Port à la Jument
             Havre Gosselin
             Port és Saies
             La Grande Grève
             Port Gorey
             Rouge Terrier
             Dixcart Bay
             Derrible Bay
             Grève de la Ville
             Les Fontaines

8.14.14   St Helier (Jersey),
          Standard Port, tidal curves   **636**
          Minor harbours and anchorages
          around Jersey:
             St Aubin
             Belcroute Bay
             St Brelade
             Grève au Lancon
             Grève de Lecq
             Bonne Nuit Bay
             Bouley Bay
             Rozel Bay
             St Catherine
             La Rocque
             Les Ecrehou
             Plateau des Minquiers

8.14.15   Gorey (Jersey)   **639**

14

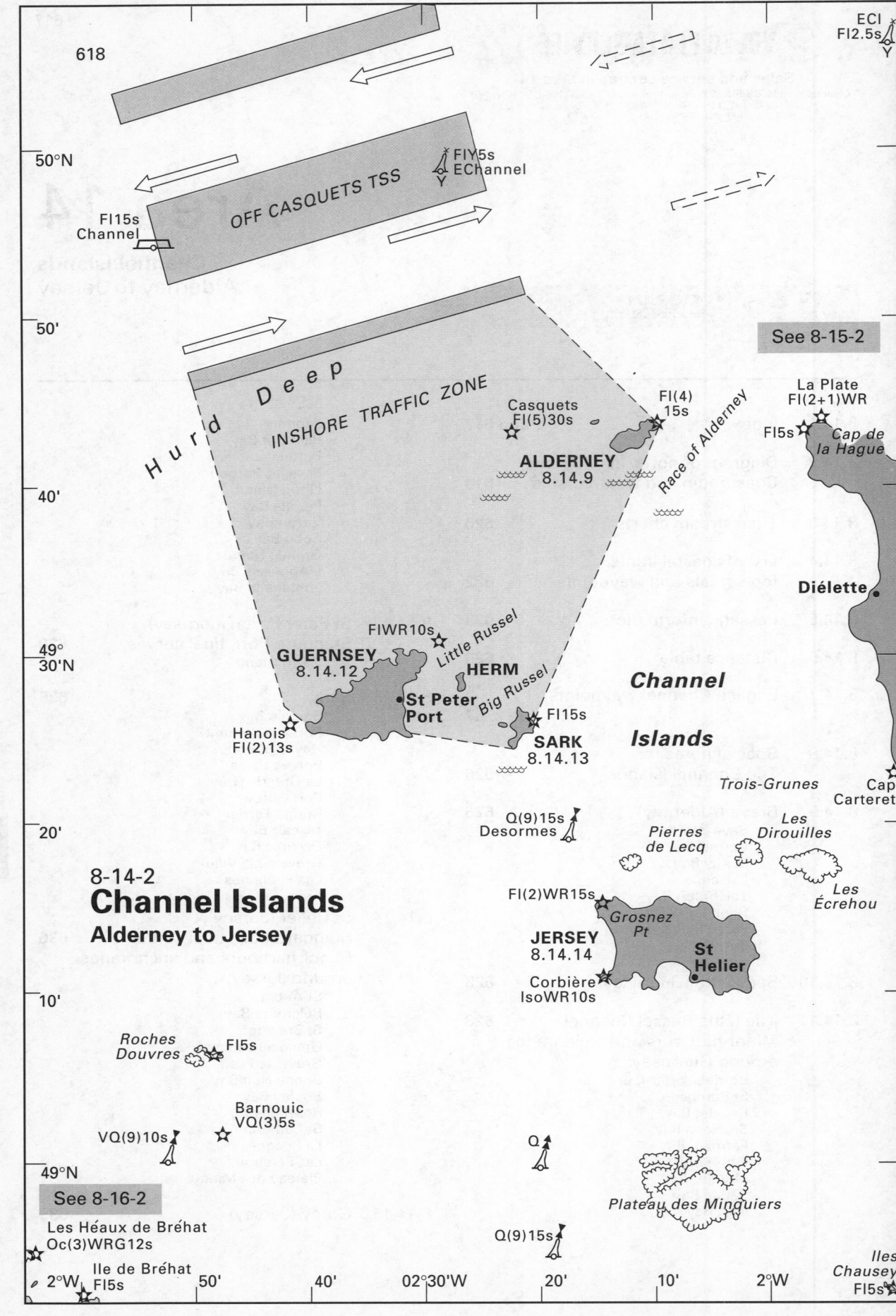

618

50°N

OFF CASQUETS TSS

Fl15s
Channel

Fl.Y5s
EChannel
Y

See 8-15-2

50'

Hurd   Deep

INSHORE TRAFFIC ZONE

Casquets
Fl(5)30s

ALDERNEY
8.14.9

Fl(4)
15s

Race of Alderney

La Plate
Fl(2+1)WR

Fl5s

Cap de
la Hague

40'

Diélette

FlWR10s

Little Russel

GUERNSEY
8.14.12

HERM

Big Russel

Channel

49°
30'N

St Peter
Port

Fl15s

SARK
8.14.13

Islands

Hanois
Fl(2)13s

Trois-Grunes

Cap
Carteret

20'

Q(9)15s
Desormes

Pierres
de Lecq

Les
Dirouilles

Les
Écrehou

8-14-2
Channel Islands
Alderney to Jersey

Fl(2)WR15s

JERSEY
8.14.14

Grosnez
Pt

St
Helier

10'

Corbière
IsoWR10s

Roches
Douvres

Fl5s

Barnouic
VQ(3)5s

VQ(9)10s

Q

49°N

See 8-16-2

Plateau des Minguiers

Les Héaux de Bréhat
Oc(3)WRG12s

Q(9)15s

Iles
Chausey

2°W   Ile de Bréhat
Fl5s

50'

40'

02°30'W

20'

10'

2°W

Fl5s

ECl
Fl2.5s
Y

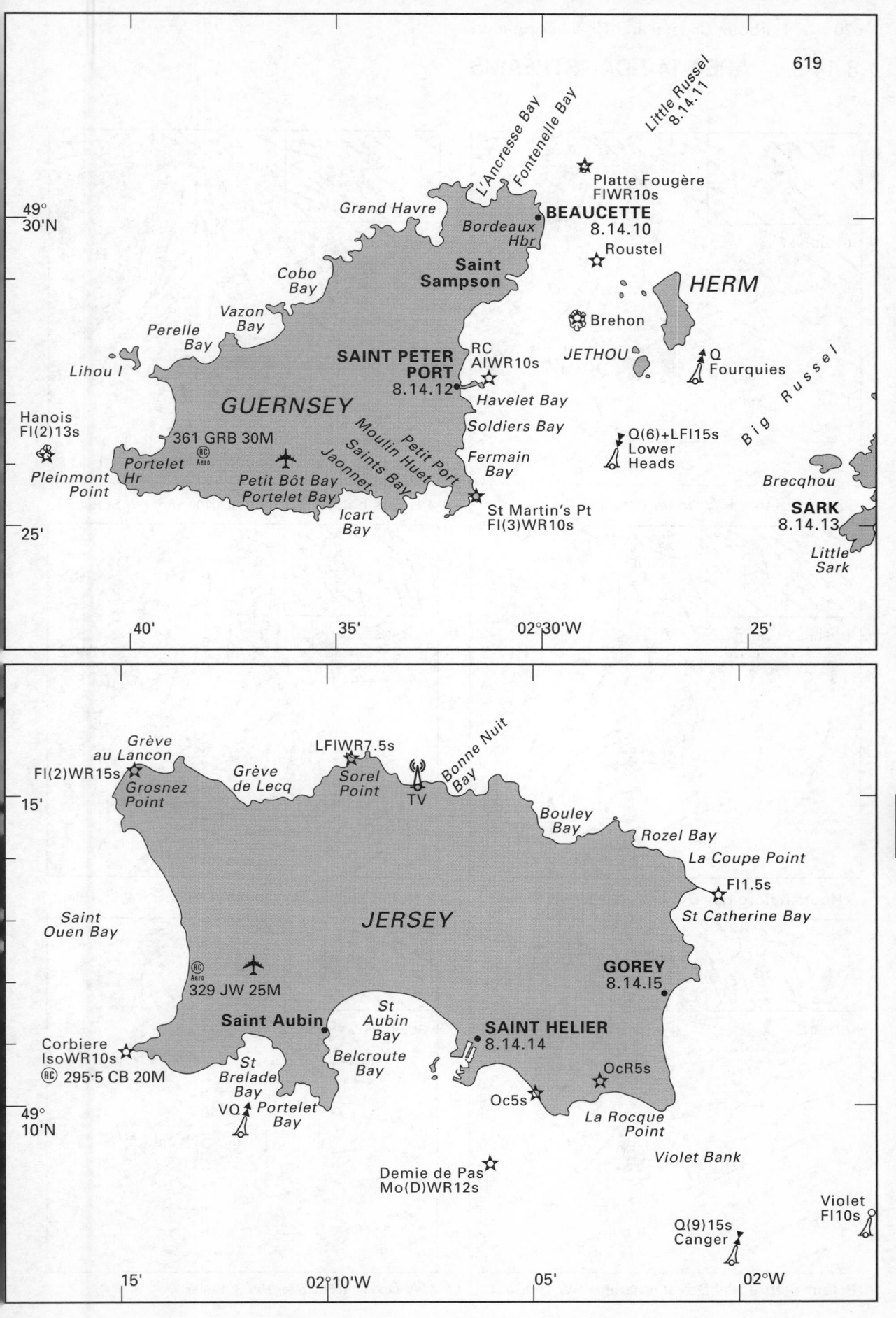

619

GUERNSEY

L'Ancresse Bay
Fontenelle Bay
Little Russel
8.14.11

Platte Fougère
FIWR10s

Grand Havre

Bordeaux
Hbr

BEAUCETTE
8.14.10

Roustel

**Saint
Sampson**

HERM

Cobo
Bay

Vazon
Bay

Brehon

JETHOU

Perelle
Bay

**SAINT PETER
PORT**

RC
AIWR10s

Q
Fourquies

Big Russel

Lihou I

8.14.12

Havelet Bay

Hanois
FI(2)13s

GUERNSEY

361 GRB 30M

RC
Aero

Soldiers Bay

Q(6)+LFI15s
Lower
Heads

Pleinmont
Point

Portelet
Hr

Petit Bôt Bay
Portelet Bay

Petit Port

Moulin Huet

Saints Bay

Jaonnet

Fermain
Bay

Brecqhou

SARK
8.14.13

Icart
Bay

St Martin's Pt
FI(3)WR10s

*Little
Sark*

49°
30'N

25'

49°
30'N

40'   35'   02°30'W   25'

Grève
au Lancon

LFIWR7.5s

Bonne Nuit

FI(2)WR15s

Grosnez
Point

Grève
de Lecq

Sorel
Point

TV

Bouley
Bay

Rozel Bay

La Coupe Point

FI1.5s

Saint
Ouen Bay

JERSEY

St Catherine Bay

RC
Aero

329 JW 25M

GOREY
8.14.I5

Corbiere
IsoWR10s

Saint Aubin

St
Aubin
Bay

SAINT HELIER
8.14.14

OcR5s

RC 295·5 CB 20M

St
Brelade
Bay

Belcroute
Bay

Oc5s

La Rocque
Point

VQ

Portelet
Bay

Demie de Pas
Mo(D)WR12s

Violet Bank

Violet
FI10s

49°
10'N

Q(9)15s
Canger

15'   02°10'W   05'   02°W

14

8-14-3   AREA 14 TIDAL STREAMS

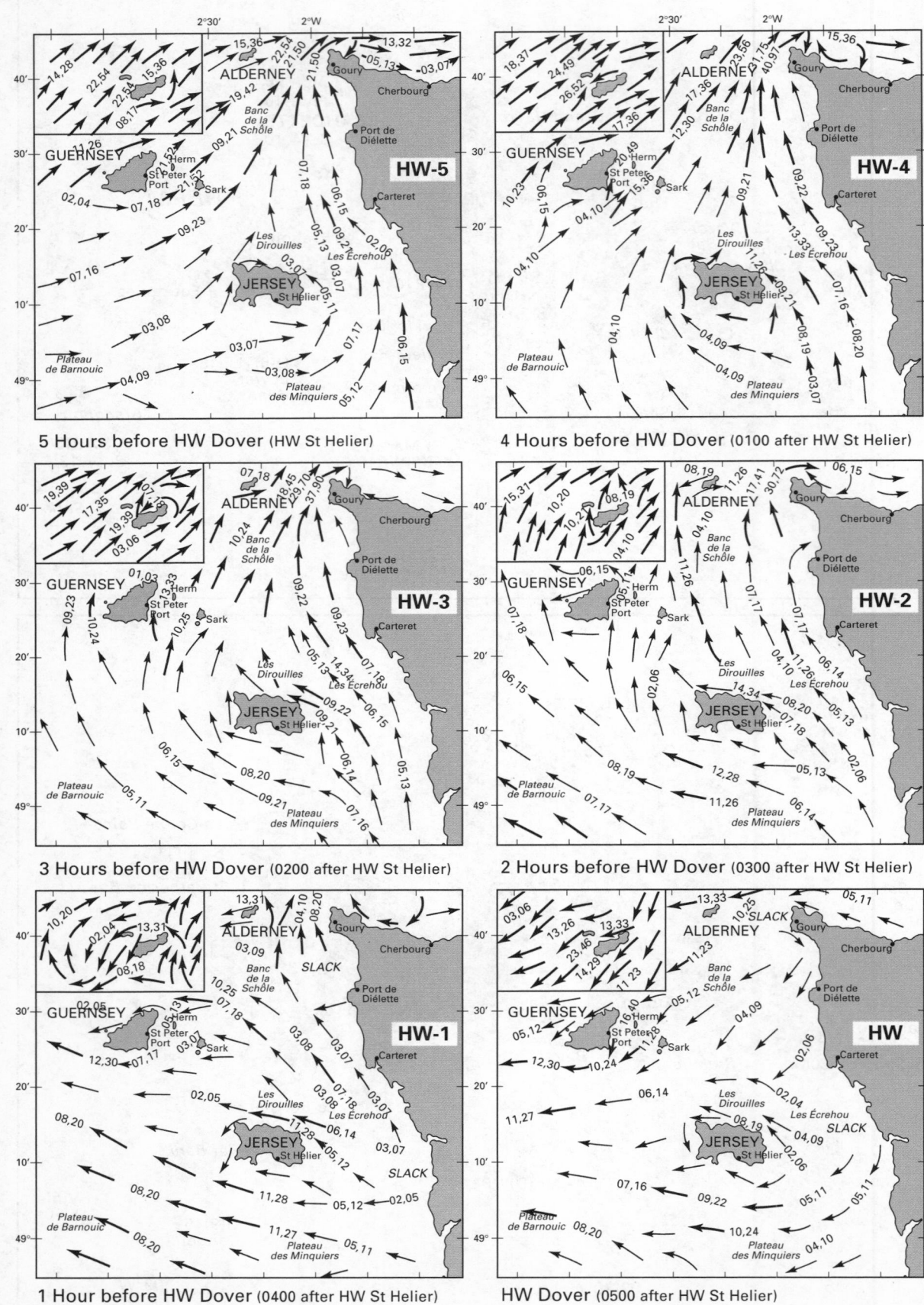

5 Hours before HW Dover (HW St Helier)

4 Hours before HW Dover (0100 after HW St Helier)

3 Hours before HW Dover (0200 after HW St Helier)

2 Hours before HW Dover (0300 after HW St Helier)

1 Hour before HW Dover (0400 after HW St Helier)

HW Dover (0500 after HW St Helier)

Westward 8.16.3   Southward 8.15.3   Northward 8.2.3   Eastward 8.19.3

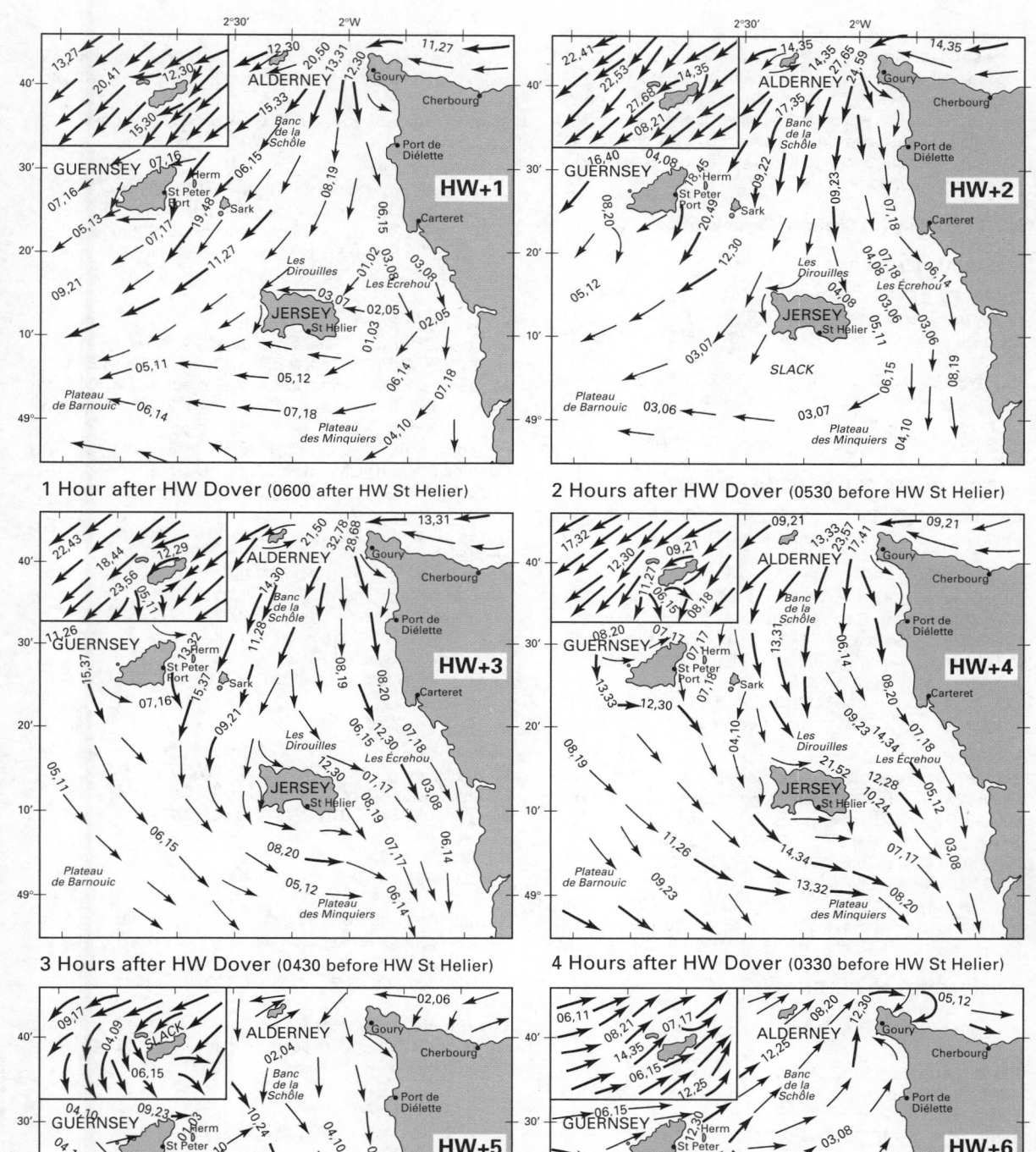

1 Hour after HW Dover (0600 after HW St Helier)

2 Hours after HW Dover (0530 before HW St Helier)

3 Hours after HW Dover (0430 before HW St Helier)

4 Hours after HW Dover (0330 before HW St Helier)

5 Hours after HW Dover (0230 before HW St Helier)

6 Hours after HW Dover (0130 before HW St Helier)

14

8.14.4 COASTAL LIGHTS, FOG SIGNALS AND WAYPOINTS

Lights with a nominal range of 15M or more are in **bold** print, places and features are in CAPITALS, and light-vessels, light floats and Lanbys in *CAPITAL ITALICS*. Unless otherwise stated lights are white. m = elevation in metres; M = nominal range in miles. Fog signals are in *italics*. Useful waypoints are underlined; use those on land with care. All geographical positions are referenced to the ED 50 datum but should be assumed to be approximate.

NOTE: For English Channel Waypoints see 8.1.7.

MID-CHANNEL MARKS

CHANNEL lt F 49°54'·42N 02°53'·67W Fl 15s 12m **25M**;   R hull with lt tr amidships; Racon (O); *Horn (1) 20s.*
E Channel buoy 49°58'·67N 02°28'·87W Fl Y 5s; Racon (T); *Whis.*
EC 1 buoy 50°05'·90N 01°48'·35W Fl Y 2·5s; Racon (T); *Whis.*
EC 2 buoy 50°12'·10N 01°12'·40W Fl (4) Y 15s; Racon (T) ; *Whis.*
EC 3 buoy 50°18'·30N 00°36'·10W Fl Y 5s; Racon (T); *Whis.*

THE CASQUETS AND ALDERNEY

Casquets 49°43'·38N 02°22'·55W Fl (5) 30s 37m **24M**; W tr, the highest and NW of three; Racon (T); *Horn (2) 60s*; H24.

- ALDERNEY
Alderney (Quenard Pt) 49°43'·81N 02°09'·77W Fl (4) 15s 37m **28M**; W ○ tr, B band; vis 085°-027°; *Siren (4) 60s.*
Château à L'Étoc Pt 49°44'·00N 02°10'·55W Iso WR 4s 20m W10M, R7M; W col; vis R071·1°-111·1°, W111·1°-151·1°; in line 111·1° with main lt.
Ldg bns 142°: Front, 49°43'·96N 02°10'·89W; W bn, ○ topmark; rear, 720m from front, BW bn, △ topmark.

- BRAYE
Ldg lts 215°: **Front**, elbow of old pier, 49°43'·46N 02°11'·83W Q 8m **17M**; vis 210°-220°; **rear**, 335m from front, Q 17m **18M**; vis 210°-220°. Both metal posts on W cols.
Bkwtr hd 49°43'·87N 02°11'·59W L Fl 10s 7m 5M.
No 1 buoy 49°43'·78N 02°11'·63W QG; SHM.
No 2 buoy 49°43'·66N 02°11'·67W QR; PHM.
Inner fairway SHM buoy, Q (2) G 5s, 49°43'·63N 02°11'·90W.
Inner fairway PHM buoy, Q (2) R 5s, 49°43'·60N 02°11'·85W.
Braye jetty hd 49°43'·59N 02°11'·92W 2 FR (vert) 8m 5M.

APPROACHES TO GUERNSEY

- LITTLE RUSSEL CHANNEL

Platte Fougère 49°30'·88N 02°29'·05W Fl WR 10s 15m **16M**; W 8-sided tr, B band; vis W155°-085°, R085°-155°; Racon (P); *Horn 45s.*
Tautenay lt bn 49°30'·17N 02°26'·74W Q (3) WR 6s 7m W7M, R6M; B and W bn; vis W050°-215°, R215°-050°.
Roustel lt bn tr 49°29'·28N 02°28'·71W Q 8m 7M; lantern on B & W chequered tr.
Platte lt bn 49°29'·15N 02°29'·50W Fl WR 3s 6m W7M, R5M; G tr; vis R024°-219°, W219°-024°.
Brehon lt bn 49°28'·34N 02°29'·20W Iso 4s 19m 9M; bn on ● tr.

BIG RUSSEL
Noire Pute 49°28'·27N 02°24'·93W Fl (2) WR 15s 8m 6M; vis W220°-040°, R040°-220°.
Fourquies buoy 49°27'·40N 02°26'·40W Q; NCM.
Lower Heads buoy 49°25'·91N 02°28'·48W Q (6) + L Fl 15s; SCM; *Bell* .

GUERNSEY

- BEAUCETTE MARINA/BORDEAUX HARBOUR
Petite Canupe lt bn 49°30'·25N 02°29'·05W Q (6) + L Fl 15s; SCM.
Beaucette ldg lts 276°: Front 49°30'·25N 02°30'·13W FR; W board with R stripe; rear, 185m from front, FR; R board with W stripe.
Bordeaux Hbr bkwtr hd 49°29'·38N 02°30'·30W; post.

- ST SAMPSON
Ldg lts 286°: Front S pier hd 49°28'·97N 02°30'·66W FR 3m 5M; vis 230°-340°; Tfc sigs; rear, 390m from front, FG 13m; clock tr. 2 FR (vert) on 3 chimneys (conspic) 300m N.
Crocq pier hd (inner) FR 11m 5M; vis 250°-340°. Tfc sigs.
N pier hd 49°28'·98N 02°30'·62W FG 3m 5M; vis 230°-340°.

- ST PETER PORT
Ldg lts 220°: **Front**, Castle bkwtr hd 49°27'·36N 02°31'·34W Al WR 10s 14m **16M**; dark ● tr, W on NE side; vis 187°-007°; RC (synch with ᎁ); *Horn 15s*; rear, Belvedere, Oc 10s 61m 14M; W ■ with Y stripe on W tr; vis 179°-269°; both intens 217°-223°.
Reffée buoy 49°27'·80N 02°31'·18W VQ (6) + L Fl 10s; SCM.
Queen Elizabeth II Marina 49°27'·79N 02°31'·78W. Dir lt 270°, Oc WRG 3s 5m 6M; vis G258°-268°, W268°-272°, R272°-282°.
Queen Elizabeth II Marina app buoy 49°27'·78N 02°31'·66W QR; PHM.
White Rock pier hd 49°27'·43N 02°31'·60W Oc G 5s 11m 14M; ● stone tr; intens 174°-354°; tfc sigs.
Pool ldg lts 265°: Front, S pier hd, 49°27'·38N 02°31'·95W Oc R 5s 10m 14M; W framework tr; rear, 160m from front, Iso R 2s 22m 3M; vis 260°-270°.
Albert Dock fish quay hd 49°27'·30N 02°31'·39W FR.

- HAVELET BAY
Oyster Rk bn 49°27'·15N 02°31'·38W; Y bn 'O'.
Oyster Rk buoy 49°27'·10N 02°31'·39W QG; SHM.
Moulinet buoy 49°27'·03N 02°31'·46W QR; PHM.
Moulinet 49°27'·01N 02°31'·49W; Y bn 'M'.

- SOLDIERS BAY
Anfré bn 49°26'·52N 02°31'·40W; Y bn 'A'.

St Martin's Pt 49°25'·37N 02°31'·61W Fl (3) WR 10s 15m 14M; flat-roofed, W bldg; vis R185°-191°, W191°-011°, R011°-081°. *Horn (3) 30s.*
Longue Pierre bn 49°25'·42N 02°31'·39W; Y bn 'LP'.

Les Hanois 49°26'·16N 02°42'·06W Fl (2) 13s 33m **20M**; Gy ● tr, B lantern, helicopter platform; vis 294°-237°; *Horn (2) 60s.* 4 FR on masts 1·27M ESE.

- PORTELET HARBOUR
Portelet Hbr bkwtr bn 49°26'·22N 02°39'·74W.

- COBO BAY/GRAND HAVRE
Grosse Rk bn 49°29'·07N 02°36'·11W 11m; B bn.
Rousse Pt bkwtr bn 49°29'·98N 02°32'·97W; B bn.

HERM

Alligande lt bn 49°27'·91N 02°28'·69W Fl (3) G 5s; Orange 'A' on B mast; Ra refl.
Épec lt bn 49°28'·04N 02°27'·81W Fl G 3s; Black 'E' on G mast.
Vermerette lt bn 49°28'·18N 02°27'·67W Fl (2) Y 5s; Orange 'V' on bn.
Percée Pass, Gate Rk 49°27'·94N 02°27'·44W Q (9) 15s; WCM.

SARK

Corbée du Nez 49°27'·15N 02°22'·08W Fl (4) WR 15s 14m 8M; vis W057°-230°, R230°-057°.
Founiais bn 49°26'·08N 02°20'·28W; SPM; Topmark 'F'.
Pt Robert 49°26'·20N 02°20'·70W Fl 15s 65m **20M**; W 8-sided tr; vis 138°-353°; *Horn (2) 30s*.

Blanchard buoy 49°25'·43N 02°17'·33W Q (3) 10s; ECM; *Bell*.

JERSEY

Desormes buoy 49°19'·00N 02°17'·90W Q (9) 15s; WCM.
Grosnez Pt 49°15'·55N 02°14'·75W Fl (2) WR 15s 50m **W19M**, **R17M**; W hut; vis W081°-188°, R188°-241°.
La Corbière 49°10'·85N 02°14'·90W Iso WR 10s 36m **W18M, R16M**; ● stone tr; vis W shore-294°, R294°-328°, W328°-148°, R148°-shore; RC; *Horn Mo (C) 60s*.

- WESTERN PASSAGE
Ldg lts 082°: Front, La Grève d'Azette 49°10'·21N 02°05'·00W Oc 5s 23m 14M; vis 034°-129°; rear, Mont Ubé 1M from front, Oc R 5s 46m 12M; vis 250°-095°; Racon (T).
Noirmont Pt 49°09'·97N 02°09'·94W Fl (4) 12s 18m 13M; B tr, W band.
Passage Rk buoy 49°09'·59N 02°12'·18W VQ; NCM.
Les Fours buoy 49°09'·65N 02°10'·08W Q; NCM.
Ruaudière Rk buoy 49°09'·80N 02°08'·51W Fl G 3s; SHM; *Bell*.
Diamond Rk buoy 49°10'·18N 02°08'·56W Fl (2) R 6s; PHM.

- SAINT AUBIN
North pier hd 49°11'·27N 02°09'·95W Iso R 4s 12m 10M; and Dir lt 254°, F WRG 5m, vis G248°-253°, W253°-255°, R255°-260°.
Fort pier hd 49°11'·18N 02°09'·52W Fl R 4s 8m 1M.

- ST HELIER
Dir lt 110° F WRG, 49°10'·80N 02°07'·00W, G096°-108°, W108°-112°, R112°-124°. (W appr to Elizabeth marina).
ECM bcn, VQ(3) 5s, 49°10'·80N 02°07'·20W.
La Vrachere IDM bcn, Fl (2) 5s, 49°11'·00N 02°07'·40W.
Red and Green Passage (Small Roads) ldg lts 022·7°: Front, Elizabeth East Berth dn 49°10'·69N 02°06'·86W Oc G 5s 10m 11M; R stripe on framework tr; rear, Albert Pier elbow, 230m from front, Oc R 5s 18m 12M; R stripe on framework tr; synch with front.
E Rock buoy 49°10'·02N 02°07'·20W QG; SHM.
Platte Rock lt bn 49°10'·22N 02°07'·27W Fl R 1·5s 6m 5M; R metal col.
Ldg lts 078°: Front, 49°10'·68N 02°06'·58W FG; rear, 80m from front, FG; both on W cols.
Victoria pier hd 49°10'·63N 02°06'·80W; *Bell*; Tfc sigs.

- EASTERN PASSAGE/VIOLET CHANNEL/LA ROCQUE
Hinguette buoy 49°09'·39N 02°07'·22W Fl (4) R 15s; PHM.
Demie de Pas lt bn tr 49°09'·07N 02°06'·05W Mo (D) WR 12s 11m W14M, R10M; B tr, Y top; vis R130°-303°, W303°-130°; Racon (T); *Horn (3) 60s*.
Icho tr 49°08'·95N 02°02'·81W (conspic)
Canger Rock buoy 49°07'·41N 02°00'·30W Q (9) 15s; WCM.
Frouquier Aubert buoy 49°06'·14N 01°58'·78W Q (6) + L Fl 15s; SCM.
Violet buoy 49°07'·87N 01°57'·05W L Fl 10s; SWM.
Petite Anquette 49°08'·52N 01°56'·21W; W bn.
Grande Anquette 49°08'·38N 01°54'·11W; W bn.

- GOREY
Ldg lts 298°: Front, pier hd 49°11'·86N 02°01'·25W Oc RG 5s 8m 12M; W framework tr; vis R304°-352°, G352°-304°; rear, 490m from front, Oc R 5s 24m 8M.
Inner Road buoy 49°11'·55N 02°00'·25W QG; SHM.

- ST CATHERINE BAY/ROZEL BAY
Verclut bkwtr hd 49°13'·39N 02°00'·57W Fl 1·5s 18m 13M; framework tr.
La Coupe Pt turret 49°13'·98N 02°01'·70W.
Rozel Bay Dir lt 245°: 49°14'·27N 02°02'·68W, F WRG 11m 5M; vis G240°-244°, W244°-246°, R246°-250°.

- BONNE NUIT BAY TO GRÈVE AU LANCON
Bonne Nuit Bay ldg lts 223°: Front, pier hd 49°15'·17N 02°07'·08W FG 7m 6M; rear, 170m from front, FG 34m 6M.
Sorel Pt 49°15'·64N 02°09'·45W L Fl WR 7·5s 50m **15M**; B & W chequered ● tr; vis W095°-112°, R112°-173°, W173°-230°, R230°-269°, W269°-273°.

OFFLYING ISLANDS

- LES ÉCREHOU
Écrevière buoy 49°15'·32N 01°52'·00W Q (6) + L Fl 15s; SCM.
Mâitre Island bn 49°17'·14N 01°55'·52W.

- PLATEAU DES MINQUIERS
NW Minquiers buoy 48°59'·70N 02°20'·50W Q; NCM; *Bell*.
SW Minquiers buoy 48°54'·40N 02°19'·30W Q (9) 15s; WCM; *Whis*.
S Minquiers buoy 48°53'·15N 02°10'·00W Q (6) + L Fl 15s; SCM.
SE Minquiers buoy 48°53'·50N 02°00'·00W Q (3) 10s; ECM; *Bell*.
NE Minquiers buoy 49°00'·90N 01°55'·20W VQ (3) 5s; ECM; *Bell*.
N Minquiers buoy 49°01'·70N 02°00'·50W Q; NCM.
Demi de Vascelin buoy 49°00'·08N 02°05'·10W; SHM; (unlit.)

8.14.5 PASSAGE INFORMATION

Current Pilots for this popular area include: *The Channel Islands* (Imray/RCC Pilotage Foundation, Heath); *Shell Channel Pilot* (Imray/Cunliffe); *Normandy and CI Pilot* (Adlard Coles/Brackenbury); *Brittany and CI Cruising Guide* (Adlard Coles/Jefferson); *N Brittany and CI Cruising* (YM/Cumberlidge).

CHANNEL ISLANDS – GENERAL (chart *2669*)

In an otherwise delightful cruising area, the main problems around the Channel Islands include fog and thick weather, the very big tidal range, strong tidal streams, overfalls and steep seas which get up very quickly. The shoreline is generally rugged with sandy bays and many offlying rks. It is important to use large scale charts, and recognised leading marks (of which there are plenty) when entering or leaving many of the hbrs and anchs. Several passages are marked by bns/perches identified by an alphabetical letter(s) in lieu of topmark.

From the N, note the Casquets TSS and ITZ, see 8.14.2. Soundings of Hurd Deep can help navigation. The powerful lights at the Casquets, Alderney (Quenard Pt), Cap de la Hague, Cap Levi and Barfleur greatly assist a night or dawn landfall. By day Alderney is relatively high and conspic. Sark is often seen before Guernsey which slopes down from S to N. Jersey is low-lying in the SE. The islands are fringed by many rky dangers. In bad visibility it is prudent to stay in hbr.

It is important to appreciate that over a 12 hour period tidal streams broadly rotate anti-clockwise around the Islands, particularly in open water and in wider chans (see 8.14.3). The E-going (flood) stream is of less duration than the W-going, but is stronger. The islands lie across the main direction of the streams, so eddies are common along the shores. The range of tide is greatest in Jersey (9·6m sp, 4·1m np), and least in Alderney (5·3m sp, 2·2m np). Streams run hard through the chans and around headlands and need to be worked carefully; neaps are easier, particularly for a first visit. Strong W'lies cause a heavy sea, usually worst from local HW – 3 to + 3.

Apart from the main hbrs described in Area 14, there are many attractive minor hbrs and anchs, see Index. In the very nature of islands a lee can usually be found somewhere. Boats which can take the ground are better able to explore the quieter hbrs. Avoid lobster pots and oyster beds.

THE CASQUETS AND ORTAC ROCK (chart 60)

Casquets lt ho (fog sig) is conspic on the largest island of this group of rks 5·5M W of Braye, Alderney (8.14.9). Off-lying dangers extend 4ca W and WSW (The Ledge and Noire Roque) and 4ca E (Pte Colotte). The tide runs very hard round and between these various obstructions. A shallow bank, on which are situated Fourquie and l'Equêt rks (dry), lies from 5ca to 1M E of Casquets, and should not be approached. Ortac rk (24m) is 3·5M E of Casquets. Ortac Chan runs N/S 5ca W of Ortac; here the stream begins to run NE at HW St Helier – 0230, and SW at HW St Helier + 0355, with sp rates up to 5½kn (7kn reported). Ortac Chan should not be used in bad weather due to tremendous overfalls; these also occur over Eight-fathom Ledge (8½ca W of Casquets), and over the Banks SW, SSW and SSE of the Casquets. An Historic Wreck lies about 300m E of Casquets lt ho (see 8.0.3g).

ALDERNEY AND THE SWINGE (chart 60)

See 8.14.9 for Braye Harbour (chart 2845) and approaches, together with pleasant bays and anchs around the island, offering shelter from different wind/sea directions. The sunken NE extremity of Admiralty Breakwater should not be crossed except in calm conditions, outside LW±2 and keeping about 50m off the hd of the Breakwater where there is 2·3m.

The Swinge lies between Burhou with its bordering rks, and the NW coast of Alderney. It can be a dangerous chan, and should only be used in reasonable vis and fair weather. On N side of the Swinge the main dangers are Boues des Kaines, almost awash at LW about 7½ca ESE of Ortac, and North Rk 2½ca SE of Burhou. On S side of the Swinge beware Barsier Rk (dries) 3½ca NNW of Fort Clonque, and Corbet Rk (0·5m high), with drying outliers, 5ca N of Fort Clonque.

The SW-going stream begins at HW St Helier + 0340, and the NE stream at HW St Helier – 0245, sp rates 7-8kn. On the NE-going stream, beware the very strong northerly set in vicinity of Ortac. The tide runs very hard, and in strong or gale force winds from S or W there are very heavy overfalls on the SW-going stream between Ortac and Les Etacs (off W end of Alderney). In strong E winds, on the NE-going stream, overfalls occur between Burhou and Braye breakwater. These overfalls can mostly be avoided by choosing the best time and route (see below), but due to the uneven bottom and strong tides broken water may be met even in calm conditions.

The best time to pass SW through the Swinge is at about HW St Helier +0400, when the SW-going stream starts; hold to the SE side of the chan since the strongest stream runs on the Burhou side. But after HW St Helier +0500, to clear the worst of the overfalls keep close to Burhou and Ortac, avoiding North Rk and Boues des Kaines.

Heading NE at about HW St Helier –0200, Great Nannel in transit with E end of Burhou clears Pierre au Vraic to the E, but passes close W of Les Etacs. On this transit, when Roque Tourgis fort is abeam, alter slightly to stbd to pass 1ca NW of Corbet Rk; keep near SE side of chan.

Pierre au Vraic (dries 1·2m) is an isolated, unmarked rock 1·8M S of Ortac and 1·8M WSW of Les Étacs, almost in the fairway to/from the Swinge. On a fair tide from Guernsey it will be well covered, but it is a serious hazard if leaving the Swinge on a SW-going Spring tide close to LW (HW Dover to HW Dover +4). See AC 60 for clearing bearings.

THE ALDERNEY RACE (chart 3653)

The Alderney Race, so called due to very strong tidal streams, runs NE/SW between Alderney and Cap de la Hague. The fairway, approx 4M wide, is bounded by Race Rk and Alderney S Banks to the NW, and to the SE by rky banks 4M WSW of Cap de la Hague, Milieu and Banc de la Schôle (least depth 2·7m). These dangers which cause breaking seas and heavy overfalls should be carefully avoided. In bad weather and strong wind-against-tide conditions the seas break in all parts of the Race and passage is not recommended. Conditions are exacerbated at sp tides.

In mid-chan the NE-going stream starts at HW St Helier – 0210 (HWD + 0530) and the SW stream at HW St Helier +0430 (HWD), sp rates both 5·5kn. Times at which streams turn do not vary much for various places, but the rates do; for example, 1M W of C de la Hague the sp rates are 7-8kn.

To obtain optimum conditions, timing is of the essence. As a rule of thumb the Race should be entered on the first of the fair tide so as to avoid the peak tidal streams with attendant overfalls/breaking seas.

Thus, bound SW, arrive off C de la Hague at about HW St Helier +0430 (HW Dover) when the stream will be slack, whilst just starting to run SW off Alderney. A yacht leaving Cherbourg at HW Dover –0300 will achieve the above timing by utilising the inshore W-going tidal eddy.

Conversely, NE bound, leave St Peter Port at approx local HW –0425 (HW Dover+3) with a foul tide so as to pass Banc de la Schôle as the first of the fair tide starts to make. A later departure should achieve a faster passage, but with potentially less favourable conditions in the Race. On the NE stream the worst overfalls are on the French side.

APPROACHES TO GUERNSEY (charts 808, 3654)

From the N/NE, The Little Russel Channel (chartlet at 8.14.11) between Guernsey and Herm gives the most convenient access to Beaucette marina (8.14.10) and St Peter Port (8.14.12 and chart 3140). With lts on Platte Fougère, Tautenay, Roustel, Platte and Bréhon, plus the ldg lts (220°) for St Peter Port, the Little Russel can be navigated day or night in reasonable vis, even at LW. But it needs care, due to rks which fringe the chan and appr, and the strong tide which also sets across the ent. In mid chan, S of Platte and NW of Bréhon, the NE-going stream begins at HW St Peter Port – 0245, and the SW stream at HW St Peter Port +0330, sp rates both 5·25kn which can raise a very steep sea with wind against tide.

The Big Russel is wider and easier; in bad weather or poor vis it may be a better approach to St Peter Port, via Lower Heads SCM lt buoy. From the NW, Doyle Passage, which is aligned 146°/326° off Beaucette, can be used but only by day with local knowledge. From S or W, the natural route is around St Martin's Pt rounding Longue Pierre bn (LP) 1·5ca ENE.

Minor hbrs and anchs around Guernsey are briefly described after the St Peter Port tidal predictions (8.14.12). In onshore winds keep well clear of Guernsey's W coast, where in bad weather the sea breaks on dangers up to 4M offshore.

HERM AND JETHOU (charts *807, 808*).

Herm (8.14.12) and Jethou (private) are reached from Little Russel via any of 7 passages all of which require reasonable vis and care with tidal streams; Alligande pass is most direct from St Peter Port. The appr from the Big Russel is more open and leads easily to pleasant ⚓s at Belvoir Bay and Shell Bay.

SARK (8.14.13 and chart *808*)

La Maseline and Creux on the E coast are the only proper hbrs, the former much used by ferries. Elsewhere around the island, whatever the wind direction, a sheltered anch can usually be found in a lee, although swell may intrude. On the NW coast, Port à La Jument and Port du Moulin in Banquette Bay offer some shelter from S and E winds. Fontaines Bay and La Grève de la Ville offer different degrees of protection on the NE coast. Derrible B, Dixcart B and Rouge Terrier are good anchs on the SE coast. Port Gorey, Les Fontaines B, La Grande Grève and Havre Gosselin are all on the W coast; the last named is crowded in season due to easy access from Guernsey. Tidal streams around Sark need careful study, especially returning from the E coast towards Guernsey when the choice between going N or S-about Sark can make a significant difference. A more detailed study is under 8.14.13.

JERSEY (charts *3655*, 1136, *1137*, 1138)

The rotary pattern of tidal streams affecting the Channel Islands as a whole dictates that when streams are slack on the N and S coasts of Jersey, they are running strongly on the E and W coasts; and vice versa. If reaching Jersey from Guernsey/Alderney at HW St Helier +4, a fair tide can be carried for at least 6 hrs down the W coast and along the S coast to St Helier. From the S, leave St Malo at about HW, keeping E of the Minquiers, in order to carry a fair tide for 6 hrs to St Helier. Follow similar tidal tactics when coasting around the island.

To N and NE of Jersey, Les Pierres de Lecq (Paternosters), Les Dirouilles and Les Ecrehou are groups of islets and drying rks, 2-4M offshore. On the N coast several bays (8.14.14) offer anchs sheltered in offshore winds. Coming from N, a convenient landfall is Desormes WCM buoy, 4M NNW of Grosnez Pt (conspic lookout tr). In St Ouen B on the W coast, which has drying rks almost 1M offshore, there are no good anchorages except NW of La Rocco tr which is sheltered in offshore winds.

Rounding the SW tip, to clear offlying dangers by 1M, keep the top of La Corbière lt ho (conspic) level with or below the clifftops behind (FR lt). The 'CB' RDF bn at the lt ho provides distance off in conjunction with the fog horn; see Table 3 (1). Coded wind info is also transmitted; see 8.14.14.

Along the S coast the NW and W Passages (buoyed) lead E past Noirmont Pt toward St Helier (8.14.14). St Brelade and St Aubin Bays (8.14.14) provide some shelter from W'lies. From the SW and S St Helier can be approached via Danger Rk Passage, Red & Green Passage or South Passage. All require good visibility to identify the transit marks and care to maintain the transits exactly. Only the R & G Passage is lit, but it needs sufficent water to pass over Fairway Rk (1·2m). The new Elizabeth marina at St Helier can be entered either from the R & G Passage or, with sufficient rise of tide, from St Aubin Bay. The latter appr on 110° passes N of Elizabeth Castle, crossing the causeway which dries approx 5·3m. It is well marked and lit.

SE of St Helier the drying, rky Violet Bank extends 1M S to Demie de Pas lt beacon, thence E past Icho Twr (conspic). It extends 1·7M S and 2M SE of La Rocque Pt. Further rky plateaux extend 1M to seaward. The Violet Channel (chart 1138), although buoyed is best avoided in bad weather, wind-over-tide or poor vis. From St Helier make good Canger Rk WCM lt buoy, thence track 078° for 2·2M to Violet SWM lt buoy. Turn N to pick up the charted ldg lines toward Gorey (8.14.15; dries) or to St Catherine Bay, both popular hbrs. The safe width of Violet Chan is only 5ca in places. Beware Decca problems due to being in the baseline extension area. The E coast of Jersey is sheltered from W'lies, but requires careful pilotage.

If bound for the adjacent French coast, proceed NE from Violet buoy via the Anquette Channel, between Petite and Grande Anquette beacons.

Les Minquiers (8.14.14), 10-18M S of St Helier, should only be entered by visitors in settled weather, with extreme caution and a good Pilot book.

14

8.14.6   DISTANCE TABLE

Approximate distances in nautical miles are by the most direct route, whilst avoiding dangers and allowing for Traffic Separation Schemes. Places in *italics* are in adjoining areas; places in **bold** are in 8.0.8, Cross-Channel Distances.

1. *Cherbourg*	1																			
2. *Cap de la Hague*	14	2																		
3. *Carteret*	41	23	3																	
4. *Granville*	75	61	38	4																
5. *St Malo*	87	73	38	23	5															
6. Casquets	31	17	32	63	70	6														
7. **Braye (Alderney)**	23	9	26	66	73	8	7													
8. Beaucette	39	25	34	59	58	15	19	8												
9. **St Peter Port**	42	28	31	55	54	18	23	4	9											
8. Les Hanois	49	35	37	58	56	23	29	14	10	10										
11. Creux (Sark)	37	23	23	50	52	18	22	11	10	16	11									
12. **St Helier**	59	45	28	30	38	43	46	33	29	32	24	12								
13. Gorey (Jersey)	47	33	16	29	38	36	35	32	29	35	20	13	13							
14. *Dahouet*	88	74	62	44	28	70	72	62	58	57	53	41	47	14						
15. *St Quay-Portrieux*	88	74	64	54	35	71	73	55	56	48	51	46	52	12	15					
16. *Paimpol*	91	77	65	56	42	67	70	54	50	45	50	45	53	24	24	16				
17. *Lézardrieux*	88	74	68	54	49	65	68	52	48	42	38	47	55	33	21	14	17			
18. *Tréguier*	94	80	72	72	60	66	72	56	52	42	58	53	63	58	46	29	22	18		
19. *Roscoff*	117	103	95	96	84	87	94	77	73	63	79	80	93	71	59	58	54	41	19	
20. *L'Aberwrac'h*	145	131	126	128	116	115	122	107	103	93	109	110	123	103	91	88	84	72	32	20

SPECIAL NOTES FOR THE CHANNEL ISLANDS   8-14-8

The Channel Islands (Jersey, Guernsey, Alderney, Sark and other smaller islands) lie, not in the Channel, but in the Bay of St. Malo. Alderney is part of the Bailiwick of Guernsey and the States of Alderney have seats in the States of Guernsey. Sark, Brecqhou, Herm and Jethou are all part of Guernsey.

History The Islands were originally part of Normandy and therefore French; the eastern ends of Jersey & Alderney are only 15 and 8·5 miles respectively from France. They could not be thought of as British until, at the earliest, the 13th century, after King John lost mainland Normandy. The French call them Les Iles Anglo-Normandes (Jersey, Guernesey, Aurigny et Sercq).

Customs The Islands are British but are not part of the UK nor of the EU. They are self-governing, with their own laws and customs regulations. British yachts entering Channel Island ports will be required to complete the local Customs declaration form and may have to produce the vessel's registration documents; they will also be subject to customs formalities on return to UK. Yachts going to France need the normal documents (passports etc) and British yachts returning to the Channel Islands from France, must, like all French yachts, wear the Q flag. (It is advisable to do so when arriving from UK, but not mandatory, except in Alderney). All Channel Islands have reciprocal medical arrangements with UK.

Charts A folio of 10 small craft Admiralty charts of the Channel Islands costs £31.95. The charts and scales are:

5604.1	CI and appr's	1:500,000
5604.2	Guernsey to Alderney	1:185,000
5604.3	Guernsey to Lezardrieux	1:185,000
5604.4	Jersey to St Malo	1:185,000
5604.5	Alderney	1:25,000
5604.6	Guernsey, Herm and Sark	1:60,000
5604.7	The Little Russel	1:25,000
5604.8	Sark; Gorey (Jersey)	1:25,000
5604.9	Jersey	1:60,000
5604.10	Appr's to St Helier	1:25,000

Weather forecasts. See 5.7.1 and 8.14.14.

Ports of Entry are Braye, Beaucette, St Sampson, St Peter Port, St Helier and Gorey.

SAR operations are directed by the Hr Mrs of St Peter Port (for the N area) and St Helier (for the S area), via St Peter Port and Jersey Radio respectively. Major incidents are co-ordinated with CROSSMA Joburg and Falmouth MRCC. Unlike the UK there are no CGs, but there are LBs at Braye, St Peter Port, St Helier and St Catherines (Jersey).

Telephones All CI telephones are part of the UK BT system.

Radio Telephone VHF Link calls to the UK made by British yachtsmen through St Peter Port or Jersey Radio will incur handling charges by British Telecom at the rate for foreign calls (see 6.4.10).

Courtesy Flags Many yachts fly a courtesy flag in Channel Island ports as a mark of politeness but it is not de rigeur. The local flags are:
Jersey W flag with R diagonal cross, with the Jersey Royal Arms (three lions passant with gold crown above) in the canton.
Guernsey R ensign with Duke William's cross in the fly. Vessels owned by Guernsey residents may wear this ensign.
Sark The English (St George's) flag with the Normandy arms in the canton.
Alderney The English (St George's) flag and in the centre a G disc charged with a gold lion.
Herm The English (St George's) flag, and in the canton the Arms of Herm (three cowled monks on a gold diagonal stripe between blue triangles containing a silver dolphin).

Cars can be hired in Jersey, Guernsey and Alderney. All cars are forbidden in Sark.

Animals The rules regarding animals are as strict as they are in UK. Landing of animals from boats is permitted only from UK, Ireland, Isle of Man or other Chan Islands, but not if the boat has visited France. Unless expressly permitted by a Revenue Officer, no vessel may lie alongside a pontoon or quay with an animal on board.

Currency is interchangeable with UK currency except in coin. Using CI notes on return to UK is not always popular! Postage stamps, issued by Jersey, Guernsey and Alderney must be used in the appropriate island. There is only one class of post; it is cheaper than UK.

BRAYE (Alderney)   8-14-9

Alderney 49°43'·83N 02°11'·42W   Rtg 1-4-1

CHARTS
AC *5604.5, 2845, 60, 3653, 2669*; SHOM 6934, 7158; ECM 1014; Imray C33A; Stanfords 7, 16

TIDES
−0400 Dover; ML 3·5; Duration 0545; Zone 0 (UT)

Standard Port ST HELIER (⟶)

Times				Height (metres)			
High Water		Low Water		MHWS	MHWN	MLWN	MLWS
0300	0900	0200	0900	11·0	8·1	4·0	1·4
1500	2100	1400	2100				
Differences BRAYE							
+0050	+0040	+0025	+0105	−4·8	−3·4	−1·5	−0·5

SHELTER
Good in Braye Hbr, except in strong N/NE winds. A total of 80 Y ⚓s are laid parallel to the Admiralty bkwtr, E of Braye jetty and near Toulouse Rk, bn. Orange buoys are for locals. No landing on Admiralty bkwtr; at its NE end beware submerged extension. ⚓ in hbr is good on sand, but only fair on rock or weed patches; keep clear of the fairway and jetty due to steamer traffic. Hbr speed limit 4kn. Access HW±2 to drying inner hbr for D, FW.

NAVIGATION
WPT 49°44'·32N 02°10'·90W, 035°/215° from/to front ldg lt 215°, 1·05M. The main hazards are strong tidal streams and the many rocks encircling Alderney. The safest appr is from the NE. Take the Swinge and the Race at/near slack water to avoid the dangerous overfalls in certain wind and tide conditions (see 8.14.5). In the Swinge calmest area is often near Corbet Rk. At mid-flood (NE-going) a strong eddy flows SW past the hbr ent. On the S side of the island during the ebb, a strong NE-going eddy runs close inshore of Coque Lihou. Give Brinchetais Ledge (E end) a wide berth to avoid heavy overfalls. An Historic Wreck is 5ca N of Quenard Pt lt ho (see 8.0.3h).

LIGHTS AND MARKS
From NW, N side of Ft Albert and end of Admiralty bkwtr 115° clear the Nannels. Iso WR 4s at Château à l'Etoc Pt, E of the hbr, vis R071°-111°, W111°-151°, in line 111° with Quenard Pt lt ho, Fl (4) 15s, clears sunken ruins of bkwtr. Ldg lts, both Q vis 210°-220°, lead 215° into hbr; front 8m 17M; rear 17m 18M. The Admty bkwtr hd has a lt, L Fl 10s 7m 5M. By day, St Anne's church spire on with W bn at Douglas Quay leads 210° to fairway which is marked by a QR and QG buoy and an inner pair of Q (2) R 5s and Q (2) G 5s buoys. End of steamer quay has 2 FR (vert) lts.

RADIO TELEPHONE
Call: *Alderney Radio* VHF Ch **74** 16 (12) (Apr to Sept, 0800-1800, daily; Oct 0800-1700 daily; Nov to Mar, 0800-1700, Mon-Fri: all LT). Note: In fog/limited vis radar assistance and RDF bearings to small craft can be provided by the Hr Mr during above hrs. Outside these hrs call St Peter Port. For the Casquets TSS see Cherbourg (8·15·9). Mainbrayce Marine Ch 80 M (Apr-mid Sept: 0800-2000LT). Water taxi call *Mainbrayce* Ch M, 0800-2359.

TELEPHONE (Dial code 01481)
Hr Mr & ⌗ 822620, ☎ 823699; Marinecall 0891 500 432; Recorded forecast for Alderney/Guernsey (06969) 8800 (available from Alderney/Guernsey); 06966 0022 recorded forecast for Alderney/Guernsey (available from UK); Police 822731; Dr 822077; ⊞ 822822; ❶ Info 822994 (H24).

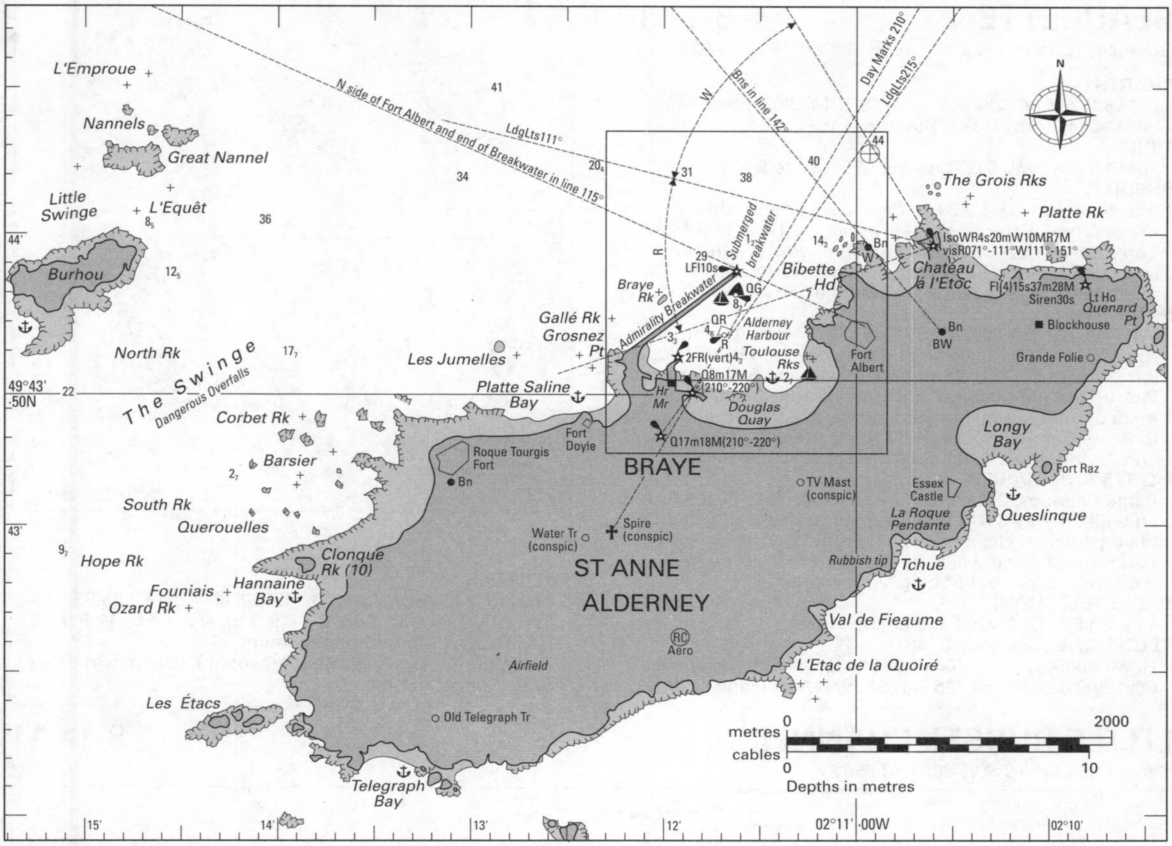

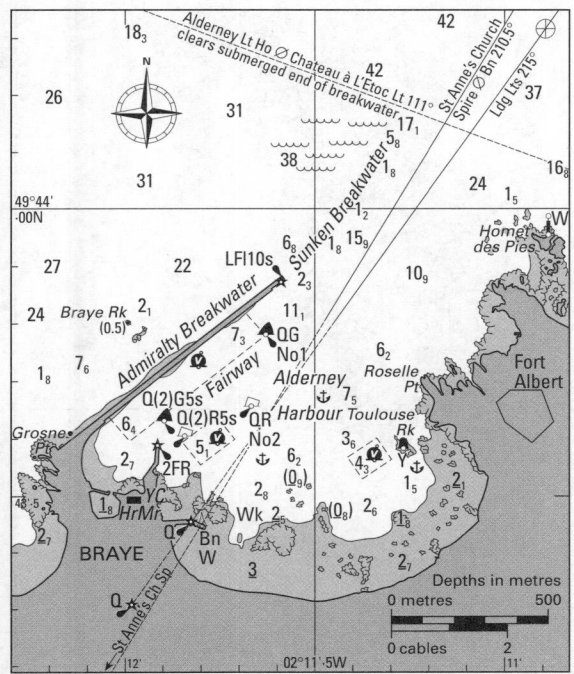

FACILITIES

Hbr ⚓ (£10 flat rate); **Jetty** , FW, C, ▣; **Sapper Slip,** FW; **Alderney SC** ☎ 822758, Bar; **Services:** Slip, FW, ME, El, Ⓔ, Gas, SM, Sh, CH, ACA, P (cans), D (Mainbrayce, inner hbr HW±2). **Town** EC Wed; V, R, Bar, ✉, Ⓑ, ✈ to Jersey, Guernsey and Southampton; Dinard and Cherbourg via Guernsey. Ferry: via Guernsey – Poole.

ANCHORAGES AROUND ALDERNEY

There are several ⚓s, all picturesque but only safe in off-shore winds. Most ⚓s are very small and many have offlying rocks. Without local knowledge, advice from the Hr Mr and a good Pilot book plus AC 60 and/or 2845, it is not recommended to enter these anchorages. None provide any facilities. Clockwise from Braye they are:

Saye Bay. Small sandy bay 4ca E of ent to Braye Hbr. Appr on transit 142° of ldg bns, opening to the E. Ent is 100m wide between Homet des Pies and Homet des Agneaux. Exposed to N'lies. Château à l'Étoc ✩ is 300m ENE.

Corblets Bay. AC 2845. Appr with BW bn △ (rear ldg mark of 142° transit for Braye) brg 210°. Leave Platte Rk (1·8m) 100m to port. Beware drying reefs closer in. ⚓ in 2·5m when Quenard lt ho and Château à l'Étoc ✩ are in line.

Longy Bay. AC 2845. Wide drying bay with good holding in sand. Appr on N between Queslingue (14m high) and rk 0·6m to stbd. ⚓ in 3·5m closer to Essex Castle than to Raz Island to await fair tide in the Race.

La Tchue. Good holding in small bay surrounded by cliffs. La Rocque Pendante to the E and smoking rubbish tip to the NW are both conspic.

Telegraph Bay. Pleasant sandy bay on SW tip of the island but ringed by rocks. Appr on NNE between Noires Putes and Coupé. Telegraph Twr is conspic until close inshore.

Hannaine Bay. A good place to await the flood tide. Appr on transit 057° of Tourgis Bn △ and SE side of Fort Clonque. Beware rks either side. ⚓ on sand in 3m, 100m S of Fort.

Platte Saline Bay. AC 2845. Good shelter from E winds.

Burhou. Temp'y ⚓ in bay in SSW of Burhou, only on SW stream; exposed at HW on the NE-going stream. Appr on 010° for the gap between Burhou and Little Burhou.

OFF CASQUETS TSS

Casquets TSS/ITZ. See 8.14.2. Orientated 075°/255° the E/W lanes and central separation zone are 5M wide and 20M long. Channel lt float and E Channel lt buoy lie at either end. The S edge is roughly defined by Hurd Deep (174m max depth). The ITZ encompasses Alderney, Guernsey & Sark. The TSS is under radar surveillance by *Jobourg Traffic* (8.15.9). Portland CG offers radio cover Ch **69** 16.

14

BEAUCETTE   8-14-10

Guernsey (Channel Islands) 49°30'.25N 02°30'.12W

CHARTS
AC *5604.6 & .7, 808, 807, 3654*; SHOM 6903, 6904, 7159; ECM 1014; Imray C33A; Stanfords 16

TIDES
−0450 Dover; ML 5·0; Duration 0550; Zone 0 (UT)

SHELTER
Excellent. Sill dries 2.37m; for access times, add 2m to the depth of water over sill given in the table at 8.14.12. Entry not advised in strong onshore winds or heavy swell. 8 Y waiting buoys are outside (water taxi, Ch 80) and tide gauges outside & inside the 18m wide ent chan.

NAVIGATION
WPT 49°30'·15N 02°28'·85W, 097°/277° from/to ent, 8½ca. Appr from Little Russel to mid-way between Platte Fougère lt tr (W with B band, 25m) and Roustel lt tr (BW chequered). Pick up the unlit fairway buoy, ldg marks/lts and four pairs of unlit lateral buoys. Beware cross tides setting on to Petite Canupe Rocks (SCM lt bn) to the N, and rocks and drying areas to the S of the approach channel.

LIGHTS AND MARKS
Petite Canupe SCM bn, Q (6) + L Fl 15s, close S of which is an unlit fairway SWM buoy, signed to Beaucette, and on the ldg line. Ldg lts/marks 277°: Front FR, R arrow on W background on stbd side of ent; rear FR, W arrow on R background, on roof of bldg, with windsock.

RADIO TELEPHONE
VHF Ch **80** (0700-2200 and at tide times).

TELEPHONE (Dial code 01481)
Hr Mr 45000, mobile (04481) 102302; ⌗ 45000; Marinecall 0891 500 432; Police 725111; St John Ambulance 725211.

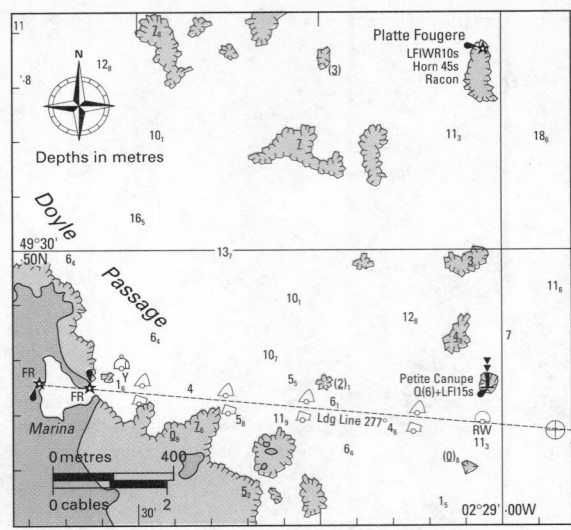

Depths in metres

FACILITIES
Marina (140+50 visitors), ☎ 45000, ⛴ 47071, £15.93, D, FW, AC, Gas, Gaz, Slip, BH (16 ton), ME, El, C (12.5 ton), Bar, R, V, ▣, Marine management.
Town EC Thurs; ✉, Ⓑ (St Sampson), ✈ (Guernsey). Ferry: St Peter Port – Poole.

LITTLE RUSSEL CHANNEL   8-14-11

See 8.14.5 and AC *807, 808* and *5604.7*

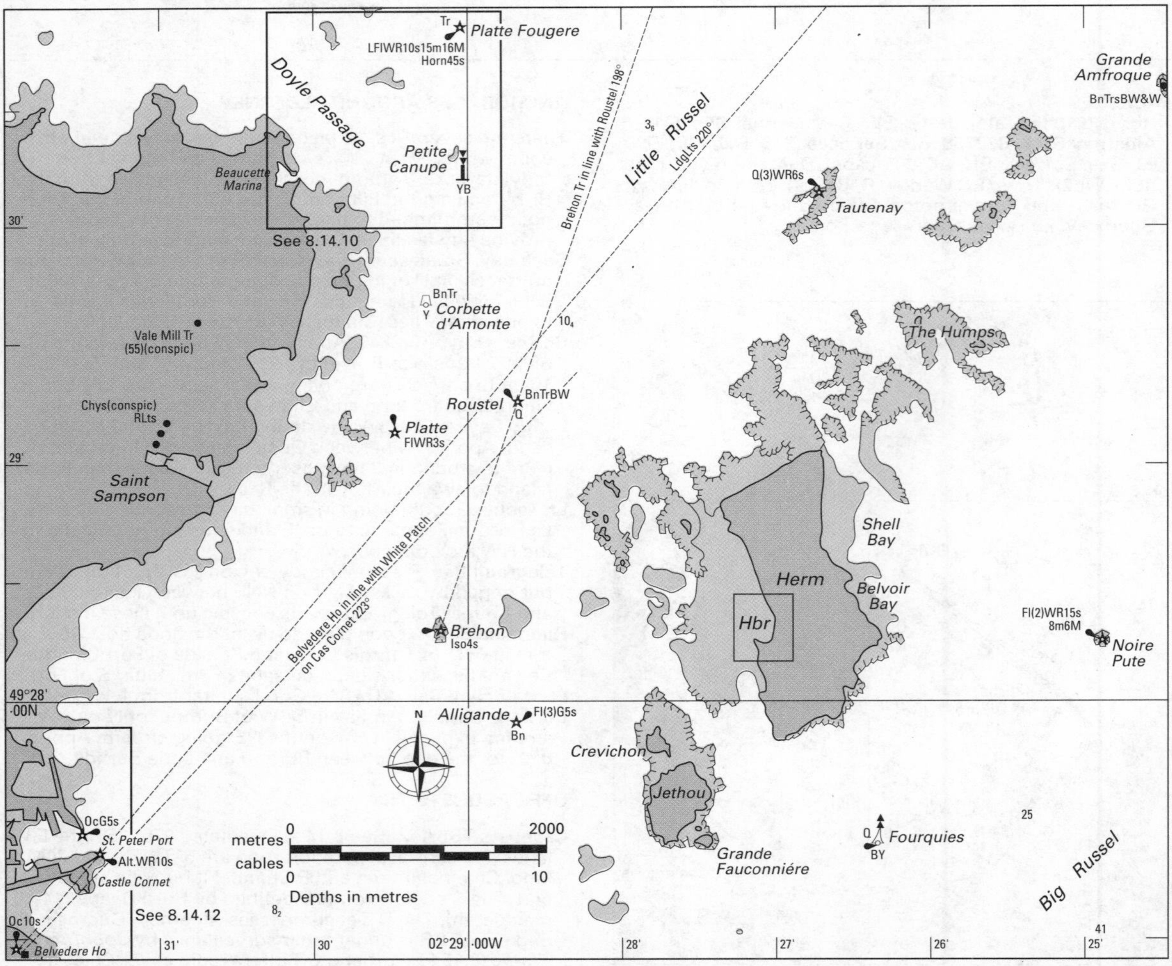

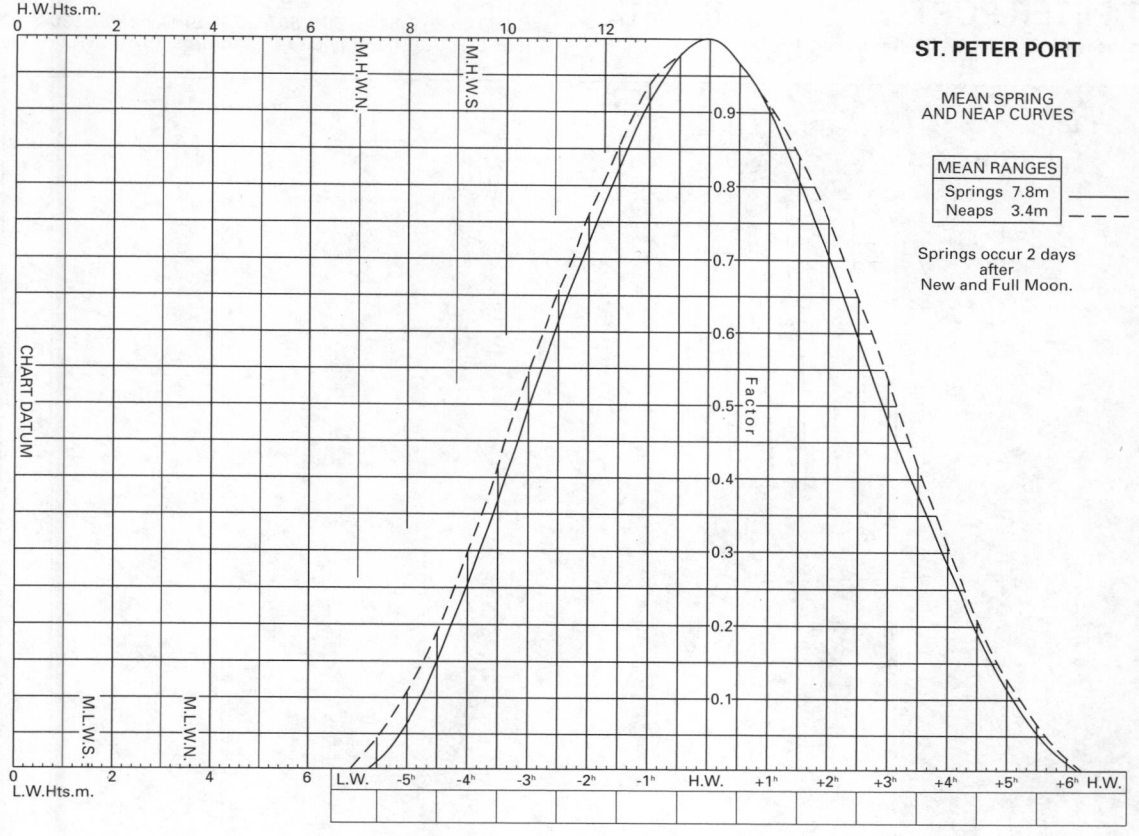

ST. PETER PORT

MEAN SPRING
AND NEAP CURVES

MEAN RANGES	
Springs 7.8m	————
Neaps 3.4m	– – – –

Springs occur 2 days
after
New and Full Moon.

HARBOURS AND ANCHORAGES AROUND GUERNSEY

Chart 808 is esential. ⚓s and hbrs are listed clockwise from Beaucette. All have buses to St Peter Port (from cliff-top level on the E and S coasts).

EAST COAST

Bordeaux Harbour. Small drying hbr full of local moorings. Rky appr with strong cross tide. Exposed to E. Café.

St Sampson's Harbour. Hbr dries 5·2m. Official port of entry. Good shelter but the disadvantages of a commercial and fishing hbr. Yachts may only enter by prior arrangement or for commercial services. WPT 49°28'·76N 02°29'·56W, the intersection of St Peter Port and St Sampson ldg lts. 3 chys on N side are conspic. Ldg lts 286°: Front, FR 3m 5M, on S Arm; rear, FG 13m, 390m from front, on clocktower. N pier hd FG 3m 5M, vis 230°-340°. Crocq pier hd, FR 11m 5M, vis 250°-340°, and tfc sigs. A Fl Y on S Arm flashes when petroleum/gas tankers are moving in the hbr; do not obstruct. Speed limit 6kn. No ⚓ in hbr. VHF Ch 12 (H24). Facilities: Call Dockmaster ☎ 720229 for entry, AB, C, FW. No special facilities for yachts. **Services:** Slip, BY, ME, El, Sh, C.

Havelet Bay. Enter between SHM buoy QG and PHM buoy QR, marking Oyster Rk, bn 'O', and Moulinet Rk, bn 'M'. Unlit SHM and PHM buoy about 100m closer inshore. Crowded ⚓ in summer; no ✺s. Landing slip close W of Castle Cornet.

Soldier's Bay. Good holding on sand; exposed to E. On appr beware rky spur off Les Terres Point. Anfré Rk (3_3), bn 'A', is 4ca offshore. Steps to cliff path. No facilities.

Fermain Bay. Good holding on sand; exposed to E. From N beware Gold Fisher Rk (2_1) and drying reefs off NE end of bay. From SE beware Gabrielle Rk (2_1). Popular tourist beach. Café, hotel, bar.

SOUTH COAST

In the centre of first bight W of St Martin's Pt, beware Mouillière (8_c). S winds can bring swell above half tide. Within this bight are:

Petit Port. Good holding on sand. Steep steps to cliff-top bar.

Moulin Huet. Good holding on sand. Tea garden and hotel.

Saints Bay. Good holding on sand. Below half tide beware uncharted rock in middle and unburied telephone cable on E side. ⚓ outside moorings with trip line. Café, hotel, bar.

Icart Bay. Beware Fourquie de la Moye (3_3) in centre of ent between Icart Pt and Pte de la Moye. In Icart Bay are:

Jaonnet. Good holding on sand off small beach or further E off rky shore. Exposed to S. No facilities. Cliff path inland.

Petit Bôt Bay. Beware drying reef on E side. A short swell often works in. Café; up hill to hotel, bar, airport, ✉, V. Better ⚓ close W at:

Portelet. Good holding on sand in small ⚓. Sheltered from N and W. No access inland. Facilities via dinghy/Petit Bôt.

WEST COAST

Good visibility and chart essential; a pilot and E'ly wind desirable. Pass outside Les Hanois, unless bound for:

Portelet Harbour. Good holding on sand. Exposed to W. ⚓ outside moorings and clear of fish farm. Rky appr; local knowledge advised. Best avoid small drying stone quay. Hotel, bar, café.

Lihou Island. ⚓ off NE corner. Sheltered from E. Between Lihou and Guernsey is a drying rocky area and causeway over which the tide runs fast. Respect bird sanctuaries on off-lying islets. No facilities.

Perelle Bay. Good holding on sand. Exposed to W; rky appr. Beware Colombelle Rk (1_5) NE of bay. ⚓ outside moorings. Bar, hotel, D & P (cans).

Vazon Bay. Wide sandy beach for settled conditions, but exposed to the W. Beware Boue Vazon (3) in appr, many lobster pots, surfers and bathers. Long surf line. Hotel, R.

Cobo Bay. Beware Boue Vazon (3) in appr and many lobster pots. Rky appr from S of Moulière. Good holding on sand; ⚓ outside local moorings. Facilities: Hotel, Bar, R, B, ✉, V, D & P (cans).

Grande Havre. Very popular, many local moorings. Rky appr, exposed to NW, sheltered from S'lies. ⚓ to W of Hommet de Grève. Stone slip, busy in summer; lying alongside not recommended. Facilities: Hotel, Bar.

L'Ancresse Bay. Good holding on sand. Exposed to the N, but good shelter from S/SW. Hotel, Bar, Café.

Fontenelle Bay. Good holding on sand. Exposed to the N. Beware drying rks on E of ent. No facilities.

14

ST PETER PORT

8-14-12

Guernsey 49°27'·41N 02°31'·45W   Rtg 1-1-1

CHARTS

AC *5604.6 & .7*, 3140, *808, 807, 3654*; SHOM 6903, 6904, 7159; ECM 1014; Imray C33A; Stanfords 16

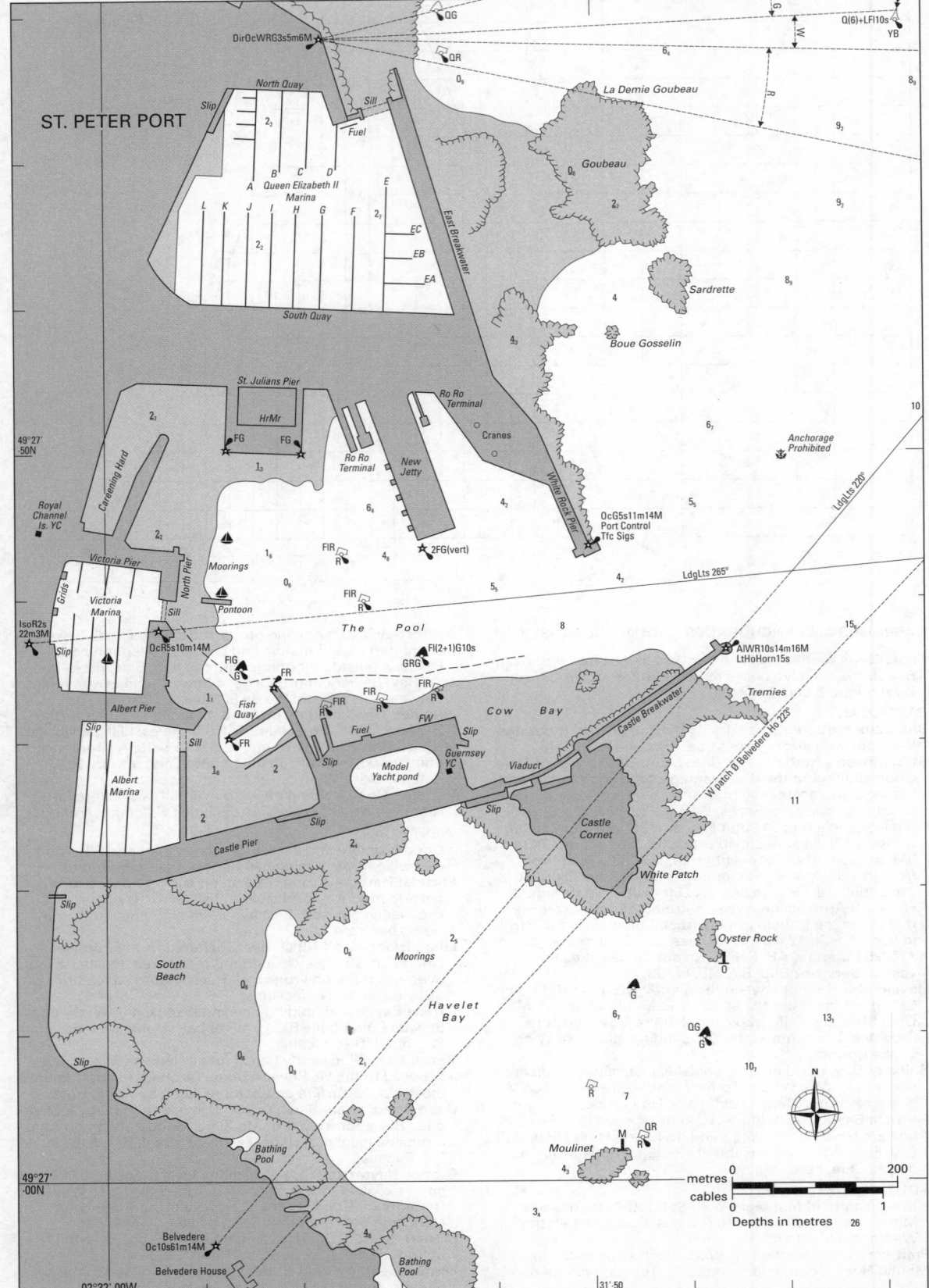

Depths in metres

TIDES

–0439 Dover; ML 5·2; Duration 0550; Zone 0 (UT)
NOTE: Now a Standard Port, predicted times and hts of HW/LW for each day of the year are shown below.
To find depth of water over the sill into Victoria marina:
1. Look up predicted time and height of HW St Peter Port.
2. Enter table below on the line for height of HW.
3. Extract depth (m) of water for time before/after HW.

Ht (m) of HW St Peter Port	Depth of Water in metres over the Sill (dries 4·4m)						
	HW	±1hr	±2hrs	±2½hrs	±3hrs	±3½hrs	±4hrs
6·20	1·85	1·67	1·30	1·03	0·75	0·47	0·20
·60	2·25	2·00	1·50	1·13	"	0·37	0·00
7·00	2·65	2·34	1·70	1·23	"	0·27	–
·40	3·05	2·67	1·90	1·33	"	0·17	–
·80	3·45	3·00	2·10	1·43	"	0·07	–
8·20	3·85	3·34	2·30	1·53	"	–	–
·60	4·25	3·67	2·50	1·63	"	–	–
9·00	4·65	4·00	2·70	1·73	"	–	–
·40	5·05	4·34	2·90	1·83	"	–	–
·80	5·45	4·67	3·10	1·93	"	–	–

SHELTER
Good, especially in Victoria Marina which has a sill 4·4m above CD, with a fixed vert pillar in mid-entrance, and gauge giving depth over sill. Access approx HW±2½ according to draft; see Table above. R/G tfc lts control ent/exit. Appr via buoyed/lit chan along S side of hbr. Marina boat will direct yachts to waiting pontoon or Y ⚓s to E of marina ent. Pontoons for tenders are each side of marina ent. Local moorings are in centre of hbr, with a secondary fairway N of them. ⚓ prohib. Queen Elizabeth II and Albert marinas are for local boats only.

NAVIGATION
WPT 49°27'·88N 02°30'·70W, 040°/220° from/to front ldg lt, 0·68M. Offlying dangers, big tidal range and strong tidal streams demand careful navigation. Easiest appr from N is via Big Russel between Herm and Sark, passing S of Lower Hds SCM lt buoy. The Little Russel is slightly more direct, but needs care especially in poor visibility; see 8.14.5 and 8.14.11 chartlet. From W and S of Guernsey, give Les Hanois a wide berth. Beware ferries and shipping. Hbr speed limits: 6kn from outer pier heads to line from New Jetty to Castle Cornet; 4kn W of that line. The RDF beacon, GY 304·50kHz (see Table 3(1)), on Castle bkwtr is synchronised with the co-located horn* to give distance finding. The horn blast begins simultaneously with the 27 sec long dash after the four GY ident signals. The number of seconds from the start of the long dash until the horn blast is heard, multiplied by 0·18 gives the distance in M from the horn.

LIGHTS AND MARKS
Appr ldg lts 220°: Front, Castle bkwtr hd Al WR 10s 14m 16M (vis 187°-007°) Horn 15s*; rear, Belvedere Oc 10s 61m 14M, intens 217°-223°. By day, White patch at Castle Cornet in line 223° with Belvedere Ho (conspic).
Inner ldg lts 265°: Front, Oc R 5s; rear, Iso R 2s, vis 260°-270° (10°). This ldg line is for the use of ferries berthing at New Jetty. It extends through moorings in The Pool, so must not be used by yachts which should appr to Victoria marina via the buoyed/lit S channel (dashed line).
Traffic Signals on White Rock pierhead:
Ⓡ (vis from seaward) = No ent
Ⓡ (vis from landward) = No exit (also shown from SW corner of New Pier).
These sigs do not apply to boats, <15m LOA, under power and keeping clear of the fairways.

RADIO TELEPHONE
For St Peter Port as a whole call *Port Control* Ch 12 (H24). Water taxi Ch 10 (0800-2359LT). If difficulty experienced in raising *Port Control* on VHF, messages may be sent via St Peter Port Radio on VHF Ch 20 or MF; see 6·5·1. Link calls Ch 62 via St Peter Port Radio. St Sampson Ch 12 (H24).

TELEPHONE (Dial code 01481)
Hr Mr 720229, 🛟714177; Marina 725987; ⌗726911; CG Sig Stn 720085; Recorded premium rate forecasts for Guernsey/Alderney are available on (06969) 8800 only from Guernsey/Alderney; recorded premium rate forecast for Guernsey/Alderney available on (06966) 0022 from UK; Marinecall 0891 500 432; Dr 711237 (H24), Pier Steps at Boots; 725211 (St John Ambulance); Police 725111.

FACILITIES
Victoria Marina (400, all visitors) ☎ 725987, £13 (£1 extra in Jul/Aug), FW, AC, Slip, ♿, ▯, R, Max LOA/draft = 12·8m/1·8m, Max stay 14 days; N Pier C (32, 20, 7 ton), AB; Castle Pier P, D, approx HW±3, 0730-1730 Mon-Sat, 0730-1200 Sun; (also fuel pontoon at QE II marina). Royal Chan Is YC ☎ 723154 Bar; Guernsey YC ☎ 722838;
Services: CH, Gas, Gaz, ACA, ME, EI, SM, BY, Ⓔ.
Town EC Thurs; P, D, V, CH, R, ▯, Bar, ✉, Ⓑ. Ferry to Poole, Cherbourg, Diélette, St Malo; Hydrofoil/catamaran to Sark, Poole, Jersey, St Malo; ✈ (Guernsey Airport).

HERM ISLAND
Access to Herm is not difficult, given adequate planning.

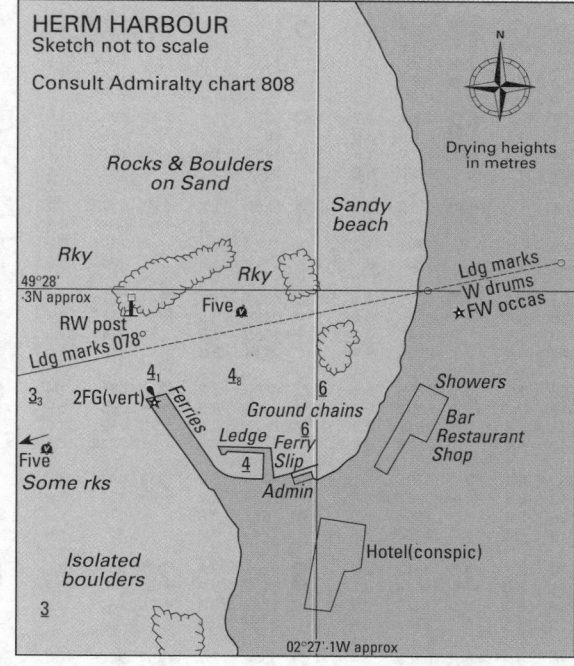

Herm Harbour
SHELTER
Good, safe in all winds. Access HW±2½. Options: a. Bilge keelers dry out on firm sand inside hbr, moored fore/aft. b. Fin keelers may dry out against outer N wall of hbr, but beware ledge/apron. c. Dry out on the beach to the NE, moored fore/aft to chains. d. 5 ⚓s to N and 5 to W of hbr dry out: rky bottom to the N; isolated boulders/sand to W.
NAVIGATION
Appr from Little Russel to skirt close N of Vermerette bn in line 074° with W patch on Hbr quay. When base of Vermerette bn is awash, there is 1m at hbr ent. The tide will be setting N. See Pilot for details of Corbette, Alligande and other passages from the W.
LIGHTS AND MARKS
Ldg lts, both FW (occas) and W drums at 078°. 2FG (vert) on quay hd. Night appr not advised for visitors.
TELEPHONE
Island Admin ☎ 722377 for permission to stay overnight.
FACILITIES
No fees; donations welcome. Showers, FW, Hotel, Bar, R, limited V. Very congested in season at weekends, but plenty of space Sun to Thurs nights; many ferries by day.

Rosière Steps
Access at all tides for landing; do not remain alongside. Caution: From just before HW to HW+2 tide sets hard onto the steps. Easiest appr is from Big Russel via Percée passage; avoid Fourquies (2₃), NCM lt buoy, and Meulettes (1₇) off SW tip of Herm. ⚓ NW of Rosière steps; good holding on sand, but exposed to S and SW. Buoys are for ferries and locals. Facilities: as Herm Hbr, 400m N.
Belvoir Bay and Shell Beach on the E coast are good ⚓s on sand, sheltered from W. Easy access from E; from S keep 400m offshore. Beach café or walk 800m to village.
Note: Jethou, Crevichon and Grande Fauconnière islands are private. No landing.

CHANNEL ISLANDS – ST. PETER PORT

LAT 49°27′N   LONG 2°31′W

TIMES AND HEIGHTS OF HIGH AND LOW WATERS

YEAR **1999**

TIME ZONE (UT)
For Summer Time add ONE hour in non-shaded areas

JANUARY

Day	Time	m	Time	m	Time	m	Time	m
1 F	0533	9.1	1205	1.4	1803	9.0		
2 SA O	0027	1.3	0623	9.4	1257	1.0	1852	9.3
3 SU	0116	1.1	0711	9.6	1344	0.9	1939	9.3
4 M	0201	1.1	0755	9.6	1428	0.9	2022	9.2
5 TU	0243	1.3	0836	9.4	1510	1.2	2102	8.9
6 W	0322	1.6	0915	9.0	1548	1.6	2140	8.6
7 TH	0359	2.1	0953	8.5	1626	2.2	2218	8.0
8 F	0436	2.7	1031	8.0	1704	2.7	2258	7.5
9 SA	0516	3.2	1114	7.4	1747	3.2	2345	7.0
10 SU	0607	3.6	1207	7.0	1841	3.6		
11 M	0046	6.8	0711	3.8	1314	6.7	1945	3.7
12 TU	0159	6.8	0821	3.8	1426	6.8	2053	3.6
13 W	0308	7.0	0928	3.5	1532	7.0	2155	3.3
14 TH	0405	7.4	1024	3.1	1626	7.4	2247	2.9
15 F	0453	7.8	1113	2.6	1715	7.8	2333	2.4
16 SA	0537	8.3	1158	2.2	1759	8.2		
17 SU ●	0016	2.1	0618	8.6	1241	1.8	1841	8.5
18 M	0057	1.7	0658	8.9	1322	1.5	1920	8.8
19 TU	0136	1.5	0736	9.1	1401	1.3	1958	8.9
20 W	0215	1.4	0814	9.2	1440	1.3	2035	8.9
21 TH	0253	1.5	0852	9.1	1518	1.4	2113	8.8
22 F	0331	1.7	0931	8.9	1557	1.6	2154	8.5
23 SA	0412	2.0	1015	8.5	1640	2.0	2238	8.2
24 SU	0458	2.4	1104	8.1	1729	2.4	2331	7.8
25 M	0555	2.8	1204	7.7	1830	2.8		
26 TU	0037	7.5	0707	3.1	1319	7.5	1947	3.0
27 W	0159	7.4	0837	3.0	1443	7.5	2113	2.9
28 TH	0320	7.7	0957	2.7	1558	7.8	2224	2.5
29 F	0427	8.1	1100	2.2	1700	8.2	2324	2.0
30 SA	0523	8.6	1156	1.7	1754	8.6		
31 SU O	0016	1.6	0613	9.1	1246	1.2	1842	9.0

FEBRUARY

Day	Time	m	Time	m	Time	m	Time	m
1 M	0104	1.3	0658	9.4	1331	1.0	1925	9.2
2 TU	0146	1.1	0740	9.5	1412	0.9	2005	9.2
3 W	0225	1.1	0818	9.4	1449	1.0	2041	9.1
4 TH	0300	1.3	0852	9.2	1523	1.4	2114	8.8
5 F	0331	1.7	0924	8.8	1553	1.8	2144	8.3
6 SA	0400	2.2	0955	8.3	1621	2.4	2215	7.8
7 SU	0430	2.7	1028	7.7	1651	2.9	2249	7.3
8 M	0504	3.2	1107	7.2	1728	3.4	2332	6.9
9 TU	0554	3.7	1159	6.7	1825	3.8		
10 W	0037	6.6	0713	3.9	1318	6.5	1949	3.9
11 TH	0206	6.6	0834	3.8	1444	6.6	2106	3.4
12 F	0325	6.9	0945	3.4	1555	7.0	2212	3.2
13 SA	0425	7.4	1045	2.8	1651	7.5	2307	2.7
14 SU	0515	8.0	1136	2.2	1740	8.1	2356	2.1
15 M	0559	8.6	1222	1.6	1824	8.6		
16 TU ●	0040	1.6	0641	9.1	1306	1.2	1904	9.0
17 W	0122	1.1	0721	9.4	1347	0.8	1943	9.3
18 TH	0202	0.9	0800	9.6	1426	0.7	2021	9.4
19 F	0240	0.9	0838	9.6	1504	0.7	2058	9.3
20 SA	0318	1.0	0917	9.4	1541	1.0	2136	9.0
21 SU	0357	1.4	0957	8.9	1621	1.5	2218	8.5
22 M	0439	2.0	1043	8.3	1705	2.2	2305	7.9
23 TU	0530	2.6	1138	7.7	1801	2.8		
24 W	0006	7.4	0638	3.1	1252	7.2	1917	3.2
25 TH	0132	7.1	0817	3.3	1429	7.1	2057	3.3
26 F	0308	7.3	0948	2.9	1552	7.4	2216	2.8
27 SA	0418	7.8	1053	2.4	1652	7.9	2314	2.3
28 SU	0512	8.4	1145	1.8	1742	8.5		

MARCH

Day	Time	m	Time	m	Time	m	Time	m
1 M	0003	1.7	0559	8.9	1231	1.3	1826	8.9
2 TU O	0048	1.3	0641	9.3	1313	1.0	1906	9.2
3 W	0127	1.1	0720	9.5	1350	0.9	1942	9.3
4 TH	0202	1.1	0755	9.4	1424	1.0	2015	9.2
5 F	0234	1.1	0826	9.3	1453	1.2	2044	9.0
6 SA	0301	1.4	0855	8.9	1519	1.6	2112	8.6
7 SU	0327	1.9	0923	8.4	1543	2.1	2139	8.1
8 M	0352	2.4	0951	7.9	1607	2.6	2207	7.6
9 TU	0421	2.9	1023	7.4	1637	3.2	2240	7.2
10 W	0459	3.4	1105	6.9	1720	3.6	2329	6.7
11 TH	0600	3.8	1210	6.4	1834	4.0		
12 F	0052	6.5	0745	3.9	1351	6.4	2021	3.9
13 SA	0237	6.6	0908	3.5	1521	6.8	2138	3.5
14 SU	0352	7.2	1015	2.9	1624	7.4	2240	2.8
15 M	0447	7.9	1110	2.2	1715	8.1	2332	2.1
16 TU	0535	8.6	1158	1.5	1800	8.7		
17 W ●	0018	1.4	0618	9.2	1242	0.9	1842	9.2
18 TH	0103	0.9	0700	9.7	1326	0.5	1922	9.6
19 F	0144	0.5	0741	9.9	1406	0.3	2001	9.8
20 SA	0224	0.4	0820	9.9	1445	0.3	2040	9.7
21 SU	0302	0.6	0900	9.6	1523	0.7	2118	9.4
22 M	0341	1.0	0940	9.1	1602	1.3	2158	8.8
23 TU	0422	1.7	1024	8.4	1645	2.1	2244	8.1
24 W	0512	2.5	1118	7.6	1738	2.9	2343	7.4
25 TH	0619	3.1	1233	7.0	1855	3.4		
26 F	0109	6.9	0802	3.4	1419	6.9	2043	3.5
27 SA	0253	7.1	0936	3.0	1539	7.3	2202	3.0
28 SU	0402	7.6	1037	2.5	1636	7.8	2257	2.4
29 M	0454	8.2	1126	1.9	1722	8.4	2343	1.9
30 TU	0538	8.7	1208	1.5	1803	8.8		
31 W O	0024	1.5	0618	9.1	1247	1.2	1840	9.1

APRIL

Day	Time	m	Time	m	Time	m	Time	m
1 TH	0102	1.2	0654	9.3	1323	1.0	1915	9.2
2 F	0135	1.1	0728	9.3	1354	1.1	1946	9.2
3 SA	0205	1.1	0758	9.2	1422	1.3	2015	9.0
4 SU	0232	1.4	0827	8.9	1446	1.6	2042	8.7
5 M	0257	1.7	0854	8.5	1511	2.0	2108	8.3
6 TU	0323	2.2	0922	8.0	1535	2.5	2135	7.9
7 W	0351	2.7	0953	7.5	1604	3.0	2207	7.4
8 TH	0426	3.2	1032	7.0	1644	3.5	2252	7.0
9 F	0519	3.6	1131	6.6	1746	3.9		
10 SA	0002	6.6	0650	3.8	1259	6.5	1930	3.9
11 SU	0141	6.7	0830	3.5	1437	6.8	2100	3.5
12 M	0309	7.2	0940	2.9	1548	7.4	2207	2.8
13 TU	0412	7.9	1038	2.2	1642	8.1	2302	2.1
14 W	0503	8.6	1129	1.4	1730	8.8	2351	1.4
15 TH	0550	9.2	1216	0.8	1815	9.3		
16 F ●	0038	0.8	0635	9.7	1302	0.4	1858	9.8
17 SA	0123	0.4	0719	10.0	1344	0.2	1939	10.0
18 SU	0205	0.3	0801	10.0	1425	0.3	2020	9.9
19 M	0246	0.4	0843	9.7	1505	0.7	2100	9.5
20 TU	0327	0.9	0925	9.1	1546	1.3	2142	8.9
21 W	0410	1.6	1011	8.4	1630	2.1	2228	8.2
22 TH	0500	2.3	1105	7.6	1724	2.9	2326	7.5
23 F	0607	3.0	1217	7.0	1837	3.4		
24 SA	0046	7.0	0739	3.3	1356	6.9	2017	3.5
25 SU	0225	7.1	0910	3.1	1513	7.2	2135	3.2
26 M	0334	7.5	1009	2.6	1608	7.7	2230	2.6
27 TU	0426	7.9	1057	2.1	1654	8.2	2315	2.2
28 W	0510	8.4	1138	1.8	1734	8.6	2355	1.8
29 TH	0549	8.7	1216	1.5	1811	8.8		
30 F O	0031	1.5	0625	8.9	1252	1.4	1845	9.0

Chart Datum: 5·06 metres below Ordnance Datum (Local)

CHANNEL ISLANDS – ST. PETER PORT

LAT 49°27′N   LONG 2°31′W

TIMES AND HEIGHTS OF HIGH AND LOW WATERS

YEAR **1999**

TIME ZONE (UT)
For Summer Time add ONE hour in non-shaded areas

Chart Datum: 5·06 metres below Ordnance Datum (Local)

MAY

Day	Time	m	Time	m	Time	m	Time	m
1 SA	0105	1.3	0659	9.0	1323	1.3	1917	9.0
2 SU	0135	1.3	0731	8.9	1351	1.5	1947	8.9
3 M	0204	1.5	0801	8.7	1418	1.7	2015	8.7
4 TU	0232	1.8	0831	8.4	1445	2.1	2043	8.4
5 W	0301	2.1	0900	8.0	1513	2.5	2112	8.0
6 TH	0331	2.5	0933	7.6	1544	2.9	2146	7.6
7 F	0407	2.9	1013	7.2	1624	3.3	2231	7.3
8 SA	0458	3.3	1109	6.9	1721	3.6	2334	7.0
9 SU	0611	3.5	1222	6.8	1842	3.7		
10 M	0054	7.0	0744	3.4	1347	7.0	2016	3.4
11 TU	0219	7.3	0900	2.8	1503	7.5	2128	2.8
12 W	0329	7.9	1001	2.2	1604	8.1	2228	2.1
13 TH	0428	8.5	1056	1.5	1657	8.7	2322	1.5
14 F	0520	9.0	1147	1.0	1746	9.3		
15 SA ●	0012	0.9	0609	9.5	1236	0.6	1833	9.7
16 SU	0100	0.5	0657	9.7	1323	0.4	1918	9.9
17 M	0147	0.4	0743	9.8	1407	0.5	2002	9.8
18 TU	0231	0.5	0828	9.5	1451	0.8	2045	9.5
19 W	0315	0.9	0913	9.1	1534	1.3	2129	9.0
20 TH	0401	1.5	1000	8.5	1619	2.0	2216	8.4
21 F	0451	2.1	1052	7.8	1711	2.7	2309	7.7
22 SA	0550	2.7	1155	7.3	1814	3.2		
23 SU	0016	7.2	0703	3.1	1315	7.0	1933	3.5
24 M	0139	7.1	0825	3.1	1431	7.1	2053	3.3
25 TU	0253	7.2	0929	2.9	1530	7.4	2152	3.0
26 W	0349	7.6	1020	2.6	1618	7.8	2240	2.6
27 TH	0435	7.9	1103	2.2	1700	8.1	2321	2.2
28 F	0516	8.2	1143	2.0	1738	8.4	2359	1.9
29 SA	0555	8.4	1219	1.8	1814	8.6		
30 SU O	0033	1.7	0631	8.5	1252	1.7	1849	8.7
31 M	0107	1.6	0706	8.6	1324	1.7	1922	8.7

JUNE

Day	Time	m	Time	m	Time	m	Time	m
1 TU	0140	1.7	0739	8.5	1355	1.9	1953	8.6
2 W	0212	1.8	0812	8.3	1426	2.1	2024	8.4
3 TH	0244	2.0	0844	8.1	1458	2.3	2056	8.2
4 F	0318	2.3	0920	7.8	1532	2.7	2133	7.9
5 SA	0357	2.6	1001	7.6	1613	3.0	2218	7.6
6 SU	0444	2.9	1051	7.3	1704	3.2	2313	7.4
7 M	0545	3.0	1153	7.2	1810	3.3		
8 TU	0020	7.4	0658	3.0	1304	7.3	1928	3.2
9 W	0135	7.5	0815	2.7	1418	7.6	2047	2.8
10 TH	0249	7.9	0924	2.3	1526	8.0	2154	2.3
11 F	0355	8.3	1025	1.8	1626	8.6	2254	1.7
12 SA	0453	8.8	1121	1.3	1720	9.0	2349	1.2
13 SU ●	0548	9.1	1214	1.0	1811	9.4		
14 M	0041	0.8	0639	9.4	1305	0.8	1900	9.7
15 TU	0131	0.6	0729	9.5	1353	0.7	1947	9.7
16 W	0219	0.6	0816	9.4	1439	0.9	2032	9.5
17 TH	0305	0.9	0902	9.1	1523	1.3	2116	9.1
18 F	0350	1.3	0948	8.6	1607	1.8	2201	8.6
19 SA	0436	1.9	1034	8.1	1653	2.4	2247	8.0
20 SU	0526	2.5	1125	7.6	1743	3.0	2340	7.5
21 M	0621	2.9	1224	7.2	1842	3.3		
22 TU	0042	7.1	0724	3.2	1332	7.0	1949	3.5
23 W	0154	7.1	0832	3.3	1438	7.1	2058	3.4
24 TH	0300	7.1	0932	3.1	1534	7.3	2155	3.1
25 F	0354	7.4	1023	2.8	1622	7.7	2243	2.7
26 SA	0441	7.6	1106	2.5	1705	8.0	2325	2.4
27 SU	0525	7.9	1146	2.3	1746	8.3		
28 M O	0004	2.1	0605	8.2	1224	2.1	1824	8.5
29 TU	0042	1.9	0644	8.3	1301	1.9	1901	8.6
30 W	0120	1.8	0721	8.4	1336	1.9	1936	8.7

JULY

Day	Time	m	Time	m	Time	m	Time	m
1 TH	0156	1.7	0757	8.4	1412	1.9	2010	8.6
2 F	0232	1.8	0832	8.4	1447	2.1	2045	8.5
3 SA	0308	2.0	0908	8.2	1523	2.2	2122	8.3
4 SU	0347	2.2	0948	8.0	1603	2.5	2204	8.1
5 M	0430	2.4	1033	7.8	1649	2.7	2253	7.9
6 TU	0521	2.6	1126	7.6	1744	2.9	2352	7.7
7 W	0623	2.7	1229	7.5	1851	3.0		
8 TH	0100	7.6	0735	2.7	1341	7.6	2009	2.9
9 F	0216	7.7	0851	2.5	1455	7.9	2127	2.5
10 SA	0330	8.0	1000	2.2	1602	8.3	2233	2.0
11 SU	0434	8.4	1102	1.8	1702	8.7	2333	1.6
12 M	0533	8.8	1158	1.4	1756	9.1		
13 TU ●	0028	1.1	0627	9.1	1252	1.1	1847	9.5
14 W	0119	0.9	0717	9.3	1340	0.9	1934	9.6
15 TH	0207	0.7	0804	9.4	1426	1.0	2019	9.6
16 F	0251	0.9	0848	9.2	1508	1.2	2100	9.3
17 SA	0333	1.2	0929	8.9	1548	1.6	2140	8.9
18 SU	0413	1.7	1008	8.4	1626	2.1	2218	8.3
19 M	0452	2.3	1048	7.8	1706	2.7	2259	7.7
20 TU	0535	2.9	1133	7.3	1750	3.2	2346	7.2
21 W	0625	3.3	1227	7.0	1846	3.6		
22 TH	0046	6.8	0724	3.6	1333	6.8	1951	3.7
23 F	0159	6.7	0831	3.6	1443	6.9	2100	3.6
24 SA	0309	6.9	0935	3.4	1544	7.2	2202	3.2
25 SU	0408	7.2	1030	3.1	1635	7.6	2253	2.8
26 M	0458	7.6	1117	2.7	1721	8.0	2339	2.4
27 TU	0543	8.0	1200	2.3	1803	8.4		
28 W O	0021	2.0	0625	8.3	1241	2.0	1843	8.7
29 TH	0102	1.7	0705	8.6	1321	1.7	1920	8.9
30 F	0142	1.5	0742	8.7	1358	1.6	1956	9.0
31 SA	0219	1.4	0818	8.8	1435	1.6	2032	9.0

AUGUST

Day	Time	m	Time	m	Time	m	Time	m
1 SU	0256	1.5	0854	8.7	1512	1.7	2109	8.9
2 M	0334	1.7	0932	8.5	1549	2.0	2148	8.6
3 TU	0413	2.0	1013	8.3	1631	2.3	2233	8.3
4 W	0459	2.3	1101	7.9	1720	2.7	2326	7.9
5 TH	0554	2.7	1159	7.6	1822	3.0		
6 F	0032	7.6	0703	3.0	1313	7.5	1942	3.1
7 SA	0154	7.5	0828	3.0	1435	7.6	2111	2.9
8 SU	0317	7.7	0947	2.7	1550	8.0	2224	2.4
9 M	0427	8.1	1052	2.2	1653	8.5	2324	1.9
10 TU	0526	8.6	1149	1.7	1747	9.0		
11 W ●	0018	1.4	0617	9.0	1240	1.3	1835	9.4
12 TH	0107	1.0	0704	9.3	1327	1.0	1920	9.6
13 F	0152	0.8	0748	9.4	1409	1.0	2001	9.7
14 SA	0232	0.9	0827	9.3	1447	1.1	2038	9.5
15 SU	0309	1.2	0903	9.1	1522	1.5	2113	9.1
16 M	0342	1.6	0936	8.6	1554	2.0	2145	8.5
17 TU	0414	2.2	1008	8.1	1624	2.5	2217	7.9
18 W	0445	2.8	1043	7.5	1658	3.1	2254	7.4
19 TH	0521	3.4	1125	7.0	1742	3.6	2341	6.8
20 F	0617	3.8	1225	6.7	1851	4.0		
21 SA	0054	6.5	0735	4.0	1348	6.6	2011	4.0
22 SU	0224	6.6	0851	3.9	1507	6.9	2125	3.6
23 M	0339	6.9	0958	3.5	1609	7.3	2226	3.1
24 TU	0435	7.4	1052	2.9	1658	7.9	2316	2.5
25 W	0522	8.0	1138	2.4	1742	8.4		
26 TH O	0001	2.0	0605	8.5	1222	1.9	1823	8.9
27 F	0044	1.5	0645	8.9	1303	1.5	1902	9.2
28 SA	0124	1.2	0723	9.1	1342	1.2	1939	9.5
29 SU	0202	1.0	0800	9.3	1421	1.1	2016	9.5
30 M	0239	1.0	0836	9.2	1456	1.2	2052	9.4
31 TU	0316	1.2	0913	9.0	1533	1.5	2131	9.1

14

CHANNEL ISLANDS – ST. PETER PORT

LAT 49°27′N   LONG 2°31′W

TIMES AND HEIGHTS OF HIGH AND LOW WATERS

YEAR **1999**

TIME ZONE (UT)
For Summer Time add ONE hour in non-shaded areas

Chart Datum: 5·06 metres below Ordnance Datum (Local)

SEPTEMBER

Day	Time	m	Day	Time	m
1 W	0354 / 0953 / 1613 / 2213	1.7 / 8.7 / 2.0 / 8.6	**16** TH	0357 / 1020 / 1612 / 2210	2.8 / 7.7 / 3.0 / 7.5
2 TH	0437 / 1038 / 1659 / 2304	2.2 / 8.2 / 2.6 / 8.0	**17** F	0424 / 1032 / 1646 / 2249	3.4 / 7.2 / 3.6 / 7.0
3 F	0529 / 1135 / 1800	2.8 / 7.6 / 3.1	**18** SA	0504 / 1120 / 1742 / 2350	3.9 / 6.7 / 4.1 / 6.5
4 SA	0011 / 0641 / 1252 / 1927	7.4 / 3.3 / 7.3 / 3.4	**19** SU	0626 / 1244 / 1926	4.3 / 6.5 / 4.2
5 SU	0144 / 0818 / 1427 / 2108	7.2 / 3.4 / 7.3 / 3.2	**20** M	0134 / 0811 / 1426 / 2050	6.4 / 4.2 / 6.7 / 3.9
6 M	0317 / 0943 / 1546 / 2221	7.5 / 3.0 / 7.8 / 2.6	**21** TU	0308 / 0926 / 1538 / 2157	6.8 / 3.7 / 7.2 / 3.3
7 TU	0424 / 1046 / 1645 / 2317	8.0 / 2.4 / 8.4 / 2.0	**22** W	0409 / 1024 / 1631 / 2250	7.4 / 3.1 / 7.9 / 2.6
8 W	0517 / 1138 / 1735	8.6 / 1.9 / 9.0	**23** TH	0456 / 1113 / 1716 / 2336	8.1 / 2.4 / 8.5 / 1.9
9 TH	0006 / 0603 / 1225 / ● 1820	1.5 / 9.1 / 1.4 / 9.4	**24** F	0540 / 1158 / 1758	8.6 / 1.8 / 9.1
10 F	0050 / 0646 / 1308 / 1901	1.1 / 9.4 / 1.1 / 9.7	**25** SA	0020 / 0620 / 1241 / O 1838	1.4 / 9.1 / 1.3 / 9.5
11 SA	0130 / 0725 / 1346 / 1938	0.9 / 9.5 / 1.0 / 9.7	**26** SU	0102 / 0659 / 1321 / 1918	0.9 / 9.5 / 0.9 / 9.8
12 SU	0207 / 0801 / 1421 / 2012	1.0 / 9.4 / 1.1 / 9.5	**27** M	0141 / 0738 / 1401 / 1956	0.7 / 9.7 / 0.8 / 9.9
13 M	0239 / 0833 / 1452 / 2043	1.2 / 9.2 / 1.4 / 9.2	**28** TU	0220 / 0816 / 1439 / 2035	0.7 / 9.7 / 0.9 / 9.7
14 TU	0308 / 0902 / 1520 / 2111	1.7 / 8.8 / 1.9 / 8.7	**29** W	0257 / 0854 / 1517 / 2115	1.0 / 9.4 / 1.3 / 9.3
15 W	0333 / 0930 / 1545 / 2140	2.2 / 8.3 / 2.4 / 8.1	**30** TH	0336 / 0934 / 1558 / 2157	1.5 / 8.9 / 1.8 / 8.7

OCTOBER

Day	Time	m	Day	Time	m
1 F	0419 / 1020 / 1644 / 2248	2.2 / 8.3 / 2.5 / 7.9	**16** SA	0348 / 0955 / 1612 / 2215	3.3 / 7.4 / 3.5 / 7.1
2 SA	0512 / 1117 / 1747 / 2357	3.0 / 7.7 / 3.1 / 7.3	**17** SU	0424 / 1038 / 1659 / 2309	3.8 / 7.0 / 3.9 / 6.7
3 SU	0628 / 1237 / 1921	3.5 / 7.2 / 3.5	**18** M	0525 / 1148 / 1829	4.3 / 6.6 / 4.2
4 M	0140 / 0813 / 1421 / 2104	7.1 / 3.6 / 7.3 / 3.3	**19** TU	0038 / 0723 / 1330 / 2011	6.5 / 4.3 / 6.7 / 3.9
5 TU	0312 / 0936 / 1536 / 2211	7.4 / 3.2 / 7.8 / 2.7	**20** W	0222 / 0848 / 1455 / 2121	6.8 / 3.9 / 7.1 / 3.4
6 W	0412 / 1034 / 1630 / 2302	8.0 / 2.5 / 8.4 / 2.1	**21** TH	0331 / 0950 / 1553 / 2217	7.4 / 3.2 / 7.8 / 2.6
7 TH	0500 / 1121 / 1717 / 2346	8.6 / 2.0 / 8.9 / 1.6	**22** F	0422 / 1042 / 1642 / 2306	8.1 / 2.5 / 8.5 / 1.9
8 F	0543 / 1204 / 1758	9.0 / 1.5 / 9.3	**23** SA	0508 / 1129 / 1728 / 2352	8.7 / 1.8 / 9.1 / 1.3
9 SA	0026 / 0621 / 1244 / ● 1836	1.3 / 9.3 / 1.3 / 9.5	**24** SU	0551 / 1215 / O 1812	9.3 / 1.2 / 9.6
10 SU	0104 / 0658 / 1320 / 1912	1.2 / 9.5 / 1.2 / 9.5	**25** M	0036 / 0633 / 1259 / 1854	0.9 / 9.7 / 0.8 / 9.9
11 M	0138 / 0731 / 1353 / 1944	1.2 / 9.4 / 1.3 / 9.4	**26** TU	0119 / 0715 / 1341 / 1937	0.7 / 9.9 / 0.7 / 10.0
12 TU	0208 / 0801 / 1422 / 2013	1.4 / 9.2 / 1.5 / 9.1	**27** W	0200 / 0756 / 1423 / 2018	0.7 / 9.9 / 0.7 / 9.8
13 W	0234 / 0829 / 1448 / 2041	1.8 / 8.9 / 1.9 / 8.7	**28** TH	0240 / 0837 / 1504 / 2101	0.9 / 9.6 / 1.1 / 9.4
14 TH	0257 / 0856 / 1513 / 2109	2.3 / 8.4 / 2.4 / 8.2	**29** F	0322 / 0920 / 1548 / 2146	1.5 / 9.1 / 1.7 / 8.7
15 F	0321 / 0924 / 1540 / 2139	2.8 / 7.9 / 2.9 / 7.6	**30** SA	0406 / 1007 / 1637 / 2239	2.2 / 8.5 / 2.4 / 8.0
			31 SU	0501 / 1104 / 1740 / 2347	3.0 / 7.8 / 3.0 / 7.4

NOVEMBER

Day	Time	m	Day	Time	m
1 M	0615 / 1221 / 1908	3.5 / 7.3 / 3.4	**16** TU	0457 / 1114 / 1744 / 2355	4.0 / 7.0 / 3.8 / 6.8
2 TU	0124 / 0754 / 1358 / 2042	7.1 / 3.6 / 7.3 / 3.2	**17** W	0619 / 1232 / 1917	4.1 / 6.9 / 3.7
3 W	0249 / 0914 / 1511 / 2147	7.4 / 3.3 / 7.7 / 2.8	**18** TH	0120 / 0758 / 1357 / 2035	6.9 / 3.9 / 7.2 / 3.3
4 TH	0348 / 1010 / 1605 / 2236	7.9 / 2.7 / 8.1 / 2.3	**19** F	0240 / 0909 / 1507 / 2138	7.4 / 3.3 / 7.7 / 2.7
5 F	0435 / 1056 / 1651 / 2320	8.4 / 2.2 / 8.6 / 2.0	**20** SA	0341 / 1007 / 1604 / 2232	8.0 / 2.6 / 8.3 / 2.1
6 SA	0516 / 1138 / 1732 / 2359	8.8 / 1.9 / 8.9 / 1.7	**21** SU	0433 / 1059 / 1656 / 2322	8.6 / 1.9 / 8.9 / 1.5
7 SU	0554 / 1216 / 1810	9.1 / 1.6 / 9.0	**22** M	0521 / 1148 / 1745	9.2 / 1.4 / 9.3
8 M	0035 / 0629 / 1252 / ● 1844	1.6 / 9.2 / 1.5 / 9.1	**23** TU	0010 / 0608 / 1237 / O 1833	1.1 / 9.6 / 0.9 / 9.7
9 TU	0108 / 0702 / 1324 / 1917	1.6 / 9.2 / 1.5 / 9.0	**24** W	0057 / 0653 / 1324 / 1919	0.8 / 9.9 / 0.7 / 9.8
10 W	0138 / 0733 / 1354 / 1948	1.7 / 9.1 / 1.7 / 8.8	**25** TH	0143 / 0738 / 1410 / 2005	0.8 / 9.9 / 0.7 / 9.7
11 TH	0204 / 0802 / 1422 / 2017	2.0 / 8.8 / 2.0 / 8.6	**26** F	0227 / 0823 / 1455 / 2051	1.0 / 9.7 / 1.0 / 9.3
12 F	0230 / 0830 / 1450 / 2047	2.3 / 8.5 / 2.4 / 8.2	**27** SA	0312 / 0909 / 1541 / 2138	1.4 / 9.3 / 1.4 / 8.8
13 SA	0257 / 0859 / 1519 / 2118	2.7 / 8.1 / 2.8 / 7.8	**28** SU	0358 / 0957 / 1630 / 2229	2.0 / 8.7 / 2.1 / 8.2
14 SU	0326 / 0932 / 1553 / 2155	3.2 / 7.7 / 3.2 / 7.4	**29** M	0450 / 1050 / 1727 / 2329	2.7 / 8.1 / 2.7 / 7.6
15 M	0403 / 1014 / 1638 / 2245	3.6 / 7.3 / 3.6 / 7.0	**30** TU	0554 / 1155 / 1837	3.2 / 7.6 / 3.1

DECEMBER

Day	Time	m	Day	Time	m
1 W	0045 / 0713 / 1315 / 1958	7.2 / 3.5 / 7.3 / 3.2	**16** TH	0539 / 1151 / 1822	3.6 / 7.3 / 3.3
2 TH	0207 / 0834 / 1430 / 2108	7.3 / 3.4 / 7.4 / 3.1	**17** F	0028 / 0656 / 1303 / 1939	7.2 / 3.6 / 7.4 / 3.2
3 F	0311 / 0936 / 1530 / 2203	7.5 / 3.1 / 7.7 / 2.8	**18** SA	0144 / 0819 / 1418 / 2053	7.4 / 3.3 / 7.6 / 2.8
4 SA	0402 / 1025 / 1619 / 2248	7.9 / 2.7 / 8.0 / 2.5	**19** SU	0257 / 0929 / 1527 / 2157	7.8 / 2.8 / 8.0 / 2.3
5 SU	0445 / 1109 / 1702 / 2329	8.2 / 2.4 / 8.2 / 2.2	**20** M	0359 / 1030 / 1627 / 2255	8.3 / 2.2 / 8.5 / 1.8
6 M	0524 / 1148 / 1742	8.5 / 2.1 / 8.4	**21** TU	0455 / 1125 / 1723 / 2349	8.8 / 1.6 / 8.9 / 1.4
7 TU	0006 / 0601 / 1225 / ● 1818	2.0 / 8.7 / 1.9 / 8.6	**22** W	0547 / 1219 / O 1816	9.3 / 1.2 / 9.3
8 W	0041 / 0636 / 1259 / 1854	1.9 / 8.9 / 1.8 / 8.6	**23** TH	0040 / 0637 / 1310 / 1906	1.0 / 9.6 / 0.8 / 9.5
9 TH	0112 / 0709 / 1331 / 1927	1.9 / 8.9 / 1.9 / 8.6	**24** F	0130 / 0726 / 1359 / 1955	0.9 / 9.8 / 0.7 / 9.5
10 F	0142 / 0742 / 1403 / 2000	2.0 / 8.7 / 2.0 / 8.5	**25** SA	0217 / 0812 / 1446 / 2041	0.9 / 9.8 / 0.7 / 9.4
11 SA	0212 / 0813 / 1434 / 2032	2.2 / 8.5 / 2.2 / 8.4	**26** SU	0302 / 0858 / 1532 / 2127	1.2 / 9.5 / 1.1 / 9.0
12 SU	0242 / 0844 / 1507 / 2105	2.5 / 8.3 / 2.5 / 8.0	**27** M	0347 / 0943 / 1618 / 2213	1.6 / 9.0 / 1.6 / 8.5
13 M	0315 / 0918 / 1542 / 2141	2.8 / 8.0 / 2.8 / 7.7	**28** TU	0433 / 1030 / 1705 / 2301	2.2 / 8.5 / 2.2 / 7.9
14 TU	0352 / 0959 / 1624 / 2226	3.1 / 7.7 / 3.0 / 7.4	**29** W	0523 / 1121 / 1757 / 2356	2.8 / 7.9 / 2.8 / 7.4
15 W	0439 / 1049 / 1716 / 2321	3.4 / 7.4 / 3.3 / 7.2	**30** TH	0620 / 1220 / 1857	3.3 / 7.4 / 3.2
			31 F	0103 / 0728 / 1330 / 2007	7.1 / 3.5 / 7.1 / 3.4

SARK   8-14-13

Sark 49°25'·87N 02°20'·35W. Rtgs: Creux 4-5-1; Maseline 3-5-3

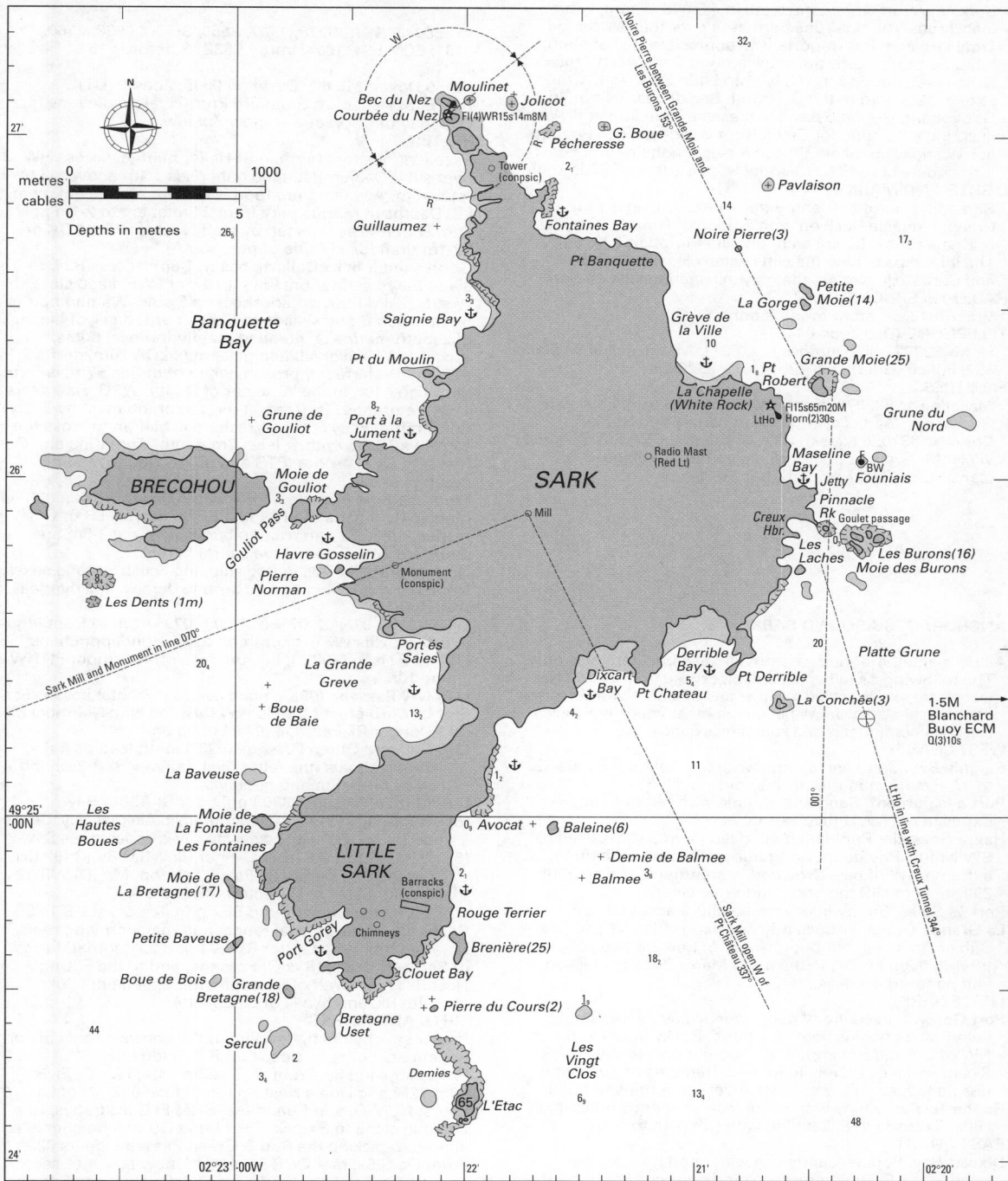

CHARTS
AC *5604.8, 808*; SHOM 6904; ECM 1014; Imray C33A; Stanfords 16

TIDES
−0450 Dover; ML 5·3; Duration 0550; Zone 0 (UT)

Standard Port ST HELIER (⟶)

Times				Height (metres)			
High Water		Low Water		MHWS	MHWN	MLWN	MLWS
0300	0900	0200	0900	11·0	8·1	4·0	1·4
1500	2100	1400	2100				
Differences SARK (MASELINE PIER)							
+0005	+0015	+0005	+0010	−2·1	−1·5	−0·6	−0·3

SHELTER
Many ⚓s (see below) sheltered in various winds, but may be disturbed, except in settled weather. There are 2 hbrs, both prone to surge/swell: **Creux** dries completely, access approx HW±2 in fair weather. Dry out bow to E wall, stern to ⚓, keeping clear of the S pier where there may be some AB at the inner end clear of steps. **Maseline** is a busy ferry hbr with no yacht berths (other than to land people); call Hr Mr Ch 13 for approval to ⚓. Moorings are private. Brecqhou Island is strictly private; landing prohibited.

NAVIGATION
Creux WPT 49°25'·30N 02°20'·30W, 164°/344° from/to ent, 0·57M. Beware large tidal range, strong streams and many lobster pots. The S-bound-only restriction in the

Goulet Passage applies to commercial vessels, not yachts. Sark is fringed by rks, but the centres of the bays are mainly clear of dangers. In the extreme SW of Little Sark near Port Gorey the detail in AC 808 is somewhat inaccurate. The tide runs hard here over the HW period.

Tidal streams: It is important to appreciate that at about half-tide the streams are slack around Sark. At HW the stream sets hard to the N, ie onto Little Sark. At LW the stream sets hard to the S, ie onto Bec du Nez (N tip). In Gouliot and Goulet passages these streams run at 6-7kn at springs. If bound for Creux from Guernsey, go N-about at HW and S-about at LW; conversely on the return. For further details see *The Channel Islands* (Heath/RCC/Imray).

LIGHTS AND MARKS
Sark Mill is hard to identify due to trees. Transits for Creux: Pinnacle Rock on with E edge of Grand Moie 001°; or Creux tunnel (white arch) on with Pt Robert lt ho 344°. The lt ho dips behind the cliffs when close in. Pt Robert and Corbée du Nez are the only navigational lts on Sark.

RADIO TELEPHONE
VHF Ch 13, summer months only.

TELEPHONE (Dial code 01481)
Hr Mr 832323; ⌧ (Guernsey) 726911; Marinecall 0891 500 432; Police (Guernsey) 725111; Dr 832045.

FACILITIES
Maseline ☎ 832070 (kiosk), M (free), C (3 ton); Ferries to Guernsey; Condor catamaran to Jersey and St Malo.
Creux ☎ 832025 (kiosk), Slip, M (free), L, FW, P & D (cans) via Hr Mr; walk or tractor up steep hill to **Village**: P & D (cans), Gas, Gaz, Kos, V, R, Bar, ⌧, Ⓑ.

ANCHORAGES AROUND SARK

All permanent moorings are private; use in emergency only. The following ⚓s (all unlit), anti-clockwise from Bec du Nez (N tip), are safe in settled weather and off-shore winds (some are only suitable over LW period). In other conditions they can be uncomfortable and sometimes dangerous:

WEST COAST
Saignie Bay. Sand and shingle with fair holding. Exposed to W. Picturesque rock formations.
Port à la Jument. Sand and shingle with fair holding. Exposed to NW. Difficult shore access.
Havre Gosselin. Popular small, deep (4-9m) ⚓, exposed to SW winds. Private mooring buoys. Beware of drying rk at extreme NW of bay. Crowded in summer. Landing, with 299 steps to cliff top and panoramic views.
Port és Saies. Sandy inlet with no shore access. N of:
La Grande Grève. Wide sandy bay exposed to W and SW. Subject to swell, but popular day ⚓. Beware two rks (drying 0.3m and ⊛) in the appr. Many steps to cliff-top and panoramic views.
LITTLE SARK
Port Gorey. ⚓ in centre of deep, weedy bay over LW only; heavy swell begins near half-flood. Rocky appr from just NW of Grande Bretagne (18m high) then 045° into bay. Rks must be positively identified. Remains of quay with unsafe ladder. Cliff walk past silver mine ruins to hotel.
Rouge Terrier. Sandy with some local moorings under high cliffs. Exposed to E. Landing with cliff path to hotel.
EAST COAST
Dixcart Bay. Popular sandy bay with good holding, but open to the S. Drying rocks extend on each side of the the approach but no dangers within the bay. Cliff path and pleasant walk to hotels.
Derrible Bay. Sandy bay with good holding. Exposed to the S. No dangers in the bay, but keep clear of SW tip of Derrible Pt when entering. Picturesque caves and steep climb ashore.
Grève de la Ville. Sand and shingle with fair holding. ⚓ close in out of tide. Exposed to E. Landing and easy walk to village.
Les Fontaines. Sand and shingle with fair holding. Reef drying 4.5m extends 1ca N from shore. ⚓ between reef and Eperquerie headland. Exposed to the E.

With grateful acknowledgements to John Frankland, author of Sark Pilotage (1996).

ST HELIER   8-14-14
Jersey (Channel Is) 49°10'·63N 02°06'·90W   Rtg 1-2-2

CHARTS
AC *5604.9 & .10*, 3278, *1137*, *3655*; SHOM 6938, 7160, 7161; ECM 534, 1014; Imray C33B; Stanfords 16

TIDES
−0455 Dover; ML 6·1; Duration 0545; Zone 0 (UT)
NOTE: St Helier is a Standard Port. Tidal predictions for each day of the year are shown below.

SHELTER
Excellent. Visitors berth in **St Helier marina**, access HW±3 over sill (CD+3·6m); hinged gate rises 1·4m above sill to retain 5m. A waiting pontoon is to W of marina ent, near LB. Depths in marina vary from 2·8m at ent to 2·1m at N end. ♥ berths as directed by staff (yachts >12m LOA or >2·1m draft, use N side of pontoon A).
Good shelter in **La Collette basin**, 1·8m; access H24, to await the tide. Caution: Ent narrow at LWS; keep close to W side; PHM buoys mark shoal on E side. Waiting berths on pontoon D and W side of C. FVs berth on W of basin.
Elizabeth marina is intended mainly for local boats; access HW±3 over sill/flap gate; max LOA 20m, drafts 2·1 to 3·5m. Preferred approach, when ht of tide >7m, is from the W on 110°, in the W sector of Dir lt F WRG. Daymarks 110° are orange ☐s: front, at dir lt; rear, on mast by E RoRo ramp. Pass S of La Vrachère IDM lt bn to cross the causeway 5·0m with at least 2m depth. At marina ent, Oc R 4s and Oc G 4s, are IPTS and tidal gauge reading depth over sill.
From the S (ie N of No 4 PHM buoy) the appr chan 338° is marked by 3 pairs of PHM and SHM buoys, Fl R or G 5s respectively. 3 Y can waiting buoys in about 1·0m are outboard either side of the lateral buoys.
No ⚓ in St Helier Rds due to shipping & fish storage boxes.
Note: For other hbrs and ⚓s around Jersey, see overleaf.

NAVIGATION
WPT 49°10'·01N 02°07'·30W, 203°/023° from/to front ldg lt, 0·74M. This WPT is common to all eight appr chans:
(1)   W Passage (082°); beware race off Noirmont Pt, HW to HW +4.
(1A) NW Passage (095°, much used by yachts) passes 6ca S of La Corbière lt ho to join W Passage abm Noirmont Pt.
(2)   Danger Rk Passage (044°) unlit; and
(3)   Red and Green Passage (023°); both lead past rky, drying shoals (the latter over Fairway Rk 1·2m) and need precision and good vis.
(4)   Middle Passage (339°) unlit, for St Aubin Bay.
(5)   S Passage (341°) is clear but unlit. Alternatively, Demie de Pas on 350° with power stn chy is easier to see D/N.
(6)   E Passage, 290° from Canger Rk WCM By, Q (9) 15s, passes S of Demie de Pas, B tr/Y top, Mo (D) WR 12s (at night stay in W sector); thence 314°.
(7)   Violet Passage around SE tip of Jersey, see 8.14.5.
Caution: very large tidal range, and many offlying reefs. Entering hbr, note Oyster Rk (W bn; R 'O' topmark) to W of Red and Green (R & G) Passage; and to the E, Dog's Nest Rk (W bn with globe topmark). Speed limit 10kn N of Platte Rk, and 5kn N of La Collette.

LIGHTS AND MARKS
Power stn chy (95m, floodlit) and W concave roofs of Fort Regent are conspic, close E of R & G ldg line.
W Passage ldg lts: Front Oc 5s 23m 14M; rear Oc R 5s 46m 12M and Dog's Nest bn (unlit) lead 082°, N of Les Fours, NCM Q, and Ruaudière, SHM Fl G 3s, buoys, to a position close to E Rock, SHM buoy QG, where course is altered to pick up the **Red & Green Passage** ldg lts 023°: Front Oc G 5s; rear Oc R 5s, synch; (now easier to see against town lts) Daymarks are red dayglow patches on front dolphin and rear lt twr. Nos 2 and 4 PHM buoys (both QR) mark the fairway N of Platte Rk (Fl R 1·5s).
Outer pier hds and dolphin are painted white and floodlit. Inner ldg lts 078°, both FG on W columns; not for yachts. For Elizabeth marina, see under SHELTER.
Entry Signals (at Port Control stn and St Helier marina)
Ⓖ lt (Oc , F or Fl)   = Enter, no exit
Ⓡ lt (Oc , F or Fl)   = Leave, no entry
Ⓡ and Ⓖ lts together   = No exit/entry
Q Ⓨ lts on Port Control Stn indicate that power-driven craft < 25m LOA may enter/dep against the displayed sigs (keeping to stbd at ent and well clear of ferries).
Note: Entry sigs are repeated at St Helier marina ent, where a large digital tide gauge shows depth over sill.

RADIO TELEPHONE

Monitor *St Helier Port Control* VHF Ch 14 (H24) for ferry movements. No marina VHF, but call *Port Control* if necessary. If unable to pass messages to *Port Control*, these can be relayed via *Jersey Radio* CRS, Ch **82 25 16** (H24) or ☎ 41121.

TELEPHONE (Dial code 01534)

Hr Mr 885588, 🕿 885599; Marina 885508; ⌗ 30232; Jersey Weather Centre *(06966) 7777; Recorded forecast *(06966) 0011 for Jersey and 0022 for CI; Marinecall 0891 500 432; Police 612612; Dr 835742 and 853178; Ⓗ 59000.

*(06966) is a Jersey dialling code for info services; it can be dialled direct from UK or prefixed 0044 from France.

FACILITIES

St Helier Marina (180+200 visitors), ☎ 885508, £12.00, FW, AC, CH, ME, El, Sh, Grid, Gas, Gaz, ▣, V, Kos;

La Collette Yacht Basin (130) ☎ 885529, is accessible H24 when marina is inaccessible; it has a few visitors berths for up to 24 hrs, FW, AC, BH (18 ton), Slip;

Continued overleaf

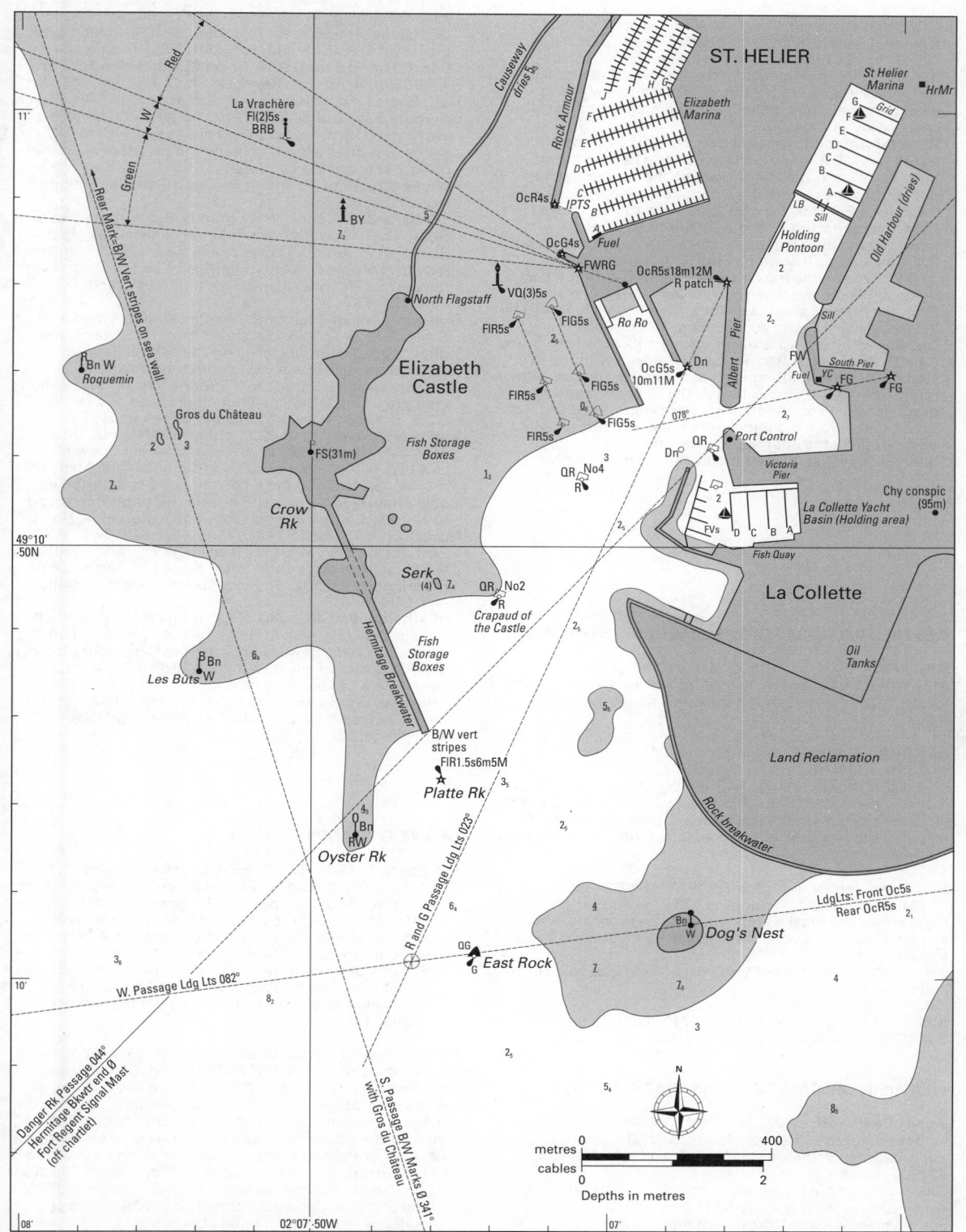

Elizabeth Marina (589; few 🅥), ☎ 885588, 🛥 885599; £12.00, FW, AC, D & P.
Hbrs Dept ☎ 885588, FW, C (various, max 32 ton), Slip, Grids, BH (18 ton); AC; **St Helier YC** ☎ 832229, R, Bar; **S Pier** (below YC) P & D (Access approx HW±3), FW.
Royal Channel Islands YC, at St Aubin: see overleaf.
Services: SM, CH, Sh, ME, El, Ⓔ, Gas. **Town** EC Thurs; P, D, CH, V, R, Bar, ✉, Ⓑ, ✈. Ro Ro Ferry: Guernsey, St Malo, Poole. Fast ferries (Mar-Nov): St Malo, Granville, Poole, Sark, Guernsey.

LA CORBIERE lt ho (8.14.4) is at 49°10'·85N 02°14'·90W, the SW tip of Jersey, 5M W of St Helier. The RDF bcn (CB 295·5kHz, see Table 3(1)) at the lt ho transmits on a six minute cycle. During each of the first 5 minutes its signal consists of Callsign CB 3 times (16 secs), then a long dash (36 secs). During the 6th minute the signal contains coded wind information.
Wind information, updated every 6 mins, is transmitted as follows: CB 3 times (16 secs), a long dash (8 secs); then 1 to 8 short dashes, indicating the average wind direction, representing the 8 cardinal points: 1 dash = NE; 2 dashes = E; 3 dashes = SE; clockwise to 8 dashes = N. Next, average wind strength on the Beaufort scale is indicated by up to 8 pips: 1 pip = Force 1; 2 pips = Force 2; 8 pips = Force 8 or more. Finally, 1 or more short dashes indicate the max gust experienced over the past 6 mins above the average wind strength already given. Example transmission: 3 dashes, then 5 pips, followed by 2 dashes = Wind direction SE, Force 5, gusting 7.
Distance-off the lt ho is given once a co-located fog horn (Mo 'C' 60s) is activated and synchronised with the RDF signal. The signal during each of the first 5 minutes is then modified to: CB 3 times, long dash (26 secs), a series of pips starting 1 second after the horn starts. Each pip that is counted before the initial horn blast is heard aboard a vessel represents approx 335m distance off the light. Several counts should be made to confirm distance-off.

WEATHER BROADCASTS BY LOCAL RADIO STATIONS

Island FM   *Daily:* Every H+30
Alderney 93·7; Guernsey 104·7MHz. Forecast and synopsis for the coastal waters of the Channel Islands, plus tide times.

BBC Radio Guernsey *Mon-Fri:* 0807, 1235, 1710LT
93·2MHz, 1116kHz   *Sat-Sun:* 0810
Forecast is broadcast live by Guernsey Airport Met Office. It covers the waters around Guernsey, Herm and Sark and includes a synopsis, coastal forecast, gale warnings and shipping movements. In summer it includes coastal station reports.

BBC Radio Jersey   *Mon-Fri:* 0635, 0810, 1835LT
88·8MHz, 1026kHz   *Sat-Sun:* 0735
Forecast for the local waters around Jersey includes a synopsis, visibility, wind direction/strength and coastal station reports.
Shipping movements are broadcast *Mon-Fri* at 0637, 0710 and 0810LT.
Tidal info is broadcast:
Mon-Fri: 0635, 0710, 0810, 1307, 1710, 1805, 1835LT;
Sat: 0709, 0735, 0809; *Sun:* 0708, 0735.

WEATHER FORECASTS BY COAST RADIO STATION

Jersey Radio VHF Ch 25, 82 and MF 1659kHz.
Forecasts for the Channel Islands (S of 50°N and E of 3°W) are broadcast at 0645, 0745, 0845LT; and at 1245, 1845, 2245UT. See 5.7.1.
Gale warnings are broadcast on receipt, at the end of the next silent period and every 6 hrs from 0307UT.
For navigational and Decca warnings see 4.10.1.3.

OTHER HARBOURS AND ANCHORAGES AROUND JERSEY

The following are the main ⚓s around the island, clockwise from St Helier:
SOUTH COAST
St Aubin. Quiet ⚓ with off-shore winds in bay (mostly dries) or yachts can dry out alongside N quay; access HW ±1. From seaward Middle Passage leads 339°, Mon Plaisir Ho in transit with tr at St Aubin Fort. Final appr is N of St Aubin Fort, via fairway in W sector of N pier head dir lt 254°, F WRG 5m, G248°-253°, W253°-255°, R255°-260°; and, same structure, Iso R 4s 12m 10M. St Aubin Fort pier head Fl R 4s 8m 1M. Facilities: AB, FW on N quay, **Slip, C (1 and 5 ton), Grid; Royal Channel Islands YC** ☎ 41023, Bar, R, M, Slip; **Services:** Sh, D, ME, SM, Sh, CH, BY, Gas, El. **Town** Bar, D, FW, ⊠, P, R, V, bus to St. Helier.
Belcroute Bay. S of St Aubin Fort. Platte and Grosse Rks are marked by poles. Excellent shelter from W to SW winds, but dries 3·5m and many moorings; or ⚓ further off in 2·4m, landing by dinghy.
Portelet Bay. W of Noirmont Pt. Good ⚓ in N'lies, either side of Janvrin Tr.
St Brelade Bay. Good shelter from N and W, but open to SW'ly swell. Beware many drying rks, especially Fournier Rk (0·9m) in centre. A quiet ⚓ is in Beau Port. Small stone jetty in NW corner; local moorings in Bouilly Port. A very popular sandy tourist beach with various hotels.
NORTH COAST
Grève au Lancon (Plemont). A wide sandy bay between Grosnez Pt, Fl (2) WR 15s, and Plemont Pt. The SE part dries. Suitable for day visits on calm days. Exposed to swell. Beware discontinued submarine cables.
Grève de Lecq. Ldg line 202°: W Martello tr on with W hotel with grey roof. ⚓ between ruined pier and The Demies 5·2m. Exposed to swell. Pub, and bus to St. Helier.
Bonne Nuit Bay. Ldg lts 223°, both FG 7/34m 6M. Conspic TV mast (232m) is ½M W of the bay. Avoid Cheval Rk close SE of ldg line. Hbr dries to sand/shingle. Many local moorings. Hotel. To the E beware Les Sambues 5·5m.
Bouley Bay. Good ⚓ on sand in 2·5m SE of pier. Exposed to NE. Rky bottom close to pier. Local moorings. Hotel.
Rozel Bay. Dir lt 245° F WRG, 11m 5M, G240°-244°, W244°-246°, R246°-250°; W sector leads between pier heads and WCM bn. Hbr, dries 1·5m to sand/shingle, and is full of moorings; ⚓ outside. Shops and pubs, bus to St Helier.
EAST COAST
St Catherine Bay. Many local moorings off inner end of Verclut bkwtr, Fl 1·5s. ⚓ S of bkwtr in 3-7m. Land on slip at root of bkwtr. Beware St Catherine Bank, rocky plateau 3·3m in centre of bay. Dinghy SC, RNLI ILB station, café.
Gorey. See 8.14.15 opposite.
La Rocque. Drying hbr, small pier, local moorings, sandy beach. Not suitable for visitors without good local knowledge. No facilities.

OFFLYING ISLANDS

Les Ecrehou. 49°17'·45N 01°55'·50W. 5M NE of Rozel, has about a dozen cottages. ML 6·2m. Arrive at about ½ tide ebbing; see 8.14.15. Appr with Bigorne Rk on 022°; when SE of Maître lle alter to 330° for FS on Marmotière ls. Beware of strong and eddying tidal streams 4 - 8kn. Pick up a buoy close SE of Marmotière or ⚓ in a pool 3ca WSW of Marmotière (with FS and houses); other islands are Maître lle (one house), Blanche and 5 other small islets. Local knowledge or a detailed pilotage book is essential. No lts.

Plateau des Minquiers. 48°58'·10N 02°03'·63W. About 12M S of Jersey (AC 3656, SHOM 7161) and ringed by six cardinal light buoys. See 8.14.15 for tides. ML 6·4m. Beware of strong and eddying tidal streams. Appr by day in good vis from Demie de Vascelin SHM buoy on 161°, Jetée des Fontaines RW bn in transit with FS on Maîtresse lle. Further transits skirt the W side of the islet to ⚓ due S of it; safe only in settled weather and light winds. Maîtresse lle has about a dozen cottages. Land at the slipway NW of the States of Jersey mooring buoy. Without local knowledge, a detailed pilotage book is essential.

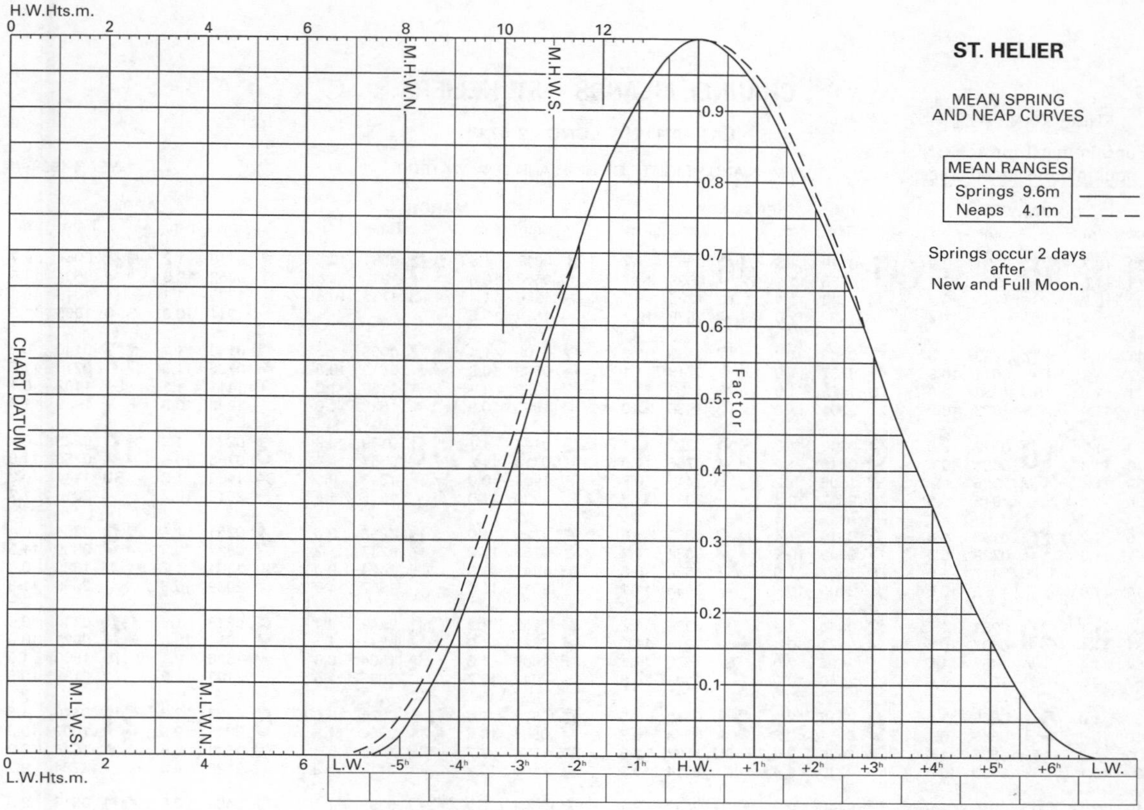

H.W.Hts.m.

ST. HELIER

MEAN SPRING
AND NEAP CURVES

MEAN RANGES
Springs 9.6m
Neaps 4.1m

Springs occur 2 days
after
New and Full Moon.

CHART DATUM

Factor

M.H.W.N. M.H.W.S.

M.L.W.S. M.L.W.N.

L.W. -5ʰ -4ʰ -3ʰ -2ʰ -1ʰ H.W. +1ʰ +2ʰ +3ʰ +4ʰ +5ʰ +6ʰ L.W.

L.W.Hts.m.

GOREY   8-14-15

Jersey 49°11'·84N 02°01'·28W   Rtg 3-4-1

CHARTS
AC *5604.8,* 1138, *3655*; SHOM 6939, 7157, 7160; ECM 534,
1014; Imray C33A; Stanfords 16

TIDES
−0454 Dover; ML 6·0; Duration 0545; Zone 0 (UT)

Standard Port ST HELIER (→)

Times				Height (metres)			
High Water		Low Water		MHWS	MHWN	MLWN	MLWS
0300	0900	0200	0900	11·0	8·1	4·0	1·4
1500	2100	1400	2100				
Differences ST. CATHERINE BAY							
0000	+0010	+0010	+0010	0·0	−0·1	0·0	+0·1
BOULEY BAY							
+0002	+0002	+0004	+0004	−0·3	−0·3	−0·1	−0·1
LES ECREHOU							
+0005	+0009	+0011	+0009	+0·1	+0·5	−0·1	0·0
LES MINQUIERS							
−0014	−0018	−0001	−0008	+0·5	+0·6	+0·1	−0·1

SHELTER
Good in the hbr (dries completely), except in S/SE winds.
Access HW±3. There are 12 drying ⚓s 150m W of pier hd.
⚓ about 2ca E of pier hd or in deeper water in the Roads;
also in St Catherine Bay to the N, except in S/SE winds.

NAVIGATION
WPT 49°10'·50N 01°57'·33W, 118°/298° from/to front ldg
lt, 2·9M. Note the very large tidal range. On appr, keep
well outside all local bns until the ldg marks are identified,
but beware Banc du Chateau (0·4m), 1M offshore to N of
298° ldg line; and Azicot Rk (dries 2·2m) just S of 298° ldg
line, 2ca from ent.
See 8.14.5 for the Violet Chan to St Helier. The Gutters
and Boat Passage across Violet Bank are not advised.

LIGHTS AND MARKS
Mont Orgueil Castle (67m) is conspic from afar. Fort
William is a W ho, R roof. There are at least 3 approaches:
a. Ldg lts 298°: front, Gorey pierhd, Oc RG 5s, W tr, vis
R304°-352°, G352°-304°; rear, Oc R 5s 8M, W ☐ Or border.

(2) Front ldg lt on with church spire 304° leads over Road
Rk (3·3m), and Azicot Rk (2·2m).
(3) Front ldg lt on with Fort William 250° leads close to Les
Arch bn (B/W with A topmark) and Pacquet Rk (0·3m).

RADIO TELEPHONE
Gorey Hbr Ch 74 (HW±3 Apr-Oct only).

TELEPHONE (Dial code 01534)
Hr Mr 853616; ☎ 30232; Marinecall 0891 500 432; for Dr
contact Hr Mr, or Hr Mr St Helier 885588.

FACILITIES
Hbr M, AB £6, P, D, FW, C (7 ton), ME, El, Sh, Gas.
Town EC Thurs; P, CH, V, R, Bar, ✉, Ⓑ, bus to St Helier.
Ferry (Mar-Nov) to Portbail, Carteret.

14

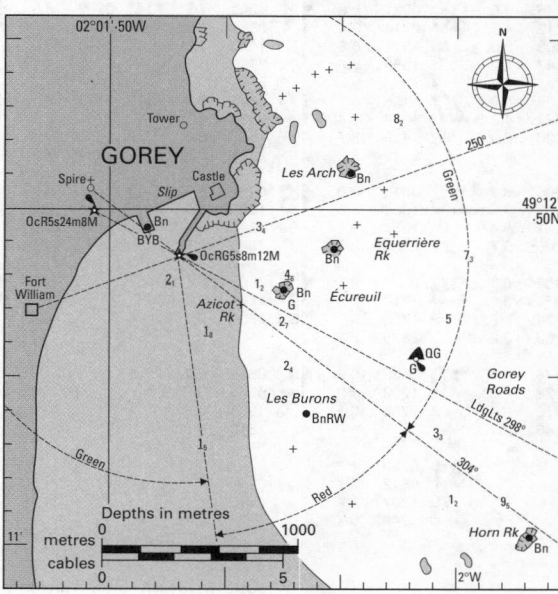

CHANNEL ISLANDS – ST. HELIER

LAT 49°11′N   LONG 2°07′W

TIMES AND HEIGHTS OF HIGH AND LOW WATERS

YEAR **1999**

TIME ZONE (UT)
For Summer Time add ONE hour in non-shaded areas

Chart Datum: 5·88 metres below Ordnance Datum (Local)

JANUARY

Day	Time	m		Day	Time	m
1 F	0533 / 1218 / 1802	10.7 / 1.6 / 10.7		**16** SA	0531 / 1209 / 1753	9.9 / 2.4 / 9.9
2 SA O	0041 / 0622 / 1311 / 1850	1.4 / 11.1 / 1.1 / 11.0		**17** SU	0029 / 0611 / 1253 / 1833	2.3 / 10.3 / 2.0 / 10.2
3 SU	0130 / 0708 / 1359 / 1935	1.2 / 11.3 / 1.1 / 11.1		**18** M	0112 / 0651 / 1336 / 1913	2.0 / 10.6 / 1.7 / 10.5
4 M	0216 / 0751 / 1444 / 2017	1.2 / 11.3 / 1.1 / 11.0		**19** TU	0152 / 0729 / 1417 / 1952	1.8 / 10.8 / 1.6 / 10.6
5 TU	0258 / 0831 / 1524 / 2057	1.4 / 11.0 / 1.4 / 10.6		**20** W	0231 / 0807 / 1457 / 2030	1.7 / 10.8 / 1.5 / 10.6
6 W	0336 / 0910 / 1600 / 2134	1.9 / 10.6 / 1.9 / 10.1		**21** TH	0308 / 0846 / 1535 / 2109	1.8 / 10.7 / 1.6 / 10.4
7 TH	0410 / 0947 / 1634 / 2211	2.4 / 10.1 / 2.5 / 9.5		**22** F	0346 / 0926 / 1613 / 2149	2.0 / 10.5 / 1.8 / 10.2
8 F	0444 / 1024 / 1708 / 2249	3.0 / 9.4 / 3.1 / 8.9		**23** SA	0425 / 1008 / 1654 / 2234	2.2 / 10.2 / 2.2 / 9.8
9 SA	0522 / 1106 / 1747 / 2335	3.5 / 8.8 / 3.6 / 8.4		**24** SU	0510 / 1057 / 1741 / 2326	2.6 / 9.7 / 2.6 / 9.3
10 SU	0609 / 1158 / 1839	4.0 / 8.3 / 4.1		**25** M	0604 / 1156 / 1841	3.0 / 9.2 / 3.0
11 M	0035 / 0712 / 1308 / 1947	8.0 / 4.3 / 8.0 / 4.2		**26** TU	0031 / 0714 / 1312 / 1956	8.8 / 3.4 / 8.8 / 3.3
12 TU	0154 / 0823 / 1426 / 2101	8.0 / 4.2 / 8.0 / 4.1		**27** W	0156 / 0838 / 1439 / 2119	8.7 / 3.4 / 8.7 / 3.2
13 W	0306 / 0932 / 1531 / 2205	8.3 / 3.9 / 8.4 / 3.7		**28** TH	0319 / 1000 / 1557 / 2233	9.0 / 3.0 / 9.1 / 2.8
14 TH	0402 / 1031 / 1624 / 2259	8.8 / 3.4 / 8.9 / 3.2		**29** F	0427 / 1110 / 1700 / 2335	9.5 / 2.5 / 9.7 / 2.2
15 F	0448 / 1122 / 1710 / 2346	9.4 / 2.8 / 9.4 / 2.7		**30** SA	0523 / 1209 / 1754	10.2 / 1.9 / 10.2
				31 SU O	0030 / 0612 / 1301 / 1840	1.7 / 10.7 / 1.4 / 10.7

FEBRUARY

Day	Time	m		Day	Time	m
1 M	0119 / 0656 / 1348 / 1922	1.3 / 11.1 / 1.1 / 11.0		**16** TU ●	0055 / 0635 / 1320 / 1858	1.7 / 10.7 / 1.3 / 10.7
2 TU	0203 / 0737 / 1429 / 2001	1.2 / 11.3 / 1.0 / 11.0		**17** W	0139 / 0716 / 1403 / 1938	1.3 / 11.1 / 1.0 / 11.0
3 W	0242 / 0815 / 1506 / 2037	1.2 / 11.2 / 1.2 / 10.8		**18** TH	0220 / 0756 / 1444 / 2017	1.1 / 11.3 / 0.8 / 11.2
4 TH	0316 / 0849 / 1537 / 2109	1.4 / 10.9 / 1.5 / 10.5		**19** F	0259 / 0834 / 1522 / 2055	1.0 / 11.3 / 0.8 / 11.1
5 F	0346 / 0921 / 1605 / 2140	1.9 / 10.4 / 2.0 / 10.0		**20** SA	0336 / 0913 / 1559 / 2133	1.2 / 11.1 / 1.1 / 10.8
6 SA	0413 / 0951 / 1630 / 2210	2.4 / 9.8 / 2.6 / 9.4		**21** SU	0413 / 0953 / 1637 / 2214	1.5 / 10.7 / 1.6 / 10.2
7 SU	0440 / 1022 / 1657 / 2242	2.9 / 9.2 / 3.2 / 8.8		**22** M	0452 / 1037 / 1719 / 2300	2.1 / 10.0 / 2.3 / 9.6
8 M	0513 / 1057 / 1734 / 2323	3.5 / 8.5 / 3.7 / 8.2		**23** TU	0541 / 1130 / 1812 / 2359	2.7 / 9.2 / 3.0 / 8.8
9 TU	0601 / 1148 / 1830	4.0 / 8.0 / 4.2		**24** W	0646 / 1243 / 1927	3.4 / 8.5 / 3.5
10 W	0029 / 0716 / 1312 / 1954	7.8 / 4.3 / 7.6 / 4.4		**25** TH	0125 / 0815 / 1422 / 2059	8.3 / 3.6 / 8.3 / 3.6
11 TH	0205 / 0841 / 1445 / 2119	7.7 / 4.2 / 7.8 / 4.1		**26** F	0302 / 0949 / 1548 / 2220	8.5 / 3.3 / 8.6 / 3.1
12 F	0323 / 0955 / 1553 / 2226	8.2 / 3.7 / 8.4 / 3.5		**27** SA	0415 / 1101 / 1652 / 2324	9.1 / 2.7 / 9.3 / 2.5
13 SA	0421 / 1055 / 1646 / 2320	8.9 / 3.0 / 9.0 / 2.8		**28** SU	0511 / 1158 / 1742	9.8 / 2.0 / 10.0
14 SU	0509 / 1146 / 1733	9.6 / 2.4 / 9.7				
15 M	0009 / 0553 / 1235 / 1816	2.2 / 10.2 / 1.8 / 10.3				

MARCH

Day	Time	m		Day	Time	m
1 M	0017 / 0558 / 1246 / 1824	1.8 / 10.5 / 1.4 / 10.5		**16** TU	0531 / 1210 / 1755	10.1 / 1.6 / 10.4
2 TU O	0103 / 0639 / 1329 / 1903	1.4 / 10.9 / 1.1 / 10.9		**17** W ●	0033 / 0615 / 1258 / 1837	1.5 / 10.8 / 1.0 / 11.0
3 W	0144 / 0718 / 1407 / 1939	1.1 / 11.2 / 0.9 / 11.0		**18** TH	0119 / 0657 / 1343 / 1918	0.9 / 11.4 / 0.5 / 11.4
4 TH	0220 / 0753 / 1441 / 2012	1.0 / 11.2 / 1.0 / 11.0		**19** F	0202 / 0737 / 1424 / 1957	0.6 / 11.7 / 0.3 / 11.6
5 F	0252 / 0825 / 1509 / 2042	1.2 / 11.0 / 1.3 / 10.7		**20** SA	0242 / 0817 / 1504 / 2036	0.4 / 11.7 / 0.3 / 11.5
6 SA	0319 / 0854 / 1534 / 2109	1.5 / 10.5 / 1.7 / 10.2		**21** SU	0321 / 0856 / 1541 / 2114	0.6 / 11.5 / 0.7 / 11.2
7 SU	0344 / 0921 / 1556 / 2135	2.0 / 10.0 / 2.2 / 9.7		**22** M	0358 / 0936 / 1619 / 2154	1.1 / 10.9 / 1.3 / 10.5
8 M	0406 / 0946 / 1619 / 2200	2.5 / 9.4 / 2.8 / 9.1		**23** TU	0437 / 1019 / 1700 / 2239	1.7 / 10.1 / 2.2 / 9.7
9 TU	0434 / 1013 / 1650 / 2232	3.1 / 8.8 / 3.4 / 8.5		**24** W	0523 / 1112 / 1751 / 2337	2.6 / 9.1 / 3.0 / 8.8
10 W	0512 / 1051 / 1735 / 2320	3.6 / 8.2 / 3.9 / 7.9		**25** TH	0627 / 1225 / 1907	3.3 / 8.3 / 3.7
11 TH	0614 / 1158 / 1848	4.1 / 7.6 / 4.3		**26** F	0103 / 0759 / 1408 / 2043	8.2 / 3.7 / 8.0 / 3.8
12 F	0051 / 0747 / 1354 / 2029	7.5 / 4.2 / 7.5 / 4.3		**27** SA	0244 / 0936 / 1535 / 2206	8.3 / 3.4 / 8.5 / 3.3
13 SA	0240 / 0915 / 1519 / 2150	7.8 / 3.8 / 8.0 / 3.7		**28** SU	0357 / 1045 / 1635 / 2307	8.9 / 2.7 / 9.1 / 2.6
14 SU	0350 / 1023 / 1619 / 2252	8.5 / 3.1 / 8.8 / 2.9		**29** M	0451 / 1138 / 1721 / 2356	9.6 / 2.1 / 9.8 / 2.0
15 M	0443 / 1120 / 1709 / 2344	9.3 / 2.3 / 9.6 / 2.1		**30** TU	0536 / 1222 / 1801	10.2 / 1.5 / 10.4
				31 W O	0039 / 0615 / 1303 / 1837	1.5 / 10.7 / 1.2 / 10.7

APRIL

Day	Time	m		Day	Time	m
1 TH	0118 / 0652 / 1339 / 1911	1.2 / 10.9 / 1.1 / 10.9		**16** F ●	0054 / 0634 / 1318 / 1855	0.7 / 11.5 / 0.3 / 11.6
2 F	0153 / 0726 / 1411 / 1943	1.1 / 11.0 / 1.1 / 10.9		**17** SA	0140 / 0716 / 1402 / 1936	0.3 / 11.8 / 0.1 / 11.8
3 SA	0224 / 0758 / 1439 / 2012	1.2 / 10.8 / 1.3 / 10.7		**18** SU	0223 / 0758 / 1444 / 2016	0.2 / 11.8 / 0.2 / 11.7
4 SU	0251 / 0827 / 1504 / 2039	1.5 / 10.5 / 1.7 / 10.3		**19** M	0304 / 0839 / 1523 / 2056	0.4 / 11.5 / 0.6 / 11.3
5 M	0316 / 0852 / 1526 / 2103	1.8 / 10.0 / 2.1 / 9.8		**20** TU	0344 / 0921 / 1603 / 2138	0.9 / 10.9 / 1.3 / 10.6
6 TU	0339 / 0915 / 1549 / 2128	2.3 / 9.5 / 2.6 / 9.3		**21** W	0426 / 1007 / 1646 / 2224	1.6 / 10.0 / 2.2 / 9.7
7 W	0406 / 0942 / 1619 / 2158	2.8 / 8.9 / 3.2 / 8.8		**22** TH	0513 / 1101 / 1738 / 2322	2.5 / 9.1 / 3.1 / 8.9
8 TH	0441 / 1019 / 1700 / 2243	3.3 / 8.4 / 3.7 / 8.2		**23** F	0616 / 1212 / 1851	3.2 / 8.3 / 3.7
9 F	0534 / 1118 / 1803 / 2357	3.8 / 7.8 / 4.1 / 7.7		**24** SA	0042 / 0742 / 1346 / 2021	8.3 / 3.6 / 8.1 / 3.8
10 SA	0658 / 1258 / 1939	4.0 / 7.5 / 4.2		**25** SU	0215 / 0911 / 1507 / 2139	8.3 / 3.4 / 8.4 / 3.4
11 SU	0148 / 0831 / 1438 / 2108	7.8 / 3.7 / 8.0 / 3.7		**26** M	0327 / 1016 / 1606 / 2238	8.7 / 2.9 / 9.0 / 2.8
12 M	0311 / 0946 / 1546 / 2216	8.4 / 3.0 / 8.7 / 2.9		**27** TU	0421 / 1107 / 1651 / 2326	9.3 / 2.4 / 9.6 / 2.3
13 TU	0411 / 1047 / 1639 / 2313	9.2 / 2.2 / 9.6 / 2.1		**28** W	0506 / 1151 / 1731	9.8 / 1.9 / 10.1
14 W	0502 / 1140 / 1728	10.1 / 1.5 / 10.4		**29** TH	0008 / 0546 / 1230 / 1807	1.9 / 10.2 / 1.7 / 10.4
15 TH	0005 / 0549 / 1231 / 1812	1.3 / 10.9 / 0.8 / 11.1		**30** F O	0046 / 0623 / 1306 / 1841	1.6 / 10.5 / 1.5 / 10.6

CHANNEL ISLANDS – ST. HELIER

LAT 49°11′N   LONG 2°07′W

TIMES AND HEIGHTS OF HIGH AND LOW WATERS

YEAR **1999**

MAY

	Time	m		Time	m
1 SA	0122 0658 1339 1913	1.4 10.6 1.5 10.7	**16** SU	0118 0656 1340 1915	0.5 11.6 0.4 11.8
2 SU	0154 0730 1409 1943	1.5 10.5 1.6 10.5	**17** M	0205 0741 1426 1959	0.4 11.6 0.5 11.7
3 M	0224 0801 1436 2011	1.6 10.3 1.9 10.3	**18** TU	0250 0825 1509 2042	0.5 11.4 0.8 11.3
4 TU	0251 0828 1501 2038	1.9 9.9 2.2 9.9	**19** W	0334 0910 1552 2125	1.0 10.8 1.4 10.7
5 W	0318 0853 1527 2105	2.3 9.5 2.6 9.5	**20** TH	0418 0957 1636 2213	1.6 10.1 2.2 9.9
6 TH	0346 0923 1558 2138	2.7 9.1 3.0 9.0	**21** F	0506 1049 1727 2307	2.4 9.3 3.0 9.1
7 F	0422 1002 1638 2223	3.1 8.6 3.5 8.6	**22** SA	0603 1151 1829	3.0 8.6 3.6
8 SA	0511 1059 1735 2329	3.4 8.2 3.8 8.1	**23** SU	0014 0713 1308 1944	8.5 3.4 8.3 3.8
9 SU	0622 1219 1857	3.6 7.9 3.9	**24** M	0132 0829 1424 2057	8.3 3.5 8.3 3.6
10 M	0057 0747 1350 2025	8.1 3.5 8.2 3.6	**25** TU	0244 0934 1525 2158	8.5 3.2 8.7 3.3
11 TU	0224 0905 1505 2137	8.5 3.0 8.8 2.9	**26** W	0342 1027 1614 2247	8.9 2.9 9.2 2.8
12 W	0332 1010 1605 2239	9.2 2.3 9.6 2.2	**27** TH	0431 1112 1656 2331	9.3 2.6 9.6 2.5
13 TH	0430 1108 1658 2335	10.0 1.6 10.4 1.5	**28** F	0513 1153 1735	9.7 2.3 10.0
14 F	0522 1202 1746	10.7 1.0 11.1	**29** SA	0011 0552 1232 1810	2.1 10.0 2.1 10.3
15 SA ●	0027 0610 1253 1831	0.9 11.3 0.6 11.5	**30** SU ○	0049 0629 1307 1845	1.9 10.2 2.0 10.4
			31 M	0125 0704 1341 1917	1.8 10.2 2.0 10.4

JUNE

	Time	m		Time	m
1 TU	0159 0737 1413 1949	1.9 10.1 2.1 10.3	**16** W	0239 0815 1458 2030	0.8 11.2 1.0 11.3
2 W	0232 0809 1442 2019	2.0 9.9 2.3 10.0	**17** TH	0325 0900 1542 2114	1.0 10.8 1.5 10.8
3 TH	0303 0839 1512 2051	2.2 9.6 2.5 9.7	**18** F	0409 0945 1624 2158	1.5 10.3 2.1 10.2
4 F	0335 0913 1545 2127	2.5 9.3 2.8 9.4	**19** SA	0453 1031 1708 2245	2.2 9.6 2.7 9.5
5 SA	0412 0954 1626 2212	2.8 9.0 3.1 9.0	**20** SU	0538 1120 1756 2337	2.8 9.0 3.3 8.9
6 SU	0458 1046 1717 2310	3.0 8.7 3.4 8.7	**21** M	0629 1217 1852	3.3 8.5 3.7
7 M	0557 1150 1824	3.2 8.5 3.5	**22** TU	0038 0728 1325 1956	8.4 3.7 8.3 3.9
8 TU	0020 0708 1306 1943	8.6 3.2 8.5 3.4	**23** W	0147 0833 1433 2101	8.3 3.7 8.3 3.8
9 W	0139 0824 1422 2058	8.8 2.9 8.9 3.0	**24** TH	0254 0935 1531 2200	8.4 3.6 8.7 3.5
10 TH	0252 0934 1530 2205	9.2 2.5 9.5 2.4	**25** F	0351 1028 1620 2250	8.7 3.3 9.1 3.1
11 F	0358 1037 1629 2307	9.8 1.9 10.1 1.8	**26** SA	0439 1115 1702 2336	9.1 2.9 9.5 2.7
12 SA	0457 1136 1723	10.4 1.4 10.7	**27** SU	0522 1158 1742	9.5 2.6 9.9
13 SU ●	0005 0550 1231 1813	1.3 10.9 1.0 11.2	**28** M ○	0018 0603 1239 1819	2.3 9.8 2.3 10.2
14 M	0059 0640 1323 1900	0.9 11.2 0.8 11.5	**29** TU	0059 0641 1317 1856	2.1 10.0 2.2 10.3
15 TU	0151 0728 1411 1946	0.7 11.3 0.8 11.5	**30** W	0139 0718 1354 1932	2.0 10.1 2.1 10.3

JULY

	Time	m		Time	m
1 TH	0216 0754 1430 2007	2.0 10.0 2.2 10.3	**16** F	0313 0846 1527 2059	1.0 10.9 1.3 11.0
2 F	0252 0830 1504 2042	2.2 9.9 2.3 10.1	**17** SA	0353 0927 1605 2138	1.4 10.5 1.8 10.5
3 SA	0328 0906 1538 2120	2.2 9.8 2.5 9.9	**18** SU	0429 1005 1640 2216	1.9 10.0 2.4 9.9
4 SU	0405 0946 1617 2202	2.3 9.6 2.7 9.6	**19** M	0503 1043 1716 2255	2.6 9.3 3.0 9.2
5 M	0446 1031 1702 2251	2.5 9.3 2.9 9.4	**20** TU	0539 1124 1757 2341	3.2 8.7 3.6 8.6
6 TU	0535 1124 1757 2350	2.8 9.0 3.1 9.1	**21** W	0623 1215 1850	3.7 8.3 4.0
7 W	0635 1228 1906	3.0 8.9 3.2	**22** TH	0040 0721 1324 1956	8.1 4.1 8.0 4.2
8 TH	0100 0745 1343 2022	9.0 3.0 8.9 3.1	**23** F	0154 0832 1440 2107	7.9 4.1 8.1 4.0
9 F	0218 0901 1500 2138	9.0 2.8 9.2 2.8	**24** SA	0307 0941 1542 2211	8.2 3.8 8.6 3.6
10 SA	0333 1012 1607 2247	9.3 2.5 9.7 2.3	**25** SU	0406 1039 1632 2305	8.6 3.4 9.1 3.1
11 SU	0439 1116 1707 2349	9.8 2.0 10.3 1.7	**26** M	0455 1128 1717 2352	9.1 2.9 9.6 2.6
12 M	0537 1215 1800	10.4 1.5 10.8	**27** TU	0539 1214 1759	9.6 2.5 10.1
13 TU ●	0046 0629 1310 1848	1.3 10.8 1.2 11.2	**28** W ○	0037 0621 1257 1838	2.2 10.0 2.2 10.4
14 W	0140 0718 1400 1934	1.0 11.1 1.0 11.4	**29** TH	0120 0701 1338 1917	1.9 10.2 2.0 10.6
15 TH	0228 0804 1445 2018	1.0 11.1 1.1 11.3	**30** F	0201 0740 1417 1954	1.7 10.4 1.8 10.7
			31 SA	0240 0817 1454 2031	1.6 10.4 1.8 10.6

AUGUST

	Time	m		Time	m
1 SU	0317 0854 1529 2108	1.7 10.3 1.9 10.5	**16** M	0357 0932 1607 2143	1.8 10.2 2.1 10.1
2 M	0353 0931 1605 2147	1.8 10.1 2.1 10.2	**17** TU	0423 1003 1634 2214	2.4 9.6 2.7 9.4
3 TU	0431 1011 1645 2230	2.1 9.8 2.4 9.8	**18** W	0449 1035 1703 2249	3.0 9.0 3.4 8.7
4 W	0513 1058 1732 2322	2.4 9.4 2.8 9.3	**19** TH	0521 1115 1745 2335	3.6 8.4 3.9 8.1
5 TH	0605 1155 1834	2.9 9.0 3.2	**20** F	0609 1214 1851	4.2 7.9 4.4
6 F	0028 0712 1310 1953	8.9 3.2 8.7 3.4	**21** SA	0052 0728 1344 2017	7.7 4.5 7.7 4.4
7 SA	0152 0835 1438 2119	8.6 3.3 8.8 3.2	**22** SU	0224 0856 1506 2136	7.7 4.3 8.1 3.9
8 SU	0318 0955 1554 2236	8.9 3.0 9.3 2.7	**23** M	0336 1006 1605 2237	8.2 3.7 8.8 3.3
9 M	0430 1104 1656 2340	9.4 2.5 9.9 2.1	**24** TU	0430 1102 1653 2328	8.9 3.1 9.4 2.6
10 TU	0529 1204 1749	10.0 1.9 10.6	**25** W	0517 1150 1737	9.5 2.5 10.1
11 W ●	0036 0619 1257 1836	1.5 10.6 1.4 11.1	**26** TH ○	0015 0559 1236 1818	2.1 10.1 2.0 10.6
12 TH	0127 0705 1345 1920	1.1 11.0 1.1 11.4	**27** F	0059 0641 1319 1858	1.6 10.5 1.6 10.9
13 F	0212 0747 1428 2000	0.9 11.1 1.0 11.4	**28** SA	0142 0720 1400 1937	1.3 10.8 1.4 11.1
14 SA	0252 0825 1505 2037	0.9 11.1 1.2 11.2	**29** SU	0222 0758 1438 2014	1.1 10.9 1.3 11.2
15 SU	0327 0900 1538 2111	1.2 10.7 1.6 10.7	**30** M	0259 0834 1514 2050	1.1 10.9 1.4 11.0
			31 TU	0335 0911 1549 2128	1.3 10.7 1.7 10.7

Chart Datum: 5·88 metres below Ordnance Datum (Local)

14

CHANNEL ISLANDS – ST. HELIER

LAT 49°11′N   LONG 2°07′W

TIMES AND HEIGHTS OF HIGH AND LOW WATERS   YEAR 1999

TIME ZONE (UT)
For Summer Time add ONE hour in non-shaded areas

SEPTEMBER

Day	Time	m	Time	m	Time	m	Time	m
1 W	0411	1.7	0949	10.3	1626	2.1	2209	10.1
2 TH	0450	2.3	1033	9.7	1710	2.7	2258	9.4
3 F	0539	3.0	1127	9.0	1808	3.3		
4 SA	0004	8.6	0646	3.5	1246	8.5	1932	3.7
5 SU	0139	8.3	0818	3.7	1425	8.5	2112	3.5
6 M	0313	8.5	0946	3.4	1544	9.0	2231	2.9
7 TU	0423	9.2	1055	2.7	1645	9.8	2331	2.1
8 W	0517	9.9	1151	2.0	1735	10.5		
9 TH	0021	1.5	0603	10.5	1240	1.5	● 1818	11.0
10 F	0107	1.1	0644	11.0	1324	1.1	1858	11.4
11 SA	0148	0.9	0722	11.2	1403	1.0	1936	11.4
12 SU	0224	1.0	0757	11.1	1437	1.1	2010	11.2
13 M	0255	1.3	0829	10.8	1507	1.5	2041	10.8
14 TU	0321	1.7	0858	10.4	1532	2.0	2109	10.2
15 W	0343	2.3	0925	9.8	1555	2.5	2136	9.5
16 TH	0405	2.9	0951	9.2	1620	3.2	2202	8.9
17 F	0433	3.5	1020	8.6	1656	3.8	2236	8.2
18 SA	0515	4.1	1106	7.9	1752	4.3	2341	7.6
19 SU	0624	4.6	1243	7.5	1925	4.6		
20 M	0142	7.4	0809	4.6	1429	7.8	2059	4.2
21 TU	0306	8.0	0933	4.0	1535	8.5	2208	3.4
22 W	0403	8.7	1033	3.2	1626	9.3	2301	2.6
23 TH	0450	9.5	1123	2.5	1712	10.0	2348	1.9
24 F	0534	10.2	1209	1.9	1754	10.7		
25 SA	0033	1.4	0615	10.8	1254	1.4	O 1834	11.2
26 SU	0117	1.0	0655	11.2	1336	1.0	1914	11.5
27 M	0158	0.8	0734	11.4	1416	0.9	1952	11.6
28 TU	0237	0.8	0811	11.4	1454	1.0	2030	11.4
29 W	0314	1.1	0848	11.1	1531	1.3	2108	10.9
30 TH	0350	1.6	0927	10.6	1609	1.9	2150	10.2

OCTOBER

Day	Time	m	Time	m	Time	m	Time	m
1 F	0430	2.3	1011	9.8	1653	2.7	2241	9.3
2 SA	0519	3.1	1107	9.0	1752	3.4	2350	8.5
3 SU	0629	3.8	1230	8.4	1921	3.9		
4 M	0131	8.1	0808	4.0	1412	8.4	2106	3.6
5 TU	0304	8.5	0937	3.5	1529	9.0	2220	2.9
6 W	0409	9.2	1041	2.8	1627	9.7	2314	2.2
7 TH	0458	9.9	1132	2.1	1713	10.4	2359	1.7
8 F	0540	10.5	1216	1.6	1755	10.9		
9 SA	0041	1.3	0618	10.9	1257	1.3	● 1832	11.1
10 SU	0119	1.2	0653	11.1	1334	1.2	1908	11.2
11 M	0152	1.3	0726	11.0	1406	1.3	1941	11.0
12 TU	0221	1.5	0757	10.8	1435	1.6	2011	10.7
13 W	0246	1.9	0824	10.4	1500	2.0	2038	10.2
14 TH	0309	2.4	0850	9.9	1524	2.5	2102	9.6
15 F	0331	2.9	0913	9.4	1550	3.1	2126	9.0
16 SA	0359	3.4	0941	8.8	1623	3.6	2158	8.4
17 SU	0438	4.0	1021	8.2	1713	4.2	2253	7.7
18 M	0538	4.5	1135	7.6	1833	4.5		
19 TU	0042	7.4	0715	4.6	1340	7.7	2012	4.2
20 W	0226	7.9	0850	4.2	1457	8.3	2129	3.5
21 TH	0329	8.6	0957	3.4	1553	9.1	2227	2.7
22 F	0419	9.5	1050	2.6	1641	10.0	2317	2.0
23 SA	0504	10.2	1139	1.9	1725	10.7		
24 SU	0004	1.3	0547	10.9	1226	1.3	O 1808	11.3
25 M	0049	0.9	0628	11.4	1311	0.9	1849	11.7
26 TU	0133	0.7	0708	11.7	1354	0.7	1930	11.8
27 W	0214	0.7	0748	11.6	1435	0.8	2011	11.6
28 TH	0254	1.0	0829	11.3	1516	1.2	2052	11.0
29 F	0334	1.6	0910	10.7	1557	1.9	2138	10.3
30 SA	0416	2.4	0957	10.0	1644	2.6	2230	9.4
31 SU	0507	3.2	1055	9.1	1744	3.4	2340	8.6

NOVEMBER

Day	Time	m	Time	m	Time	m	Time	m
1 M	0618	3.9	1215	8.5	1910	3.8		
2 TU	0113	8.2	0751	4.0	1348	8.5	2045	3.6
3 W	0241	8.5	0915	3.6	1503	8.9	2155	3.1
4 TH	0343	9.1	1016	3.0	1559	9.5	2247	2.5
5 F	0431	9.7	1105	2.5	1646	10.0	2331	2.1
6 SA	0511	10.2	1148	2.1	1727	10.4		
7 SU	0010	1.8	0548	10.6	1227	1.8	● 1804	10.7
8 M	0047	1.7	0623	10.8	1303	1.7	● 1839	10.8
9 TU	0120	1.7	0656	10.8	1336	1.7	1913	10.7
10 W	0150	1.8	0727	10.7	1406	1.9	1943	10.5
11 TH	0217	2.1	0755	10.4	1434	2.1	2011	10.0
12 F	0242	2.5	0822	10.0	1501	2.5	2037	9.6
13 SA	0308	2.9	0848	9.6	1529	3.0	2104	9.2
14 SU	0337	3.3	0917	9.1	1603	3.4	2139	8.6
15 M	0414	3.8	0958	8.6	1648	3.8	2229	8.1
16 TU	0506	4.2	1058	8.1	1753	4.1	2346	7.8
17 W	0624	4.4	1230	7.9	1920	4.1		
18 TH	0124	7.9	0758	4.1	1402	8.3	2041	3.6
19 F	0242	8.5	0912	3.5	1509	9.0	2147	2.9
20 SA	0341	9.3	1013	2.8	1605	9.8	2243	2.2
21 SU	0432	10.1	1107	2.1	1655	10.5	2334	1.5
22 M	0519	10.8	1158	1.5	1742	11.1		
23 TU	0023	1.1	0601	11.4	1248	1.0	O 1828	11.5
24 W	0110	0.8	0647	11.7	1335	0.8	1912	11.7
25 TH	0156	0.8	0731	11.7	1421	0.9	1957	11.5
26 F	0240	1.1	0815	11.4	1506	1.2	2042	11.0
27 SA	0324	1.6	0900	10.9	1551	1.7	2130	10.4
28 SU	0409	2.3	0948	10.2	1636	2.4	2221	9.6
29 M	0459	3.0	1042	9.5	1735	3.0	2322	8.9
30 TU	0600	3.6	1149	8.9	1844	3.5		

DECEMBER

Day	Time	m	Time	m	Time	m	Time	m
1 W	0037	8.5	0716	3.9	1307	8.6	2003	3.7
2 TH	0158	8.4	0833	3.8	1422	8.7	2113	3.5
3 F	0305	8.8	0938	3.5	1523	9.0	2210	3.1
4 SA	0357	9.2	1030	3.1	1613	9.4	2257	2.8
5 SU	0440	9.7	1115	2.7	1657	9.8	2338	2.5
6 M	0519	10.1	1155	2.4	1737	10.1		
7 TU	0015	2.3	0555	10.4	1233	2.2	● 1813	10.3
8 W	0051	2.2	0629	10.5	1309	2.1	1848	10.3
9 TH	0124	2.2	0702	10.5	1343	2.1	1922	10.2
10 F	0155	2.3	0734	10.4	1416	2.2	1953	10.0
11 SA	0225	2.5	0804	10.1	1447	2.4	2023	9.8
12 SU	0254	2.7	0834	9.8	1518	2.7	2054	9.4
13 M	0325	3.1	0906	9.5	1552	3.0	2129	9.1
14 TU	0401	3.4	0946	9.1	1633	3.3	2214	8.7
15 W	0446	3.7	1036	8.7	1725	3.5	2312	8.4
16 TH	0546	3.9	1142	8.5	1831	3.6		
17 F	0024	8.3	0703	3.9	1301	8.5	1948	3.5
18 SA	0145	8.5	0823	3.6	1419	8.9	2102	3.1
19 SU	0258	9.1	0934	3.0	1527	9.4	2208	2.5
20 M	0400	9.8	1037	2.4	1627	10.1	2307	2.0
21 TU	0455	10.4	1135	1.8	1722	10.7		
22 W	0002	1.5	0545	11.0	1230	1.3	O 1813	11.1
23 TH	0054	1.1	0634	11.4	1323	1.0	1902	11.4
24 F	0144	1.0	0720	11.6	1413	0.9	1949	11.4
25 SA	0231	1.1	0806	11.5	1500	1.0	2035	11.1
26 SU	0317	1.4	0852	11.2	1546	1.4	2121	10.7
27 M	0401	1.9	0937	10.6	1630	1.9	2207	10.1
28 TU	0446	2.5	1024	10.0	1715	2.5	2255	
29 W	0533	3.1	1114	9.3	1804	3.2	2348	8.8
30 TH	0626	3.7	1212	8.7	1902	3.7		
31 F	0054	8.4	0729	4.0	1323	8.4	2009	3.9

Chart Datum: 5·88 metres below Ordnance Datum (Local)

VOLVO PENTA SERVICE

Sales and service centres in area 15
France *Volvo Penta France* , 55 Avenue des Champs Pierreux, 92757 Cedex
Tel +33 1 55175445, Fax +33 1 55175261

Area 15

Central North France
Pointe de Barfleur to
St. Quay-Portrieux

VOLVO PENTA

8.15.1	Index	**Page 643**
8.15.2	Diagram of ports, lts, RDF bns, Coast radio and weather stns	**644**
8.15.3	Tidal stream charts	**646**
8.15.4	List of coastal lights, fog signals and waypoints	**648**
8.15.5	Passage information	**650**
8.15.6	Distance table	**651**
8.15.7	English Channel waypoints	**See 8.1.7**
8.15.8	Special notes for France	**652**
8.15.9	French glossary	**653**
8.15.10	Cherbourg, Standard Port, tidal curves Port de Lévi Port du Becquet	**656**
8.15.11	Omonville-la-Rogue Port Racine	**661**
8.15.12	Dielette Goury	**662**
8.15.13	Carteret	**662**
8.15.14	Portbail	**663**
8.15.15	Granville	**664**
8.15.16	Iles Chausey	**664**
8.15.17	St. Malo (Dinard) Standard Port, tidal curves Rotheneuf Cancale	**668**
8.15.18	River Rance/Dinan Plouër Lyvet	**670**
8.15.19	Inland waterways of Brittany	**671**
8.15.20	Dahouet Saint Cast Erquy Val André	**672**
8.15.21	Le Légué/St Brieux	**672**
8.15.22	Binic	**673**
8.15.23	St. Quay-Portrieux	**674**

15.

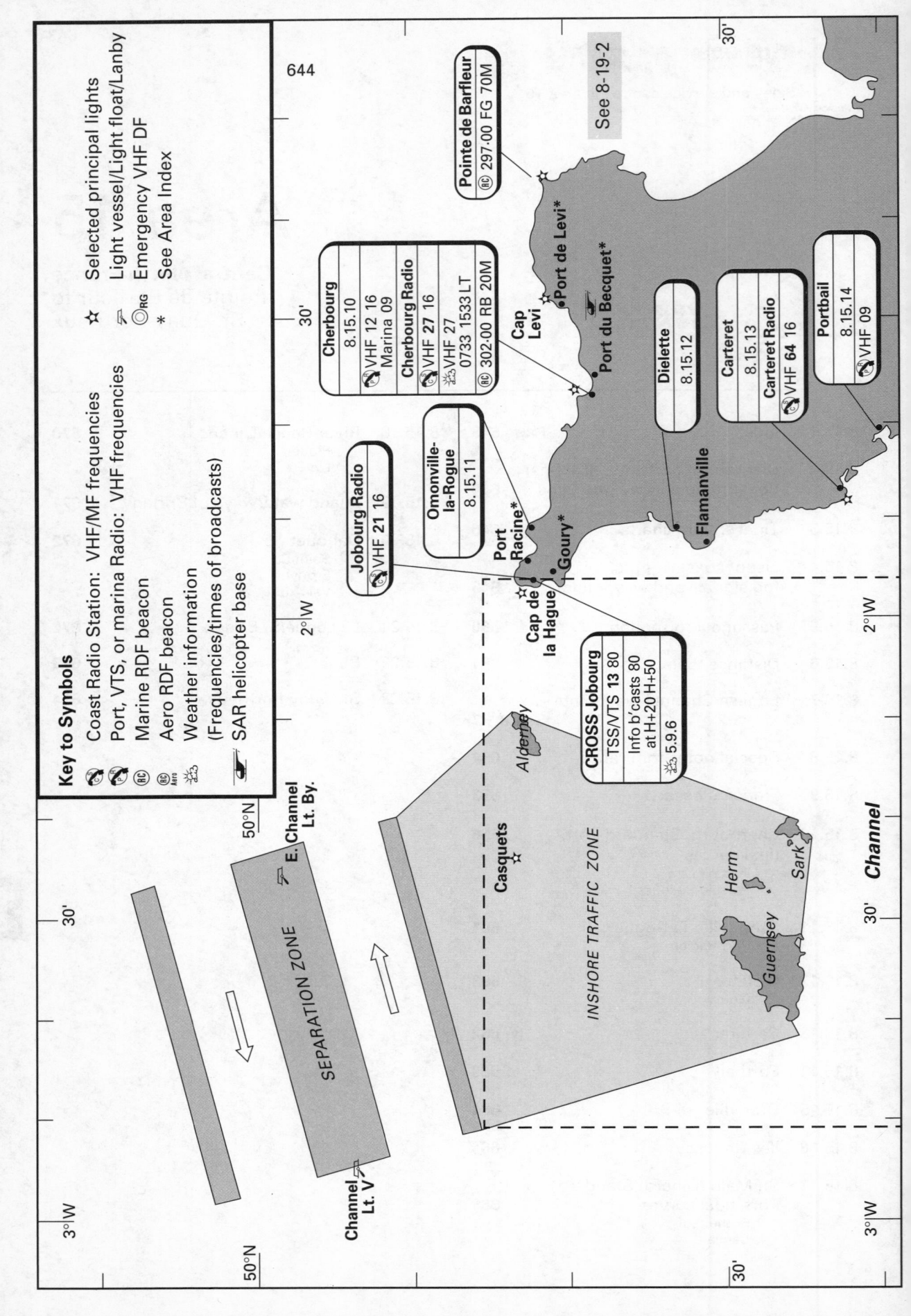

644

Key to Symbols

Coast Radio Station: VHF/MF frequencies
Port, VTS, or marina Radio: VHF frequencies
Marine RDF beacon
Aero RDF beacon
Weather information
(Frequencies/times of broadcasts)
SAR helicopter base

☆ Selected principal lights
⌐ Light vessel/Light float/Lanby
◎RG Emergency VHF DF
* See Area Index

See 8-19-2

Pointe de Barfleur
RC 297·00 FG 70M

Cherbourg
8.15.10
VHF 12 16 Marina 09

Cherbourg Radio
VHF 27 16
VHF 27
0733 1533 LT
RC 302·00 RB 20M

Omonville-la-Rogue
8.15.11

Jobourg Radio
VHF 21 16

Dielette
8.15.12

Carteret
8.15.13
Carteret Radio
VHF 64 16

Portbail
8.15.14
VHF 09

Cap Levi

Port de Levi*

Port du Becquet*

Port Racine*

Goury*

Cap de la Hague

Flamanville

CROSS Jobourg
TSS/VTS 13 80
Info b'casts 80
at H+20 H+50
5.9.6

E. Channel Lt. By.

50°N

SEPARATION ZONE

Channel Lt. V

Alderney

Casquets
☆

INSHORE TRAFFIC ZONE

Herm

Guernsey

Sark

Channel

3°W   30'   2°W   30'

50°N

30'

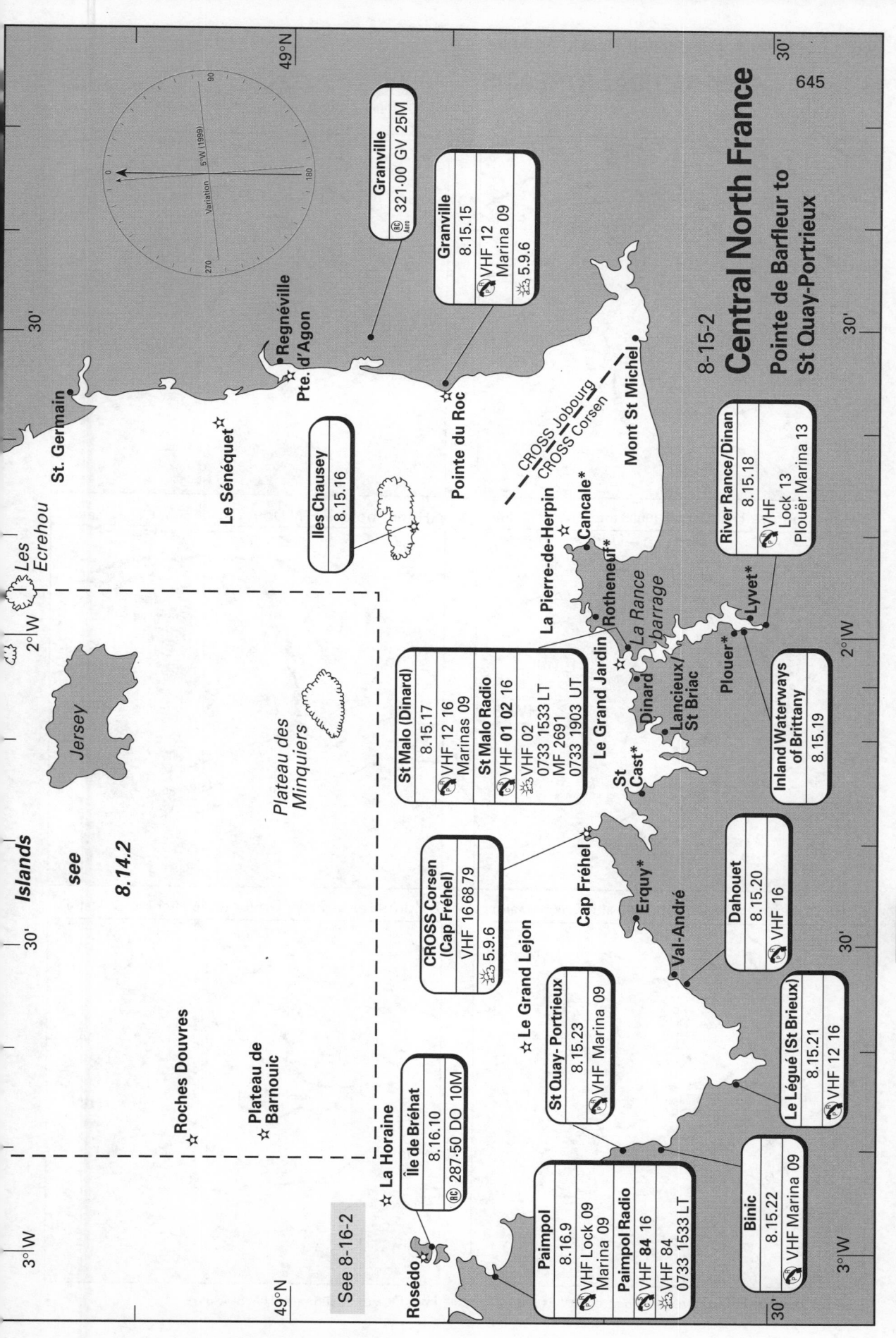

Central North France

Pointe de Barfleur to St Quay-Portrieux

8-15-2

645

15

49°N

30'

30'

Variation

5°W (1999)

St. Germain

Les Ecrehou

2°W

Jersey

Roches Douvres ☆

Plateau de Barnouic ☆

Plateau des Minquiers

Islands

see

8.14.2

3°W

30'

49°N

See 8-16-2

Regnéville ●

Pte. d'Agon ☆

Le Sénéquet ☆

Granville
Ⓡ🅒 321·00 GV 25M
Aero

Granville
8.15.15
🚤 VHF 12
Marina 09
⚓ 5.9.6

Pointe du Roc ☆

Iles Chausey
8.15.16

☆

CROSS Jobourg
CROSS Corsen

Mont St Michel ●

Cancale* ☆

La Pierre-de-Herpin ☆

Rotheneuf* ☆

Le Grand Jardin ☆

La Rance barrage

Dinard

St Malo (Dinard)
8.15.17
🚤 VHF 12 16
Marinas 09
St Malo Radio
🚤 VHF 01 02 16
📻 VHF 02
0733 1533 LT
MF 2691
0733 1903 UT

River Rance/Dinan
8.15.18
🚤 VHF
Lock 13
Plouër Marina 13

Lyvet* ●

Plouer* ●

Lancieux/ St Briac ●

Inland Waterways of Brittany
8.15.19

2°W

CROSS Corsen (Cap Fréhel)
VHF 16 68 79
⚓ 5.9.6

Cap Fréhel ☆

Erquy* ●

St Cast* ☆

Val-André ●

Dahouet
8.15.20
🚤 VHF 16

30'

☆ Le Grand Lejon

St Quay-Portrieux
8.15.23
🚤 VHF Marina 09

Le Légué (St Brieux)
8.15.21
🚤 VHF 12 16

Binic
8.15.22
🚤 VHF Marina 09

Rosédo ☆

Île de Bréhat
8.16.10
Ⓡ🅒 287·50 DO 10M

☆ La Horaine

Paimpol
8.16.9
🚤 VHF Lock 09
Marina 09
Paimpol Radio
🚤 VHF 84 16
📻 VHF 84
0733 1533 LT

3°W

30'

8-15-3   AREA 15 TIDAL STREAMS

> Due to very strong tidal stream rates, eddies may occur. Where possible these are shown, but in many areas there is insufficient information or the eddies are unstable.

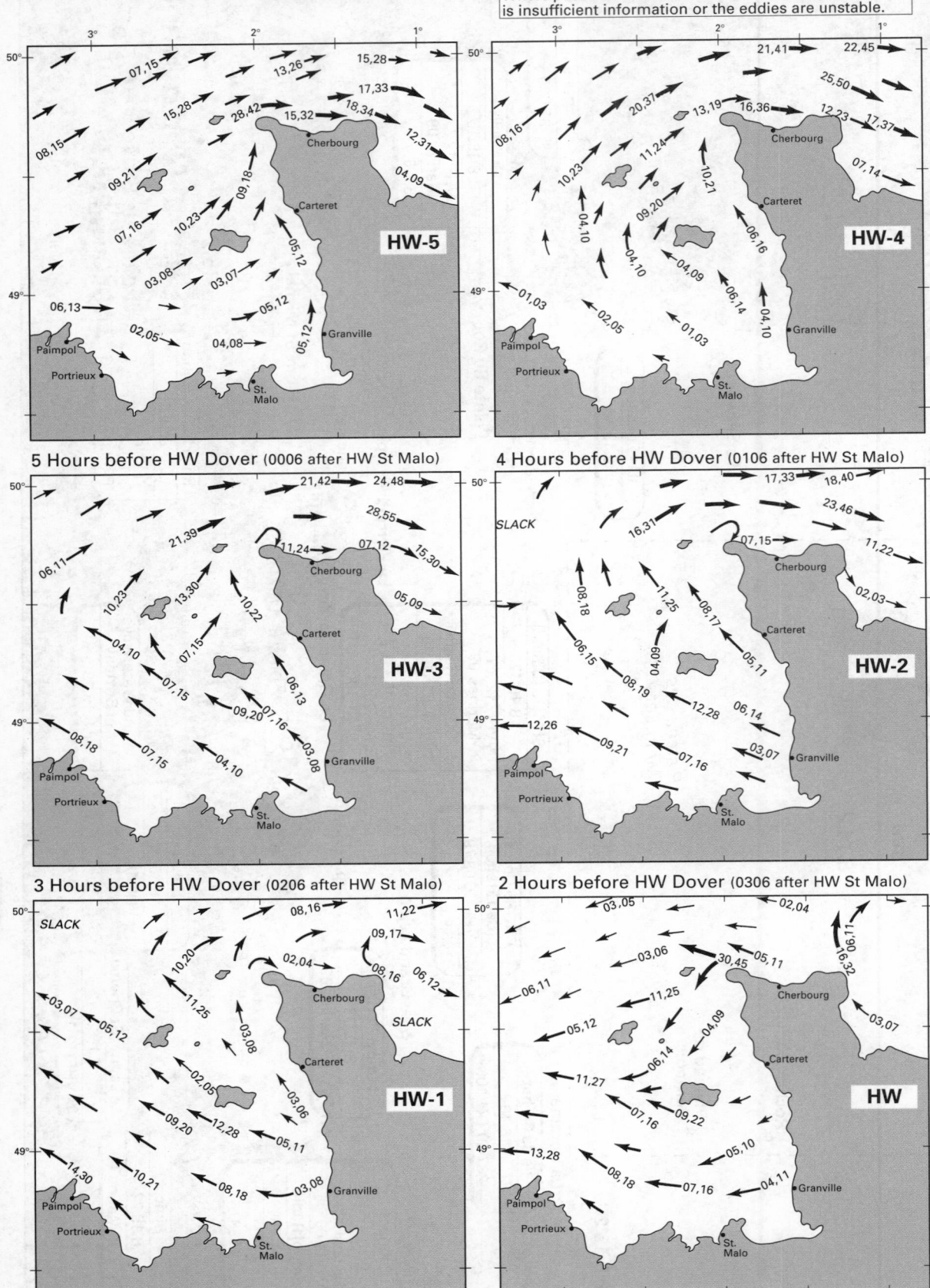

5 Hours before HW Dover (0006 after HW St Malo)

4 Hours before HW Dover (0106 after HW St Malo)

3 Hours before HW Dover (0206 after HW St Malo)

2 Hours before HW Dover (0306 after HW St Malo)

1 Hour before HW Dover (0406 after HW St Malo)

HW Dover (0506 after HW St Malo)

Westward 8.16.3   Channel Islands 8.14.3   Eastward 8.19.3   Northward 8.2.3

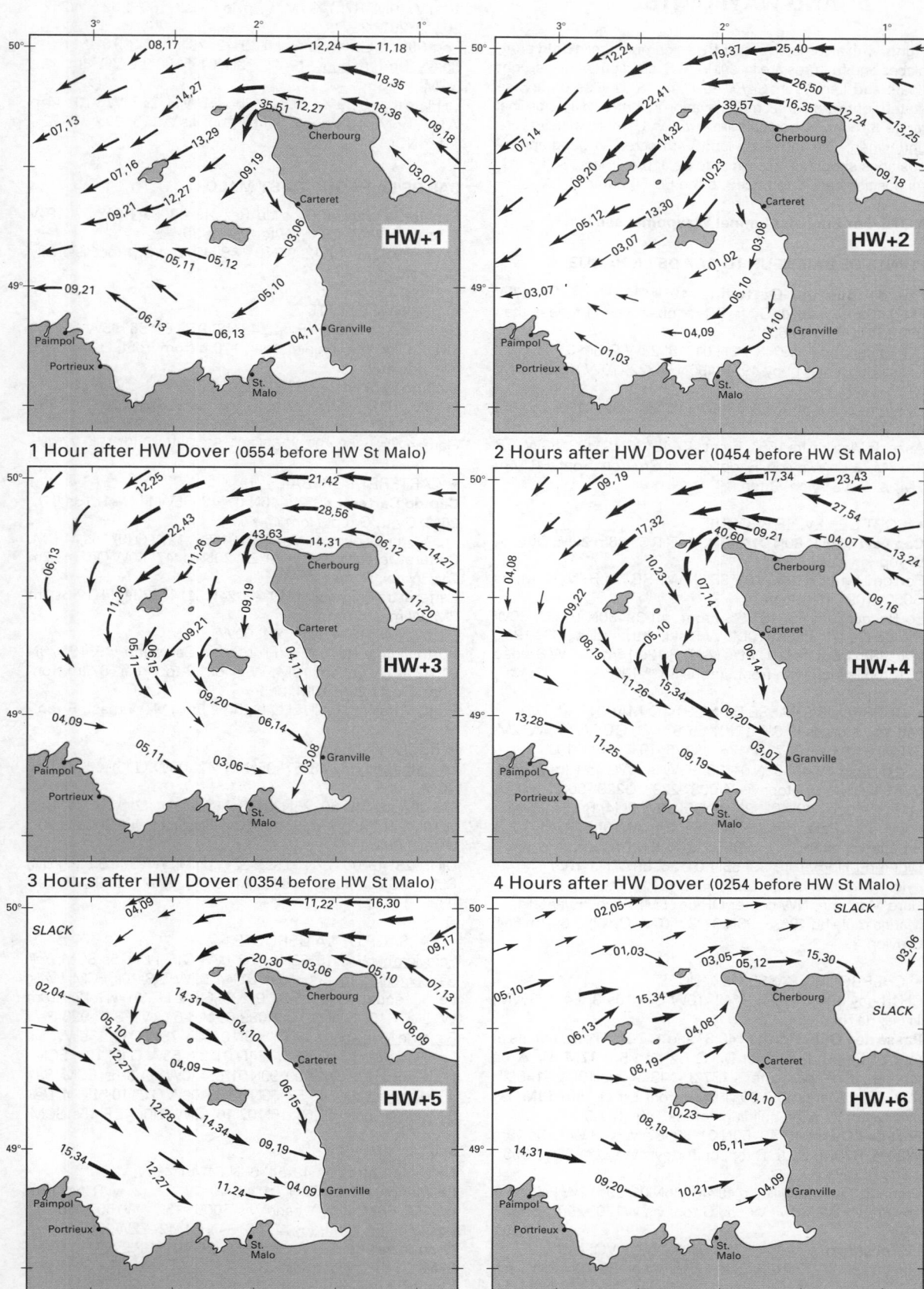

1 Hour after HW Dover (0554 before HW St Malo)

2 Hours after HW Dover (0454 before HW St Malo)

3 Hours after HW Dover (0354 before HW St Malo)

4 Hours after HW Dover (0254 before HW St Malo)

5 Hours after HW Dover (0154 before HW St Malo)

6 Hours after HW Dover (0054 before HW St Malo)

15

8.15.4 COASTAL LIGHTS, FOG SIGNALS AND WAYPOINTS

Lights with a nominal range of 15M or more are in **bold** print, places and features are in CAPITALS, and light-vessels, light floats and Lanbys in *CAPITAL ITALICS*. Unless otherwise stated lights are white. m = elevation in metres; M = nominal range in miles. Fog signals are in *italics*. Useful waypoints are underlined; use those on land with care. All geographical positions should be assumed to be approximate. See 3.4.1. All positions are referenced to the ED 50 datum.

NOTE: For English Channel Waypoints see 8.1.7.

POINTE DE BARFLEUR TO CAP DE LA HAGUE

Pte de Barfleur-Gatteville 49°41'·83N 01°15'·87W Fl (2) 10s 72m **29M**; Gy tr, B top; obsc when brg less than 088°; RC; *Horn (2) 60s.*
Les Équets buoy 49°43'·68N 01°18'·28W Q 8m 3M; NCM.
Basse du Rénier buoy 49°44'·90N 01°22'·10W VQ 8m 4M; NCM; *Whis.*
La Pierre Noire buoy 49°43'·57N 01°28'·98W Q (9) 15s 8m 4M; WCM.
Anse de Vicq ldg lts 158°. Front, 49°42'·26N 01°23'·88W FR 8m 7M; ▲ on W pylon, R top; rear, 403m from front, FR 14m 7M; ▲ on W pylon, R top.

- PORT DE LÉVI/LE BECQUET
Cap Lévi 49°41'·80N 01°28'·40W Fl R 5s 36m **22M**; Gy ☐ tr; W top.
Port de Lévi 49°41'·30N 01°28'·27W F RG 7m,R7M, G7M; vis G050°-109°, R109°-140°.
Le Becquet ldg lts 186·5°. Front, 49°39'·30N 01°32'·80W Dir Oc (2+1) 12s 8m 10M; W 8-sided tr; intens 183°-190°; rear, 49m from front, Dir Oc (2+1) R 12s 13m 7M; W 8-sided tr, R top; synch with front, intens 183°-190°.

- CHERBOURG PASSE DE L'EST TO MARINA
Fort des Flamands 49°39'·16N 01°35'·53W Dir Q WRG 13m W12M, R10M, G10M; vis G173·5°-176°, W176°-183°, R183°-193°.
Fort de l'Est 49°40'·33N 01°35'·93W Iso WG 4s 19m W12M, G9M; W pylon, G top; vis W008°-229°, G229°-008°.
La Truite buoy 49°40'·39N 01°35'·39W Fl (4) R 15s; PHM.
Forte d'Île Pelée Oc (2) WR 6s 19m W10M, R7M; W & R pedestal on fort; vis W055°-120°, R120°-055°.
Digue du Homet 49°39'·53N 01°36'·88W FG 10m 8M; W pylon, G top on blockhouse; *Horn (2+1) 60s.*
Gare Maritime, NW corner QR 6m 6M; W col, R lantern.
Marina môle hd 49°38'·93N 01°37'·07W Oc (2) G 6s 7m 6M; G pylon.

- CHERBOURG PASSE DE L'OUEST
CH1 buoy 49°43'·30N 01°42'·10W L Fl 10s 8m 4M; SWM; *Whis*; Ra refl.
Passe de l'Ouest ldg lts 140·3° and 142·2°. **Front**, two lts at root of Digue du Homet Dir Q (2 hor) 5m **17M**, W ▲ on parapet, 63m apart, intens 137·3°-143·3° and 139·2°-145·2°; rear, Gare Maritime 0·99M from front Dir Q 35m **19M**, Gy pylon with W ▲ on building, intens 140°-142·5°.
Fort de l'Ouest 49°40'·50N 01°38'·87W Fl (3) WR 15s 19m **W24M, R20M**; Gy tr, R top, on fort; vis W122°-355°, R355°-122°; RC; *Horn (3) 60s.*
Digue de Querqueville hd 49°40'·36N 01°39'·72W Fl (4) WG 15s 8m W6M, G4M; W col, G top; vis W120°-290°, G290°-120°.
Le Tenarde buoy 49°48'·78N 01°37'·67W VQ; NCM.
Ldg lts 124·3°. Front, Digue du Homet hd FG 10m 8M; rear, 0·75M from front, Terre-plein de Mielles, Iso G 4s 16m 7M; W col, B bands; both intens 114·3°-134·3°.

- OMONVILLE-LA-ROGUE/PORT RACINE
Omonville-la-Rogue 49°42'·33N 01°50'·10W Iso WRG 4s 13m W10M, R7M, G7M; W pylon; vis G180°-252°, W252°-262°, R262°-287°.
Port Racine bkwtr hd (unlit) 49°42'·78N 01°53'·70W.
Basse Bréfort buoy 49°43'·70N 01°51'·05W VQ 8m 4M; NCM; *Whis.*
La Plate lt bn tr 49°44'·02N 01°55'·65W Fl (2+1) WR 10s 11m W9M, R6M; Y 8-sided tr, with B top; vis W115°-272°, R272°-115°; NCM.

CAP DE LA HAGUE TO ST MALO

Cap de la Hague (Gros du Raz) 49°43'·37N 01° 57'·19W Fl 5s 48m **23M**; Gy tr, W top; *Horn 30s.*
La Foraine buoy 49°42'·95N 01°58'·40W; WCM; (occasionally submerged.)

- GOURY/DIÉLETTE
Goury ldg lts 065·2°. Front, 49°42'·95N 01°56'·55W QR 5m 7M; R ☐ on W ☐ on pier; rear, 116m from front, Q 11m 7M; W pylon on hut.
Diélette W bkwtr, 49°33'·23N 01°51'·73W, Iso WRG 4s 12m W10M, R7M, G7M; W tr, G top; vis G070°-135°, W135°-145°, R145°-180°; and Fl G 4s 6m 2M; vis 115°-358°.
Flamanville buoy 49°32'·62N 01°53'·93W Q (9) 15s; WCM.

- CARTERET/PORTBAIL
Cap de Carteret 49°22'·46N 01°48'·35W Fl (2+1) 15s 81m **26M**; Gy tr, G top; *Horn (3) 60s.*
Trois-Grunes buoy 49°21'·88N 01°55'·12W Q (9) 15s; WCM.
Carteret Jetée Ouest hd 49°22'·20N 01°47'·40W Oc R 4s 7m 7M; W col, R top.
Carteret training wall hd 49°22'·24N 01°47'·23W Fl G 2·5s 4m 2M; W mast, G top.
PB buoy 49°18'·47N 01°44'·60W; SWM.
Portbail ldg lts 042°. Front, La Caillourie 49°19'·79N 01°42'·40W Q 14m 10M; W pylon, R top; rear, 870m from front, Oc 4s 20m 10M; belfry.
Portbail training wall hd Q (2) R 5s 5m 1M; W mast, R top.

- REGNÉVILLE
La Catheue buoy 48°57'·95N 01°42'·00W Q (6) + L Fl 15s; SCM.
Pte d'Agon 49°00'·25N 01°34'·60W Oc (2) WR 6s 12m W10M, R7M; W tr, R top, W dwelling; vis R063°-110°, W110°-063°.
Dir lt 028° 49°00'·77N 01°33'·28W dir Oc WRG 4s 9m W12M, R9M, G9M; House; vis G024°-027°, W027°-029°, R029°-033°.

- PASSAGE DE LA DÉROUTE
Écrévière buoy 49°15'·33N 01°52'·08W Q (6) + L Fl 15s; SCM; *Bell.*
Bas Jourdan buoy 49°06'·90N 01°44'·07W Q (3) 10s; ECM; *Whis.*
Le Sénéquet 49°05'·54N 01°39'·65W Fl (3) WR 12s 18m W13M, R10M; W tr; vis R083·5°-116·5°, W116·5°-083·5°.
Basse le Marié buoy 49°01'·89N 01°48'·76W Q (9) 15s; WCM.
Les Ardentes buoy 48°57'·84N 01°51'·53W Q (3) 10s; ECM.
NE Minquiers buoy 49°00'·90N 01°55'·20W VQ (3) 5s; ECM; *Bell.*
SE Minquiers buoy 48°53'·50N 02°00'·00W Q (3) 10s; ECM; *Bell.*
S Minquiers buoy 48°53'·15N 02°10'·00W Q (6) + L Fl 15s; SCM.

- ÎLES CHAUSEY
La Petite Entrée bn 48°54'·60N 01°49'·48W; WCM.
Le Pignon 48°53'·52N 01°43'·40 W Oc (2) WR 6s 10m W11M, R8M; B tr, Y band; vis R005°-150°, W150°-005°.
Basse du Founet buoy 48°53'·34N 01°42'·22W; ECM.
Grande Île (Pte de la Tour) 48° 52'·25N 01°49'·27W Fl 5s 39m **23M**; Gy ☐ tr; *Horn 30s.*
Channel buoy 48°52'·18N 01°49'·00W Fl G 2s; SHM.
La Crabière Est lt bn tr 48°52'·52N 01°49'·30W Oc WRG 4s

5m W9M, R6M, G6M; B tr, Y top; vis W079°-291°, G291°-329°, W329°-335°, R335°-079°.

Anvers wk buoy 48°53'·90N 01°40'·84W Q (3) 10s; ECM.
Le Videcoq buoy 48°49'·70N 01°42'·02W VQ (9) 10s; WCM.

• GRANVILLE
Pointe du Roc 48°50'·11N 01°36'·70W Fl (4) 15s 49m **23M**; Gy tr, R top.
Le Loup lt bn 48°49'·63N 01°36'·17W Fl (2) 6s 8m 11M; IDM.
Hérel marina hd 48°49'·96N 01°35'·82W Fl R 4s 12m 8M; W ○ tr, R top; *Horn (2) 40s.*
Commercial Port Jetée Ouest hd 48°49'·92N 01°36'·16W Iso R 4s 12m 6M; R pylon.

• CANCALE/ROTHENEUF
La Pierre-de-Herpin 48°43'·83N 01°48'·83W Oc (2) 6s 20m **17M**; W tr, B top and base; *Siren Mo (N) 60s.*
Cancale jetty hd 48°40'·16N 01°51'·04W Oc (3) G 12s 12m 7M; W pylon, G top, G hut; obsc when brg less than 223°.
Rothneuf entrance bn 48°41'·42N 01°57'·61W; SHM; (unlit.)

ST MALO TO ST QUAY PORTRIEUX

• APPROACHES TO ST MALO
La Plate lt bn tr 48°40'·85N 02°01'·83W Fl WRG 4s 11m, W11M, R7M, G7M; vis W140°-203°, R203°-210°, W210°-225°, G225°-140°.
Brunel buoy 48°40'·88N 02°05'·26W Q (9) 15s; WCM; *Bell.*

• CHENAL DE LA PETITE PORTE/RADE DE ST MALO
Ldg lts 130°. Front, **Le Grand Jardin** 48°40'·27N 02°04'·90W Fl (2) R 10s 24m **15M**; Gy tr, R top; RC; rear, **La Balue**, 4·08M from front, dir FG 69m **24M**; Gy □ tr; intens 128·2°-129·7°.
Bassé NE buoy 48°42'·51N 02°09'·34W Q; NCM; *Bell.*
Fairway buoy 48°41'·42N 02°07'·21W L Fl 10s; SWM; *Whis.*
Les Courtis lt bn 48°40'·52N 02°05'·72W Fl (3) G 12s 14m 8M.

• CHENAL DE LA GRANDE PORTE
Ldg lts 089·1°. **Front**, **Le Grand Jardin** Fl (2) R 10s 24m **15M**; rear, **Rochebonne** 4·2M from front 48°40'·32N 01°58'·61W dir FR 40m **24M**; Gy □ tr, R top; intens 088·2°-089·7°.
Le Sou buoy 48°40'·15N 02°05'·24W VQ (3) 5s; ECM; *Bell.*
No 1 buoy 48°40'·24N 02°05'·97W Fl G 4s; SHM; *Whis.*
No 2 buoy 48°40'·27N 02°07'·48W Fl (3) R 12s; PHM; *Whis.*
Banchenou buoy 48°40'·52N 02°11'·42W Fl (5) G 20s; SHM.
Ldg lts 128·7°. Front, **Les Bas-Sablons** 48°38'·22N 02°01'·23W Dir FG 20m **22M**; W □ tr, B top; intens 127·5°-130·5°. Common rear, **La Balue**, 0·9M from front Dir FG 69m **25M**; Gy □ tr; intens 128·2°-129·7°.
Basse du Buron No 12 buoy 48°39'·46N 02°03'·44W L Fl R 10s; PHM.
Le Buron lt bn 48°39'·38N 02°03'·60W Fl (2) 6s 15m 8M; G tr.
Plateau Rance Nord 48°38'·71N 02°02'·27W VQ; NCM.
Plateau Rance Sud 48°38'·52N 02°02'·23W Q (6) + L Fl 15s; SCM.

• ST MALO
Ldg lts 070·7°. Écluse du Naye Front, 48°38'·64N 02°01'·46W FR 7m 3M; rear, FR 23m 8M vis 030°-120°.
Crapaud de la Cité SHM buoy, Fl (4) G 15s, 48°38'·41N 02°01'·93W.
Môle des Noires hd 48°38'·58N 02°01'·85W Fl R 5s 11m 13M; W tr, R top; obsc 155°-159°, 171°-178°, and when brg more than 192°; *Horn (2) 20s.*
Bas-Sablons marina môle hd 48°38'·48N 02°01'·63W Fl G 4s 7m 5M; Gy mast.

• LA RANCE
La Jument lt bn tr 48°37'·50N 02°01'·68W Fl (5) G 20s 6m 3M; G tr, SHM.
Tidal barrage, NW wall Fl G 4s 6m 5M, G pylon, vis 191°-291°.
NE dolphin Fl (2) R 6s 6m 5M; vis 040°-200°.

• ST BRIAC/ST CAST
Embouchure du Fremur. Dir lt 125° 48°37'·1N 02°08'·2W Dir Iso WRG 4s 10m W13M, R11M, G11M; W mast on hut, vis G121·5°-124·5°, W124·5°-125·5°, R125·5°-129·5°.
St Cast môle hd 48°38'·47N 02°14'·50W Iso WG 4s 11m W11M, G8M; G and W structure; vis W204°-217°, G217°-233°, W233°-245°, G245°-204°.

Cap Fréhel 48°41'·10N 02°19'·07W Fl (2) 10s 85m **29M**; Brown □ tr, G lantern; *Horn (2) 60s.*

• CHENAL D'ERQUY/ERQUY/VAL-ANDRÉ
Les Justières buoy 48°40'·66N 02°26'·43W Q (6) + L Fl 15s; SCM.
Basses du Courant buoy 48°39'·29N 02°29'·08W VQ (6) + L Fl 10s; SCM.
Erquy S môle hd 48°38'·13N 02°28'·60W Oc (2+1) WRG 12s 11m W11M, R8M, G8M; W tr, R top; vis R055°-081°, W081°-094°, G094°-111°, W111°-120°, R120°-134°.
Erquy inner jetty hd 48°38'·16N 02°28'·31W Fl R 2·5s 10m 3M; R and W tr.
Val-Andre jetty hd 48°35'·89N 02°33'·24W.

• PORT DE DAHOUET
La Dahouet buoy 48°35'·28N 02°35'·28W; NCM.
La Petite-Muette 48°34'·91N 02°34'·21W Fl WRG 4s 10m W9M, R6M, G6M; ▲ on G & W tr; vis G055°-114°, W114°-146°, R146°-196°. Fl (2) G 6s; vis 156°-286° 240m SE.

• BAIE DE SAINT BRIEUC
Grand Léjon 48°44'·95N 02°39'·90W Fl (5) WR 20s 17m **W18M**, R14M; R tr, W bands; vis R015°-058°, W058°-283°, R283°-350°, W350°-015°.
Le Rohein lt bn tr 48°38'·88N 02°37'·68W VQ (9) WRG 10s 13m W10M, R7M, G7M; WCM; vis R072°-105°, W105°-180°, G180°-193°, W193°-237°, G237°-282°, W282°-301°. G301°-330°, W330°-072°.

• LE LÉGUÉ (St BRIEUC)
Le Légué buoy 48°34'·38N 02°41'·07W Mo (A)10s; SWM; *Whis.*
Pointe à l'Aigle jetty 48°32'·15N 02°43'·05W VQ G 13m 8M; W tr, G top; vis 160°-070°.
Custom House jetty 48°31'·96N 02°43'·34W Iso G 4s 6m 2M, W cols, G top.

• BINIC
Binic, môle de Penthièvre hd 48°36'·13N 02°48'·84W Oc (3) 12s 12m 11M; W tr, G gallery; unintens 020°-110°.

• SAINT-QUAY-PORTRIEUX
Caffa buoy 48°37'·89N 02°43'·00W Q (3) 10s; ECM.
La Roselière buoy 48°37'·51N 02°46'·31W VQ (9) 10s; WCM.
Elbow 48°39'·05N 02°49'·01W dir Iso WRG 4s **W15M**, R11M, G11M; vis 159°-179°, G179°-316°, W316°-320·5°, R320·5°-159°; reserve lt ranges 12/9M.
Île Harbour Roches de Saint-Quay 48°40'·05N 02°48'·42W Oc (2) WRG 6s 16m W10M, R8M, G8M; W tr and dwelling, R top; vis R011°-133°, G133°-270°, R270°-306°, G306°-358°, W358°-011°.
NE Môle hd 48°38'·90N 02°48'·84W Fl (3) G 12s 2M; G tr.
Herflux dir lt 130° 48°39'·13N 02°47'·87W Dir Fl (2) WRG 6s W8M, R6M, G6M; vis G115°-125°, W125°-135°, R135°-145°; SCM.

15

8.15.5   PASSAGE INFORMATION

Current Pilots for this area include: *Shell Channel Pilot* (Imray/ Cunliffe); *Normandy and CI Pilot* (Adlard Coles/Brackenbury) as far W as St Malo; *Brittany and CI Cruising Guide* (Adlard Coles/Jefferson); *N Brittany and CI Cruising* (YM/Cumberlidge); *N Brittany Pilot* (Imray/RCC) W'ward from St Malo; *Admiralty Channel Pilot.* Charts *2669* and *1106 cover the* whole area. For French Glossary see 8.15.9.

Off the French coastline between Pte de Barfleur and Cap Lévi rky shoals extend up to 2·5M seaward. From C. Lévi around C. de la Hague and S to C. de Flamanville the coast is cleaner with few dangers extending more than 1M offshore. Southward to Mont St Michel and W to St Malo the coast changes to extensive offshore shoals, sand dunes studded with rks and a series of drying hbrs. From St Malo to St Quay-Portrieux the coast is characterised by deep bays (often drying), a few rugged headlands and many offlying rks.

The sea areas around this coast, including the Channel Islands, are dominated by powerful tidal streams with an anti-clockwise rotational pattern and a very large tidal range. Across the top of the Cotentin Peninsula and between C. de la Hague and Alderney the main English Channel tidal streams are rectilinear E/W. Neap tides are best, particularly for a first visit, and tidal streams need to be worked carefully. Boats which can take the ground have an advantage for exploring the shallower hbrs. Be careful to avoid lobster pots, and oyster and mussel beds in some rivers and bays.

CROSSING FROM UK TO CHERBOURG OR ALDERNEY

The popular cross-Channel route from hbrs between Portland and Chichester to those on the Cotentin peninsula or in the Channel Islands is normally straightforward in summer, but can never be taken for granted. Review the planning guide-lines in 8.3.5, especially at the start of the season. Cross-Channel distances are in 8.0.8 and waypoints in 8.1.7. Note any tidal constraints shown under the departure hbr itself. Other local factors to be considered include:

Portland & Weymouth: the Portland Race and Shambles Bank both require a wide berth. Check the tidal streams for possible wind-over-tide conditions.

Poole: leave hbr on the ebb, but at springs with a S/SE wind beware short steep seas in the Swash Channel; off Handfast, Peveril and Anvil Pts overfalls occur with wind against tide. From **Solent ports** decide whether to leave via the Needles or east of the IOW. The former usually requires a fair tide through Hurst Narrows (HW Portsmouth –1 to +4½) which in turn will dictate your ETD from hbr. The latter has no tidal gate, but is longer and may give a less favourable slant if the wind is in the SW; in W'lies it offers better shelter in the lee of the IOW. In practice the nearer exit may prove to be the obvious choice.

On passage the greatest hazard is likely to be crossing the shipping lanes, especially if fog/poor vis are forecast when it may be safest not to sail. Whether crossing at the Casquets TSS (8.14.2), or further up-Channel, is almost academic; the risk of collision with another ship is the same.

Finally, review destination(s) and possible hbrs of refuge:
Braye (Alderney), whilst accessible at all times, presents a slight risk, especially at springs, of being swept past Alderney on a W-going tide. The yacht may then clew up in Guernsey, having unwittingly negotiated the Swinge or the Alderney Race. The moral is to plan and monitor track so as to approach from well up-tide. (For Guernsey, Sark & Jersey see 8.14.5). **French ports** on the W side of the Cotentin (Diélette to Granville) are tidally constrained and exposed to the W; they are however in a lee with anticyclonic Easterlies.

Cherbourg is accessible at all times. On closing the coast especially at springs, a very large drift angle may be needed to maintain track. To the E (see Area 19), **Barfleur** dries; **St Vaast** is a safe anch, if awaiting lock opening into marina.

POINTE DE BARFLEUR TO CAP DE LA HAGUE   (AC *1106*)

The N coast of the Cotentin Peninsula runs E/W for 26M, mostly bordered by rks which extend 2·5M offshore from Pte de Barfleur to C. Lévi, and 1M offshore between Pte de Jardeheu and C. de la Hague. Tidal streams reach 5kn at sp, and raise a steep sea with wind against tide.

Pte de Barfleur has dangers up to 2M offshore, and a race, in which the sea breaks heavily, extends 3-4M NE and E from the lt ho. In bad weather, particularly with winds from NW or SE against the tide, it is necessary to keep at least 6M to seaward to avoid the worst effects; in calmer conditions the Pte can be rounded close inshore. The inner passage be-tween Pte de Barfleur and C. Lévi, keeping S of three cardinal buoys, is not recommended without local knowledge except in good weather and visibility when the transits shown on chart *1106* can be used. Tidal streams run strongly with considerable local variations.

Off C. Lévi a race develops with wind against tide, and extends nearly 2M to N. Port Lévi and Port de Becquet are two small drying hbrs E of Cherbourg. Off Cherbourg (8.15.10) the stream is E-going from about HW – 0430 and W-going from HW + 0230.

Close inshore between Cherbourg and C. de la Hague a back eddy runs W. As an alternative to Omonville (8.15.11) there is anch in Anse de St Martin, about 2M E of C. de la Hague, open to N, but useful to await the tide in the Alderney Race.

THE ALDERNEY RACE   (chart *3653*)

The Alderney Race, so called due to very strong tidal streams, runs SW/NE between C. de la Hague and Alderney. The fairway, approx 4M wide, is bounded by Race Rk and Alder-ney S Banks to the NW, and to the SE by rky banks 4M WSW of C. de la Hague, Milieu and Banc de la Schôle (least depth 2·7m). These dangers which cause breaking seas and heavy overfalls should be carefully avoided. In bad weather and strong wind-against-tide conditions the seas break in all parts of the Race and passage is not recommended. Conditions are exacerbated at sp tides.

In mid-chan the the SW-going stream starts at HW St Helier + 0430 (HW Dover) and the NE-going stream at HW St Helier –0210 (HW Dover + 0530), sp rates both 5·5kn. The times at which the stream turns do not vary much for various places, but the rates do; for example, 1M W of C. de la Hague the sp rates reach 7 to 8kn.

To obtain optimum conditions, timing is of the essence. As a rule of thumb the Race should be entered on the first of the fair tide so as to avoid the peak tidal stream with attendant overfalls/seas.

Thus, bound SW, arrive off C. de la Hague at around HW St Helier + 0430 (HW Dover) when the stream will be slack, whilst just starting to run SW off Alderney. A yacht leaving Cherbourg at HW Dover – 0300 will achieve the above timing by utilising the inshore W-going tidal eddy.

Conversely, NE bound, leave St Peter Port, say, at approx local HW St Helier – 0430 (HWD+3) with a foul tide so as to pass Banc de la Schôle as the first of the fair tide starts to make. A later departure should achieve a faster passage, but with potentially less favourable conditions in the Race. On the NE stream the worst overfalls are on the French side.

CAP DE LA HAGUE TO ST MALO
(charts *3659*, 3656, *3655*, *3653*)

The Jobourg radar surveillance station (CROSS) and atomic energy station Chy (R lts) are conspic about 3-4M SE of Gros du Raz (lt, fog sig), off C de la Hague. 5M S of C de la Hague beware Les Huquets de Jobourg, an extensive bank of drying and submerged rks, and Les Huquets de Vauville (dry) close SE of them.

The W coast of the Cotentin Peninsula is exposed, and is mostly rky and inhospitable; along much of this coast S of Carteret there is little depth of water, so that a nasty sea can build. The drying hbrs/non-tidal marinas* at Goury, Dielette* (8.15.12), Carteret* (8.15.13) and Portbail (8.15.14) are more readily accessible if cruising from S to N on the tide, since all hbrs are restricted by drying approaches.

The two main chans from/to the Alderney Race are Déroute de Terre and, further offshore, Passage de la Déroute. Neither chan are well marked in places, and are not advised at night. The former leads between Plateau des Trois Grunes and Carteret, between Basses de Portbail and Bancs Félés, between Le Sénéquet E tr and Basse Jourdan, and E of Îles Chausey toward Pte du Roc, off Granville (8.15.15). The S end of this chan, E of Îles Chausey, is very shallow; for detailed directions see *Channel Pilot*.

The Passage de la Déroute passes W of Plateau des Trois Grunes, between Basses de Taillepied and Les Écrehou, between Chaussée de Boeufs and Plateau de l'Arconie, E and SE of Les Minquiers and Les Ardentes, and W of Îles Chausey (8.15.16).

To the S of Granville is the drying expanse of B du Mont St Michel. Proceeding W, the drying hbr of Cancale (8.15.17) with many oyster beds and a fair weather anch SE of Île des Rimains, lies 4M S of Pte du Grouin, off which the many dangers are marked by La Pierre-de-Herpin (lt, fog sig). The large drying inlet of Rothéneuf, with anch off in good weather, is 4M E of St Malo (8.15.17 and chart 2700).

ST MALO TO L'OST PIC (charts *3674*, *3659*)

In the apprs to St Malo (chart 2700) are many islets, rks and shoals, between which are several chans that can be used in good vis. Tidal streams reach 4kn at sp, and can set across chans. From E and N, with sufficient rise of tide and good vis,

Chenal de la Bigne, Chenal des Petits Pointus or Chenal de la Grande Conchée can be used, but they all pass over or near to drying patches. From the W and NW, Chenal de la Grande Porte and Chenal de la Petite Porte are the easiest routes and are well marked/lit. Chenal du Décollé is a shallow, demanding inshore route from the W, and no shorter than Chenal de la Grande Porte.

By passing through the lock at W end of the R. Rance barrage (8.15.18) it is possible to cruise up river to Dinan, via the lock at Châtelier (SHOM chart 4233). At Dinan is the entrance to the Canal d'Ille et Rance to Biscay (8.15.19).

6M NW of St Malo beware Le Vieux-Banc (dries). Here the E-going stream begins at HW St Helier – 0555, and the W-going at HW St Helier – 0015, sp rates 2·5kn. There are W-going eddies very close inshore on the E-going stream. Between St Malo and C. Fréhel is St Cast hbr (8.15.20), and there are anchs S of Île Agot in the apprs to the drying hbr of St Briac, in B de l'Arguenon and B de la Fresnaye. From C. Fréhel to C. d'Erquy there are no worthwhile hbrs.
About 3ca off Cap d'Erquy, and inshore of the various rky patches close to seaward Chenal d'Erquy runs WSW/ENE into the E side of the B de St Brieuc. Erquy is a pleasant, drying hbr, but often crowded with fishing boats. The Plateau du Rohein (lt), at W end of a long ridge, is 6M W of C. d'Erquy. There are several rky shoals within the B itself, some extending nearly 2M offshore.

To seaward of Bay de St Brieuc is Grand Léjon (lt), a rky shoal 9M NE of St Quay-Portrieux. Rks extend 2½ca W and 8ca NNE of the lt ho. Petit Léjon (dries) lies 3·5M SSE of lt ho. From the N/NW, keep W of these dangers via a chan 3-4M wide which gives access to the shallow, partly drying S end of the Bay and the hbrs of Val André, Dahouet (8.15.20), Le Légué/St Brieux (8.15.21), and Binic (8.15.22). On the W side of Bay de St Brieuc, Roches de St Quay and offlying patches extend 4M E from St Quay-Portrieux (8.15.23) which can only be approached from NW or SE.

To the N and NE of L'Ost-Pic extensive offshore shoals guard the approaches to Paimpol (8.16.9), Ile de Bréhat and the Trieux river. Further N, the Plateau de Barnouic and Plateau des Roches Douvres (lt, fog sig, RC) should be avoided. Here the E-going stream begins at about HW St Malo – 0400 and the W-going at about HW St Malo +0100 with Sp rates exceeding 4kn.

8.15.6   DISTANCE TABLE

Approximate distances in nautical miles are by the most direct route, whilst avoiding dangers and allowing for Traffic Separation Schemes. Places in *italics* are in adjoining areas; places in **bold** are in 8.0.8, Cross-Channel Distances.

		1	2	3	4	5	6	7	8	9	10	11	12	13	14	15	16	17	18	19	20
1.	*Calais*	**1**																			
2.	*Barfleur*	148	**2**																		
3.	**Cherbourg**	160	20	**3**																	
4.	Omonville	163	27	10	**4**																
5.	Cap de la Hague	167	32	18	6	**5**															
6.	*Braye (Alderney)*	172	41	25	15	9	**6**														
7.	**St Peter Port**	193	60	44	34	28	23	**7**													
8.	*Creux (Sark)*	190	55	37	29	23	22	10	**8**												
9.	**St Helier**	213	77	64	51	45	46	29	24	**9**											
8.	Carteret	192	55	41	29	23	28	31	23	26	**10**										
11.	Portbail	196	59	49	33	27	32	35	27	25	5	**11**									
12.	Iles Chausey	222	87	69	61	55	58	48	43	25	33	30	**12**								
13.	Granville	227	93	75	67	61	66	55	50	30	38	35	9	**13**							
14.	Dinan	250	117	102	91	85	85	66	64	50	62	59	29	35	**14**						
15.	**St Malo**	238	105	90	79	73	73	54	52	38	50	47	17	23	12	**15**					
16.	Dahouet	240	106	88	80	74	72	54	52	41	60	59	37	45	41	29	**16**				
17.	Le Légué/St Brieux	244	110	96	86	78	76	57	56	46	69	69	41	49	45	33	8	**17**			
18.	Binic	244	115	95	84	78	75	56	55	46	70	70	43	51	45	33	10	8	**18**		
19.	**St Quay-Portrieux**	244	106	88	80	74	73	56	51	46	64	64	47	54	47	35	11	7	4	**19**	
20.	*Lézardrieux*	238	106	88	80	74	68	48	38	47	68	71	53	54	61	49	33	32	30	21	**20**

15

SPECIAL NOTES FOR FRANCE
(Areas 15 to 19)   8-15-8

Some minor differences in the information for French hbrs are: Instead of 'County' the 'Département' is given. French Standard Time is –0100 (ie 1300 Standard Time in France is 1200UT), DST not having been taken into account (see 7.1.2.)

For details of documentation apply to the French Tourist Office, 178 Piccadilly, London, W1V 0AL; ☎ 0171-629 2869, 📠 0171-493 6594, Info 0891 244123.

AFFAIRES MARITIMES
In every French port there is a representative of the central government, L'Administration Maritime, known as Affaires Maritimes. This organisation watches over all maritime activities (commercial, fishing, pleasure) and helps them develop harmoniously. Information on navigation and other maritime issues can be supplied by a local representative whose ☎ is given under each port. The Head Office is: Ministère Chargé de la Mer, Bureau de la Navigation de Plaisance, 3 Place Fontenoy, 75007 Paris, ☎ 01·44·49·80·00.

CHARTS
Two types of French chart are shown: SHOM as issued by the *Service Hydrographique et Oceanographique de la Marine*, the French Navy's Hydrographic Service; ECM *Éditions Cartographiques Maritimes* are charts for sea and river navigation. Notes: Under 'Facilities', SHOM means a chart agent. Any new edition of a SHOM chart receives a new, different chart number. SHOM charts refer elevations of lights, bridges etc to Mean Level (ML), not to MHWS as on Admiralty charts.

TIDAL COEFFICIENTS
See 8.16.25 for Coefficients based on Brest, together with explanatory notes and French tidal terms.

MÉTÉO (Weather)
The BQR (*Bulletin Quotidien des Renseignements*) is a very informative daily bulletin displayed in Hr Mr Offices and YC's. Some weather terms are in the Glossary 8.15.9. For each French port, under **TELEPHONE**, Météo is the ☎ of a local Met Office. Auto gives the ☎ for recorded Inshore and Coastal forecasts; dial 08.36.68.08.dd (dd is the Département No, shown under each port). To select the Inshore (*rivage*) or Coastal (*côte;* out to 20M offshore) bulletin, say "STOP" as your choice is spoken.
Inshore bulletins are 5 day forecasts, also containing local info on tides, signals, sea temperature, surf conditions, etc. Coastal bulletins (for 5 areas from the Belgian to Spanish borders) contain strong wind/gale warnings, general synopsis, 24hrs forecast and outlook.
For recorded Offshore bulletins for Channel/N. Sea, Atlantic or Mediterranean, Figs 5(6) & (7), dial ☎ 08.36.68.08.08. To select desired offshore area say "STOP" as it is named. Offshore bulletins contain strong wind/gale warnings, the general synopsis and forecast, and the 5 day outlook.

PUBLIC HOLIDAYS
New Year's Day, Easter Sunday and Monday, Labour Day (1 May), Ascension Day, Armistice Day 1945 (8 May), Whit Sunday and Monday, National (Bastille) Day (14 July), Feast of the Assumption (15 Aug), All Saints' Day (1 Nov), Remembrance Day (11 Nov), Christmas Day.

FRENCH GLOSSARY: see 8.15.9 on facing page.

FACILITIES.
At some marinas fuel can only be obtained/paid for by using a French credit card (of the smart variety) in a slot machine. If not in possession of such a card, it may be possible to persuade a Frenchman to use his card on your behalf and to reimburse him in cash.
The cost shown for a visitor's overnight berth is unavoidably the previous year's figure (as in similar publications). It is based on high season rates and is calculated on LOA, although beam may be taken into account at some ports. Low season rates and concessions can much reduce costs. The fee usually includes electricity, but rarely showers which range between FF8 and FF12.

TELEPHONES
☎ Nos contain 10 digits, the first 2 digits being Zone codes (01 to 05), as appropriate to location. Mobile ☎ Nos are prefixed 06. Info Nos, eg the recorded weather (Auto) are prefixed 08. The ringing tone is long, equal on/off tones (slower than UK engaged tone). Rapid pips mean the call is being connected. Engaged tone is like that in UK. A recorded message means ☎ No unobtainable.
To telephone France from UK, dial 00 33, followed by the 9 digit number, ie omitting the 0 from the Zone code prefix. To telephone UK from France dial 00 44 followed by the Area Code (omitting the first 0) and the number.
Emergencies: Dial 18 for Fire, 17 Police, 15 Ambulance; or 112 as used in all EC countries.
Phonecards for public 'phones may be bought at the PTT or at many cafés and tabacs. Cheap rates are 2130-0800 Mon-Sat; all day Sun.

SIGNALS
Standard sets of Traffic, Storm Warning and Tidal signals apply in all French ports unless otherwise stated.
Traffic Signals

Day		Night		
Full Code	Simplified Code	Full Code	Simplified Code	
● ▲ ●	or **R** Flag	Ⓡ Ⓦ Ⓡ	or Ⓡ	NO ENTRY
▼ ▲	**R** Flag or over **G** Flag	Ⓖ Ⓦ Ⓡ	or Ⓡ Ⓖ	NO ENT/DEP
▼ ▼	or **G** Flag	Ⓖ Ⓦ Ⓖ	or Ⓖ	NO DEP
● ● ●	**R** **R** Balls **R**	Ⓡ Ⓡ Ⓡ		EMERGENCY NO ENTRY
INTERNATIONAL CODE SIGNAL		Ⓖ Ⓖ Ⓖ		PORT OPEN

A Black Flag indicates a shipping casualty in the area. Flag 'P' sometimes indicates that lock or dock gates are open.

Storm Signals (International System)

Day	Night	
▲	Ⓡ Ⓡ	N.W. gale
▲	Ⓡ Ⓦ	N.E. gale
▼	Ⓦ Ⓦ	S.W. gale
▼	Ⓦ Ⓡ	S.E. gale
●	Ⓦ Ⓖ	Strong wind (force 6-7)
✚	Ⓡ Ⓖ Ⓡ	Hurricane (force 12) any direction
▬	} colour of flags is variable	Wind veering
▬	}	Wind backing

In France, Ⓦ Lts, Q or IQ, by day only, indicate forecast wind >F6, as follows: Q = within 3 hrs; IQ = within 6 hrs.

Tidal Signals

There are two sets of signals, one showing the state of the tide and the other showing the height of tide.

a.   State of the tide is shown by:

	Day		Night
High Water . . .	⊠	W Flag	Ⓦ Ⓦ
		B Cross	
Tide falling . . .	▼		Ⓦ
			Ⓦ
Low Water . . .	▷	Bu Flag	Ⓖ Ⓖ
Tide rising . . .	▲		Ⓖ
			Ⓦ

b.   The height of tide signals show the height above CD by adding together the values of the various shapes. Day: ▼ = 0·2m; ■ = 1·0m; ● = 5·0m. Night: Ⓖ = 0·2m; Ⓡ = 1·0m; Ⓦ = 5·0m. The three different shapes are shown horizontally, with ▼s to the left of ■s and ●s to the right, viewed from seaward. Lights are disposed similarly.

The following examples will help to explain:

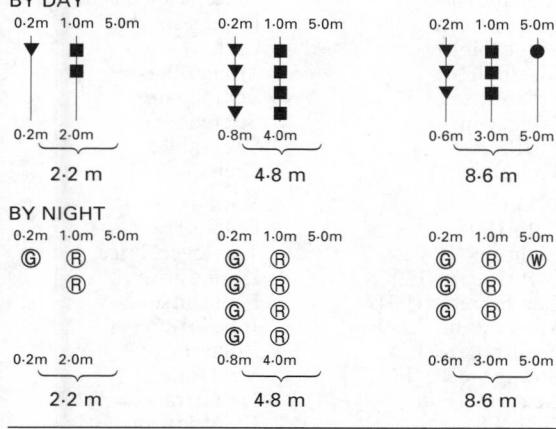

BY DAY

0·2m	1·0m	5·0m
0·2m	2·0m	
2·2 m		

0·2m	1·0m	5·0m
0·8m	4·0m	
4·8 m		

0·2m	1·0m	5·0m
0·6m	3·0m	5·0m
8·6 m		

BY NIGHT

0·2m	1·0m	5·0m
0·2m	2·0m	
2·2 m		

0·2m	1·0m	5·0m
0·8m	4·0m	
4·8 m		

0·2m	1·0m	5·0m
0·6m	3·0m	5·0m
8·6 m		

TOLLS AND QUALIFICATIONS ON INLAND WATERWAYS

Tolls are due on waterways managed by Voies Navigable de France (VNF), ie those E of a line Le Havre to Bordeaux, and the R. Loire. See also 8.15.19 and 8.18.21.
In 1998 licences were available for either one year, 30 days (not necessarily consecutive), 16 consecutive days or 1 day. The rates, based on 5 categories of boat area, ie LOA x Beam (m) = m², were as follows in French francs:

	<12m²	12-25m²	25-40m²	40-60m²	>60m²
1 Year	463	669	1339	2163	2678
30 days	267	479	845	1313	1628
16 days	103	206	309	412	515
1 day	50	101	151	202	252

Licence stickers (*vignettes*) must be visibly displayed stbd side forward; they are obtainable in person or by post from VNF offices at Le Havre, Rouen, Calais and Dunkerque and at larger centres on the canals; or from: Librairie VNF, 18 Quai d'Austerlitz, 75013 Paris; ☎ 01.45.84.85.69.
Detailed brochure from: French National Tourist Office, 178 Piccadilly, London W1V 0AL; ☎ 0171 629 2869, 📠 0171 493 6594; Info 0891 244123.
or: VNF Head Office, 175 Rue Ludovic Boutleux, BP 820, 62408 Bethune, France. ☎ 03.21.63.24.54; 📠 03.21.63.24.42.

Helmsmen of craft <15m LOA and not capable of >20 kph (11kn) must have a Helmsman's Overseas Certificate of Competence or International Certificate of Competence, plus a copy of the French CEVNI rules. For larger, faster craft the requirements are under review.

Foreign vessels >25m LOA must get permission to navigate or ⚓ in French inland waters and must keep watch on Ch 16 or other nominated frequency.

8.15.9 GLOSSARY GLOSSAIRE

English	Français
A. NAVIGATION	**NAVIGATION**
Marks, Buoys, Beacons	**Bouées et Balises**
Beacon (Bn)	Balise
Buoy	Bouée
Can (PHM buoy)	Plate, cylindrique
Chequered	A damier
Column	Colonne
Cone, conical (SHM buoy)	Cone, conique
Diamond (◇ shape)	Losange
Dividers	Compas à pointes sèches
Dolphin	Duc d'Albe
Framework Tower	Charpente
Isolated danger (IDM buoy)	Danger isolé
Landfall (SWM buoy)	Atterrisage
Landmark	Amer
Leading line, transit	Alignement
Perch	Perche, pieu
Pilot Station	Station de pilotage
Port (side)	Bâbord
Radio beacon	Radiobalise
Signal station	Sémaphore
Special mark (SPM buoy)	Marque spéciale
Square (□)	Carré
Starboard (Stbd)	Tribord
Topmark	Voyant
Tower (Tr)	Tour, tourelle
Watch Tr, lookout	Vigie

Colours	**Couleurs**
Black (B)	Noir
Blue (Bu)	Bleu (Bl)
Green (G)	Vert (V)
Grey	Gris
Red, (R)	Rouge
Stripe	Raie
White (W)	Blanc (B)
Yellow (Y)	Jaune (J)

Lights	**Feux**
Alternating (Al)	Feu alternatif
Extinguished (Lt)	Éteint
Fixed (F)	Feu fixe
Fixed and Flashing (F Fl)	Fixe É
Flashing	Feux à éclats
Interrupted quick flashing (IQ)	Scintillant, interrompu
Isophase (Iso)	Feu isophase (Iso)
Leading Light	Feu d'alignement
Lighthouse	Phare
Lightship	Bateau-phare
Obscured	Masqué
Occulting (Oc)	Feu à occultations (Oc)
Quick flashing (Q)	Feu scintillant, (Scint)
Very quick flashing (VQ)	Feu scintillant rapide

Fog Signals	**Signaux de brume**
Bell	Cloche
Explosive (fog)	Explosif
Foghorn	Corne de brume
Reed (horn)	Trompette
Siren	Sirène
Whistle	Sifflet

Compass	**Compas**
Compass, hand-bearing	Compas de relèvement
East (E)	Est
North (N)	Nord
South (S)	Sud
West (W)	Ouest

15

Tides/Depths — Marées/Profondeur

Tides/Depths	Marées/Profondeur
Bay	Anse
Beach, sandy	Grève, plage
Channel	Chenal, Passe
Chart Datum (CD)	Zéro des cartes
Cliff	Falaise
Coastline	Contour de la côte
Draught	Tirant d'eau
Echosounder	Échosondeur
Estuary	Estuaire
Flood/ebb stream	Courant de flot de jusant
Gulf	Golfe
Height, headroom, clearance	Tirant d'air
High Water (HW)	Pleine Mer
Island	Ile
Knots (kn)	Nœuds
Low Water (LW)	Basse Mer
Peninsula	Presqu'île
Point, headland	Pointe, pte
Mean Sea level	Niveau de la mer moyen
Mean (tide)	Mi-marée
Narrows	Goulet
Neaps (np)	Morte eau
Range	Amplitude
Rate (tide)	Vitesse
River	Fleuve, rivière
Sandhill, dunes	Dunes
Slack water, stand	Etale
Springs (sp)	Vive eau
Strait(s)	Pertuis
Tidal stream atl as	Atlas des Marées
Tide Tables	Annuaire des Marées

Features — Marques distinctives

Features	Marques distinctives
Bridge	Pont
Castle	Château
Conspicuous (conspic)	Amer remarquable
Railway	Chemin de fer
Steeple, spire	Clocher, flèche
Water tower	Château d'eau
Windmill	Moulin à vent

Dangers/Seabed — Dangers/Fonds

Dangers/Seabed	Dangers/Fonds
Aground	Dérive, Échoué
Bank	Chaussée, rive
Breakers	Brisants
Clay	Argile
Mud (M)	Vase (V)
Prohibited area	Zone interdite
Sand (S)	Sable (S)
Seaweed, kelp	Algues
Shoal	Haut fond, Basse
Stony, shingly	Cailloux, galets
Reef	Récif
Rock, stone	Roche, pierre
Wreck	Épave

Ports/Harbours — Ports

Ports/Harbours	Ports
Alongside berth (AB)	Accostage
Anchorage (⚓)	Mouillage
Basin	Darse, bassin
Breakwater, mole	Digue
Breakwater, wave-break	Brise-lames
Concrete	Béton
Dolphin	Bouée de corps mort
Downstream	Aval
Dredged	Dragué
Drying berth	Assèchage
Ferry	Bac
Finger berth/pontoon	Catway
Fishing harbour	Port de pêche
Fixed bridge	Pont fixe
Harbour Master	Maitre de Port

Inner harbour	Arrière Port
Jetty	Jetée
Landing (L)	Escalier du quai
Lifeboat (LB)	Canot de sauvetage
Lifting bridge	Pont basculant
Lock	Écluse, Sas
Mooring buoy	Corps-mort
Mooring	Coffre d'amarrage
Outer harbour	Avant Port
Post, pile (mooring)	Poteau
Roadstead	Rade
Slipway (slip)	Cale
Stone	Maçonnerie
Swing bridge	Pont tournant
Upstream	Amont
Yacht harbour, marina	Port de plaisance

B. METEOROLOGY — MÉTÉO

Pressure — Pression

Pressure	Pression
Forecast	Prévision
Front, warm/cold	Front, chaud/froid
High pressure	Haute pression, anticyclone
Low pressure	Dépression, bas
Ridge (high)	Crête
Rise/fall	Monter/baisser
Settled	Stationnaire
To deepen	Se creuser
To fill	Se combler
Trough (low)	Creux

Wind — Vent

Wind	Vent
Calm (F0)	Calme
Light airs (F1)	Très légère brise
Light breeze (F2)	Légère brise
Gentle breeze (F3)	Petite brise
Moderate breeze (F4)	Jolie brise
Fresh breeze (F5)	Bonne brise
Strong breeze (F6)	Vent frais
Near gale (F7)	Grand frais
Gale (F8)	Coup de vent
Severe gale (F9)	Fort coup de vent
Storm (F10)	Tempête
Back	Adonner...
Freshening	Fraîchissant
Gust	Rafale
Lull	Accalmie
Moderating	Décroissant
Squall	Grain
Veer	Vire au...

Precipitation — Précipitation

Precipitation	Précipitation
Drizzle	Bruine, crachin
Hail	Grêle
Rain	Pluie
Shower	Averse
Sleet	Neige et pluie
Thunderstorm	Orage

Cloud & Visibility — Ciel et Visibilité

Cloud & Visibility	Ciel et Visibilité
Clearing up	Éclaircie
Cloudy	Nuageux
Mist	Brume
Fog	Brouillard
Overcast	Couvert

Sea state — Mer

Sea state	Mer
Choppy	Croisée
Moderate	Agitée,
Overfalls (tide race)	Remous (violents)
Rough	Fort
Smooth	Belle
Swell	Houle

C THE BOAT / LE BATEAU

Sails/Spars/Rigging — Voiles/Mâts/Gréement

Backstay	Pataras
Batten (sail)	Latte
Boom	Bôme
Bosun's chair	Chaise de gabier
Ensign	Pavillon
Forestay	Etai
Genoa	Génois
Halyard	Drisse
Mainsail	Grand voile
Mast	Mât
Mast, to step/unstep	Mâter/démâter
Shackle	Manille
Sheet	Ecoute
Spinnaker boom	Tangon de spi
Splice	Epissure
Stainless steel	Acier inoxydable
Staysail	Trinquette
Topping lift	Balancine
Turnbuckle, bottle-screw	Ridoir
Whipping twine	Fil à surlier

On deck — Sur le pont

Anchor	Ancre
Beam, breadth	Largeur
Bilge pump	Pompe de cale
Boat hook	Gaffe
Bucket	Seau
Fender	Défense
Glass fibre (GRP)	Fibre de verre
Life jacket	Gilet de sauvetage
Oar	Aviron
Pulpit/pushpit	Balcon avant/arrière
Rudder	Gouvernail, safran
Tender	Annexe
Tiller	Barre
Varnish	Vernis
Winch handle	Manivelle de winch

Below deck — Sous le pont

Corkscrew	Tire-bouchon
Galley	Cuisine
Gas cooker	Réchaud à gaz
Matches	Allumettes
Plug	Bouchon
Saucepan	Casserole
Tap	Robinet

Electrics — Électrique

Battery (ships)	Batterie
Bulb, lamp	Ampoule
Distilled water	Eau distillée
Fuse	Fusible
Insulating tape	Adhésif isolant
Navigation lights	Feux de route
Solder	Soudure
Switch	Interrupteur

Engine — Moteur

Alternator	Alternateur
Drive-belt	Courroie
Fuel filter	Filtre à combustible
Gasket	Garniture, joint
Grease	Graisse
Injector	Injecteur
Impeller	Turbine de pompe à eau
Nut and bolt	Ecrou et boulon
Oil, lubricating	Huile
Propeller	Hélice
Sea-cock	Vanne
Spark plug	Bougie
Split pin	Goupille fendue
Starter motor	Démarreur
To bleed (air)	Purger l'air
Washer	Rondelle

Tools — Outils

Feeler gauge	Calibre d'épaisseur
File (wood/metal)	Lime
Hacksaw	Scie à métaux
Hammer	Marteau
Pliers	Pince
Screwdriver	Tournevis
Spanner, adjustable	Clé à molette
Vice	Étau

D. ASHORE / A TERRE

Nautical — Nautique

Boat hoist (BH)	Élévateur
Boatyard (BY)	Chantier naval
Chandlery (CH)	Accastillage
Coastguard (CG)	Sémaphore
Crane (C)	Grue
Customs (#)	Douane
Diesel (D)	Gas-oil, diesel
Dustbin	Poubelle
Engineer (ME)	Mécanicien
Fresh water (FW)	Eau douce, potable
Fuel	Carburant
Methylated spirits	Alcool à brûler
Paraffin	Petrole
Petrol (P)	Essence
Power point (AC)	Prise d'électricité
Shipwright (Sh)	Constructeur
Sailmaker (SM)	Voilier

Non-nautical, Shopping — Avitaillement

Airport (✈)	Aéroport
Bakery	Boulangerie
Butcher	Boucherie
Chemist	Pharmacie
Dentist	Dentiste
Doctor	Médecin
Hospital E	Hopital
Ironmonger	Quincaillerie
Launderette (▣)	Laverie
Market, food (V)	Marché
Off licence	Vins et de spiriteaux
Post Office (✉)	Bureau de Poste
Railway station (⇌)	Gare
Stamps	Timbres

E. FIRST AID / PREMIERS SOINS

Acute infection	Infection aiguë
Appendicitis	Appendicite
Burn	Brûlure
Coma	dans le coma
Coughing blood	Cracher le sang
Delirium	Delirium
Drowning	Noyade
Fracture	Fracture
Head injury	Traumisme cranien
Haemorrhage	Hémorragie
Laceration	Déchirure
Perforated ulcer	Ulcère perforé
Poisoning	Empoisonnement
Sting (insect, jellyfish)	Piqûre

15

CHERBOURG   8-15-10
Manche 49°39'·00N 01°37'·03W (Marina ent)   Rtg 1-1-2

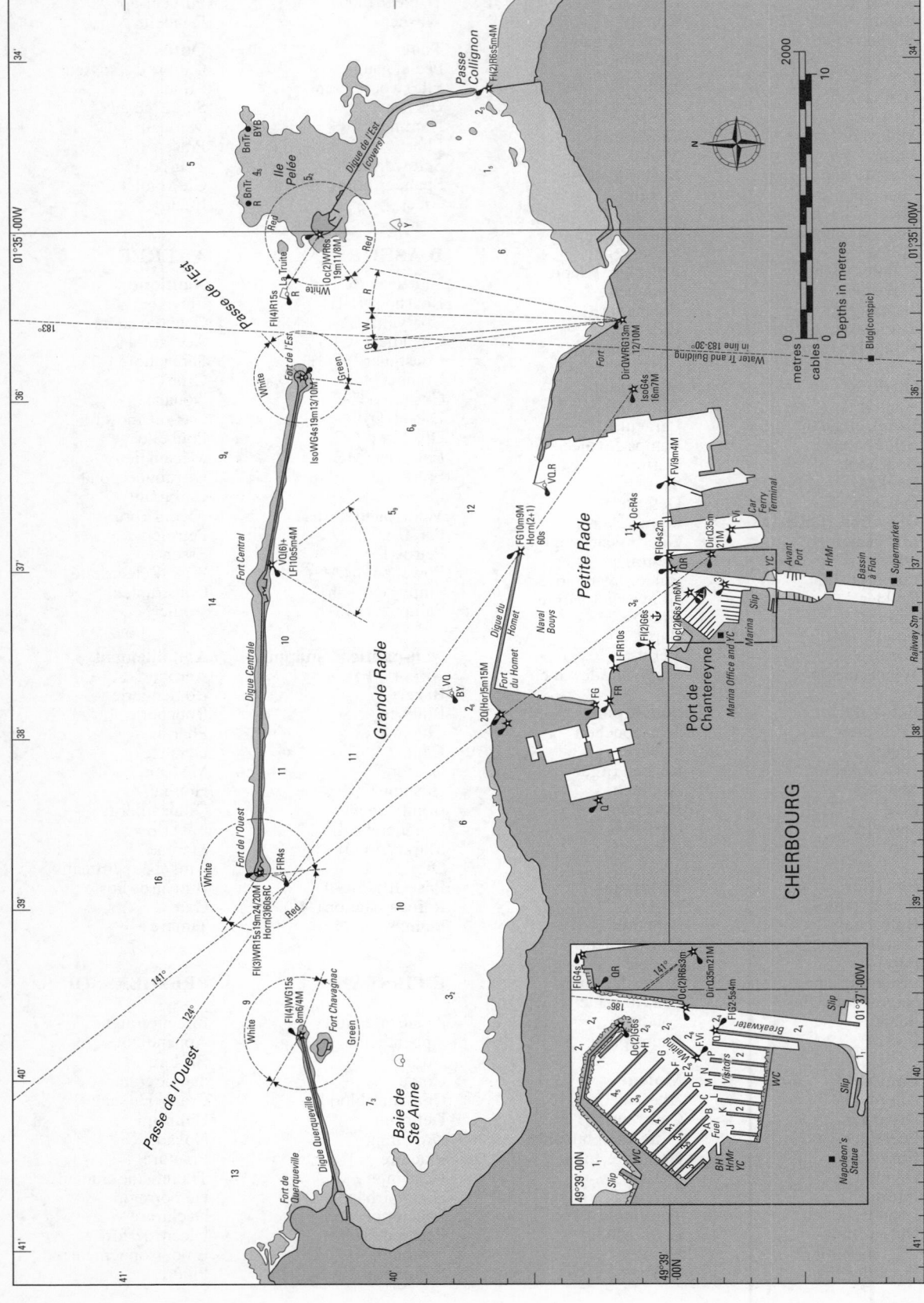

CHERBOURG continued

CHARTS
AC 2602, *1106, 2669*; SHOM 7086, 7092, 7120; ECM 528, 1014; Imray C32, C33A; Stanfords 7, 16

TIDES
−0308 Dover; ML 3·8; Duration 0535; Zone −0100

Cherbourg is a Standard Port and tidal predictions for every day of the year are given below.

SHELTER
Excellent; hbr accessible in all tides and weather. Visitors berth on pontoons M, N, P & Q, on S side of Chantereyne Marina. There is also a small craft ⚓ N of marina bkwtr. Lock into Bassin à Flot (HW±1) is normally for commercial vessels only.

NAVIGATION
WPT **Passe de l'Ouest** 49°41'·10N 01°39'·80W, 321°/141° from/to W ent, 0·85M. Note: CH1 SWM spar buoy, L Fl 10s, bears 323° from Fort de l'Ouest 3·5M.
WPT **Passe de l'Est** 49°41'·00N 01°35'·70W, 000°/180° from/to E ent, 0·65M. For coastal features from Cap de la Hague to Pte de Barfleur see 8.15.5.
There are 3 ents:
(1) Passe de l'Ouest (W ent) is the easiest. Rks extend about 80m from each bkwtr. From W, the white sector of Fort de l'Ouest lt (bearing more than 122° by day) keeps clear of offlying dangers E of Cap de la Hague.
(2) Passe de l'Est (E ent) carries 6m. Keep to W side of chan (but at least 80m off Fort de l'Est) to avoid dangers W of Ile Pelée marked by PHM buoy, Fl (4) R 15s, and by 2 unlit bn trs on N side which must be given a wide berth.
(3) Passe Collignon is a shallow (2m) chan, 93m wide, through Digue de l'Est (covers), near the shore. Not recommended except in good conditions and near HW.

LIGHTS AND MARKS
There are three powerful lts near Cherbourg:
(1) To the E, Cap Levi, Fl R 5s 36m 22M; and further E,
(2) Pte de Barfleur, Fl (2) 10s 72m 29M;
(3) To the W, Cap de la Hague, Fl 5s 48m 23M;
Further W, the lts of Alderney (Quenard Pt, Fl (4) 15s 37m 28M) and Casquets, Fl (5) 30s 37m 24M, can often be seen. See 8.14.4, 8.15.4 and 8.19.4 for details.
Fort de l'Ouest lt, at W end of Digue Centrale, Fl (3) WR 15s 19m 24/20M, vis W122°-355°, R355°-122°, RC, Reed (3) 60s. Close SSW is PHM buoy, Fl R 4s, marking shoal.
Passe de l'Ouest ldg lts 140·5°: Gare Maritime lt, Dir Q 35m 21M, in line with centre of 2Q (hor) 5m 15M at base of Digue du Homet. Grande Rade ldg lts 124°: Front FG 10m 9M, W pylon, G top, on blockhouse; rear, 0·75M from front, Iso G 4s 16m 12M, W column, B bands, W top, intens 114°-134°.
Passe de l'Est is covered by W sector (176°-183°) of Dir lt, Q WRG 13m 12/10M, at Fort des Flamands.
Inside Petite Rade steer 200° for marina ent, QR and Oc (2) G 6s. Shore lights may be confusing and mask nav lts.

RADIO TELEPHONE
Marina: call *Chantereyne* Ch 09 (0800-2300LT).
Cherbourg commercial port: call *Le Homet* Ch 12 16.
Jobourg Traffic Ch **13** 16 (H24) provides radar surveillance of the Casquets TSS/ITZ (see Fig 10 (4) and 8.15.2) and from Mont St Michel to Cap d'Antifer. Radar assistance is available on request, Ch 80, to vessels in the sector from due W to due N, from Jobourg Centre at 49°41'N 01°54'·5W. Jobourg also broadcasts traffic, nav and weather info in English and French on Ch 80 at H+20 & H+50; and at H+05 & H+35, when visibility < 2M.

TELEPHONE
Hr Mr (Port) 02·33·44·00·13; Hr Mr (Marina) 02·33·87·65·70; Aff Mar 02·33·23·36·12; CROSS 02·33·52·72·13; ⌗ 02·33·44·16·00; Météo 02·33·53·53·44; Auto 08.36.68.08.50; Police 02·33·44·20·22; 🏥 02·33·52·61·45; Dr 02·33·53·05·68; Brit Consul 01·33·44·20·13.

FACILITIES
Port de Plaisance ☎ 02.33.87.65.70, 📠 02.33.53.21.12, access H24, (900+300 visitors), FF111, Slip, AC, FW, ME, EI, Sh, BH (30 ton), CH, P & D (0800-1200; 1400-1900), ♿;
YC de Cherbourg ☎ 02·33·53·02·83, FW, R, Bar;
Services: ME, EI, Ⓔ, Sh, CH, M, SM, SHOM.
City P, D, Gaz, V, R, Bar, ✉, ⊚, Ⓑ, ⇌, ✈ (☎ 02.33.22.91.32). Ferry: Portsmouth, Southampton, Poole; Weymouth (summer only).

MINOR HARBOURS TO THE EAST OF CHERBOURG

PORT DU BECQUET, Manche, 49°39'·30N 01°32'·80W. AC *1106*; SHOM 7092. Tides as 8.15.10. Shelter is good except in winds from N to E when a strong scend occurs. Secure to S of jetty (which lies E/W). Ldg lts 186·5°: Front Dir Oc (2+1) 12s 8m 10M, W 8-sided tr, intens 183·5°-190·5°; rear, 48m from front, Dir Oc (2+1) R 12s 13m 7M, synch, also in W 8-sided tr. Facilities: very few; all facilities at Cherbourg 2·5M.

PORT DE LÉVI, Manche, 49°41'·30 N 01°28'·30W. AC *1106*; SHOM 7092, 5609; HW −0310 on Dover (UT); +0024 on Cherbourg. HW ht +0·2m on Cherbourg. Shelter good except in winds SW to N. Secure on NE side below white wall. Lt is F RG 7m 7M, G050°-109°, R109°-140°. Keep in G sector. By day keep the white wall and lt between the white marks on each pier hd. Beware lobster pots. Facilities: None. Fermanville (1·5M) has V, R, Bar.

FOR CONTINUATION EASTWARD, SEE AREA 19

Plus ça change ...

There are few things in this world that produce a greater sense of satisfaction than to sail your own boat across the sea and into a foreign port. She may be only ten tons, but you have most of the rights – as well as the responsibilities – inherent in captaining the largest ship afloat, including (bureaucracy be praised!) the right to take tobacco and liquor 'out of bond', in other words free of Customs Duty. To visit Monsieur Henri Ryst's ship-chandling office and see hard liquor, like Scotch and gin, listed at less than a quarter of the price ashore, cognac at a third, cigarettes at a fifth – it is enough to raise the morale of even the tiredest Scotsman; and then to have Monsieur Ryst apologise for not delivering until five p.m. – because he has to victual the Queen Mary! And finally the moment when all those beautiful bottles are collected in the dinghy and taken back to the ship to be stored lovingly away against the day they will be drunk, the crew all lending a willing hand amongst a litter of paper and straw.

It is for this that one puts in to Cherbourg ...... Why else, when close-by are such attractive little ports as Omonville-la-Rogue?

Harvest of Journeys: Hammond Innes/William Collins Sons & Co Ltd, 1960.

AGENTS WANTED

If you are interested in becoming our agent for any of the following ports, please write to: The Editor, Edington House, Trent, Sherborne, Dorset DT9 4SR, England – and get your free copy of the Almanac annually. You do not have to live in a port to be the agent, but should at least be a fairly regular visitor.

Plymouth	Port Haliguen
Walton-on-the-Naze	La Trinité-sur-Mer
Hopeman	Piriac
Burghead	St Nazaire/Loire
Findhorn	Pornic
Nairn	St Gilles-Croix-de-Vie
Inverness	Les Sables d'Olonne
Loch Aline	River Seudre
Craobh	Port Bloc/Gironde
Workington	Anglet/Bayonne
Lough Swilly	St Jean-de-Luz
Portbail	Hendaye
St Malo/Dinard	Grandcamp-Maisy
Le Légué/St Brieuc	Port-en-Bessin
Lampaul	Ouistreham/Caen
L'Aberildut	Dives
Douarnenez	St Valéry-en-Caux
Lorient	Dunkerque
River Étel	Emden
Le Palais (Belle Ile)	Langeoog

15

TIME ZONE –0100
(French Standard Time)
Subtract 1 hour for UT

For French Summer Time add
ONE hour in non-shaded areas

FRANCE – CHERBOURG

LAT 49°39′N   LONG 1°38′W

TIMES AND HEIGHTS OF HIGH AND LOW WATERS

YEAR **1999**

JANUARY

Day	Time / m	Time / m	Day	Time / m	Time / m
1 F	0215 1.3 / 0752 6.4	1446 1.1 / 2022 6.3	**16** SA	0224 1.9 / 0759 5.9	1447 1.6 / 2021 5.8
2 SA O	0307 1.2 / 0842 6.5	1535 0.9 / 2112 6.4	**17** SU ●	0304 1.7 / 0837 6.1	1525 1.4 / 2059 6.0
3 SU	0354 1.1 / 0928 6.6	1622 0.9 / 2158 6.4	**18** M	0343 1.5 / 0915 6.2	1604 1.2 / 2137 6.1
4 M	0439 1.2 / 1011 6.6	1705 1.0 / 2241 6.3	**19** TU	0421 1.4 / 0952 6.3	1643 1.1 / 2215 6.2
5 TU	0521 1.3 / 1052 6.4	1746 1.1 / 2322 6.1	**20** W	0500 1.3 / 1031 6.4	1721 1.0 / 2255 6.1
6 W	0602 1.5 / 1132 6.2	1826 1.4	**21** TH	0539 1.3 / 1111 6.3	1800 1.1 / 2335 6.1
7 TH	0001 5.9 / 0641 1.8	1210 5.9 / 1904 1.7	**22** F	0619 1.4 / 1152 6.2	1841 1.3
8 F	0041 5.6 / 0721 2.1	1250 5.5 / 1945 2.1	**23** SA	0017 5.9 / 0702 1.6	1235 5.9 / 1926 1.5
9 SA	0124 5.3 / 0805 2.4	1335 5.2 / 2031 2.4	**24** SU	0101 5.7 / 0751 1.9	1323 5.7 / 2017 1.8
10 SU	0215 5.0 / 0859 2.7	1431 4.9 / 2129 2.6	**25** M	0155 5.4 / 0849 2.1	1423 5.4 / 2119 2.0
11 M	0318 4.9 / 1006 2.8	1541 4.8 / 2241 2.7	**26** TU	0303 5.3 / 1000 2.3	1540 5.3 / 2234 2.2
12 TU	0430 4.9 / 1121 2.7	1656 4.8 / 2353 2.6	**27** W	0425 5.3 / 1121 2.2	1703 5.3 / 2355 2.1
13 W	0537 5.1 / 1227 2.5	1803 5.0	**28** TH	0541 5.5 / 1237 1.9	1817 5.5
14 TH	0053 2.4 / 0631 5.3	1321 2.2 / 1856 5.3	**29** F	0105 1.9 / 0646 5.8	1341 1.6 / 1920 5.8
15 F	0142 2.1 / 0718 5.6	1406 1.9 / 1941 5.6	**30** SA	0205 1.6 / 0743 6.1	1437 1.3 / 2015 6.1
			31 SU O	0258 1.4 / 0833 6.3	1526 1.1 / 2103 6.3

FEBRUARY

Day	Time / m	Time / m	Day	Time / m	Time / m
1 M	0344 1.2 / 0917 6.5	1609 0.9 / 2145 6.3	**16** TU ●	0325 1.3 / 0859 6.3	1547 1.0 / 2122 6.2
2 TU	0426 1.2 / 0957 6.5	1649 0.9 / 2224 6.3	**17** W	0406 1.1 / 0939 6.5	1627 0.8 / 2202 6.4
3 W	0504 1.2 / 1034 6.5	1726 1.0 / 2300 6.2	**18** TH	0446 1.0 / 1019 6.6	1706 0.7 / 2241 6.4
4 TH	0539 1.3 / 1109 6.3	1800 1.2 / 2333 6.0	**19** F	0525 0.9 / 1059 6.6	1745 0.7 / 2320 6.4
5 F	0613 1.5 / 1142 6.0	1832 1.5	**20** SA	0605 1.0 / 1139 6.5	1825 0.9 / 2359 6.2
6 SA	0006 5.8 / 0645 1.8	1214 5.7 / 1905 1.8	**21** SU	0646 1.2 / 1219 6.2	1907 1.2
7 SU	0038 5.5 / 0721 2.1	1247 5.4 / 1940 2.2	**22** M	0040 5.9 / 0732 1.6	1304 5.8 / 1955 1.7
8 M	0114 5.2 / 0801 2.4	1327 5.0 / 2024 2.5	**23** TU	0128 5.6 / 0826 1.9	1400 5.4 / 2054 2.1
9 TU	0202 4.9 / 0855 2.7	1425 4.7 / 2124 2.8	**24** W	0233 5.2 / 0935 2.2	1518 5.1 / 2211 2.4
10 W	0313 4.7 / 1009 2.8	1551 4.6 / 2248 2.9	**25** TH	0402 5.1 / 1102 2.3	1653 5.1 / 2341 2.4
11 TH	0443 4.7 / 1135 2.7	1723 4.7	**26** F	0529 5.2 / 1227 2.1	1813 5.3
12 F	0010 2.7 / 0556 5.0	1245 2.4 / 1828 5.0	**27** SA	0058 2.1 / 0638 5.6	1334 1.7 / 1916 5.6
13 SA	0111 2.4 / 0651 5.4	1338 2.0 / 1918 5.4	**28** SU	0159 1.8 / 0735 5.9	1428 1.4 / 2007 5.9
14 SU	0200 2.0 / 0736 5.7	1424 1.6 / 2001 5.7			

MARCH

Day	Time / m	Time / m	Day	Time / m	Time / m
1 M	0249 1.5 / 0822 6.2	1514 1.1 / 2050 6.2	**16** TU	0219 1.6 / 0755 6.0	1441 1.2 / 2020 6.1
2 TU O	0331 1.3 / 0902 6.4	1553 1.0 / 2128 6.3	**17** W ●	0303 1.2 / 0838 6.4	1524 0.8 / 2102 6.4
3 W	0408 1.1 / 0939 6.4	1629 0.9 / 2202 6.3	**18** TH	0346 0.9 / 0921 6.6	1606 0.6 / 2143 6.6
4 TH	0442 1.1 / 1012 6.4	1701 1.0 / 2233 6.2	**19** F	0427 0.7 / 1002 6.8	1646 0.5 / 2223 6.6
5 F	0514 1.2 / 1044 6.3	1732 1.1 / 2303 6.1	**20** SA	0508 0.6 / 1043 6.8	1726 0.6 / 2303 6.6
6 SA	0544 1.3 / 1113 6.1	1801 1.4 / 2331 5.9	**21** SU	0548 0.7 / 1123 6.6	1807 0.8 / 2341 6.4
7 SU	0613 1.4 / 1141 5.8	1830 1.7 / 2358 5.6	**22** M	0630 1.0 / 1204 6.3	1850 1.2
8 M	0644 1.6 / 1209 5.5	1900 2.0	**23** TU	0022 6.0 / 0715 1.4	1249 5.8 / 1937 1.7
9 TU	0028 5.3 / 0719 2.2	1242 5.1 / 1937 2.4	**24** W	0108 5.6 / 0808 1.8	1344 5.4 / 2036 2.2
10 W	0106 5.0 / 0803 2.5	1329 4.8 / 2026 2.7	**25** TH	0211 5.2 / 0918 2.2	1506 5.0 / 2157 2.5
11 TH	0203 4.7 / 0906 2.8	1446 4.5 / 2143 2.9	**26** F	0343 5.0 / 1048 2.3	1646 4.9 / 2331 2.5
12 F	0337 4.6 / 1035 2.8	1637 4.5 / 2321 2.9	**27** SA	0515 5.1 / 1214 2.1	1806 5.2
13 SA	0515 4.8 / 1202 2.5	1757 4.9	**28** SU	0047 2.2 / 0625 5.4	1320 1.8 / 1904 5.6
14 SU	0037 2.5 / 0620 5.2	1305 2.1 / 1851 5.3	**29** M	0146 1.9 / 0719 5.7	1412 1.5 / 1949 5.9
15 M	0132 2.0 / 0710 5.6	1355 1.6 / 1937 5.7	**30** TU	0232 1.6 / 0803 6.0	1454 1.3 / 2029 6.1
			31 W O	0311 1.3 / 0841 6.2	1531 1.1 / 2103 6.2

APRIL

Day	Time / m	Time / m	Day	Time / m	Time / m
1 TH	0346 1.2 / 0916 6.3	1603 1.1 / 2135 6.2	**16** F ●	0321 0.8 / 0857 6.6	1541 0.5 / 2119 6.6
2 F	0417 1.2 / 0948 6.3	1634 1.1 / 2205 6.2	**17** SA	0405 0.6 / 0941 6.8	1624 0.4 / 2202 6.7
3 SA	0447 1.2 / 1017 6.2	1703 1.2 / 2233 6.1	**18** SU	0448 0.5 / 1025 6.8	1707 0.5 / 2243 6.7
4 SU	0516 1.3 / 1045 6.0	1731 1.4 / 2300 5.9	**19** M	0531 0.6 / 1108 6.6	1750 0.8 / 2324 6.4
5 M	0545 1.5 / 1112 5.8	1759 1.7 / 2326 5.7	**20** TU	0615 0.9 / 1151 6.3	1834 1.3
6 TU	0615 1.7 / 1141 5.5	1829 2.0 / 2355 5.5	**21** W	0007 6.1 / 0702 1.3	1238 5.8 / 1924 1.8
7 W	0648 2.0 / 1214 5.2	1903 2.3	**22** TH	0054 5.6 / 0756 1.8	1335 5.3 / 2024 2.3
8 TH	0031 5.2 / 0728 2.3	1257 4.9 / 1948 2.6	**23** F	0156 5.2 / 0904 2.1	1454 5.0 / 2143 2.6
9 F	0122 4.8 / 0824 2.6	1404 4.6 / 2057 2.9	**24** SA	0321 5.0 / 1028 2.3	1626 4.9 / 2309 2.5
10 SA	0243 4.6 / 0945 2.7	1546 4.6 / 2232 2.9	**25** SU	0447 5.0 / 1148 2.2	1741 5.2
11 SU	0425 4.7 / 1114 2.5	1716 4.8 / 2355 2.5	**26** M	0021 2.3 / 0556 5.3	1251 1.9 / 1836 5.5
12 M	0540 5.1 / 1225 2.1	1816 5.3	**27** TU	0118 2.0 / 0650 5.6	1342 1.7 / 1920 5.7
13 TU	0057 2.1 / 0636 5.5	1320 1.6 / 1905 5.7	**28** W	0204 1.7 / 0734 5.8	1425 1.5 / 1959 5.9
14 W	0149 1.6 / 0725 6.0	1410 1.1 / 1951 6.1	**29** TH	0244 1.5 / 0814 6.0	1501 1.3 / 2034 6.1
15 TH	0236 1.1 / 0812 6.3	1456 0.8 / 2036 6.4	**30** F O	0319 1.4 / 0849 6.0	1535 1.3 / 2107 6.1

Chart Datum: 3·33 metres below Lallemand System (Mean Sea Level, Marseilles)

TIME ZONE –0100
(French Standard Time)
Subtract 1 hour for UT
For French Summer Time add ONE hour in non-shaded areas

FRANCE – CHERBOURG

LAT 49°39′N   LONG 1°38′W

TIMES AND HEIGHTS OF HIGH AND LOW WATERS

YEAR **1999**

MAY

Day	Time	m	Day	Time	m
1 SA	0351 / 0922 / 1605 / 2137	1.3 / 6.1 / 1.3 / 6.1	**16** SU	0344 / 0921 / 1603 / 2141	0.6 / 6.7 / 0.6 / 6.7
2 SU	0421 / 0952 / 1635 / 2205	1.3 / 6.0 / 1.4 / 6.0	**17** M	0430 / 1008 / 1649 / 2225	0.6 / 6.6 / 0.7 / 6.6
3 M	0451 / 1021 / 1704 / 2233	1.5 / 5.9 / 1.5 / 5.9	**18** TU	0516 / 1054 / 1734 / 2309	0.6 / 6.5 / 1.0 / 6.4
4 TU	0521 / 1050 / 1734 / 2303	1.5 / 5.8 / 1.7 / 5.8	**19** W	0602 / 1140 / 1821 / 2354	0.9 / 6.2 / 1.4 / 6.1
5 W	0552 / 1122 / 1805 / 2335	1.6 / 5.6 / 1.9 / 5.6	**20** TH	0651 / 1228 / 1912	1.2 / 5.8 / 1.8
6 TH	0626 / 1158 / 1840	1.8 / 5.3 / 2.2	**21** F	0043 / 0744 / 1323 / 2010	5.7 / 1.7 / 5.4 / 2.2
7 F	0013 / 0707 / 1241 / 1926	5.3 / 2.1 / 5.0 / 2.5	**22** SA	0140 / 0845 / 1430 / 2118	5.4 / 2.0 / 5.1 / 2.5
8 SA	0101 / 0759 / 1340 / 2029	5.0 / 2.3 / 4.8 / 2.7	**23** SU	0250 / 0955 / 1547 / 2232	5.1 / 2.2 / 5.0 / 2.5
9 SU	0209 / 0909 / 1502 / 2151	4.8 / 2.4 / 4.7 / 2.7	**24** M	0404 / 1106 / 1657 / 2339	5.0 / 2.2 / 5.1 / 2.4
10 M	0334 / 1029 / 1627 / 2312	4.8 / 2.3 / 4.9 / 2.6	**25** TU	0512 / 1209 / 1755	5.1 / 2.1 / 5.3
11 TU	0452 / 1141 / 1734	5.1 / 2.0 / 5.3	**26** W	0038 / 0610 / 1302 / 1843	2.2 / 5.3 / 1.9 / 5.5
12 W	0018 / 0555 / 1243 / 1829	2.1 / 5.5 / 1.6 / 5.7	**27** TH	0128 / 0700 / 1348 / 1925	2.0 / 5.5 / 1.8 / 5.7
13 TH	0115 / 0650 / 1337 / 1920	1.6 / 5.9 / 1.2 / 6.1	**28** F	0211 / 0743 / 1429 / 2003	1.8 / 5.7 / 1.6 / 5.9
14 F	0207 / 0742 / 1428 / 2008	1.2 / 6.2 / 0.9 / 6.4	**29** SA	0250 / 0822 / 1505 / 2039	1.6 / 5.8 / 1.6 / 6.0
15 SA ●	0256 / 0832 / 1516 / 2055	0.9 / 6.5 / 0.7 / 6.6	**30** SU O	0324 / 0857 / 1538 / 2111	1.5 / 5.8 / 1.5 / 6.0
			31 M	0358 / 0930 / 1611 / 2142	1.4 / 5.8 / 1.5 / 6.0

JUNE

Day	Time	m	Day	Time	m
1 TU	0430 / 1001 / 1642 / 2213	1.4 / 5.8 / 1.6 / 5.9	**16** W	0503 / 1042 / 1721 / 2256	0.7 / 6.4 / 1.1 / 6.4
2 W	0503 / 1033 / 1715 / 2246	1.5 / 5.7 / 1.7 / 5.9	**17** TH	0550 / 1129 / 1808 / 2342	0.9 / 6.2 / 1.3 / 6.2
3 TH	0536 / 1109 / 1749 / 2322	1.6 / 5.6 / 1.9 / 5.7	**18** F	0637 / 1215 / 1856	1.2 / 5.9 / 1.7
4 F	0612 / 1147 / 1826	1.7 / 5.5 / 2.0	**19** SA	0027 / 0725 / 1303 / 1946	5.9 / 1.5 / 5.6 / 2.0
5 SA	0003 / 0653 / 1231 / 1911	5.5 / 1.8 / 5.3 / 2.2	**20** SU	0116 / 0815 / 1355 / 2041	5.6 / 1.9 / 5.3 / 2.3
6 SU	0049 / 0741 / 1322 / 2008	5.3 / 2.0 / 5.1 / 2.4	**21** M	0210 / 0911 / 1454 / 2143	5.2 / 2.1 / 5.1 / 2.5
7 M	0145 / 0841 / 1426 / 2117	5.1 / 2.1 / 5.0 / 2.5	**22** TU	0312 / 1013 / 1559 / 2247	5.0 / 2.3 / 5.0 / 2.5
8 TU	0253 / 0950 / 1540 / 2231	5.1 / 2.1 / 5.1 / 2.3	**23** W	0418 / 1117 / 1703 / 2350	5.0 / 2.2 / 5.1 / 2.4
9 W	0406 / 1101 / 1650 / 2340	5.2 / 1.9 / 5.3 / 2.1	**24** TH	0523 / 1216 / 1800	5.0 / 2.2 / 5.3
10 TH	0515 / 1206 / 1752	5.4 / 1.7 / 5.6	**25** F	0047 / 0622 / 1310 / 1850	2.2 / 5.2 / 2.1 / 5.5
11 F	0043 / 0617 / 1307 / 1849	1.7 / 5.8 / 1.4 / 6.0	**26** SA	0137 / 0712 / 1356 / 1933	2.0 / 5.4 / 1.9 / 5.7
12 SA	0140 / 0715 / 1402 / 1942	1.3 / 6.1 / 1.1 / 6.3	**27** SU	0221 / 0756 / 1437 / 2013	1.8 / 5.5 / 1.8 / 5.8
13 SU ●	0234 / 0811 / 1455 / 2034	1.0 / 6.3 / 0.9 / 6.5	**28** M O	0300 / 0835 / 1514 / 2049	1.6 / 5.7 / 1.7 / 5.9
14 M	0326 / 0904 / 1545 / 2123	0.8 / 6.5 / 0.9 / 6.6	**29** TU	0336 / 0911 / 1550 / 2123	1.5 / 5.8 / 1.6 / 6.0
15 TU	0415 / 0954 / 1634 / 2210	0.7 / 6.5 / 0.9 / 6.6	**30** W	0412 / 0945 / 1625 / 2157	1.4 / 5.8 / 1.6 / 6.0

JULY

Day	Time	m	Day	Time	m
1 TH	0447 / 1020 / 1700 / 2233	1.4 / 5.8 / 1.6 / 6.0	**16** F	0535 / 1113 / 1751 / 2324	0.9 / 6.2 / 1.3 / 6.3
2 F	0523 / 1056 / 1736 / 2311	1.4 / 5.8 / 1.7 / 5.9	**17** SA	0617 / 1154 / 1833	1.1 / 6.0 / 1.5
3 SA	0600 / 1136 / 1815 / 2352	1.4 / 5.7 / 1.8 / 5.8	**18** SU	0005 / 0658 / 1234 / 1914	6.0 / 1.4 / 5.7 / 1.8
4 SU	0639 / 1217 / 1858	1.5 / 5.6 / 1.9	**19** M	0045 / 0738 / 1314 / 1958	5.7 / 1.7 / 5.4 / 2.1
5 M	0034 / 0724 / 1302 / 1947	5.6 / 1.7 / 5.4 / 2.1	**20** TU	0127 / 0822 / 1400 / 2047	5.4 / 2.1 / 5.2 / 2.4
6 TU	0122 / 0815 / 1354 / 2046	5.4 / 1.8 / 5.3 / 2.2	**21** W	0216 / 0914 / 1455 / 2148	5.1 / 2.4 / 5.0 / 2.6
7 W	0219 / 0915 / 1457 / 2154	5.3 / 1.9 / 5.2 / 2.2	**22** TH	0319 / 1018 / 1604 / 2259	4.8 / 2.6 / 4.9 / 2.6
8 TH	0327 / 1024 / 1610 / 2307	5.3 / 2.0 / 5.3 / 2.1	**23** F	0434 / 1128 / 1715	4.8 / 2.6 / 5.0
9 F	0442 / 1135 / 1722	5.3 / 1.9 / 5.5	**24** SA	0007 / 0546 / 1233 / 1816	2.5 / 4.9 / 2.4 / 5.2
10 SA	0016 / 0553 / 1242 / 1826	1.8 / 5.6 / 1.6 / 5.8	**25** SU	0105 / 0645 / 1326 / 1906	2.3 / 5.1 / 2.2 / 5.4
11 SU	0119 / 0658 / 1344 / 1925	1.5 / 5.8 / 1.4 / 6.1	**26** M	0154 / 0733 / 1412 / 1949	2.1 / 5.4 / 2.0 / 5.7
12 M	0218 / 0758 / 1440 / 2019	1.2 / 6.1 / 1.2 / 6.4	**27** TU	0236 / 0815 / 1453 / 2029	1.7 / 5.6 / 1.8 / 5.9
13 TU ●	0312 / 0852 / 1532 / 2110	0.9 / 6.3 / 1.1 / 6.5	**28** W O	0315 / 0853 / 1531 / 2106	1.5 / 5.8 / 1.6 / 6.0
14 W	0403 / 0943 / 1621 / 2157	0.8 / 6.4 / 1.0 / 6.5	**29** TH	0353 / 0929 / 1608 / 2142	1.3 / 5.9 / 1.5 / 6.2
15 TH	0450 / 1030 / 1707 / 2242	0.8 / 6.3 / 1.1 / 6.5	**30** F	0430 / 1005 / 1645 / 2219	1.2 / 6.0 / 1.4 / 6.2
			31 SA	0507 / 1042 / 1722 / 2257	1.1 / 6.0 / 1.4 / 6.2

AUGUST

Day	Time	m	Day	Time	m
1 SU	0544 / 1120 / 1800 / 2337	1.1 / 6.0 / 1.4 / 6.1	**16** M	0625 / 1159 / 1837	1.3 / 5.9 / 1.7
2 M	0623 / 1200 / 1841	1.2 / 5.9 / 1.6	**17** TU	0009 / 0658 / 1232 / 1912	5.8 / 1.7 / 5.6 / 2.0
3 TU	0017 / 0704 / 1240 / 1926	5.9 / 1.4 / 5.7 / 1.8	**18** W	0043 / 0733 / 1307 / 1953	5.5 / 2.1 / 5.3 / 2.4
4 W	0100 / 0750 / 1326 / 2018	5.7 / 1.6 / 5.5 / 2.0	**19** TH	0122 / 0815 / 1351 / 2045	5.1 / 2.4 / 5.0 / 2.7
5 TH	0151 / 0845 / 1423 / 2123	5.5 / 1.9 / 5.3 / 2.2	**20** F	0215 / 0913 / 1456 / 2158	4.8 / 2.8 / 4.8 / 2.8
6 F	0257 / 0954 / 1539 / 2240	5.3 / 2.1 / 5.2 / 2.2	**21** SA	0338 / 1034 / 1626 / 2323	4.6 / 2.9 / 4.7 / 2.8
7 SA	0421 / 1113 / 1702 / 2359	5.2 / 2.1 / 5.4 / 2.0	**22** SU	0512 / 1156 / 1744	4.7 / 2.8 / 4.9
8 SU	0542 / 1228 / 1814	5.4 / 2.0 / 5.6	**23** M	0033 / 0619 / 1259 / 1840	2.5 / 5.0 / 2.5 / 5.3
9 M	0108 / 0651 / 1333 / 1915	1.7 / 5.7 / 1.7 / 6.0	**24** TU	0126 / 0709 / 1348 / 1925	2.1 / 5.3 / 2.1 / 5.6
10 TU	0208 / 0751 / 1431 / 2010	1.3 / 6.0 / 1.4 / 6.3	**25** W	0211 / 0751 / 1430 / 2006	1.8 / 5.6 / 1.8 / 5.9
11 W ●	0302 / 0844 / 1521 / 2059	1.1 / 6.2 / 1.2 / 6.5	**26** TH	0252 / 0831 / 1509 / 2045	1.5 / 5.9 / 1.5 / 6.2
12 TH	0350 / 0931 / 1607 / 2143	0.9 / 6.3 / 1.1 / 6.6	**27** F O	0331 / 0909 / 1548 / 2123	1.2 / 6.1 / 1.3 / 6.4
13 F	0434 / 1012 / 1649 / 2223	0.9 / 6.4 / 1.1 / 6.5	**28** SA	0409 / 0946 / 1626 / 2201	1.0 / 6.2 / 1.2 / 6.5
14 SA	0514 / 1050 / 1727 / 2301	0.9 / 6.3 / 1.2 / 6.4	**29** SU	0447 / 1023 / 1704 / 2239	0.9 / 6.3 / 1.1 / 6.5
15 SU	0551 / 1126 / 1803 / 2336	1.1 / 6.1 / 1.4 / 6.2	**30** M	0524 / 1101 / 1742 / 2318	0.9 / 6.3 / 1.1 / 6.4
			31 TU	0602 / 1138 / 1821 / 2357	1.0 / 6.2 / 1.3 / 6.2

15

Chart Datum: 3·33 metres below Lallemand System (Mean Sea Level, Marseilles)

TIME ZONE –0100
(French Standard Time)
Subtract 1 hour for UT

For French Summer Time add
ONE hour in non-shaded areas

FRANCE – CHERBOURG

LAT 49°39′N   LONG 1°38′W

TIMES AND HEIGHTS OF HIGH AND LOW WATERS   YEAR **1999**

SEPTEMBER

Day	Time	m	Day	Time	m
1 W	0642 / 1217 / 1904	1.3 / 5.9 / 1.6	16 TH	0001 / 0650 / 1219 / 1907	5.5 / 2.1 / 5.4 / 2.3
2 TH	0039 / 0727 / 1300 / 1955	5.9 / 1.6 / 5.7 / 1.9	17 F	0034 / 0725 / 1255 / 1950	5.2 / 2.5 / 5.1 / 2.6
3 F	0130 / 0821 / 1357 / 2059	5.5 / 2.0 / 5.4 / 2.2	18 SA	0119 / 0814 / 1350 / 2054	4.8 / 2.9 / 4.8 / 2.9
4 SA	0239 / 0932 / 1517 / 2224	5.2 / 2.4 / 5.1 / 2.4	19 SU	0235 / 0931 / 1523 / 2229	4.5 / 3.1 / 4.6 / 2.9
5 SU	0414 / 1102 / 1651 / 2351	5.1 / 2.4 / 5.2 / 2.2	20 M	0431 / 1113 / 1705 / 2355	4.5 / 3.0 / 4.8 / 2.7
6 M	0541 / 1223 / 1807	5.3 / 2.2 / 5.5	21 TU	0549 / 1226 / 1808	4.9 / 2.7 / 5.2
7 TU	0102 / 0649 / 1328 / 1908	1.8 / 5.6 / 1.8 / 5.9	22 W	0054 / 0640 / 1319 / 1856	2.2 / 5.3 / 2.2 / 5.6
8 W	0200 / 0744 / 1422 / 1959	1.4 / 6.0 / 1.5 / 6.2	23 TH	0141 / 0723 / 1402 / 1939	1.8 / 5.7 / 1.8 / 6.0
9 TH	0250 / 0830 / 1508 / ● 2043	1.1 / 6.2 / 1.3 / 6.5	24 F	0223 / 0803 / 1443 / 2019	1.4 / 6.0 / 1.4 / 6.3
10 F	0333 / 0911 / 1549 / 2123	1.0 / 6.4 / 1.2 / 6.6	25 SA	0304 / 0843 / 1523 / ○ 2059	1.1 / 6.3 / 1.1 / 6.5
11 SA	0412 / 0948 / 1625 / 2159	0.9 / 6.4 / 1.1 / 6.5	26 SU	0344 / 0922 / 1603 / 2138	0.8 / 6.5 / 0.9 / 6.7
12 SU	0447 / 1022 / 1659 / 2232	1.0 / 6.3 / 1.2 / 6.4	27 M	0423 / 1000 / 1642 / 2218	0.7 / 6.6 / 0.9 / 6.7
13 M	0519 / 1053 / 1731 / 2303	1.1 / 6.2 / 1.4 / 6.2	28 TU	0502 / 1038 / 1722 / 2258	0.7 / 6.5 / 0.9 / 6.6
14 TU	0550 / 1122 / 1801 / 2332	1.4 / 6.0 / 1.6 / 5.9	29 W	0541 / 1116 / 1802 / 2338	0.9 / 6.4 / 1.1 / 6.3
15 W	0619 / 1150 / 1832	1.7 / 5.7 / 1.9	30 TH	0622 / 1156 / 1846	1.3 / 6.1 / 1.5

OCTOBER

Day	Time	m	Day	Time	m
1 F	0022 / 0708 / 1240 / 1937	5.9 / 1.7 / 5.8 / 1.9	16 SA	0648 / 1215 / 1911	2.5 / 5.2 / 2.5
2 SA	0115 / 0804 / 1338 / 2044	5.5 / 2.2 / 5.4 / 2.3	17 SU	0041 / 0730 / 1304 / 2005	4.9 / 2.8 / 4.9 / 2.8
3 SU	0230 / 0920 / 1503 / 2214	5.1 / 2.6 / 5.1 / 2.4	18 M	0147 / 0837 / 1423 / 2128	4.6 / 3.1 / 4.7 / 2.9
4 M	0412 / 1056 / 1642 / 2344	5.0 / 2.6 / 5.2 / 2.2	19 TU	0333 / 1017 / 1609 / 2303	4.6 / 3.1 / 4.7 / 2.7
5 TU	0537 / 1216 / 1757	5.3 / 2.3 / 5.5	20 W	0505 / 1143 / 1725	4.8 / 2.8 / 5.1
6 W	0052 / 0639 / 1317 / 1854	1.9 / 5.6 / 1.9 / 5.9	21 TH	0012 / 0601 / 1241 / 1818	2.3 / 5.3 / 2.3 / 5.5
7 TH	0146 / 0727 / 1406 / 1940	1.5 / 6.0 / 1.6 / 6.2	22 F	0104 / 0647 / 1329 / 1904	1.9 / 5.7 / 1.8 / 5.9
8 F	0231 / 0809 / 1448 / 2021	1.2 / 6.2 / 1.4 / 6.4	23 SA	0150 / 0730 / 1413 / 1948	1.4 / 6.1 / 1.4 / 6.3
9 SA	0311 / 0846 / 1526 / ● 2058	1.1 / 6.4 / 1.3 / 6.5	24 SU	0233 / 0812 / 1456 / ○ 2031	1.1 / 6.4 / 1.1 / 6.6
10 SU	0346 / 0919 / 1559 / 2131	1.1 / 6.3 / 1.2 / 6.4	25 M	0316 / 0854 / 1539 / 2113	0.8 / 6.6 / 0.9 / 6.8
11 M	0418 / 0950 / 1631 / 2202	1.2 / 6.3 / 1.3 / 6.3	26 TU	0358 / 0934 / 1621 / 2156	0.7 / 6.7 / 0.8 / 6.8
12 TU	0448 / 1019 / 1700 / 2231	1.5 / 6.2 / 1.4 / 6.1	27 W	0440 / 1015 / 1703 / 2239	0.7 / 6.7 / 0.8 / 6.7
13 W	0517 / 1047 / 1730 / 2259	1.5 / 6.1 / 1.6 / 5.9	28 TH	0522 / 1056 / 1746 / 2323	1.0 / 6.5 / 1.0 / 6.4
14 TH	0545 / 1113 / 1759 / 2327	1.8 / 5.8 / 1.8 / 5.6	29 F	0606 / 1139 / 1832	1.3 / 6.2 / 1.4
15 F	0615 / 1141 / 1832 / 2358	2.1 / 5.5 / 2.2 / 5.3	30 SA	0010 / 0655 / 1226 / 1925	6.0 / 1.8 / 5.9 / 1.8
			31 SU	0106 / 0753 / 1325 / 2032	5.5 / 2.3 / 5.4 / 2.2

NOVEMBER

Day	Time	m	Day	Time	m
1 M	0221 / 0910 / 1447 / 2159	5.2 / 2.6 / 5.2 / 2.4	16 TU	0115 / 0801 / 1342 / 2040	4.8 / 2.9 / 4.9 / 2.7
2 TU	0356 / 1040 / 1618 / 2323	5.1 / 2.7 / 5.4 / 2.3	17 W	0236 / 0921 / 1507 / 2203	4.7 / 3.0 / 4.8 / 2.6
3 W	0515 / 1155 / 1731	5.3 / 2.4 / 5.4	18 TH	0404 / 1047 / 1628 / 2319	4.9 / 2.8 / 5.0 / 2.4
4 TH	0028 / 0613 / 1254 / 1827	2.0 / 5.6 / 2.1 / 5.7	19 F	0512 / 1156 / 1732	5.2 / 2.4 / 5.4
5 F	0120 / 0659 / 1342 / 1913	1.7 / 5.9 / 1.8 / 6.0	20 SA	0021 / 0606 / 1252 / 1825	1.9 / 5.6 / 1.9 / 5.8
6 SA	0204 / 0740 / 1423 / 1954	1.5 / 6.1 / 1.6 / 6.1	21 SU	0114 / 0654 / 1342 / 1915	1.5 / 6.0 / 1.5 / 6.2
7 SU	0243 / 0816 / 1459 / 2031	1.4 / 6.2 / 1.5 / 6.2	22 M	0203 / 0740 / 1429 / 2003	1.2 / 6.4 / 1.1 / 6.5
8 M	0317 / 0849 / 1533 / ● 2104	1.4 / 6.3 / 1.4 / 6.2	23 TU	0250 / 0826 / 1516 / ○ 2050	0.9 / 6.6 / 0.9 / 6.7
9 TU	0349 / 0920 / 1604 / 2135	1.4 / 6.3 / 1.4 / 6.2	24 W	0336 / 0911 / 1602 / 2137	0.8 / 6.8 / 0.8 / 6.7
10 W	0420 / 0949 / 1635 / 2204	1.5 / 6.2 / 1.5 / 6.0	25 TH	0421 / 0956 / 1647 / 2224	0.8 / 6.8 / 0.8 / 6.6
11 TH	0449 / 1017 / 1705 / 2233	1.6 / 6.1 / 1.6 / 5.9	26 F	0507 / 1041 / 1734 / 2312	1.0 / 6.6 / 1.0 / 6.4
12 F	0519 / 1045 / 1735 / 2303	1.9 / 5.9 / 1.8 / 5.7	27 SA	0554 / 1126 / 1822	1.4 / 6.3 / 1.3
13 SA	0549 / 1116 / 1808 / 2337	2.1 / 5.7 / 2.0 / 5.4	28 SU	0001 / 0644 / 1215 / 1915	6.0 / 1.8 / 6.0 / 1.7
14 SU	0622 / 1152 / 1846	2.4 / 5.4 / 2.3	29 M	0056 / 0741 / 1310 / 2016	5.6 / 2.2 / 5.6 / 2.0
15 M	0019 / 0703 / 1237 / 1934	5.1 / 2.7 / 5.1 / 2.5	30 TU	0202 / 0848 / 1418 / 2128	5.3 / 2.5 / 5.3 / 2.3

DECEMBER

Day	Time	m	Day	Time	m
1 W	0318 / 1004 / 1535 / 2243	5.1 / 2.6 / 5.2 / 2.3	16 TH	0151 / 0838 / 1416 / 2112	5.0 / 2.7 / 5.1 / 2.4
2 TH	0432 / 1116 / 1647 / 2349	5.2 / 2.5 / 5.2 / 2.2	17 F	0303 / 0952 / 1530 / 2225	5.0 / 2.6 / 5.1 / 2.3
3 F	0533 / 1218 / 1749	5.4 / 2.3 / 5.4	18 SA	0416 / 1107 / 1642 / 2336	5.2 / 2.4 / 5.3 / 2.0
4 SA	0045 / 0623 / 1310 / 1840	2.1 / 5.6 / 2.1 / 5.6	19 SU	0522 / 1213 / 1746	5.5 / 2.1 / 5.6
5 SU	0132 / 0707 / 1354 / 1925	1.9 / 5.8 / 1.9 / 5.8	20 M	0038 / 0620 / 1312 / 1845	1.7 / 5.9 / 1.7 / 6.0
6 M	0213 / 0746 / 1433 / 2004	1.7 / 6.0 / 1.7 / 5.9	21 TU	0135 / 0713 / 1406 / 1940	1.4 / 6.2 / 1.3 / 6.3
7 TU	0250 / 0822 / 1509 / ● 2040	1.7 / 6.1 / 1.6 / 6.0	22 W	0228 / 0804 / 1458 / ○ 2033	1.1 / 6.5 / 1.0 / 6.5
8 W	0324 / 0855 / 1542 / 2114	1.6 / 6.1 / 1.5 / 6.0	23 TH	0319 / 0854 / 1548 / 2124	1.0 / 6.7 / 0.8 / 6.6
9 TH	0357 / 0926 / 1614 / 2144	1.7 / 6.1 / 1.5 / 5.9	24 F	0408 / 0942 / 1636 / 2214	1.0 / 6.7 / 0.7 / 6.6
10 F	0428 / 0956 / 1646 / 2215	1.7 / 6.1 / 1.6 / 5.9	25 SA	0456 / 1029 / 1724 / 2302	1.0 / 6.7 / 0.8 / 6.4
11 SA	0500 / 1027 / 1719 / 2248	1.8 / 6.0 / 1.7 / 5.7	26 SU	0544 / 1116 / 1812 / 2350	1.3 / 6.5 / 1.1 / 6.1
12 SU	0532 / 1101 / 1752 / 2324	2.0 / 5.8 / 1.8 / 5.6	27 M	0632 / 1202 / 1900	1.6 / 6.2 / 1.4
13 M	0607 / 1138 / 1829	2.2 / 5.6 / 2.0	28 TU	0038 / 0721 / 1249 / 1950	5.8 / 1.9 / 5.9 / 1.8
14 TU	0004 / 0646 / 1220 / 1913	5.3 / 2.4 / 5.4 / 2.2	29 W	0129 / 0813 / 1341 / 2044	5.5 / 2.2 / 5.5 / 2.1
15 W	0052 / 0736 / 1312 / 2006	5.1 / 2.6 / 5.2 / 2.3	30 TH	0226 / 0912 / 1441 / 2146	5.2 / 2.5 / 5.2 / 2.4
			31 F	0330 / 1019 / 1549 / 2253	5.1 / 2.6 / 5.0 / 2.5

Chart Datum: 3·33 metres below Lallemand System (Mean Sea Level, Marseilles)

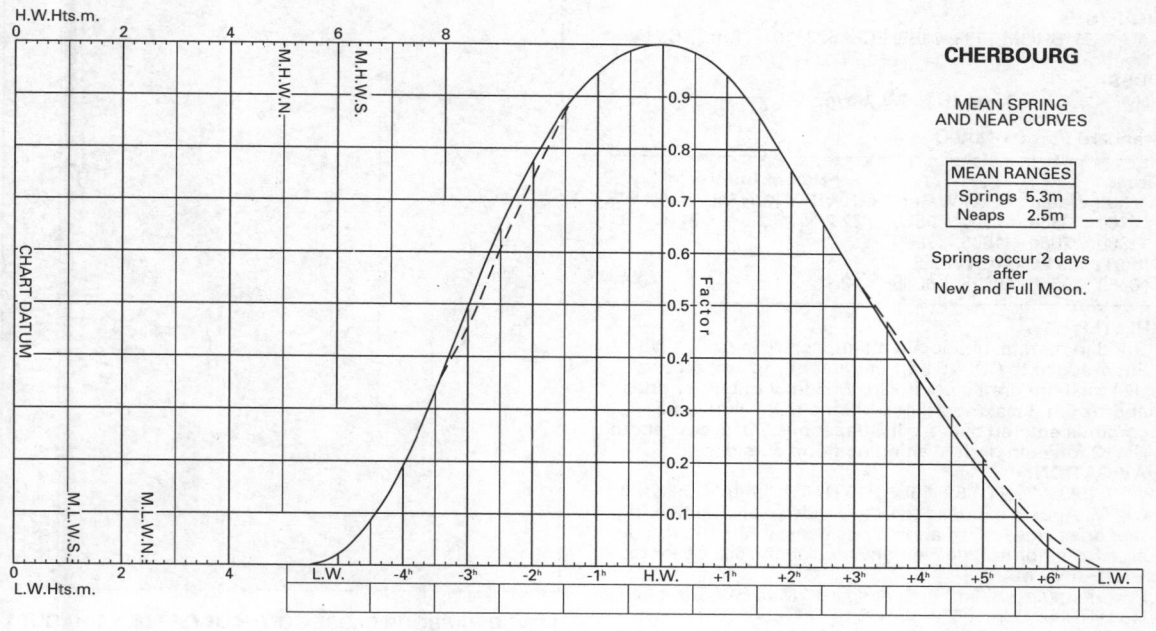

CHERBOURG

MEAN SPRING
AND NEAP CURVES

MEAN RANGES	
Springs 5.3m	——
Neaps 2.5m	- - -

Springs occur 2 days
after
New and Full Moon.

OMONVILLE-LA-ROGUE   8-15-11

Manche 49°42'·34N 01°49'·78W   Rtg 3-4-2

CHARTS
AC *1106, 2669*; SHOM 5636, 7120, 7158; ECM 528, 1014; Imray C33A; Stanfords 7, 16

TIDES
−0330 Dover; ML 3·6; Duration 0545; Zone −0100

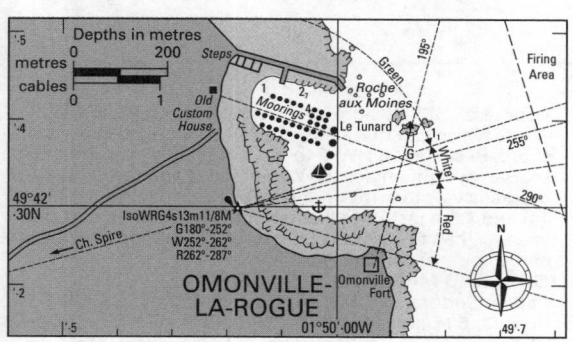

Standard Port CHERBOURG (←—)

Times				Height (metres)			
High Water		Low Water		MHWS	MHWN	MLWN	MLWS
0300	1000	0400	1000	6·4	5·0	2·5	1·1
1500	2200	1600	2200				
Differences OMONVILLE							
−0025	−0030	−0022	−0022	−0·3	−0·2	−0·2	−0·1
GOURY							
−0100	−0040	−0105	−0120	+1·7	+1·6	+1·0	+0·3

SHELTER
Good, except in strong winds from N to SE. There are 4 W conical ⚓s or ⚓ S of bkwtr; beware rks off outer end.

NAVIGATION
WPT 49°42'·50N 01°48'·60W, 075°/255° from/to Omonville lt, 1·0M. Ent is 100m wide, between rks extending N from Omonville Fort, and running ESE from bkwtr marked by Le Tunard, G bn tr. From W or N, keep clear of Basse Bréfort (depth 1m, marked by NCM buoy, VQ) 0·6M N of Pte de Jardeheu. Appr on 195° transit (below), passing 100m E of Le Tunard and into W sector of lt before turning stbd 290° for old Custom Ho and moorings. From E, appr on 255° transit in W sector of lt, until S of Le Tunard.
To ENE of port is a military firing area; when active, a R flag is flown from the bkwtr head.

LIGHTS AND MARKS
Omonville lt, Iso WRG 4s 13m 11/8M, on W framework tr with R top, vis G180°-252°, W252°-262°, R262°-287°. Lt in transit 255° with ⊕ steeple, 650m beyond, leads S of Le Tunard. From N, Le Tunard leads 195° in transit with fort. Street lts adequately illuminate the hbr area.

RADIO TELEPHONE
None. For Casquets TSS see Cherbourg (8.15.10).

TELEPHONE
Aff Mar 02·33·53·21·76; ⌗ 02·33·53·05·60; CROSS 02·33·52·72·13; 02·33·52·71·33; Météo 02·33·22·91·77; Auto 08.36.68.08.50; Police 02·33·52·72·02; Dr 02·33·53·08·69; Brit Consul 01·33·44·20·13.

FACILITIES
Jetty M, L, FW, AB, V, R, Bar. **Village** V, Gaz, R, Bar, nearest fuel (cans) at Beaumont-Hague 5km, ✉, Ⓑ, ⇌ (bus to Cherbourg), ✈. Ferry: See Cherbourg.

ADJACENT HARBOUR

PORT RACINE, Manche, 49°42'·78N 01°53'·70W. AC *1106, 3653;* SHOM 5636. Tides as 8.15.11. Port Racine (said to be the smallest hbr in France) is in the SW corner of Anse de St. Martin. This bay, 2M E of Cap de la Hague, has ⚓s sheltered from all but onshore winds. From N, appr with conspic chy (279m) at atomic stn brg 175°; or from NE via Basse Bréfort NCM buoy, VQ, on with St Germain des Vaux spire brg 240°. Both lines clear La Parmentière rks awash in centre of bay and Les Herbeuses and Le Grun Rks to W and E respectively. ⚓ or moor off the hbr which is obstructed by lines; only accessible by dinghy. R is only facility.

15

DIÉLETTE   8-15-12

Manche, 49°33′·30′N 01°51′·80′W   Rtg 3-2-2

CHARTS
AC *3653*; SHOM 7133, 7158; ECM 528, 1014; Imray C33A; Stanfords 16

TIDES
HW −0430 on Dover (UT); ML 5·2m

Standard Port ST-MALO (→)

Times				Height (metres)			
High Water		Low Water		MHWS	MHWN	MLWN	MLWS
0100	0800	0300	0800	12·2	9·2	4·3	1·6
1300	2000	1500	2000				
Differences FLAMANVILLE							
+0050	+0050	+0025	+0045	−2·7	−1·8	−1·1	−0·5

SHELTER
Good in marina, but do not attempt entry in strong W'lies. Ent dredged to CD, NE part of outer hbr to 2m; access H24 for 1·5m draft if coeff <80. W side of outer hbr dries approx 5m (local moorings). Marina (1·5-2·5m) in SE corner is entered over a sill 4·0m above CD; access about HW±3 for 1·5m draft, waiting pontoon outside.

NAVIGATION
WPT 49°33′·55N 01°52′·15W, 320°/140° from/to W bkwtr lt, 0·40M. Appr is exposed to W'ly winds/swell. Caution: rky reef dries close NE of appr; cross tides at hbr ent. Prohib area from hbr to C de Flamanville extends 5ca offshore.

LIGHTS AND MARKS
Power stn chys (72m) are conspic 1·2M to SW. Dir lt 140°, Iso WRG 4s 12m 10/7M, W tr/G top at hd of West bkwtr, vis G070°-135°, W135°-145° (10°), R145°-180°; on same tr is a lower lt, Fl G 4s 6m 2M. N bkwtr hd, Fl R 4s 8m 5M, W mast/R top. Spur, close SE at ent to new basin, is Fl (2) R 6s 6m 1M. Opposite spur, Fl G 6s 6m 2M, vis 115°-358°.

RADIO TELEPHONE
VHF Ch 09, 0830-2000LT.

TELEPHONE
Hr Mr 02·33.53.68.78, ☎ 02·33.53.68.79; ⌗ 02·33.23.34.00; Aff Mar 02·33.23.36.13; Météo 08·36·68·12·34; CROSS 02·33.52.72.13; SNSM 02·33.04.93.17; YC ☎ 02·33·20·14·08.

FACILITIES
Marina (410) FF117, AC, FW, Fuel, Slip, C (10ton); **Village**, V, Bar, R. Also facilities at Flamanville (1·3M). Ferry to CI.

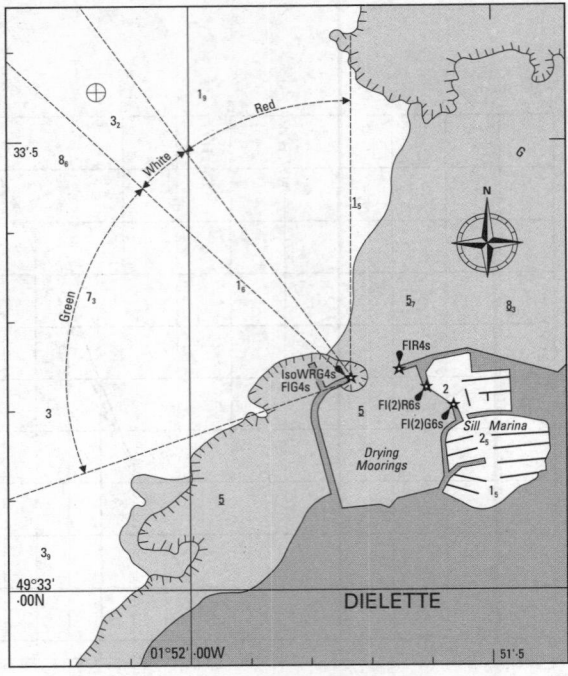

MINOR HARBOUR CLOSE SOUTH OF CAP DE LA HAGUE

GOURY, Manche, 49°43′·00N 01°56·70′W. AC *1106, 3653*; SHOM 7133 (essential large scale chart) , 5636, 7158. HW −0410 on Dover (UT); ML 5·1m. See 8.15.11. For visitors, appr at slack water nps with no swell and good vis; a fair wx hbr only, dries to flat sand/mud. Cap de la Hague lt, Fl 5s, is 0·5M NW of hbr; La Foraine WCM buoy is 1·1M to the W. Ldg lts: Front QR 4m 7M, on bkwtr hd; rear (110m from front), Q 10m 12M, intens 057°-075°, lead 065° between Charlin to S and Les Grois to N. By day, W patch with R ■ at end of bkwtr on with W pylon of rear ldg lt, 065°. ⌕ W of the 2 LB slips in 1·7m or dry out on the NE side of the bkwtr. Facilities: R, Bar at Auderville (0·5M).

CARTERET   8-15-13

Manche 49°22′·20N 01°47′·38W   Rtg 3-2-2

CHARTS
AC *3655, 2669*; SHOM 7133, 7157, 7158; ECM 1014; Imray C33A; Stanfords 16

TIDES
−0440 Dover; ML 5·9; Duration 0545; Zone −0100

Standard Port ST-MALO (→)

Times				Height (metres)			
High Water		Low Water		MHWS	MHWN	MLWN	MLWS
0100	0800	0300	0800	12·2	9·2	4·3	1·6
1300	2000	1500	2000				
Differences CARTERET							
+0035	+0025	+0020	+0035	−1·6	−1·1	−0·6	−0·3

SHELTER
Good in non-tidal marina (sill is 4m above CD; lifting gate retains 2·3m within); access HW−2½ to +3 for 1·5m draft. Ⓥ berths on far side of the most E'ly pontoon (F). If too late on the tide for the marina, possible waiting berth on W Jetty (clear of ferry) where a 1·5m draft boat can stay afloat for 6 hrs np, 9hrs sp. The tiny Port des Américains and drying basin, close W of marina, have up to 5m at HW.

NAVIGATION
WPT 49°21′·18N 01°47′·50W (off chartlet), 189°/009° from/to W Jetty lt, 1M. From N/NW, keep well off shore on appr to avoid rks 1M N of Cap de Carteret extending about 1M from coast. From W, about 4M off shore, beware Trois Grune Rks (dry 1·6m) marked by WCM buoy, Q (9) 15s. Appr dries ½M offshore and is exposed to fresh W/SW winds which can make ent rough. There are no safe ⌕s off shore. Best appr at HW−2 to avoid max tidal stream, 4½kn sp. Bar, at right angles to W Jetty, dries 4m; the chan dries progressively to firm sand, and is dredged to drying hts of 4m and 4·5m just W of the marina. Best water is mid-chan initially, then to outside of bend. The outer end of W bkwtr partly cover at springs. No ⌕ in river.

LIGHTS AND MARKS
Cap de Carteret, Fl (2+1) 15s 81m 26M, grey tr, G top, Horn (3) 60s, and conspic Sig Stn are 8ca WxN of the ent. W Jetty, Oc R 4s 6m 8M, W col, R top; E bkwtr, Fl G 2·5s, W mast G top. These lts in transit lead about 009° to ent. The bend in the chan is marked by a PHM bn, Fl (2) R 6s, & a SHM bn, Fl (2) G 6s. Marina sill is marked by a PHM bn, Fl (3) R 12s, and a SHM bn, Fl (3) G 12s; plus Y poles. Caution: a metal frame is said to project from the PHM bn.

RADIO TELEPHONE
VHF Ch 16 64. Marina Ch 09.

TELEPHONE
Hr Mr 02·33.44.00.13; CROSS 02·33.52.72.13; ⌗ 02·33·04· 90.08; Météo 02·33.22.91.77; Auto 08.36.68.08.50; Police 02·33.53.80.17; Ⓗ (Valognes) 02·33.40.14.39; Brit Consul 01·33.44.20.13.

FACILITIES
Port de Plaisance "Le Port des Iles" ☎ 33·04·70·84, ☎ 33040837, (260 + 60 visitors), FF109, AC, FW, CH, Fuel; **West Jetty** AB free for 6 hrs, then at 50% of marina rate, Slip, FW, R, Bar; **Cercle Nautique de Barneville-Carteret** ☎ 33.53.88.29, Slip, M, Bar.
Town ME, P & D (cans), V, Gaz, R, Bar, ✉, Ⓑ (Barneville), ⇌ (Valognes), ✈ (Cherbourg). Ferry: Cherbourg, Jersey.

CARTERET *continued*

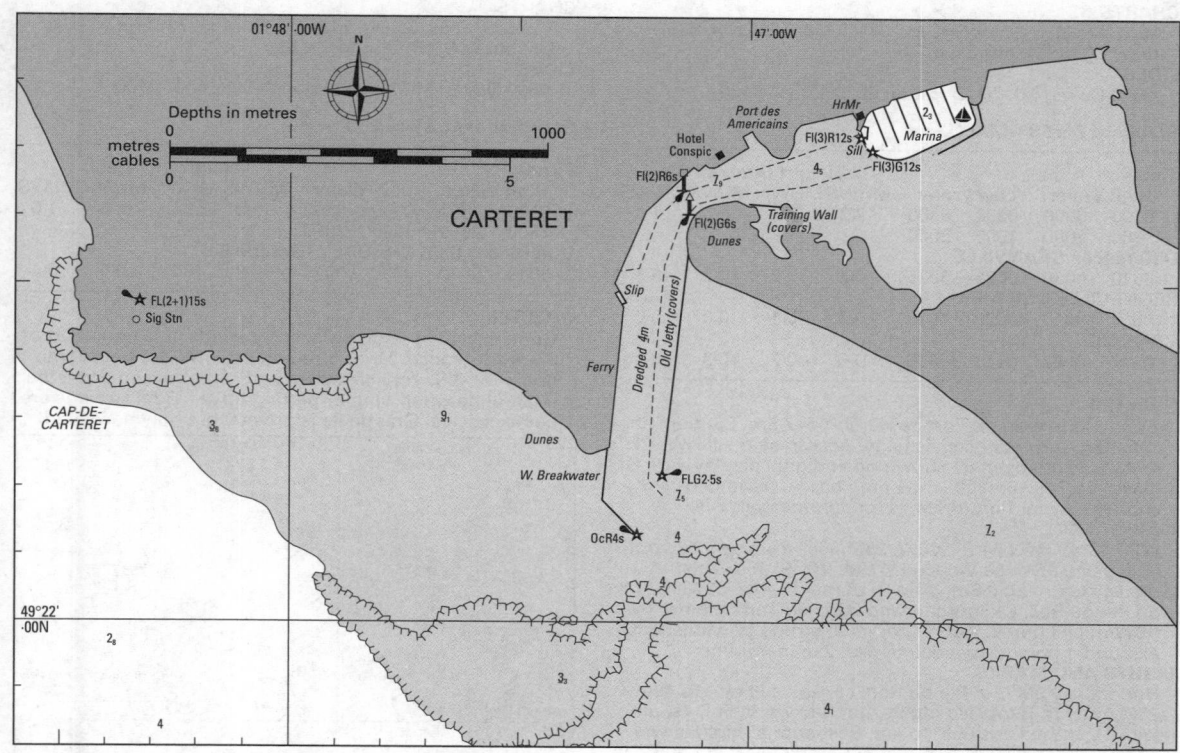

PORTBAIL   8-15-14

Manche 49°19'·46N 01°42'·85W   Rtg 3-4-2

CHARTS
AC *3655, 2669*; SHOM 7133, 7157; ECM 1014; Imray C33A; Stanfords 16

TIDES
HW −0440 on Dover (UT); ML 6·3m; Duration 0545

Standard Port ST-MALO (→)

Times				Height (metres)			
High Water		Low Water		MHWS	MHWN	MLWN	MLWS
0100	0800	0300	0800	12·2	9·2	4·3	1·6
1300	2000	1500	2000				
Differences PORTBAIL							
+0035	+0030	+0030	+0035	−0·8	−0·5	−0·3	−0·1
ST GERMAIN-SUR-AY							
+0030	+0030	+0040	+0040	−0·7	−0·4	−0·1	0·0
LE SÉNÉQUET							
+0020	+0020	+0028	+0028	−0·3	−0·2	0·0	0·0

SHELTER
Good. Hbr dries 7·0m, but access HW±½ at np, HW±2½ at sp for 1m draft. Drying basin to E of jetty: visitors berth on pontoon parallel with NW side of basin or moor on first line of buoys parallel to jetty. Portbail is 4M SE of Carteret.

NAVIGATION
WPT 49°18'·30N 01°44'·49W (off chartlet, abeam "PB" SWM buoy), 222°/042° from/to chan buoys, 1·4M. Beware very strong tide over bar. Ldg line crosses sand banks (drying about 8ca offshore) to a pair of unlit PHM/SHM buoys. Thence via chan dredged 5·2m; on port side a training wall (covers at HW) is marked by R spar bns, the first Q (2) R 5s.

LIGHTS AND MARKS
A Water Tr (43m) is conspic 6ca NNW of ent. Ldg lts 042°: Front (La Caillourie) QW 14m 10M, W pylon, R top; rear, 870m from front, Oc 4s 20m 10M (church spire). Training wall hd, Q (2) R 5s 5m 2M.

RADIO TELEPHONE
VHF Ch 09.
TELEPHONE
Hr Mr ☎ 02·33·04·83·48 (15 Jun-31 Aug).
FACILITIES
Quay FF50, FW, D, P, AC, C (5 ton); **Cercle Nautique de Portbail-Denneville** ☎ 02·33·04·86·15, Bar, R; **YC de Portbail** ☎ 02·33·04·83·48, AB, C, Slip; **Services:** Sh, ME, El. **Town** (½M by causeway) Bar, ⓑ, ✉, R, V, ⇌ (Valognes).

15

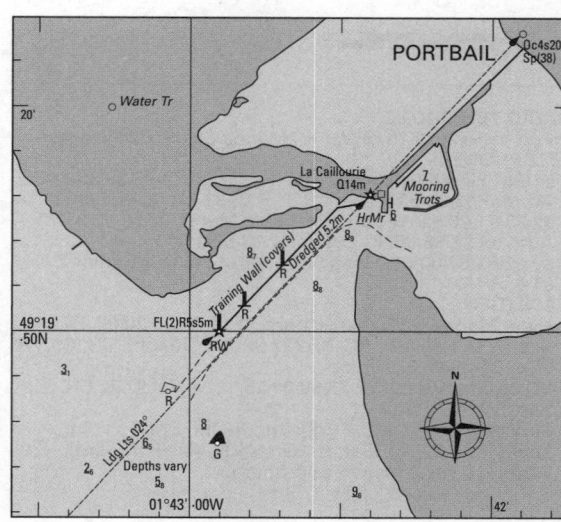

GRANVILLE   8-15-15

Manche 48°49'·97N 01°35'·88W   Rtg 3-1-2

CHARTS
AC 3672, 3656, *3659*; SHOM 7341, 7156; ECM 534, 535; Imray C33B; Stanfords 16

TIDES
–0510 Dover; ML 7·1; Duration 0525; Zone –0100

Standard Port ST-MALO (→)

Times				Height (metres)			
High Water		Low Water		MHWS	MHWN	MLWN	MLWS
0100	0800	0300	0800	12·2	9·2	4·3	1·6
1300	2000	1500	2000				
Differences GRANVILLE							
+0010	+0010	+0025	+0015	+0·7	+0·6	+0·2	–0·1
REGNÉVILLE-SUR-MER							
+0018	+0018	+0028	+0028	–0·2	–0·1	0·0	0·0
CANCALE							
–0002	–0002	+0012	+0006	+0·8	+0·7	+0·3	+0·1

SHELTER
Good in the marina, Port de Hérel, 1·5–2·5m. Caution: at ent sharp turn restricts visibility. Access over sill HW –2½ to +3½. Depth over sill shown on lit digital display atop S bkwtr: eg 76=7·6m; 00 = no entry; hard to read in bright sun. The Avant Port (dries) is for commercial/ FVs.

NAVIGATION
WPT 48°49'·40N 01°37'·00W, 235°/055° from/to S bkwtr lt (Fl R 4s), 0·95M. Le Videcoq WCM, VQ (9) 10s Whis, marks rks drying 0·8m, 3¼M W of Pte du Roc. Beware rks off Pte du Roc, La Fourchie and Banc de Tombelaine, 1M SSW of Le Loup lt. Appr is rough in strong W winds. Ent/exit under power; speed limit 4kn, 2kn in marina.

LIGHTS AND MARKS
Hbr ent is 0·6M E of Pte du Roc (conspic), Fl (4) 15s 49m 23M, grey tr, R top. No ldg lts, but S bkwtr lt, Fl R 4s, on with TV mast leads 055° to ent. Best appr at night is with Le Loup bearing 085° to avoid pot markers off Pte du Roc; hbr lts are hard to see against town lts. Turn port at bkwtr to cross the sill between R/G piles, Oc R/G 4s. Sill of bathing pool to stbd is marked by 5 R piles, lit Fl Bu 4s.

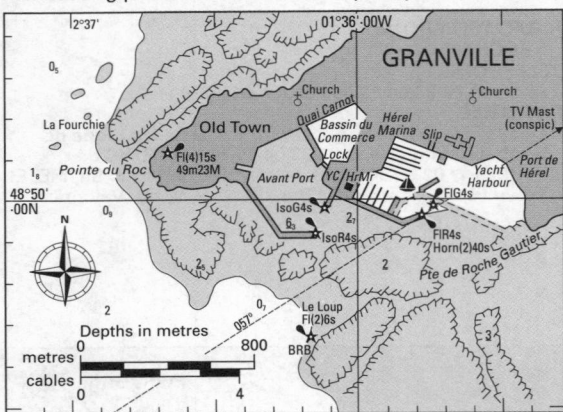

RADIO TELEPHONE
Port VHF Ch 12 16 (HW±1½). Marina Ch 09, H24 in season.

TELEPHONE
Hr Mr (Hérel) 02·33·50·20·06; Hr Mr (Port) 02·33·50·17·75; Aff Mar 02·33·50·00·59; CROSS 02·33·52·72·13; SNSM 02·33·61·26·51; ⊞ 02·33·50·19·90; Météo 02·33·22·91·77; Auto 08.36.68.08.50; Police 02·33·50·01·00; Dr 02·33·50·00·07; Hosp 02·33·90·74·75; Brit Consul 01.33.44.20.13.

FACILITIES
Hérel Marina (850+150 visitors) ☎ 02·33·50·20·06, FF100, Slip, P, D, FW, ME, AC, BH (12 ton), C (10 ton), CH, Gaz, R, ▣, V, Bar, SM, El, Sh, ⬚;
YC de Granville ☎ 02·33·50·04·25, L, M, BH, D, P, CH, ▣, Slip FW, AB, Bar;
Services: CH, M, ME, El, Ⓔ, Sh, SHOM, SM.
Town P, D, ME, V, Gaz, R, Bar, ✉, Ⓑ, ⇌, ✈ (Dinard).
Ferry: UK via Jersey or Cherbourg.

ILES CHAUSEY   8-15-16

Manche 48°52'·20N 01°49'·00W (S ent)   Rtg 3-5-1

CHARTS
AC 3656, *3659*; SHOM 7134, 7156, 7155, 7161; ECM 534, 535; Imray C33B; Stanfords 16

TIDES
–0500 Dover; ML 7·4; Duration 0530; Zone –0100

Standard Port ST-MALO (→)

Times				Height (metres)			
High Water		Low Water		MHWS	MHWN	MLWN	MLWS
0100	0800	0300	0800	12·2	9·2	4·3	1·6
1300	2000	1500	2000				
Differences ILES CHAUSEY (Grande Ile)							
+0010	+0010	+0020	+0015	+0·8	+0·7	+0·5	+0·4

SHELTER
Good except in strong NW or SE winds. It is not a Port of Entry for France. Moor fore-and-aft to W ⚓s, free; some dry at MLWS. Very crowded Sat/Sun in season. Note the tidal range when ⚓ing or picking up ⚓. Tidal streams are not excessive. Grande Ile is private, but may be visited.

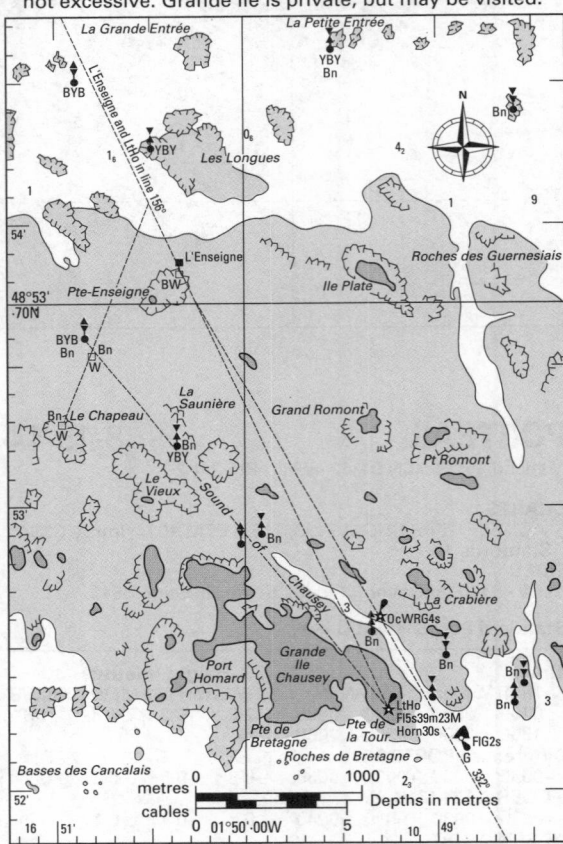

NAVIGATION
WPT 48°51'·50N 01°48'·48W, 152°/332° from/to La Crabière lt, 1·2M. The easier route into the Sound is from the S, but beware rks E and S of Pte de la Tour, marked by ECM bns. The N route requires adequate ht of tide, SHOM 7134 or detailed SDs for transits, and/or local knowledge. Dangerous wk reported N of La Petite Entree (off chartlet).

LIGHTS AND MARKS
Pte de la Tour, Fl 5s, is conspic. La Crabière, Oc WRG 4s 5m 9/6M, B tr, Y top; see 8.15.4. From N, L'Enseigne bn tr (19m) on with Pte de la Tour lt ho leads 156°. From S, La Crabière on with L'Enseigne leads 332°.

RADIO TELEPHONE None.

TELEPHONE
Police 02·33·52·72·02; CROSS 02·33·52·72·13; Auto 08.36.68.08.50.

FACILITIES
R. Tourelle L, ◫. **Village** FW & V (limited), Gaz, R, Bar. See also Granville. Ferry to UK via Granville and Jersey.

TIME ZONE –0100
(French Standard Time)
Subtract 1 hour for UT
For French Summer Time add ONE hour in non-shaded areas

FRANCE – ST. MALO

LAT 48°38'N   LONG 2°02'W

TIMES AND HEIGHTS OF HIGH AND LOW WATERS

YEAR **1999**

JANUARY

Day	Time	m	Day	Time	m
1 F	0039 / 0609 / 1311 / 1839	2.0 / 12.0 / 1.8 / 12.1	**16** SA	0040 / 0613 / 1302 / 1835	3.1 / 10.9 / 2.7 / 10.9
2 SA O	0135 / 0700 / 1405 / 1930	1.6 / 12.4 / 1.4 / 12.3	**17** SU	0123 / 0654 / 1346 / 1916	2.7 / 11.4 / 2.3 / 11.3
3 SU	0225 / 0748 / 1454 / 2017	1.5 / 12.6 / 1.3 / 12.3	**18** M	0204 / 0732 / 1427 / 1954	2.4 / 11.7 / 2.0 / 11.6
4 M	0310 / 0832 / 1538 / 2100	1.5 / 12.5 / 1.4 / 12.1	**19** TU	0244 / 0810 / 1509 / 2032	2.1 / 11.9 / 1.8 / 11.7
5 TU	0350 / 0912 / 1617 / 2140	1.8 / 12.2 / 1.8 / 11.7	**20** W	0323 / 0848 / 1549 / 2111	2.0 / 12.0 / 1.8 / 11.8
6 W	0426 / 0951 / 1653 / 2217	2.2 / 11.8 / 2.3 / 11.2	**21** TH	0402 / 0927 / 1627 / 2150	2.0 / 12.0 / 1.9 / 11.6
7 TH	0457 / 1027 / 1727 / 2253	2.8 / 11.1 / 3.0 / 10.5	**22** F	0440 / 1006 / 1706 / 2229	2.2 / 11.7 / 2.1 / 11.3
8 F	0533 / 1103 / 1800 / 2329	3.4 / 10.4 / 3.6 / 9.9	**23** SA	0520 / 1047 / 1747 / 2312	2.6 / 11.2 / 2.5 / 10.8
9 SA	0609 / 1142 / 1837	4.0 / 9.7 / 4.2	**24** SU	0602 / 1133 / 1832	3.0 / 10.7 / 3.0
10 SU	0012 / 0653 / 1230 / 1927	9.3 / 4.5 / 9.2 / 4.6	**25** M	0001 / 0653 / 1230 / 1927	10.3 / 3.5 / 10.2 / 3.5
11 M	0108 / 0753 / 1338 / 2033	8.9 / 4.8 / 8.8 / 4.8	**26** TU	0105 / 0758 / 1346 / 2038	9.9 / 3.9 / 9.8 / 3.8
12 TU	0224 / 0913 / 1458 / 2149	8.8 / 4.8 / 8.9 / 4.6	**27** W	0227 / 0922 / 1512 / 2203	9.8 / 3.9 / 9.9 / 3.6
13 W	0340 / 1023 / 1608 / 2256	9.2 / 4.4 / 9.3 / 4.1	**28** TH	0349 / 1046 / 1630 / 2319	10.1 / 3.5 / 10.3 / 3.1
14 TH	0440 / 1125 / 1704 / 2352	9.8 / 3.8 / 9.9 / 3.5	**29** F	0500 / 1157 / 1735	10.7 / 2.8 / 11.0
15 F	0529 / 1216 / 1752	10.4 / 3.2 / 10.5	**30** SA	0025 / 0559 / 1259 / 1831	2.5 / 11.4 / 2.1 / 11.6
			31 SU O	0122 / 0651 / 1353 / 1920	2.0 / 12.0 / 1.7 / 12.0

FEBRUARY

Day	Time	m	Day	Time	m
1 M	0211 / 0736 / 1440 / 2003	1.7 / 12.3 / 1.4 / 12.1	**16** TU ●	0147 / 0716 / 1411 / 1939	2.1 / 11.8 / 1.7 / 11.9
2 TU	0254 / 0816 / 1521 / 2042	1.6 / 12.4 / 1.4 / 12.1	**17** W	0231 / 0756 / 1455 / 2018	1.7 / 12.3 / 1.3 / 12.2
3 W	0331 / 0853 / 1556 / 2117	1.7 / 12.3 / 1.6 / 11.9	**18** TH	0313 / 0835 / 1537 / 2057	1.3 / 12.6 / 1.0 / 12.4
4 TH	0404 / 0927 / 1627 / 2149	1.9 / 12.0 / 2.0 / 11.6	**19** F	0353 / 0914 / 1616 / 2136	1.2 / 12.6 / 1.1 / 12.3
5 F	0432 / 0958 / 1655 / 2219	2.3 / 11.5 / 2.5 / 11.0	**20** SA	0431 / 0953 / 1654 / 2214	1.4 / 12.4 / 1.7 / 12.0
6 SA	0501 / 1027 / 1720 / 2247	2.8 / 10.9 / 3.1 / 10.4	**21** SU	0508 / 1032 / 1732 / 2253	1.8 / 11.9 / 1.9 / 11.4
7 SU	0527 / 1057 / 1747 / 2318	3.4 / 10.2 / 3.7 / 9.8	**22** M	0547 / 1115 / 1812 / 2338	2.5 / 11.1 / 2.7 / 10.7
8 M	0559 / 1132 / 1822 / 2358	4.0 / 9.6 / 4.3 / 9.2	**23** TU	0632 / 1206 / 1901	3.2 / 10.3 / 3.4
9 TU	0644 / 1222 / 1915	4.5 / 8.9 / 4.8	**24** W	0036 / 0732 / 1319 / 2010	10.0 / 3.8 / 9.6 / 4.0
10 W	0101 / 0752 / 1344 / 2036	8.7 / 4.9 / 8.5 / 5.0	**25** TH	0159 / 0901 / 1455 / 2144	9.5 / 4.1 / 9.0 / 4.0
11 TH	0236 / 0934 / 1522 / 2207	8.6 / 4.8 / 8.7 / 4.7	**26** F	0335 / 1034 / 1622 / 2307	9.6 / 3.8 / 9.8 / 3.5
12 F	0401 / 1045 / 1634 / 2317	9.1 / 4.3 / 9.3 / 4.1	**27** SA	0451 / 1148 / 1728	10.3 / 3.0 / 10.6
13 SA	0502 / 1146 / 1728	9.8 / 3.5 / 10.1	**28** SU	0014 / 0549 / 1248 / 1820	2.8 / 11.0 / 2.3 / 11.3
14 SU	0012 / 0551 / 1238 / 1815	3.4 / 10.6 / 2.8 / 10.8			
15 M	0101 / 0635 / 1326 / 1858	2.7 / 11.3 / 2.2 / 11.4			

MARCH

Day	Time	m	Day	Time	m
1 M	0109 / 0637 / 1339 / 1904	2.2 / 11.7 / 1.8 / 11.7	**16** TU	0035 / 0611 / 1301 / 1835	2.7 / 11.2 / 2.0 / 11.5
2 TU O	0155 / 0719 / 1422 / 1943	1.8 / 12.1 / 1.5 / 12.0	**17** W ●	0125 / 0655 / 1350 / 1918	1.9 / 12.0 / 1.3 / 12.2
3 W	0234 / 0755 / 1458 / 2018	1.6 / 12.3 / 1.4 / 12.1	**18** TH	0212 / 0737 / 1437 / 1959	1.2 / 12.6 / 0.8 / 12.7
4 TH	0308 / 0829 / 1530 / 2049	1.5 / 12.3 / 1.5 / 12.0	**19** F	0257 / 0818 / 1520 / 2039	0.8 / 13.0 / 0.5 / 12.9
5 F	0338 / 0859 / 1557 / 2118	1.6 / 12.1 / 1.7 / 11.8	**20** SA	0338 / 0858 / 1600 / 2118	0.6 / 13.1 / 0.5 / 12.9
6 SA	0405 / 0928 / 1623 / 2145	1.9 / 11.8 / 2.1 / 11.4	**21** SU	0418 / 0937 / 1636 / 2156	0.8 / 12.8 / 0.9 / 12.4
7 SU	0431 / 0955 / 1646 / 2212	2.4 / 11.3 / 2.7 / 10.9	**22** M	0455 / 1017 / 1716 / 2236	1.3 / 12.2 / 1.6 / 11.7
8 M	0455 / 1022 / 1710 / 2239	2.9 / 10.6 / 3.3 / 10.2	**23** TU	0534 / 1059 / 1755 / 2319	2.1 / 11.3 / 2.5 / 10.8
9 TU	0522 / 1051 / 1738 / 2310	3.5 / 9.9 / 4.0 / 9.5	**24** W	0618 / 1150 / 1843	3.0 / 10.3 / 3.4
10 W	0558 / 1130 / 1820 / 2357	4.2 / 9.1 / 4.6 / 8.9	**25** TH	0016 / 0717 / 1303 / 1952	9.9 / 3.8 / 9.6 / 4.1
11 TH	0653 / 1236 / 1929	4.7 / 8.5 / 5.1	**26** F	0141 / 0847 / 1443 / 2129	9.0 / 4.2 / 9.1 / 4.2
12 F	0126 / 0821 / 1431 / 2111	8.4 / 5.0 / 8.3 / 5.1	**27** SA	0320 / 1020 / 1610 / 2253	9.4 / 3.8 / 9.6 / 3.7
13 SA	0318 / 1004 / 1601 / 2239	8.6 / 4.5 / 8.9 / 4.4	**28** SU	0436 / 1132 / 1712 / 2357	10.0 / 3.1 / 10.3 / 3.0
14 SU	0431 / 1111 / 1701 / 2341	9.4 / 3.7 / 9.8 / 3.7	**29** M	0531 / 1229 / 1800	10.7 / 2.5 / 11.0
15 M	0525 / 1209 / 1750	10.3 / 2.8 / 10.7	**30** TU	0048 / 0616 / 1316 / 1841	2.4 / 11.3 / 2.0 / 11.5
			31 W O	0131 / 0655 / 1355 / 1917	2.0 / 11.7 / 1.7 / 11.8

APRIL

Day	Time	m	Day	Time	m
1 TH	0208 / 0730 / 1429 / 1949	1.7 / 11.9 / 1.6 / 12.0	**16** F ●	0148 / 0712 / 1413 / 1935	1.1 / 12.7 / 0.6 / 12.9
2 F	0240 / 0801 / 1459 / 2019	1.6 / 12.0 / 1.6 / 12.0	**17** SA	0236 / 0756 / 1459 / 2017	0.6 / 13.1 / 0.3 / 13.1
3 SA	0309 / 0831 / 1527 / 2047	1.6 / 12.0 / 1.7 / 11.9	**18** SU	0321 / 0839 / 1541 / 2058	0.4 / 13.2 / 0.4 / 13.0
4 SU	0338 / 0859 / 1553 / 2114	1.8 / 11.8 / 2.0 / 11.6	**19** M	0402 / 0921 / 1620 / 2139	0.6 / 12.8 / 0.9 / 12.6
5 M	0404 / 0926 / 1617 / 2141	2.1 / 11.3 / 2.5 / 11.1	**20** TU	0442 / 1003 / 1658 / 2220	1.1 / 12.1 / 1.6 / 11.8
6 TU	0429 / 0954 / 1641 / 2208	2.6 / 10.7 / 3.1 / 10.5	**21** W	0523 / 1048 / 1741 / 2306	1.9 / 11.2 / 2.5 / 10.9
7 W	0457 / 1023 / 1708 / 2238	3.2 / 10.0 / 3.7 / 9.8	**22** TH	0609 / 1140 / 1830	2.8 / 10.2 / 3.4
8 TH	0530 / 1100 / 1746 / 2319	3.8 / 9.3 / 4.4 / 9.1	**23** F	0003 / 0708 / 1250 / 1936	10.0 / 3.6 / 9.4 / 4.1
9 F	0618 / 1155 / 1845	4.4 / 8.7 / 4.9	**24** SA	0122 / 0829 / 1420 / 2106	9.3 / 4.0 / 9.1 / 4.2
10 SA	0030 / 0733 / 1336 / 2019	8.5 / 4.8 / 8.4 / 5.0	**25** SU	0253 / 0953 / 1544 / 2224	9.3 / 3.8 / 9.4 / 3.8
11 SU	0228 / 0911 / 1520 / 2155	8.5 / 4.5 / 8.8 / 4.5	**26** M	0407 / 1102 / 1643 / 2326	9.6 / 3.3 / 10.1 / 3.2
12 M	0352 / 1031 / 1626 / 2304	9.2 / 3.7 / 9.7 / 3.6	**27** TU	0501 / 1157 / 1730	10.3 / 2.8 / 10.7
13 TU	0451 / 1134 / 1719	10.2 / 2.8 / 10.6	**28** W	0016 / 0546 / 1242 / 1810	2.7 / 10.9 / 2.4 / 11.1
14 W	0003 / 0541 / 1231 / 1806	2.6 / 11.1 / 1.9 / 11.6	**29** TH	0058 / 0625 / 1321 / 1846	2.3 / 11.2 / 2.1 / 11.5
15 TH	0057 / 0627 / 1324 / 1851	1.8 / 12.0 / 1.1 / 12.4	**30** F O	0136 / 0700 / 1356 / 1919	2.0 / 11.5 / 1.9 / 11.7

15

Chart Datum: 6·29 metres below Lallemand System (Mean Sea Level, Marseilles)

TIME ZONE –0100
(French Standard Time)
Subtract 1 hour for UT
For French Summer Time add
ONE hour in non-shaded areas

FRANCE – ST. MALO

LAT 48°38'N   LONG 2°02'W

TIMES AND HEIGHTS OF HIGH AND LOW WATERS

YEAR **1999**

MAY

Day	Time	m	Day	Time	m
1 SA	0209 / 0733 / 1427 / 1950	1.9 / 11.6 / 1.9 / 11.8	16 SU	0214 / 0735 / 1437 / 1956	0.7 / 12.9 / 0.5 / 13.0
2 SU	0241 / 0803 / 1457 / 2019	1.8 / 11.6 / 1.9 / 11.7	17 M	0302 / 0821 / 1522 / 2040	0.6 / 12.9 / 0.6 / 12.9
3 M	0312 / 0833 / 1525 / 2048	1.9 / 11.5 / 2.1 / 11.5	18 TU	0347 / 0907 / 1605 / 2124	0.7 / 12.6 / 1.1 / 12.5
4 TU	0340 / 0903 / 1552 / 2117	2.1 / 11.2 / 2.5 / 11.2	19 W	0430 / 0952 / 1645 / 2208	1.2 / 12.0 / 1.7 / 11.8
5 W	0409 / 0933 / 1619 / 2147	2.5 / 10.8 / 3.0 / 10.7	20 TH	0513 / 1039 / 1724 / 2255	1.9 / 11.2 / 2.5 / 11.0
6 TH	0439 / 1006 / 1649 / 2219	3.0 / 10.2 / 3.5 / 10.1	21 F	0559 / 1129 / 1813 / 2348	2.7 / 10.3 / 3.3 / 10.2
7 F	0514 / 1044 / 1727 / 2301	3.5 / 9.6 / 4.1 / 9.4	22 SA	0653 / 1229 / 1915	3.4 / 9.6 / 4.0
8 SA	0600 / 1135 / 1822	4.0 / 9.0 / 4.5	23 SU	0053 / 0758 / 1342 / 2028	9.6 / 3.8 / 9.2 / 4.2
9 SU	0003 / 0704 / 1254 / 1940	8.9 / 4.3 / 8.7 / 4.7	24 M	0209 / 0910 / 1458 / 2140	9.3 / 3.9 / 9.3 / 4.0
10 M	0135 / 0827 / 1429 / 2109	8.8 / 4.2 / 9.0 / 4.3	25 TU	0322 / 1016 / 1602 / 2242	9.4 / 3.7 / 9.7 / 3.6
11 TU	0304 / 0955 / 1543 / 2223	9.3 / 3.6 / 9.7 / 3.5	26 W	0421 / 1112 / 1652 / 2334	9.8 / 3.3 / 10.2 / 3.2
12 W	0410 / 1056 / 1642 / 2327	10.1 / 2.7 / 10.6 / 2.7	27 TH	0509 / 1201 / 1735	10.3 / 2.9 / 10.6
13 TH	0506 / 1157 / 1734	11.0 / 2.0 / 11.5	28 F	0020 / 0551 / 1243 / 1814	2.8 / 10.7 / 2.6 / 11.0
14 F	0026 / 0557 / 1255 / 1823	1.8 / 11.8 / 1.3 / 12.3	29 SA	0101 / 0629 / 1322 / 1849	2.5 / 11.0 / 2.4 / 11.3
15 SA	0122 / 0647 / 1348 / 1910	1.2 / 12.5 / 0.8 / 12.8	30 SU	0138 / 0705 / 1357 / 1923	2.3 / 11.2 / 2.2 / 11.4
			31 M	0213 / 0739 / 1430 / 1955	2.1 / 11.2 / 2.2 / 11.5

JUNE

Day	Time	m	Day	Time	m
1 TU	0248 / 0812 / 1502 / 2027	2.1 / 11.2 / 2.3 / 11.4	16 W	0333 / 0856 / 1550 / 2112	0.9 / 12.4 / 1.3 / 12.4
2 W	0320 / 0845 / 1533 / 2059	2.2 / 11.1 / 2.5 / 11.2	17 TH	0418 / 0942 / 1632 / 2156	1.3 / 11.9 / 1.8 / 12.0
3 TH	0353 / 0919 / 1604 / 2132	2.4 / 10.8 / 2.8 / 10.9	18 F	0501 / 1026 / 1714 / 2240	1.8 / 11.3 / 2.4 / 11.3
4 F	0426 / 0955 / 1638 / 2209	2.8 / 10.4 / 3.2 / 10.4	19 SA	0543 / 1111 / 1751 / 2325	2.4 / 10.6 / 3.0 / 10.6
5 SA	0504 / 1035 / 1717 / 2252	3.1 / 10.0 / 3.6 / 9.9	20 SU	0627 / 1158 / 1839	3.1 / 10.0 / 3.6
6 SU	0548 / 1122 / 1807 / 2345	3.5 / 9.6 / 4.0 / 9.5	21 M	0015 / 0716 / 1252 / 1936	9.9 / 3.7 / 9.4 / 4.1
7 M	0643 / 1224 / 1911	3.8 / 9.3 / 4.2	22 TU	0114 / 0812 / 1355 / 2041	9.4 / 4.0 / 9.2 / 4.2
8 TU	0056 / 0751 / 1340 / 2027	9.3 / 3.8 / 9.4 / 4.0	23 W	0222 / 0915 / 1505 / 2146	9.2 / 4.1 / 9.2 / 4.1
9 W	0215 / 0905 / 1456 / 2143	9.5 / 3.5 / 9.8 / 3.6	24 TH	0329 / 1018 / 1606 / 2247	9.3 / 3.9 / 9.6 / 3.8
10 TH	0328 / 1021 / 1603 / 2252	10.1 / 3.0 / 10.5 / 2.9	25 F	0427 / 1116 / 1658 / 2340	9.6 / 3.5 / 10.0 / 3.3
11 F	0431 / 1124 / 1702 / 2356	10.8 / 2.3 / 11.2 / 2.2	26 SA	0517 / 1206 / 1742	10.1 / 3.2 / 10.5
12 SA	0529 / 1226 / 1757	11.5 / 1.7 / 11.9	27 SU	0027 / 0601 / 1250 / 1823	2.9 / 10.5 / 2.8 / 10.9
13 SU	0056 / 0624 / 1324 / 1849	1.5 / 12.1 / 1.3 / 12.4	28 M	0110 / 0642 / 1330 / 1901	2.6 / 10.8 / 2.6 / 11.1
14 M	0152 / 0717 / 1416 / 1938	1.1 / 12.4 / 1.0 / 12.7	29 TU	0150 / 0720 / 1407 / 1936	2.4 / 11.0 / 2.5 / 11.3
15 TU	0244 / 0807 / 1505 / 2026	0.9 / 12.5 / 1.0 / 12.7	30 W	0227 / 0756 / 1443 / 2011	2.3 / 11.1 / 2.4 / 11.4

JULY

Day	Time	m	Day	Time	m
1 TH	0304 / 0831 / 1518 / 2046	2.2 / 11.1 / 2.4 / 11.4	16 F	0403 / 0926 / 1616 / 2139	1.3 / 12.0 / 1.7 / 12.1
2 F	0340 / 0907 / 1553 / 2122	2.2 / 11.1 / 2.5 / 11.2	17 SA	0443 / 1006 / 1653 / 2217	1.7 / 11.6 / 2.1 / 11.6
3 SA	0417 / 0945 / 1630 / 2200	2.4 / 10.9 / 2.7 / 11.0	18 SU	0519 / 1044 / 1725 / 2255	2.2 / 11.0 / 2.7 / 10.9
4 SU	0455 / 1024 / 1709 / 2241	2.6 / 10.6 / 3.0 / 10.6	19 M	0553 / 1121 / 1803 / 2333	2.9 / 10.4 / 3.3 / 10.2
5 M	0537 / 1108 / 1753 / 2328	2.9 / 10.3 / 3.3 / 10.2	20 TU	0628 / 1201 / 1843	3.5 / 9.7 / 3.9
6 TU	0624 / 1158 / 1846	3.2 / 10.0 / 3.6	21 W	0017 / 0711 / 1250 / 1935	9.5 / 4.1 / 9.2 / 4.4
7 W	0024 / 0720 / 1300 / 1950	9.9 / 3.4 / 9.8 / 3.8	22 TH	0114 / 0808 / 1356 / 2045	9.0 / 4.4 / 8.9 / 4.6
8 TH	0134 / 0827 / 1414 / 2106	9.8 / 3.5 / 9.8 / 3.6	23 F	0228 / 0919 / 1514 / 2159	8.8 / 4.5 / 9.0 / 4.4
9 F	0251 / 0946 / 1529 / 2223	10.0 / 3.3 / 10.2 / 3.2	24 SA	0344 / 1031 / 1621 / 2304	9.0 / 4.2 / 9.4 / 3.9
10 SA	0403 / 1056 / 1637 / 2333	10.4 / 2.8 / 10.8 / 2.6	25 SU	0446 / 1132 / 1714 / 2358	9.5 / 3.7 / 10.0 / 3.3
11 SU	0510 / 1203 / 1739	11.0 / 2.3 / 11.5	26 M	0536 / 1222 / 1800	10.1 / 3.2 / 10.6
12 M	0037 / 0610 / 1305 / 1835	2.0 / 11.6 / 1.8 / 12.0	27 TU	0045 / 0621 / 1307 / 1841	2.9 / 10.5 / 2.9 / 11.0
13 TU	0136 / 0706 / 1400 / 1926	1.5 / 12.0 / 1.5 / 12.4	28 W	0129 / 0702 / 1349 / 1920	2.5 / 10.9 / 2.5 / 11.3
14 W	0231 / 0757 / 1451 / 2014	1.2 / 12.2 / 1.4 / 12.6	29 TH	0210 / 0740 / 1428 / 1957	2.2 / 11.2 / 2.3 / 11.6
15 TH	0319 / 0843 / 1536 / 2058	1.1 / 12.2 / 1.4 / 12.5	30 F	0250 / 0817 / 1506 / 2033	2.0 / 11.4 / 2.1 / 11.7
			31 SA	0331 / 0854 / 1544 / 2110	1.8 / 11.5 / 2.0 / 11.8

AUGUST

Day	Time	m	Day	Time	m
1 SU	0407 / 0932 / 1621 / 2148	1.8 / 11.5 / 2.1 / 11.7	16 M	0448 / 1010 / 1653 / 2220	2.1 / 11.3 / 2.4 / 11.2
2 M	0445 / 1010 / 1659 / 2227	2.0 / 11.3 / 2.3 / 11.3	17 TU	0515 / 1041 / 1723 / 2251	2.7 / 10.7 / 3.1 / 10.5
3 TU	0523 / 1050 / 1739 / 2309	2.3 / 11.0 / 2.7 / 10.9	18 W	0541 / 1112 / 1754 / 2325	3.4 / 10.0 / 3.7 / 9.7
4 W	0605 / 1134 / 1824 / 2358	2.7 / 10.5 / 3.2 / 10.3	19 TH	0613 / 1150 / 1834	4.0 / 9.4 / 4.4
5 TH	0653 / 1229 / 1921	3.2 / 10.1 / 3.7	20 F	0010 / 0700 / 1246 / 1937	9.0 / 4.6 / 8.8 / 4.8
6 F	0102 / 0755 / 1341 / 2037	9.9 / 3.6 / 9.8 / 3.9	21 SA	0124 / 0814 / 1417 / 2114	8.5 / 5.0 / 8.5 / 4.9
7 SA	0225 / 0920 / 1506 / 2203	9.7 / 3.7 / 9.9 / 3.6	22 SU	0302 / 0947 / 1546 / 2230	8.5 / 4.8 / 8.9 / 4.4
8 SU	0348 / 1039 / 1624 / 2320	10.0 / 3.3 / 10.4 / 3.0	23 M	0418 / 1101 / 1649 / 2331	9.1 / 4.2 / 9.6 / 3.7
9 M	0501 / 1150 / 1731	10.6 / 2.7 / 11.1	24 TU	0513 / 1157 / 1738	9.8 / 3.5 / 10.3
10 TU	0026 / 0603 / 1252 / 1827	2.3 / 11.3 / 2.1 / 11.8	25 W	0022 / 0600 / 1245 / 1821	3.0 / 10.5 / 2.9 / 11.0
11 W	0125 / 0657 / 1348 / 1915	1.7 / 11.8 / 1.7 / 12.3	26 TH	0108 / 0642 / 1329 / 1901	2.4 / 11.1 / 2.4 / 11.5
12 TH	0218 / 0744 / 1436 / 1959	1.3 / 12.1 / 1.4 / 12.5	27 F	0151 / 0721 / 1411 / 1939	1.9 / 11.5 / 2.0 / 12.0
13 F	0304 / 0826 / 1518 / 2039	1.2 / 12.2 / 1.4 / 12.5	28 SA	0234 / 0759 / 1452 / 2016	1.6 / 11.9 / 1.6 / 12.3
14 SA	0343 / 0904 / 1554 / 2115	1.3 / 12.1 / 1.6 / 12.4	29 SU	0314 / 0836 / 1531 / 2054	1.3 / 12.1 / 1.5 / 12.4
15 SU	0418 / 0938 / 1626 / 2149	1.6 / 11.8 / 1.9 / 11.9	30 M	0354 / 0914 / 1609 / 2131	1.2 / 12.2 / 1.5 / 12.3
			31 TU	0430 / 0951 / 1646 / 2209	1.4 / 12.0 / 1.8 / 11.9

Chart Datum: 6·29 metres below Lallemand System (Mean Sea Level, Marseilles)

TIME ZONE –0100
(French Standard Time)
Subtract 1 hour for UT

For French Summer Time add
ONE hour in non-shaded areas

FRANCE – ST. MALO

LAT 48°38′N   LONG   2°02′W

TIMES AND HEIGHTS OF HIGH AND LOW WATERS

YEAR **1999**

SEPTEMBER

Day	Time	m	Day	Time	m
1 W	0507 / 1029 / 1723 / 2249	1.9 / 11.5 / 2.3 / 11.3	**16** TH	0500 / 1029 / 1714 / 2242	3.3 / 10.3 / 3.6 / 9.9
2 TH	0546 / 1111 / 1805 / 2337	2.5 / 10.9 / 3.0 / 10.5	**17** F	0527 / 1100 / 1748 / 2318	4.0 / 9.6 / 4.3 / 9.1
3 F	0631 / 1203 / 1859	3.2 / 10.2 / 3.7	**18** SA	0605 / 1144 / 1840	4.7 / 8.8 / 4.9
4 SA	0040 / 0732 / 1318 / 2019	9.8 / 3.9 / 9.6 / 4.1	**19** SU	0021 / 0709 / 1313 / 2007	8.4 / 5.2 / 8.3 / 5.2
5 SU	0211 / 0904 / 1455 / 2155	9.4 / 4.1 / 9.6 / 3.9	**20** M	0218 / 1021 / 1509 / 2151	8.2 / 5.3 / 8.5 / 4.8
6 M	0345 / 1030 / 1620 / 2314	9.7 / 3.7 / 10.2 / 3.2	**21** TU	0348 / 1028 / 1708 / 2300	8.8 / 4.6 / 9.3 / 3.9
7 TU	0458 / 1142 / 1723	10.4 / 2.9 / 11.0	**22** W	0447 / 1128 / 1711 / 2354	9.6 / 3.8 / 10.2 / 3.1
8 W	0018 / 0555 / 1242 / 1815	2.4 / 11.2 / 2.2 / 11.7	**23** TH	0534 / 1218 / 1755	10.5 / 2.9 / 11.0
9 TH ●	0113 / 0642 / 1333 / 1859	1.7 / 11.8 / 1.8 / 12.2	**24** F	0042 / 0616 / 1305 / 1837	2.3 / 11.3 / 2.2 / 11.8
10 F	0200 / 0724 / 1417 / 1939	1.4 / 12.1 / 1.5 / 12.5	**25** SA O	0128 / 0657 / 1350 / 1916	1.7 / 11.9 / 1.6 / 12.3
11 SA	0242 / 0802 / 1454 / 2015	1.3 / 12.3 / 1.4 / 12.5	**26** SU	0213 / 0736 / 1433 / 1955	1.2 / 12.4 / 1.2 / 12.7
12 SU	0316 / 0835 / 1527 / 2047	1.4 / 12.2 / 1.5 / 12.3	**27** M	0255 / 0815 / 1514 / 2034	0.9 / 12.7 / 1.0 / 12.9
13 M	0347 / 0906 / 1556 / 2117	1.6 / 12.0 / 1.8 / 12.0	**28** TU	0335 / 0853 / 1554 / 2113	0.9 / 12.7 / 1.1 / 12.7
14 TU	0413 / 0935 / 1622 / 2145	2.1 / 11.5 / 2.3 / 11.4	**29** W	0412 / 0931 / 1632 / 2152	1.1 / 12.4 / 1.5 / 12.2
15 W	0437 / 1002 / 1648 / 2213	2.6 / 11.0 / 2.9 / 10.7	**30** TH	0451 / 1010 / 1710 / 2233	1.7 / 11.8 / 2.2 / 11.4

OCTOBER

Day	Time	m	Day	Time	m
1 F	0529 / 1053 / 1752 / 2321	2.5 / 11.0 / 3.0 / 10.5	**16** SA	0452 / 1022 / 1715 / 2242	4.0 / 9.8 / 4.2 / 9.3
2 SA	0615 / 1146 / 1848	3.4 / 10.2 / 3.8	**17** SU	0526 / 1100 / 1800 / 2334	4.6 / 9.1 / 4.8 / 8.6
3 SU	0028 / 0718 / 1305 / 2012	9.6 / 4.1 / 9.5 / 4.2	**18** M	0621 / 1209 / 1914	5.2 / 8.4 / 5.2
4 M	0205 / 0853 / 1446 / 2148	9.2 / 4.4 / 9.4 / 4.0	**19** TU	0121 / 0756 / 1419 / 2110	8.2 / 5.4 / 8.4 / 5.0
5 TU	0339 / 1021 / 1609 / 2303	9.6 / 3.8 / 10.1 / 3.2	**20** W	0307 / 0941 / 1540 / 2219	8.7 / 4.9 / 9.1 / 4.1
6 W	0446 / 1129 / 1708	10.4 / 3.1 / 10.9	**21** TH	0411 / 1050 / 1636 / 2317	9.5 / 4.0 / 10.0 / 3.2
7 TH	0003 / 0537 / 1224 / 1755	2.4 / 11.1 / 2.4 / 11.6	**22** F	0500 / 1144 / 1723	10.5 / 3.0 / 11.0
8 F	0053 / 0620 / 1311 / 1836	1.9 / 11.7 / 1.9 / 12.0	**23** SA	0009 / 0545 / 1234 / 1806	2.3 / 11.4 / 2.2 / 11.8
9 SA ●	0136 / 0659 / 1351 / 1914	1.6 / 12.0 / 1.7 / 12.2	**24** SU O	0059 / 0628 / 1323 / 1849	1.6 / 12.1 / 1.5 / 12.5
10 SU	0213 / 0733 / 1426 / 1947	1.5 / 12.1 / 1.6 / 12.3	**25** M	0147 / 0710 / 1410 / 1932	1.0 / 12.7 / 1.0 / 12.9
11 M	0246 / 0805 / 1457 / 2018	1.6 / 12.1 / 1.7 / 12.1	**26** TU	0232 / 0751 / 1455 / 2014	0.7 / 13.0 / 0.8 / 13.1
12 TU	0314 / 0834 / 1526 / 2046	1.8 / 11.9 / 1.9 / 11.9	**27** W	0315 / 0832 / 1537 / 2055	0.8 / 13.0 / 0.9 / 12.8
13 W	0340 / 0901 / 1553 / 2114	2.1 / 11.6 / 2.3 / 11.4	**28** TH	0355 / 0913 / 1618 / 2138	1.1 / 12.7 / 1.4 / 12.3
14 TH	0404 / 0928 / 1618 / 2141	2.6 / 11.1 / 2.9 / 10.8	**29** F	0434 / 0954 / 1700 / 2222	1.7 / 12.0 / 2.1 / 11.4
15 F	0427 / 0954 / 1644 / 2209	3.3 / 10.5 / 3.5 / 10.0	**30** SA	0517 / 1040 / 1745 / 2312	2.6 / 11.2 / 2.9 / 10.5
			31 SU	0604 / 1135 / 1842	3.5 / 10.3 / 3.7

NOVEMBER

Day	Time	m	Day	Time	m
1 M	0019 / 0706 / 1250 / 2000	9.6 / 4.2 / 9.6 / 4.1	**16** TU	0553 / 1133 / 1837	4.8 / 8.9 / 4.8
2 TU	0147 / 0836 / 1423 / 2126	9.2 / 4.4 / 9.5 / 4.0	**17** W	0023 / 0707 / 1308 / 2000	8.6 / 5.1 / 8.7 / 4.8
3 W	0315 / 0958 / 1542 / 2238	9.5 / 4.0 / 9.9 / 3.4	**18** TH	0204 / 0840 / 1444 / 2133	8.8 / 4.9 / 9.1 / 4.2
4 TH	0420 / 1103 / 1641 / 2336	10.2 / 3.3 / 10.6 / 2.8	**19** F	0321 / 1000 / 1550 / 2233	9.4 / 4.1 / 9.9 / 3.4
5 F	0509 / 1156 / 1727	10.8 / 2.7 / 11.1	**20** SA	0419 / 1103 / 1644 / 2332	10.3 / 3.2 / 10.8 / 2.5
6 SA	0024 / 0551 / 1241 / 1808	2.3 / 11.4 / 2.3 / 11.5	**21** SU	0510 / 1200 / 1734	11.2 / 2.4 / 11.6
7 SU	0105 / 0629 / 1321 / 1845	2.1 / 11.7 / 2.1 / 11.8	**22** M	0028 / 0557 / 1254 / 1822	1.8 / 12.0 / 1.7 / 12.3
8 M ●	0141 / 0704 / 1356 / 1919	2.0 / 11.9 / 2.0 / 11.8	**23** TU O	0120 / 0644 / 1346 / 1909	1.2 / 12.7 / 1.2 / 12.8
9 TU	0214 / 0735 / 1428 / 1950	2.0 / 11.9 / 2.0 / 11.8	**24** W	0210 / 0729 / 1436 / 1956	0.9 / 13.0 / 0.9 / 13.0
10 W	0243 / 0805 / 1458 / 2020	2.1 / 11.8 / 2.1 / 11.6	**25** TH	0256 / 0814 / 1522 / 2042	0.9 / 13.0 / 1.0 / 12.8
11 TH	0311 / 0833 / 1527 / 2049	2.3 / 11.6 / 2.4 / 11.3	**26** F	0340 / 0859 / 1607 / 2128	1.2 / 12.7 / 1.3 / 12.3
12 F	0338 / 0901 / 1555 / 2118	2.7 / 11.2 / 2.8 / 10.8	**27** SA	0422 / 0944 / 1652 / 2214	1.8 / 12.1 / 1.9 / 11.5
13 SA	0403 / 0930 / 1624 / 2148	3.2 / 10.7 / 3.3 / 10.2	**28** SU	0502 / 1030 / 1738 / 2304	2.5 / 11.4 / 2.6 / 10.7
14 SU	0431 / 1000 / 1656 / 2223	3.8 / 10.1 / 3.9 / 9.6	**29** M	0550 / 1122 / 1831	3.3 / 10.6 / 3.4
15 M	0504 / 1037 / 1738 / 2309	4.4 / 9.5 / 4.4 / 9.0	**30** TU	0002 / 0646 / 1225 / 1934	9.9 / 4.0 / 9.9 / 3.9

DECEMBER

Day	Time	m	Day	Time	m
1 W	0111 / 0800 / 1341 / 2045	9.4 / 4.3 / 9.5 / 4.0	**16** TH	0633 / 1216 / 1916	4.5 / 9.3 / 4.3
2 TH	0229 / 0915 / 1458 / 2155	9.4 / 4.2 / 9.6 / 3.9	**17** F	0100 / 0746 / 1338 / 2029	9.2 / 4.5 / 9.3 / 4.1
3 F	0338 / 1022 / 1602 / 2255	9.7 / 3.8 / 10.0 / 3.5	**18** SA	0222 / 0906 / 1458 / 2148	9.4 / 4.2 / 9.7 / 3.7
4 SA	0433 / 1118 / 1654 / 2346	10.2 / 3.4 / 10.4 / 3.1	**19** SU	0333 / 1021 / 1604 / 2255	10.1 / 3.5 / 10.4 / 3.0
5 SU	0519 / 1206 / 1738	10.7 / 3.0 / 10.8	**20** M	0434 / 1127 / 1703 / 2357	10.9 / 2.8 / 11.2 / 2.5
6 M	0030 / 0559 / 1249 / 1817	2.8 / 11.1 / 2.7 / 11.1	**21** TU	0530 / 1228 / 1759	11.7 / 2.0 / 11.9
7 TU ●	0109 / 0636 / 1326 / 1854	2.5 / 11.4 / 2.5 / 11.3	**22** W O	0055 / 0622 / 1325 / 1852	1.7 / 12.3 / 1.5 / 12.4
8 W	0144 / 0710 / 1401 / 1928	2.4 / 11.5 / 2.4 / 11.4	**23** TH	0150 / 0713 / 1419 / 1943	1.3 / 12.7 / 1.1 / 12.7
9 TH	0217 / 0742 / 1434 / 2000	2.4 / 11.6 / 2.4 / 11.3	**24** F	0240 / 0802 / 1510 / 2032	1.1 / 12.9 / 1.0 / 12.6
10 F	0248 / 0813 / 1507 / 2032	2.5 / 11.5 / 2.5 / 11.2	**25** SA	0328 / 0849 / 1557 / 2119	1.3 / 12.8 / 1.2 / 12.3
11 SA	0318 / 0844 / 1539 / 2103	2.8 / 11.3 / 2.7 / 10.9	**26** SU	0412 / 0934 / 1642 / 2205	1.6 / 12.4 / 1.6 / 11.8
12 SU	0348 / 0915 / 1610 / 2136	3.1 / 11.0 / 3.0 / 10.6	**27** M	0455 / 1018 / 1726 / 2249	2.2 / 11.8 / 2.2 / 11.1
13 M	0418 / 0948 / 1644 / 2212	3.4 / 10.6 / 3.4 / 10.1	**28** TU	0536 / 1103 / 1809 / 2334	2.8 / 11.1 / 2.4 / 10.4
14 TU	0453 / 1026 / 1724 / 2254	3.8 / 10.1 / 3.8 / 9.7	**29** W	0617 / 1151 / 1856	3.5 / 10.3 / 3.6
15 W	0536 / 1112 / 1813 / 2348	4.2 / 9.6 / 4.1 / 9.3	**30** TH	0025 / 0708 / 1246 / 1949	9.8 / 4.0 / 9.7 / 4.1
			31 F	0126 / 0813 / 1355 / 2052	9.3 / 4.4 / 9.3 / 4.3

15

Chart Datum: 6·29 metres below Lallemand System (Mean Sea Level, Marseilles)

ST MALO/DINARD   8-15-17

Ille et Vilaine 48°38'·35N 02°01'·80W Rtgs: (Vauban) 3-4-1;
(Sablons) 3-3-1

CHARTS
AC 2700, *3659, 2669*; SHOM 7130, 7155, 7156, 6966; ECM
535; Imray C33B; Stanfords 16

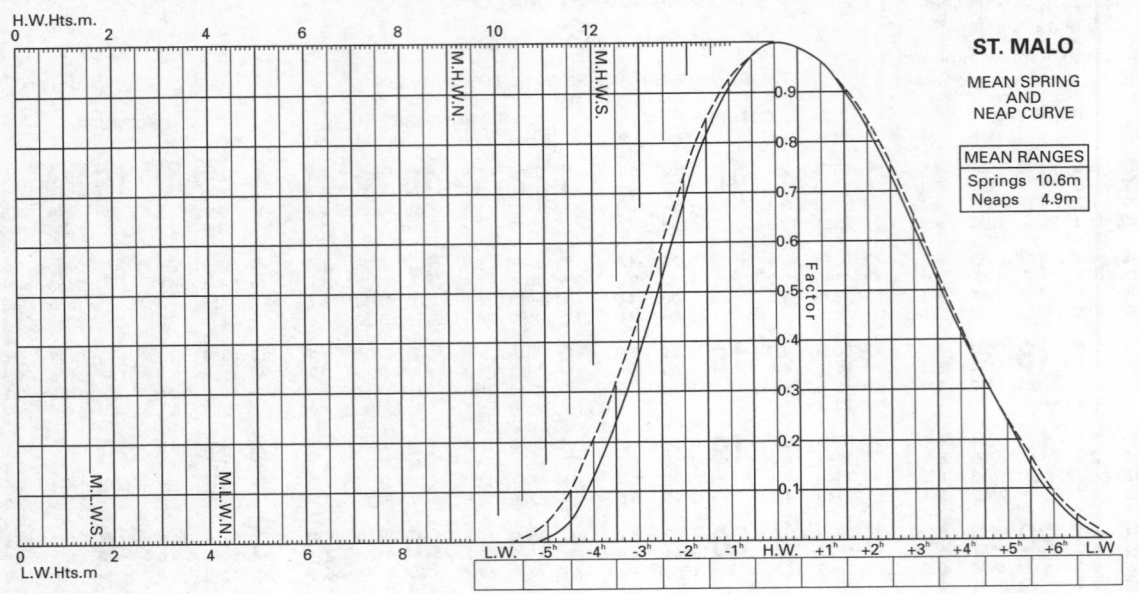

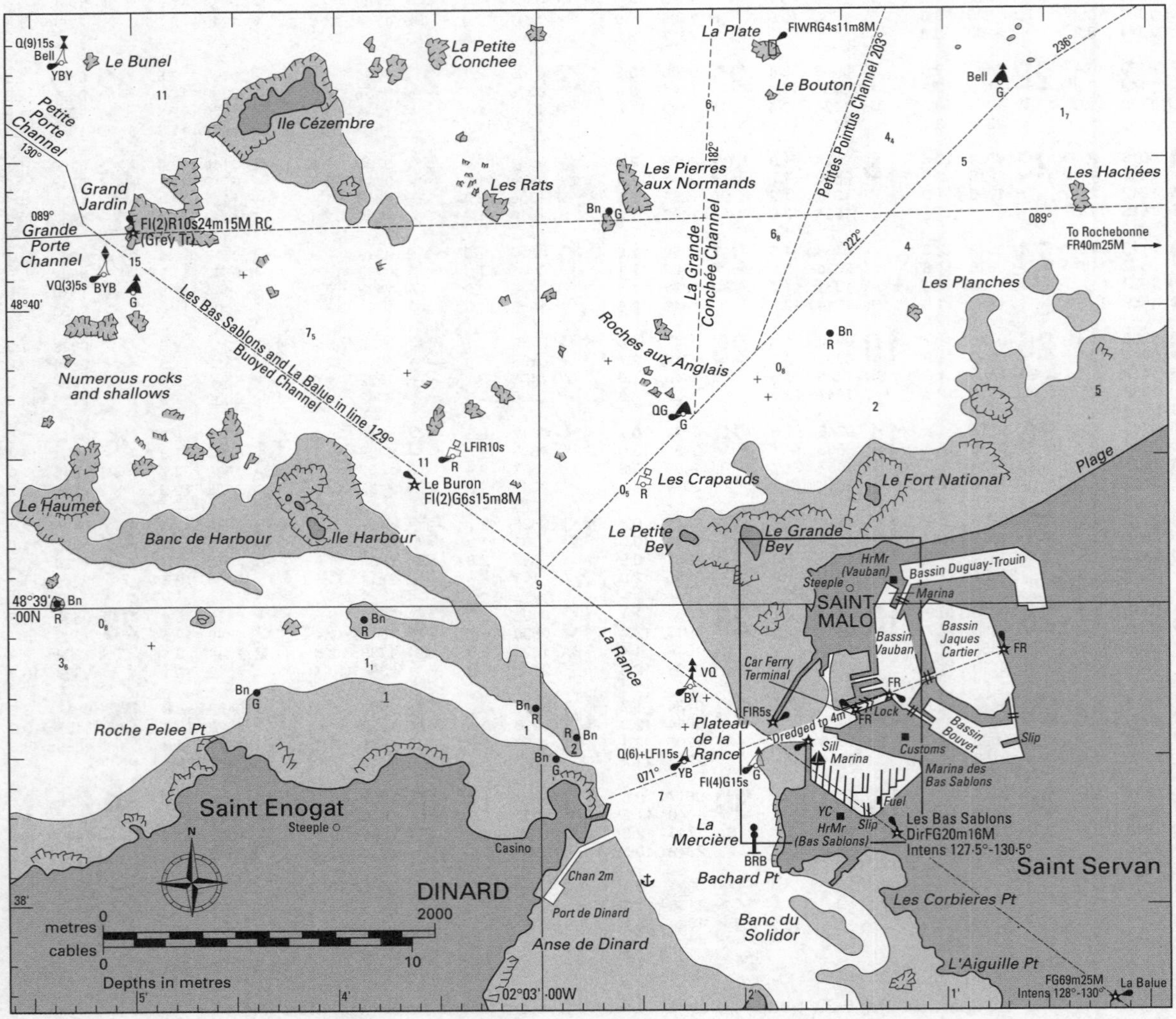

ST. MALO

MEAN SPRING
AND
NEAP CURVE

MEAN RANGES
Springs 10.6m
Neaps 4.9m

ST MALO/DINARD *continued*

TIDES
−0506 Dover; ML 6·8; Duration 0535; Zone −0100
Saint-Malo is a Standard Port and the tidal predictions for each day of the year are given above.

SHELTER
Two options: (1) Lock into the Bassin Vauban, min depth 6m. Excellent shelter near the walled city. Bassin Duguay-Trouin, via bridge, is better for long stay. No ⚓ in basins; 3kn speed limit. Outside the lock are 3 waiting buoys N of appr chan; keep clear of vedette and Condor berths. See next column for lock times and signals.
(2) Good shelter nearer St Servan in Bas Sablons marina, entered over sill 2m above CD. Ⓥ berths are 32-66 (even side) and 43-75 (odd side) on Pontoon A, and 92-102 and 91-101 on Pontoon B. N end of pontoon 'A' is exposed to NW winds. Caution: marina ent is only 40m wide, close S of ferry pier extending W from N corner of Bas-Sablons basin and beyond marina bkwtr, Fl G 4s 7m 5M. Two W waiting buoys outside. Depth of water over sill is shown on a digital gauge atop the bkwtr, visible only from seaward; inside, a conventional gauge at base of bkwtr shows depths <3m.
At **Dinard** there is a yacht ⚓ and moorings, reached by a beaconed chan, all dredged 2m, but virtually filled by local boats. (Marina planned).

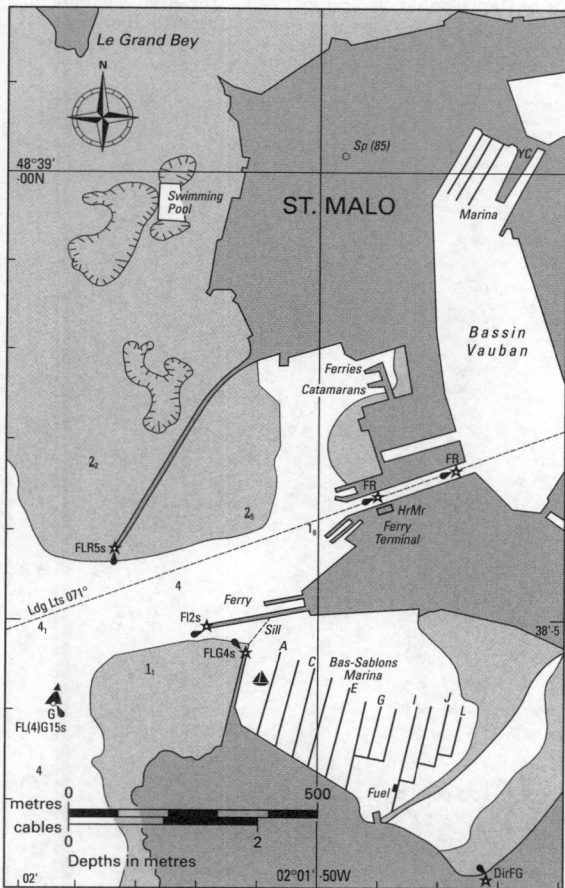

NAVIGATION
WPT Fairway SWM buoy, L Fl 10s Whis, 48°41'·42N 02°07'·20W, 307°/127° from/to Grand Jardin lt, 1·9M. Care is needed due to many dangerous rks around the appr chans, plus strong tidal streams. The 3 main chans are:
1. Petite Porte (130°/129°); best from N or NW and at night.
2. Grande Porte (089°/129°); from the W.
These 2 chans meet at Le Grand Jardin lt and continue 129°.
3. La Grande Conchée (182°); most direct from N.
The first two are well lit. In fresh W'lies it can be quite rough in the vicinity of Le Grand Jardin.

LIGHTS AND MARKS
Chenal de la Petite Porte: Ldg Its 130°, front, Le Grand Jardin, Fl (2) R 10s 24m 15M, grey tr; rear, La Balue, FG 69m 25M.
Chenal de la Grande Porte: Ldg Its 089°, front, Le Grand Jardin; rear, Rochebonne, FR 40m 24M, (off chartlet) 4·2M from front; leads into Chenal de la Petite Porte.
Inner ldg Its 129° from Le Grand Jardin lt ho: Front, Les Bas Sablons, FG 20m 16M; rear, La Balue (as above).
La Plate lt, Fl WRG 4s 11m 9/6M, W140°-203°, R203°-210°, W210°-225°, G225°-140°.
St Malo lock: Ldg Its, 2 FR, 071° into lock. Lock operates five times in each direction, ie
Inbound: HW −2½, −1½, −½, HW+½, +1½.
Outbound: HW −2, −1, HW, +1, +2.
Freeflow operation is rare due to road traffic over bridge.
Lock sigs:

Ⓖ
Ⓦ } No ent to lock without instructions
Ⓖ

Ⓖ
Ⓖ } Boats may enter lock
Ⓖ

Ⓡ
Ⓡ } No ent. Keep 200m from gates
Ⓡ

Ⓨ alongside the top lt shows that both gates are open; instructions are the same, but beware current.
2 Ⓡ over Ⓖ = all movements prohib, except departure of large ships.

RADIO TELEPHONE
Call: *St Malo Port* or *Grand Jardin* VHF Ch **12** 16 (H24).
Port Vauban and Les Bas Sablons marinas Ch 09.

TELEPHONE
ST MALO: Port Hr Mr 02·99·20·25·01; Hr Mr (Vauban) 02·99·56·51·91; Hr Mr (Sablons) 02·99·81·71·34; Aff Mar 02·99·56·87·00; CROSS 02·98·89·31·31; SNSM 02·98·89·31·31; ⌗ 02·99·81·65·90; Météo 02·99·46·10·46; Auto 08·36·68·08·35; Police 02·99·81·52·30; Ⓗ 02·99·56·56·19; Brit Consul 02·99·46·26·64.
DINARD: Hr Mr 02·99·46·65·55; ⌗ 02·99·46·12·42; Météo 02·99·46·10·46; Auto 08·36·68·08·35; Ⓗ 02·99·46·18·68.

FACILITIES
ST MALO: **Bassin Vauban** (250 + 100 Ⓥ) ☎ 02·99·56·51·91, 🕾 02·99·56·57·81, FF91.50, FW, AC, C (1 ton); **Société Nautique de la Baie de St. Malo** ☎ 02·99·40·84·42, Bar (visitors welcome).
ST SERVAN: **Marina Les Bas-Sablons** (1216 + 64 visitors on Pontoon A, berths 43-75 and 32-64) ☎ 02·99·81·71·34, 🕾 02·99·81·91·81, FF93.50, Slip, C, AC, FW, CH, BH (10 ton), Gaz, R, YC, Bar, P & D at Pontoon I; Note: Fuel may only be paid for by French credit card.
Services: El, Ⓔ, ME, CH, Sh, C, BY, SM, SHOM.
Town Slip, P, Gaz, D, ME, El, Sh, C, V, R, Bar, ✉, Ⓑ, ⇌, ✈ (Dinard). Ferry: Portsmouth, Poole or Jersey.
DINARD: **Port de Dinard** ☎ 02·99·46·65·55, Slip, ⚓, M FF83, P, D, L, FW, temp AB; **YC de Dinard** ☎ 02·99·46·14·32, Bar; **Services:** ME, El, Ⓔ, Sh, M, SM.
Town P, D, ME, El, CH, V, Gaz, R, Bar, ✉, Ⓑ, ⇌, ✈.

OTHER HARBOURS EAST OF ST MALO

CANCALE, Ille-et-Vilaine, 48°40'·10N 01°51'·10W. AC *3659*; SHOM 7131, 7155. HW −0510 on Dover (UT); ML 7·2m; Duration 0535. See 8.15.15. A drying hbr just inside Bay of Mont St Michel, 1M SW of Pte de la Chaine. Area dries to about 1M off-shore; ⚓ off Pte de la Chaine in deep water. Drying berths usually available in La Houle, the hbr in Cancale. Exposed to winds SW to SE. Jetty hd lt Oc (3) G 12s 12m 8M, obsc when brg < 223°. Facilities: **Quay** D, P, C (1·5 ton), FW; **Services:** El, M, ME, Sh; **Club Nautique de Cancale** ☎ 02·99·89·90·22.
Town (famous for oysters), Ⓑ, Bar, D, P, ✉, R, V.

ROTHENEUF, Ille-et-Vilaine, 48°41'·42N 01°57'·56W. AC 2700, *3659*; SHOM 7131, 7155. HW −0510 on Dover (UT); Tides as for St. Malo; ML 7·0m; Duration 0540. Complete shelter in hbr which dries completely. ⚓ outside in 4m just N of spar bn marking ent. Rks on both sides of ent which is less than 170m wide. Safest to enter when rks uncovered. Ldg line at 163°, W side of Pte Benard and old converted windmill. There are no lts. Facilities: FW, Slip.
Village Bar, D, P, R, V.

15

RIVER RANCE/DINAN   8-15-18

Ille-et-Vilaine 48°37'·10N 02°01'·62W (Barrage)   Rtg 3-3-1

CHARTS
AC 2700, *3659*; SHOM 4233, 7130; Imray C33B

TIDES
Standard Port ST MALO (◀—) Zone –0100

Water levels up-river of the Rance hydro-electric tidal barrage are strongly affected by the operation of the sluice gates and occasional use of the turbines as pumps. On most days from 0700 – 2100LT, 4m above CD is maintained. There is generally 8·5m above CD for a period of 4 hours from 0700 – 2000LT.

A French language pamphlet, issued by Électricité de France, should be obtained from Hr Mr's at St Malo or Bas Sablons, or from the office at the barrage lock. It gives forecasts for the summer months of when heights of 4m and 8·5m above CD will occur in the period 0700 – 2000LT. The local daily paper *Ouest-France* gives a forecast for the next day of HW and LW up-stream of the barrage, under the heading *Usine Marémotrice de la Rance*. A visit to the barrage exhibition centre by the lock may be instructive.

SHELTER
Good shelter up-river dependent on wind direction. The principal ⚓s/moorings on the E bank are at St Suliac and Mordreuc, and at La Richardais, La Jouvente, Le Minihic and La Pommeraie on the W bank. Marinas at Plouër, Lyvet (E bank, beyond Chatelier lock) and Dinan: see opp.

NAVIGATION
From St Malo/Dinard, appr the lock at the W end of the barrage between a prohib area to port, marked by PHM buoys and wire cables, and Pointe de La Jument to stbd. White waiting buoys are on the W side of the appr chan, either side of the lock.

Lock opening by day on the hour, every hour provided the level is at least 4m above CD; from 2030 – 0430 opening is on request. Yachts should arrive at H –20 mins, ideally HW –3. The lifting road-bridge across the lock opens between H and H +15. Boats leaving the lock have priority. Up-river of the lock a further prohib area to port is marked as above.

The 3M chan to St Suliac has min depth of 2m; the next 6M to the Chatelier lock partially dries. The suspension bridge and road bridge at Port St. Hubert have 23m clearance. A viaduct 1M beyond Mordreuc has 19m clearance.

The Chatelier lock and swing bridge operate 0800-2000LT, provided there is at least 8·5m rise of tide. HW Chatelier is 2-3 hours after HW St Malo depending on the barrage. Allow 2-3 hours from the barrage to Chatelier. The final 3M to Dinan is unobstructed overhead and has a published min depth in the marked chan of 1·8m; check with lock-keeper. Dinan gives access to the Ille et Rance Canal and River Vilaine to Biscay (see 8.15.19).

LIGHTS AND MARKS
Approaching the barrage from seaward:
Pte de la Jument bn tr, Fl (5) G20s 6m 4M; PHM Prohib Area buoy opposite, Fl R 4s.
NW side of lock, Fl G 4s, with G △ on W background.
First dolphin, Fl R (2) 6s, with R □ on W background.
Approaching from Dinan:
PHM, Oc R 4s, at S end of Prohib Area.
Last dolphin, Oc R (2) 6s, with R □ on W background.
SW side of lock, Iso G4s, G △ on W background.
Lock entry sigs are modified IPTS:
3 vert G □s   = Entry permitted.
3 vert R □s   = Entry prohibited.
Vert G W G □s = Proceed as individually instructed by lock keeper.
Additional sigs on the barrage to the E of the lock show the direction of flow through the turbines.
The chan up-river is partly buoyed and marked by stakes.

RADIO TELEPHONE
Barrage lock: VHF Ch 13.

TELEPHONE
Water levels/navigation 02·99·46·14·46; Barrage/lock info 02·99·46·21·87; Hr Mr (Richardais) 02·99·46·24·20; Hr Mr (Plouër) 02·96·86·83·15; Chatelier lock 02·96·39·55·66; Hr Mr (Lyvet) 02·96·83·35·57; Hr Mr (Dinan) 02·96·39·04·67; Météo 02·99·46·10·46; Auto 08.36.68.08.35; Aff Mar 02·96·39·56·44; Police 02·99·81·52·30; Brit Consul 02·99·46·26·64.

FACILITIES
St. Suliac Slip, M, Bar, R, V, Divers (Convoimer);
Mordreuc Slip, L, M, Bar, R, P, V; **La Richardais** El, ME, Sh.

Villages: Bar, D, P, ✉, R, V, Ⓑ; **La Jouvente** AB, Bar, R; **Le Minihic** M, L, Slip, ME, El, Sh; **La Pommeraie** M, L, SC, R.

MARINAS ON THE RIVER RANCE

PLOUËR, Côtes d'Armor, 49°32'·00N 01°58'·00W. Rtg 3-3-2. Marina is on the W bank of the R Rance, 6M above the barrage and 0·5M above the two St Hubert bridges. Access approx HW±3, when tide is 8m above CD, giving at least 1·5m water above rising gate. Approach on about 285°, ent in line with Plouër church spire. Unlit PHM and SHM perches are 30m from ent at S end of bkwtr. Ent is marked by FR and FG lts which are lit, by day or night, whenever access is available. Depth gauge (hard to read) has W flood-light. Facilities: **Marina** (240+ ♥ on pontoon B) ☎ 02·96·86·83·15. VHF Ch 09. AB FF38-72, Slip, AC, CH, FW, BY, C, ME, BH (10-14 ton), R, Bar, limited V.

LYVET, Hr Mr ☎ 02·96·83·35·57; **Marina** (175 berths) AC, FW, R, Bar, limited V. Immediately upstream of Chatelier lock, on the E bank.

DINAN, Hr Mr ☎ 02·96·39·56·44; **Marina** AC, FW, P, D, C for masts, R, Bar. Berths line the W bank of the river, with finger pontoons close to the Port. Low bridge beyond Port has 2·5m headroom, giving access to the Ille et Rance canal. **Town** (75m above water level) V, R, ✉, Ⓑ, ⚞, ✈ (Dinard).

Ille et Rance canal (see opposite): On the Breton canals the tolls charged elsewhere in France (see 8.15.8) are not envisaged. A certificate of competence is not required, unless LOA >15m or speed >20kph/11kn.

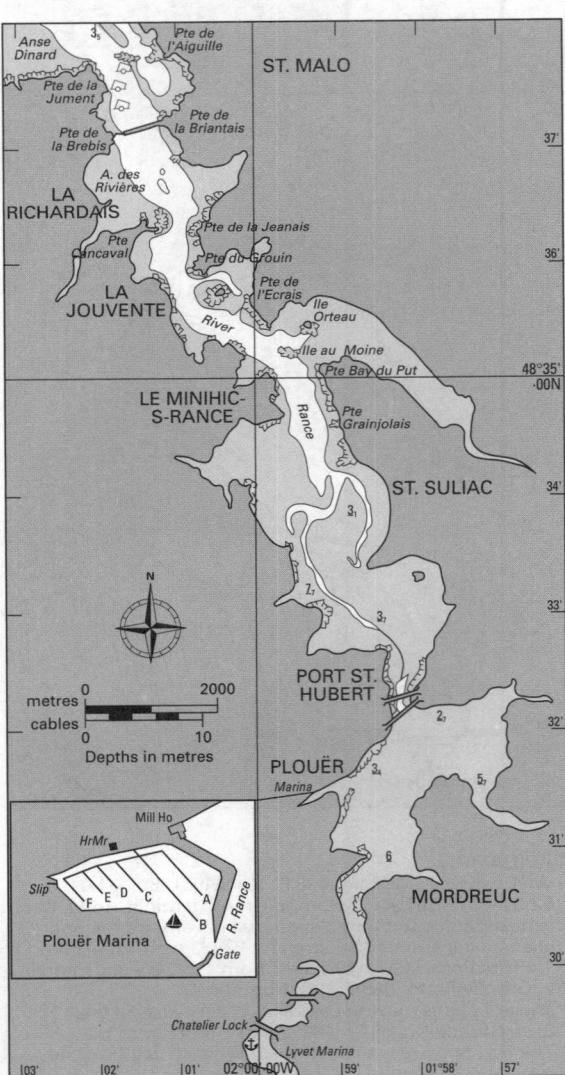

INLAND WATERWAYS OF BRITTANY

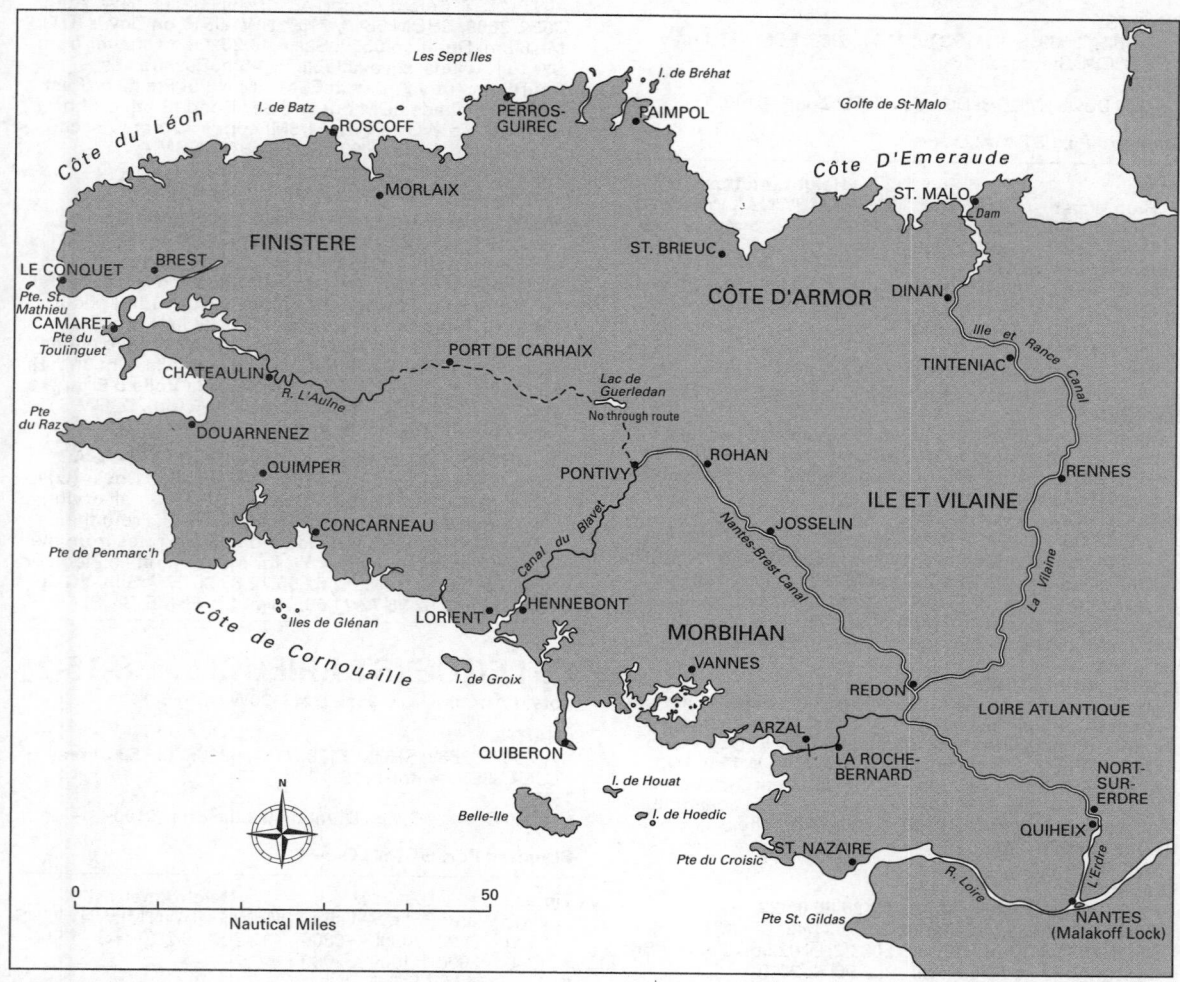

NAVIGATION

Canals and rivers across and within Brittany enable boats of limited water and air drafts to go from the Channel to the Bay of Biscay avoiding the passage around Finistere. Dinan to Arzal takes about 5 days. Distances, number of locks, boat size and speed limits are summarised opposite.

LOCKS

From Apr to Sept locks are worked 7 days a week 0800-1930LT, closing for lunch 1230-1330 approx. All locks are attended, but a fair measure of self-help is the order of the day. In Jul/Aug, in order to conserve water, locks may open on the hour only (and at H+30 if traffic demands).

ACCESS

For prior estimate of max draught possible, write: Equipement, Ille et Vilaine, 1 Avenue de Mail, 35000 Rennes. (☎ 02·99.59.20.60; ☎ 02·99.54.03.99); or obtain recorded information update on ☎ 02·99.59.11.12.
For latest info on the Ille et Rance Canal/R Vilaine, contact: Rennes ☎ 02·99.59.20.60 or Redon ☎ 02·99.71.03.78.
For the Lorient-Nantes Canal, contact:
Nantes ☎ 02·40.71.02.00; Hennebont ☎ 02·97.85.15.15; Lorient ☎ 02·97.21.21.54; Pontivy ☎ 02·97.25.55.21.
Closures *(Chômages)* for maintenance are scheduled in late autumn and in winter each Wednesday (approx first week in November to last week in March).

INFORMATION

For maps and guide books write (with SAE) to:
Comité des Canaux Bretons,
Service de Documentation du Comité,
12 rue de Jemmapes, 44000 Nantes (☎ 02·40.47.42.94).
Inland Waterways of France: D Edwards-May (Imray) and the ECM Carte-Guide No 12 are recommended.
TOLLS may be due on the R Loire only; see 8.15.8 for rates.

SUMMARY	Length km	No of locks	Max draft m	Max air draft m	Max LOA m	Max beam m	Speed limit kn
St MALO-ARZAL (Ille et Rance Canal and La Vilaine)							
R Rance-Dinan	29·0	1	1·3	19	25	–	5·4
Ille et Rance Canal							
Dinan-Rennes	79·0	48	1·2	2·5	25	4·5	4·3
Rennes-Redon	89·0	13	1·2	3·2/2·6*	25	4·5	4·3
Redon-Arzal	42·0	1	1·3	–			
*Depending on water level							
LORIENT - NANTES (See 8.17.14)							
Canal du Blavet							
Lorient-Pontivy	70	28	1·4	2·6	25	4·6	4·3
Nantes-Brest Canal							
	184·3	106	–	3	25	4·6	4·3
Pontivy-Rohan			0·8 (possible closure)				
Rohan-Josselin			1·0				
Josselin-Redon			1·4				
Redon-Quiheix			1·1				
L'Erdre River	27·6	1	1·4	3·8	400	6·2	13·5
R Loire, above Nantes (8.17.28), may be navigable to Angers.							
R L'AULNE (See 8.16.28)							
Brest-Chateaulin	42	1	3·0	N/A	25		–
Chateaulin-Carhaix							
	72	33	1·1	2·5	25	4·6	4·3

15

DAHOUET   8-15-20
Côte d'Armor 48°34'·85N 02°34'·30W   Rtg 3-2-2

CHARTS
AC *3674*, 2669; SHOM 7310, 7154, 6966; ECM 536; Imray
C33B, C34; Stanfords 16

TIDES
−0520 Dover; ML 6·3; Duration 0550; Zone −0100

Standard Port ST-MALO (←—)

Times				Height (metres)			
High Water		Low Water		MHWS	MHWN	MLWN	MLWS
0100	0800	0300	0800	12·2	9·2	4·3	1·6
1300	2000	1500	2000				
Differences DAHOUET							
−0006	−0006	−0020	−0015	−0·9	−0·6	−0·3	−0·3
ERQUY							
−0005	0000	−0018	−0012	−0·6	−0·4	−0·1	−0·1
SAINT CAST							
−0002	−0002	−0005	−0005	−0·2	−0·1	−0·1	−0·1

SHELTER
Good, but ent (dries <u>4</u>m) unsafe in fresh NW winds; a bar
may form after strong NW'lies. Outer hbr (FVs) dries
<u>5</u>·5m; access HW±2. Marina, min depth 2·5m, accessible
over sill 5·5m above CD.

NAVIGATION
WPT 48°35'·28N 02°35'·28W, unlit NCM By, 297°/117°
from/to La Petite Muette SHM lt tr, 0·8M; appr in W sector
(see 8.15.20 chartlet) until close in. Hbr ent is a narrow
break in the cliffs. Pick up 148° transit of 2 W bns, leaving
these to port and Petite Muette to stbd. The W ent, S of
Petite Muette is dangerous. There are rks W and SW of
the ent.

LIGHTS AND MARKS
The wide beach at Val André and the W chapel at hbr ent
are both conspic; see also 8.15.20 for other conspic
marks in the bay. Appr is marked by G/W lt tr, La Petite
Muette, Fl WRG 4s 10m 9/6M, G055°-114°, W114°-146°,
R146°-196°. Stone pagoda is seen NE of ent. SHM bn, Fl
(2) G 6s, vis 156°-286°, marks the narrow ent abeam the 2
W ldg bns. Sill ent has PHM and SHM perches.

RADIO TELEPHONE
VHF Ch 09 16.

TELEPHONE
Hr Mr 02·96·72·82·85; Météo 02·36·65·02·22;
⑂ 02·96·74·75·32; Aff Mar 02·96·72·31·42; CROSS
02·98·89·31·31; Auto 08.36.68.08.22; Ⓗ 02·96·45·23·28; Brit
Consul 02·99·46·26·64; Police 02·96·72·22·18.

FACILITIES
Marina (318+20) ☎ 02·96·72·82·85, FF87, FW, AC, BH (10
ton), Slip, C (14 ton); **Quay** P, D, C (4 ton); **YC du Val-
André** ☎ 02·96·72·95·28;
Services: CH, El, ME, Sh. **Town**, V, R, Bar, ⇌ (Lamballe),
✈ (St. Brieuc). Ferry: St. Malo-Portsmouth.

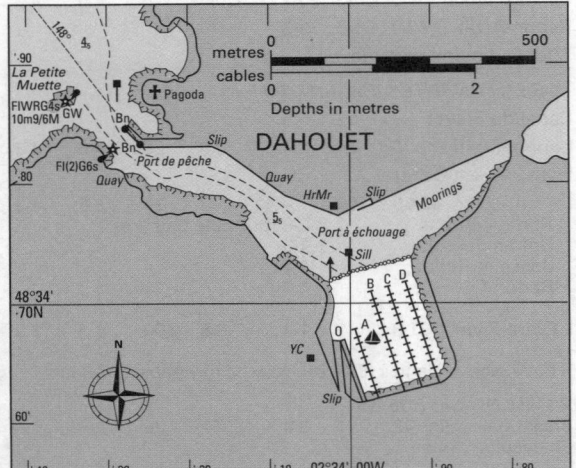

OTHER HARBOURS BETWEEN ST MALO AND DAHOUET

SAINT CAST, Côte d'Armor, 48°38'·45N 02°14'·51W. AC
3659, 2669; SHOM 5646, 7155. HW −0515 on Dover (UT);
ML 6·8m; Duration 0550. See 8.15.20. Good shelter from
SW to N winds; ⚓s available in 1·8m. Beware Les
Bourdinots (dry <u>2</u>m) with ECM ¾M NE of Pte de St Cast,
and La Feuillade (IDM bn) and Bec Rond (R bn) off hbr.
Mole hd, Iso WG 4s 11m 11/8M; appr in either W sector
(see 8.15.4). Hr Mr ☎ 02·96·41·88·34; SNSM
☎ 02·96·41·88·34; Facilities: **YC** ☎ 02·96·41·91·77.
Town CH, El, ME, Sh, Ⓑ, Bar, D, P, ✉, R, V.

ERQUY, Côte d'Armor, 48°38'·10N 02°28'·60W. AC 3672,
3674, 2669; SHOM 7310, 7154. HW −0515 on Dover (UT);
ML 6·5m; Duration 0550. See 8.15.20. Sheltered from E,
but exposed to SW/W winds. Hbr dries and is usually full
of FVs. Beware Plateau des Portes d'Erquy (dry) about
2M to W. From S, beware rks off Pte de la Houssaye.
Mole hd lt Oc (3+1) WRG 12s 11m 11/8M; appr in either
W sector (see 8.15.4). Inner jetty hd Fl R 2·5s 10m 3M. Hr
Mr and ⑂ ☎ 02·96·72·19·32; **Cercle de la Voile d'Erquy**
☎ 02·96·72·32·40; Facilities: **Quay** C (3·5 ton), D, FW, P;
Town CH, El, ME, Sh, R, V, Bar.

VAL-ANDRÉ, Côte d'Armor, 48°35'·88N 02°33'·24W. AC
3674, 2669; SHOM 7310, 7154. HW −0520 on Dover (UT);
ML 6·1m; Duration 0550. Tides as 8.15.20. Small drying
hbr exposed to S/SW winds; access HW±3. From the E
beware Le Verdelet, and Platier des Trois Têtes from the
W. Berth on the quay, ask YC for mooring off Le Piegu or
⚓ off. Facilities: Hr Mr ☎ 02·96·72·83·20, FW, Slip; **YC du
Val-André** ☎ 02·96·72·21·68; **Town** CH, El, ME, Sh, Bar, R, V.

LE LÉGUÉ (ST BRIEUC)   8-15-21
Côte d'Armor 48°31'·95N 02°43'·30W   Rtg 3-1-3

CHARTS
AC *3674*, 2669; SHOM 7128, 7154, 6966; ECM 536; Imray
C34, C33B; Stanfords 16

TIDES
−0520 Dover; ML 6·5; Duration 0550; Zone −0100

Standard Port ST-MALO (←—)

Times				Height (metres)			
High Water		Low Water		MHWS	MHWN	MLWN	MLWS
0100	0800	0300	0800	12·2	9·2	4·3	1·6
1300	2000	1500	2000				
Differences LE LÉGUÉ							
+0005	+0005	−0013	−0003	−0·7	−0·3	−0·2	−0·2

SHELTER
Very good in Le Légué (the port for St Brieuc), especially
in the wet basin. Yachts use Bassin No 2 (min 3m) near
viaduct. Lock opens HW −2 to HW+1 sp; HW ±1 nps. The
lock sill is 5·0m above CD. Yachts can wait against Le Quai
Gilette (N bank), but soft mud slopes very steeply to chan.

NAVIGATION
WPT 48°34'·39N 02°41'·09W, Le Légué SWM buoy, Fl Mo
(A) 10s, Whis, 030°/210° from/to Pte de l'Aigle lt, 2·6M.
Appr via buoyed chan (via some gaps); not advised in
strong N/NE winds. The area dries E/SE of conspic Pte du
Roselier. Keep close to Pte à l'Aigle to avoid Les Galettes.

LIGHTS AND MARKS
Conspic marks: Rohein tr, from N, and Le Verdelet Is
from E (beware Plateau des Jaunes). No ldg lines; 2 lts
on the NW bank of the river de Gouet ent: Pte de l'Aigle,
QG 13m 8M, vis 160°-070°, W tr G top. Jetée de la
Douane (W columns with G top), Iso G 4s 6m 2M.

RADIO TELEPHONE
Call: *Légué Port* VHF Ch 12 16 (approx HW−2 to +1½).

TELEPHONE
Hr Mr 02·96·33·35·41; Aff Mar 02·96·61·22·61; CROSS
02·98·89·31·31; Météo 02·99·46·10·46 and VHF Ch 13; Auto
08·36·68·08·22; SNSM 02·96·88·35·47; ⑂ 02·96·33·33·03;
Police 02·96·94·52·25; Dr St Brieuc 02·96·61·49·07; Brit
Consul 02·99·46·26·64.

FACILITIES
Quai (100+20 visitors), AB FF61, C (30 ton); P & D (cans on
quai or tanker); **Services:** Sh, ME, El, CH, SM, Ⓔ, El, CH.
Town (St Brieuc) P & D (cans), FW, Gaz, V, R, Bar, ✉, Ⓑ,
⇌, ✈. Ferry: St Malo.

LE LÉGUÉ/ST BRIEUC *continued*

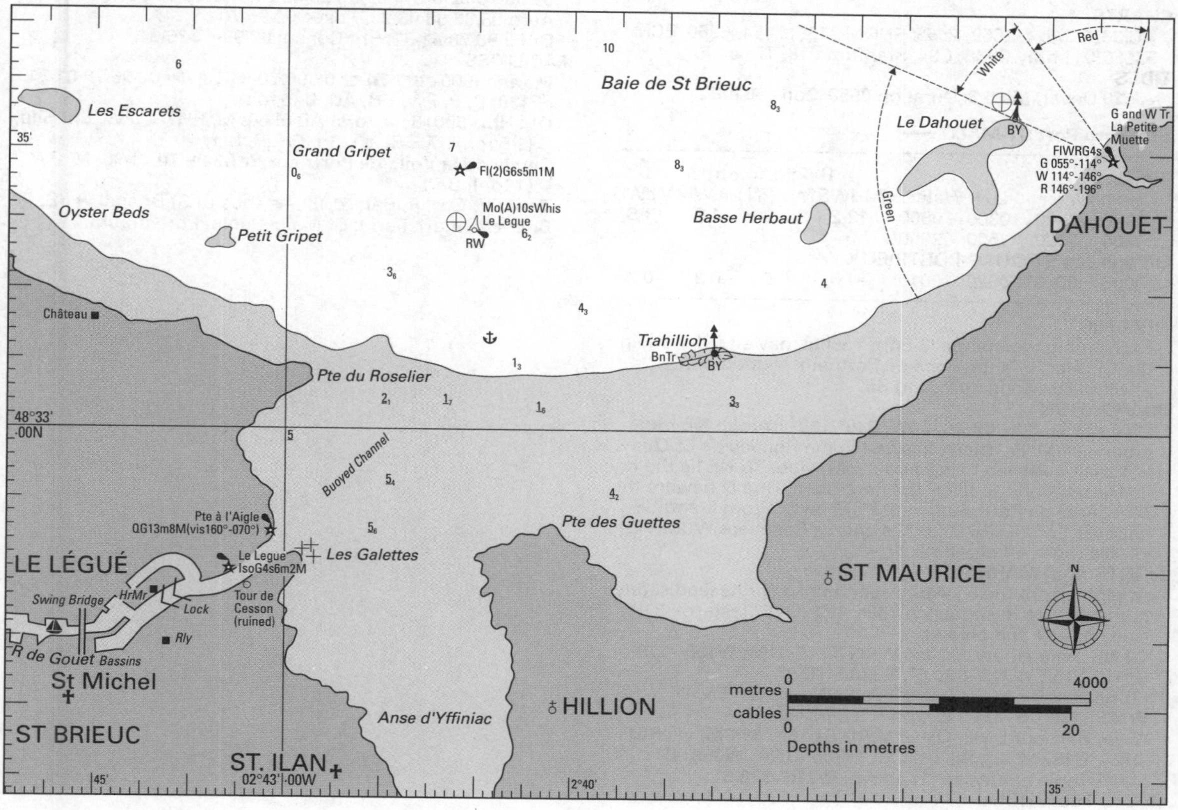

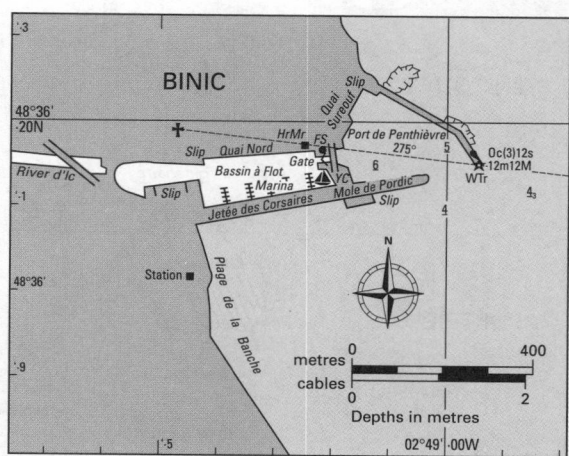

Les Escarets
Baie de St Brieuc
Le Dahouet
Grand Gripet
Fl(2)G6s5m1M
Mo(A)10sWhis
Le Legue
RW
White
Red
Green
G and W Tr
La Petite Muette
FlWRG4s
G 055°-114°
W 114°-146°
R 146°-196°
BY
Oyster Beds
Petit Gripet
Basse Herbaut
DAHOUET
Château
Trahillion
BnTr
Pte du Roselier
48°33'·00N
Buoyed Channel
Pte à l'Aigle
QG13m8M(vis160°-070°)
Pte des Guettes
Les Galettes
LE LÉGUÉ
Le Legue
IsoG4s6m2M
Swing Bridge
HrMr
Lock
Tour de Cesson (ruined)
Rly
R de Gouet
Bassins
St Michel
ST BRIEUC
ST MAURICE
Anse d'Yffiniac
HILLION
ST. ILAN
02°43'·00W
2°40'
metres
cables
Depths in metres

BINIC 8-15-22

Côte d'Armor 48°36'·12N 02°48'·90W Rtg 4-3-2

CHARTS

AC *3674*, 2669; SHOM 7128, 7154, 6966; ECM 536; Imray C33B; Stanfords 16

TIDES

–0525 Dover; ML 6·3; Duration 0550; Zone –0100

Standard Port ST-MALO (⟵)

Times				Height (metres)			
High Water		Low Water		MHWS	MHWN	MLWN	MLWS
0100	0800	0300	0800	12·2	9·2	4·3	1·6
1300	2000	1500	2000				
Differences BINIC							
–0003	–0003	–0025	–0010	–0·8	–0·6	–0·3	–0·3

SHELTER

Good, especially in Bassin à Flot/marina (1·5-3m). Easy access HW±3 by day/night to Avant Port (dries), except in E winds. Lock opens, in working hrs, approx HW–1 to HW near sp, if tide reaches 9·5m; no opening near nps, when gate may be closed for 4 or 5 days.

NAVIGATION

WPT 48°37'·00N 02°42'·00W, 078°/258° from/to ent, 4·7M. Best appr from E, from Baie de St Brieuc (see 10·18·5) keeping E of Caffa ECM, from which ent bears 246°; or from N through Rade de Portrieux. Ent between moles dries 4·2m.

LIGHTS AND MARKS

Ldg line 275°, N mole hd lt tr, Oc (3) 12s 12m 12M, W tr, G gallery, on with church spire.

Gate and sliding bridge sigs on mast N of gate:

By day: St Andrew's Cross, B on W flag = Gate open
By night: Ⓦ and Ⓡ (hor) = No entry
Ⓦ and Ⓖ (hor) = No exit
Ⓡ and Ⓖ (hor) = No exit/entry

RADIO TELEPHONE

VHF Ch 09.

TELEPHONE

Hr Mr 02·96·73·61·86, ⛴ 02·96.73.72.38; Aff Mar 02·96·70·42·27; SNSM 02·96.73.74.41; CROSS 02·98·89·31·31; # 02·96·74·75·32; Météo 02·99·46·10·46; Auto 08·36·68·08·22; Police 02·96·73·60·32; Dr 02·96·42·61·05; Ⓗ 02·96.94.31.71; Brit Consul 02·99·46·26·64.

FACILITIES

Bassin (540+60), AB FF71.20, FW, AC, C (20 ton), Slip; **Club Nautique de Binic** ☎ 02·96·73·31·67; **Services:** CH, ME, El, Ⓔ, Sh, SM, SHOM. **Town** P, V, Gaz, ⊡, R, Bar, ✉, Ⓑ, ⇌ (bus to St Brieuc), ✈ (St Brieuc). Ferry: St Malo.

15

BINIC
48°36'·20N
Slip
Quai Surcouf
Port de Penthièvre
275°
Oc(3)12s 12m12M
WTr
HrMr
FS
Slip
Quai Nord
Gate
Bassin à Flot
Marina
YC
River d'Ic
Slip
Jetée des Corsaires
Mole de Pordic
Slip
Station
Plage de la Banche
48°36'
metres
cables
Depths in metres
02°49'·00W

ST QUAY-PORTRIEUX   8-15-23

Côte d'Armor 48°38′·90N 02°48′·88W   Rtg 2-2-2

CHARTS

AC 3672, *3674*, 2669, *2668*; SHOM 7128, 7154, 6966; ECM
536, 537; Imray C33B, C34; Stanfords 16, 17

TIDES

−0520 Dover; ML 6·3; Duration 0550; Zone −0100

Standard Port ST-MALO (←)

Times				Height (metres)			
High Water		Low Water		MHWS	MHWN	MLWN	MLWS
0100	0800	0300	0800	12·2	9·2	4·3	1·6
1300	2000	1500	2000				
Differences ST QUAY-PORTRIEUX							
−0005	0000	−0020	−0010	−1·0	−0·6	−0·3	−0·2

SHELTER

Excellent in the marina (3·5m). Yachts may also dry out in
the Old Hbr. ⚓ in the Rade de Portrieux is good but
affected by winds from N to SE.

NAVIGATION

WPT 48°41′·00N 02°49′·60W, 349°/169° from/to NE mole
elbow, 2·0M. Portrieux lies inside the Roches de St Quay,
the chan between being about ½M wide. To NE lie the rky
Ile Harbour and to the E Rochers Déan. Due N beware the
Moulières de Portrieux, unlit ECM bn tr. From E and SE
appr via Caffa ECM Q (3) 10s and La Roselière WCM VQ
(9) 10s (both off chartlet).

LIGHTS AND MARKS

At night, from the N, White sectors of 4 Dir lts lead safely
to the marina in sequence 169°, 130°, 185° (astern), 318°
(see chartlet and below):
(1) NE mole elbow, Dir Iso WRG 4s 15/11M, **W159°-179°**,
G179°-316°, W316°-320.5°, R320.5°-159°.
(2) Herflux Dir lt, Fl (2) WRG 6s 8/6M, vis G115°-125°,
W125°-135°, R135°-145°; on Rochers Déan.
(3) Ile Harbour Dir lt, Oc (2) WRG 6s 16m 11/8M, vis R011°
-133°, G133°-270°, R270°-306°, G306°-358°, **W358°-011°**.
(4) NE mole elbow, as (1) above, **W316°-320.5°**.

RADIO TELEPHONE

VHF Ch 09 (0830-1230; 1330-1830LT. H24 in season).

TELEPHONE

Marina 02·96·70·81·30; Hr Mr (Old Hbr) 02·96·70·95·31;
Aff Mar 02·96·70·42·27; CROSS 02·98·89·31·31; SNSM
02·96·70·52·04; ⌗ 02·96·33·33·03; Météo 02·99·46·10·46;
Auto 08.36.68.08.22; Police 02·96·70·61·24;
Dr 02·96·70·41·31; Brit Consul 02·99·46·26·64.

FACILITIES

Marina (900+100 Ⓥ) ☎ 02·96·70·81·30, 🛥 02·96·70·81·31,
FF130, D, P, FW, BH, AC, C (5 ton);
Old Hbr (500+8 visitors) AB FF60, M, P, D, L, FW, Sh, Slip,
C (1·5 ton), ME, El, Ⓔ, Sh, CH, R, Bar;
Cercle de la Voile de Portrieux ☎ 02·96·70·41·76, M, FW,
C (1 ton), Bar;
Town V, Gaz, R, Bar, ✉, Ⓑ, ⇌ (bus to St Brieuc), ✈ (St
Brieuc/Armor). Ferry: St Malo–Poole, Portsmouth.

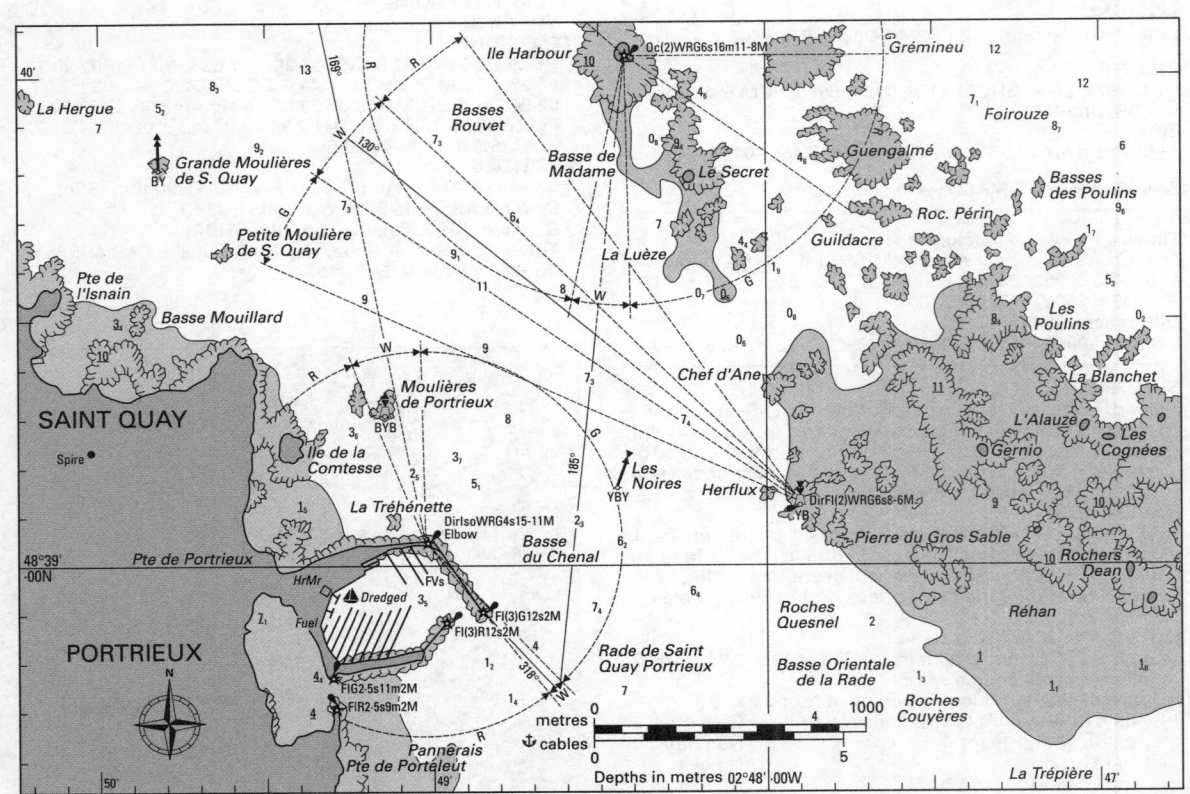

VOLVO PENTA SERVICE

Sales and service centres in area 16
Names and addresses of Volvo Penta dealers in
this area are available from:
France *Volvo Penta France* , 55 Avenue des Champs Pierreux, 92757 Cedex
Tel +33 1 55175445, Fax +33 1 55175261

VOLVO PENTA

Area 16

North Brittany
Paimpol to Raz de Sein

8.16.1	Index	**Page 675**
8.16.2	Diagram of ports, lights, RDF bns, Coast radio and weather stns	**676**
8.16.3	Tidal stream charts	**678**
8.16.4	List of coastal lights, fog signals and waypoints	**680**
8.16.5	Passage information	**684**
8.16.6	Distance table	**685**
8.16.7	English Channel waypoints	**See 8.1.7**
8.16.8	Special notes for France	**See 8.15.8**
8.16.9	Paimpol	**686**
8.16.10	Ile de Bréhat	**686**
8.16.11	Lézardrieux	**687**
8.16.12	Pontrieux	**688**
8.16.13	Tréguier Port Blanc	**689**
8.16.14	Perros-Guirec	**690**
8.16.15	Ploumanac'h Trégastel	**690**
8.16.16	Trébeurden	**691**
8.16.17	Lannion Les Sept Iles Locquemeau Locquirec Primel-Trégastel	**692**
8.16.18	Morlaix Penzé River Moguériec Pontusval	**693**
8.16.19	Roscoff Ile de Batz	**694**
8.16.20	L'Aberwrac'h	**695**
8.16.21	L'Aberbenoit	**695**
8.16.22	Baie de Lampaul Baie du Stiff	**696**
8.16.23	L'Aberildut	**696**
8.16.24	Chenal du Four	**697**
8.16.25	Tidal coefficients Portsall Argenton Ile de Molène	**698**
8.16.26	Le Conquet	**699**
8.16.27	Brest, Standard Port, tidal curves Anse de Berthaume	**700**
8.16.28	Le Rade de Brest	**700**
8.16.29	Camaret	**705**
8.16.30	Morgat	**705**
8.16.31	Douarnenez	**706**

16

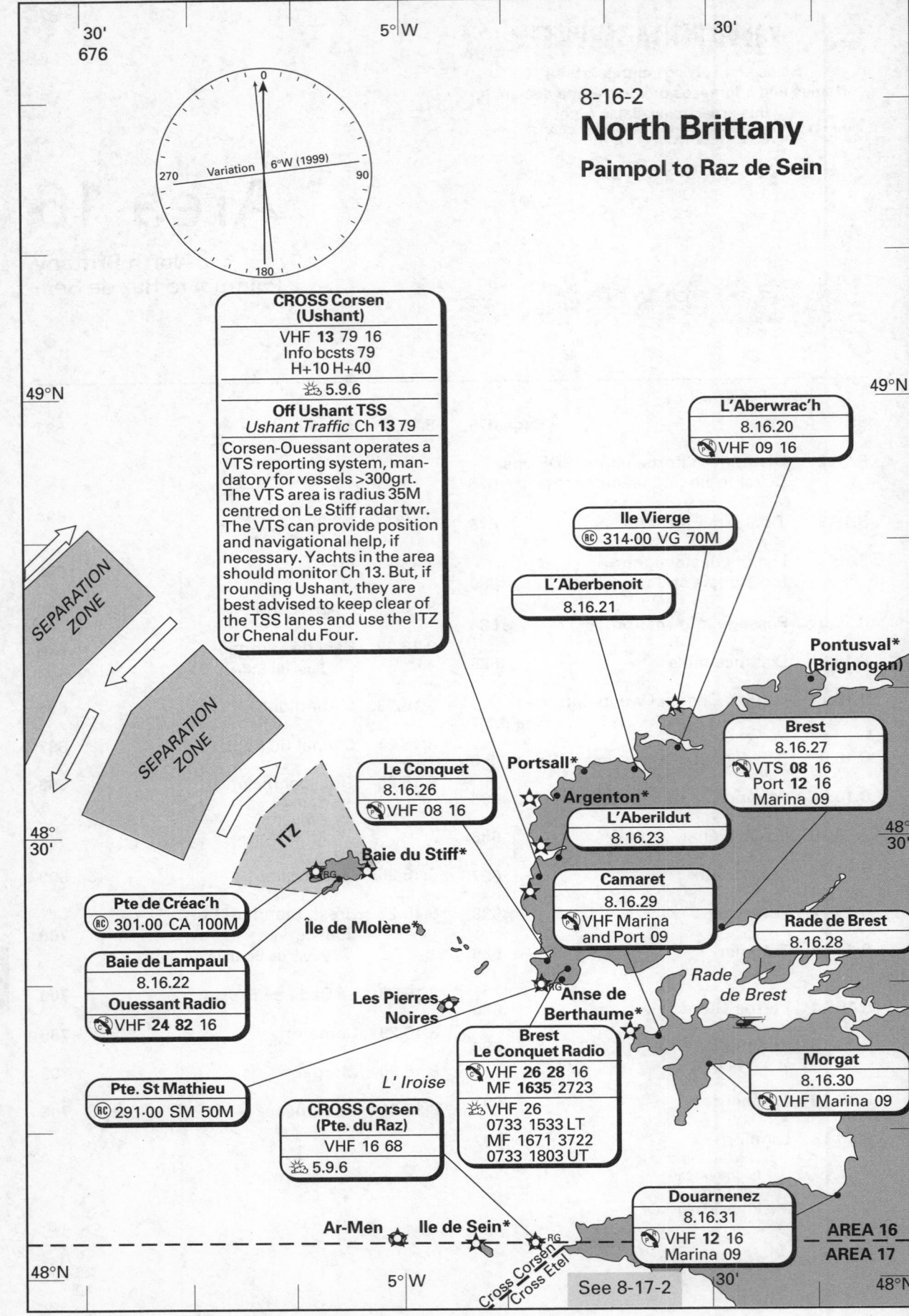

30'
676

5°W

30'

270 — Variation 6°W (1999) — 90

0

180

8-16-2
North Brittany
Paimpol to Raz de Sein

49°N

49°N

CROSS Corsen (Ushant)

VHF **13** 79 16
Info bcsts 79
H+10 H+40
☼ 5.9.6

Off Ushant TSS
Ushant Traffic Ch **13** 79

Corsen-Ouessant operates a VTS reporting system, mandatory for vessels >300grt. The VTS area is radius 35M centred on Le Stiff radar twr. The VTS can provide position and navigational help, if necessary. Yachts in the area should monitor Ch 13. But, if rounding Ushant, they are best advised to keep clear of the TSS lanes and use the ITZ or Chenal du Four.

L'Aberwrac'h
8.16.20
VHF 09 16

Ile Vierge
Ⓡ 314·00 VG 70M

L'Aberbenoit
8.16.21

Pontusval*
(Brignogan)

Brest
8.16.27
VTS **08** 16
Port **12** 16
Marina 09

SEPARATION ZONE

SEPARATION ZONE

ITZ

48° 30'

48° 30'

Le Conquet
8.16.26
VHF 08 16

Portsall*

Argenton*

L'Aberildut
8.16.23

Camaret
8.16.29
VHF Marina and Port 09

Rade de Brest
8.16.28

Baie du Stiff*

Pte de Créac'h
Ⓡ 301·00 CA 100M

Île de Molène*

Baie de Lampaul
8.16.22
Ouessant Radio
VHF **24 82** 16

Les Pierres Noires

Anse de Berthaume*

Rade de Brest

Morgat
8.16.30
VHF Marina 09

L' Iroise

Brest
Le Conquet Radio
VHF **26 28** 16
MF **1635** 2723
☼VHF 26
0733 1533 LT
MF 1671 3722
0733 1803 UT

Pte. St Mathieu
Ⓡ 291·00 SM 50M

CROSS Corsen
(Pte. du Raz)
VHF 16 68
☼ 5.9.6

Douarnenez
8.16.31
VHF **12** 16
Marina 09

Ar-Men

Ile de Sein*

Cross Corsen
Cross Etel

AREA 16
AREA 17

48°N

48°N

5°W

30'

See 8-17-2

4°W · 30' · 3°W

49°N

48°
30'

48°N · 4°W

Paimpol
8.16.9
📻 VHF 09
Lock 09
Paimpol Radio
📻 VHF **84** 16
🌦VHF 84
0733 1533 LT

AREA 16 | AREA 14

See 8-14-2

Perros-Guirec
8.16.14
📻 VHF **09** 16

Ploumanac'h
8.16.15
📻 VHF 09

Tréguier
8.16.13
📻 VHF Marina 09

Les
Sept Iles*

Ile de Bréhat
8.16.10
(RC) 287·50 DO 10

Roscoff
8.16.19
📻VHF **12** 16

Les Triagoz

Tregastel*

⊙RG

Plougasnou Radio
📻VHF **81** 16
🌦VHF 81
0733 1533 LT

Kerprigent

**Port
Blanc***

AREA 15

See 8-15-2

Ile de
Batz* ⊙RG

Primel*

Bec-Léguer

Locquémeau*

Lannion
8.16.17

Lézardrieux
8.16.11
📻VHF 09

Locquirec

Penzé River*

Moguériec*

**CROSS Corsen
(Ile de Batz)**
🌦 5.9.6

Trébeurden
8.16.16
📻 VHF **09** 16

Lannion
(RC)
Aero 345·00 LN 50M

Pontrieux
8.16.12
📻VHF **12** 16
Lock 12

3°W

16

Morlaix
8.16.18
📻VHF 09 16

Key to Symbols

📻 Coast Radio Station: VHF/MF frequencies
📻 Port, VTS, or marina Radio: VHF frequencies
(RC) Marine RDF beacon
(RC)Aero Aero RDF beacon
🌦 Weather information
(Frequencies/times of broadcasts)
🚁 SAR helicopter base
☆ Selected principal lights
⚲ Light vessel/Light float/Lanby
⊙RG Emergency VHF DF
* See Area Index

8-16-3   AREA 16 TIDAL STREAMS

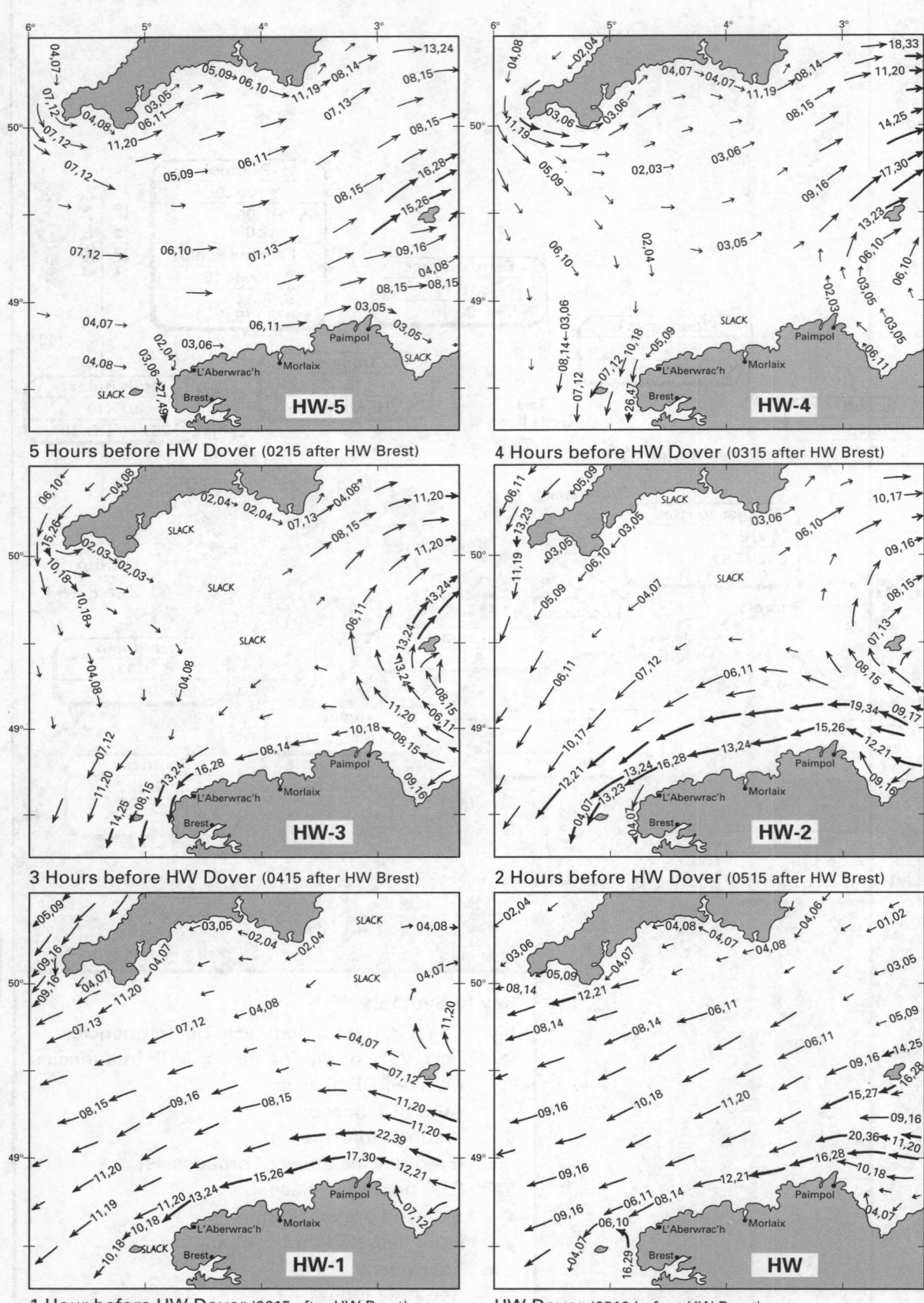

5 Hours before HW Dover (0215 after HW Brest)

4 Hours before HW Dover (0315 after HW Brest)

3 Hours before HW Dover (0415 after HW Brest)

2 Hours before HW Dover (0515 after HW Brest)

1 Hour before HW Dover (0615 after HW Brest)

HW Dover (0510 before HW Brest)

Southward 8.17.3   Eastward 8.15.3   Northward 8.1.3

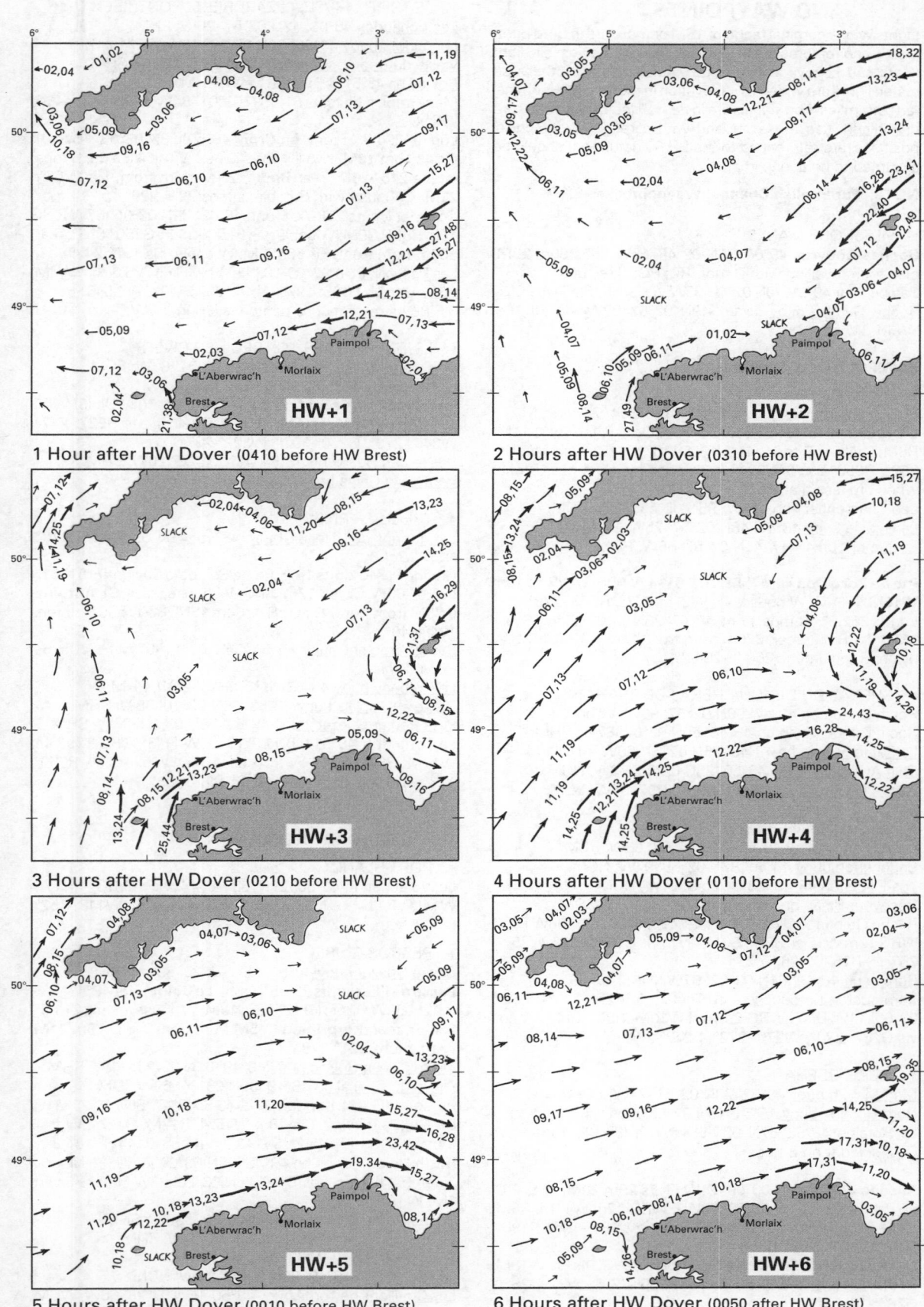

1 Hour after HW Dover (0410 before HW Brest)

2 Hours after HW Dover (0310 before HW Brest)

3 Hours after HW Dover (0210 before HW Brest)

4 Hours after HW Dover (0110 before HW Brest)

5 Hours after HW Dover (0010 before HW Brest)

6 Hours after HW Dover (0050 after HW Brest)

16

8.16.4 COASTAL LIGHTS,FOG SIGNALS AND WAYPOINTS

Lights with a nominal range of 15M or more are in **bold** print, places and features are in CAPITALS, and light-vessels, light floats and Lanbys in *CAPITAL ITALICS*. Unless otherwise stated lights are white. m = elevation in metres; M = nominal range in miles. Fog signals are in *italics*. Useful waypoints are underlined; use those on land with care. All geographical positions are referenced to the ED 50 datum but should be assumed to be approximate.

NOTE: For English Channel Waypoints see 8.1.7.

- OFFSHORE MARKS
Roches Douvres 49°06'·35N 02°48'·65W Fl 5s 60m **28M**; pink tr on dwelling with G roof; RC; RG; *Siren 60s.*
Barnouic lt tr 49°01'·70N 02°48'·33W VQ (3) 5s 15m 7M; ECM.
Roche Gautier buoy 49°00'·49N 02°52'·92W VQ (9) 10s; WCM; *Whis.*

PAIMPOL TO ÎLE DE BRÉHAT

- PAIMPOL
Les Calemarguiers buoy 48°47'·04N 02°54'·77W; ECM.
L'Ost Pic lt tr 48°46'·82N 02°56'·33W Oc WR 4s 20m W11M, R8M; 2 W trs, R tops; vis W105°-116°, R116°-221°, W221°-253°, R253°-291°, W291°-329°; obsc by islets near Bréhat when brg less than 162°.
Les Charpentiers bn 48°47'·95N 02°55'·92W; ECM.
La Gueule buoy 48°47'·48N 02°57'·25W; PHM.
La Jument bn 48°47'·41N 02°57'·88W; PHM.

Pte de Porz-Don 48°47'·53N 03°01'·47W Oc (2) WR 6s 13m **W15M**, R11M; W house; vis W269°-272°, R272°-279°.
Ldg lts 262·2°. Kernoa, front, 48°47'·26N 03°02'·37W FR 5m 7M; W & R hut; rear, 370m from front, Dir FR 12m 14M; W pylon, R top; intens 260·2°-264·2°.

- CHENAL DU DENOU/CHENAL DE BRÉHAT
Roc'h Denou bn 48°47'·90N 02°57'·96W; W bn.
Roc'h Denou Vihan bn 48°48'·50N 02°57'·87W; SHM.
La Petite Moisie bn 48°48'·65N 02°57'·60W; PHM.
Cain Ar Monse buoy 48°50'·22N 02°56'·73W; NCM.
Roche Guarine buoy 48°51'·69N 02°57'·54W; ECM.

- CHENAL DU FERLAS
Lel Ar Serive buoy 48°50'·04N 02°58'·68W; SCM.
Cadenenou buoy 48°49'·87N 02°58'·97W; NCM.
Les Piliers bn 48°49'·83N 02°59'·91W; NCM.
Réceveur Bihan bn 48°49'·76N 03°01'·87W; SCM.
Roche Quinonec Dir lt 257·3°, 48°49'·43N 03°03'·58W Dir Q WRG 12m W10M, R8M, G8M; Gy tr; vis G254°-257°, W257°-257·7°, R257·7°-260·7°.
Rompa bn 48°49'·64N 03°02'·67W; IDM.
Kermouster, Embouchure du Trieux Dir lt 271°, 48°49'·62N 03°05'·11W Dir Fl WRG 2s 16m W10M, R8M, G8M; W col; vis G267°-270°, W270°-272°, R272°-274°.

- ÎLE DE BRÉHAT
Men-Marc'h buoy 48°52'·23N 02°51'·71W; ECM.
Nord Horaine buoy 48°54'·48N 02°55'·08W; NCM.
La Horaine 48°53'·57N 02°55'·15W Fl (3) 12s 13m 11M; Gy 8-sided tr on B hut.

Rosédo 48°51'·51N 03°00'·21W Fl 5s 29m **20M**; W tr; RC.
Le Paon 48°51'·98N 02°59'·08W F WRG 22m W11M, R8M, G8M; Y tr; vis W033°-078°, G078°-181°, W181°-196°, R196°-307°, W307°-316°, R316°-348°.
Men-Joliguet 48°50'·18N 03°00'·12W Iso WRG 4s 6m W13M, R10M, G10M; WCM bn tr; vis R255°-279°, W279°-283°, G283°-175°.

LÉZARDRIEUX TO TRÉGUIER

- LE TRIEUX RIVER, LÉZARDRIEUX/PONTRIEUX
Les Echaudés 48°53'·42N 02°57'·26W; PHM.
Les Sirlots buoy 48°53'·00N 02°59'·48W; SHM; *Whis.*
Vieille du tréou bn tr 48°52'·05N 03°01'·00W; SHM.
Gosrod bn 48°51'·48N 03°01'·14W; PHM.
Men Grenn lt bn tr 48°51'·27N 03°03'·84W Q (9) 15s 7m 7M; WCM.
Ldg lts 224·7°: Front, **La Croix** 48°50'·28N 03°03'·16W Dir Oc 4s 15m **19M**; two Gy ● trs joined, W on NE side, R tops; intens 215°-235°; rear **Bodic**, 2·1M from front, Dir Q 55m **22M**; W house with G gable; intens 221°-229°.
Coatmer ldg lts 218·7°: Front, 48°48'·32N 03°05'·67W F RG 16m R9M, G9M; W gable; vis R200°-250°, G250°-053°; rear, 660m from front, FR 50m 9M; W gable; vis 197°-242°.
Les Perdrix lt tr 48°47'·80N 03°05'·71W Fl (2) WG 6s 5m W6M, G3M; G tr; vis G165°-197°, W197°-202·5°, G202·5°-040°.
3 F Bu lts mark marina pontoons, 750m SSW.

- LE TRIEUX RIVER TO TRÉGUIER RIVER
An Ogejou Bihan bn 48°53'·44N 03°01'·83W; ECM.
La Moisie bn 48°53'·89N 03°02'·15W; ECM.
Les Héaux de Bréhat 48°54'·57N 03°05'·10W Oc (3) WRG 12s 48m **W15M**, R11M, G11M; Gy ● tr; vis R227°-247°, W247°-270°, G270°-302°, W302°-227°.
Basse des Héaux bn 48°54'·13N 03°05'·20W; SHM.
Pont de la Gaîne bn 48°53'·20N 03°07'·26W; PHM.

- TRÉGUIER RIVER
La Jument des Héaux buoy 48°55'·41N 03°07'·95W VQ; NCM; *Bell.*
Grande Passe ldg lts 137°: Front, Port de la Chaîne 48°51'·61N 03°07'·80W Oc 4s 12m 11M; W house; rear, **St Antoine**, 0·75M from front, Dir Oc R 4s 34m **15M**; R&W house; intens 134°-140°.
Basse Crublent buoy 48°54'·35N 03°11'·07W Fl (2) R 6s; PHM; *Whis.*
Le Corbeau buoy 48°53'·42N 03°10'·20W; PHM.
Pierre à l'Anglais buoy 48°53'·30N 03°10'·38W; SHM.
Petit Pen ar Guézec buoy 48°52'·58N 03°09'·34W; SHM.
La Corne lt tr 48°51'·40N 03°10'·53W Fl (3) WRG 12s 14m W11M, R8M, G8M; W tr, R base; vis W052°-059°, R059°-173°, G173°-213°, W213°-220°, R220°-052°.

TRÉGUIER TO TRÉBEURDEN

- PORT-BLANC
Le Voleur lt tr 48°50'·27N 03°18'·44W Fl WRG 4s 17m W14M, R11M, G11M; W tr; vis G140°-148°, W148°-152°, R152°-160°.

- PERROS-GUIREC
Basse Guazer buoy 48°51'·65N 03°20'·89W; PHM.
Passe de l'Est ldg lts 224·5°: Front, **Le Colombier** 48°47'·93N 03°26'·58W Dir Oc (4) 12s 28m **15M**; W house; intens 214·5°-234·5°; rear, **Kerprigent**, 1·5M from front, Dir Q 79m **21M**; W tr; intens 221°-228°.
Pierre à Jean Rouzic buoy 48°49'·61N 03°24'·11W; SHM.
Pierre du Chenal bn 48°49'·35N 03°24'·59W; IDM.
Passe de l'Ouest. **Kerjean** Dir lt 143·6° 48°47'·85N 03°23'·31W Dir Oc (2+1) WRG 12s 78m **W15M**, R12M, G12M; W tr, B top; vis G133·7°-143·2°, W143·2°-144·8°, R144·8°-154·3°.
Roc'h Hu de Perros bn 48°48'·88N 03°24'·87W; PHM.
Jetée Est (Linkin) hd 48°48'·26N 03°26'·23W Fl (2) G 6s 4m 9M; W pile, G top.
Roche Bernard bn 48°49'·50N 03°25'·38W; SHM.
La Fronde buoy 48°49'·93N 03°25'·90W; SHM.
Bilzic bn 48°50'·27N 03°25'·65W; PHM.
La Horaine bn 48°49'·95N 03°27'·18W; NCM.
Les Couillons de Tomé buoy 48°50'·95N 03°25'·60W; WCM.

- PLOUMANAC'H
Men-Ruz 48°50'·32N 03°28'·90W Oc WR 4s 26m W12M, R9M; pink ■ tr; vis W226°-242°, R242°-226°; obsc by Pte de Trégastel when brg less than 080°, and part obsc by Les Sept-Îles 156°-207°, and by Île Tomé 264°-278°.

- LES SEPT-ÎLES
Île-aux-Moines 48°52'·78N 03°29'·33W Fl (3) 15s 59m **24M**; Gy tr and dwelling; obsc by Îlot Rouzic and E end of Île Bono 237°-241°, and in Baie de Lannion when brg less than 039°.
Les Dervinis buoy 48°52'·41N 03°27'·23W; SCM.

- TRÉGASTEL
Île Dhu bn 48°50'·43N 03°31'·13W; PHM.
Le Taureau bn 48°50'·47N 03°31'·51W; SHM.

Les Triagoz 48°52'·35N 03°38'·73W Oc (2) WR 6s 31m W14M, R11M; Gy ■ tr, R lantern; vis W010°-339°, R339°-010°; obsc in places 258°-268° by Les Sept-Îles.
Bar ar Gall buoy 48°49'·80N 03°36'·00W VQ (9) 10s; WCM.
Le Crapaud buoy 48°46'·65N 03°40'·40W Q (9) 15s; WCM.

- TRÉBEURDEN
Ar Gouredec buoy 48°46'·49N 03°36'·40W VQ (6) + L Fl 10s; SCM.
buoy 48°46'·54N 03°35'·89W Fl (2) R 6s; PHM.
Pt de Lan Kerellec 48°46'·80N 03°34'·98W Iso WRG 4s; W8M, R5M, G5M; vis G058°-064°, W064°-069°, R069°-130°.

TRÉBEURDEN TO ROSCOFF

- LÉGUER RIVER, LANNION
Kinierbel buoy 48°44'·20N 03°34'·95W; SHM; *Bell*.
Beg-Léguer 48°44'·40N 03°32'·83W Oc (4) WRG 12s 60m W12M, R9M, G9M; W face of W house, R lantern; vis G007°-084°, W084°-098°, R098°-129°.

- LOCQUÉMEAU
Ldg lts 121°: Front, 48°43'·48N 03°34'·40W FR 21m 6M; W pylon, R top; vis 068°-228°; rear, 484m from front Oc (2+1) R 12s 39m 7M; W gabled house; vis 016°-232°.
Locquémeau buoy 48°43'·94N 03°35'·73W; SHM; *Whis*.

- PRIMEL
Ldg lts 152°: Front, 48°42'·52N 03°49'·10W FR 35m 6M; W □, R stripe on pylon; vis 134°-168°; rear, 172m from front, FR 56m 6M; W □, R stripe.
Jetty hd 48°42'·82N 03°49'·53W Fl G 4s 6m 7M.
Méloine buoy 48°45'·65N 03°50'·55W; WCM; *Whis*.

- BAIE DE MORLAIX
Chenal du tréguier ldg lts 190·5°: Front, Île Noire 48°40'·41N 03°52'·44W Oc (2) WRG 6s 15m W11M, R8M, G8M; W □ tr, R top; vis G051°-135°, R135°-211°, W211°-051°; obsc in places. Common rear, **La Lande** 48°38'·26N 03°53'·04W Fl 5s 85m **23M**; W □ tr, B top; obsc by Pte Annelouesten when brg more than 204°.
La Pierre Noire bn 48°41'·71N 03°53'·97W; SHM.
La Chambre bn 48°40'·80N 03°52'·41W; SHM.
Grande Chenal ldg lts 176·4°: Front, **Île Louet** 48°40'·47N 03°53'·24W Oc (3) WG 12s 17m **W15M**; G10M; W □ tr, B top; vis W305°-244°, G244°-305°, vis 139°-223° from offshore, except when obsc by Is. Common rear, **La Lande** above.
Pot de Fer buoy 48°44'·29N 03°53'·93W; ECM.
Vieille bn 48°42'·66N 03°54'·03W; SHM.
Stolvezen buoy 48°42'·71N 03°53'·32W; PHM.
La Noire bn 48°42'·61N 03°52'·11W; SHM.
Ricard bn 48°41'·60N 03°53'·40W; SHM.
Barre de-Flot No. 1 buoy 48°40'·24N 05°52'·86W; SHM.
Marine farm prohib area buoy 48°43'·00N 03°54'·10W VQ (6) + L Fl 10s; SCM.

- BLOSCON/ROSCOFF
Le Menk lt bn tr 48°43'·35N 03°56'·60W Q (9) WR 15s 6m W5M, R3M; vis W160°-188°; WCM.
Bloscon jetty hd 48°43'·27N 03°57'·59W Fl WG 4s 9m W10M, G7M; W tr, G top, vis W206°-216°, G216°-206°; RC. In fog Fl 2s.
Ar Pourven buoy 48°43'·10N 03°57'·61W Q; NCM.
Astan buoy 48°44'·95N 03°57'·55W VQ (3) 5s 9m 6M; ECM; *Whis*; Ra refl.
Basse de Bloscon buoy 48°43'·77N 03°57'·48W VQ; NCM.
Ar-Chaden lt bn 48°43'·99N 03°58'·15 W Q (6) + L Fl WR 15s 14m W8M, R6M; vis R262°-289·5°, W289·5°-293°, R293°-326°, W326°-110°; SCM.
Men-Guen-Bras lt bn 48°43'·81N 03°57'·95W Q WRG 14m W9M, R6M, G6M; vis W068°-073°, R073°-197°, W197°-257°, G257°-068°; NCM.
Roscoff ldg lts 209°: Front, N Môle 48°43'·62N 03°58'·57W Oc (2+1) G 12s 7m 7M; W col, G top; vis 078°-318°; **rear**, 430m from front, Oc (2+1) 12s 24m **15M**; Gy ■ tr, W on NE side; vis 062°-242°.
jetty hd 48°43'·98N 03°58'·87W F Vi; W & Purple **I**.

ÎLE DE BATZ TO ÎLE VIERGE

- ÎLE DE BATZ
Lt Ho 48°44'·78N 04°01'·55W Fl (4) 25s 69m **23M**; Gy tr; auxiliary lt FR 65m 7M; same tr; vis 024°-059°.

- CANAL DE L'ÎLE DE BATZ
Perroch NCM bn, 48°44'·17N 03°59'·62W.
Île aux Moutons landing stage SCM, VQ (6) + L Fl 10s 3m 7M, 48°44'·31N 04°00'·43W.
L'Oignon NCM bn, 48°44'·10N 04°01'·27W.
Basse Plate NCM bn, 48°44'·32N 04°02'·44W.

- MOGUÉRIEC.
Ldg lts 162°: Front, jetty hd, 48°41'·40N 04°04'·40W, Iso WG 4s 9m W11M, G6M; W tr, G top; vis W158°-166°, G166°-158°; rear, 440m from front, FG 22m 7M; W Col, G top; vis 142°-182°.

- PONTUSVAL
Pointe de Pontusval buoy 48°41'·51N 04°19'·12W; ECM.
Ar Peich buoy 48°40'·95N 04°19'·08W; SHM.
An Neudenn bn 48°40'·72N 04°19'·01W; PHM.
Pte de Beg-Pol 48°40'·73N 04°20'·70W Oc (3) WR 12s 16m W10M, R7M; W □ tr, B top, W dwelling; vis W shore-056°, R056°-096°, W096°-shore. QY and FR lts on towers 2·4M S.

Aman-ar-Ross buoy 48°41'·94N 04°26'·96W Q 9m 7M; NCM; *Whis*.
Barr Ar-Skoaz buoy 48°38'·29N 04°29'·99W; PHM.
Lizen Ven Ouest buoy 48°40'·55N 04°33'·68W VQ (9) 10s 8m 5M; WCM; *Whis*.
Île-Vierge 48°38'·38N 04°33'·97W Fl 5s 77m **27M**; Gy tr; vis 337°-325°; RC; *Horn 60s*.

ÎLE VIERGE TO LE FOUR

- L'ABERWRAC'H
Libenter buoy 48°37'·57N 04°38'·35W Q (9) 15s 8m 6M; Ra refl; WCM; *Whis*.
Ldg lts 100·1°: Front, Île Wrac'h 48°36'·95N 04°34'·47W QR 20m 7M; W □ tr, Or top, dwelling; rear, Lanvaon 1·63M from front, Dir Q 55m 12M; W □ tr, Or ▲ on top; intens 090°-110°.
Trepied buoy 48°37'·35N 04°37'·47W; PHM.
Grand Pot de Beurre bn 48°37'·27N 04°36'·39W; PHM.
Petit Pot de Beurre bn 48°37'·18N 04°36'·13W; ECM.
Basse de la Croix buoy 48°36'·98N 04°35'·90W Fl (3) G 12s; SHM.

16

Breac'h Ver lt tr 48°36'·70N 04°35'·30W Fl G 2·5s 6m 3M; ▲ on tr; SHM.
Dir lt 128°, N bkwtr 48°35'·95N 04°33'·72W Dir Oc (2) WRG 6s 5m W13M, R11M, G11M; vis G125·7°-127·2°, W127·2°-128·7°, R128·7°-130·2°.

● L'ABER BENOÎT
Petite Fourche buoy 48°37'·05N 04°38'·67W; WCM.
Rusven Ouest buoy 48°36'·15N 04°39'·34W.
Rusven Est buoy 48°36'·37N 04°38'·53W; SHM.
Basse de Chenal 48°35'·87N 04°38'·44W; SWM.
Poul Orvil buoy 48°35'·58N 04°38'·20W; WCM.
La Jument bn 48°35'·19N 04°37'·30W: PHM.
Le Chien bn 48°34'·73N 04°36'·80W; IDM.

Le Relec buoy 48°36'·05N 04°40'·76W; ECM.

● PORTSALL/ARGENTON
Corn-Carhai 48°35'·25N 04°43'·86W Fl (3) 12s 19m 9M; W 8-sided tr, B top.
Basse Paupian buoy 48°35'·38N 04°46'·16W; WCM.
Grande Basse de Portsall buoy 48°36'·78N 04°46'·05W   VQ (9) 10s 9m 4M; Ra refl; WCM; Whis.
Bosven Aval bn 48°33'·88N 04°44'·18W; W bn tr.
Men ar Pic bn 48°33'·72N 04°43'·93W; G bn tr.
Portsall 48°33'·89N 04°42'·18W Oc (4) WRG 12s 9m W13M, R10M, G10M; W col, R top: vis G058°-084°, W084°-088°, R088°-058°.
Île Dolvez front ldg mark 086° 48°31'·32N 04°46'·13W; W bn.

Le Four 48°31'·45N 04°48'·23W Fl (5) 15s 28m 18M; Gy ● tr; Horn (3+2) 60s.

Le Taureau WCM bn tr 48°31'·51N 04°47'·26W.

CHENAL DU FOUR
L'ABER-ILDUT
L'Aber-Ildut 48°28'·32N 04°45'·47W Dir Oc (2) WR 6s 12m W25M, R20M; W bldgs; vis W081°-085°, R085°-087°.

ldg lts 158·5°: Front, Kermorvan 48°21'·80N 04°47'·31W Fl 5s 20m 22M; rear, Pte de St Mathieu Fl 15s 56m 29M. Dir F 54m; same tr; intens 157·5°-159·5° (see above).
Les Plâtresses 48°26'·35N 04°50'·85W Fl RG 4s 17m 6M; W tr; vis R343°-153°, G153°-333°.
La Valbelle buoy 48°26'·55N 04°49'·90W Fl (2) R 6s 8m 5M; PHM; Whis.
SE Plâtresses buoy 48°26'·03N 04°50'·43W; SHM.
Le Tendoc buoy 48°25'·73N 04°49'·36W; PHM.
Saint Paul buoy 48°24'·93N 04°49'·08W Oc (2) R 9s; PHM.
Taboga buoy 48°23'·88N 04°47'·99W; IDM.

Pte de Corsen 48°24'·95N 04°47'·52W Dir Q WRG 33m W12M, R8M, G8M; W hut; vis R008°-012°, W012°-015°, G015°-021°.
Kermorvan 48°21'·80N 04°47'·31W Fl 5s 20m 22M; W☐ tr; obsc by Pte de St Mathieu when brg less than 341°.
Rouget buoy 48°22'·10N 04°48'·79W Fl G 4s; SHM; Whis.
La Grande Vinotière lt tr 48°22'·00N 04°48'·33W L Fl R 10s 15m 5M; R 8-sided tr.

● LE CONQUET
Môle Sainte Barbe 48°21'·64N 04°46'·94W Oc G 4s 5m 6M.

Bas des Renards buoy 48°21'·05N 04°47'·50W; IDM.
Lochrist 48°20'·63N 04°45'·73W Dir Oc (3) 12s 49m 22M; W 8-sided tr, R top; intens 135°-140°.
Tournant et Lochrist buoy 48°20'·70N 04°48'·03W Iso R 4s; PHM.
Ar C'hristian Braz bn 48°20'·75N 04°50'·10W; ECM.
ldg lts 007°: Front, Kermorvan 48°21'·80N 04°47'·31W   Fl 5s 20m 22M; rear, trézien 48°25'·48N 04°46'·65W Dir Oc (2) 6s 84m 20M; Gy tr, W on S side; intens 003°-011°.

Pte de St Mathieu 48°19'·85N 04°46'·17W Fl 15s 56m 29M; W tr, R top. Dir F 54m 28M; same tr; intens 157·5°-159·5°; RC. 54m 291° from St Mathieu Q WRG 26m, W14M, R11M, G11M; W tr; vis G085°-107°, W107°-116°, R116°-134°.
La Fourmi buoy 48°19'·31N 04°47'·88W; SHM.
Les Vieux-Moines 48°19'·40N 04°46'·55W Fl R 4s 16m 5M; R 8-sided tr; vis 280°-133°; PHM.

CHENAL DE LA HELLE

Ldg lt 137·9°: Front, Kermorvan 48°21'·80N 04°47'·31W Fl 5s 20m 22M; rear, Lochrist 48°20·63N 04°45'·73W Dir Oc (3) 12s 49m 22M (see above).
Luronne buoy 48°26'·67N 04°53'·70W; WCM; Bell.
ldg lts 293·5°: Front, Le Faix lt tr 48°25'·78N 04°53'·82W VQ; 16m 8M; NCM; rear, Le Stiff 48°28'·60N 05°03'·10W Fl (2) R 20s 85m 24M (see below).
Ldg lt 142·5° for Chenal de La Helle: Front, Kermorvan 48°21'·80N 04°47'·31W Fl 5s 20m 22M (see above); rear, two W bns 48°20'·17N 04°45'·44W.
Pourceaux buoy 48°24'·07N 04°51'·22W Q; NCM.
S. Pierre buoy 48°23'·15N 04°49'·00W; SHM.

OUESSANT AND ÎLE DE MOLÈNE

Men-Korn lt bn tr 48°27'·95N 05°01'·22W VQ (3) WR 5s 21m W8M, R8M; vis W145°-040°, R040°-145°; ECM.
Le Stiff 48°28'·60N 05°03'·10W Fl (2) R 20s 85m 24M; two adjoining W trs.
Gorle Vihan bn 48°28'·40N 05°02'·50W; IDM.
Port du Stiff, Môle Est Hd 48°28'·18N 05°03'·16W Dir Q WRG 11m W10M, R7M, G7M; W tr, G top; vis G251°-254°, W254°-264°, R264°-267°.

OUESSANT SW LANBY 48°31'·20N 05°49'·10W Fl 4s 10m 20M; RC; Racon (M).
NE buoy 48°45'·90N 05°11'·60W L Fl 10s 9m 8M; Whis; Racon.
Créac'h 48°27'·62N 05°07'·72W Fl (2) 10s 70m 32M; W tr, B bands; obsc 247°-255°; Racon (C), RC, RG; Horn (2) 120s.
Nividic lt tr 48°26'·80N 05°08'·95W VQ (9) 10s 28m 9M; W 8-sided tr, R bands; obsc by Ouessant 225°-290°. Helicopter platform.
La Jument 48°25'·40N 05°07'·95W Fl (3) R 15s 36m 22M; Gy 8-sided tr, R Top; vis 241°-199°; Horn (3) 60s.
Men ar Froud SCM bn tr, 48°26'·70N 05°03'·57W.

Kéréon (Men-Tensel) 48°26'·30N 05°01'·45W Oc (2+1) WR 24s 38m W17M, R7M; Gy tr; vis W019°-248°, R248°-019°; Horn (2+1) 120s.
Pierres-Vertes buoy 48°22'·26N 05°04'·68W VQ (9) 10s 9m 5M; WCM; Whis; Ra refl.

● ÎLE DE MOLÈNE
Les trois-Pierres 48°24'·75N 04°56'·75W Iso WRG 4s 15m W9M, R6M, G6M; W col; vis G070°-147°, W147°-185°, R185°-191°, G191°-197°, W197°-213°, R213°-070°.
Molène, Old Môle Hd Dir lt 191° 48°23'·91N 04°57'·18W Dir Fl (3) WRG 12s 6m W9M, R7M, G7M; vis G183°-190°, W190°-192°, R192°-203°. Chenal des Laz Dir lt 261°, Dir   Fl (2) WRG 6s 9m W9M, R7M, G7M; same structure; vis G252·5°-259·5°, W259·5°-262·5°, R262·5°-269·5°.

L'IROISE/BREST AND APPROACHES

Pierres Noires buoy 48°18'·54N 04°58'·18W; SCM; Bell.
Les Pierres Noires 48°18'·73N 04°54'·80W Fl R 5s 27m 19M; W tr, R top; Horn (2) 60s.
Basse Royale buoy 48°17'·52N 04°49'·52W Q (6) + L Fl 15s; SCM.
Vandrée buoy 48°15'·30N 04°48'·17W VQ (9) 10s; Whis; WCM.

La Parquette 48°15'·96N 04°44'·25W Fl RG 4s 17m R6M, G6M; W 8-sided tr, B diagonal stripes; vis R244°-285°, G285°-244°.

• GOULET DE BREST
Roc du Charles Martel buoy 48°18'·90N 04°42'·10W Fl (4) R; PHM; *Whis*.
Swansea Vale buoy 48°18'·27N 04°38'·75W Fl (2) 6s; *Whis*; IDM.

• BREST
Pénoupèle buoy 48°28'·51N 04°30'·43W Fl (3) R 12s; PHM.
Port Militaire, Jetée Sud hd 48°22'·17N 04°29'·37W QR 10m 5M; W tr, R top; vis 094°-048°.
Jetée Est hd 48°22'·22N 04°29'·12W QG 10m 8M; W tr,   G top; vis 299°-163°.
Ldg lts 344°: Front, 48°22'·85N 04°29'·53W VQ WRG; 24m; W10M, R5M, G5M; vis G 334°-342°, W342°-346°, R346°-024°; rear, 118m from front, Dir VQ 32m 10M.
La Penfeld ldg lts 314°: Front 48°22'·93N 04°29'·85W Dir Iso R 5s 9m 10M; rear, 17m from front, Dir Iso R 5s 16m 12M; both intens 309°-319°.
Port de Commerce Jetée du Sud W hd 48°22'·66N 04°29'·02W Fl G 4s 10m 6M; vis 022°-257°.
Port de Commerce Jeteé du Sud E hd 48°22'·76N 04°28'·39W Oc (2) R 6s 8m 5M; W pylon, R top; vis 018°-301°.
R2 buoy 48°22'·07N 04°28'·66W Fl (2) R 6s; PHM.
R1 buoy 48°21'·80N 04°28'·22W Fl G 4s; SHM.
R4 buoy 48°22'·28N 04°27'·91W Fl R 10s; PHM.
Lt bn 48°22'·74N 04°26'·45W Fl (4) R 15s; R □ on pile.
Moulin Blanc buoy 48°22'·85N 04°25'·90W Fl (3) R 12s; PHM.

• LE MOULIN BLANC
MB1 buoy 48°23'·29N 04°25'·66W Fl G 2s; SHM.

• CAMARET
Môle Nord hd 48°16'·92N 04°35'·20W Iso WG 4s 7m W12M, G9M; W pylon, G top; vis W135°-182°, G182°-027°.
Môle Sud hd 48°16'·69N 04°35'·25W Fl (2) R 6s 9m 5M; R pylon.
Pointe du Toulinguet 48°16'·88N 04°37'·64W Oc (3) WR 12s 49m **W15M**, R11M; W □ tr on bldg; vis W shore-028°, R028°-090°, W090°-shore.
Pte du Petit-Minou 48°20'·26N 04°36'·80W Fl (2) WR 6s 32m **W19M**, **R15M**; Gy tr, R top; vis Rshore-252°, W252°-260°, R260°-307°, W(unintens) 307°-015°,W015°-065·5°, W070·5°-shore. Same structure, ldg lts 068°: **Front**, Dir Q 30m **23M**, intens 067·3°-068·8°; **rear**, **Pte du Portzic**, Dir Q 56m **22M**; intens 065°-071°
Fillettes buoy 48°19'·81N 04°35'·58W VQ (9); WCM; *Whis*.
Kerviniou buoy 48°19'·81N 04°35'·20W Fl (2) R 6s; PHM.
Roche Mengam 48°20'·40N 04°34'·48W Fl (3) WR 12s 10m W11M, R8M, R tr, B bands; vis R034°-054°, W054°-034°.
Pte du Portzic 48°21'·55N 04°31'·96W Oc (2) WR 12s 56m **W19M**, **R15M**; Gy tr; vis R219°-259°, W259°-338°, R338°-000°, W000°-065·5°, W070·5°-219°. Same structure Dir Q (6) + L Fl 15s 54m **23M**; intens 045°-050°.

L'IROISE/BAIE DE DOUARNENEZ
Basse Du Lis buoy 48°13'·05N 04°44'·46W Q (6) + L Fl 15s 9m 6M; SCM HFP; *Whis*.
Le Chevreau buoy 48°13'·35N 04°36'·85W; WCM.
Le Bouc buoy 48°11'·58N 04°37'·29W Q (9) 15s; WCM; *Whis*.

Basse Vieille buoy 48°08'·30N 04°35'·68W Fl (2) 6s 8m 7M; IDM HFP; *Whis*; Ra refl.

• MORGAT
Pointe de Morgat 48°13'·24N 04°29'·72W Oc (4) WRG 12s 77m **W15M**, R11M, G10M; W □ tr, R top, W dwelling; vis W shore-281°, G281°-301°, W301°-021°, R021°-043°; obsc by Pte du Rostudel when brg more than 027°.
Mole hd 48°13'·57N 04°29'·92W Oc (2) WR 6s 8m W9M, R6M; W&R framework tr; vis Wshore-257°, R257°-shore.
Marina ent through wavebreak pontoons marked by Fl G 4s to stbd and Fl R 4s to port.

• DOUARNENEZ
Épi de Biron hd 48°06'·15N 04°20'·38W QG 7m 6M; W col, G top.
Île Tristan 48°06'·20N 04°20'·17W Oc (3) WR 12s 35m W13M, R10M; Gy tr, W band, B top; vis W shore-138°, R138°-153°, W153°-shore; obsc by Pte de Leidé when brg less than 111°.
Bassin Nord, N Mole E hd 48°06'·02N 04°19'·20W Iso G 4s 9m 4M; W & G pylon.
S Mole N hd Oc (2) R 6s 6m 6M; W&R pylon.
Elbow, Môle de Rosmeur hd 48°05'·86N 04°19'·15W Oc G 4s 6m 6M; W pylon, G top; vis 170°-097°.

Pointe du Millier 48°05'·99N 04°27'·85W Oc (2) WRG 6s 34m **W16M**, R12M, G11M; W house; vis G080°-087°, W087°-113°, R113°-120°, W120°-129°, G129°-148°, W148°-251°, R251°-258°; part obsc 255·5°-081·5°.
Basse Jaune buoy 48°05'·25N 04°42'·35W; IDM.
Tévennec 48°04'·33N 04°47'·64W Q WR 28m W10M R7M; W □ tr and dwelling; vis W090°-345°, R345°-090°; Dir lt Fl 4s 24m 12M; same tr; intens 324°-332°.

RAZ DE SEIN

The lights below are also listed in 8.17.4 for the convenience of yachts navigating the Raz de Sein.

• RAZ DE SEIN
La Vieille 48°02'·49N 04°45'·31W Oc (2+1) WRG 12s 33m **W17M**, R14M, G13M; Gy ■ tr; vis W290°-298°, R298°-325°, W325°-355°, G355°-017°, W017°-035°, G035°-105°, W105°-123°, R123°-158°, W158°-205°; R lt on radio mast 3·4M ENE; *Horn (2+1) 60s*.
La Plate 48°02'·36N 04°45'·50W VQ (9) 10s 19m 8M; WCM.
Le Chat 48°01'·44N 04°48'·80W Fl (2) WRG 6s 27m W9M, R6M, G6M; SCM; vis G096°-215°, W215°-230°, R230°-271°, G271°-286°, R286°-096°; Ra refl.

• CHAUSSÉE DE SEIN/ÎLE DE SEIN (E to W)
Cornoc-An-Ar-Braden buoy 48°03'·30N 04°50'·80W Fl G 4s; SHM; *Whis*.
Île de Sein (main lt) 48°02'·70N 04°51'·95W Fl (4) 25s 49m **29M**; W tr, B top; RC.
Men-Brial, (115°/0.8M from main lt), Oc (2) WRG 6s 16m W12M, R9M, G7M; G & W tr; vis G149°-186°, W186°-192°, R192°-221°, W221°-227°, G227°-254°.
Ar Guéveur 48°02'·00N 04°51'·32W; W tr 20m; *Dia 60s*.
Ar-Men 48°03'·06N 04°59'·80W Fl (3) 20s 29m **23M**; W tr, B top; *Horn (3) 60s*.
Chaussée de Sein buoy 48°03'·80N 05°07'·70W VQ (9) 10s 9m 8M; WCM HFP; Racon (O); *Whis*.

16

8.16.5 PASSAGE INFORMATION

NORTH BRITTANY (charts 2643 *2644 2668*)

Refer to *North Brittany Pilot* (Imray/RCC); Admiralty *Channel Pilot* (NP 27); *North Brittany and CI Cruising* (YM/Cumberlidge); *Brittany and CI Cruising Guide* (Adlard Coles/Jefferson), and *Shell Channel Pilot* (Imray/Cunliffe). For French Glossary see 8.15.9, and 8.17.5 for Breton words with navigational value.

Good landfall marks must be carefully identified before closing this rock-strewn coast. Closer inshore the tidal streams and currents vary, and overfalls are best avoided. In rough weather, low visibility (fog and summer haze are frequent) or if uncertain of position, it may be prudent to lie off and wait for conditions to improve; there are few safe havens. A high degree of planning is needed to achieve safe pilotage. In the W of the area the size of Atlantic swells can much reduce the range at which objects, especially floating marks, are seen.

PAIMPOL TO PLOUMANAC'H (AC 3670)

In the offing, between 11M and 18M NNE of Île de Bréhat, are Plateau de Barnouic (lit) and Plateau des Roches Douvres (lt, fog sig, RC), both with drying and submerged rks, to be given a wide berth particularly in poor vis.

Approaching from the SE, keep to seaward of the three ECM buoys off L'Ost-Pic or enter B de Paimpol (8.16.9) from a point about 1M E of the most N'ly ECM (Les Charpentiers). The Ferlas chan (AC 3673) runs S of Île de Bréhat (8.16.10), and is useful if entering/leaving R. Trieux from/to the E. It is well marked and not difficult, but best taken at half tide due to unmarked rks in chan almost awash at or near LW.

For the many yachts approaching from Guernsey, Les Héaux-de-Bréhat lt ho is a conspic landfall day/night for either Tréguier or Lézardrieux. Closer in or from the E, La Horaine (lt bn) is the best landfall for the latter. It marks the Plateaux de la horaine and des Échaudés and other rks to the SE. In poor visibility it should be closed with caution and left at least 7ca to the SE, as the flood stream sets strongly onto it. The Grand Chenal is the main, lit chan into R. de trieux for Lézardrieux (8.16.11) and up-river to Pontrieux (8.16.12). From NW the unlit Chenal de La Moisie leads SSE to join the Grand Chenal at Île de Bréhat (8.16.10).

Between Lézardrieux and Tréguier (8.16.13) the Passage de la Gaine is a useful inshore route, avoiding a detour round Les Heaux. It is unlit and needs good vis, but if taken at above half tide, presents no problem in fair weather. The Grande Passe into R. de Tréguier is well lit, but ldg marks are less easy to see by day. The NE Passage should be used with caution.

Between Basse Crublent lt buoy and Port Blanc unmarked rks extend 2M offshore. Port Blanc (AC 3672) can be difficult to identify by day. Perros-Guirec (8.16.14) is approached either side of Ile Tomé from NE or NW via well lit/marked chans (AC 3672). Ploumanac'h (8.16.15) can only be entered by day.

LES SEPT ÎLES TO BAIE DE MORLAIX (AC 3669)

Les Sept Îles (8.16.17 and AC 3670) consist of five main islands and several islets, through which the tide runs strongly. Île aux Moines is lit, and all the islands are bird sanctuaries. Further W, Plateau des Triagoz has offlying dangers WSW and NE of the lt, where the sea breaks heavily. Here the stream turns ENE at HW Brest – 0325, and WSW at HW Brest +0245, sp rates both 3·8kn.

Trégastel Ste Anne (8.16.15) is a small anchorage W of Ploumanac'h. To the SW the coast as far as Trébeurden (8.16.16) is not easily approached due to many offlying rks. The radome NE of Trébeurden is conspic. Further S in the B de Lannion is Locquémeau and anchs near the mouth of the drying R. Léguier up to Lannion (8.16.17). Primel (8.16.17), at the E ent to Baie de Morlaix, provides a good deep anch. To the N is the drying Plateau de la Méloine.

The B de Morlaix (8.16.18 and AC 2745) is bestrewn with drying rks and shoals, all marked. Careful pilotage and adequate visibility are needed to negotiate any of the chans which are narrow in parts. The Grand Chenal passes close E of Île Ricard with Île Louet and La Lande (both lit) in transit 176°; abeam Calhic bn tr alter to port to transit between Château du Taureau (conspic) and Île Louet. Continue SSE for the river up to Morlaix. The anchorage NE of Carantec is reached from Chenal Ouest de Ricard.

ÎLE DE BATZ TO LE FOUR (charts 3668, 3669)

N of Île de Batz the E-going stream begins at HW Brest – 0435, and the W-going stream at HW Brest +0105, sp rates 3·8kn. Approaching Roscoff (8.16.19) from NE, leave Basse Astan ECM lt buoy to stbd steering with Men Guen Bras NCM lt bn in transit 213° with Chapelle St Barbe to round Ar Chaden for Roscoff hbr (dries); or transit W via Canal de L'Île de Batz.

In daylight and above half tide Canal de L'Île de Batz is a useful short cut between the island and the mainland. From near Ar Chaden steer 275° for the Vi bn at end of the conspic Roscoff ferry pier. Pass 30m N of this bn, and at this point alter to 300° for Run Oan SCM. Thence steer 283°, leaving Perroch NCM bn 100m to port. When clear of this rky, drying shoal alter to 270°, leaving Por Kernock hbr bkwtrs well to stbd and aiming midway between L'Oignon NCM and La Croix SCM. When these are abeam steer 281° for Basse Plate NCM bn; thence West into open waters.

Proceeding W from Île de Batz toward Le Four there are many off-lying dangers, in places 3M offshore. Swell may break on shoals even further to seaward. The tide runs strongly, and in poor vis or bad weather it is a coast to avoid. But in good conditions this is an admirable cruising ground with delightful hbrs such as Moguériec and Pontusval (8.16.18), L'Aberwrac'h (8.16.20), L'Aberbenoit (8.16.21), Portsall and Argenton (8.16.25). N of L'Aberwrac'h is Île Vierge lt ho, reputedly the tallest in the world, and a conspic landmark. Off Le Libenter, at N side of L'Aberwrac'h ent, the E-going stream starts at HW Brest – 0500, sp rate 3·8kn, and the W-going stream at HW Brest + 018.

W of L'Aberwrac'h is an inshore chan leading past Portsall to Le Four (lt bn). This is a sheltered short-cut, but must only be used by day and in good visibility. AC 1432 or SHOM 5772 and full directions, as in *North Brittany Pilot*, are needed.

OUESSANT (USHANT) (chart 2694)

Île Ouessant lies 10M off NW Brittany. It is a rky island, with dangers extending 5ca to NE, 7½ca to SE, 1·5M to SW and 1M to NW; here Chaussée de Keller is a dangerous chain of drying and submerged rks running 1M W of Île de Keller and into the ITZ. Apart from Lampaul (8.16.22) the only other anch is B du Stiff which gives some shelter in moderate winds between S and NW. Tidal streams are strong close to the island, and in chans between it and mainland. Off Pte de Créac'h (lt, fog sig, RC) the stream turns NNE at HW Brest – 0550, and SSW at HW Brest + 0045, sp rate 5·5kn.

The route outside Ouessant TSS, 8.16.2, has little to commend it. Unless bound to/from Spain/Portugal it adds much to the distance and is exposed to sea and swell. Yachts should round Ouessant via the ITZ or the inshore channels. Besides being an important landfall, Ouessant in thick weather is an unhealthy area, and it is prudent to stay in harbour until the vis improves. But in fair weather and reasonable visibility the pilotage in the chans between it and the mainland is not very demanding. They are well buoyed and marked (see 8.16.24), but the tide runs hard in places, causing overfalls when against wind >Force 5.

The three main chans between the island and mainland are: The Chenal du Four, inshore and most direct and popular; Chenal de la Helle, an alternative to N part of Chenal du Four (partly used for access to Île Molène), is not so direct but better in bad weather. Passage du Fromveur, close SE of Ouessant, is easiest but longer and can become extremely rough; tidal streams may exceed 8kn.

CHENAL DU FOUR (8.16.24 and AC 3345, 2694)

It is imperative to work the tides to best advantage through this passage: 1M W of Le Four the S-going stream begins at HW Brest + 0130; the N-going stream at HW Brest – 0545, sp rates 3·6kn. Further S, off Pte de Corsen, the stream is weaker, max 2·3kn at sp. The tide runs strongest at S end of Chenal du Four, off Le Conquet. Here the S-going stream starts at HW Brest + 0015, max 5kn; the N-going stream begins at HW Brest – 0550, 5·2kn max at sp. Wind-over-tide effects may be considerable.

Yachts are less rigidly tied to transits/dir lts than large ships and the following pilotage sequence can be used day or night, buoy-hopping as necessary if transits are obscured:
From 1·2M W of Le Four, track 180° (04°50'W: clear of Les Liniou reef to port) for 5M to Valbelle PHM lt buoy. Here pick up the transit 158·5°of Pte de Kermorvan on with Pte St Mathieu. Maintain this transit until Pte de Corsen lt bears 012° astern; then alter 192° to pass between La Grande Vinotière lt bn and Roche du Rouget lt buoy. Stand on until Le Faix lt bn is on with Grand Courleau bn 325° astern; alter 145° to maintain this track for 2·3M when open water will be reached with Vieux-Moines lt bn 4ca abeam to port.

Double check all lt/marks; do not confuse St Mathieu with Lochrist. L'Aberildut (8.16.23), 3·5M SSE of Le Four, and Le Conquet (8.16.26), 3ca SE of Pte de Kermorvan are the only ports off the Chenal du Four; but in offshore winds anch can be found in Anse de Porsmoguer and Anse des Blancs-Sablons, both between Corsen and Kermorvan.

Homeward-bound, or along the N coast of France, enter the S end of Chenal du Four at LW Brest; a fair tide can then be carried through the chan and NE past Île Vierge. The reverse sequence of pilotage is followed.

CHENAL DE LA HELLE (8.16.24 and AC 3345, 2694)

At N end of Chenal de la Helle the ENE stream starts at HW Brest – 0520 (sp rate 2·8kn), and the SW stream at HW Brest – 0045 (sp rate 3·8kn). The Ch de la Helle converges at a 20° angle with the Ch du Four. From the N, steer SW from Le Four towards Ile de Molène lt to pick up the 138° transit of Pte de Kermorvan and Lochrist close to Luronne unlit WCM buoy. Maintain this transit until Le Faix lt bn and Le Stiff lt ho are in transit 293° astern; steer 113° for 8ca until Pte de Kermorvan is on with 2 W bns (Pignons de Kéravel) at 142°. This transit avoids Basse St Pierre (4·7m) and intercepts the Ch du Four 7ca N of Grande Vinotière.

APPROACHES TO BREST (charts 798, 3427, 3428)

The outer approaches lie between Chaussée des Pierres Noires and Pte St Mathieu to the N and Pte du Toulinguet to the S. From the W steer on the 068° transit of Petit Minhou and Portzic on the N shore. From the S steer toward Petit Minhou to pick up the transit, but beware rks 7M W and SW of Pte du Toulinguet. Yachts <25m LOA are exempt from VTM, but should monitor VHF Ch 08 or 16.
Abeam Petit Minhou lt ho the Goulet (Narrows) de Brest narrows to 1M; there are well-marked drying rks almost in mid-stream. A course of 075° through the Passe Nord leaves Roc Mengam lt bn 2ca to stbd. Tidal streams attain 4·5kn in the Goulet. In Passe Sud there is a useful back-eddy close inshore which runs ENE during the ebb. Once beyond Pte du Portzic a buoyed chan leads ENE past the Naval and commercial hbrs to the Moulin Blanc marina (8.16.27). The Rade de Brest (8.16.28) opens to the S and E.

L'IROISE/BAIE DE DOUARNENEZ (charts 3427, 798)

L'Iroise is the area between Chaussée des Pierres Noires and Chaussée de Sein; the B de Douarnenez lies further E. On the NE side of L'Iroise (chart 3427) a chain of rks extends 7M W from Pte du Toulinguet. There are several chans through these rks, of which the simplest for Brest (8.16.27) and Camaret (8.16.29) is the 3ca wide Chenal du Toulinguet which runs NNW between La Louve bn tr (1ca W of Pte du Toulinguet) on E side and Le Pohen rk on the W side.
Here the N-going stream begins at HW Brest – 0550, and the S-going at HW Brest + 0015, sp rates 2·75kn. 2·5M NW of C. de la Chèvre is Le Chévreau (dries), with La Chèvre 5ca to NE of it (1·25M WSW of Pte de Dinan). 7M W of Pte de Dinan lies Basse du Lis, rky shoals with depth of 2·4m.

The B de Douarnenez is entered between C. de la Chèvre and Raz de Sein. Off C. de la Chèvre various dangers, on which the sea breaks, extend SW for 2·25M to Basse Vieille (dries), lt buoy. Morgat (8.16.30) lies 4M NNE of C. de la Chèvre. Beware group of drying rks, including La Pierre-Profonde and Le Taureau close SSW of Les Verrès (rk 9m high), which lies nearly 2·5M ESE of Morgat.

Approaching Douarnenez (8.16.31) beware Basse Veur and Basse Neuve. The S shore of the B is clear of dangers more than 2ca offshore, except for Duellou Rk (4m high) 5ca offshore, and other rks 1M eastward. Further W beware Basse Jaune, an isolated rk (dries) about 1M N of Pte du Van.

8.16.6   DISTANCE TABLE

Approximate distances in nautical miles are by the most direct route, whilst avoiding dangers and allowing for Traffic Separation Schemes. Places in *italics* are in adjoining areas; places in **bold** are in 8.0.8, Cross-Channel Distances.

		1	2	3	4	5	6	7	8	9	10	11	12	13	14	15	16	17	18	19	20
1.	*St Quay-Portrieux*	1																			
2.	Paimpol	24	2																		
3.	Bréhat (Port Clos)	15	8	3																	
4.	Lézardrieux	21	14	6	4																
5.	**Tréguier**	46	29	22	22	5															
6.	Perros-Guirec	37	35	28	28	21	6														
7.	Ploumanac'h	40	33	27	29	25	6	7													
8.	Trébeurden	48	44	38	40	32	17	11	8												
9.	**Lannion**	52	48	42	44	33	21	15	6	9											
8.	Morlaix	67	64	58	60	46	36	30	23	24	10										
11.	**Roscoff**	59	58	52	54	41	28	22	17	19	12	11									
12.	**L'Aberwrac'h**	91	88	82	84	72	60	54	49	51	48	32	12								
13.	L'Aberbenoit	92	89	83	85	76	61	55	50	52	45	33	7	13							
14.	Lampaul	114	110	104	106	98	83	77	72	74	67	55	29	28	14						
15.	**Le Conquet**	114	110	104	106	98	83	77	72	71	68	55	29	23	17	15					
16.	Brest (marina)	125	119	114	114	107	92	86	83	87	79	67	42	41	31	18	16				
17.	Camaret	124	120	114	116	108	93	87	82	81	78	65	39	33	27	13	10	17			
18.	Morgat	134	130	124	126	118	103	97	92	91	88	75	49	43	37	20	24	16	18		
19.	Douarnenez	139	135	129	131	123	108	102	97	96	93	80	54	48	42	25	29	21	11	19	
20.	*Audierne*	144	139	133	135	128	113	108	102	101	98	86	55	53	40	30	34	28	27	30	20

8.16.7 English Channel Waypoints: See 8.1.7   **8.16.8** Special Notes for France: See 8.15.8

16

PAIMPOL   8-16-9

Côte d'Armor 48°47'·06N 03°02'·47W   Rtg 3-3-2

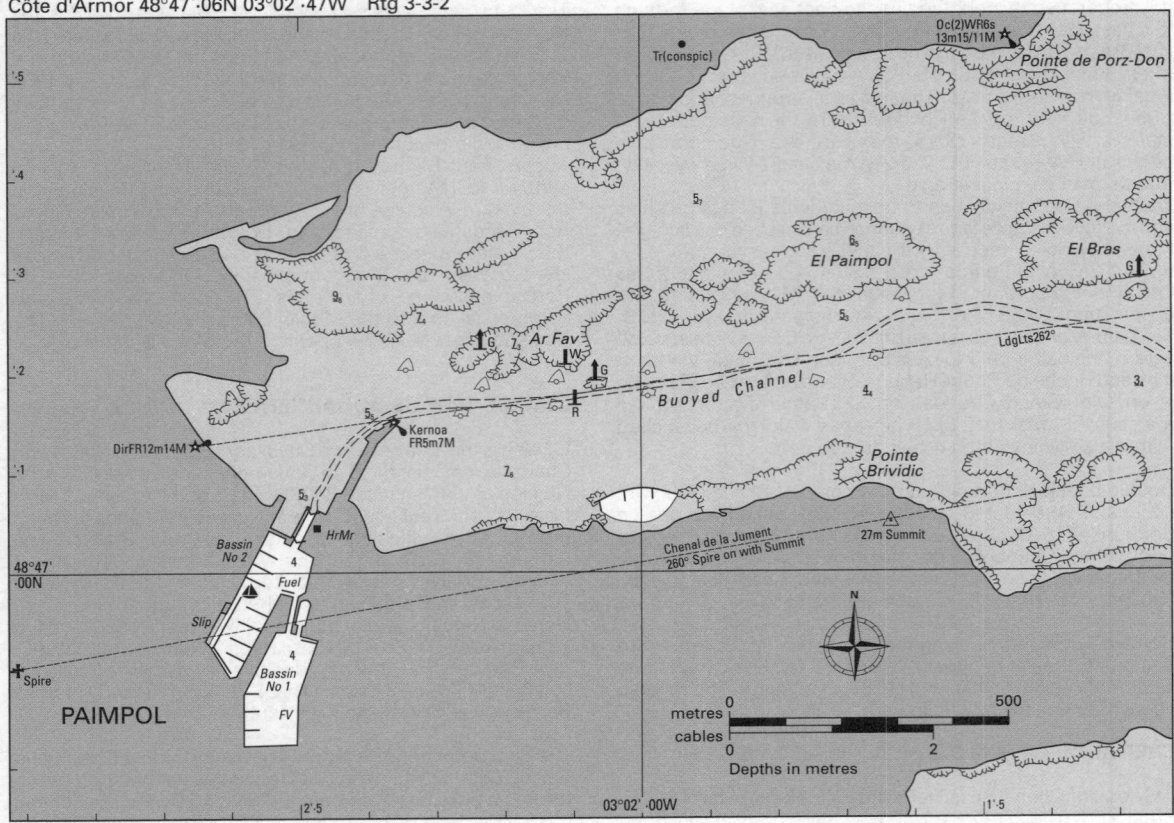

CHARTS
AC 3673, 3670, *2668*; SHOM 7127, 831, 7154; ECM 537; Imray C34; Stanfords 17
TIDES
Dover –0525; ML 6·1; Duration 0600; Zone –0100

Standard Port ST MALO (←)

Times				Height (metres)			
High Water		Low Water		MHWS	MHWN	MLWN	MLWS
0100	0800	0300	0800	12·2	9·2	4·3	1·6
1300	2000	1500	2000				
Differences PAIMPOL							
–0005	–0010	–0035	–0025	–1·4	–0·8	–0·5	–0·2

SHELTER
Good shelter from all winds in hbr, but few ⚓s as most of the Anse de Paimpol dries, including the appr chan to hbr. Lock opens HW ±2 when height of HW <10m; HW ±2½ when HW >10m. Visitors' berths at pontoon A, Basin No 2, min depth 3·8m. Larger yachts berth in Basin No 1.
NAVIGATION
WPT 48°47'·88N 02°54'·50W, 080°/260° from/to summit of Pte Brividic 4·7M. Chenal de la Jument is the normal appr from the E. After La Jument PHM bn tr, either ⚓ to await the tide; or alter 262° for small unlit buoys/bns marking final 1M of chan; hard to see against a low evening sun. The drying rks (El Paimpol, El Bras and Ar Fav) are close N of the ldg line. An alternative appr from Ile de Bréhat at HW+2 lies E of Les Piliers NCM bn tr, thence S past Pte de la Trinité; or appr from further E via Chenal du Denou 193°. Bearing in mind the large tidal range, there is enough water in the bay from half-flood for most craft.
LIGHTS AND MARKS
4M E is L'Ost-Pic lt, Oc WR 4s 20m 11/8M, conspic □ W tr. Pte de Porz-Don, Oc (2) WR 6s 13m 15/11M, vis W269°-272°, R272°-279°, is 7ca ENE of hbr ent. W sector leads 270° to the inner ldg lts 262°. A conspic tr (52m) is 3ca W of Porz -Don.
Outer ldg marks 260° for Chenal de la Jument: Paimpol ✠ spire on with the summit (27m) of Pte Brividic.

Inner ldg lts 262°: front, Jetée de Kernoa, FR 5m 7M; rear, Dir FR 12m 14M, intens 260°-264°.
RADIO TELEPHONE
VHF Ch 09 (0800-1200LT and lock opening hrs).
TELEPHONE
Hr Mr 02·96.20.47.65; Port Mgr 02·96·20·80·77; ⌗ 02·96·20·81·87; Aff Mar 02·96·20·84·30; CROSS 02·98·89·31·31; Auto 08·36·68·08·22; Police 02·96·20·80·17; Ⓗ 02·96·20·86·02; Dr 02·96·20·80·04; Brit Consul 02·99·46·26·64.
FACILITIES
Basin No 2 (marina 280+20 visitors), FF103, FW, AC, D (quay), P (cans), ME, EI, ⌂; **Basin No 1** C (6 and 4 ton); **Quai de Kernoa** P, ME; **Quai neuf** Slip, M, FW, AB; **Services:** Sh, CH, SHOM, Ⓔ.
Town P, CH, V, R, Bar, Gaz, ⊡, ⊠, Ⓑ, ⇌, ✈ Dinard, Brest, Rennes. Ferry: Roscoff, St Malo.

ILE DE BRÉHAT   8-16-10

Côte d'Armor 48°51'·00N 03°00'·00W   Rtg 2-4-1

CHARTS
AC 3673, 3670, *2668*; SHOM 7127, 831, 832; ECM 537; Imray C34; Stanfords 17
TIDES
–0525 Dover; ML 5·8; Duration 0605; Zone –0100

Standard Port ST MALO (←)

Times				Height (metres)			
High Water		Low Water		MHWS	MHWN	MLWN	MLWS
0100	0800	0300	0800	12·2	9·2	4·3	1·6
1300	2000	1500	2000				
Differences LES HEAUX DE BRÉHAT							
–0018	–0017	–0050	–0050	–2·4	–1·6	–0·7	–0·3
ILE DE BRÉHAT							
–0008	–0013	–0040	–0037	–1·8	–1·2	–0·5	–0·3

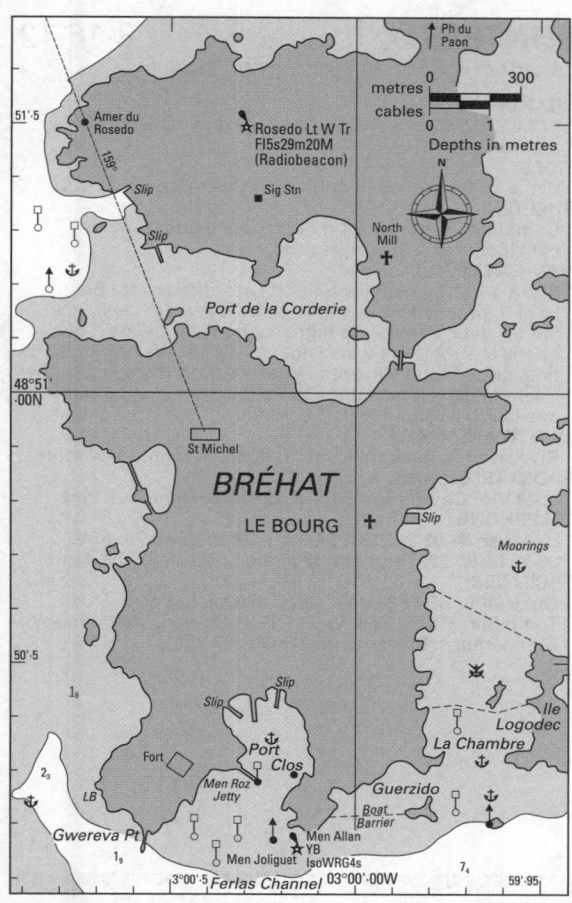

LÉZARDRIEUX   8-16-11

Côte d'Armor 48°47′·41N 03°05′·83W   Rtg 1-1-2

CHARTS
AC 3673, 3670, *2668*; SHOM 7126, 7127, 831, 7152; ECM 537; Imray C34; Stanfords 17

TIDES
−0510 Dover; ML 5·9; Duration 0610; Zone −0100

Standard Port ST MALO (←)

Times				Height (metres)			
High Water		Low Water		MHWS	MHWN	MLWN	MLWS
0100	0800	0300	0800	12·2	9·2	4·3	1·6
1300	2000	1500	2000				
Differences LÉZARDRIEUX							
−0010	−0010	−0047	−0037	−1·7	−1·2	−0·6	−0·3

SHELTER
Very good in all weathers. The Trieux River and marina pontoons are accessible H24. Very close SW, a marina extension (247 berths) has some ◑ berths (2·4m inside). Access over sill 4·9m above CD, with automatic flap. As sill covers on the flood to 6·15m CD, flap automatically drops to give 1·25m clearance. A depth gauge shows water over sill. IPTS in use. See chartlet overleaf. Multi-hulls and boats >12·5m LOA should moor on ◑s in the stream. Yachts can go about 12km up river (via bridge, clearance 17m) to lock in at Pontrieux (8.16.12).

NAVIGATION
WPT 48°55′·00N 02°56′·20W, 045°/225° from/to front ldg lt 225° (La Croix), 6·7M. Roches Douvres and Barnouic are dangers in the outer apps; closer in, are the Plateau de la Horaine and rky shoals to the W. Off river ent beware strong cross streams. The 3 well-marked ent chans are: Ferlas Chan from the E, running S of Ile de Bréhat; Grand Chenal, main chan from NE, best for strangers; and Moisie, unlit from the NW, which also connects with Passe de la Gaine from/to Tréguier (8.16.13).

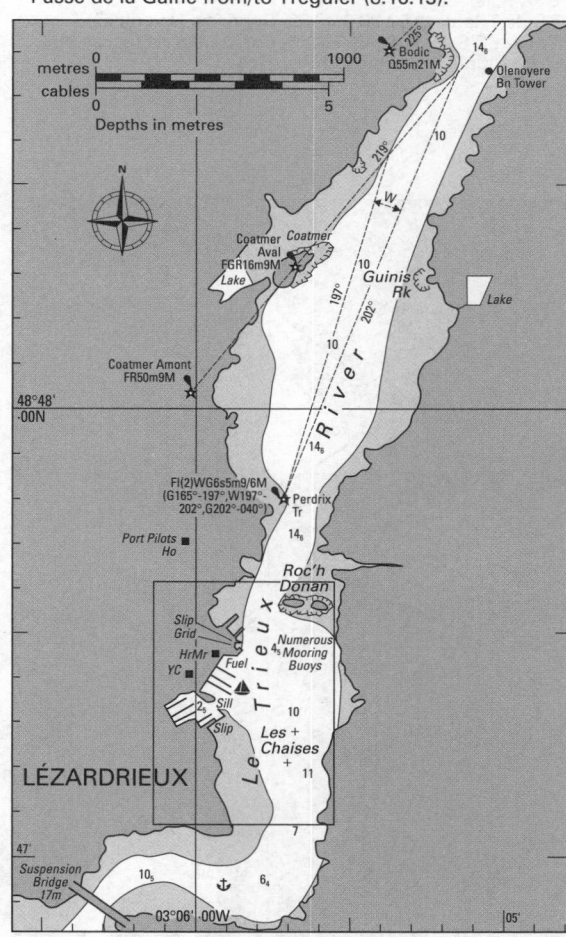

ILE DE BREHAT continued

SHELTER
Port Clos: drying main hbr; good shelter, but busy with vedettes. No AB; ⚓ clear of fairway. (Due to cables across the Ferlas Chan, ⚓ is prohib to the SW of Port Clos).
Port de la Corderie: hbr dries; get well out of strong tides. Good shelter, except in W winds.
E of Le Bourg there are free drying private ◑s near ⚓.
La Chambre: ⚓ in upper reaches just S of the ⚒ area. Slip can be floodlit by pressing button on lamp post at top of slip.
Guerzido in the Chenal de Ferlas is good holding, partly out of the strong tides. There are ◑s or ⚓ E of Men Allan and close to the buoys of the boat barrier.

NAVIGATION
WPT Ferlas chan 48°49′·45N 02°55′·00W, 098°/278° from/to La Croix lt, 5·5M. See also 8.16.11. On appr, beware La Horaine, Men Marc'h and C'hign Bras closer in.

LIGHTS AND MARKS
For the three principal lts on Ile de Bréhat, see 8.16.4.

RADIO TELEPHONE
Sémaphore de Bréhat VHF Ch 16 10, Day only.

TELEPHONE
Hr Mr none; CROSS 02·98·89·31·31; SNSM 02·96·20·00·14; Auto 08·36·68·08·22; ∰ 02·96·20·81·87; Police 02·96·20·80·17; Dr 02·96·20·00·99; Brit Consul 02·99·46·26·64.

FACILITIES
Hbrs M, FW, P from fuel barge at Port Clos, Slip, full access at HW; **CN de Bréhat**, FW, Bar; **Services:** ME. **Village** V, Gaz, Bar, ⊠, Ⓑ (Paimpol), ⇌ (ferry to Pte de l'Arcouest, bus to Paimpol), ✈ (Dinard, Brest, Rennes to London). Ferry: Plymouth-Roscoff. No cars on island.

16

LIGHTS AND MARKS

Offshore lts: Roches Douvres, Fl 5s 60m 28M, pink tr. Barnouic ECM bn tr, VQ (3) 5s 15m 9M.
Les Héaux de Bréhat, Oc (3) WRG 12s 48m 17/12M, gy tr. Pte du Paon and Rosédo, on Bréhat, see 8.16.4 and .10.
The ldg marks/lts for the ent chans are:

(1) Ferlas chan:
W sector of Men Joliguet lt bn tr 271° (see 8.16.10).
W sector of Roche Quinonec Dir Q WRG 257°.
W sector of Kermouster Dir Fl WRG 2s leads 271° to join Coatmer ldg line.

(2) Grand Chenal ldg lts 225°: Front, La Croix Oc 4s 15m 19M; two grey trs joined, W on NE side with R tops, intens 215°-235°; rear, Bodic (2·1M from front) Q 55m 22M (intens 221°-229°).

(3) Moisie chan: Amer du Rosédo W obelisk on 159° with St Michael's chapel (both conspic on Ile de Bréhat).

Within the Trieux river:

(4) Coatmer ldg lts 219°: front F RG 16m 9/9M, vis R200°-250°, G250°-053°; rear, 660m from front, FR 50m 9M.

(5) W sector 200° of Les Perdrix G tr, Fl (2) WG 6s.

Beware, at night, the unlit Roc'h Donan 2½ca S of Perdrix. The only lts beyond Perdrix are F Bu lts at the outboard ends of the 3 tidal marina pontoons, and a Fl R 4s and Fl G 4s buoy 50 - 100m E of the ent to new marina; also unlit perches: PHM/SHM at ent; 1 ECM 50m NE of ent, and 5 Y SPM marking the limits of the marina.

RADIO TELEPHONE

VHF Ch 09 (0730-2200 Jul/Aug. 0800-1200 and 1400-1800 rest of year).

TELEPHONE

Hr Mr 02·96·20·14·22; Aff Mar at Paimpol 02·96·20·84·30; CROSS 02·98·89·31·31; ☼ at Paimpol 02·96·20·81·87; Auto 08·36·68·08·22; Police 02·96·20·8·17; Dr 02·96·20·8·30; Brit Consul 02·99·46·26·64.

FACILITIES

Marina (477; **◐** as directed by Hr Mr), ☎ 02·96·20·14·22, FF98, Slip, P, D, FW, AC, ME, El, CH, SM, Sh, C (6 ton), Gaz, R, ▣, Bar.
YC de Trieux ☎ 02·96·20·8·39. Services: Divers, Ⓔ;
Town EC Sun; P, D, V, Gaz, R, Bar, ✉, Ⓑ, ⇌ (occas bus to Paimpol), ✈ Lannion. Ferry: Roscoff.

PONTRIEUX   8-16-12

Côte d'Armor 48°42'·80N 03°08'·90W   Rtg 3-4-1

CHARTS

ECM 537; AC 3673 and SHOM 7126 downstream of Lézardrieux

TIDES

HW at Pontrieux Lock is at HW ST MALO. See also 8.16.11.

SHELTER

Complete shelter in 2-4m depth alongside Quay (SE bank), approx 1km above lock.

NAVIGATION

See 8.16.11 for approach up to Lézardrieux. Not before HW –3, proceed via suspension bridge (17m clearance) 6M up-river, keeping to high, rky bank on bends. Lock opens HW –2 (–1 at weekends) to HW+1. Waiting buoy (½ tide) close E and slip with FW and AC on the bend. Below Château de la Roche Jagu there is also a waiting buoy available HW±3.

LIGHTS AND MARKS

River is unlit (beware sand dredgers at night); few marks.

RADIO TELEPHONE

Lock VHF Ch 12, HW –2 to +1. ☎ link to Pontrieux Port.

TELEPHONE

Hr Mr ☎/⌨ 02·96·95·34·87; Lock 02·96·95·60·70; Auto 08·36·68·08·22. There is a ☎ at the Château Roche Jagu.

FACILITIES

Quay (100) AB FF81, FW, AC, C (6 ton), R, Bar, ♿.
Town Bar, FW, R, Slip, V, Gaz, P, D, Ⓑ, ✉, ▣, ⇌ Paimpol/Guingamp, ✈ Brest, Rennes & Dinard.

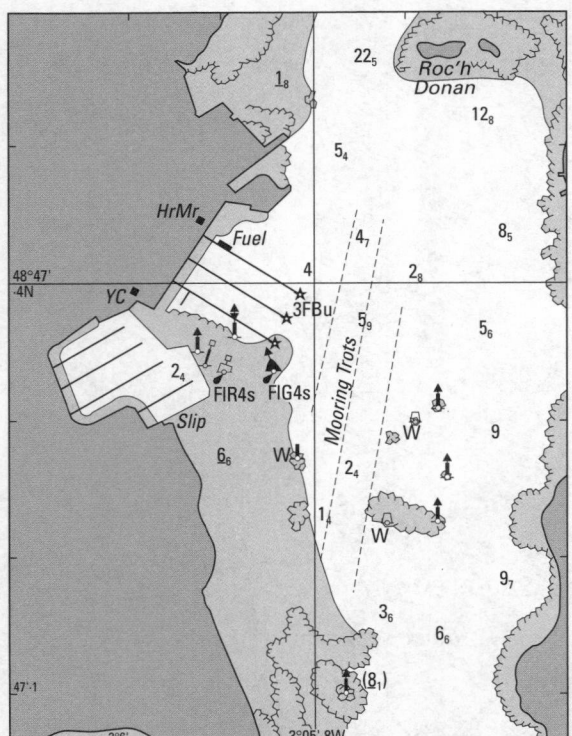

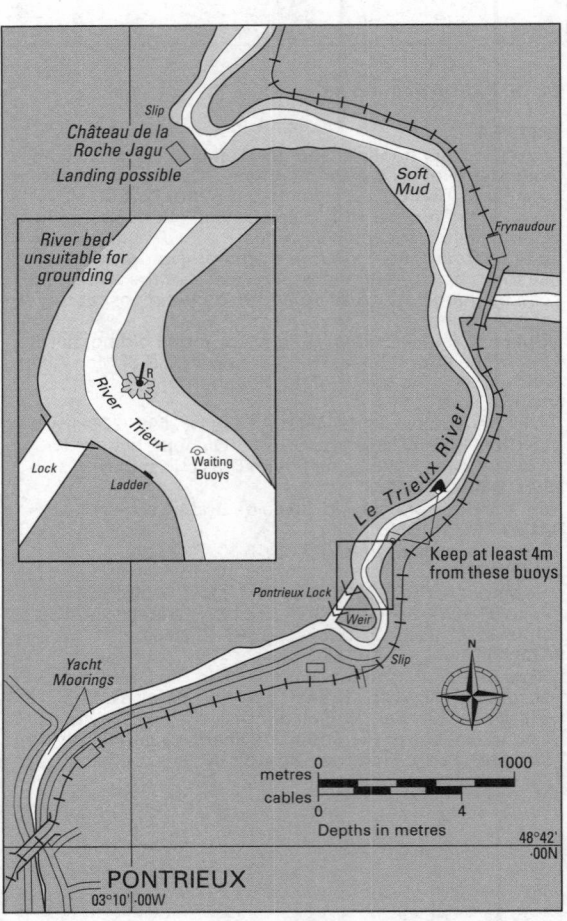

TRÉGUIER   8-16-13
Côte d'Armor 48°47'·27N 03°13'·18W   Rtg 1-2-1

CHARTS
AC 3672, 3670, *2668*; SHOM 7126, 7152; ECM 537; Imray C34; Stanfords 17

TIDES
–0540 Dover; ML 5·7; Duration 0600; Zone –0100
Standard Port ST MALO (←—)

Times				Height (metres)			
High Water		Low Water		MHWS	MHWN	MLWN	MLWS
0100	0800	0300	0800	12·2	9·2	4·3	1·6
1300	2000	1500	2000				
Differences TRÉGUIER							
–0005	–0010	–0055	–0040	–2·3	–1·5	–0·7	–0·3
PORT-BÉNI							
–0017	–0022	–0100	–0045	–2·4	–1·5	–0·6	–0·2

SHELTER
Good in marina; always berth head to tide which runs hard through the pontoons. Possible ⚓s, keeping clear of the chan: 7ca SW of La Corne lt tr, but exposed to N'lies; N and S of La Roche Jaune village; in pool 1ca NE of No 10 buoy (1M N of marina).

NAVIGATION
WPT 48°55'·25N 03°13'·00W, 317°/137° from/to front ldg lt, 5M (Grande Passe). There are three ent chans:
(1) Grande Passe: well marked/lit, but marks are hard to see by day. Caution: strong tidal streams across the chan.
(2) Passe de la Gaine: well marked, navigable with care by day in good vis. Unlit short cut to/from Lézardrieux.
(3) Passe du Nord-Est: unlit, dangerous with winds from W and NW as sea breaks across the chan.
Within the R Jaudy it is important to heed channel buoys and bns, eg keep E of an unlit SHM buoy 300m SW of La Corne lt ho to avoid the drying bank which it marks. Speed limit is 6kn above La Roche Jaune.

LIGHTS AND MARKS
Important marks: La Corne WR lt tr, Fl (3) WRG 12s 11/8M; 6ca to the N is Men Noblance WB bn tr on SE corner of Ile d'Er; and 4ca SW is Skeiviec W bn tr. The spire of Tréguier cathedral is 4·6M SSW of La Corne, but may be obscured by high wooded banks when entering the river estuary in the vicinity of Pen ar Guézec.
Ldg lts/marks for the appr chans:
(1) For Grande Passe 137°: front, Port de la Chaine, Oc 4s 12m 12M, white ho; rear, St Antoine Dir Oc R 4s 34m 15M, RW ho. At Pen ar Guézec unlit SHM buoy steer 216° in the W sector of La Corne lt.
Note: The ldg marks are very hard to identify by day. From Basse Crublent PHM buoy the Pleubian spire and water tower offer a clear transit 154° towards the Pierre à l'Anglais and Le Corbeau lateral buoys.
(2) For Passe de la Gaine 242°: Men Noblance bn tr, W with horiz B band, on with rear mark (W wall with B vert stripe) below the skyline and just right of conspic Plougrescant ✠. Hold this transit exactly to stay in narrow, marked chan; but marks hard to see from afar, especially against a low sun or in poor visibility.
(3) Passe du Nord-Est, for direct appr to La Corne having cleared W of La Jument NCM By and adjacent rky shoals: Tréguier cathedral spire and Skeiviec at 207°.

RADIO TELEPHONE
Marina Ch 09 (In season: Mon-Sat 0800-1200, 1330-2100; Sun 0800-1000, 1600-1800. Out of season: Sun/Mon closed; Tue-Sat 0800-1200, 1330-1700. All LT).

TELEPHONE
Hr Mr 02·96·92·42·37; Aff Mar 02·96·20·84·30 (Paimpol); CROSS 02·96·54·11·11; ⊞ 02·96·92·31·44; Auto 08·36·68·08·22; Police 02·96·92·32·17; Dr 02·96·92·32·14; ⊞ 02·96·05·71·11 (Lannion); Brit Consul 02·99·46·26·64.

FACILITIES
Marina (200+130 ⓥ), ☎ 02·96·92·42·37, ⚓ 02·96·92·29·25 (indicate for Port de Plaisance), FF80, Slip, FW, ME, C (8 ton), D (on most N'ly pontoon HW±1), CH, El, Sh, AC, Bar, R, Gaz, ⧉; **Bar du Port de Plaisance** ☎ 02·96·92·42·37, excellent facilities, open all year. **Club Nautique de Tréguier** 02·96·92·37·49 Bar, opp marina. **Services:** M, CH; **Town** EC Mon; Market Wed, P, FW, CH, V, Gaz, R, Bar, ✉, Ⓑ, V (small supermarket just W of cathedral delivers to boats), ⇌ (bus to Paimpol and Perros-Guirec), ✈ (St Brieuc, Lannion). Ferry: Roscoff, St Malo.

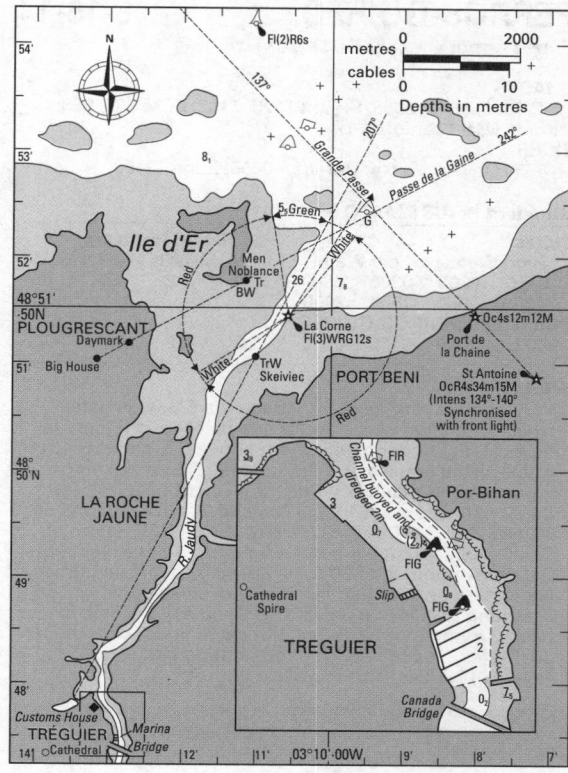

16

MINOR HARBOUR, approx 8M ENE of PERROS-GUIREC

PORT BLANC, Côte d'Armor, 48°50'·60N 03°18'·80W, AC 3672, 3670; SHOM 7125, 7152. HW –0545 on Dover (UT); HW–0040 and ht –2·0m on St Malo; ML 5·3m; Duration 0600. Good natural hbr (known as Port Bago), but open to winds between NW and NNE. Appr on 150° toward Le Voleur Dir lt, Fl WRG 4s 17m 14/11M, G140°-148°, W148°-152°, R152°-160°. Note: the former rear ldg mark is reported ruined/obsc'd. The most conspic daymark is a 16m high W obelisk on Ile du Chateau Neuf, to stbd of appr chan; a less obvious W tr is to port on Ile St Gildas. There are 30 W ⚓s in the pool or yachts can ⚓ off or dry out alongside quays, 1·3m. Facilities: AB FF30, FW, AC, C (16 ton), Slip; **Services:** CH, El, ME, Sh. **Town** Bar, R, V.

PERROS-GUIREC   8-16-14

Côte d'Armor 48° 48'·23N 03° 26'·12W   Rtg 3-2-2

CHARTS
AC 3672, 3670, *2668*; SHOM 7125, 7152; ECM 537, 538;
Imray C34; Stanfords 17

TIDES
–0550 Dover; ML 5·4; Duration 0605; Zone –0100

Standard Port ST MALO (←)

Times				Height (metres)			
High Water		Low Water		MHWS	MHWN	MLWN	MLWS
0100	0800	0300	0800	12·2	9·2	4·3	1·6
1300	2000	1500	2000				
Differences PERROS-GUIREC							
–0030	–0040	–0115	–0055	–2·9	–1·8	–0·9	–0·3

SHELTER
Very good in marina (2·5m). Enter via 6m wide gate,
which is opened when rise of tide reaches 7m (there is
no lock). Sill under gate is 3·5m above CD, giving 3·5m
water inside gateway on first opening. Gate opening
times depend mainly on tidal Coefficient (8.16.25), ie:
Coeff >70, approx HW±1½; Coeff 60-70, HW±1; Coeff 50-
60, HW–1 to +½; Coeff 40-50, HW–½ to HW. Caution: at
Coeff <40, gate may not open for up to 4 days (neaped).
Gate may open up to 30 mins ahead of published times,
depending on weather, but does not close early.
Retaining wall is marked by R & W poles. ⚓ prohib in
basin. Drying moorings 1ca E of Jetée du Linkin. Off Pte
du Chateau in approx 3m good holding and safe ⚓,
except in NE'lies, plus 2 W ⬤s.

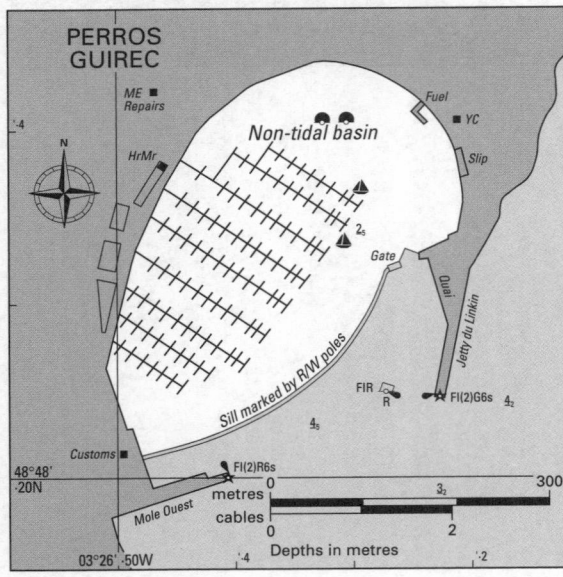

NAVIGATION
WPT 48°52'·40N 03°20'·00W, 045°/225° from/to front ldg lt
(Le Colombier), 6·4M. Beware Ile Tomé in the ent to Anse
de Perros; rks extend 7ca off the W side and 6ca E of the N
side. Explosive dumping ground is 8ca NNE of the island.

LIGHTS AND MARKS
From NE: Ldg lts 225°: front Le Colombier Dir Oc (4) 12s
28m 18M, intens 220°-230°; rear Kerprigent (1·5M from
front) Q 79m 22M, intens 221°-228°.
Passe de l'Ouest: Kerjean Dir lt 144° Oc (2+1) WRG 12s
78m 15/13M, vis G134°-143°, W143°-144°, R144°-154°.
Gate sigs (flags/lts): Ⓖ over Ⓡ = closed;
Ⓖ = open, priority to enter; Ⓡ = open, priority to leave.

RADIO TELEPHONE
VHF Ch 09 16.

TELEPHONE
Hr Mr 02·96.49.80.50, ☎ 02·96.23.37.19; Basin gate
02·96.23.19.03; Aff Mar 02·96.23.13.78; ⌗ 02·96.23.18·12;
CROSS 02·98·89.31.31; SNSM 02·96.20.00.45; Auto
08·36.68.08·22; Police 02·96.23.20.17; Dr 02·96.23.20.01;
Brit Consul 02·99.46.26.64.

FACILITIES
Marina (600+50 Ⓥ) ☎ 02·96·49·80·50, FF120, P, D, FW,
ME, AC, El, Sh, C (7 ton), CH, V, R, SM, Gas, Gaz, Kos, Ⓞ;
Services: Ⓔ, SHOM; **Town** CH, V, Gaz, R, Bar, ✉, Ⓑ, ⇌
(Lannion), ✈ (Morlaix/Lannion). Ferry: Roscoff.

PLOUMANAC'H   8-16-15

Côte d'Armor 48° 50'·35N 03° 29'·14W   Rtg 3-4-1

CHARTS
AC 3669, 3670, *2668*; SHOM 7125, 7152; ECM 537, 538;
Imray C34; Stanfords 17

TIDES
–0550 Dover; ML 5·5; Duration 0605; Zone –0100

Standard Port ST MALO (←)

Times				Height (metres)			
High Water		Low Water		MHWS	MHWN	MLWN	MLWS
0100	0800	0300	0800	12·2	9·2	4·3	1·6
1300	2000	1500	2000				
Differences PLOUMANAC'H							
–0023	–0033	–0112	–0053	–2·9	–1·8	–0·7	–0·2

SHELTER
Good; ⬤s are first line of dumbell buoys. A sill, drying
2·55m, retains at least 1·8m within. Depth gauges are on
the 4th (unreliable) and the last PHM stakes. If the
concrete base of the 3rd SHM stake is covered, depth
over sill is >1·2m. Inside the sill, for best water keep to
port and appr moorings from N. FV moorings to stbd of
ent. SE and SW sides of hbr are very shallow.

NAVIGATION
WPT 48°51'·50N 03°29'·00W, 008°/188°, 1·25M from/to ent
between Mean Ruz lt ho and Chateau Costaeres (conspic).
Ent is difficult in strong NW'lies. From/to NW, beware An
Dreuzinier, unmarked rks (drying 1·4m), 100m N and NE
of No 1 SHM stake; not a problem with sufficient rise of
tide, but near LW keep very close W of a line through the
first two PHM stakes. Chan is marked by unlit stakes.

LIGHTS AND MARKS
Mean Ruz lt ho, Oc WR 4s, to E with adjacent sig stn, conspic.

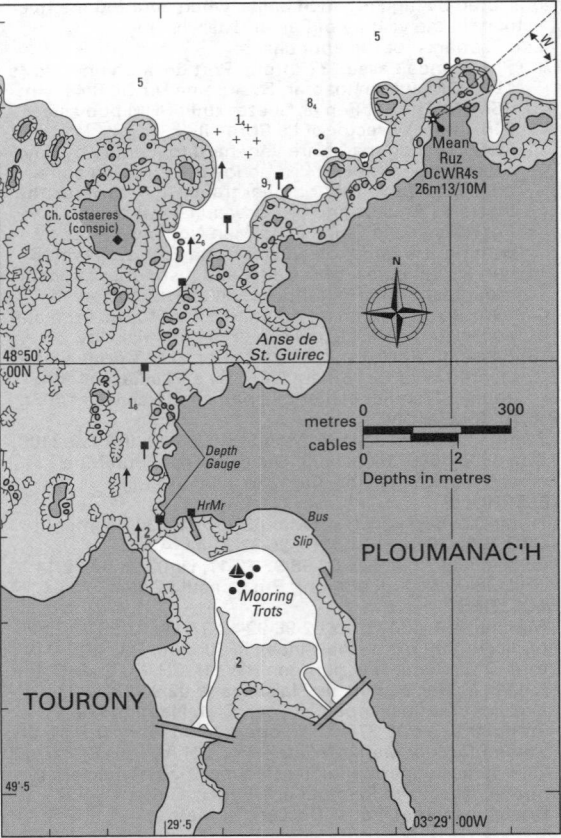

RADIO TELEPHONE
VHF Ch 09.
TELEPHONE
Hr Mr 02·96.91.44.31/02·96.23.37.82; Auto 08·36.68·08·22; SNSM 02·96.20.00.45; Dr 02·96.91.42.00; ME 02·96.23.31.40.
FACILITIES
Port de Plaisance (230 + 50 Ⓥ) M, FF105; **Quai Bellevue** FW, AC, L, Slip, P & D cans; Bus to Lannion & Perros; **YC Société Nautique de Perros Guirec.** Ferry: See Roscoff.

ANCHORAGE 1M WEST OF PLOUMANAC'H

TRÉGASTEL, Côte d'Armor, 48°50'·10N 03°31'·20W, AC 3669, 3670; SHOM 7152. HW –0550 on Dover (UT); +0005 and –1·8m on Brest HW; ML 5·1m; Duration 0605. Use 8.16.15 differences. Good ⚓ in 2m, but exposed to winds from W to N. Ent, 2ca W of La Pierre Pendue (conspic rk), is marked by PHM bn on Ile Dhu and SHM buoy off Le Taureau, rk drying 4·5m (bn destroyed). Turreted house, conspic, brg approx 165° leads between Ile Dhu and Le Taureau. Thence after 2 more PHM and 1 SHM bns, turn E to the ⚓ or Orange ⚓s S of Ile Ronde. Facilities: Slip; **Club Nautique de Trégastel** ☎ 02·96.23·45.05; **Town** (Ste Anne, 0·5M inland) CH, Ⓑ, ⊠, Ⓞ, Bar, R, V.

TRÉBEURDEN   8-16-16
Côte d'Armor 48°46'·35N 03°35'·06W   Rtg 3-2-2

CHARTS
AC 3669; SHOM 7125, 7124, 7151; ECM 537, 538; Imray C34; Stanfords 17
TIDES
–0605 Dover; ML 5·5; Duration 0605; Zone –0100

Standard Port BREST (⟶)

Times				Height (metres)			
High Water		Low Water		MHWS	MHWN	MLWN	MLWS
0000	0600	0000	0600	6·9	5·4	2·6	1·0
1200	1800	1200	1800				
Differences TRÉBEURDEN							
+0100	+0110	+0120	+0100	+2·3	+1·9	+0·9	+0·4

SHELTER
Good in marina (3·5m). Access HW±3½ (±4¼ at sp) over moving sill (2m CD; 15m wide) at stbd side of ent; rest of sill is fixed 3·5m. Tide gauge floodlit, port side of sill. Ⓥ on pontoon F (2nd from ent). Do not manoeuvre within 10 mins of the sill dropping, due to strong underwater inrush. 15 deep-water waiting buoys outside, or ⚓ off NE side of Ile Milliau, but exposed to W'lies.
NAVIGATION
WPT 48°45'·13N 03°40'·68W, 246°/066° from/to Lan Kerellec Dir lt, 4·1M. From W, appr is clear. From E and N, round Bar ar Gall and Le Crapaud WCM buoys; continue S for 1·5M, then alter 066° toward Ile Milliau (conspic CG bldg); thence as below to enter the marked chan to marina ent. From Ar Gouredec SCM buoy, VQ (6) + L Fl 10s, ✠ spire (conspic) brg 098° leads to ent via chan buoyed as shown.
LIGHTS AND MARKS
Le Crapaud WCM buoy, Q (9) 15s. Lan Kerellec Dir lt, Iso WRG 4s 8/5M, G058°-064°, W064°-069°, R069°-130°, leads 066° past Ile Milliau. IPTS (sigs 2 & 4) on bkwtr and on sill gateway; 4 Y SPM bns mark fixed sill.
RADIO TELEPHONE
Call *Port Trébeurden* VHF Ch 09 16.
TELEPHONE
Hr Mr ☎ 02·96.23·64.00; Aff Mar 02·96.37.06.52; CROSS 02·98·89.31.31; SNSM 02·96.23·53.82; ⌗ 02·96.92·31.44; Police 02·96.23.51.96 (Jul/Aug); Ⓗ (Lannion) 02·96.05.71.11.
FACILITIES
Marina (400 + 160 Ⓥ), ☎ as Hr Mr, ⛟ 02·96.47.40.87, FF105, FW, AC, P, D, BY, C (20 ton); **YC de Trébeurden** ☎ 96·37·00.40 (July-Aug); **Services:** BY, ME, El, Sh, CH. **Town** V, R, Bar, ⊠, Ⓑ, ✈ (Lannion). Ferry: Roscoff/St.Malo.

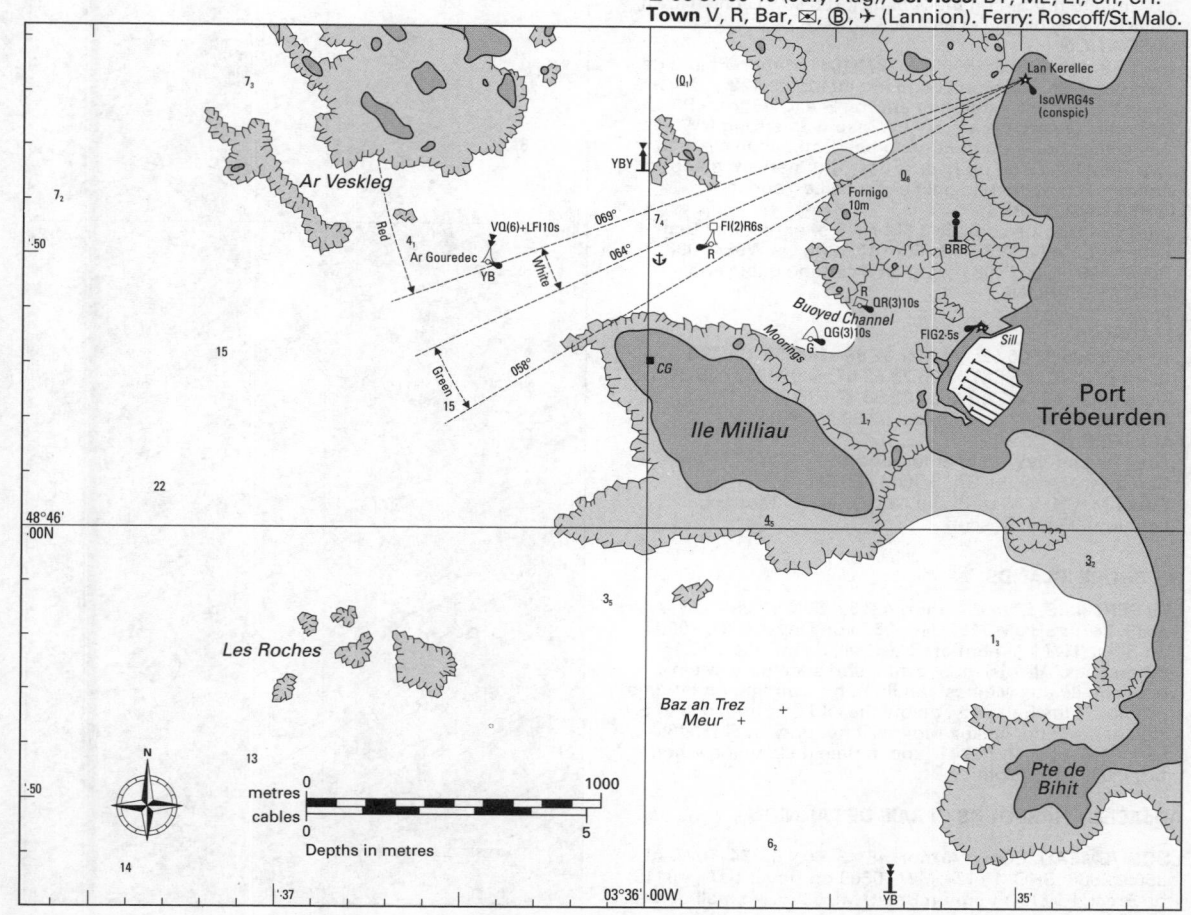

LANNION (Léguer River)   8·16·17

Côte d'Armor 48°44'·00N 03°33'·50W   Rtg 3-4-2

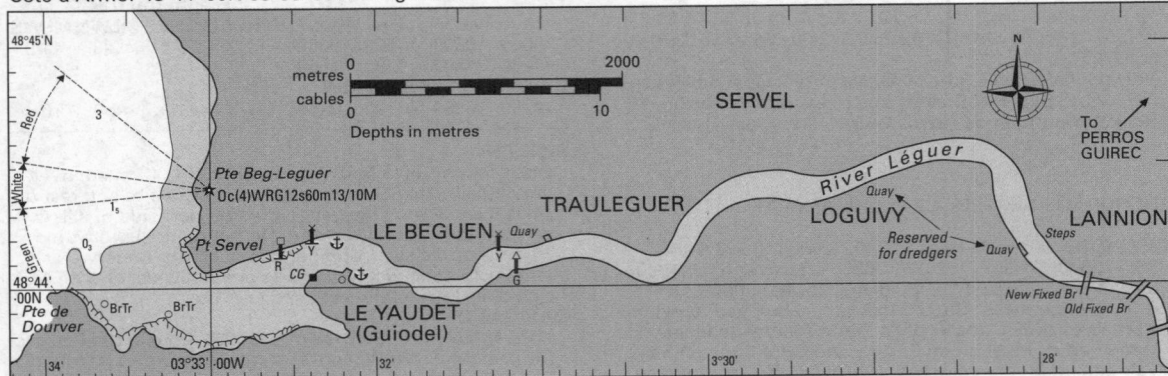

CHARTS
AC 3669, *2668*; SHOM 7124, 7151; ECM 537, 538; Imray C34; Stanfords 17

TIDES
–0605 Dover; ML 5·4; Duration: no data; Zone –0100

Standard Port BREST (→)

Times				Height (metres)			
High Water		Low Water		MHWS	MHWN	MLWN	MLWS
0000	0600	0000	0600	6·9	5·4	2·6	1·0
1200	1800	1200	1800				
Differences LOCQUIREC							
+0058	+0108	+0120	+0100	+2·2	+1·8	+0·8	+0·3

SHELTER
Good, except in strong W/NW winds. ⚓ in estuary or in non-drying pools off Le Yaudet and Le Beguen. It may be possible to dry out on the N bank just below Lannion town, but a recce by dinghy or on foot is advised.

NAVIGATION
WPT 48°44'·40N 03°36'·60W, 284°/104° from/to Pointe de Dourven 1·9M (also on Locquemeau ldg lts 122°). Beware drying sandbank extending approx 2ca N/NE from Pte de Dourven. No access at very LW, esp with strong NW'lies when seas break on the drying bar. Enter chan close to two G bn trs. Chan up river is easy, but narrow, steep-to and marked by trs/bns only as far as Le Yaudet.

LIGHTS AND MARKS
Large W radome conspic 3·5M NNE of ent. Pointe Beg-Léguer lt, Oc (4) WRG 12s 60m 13/10M; vis W084°-098°, R098°-129°, G007°-084°; lt is on a cottage gable end.

RADIO TELEPHONE
None.

TELEPHONE
Hr Mr 02·96·37·06·52; Aff Mar 02·96·37·06·52; CROSS 02·98·89·31·31; SNSM 02·96·23·52·07; ⌗ 02·96·37·45·32; Auto 08·36·68·08·22; Police 02·96·37·03·78; Dr 02·96·37·42·52; Brit Consul 02·99·46·26·64.

FACILITIES
Quai de Loguivy AB in emergency, Slip, FW, C (1 ton). **Services:** M, ME, El, Sh, SHOM, Ⓔ, CH. **Town** M, CH, V, Gaz, R, Bar, ✉, Ⓑ, ⇌, ✈ (Morlaix, Lannion). Ferry: Roscoff.

OFFSHORE ISLANDS

LES SEPT ILES, Côte d'Armor, 48° 52'·80N 03°29'·10W, AC 3669, 3670; SHOM 7152. HW-0550 on Dover (UT); +0005 on Brest. HW ht –1·8m on Brest. ML 5·2m. Use 8.16.15 differences. All 7 islands form a bird sanctuary. Main ⚓ between Île aux Moines and Ile Bono. Landing on latter is prohib. ⚓ due E of jetty; below the Old Fort, or close to S side of Ile Bono. Île aux Moines lt ho, grey tr, Fl (3) 15s 59m 24M, obsc 237°-241° and in Baie de Lannion when brg < 039°. No facilities.

ADJACENT HARBOURS IN BAIE DE LANNION

LOCQUEMEAU, Côte d'Armor, 48°43'·60N 03°34'·70W, AC 3669, 2668; SHOM 7124. HW –0600 on Dover (UT); +0110 on Brest; HW ht +1·5m on Brest; ML 5·3m. A small drying hbr by ent to Lannion River (8.16.17). There are two quays: the outer is accessible at LW, but open to W 'lies. Yachts can dry out at inner quay, on S side. Ldg lts 122° to outer quay: front FR 21m 6M, vis 068°-228°, W pylon + R top; rear, 484m from front, Oc (2+1) R 12s 39m 7M, W gable and R gallery. **Services:** ME, El, Sh; **Town** Bar.

LOCQUIREC, Côte d'Armor, 48°41'·50N 03°38'·68W. AC 3669, 2668; SHOM 7124. Tidal data as for Locquemeau, above. Small drying hbr at mouth of R Le Douron, with good shelter from W/SW winds. The whole estuary dries to shifting sandbanks (2·9m to 6·1m). Access HW±3. No lights, but a NCM buoy is 7ca N of Pte de Locqueric and a SHM bn tr (6ca S of the hbr) is conspic as the bay opens up. A pleasant temp ⚓, or overnight if able to take the ground. Many moorings, inc 10 🅐s. Land at slip.

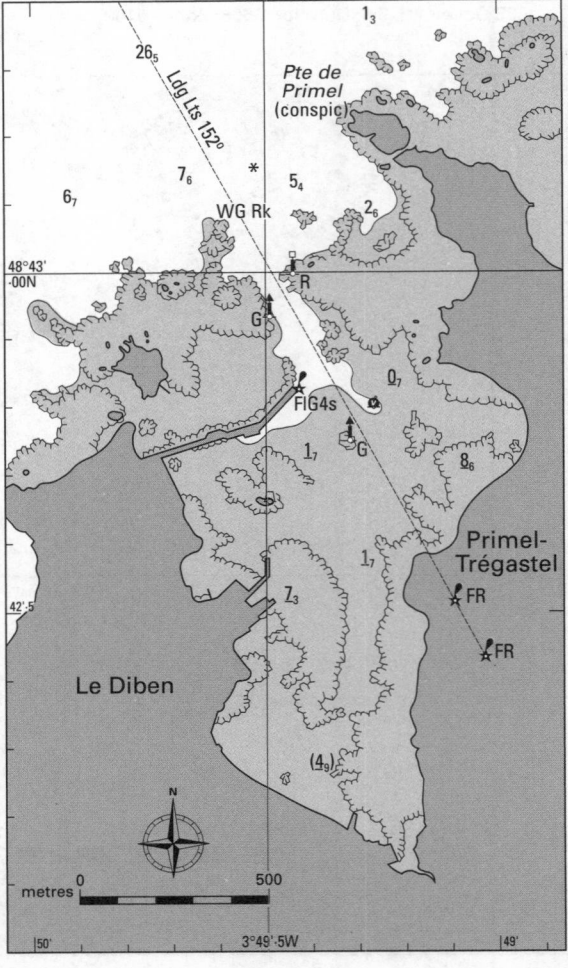

PRIMEL-TRÉGASTEL, Finistere, 48°42´.80N 03°49´.30W, AC 2745, 3669; SHOM 7095, 7151. HW −0610 on Dover (UT); ML 5·3m; Duration 0600. See Anse de Primel (8.16.18) and facing chartlet. All tides access. Good ⚓, but open to N/NW'lies; seas break across ent in strong winds. Beware drying rks off Pte de Primel to E, and off Ar Zammeguez (3m high, painted W/G) to W of ent. Enter exactly on daymarks 152°, both are W ☐ walls with R vert stripe, on hillside; or co-located ldg lts, both FR 35/56m 6M, front vis 134°-168°. Pass between a PHM and SHM bn, the former quite short. 15 (10 deep water) ⚓s or ⚓ to SE or SW of bkwtr hd, Fl G 4s 6m 7M, in 2-9m. Le Diben on W side is FV port. Drying upper reaches are well sheltered. VHF Ch 09 16 (season). Hr Mr ☎ 02.98.62.28.40.
Facilities: C (25 ton), FW, Slip, CH, El, ME, Sh, Ⓔ, R, Bar.

MORLAIX   8-16-18

Finistere 48°35'.50N 03°50'.50W   Rtg 3-2-1

CHARTS
AC 2745, 3669; SHOM 7095, 7151; ECM 538; Imray C34, C35; Stanfords 17

TIDES
−0610 Dover; ML 5·3; Duration 0610; Zone −0100

Standard Port BREST (→)

Times				Height (metres)			
High Water		Low Water		MHWS	MHWN	MLWN	MLWS
0000	0600	0000	0600	6·9	5·4	2·6	1·0
1200	1800	1200	1800				

Differences MORLAIX (CHÂTEAU DU TAUREAU)
+0055 +0105 +0115 +0055 +2·0 +1·7 +0·8 +0·3
ANSE DE PRIMEL
+0100 +0110 +0120 +0100 +2·1 +1·7 +0·8 +0·3

SHELTER
Good in the bay and at Dourduff (dries), clear of extensive oyster beds marked by small orange buoys/stakes. Boats can go 5M up to Morlaix town and lock in to the Bassin à Flot; lock opens by day only, at HW −1½, HW and HW+1. Complete shelter at the marina; ❤'s pontoon on E bank, just N of slip and YC. A movable footbridge across the marina abeam the YC, is usually open during lock hours.

NAVIGATION
WPT 48°42´.71N 03°53´.44W, abeam Stolvezen PHM buoy, 356°/176° from/to Ile Louet lt, 2·25M (Grand Chenal). The three ent channels all have rky dangers:
(1) Chenal Ouest 188°, W of Ricard Is. Deepest chan, but unlit.
(2) Grand Chenal 176°, E of Ricard Is, shallower but lit.
(3) Chenal de Tréguier, 190°, best at night, but almost dries.
Strong N'lies can raise a steep sea even in the estuary.
The Penzé river lies W of Ile de Callot.

LIGHTS AND MARKS
Grand Chenal ldg lts 176°: front Ile Louet, Oc (3) WG 12s; rear La Lande, Fl 5s.
Chenal de Tréguier ldg lts 190°: Ile Noire, Oc (2) WRG 6s; rear La Lande, Fl 5s.
River up to Morlaix, 3M above Dourduff, is buoyed but unlit.

RADIO TELEPHONE
Port and marina VHF Ch 09 16.

TELEPHONE
Hr Mr 02.98.62.13.14; Lock 02.98.88.54.92; Aff Mar 02.98.62.8.47; CROSS 02.98.89.31.31; SNSM 02.98.88.00.76; ⊞ 02.98.88.06.31; Auto 08.36.68.08.29; Police 02.98.88.58.13; Ⓗ 02.98.62.61.60; Brit Consul 02.99.46.26.64.

FACILITIES
Marina (180+30 visitors) ☎ 02.98.62.13.14, access as lock times, FF74, AC, FW, C (8 ton), P & D, Slip, ME, El, Sh, CH; **YC de Morlaix** ☎ 02.98.62.08.51;
Town P, D, SM, Ⓔ, SHOM, V, Gaz, R, Bar, ⊠, Ⓑ, Ⓞ, ⇌, ✈. Ferry: Roscoff.

ANCHORAGES N AND NW OF MORLAIX
PENZÉ RIVER, Finistere, Ent 48°42´.00N 03°56´.40W, AC 2745, SHOM 7095. HW −0610 on Dover (UT), +0105 on Brest; HW ht +1·2m Brest; ML 5·0m; Duration 0605. From NNW appr between Cordonnier and Guerhéon bn trs at mid-flood or, for deeper water, from the ENE between Les Bizeyer reef and Le Paradis bn tr; thence pass W of Ile Callot. A short cut from Morlaix estuary to the Penzé is the drying Passe aux Moutons, between Carantec and Ile

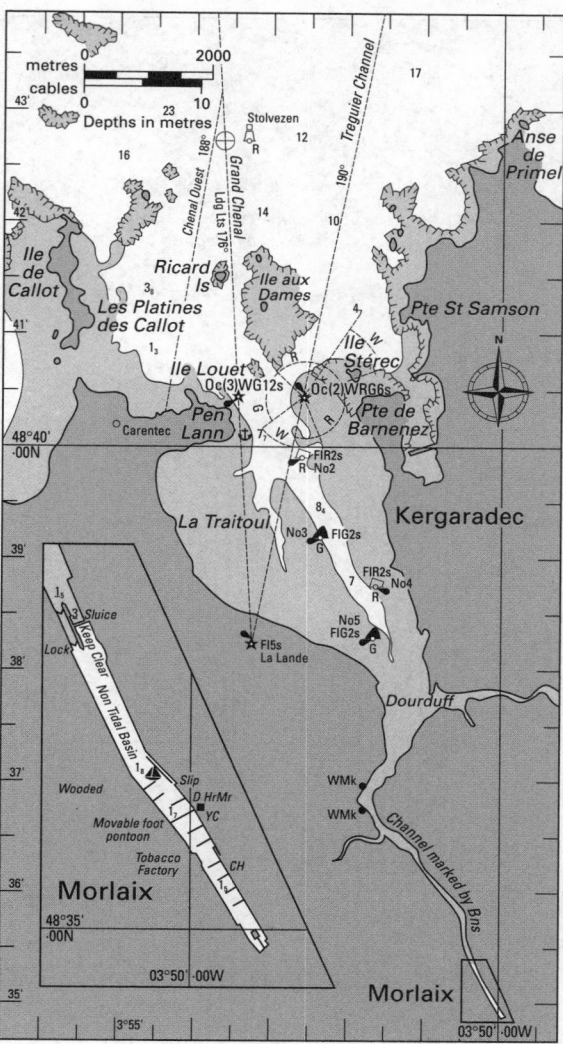

Callot, with adequate rise. The ⚓ NE of Carantec is open, especially to NW; landing stage dries about 4·6m. Yachts can dry out inside Pempoul bkwtr off St Pol-de-Léon. Further S the chan narrows and is scantily marked only by oyster withies and local moorings. SW of Pte de Lingos shelter is better; or moor off St Yves where the old ferry slips provide landing places. S of the Pont de la Corde (11m clearance) the river is buoyed and navigable on the tide for 3M to complete shelter at Penzé. Facilities at Carantec: El, ME, Sh, M, CH, P, D, Ⓔ. **Town** Ⓑ, Bar, ⊠, R, V. **Penzé** AB (drying), limited V, R, Bar.

OTHER HARBOURS WEST OF ROSCOFF

MOGUÉRIEC, Finistere, 48°40´.40N 04°04´.40W, AC 3669, 2668; SHOM 7151. Tides approx as for Ile de Batz (8.16.19). A small drying fishing hbr, 3M SSW of W ent to Canal de Batz, open to NW swell. Ldg lts 162°: both W trs/G tops, front on jetty, Iso WG 4s 9m, W158°-166°; rear FG 22m. Beware Méan Névez rk, dries 3·3m, to W of appr. ⚓ close SW of Ile de Siec, or 3ca WSW of Ar Skeul WCM bn tr in 4m, or 2ca NNE of Moguériec's drying jetty. Facilities: V, R, Bar, P.

PONTUSVAL, Finistere, 48°40´.65N 04°19´.08W, AC 3668, 2644; SHOM 7150. HW +0605 on Dover (UT); ML 4·7m; Duration 0600; see 8.16.19 (BRIGNONAN). App from ECM buoy (48°41´.51N 04°19´.12W) via ldg marks 178° W bn on with ch spire 1M S. Ent between An Neudenn R bn tr to E and 3 white-topped rks to W. ⚓ here in approx 4m or dry out closer in. Hbr is open to N winds and often full of FVs. Entry at night prohib. Facilities: Bar, FW, R, V.

16

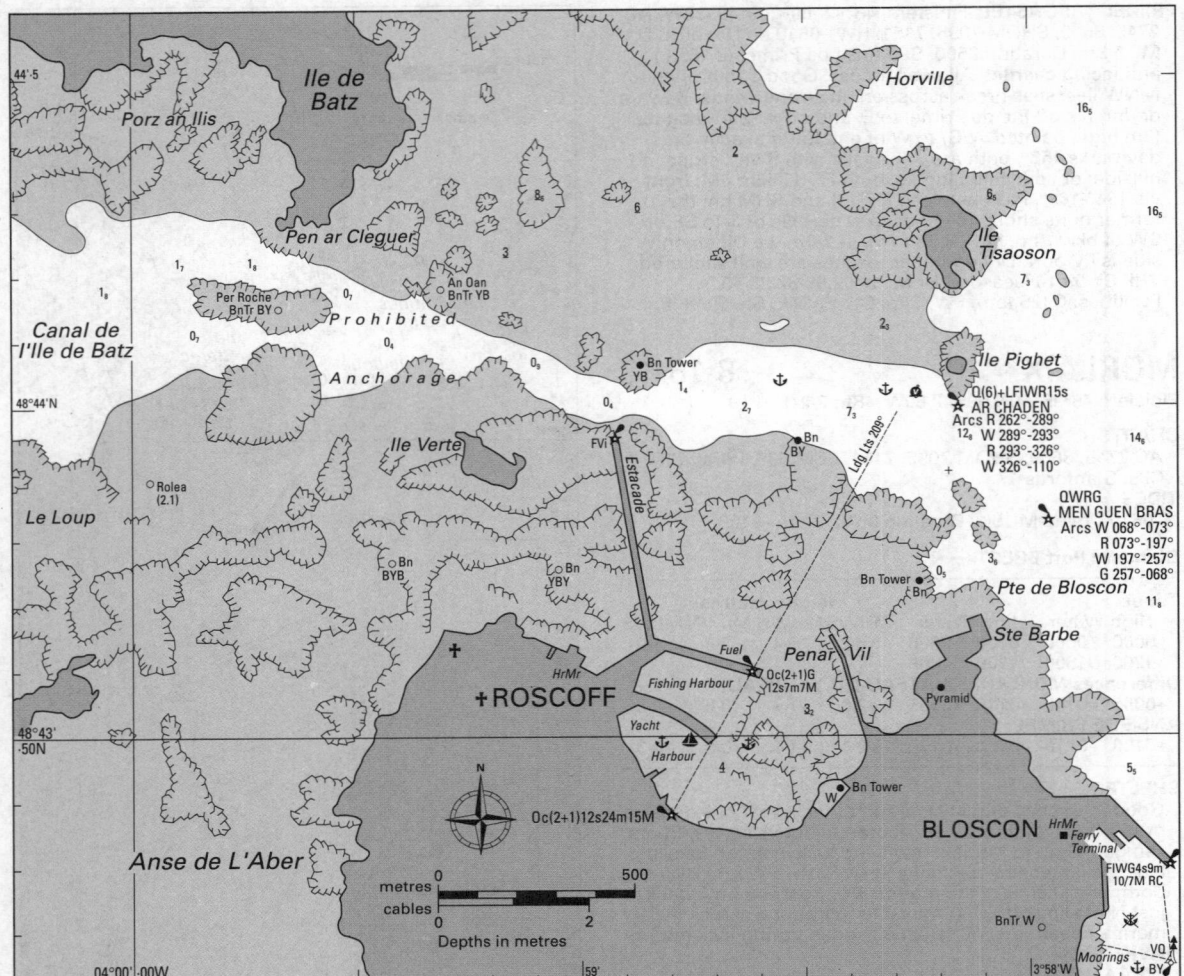

ROSCOFF   8-16-19

Finistere 48°43'·60N 03°58'·50W   Rtg 3-3-1
CHARTS
AC 2745, 3669; SHOM 7095, 7151; ECM 538; Imray C35;
Stanfords 17
TIDES
−0605 Dover; ML 5·2; Duration 0600; Zone −0100
Standard Port BREST (⟶)

Times				Height (metres)			
High Water		Low Water		MHWS	MHWN	MLWN	MLWS
0000	0600	0000	0600	6·9	5·4	2·6	1·0
1200	1800	1200	1800				
Differences ROSCOFF							
+0055	+0105	+0115	+0055	+1·9	+1·6	+0·8	+0·3
ILE DE BATZ							
+0045	+0100	+0105	+0055	+2·0	+1·6	+0·9	+0·4
BRIGOGNAN							
+0040	+0045	+0055	+0040	+1·1	+0·9	+0·3	+0·1

SHELTER
Good in Roscoff (dries 4·9m) except in strong N/E winds.
Access HW±2. AB on S side of jetty in Yacht Hbr, but FVs
leave little room; or dry out against road wall or secure to
⚓ in SW corner. Close W of Ar Chaden are W ⚓s in 4-5m.
Bloscon ferry hbr should only be entered with Hr Mr's
approval, but ⚓s or ⚓ to the S, clear of ferries (good for
crew change). Beware foul ground inshore and WIP.
NAVIGATION
WPT 48°46'·00N 03°55'·80W, 033°/213° from/to Men Guen
Bras lt, 2·6M. The ent to Roscoff needs care due to many
large rks in the area; best to enter near HW. See 8.16.5
for pilotage in the Canal de l'Ile de Batz. Chans are well
marked and must be kept to. Appr to Bloscon is easier.

LIGHTS AND MARKS
Ile de Batz lt ho (conspic) Fl (4) 25s 69m 23M. At E end of
Canal de l'Ile de Batz are Ar Chaden Q (6)+L Fl WR 15s,
SCM bn tr, & Men-Guen-Bras Q WRG, NCM. Ldg lts/marks
209° for Roscoff hbr: both Oc (2+1) G 12s, front 7m 7M, W
col, G top, with B/W vert stripes on end of mole; rear
conspic W lt ho 24m 15M. Bloscon ferry jetty Fl WG 4s,
W200°-210°, G210°-200°, appr in W sector; in fog, Fl W 2s.
RADIO TELEPHONE
Roscoff Ch 09. *Bloscon* Ch 12 16; 0830-1200, 1330-1800LT.
TELEPHONE
Hr Mr (Port de Plaisance) 02·98·69·76·37; Hr Mr (Roscoff)
02·98·61·27·84; Aff Mar 02·98·69·70·15; CROSS 02·98·89·
31·31; SNSM 02·98·61·27·84; ⌗ (Roscoff) 02·98·69·19·67;
⌗ (Bloscon) 02·98·61·27·86; Auto 08·36.68.08.29; Police
02·98·69·00·48; Ⓗ 02·98·88·40·22; Dr 02·98·69·71·18; Brit
Consul 02·99·46·26·64.
FACILITIES
Vieux Port (220+30 visitors) ☎ 02·98·69·76·37, AB (with
fender board), FW, AC, M; **Quai Neuf** Reserved for FVs, C
(5 ton); **Club Nautique de Roscoff** ☎ 02·98·69·72·79, Bar;
Bloscon M, L, Slip.
Services: BY, ME, El, Sh, CH. **Town** P, D, ME, El, Sh, CH,
Gaz, V, R, Bar, ⊠, Ⓑ, ⇌, ✈ (Morlaix). Ferry: Plymouth.

HARBOUR/ANCHORAGE CLOSE NORTH

ILE DE BATZ, Finistere, 48°44'·50N 04°00'·50W, AC 2745,
3669; SHOM 7095; HW +0610 Dover (UT); ML 5·2m. See
8.16.19. Porz-Kernoc'h gives good shelter but dries. E slip
is reserved for ferries. ⚓ in E or W parts of the chan
depending on wind, but holding ground poor. ⚓ prohib in
area W of Roscoff landing slip. Ile de Batz lt ho Fl (4) 25s.
Facilities: a few shops.

L'ABERWRAC'H   8-16-20

Finistere 48°36'·75N 04°35'·30W   Rtg 3-4-1

CHARTS
AC 1432, 2644; SHOM 7094, 7150; ECM 539; Imray C35; Stanfords 17

TIDES
+0547 Dover; ML 4·5; Duration 0600; Zone –0100

Standard Port BREST (→)

Times				Height (metres)			
High Water		Low Water		MHWS	MHWN	MLWN	MLWS
0000	0600	0000	0600	6·9	5·4	2·6	1·0
1200	1800	1200	1800				
Differences L'ABERWRAC'H, ILE CÉZON							
+0030	+0030	+0038	+0037	+0·8	+0·7	+0·2	0·0

SHELTER
Good, except in strong NW'lies. At La Palue either berth on the single pontoon (max LOA = 12m) or pick up one of 30 numbered W ⚓s. Free water taxi in summer every H, 0800-2200. Excellent shelter in all winds at Paluden, 1·5M up-river (off chartlet), on dumbell ⚓s; plus landing jetty, but ⚓ prohib.

NAVIGATION
WPT for Grand Chenal 48°37'·40N 04°38'·40W, 280°/100° from/to front ldg lt 2·6M. Keep clear of Le Libenter bank marked by WCM buoy, Q (9) 15s (Whis), brg 254° from Ile Vierge lt 3·0M; also Basse Trousquennou to S.
Two outer appr chans lead to the inner 128° appr line:
(1) Grand Chenal 100° (well lit and best for strangers) runs S of Libenter, Grand and Petit Pot de Beurre.
(2) Chenal de la Malouine, a narrow short cut from N/E, only by day and in good weather: 176° transit of Petit Pot de Beurre with Petite Ile de la Croix W bn; great precision is required. Caution: breakers and cross-tides.

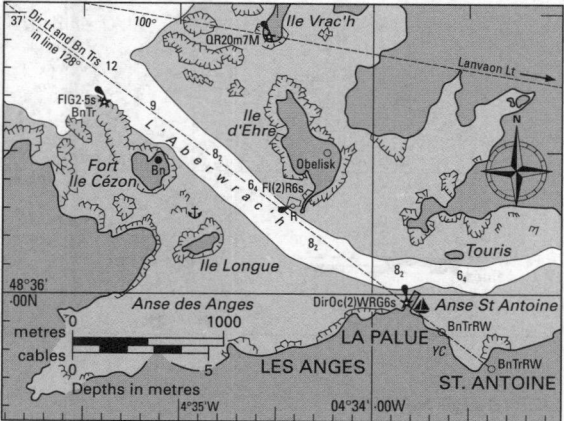

LIGHTS AND MARKS
Ile-Vierge lt ho Fl 5s 77m 27M, Gy tr, Horn 60s, RC, vis 337°–325° (348°). For the Grand Chenal the 100° ldg lts/marks are: front QR, Ile Vrac' h, W □ tr orange top; and, 1·63M to the rear, Dir Q, Lanvaon, W □ tr orange △ on top. Then Dir Oc (2) WRG 6s, W127·2°-128·7°, leads 128° almost to the pontoon at La Palue. Unlit up river.

RADIO TELEPHONE
VHF Ch 09 16 (0700-2200LT in season).

TELEPHONE
Hr Mr 02·98·04·91·62; Aff Mar 02·98·04·90·13; CROSS/SNSM 02·98·89·31·31; ⌗ 02·98·04·90·27; Météo 02·98·84·60·64; Auto 08·36·68·08·29; Police 02·98·04·00·18; Ⓗ 02·98·46·11·33; Dr 02·98·04·91·87; SAMU 15; Brit Consul 02·99·46·26·64.

FACILITIES
Pontoon (30, some Ⓥ) ☎ 02·98·04·91·62, FF98, M, D, FW, ME, El, CH, BH (12 ton); **YC des Abers** ☎ 02·98·04·92·60, Bar, Ⓧ; **Services**: Sh, Ⓔ, Slip, C (3 ton mobile). **Town** P, V, Gaz, R, Ⓧ, P, Bar, ✉, Ⓑ (Landeda, every a.m. except Mon), ⇌, ✈, (bus to Brest). Ferry: Roscoff.

L'ABERBENOIT   8-16-21

Finistere 48°34'·65N 04°36'·80W   Rtg 3-4-1

CHARTS
AC 1432, 2644; SHOM 7094, 7150; ECM 539, 540; Imray C35; Stanfords 17

TIDES
+0535 Dover; ML 4·7; Duration 0555; Zone –0100

Standard Port BREST (→)

Times				Height (metres)			
High Water		Low Water		MHWS	MHWN	MLWN	MLWS
0000	0600	0000	0600	6·9	5·4	2·6	1·0
1200	1800	1200	1800				
Differences L'ABERBENOIT							
+0022	+0025	+0035	+0020	+1·0	+0·9	+0·4	+0·2
PORTSALL							
+0015	+0020	+0025	+0015	+0·6	+0·5	+0·1	0·0

SHELTER
Excellent, but do not enter at night, in poor vis nor in strong WNW winds; best near LW when dangers can be seen. Six ⚓s and ⚓ as shown or further up-river. R navigable on the tide to Tréglonou bridge 3M upstream. Beware oyster beds.

NAVIGATION
WPT 48°37'·05N 04°38'·67W, Petite Fourche WCM, 337°/157° from/to Ile Guénioc, 1M. From WPT track 168° for 1M until abeam Ile Guénioc; thence 134° past Basse du Chenal and Karreg ar Poul Doun PHM bns to Men Renead SHM buoy. Alter stbd 160° to pass close to La Jument rk (PHM bn and R paint patch); thence 140°, passing 2 SHM buoys and leaving Le Chien IDM bn to port, leads to the fairway.

LIGHTS AND MARKS
Unlit. Chan bns and buoys must be carefully identified.

RADIO TELEPHONE
None.

TELEPHONE
Hr Mr nil; CROSS/SNSM 02·98·89·31·31; ⌗ 02·98·04·90·27; Météo 02·98·84·60·64; Auto 08·36·68·08·29; Police 02·98·48·8·10; Dr 02·98·89·75·67; Brit Consul 02·99·46·26·64.

FACILITIES
Le Passage Slip, M (free), L, FW; **Tréglonou** Slip; **Services**: Sh, ME, El. **Town** Gaz, ✉, Ⓑ (Ploudalmezeau), ⇌, ✈ (bus to Brest). Ferry: Roscoff.

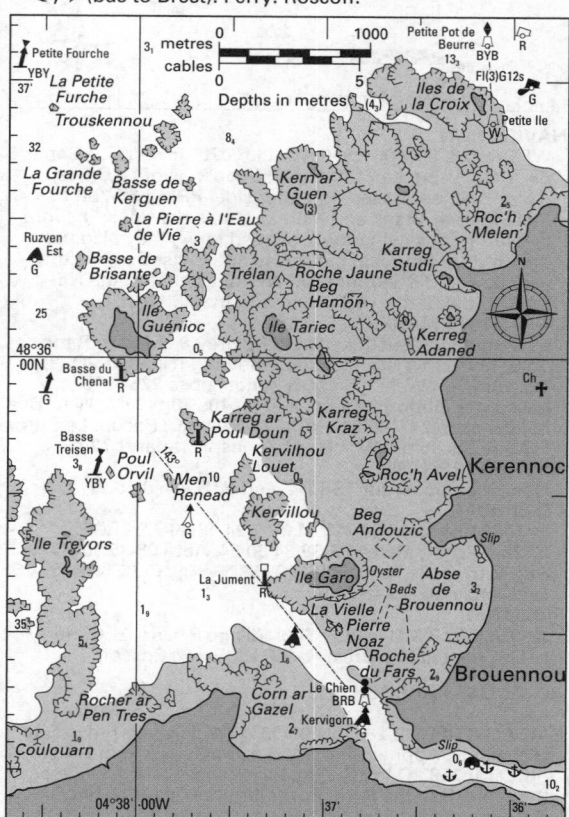

16

LAMPAUL (ILE D'OUESSANT) 8-16-22

Finistere 48°26'·70N 05°07'·40W   Rtg 4-5-2

CHARTS
AC 2694; SHOM 7123, 7149; ECM 540; Imray C36; Stan 17
TIDES
+0522 Dover; ML 3·9; Duration 0555; Zone –0100

Standard Port BREST (→)

Times				Height (metres)			
High Water		Low Water		MHWS	MHWN	MLWN	MLWS
0000	0600	0000	0600	6·9	5·4	2·6	1·0
1200	1800	1200	1800				
Differences BAIE DE LAMPAUL							
+0005	+0005	–0005	+0003	0·0	–0·1	–0·1	0·0
ILE DE MOLENE							
+0012	+0012	+0017	+0017	+0·4	+0·3	+0·2	+0·1

SHELTER
Bay is open to SW winds and swell; only usable in settled weather, prone to poor vis, esp in July. There are approx 24 ✿s to S of the small drying hbr to E of pier, ent 15m wide, which normally has no room for visitors.

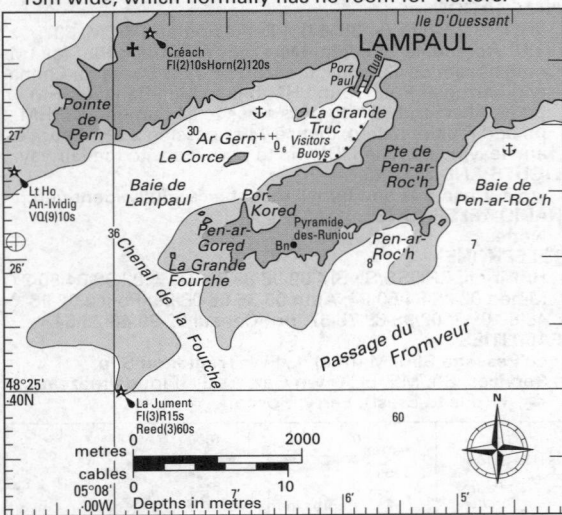

NAVIGATION
WPT 48°26'·30N 05°09'·00W, 250°/070° from/to Le Corce Rk, 1·4M. Bring Le Stiff lt ho 055° open N of Le Corce, which may be passed on either side. PHM/SHM bn trs mark Men-ar-Blank and Men-ar-Groas rks closer inshore. Beware ferries using the T-shaped quay; they also use the Ch de la Fourche, but this is not advised for visiting yachts. The ITZ extends 5M NW of Ushant to the NE-bound lane of the TSS (see diagram in 8.16.2).
LIGHTS AND MARKS
La Jument Fl (3) R 15s 36m 22M; grey 8-sided tr, R top; obsc 199°-241°; Horn (3) 60s. An-Ividig (Nividic) VQ (9) 10s 28m 9M; W 8-sided tr, R bands; obsc 225°-290°; helicopter platform. Creac'h Fl (2) 10s 70m 34M; W tr, B bands; obsc 247°-255°; Horn (2) 120s; RC; Racon. Le Stiff Fl (2) R 20s 85m 24M; close to conspic radar tr 72m.
RADIO TELEPHONE
None. For Ouessant TSS/ITZ and VTS see 8.16.27.
TELEPHONE
Hr Mr 02·98·89 20 05; Aff Mar 02·94·48·80·27; CROSS 02·98·89·31·31; Météo 02·98·84·60·64; Auto 08·36.68·08·29; SNSM 02·98.89·70·04; Police 02·98.68·8·39; Dr 02·98·89·92·70; Brit Consul 02·99.46·26·64.
FACILITIES
✿, AB, FW, P & D (cans), Slip. **Village** R, Gaz, ✉, Ⓑ, ferry to Le Conquet and Brest ⇌, ✈. UK Ferry: Roscoff.

ADJACENT HARBOUR

BAIE DU STIFF, 48°28'·13N 05°03'·18W, is sheltered in S to NW winds. Appr is clear apart from Gorle Vihan with IDM bn. Dir lt 259°, Q WRG 11m 10/7M, vis W254°-264°, is on the mole. S of the lt ho, Porz Liboudou is for ferries, but 9 R ✿s are available in 5m. Holding is poor; little room to ⚓.

L'ABERILDUT 8-16-23

Finistere 48°28'·30N 04°45'·72W   Rtg 3-3-1

CHARTS
AC 3345, 2694, 2644; SHOM 7122, 7149; ECM 540; Imray C36; Stanfords 17
TIDES
+0520 on Dover (UT); ML 4·2m; Zone –0100

Standard Port BREST (→)

Times				Height (metres)			
High Water		Low Water		MHWS	MHWN	MLWN	MLWS
0000	0600	0000	0600	6·9	5·4	2·6	1·0
1200	1800	1200	1800				
Differences L'ABERILDUT							
+0010	+0010	+0023	+0010	+0·4	+0·3	0·0	0·0

SHELTER
Very good inside, but appr is open to W winds; access all tides and at night with care. Hbr partly dries, but a narrow chan at the ent has 2m, with pools to 6m inside. Beyond the FV quay (NW side) a pontoon provides landing and fuel. Some ✿s; little room to ⚓, but ⚓s outside as chartlet. A useful passage hbr to await the tide in the Ch du Four.
NAVIGATION
WPT 48°28'·12N 04°48'·13W, 263°/083° from/to Dir lt, 1·6M. From N beware Les Liniou Rks 1·5M NNW of the WPT and Plateau des Fourches 1·2M SSW. Appr is fairly easy in good vis, but beware strong cross tides. At the ent leave both Men Tassin PHM bn and Roche du Crapaud, a large rounded rk, close to port to clear drying spit on S side of the narrow ent. For Chenal du Four see opposite and 8.16.5.

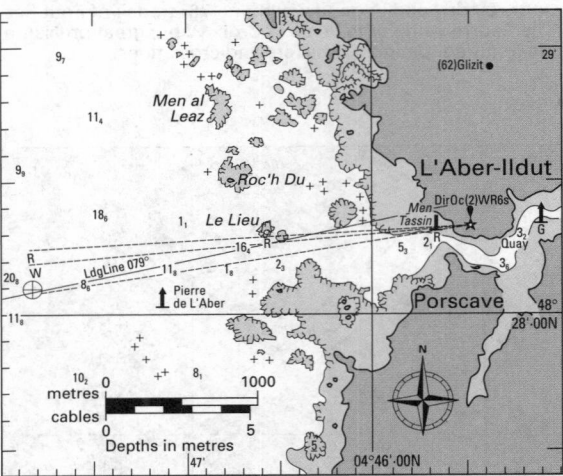

LIGHTS AND MARKS
Le Four tr, Fl (5) 15s 28m 18M, gy tr, siren (3+2) 60s, is 3·35M N of the WPT. Pointe de Corsen lt, Dir Q WRG 33m 12/8M, is 3·2M S of the WPT.
A stern transit 258° of Kéréon lt, gy tr, Oc (2+1) WR 24s 38m 17M, with La Jument lt, Fl (3) R 15s 36m 22M, gy tr + R top, (both off Ouessant) leads to the W sector of a powerful Dir lt 083°, Oc (2) WR 6s 12m 25/20M, vis W081°-085°, R085°-087°, on W bldg at hbr ent; good daymark. Ldg marks (difficult to see from afar): front, Lanildut spire on with Brélès spire leads 079° into fairway. Drying rks are marked by Pierre de l'Aber SHM bn and Le Lieu PHM bn tr 5m; the latter is easier to see.
RADIO TELEPHONE
None.
TELEPHONE
Hr Mr 02·98·04.36.40 (Jun-Sep); Aff Mar 02·98·48·66.54; Auto 08·36.68.08·29; ⌗ 02·98.44.35.20; CROSS/SNSM 02·98.89.31.31; Police 02·98·48·8·10; Dr 02·98.04.33.08·
FACILITIES
Hbr, M (300, inc 12 ✿s; FF52), FW, D, slips, AC at FV quay;
Services: BY, Sh, ME, El, CH, M.
Village V, R, Bar, ✉. All needs at Brest 25km. Ferry: Roscoff.

CHENAL DU FOUR and CHENAL DE LA HELLE

See 8.16.5 for notes on these passages

Fl(5)15s

LE FOUR

31'

48

8_1

40

30'

8_4

Les Liniou

3_6

6_8

29'

Saint-Mathieu and Kermorvan Ldg Lts 158°

CHENAL DU FOUR

70

46

DirOc(2)WRG6s

Chenal de L'Aber Ildut 083°

28'

13$_1$

CHENAL DE LA HELLE

Lochrist and Kermorvan Ldg Lts 138°

5_8

23

Plateau des Fourches

27'

5_3

6

Fl(2)R6s
Valbelle
R

Luronne
YBY

5

6_7

Platresses
FlRG4s

Platresses SE
0_1 G

26'

7_5

Le Faix
VQ
BY

1_7

Tendoc
R

14_1

Trezien
DirOc(2)6s

48°25'
·00N

PLATEAU
DE LA
HELLE

Le Stiff Lt in line with Le Faix Bn Tr 293°

Oc(2)R6s
Saint-Paul
R   4,

DirQWRG

Les Trois Pierres
IsoWRG4s

6_5

Pointe de Corsen

5_4

7_8

24'

DirFl(3)WRG12s
Ile DirFl(2)WRG6s
Molene

Pourceaux Q
BY

Taboga
9_8 BRB

1_4

Saint-Pierre
G

23'

Ile de Quemenes

2_4

9_5

7_8

Grand
Courleau BY

Rouget
FlG4s
G

22'

Grande Vinotiere
LFlR10s
R

Fl5s
Pte de Kermorvan

2_8

114°-35s°

5_5

LE CONQUET

*Ile de
Beniguet*

6_1

21'

N

IsoR4s
R

DirOc(3)12s
Lochrist

metres   0   4000
sea miles
              0   2
Depths in metres

9_6

145°-325s°

Fl15s
DirF
QWRG

Ldg Lts 007°

Pte St Mathieu

20'

4_1

La Fourmi
G

Vieux-Moines
FlR4s
R

9_1

0_2

57'   56'   55'   54'   53'   52'   51'   04°50'·00W   49'   46'

16

BREST TIDAL COEFFICIENTS 1999

Date	Jan am	Jan pm	Feb am	Feb pm	Mar am	Mar pm	Apr am	Apr pm	May am	May pm	June am	June pm	July am	July pm	Aug am	Aug pm	Sept am	Sept pm	Oct am	Oct pm	Nov am	Nov pm	Dec am	Dec pm
1	91	95	97	98	88	91	93	93	86	85	78	77	78	78	85	83	82	76	70	63	49	48	50	
2	98	99	98	97	94	96	92	91	84	83	75	73	77	75	81	78	70	63	55	50		50	51	53
3	100	99	95	92	97	97	89	86	80	78	70	68	73	71	74	70	57	53		47	54	59	56	59
4	98	95	89	84	96	94	83	79	75	71	64	61	69	66	66	62		50	47	50	64	69	62	66
5	92	88	79	74	91	87	75	70	67	63	58	55	63	61	59		50	52	55	61	73	77	69	72
6	83	78	68	62	83	79	65	60	58	54	52	50	59	57	56	55	56	62	67	74	80	83	74	76
7	72	66	56	50	73	68	54	49	49	45	49			56	55	58	69	75	79	84	85	86	78	79
8	60	55	45	40	62	56	43	38	42	40	49	51	57	58	61	67	81	87	88	91	87	87	79	79
9	49	45	36	33	50	44	35			40	54	59	61	65	72	78	91	95	93	94	86	85	79	78
10	41	39		33	38	34	33	34	41	46	64	70	69	74	84	89	97	98	94	94	83	80	77	75
11	38		34	38	31	31	37	42	51	58	76	82	79	85	93	96	98	98	92	90	78	74	73	71
12	38	40	43	49		33	49	57	65	73	88	93	89	93	98	99	96	93	87	83	70	66	68	65
13	43	48	55	61	37	44	65	74	80	88	98	101	96	99	99	98	89	84	79	74	62	57	61	58
14	52	57	67	74	50	58	82	90	94	100	103	104	100	100	96	93	80	74	69	64	52	47	54	51
15	61	66	80	85	66	74	97	103	105	108	104	102	99	97	88	83	68	62	58	52	43	39	48	46
16	71	75	90	94	81	88	108	112	110	111	100	96	94	90	78	72	56	49	47	41	37	36	45	45
17	79	82	98	101	95	101	114	114	110	107	92	87	85	80	66	60	43	37	36	32	37		47	
18	85	87	102	103	105	109	113	110	103	98	81	75	74	68	53	47	33	30	30		40	45	50	55
19	89	90	102	100	111	111	106	100	92	85	69	63	63	57	42	37		29	31	34	51	58	61	67
20	90	90	97	93	111	108	93	85	78	71	58	54	52	47		34	31	35	39	46	66	73	74	80
21	89	87	88	82	104	99	77	69	64	58		50		43	33	34	41	48	53	61	80	87	86	92
22	84	81	75	68	93	85	61	54	54		48	46	41	40	37	41	55	62	69	76	94	99	97	100
23	77	73	62	56	77	69	50		50	49	47	48	40	42	46	51	70	76	84	90	103	106	103	105
24	68	64	51		61	54	48	48	49	51	50	52	45	48	57	63	83	89	97	102	108	108	105	104
25	60	57	50	51	49	47	50	54	53	56	55	58	53	57	69	74	94	99	106	108	107	104	102	98
26	55		54	59		47	59	63	60	63	62	64	61	65	80	84	102	105	110	109	100	95	94	89
27	56	58	65	71	51	56	68	72	66	69	67	70	69	73	88	92	106	106	107	104	89	82	83	77
28	61	66	77	83	62	68	76	79	72	74	72	74	76	79	95	96	104	101	99	93	75	69	71	65
29	72	77			74	79	82	84	76	77	76	77	82	84	97	97	97	92	86	79	62	57	59	54
30	83	87			83	87	85	86	78	79	78	78	85	86	96	94	85	78	71	63	53	51	50	47
31	91	94			90	92			79	79			87	86	91	87			57	52				46

TIDAL COEFFICIENTS   8-16-25

These indicate at a glance the magnitude of the tide on any particular day by assigning a non-dimensional coefficient to the twice-daily range of tide. The coefficient is based on a scale of 45 for mean neap (morte eau) and 95 for mean spring (vive eau) ranges. The coefficient is 70 for an average tide. A very small np tide may have a coefficient of only 20, whilst a very big sp tide might be as high as 120. The ratio of the coefficients of different tides equals the ratio of their ranges; the range, for example, of the largest sp tide (120) is six times that of the smallest np tide (20).

The table opposite is for Brest, but holds good elsewhere along the Channel and Atlantic coasts of France.

French tide tables, similar to Admiralty tide tables as in this Almanac, show for Secondary ports their time and height differences against the appropriate standard port for vive eau (springs) and for morte eau (neaps). The tidal coefficient for the day may be used to decide which correction(s) to apply. In general it is satisfactory to use the vive eau corrections for coefficients over 70 and the morte eau corrections for the others. Where it is necessary to obtain more accurate corrections (in estuaries for example) this can be done by interpolating or extrapolating.

Coefficients may also be used to determine rates of tidal streams on a given day, using a graph similar in principle to that shown in Fig 7 (7). On the vertical axis plot tidal coefficients from 20 at the bottom to 120 at the top. The horizontal axis shows tidal stream rates from zero to (say) five knots. From the tidal stream atlas or chart, plot the np and sp rates against coefficient 45 and 95 respectively; join these two points. Entering with the tidal coefficient for the day in question, go horizontally to the sloping line, then vertically to read the required rate on the horizontal axis.

French translations of common tidal terms are as follows:

HW	Pleine mer (PM)
LW	Basse mer (BM)
Springs	Vive eau (VE)
Neaps	Morte eau (ME)
CD	Zero des cartes
MHWS	Pleine mer moyenne de VE
MHWN	Pleine mer moyenne de ME
MLWN	Basse mer moyenne de ME
MLWS	Basse mer moyenne de VE

ADJACENT HARBOURS

PORTSALL, Finistere, 48°33′·85N 04°42′·95W. AC 1432, 3688; SHOM 7094, 7150. HW +0535 on Dover (UT); ML 4·4m; Duration 0600. See 8.16.21. Small drying hbr at head of bay. Access HW±3. Good shelter except in strong N winds. Ldg marks: Le Yurc'h rk (7m) on with Ploudalmézeau spire leads 109°; thence 085° on W & RW marks. By night use W sector 084°–088° of lt Oc (4) WRG 12s 9m 13/10M, W col/R top. Appr marked by 5 bn trs. Beware many rks for about 2M off-shore. ↓ to W of ent, or go alongside quay in hbr. Facilities: Aff Mar ☎ 98·48·66·54; SNSM ☎ 02·98·48·77·44; Dr ☎ 02·98·48·8·46; **Quay** C (0·5 ton), D, FW, P, Slip; **Club Naut** ☎ 02·98·48·63·10; **Coop de Pêcheurs** ☎ 02·98·48·63·26, CH. **Town** Bar, ⊠, R, V.

ARGENTON, Finistere, 48°31′·32N 04°46′·25W. AC 3347, 2694; SHOM 7122. HW +0535 on Dover (UT); ML 4·6m; Duration 0600; use PORTSALL diffs 8.16.21. Small drying hbr; good shelter except in W winds when a swell comes up the bay into the hbr. Access HW±3. Appr 086° on 2 W bns & RW wall. Le Four lt Fl (5) 15s is 1·4M to W. Beware strong E-W tides. ↓ in deep water off hbr ent. 10 ♠s. Facilities: FW, P on quay; **SC** ☎ 02·98·89·54·04. **Town** Bar, R, V.

ILE DE MOLENE, Finistere, 48°24′·13N 04°57′·26W. AC 2694; SHOM 7123, 7122, 7149. HW +0520 on Dover (UT); ML 4·6m; see 8.16.22. Hbr, part-drying, is easier at nps, good wx/vis. Beware strong tidal streams. Best appr is via Ch de la Helle, twixt Le Faix bn tr, VQ 16m, and Luronne WCM buoy. Track W to pick up ldg marks 215°: front, Trois Pierres bn, Iso WRG 4s, 15m; rear, RW N. Mill bn tr. Nearing front mark, alter stbd to align spire 199° between ECM bn tr and WCM buoy. ↓ S of N bkwtr hd in about 1·5m; 10 ♠s in inner hbr, FF30. Dir lt 191°, Fl (3) WRG 12s, W190°–192°, is on old S pier; same lt, but Fl (2) WRG 6s, also covers Chenal des Las (W259·5°-262·5°). Facilities: FW, V, CH, R, Bar, ⊠.

LE CONQUET   8-16-26

Finistere 48°21′·60N 04°47′·15W Rtg 3-4-2

CHARTS
AC 3345, 2694; SHOM 7122, 7149, 7148; ECM 540; Imray C36; Stanfords 17

TIDES
+0535 Dover; ML 3·9; Duration 0600; Zone –0100

Standard Port BREST (→)

Times				Height (metres)			
High Water		Low Water		MHWS	MHWN	MLWN	MLWS
0000	0600	0000	0600	6·9	5·4	2·6	1·0
1200	1800	1200	1800				
Differences LE CONQUET							
–0005	0000	+0007	+0007	–0·1	–0·1	–0·1	0·0

SHELTER
Good except in strong W winds. A busy fishing port with few yacht facilities. AB only briefly at quay for loading. ↓ prohib in Avant Port. Yachts can ↓ further up hbr but it dries and may be foul.

NAVIGATION
WPT 48°21′·50N 04°48′·50W, 263°/083° from/to Mole Ste Barbe lt, 1M. From the NW, beware the Grande Vinotière rks. Also note strong cross streams in the Chenal du Four.

LIGHTS AND MARKS
Ldg line 095° lt on Mole Ste Barbe, Oc G 4s in line with spire of Le Conquet church. La Louve R bn tr and end of Mole St Christophe in line at 079°.

RADIO TELEPHONE
Le Conquet Port (Hr Mr) VHF 11 16. Call: *St Mathieu* VHF Ch 16 for Chenal du Four and Chenal de la Helle (see 8.16.9).

TELEPHONE
Hr Mr 02·98·89·08·07; Aff Mar 02·98·89·00·05; Météo 02·98·84·60·64; Auto 08·36·68·08·29; CROSS 02·98·89·31·31; SNSM 02·98·89·02·07; Police 02·98·89·00·13; Dr 02·98·89·01·86; Brit Consul 02·99·46·26·64.

FACILITIES
Hbr Slip, M, L, D; **Services:** ME, EI, P (cans), CH. **Town** P, D, FW, ME, EI, V, Gaz, R, Bar, ⊠, Ⓑ, ⇌ (bus to Brest), ✈ (Brest). Ferry: Roscoff.

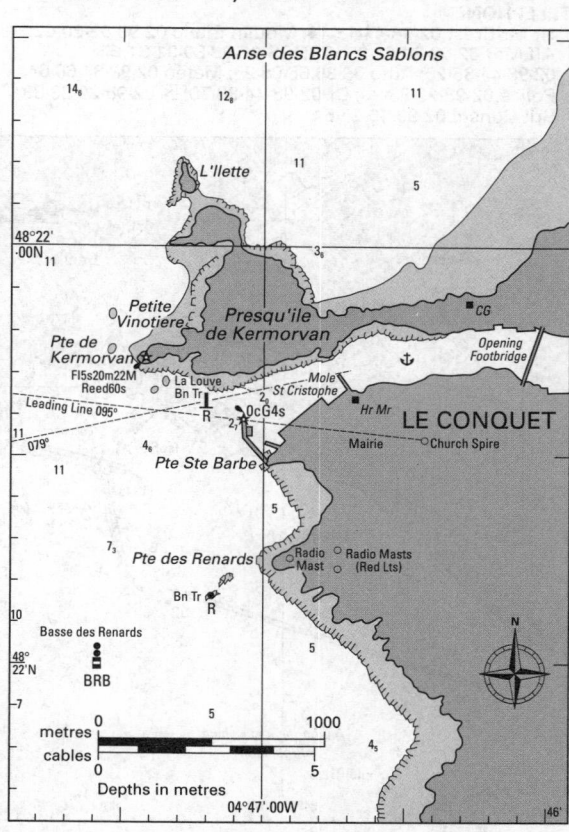

16

BREST   8-16-27

Finistere 48°21'·30N 04°25·70W (Moulin Blanc)   Rtg 1-1-2

CHARTS

AC 3428, 3427, 798; SHOM 7397, 7398, 7399, 7400, 7401, 7149, 7172; ECM 542; Imray C36; Stanfords 17

TIDES

+0520 Dover; ML 4·0; Duration 0605; Zone –0100
NOTE: Brest is a Standard Port. Tidal predictions for every day are given below; tidal coefficients are above.

SHELTER

Excellent in Brest, and at many ⚓s in the Rade de Brest (50 sq miles). Access at any tide H24. Yachts should use Moulin Blanc marina, not the Port du Commerce. Brest is a busy commercial, naval and fishing port. The Port Militaire and a zone round Ile Longue are prohib areas.

NAVIGATION

WPT 48°18'·30N 04°44'·00W, 248°/068° from/to front ldg lt (Pte du Petit Minou), 5·3M. Tidal streams run hard in the Goulet de Brest. In mid-chan beware rks, well marked; pass either side. As WPT to Marina, use Moulin Blanc PHM buoy, Fl (3) R 12s, 48°22'·85N 04°25'·90W, 207°/027° from/to MB1 and MB2 chan buoys, 0·55M.

LIGHTS AND MARKS

Apprs marked by lts at Pte St Mathieu, Pte du Petit Minou and Pte du Portzic. Oceanopolis bldg, W roof, is conspic. Marina, 2M E of the Port de Commerce, has buoyed chan; MB4 lt and the ECM lt By can be obsc'd by berthed craft.

RADIO TELEPHONE

Call: *Brest Port* (at Pte du Portzic) VHF Ch 08 16 (controls apprs to Brest). All vessels entering keep watch on Ch 16. Marina Ch 09 16 (H24).

Corsen-Ouessant, callsign *Ouessant Traffic* on Ch 13 79, operates a VTS reporting system which is mandatory for vessels > 300grt; see Chapter 6, Table 6(2). It also passes to CROSS Corsen (MRCC) traffic info over a far larger area from Mont St Michel in the E and Pte de Penmarch in the S, thence out to 8°W. It broadcasts tfc info, urgent warnings and special weather bulletins in English and French, on Ch 79 at H+10 and +40. Routine weather bulletins are detailed in Chapter 5, 5.10.5. Position and navigational help can be given to any craft, if necessary; monitor Ch 16 whilst in the area.

TELEPHONE

Hr Mr Brest 02·98·44·13·44; Moulin Blanc 02·98·02·20·02; Aff Mar 02·98·80·62·25; CROSS 02·98·89·31·31; ⌗ 02·98·44·35·20; Auto 08·36·68·08·29; Météo 02·98·84·60·64; Police 02·98·22·83·90; Dr 02·98·44·38·70; Ⓗ 02·98·22·33·33; Brit Consul 02·99·46·26·64.

FACILITIES (MOULIN BLANC)

Marina (1225+100 Ⓥ), ☎ 02·02·98·02·20·02, 🚤
02·98·41·67·91, FF105, P & D H24, FW, AC, Slip, ME, EI, Ⓔ, SHOM, Sh, C (3 & 12 ton), BH (14 & 35 ton), SM, CH, Gaz, R, Ⓡ, V, Bar; **Sté des Régates de Brest** ☎ 02·98·02·53·36, R.
BREST **Services:** CH, SM, ME, EI, Sh, Ⓔ, SHOM.
City all facilities, Gaz, ✉, Ⓑ, ⇄, ✈. Ferry: Roscoff.

ADJACENT ANCHORAGE TO THE WEST

ANSE DE BERTHAUME, 48°20'·50N 04°41'·75W. AC 3427. A useful passage ⚓ if awaiting the tide E into Goulet de Brest; N into Ch du Four, or S toward Raz de Sein. Good shelter in W'lies. ⚓ in 5m off slip N of Fort de Berthaume (conspic); 1ca NE, beware Le Chat rk, dries 6·8m. No lts.

RADE DE BREST   8-16-28

Finistere

TIDES

In most of the bays in the Rade de Brest tidal streams are weak, but in the main rivers they can exceed 2kn at sp.

SHELTER AND NAVIGATION

The Rade de Brest offers a sheltered cruising ground, useful in bad weather, with many attractive ⚓s.
To the NE, ½M beyond Pont Albert-Louppe (2 bridges: 29m and 25m clearance) is a good ⚓ at Le Passage. It is possible to explore R L'Elorn for about 6M to the drying port of Landerneau; keep well inboard of chan buoys.
On the S side of Rade de Brest are various naval sites with prohib ⚓ around Ile Longue. There are however ⚓s at Le Fret, on SE side of Ile Longue, and at Roscanvel on E side of the Quelern Peninsula.
To the SE, L'Aulne is a lovely river with steep wooded banks. Near the mouth of its estuary, on the N shore, is a good ⚓ and W ⚓s in 3m in Anse de l'Auberlach. Further E, 3 small drying rivers run into the Aulne from the north: R Daoulas, R de l'Hôpital and R du Faou and offer shelter for boats which can dry out.
Up the Aulne there are ⚓s near Landévennec, below Térénez bridge (27m), and also 1½M above that bridge. At Guily-Glaz, 14M above Landévennec, a lock (open HW Brest –2 to +1½) opens into the canalised river to Port Launay (AB on quay, FF20, AC, FW, R), and 3M further on to Chateaulin, AB on pontoons; most facilities.

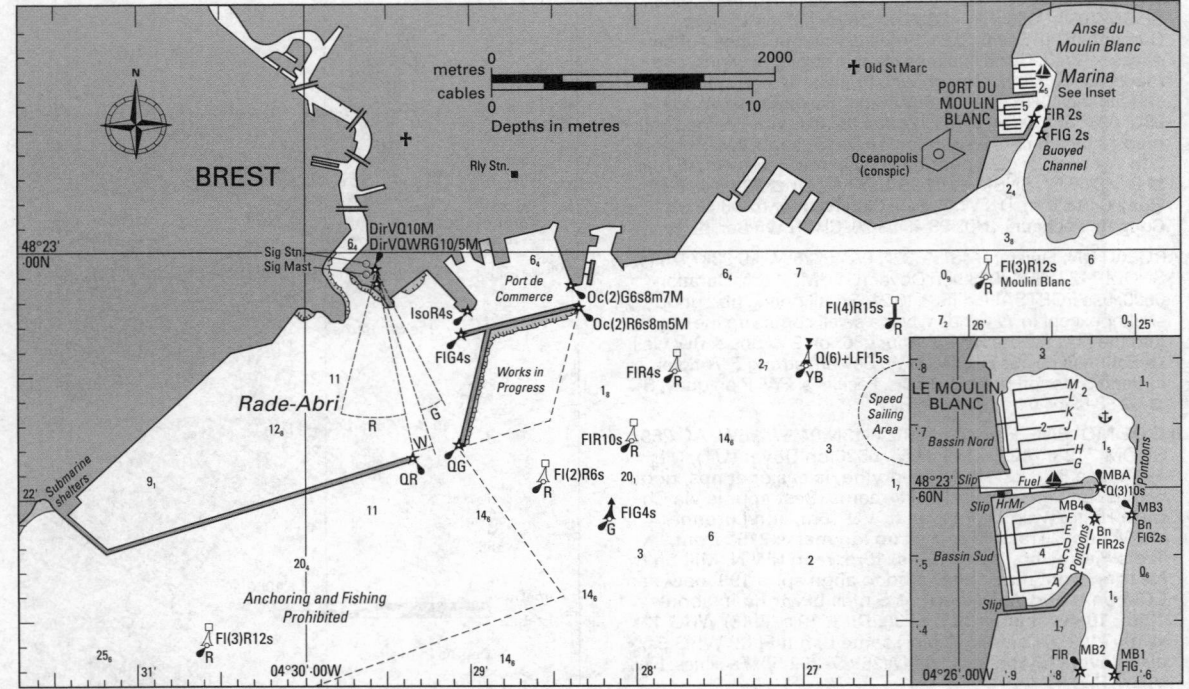

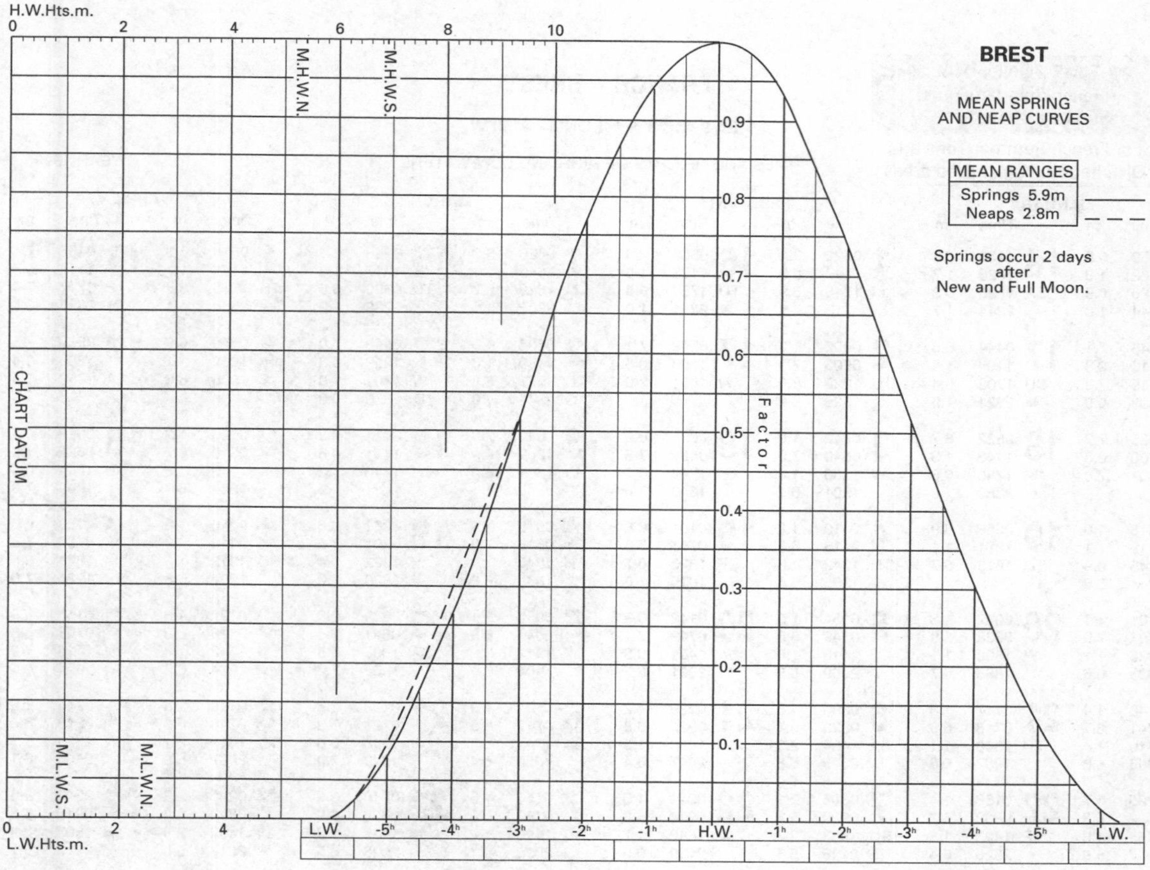

H.W.Hts.m.

CHART DATUM

M.H.W.N.
M.H.W.S.
M.L.W.S.
M.L.W.N.

Factor

0.9
0.8
0.7
0.6
0.5
0.4
0.3
0.2
0.1

L.W.Hts.m.

L.W. -5ʰ -4ʰ -3ʰ -2ʰ -1ʰ H.W. -1ʰ -2ʰ -3ʰ -4ʰ -5ʰ L.W.

BREST

MEAN SPRING
AND NEAP CURVES

MEAN RANGES
Springs 5.9m ———
Neaps 2.8m - - - -

Springs occur 2 days
after
New and Full Moon.

RADE DE BREST *continued*

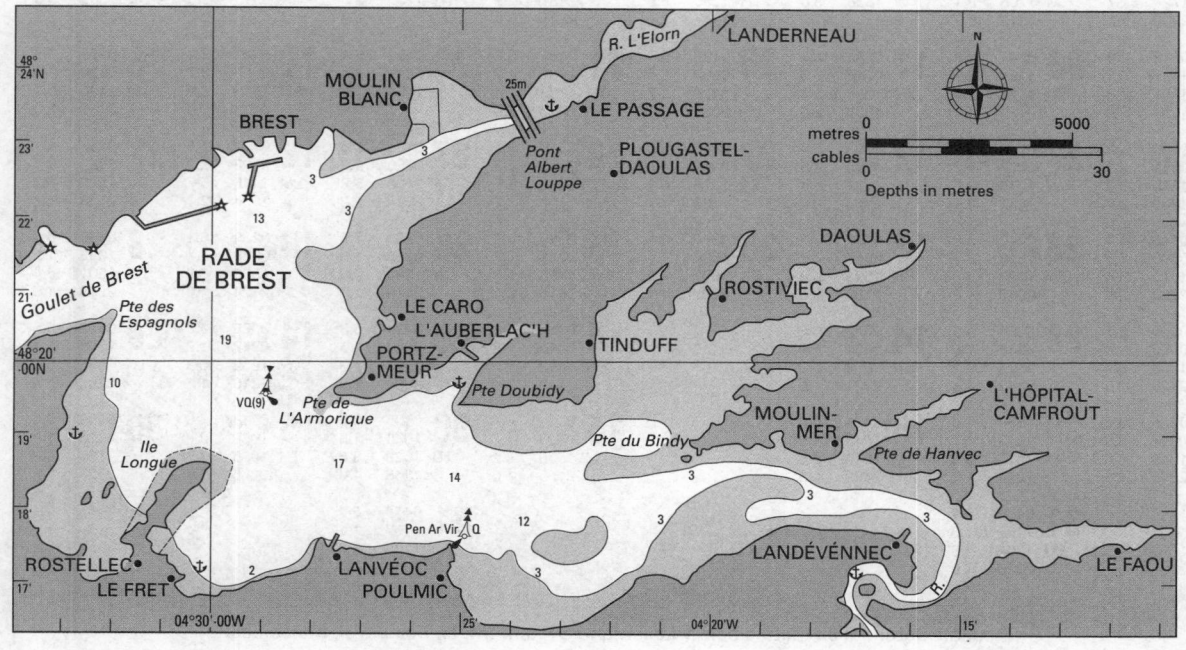

TIME ZONE –0100
(French Standard Time)
Subtract 1 hour for UT

For French Summer Time add ONE hour in non-shaded areas

FRANCE – BREST

LAT 48°23′N   LONG 4°30′W

TIMES AND HEIGHTS OF HIGH AND LOW WATERS

YEAR **1999**

JANUARY

Date	Time	m	Date	Time	m
1 F	0359 / 1022 / 1626 / 2244	6.9 / 1.0 / 6.9 / 1.0	**16** SA	0405 / 1025 / 1625 / 2244	6.3 / 1.7 / 6.2 / 1.7
2 SA O	0448 / 1112 / 1715 / 2332	7.1 / 0.8 / 7.0 / 0.9	**17** SU ●	0444 / 1104 / 1703 / 2321	6.5 / 1.5 / 6.4 / 1.5
3 SU	0535 / 1200 / 1801	7.2 / 0.8 / 7.0	**18** M	0522 / 1143 / 1740 / 2359	6.7 / 1.3 / 6.6 / 1.3
4 M	0018 / 0619 / 1245 / 1844	1.0 / 7.1 / 0.9 / 6.8	**19** TU	0559 / 1221 / 1818	6.9 / 1.1 / 6.7
5 TU	0101 / 0701 / 1328 / 1925	1.1 / 7.0 / 1.1 / 6.6	**20** W	0037 / 0638 / 1300 / 1856	1.3 / 6.9 / 1.1 / 6.7
6 W	0143 / 0741 / 1410 / 2006	1.4 / 6.7 / 1.4 / 6.3	**21** TH	0117 / 0718 / 1340 / 1937	1.3 / 6.9 / 1.1 / 6.6
7 TH	0225 / 0822 / 1453 / 2047	1.7 / 6.3 / 1.8 / 5.9	**22** F	0158 / 0800 / 1423 / 2020	1.4 / 6.7 / 1.3 / 6.4
8 F	0307 / 0903 / 1537 / 2132	2.1 / 5.9 / 2.2 / 5.6	**23** SA	0243 / 0845 / 1509 / 2108	1.6 / 6.5 / 1.6 / 6.1
9 SA	0353 / 0951 / 1626 / 2226	2.4 / 5.6 / 2.6 / 5.3	**24** SU	0333 / 0937 / 1602 / 2205	1.8 / 6.2 / 1.8 / 5.8
10 SU	0446 / 1048 / 1724 / 2330	2.7 / 5.3 / 2.7 / 5.2	**25** M	0432 / 1038 / 1705 / 2313	2.1 / 5.9 / 2.1 / 5.7
11 M	0548 / 1157 / 1831	2.8 / 5.2 / 2.8	**26** TU	0541 / 1151 / 1817	2.2 / 5.7 / 2.2
12 TU	0040 / 0659 / 1310 / 1939	5.2 / 2.8 / 5.2 / 2.7	**27** W	0032 / 0657 / 1310 / 1933	5.7 / 2.2 / 5.8 / 2.1
13 W	0146 / 0805 / 1413 / 2036	5.4 / 2.6 / 5.4 / 2.4	**28** TH	0148 / 0812 / 1423 / 2043	5.9 / 2.0 / 6.0 / 1.8
14 TH	0240 / 0859 / 1503 / 2123	5.7 / 2.3 / 5.7 / 2.2	**29** F	0254 / 0918 / 1525 / 2142	6.3 / 1.6 / 6.3 / 1.5
15 F	0325 / 0944 / 1546 / 2205	6.0 / 2.0 / 6.0 / 1.9	**30** SA	0350 / 1013 / 1617 / 2234	6.6 / 1.3 / 6.6 / 1.2
			31 SU O	0438 / 1102 / 1704 / 2320	6.9 / 1.0 / 6.8 / 1.0

FEBRUARY

Date	Time	m	Date	Time	m
1 M	0522 / 1147 / 1746	7.1 / 0.9 / 6.9	**16** TU ●	0503 / 1123 / 1723 / 2341	6.9 / 1.0 / 6.8 / 1.0
2 TU	0002 / 0603 / 1228 / 1825	1.0 / 7.1 / 0.9 / 6.9	**17** W	0542 / 1203 / 1801	7.1 / 0.8 / 7.0
3 W	0042 / 0640 / 1306 / 1901	1.0 / 7.0 / 1.0 / 6.7	**18** TH	0021 / 0621 / 1242 / 1840	0.9 / 7.3 / 0.7 / 7.0
4 TH	0119 / 0715 / 1342 / 1935	1.2 / 6.8 / 1.3 / 6.5	**19** F	0101 / 0701 / 1323 / 1919	0.8 / 7.3 / 0.7 / 7.0
5 F	0154 / 0749 / 1418 / 2009	1.5 / 6.5 / 1.6 / 6.2	**20** SA	0142 / 0742 / 1405 / 2001	0.9 / 7.1 / 0.9 / 6.7
6 SA	0230 / 0823 / 1454 / 2045	1.8 / 6.1 / 2.0 / 5.8	**21** SU	0226 / 0825 / 1450 / 2047	1.2 / 6.8 / 1.3 / 6.0
7 SU	0308 / 0900 / 1533 / 2126	2.1 / 5.8 / 2.3 / 5.5	**22** M	0314 / 0914 / 1540 / 2139	1.5 / 6.3 / 1.7 / 6.0
8 M	0351 / 0944 / 1620 / 2219	2.5 / 5.4 / 2.7 / 5.2	**23** TU	0410 / 1013 / 1640 / 2246	1.9 / 5.9 / 2.1 / 5.6
9 TU	0444 / 1044 / 1720 / 2330	2.8 / 5.1 / 2.9 / 5.0	**24** W	0518 / 1128 / 1754	2.3 / 5.6 / 2.4
10 W	0552 / 1204 / 1836	3.0 / 5.0 / 3.0	**25** TH	0010 / 0639 / 1256 / 1917	5.5 / 2.4 / 5.5 / 2.4
11 TH	0051 / 0712 / 1328 / 1953	5.1 / 2.9 / 5.1 / 2.8	**26** F	0136 / 0802 / 1416 / 2033	5.7 / 2.2 / 5.7 / 2.1
12 F	0203 / 0822 / 1432 / 2052	5.4 / 2.6 / 5.4 / 2.4	**27** SA	0246 / 0910 / 1518 / 2133	6.0 / 1.8 / 6.1 / 1.7
13 SA	0257 / 0916 / 1521 / 2139	5.7 / 2.2 / 5.8 / 2.0	**28** SU	0340 / 1004 / 1607 / 2222	6.4 / 1.4 / 6.5 / 1.4
14 SU	0342 / 1001 / 1604 / 2221	6.2 / 1.7 / 6.2 / 1.6			
15 M	0424 / 1043 / 1644 / 2302	6.5 / 1.3 / 6.5 / 1.3			

MARCH

Date	Time	m	Date	Time	m
1 M	0426 / 1049 / 1649 / 2305	6.7 / 1.1 / 6.7 / 1.1	**16** TU	0358 / 1017 / 1620 / 2238	6.6 / 1.2 / 6.6 / 1.2
2 TU O	0506 / 1130 / 1727 / 2344	6.9 / 1.0 / 6.8 / 1.0	**17** W ●	0440 / 1059 / 1701 / 2320	7.0 / 0.8 / 7.0 / 0.8
3 W	0542 / 1207 / 1801	7.0 / 0.9 / 6.9	**18** TH	0521 / 1141 / 1740	7.3 / 0.5 / 7.2
4 TH	0019 / 0615 / 1240 / 1833	1.0 / 7.0 / 1.0 / 6.8	**19** F	0001 / 0601 / 1222 / 1820	0.6 / 7.5 / 0.4 / 7.3
5 F	0052 / 0647 / 1312 / 1904	1.1 / 6.8 / 1.2 / 6.4	**20** SA	0042 / 0641 / 1303 / 1900	0.5 / 7.5 / 0.5 / 7.2
6 SA	0124 / 0717 / 1344 / 1934	1.3 / 6.6 / 1.5 / 6.4	**21** SU	0125 / 0723 / 1346 / 1942	0.7 / 7.3 / 0.8 / 7.0
7 SU	0156 / 0748 / 1416 / 2006	1.6 / 6.3 / 1.8 / 6.1	**22** M	0210 / 0808 / 1432 / 2028	0.9 / 6.9 / 1.2 / 6.5
8 M	0230 / 0820 / 1449 / 2040	2.0 / 5.9 / 2.2 / 5.7	**23** TU	0258 / 0857 / 1523 / 2121	1.4 / 6.3 / 1.7 / 6.1
9 TU	0307 / 0857 / 1529 / 2124	2.3 / 5.5 / 2.6 / 5.3	**24** W	0354 / 0957 / 1623 / 2228	1.9 / 5.8 / 2.2 / 5.6
10 W	0354 / 0947 / 1621 / 2226	2.7 / 5.1 / 2.9 / 5.0	**25** TH	0502 / 1114 / 1737 / 2354	2.3 / 5.4 / 2.5 / 5.4
11 TH	0455 / 1101 / 1733 / 2352	3.0 / 4.9 / 3.1 / 5.0	**26** F	0625 / 1245 / 1903	2.4 / 5.4 / 2.5
12 F	0615 / 1236 / 1902	3.0 / 4.9 / 2.9	**27** SA	0123 / 0750 / 1405 / 2020	5.6 / 2.2 / 5.6 / 2.2
13 SA	0119 / 0740 / 1356 / 2016	5.2 / 2.7 / 5.2 / 2.6	**28** SU	0231 / 0856 / 1503 / 2118	5.9 / 1.9 / 6.0 / 1.8
14 SU	0224 / 0843 / 1452 / 2109	5.6 / 2.2 / 5.7 / 2.1	**29** M	0324 / 0947 / 1549 / 2204	6.3 / 1.5 / 6.3 / 1.5
15 M	0314 / 0933 / 1538 / 2155	6.1 / 1.7 / 6.2 / 1.6	**30** TU	0407 / 1030 / 1628 / 2245	6.6 / 1.3 / 6.6 / 1.3
			31 W O	0444 / 1107 / 1703 / 2321	6.7 / 1.1 / 6.7 / 1.1

APRIL

Date	Time	m	Date	Time	m
1 TH	0518 / 1141 / 1735 / 2354	6.8 / 1.1 / 6.8 / 1.1	**16** F ●	0456 / 1116 / 1717 / 2339	7.4 / 0.5 / 7.4 / 0.5
2 F	0549 / 1212 / 1805	6.8 / 1.1 / 6.8	**17** SA	0539 / 1200 / 1759	7.5 / 0.4 / 7.4
3 SA	0025 / 0618 / 1243 / 1834	1.2 / 6.7 / 1.3 / 6.7	**18** SU	0023 / 0622 / 1244 / 1842	0.4 / 7.5 / 0.5 / 7.3
4 SU	0056 / 0648 / 1312 / 1904	1.3 / 6.6 / 1.5 / 6.5	**19** M	0108 / 0706 / 1329 / 1926	0.5 / 7.3 / 0.8 / 7.0
5 M	0127 / 0718 / 1342 / 1934	1.6 / 6.3 / 1.8 / 6.2	**20** TU	0155 / 0753 / 1416 / 2014	0.9 / 6.8 / 1.2 / 6.6
6 TU	0159 / 0748 / 1415 / 2007	1.8 / 6.0 / 2.1 / 5.9	**21** W	0245 / 0845 / 1508 / 2108	1.3 / 6.3 / 1.7 / 6.1
7 W	0235 / 0824 / 1452 / 2047	2.2 / 5.6 / 2.5 / 5.5	**22** TH	0342 / 0945 / 1608 / 2215	1.8 / 5.8 / 2.2 / 5.7
8 TH	0319 / 0910 / 1541 / 2144	2.5 / 5.3 / 2.8 / 5.2	**23** F	0448 / 1100 / 1719 / 2334	2.2 / 5.4 / 2.5 / 5.5
9 F	0415 / 1017 / 1646 / 2303	2.8 / 5.0 / 3.0 / 5.0	**24** SA	0606 / 1224 / 1840	2.4 / 5.3 / 2.5
10 SA	0528 / 1147 / 1811	2.8 / 4.9 / 3.0	**25** SU	0057 / 0725 / 1339 / 1954	5.5 / 2.3 / 5.5 / 2.3
11 SU	0031 / 0653 / 1313 / 1933	5.2 / 2.7 / 5.2 / 2.6	**26** M	0205 / 0830 / 1436 / 2051	5.8 / 2.0 / 5.9 / 2.0
12 M	0144 / 0803 / 1416 / 2034	5.6 / 2.2 / 5.7 / 2.1	**27** TU	0257 / 0920 / 1522 / 2138	6.1 / 1.7 / 6.2 / 1.7
13 TU	0239 / 0858 / 1506 / 2124	6.1 / 1.7 / 6.2 / 1.6	**28** W	0340 / 1003 / 1601 / 2218	6.3 / 1.5 / 6.4 / 1.5
14 W	0328 / 0947 / 1552 / 2210	6.6 / 1.2 / 6.7 / 1.1	**29** TH	0417 / 1040 / 1635 / 2254	6.5 / 1.4 / 6.5 / 1.4
15 TH	0413 / 1032 / 1635 / 2255	7.0 / 0.7 / 7.1 / 0.7	**30** F O	0450 / 1113 / 1707 / 2327	6.6 / 1.3 / 6.6 / 1.3

Chart Datum: 3·64 metres below Lallemand System (Mean Sea Level, Marseilles)

TIME ZONE –0100
(French Standard Time)
Subtract 1 hour for UT

For French Summer Time add
ONE hour in non-shaded areas

FRANCE – BREST

LAT 48°23'N LONG 4°30'W

TIMES AND HEIGHTS OF HIGH AND LOW WATERS

YEAR **1999**

MAY

Day	Time	m	Time	m	Time	m	Time	m
1 SA	0521	6.6	1144	-1.3	1737	6.6	2358	1.3
16 SU	0519	7.4	1139	0.5	1740	7.4		
2 SU	0552	6.5	1214	1.4	1808	6.6		
17 M	0005	0.4	0605	7.3	1226	0.6	1826	7.3
3 M	0030	1.4	0622	6.4	1245	1.6	1838	6.4
18 TU	0052	0.6	0652	7.1	1313	0.9	1913	7.0
4 TU	0102	1.6	0653	6.2	1316	1.8	1910	6.2
19 W	0141	0.9	0741	6.7	1402	1.2	2002	6.7
5 W	0135	1.8	0726	6.0	1349	2.0	1944	6.0
20 TH	0233	1.3	0833	6.3	1454	1.7	2056	6.2
6 TH	0212	2.0	0802	5.7	1427	2.3	2025	5.7
21 F	0328	1.7	0931	5.8	1551	2.1	2156	5.8
7 F	0255	2.3	0848	5.4	1514	2.6	2118	5.4
22 SA	0428	2.1	1036	5.5	1654	2.4	2304	5.6
8 SA	0348	2.5	0949	5.2	1614	2.8	2227	5.3
23 SU	0536	2.3	1148	5.4	1804	2.5		
9 SU	0452	2.6	1106	5.1	1729	2.8	2346	5.3
24 M	0017	5.5	0647	2.3	1259	5.4	1914	2.4
10 M	0608	2.5	1227	5.3	1848	2.5		
25 TU	0125	5.6	0752	2.2	1359	5.6	2015	2.2
11 TU	0059	5.6	0720	2.2	1335	5.7	1955	2.1
26 W	0221	5.8	0845	2.0	1447	5.9	2105	2.0
12 W	0201	6.0	0821	1.7	1431	6.2	2050	1.6
27 TH	0307	6.0	0930	1.8	1529	6.1	2147	1.8
13 TH	0255	6.5	0915	1.2	1521	6.6	2141	1.1
28 F	0347	6.1	1009	1.7	1605	6.3	2225	1.7
14 F	0344	6.9	1004	0.8	1609	7.0	2230	0.7
29 SA	0422	6.2	1044	1.6	1639	6.4	2300	1.6
15 SA ●	0432	7.2	1052	0.6	1654	7.3	2317	0.5
30 SU O	0456	6.3	1117	1.6	1712	6.5	2334	1.5
31 M	0529	6.3	1150	1.6	1745	6.5		

JUNE

Day	Time	m	Time	m	Time	m	Time	m
1 TU	0008	1.5	0601	6.3	1222	1.6	1818	6.4
16 W	0039	0.6	0640	6.9	1259	0.9	1900	7.0
2 W	0041	1.6	0634	6.2	1255	1.8	1852	6.3
17 TH	0128	0.9	0728	6.7	1347	1.2	1948	6.7
3 TH	0116	1.7	0709	6.0	1330	1.9	1929	6.1
18 F	0217	1.2	0817	6.3	1435	1.6	2037	6.4
4 F	0154	1.8	0748	5.8	1409	2.1	2011	5.9
19 SA	0307	1.6	0907	5.9	1526	1.9	2128	6.0
5 SA	0237	2.0	0832	5.6	1455	2.3	2100	5.7
20 SU	0359	1.9	1001	5.6	1620	2.2	2224	5.7
6 SU	0326	2.2	0926	5.4	1550	2.4	2159	5.6
21 M	0456	2.2	1101	5.4	1719	2.4	2326	5.6
7 M	0423	2.3	1031	5.4	1654	2.5	2307	5.5
22 TU	0558	2.4	1205	5.3	1823	2.5		
8 TU	0530	2.3	1143	5.4	1806	2.4		
23 W	0032	5.4	0702	2.4	1309	5.4	1928	2.5
9 W	0017	5.7	0640	2.1	1253	5.7	1915	2.1
24 TH	0135	5.4	0802	2.3	1406	5.6	2025	2.3
10 TH	0123	6.0	0745	1.8	1356	6.1	2017	1.7
25 F	0230	5.6	0853	2.2	1454	5.8	2114	2.1
11 F	0223	6.4	0844	1.4	1452	6.5	2114	1.3
26 SA	0316	5.8	0937	2.0	1536	6.0	2157	1.9
12 SA	0319	6.7	0939	1.1	1545	6.8	2208	0.9
27 SU	0356	5.9	1016	1.8	1614	6.2	2235	1.7
13 SU ●	0412	7.0	1031	0.8	1636	7.1	2259	0.7
28 M	0433	6.1	1053	1.7	1651	6.3	2312	1.6
14 M	0502	7.1	1121	0.7	1725	7.2	2350	0.6
29 TU	0508	6.2	1128	1.6	1726	6.4	2348	1.5
15 TU	0552	7.1	1210	0.8	1813	7.2		
30 W	0543	6.2	1203	1.6	1801	6.5		

JULY

Day	Time	m	Time	m	Time	m	Time	m
1 TH	0024	1.5	0619	6.2	1238	1.6	1838	6.4
16 F	0111	0.8	0711	6.7	1328	1.1	1928	6.8
2 F	0100	1.5	0655	6.2	1315	1.7	1915	6.4
17 SA	0156	1.1	0753	6.4	1411	1.4	2010	6.5
3 SA	0138	1.5	0734	6.1	1354	1.8	1956	6.2
18 SU	0239	1.5	0835	6.1	1455	1.7	2052	6.1
4 SU	0219	1.6	0816	5.9	1438	1.9	2041	6.1
19 M	0323	1.8	0919	5.8	1540	2.1	2138	5.7
5 M	0305	1.8	0904	5.8	1527	2.1	2132	5.9
20 TU	0410	2.2	1008	5.5	1630	2.4	2230	5.4
6 TU	0356	2.0	1000	5.6	1624	2.2	2232	5.8
21 W	0504	2.5	1106	5.2	1728	2.6	2333	5.2
7 W	0456	2.1	1105	5.6	1730	2.2	2339	5.8
22 TH	0605	2.7	1213	5.2	1834	2.7		
8 TH	0603	2.1	1216	5.7	1841	2.1		
23 F	0043	5.1	0713	2.7	1321	5.3	1943	2.6
9 F	0050	5.9	0713	1.9	1326	5.9	1949	1.8
24 SA	0151	5.3	0815	2.5	1421	5.5	2041	2.4
10 SA	0158	6.1	0819	1.7	1430	6.3	2053	1.5
25 SU	0246	5.5	0907	2.3	1509	5.8	2130	2.1
11 SU	0301	6.4	0920	1.4	1529	6.6	2152	1.1
26 M	0332	5.7	0950	2.0	1552	6.0	2212	1.8
12 M	0358	6.7	1016	1.1	1622	6.9	2246	0.9
27 TU	0412	6.0	1030	1.8	1630	6.3	2251	1.6
13 TU ●	0451	6.9	1108	0.9	1713	7.1	2337	0.7
28 W	0449	6.2	1108	1.5	1708	6.5	2329	1.4
14 W	0540	6.9	1156	0.9	1800	7.1		
29 TH	0526	6.3	1144	1.5	1744	6.6		
15 TH	0025	0.7	0626	6.9	1243	0.9	1845	7.0
30 F	0006	1.3	0602	6.5	1221	1.4	1821	6.7
31 SA	0043	1.2	0639	6.5	1258	1.4	1859	6.7

AUGUST

Day	Time	m	Time	m	Time	m	Time	m
1 SU	0121	1.2	0717	6.4	1337	1.4	1938	6.6
16 M	0206	1.4	0758	6.3	1420	1.6	2013	6.2
2 M	0200	1.3	0757	6.3	1419	1.6	2020	6.4
17 TU	0243	1.8	0835	5.9	1458	2.0	2050	5.8
3 TU	0243	1.5	0841	6.1	1505	1.8	2107	6.2
18 W	0323	2.2	0915	5.6	1541	2.4	2134	5.4
4 W	0331	1.7	0919	5.9	1558	2.0	2202	5.9
19 TH	0409	2.6	1006	5.2	1633	2.7	2231	5.1
5 TH	0428	2.0	1033	5.7	1702	2.2	2309	5.7
20 F	0506	2.9	1114	5.0	1739	2.9	2347	4.9
6 F	0535	2.2	1147	5.6	1815	2.2		
21 SA	0619	3.0	1234	5.0	1857	2.9		
7 SA	0026	5.7	0650	2.2	1306	5.7	1932	2.1
22 SU	0111	5.0	0736	2.8	1347	5.3	2009	2.6
8 SU	0144	5.8	0804	2.0	1418	6.1	2042	1.7
23 M	0218	5.3	0837	2.5	1443	5.6	2103	2.3
9 M	0252	6.1	0909	1.6	1519	6.4	2144	1.3
24 TU	0307	5.6	0925	2.2	1528	6.0	2147	1.9
10 TU	0350	6.5	1006	1.3	1613	6.8	2237	1.0
25 W	0349	6.0	1006	1.8	1608	6.4	2228	1.5
11 W ●	0441	6.7	1056	1.1	1701	7.0	2325	0.8
26 TH	0428	6.3	1045	1.5	1646	6.7	2306	1.2
12 TH	0526	6.9	1142	0.9	1745	7.1		
27 F O	0505	6.6	1123	1.3	1724	6.9	2344	1.0
13 F	0009	0.8	0608	6.9	1224	0.9	1825	7.1
28 SA	0542	6.8	1201	1.1	1801	7.1		
14 SA	0050	0.9	0647	6.8	1304	1.1	1902	6.9
29 SU	0022	0.9	0618	6.9	1239	1.0	1838	7.1
15 SU	0129	1.1	0723	6.6	1342	1.3	1938	6.6
30 M	0100	0.9	0656	6.8	1318	1.1	1917	7.0
31 TU	0140	1.0	0735	6.7	1400	1.3	1959	6.7

16

Chart Datum: 3·64 metres below Lallemand System (Mean Sea Level, Marseilles)

TIME ZONE –0100
(French Standard Time)
Subtract 1 hour for UT

For French Summer Time add
ONE hour in non-shaded areas

FRANCE – BREST

LAT 48°23′N   LONG   4°30′W

TIMES AND HEIGHTS OF HIGH AND LOW WATERS   YEAR **1999**

SEPTEMBER

No	Day	Time	m	Time	m	Time	m	Time	m
1	W	0222	1.3	0818	6.4	1445	1.6	2045	6.4
2	TH	0310	1.7	0908	6.1	1538	1.9	2139	6.0
3	F	0405	2.1	1010	5.7	1642	2.2	2249	5.6
4	SA	0515	2.4	1129	5.5	1800	2.4		
5	SU	0015	5.5	0636	2.4	1257	5.6	1924	2.2
6	M	0140	5.7	0757	2.2	1412	6.0	2038	1.9
7	TU	0248	6.1	0902	1.8	1512	6.4	2136	1.4
8	W	0341	6.4	0956	1.4	1601	6.8	2225	1.1
9	TH	0427	6.7	1042	1.1	1645	7.0	●2309	0.9
10	F	0508	6.9	1124	1.0	1724	7.1	2349	0.9
11	SA	0545	6.9	1202	1.0	1800	7.1		
12	SU	0025	0.9	0619	6.9	1237	1.1	1833	6.9
13	M	0059	1.1	0650	6.7	1311	1.3	1904	6.7
14	TU	0132	1.4	0722	6.4	1345	1.6	1936	6.3
15	W	0204	1.8	0754	6.1	1419	2.0	2008	5.9
16	TH	0239	2.2	0829	5.7	1458	2.4	2046	5.5
17	F	0319	2.6	0912	5.4	1544	2.8	2135	5.1
18	SA	0410	3.0	1015	5.0	1646	3.0	2250	4.9
19	SU	0522	3.1	1142	5.0	1807	3.1		
20	M	0027	4.9	0651	3.1	1309	5.2	1931	2.8
21	TU	0146	5.2	0804	2.7	1412	5.6	2031	2.4
22	W	0239	5.6	0855	2.3	1459	6.0	2118	1.9
23	TH	0322	6.1	0939	1.8	1541	6.5	2200	1.5
24	F	0402	6.5	1019	1.4	1621	6.8	2240	1.1
25	SA	0441	6.8	1059	1.1	1659	7.1	○2319	0.8
26	SU	0518	7.1	1138	0.9	1738	7.3	2358	0.7
27	M	0556	7.2	1218	0.8	1816	7.4		
28	TU	0038	0.7	0635	7.2	1259	0.8	1857	7.2
29	W	0119	0.9	0715	7.0	1342	1.1	1940	6.9
30	TH	0203	1.2	0759	6.6	1429	1.5	2027	6.4

OCTOBER

No	Day	Time	m	Time	m	Time	m	Time	m
1	F	0252	1.7	0850	6.2	1523	1.9	2125	5.9
2	SA	0350	2.2	0955	5.8	1630	2.3	2240	5.5
3	SU	0502	2.5	1119	5.5	1751	2.5		
4	M	0011	5.4	0627	2.6	1249	5.6	1918	2.3
5	TU	0134	5.6	0748	2.3	1403	6.0	2028	1.9
6	W	0236	6.0	0850	1.9	1458	6.4	2122	1.5
7	TH	0325	6.4	0940	1.5	1544	6.7	2208	1.2
8	F	0407	6.7	1024	1.3	1625	6.9	2248	1.1
9	SA	0445	6.9	1102	1.1	1701	7.0	●2324	1.0
10	SU	0519	6.9	1137	1.1	1733	6.9	2357	1.1
11	M	0550	6.9	1210	1.2	1804	6.8		
12	TU	0029	1.3	0620	6.7	1242	1.4	1834	6.6
13	W	0059	1.5	0650	6.5	1314	1.7	1904	6.3
14	TH	0130	1.9	0721	6.2	1347	2.0	1935	6.0
15	F	0202	2.2	0754	5.9	1423	2.3	2010	5.6
16	SA	0239	2.6	0833	5.5	1506	2.7	2055	5.4
17	SU	0326	2.9	0928	5.2	1602	2.9	2201	4.9
18	M	0431	3.1	1049	5.0	1716	3.0	2335	4.9
19	TU	0558	3.1	1220	5.1	1842	2.9		
20	W	0102	5.1	0720	2.8	1331	5.5	1951	2.3
21	TH	0202	5.6	0819	2.4	1424	6.0	2042	1.9
22	F	0249	6.1	0906	1.8	1509	6.5	2128	1.5
23	SA	0332	6.6	0950	1.4	1552	6.9	2211	1.0
24	SU	0413	7.0	1032	1.0	1633	7.3	○2253	0.7
25	M	0453	7.2	1114	0.7	1714	7.4	2335	0.6
26	TU	0534	7.4	1157	0.6	1756	7.5		
27	W	0017	0.6	0615	7.3	1241	0.7	1839	7.3
28	TH	0102	0.9	0659	7.1	1325	1.0	1925	6.9
29	F	0148	1.2	0746	6.8	1417	1.4	2016	6.4
30	SA	0239	1.7	0840	6.3	1513	1.8	2116	5.9
31	SU	0338	2.2	0945	5.9	1619	2.2	2230	5.5

NOVEMBER

No	Day	Time	m	Time	m	Time	m	Time	m
1	M	0449	2.5	1104	5.6	1737	2.4	2355	5.4
2	TU	0609	2.6	1228	5.7	1858	2.3		
3	W	0113	5.6	0726	2.4	1340	5.9	2005	2.0
4	TH	0213	6.0	0827	2.0	1435	6.2	2058	1.7
5	F	0301	6.3	0917	1.7	1521	6.5	2143	1.5
6	SA	0342	6.5	1000	1.5	1600	6.6	2222	1.4
7	SU	0419	6.7	1038	1.4	1635	6.7	2258	1.3
8	M	0452	6.8	1112	1.4	1707	6.7	●2330	1.4
9	TU	0523	6.8	1145	1.4	1738	6.6		
10	W	0001	1.5	0554	6.7	1217	1.5	1809	6.5
11	TH	0032	1.7	0625	6.5	1249	1.7	1840	6.3
12	F	0103	1.9	0656	6.3	1322	1.9	1912	6.0
13	SA	0135	2.2	0730	6.0	1358	2.2	1947	5.7
14	SU	0212	2.5	0808	5.7	1439	2.5	2029	5.4
15	M	0256	2.7	0858	5.4	1529	2.7	2126	5.2
16	TU	0352	2.9	1004	5.2	1631	2.8	2243	5.0
17	W	0505	3.0	1124	5.2	1747	2.8		
18	TH	0006	5.2	0626	2.8	1240	5.5	1900	2.5
19	F	0116	5.6	0733	2.4	1341	5.9	2001	2.0
20	SA	0211	6.0	0829	1.9	1433	6.4	2053	1.6
21	SU	0259	6.5	0918	1.5	1521	6.8	2141	1.1
22	M	0345	6.9	1005	1.1	1608	7.2	2227	0.8
23	TU	0430	7.2	1052	0.7	1653	7.4	○2313	0.7
24	W	0514	7.4	1139	0.6	1740	7.4		
25	TH	0000	0.7	0600	7.4	1226	0.6	1827	7.2
26	F	0047	0.9	0647	7.2	1315	0.9	1915	6.9
27	SA	0136	1.2	0736	6.9	1406	1.2	2007	6.5
28	SU	0227	1.6	0829	6.5	1501	1.6	2105	6.0
29	M	0324	2.0	0929	6.1	1602	2.0	2209	5.7
30	TU	0427	2.4	1037	5.8	1710	2.3	2321	5.5

DECEMBER

No	Day	Time	m	Time	m	Time	m	Time	m
1	W	0537	2.5	1151	5.6	1822	2.4		
2	TH	0034	5.5	0648	2.5	1302	5.7	1929	2.2
3	F	0137	5.7	0753	2.3	1402	5.9	2026	2.0
4	SA	0230	6.0	0847	2.1	1451	6.1	2114	1.9
5	SU	0314	6.2	0932	1.9	1533	6.2	2155	1.7
6	M	0352	6.4	1012	1.7	1611	6.4	2232	1.6
7	TU	0427	6.5	1049	1.6	1645	6.4	●2306	1.6
8	W	0501	6.6	1123	1.6	1717	6.4	2338	1.6
9	TH	0533	6.6	1156	1.6	1750	6.4		
10	F	0010	1.7	0606	6.5	1230	1.7	1822	6.3
11	SA	0043	1.8	0639	6.4	1304	1.8	1855	6.1
12	SU	0116	2.0	0714	6.2	1339	1.9	1931	5.9
13	M	0152	2.2	0752	6.0	1418	2.1	2011	5.7
14	TU	0234	2.4	0836	5.8	1503	2.3	2059	5.5
15	W	0323	2.6	0929	5.6	1555	2.5	2159	5.3
16	TH	0422	2.7	1034	5.5	1658	2.5	2310	5.3
17	F	0532	2.7	1145	5.6	1808	2.4		
18	SA	0023	5.5	0644	2.5	1254	5.8	1917	2.1
19	SU	0129	5.9	0749	2.1	1357	6.2	2018	1.8
20	M	0227	6.3	0848	1.6	1454	6.5	2113	1.4
21	TU	0320	6.7	0942	1.2	1547	6.9	2206	1.0
22	W	0411	7.1	1034	0.9	1638	7.1	○2256	0.8
23	TH	0500	7.3	1125	0.7	1728	7.2	2346	0.7
24	F	0549	7.4	1214	0.6	1817	7.2		
25	SA	0035	0.8	0637	7.3	1304	0.7	1905	7.0
26	SU	0123	1.0	0725	7.1	1353	1.0	1954	6.6
27	M	0212	1.4	0814	6.7	1443	1.4	2044	6.3
28	TU	0302	1.7	0904	6.3	1535	1.8	2136	5.9
29	W	0355	2.1	0958	5.9	1631	2.2	2234	5.6
30	TH	0453	2.4	1059	5.6	1732	2.4	2339	5.4
31	F	0557	2.6	1207	5.4	1839	2.5		

Chart Datum: 3·64 metres below Lallemand System (Mean Sea Level, Marseilles)

CAMARET   8-16-29

Finistere 48°16'·80N 04°35'·19W   Rtg 1-1-2

CHARTS

AC 3427, 798; SHOM 7401, 7148, 7149; Imray C36; ECM 540, 542; Stanfords 17

TIDES

+0500 Dover; ML 3·8; Duration 0610; Zone –0100

Standard Port BREST (←—)

Times				Height (metres)			
High Water		Low Water		MHWS	MHWN	MLWN	MLWS
0000	0600	0000	0600	6·9	5·4	2·6	1·0
1200	1800	1200	1800				
Differences CAMARET							
–0010	–0010	–0013	–0013	–0·3	–0·3	–0·1	0·0

SHELTER

Good, except in strong E winds. Plaisance La Pointe (5m) is mainly for visitors, but Styvel has some visitors berths for smaller craft (dredged 1·5m) and is nearer town. SW side of hbr mostly dries; FVs berth on SSE side.

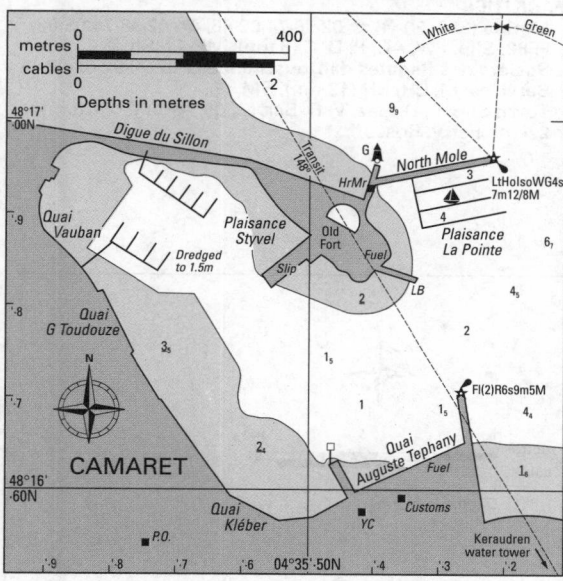

NAVIGATION

WPT 48°18'·00N 04°36'·00W, 335°/155° from/to N mole lt, 1·2M. Beware rks W of Pte du Grand Gouin. ⚓ in hbr prohib.

LIGHTS AND MARKS

Lt ho at E end of N mole, Iso WG 4s, W135°-182°, G182°-027°; appr in W sector. The G SHM bn tr at the W end of the N mole is very conspic; also Tour Vauban and chapel close SW. Ldg line at 148°: front mark = top of the old fort; rear = Keraudren water tr on hill behind.

RADIO TELEPHONE

VHF Ch 09. For Ouessant Traffic see 8.16.2 and 8.16.27.

TELEPHONE

Hr Mr 02·98·27·95·99; Aff Mar 02·98·27·93·28; SNSM 02·98·27·94·76; CROSS 02·98·89·31·31; ⊞ 02·98·27·93·02; Auto 08·36.68·08·29; Police 02·98·27·00·22; Dr 02·98·57·91·35; Brit Consul 01·40·63·16·02.

FACILITIES

Plaisance La Pointe (100+80 visitors) ☎ 02·98·27·95·99, FF95.50, FW, AC, C (8 ton), D, Access H24;
Plaisance 'Styvel' (200+30 visitors), FW, AC, &, Access H24, dredged 1·5m;
Services: M, ME, El, Ⓔ, Sh, CH, P, C (5 ton), SM, SHOM.
Town P, V, Gaz, R, Bar, ✉, Ⓑ, ⇌ (Brest), ✈ (Brest or Quimper). Ferry: Roscoff.

MORGAT   8-16-30

Finistere 48°13'·62N 04°29'·69W   Rtg 2-3-1

CHARTS

AC 798; SHOM 6676, 6099; Imray C36; ECM 541, 542; Stanfords 17

TIDES

+0500 Dover; ML 3·8; Duration No data; Zone –0100

Standard Port BREST (←—)

Times				Height (metres)			
High Water		Low Water		MHWS	MHWN	MLWN	MLWS
0000	0600	0000	0600	6·9	5·4	2·6	1·0
1200	1800	1200	1800				
Differences MORGAT							
–0008	–0008	–0020	–0010	–0·4	–0·4	–0·2	0·0

SHELTER

The port is exposed to winds from the W and N, but the marina is protected by floating concrete wavebreaks. There are pleasant day ⚓s between Morgat and Cap de la Chèvre in the bays of St Hernot, St Norgard & St Nicolas; sheltered from the W. Also 2·5M to E in lee of Is de l'Aber.

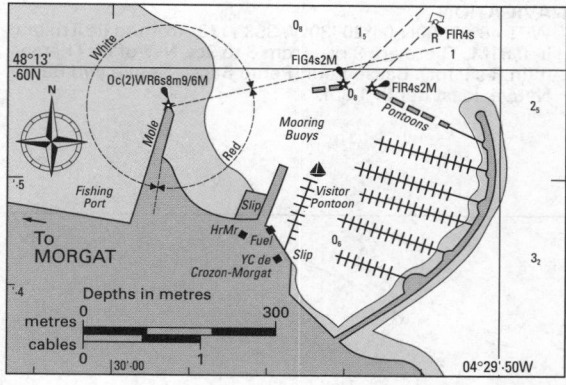

NAVIGATION

WPT 48°12'·00N 04°28'·00W, 147°/327° from/to E bkwtr hd, 1·9M. There are rks close under the cliffs S of Pte de Morgat, and Les Verres 2M ESE of ent. Ent chan, dredged 1·5m, is marked by PHM buoy Fl R 4s, close SE of which is depth of 1m. Fl R/G 4s lts are at end of wavebreaks.

LIGHTS AND MARKS

Pte de Morgat lt, Oc (4) WRG 12s 77m 15/10M, is 4ca S of hbr; G sector covers Les Verres. Appr in W sector, 007°-257°, of inner Mole lt, Oc (2) WR 6s 8m 9/6M.

RADIO TELEPHONE

Marina VHF Ch 09.

TELEPHONE

Hr Mr 02·98·27·01·97; Aff Mar 02·98·27·09·95; CROSS 02·98·89·31·31; Auto 08·36.68·08·29; SNSM 02·98·27·00 41; ⊞ 02·98·27·93·02; Police 02·98·27·00·22; Ⓗ 02·98·27·05·33; Brit Consul 01·40·63·16·02.

FACILITIES

Marina (550+50 Ⓥ), ☎ 02·98·27·01·97, ⚓ 02·98·27·19·76, FF77.50, AC, FW, C (8 ton), Slip, CH, D, P, ME, Access H24;
YC du Crozon-Morgat ☎ 98·27·01·98;
Services: M, C (6 ton), El, Sh, Ⓔ.
Town (Crozon), V, Gaz, R, Bar, ✉, Ⓑ, ⇌, ✈ (Brest or Quimper). Ferry: Roscoff.

16

DOUARNENEZ 8-16-31

Finistere 48°06'·17N 04°20'·32W Rtg 3-2-2

CHARTS
AC 798; SHOM 6677, 6099; Imray C36; ECM 542; Stanfords 17

TIDES
+0500 Dover; ML 3·7; Duration 0615; Zone –0100

Standard Port BREST (⟵)

Times				Height (metres)			
High Water		Low Water		MHWS	MHWN	MLWN	MLWS
0000	0600	0000	0600	6·9	5·4	2·6	1·0
1200	1800	1200	1800				
Differences DOUARNENEZ							
–0010	–0015	–0018	–0008	–0·5	–0·5	–0·3	–0·1

SHELTER
Very good; access H24, all weathers and tides to visitors' berths in the marina (1·5m) at Tréboul, or in the river outside (subject to wash from passing traffic). About 2ca S of the marina the river has been dammed to form a non-tidal basin (3·2m), Port Rhu, as a museum for classic craft; limited access via a lock opening HW±1½ sp, HW±½ nps. The Fishing hbr is prohib to yachts and Port du Rosmeur is full of moorings.

NAVIGATION
WPT 48°07'·00N 04°20'·30W, 353°/173° from/to Ile Tristan lt, 0·81M. There are 3 rks, from 3 to 9ca NW of Ile Tristan lt (in R sector), Basse Veur, Petite Basse Neuve and Basse Neuve, least depth 1·8m.

LIGHTS AND MARKS
Approx 5M to W is Pte du Milier lt, Oc (2) WRG 6s 34m 16/11M, G080°-087°, W087°-113°, R113°-120°, W120°-129°, G129°-148°, W148°-251°, R 251°-258°.
Ile Tristan Oc (3) WR 12s 33m 13/10M, vis R138°-153°, W elsewhere; R sector covers Basse Veur and Basse Neuve, least depth 1·8m.
On the high road bridge at S end of Port Rhu, Dir lt 157°, Fl (5) WRG 20s 16m 5/4M, covers the Grande Passe and river; vis G154°-156°, W156°-158°, R158°-160°.
Port Rhu lock ent is marked by a Fl R 5s and a Fl G 5s.

RADIO TELEPHONE
Marina VHF Ch 09 (0700-1200 and 1330-2100LT in season; out of season 0830-1200, 1330-1730LT). Port Ch 12 16.

TELEPHONE
Hr Mr (Plaisance) 02·98·74·02·56; Aff Mar 02·98·92·00·91; CROSS 02·98·89·31·31; SNSM 02·98·89·63·16; ⌗ 02·98·92·01·45; Météo 02·98·84·60·64; Auto 08·36·68·08·29; Police 02·98·92·01·22; Ⓗ 02·98·92·25·00; Brit Consul 01·40·63·16·02.

FACILITIES
Marina (380+30 Ⓥ) ☎ 02·98·74·02·56, 🖅 02·98·74.05.08, FF82, Slip, FW, AC, P, D, C (6 ton), ME, El, Sh, Ⓒ;
Société des Regates de Douarnenez ☎ 02·98·92·02·03;
Services: M, CH, BH (12 ton), SM, Ⓔ.
Town Slip, P, D, Gaz, V, R, Bar, ✉, Ⓑ, ⇌ and ✈ (Quimper 22km). Ferry: Roscoff.

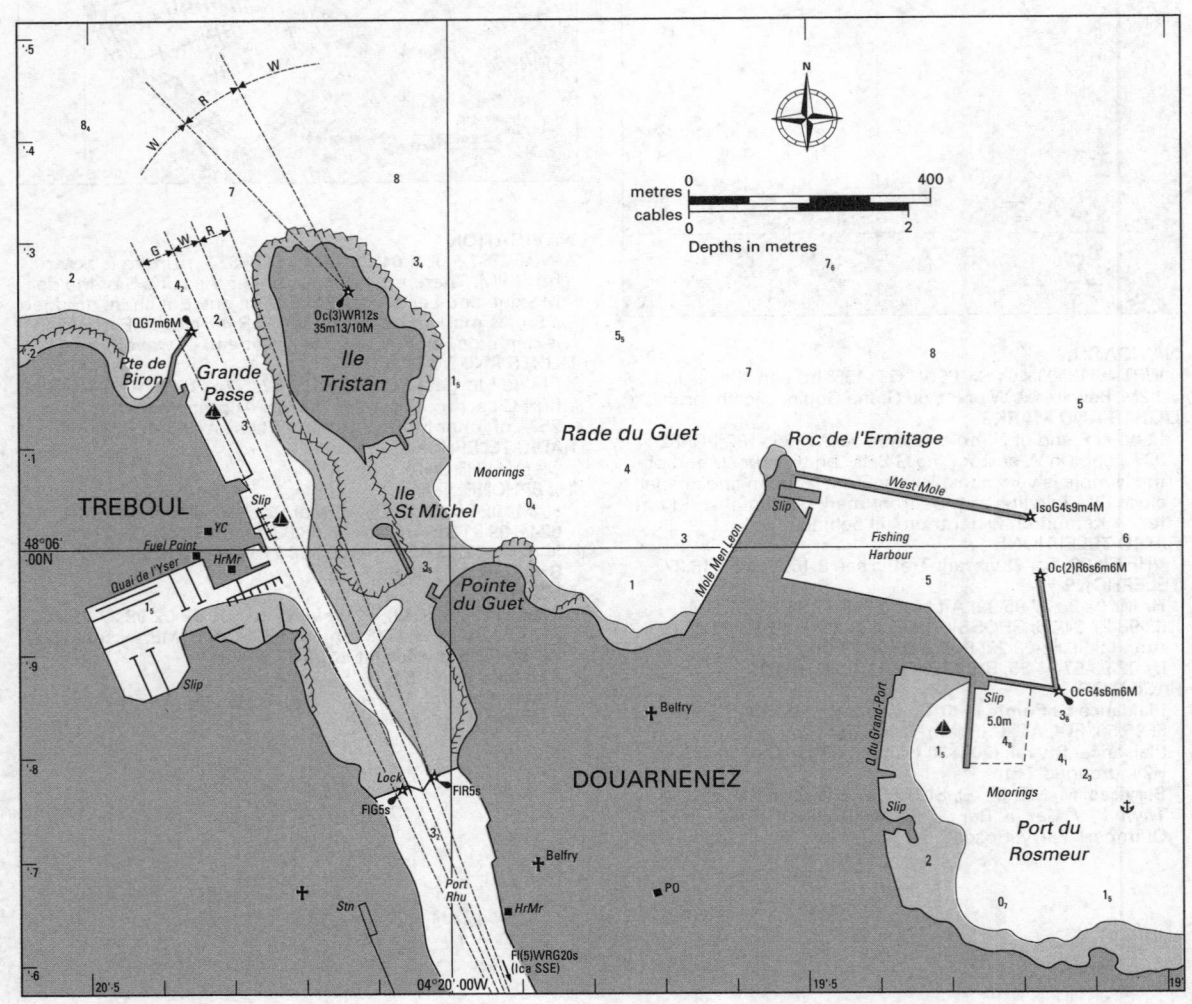

VOLVO PENTA SERVICE

Sales and service centres in area 17
Names and addresses of Volvo Penta dealers in
this area are available from:

France *Volvo Penta France* , 55 Avenue des Champs Pierreux, 92757 Cedex
Tel +33 1 55175445, Fax +33 1 55175261

Area 17

South Brittany
Raz de Sein to River Loire

VOLVO PENTA

8.17.1	Index	**Page 707**
8.17.2	Diagram of ports, lights, RDF bns, Coast radio and weather stns	**708**
8.17.3	Tidal stream charts	**710**
8.17.4	List of coastal lights, fog signals and waypoints	**712**
8.17.5	Passage information	**717**
8.17.6	Distance table	**718**
8.17.7	Special notes for France	**See 8.15.8**
8.17.8	Audierne Ile de Sein St Guénolé Le Guilvinec Lesconil	**719**
8.17.9	Loctudy	**720**
8.17.10	Bénodet	**720**
8.17.11	Port-la-Forêt	**721**
8.17.12	Concarneau Iles de Glénan Aven and Bélon Rivers Brigneau Merrien Doëlan Le Pouldu	**722**
8.17.13	Port Tudy (Ile de Groix) Loc Maria	**723**
8.17.14	Lorient	**724**
8.17.15	River Etel	**725**
8.17.16	Le Palais (Belle Ile) Sauzon	**726**
8.17.17	Port Haliguen Port Maria	**726**
8.17.18	La Trinité-sur-Mer	**727**
8.17.19	Crouesty Ile Houat	**727**
8.17.20	Golfe du Morbihan	**728**
8.17.21	Vannes	**730**
8.17.22	Vilaine River Penerf	**731**
8.17.23	Piriac Ile Dumet	**732**
8.17.24	La Turballe	**732**
8.17.25	Le Croisic	**733**
8.17.26	Le Pouliguen	**733**
8.17.27	Pornichet	**734**
8.17.28	River Loire and St Nazaire Port de Comberge Port de la Gravette Saint-Gildas	**735**

17

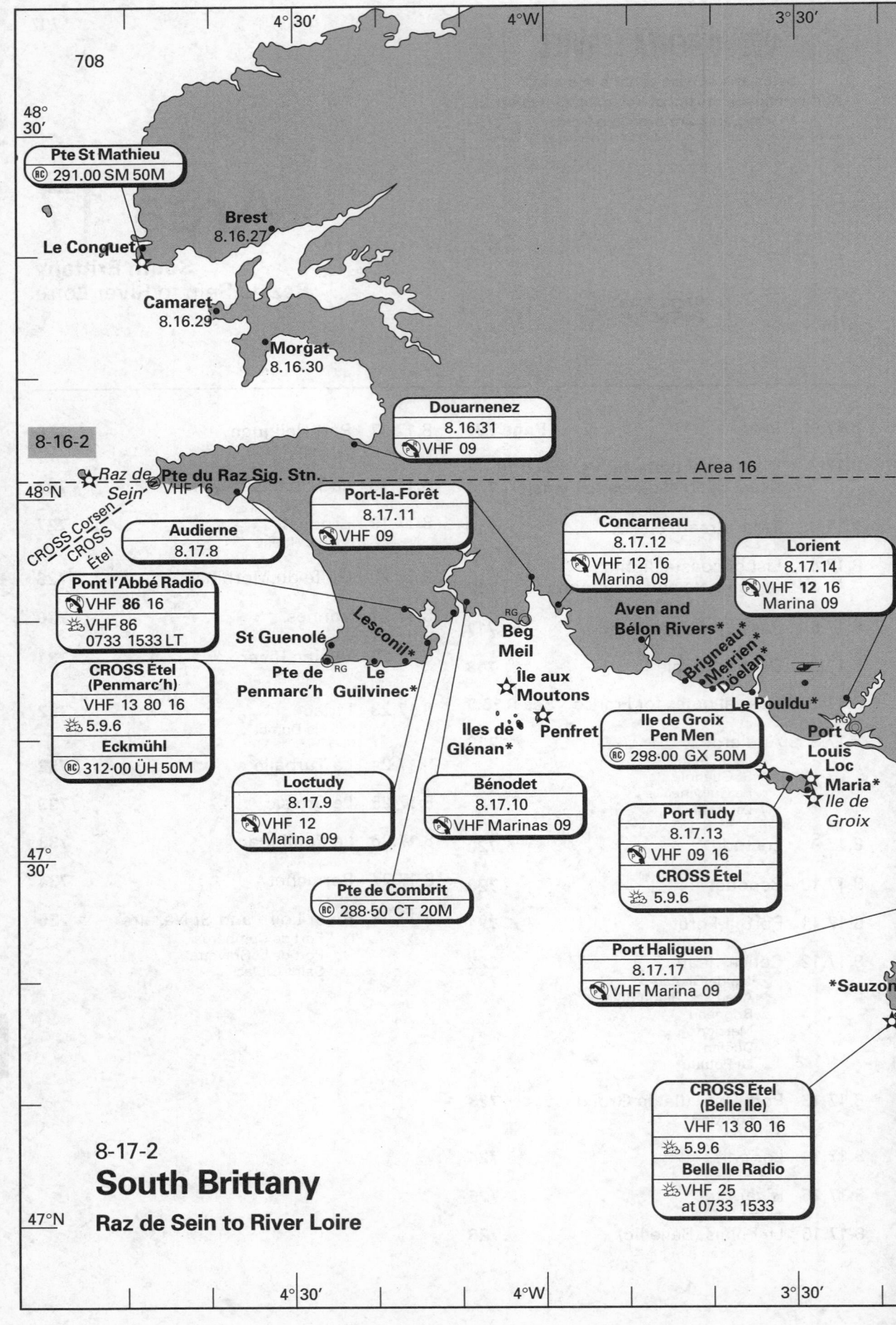

708

Pte St Mathieu
(RC) 291.00 SM 50M

Brest
8.16.27

Le Conquet

Camaret
8.16.29

Morgat
8.16.30

Douarnenez
8.16.31
VHF 09

8-16-2

Raz de Sein · **Pte du Raz Sig. Stn.**
VHF 16

48°N

CROSS Corsen

CROSS Étel

Audierne
8.17.8

Port-la-Forêt
8.17.11
VHF 09

Area 16

Concarneau
8.17.12
VHF 12 16
Marina 09

Lorient
8.17.14
VHF **12** 16
Marina 09

Pont l'Abbé Radio
VHF **86** 16
VHF 86
0733 1533 LT

Lesconil*

St Guenolé

Beg
Meil

RG

**Aven and
Bélon Rivers***

Brigneau*
Merrien *
Döelan*

**CROSS Étel
(Penmarc'h)**
VHF 13 80 16
5.9.6
Eckmühl
(RC) 312·00 ÜH 50M

Pte de
Penmarc'h

RG

Le
Guilvinec*

Île aux
Moutons

Penfret

**Ile de Groix
Pen Men**
(RC) 298·00 GX 50M

Le Pouldu*

Port
Louis
Loc
Maria*

Iles de
Glénan*

Loctudy
8.17.9
VHF 12
Marina 09

Bénodet
8.17.10
VHF Marinas 09

Port Tudy
8.17.13
VHF 09 16
CROSS Étel
5.9.6

*Ile de
Groix*

47°
30'

Pte de Combrit
(RC) 288·50 CT 20M

Port Haliguen
8.17.17
VHF Marina 09

*Sauzon

**CROSS Étel
(Belle Ile)**
VHF 13 80 16
5.9.6
Belle Ile Radio
VHF 25
at 0733 1533

8-17-2
South Brittany
Raz de Sein to River Loire

47°N

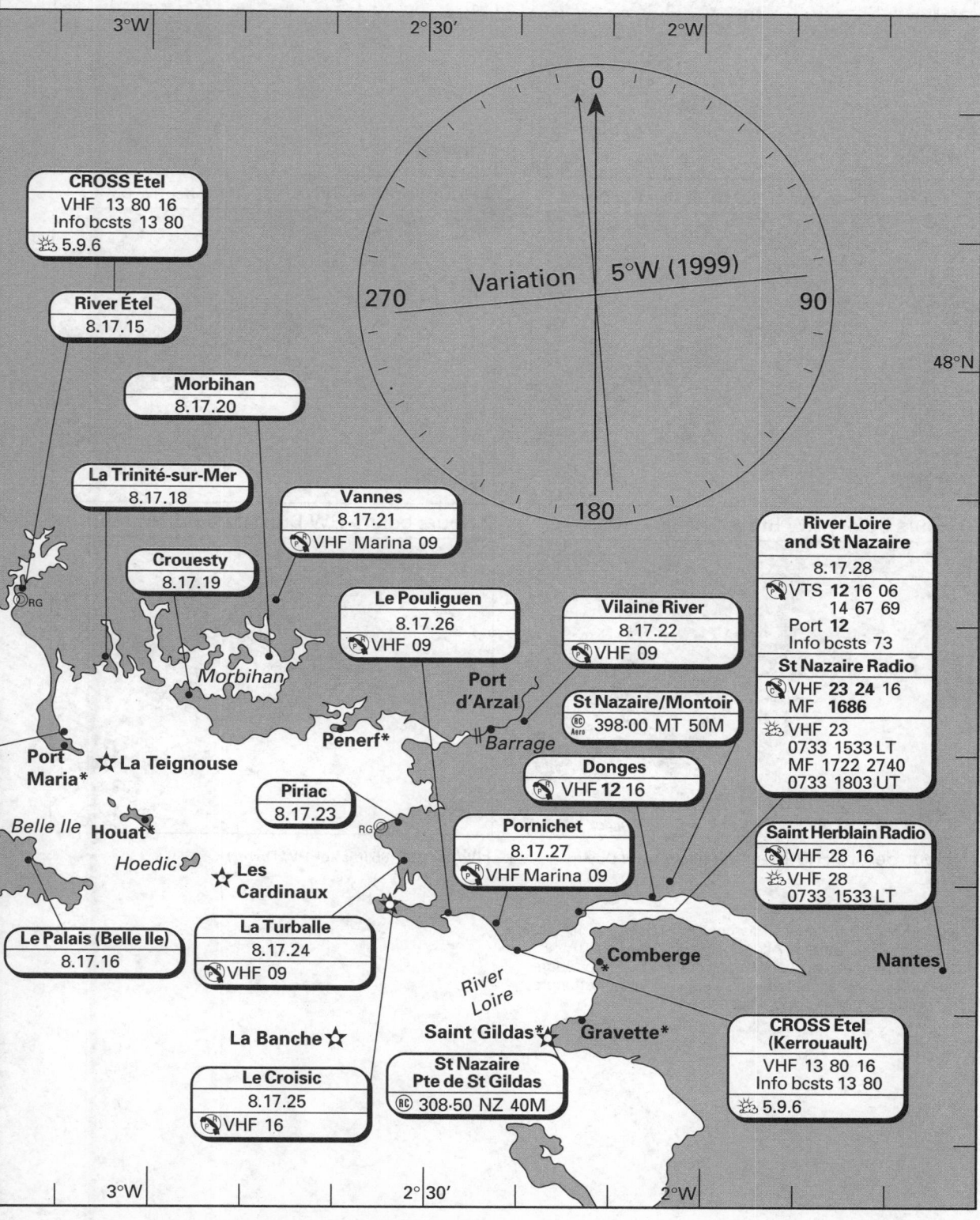

Key to Symbols

Coast Radio Station: VHF/MF frequencies
Port, VTS, or marina Radio: VHF frequencies
Marine RDF beacon
Aero RDF beacon
Weather information
(Frequencies/times of broadcasts)

SAR helicopter base
Selected principal lights
Light vessel/Light float/Lanby
Emergency VHF DF
See Area Index

3°W   2° 30'   2°W

CROSS Etel
VHF 13 80 16
Info bcsts 13 80
5.9.6

River Étel
8.17.15

Variation 5°W (1999)

270   90   0   180

48°N

Morbihan
8.17.20

La Trinité-sur-Mer
8.17.18

Vannes
8.17.21
VHF Marina 09

River Loire
and St Nazaire
8.17.28
VTS 12 16 06
14 67 69
Port 12
Info bcsts 73

St Nazaire Radio
VHF 23 24 16
MF 1686
VHF 23
0733 1533 LT
MF 1722 2740
0733 1803 UT

Crouesty
8.17.19

Le Pouliguen
8.17.26
VHF 09

Vilaine River
8.17.22
VHF 09

Morbihan

Port
d'Arzal

St Nazaire/Montoir
398·00 MT 50M

Penerf*   Barrage

Port
Maria*   La Teignouse

Piriac
8.17.23

Donges
VHF 12 16

Belle Ile   Houat*

RG

Pornichet
8.17.27
VHF Marina 09

Saint Herblain Radio
VHF 28 16
VHF 28
0733 1533 LT

Hoedic   Les
Cardinaux

Le Palais (Belle Ile)
8.17.16

La Turballe
8.17.24
VHF 09

Comberge
*

Nantes

17

River
Loire

La Banche

Saint Gildas*   Gravette*

CROSS Etel
(Kerrouault)
VHF 13 80 16
Info bcsts 13 80
5.9.6

Le Croisic
8.17.25
VHF 16

St Nazaire
Pte de St Gildas
308·50 NZ 40M

3°W   2° 30'   2°W

8-17-3   AREA 17 TIDAL STREAMS

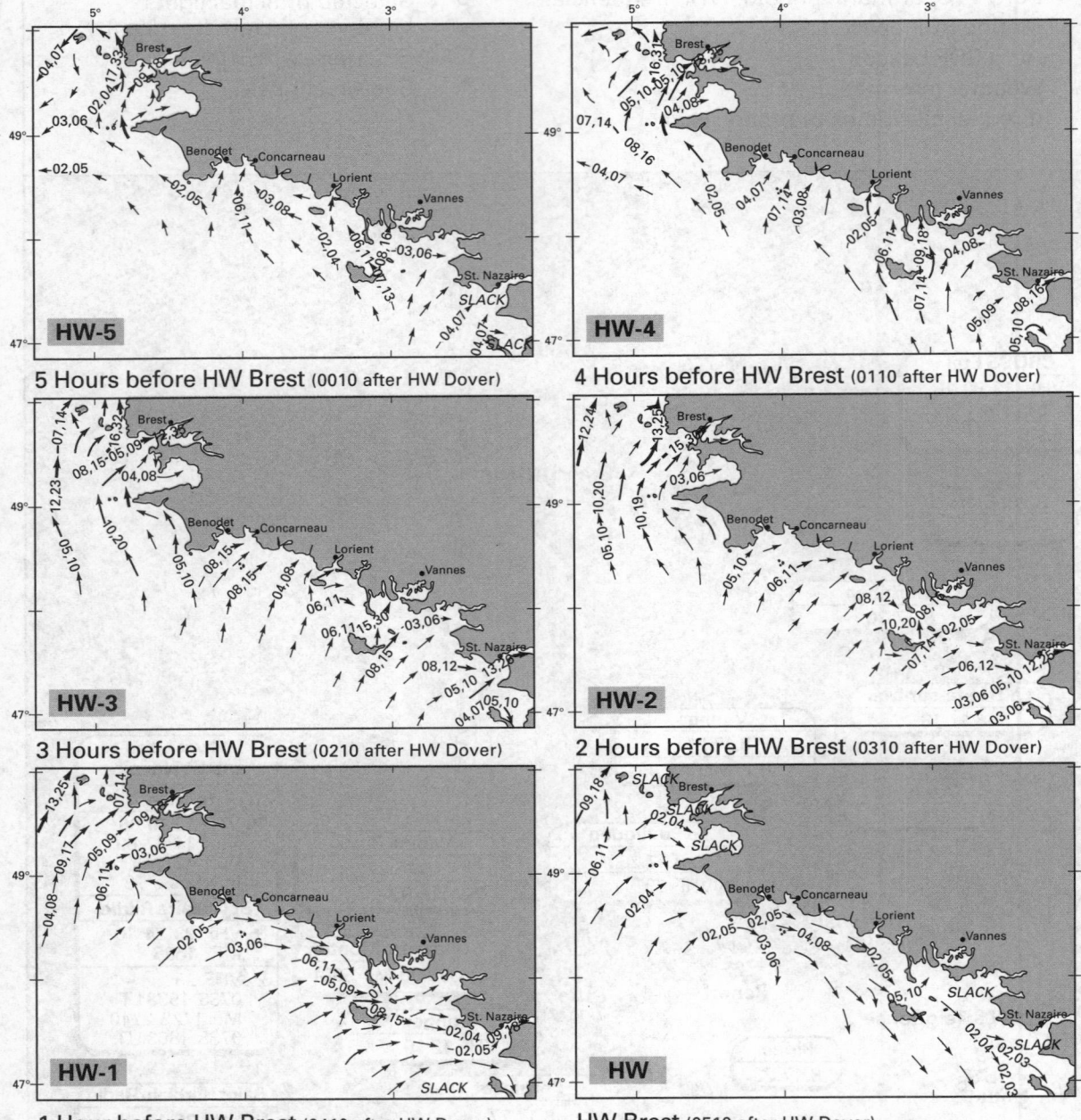

5 Hours before HW Brest (0010 after HW Dover)

4 Hours before HW Brest (0110 after HW Dover)

3 Hours before HW Brest (0210 after HW Dover)

2 Hours before HW Brest (0310 after HW Dover)

1 Hour before HW Brest (0410 after HW Dover)

HW Brest (0510 after HW Dover)

Note: These tidal stream chartlets are based on NP 265
(Admiralty Tidal Stream Atlas for France, W Coast) which
uses data from actual observations out to 15-25M offshore.
The equivalent French Atlas gives data for further offshore,
but based on computer predictions.

Northward 8.16.3   Southward 8.18.3

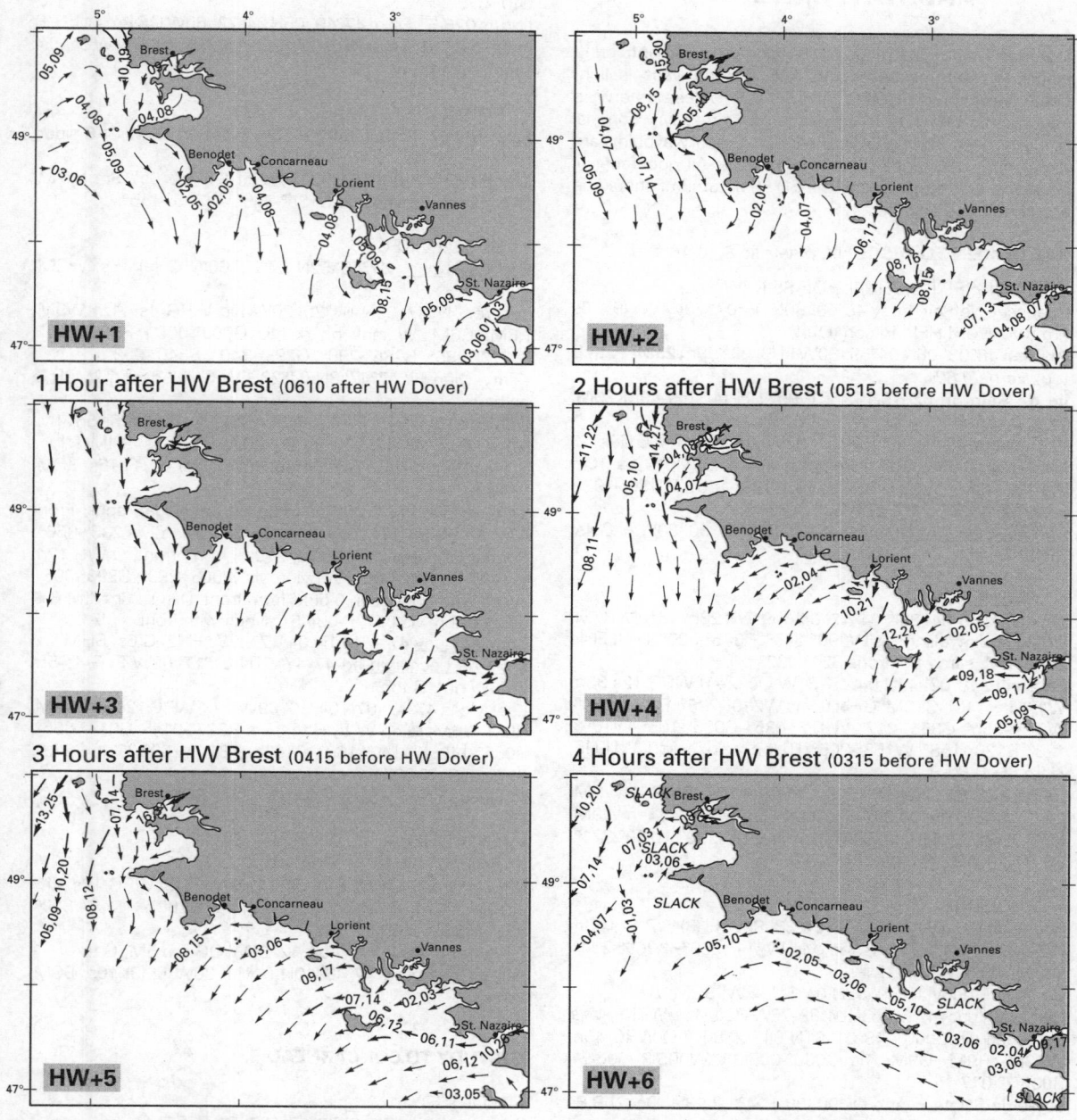

HW+1
1 Hour after HW Brest (0610 after HW Dover)

HW+2
2 Hours after HW Brest (0515 before HW Dover)

HW+3
3 Hours after HW Brest (0415 before HW Dover)

HW+4
4 Hours after HW Brest (0315 before HW Dover)

HW+5
5 Hours after HW Brest (0215 before HW Dover)

HW+6
6 Hours after HW Brest (0115 before HW Dover)

17

Note: These tidal stream chartlets are based on NP 265 (Admiralty Tidal Stream Atlas for France, W Coast) which uses data from actual observations out to 15-25M offshore. The equivalent French Atlas gives data for further offshore, but based on computer predictions.

8.17.4 COASTAL LIGHTS, FOG SIGNALS AND WAYPOINTS

Lights with a nominal range of 15M or more are in **bold** print, places and features are in CAPITALS, and light-vessels, light floats and Lanbys in *CAPITAL ITALICS*. Unless otherwise stated lights are white. m = elevation in metres; M = nominal range in miles. Fog signals are in *italics*. Useful waypoints are underlined; use those on land with care. All geographical positions are referenced to the ED 50 datum but should be assumed to be approximate.

RAZ DE SEIN TO LESCONIL (See also 8.16.4)

● CHAUSSÉE DE SEIN/ÎLE DE SEIN (W to E)
Chaussée de Sein buoy 48°03'·80N 05°07'·70W VQ (9) 10s 9m 8M; WCM HFP; Racon (O); *Whis*.
Ar-Men 48°03'·06N 04°59'·80W Fl (3) 20s 29m **23M**; W tr, B top; *Horn (3) 60s*.
Île de Sein 48°02'·70N 04°51'·95W Fl (4) 25s 49m **29M**; W tr, B top; RC.
Ar Guéveur 48°02'·00N 04°51'·32W 20m; W tr; *Dia 60s*.
Men-Brial, 0·8M 115° from main lt, Oc (2) WRG 6s 16m W12M, R9M, G7M; G&W tr; vis G149°-186°, W186°-192°, R192°-221°, W221°-227°, G227°-254°.
Cornoc-An-Ar-Braden buoy 48°03'·30N 04°50'·80W Fl G 4s; SHM; *Whis*.

● RAZ DE SEIN
Tévennec 48°04'·33N 04°47'·64W Q WR 28m W10M R7M; W □ tr and dwelling; vis W090°-345°, R345°-090°; Dir lt Fl 4s 24m 12M; same tr; intens 324°-332°.
La Vieille 48°02'·49N 04°45'·31W Oc (2+1) WRG 12s 33m **W17M**, R14M, G13M; Gy ■ tr; vis W290°-298°, R298°-325°, W325°-355°, G355°-017°, W017°-035°, G035°-105°, W105°-123°, R123°-158°, W158°-205°; R lt on radio mast 3·4M ENE; *Horn (2+1) 60s*.
La Plate 48°02'·36N 04°45'·50W VQ (9) 10s 19m 8M; WCM.
Le Chat 48°01'·44N 04°48'·80W Fl (2) WRG 6s 27m W9M, R6M, G6M; SCM; vis G096°-215°, W215°-230°, R230°-271°, G271°-286°, R286°-096°; Ra refl.

● AUDIERNE
Pointe de Lervily 48°00'·11N 04°33'·84W Fl (3) WR 12s 20m W14M, R11M; W tr, R top; vis W211°-269°, R269°-294°, W294°-087°, R087°-121°.
Gamelle E buoy 47°59'·52N 04°31'·96W; SCM; *Bell*.
Gamelle W buoy 47°59'·53N 04°32'·76W VQ (9) 10s; WCM; *Whis*.
Kergadec dir lt 006°: 48°01'·01N 04°32'·80W Q WRG 43m W12M, R9M, G9M; vis G000°-005·3°, W005·3°-006·7°, R006·7°-017°.
Jetée de Sainte-Évette 48°00'·38N 04°32'·98W Oc (2) R 6s 2m 7M; R lantern; vis 090°-270°.
Passe de l'Est ldg lts 331°: Front, Jetée de Raoulic 48°00'·60N 04°32'·37W Fl (3) WG 12s 11m W14M, G9M; W ○ tr; vis W shore-034°, G034°-shore, but may show W037°-055°; rear, Kergadec, 0·5M from front, Dir FR 44m 9M ; W 8-sided tr, R top; intens 321°-341°.

● PORS POULHAN
W side of ent 47°59'·15N 04°27'·80W QR 14m 9M; W ○ tr, R lantern.

● SAINT GUÉNOLÉ
Chenal de Groumilli ldg lts 123°: Front, 47°48'·20N 04°22'·60W FG 9m 9M; Or ● on W tr, B bands; rear, 300m from front, FG 13m 9M ; Or ● on W tr, B bands.
Basse Gaouac'h buoy 47°48'·66N 04°24'·13W Fl (3) G 12s; SHM; *Whis*.
Scoedec 47°48'·46N 04°23'·10W Fl G 2·5s 6m 3M; G tr.

Ldg lts 055·4°: Front, 47°48'·75N 04°22'·65W VQ 5m 2M; G&W col; rear, 320m from front, F Vi 12m 1M; G&W col; vis 040°-070°.
Ldg lts 026·5°: Front 47°49'·05N 04°22'·60W QR 8m 4M;   R mast; rear, 51m from front, QR 12m 4M; mast, R & W bands; synch with front.

● POINTE DE PENMARC'H
Eckmühl 47°47'·95N 04°22'·35W Fl 5s 60m **23M**; Gy 8-sided tr; RC; *Horn 60s*.
Menhir 47°47'·80N 04°23'·90W Fl (2) WG 6s 19m W7M, G4M; W tr, B band; vis G135°-315°, W315°-135°.

● LE GUILVINEC
Cap Caval buoy 47°46'·52N 04°22'·60W Q (9) 15s; WCM; *Whis*.
Locarec 47°47'·33N 04°20'·30W Iso WRG 4s 11m W9M, R6M, G6M; W tank on rk; vis G063°-068°, R068°-271°, W271°-285°, R285°-298°, G298°-340°, R340°-063°.
Kérity. Men Hir 47°47'·3N 04°20'·6W Fl R 2·5s 6m 2M; R ■ on bn.
Detached bkwtr hd 47°47'·6N 04°20'·9W Fl (2) G 6s 5m 1M.
Névez buoy 47°45'·90N 04°20'·00W Fl G 2·5s; SHM.
Spinec buoy 47°45'·24N 04°18'·80W Q (6) + L Fl 15s; SCM; *Whis*.
Le Guilvinec ldg lts 053°. Môle de Léchiagat, spur, Front 47°47'·49N 04°17'·00W Q 7m 8M; W pylon; vis 233°-066°.
Rocher Le Faoute's, Middle, 210m from front, Q WG 12m W14M, G11M; R ● on W pylon; vis W006°-293°, G293°-006°; synch with front; rear, 0·58M from front, Dir Q 26m 8M; R ● on W pylon; vis 051·5°-054·5°; synch with front.
Capelan buoy 47°47'·21N 04°17'·47W Fl (2) G 6s; SHM.
Môle de Léchiagat hd 47°47'·51N 04°17'·09W Fl G 4s 5m 7M; W hut, G top.
Lost Moan 47°47'·07N 04°16'·69W Fl (3) WRG 12s 8m W9M, R6M, G6M; ■ on W tr, R top; vis R327°-014°, G014°-065°, R065°-140°, W140°-160°, R160°-268°, W268°-273°, G273°-317°, W317°-327°.
Ar Guisty bn 47°45'·69N 04°15'·50W; SCM.

● LESCONIL
Reissant bn 47°46'·45N 04°13'·43W; SCM.
Men-ar-Groas 47°47'·86N 04°12'·60W Fl (3) WRG 12s 14m W10M, R7M, G7M; W tr, G top; vis G268°-313°, W313°-333°, R333°-050°.
E bkwtr hd 47°47'·77N 04°12'·56W QG 5m 5M; G tr.
Karek Greis buoy 47°46'·10N 04°11'·30W Q (3) 10s; ECM; *Whis*.

LOCTUDY TO CONCARNEAU

● LOCTUDY
Rostolou buoy 47°46'·70N 04°07'·20W; ECM.
Roc'h Hélou buoy 47°47'·17N 04°08'·00W; WCM.
Bas Boulanger buoy 47°47'·40N 04°09'·05W VQ (6) + L Fl 10s; SCM.
Bilien buoy 47°49'·17N 04°08'·02W VQ (3) 5s; ECM; *Whis*.
Chenal de Bénodet buoy 47°48'·60N 04°06'·96W; ECM.
Basse Malvic buoy 47°48'·52N 04°06'·53W; WCM.
Pointe de Langoz, S side 47°49'·94N 04°09'·48W Fl (4) WRG 12s 12m **W15M**, R11M, G11M; W tr, R top; vis W115°-257°, G257°-284°, W284°-295°, R295°-318°, W318°-328°, R328°-025°.
Men Audierne bn 47°50'·37N 04°08'·98W; SHM.
Karek-Saoz 47°50'·08N 04°09'·30W QR 3m 2M; R tr.
Les Perdrix 47°50'·31N 04°09'·88W Fl WRG 4s 15m W11M, R8M, G8M; ▲ on B&W tr; vis G090°-285°, W285°-295°, R295°-090°.
Le Blas 47°50'·34N 04°10'·15W Fl (3) G 12s 5m 1M; G ▲ on truncated col.

• BENODET
Ldg lts 345·5°: Front, **Pte du Coq** 47°52'·38N 04°06'·61W, Dir Oc (2+1) G 12s 11m **17M**; W ○ tr, G stripe; intens 345°-347°. Common rear Pyramide, 336m from front, Oc (2+1) 12s 48m 11M; W tr, G top; vis 338°-016°, synch with front.
Ldg lts 000·5°: Front, Pte de Combrit 47°51'·92N 04°06'·70W, Oc (3+1) WR 12s 19m W12M , R9M; W □ tr, Gy corners; vis W325°-017°, R017°-325°; RC. Common rear, Pyramide, 0·63M from front.
Les Verrés bn 47°51'·61N 04°06'·06W; SHM.
Le Four bn 47°51'·85N 04°06'·32W; SHM.
Pte du Toulgoet Fl R 2s 2m 1M; R mast.

Le Taro bn 47°50'·57N 04°04'·86W; WCM.
Men Déhou bn 47°48'·18N 04°04'·63W; ECM.
Les Poulains bn 47°47'·75N 04°03'·40W; NCM.
La Voleuse buoy 47°48'·81N 04°02'·40W Q (6) + L Fl 15s; SCM; *Whis*.
La Vache bn 47°49'·60N 04°02'·53W; SHM.
Men Vras bn 47°49'·72N 04°01'·50W; ECM.

• BEG-MEIL
Linuen bn 47°50'·71N 03°57'·70W; SCM.
Chaussée de Beg'Meil buoy 47°50'·82N 03°57'·23W Q (3) 10s; ECM.
Laouen Pod bn 47°51'·29N 03°57'·91W; ECM.
Quay hd 47°51'·72N 03°58'·85W Fl R 2s 6m 1M; R & W col.

• PORT-LA-FORÊT
Le Scoré bn 47°52'·81N 03°57'·48W; SCM.
Les Ormeaux bn 47°53'·33N 03°58'·25W; PHM.
Channel buoy 47°53'·46N 03°58'·05W Fl (2) G 6s; SHM.
Cap Coz mole hd 47°53'·55N 03°58'·20W Fl (2) R 6s 5m 6M.
Kerleven mole hd Fl G 4s 8m 6M.

• CONCARNEAU
Ldg lts 028·5°: Front, La Croix 47°52'·22N 03°55'·00W Oc (3) 12s 14m 13M; R&W tr; vis 006·5°-093°; **rear**, **Beuzec**, 1·34M from front, Dir Q 87m **23M**; spire; intens 026·5°-030·5°.
Le Cochon 47°51'·53N 03°55'·47W Fl (3) WRG 12s 5m W9M, R6M, G6M; G tr; vis G048°-205°, R205°-352°, W352°-048°; SHM.
Basse du Chenal PHM buoy, QR, 47°51'·58N 03°55'·60W.
Men Fall buoy 47°51'·82N 03°55'·20W Fl G 4s; SHM.
Kersos bn 47°51'·87N 03°54'·85W; SHM.
Lanriec 47°52'·07N 03°54'·56W QG 13m 8M; G lt window on W gable; vis 063°-078°.
La Médée 47°52'·12N 03°54'·71W Fl R 2·5s 9m 4M; R tr: PHM.
Marina hd 47°52'·20N 03°54'·72W Fl (3) R 12s; R □ on post.

• BAIE DE POULDOHAN
Petit Taro bn 47°51'·17N 03°55'·21W; WCM.
Pouldohan 47°51'·03N 03°53'·61W Fl G 4s 7m 8M; W ○ tr, G top; vis 053°-065°.
Roché Tudy bn 47°50'·58N 03°54'·41W; SHM.

ÎLES DE GLENAN

• ÎLES DE GLÉNAN/ÎLE AUX MOUTONS
Basse Pérennès buoy 47°41'·15N 04°06'·05W Q (9) 15s 8m 5M; WCM; *Whis*; Ra refl.
Jument de Glénan buoy 47°38'·80N 04°01'·32W Q (6) + L Fl 15s 10m 4M; SCM; *Whis*; Ra Refl.
Penfret 47°43'·32N 03°57'·10W Fl R 5s 36m **21M**; W ○ tr, R top; auxiliary lt Dir Q 34m 12M; same tr; vis 295°-315°.
Île Cigogne 47°43'·10N 03°59'·59W, W tr B top.
Les Bluniers bn 47°43'·42N 04°03'·73W; WCM.
Broc'h bn 47°43'·22N 04°01'·31W; NCM.

La Pie lt bn 47°43'·81N 03°59'·67W; Fl (2) 6s 9m 3M; IDM.
Île de Bananec bn 47°43'·32N 03°59'·11W; ECM.
Rouge de Glénan buoy 47°45'·50N 04°03'·90W VQ (9) 10s 8m 8M; WCM; *Whis*; Ra refl.
Île-aux-Moutons 47°46'·55N 04°01'·62W Oc (2) WRG 6s 18m **W15M**, R11M, G11M; W □ tr and dwelling; vis W035°-050°, G050°-063°, W063°-081°, R081°-141°, W141°-292°, R292°-035°; **auxiliary lt** Dir Oc (2) 6s 17m **24M**; same tr; synch with main lt, intens 278·5°-283·5°.
Grand Pourceaux buoy 47°46'·05N 04°00'·75W Q; NCM.
Rochers Leuriou bn 47°45'·20N 03°59'·90W; ECM.
Jaune de Glénan buoy 47°42'·60N 03°49'·75W Q (3) 10s; ECM; *Whis*.
Cor-Loch buoy 47°42'·28N 03°52'·22W; IDM.
Basse an Ero buoy 47°40'·47N 03°55'·38W; SCM.
Laoennou buoy 47°39'·70N 03°54'·60W; IDM.

CONCARNEAU TO ÎLE DE GROIX

• TRÉVIGNON TO PORT MANECH
Les Soldats lt bn 47°47'·91N 03°53'·32W VQ (9) 10s; WCM.
Môle Hd 47°47'·72N 03°51'·20W Fl G 4s 5m 8M; W col, G top.
Trévignon bkwtr root 47°47'·65N 03°51'·22W Oc (3+1) WRG 12s 11m W14M, R11M, G11M; W □ tr, G top; vis W004°-051°, G051°-085°, W085°-092°, R092°-127°, R322°-351°.
Men Du bn 47°46'·44N 03°50'·40W; IDM.
Corn Vas buoy 47°45'·92N 03°50'·18W; WCM.
Men ar tréas buoy 47°45'·84N 03°49'·58W; SCM.
Île Verte bn 47°46'·35N 03°47'·95W; ■ tr.
Île de Raguénès 47°46'·95N 03°47'·65W; SCM.

• PORT MANECH/AVEN AND BÉLON RIVERS
Pointe de Beg-ar-Vechen 47°48'·03N 03°44'·30W Oc (4) WRG 12s 38m W10M, R7M, G7M; W & R tr; vis W (unintens) 050°-140°, W140°-296°, G296°-303°, W303°-311°, R311°-328° over Les Verrès, W328°-050°; obsc by Pte de Beg-Morg when brg less than 299°.
Les Verrès bn 47°46'·70N 03°42'·60W; IDM.

• BRIGNEAU/MERRIEN/DOËLAN
Brigneau mole hd 47°46'·95N 03°40'·10W Oc (2) WRG 6s 7m W12M, R9M, G9M; W col, R top; vis G280°-329°, W329°-339°, R339°-034°.
Brigneau buoy 47°46'·15N 03°39'·99W; SWM; *Whis*.
Merrien 47°47'·05N 03°38'·82W QR 26m 7M; W ○ tr, R top; vis 004°-009°.
Port de la Merrien buoy 47°46'·52N 03°39'·09W; SCM.
Doëlan ldg lts 013·8°: Front, 47°46'·35N 03°36'·42W Oc (3) WG 12s 20m W13M, G10M; W tr, G band and top; vis W shore-305°, G305°-314°, W314°-shore; rear, 326m from front, QR 27m 9M; W tr, R band and top.

• LE POULDU TO LOMENER/RIVIÈRE DE QUIMPERLÉ
Le Pouldu ent bn 47°45'·76N 03°32'·11W; PHM.
Grand Cochon buoy 47°43'·09N 03°30'·73W; SCM.
Kerroc'h 47°42'·00N 03°27'·53W Oc (2) WRG 6s 22m W11M, R8M, G8M; W tr, R top; vis R096·5°-112°·5, G112·5°-132°, R132°-302°, W302°-096·5°.
Anse de Stole Dir lt 357·2°, 47°42'·33N 03°25'·57W Dir Q WRG 13m W10M, R8M, G8M; W tr, R top; vis G349·2°-355·2°, W355·2°-359·2°, R359·2°-005·2°.

• ÎLE DE GROIX/PORT TUDY/LOCMARIA
Pen Men 47°38'·87N 03°30'·48W Fl (4) 25s 59m **29M**; W ○ tr, B top; vis 309°-275°; RC.
Pointe des Chats 47°37'·30N 03°25'·25W Fl R 5s 16m **19M**; W ○ tr and dwelling.
Port Tudy môle N hd 47°38'·78N 03°26'·62W Iso G 4s 12m 6M; W tr, G top.
Pointe de la Croix 47°38'·10N 03°25'·20W Oc WR 4s 16m

17

W12M, R9M; W pedestal, R lantern; vis W169°-336°, R336°-345°, W345°-353°.
Edouard de Cougy buoy 47°37'·97N 03°23'·80W; ECM.
Les Chars buoy 47°35'·74N 03°23'·50W Q (6) + L Fl 15s; SCM; *Whis*.

LORIENT

- PASSE OUEST

Ldg lts 057°: Front, Les Sœurs 47°42'·22N 03°21'·70W   Dir Q 11m 13M, R tr, W bands; vis intens 042·5°-058·5°, (4M) 058·5°-042·5°; rear **Port Louis**, 740m from front, Dir Q 22m **18M**; W daymark, R bands on bldg. Its intens 042·5°-058·5°, (4M) 058·5°-042·5°.
'L' Banc des truics buoy 47°40'·82N 03°24'·40W Q (9) 15s; WCM.
A2 Locqueltas buoy 47°41'·00N 03°24'·90W Fl R 2·5s; PHM.
A5 buoy 47°41'·56N 03°23'·02W Fl (2) G 6s; SHM.
A7 buoy 47°41'·77N 03°22'·58W Fl G 2·5s; SHM.
Les trois Pierres 47°41'·58N 03°22'·40W Q RG 11m R6M, G6M; B tr, R bands; vis G060°-196°, R196°-002°.
Île aux Souris 47°42'·22N 03°21'·43W Dir Q WG 6m W3M, G2W; G tr; vis W041·5°-043·5°, G043·5°-041·5°.

- PASSE DU SUD

Ldg lts 008·5°: **Front**, Fish Market 47°43'·82N 03°21'·67W Dir QR 16m **17M**; R ■ on Gy tr; intens 006°-011°; **rear**, Kergroise-La Perrière 515m from front Dir QR 34m **16M**; R ■, W stripe on Gy tr; synch with front; intens 006°-011°.
Bastresse Sud buoy 47°40'·83N 03°22'·01W QG; SHM; *Bell*.
Les Errants buoy 47°41'·16N 03°22'·29W Fl (2) R 6s; PHM.

- ENTRANCE CHANNEL

Île Saint Michel Passe de la Citadelle ldg lts 016·5°: **Front**, 47°41'·53N 03°21'·54W Dir Oc (3) G 12s 8m **16M**; W tr, G top; **rear**, 306m from front, Dir Oc (3) G 12s 14m **16M**; W tr, G top; synch with front; both intens 014·5°-017·5°.
La Potée de Beurre bn 47°42'·30N 03°21'·90W; SHM.
Chan W side, La Petite Jument 47°42'·63N 03°21'·98W Oc R 4s 5m 6M; R tr; vis 182°-024°.
Chan E side, Tourelle de la Citadelle 47°42'·66N 03°21'·86W Oc G 4s 6m 6M; G tr; vis 009°-193°.
Chan W side Le Cochon Fl R 4s 5m 5M; R tr, G band.

- KERNEVEL

Banc du Turc buoy 47°43'·39N 03°21'·77W Fl (3) G 12s; SHM.
Port de Kernevel Marina ent buoy 47°43'·47N 03°22'·01W Fl Y 2·5s 3m 2M; SPM with can topmark.
Ldg lts 217° 47°43'·08N 03°22'·23W **Front**, Dir QR 10m **15M**; R ■ on R&W tr; intens 215°-219°; **rear**, 290m from front, Dir QR 18m **15M**; W □ tr, R top; synch with front; intens 215°-219°.

- PORT-LOUIS

Jetty 47°42'·76N 03°21'·29W Iso G 4s 7m 6M; W tr, G top.

- KÉROMAN/FISHING HARBOUR/RADE DE PENMANÉ

Submarine base Ldg lts 350°: **Front**, 47°43'·66N 03°21'·93W Dir Oc (2) R 6s 25m **15M**; **rear**, 91m from front, Dir Oc (2) R 6s 31m **15M**; R&W topmark on Gy pylon, R top; lts synch and intens 348°-353°.
E side of ent 47°43'·68N 03°21'·79W Fl RG 4s 7m 6M; W tr, G top; vis G000°-235°, R235°-360°.
Pengarne 47°43'·94N 03°21'·13W Fl G 2·5s 3m 4M; G tr.
Pointe de l'Espérance Dir lt 037° 47°44'·57N 03°20'·58W Dir Q WRG 8m W10M, R8M, G8M; W tr, G top; vis G034·2°-036·7°, W036·7°-037·2°, R037·2°-047·2°.
Ro-Ro Terminal 47°44'·48N 03°20'·88W Oc (2) R 6s 7m 6M.
Lorient Marina ent buoy No 8 47°44'·61N 03°20'·90W   Fl R 2·5s; PHM.

LORIENT TO BELLE ÎLE

- RIVIÈRE D'ÉTEL

Roheu bn 47°38'·57N 03°14'·68W; SCM.
W side ent 47°38'·75N 03°12'·82W Oc (2) WRG 6s 13m W9M, R6M, G6M; R tr; vis W022°-064°, R064°-123°, W123°-330°, G330°-022°; 2 FR on radio mast 2·3M NW; FR and F on radio masts 2·4M NW.
Les Pierres Noires bn 47°35'·55N 03°13'·25W; IDM.

- PORT MARIA

Le Pouilloux buoy 47°27'·97N 03°08'·93W; SCM.
Ldg lts 006·5°: Front, 47°28'·65N 03°07'·15W Dir QG 5m 13M; W tr, B band; rear, 230m from front, Dir QG 13m 13M; W tr, B band; both intens 005°-008°.
Main light 47°28'·85N 03°07'·42W Q WRG 28m W14M, R10M, G10M; W tr; vis W246°-252°, W291°-297°, G297°-340°, W340°-017°, R017°-051°, W051°-081°, G081°-098°, W098°-143°.
Baz an tréac'h buoy 47°27'·98N 03°07'·10W; IDM.
S bkwtr hd 47°28'·60N 03°07'·23W Oc (2) R 6s 9m 7M; W tr, R top.

- PLATEAU DES BIRVIDEAUX

Tower 47°29'·20N 03°17'·45W Fl (2) 6s 24m 10M; B tr, R bands; IDM.

- BELLE ÎLE/SAUZON/LE PALAIS

Pte des Poulains 47°23'·37N 03°15'·08W Fl 5s 34m **23M**; W □ tr and dwelling; vis 023°-291°.
Les Poulains buoy 47°23'·42N 03°16'·65W; WCM.
Goulphar 47°18'·67N 03°13'·67W Fl (2) 10s 87m **26M**; Gy tr.
La Truie bn 47°17'·10N 03°11'·62W; IDM.
N Poulains buoy 47°23'·70N 03°14'·86W; NCM.
Bas Gareau bn 47°22'·85N 03°12'·97W; SHM.
Sauzon Jetée NW Hd 47°22'·58N 03°13'·00W Fl G 4s 8m 8M.
Jetée SE Hd Fl R 4s 8m 8M; W tr, R top.
Le Palais jetée Nord 47°20'·90N 03°09'·00W Fl (2+1) G 12s 11m 7M; W tr; obsc 298°-170°.
La Truie du Bugul bn 47°19'·60N 03°06'·50W; NCM.
Pointe de Kerdonis 47°18'·65N 03°03'·50W Fl (3) R 15s 35m **15M**; W □ tr and dwelling; obsc by Pointes d'Arzic and de Taillefer 025°-129°.
Les Galères buoy 47°18'·80N 03°02'·75W; ECM.

BAIE DE QUIBERON AND GOLFE DU MORBIHAN

- CHAUSSÉE AND PASSAGE DE LA TEIGNOUSE

Le Four bn 47°27'·80N 03°06'·48W; SCM.
Bas Cariou buoy 47°27'·00N 03°06'·33W; WCM; *Bell*.
Bas du Chenal buoy 47°26'·70N 03°05'·70W; SCM.
Goué Vaz N buoy 47°26'·27N 03°05'·35W; NCM.
Goué Vaz S buoy 47°25'·84N 03°04'·80W Q (6) + L Fl 15s; SCM; *Whis*.
Basse du Milieu buoy 47°26'·00N 03°04'·10W Fl (2) G 6s 9m 2M; SHM HFP.
Goué Vaz E buoy 47°26'·30N 03°04'·20W Fl (3) R 12s; PHM.
La Teignouse 47°27'·50N 03°02'·67W Fl WR 4s 19m 15/11M; W ○ Tr, R top vis W033°-039°, R039°-033°.
NE Teignouse buoy 47°26'·62N 03°01'·80W Fl (3) G 12s; SHM.
Basse Nouvelle buoy 47°27'·02N 03°01'·85W Fl R 2·5s; PHM.
Quiberon S buoy 47°30'·10N 03°02'·30W Q (6) + L Fl 15s; SCM.

- PORT HALIGUEN

New bkwtr hd 47°29'·36N 03°05'·90W Oc (2) WR 6s 10m W11M, R8M; W tr, R top; vis W233°-240·5°, R240·5°-299°, W299°-306°, R306°-233°.

Quiberon N buoy 47°29'·68N 03°02'·52W; NCM.
Explosive wreck buoy 47°31'·25N 03°05'·36W; IDM.
Men er Roue bn 47°32'·33N 03°06'·00W; IDM.

- RIVIÈRE DE CRAC'H/LA TRINITÉ-SUR-MER
Ldg lts 347°: Front, 47°34'·14N 03°00'·29W Q WRG 11m
W10M, R7M, G7M; W tr, G top; vis G321°-345°, W345°-
013·5°, R013·5°-080°; **rear**, 560m from front, Dir Q 21m **15M**;
W ○ tr, G top; synch with front, intens 337°-357°.
Le Rat buoy 47°32'·89N 03°01'·69W; IDM.
Souris buoy 47°32'·03N 03°01'·14W; IDM.
Petit Trého buoy 47°33'·55N 03°00'·67W Fl (4) R 15s; PHM.
La Trinité-sur-Mer dir lt 347°: 47°35'·09N 03°00'·90W Dir Oc
WRG 4s 9m W13M, R11M, G11M; W tr; vis G345°-346°,
W346°-348°, R348°-349°.
S pier hd 47°35'·15N 03°01'·42W Oc (2) WR 6s 6m W10M,
R7M; W tr, R top; vis R090°-293·5°, W293·5°-300·5°, R300·5°-
329°.

Buissons de Méaban buoy 47°31'·71N 02°58'·42W; SCM.
Méaban buoy 47°30'·83N 02°56'·14W; SCM.

- GOLFE DU MORBIHAN
Le Grand Mouton 47°33'·77N 02°54'·78W QG 4m 3M;
G tripod.
Le Grégan 47°33'·96N 02°54'·96W Q (6) + L Fl 15s 3m 8M;
SCM.
Auray No 13 bn 47°39'·53N 02°58'·57W; SHM.
Creizic S buoy 47°34'·68N 02°52'·75W; SCM.
Creizic N buoy 47°35'·00N 02°52'·12W; NCM.
Les Rechauds bns 47°36'·25N 02°51'·20W; 2 x SHM.
Truie d'Arradon bn 47°36'·63N 02°50'·18W; PHM.
Roguédas 47°37'·18N 02°47'·19W Fl G 2·5s 4m 4M; G tr.

- PLATEAU DU GRAND MONT
Basse de S Gildas buoy 47°29'·83N 02°52'·30W; WCM.
Roc de l' Epieu buoy 47°29'·55N 02°52'·86W; IDM.
Chimère buoy 47°28'·90N 02°53'·90W; SCM.
Basse du Grand Mont buoy 47°29'·05N 02°51'·08W; SCM.

- CHAUSSÉE DU BÉNIGUET
Les Esclassiers W bn 47°25'·72N 03°03'·00W; WCM.
Le Grand Coin bn 47°24'·50N 03°00'·20W; ECM.

- ÎLE DE HOUAT
Le Rouleau bn 47°23'·74N 03°00'·20W; WCM.
Bonnenn Vraz bn 47°24'·30N 02°59'·80W; WCM.
Port de Saint-Gildas môle Nord 47°23'·63N 02°57'·26W Fl (2)
WG 6s 8m W9M, G6M; W tr, G top; vis W168°-198°, G198°-
210°, W210°-240°, G240°-168°.
Men Grouiz bn 47°22'·82N 02°54'·97W; ECM.
Er Rouzez buoy 47°22'·08N 02°54'·28W; ECM.

Pot de Feu buoy 47°21'·75N 02°59'·70W; IDM.

- ÎLE DE HÖEDIC
Er Palaire bn 47°20'·23N 02°54'·95W; WCM.
Les Sœurs bn 47°21'·20N 02°54'·70W; WCM.
La Chèvre bn 47°21'·16N 02°52'·50W; IDM.
Port de l'Argol bkwtr hd 47°20'·75N 02°52'·46W Fl WG 4s
10m W9M , G6M ; W tr, G top; vis W143°-163°, G163°-183°,
W183°-203°, G203°-143°.
Le Chariot buoy 47°18'·94N 02°52'·90W; SCM.
Les Grands Cardinaux 47°19'·35N 02°50'·08W Fl (4) 15s 28m
13M; R and W tr.
Cohfournik bn 47°19'·48N 02°49'·72W; ECM.
Er Guéranic bn 47°20'·58N 02°50'·43W; ECM.

CROUESTY TO LE CROISIC

- PORT NAVALO/CROUESTY EN ARZON
Pte de Port-Navalo 47°32'·93N 02°55'·02W Oc (3) WRG 12s
32m **W15M**, R11M , G11M ; W tr and dwelling; vis W155°-
220°, G317°-359°, W359°-015°, R015°-105°.
Ldg lts 058°: **Front**, 47°32'·60N 02°53'·85W Dir Q 10m **19M**;
R panel with W vert stripe; intens 056·5°-059·5°; **rear**, 315m
from front, Dir Q 27m **19M**; Gy tr; intens 056·5°-059·5°.
N jetty hd Oc (2) R 6s 9m 7M; R and W □ tr, R top.
S jetty hd 47°32'·51N 02°54'·02W Fl G 4s 9m 7M; G/ W ■ tr.

- PLATEAU DE SAINT JACQUES/SAINT-JACQUES-EN-
SARZEAU
Bas Rohaliguen S Jacques buoy 47°28'·25N 02°47'·45W;
SCM.
Saint-Jacques-en-Sarzeau lt tr 47°29'·22N 02°47'·45W   Oc
(2) R 6s 5m 6M; W 8-sided tr, R top.

- PLATEAU DE LA RECHERCHE
Recherche buoy 47°25'·65N 02°50'·27W Q (9) 15s; WCM.
Locmariaquer buoy 47°25'·88N 02°47'·30W; IDM.

- PÉNERF
Le Pignon 47°30'·10N 02°38'·85W Fl (3) WR 12s 6m W9M,
R6M; R ■ on tr; vis R028·5°-167°, W167°-175°, R175°-
349·5°, W349·5°-028·5°.

- VILAINE RIVER
Basse de Kervoyal 47°30'·43N 02°32'·55W Dir Q WR W8M,
R5M; vis W269°-271°, R271°-269°; SCM on B tr.
Basse Bertrand 47°31'·10N 02°30'·63W Iso WG 4s 6m
W9M, G6M; G tr; vis W040°-054°, G054°-227°, W227°-234°,
G234°-040°.
Penlan 47°31'·05N 02°30'·06W Oc (2) WRG 6s 26m **W15M**,
R11M, G11M; W tr, R bands; vis R292·5°-025°, G025°-052°,
W052°-060°, R060°-138°, G138°-180°.
Pointe du Scal, 47°29'·72N 02°26'·78W QG 12s 8m 4M;
W □ tr, G top.

- ÎLE DUMET
Fort 47°24'·80N 02°37'·10W Fl (2+1) WRG 15s 14m W7M,
R4M, G4M; W col, G top on fort; vis G090°-272°, W272°-
285°, R285°-325°, W325°-090°.
E Île Dumet buoy 47°25'·20N 02°35'·00W Q (3) 10s; ECM.

- MESQUER
Jetty hd 47°25'·32N 02°27'·95W Oc (3+1) WRG 12s 7m
W10M, R7M, G7M; W col and bldg; vis W067°-072°, R072°-
102°, W102°-118°, R118°-293°, W293°-325°, G325°-067°.

- PIRIAC-SUR-MER
Inner mole hd 47°23'·00N 02°32'·65W Oc (2) WRG 6s 8m
W10M, R7M, G7M; W col; vis R066°-148°, G148°-194°,
W194°-201°, R201°-221°; *Siren 120s*.
Les Bayonelles buoy 47°22'·58N 02°34'·90W Q (9) 15s;
WCM; *Whis*.
Oil pipeline 47°22'·15N 02°32'·70W Oc (2+1) WRG 12s 14m
W12M, R9M, G9M; W □, R stripe on R tr; vis G300°-036°,
W036°-068°, R068°-120°.

- LA TURBALLE/LE CROISIC
La Turballe ldg lts 006·5° both Dir F Vi 11/19m 3M, both intens
004°-009°.
Jetée de Garlahy 47°20'·77N 02°30'·83W Fl (4) WR 12s 13m
W10M, R7M; W pylon, R top; vis R060°-315°, W315°-060°.
Basse Hergo 47°18'·68N 02°31'·62W Fl G 2·5s 5m 3M; SHM.
Jetée de Tréhic hd 47°18'·55N 02°31'·34W Iso WG 4s 12m
W13M, G10M; Gy tr, G top; vis G042°-093°, W093°-137°,
G137°-345°; F Bu fog det lt.
Le Grand Mabon 47°18'·11N 02°30'·94W Fl R 2·5s 6m 2M;
R pedestal.

17

LE CROISIC TO PTE DE ST GILDAS

- ### PLATEAU DU FOUR/BANC DE GUÉRANDE
<u>Bonen du Four buoy</u> 47°18'·60N 02°39'·20W Q; NCM; *Whis.*
Le Four 47°17'·94N 02°37'·96W Fl 5s 23m **19M**; W tr, B stripes, G top.
<u>W Basse Capella buoy</u> 47°15'·67N 02°44'·66W Q (9) 15s; WCM; *Whis.*
<u>Goué-Vas-du-Four buoy</u> 47°14'·96N 02°38'·13W Q (6) + L Fl 15s; SCM.
<u>S Banc Guérande buoy</u> 47°08'·87N 02°42'·74W VQ (6)   + L Fl 10s; SCM; *Whis.*

- ### PLATEAU DE LA BANCHE
<u>W Banche buoy</u> 47°11'·65N 02°32'·34W VQ (9) 10s; WCM; *Whis.*
<u>NW Banche buoy</u> 47°12'·90N 02°30'·95W Q 8m 4M; NCM HFP; *Bell.*
La Banche 47°10'·70N 02°28'·00W Fl (2+1) WR 15s 22m **W17M**, R11M; B tr, W bands; vis R266°-280°, W280°-266°.
<u>SE Banche buoy</u> 47°10'·47N 02°26'·02W; ECM.

- ### BAIE du POULIGUEN APPROACHES (Baie de la Baule)
<u>Penchateau buoy</u> 47°15'·36N 02°24'·30W Fl R 2·5s; PHM.
<u>Les Guérandaises buoy</u> 47°15'·06N 02°24'·23W Fl G 4s; SHM.
<u>Les Evens buoy</u> 47°14'·47N 02°22'·46W; PHM.
<u>Les Troves buoy</u> 47°14'·25N 02°22'·30W; SHM.
<u>NNW Pierre Percée</u> 47°13'·67N 02°20'·54W; NCM.
La Vieille bn 47°14'·09N 02°19'·43W; SCM.
Sud de la Vieille buoy 47°13'·81N 02°19'·41W; IDM.
Le Caillou buoy 47°13'·71N 02°19'·11W; NCM.
Le Petit Charpentier bn 47°13'·40N 02°18'·87W; SCM.

- ### LE POULIGUEN.
Les Petits Impairs 47°16'·08N 02°24'·53W Fl (2) G 6s 6m 2M; G ▲, on tr.
S Jetty 47°16'·48N 02°25'·30W QR 13m 9M; W col; vis 171°-081°.

- ### PORT DE PORNICHET
La Baule <u>S bkwtr hd</u> 47°15'·55N 02°21'·07W Iso WG 4S 11m W10M, G7M; W tr, G top; vis G084°-081°, W081°-084°.
South ent QG 3m 1M.
North ent QR 4m 1M.

Le Grand Charpentier 47°12'·90N 02°19'·05W Q WRG 22m W14M, R10M, G10M, Gy tr, G lantern; vis G020°-049°, W049°-111°, R111°-310°, W310°-020°; Helicopter platform; Sig stn 1·5M NE.

- ### LOIRE APPROACHES
<u>Loire Approach buoy SN1</u> 47°00'·15N 02°39'·75W L Fl 10s 8m 5M; SWM HFP; *Whis;* Racon (Z).
<u>Loire Approach buoy SN2</u> 47°02'·15N 02°33'·45W Iso 4s 8m 5M; SWM HFP; Ra refl.
<u>Thérésia buoy</u> 47°04'·92N 02°27'·20W Fl R 2·5s; PHM.
<u>Les Chevaux buoy</u> 47°03'·58N 02°26'·29W Fl G 2·5s; SHM.
<u>La Couronnée buoy</u> 47°07'·67N 02°20'·00W QG 8m 6M; SHM HFP; Racon.
<u>Lancastria buoy</u> 47°08'·92N 02°20'·39W VQR 8m 2M; PHM HFP; Ra Refl.

- ### PLATEAU DE LA LAMBARDE
<u>SE Lambarde buoy</u> 47°10'·10N 02°20·72W Q (6) + L Fl 15s; SCM; *Bell.*
NW Lambard buoy 47°10'·88N 02°22'·78W; WCM.

- ### PASSE DES CHARPENTIERS
Portcé Ldg lts 025·5°: **Front**, 47°14'·62N 02°15'·36W Dir Q 6m **22M** ; W col; intens 024·7°-026·2°; **rear**, 0·75M from front, Q 36m **27M**; W tr; intens 024·7°-026·2° (H24).
<u>No 1 buoy</u> 47°10'·02N 02°18'·35W VQ G; SHM.
<u>No 7 buoy</u> 47°13'·37N 02°16'·02W VQ G; SHM.
Pointe d'Aiguillon 47°14'·60N 02°15'·70W Oc (4) WR 12s 27m **W15M**, R11M; W tr; vis W233°-293°, W297°-300°, R300°-327°, W327°-023°, W027°-089°.

- ### VILLE-ES-MARTIN
Jetty hd 47°15'·40N 02°13'·58W Fl (2) 6s 10m 12M; W tr, R top.
Les Morées 47°15'·05N 02°12'·95W Fl (3) WR 12s 11m W9M, R6M; G tr; vis W058°-224°, R300°-058°.

- ### SAINT-NAZAIRE
W jetty Oc (4) R 12s 11m 10M; W tr, R top.
<u>East jetty</u> 47°16'·05N 02°12'·06W Oc (4) G 12s 11m 11M; W tr, G top.
Old Môle hd 47°16'·33N 02°11'·74W Oc (2+1) 12s 18m 11M; W tr, R top; vis 153·5°-063·5°; weather signals.
<u>Basse Nazaire S buoy</u> 47°16'·27N 02°11'·57W Q (6) + L Fl 15s; SCM.

- ### POINTE DE MINDIN
W môle 47°16'·27N 02°10'·04W Fl G 2·5s 6m 3M.

- ### LE POINTEAU/PORT DE COMBERGE/PORT DE LA GRAVETTE
<u>Le Pointeau Digue S hd</u> 47°14'·08N 02°10'·89W Fl WG 4s 4m W10M, G6M; G & W ○ hut; vis G050°-074°, W074°-149°, G149°-345°, W345°-050°.
<u>Port de Comberge S jetty</u> 47°10'·60N 02°09'·95W Oc WG 4s 7m W9M, G5M; W tr, G top; vis W123°-140°, G140°-123°.
<u>Port de la Gravette jetty hd</u> 47°09'·80N 02°12'·60W Fl (3) WG 12s 7m W8M, G5M; W structure, G top; vis G224°-124°, W124°-224°.

- ### SAINT GILDAS (Anse de Boucau)
Pte de Saint Gildas 47°08'·10N 02°14'·67W Q WRG 23m W11M, R6M, G6M; framework tr on W house; vis R264°-308°, G308°-078°, W078°-088°, R088°-174°, W174°-180°, G180°-264°; RC.

RIVER LOIRE TO NANTES

<u>Bridge (channel centre)</u> 47°17·16N 02°10'·16W Iso 4s 55m.

- ### DONGES
SW dolphin 47°18'·12N 02°04'·90W Fl G 4s 12m 5M; Gy col.
NE dolphin (close ENE) Iso G 4s 12m 4M; G col.
Jetty hd 47°18'·35N 02°04'·11W Fl (2) R 6s 9m 9M.

- ### PAIMBŒUF
Môle Hd 47°17'·50N 02°01'·88W Oc (3) WG 12s 9m W10M, G7M; W ○ tr, G top; vis G shore-123°, W123°-shore.
Île du Petit Carnet 47°17'·29N 02°00'·29W Fl G 2·5s 8m 3M; W framework tr, G top.
From Paimbœuf to Nantes lts on S side are G, and N Red.

- ### PORT DE TRENTE MOULT/NANTES
<u>Trente Moult bn off</u> 47°11'·83N 01°34'·63W; SPM.
Quai du Président Wilson Hd 47°12'·02N 01°34'·37W Fl R 2·5s.

8.17.5 PASSAGE INFORMATION

SOUTH BRITTANY (charts 2643, 2646)

The *North Biscay Pilot* (Imray/RCC) or the Admiralty *Bay of Biscay Pilot* are recommended. The *French Pilot* (Vol 3) (Nautical/Robson), although out of print, contains many unique almost timeless sketches and transits. French charts (SHOM) are often larger scale than Admiralty charts, and hence more suitable for inshore waters. For French Glossary, see 8.15.9. The following Breton words have navigational significance: *Aber*: estuary. *Aven*: river, stream. *Bann*: hill. *Bian*: small. *Bras*: great. *Du*: black. *Enez, Inis*: island. *Garo*: rough, hard. *Glas*: green. *Goban*: shoal. *Gwenn*: white. *Karreg*: rock. *Ker*: house. *Men, mein*: rock, stone. *Morlenn*: creek. *Penn*: strait. *Porz*: harbour. *Raz*: tide race. *Ruz*: red. *Trez*: sand.

Mist and haze are quite common in the summer, fog less so. Winds are predominantly from SW to NW, often light and variable in summer, but in early and late season N or NE winds are common. Summer gales are infrequent, and are usually related to passing fronts. In summer the sea is often calm or slight, but swell, usually from W or NW, can severely affect exposed anchorages. When crossing B of Biscay, allow for a likely set to the E, particularly after strong W winds.

A particular feature of this coast during the summer is the sea and land breeze cycle, known locally as the *vent solaire*. After a quiet forenoon, a W'ly sea breeze sets in about midday, blowing onshore. It slowly veers to the NW, almost parallel to the coast, reaching Force 4 by late afternoon; it then veers further to the N, expiring at dusk. Around midnight a land breeze may pipe up from the NE and freshen sufficiently to kick up rough seas – with consequent disruption to moorings and anchs open to the NE. By morning the wind has abated.

Tidal streams are weak offshore, but can be strong in estuaries, channels and around headlands, especially nearer the English Chan. The tidal stream chartlets at 8.17.3 are based on NP 265 (Admiralty Tidal Stream Atlas for France, W Coast) which uses data from actual observations out to 15-25M offshore. The equivalent French Atlas gives more data, but based on computer predictions.

Inland waterways (8.15.19) can be entered from Lorient (8.17.14), Vilaine R (8.17.22) and the R. Loire (8.17.28).

RAZ DE SEIN TO BENODET (chart 2351)

Chaussée de Sein (chart 798) is a chain of islands, rks and shoals extending 15M W from the Pte du Raz. A WCM lt buoy marks the seaward end. For directions on Île de Sein (8.17.8) and Raz de Sein see *North Biscay Pilot* (RCC/Imray).

Raz de Sein (chart 798) is the chan between Le Chat bn tr (at E end of Chaussée de Sein) and the dangers extending 8ca off Pte du Raz, the extremity of which is marked by La Vieille lt ho and La Plate lt tr. The Plateau de Tévennec is 2M N of Raz de Sein; it consists of islets, rks and shoals which extend 5ca in all directions from the lt ho thereon. Other dangers on the N side of the Raz are rks and shoals extending nearly 1M W and WSW from Pte du Van, and Basse Jaune (dries) 1M to N. On the S side the main dangers, all 1·5M off La Vieille, are: to the SW, Kornog Bras, a rk with depth of 3m; to the S, Masklou Greiz, rky shoals on which sea can break heavily; and to the SE, Roche Moulleg.

In the middle of Raz de Sein the NE-going (flood) stream begins at HW Brest + 0550, sp rate 6·5kn; the SW-going (ebb) stream begins at HW Brest − 0030, sp rate 5·5kn. There are eddies near La Vieille on both streams. In good weather, near np, and with wind and tide together, the Raz presents no difficulty, but in moderately strong winds it should be taken at slack water, which lasts for about ½ hour at end of flood stream. In strong winds the chan must not be used with wind against tide, when there are overfalls with a steep breaking sea.

The B des Trépassés (1·5M ENE of La Vieille) is possible anch to await the S-going tide. Port Bestrée or Anse du Loc'h (1M and 4M E of Pte du Raz) may be suitable anchs if N-bound.

Audierne (8.17.8) lies between Raz de Sein and Pte de Penmarc'h (lt, fog sig, RC) off which dangers extend 1M to NW, W and S, and 3M to SE, and breaking seas occur in strong winds. The fishing hbrs of St Guénolé, Le Guilvinec (8.17.8) and Lesconil provide excellent shelter, but have difficult ents. Loctudy (8.17.9) is well sheltered from W/SW.

BENODET TO LORIENT (chart 2352)

Îles de Glénan (chart 3640, SHOM 6648, 8.17.12), lie to seaward of Loctudy and Concarneau. With offlying dangers they stretch 5M from W to E and 4M from N to S. The islands are interesting to explore, but anchs are rather exposed. Between Îles de Glénan and Bénodet lie Les Pourceaux, reefs which dry, and Île aux Moutons which has dangers extending SW and NW.

Along the coast the larger ports are Bénodet (8.17.10), Port-la-Forêt (8.17.11) and Concarneau (8.17.12). Anse de Bénodet has rky shoals on both sides but is clear in the middle. The coast from Pte de Mousterlin to Beg Meil is fringed by rks, many of which dry, extending 1M offshore. Chaussée de Beg Meil extends 8½ca SE, where Linuen rk (dries) is marked by bn. From Concarneau to Pte de Trévignon rks extend nearly 1·5M offshore in places.

Between Pte de Trévignon and Lorient are rky cliffs and several interesting lesser hbrs and anchs, delightful in fair weather; but most dry and are dangerous to approach in strong onshore winds. These include the Aven and Belon rivers, Brigneau, Merrien (mostly dries), Doëlan (but most of hbr dries) and Le Pouldu (Rivière de Quimperlé). All are described in 8.17.12 and the *North Biscay Pilot*.

Hazards SE and E of Pte de Trévignon include: Men Du, a rk 0·3m high, marked by IDM bn, about 1·25M SE of the same pt. Corn Vas, depth 1·8m, and Men ar Tréas, a rk which dries, are close S, both buoyed. Île Verte lies 6ca S of Ile de Raguénès, with foul ground another 2ca to S. The approaches to Aven and Bélon Rivers are clear, except for Le Cochon and Les Verrés (IDM bn) to the SE. Between Le Pouldu and Lorient, Grand Cochon (SCM buoy) and Petit Cochon lie about 1M offshore.

LORIENT TO QUIBERON (charts 2352, 2353)

The great seaport of Lorient (8.17.14) has sheltered apprs and 4 marinas. Île de Groix lies 4M SW. Its main offlying dangers are to the E and SE: shoals off Pte de la Croix; Les Chats which extend 1M SE from Pte des Chats; and shoals extending 7½ca S of Loc Maria. Port Tudy (8.17.13), on N coast, is the main hbr, and is easy of access and well sheltered except from NE.

7M SE of Lorient, River Étel (8.17.15) is an attractive hbr with a difficult ent which must only be approached in good weather and on the last of the flood. Further S do not appr the isthmus of the Quiberon peninsula closely due to rky shoals. 6M W of Quiberon lies Plateau des Birvideaux (lt), a rky bank (depth 4·6m) on which the sea breaks in bad weather.

Belle Île has no dangers more than 2½ca offshore, apart from buoyed rks which extend 7½ca W of Pte des Poulains, and La Truie rk marked by IDM bn tr 5ca off the S coast. The S coast is much indented and exposed to swell from W. In good settled weather (only) and in absence of swell there is an attractive anch in Port du Vieux Château (Ster Wenn), 1M S of Pte des Poulains; see *North Biscay Pilot*. On the NE coast lie Le Palais (8.17.16) and Sauzon, which partly dries but has good anch off and is sheltered from S and W. Off Le Palais the ESE-going (flood) stream begins at HW Brest − 0610, and the WNW-going at HW Brest + 0125, sp rates 1·5kn.

17

BAIE DE QUIBERON (chart 2353)

B de Quiberon is an important and attractive yachting area, with centres at Port Haliguen (8.17.17), La Trinité (8.17.18), Crouesty (8.17.19) and the Morbihan (8.17.20). The S side of the bay is enclosed by a long chain of islands, islets, rks and shoals from Presqu'île de Quiberon to Les Grands Cardinaux 13M SE. This chain includes the attractive islands of Houat (8.17.19) and Hoëdic, well worth visiting, preferably mid-week. The Bay is open to the E and SE.

From W or S, enter the B via Passage de la Teignouse in W sector (033°-039°) of La Teignouse lt ho; thence 068° between Basse Nouvelle lt buoy and NE Teignouse lt buoy. In this chan the NE-going (flood) stream begins at HW Brest – 0610, and the SW-going at HW Brest – 0005, sp rates 3·75 kn; in strong winds it is best to pass at slack water. Good alternative chans are Passage du Béniguet, NW of Houat, and Passage des Soeurs, NW of Hoëdic.

The Golfe du Morbihan, on the N side of B de Quiberon, is an inland sea containing innumerable islands and anchs. Port Navalo anch is on the E side of the ent with Port du Crouesty close SE. Inside, River Auray flows in from the NW and the city of Vannes (8.17.21) is on the N side. Sp stream rates in the vicinity of Grand Mouton achieve 8kn and elsewhere in the ent can exceed 4kn. Flood commences HW Brest – 0400 and turns at HW Brest + 0200.

CROUESTY TO LE CROISIC (chart 2353)

Eastwards from the Morbihan, dangers extend 1M seaward of Pte de St Jacques, and 3M offshore lies Plateau de la Recherche with depths of 1·8m. SE of Penerf (8.17.22), which provides good anch, Plateau des Mats is an extensive rky bank, drying in places, up to 1·75M offshore.

Approaching the R. Vilaine (8.17.22) beware La Grande Accroche, a large shoal with least depth 1m, astride the ent. The main lit chan keeps NW of La Grande Accroche, to the bar on N side thereof. Here the flood begins at HW Brest – 0515, and the ebb at HW Brest + 0035, sp rates 2·5kn. In SW winds against tide the sea breaks heavily; when the Passe de la Varlingue, 5ca W of Pte du Halguen, is better, but beware La Varlingue (dries). At Arzal/Camoël yachts can lock into the non-tidal river for canal to Dinan/St Malo (see 8.15.18/19).

S of Pte du Halguen other dangers, close inshore, are the rky shoals, depth 0·6m, of Basse de Loscolo and Basse du Bile. Off Pte du Castelli, the Plateau de Piriac extends about 1·75M NW with depths of 2·3m and drying rks closer inshore. The small hbr of Piriac (8.17.23) lies on the N side of Pointe du Castelli and Les Bayonelles (dry) extend 5ca W. A chan runs between Plateau de Piriac and Île Dumet (lt), which is fringed by drying rks and shoals particularly on N and E sides.

In the Rade du Croisic are the hbrs of La Turballe (8.17.24) and Le Croisic (8.17.25). Off Pte du Croisic dangers extend 1M to N and W. Plateau du Four, a dangerous drying bank of rks, lies about 4M W and WSW of Pte du Croisic, marked by buoys and lt ho near N end. Between Pte du Croisic and Pte de Penchâteau, Basse Lovre is a rky shoal with depths of 1m, 5ca offshore.

LE CROISIC TO R. LOIRE (chart 2353, 3216)

From Chenal du Nord, B du Pouliguen (8.17.26) is entered between Pte de Penchâteau and Pte du Bec, 3M to E. In SE corner of bay is the yacht hbr of Pornichet (8.17.27). The B is partly sheltered from S by rks and shoals extending SE from Pte de Penchâteau to Le Grand Charpentier, but a heavy sea develops in strong S-SW winds. The W chan through these rks runs between Penchâteau and Les Guérandaises lateral buoys; other chans lie further E.

The River Loire estuary (chart 3216), which carries much commercial tfc, is entered via either the Chenal du Nord or the Chenal du Sud. The former runs ESE between the mainland and two shoals, Plateau de la Banche and Plateau de la Lambarde; these lie about 4M S of B du Pouliguen. Chenal du Sud, the main DW chan, leads NE between Plateau de la Lambarde and Pte de St Gildas. Here the in-going stream begins at HW Brest – 0500, and the out-going at HW Brest + 0050, sp rates about 2·75kn.

In the near apprs to St Nazaire (8.17.28 and charts 2985, 2989) beware Le Vert, Les Jardinets and La Truie (all dry) which lie close E of the chan. The river is navigable as far as Nantes. On the E side of the estuary, between the Loire bridge and Pte de St Gildas, are the small drying hbrs of Comberge, La Gravette and St Gildas (8.17.28).

8.17.6   DISTANCE TABLE

Approximate distances in nautical miles are by the most direct route, whilst avoiding dangers and allowing for Traffic Separation Schemes. Places in *italics* are in adjoining areas; places in **bold** are in 8.0.8, Cross-Channel Distances.

1. *Le Conquet*	**1**																			
2. *Camaret*	13	**2**																		
3. *Morgat*	22	16	**3**																	
4. *Douarnenez*	29	21	11	**4**																
5. Audierne	30	28	27	30	**5**															
6. Loctudy	55	55	53	55	30	**6**														
7. Bénodet	58	58	57	60	33	4	**7**													
8. Port-la-Forêt	65	64	63	66	36	12	12	**8**												
9. Concarneau	63	62	61	64	37	12	11	4	**9**											
8. Lorient	84	86	85	88	61	38	36	33	32	**10**										
11. Le Palais (Belle Ile)	95	99	98	101	74	54	52	48	47	26	**11**									
12. Port Haliguen	100	105	104	107	80	59	57	55	53	32	11	**12**								
13. La Trinité	108	110	109	112	85	64	62	60	58	37	16	8	**13**							
14. Crouesty	108	110	109	112	85	64	62	60	58	37	16	9	8	**14**						
15. Vannes	120	121	120	123	96	75	73	71	69	48	27	20	19	12	**15**					
16. Arzal/Camöel	131	130	129	132	105	84	82	80	78	57	36	31	31	28	37	**16**				
17. Le Croisic	124	125	124	127	100	79	77	75	73	48	27	26	26	22	33	18	**17**			
18. La Baule/Pornichet	134	131	130	133	106	85	82	80	78	55	36	36	36	30	40	30	13	**18**		
19. St Nazaire	145	138	137	140	113	95	91	90	87	66	41	42	45	40	50	39	24	12	**19**	
20. Pornic	146	149	148	151	124	105	101	100	97	72	45	47	49	43	55	42	24	18	16	**20**

8.17.7   Special notes for France: See 8.15.8

AUDIERNE   8-17-8

Finistere 48°00'·61N 04°32'·33W   Rtg 3-3-1

CHARTS
AC 3640, 2351; SHOM 7147, 7148; Imray C36, C37; ECM 541

TIDES
+0440 Dover; ML 3·1; Duration 0605; Zone 0100

Standard Port BREST (←——)

Times				Height (metres)			
High Water		Low Water		MHWS	MHWN	MLWN	MLWS
0000	0600	0000	0600	6·9	5·4	2·6	1·0
1200	1800	1200	1800				
Differences AUDIERNE							
−0035	−0030	−0035	−0030	−1·7	−1·3	−0·6	−0·2
ILE DE SEIN							
−0005	−0005	−0010	−0005	−0·7	−0·6	−0·2	−0·1
LE GUILVINEC							
−0010	−0025	−0025	−0015	−1·8	−1·4	−0·6	−0·1
LESCONIL							
−0008	−0028	−0028	−0018	−1·9	−1·4	−0·6	−0·1

SHELTER
Good in marina, 3 pontoons 2ca SW of the bridge. Access HW−2 to +1 for 2m draft, except in strong SE-SW winds when seas break at the ent. Chan dredged about 1m, but drying banks close to stbd. Quays reserved for FVs. At **Ste Evette** a long bkwtr, Oc (2) R 6s, gives good shelter, except in SE-SW winds when swell enters. Many unmarked W 🛟s to the N leave no room to ⚓ in lee of bkwtr. Keep clear of slip area as vedettes enter with much verve.

NAVIGATION
WPT 47°59'·54N 04°32'·91W, 186°/006° from/to Kergadec lt, 1·5M. Appr between La Gamelle, rks drying 0·9m in the middle of the bay, and Le Sillon de Galets rks to the W; see clearing brg 016°, W pyramid and bkwtr lt. Or from the SE, leave La Gamelle to port. Appr is difficult in strong SE-SW winds. Inside the ent, dredged chan initially favours the W bank with ldg marks, vert R/W chevrons, in line 359°. At root of bkwtr chan turns NE, with 2nd set of R/W chevrons on fish shed in transit 045°; cross river to abeam fish market on stbd side, then alter 90° port to marina. Keep close to FV quays and yacht pontoons; banks dry to stbd.

LIGHTS AND MARKS
By day from the WPT, Kergadec, W 8-sided lt tr, R top, on with old lt ho (hard to see) leads 006°. At night stay in the W sector (005°-007°) of Kergadec, Dir Q WRG 43m 12/9M. From SE, ldg marks/lts at 331°: Front Fl (3) WG 12s 11m 14/9M, W ○ tr on hbr bkwtr; rear FR 44m 9M (Kergadec).

RADIO TELEPHONE
None. Adjacent sig stn at Pte du Raz Ch 16.

TELEPHONE
Hr Mr 02.98.70.07.91; Aff Mar 02.98.70.03.33; CROSS 02.98.89.31.31; SNSM 02.98.70.03.31; ⊞ 02.98.94.68.67; Auto 08.36.68.08.29; Police 02.98.70.04.38; Ⓗ 02.98.75.10.10; Brit Consul 01.40.63.16.02.

FACILITIES
Port de Plaisance (100 + 20 Ⓥ), ☎ 02.98.75.04.93, FF101, AC, FW, CH, ME, El, Ⓔ, Sh, Bar, R, V; **Poulgoazec** (E bank) C (15 ton), Slip. **Town** P & D (cans), V, Gaz, R, Bar, ✉, Ⓑ, bus to Quimper ⇌, ✈. Ferry: Roscoff. **Ste Evette**, Hr Mr ☎ 02.98.70.00.28, access H24, M, ◙, Showers.

ADJACENT HARBOURS AND ANCHORAGES

ILE DE SEIN, Finistere, 48°02'·40N 04°50'·80W. AC 798, 2351; SHOM 5252, 7148. Tides, see above; ML 3·8m. Ile de Sein is the only inhabited Is in the Chaussée de Sein, a chain of islands, rks and shoals extending 15M W from the Pte du Raz. The outer end has a WCM lt buoy and 5M E is Ar-Men lt tr, Fl (3) 20s 29m, horn (3) 60s. The E end is separated from the mainland by the Raz de Sein; see 8.17.5 for passage details. Ile de Sein is worth visiting in fair weather, good vis and preferably near nps. Best appr is from the N, 187° via Chenal d'Ezaudi, with Men-Brial lt ho, Oc (2) WRG 6s, on with third house (W with B stripe) from left (close S of lt ho). Chan between drying rks is entered at Cornoc-An-Ar-Braden SHM By, Iso G 4s and tide sets across the chan, which is marked by bn trs. There are also chans from NE and E. ⚓ off or inside the mole, but open to N and E. Hbr partly dries. See *North Biscay Pilot* (RCC/Imray) for directions. Facilities: limited V, R, CH, Sh.

ST GUÉNOLÉ, Finistere, 47°48'·70N 04°22'·90W. AC 2351; SHOM 6645, 7146; ECM 543. Strictly a fishing port; yachts not welcomed. Access difficult in fresh W'lies, impossible in heavy weather. 3 sets of ldg marks/lts. Lts as 8.17.4. Pilot book & SHOM 6645 essential. Hr Mr ☎ 02.98.58.60.43.

LE GUILVINEC, Finistere, 47°47'·52N 04°17'·10W. AC 3640, 2351; SHOM 6646, 7146. HW + 0447 on Dover (UT); ML 3·0m. See 8.17.8. Good shelter and useful passage port; hbr (3m) accessible H24 for <2·5m draft, but total priority to FVs; no ent/exit 1600-1830. At NE end of hbr (amongst hosts of lesser buoys), secure to one large W 🛟; max stay 24hrs. Good ⚓ off ent in lee of reef but stay clear of fairway. Beware Lost Moan Rks SE of ent marked by RW bn tr, Fl (3) WRG 12s 8m 9/6M. Ent is easy if vis is adequate to see ldg lts/marks. Three ldg lts, all synch, in line 053°: front, Mole de Lechiagat Q 7m 8m, W pylon, vis 233°-066°; middle, Rocher Le Faoutés, 210m from front, QWG 12m 14/11M, R □ on W pylon, vis W006°-293°, G293°-006°; rear, 0·58M from front, Dir Q 26m 8M, R □ on W pylon with R stripe, vis 051·5°-054·5°. VHF Ch 12. Facilities: Hr Mr ☎ 02.98.58.05.67; Aff Mar ☎ 02.98-58-13-13; ⊞, C, FW, D, P, El, ME, Sh, CH, Ⓔ.

LESCONIL, Finistere, 47°47'·76N 04°12'·57W. AC 3640, 2351; SHOM 6646, 7146; ECM 543. Tides, see left column; ML 3m. Fishing port 3M SW of Loctudy; yachts tolerated at their own risk. Do not enter/leave 1630-1830LT due to FV inrush. Appr from Karek Greis ECM buoy, Q (3) 10s, on ldg line 325°, belfry just open W of Men ar Groas lt ho, Fl (3) WRG 12s 14m 10/7M; at night in W sector 313°-333°. Bkwtr lts are QG and Oc R 4s. Possible drying mooring inside S bkwtr; no 🛟s, no AB on quays. Hr Mr ☎ 02.98.82.22.97. Facilities of fishing port.

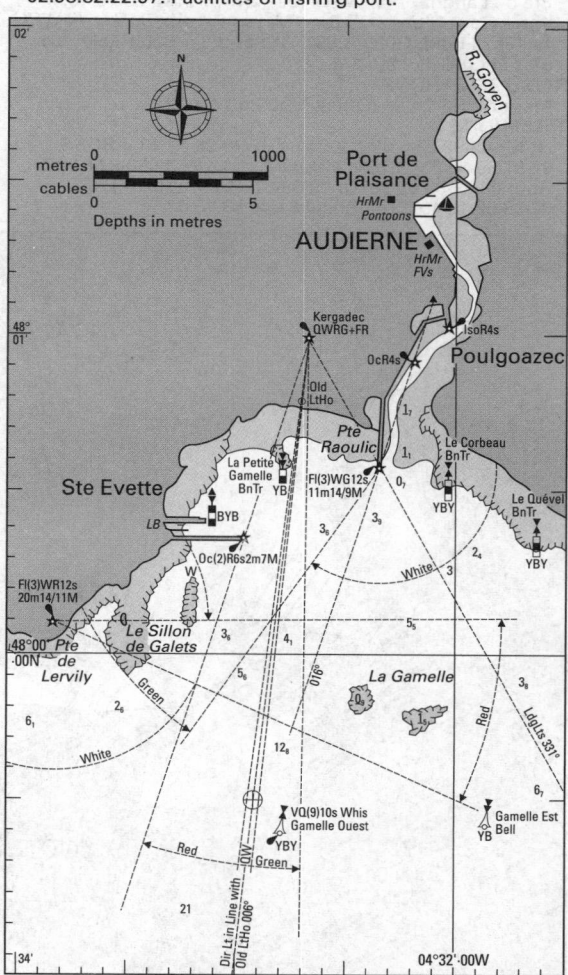

17

LOCTUDY   8-17-9

Finistere 47°50´·30N 04°10´·50W   Rtg 3-2-2

CHARTS
AC 3641, 2351/2; SHOM 6649, 6679, 7146; ECM 543;
Imray C37, 38

TIDES
+0505 Dover (UT); ML 3·0; Duration 0615; Zone –0100

Standard Port BREST (⟵)

Times				Height (metres)			
High Water		Low Water		MHWS	MHWN	MLWN	MLWS
0000	0600	0000	0600	6·9	5·4	2·6	1·0
1200	1800	1200	1800				
Differences LOCTUDY							
–0013	–0033	–0035	–0025	–1·9	–1·5	–0·7	–0·2

SHELTER
Excellent in marina and hbr, except in strong ESE winds.
The many ⚓s and moorings in the river leave little space
to ⚓. Keep clear of FVs, esp 17-1900LT daily when yachts
are discouraged from entering/leaving hbr.

NAVIGATION
WPT 47°50´·12N 04°08´·86W, 105°/285° from/to Les Perdrix
lt, 0·73M. From S and W, leave Bas Bilien ECM, VQ (3), to
port, thence to WPT. From E/NE, give Men Audierne SHM
bn a wide berth. Bar has least depth 0·9m, deeper to the
N. Sp ebb runs at 3½kn; enter under power only. Appr 285°
(to clear unmarked Karek Croisic rk) in W sector of Les Perdrix
lt; when 300m short, alter port onto 274° as marina and
Chateau Laubrière (conspic) come in transit. Beware rky
ledges close S of Les Perdrix and SHM bn, Fl (3) G 12s.
Pont l'Abbé (3M up-river) dries about 2m, but is accessible
to shoal draft boats on the flood; chan marked by perches.

LIGHTS AND MARKS
Pte de Langoz Fl (4) WRG 12s 12m 15/11M (see 8.15.4).
Karek-Saoz R bn tr QR 3m 1M. Les Perdrix B/W tr, Fl WRG
4s 15m 11/8M, G090°-285°, W285°-295°, R295°-090°. Le
Blas Fl (3) G 12s 5m 1M.

RADIO TELEPHONE
Marina VHF Ch 09 (Office hrs); Port Ch 12.

TELEPHONE
Hr Mr 02·98·87·51·36; Aff Mar 02·98·58·13·13; CROSS
02·97·55·35·35; SNSM 02·98·87·41·12; ⌗ 02·98·87·61·12;
Auto 08·36·68·08·29; Dr 02·98·87·41·80; Ⓗ (6km)
02·98·82·40·40; Brit Consul 01·40·63·16·02.

FACILITIES
Marina (592 + 65 visitors;) ☎ 02·98·87·51·36, FF125, FW,
AC, Slip, D & P, C (9 tons), CH, Sh, ME, El; ♿.
Town Bar, V, R, Dr, ⌷, Ⓑ.

BÉNODET   8-17-10

Finistere 47°51´·80N 04°06´·40W   Rtg 2-1-1

CHARTS
AC 3641, 2352; SHOM 6679, 6649, 7313, 7146; ECM 543;
Imray C37

TIDES
+0450 Dover; ML 3·1; Duration 0610; Zone –0100

Standard Port BREST (⟵)

Times				Height (metres)			
High Water		Low Water		MHWS	MHWN	MLWN	MLWS
0000	0600	0000	0600	6·9	5·4	2·6	1·0
1200	1800	1200	1800				
Differences BÉNODET							
0000	–0020	–0023	–0013	–1·7	–1·3	–0·5	–0·1
CORNIGUEL							
+0015	+0010	–0015	–0010	–2·0	–1·6	–1·0	–0·7

SHELTER
Marinas at Ste Marine (W bank, town of Combrit) and at Anse
de Penfoul (E bank, Bénodet), both accessible H24 at any tide.
Caution: In both marinas, best to arr/dep near slack water to
avoid the strong stream, esp 4kn ebb, through the pontoons
with risk of damage. Some ⚓s available. ⚓ in Anse du Trez in
offshore winds. Speed limit 3kn in hbr.
R Odet is navigable near HW to Quimper, but masted
vessels must ⚓ at Poulguinan bridge (5·8m clearance), 1M
beyond Corniguel and 0·5M below the city; pleasant ⚓s at
Anse de Combrit, Anse de Kérautret, Porz Keraign, Porz
Meilou, Anse de Toulven and SW of Lanroz. N of Lanroz
the river shoals progressively to 0·5m in places. SHOM
6679 is recommended.

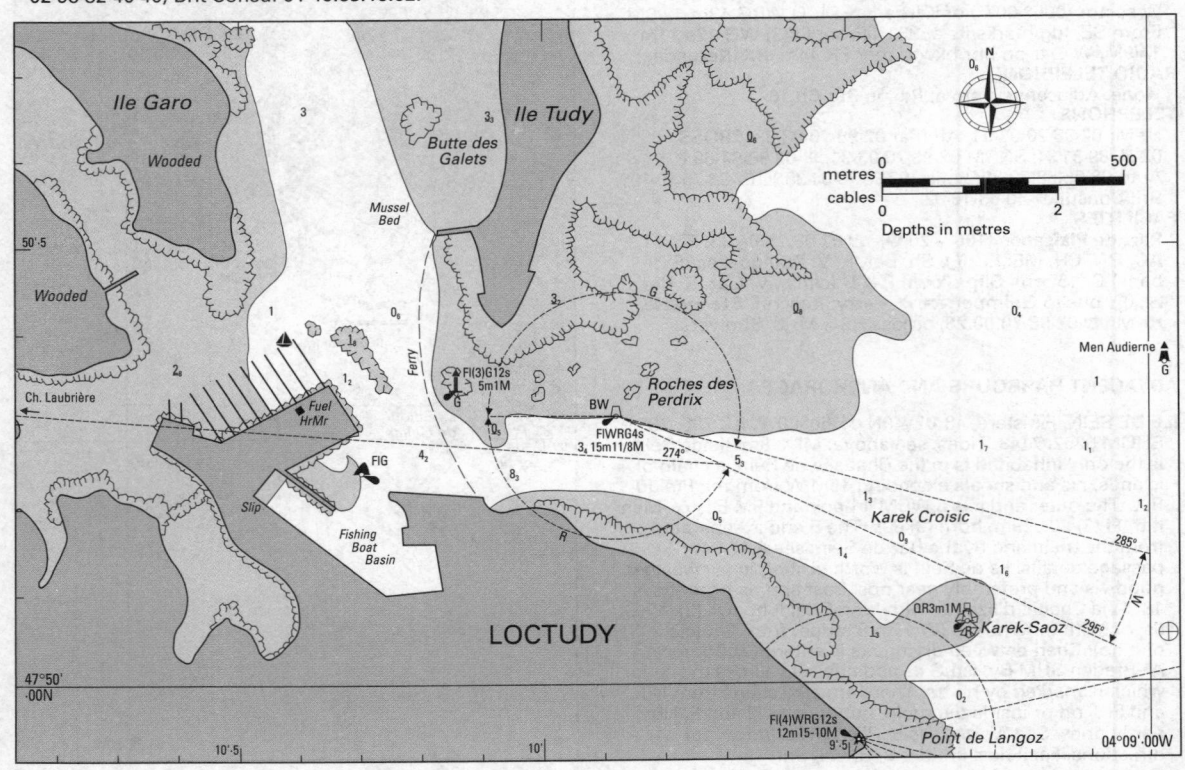

BÉNODET *continued*

NAVIGATION

WPT 47°51'·00N 04°06'·10W, 166°/346° from/to front ldg lt, 1·43M. The centre of the bay is clear for small craft, but beware Roches de Mousterlin at the SE end of the bay and various rks off Loctudy to the SW. There is a tanker chan past the Ile aux Moutons, 6M SSE of hbr.

LIGHTS AND MARKS

Ldg lts/daymarks 346°: Front, Oc (2+1) G 12s 11m 17M, intens 345°-347°, W ○ tr, G vert stripe, G top (hard to see until close); rear Oc (2+1) 12s 48m 11M, conspic W tr, G top, synch. Ile-aux-Moutons (6M SSE), Oc (2) WRG 6s 18m 15/11M + Dir Oc (2) 6s 17m 24M, intens 278°-283°.

RADIO TELEPHONE

Both marinas VHF Ch 09 (0800-2000LT in season).

TELEPHONE

Hr Mr 02·98·56·38·72; Aff Mar 02·98·57·03·82; CROSS 02·97·55·35·35; SNSM 02·98·57·02·00; ⌖ 02·98·55·04·19; Météo 02·98·94·03·43; Dr 02·98·57·22·21; Brit Consul 01·40·63·16·02.

FACILITIES

BÉNODET: **Anse de Penfoul Marina** (510+40 Ⓥ AB; also 175 buoys +15 ⚓) ☎ 02·98·57·05·78, 🖅 02.98.57.00.21, AC, FW, ⬚, R, CH, ME, V, P, D, M, El, Ⓔ, Sh, C, SM, Divers. **Quay** C (10 ton). **Town** All facilities, Gaz, ✉, Ⓑ, bus to Quimper ⇌, ✈.

COMBRIT: **Sainte Marine Marina** (350+70 Ⓥ), FF118 or FF76 for ⚓, ☎ 02·98·56·38·72, 🖅 02·98·51·95·17, AC, CH, FW. **Town** V, R, Bar, ⬚, Ⓔ. Pedestrian ferry to Bénodet.

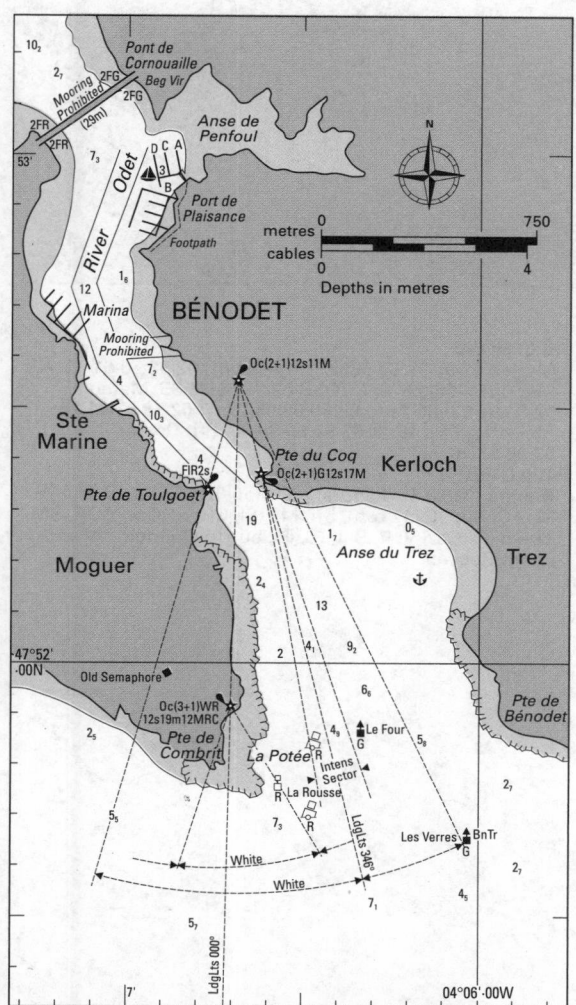

PORT-LA-FORÊT   8-17-11

Finistere 47°53'·55N 03°58'·17W   Rtg 2-1-2

CHARTS

AC 3641, 2352; SHOM 6650, 7146; ECM 543, 544; Imray C38

TIDES

+0450 Dover; ML 2·9; Duration 0615; Zone –0100

Use Differences CONCARNEAU 8.17.12

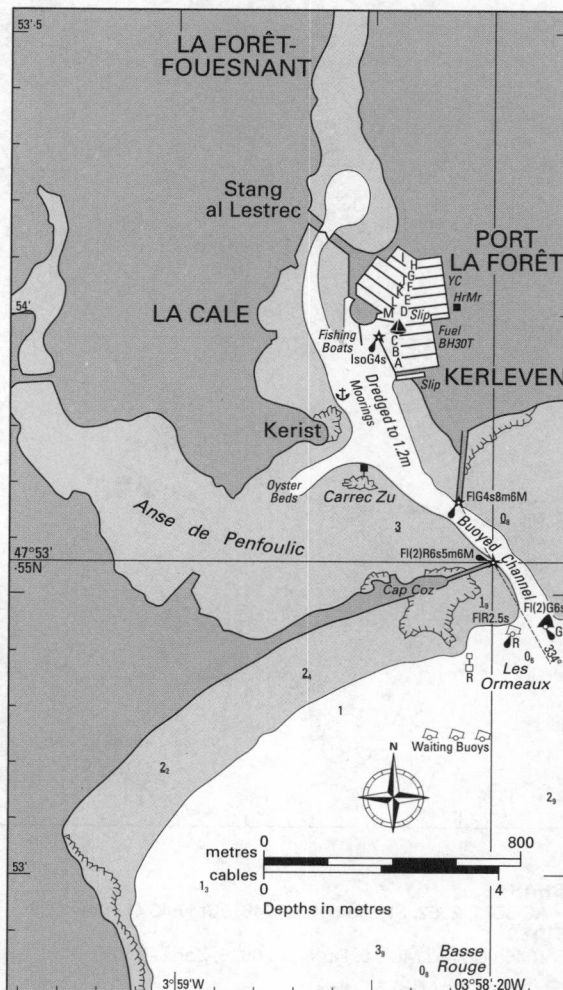

17

SHELTER

Very good in marina (2m); Ⓥ pontoon C-D. There is ⚓ inside Cap Coz and moorings to W of the inner chan, dredged 1·2m .

NAVIGATION

WPT 47°52'·77N 03°57'·62W, 154°/334° from/to Cap-Coz lt, 0·88M. Beware Basse Rouge 6·5ca S of Cap Coz, Le Scoré (unlit SCM bn) and buoyed oyster farms in apprs. At sp a shoal patch 0·9m just S of the ent denies access LW±1½; there are 3 W waiting buoys close WSW of the ent.

LIGHTS AND MARKS

Cap Coz, Fl (2) R 6s 5m 6M, and Kerleven bkwtr lt, Fl G 4s 8m 6M, lead 334° into chan marked with buoys and bns; the first pair of chan buoys are lit, Fl R 2·5s and Fl (2) G 6s.

RADIO TELEPHONE

VHF Ch 09.

TELEPHONE

Hr Mr 02·98·56·98·45; Aff Mar 02·98·56·01·98; Rescue CROSS-Etel 02·97·55·35·35; Auto 08.36.68.08.29; SNSM 02·98·56·98·25; ⌖ (Concarneau) 02·98·97·01·73; Police 02·98·56·00·11; Ⓗ (Concarneau) 02·98·50·30·30; Brit Consul 01·40·63·16·02.

FACILITIES

Marina (900+100 Ⓥ) ☎ 02·98·56·98·45, 🖅 02.98.56.81.31, FF120, AC, D, P, FW, ME, El, Sh, CH, Gaz, R, ⬚, SM, V, Bar, BH (16 ton), C (4 ton), Slip (multi hull).

Town Gaz, ✉, Ⓑ, ⇌, ✈ Quimper. Ferry: Roscoff.

CONCARNEAU   8-17-12
Finistere 47°52'·10N 03°54'·68W   Rtg 2-1-1

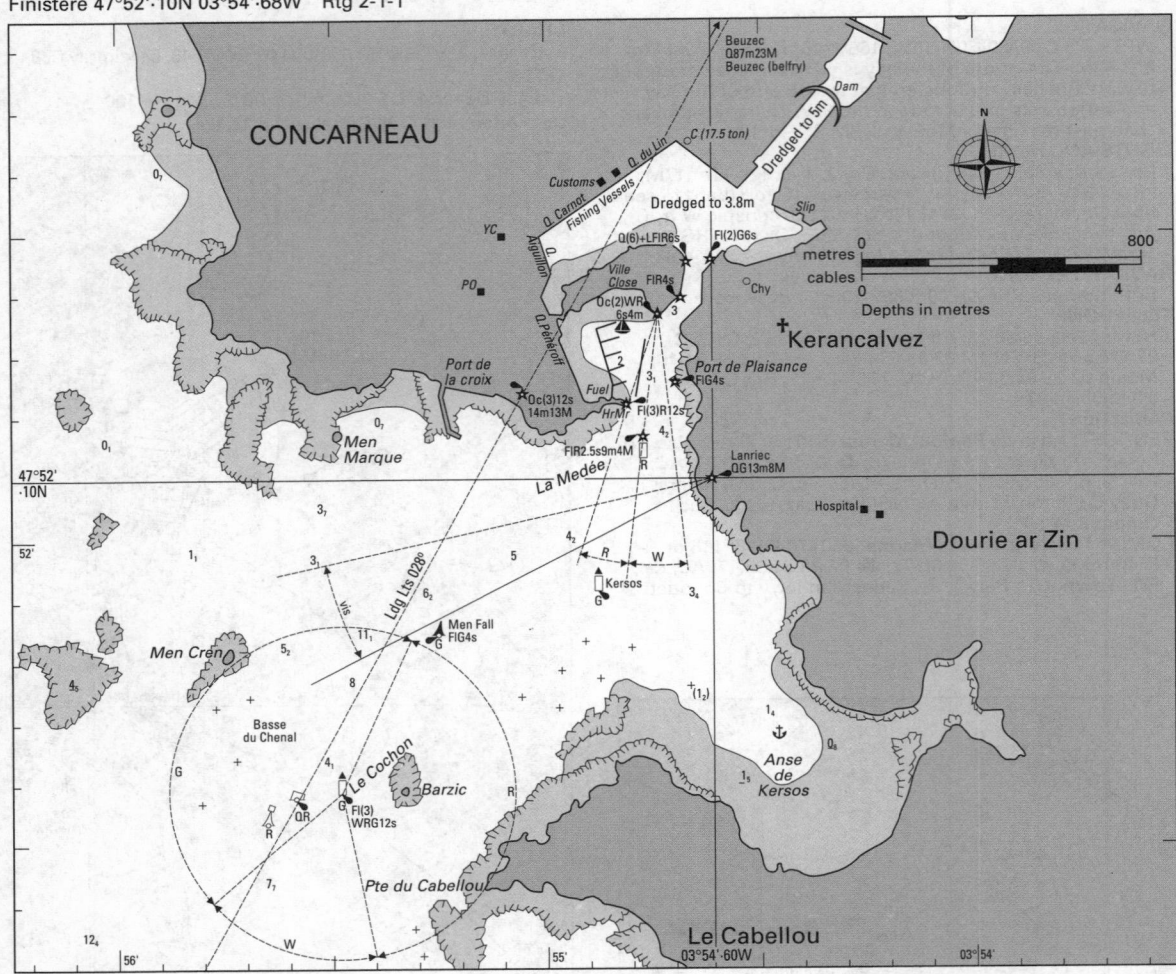

CHARTS
AC 3641, 2352; SHOM 6650, 7146; ECM 543/4; Imray C38
TIDES
+0455 Dover; ML 3·0; Duration 0615; Zone −0100

Standard Port BREST (←—)

Times				Height (metres)			
High Water		Low Water		MHWS	MHWN	MLWN	MLWS
0000	0600	0000	0600	6·9	5·4	2·6	1·0
1200	1800	1200	1800				
Differences CONCARNEAU							
−0010	−0030	−0030	−0020	−1·9	−1·5	−0·7	−0·2
ILE DE PENFRET (Iles de Glénan)							
−0005	−0030	−0028	−0018	−1·9	−1·5	−0·7	−0·2

SHELTER
Good, except in strong S'lies. The marina (2m) has an anti-wash barrier. The Arrière Port is solely for FVs; yacht pontoon on NE corner of La Ville Close is only for locals.
NAVIGATION
WPT 47°50'·00N 03°56'·80W, 208°/028° from/to front ldg lt 028°, 2·52M. Beware rks around Men Cren and Le Cochon.
LIGHTS AND MARKS
Ldg lts 028°: front Oc (3) 12s 14m 13M, RW tr which is hard to see against bldgs behind; rear, 1·35M from front, Q 87m 23M, spire on skyline. Steer between Le Cochon G bn tr, Fl WRG 12s, and Basse du Chenal PHM buoy, QR; the former is easier to see than the ldg marks. Past Men Fall SHM buoy Fl G 4s, steer 070° for Lanriec lt, QG 13m 8M, vis 063°-078°, G window on W gable, LANRIEC below.
RADIO TELEPHONE
Marina Ch 09 (0700-2100LT in season). FV hbr Ch 12 16 (H24).

TELEPHONE
Marina 02·98·97·57·96; Hr Mr (FV hbr) 02·98·50·61·00; Aff Mar 02·98·50·69·76; CROSS 02·97·55·35·35; Météo 02·98·94·03·43; Auto 08.36.68.08.29; ⌗ 02·98·97·01·73; Police 17; Fire 18; Ⓗ 02·98·50·30·30; Brit Consul 01·40·63·16·02.
FACILITIES
Marina (238 + 50 visitors; pontoon 'D'), FF130, P, D, FW, M, AC, Slip, C (17 ton), Sh, ME, El, CH, SHOM, ACA, SM.
Town Ⓔ, Gaz, V, R, Bar, ✉, Ⓑ, bus to Quimper ⇌ and ✈.
Ferry: Roscoff.

OTHER HARBOURS AND ANCHORAGES BETWEEN CONCARNEAU AND LORIENT

ILES DE GLÉNAN, 47°43'·04N 03°59'·51W (twr on Île Cigogne). A good Pilot and large-scale chart are essential: AC 3640; SHOM 6648 (larger scale than AC 3640), 7146, 7313; ECM 243. Tides see 8.17.12. A low-lying archipelago, 10M SSW of Concarneau, with Ile aux Moutons and Les Pourceaux, both rky plateaux, to the N. Cardinal buoys mark Basse Jaune, a partly drying shoal to the E, and the SE, S and SW limits of the Islands. Visit in settled weather as ⌕s can be exposed. There is enough water HW±3 for most boats, but below half-tide careful pilotage is needed. **Conspic marks** are Penfret, highest island with lt Fl R 5s 36m 21M & Dir Q; and the tower (W with B top) on Ile Cigogne, HQ of Centre Nautique. **Approaches**: Easiest is from the N, via WPT 47°44'·0N 03°57'·5W, to W side of Penfret, with bn on Ile Guéotec brg 192°. ⌕ there or proceed W to ⌕s and ⌕ in La Chambre, S of Ile de St Nicolas; at W end a wind turbine (5 FR) is conspic. Also from N, Cigogne tr in transit 181° with chy on Ile du Loc'h leads close E of La Pie IDM bn, Fl (2) 6s 9m 3M, to ⌕ NW of Ile de Bananec; or SE into the pool. From the W, Chenal des Bluiniers 095° dries 0·8m between Ile Drénec and St Nicolas. S apprs and night navigation are not advised. Other ⌕s: E side of Penfret; close E of Cigogne; and N of Ile du Loc'h. ⌕s 50FF. R, Bar in St Nicolas, limited V.

AVEN and BELON RIVERS, Finistere, 47°48'·05N 03°44'·20W, AC 2352; SHOM 7138, 7031; ECM 544. HW +0450 on Dover (UT), –0030 on Brest. HW ht –1·9m on Brest; ML 2·8m; Duration 068. Both rivers are shallow in their upper reaches and have bars, shown on SHOM 7138 as dredged 0·6m. Seas rarely break on the Aven bar, but the Belon bar is impassable in bad weather. Beware Les Cochons de Rousbicout (drying 0·3m) to SW of ent and Les Verres to SE. Port Manech has ⌕s and a good ⌕ in 2·5m outside the bar which dries 0·9m. Very good shelter at Rosbras up the **Aven**; Pont-Aven, 3·6M up-river, only accessible for shoal craft. Moorings in 2·5m; or AB at the quay dries 2·5m. For the **Belon**, appr near HW from close to Pte de Kerhermen and hug the E shore to cross the bar (dries 0·3m); SHOM 7138/ pilot book is advisable. 1M up-river are 3 large ⌕s or ⌕ in deep water; ⌕s trots further up. Port Manech has only lt, Oc (4) WRG 12s 38m 10/7M, see 8.17.4 for sectors. Night entry not advised. Facilities (Aven): Aff Mar ☎ 02.98.06.00.73; **YC de l'Aven** (Port Manech). **Town** ME, Slip, C, FW, P&D, R, Bar.

BRIGNEAU, Finistere, 47°476'·82N 03°40'·00W. AC 2352; SHOM 7138, 7031; ECM 544. –0020 on Brest; ML 2·8m. Small drying, fair weather hbr. Strong onshore winds render the ent dangerous and the hbr untenable due to swell. Unlit RW buoy is 8ca S of hbr ent. By day bkwtr lt and rear W panel (hard to see) lead 331° to ent, close E of ruined factory. Dir lt on bkwtr, Oc (2) WRG 6s 7m 12/9M, W tr/R top, W329°- 339°. Some ⌕s or AB on W quay, dries. Facilities: FW, AC, V.

MERRIEN, Finistere, 47°46'·51N 03°38'·98W. AC 2352; SHOM 7138, 7031; ECM 544. HW –0020 on Brest; ML 2·8m. Drying inlet with rky ledges either side of apprs. Ldg marks 005°: front W☐ lt tr/R top; rear, house gable. Dir lt QR 26m 7M, vis 004°-009°. ⌕ outside ent or moor to ⌕ or AB on quay SE side. Avoid oyster beds beyond quay. Facilities: FW, AC, R.

DOËLAN, Finistere, 47°46'·20N 03°36'·45W. AC 2352; SHOM 7138, 7031; ECM 544. HW +0450 on Dover (UT), –0035 on Brest ; HW ht –2·2m on Brest; ML 3·1m; Duration 0607. Fair weather only, open to onshore winds. Drying AB at quays; or afloat on W buoys just N and S of bkwtr. Conspic factory chy E of front ldg lt. Daymark, W bn/B stripe, (about 1km NNE of rear ldg lt) on with ldg lts 014°: front Oc (3) WG 12s 20m 13/10M, W tr/G band & top, W shore -305°, G305°- 314°, W314°-shore; rear QR 27m 9M, W tr/R band & top. Facilities: Aff Mar ☎ 02.98.96.62.38; **Services**: CH, El, Ⓔ, ME, Sh. **Town** D, P, FW, Dr, ✉, R, V, Bar.

LE POULDU (La Laïta or Quimperlé River), Finistere, 47°45'·70N 03°32'·20W. AC 2352; SHOM 7138, 7031; ECM 544. HW – 0020 on Brest; ML 2·8m. Strictly a fair weather hbr, but once inside a small marina on the E bank provides adequate shelter for small yachts; or ⌕ in deeper pools upstream. At HW appr the estuary ent close E of a W ○ tr on low cliffs. The ent favours the W side, but chan shifts often and local advice is needed. In onshore winds the bar is dangerous on the ebb. Tides reach 6kn at sp. No lights. Facilities: FW, V, R, Bar.

PORT TUDY   8-17-13

Morbihan (Ile de Groix) 47°38'·74N 03°26'·63W   Rtg 2-4-2

CHARTS
AC 2352, 2646; SHOM 7139, 7031, 7032; ECM 544; Imray C38

TIDES
+0505 Dover; ML 3·1; Duration 0610; Zone –0100

Standard Port BREST (←—)

Times				Height (metres)			
High Water		Low Water		MHWS	MHWN	MLWN	MLWS
0000	0600	0000	0600	6·9	5·4	2·6	1·0
1200	1800	1200	1800				
Differences PORT TUDY (Ile de Groix)							
0000	–0025	–0025	–0015	–1·8	–1·4	–0·6	–0·1

SHELTER
Very good in marina or on pontoons outside, dredged 0·9-2·4m. Access via lock to marina HW –1½ to +2, (0630- 2200) or less at small coefficients. Outer hbr is open to swell in strong N/NE winds, access H24. Moor fore and aft to buoys; max draft 3m. No ⌕ in hbr, often very crowded. Caution: ferries navigating with panache.

NAVIGATION
WPT 47°39'·14N 03°26'·28W, (100m E of Speerbrecker ECM buoy), 039°/219° from/to N mole hd lt, 0·5M. Remain in R sector of E mole hd lt. Beware a large unlit mooring buoy 0·6M NW of ent and rks SE of appr. From E or SE pass N of Basse Melite NCM buoy. Use SHOM 7139 for exploring the island, including Locmaria and Port Lay.

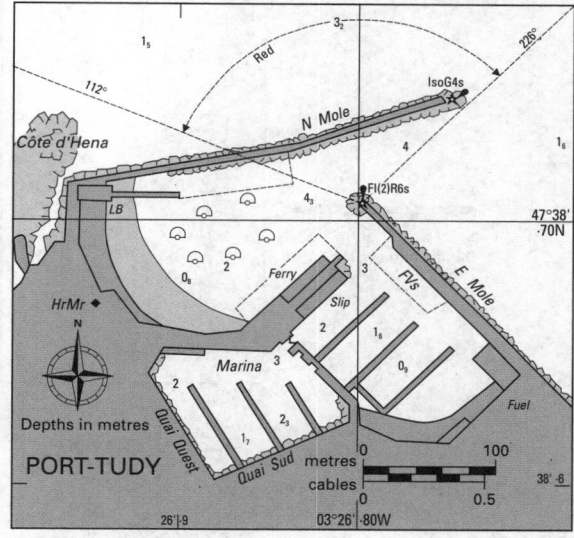

LIGHTS AND MARKS
Pen-Men lt ho (at NW end of island), Fl (4) 25s 59m 29M, W ☐ tr, B top. Pte de la Croix lt (at E end of island), Oc WR 4s 16m 12/9M. Ldg line at 220°, church spire in line with W end of N mole. By night, mole hd lts in transit 219° clear offlying rks to the NE.

RADIO TELEPHONE
VHF Ch 09 16 during lock opening times.

TELEPHONE
Hr Mr 02.97.86.54.62; Aff Mar 02.97.37.16.22; CROSS 02.97.55.35.35; SNSM 02.97.86.82.87; ⌗ 02.97.86.80.93; Auto 08.36.68.08.56; Police 02.97.86.81.17; ⊞ (Lorient) 02.97.83.04.02.

FACILITIES
Marina (150), FF173, FF50 on buoy, FW, AC; **Quay** P & D (cans, 0800–1200 & 1400–1900, ☎ 02.97.86.80.96), ME, El, Sh, C (3 ton), CH. **Town** V, R, ◎, ✉, Bar. Ferry to Lorient.

OTHER HARBOUR ON ILE DE GROIX

LOCMARIA, Morbihan, 47°37'·85N 03°26'·28W. AC 2352, SHOM 7139; –0020 Brest; ML 2·8m. Appr is open to the S, but tiny drying hbr gives shelter in offshore winds. Steer N for G bn tr initially; then ldg line 350°, W bn on with conspic Ho. Close in, 2 PHM bns and a SCM and NCM bn mark the unlit chan. Limited space inside to dry out; or ⌕ outside the hbr W of the ldg line. Facilities in village, V, R.

17

LORIENT

8-17-14

Morbihan 47°42'·64N 03°21'·92W   Rtg 1-1-2

CHARTS
AC 304, 2352; SHOM 7140, 7139, 7031, 7032; ECM 544, 545; Imray C38

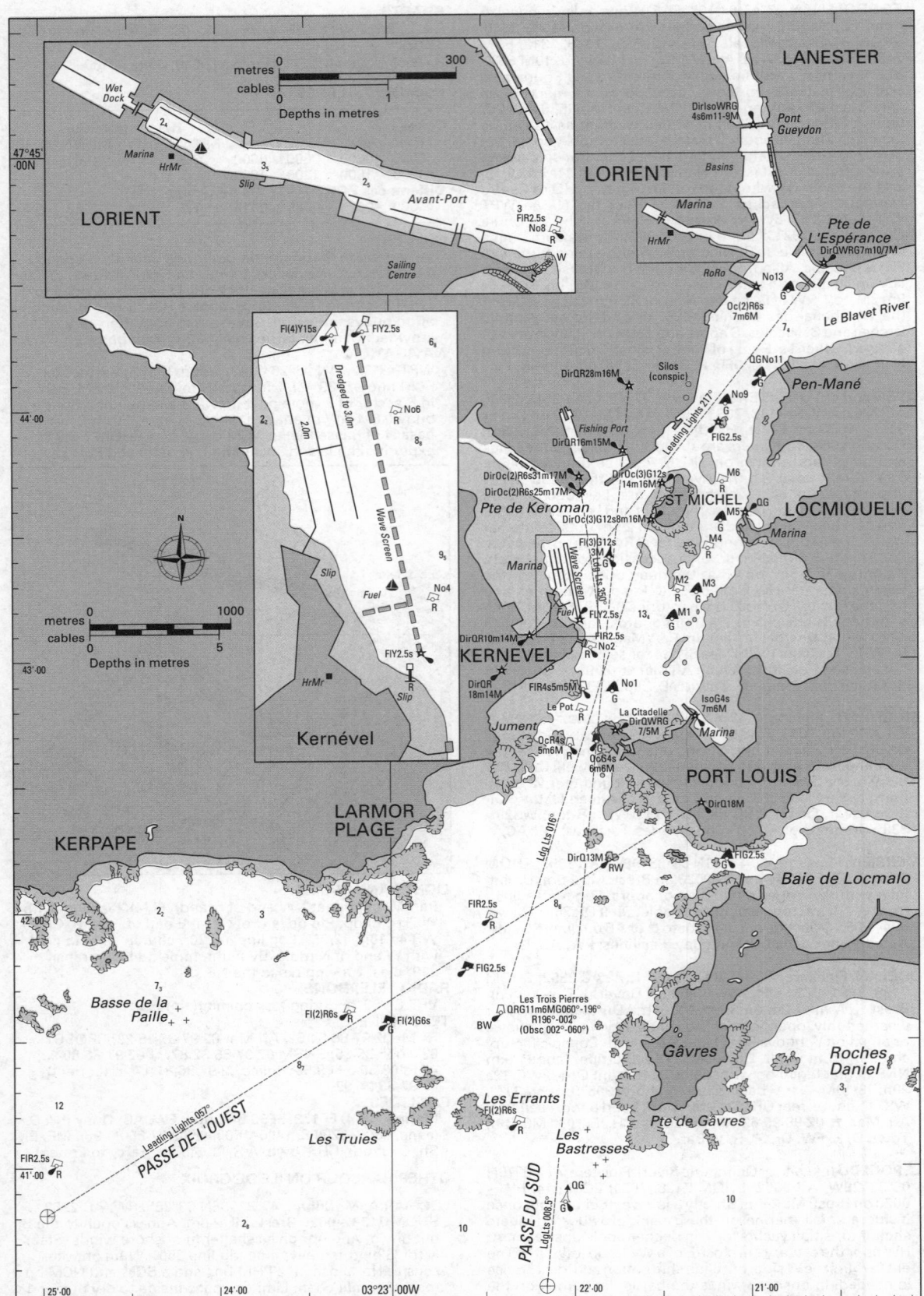

TIDES
+0455 Dover; ML 3·1; Duration 0620; Zone –0100

Standard Port BREST (←—)

Times				Height (metres)			
High Water		Low Water		MHWS	MHWN	MLWN	MLWS
0000	0600	0000	0600	6·9	5·4	2·6	1·0
1200	1800	1200	1800				
Differences LORIENT							
+0003	–0022	–0020	–0010	–1·8	–1·4	–0·6	–0·2
PORT LOUIS							
+0004	–0021	–0022	–0012	–1·8	–1·4	–0·6	–0·1
PORT D'ETEL							
+0020	–0010	+0030	+0010	–2·0	–1·3	–0·4	+0·5

SHELTER
Very good. Ile de Groix shelters the ent from SW'lies. Hbr access all tides/weather. 4 marinas at: **Kernével**, W of main chan (enter between 2 Y buoys at N end of wave-break, thence ❶ berths at S end); **Port Louis** (E of La Citadelle); **Locmiquélic** (E of Ile Ste Michel); and **Port du Lorient** in the city: berth in Avant Port or lock into the Bassin à Flot, HW±1 sp, ±15 mins nps; access HJ. No ⚓ in chans and hbr, but moorings ENE of La Citadelle and ⚓ for shoal draft in B de Locmalo. R Blavet is navigable on the flood for 6M to Hennebont where there are 🚤s and a pontoon in complete shelter; also moorings below first of 3 bridges, 21m least clearance. Caution: 0.3m patches beyond the first bridge. See 8.15.18 for canal access.

NAVIGATION
WPT Passe du Sud 47°40'·50N 03°22'·40W, 188°/008° from/to front ldg lt, 3·35M. WPT Passe de l'Ouest, 47°40'·80N 03°24'·92W, 237°/057° from/to front ldg lt, 3·0M. There are few navigational dangers if ldg lines are kept to, but yachts must keep clear of shipping in the main chan. Abeam La Citadelle a secondary yacht chan parallels the main chan to W of La Jument R bn tr, Oc R 4s and Le Cochon RGR bn tr, Fl R 4s.

LIGHTS AND MARKS
Conspic daymarks are water tr 8ca W of Kernevel, La Citadelle to stbd of ent, submarine pens at Pte de Keroman and 2 silos N of Ile St Michel.
Ldg and Dir lts as seen from seaward in sequence:
(1) Passe de l'Ouest: ldg lts 057°, both Dir Q; Front, Les Soeurs, 11m 13M; R tr, W bands. Rear, Port Louis 740m from front, 22m 18M; W daymark, R bands on bldg.
(2) Passe du Sud: ldg lts 008·5°, both Dir QR, intens 006°-011°, synch; Front, 16m 15M; R □, G bands on Gy tr. Rear, Kergroise, 515m from front, 28m 16M; R □, W stripe on Gy framework tr.
(3) Les Trois Pierres: QRG 11m 6M; conspic B tr, W bands, G 060°-196°, R196°-002°.
(4) Ile Saint-Michel: ldg lts 016·5°, both Dir Oc (3) G 12s 8/14m 16M, intens 015°-018°; W trs, G tops.
(5) Pte de Keroman: ldg lts 350°, both Dir Oc (2) R 6s 17M, synch, intens 349°-351°. Front, 25m; R ho, W bands; Rear, 31m; RW topmark on Gy pylon, R top.
(6) Kernével: ldg lts 217°, both Dir QR 14M, intens 215°-219°; Front, 10m. Rear, 18m; W □ tr, R top.
(7) Pte de l'Esperance: Dir lt 037°: Dir Q WRG 8m 10/7M; G034·2°-036·7°, W036·7°-037·2°, R037·2°-047·2°.
(8) Pont Gueydon: Dir lt 352°: Iso WRG 4s 6m 11/9M; G350°-351·5°, W351·5°-352·5°, R352·5°-355·5°.

RADIO TELEPHONE
Vigie Port Louis VHF Ch 11 16 (H24). Marinas Ch 09 (HO).

TELEPHONE
Aff Mar 02·97·37·16·22; CROSS 02·97·55·35·35; SNSM 02·97·64·32·42; ☷ 02·97·37·29·57; Météo 02·97·64·34·86; Auto 08·36·68·08·56; Police 02·97·64·27·17; Ⓗ 02·97·37·51·33; Brit Consul 01·40·63·16·02.

FACILITIES (from seaward)
Kernével Marina (410+60 ❶) ☎ 02·97·65·48·25; FF115. H24 access, depth 3m; FW, AC, P & D (S end of marina; call Ch 09), ⬛, Slip, BH (25 ton), C (100 ton), YC ☎ 02·97·47·47·25.
Port-Louis Marina (160+20 ❶), ☎ 02·97·82·18·18, dredged 2m, FW, AC, C (150 ton).
Locmiquélic Marina, (217+10 ❶) ☎ 02·97·33·59·51, 🚤 02·97·33·89·25, depth 1·5-3m, FW, AC, C (40 ton), ⬛.
Lorient Marina (320+50 ❶) ☎ 02·97·21·10·14; FF115, Avant Port 2·5-3m depth, 2·5m in Bassin à Flot; FW, AC, ⬛, Slip, BH (25 ton), C (100 ton), ME, EI, Ⓔ, Sh, CH, SHOM, ACA, SM, P&D @ Kernevel; **Club Nautique de Lorient**, Bar, C (1½ ton), FW, Slip. **City** All facilities, ✉, Ⓑ, ⇌, ✈.

RIVER ÉTEL   8-17-15
Morbihan 47°39'·60N 03°12'·38W   Rtg 4-4-2

CHARTS
AC 2352; SHOM 7138, 7032; ECM 545; Imray C38

TIDES
+0505 Dover (UT); ML 3·2m; Duration 0617. See 8.17.14

SHELTER
Excellent at marina (1·5-2m) on E bank 1M up-river from the ent, inside the town quay (FVs). Possible ⚓s S of conspic LB ho, off Le Magouër on the W bank or above town (beware strong streams). Pont Lorois (1·3M N) has 9·5m clearance.

NAVIGATION
WPT 47°38'·38N 03°12'·90W, 219°/039° from/to water tr (off chartlet), 1·47M. Appr only by day, in good visibility, at about HW –1½ on the last of the flood, with conspic water tr brg 039°. Bar dries approx 0·4m; buoyed/lit chan shifts. For directions in simple French, call *Semaphore d'Etel* Ch 13. If no VHF, pre-notify ETA by ☎; fly ensign at mast-head; expect visual sigs from Fenoux mast, close NW of ent: Waggle of semaphore arrow = acknowledged; obey signals:
Arrow vert = maintain present course.
Arrow inclined = alter course in direction indicated.
Arrow horiz = no entry for all vessels; conditions dangerous.
● hoisted = no ent for undecked boats and craft <8m LOA.
R flag = insufficient depth over bar. Once inside, the chan is narrow, but well marked, up to Pte Saint-Germain.

LIGHTS AND MARKS
Lt W side of ent, Oc (2) WRG 6s 13m 9/6M, W022°-064°, R064°-123°, W123°-330°, G330°-022°; no ⚓ within 5ca of it. Épi de Plouhinic bn, Fl R 2·5s 7m 2M, marks groyne at ent.

RADIO TELEPHONE
Call *Semaphore d'Etel* VHF Ch 13 16 (see above). Marina Ch 13 16 (HW–3 to +2). For CROSS Étel, see 8.15.8.

TELEPHONE
Hr Mr 02·97·55·46·62, 🚤 02·97·55·34·14; Aff Mar 02·97·55·30·32; Auto 08·36·65·02·56; CROSS 02·97·55·35·35; Sig Tr 02·97·55·35·59; Police 02·97·55·32·11.

FACILITIES
Marina (180 + 20 visitors) FW, AC, C (6 ton), Slip; **Quay** P & D (cans), CH, EI, ME, Sh. **Town** Bar, Dr, R, V, ⬛, Bus to ⇌ (Auray 15km) and ✈ (Lorient 32km).

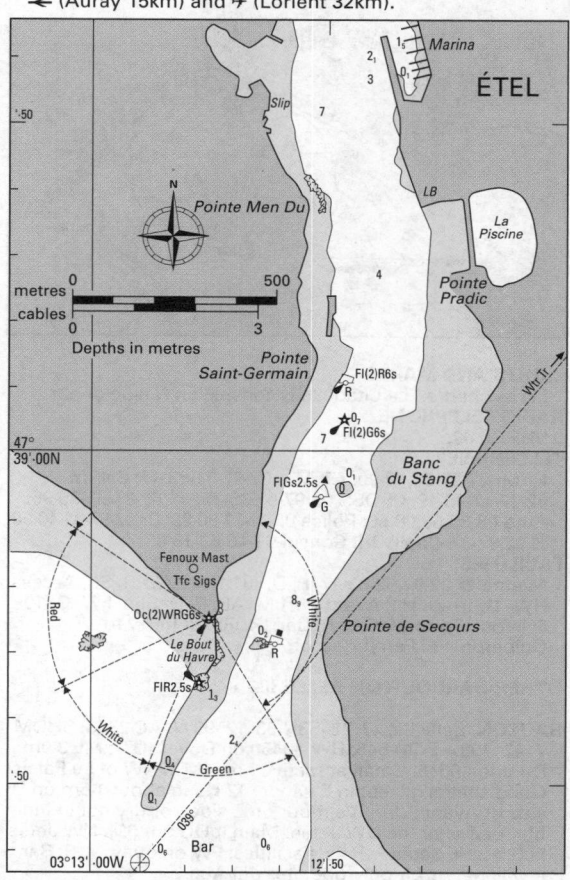

LE PALAIS (BELLE ILE)   8-17-16
Morbihan 47°20'·89N 03°08'·98W   Rtg 2-3-1

CHARTS
AC 2353; Imray C39; SHOM 7142, 7032; ECM 545
TIDES
+0458 Dover; ML 3·1; Duration 0615; Zone –0100

Standard Port BREST (←—)

Times				Height (metres)			
High Water		Low Water		MHWS	MHWN	MLWN	MLWS
0000	0600	0000	0600	6·9	5·4	2·6	1·0
1200	1800	1200	1800				
Differences LE PALAIS							
+0007	–0028	–0025	–0020	–1·8	–1·4	–0·7	–0·3
ILE DE HOUAT							
+0010	–0025	–0020	–0015	–1·7	–1·3	–0·6	–0·2
ILE DE HÖEDIC							
+0010	–0035	–0027	–0022	–1·8	–1·4	–0·7	–0·3

SHELTER
Good, except in strong E'lies which cause marked swell. Very crowded in season. Deep draft yachts moor on 3 trots of ⚓s inside Mole Bourdelle; shallow draft on ⚓s to port. Inner hbr mostly dries. Lock into the Bassin à Flot opens HW –1½ to +1 (0600-2200LT), for berths on S side in 2·5m; thence via lifting bridge into marina (1·7m).
NAVIGATION
WPT 47°21'·20N 03°08'·00W, 065°/245° from/to Jetée Nord lt, 0·80M. No navigational dangers, but beware fast ferries. ⚓ between Sauzon (see below) and Le Palais is prohib.

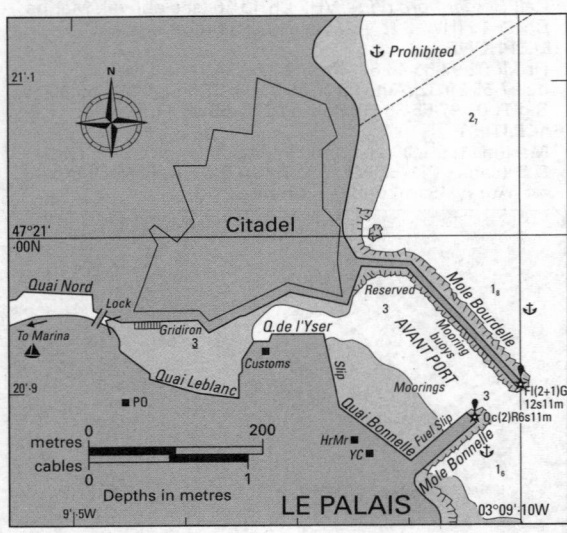

LE PALAIS

LIGHTS AND MARKS
Lts as chartlet. La Citadelle is conspic on N side of hbr.
RADIO TELEPHONE
VHF Ch 09.
TELEPHONE
Hr Mr 02·97·31·42·90; Aff Mar 02·97·31·83·17; SNSM 02·97·47·48·49; CROSS 02·97·55·35·35; ⊞ 02·97·31·85·95; Auto 08.36.68.08.56; Police 02·97·31·80·22; Dr 02·97·31·40·90; Ⓗ 02·97·31·48·48; Brit Consul 01·40·63·16·02.
FACILITIES
Marina ☎ 02·97·52·83·17, P, D, AC, FW, ME, EI, Sh, Access HW–1½ to +1, HJ; Avant Port M, AB, P, D, Slip, FW, C (10 & 5 ton). Town V, Gaz, R, Bar, ⊠, Ⓑ, ⇌ (ferry to Quiberon), ✈. Ferry: Roscoff.

OTHER HARBOUR ON BELLE ILE
SAUZON, Belle Ile, 47°22'·53N 03°12'·93W. AC 2353; SHOM 7142, 7032; ECM 545; HW +0450 on Dover (UT); ML 3·0m; Duration 0615. Small attractive hbr, 4M WNW of Le Palais. Good shelter except in E winds. 12 ⚓s in about 1·5m on W side of Avant Port (FVs moor on E side), or dry out in inner hbr, or ⚓ N of the NW Jetée. Main lt QG 9m 6M. NW Jetée Fl G 4s. SE Jetée Fl R 4s. Facilities: FW on quay; V, R, Bar in village. Hr Mr only operates Jul/Aug.

PORT HALIGUEN   8-17-17
Morbihan 47°29'·40N 03°06'·00W   Rtg 1-2-2

CHARTS
AC 2353; Imray C38, 39; SHOM 7141, 7032, 7033; ECM 545
TIDES
+0500 Dover; ML 3·1; Duration 0615; Zone –0100
Standard Port BREST (←—)

Times				Height (metres)			
High Water		Low Water		MHWS	MHWN	MLWN	MLWS
0000	0600	0000	0600	6·9	5·4	2·6	1·0
1200	1800	1200	1800				
Differences PORT HALIGUEN							
+0015	–0020	–0015	–0010	–1·7	–1·3	–0·6	–0·3
LA TRINITÉ							
+0020	–0020	–0015	–0005	–1·5	–1·1	–0·5	–0·2

SHELTER
Good, but uncomfortable in strong NW to NE winds. Access H24 at all tides. Marina boat will meet. Visitors usually berth alongside on pontoon 'V' to stbd of ent.
NAVIGATION
WPT 47°29'·80N 03°05'·00W, 060°/240° from/to bkwtr lt, 0·75M. From W or S, appr via Passage de la Teignouse. Banc de Quiberon, marked by NCM and SCM buoys, is shoal (1·5m) at S end. 500m ENE of bkwtr lt in R sector 240°-299°, beware 1·8m shoal, with unlit SCM buoy.
LIGHTS AND MARKS
W sector 246°-252° of Port-Maria main lt, Q WRG 28m 14/10M, leads N of Banc de Quiberon; W sector 299°-306° of bkwtr lt, Oc (2) WR 6s 10m 12/9M, leads S of it.
RADIO TELEPHONE
VHF Ch 09.
TELEPHONE
Hr Mr 02·97·50·20·56; ⊞ 02·97·55·73·46; CROSS 02·97·55·35·35; SNSM 02·97·50·14·39; Météo 02·97·64·34·86; Auto 08.36.68.08.56; Police 02·97·50·07·39; Dr 02·97·50·13·94.
FACILITIES
Marina (760 + 100 Ⓥ) ☎ 02·97·50·20·56, FF115, Slip, P, D, C (2 ton), BH (13 ton), ME, EI, Sh, AC, CH, FW, Ⓙ, SM, Bar, R, V. Town (Quiberon) V, Gaz, R, Ice, Bar, ⊠, Ⓑ, ⇌, ✈.

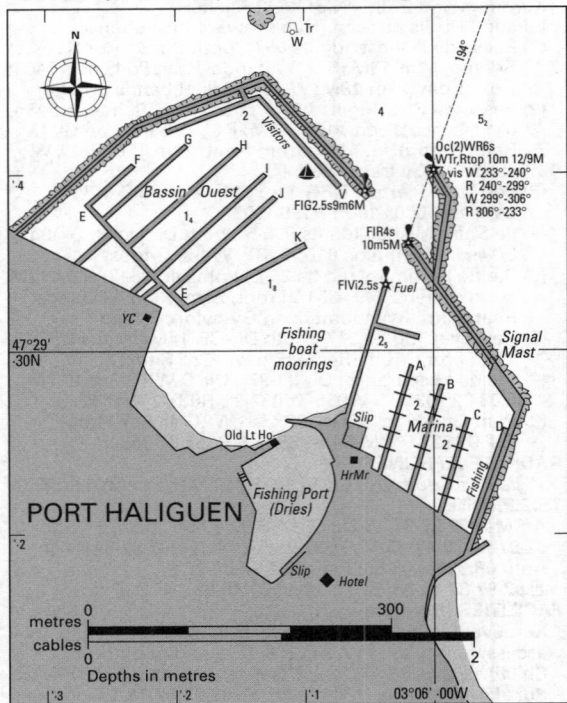

PORT HALIGUEN

PORT MARIA, Morbihan 47°28'·65N 03°07'·25W. AC 2353; SHOM 5352, 7032. Tides as 8.17.17. Shelter good in all winds, but busy ferry/FV port; only suitable for yachts as a refuge or in emergency. Access dangerous in strong SE–SW winds. N half hbr dries. E mole reserved for ferries. ⚓ in SW of hbr in approx 2m. Hr Mr/Aff Mar ☎ 02·97·50·08·71; Facilities: ⊞, C (6 ton), FW at E quay, EI, ME, Sh, SHOM.

LA TRINITÉ-SUR-MER   8-17-18

Morbihan 47°34'·06N 03°00'·60W   Rtg 2-1-2

CHARTS
AC 2358, 2353; Imray C39; SHOM 7141, 7033, 7034; ECM 545, 546

TIDES
+0455 Dover; ML 3·2; Duration 0610; Zone –0100

Standard Port BREST (←). Differences see 8.17.17.

SHELTER
Very good, except in strong SE/S winds near HW when La Vaneresse sandbank is covered. Access H24 at all tides. Marina boat will meet. No ⚓/fishing in river. Speed limit 5kn.

NAVIGATION
WPT 47°31'·90N 02°59'·53W, 167°/347° from/to front ldg lt, 2·3M. No navigational dangers; the river is marked by buoys and perches. Best water close to E bank. Beware many oyster beds, marked with perches.

LIGHTS AND MARKS
Conspic daymarks include: Mousker rk, off-white top; caravan site 3ca NNE; and ⊞ spire at La Trinité. Ldg marks (below) are difficult to see by day. Pte de Kernevest ldg lts 347°: Front Q WRG 11m 10/7M (W345°-013°); rear Dir Q 21m 15M, synch, intens 337°-357°. 1M up-river: Dir lt 347°, Oc WRG 4s 9m 13/11M (W346°-348°). S Pier, Oc (2) WR 6s (W293°-300°). ⓥ pontoon is first beyond ☆ Iso R 4s.

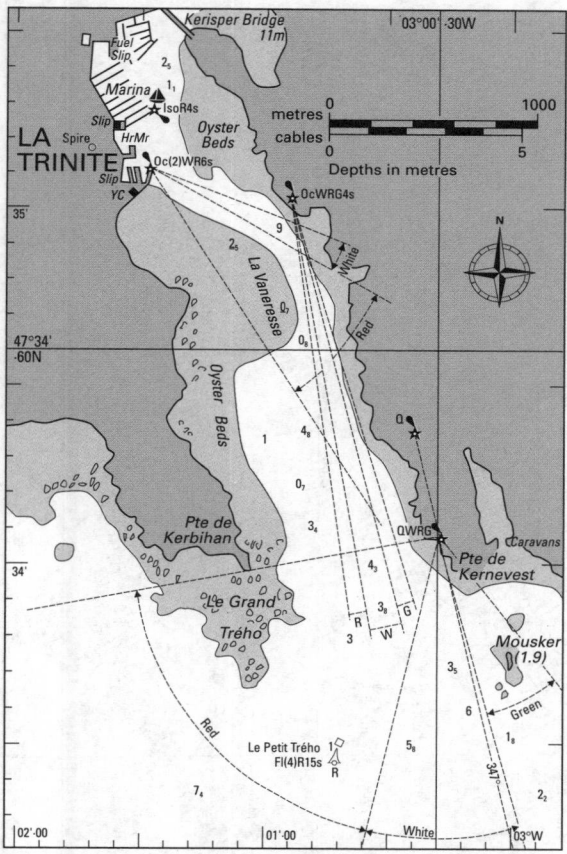

RADIO TELEPHONE
Marina VHF Ch 09.

TELEPHONE
Hr Mr 02·97·55·71·49; Aff Mar 02·97·24·01·43 at Auray; CROSS 02·97·55·35·35; SNSM 02·97·55·02·30; ☷ 02·97·55·73·46; Météo 02·97·64·34·86; Auto 08.36.68.08.56; Police 02·97·55·71·62; Dr 02·97·55·74·03; Brit Consul 01·40·63·16·02.

FACILITIES
Marina (900+100 ⓥ) ☎ 02·97·55·71·27, AC, P, D, FW, BH (36 ton), Gridiron, M, ME, El, CH, SHOM, Ⓔ, SM, Sh; **Club Nautique** ☎ 02·97·55·73·48. **Town** V, Gaz, R, Bar, Ice, ✉, Ⓑ, ⇌ (Auray), ✈ (Lorient). Ferry: Roscoff or St Malo.

CROUESTY   8-17-19

Morbihan 47°32'·52N 02°54'·03W   Rtg 1-1-2

CHARTS
AC 2358, 2353; Imray C39; SHOM 6992, 7034, 7033; ECM 546

TIDES
+0505 Dover; ML 3·0; Duration 0555; Zone –0100

Standard Port BREST (←)

Times				Height (metres)			
High Water		Low Water		MHWS	MHWN	MLWN	MLWS
0000	0600	0000	0600	6·9	5·4	2·6	1·0
1200	1800	1200	1800				
Differences PORT NAVALO							
+0030	–0005	–0010	–0005	–2·0	–1·5	–0·8	–0·3

SHELTER
Good, protected from W'lies by Quiberon Peninsula; additional shelter in very large marina which contains 5 large separate basins. ⓥ pontoons on S side of fairway.

NAVIGATION
WPT 47°32'·04N 02°55'·21W, 238°/058° from/to front ldg lt, 1·1M. There are no navigational dangers, the ent being well marked and dredged 1·8m. See also Morbihan 8.17.20.

LIGHTS AND MARKS
Ldg lts 058°: both Dir Q 10/27m 19M, intens 056·5°-059·5°. By day, front W vert stripe on R panel; rear grey lt ho. Bkwtr hds: N = Oc (2) R 6s, S = Fl G 4s, plus lead-in buoys.

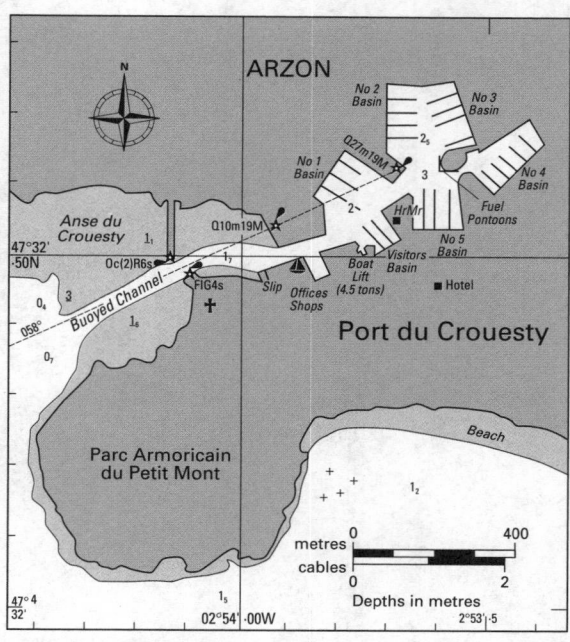

RADIO TELEPHONE
VHF Ch 09.

TELEPHONE
Hr Mr 02·97·53·73·33; Aff Mar 02·97·41·84·10; ☷ 02·97·63·18·71; CROSS 02·97·55·35·35; Auto 08.36.65.08.56; SNSM 02·97·41·35·35; Police 02·97·53·71·65; Dr 02·97·53·71·61; Brit Consul 01·40·63·16·02.

FACILITIES
Marina (1000+120 ⓥ) ☎ 02·97·53·73·33, ⌂ 02·97·53·90·22, P, D, AC, FW, ME, El, Sh, Slip, BH (45 ton), C (10 ton), CH, Bar, M, Ⓔ, SM. **Town** V, Gaz, R, Bar, ✉ & Ⓑ (Arzon), ⇌ (Vannes), ✈ (Vannes, Lorient, St Nazaire).

ISLAND HARBOUR IN THE BAIE DE QUIBERON

ÎLE HOUAT, 47°23'·60N 02°57'·25W. AC 2353; SHOM 7033. HW +0505 on Dover (UT); ML 3·1m; Duration 0605; See 8.17.16. Good shelter, except from N/NE'lies, at Port St Gildas, near E end of the N coast. Appr from N or NE passing abeam La Vieille rk (conspic 14m). Avoid rks 6m inboard of bkwtr and 15m off lt tr. Moor on double trots; no ⚓ in hbr. S part of hbr dries. Keep clear of ferries and FVs on W and N quays. Lts as 8.17.4. Few facilities.

17

GOLFE DU MORBIHAN
Morbihan 47°32'·92N 02°55'·26W   Rtg 3-3-1

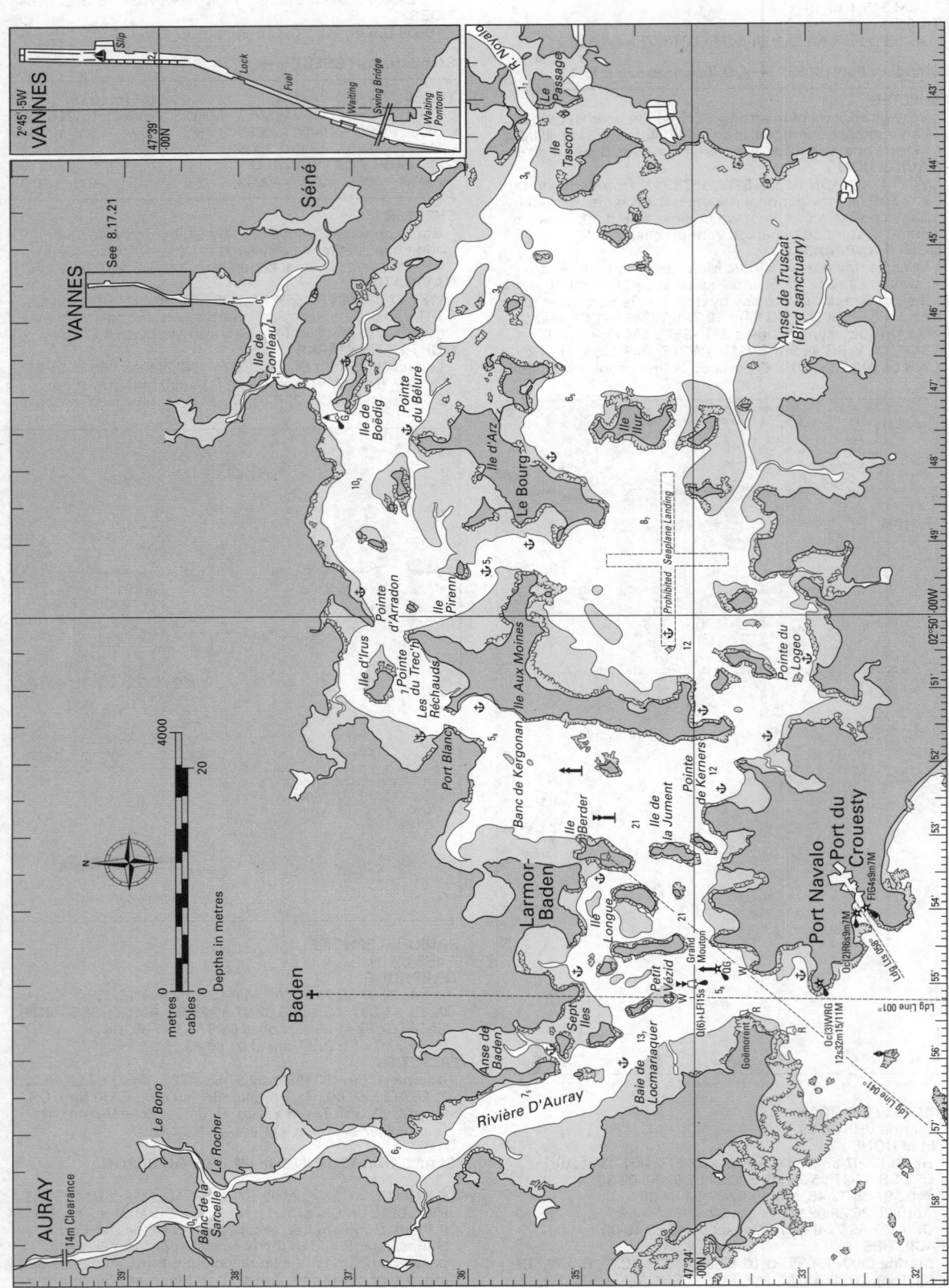

CHARTS
AC 2358, 2353; Imray C39; SHOM 6992, 7034, 7033; ECM 546

TIDES
−0515 Dover; ML 3·0; Zone −0100

Standard Port BREST (←—)

Times				Height (metres)			
High Water		Low Water		MHWS	MHWN	MLWN	MLWS
0000	0600	0000	0600	6·9	5·4	2·6	1·0
1200	1800	1200	1800				
Differences PORT NAVALO							
+0030	−0005	−0010	−0005	−2·0	−1·5	−0·8	−0·3
AURAY							
+0055	0000	+0020	+0005	−2·0	−1·4	−0·8	−0·2
VANNES							
+0220	+0200	+0200	+0125	−3·6	−2·7	−1·6	−0·5
ARRADON							
+0155	+0145	+0145	+0130	−3·7	−2·7	−1·6	−0·5
LE LOGEO							
+0155	+0145	+0145	+0125	−3·7	−2·7	−1·6	−0·5

The Golfe du Morbihan is an inland sea of about 50sq miles with deep apprs and ent. It contains many islands, all but two privately owned. The many ⚓s (see chartlet and below) are increasingly restricted by extensive moorings. It is essential to use chain when ⚓ing, unless well out of the tide. Avoid numerous oyster beds, marked by withies and bird sanctuaries, especially in SE. Much of E & SE dries. Vannes, see 8.17.21.

NAVIGATION
WPT 47°32'·04N 02°55'·21W, 181°/001° from/to Petit Vézid front ldg mark, 2·2M. Beware very strong tides in the ent and some narrow chans, max 5¾kn sp ebb (8kn reported), but easing in the upper reaches. For a first visit, springs should be avoided; it is likely to be impossible for an aux yacht to enter against a sp ebb. Abeam Grand Mouton the flood and ebb begin 3hrs before and 3hrs after HW Brest respectively; slack water lasts about 30mins at sp and 1hr at nps. HW times become later the further E one goes into the Morbihan, ie HW Vannes is 2 hrs after HW Pt Navalo. But HW at Port Navalo and Auray are within 25 mins of each other.
At the ent the flood divides: a weaker flow into the River Auray; but the major stream rushes NE into the main chan, setting strongly toward Petit & Grand Mouton rks. To avoid these, keep up to the ldg line until safely past Grand Mouton, but beware shoals to port off Goémorent R bn tr.
Beware very strong streams between Île Berder and Île de la Jument, and between Pte de Toulindag and Port Blanc where Les Réchauds rks are marked by 2 SHM bns. Caution: frequent ferries cross the narrows between Port Blanc and Île aux Moines. Due to an eddy around Île d'Irus the stream runs mainly SW between Les Réchauds and Pte d'Arradon.
Pilotage is not difficult, but due to higher than usual speeds over the ground, it helps to pre-plot the desired trks/distances within the channels; marks can then be more readily identified and track adjusted with ease, especially if beating.

LIGHTS AND MARKS
At the ent ldg daymarks on 001° are: front Petit Vézid W obelisk (looks like a yacht sail from afar), rear Baden ✠ spire (3·3M); maintain until abeam Port Navalo lt ho. Chans and dangers are well marked; the only lts are: Port Navalo Oc (3) WRG 12s 32m 15/11M at ent, W sector 359°-015°. Inside ent: Grand Mouton SHM bn, QG and Le Grégan SCM bn, Q (6) + L Fl 15s. Roguédas SHM bn, Fl G 2·5s, at W end of Île de Boëdig marks appr to Vannes.

SHELTER AND FACILITIES (clockwise from ent)
PORT NAVALO: ⚓ in bay, but space limited by moorings, and exposed to W/NW winds. Convenient to await the tide. All facilities. ⌗ ☎ 02·97·53·82·12; Police 02·97·24·17·17.
LOCMARIAQUER: Drying ⚓ off village quay; ferries use the buoyed chan to jetty. V, R, ME.
SEPT ÎLES: Small, quiet ⚓; chan leads into Anse de Baden.
LE ROCHER: Good shelter, but almost full of moorings. Further N the river almost dries, but can be navigated on the tide.
BONO: Moor or ⚓ (rky bottom) off Banc de la Sarcelle.
Village, AB in drying basin, ME, R, V, Gaz, ⊠.

AURAY: Access at mid-flood via a bridge, 3ca S of town, with 14m clearance MHWS. Note: this clearance, coupled with little depth of water, may need careful calculations for safe passage by high-masted yachts. Moor in a pool S of the bridge; 12 ⚓s or drying AB at St Goustan beyond. Aff Mar ☎ 02.97.24.01.43, 🕿 02.97.50.72.66. Facilities: ME, El, Sh, SHOM, CH. **Town** R, V, Bar, ⊠, ⇌.
ILE LONGUE: near SE tip ⚓ out of the stream. No landing.
LARMOR BADEN: good ⚓s to S, but many moorings. Aff Mar ☎ 02·97·57·05·66. Village: quay, slip, C, V, R, Bar, ⊠.
ILE BERDER: pleasant ⚓ E of the island; causeway to mainland.
PORT BLANC: Hr Mr ☎ 02·97·26·30·57, 🕿 02·97·26·30·16. FW, P & D at pontoon, but many moorings. Quay, slip, cash terminal. Ferry every ½hr to Île aux Moines.
ILE AUX MOINES: a much-frequented, public island. The narrows between the mainland and Les Réchauds rks can be rough. ⚓ off N end, landing at Pte du Trec'h or pick up ⚓ (see Hr Mr) off Pte des Réchauds where there is a small marina. Water taxi available; call VHF Ch 09 or sound foghorn. Hr Mr ☎ 02·97·26·30·57, D, FW. Other quieter ⚓s off W side and S tip of island.
ARRADON: limited ⚓, exposed to S'ly. M, Slip, FW, ME. Hr Mr ☎ 02·97·44·01·23.
ILE PIRENN: exposed ⚓ in tidal stream.
ILE D'ARZ: a public island. ⚓ NE of Pte du Béluré; E of Le Bourg (good shelter), or to the W, depending on winds. Rudevent village: ME, El, Sh.
ILE DE BOËDIG: sheltered ⚓ in chan N of the E end of island.
ILE DE CONLEAU: ⚓ or moor in bight just S of village, as space permits. ME, El, Sh, R in village.
SÉNÉ: ME.
VANNES: see 8.17.21.
R NOYALO : ⚓ off Pte du Passage (depths up-river are uncertain) or in Anse de Truscat, 2M to SW of river ent.
KERNERS: ⚓ off the Anse de Kerners or Anse de Pen Castel in 3 to 6m.
ILE DE LA JUMENT (or Ar Gazek): good shelter to E of island out of the tide; convenient for leaving on the tide.

17

VANNES   8-17-21

Morbihan 47°38'·45N 02°45'·62W   Rtg 3-2-1

CHARTS
AC 2358, 2353; Imray C39; SHOM 7034; ECM 546

TIDES
See GOLFE DU MORBIHAN 8.17.20. ML 2·0m; Zone –0100

SHELTER
Very good, protected from all winds. Access by day only. Waiting pontoons, with intercom to Hr Mr, are down and upstream of **swing bridge**, which only opens whilst lock gate into wet basin is open, ie HW±2½. Bridge opens at H and H+30 in season (15 Jun-15 Sep) and at weekends; but only at H out of season. Outbound craft have priority over arrivals. NB: during the first and final ½ hour periods when the lock is open, the bridge will open on request VHF Ch 09.

The narrow **lock gate**, remotely-controlled by the Hr Mr, opens HW±2½ (in season 0700-2200LT; out of season 0900-1800 Mon-Sat; and 0700-2100LT Sun). Lock sill, 1·3m above CD, retains 2·4m inside wet basin.

Note: HW Vannes –2½ happens to be HW Port Tudy (8.17.13) which is used by the Hr Mr to determine when the lock opens. *Horaires d'Ouverture du Bassin* (a free annual schedule of lock hrs) is available from: Bureau du Port de Plaisance, La Rabine, 56000 Vannes.

Berths: Marina boat may indicate a vacant finger pontoon; otherwise visitors berth N/S on pontoons D and G just S of movable inner foot-bridge (*passerelle*).

NAVIGATION
WPT: see 8.17.20. After Roguédas SHM lt bn do not cut the corner. Where the chan turns N can be identified by a pink house on the E bank. Thereafter passage past Ile de Conleau is easy and well marked. Beacon'd appr chan to Vannes is narrow, least depth 0·7m; only advised near HW.

LIGHTS AND MARKS
Bridge sigs (vert) on bridge's central pier are:
2 Ⓡ = no passage; 2 Oc Ⓡ = standby; 2 Ⓖ = proceed;
2 Oc Ⓖ = only transit if committed;
Ⓨ = unmasted boats may transit.
Lock sigs: Ⓖ and Ⓡ = Lock closed; No lts = Lock open.

RADIO TELEPHONE
VHF Ch 09. (Summer 0830-2100; winter HW±2½ and 0900-1200 and 1330-1800).

TELEPHONE
Hr Mr 02·97·54·16·08, 02·97·54·00·47; Aff Mar 02·97·63·40·95, ☎ 02.97.63.46.77; ☰ 02·97·63·18·71; CROSS 02·97·55·35·35, ☎ 02.97.63.71.75; SNSM 02·97·26·00·56; Météo 02·97·42·49·49; Auto 08.36.65.08.56; Police 02·97·47·19·20; Dr 02·97·47·47·25; Ⓗ 02·97·01·41·41, ☎ 02.97.01.40.07; Brit Consul 01·40·63·16·02.

FACILITIES
Marina (240+60 Ⓥ), ☎ 02·97·54·16·08, ☎ 02.97.42.48.80, FF99, Slip, ◎, FW, AC, ME, C (12 ton); P & D @ HW±2½ from pontoon on E side of canal, just S of lock.
City V, R, Sh, CH, El, Ⓔ, CH, SM, SHOM, ✉, Ⓑ, ⇌, ✈ (Vannes, Lorient or St Nazaire).

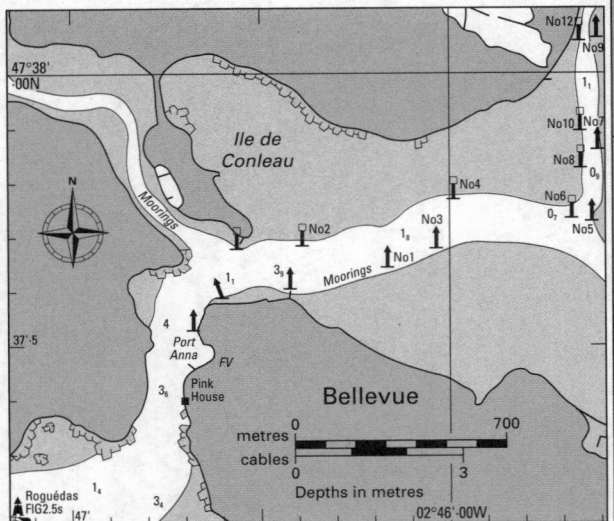

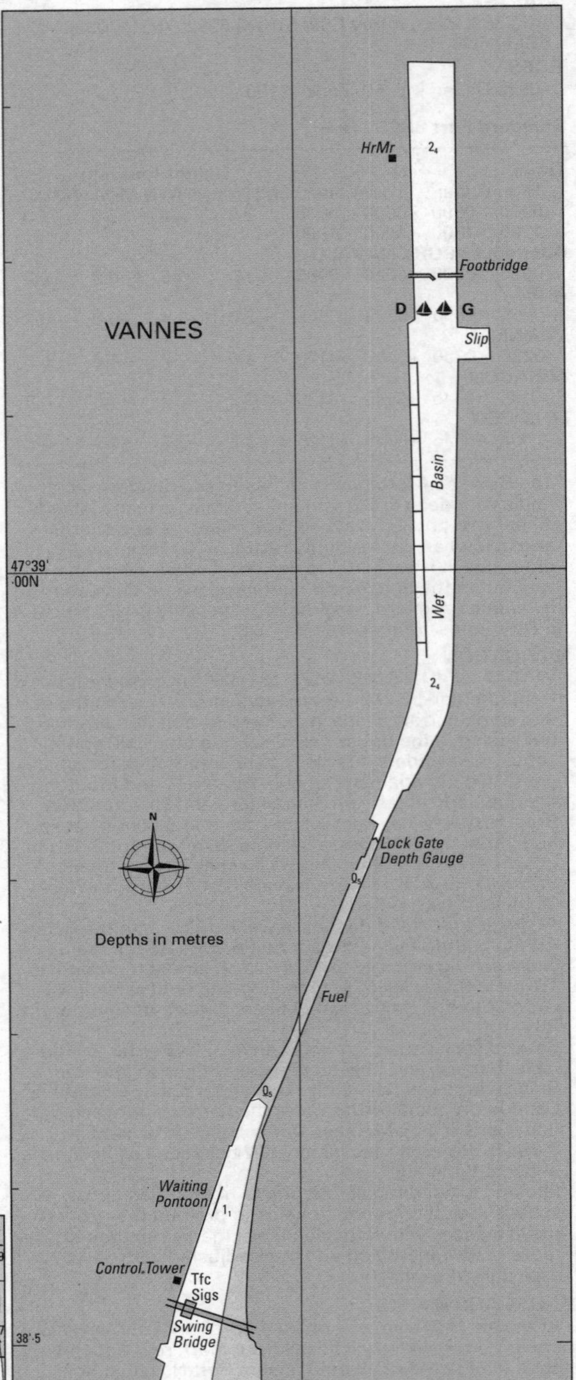

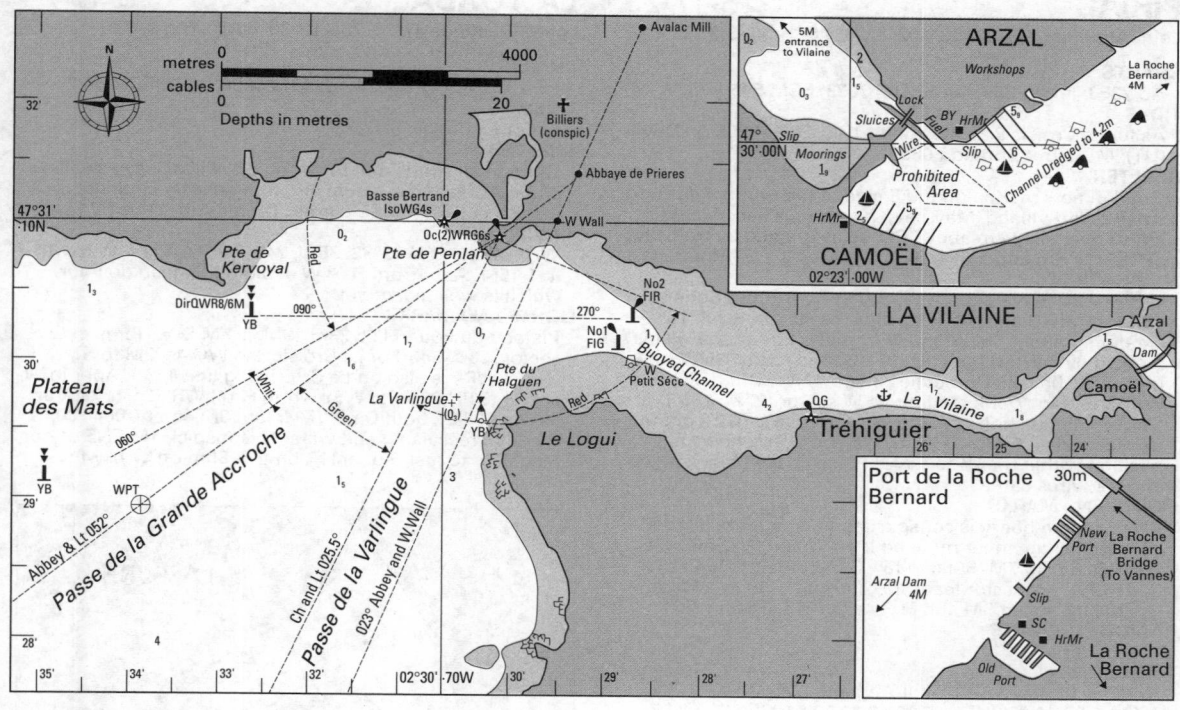

VILAINE RIVER   8-17-22

Morbihan 47°30'·40N 02°28'·60W   Rtg 3-1-2

CHARTS

AC 2353; SHOM 2381, 5418, 7033; ECM 546; Imray C39

TIDES

+0500 Dover; ML (Penerf) 3·3; Duration 0610; Zone –0100

Standard Port BREST (◄—)

Times				Height (metres)			
High Water		Low Water		MHWS	MHWN	MLWN	MLWS
0000	0600	0000	0600	6·9	5·4	2·6	1·0
1200	1800	1200	1800				
Differences PENERF							
+0020	–0025	–0015	–0015	–1·5	–1·1	–0·6	–0·3
TRÉHIGUIER							
+0035	–0020	–0005	–0010	–1·4	–1·0	–0·5	–0·3

SHELTER

Good shelter up-river: buoys at Tréhiguier; above Arzal dam in non-tidal waters, marinas at Arzal (N bank) and Camoël (S bank); and 5M upstream at La Roche Bernard on **Ⓥ** pontoon between old and new ports; also at Foleux marina, 4½M further up-river. Masted yachts can transit a swing bridge at Cran to reach Redon where there is a marina, crane and access to Brittany canals (8.15.18).

NAVIGATION

WPT Passe de la Grande Accroche 47°29'·00N 02°33'·90W, 232°/052° from/to Penlan lt, 3·3M. La Vilaine has a bar (min 0·5m), on which seas break in strong onshore winds esp at sp ebb. Best to enter/leave on last of the flood. River is well buoyed up to Tréhiguier and adequately so beyond; keep strictly to buoyed chan as silting occurs. Arzal dam lock opens at H, up to 9 times per day, 0700–2200 (LT) in Jul/ Aug; in other months 0800, 0900, 1200, 1400, 1600, 1700, 1900, 2000LT. But times vary daily; call Hr Mr VHF Ch 09 or recorded ☎ 97·45·01·15. Keep strictly to the buoyed chan to avoid the prohib area (Y buoys) below/above the dam. There is **Ⓐ** or room to ⚓ below the dam to await lock opening.

LIGHTS AND MARKS

There are three apprs and ldg lines to river ent:
(1) Passe de la Grande Accroche: Penlan lt ho on with Abbey de Prières at 052°. Marks are reportedly conspic by day.
(2) Penlan lt on with Billiers ch tr 023°, leaving Varlingue Rk (dries 0·3m) close to stbd.
(3) Passe de la Varlingue: W wall (not conspic) ≠ Abbey Tr 023°, keeping close to WCM bn and oyster poles off Le Logui.

Two principal lights are visible in the approaches:
(1) Basse Bertrand G tr, Iso WG 4s 6m 9/6M, W040°-054°, G054°-227°, W227°-234°, G234°-040°.
(2) Penlan, W tr, R bands Oc (2) WRG 6s 26m 15/11M, R292°-025°, G025°-052°, W052°-060°, R060°-138°, G138°-180°. At the river mouth Petit Sécé W bn tr is easier to see than Nos 1 and 2 chan buoys.

RADIO TELEPHONE

Lock VHF Ch 18 (HX); Arzal-Camoël marina Ch 09 (French); no VHF at La Roche Bernard.

TELEPHONE

ARZAL/CAMOËL: Hr Mr 02·99·90·05·86; Aff Mar 02·99·90·32·62; CROSS 02·97·55·35·35; ⌗ 02·97·63·18·71 at Vannes; Auto 08·36·68·08·56; Brit Consul 01·40·63·16·02; Dr 02·97·45.01.21; Ⓗ 02·99.90.61.20.
LA ROCHE BERNARD: Hr Mr 02·99·90·62·17.

FACILITIES

ARZAL/CAMOËL: **Marina** (630 total, inc 25 visitors on each bank) ☎ 02·99·90·05·86, FF90, FW, AC, Ⓞ, C (15 ton), P, D, Gaz, SM, ME, El, Sh, CH, Ⓔ, R, Bar. Note: these facilities are all at Arzal. Camoël has Hr Mr and showers.
Towns (both 3km) V, R, Bar, Ⓑ, ⊠.
LA ROCHE BERNARD: **New Port** (110) ☎ 02·99·90·62·17, FF70, FW, AC, M, ME, El, Ⓔ, Sh, CH; **Old Port** (200), P, D, Ⓞ, C, AC, CH, FW, Slip. **Town** V, Gaz, R, Bar, Ice, ⊠, Ⓑ, ⇌ (Pontchateau), ✈ (Nantes or Rennes).
Foleux: ☎ 02·99·91·80·87. Marina on N bank; buoys off both banks. FW, AC, R.

ADJACENT HARBOUR

PENERF, Morbihan, 47°30'·10N 02°38'·80W, AC 2353; SHOM 5418, 7033. HW +0515 on Dover (UT); Duration 0610; ML 3·3m. See 8.17.22. Shelter good, except in fresh W'lies. SDs and SHOM 5418 are advised. Appr between Penvins PHM buoy and Borenis SHM buoy. Ldg marks: Le Pignon PHM lt bn on 359° with Le Tour du Parc spire. The 3 ents are not easy: **Passe de l'Ouest** is shoal and ill marked. **Passe du Centre** is the widest and easiest, ldg 150m W of a drying reef, marked by La Traverse SHM bn, N of which depth is 0·5m; thence 40m E of Le Pignon. **Passe de l'Est** has 4m, but is narrower and rks are close to stbd. It leads E of La Traverse and Le Pignon bns to join Passe du Centre. In the river, head ENE for 1M to **Ⓐ** off Penerf quay. Beware oyster beds. Le Pignon lt, Fl (3) WR 12s 6m 9/6M, W sector 349°-028° covers the appr, but night entry not advised. Facilities: P & D (on quay), Slip, CH, El, ME, Sh. **Village** Bar, Dr, R, V.

17

PIRIAC   8-17-23

Loire Atlantique 47°23´·00N 02°32´·63W   Rtg 3-3-2

CHARTS
AC 2353; Imray C39, 40; SHOM 7033; ECM 546

TIDES
As for Le Croisic 8.17.25. Zone –0100. HW +0505 on Dover (UT); ML 3·1m; Duration 0605.

SHELTER
Good in new marina on the E side of the drying FV hbr in small resort village. May be exposed to N'lies. Access HW±3 over sill 2·4m above CD; sill is marked by traffic lts (IPTS), a PHM and a SHM perch and by 4 Y SPM perches.

NAVIGATION
WPT 47°24´·30N 02°32´·10W, 017°/197° from/to hbr ent, 1·25M. From S and SW keep clear of Plateau de Piriac extending about 1M W and N from the hbr; to the W it is marked by a WCM buoy, Q (9) 15s, and to the NNW by 2 unlit NCM bns. Ile Dumet lies 3.5M WNW with lt, Fl (2+1) WRG 15s 14m 7/4M; at night its W sector (272° -285°) used in conjunction with the W sector (067°-072°) of Pte de Mesquer lt, Oc (3+1) WRG 12s 7m 10/7M, helps to position within the W sector of Piriac lt, see below; night appr requires care.

LIGHTS AND MARKS
Piriac church belfry is conspic daymark, approx aligned 197° with chan. Inner mole hd lt on W bcn tr, Dir Oc (2) WRG 6s 8m 10/7M, R066°-148°, G148°-194°, W194°-201°, R201°-221°; W sector leads 197° through hbr ent. Bkwtr lts are Fl G 4s 5m 5M and Fl R 4s 4m 5M. IPTS at sill.

RADIO TELEPHONE
VHF Ch 09.

TELEPHONE
Hr Mr ☎ 02·40·23·52·32 (Jul-Aug only), 🛥 02·40·15·51·78. Aff Mar 02·40·23·33·35; ⌗ 02·40·23·32·51; CROSS 02·97·55·35·35; Auto 08·36·68·08·44; SNSM 02·40·23·55·74.

FACILITIES
Marina (480+20 visitors), FW, AC, D, P (cans) on quay, Slip, C (9 tons), CH, Ⓔ, El, ME, Sh; drying M, in FV hbr.

Ile Dumet, 3·5M WNW of Piriac, has pleasant ⚓ on NE side in 2m, clear of mussel beds. Appr with lt ho, Fl (2+1) WRG 15s 14m 7/4M, bearing 215°.

LA TURBALLE   8-17-24

Loire Atlantique 47°20´·78N 02°30´·80W   Rtg 3-2-2

CHARTS
AC 2353; Imray C39, 40; SHOM 6826, 7033; ECM 546

TIDES
As for Le Croisic 8.17.25

SHELTER
Good in all winds, but in strong SSW'lies heavy swell can enter. Access H24. Inside ent, turn smartly stbd into marina (1·5-2m) in SE corner. There is an active FV fleet.

NAVIGATION
WPT 47°20´·25N 02°32´·35W, 245°/065° from/to W bkwtr lt, 1·15M. Appr from S or W avoiding Plateau du Four, which is well marked/lit.

LIGHTS AND MARKS
Plateau du Four, Fl 5s 23m 19M, is 5M SW. Hbr is in G sector (136°-345°) of Le Croisic, Iso WG 4s, 2M to S. (Note: WPT is also on Le Croisic ldg line 156°). Appr in W sector (315°-060°) of W bkwtr lt, Fl (4) WR 12s, to pick up ldg lts 006·5°, both Dir F Vi 11/19m 3M, intens 004°-009°. By day Trescalan ⊕ and water tr (conspic), 1M ENE of hbr, lead 070° to just S of ent. R bn tr is 80m off W bkwtr.

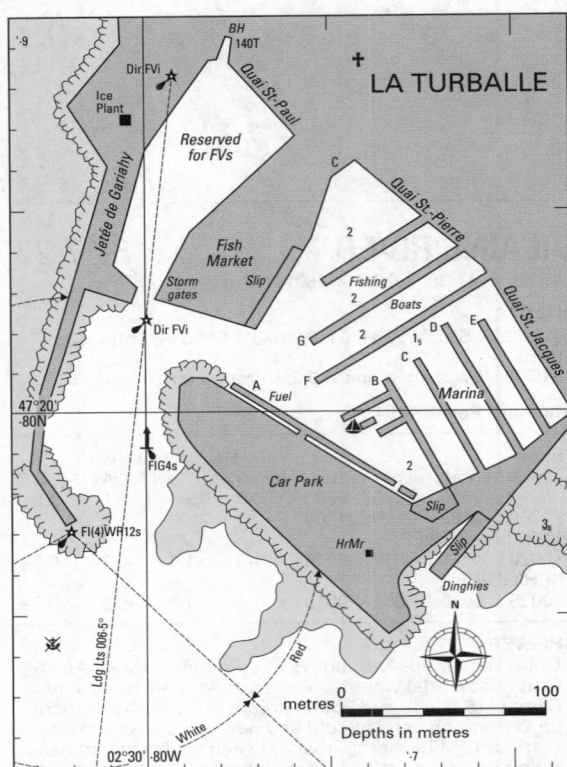

RADIO TELEPHONE
VHF Ch 09.

TELEPHONE
Hr Mr 02·40·62·80·40; Aff Mar 02·40·23·33·35; ⌗ 02·40·23·32·51; Auto 08·36·68·08·44; SNSM 02·40·23·42·67.

FACILITIES
Marina (290+20 visitors, pontoon B), ☎ 02·40·62·80·40, FF95, FW, AC, Slip, M, C (16 tons), BH (140 tons), D (H24), P at garage 500m, ME, El, Ⓔ, Sh, CH, ⌂ in Master Hbr House (Capitainerie), Gaz, R, SM, YC, SHOM, Ice.
Town V, R, Ⓑ, ✉, Ⓞ, Dr, Bus to St Nazaire and Nantes.

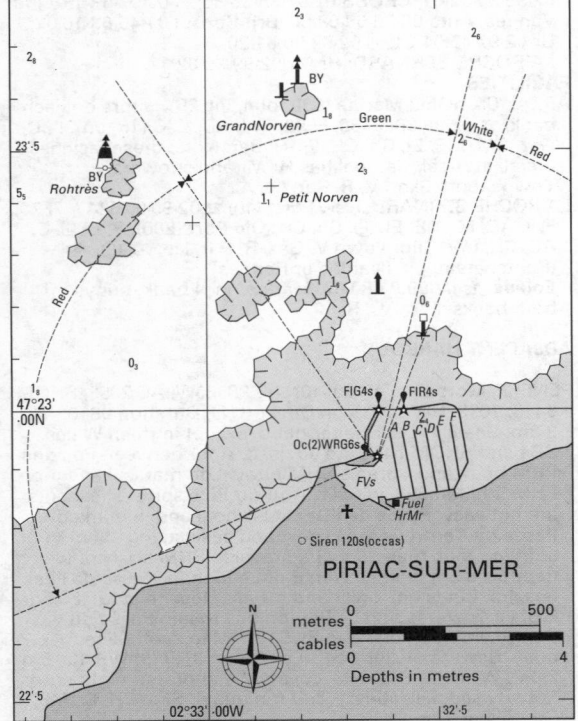

LE CROISIC   8-17-25

Loire Atlantique 47°18'·56N 02°31'·27W   Rtg 3-2-1

CHARTS
AC 2353, 2986, 2646; Imray C39; SHOM 6826, 7033, 7395; ECM 546, 547

TIDES
+0450 Dover; ML 3·3; Duration 0605; Zone −0100

Standard Port BREST (←—)

Times				Height (metres)			
High Water		Low Water		MHWS	MHWN	MLWN	MLWS
0000	0600	0000	0600	6·9	5·4	2·6	1·0
1200	1800	1200	1800				
Differences LE CROISIC							
+0015	−0040	−0020	−0015	−1·5	−1·1	−0·6	−0·3

SHELTER
Five drying (1·7m) basins, called *Chambres* are formed by islands (*Jonchères*). Berth in the last *Chambre*, bows to pontoon or against the wall, access HW±1. See Hr Mr for mooring or ⚓ in Le Poul which is crowded; tripping line is advised. Safest ⚓ in Pen Bron Creek; streams run hard.

NAVIGATION
WPT 47°19'·00N 02°31'·80W, 336°/156° from/to front ldg lt, 1·2M. Sp tides reach 4kn. Safest ent is HW±1 sp, HW±2 np. Beware the rks at Hergo Tr, SHM, Fl G 2·5s. Note: the W sector (093°-137°) of Tréhic lt, Iso WG 4s, which leads clear of distant dangers, will lead onto close-in dangers. Keep to the ldg lines as appr and hbr dry extensively to the E.

LIGHTS AND MARKS
The sanatorium, hospital and ch belfry are conspic.
Outer ldg lts 156°: both Dir Oc (2+1) 12s 10/14m 18M; intens 154°-158°, synch; Y □s on W pylons, rear has G top.
Middle ldg lts 174°: both QG 5/8m 11M; vis 170°-177°; Y □s with G stripe on G & W pylons, almost obsc'd by trees.
Inner ldg lts QR 134°; R/W chequered □s on Fish market roof.

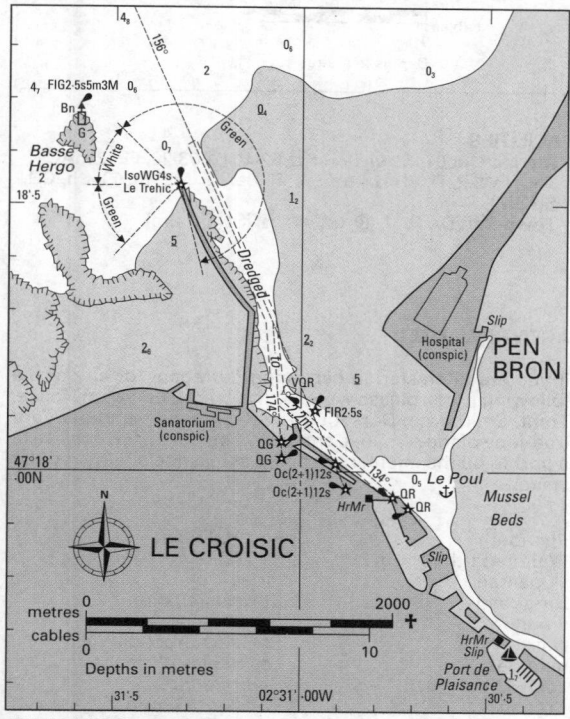

LE CROISIC

RADIO TELEPHONE
VHF Ch 09 (0800-1200; 1330-2000 in season).

TELEPHONE
Hr Mr 02·40·23·10·95; Aff Mar 02·40·23·06·56; CROSS 02·97·55·35·35; SNSM 02·40·23·01·17; ⊞ 02·40·23·05·38; Météo 02·40·90·08·80; Police 02·40·23·00·19; Dr 02·40·23·01·70; Ⓗ 02·40·23·01·12; Brit Consul 01·40·63·16·02.

FACILITIES
Marina (5th Chambre; 220+15 Ⓥ), FF60, FW, ME, El, Sh; **Quai** Slip, C (8 & 180 ton), CH, Ⓔ, YC, Divers, 🅶. **Town** P & D (cans), V, Gaz, R, Bar, ⊠, Ⓑ, ⇌, ✈ (St Nazaire).

LE POULIGUEN   8-17-26

Loire Atlantique 47°16'·40N 02°25'·40W   Rtg 3-2-2

CHARTS
AC 2986, 2353, 2646; Imray C39; SHOM 6797, 7395; ECM 547

TIDES
Sp +0435 Dover, Nps +0530 Dover; ML 3·3; Duration Sp 0530, Nps 0645; Zone −0100

Standard Port BREST (←—)

Times				Height (metres)			
High Water		Low Water		MHWS	MHWN	MLWN	MLWS
0000	0600	0000	0600	6·9	5·4	2·6	1·0
1200	1800	1200	1800				
Differences LE POULIGUEN							
+0020	−0025	−0020	−0025	−1·5	−1·1	−0·6	−0·3

SHELTER
Very good, except in SE winds. 30 Ⓥ berths on pontoon A, to stbd at ent. Yachts up to 2m draft can stay afloat. Beware strong ebb tide. Fixed bridge up-river has 1m clearance MHWS. Le Pornichet, 3M to the E, is an easier approach and ent. Reefs running 4M SE towards Grand Charpentier lt ho, Q WRG, form a barrier across the Baie du Pouliguen which may be entered through any of 4 passes. In strong S winds, beware swell and breakers.

NAVIGATION
WPT 47°15'·20N 02°25'·00W, 250°/070° from/to Penchâteau PHM buoy, Fl R 2·5s, 0·58M. Best appr at HW −1 from W/SW between Pte de Penchateau and Les Evens (drying reef). From Penchâteau and Basse Martineau PHM light buoys, leave La Vieille SHM perch and Petits Impairs bn, Fl (2) G 6s, to stbd, and 3 PHM bns well to port. The inner chan shifts, dries approx 1·5m and is marked at longish intervals by one PHM and 5 SHM poles.

LIGHTS AND MARKS
W jetty, QR 13m 9M, vis 171°-081°, is a slim white column, R top, conspic. The final SHM pole marks the narrowing chan and E training wall which covers. Navigational lights are very hard to see against shore lts of La Baule and night appr is not advised.

RADIO TELEPHONE
Pouliguen VHF Ch 09, 0900-1230 & 1400-1900LT.

TELEPHONE
Hr Mr 02·40·11·97·97, ☏ 02·40·11·97·98; ⊞ 02·40·61·32·04; Aff Mar 02·40·42·32·55; SNSM 02·40·61·03·20; CROSS 02·97·55·35·35; Météo 02·40·90·00·80; Auto 08.36.68.08.44; Police 02·40·24·48·17; Dr 02·40·60·51·73.

FACILITIES (Le Pouliguen)
Quai (Pontoons 850+30 Ⓥ) ☎ 02·40·60·03·50, Slip, P, D, AC, FW, C (18 ton), M, ME, Sh, CH, Ⓔ, El, Divers, SM; **La Baule YC** ☎ 02·40·60·57·87 (allots berths to visitors). **Town** V, Gaz, R, Bar, ⊠, Ⓑ, ⇌, ✈ (St Nazaire).

HISTORICAL NOTE: 240 years ago ......

The **Battle of Quiberon Bay** was fought on 20 November 1759 between the British Channel Fleet under Admiral Sir Edward Hawke and the French Fleet under Marshal de Conflans. The action took place in the waters, then mostly uncharted, between Belle Île, Île Hoedic and Le Croisic. A WNW near-gale was blowing with frequent severe squalls. Several ships were lost on the Plateau du Four, on Les Cardinaux, rocks off Île Hoedic, and on the mainland lee shore.

The British victory was commemorated by the song *Heart of Oak*, written by David Garrick, which has taken its place among the great battle songs of the world.

Come cheer up, my lads, 'tis to glory we steer,
To add something more to this wonderful year:
To honour we call you, not press you like slaves,
For who are so free as we sons of the waves?
* Heart of oak are our ships, heart of oak are our men;*
* We always are ready, steady boys, steady,*
* We'll fight, and we'll conquer again and again.*

17

PORNICHET   8-17-27
Loire Atlantique 47°15´·55N 02°21´·05W   Rtg 1-1-2

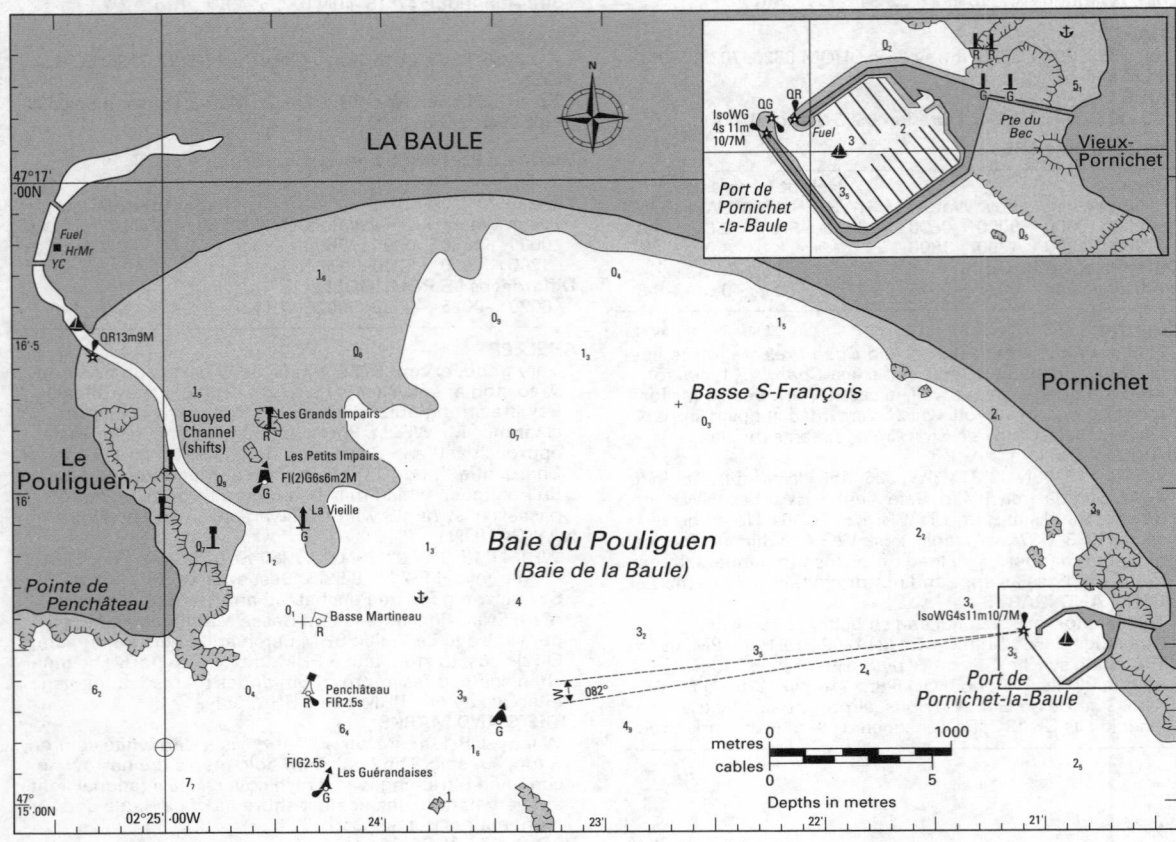

CHARTS
AC 2989, 2986, 2353; Imray C39; SHOM 6797, 7395; ECM 547

TIDES
Sp +0435 Dover, Nps +0530 Dover; ML 3·3; Duration Sp 0530, Nps 0645; Zone –0100

Standard Port BREST (←)

Times				Height (metres)			
High Water		Low Water		MHWS	MHWN	MLWN	MLWS
0000	0600	0000	0600	6·9	5·4	2·6	1·0
1200	1800	1200	1800				
Differences PORNICHET							
+0020	–0045	–0022	–0022	–1·4	–1·0	–0·5	–0·2

SHELTER
A very large artificial marina at the E end of the B de la Baule, with excellent shelter and facilities. Access at all tides for up to 2·5m draft, but engine required in narrow ent in W'ly >Force 8. Drying ⚓ as shown on chartlet inset.

NAVIGATION
Appr from the W, as for Le Pouliguen (3M), then direct via W sector (082°) of Iso WG 4s bkwtr lt; also from SW, track 035° between Les Evens PHM and Les Troves SHM unlit bns; or from SSE track 335° from Grand Charpentier lt.

LIGHTS AND MARKS
Navigational lts are very hard to see against shore lts of La Baule. S bkwtr Iso WG 4s 11m 10/7M, W081°-084° (3°), G084°-081° (357°). Inside ent, QR 4m 1M and QG 3m 1M on perches define the channel.

RADIO TELEPHONE
VHF Ch 09.

TELEPHONE
Aff Mar 02·40·60·56·13; CROSS 02·97·55·35·35; ⌗ 02·40·61·32·04; Météo 02·40·90·08·80; Auto 08·36·68·08·44; Ⓗ (St Nazaire) 02·40·90·60·60; Dr (La Baule) 02·40·60·17·20; Brit Consul 01·40·63·16·02.

FACILITIES
Marina (1000+150 visitors) ☎ 02·40·61·03·20, FF125, AC, Slip, FW, P, D, BH (24 ton), V, R, Bar, ⊡, ME, EI, Ⓔ, Sh, CH, SHOM.
Town Bar, Dr, R, V, Ⓑ, ✉, ⇌, ✈ (St Nazaire).

RIVER LOIRE/ST NAZAIRE

Loire Atlantique   Rtg (St Nazaire) 3-3-2   **8-17-28**

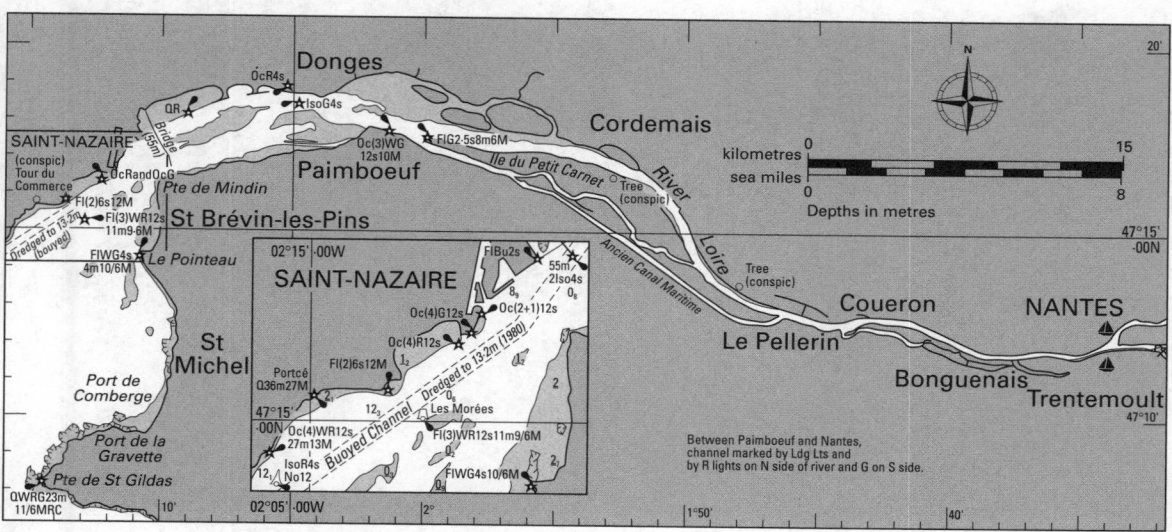

CHARTS
AC 2985, 2989, 2986; Imray C40; SHOM 6797, 7396, 7395;
ECM 248, 547
TIDES
St Nazaire: Sp +0445 Dover, Nps –0540 Dover; ML 3·6;
Duration Sp 0640, Nps 0445; Zone –0100

Standard Port BREST (←)

Times				Height (metres)			
High Water		Low Water		MHWS	MHWN	MLWN	MLWS
0000	0600	0000	0600	6·9	5·4	2·6	1·0
1200	1800	1200	1800				
Differences ST NAZAIRE							
+0030	–0040	–0010	–0010	–1.1	–0.8	–0.4	–0.2
LE GRAND CHARPENTIER							
+0015	–0045	–0025	–0020	–1.5	–1.1	–0.6	–0.3
DONGES							
+0040	–0030	0000	0000	–0.9	–0.7	–0.5	–0.4
CORDEMAIS							
+0055	–0005	+0105	+0030	–0.7	–0.5	–0.7	–0.4
LE PELLERIN							
+0110	+0010	+0145	+0100	–0.7	–0.5	–0.9	–0.4
NANTES (Chantenay)							
+0133	+0055	+0215	+0125	–0.6	–0.3	–0.8	–0.1

SHELTER
Hbr is mainly naval and commercial, but yachts can berth
at S end of Bassin Penhoet; ent via E lock and Bassin de St
Nazaire. ⚓ in Bonne Anse.
NAVIGATION
WPT 47°07'·95N 02°20'·00W, 205°/025° from/to front ldg lt,
7·3M, via S chan. Or appr from W, via N chan, to join dredged
chan (13·2m) SE of Grand Charpentier lt Q WRG. In strong W
winds the bar (outside chan) is only safe HW –3 to HW.
R Loire navigable 28M to Nantes and ent to canals (8.15.18).
Tolls may be due above Nantes; see 8.15.8.
LIGHTS AND MARKS
Appr ldg lts 025½°: both Q 6/36m 22/27M, intens 024°-027°.
RADIO TELEPHONE
St Nazaire Port VHF Ch **12** 16 06 14 67 69 (H24). Other stns:
Donges Ch 12 16 (occas); Nantes Ch 12 16 06 67 69 (0700-
1100, 1300-1700, except Sun); water level reports (St Nazaire
to Nantes) broadcast on Ch 73 every 15min from H+00.
TELEPHONE
ST NAZAIRE Hr Mr 02·40·00·45·20; Aff Mar 02·40·22·46·32;
CROSS 02·97·55·35·35; SNSM 02·40·61·03·20; ⌗
02·40·66·82·65; Météo 02·40·90·00·80; Auto 08.36.68.08.44;
Police 02·40·70·55·00; Dr 02·40·22·15·32; Ⓗ 02·40·90·60·60.
NANTES Hr Mr 02·40·44·20·54; Aff Mar 02·40·73·18·70;
⌗ 02·40·73·39·55; Météo 02·40·84·80·19; Ⓗ 02·40·48·33·33;
Brit Consul 01·40·63·16·02.

FACILITIES
ST NAZAIRE **Quai** P, D, L, FW, C, M, ME, El, Sh, CH, Ⓔ,
SHOM. **Town** V, Gaz, R, Bar, ✉, Ⓑ, ⇌, ✈.
NANTES **Quai** FW, C, CH, SHOM, ME, El, Ⓔ; **Trentemoult**
AB. **City** all facilities: ✉, Ⓑ, ⇌, ✈. Ferry: St Malo/Roscoff.

MINOR HARBOURS BETWEEN SAINT-NAZAIRE AND POINTE DE SAINT-GILDAS

The following three small hbrs lie NE of Pte de St-Gildas,
on the E side of the R Loire estuary; see chartlet above.
They are flanked by shellfish beds on rky ledges drying
to about 4ca offshore; they are sheltered from W'lies but
open to N'lies. Charts are AC 2986, 2981, 3216; SHOM
7395, 6797; ECM 547. Tidal data may be interpolated
from Le Grand Charpentier, St-Nazaire (8.17.26) and
Pornic (8.18.9). The bay is shallow. Note: 4M N of Pte de
St-Gildas is La Truie rk, drying 2·6m and marked by unlit
IDM bn; 1·3M SSW of it is a shoal patch 0·7m.

PORT DE COMBERGE, Loire Atlantique, 47°10'·60N
02°09'·50W; this is position of S bkwtr lt, Oc WG 4s 7m 9/5M,
W tr with G top, W123°-140°, G elsewhere. Appr in the W
sector or by day on 136° with the bkwtr lt in transit with the
disused lt ho beyond. Beware Les Moutons, rk drying 0·4m,
7½ca NW of the bkwtr lt, close to the approach track. The ent
is narrow; tiny hbr dries about 2m, access from half-flood.
Hr Mr ☎ 02.40.27.82.85; Facilities: M, FW, YC, Slip, C (6 ton),
L. Other facilities at nearby town of St Michel-Chef-Chef.

PORT DE LA GRAVETTE, Loire Atlantique, 47°09'·71N
02°12'·60W; this is position of the lt on end of the bkwtr, Fl
(3) WG 12s 7m 8/5M, W sector 124°-224°, G elsewhere. The
hbr is 2·2M NE of Pte de St-Gildas. Daymarks are bkwtr lt
in transit 130° with La Treille water tr, 2M inland. Shellfish
beds to the W and E are marked by unlit NCM bns. On
rounding the 600m long bkwtr, turn stbd between lateral
buoys; there is about 1·2m water in the N part of the hbr
which dries closer in. Many local moorings, few facilities.

SAINT-GILDAS (Anse du Boucau), Loire Atlantique, 47°08'·45N
02°14'·65W. The hbr is 5ca N of Pte de St Gildas lt ho, Q
WRG 23m 11/6M (see 8.17.4). The hbr bkwtr extends 3ca N,
with a large automatic tide gauge and ☆ Fl (2) G 6s at its N
end. An unlit SHM bn, and a SHM buoy, Fl G 2·5s (May-
Sept), lie 1ca and 2ca NW of bkwtr hd. Appr from about
1M N of Pte de St-Gildas on a brg of 177° or at night in its
W sector 174°-180°. L'Ilot rky ledge is marked by a PHM bn.
Pick up a mooring in 1·5m in the N part of the hbr or dry
out further S. Hr Mr ☎ 02.40.21.60.07. VHF Ch 09.
Facilities: Slips, YC, FW, C (5 ton), V at Préfailles 1M to E.

17

VOLVO PENTA SERVICE

Sales and service centres in area 18
Names and addresses of Volvo Penta dealers in this area are available from:
France *Volvo Penta France* , 55 Avenue des Champs Pierreux, 92757 Cedex
Tel +33 1 55175445, Fax +33 1 55175261. **Spain** *Volvo Penta España SA*, Paeso
De La Castellana 130, 28046 Madrid Tel +34 1 5666100 Fax +34 1 5666200

VOLVO PENTA

Area 18

South Biscay
River Loire to Spanish Border

8.18.1	Index	**Page 737**
8.18.2	Diagram of ports, lights, RDF bns, Coast radio and weather stns	**738**
8.18.3	Tidal stream charts	**740**
8.18.4	List of lights, fog signals and waypoints	**742**
8.18.5	Passage information	**745**
8.18.6	Distance table	**746**
8.18.7	Special notes for France	**See 8.15.8**
8.18.8	French glossary	**See 8.15.9**
8.18.9	Pornic	**747**
8.18.10	L'Herbaudière (Ile de Noirmoutier) Noirmoutier-en-l'Ile Fromentine	**748**
8.18.11	Port Joinville, Ile d'Yeu Port de la Meule	**749**
8.18.12	St Gilles-Croix-de-Vie	**750**
8.18.13	Les Sables d'Olonne	**751**
8.18.14	Bourgenay	**751**
8.18.15	Ars-en-Ré Jard-sur-Mer L'Aiguillon/La Faute-sur-Mer Marans La Flotte, Ile de Ré	**752**
8.18.16	St Martin, Ile de Ré	**753**
8.18.17	La Rochelle	**754**
8.18.18	Ile d'Oléron (Le Douhet, Port St Denis) Le Chateau Boyardville	**755**
8.18.19	Rochefort Ile d'Aix	**756**
8.18.20	Seudre River (Marennes, La Tremblade)	**757**
8.18.21	La Gironde & Canals (Pointe de Grave, Standard Port, tidal curves)	**758**
8.18.22	Royan Meschers-sur-Gironde Mortagne-sur-Gironde Pauillac Blaye Bordeaux	**759**
8.18.23	Port Bloc	**760**
8.18.24	Arcachon La Vigne Fontainevieille Audenge Andernos	**764**
8.18.25	Landes range	**765**
8.18.26	Capbreton	**766**
8.18.27	Anglet/Bayonne	**766**
8.18.28	St Jean-de-Luz	**767**
8.18.29	Hendaye	**768**

18

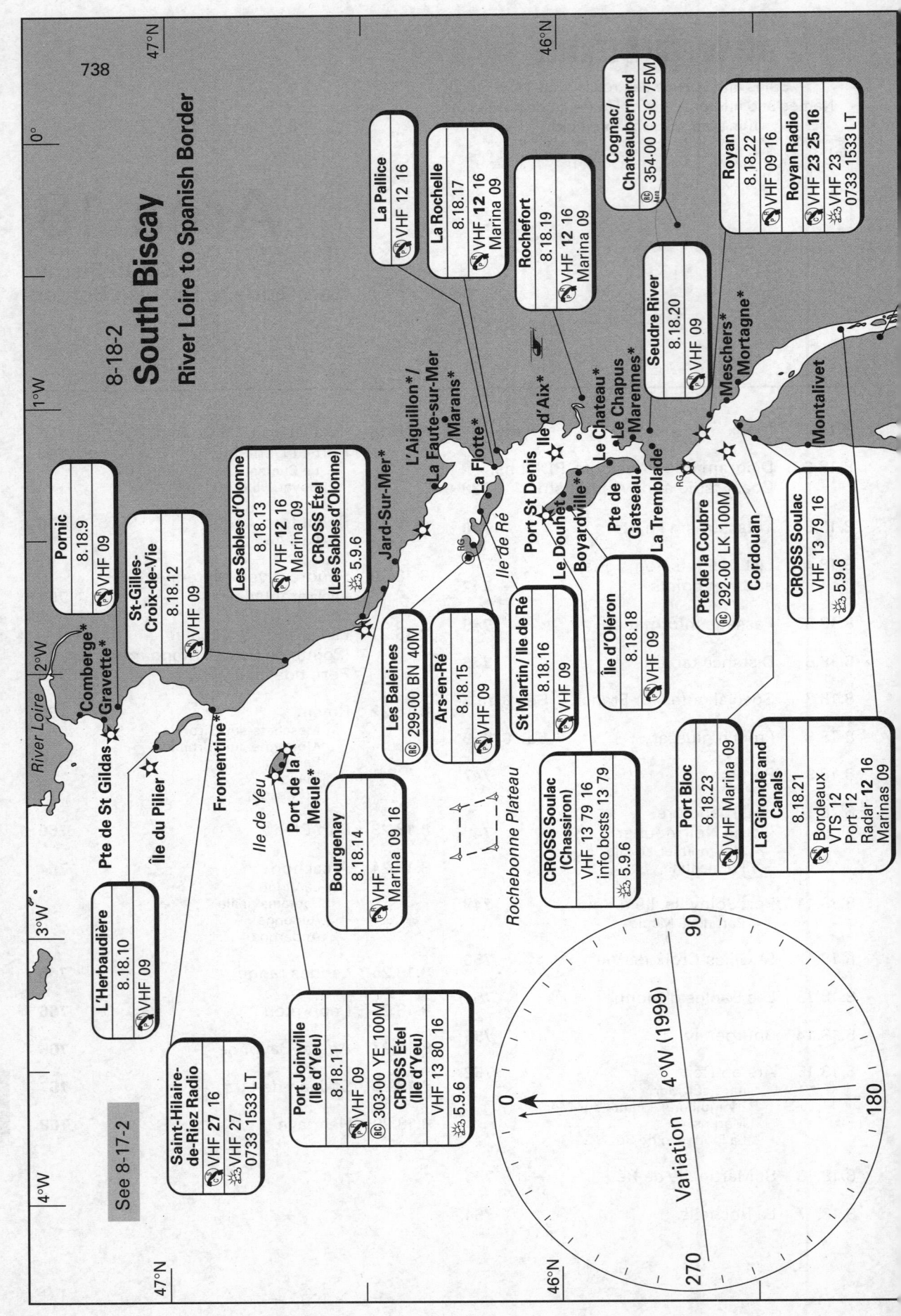

8-18-2
South Biscay
River Loire to Spanish Border

738

See 8-17-2

Saint-Hilaire-de-Riez Radio
VHF **27** 16
VHF 27
0733 1533 LT

L'Herbaudière
8.18.10
VHF 09

Pornic
8.18.9
VHF 09

St-Gilles-Croix-de-Vie
8.18.12
VHF 09

Les Sables d'Olonne
8.18.13
VHF **12** 16
Marina 09
CROSS Étel
(Les Sables d'Olonne)
5.9.6

La Pallice
VHF 12 16

La Rochelle
8.18.17
VHF **12** 16
Marina 09

Rochefort
8.18.19
VHF **12** 16
Marina 09

Cognac/Chateaubernard
354·00 CGC 75M

Royan
8.18.22
VHF 09 16
Royan Radio
VHF **23** 25 16
VHF 23
0733 1533 LT

Seudre River
8.18.20
VHF 09

Port Joinville (Ile d'Yeu)
8.18.11
VHF 09
303·00 YE 100M
CROSS Étel
(Ile d'Yeu)
VHF 13 80 16
5.9.6

Bourgenay
8.18.14
VHF
Marina 09 16

Les Baleines
299·00 BN 40M

Ars-en-Ré
8.18.15
VHF 09

St Martin/ Ile de Ré
8.18.16
VHF 09

Ile d'Oléron
8.18.18
VHF 09

Pte de la Coubre
292·00 LK 100M

CROSS Soulac
VHF 13 79 16
5.9.6

CROSS Soulac
(Chassiron)
VHF 13 79 16
info bcsts 13 79
5.9.6

Port Bloc
8.18.23
VHF Marina 09

La Gironde and Canals
8.18.21
Bordeaux
VTS 12
Port 12
Radar **12** 16
Marinas 09

River Loire

Comberge*
Gravette*

Pte de St Gildas

Ile du Pilier

Fromentine*

Ile d'Yeu

Port de la Meule*

Jard-Sur-Mer*

L'Aiguillon*/
La Faute-sur-Mer
Marans*

La Flotte*

Ile de Ré

Port St Denis
Le Douhet
Boyardville*

Ile d'Aix*
Le Chateau*
Le Chapus*
Marennes*
Pte de Gatseau
La Tremblade

Meschers*
Mortagne*

Montalivet

Cordouan

Rochebonne Plateau

Variation
4°W (1999)

0
90
180
270

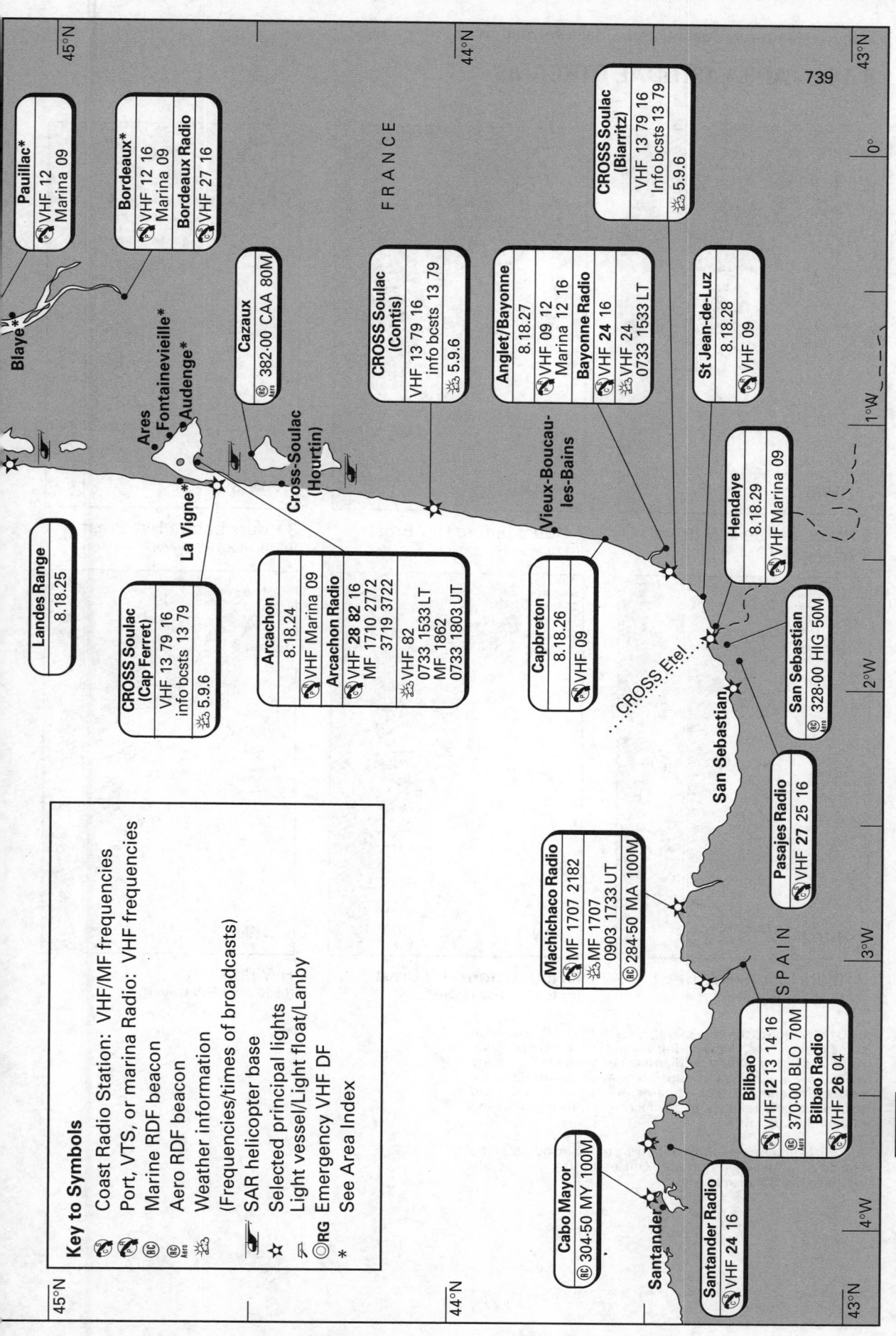

Key to Symbols

- Coast Radio Station: VHF/MF frequencies
- Port, VTS, or marina Radio: VHF frequencies
- Marine RDF beacon
- Aero RDF beacon
- Weather information
  (Frequencies/times of broadcasts)
- SAR helicopter base
- Selected principal lights
- Light vessel/Light float/Lanby
- ○RG Emergency VHF DF
- * See Area Index

45°N

Pauillac*
| VHF 12 |
| Marina 09 |

Bordeaux*
| VHF 12 16 |
| Marina 09 |
| **Bordeaux Radio** |
| VHF 27 16 |

Blaye**

FRANCE

Cazaux
| 382·00 CAA 80M |

Ares
Fontainevieille*
Audenge*

La Vigne*

Cross-Soulac
(Hourtin)

**CROSS Soulac
(Contis)**
| VHF 13 79 16 |
| info bcsts 13 79 |
| 5.9.6 |

Anglet/Bayonne
8.18.27
| VHF 09 12 |
| Marina 12 16 |
| **Bayonne Radio** |
| VHF 24 16 |
| VHF 24 |
| 0733 1533 LT |

**CROSS Soulac
(Biarritz)**
8.18.28
| VHF 13 79 16 |
| Info bcsts 13 79 |
| 5.9.6 |

St Jean-de-Luz
8.18.28
| VHF 09 |

Landes Range
8.18.25

**CROSS Soulac
(Cap Ferret)**
| VHF 13 79 16 |
| info bcsts 13 79 |
| 5.9.6 |

Arcachon
8.18.24
| VHF Marina 09 |
| **Arcachon Radio** |
| VHF 28 82 16 |
| MF 1710 2772 |
| 3719 3722 |
| VHF 82 |
| 0733 1533 LT |
| MF 1862 |
| 0733 1803 UT |

Vieux-Boucau-
les-Bains

Capbreton
8.18.26
| VHF 09 |

CROSS Etel

Hendaye
8.18.29
| VHF Marina 09 |

San Sebastian
| 328·00 HIG 50M |

San Sebastian

Machichaco Radio
| MF 1707 2182 |
| MF 1707 |
| 0903 1733 UT |
| 284·50 MA 100M |

Pasajes Radio
| VHF 27 25 16 |

SPAIN

Cabo Mayor
| 304·50 MY 100M |

Santander

Santander Radio
| VHF 24 16 |

Bilbao
| VHF 12 13 14 16 |
| 370·00 BLO 70M |
| **Bilbao Radio** |
| VHF 26 04 |

44°N

45°N

44°N

43°N

43°N

45°N

44°N

43°N

45°N

44°N

43°N

0°

1°W

2°W

3°W

4°W

739

18

8-18-3 AREA 18 TIDAL STREAMS

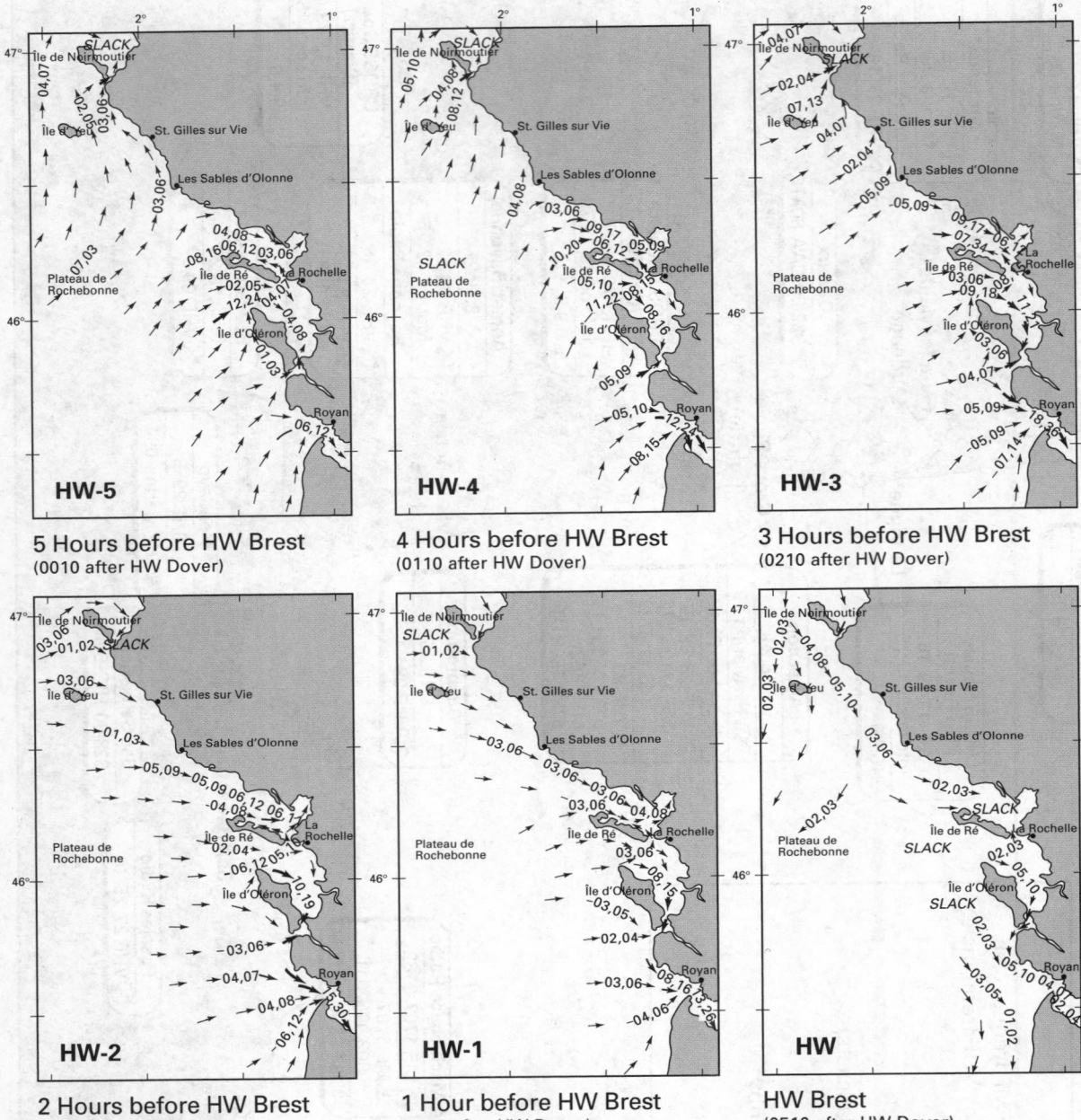

HW-5

5 Hours before HW Brest
(0010 after HW Dover)

HW-4

4 Hours before HW Brest
(0110 after HW Dover)

HW-3

3 Hours before HW Brest
(0210 after HW Dover)

HW-2

2 Hours before HW Brest
(0310 after HW Dover)

HW-1

1 Hour before HW Brest
(0410 after HW Dover)

HW

HW Brest
(0510 after HW Dover)

CAUTION: Due to the very strong rates of the tidal streams in
some of the areas, many eddies may occur. Where possible
some indication of these eddies has been included. In many
areas there is either insufficient information or the eddies are
unstable. Generally tidal streams are weak offshore and
strong winds have a very great effect on the rate and direction
of the tidal streams.

NOTE: No tidal stream information is published by either the
French or British Hydrographic Offices for the area southwards to the Spanish border.

Northward 8.17.3

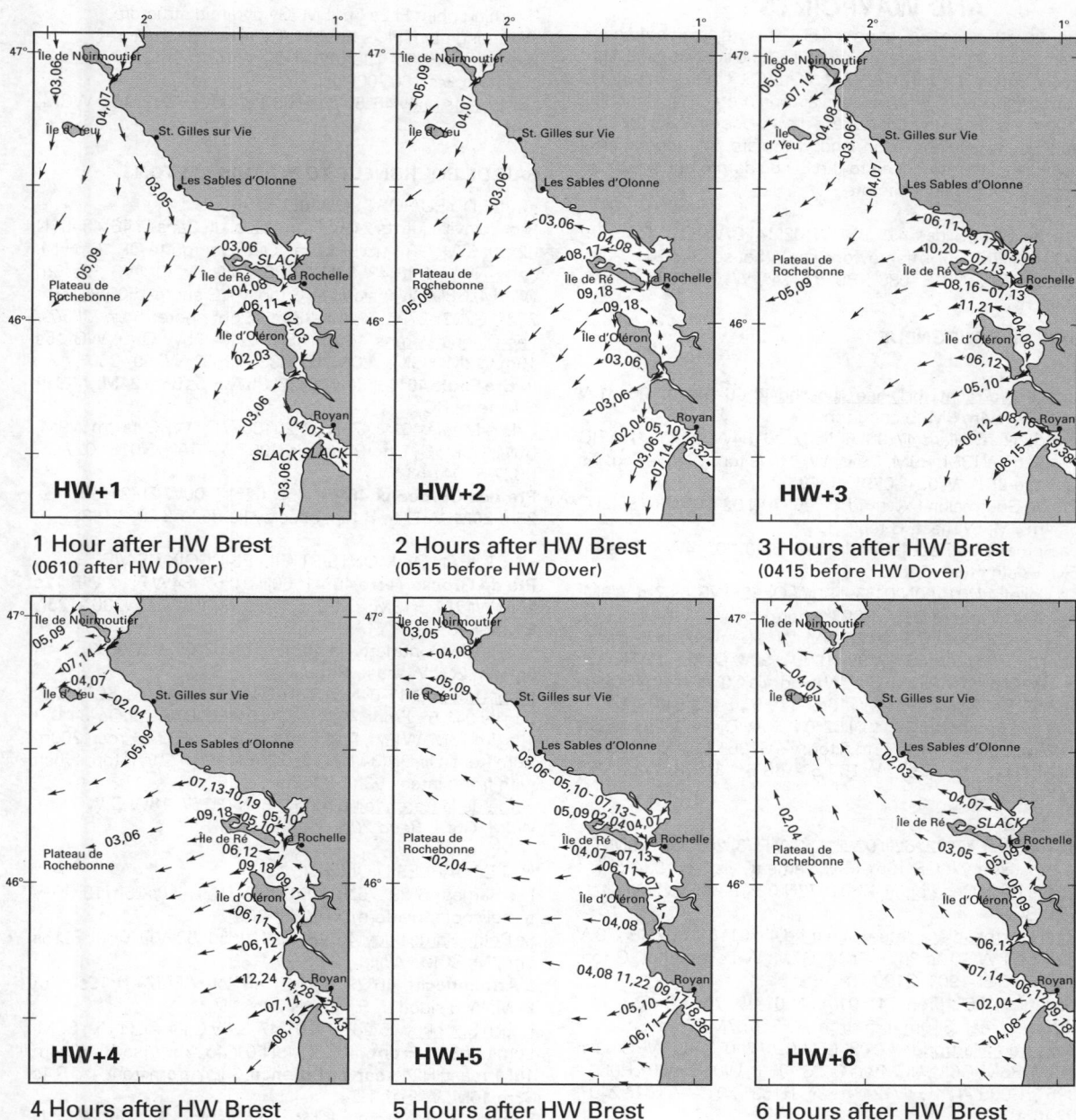

HW+1
1 Hour after HW Brest
(0610 after HW Dover)

HW+2
2 Hours after HW Brest
(0515 before HW Dover)

HW+3
3 Hours after HW Brest
(0415 before HW Dover)

HW+4
4 Hours after HW Brest
(0315 before HW Dover)

HW+5
5 Hours after HW Brest
(0215 before HW Dover)

HW+6
6 Hours after HW Brest
(0115 before HW Dover)

CAUTION: Due to the very strong rates of the tidal streams in some of the areas, many eddies may occur. Where possible some indication of these eddies has been included. In many areas there is either insufficient information or the eddies are unstable. Generally tidal streams are weak offshore and strong winds have a very great effect on the rate and direction of the tidal streams.

NOTE: No tidal stream information is published by either the French or British Hydrographic Offices for the area southwards to the Spanish border.

18

8.18.4 COASTAL LIGHTS, FOG SIGNALS AND WAYPOINTS

Lights with a nominal range of 15M or more are in **bold** print, places and features are in CAPITALS, and light-vessels, light floats and Lanbys in *CAPITAL ITALICS*. Unless otherwise stated lights are white. m = elevation in metres; M = nominal range in miles. Fog signals are in *italics*. Useful waypoints are underlined; use those on land with care. All geographical positions are referenced to the ED 50 datum but should be assumed to be approximate.

Pte de Saint-Gildas 47°08'·10N 02°14'·67W Q WRG 23m W11M, R6M, G6M; framework tr on W house; vis R264°-308°, G308°-078°, W078°-088°, R088°-174°, W174°-180°, G180°-264°; RC.

BAIE DE BOURGNEUF

• PORNIC

Noëveillard Yacht Hbr Digue Ouest hd 47°06'·53N 02°06'·61W Fl (2) R 6s 4m 3M; B col, R top.
Pte de Noëveillard 47°06'·68N 02°06'·84W Oc (3+1) WRG 12s 22m W13M, R9M, G9M; W □ tr, G top, W dwelling; vis G shore-051°, W051°-079°, R079°-shore.
Pte de Gourmalon bkwtr hd 47°06'·70N 02°06'·40W Fl (2) G 6s 4m 8M; W mast, G top.
La Bernerie-en-Retz jetty hd 47°04'·6N 02°02'·4W Fl R 2s 4m 5M; W structure, R top.
Le Collet 47°01'·80N 01°59'·00W Oc (2) WR 6s 7m W9M, R6M; vis W shore-093°, R093°-shore.
Ldg lts 118° both QG 4/12m 6M; W □ G stripe, on W pylon.
Étier des Brochets 46°59'·90N 02°01'·90W Oc (2+1) WRG 12s 8m W10M, R7M, G7M; G tr, W band; vis G071°-091°, W091°-102·5°, R102·5°-116·5°, W116·5°-119·5°, R119·5°-164·5°.
Bec de l'Époids 46°56'·40N 02°04'·50W Dir Iso WRG 4s 6m W12M, R9M, G9M; W □ tr, R top; vis G106°-113·5°, R113·5°-122°, G122°-157·5°, W157·5°-158·5°, R158·5°-171·5°, W171·5°-176°.

• ÎLE DE NOIRMOUTIER

Île du Pilier 47°02'·62N 02°21'·53W Fl (3) 20s 33m **29M**; Gy ▲ tr. Auxiliary lt QR 10m 11M, same tr; vis 321°-034°.
Passe de la Grise buoy 47°01'·73N 02°19'·90W Q (6) + L Fl 15s; SCM.
P de l'Herbaudière Jetée Ouest hd 47°01'·69N 02°17'·79W Oc (2+1) WG 12s 9m W10M, G7M; W col and hut, G top; vis W187·5°-190°, G190°-187·5°.
Ldg lts 187·5°: Front, 47°01'·65N 02°17'·76W Q 10m 7M; Gy mast; rear, 310m from front, Q 26m 7M; Gy mast.
Basse du Martroger 47°02'·65N 02°17'·05W Q WRG 11m W9M, R6M, G6M; NCM; vis G033°-055°, W055°-060°, R060°-095°, G095°-124°, W124°-153°, R153°-201°, W201°-240°, R240°-033°.
Pierre Moine 47°03'·43N 02°12'·30W Fl (2) 6s 14m 9M; IDM.
Pte des Dames 47°00'·73N 02°13'·18W Oc (3) WRG 12s 34m **W19M**, **R15M**, **G15M**; W □ tr; vis G016·5°-057°, R057°-124°, G124°-165°, W165°-191°, R191°-267°, W267°-357°, R357°-016·5°.
Noirmoutier Jetty hd 46°59'·30N 02°12'·95W Oc (2) R 6s 6m 6M; W col, R top.
Pte de Devin 46°59'·20N 02°17'·40W Oc (4) WRG 12s 10m W11M, R8M, G8M; W col and hut, G top; vis G314°-028°, W028°-035°, R035°-134°.

• FROMENTINE

Pte de Notre Dame-de-Monts 46°53'·30N 02°08'·50W Dir Oc (2) WRG 6s 21m W13M, R10M, G10M; W tr, B top; vis G000°-043°, W043°-063°, R063°-073°, W073°-094°, G094°-113°, W113°-116°, R116°-175°, G175°-196°, R196°-230°.
Bridge, each side on centre span Iso 4s 32m **18M**; H24.
Tourelle Milieu 46°53'·60N 02°09'·00W Fl (4) R 15s 6m 5M; R ■ on tr.

• ROUTE DU GOIS CAUSEWAY

E shore Fl R 4s 6m 6M; R hut; vis 038°-218°.
E turning point Fl 2s 5m 5M; Gy pyramid structure.
W turning point Fl 2s 5m 3M; Gy pyramid structure.
Bassotière 46°56'·10N 02°08'·90W Fl G 2s 7m 2M; W tripod, G lantern; vis 180°-000°.
Les Boeufs buoy 46°55'·10N 02°28'·00W VQ (9) 10s; WCM; *Bell.*

BAIE DE BOURGNEUF TO PERTUIS BRETON

• ÎLE D'YEU/PORT JOINVILLE

Port Joinville ldg lts 219°: Front, Quai du Canada 46°43'·67N 02°20'·87W QR 11m 5M; rear, Quai Georgette QR 16m 5M.
Jetty NW hd 46°43'·83N 02°20'·73W Oc (3) WG 12s 9m W11M, G8M; W 8-sided tr, G top; vis G shore-150°, W150°-232°, G232°-279°, W279°-285°, G285°-shore; *Horn (3) 30s.*
Les Chiens Perrins 46°43'·65N 02°24'·55W Q (9) WG 15s 16m W8M, G5M; WCM; vis G330°-350°, W350°-200°.
Petite Foule 46°43'·20N 02°22'·85W Fl 5s 56m **24M**; W □ tr, G lantern; RC.
P de la Meule 46°41'·75N 02°20'·60W Oc WRG 4s 9m W9M, R6M, G5M; Gy □ tr, R top; vis G007·5°-018°, W018°-027·5°, R027·5°-041·5°.
Pte des Corbeaux 46°41'·45N 02°17'·00W Fl (2+1) R 15s 25m **20M**; W □ tr, R top; obsc by Île de Yeu 083°-143°.

• ST JEAN DE MONTS/ST GILLES-CROIX-DE-VIE

Pte de Grosse Terre 46°41'·60N 01°57'·84W Fl (4) WR 12s 25m **W17M**, R13M; W truncated conical tr; vis W290°-125°, R125°-145°.
St Jean de Monts jetty hd 46°47'·15N 02°05'·05W Q (2)   R 5s 10m 2M; W mast, R top.
Pilours buoy 46°41'·04N 01°58'·01W Q (6) + L Fl 15s; SCM; *Bell.*
Ldg lts 043·5°: Front, 46°41'·92N 01°56'·67W Dir Oc (3+1) 12s 7m 13M; W □ tr, R top; intens 033·5°-053·5°; rear, 260m from front, Dir Oc (3+1) R 12s 28m 13M; W □ tr, R top; synch with front; intens 033·5°-053·5°.
Jetée de la Garenne hd 46°41'·51N 01°57'·18W Q WG 8m, W8M, G6M; *Reed 20s.*

• LES SABLES D'OLONNE

Les Barges 46°29'·76N 01°50'·42W Fl (2) R 10s 25m 13M; Gy tr, helicopter platform; vis 265°-205°.
La Petite Barge buoy 46°28'·96N 01°50'·53W Q (6) + L Fl 15s 8m 7M; SCM; *Whis.*
L'Armandèche 46°29'·47N 01°48'·21W Fl (2+1) 15s 42m **24M**; W 6-sided tr, R top; vis 295°-130°.
Nouch Sud buoy 46°28'·63N 01°47'·33W Q (6) + L Fl 15s; SCM.
Ldg lts 033°: **Front**, 46°29'·48N 01°46'·28W Iso R 4s 14m **16M**; mast; H24; **rear**, **La Potence**, 330m from front, Iso R 4s 33m **16M**; W □ tr; H24.
Ldg lts 320°: Front, Jetée des Sables hd, 46°29'·49N 01°47'·43W QG 11m 8M; W tr, G top; rear, Tour de la Chaume, 465m from front, Oc (2+1) 12s 33m 13M; large Gy ■ tr, W turret.
Ldg lts 327°: Front, FR 6m 11M; R line on W hut; rear, 65m from front, FR 9m 11M; R line on W tr; intens 324°-330°.
Jetée St Nicolas hd 46°29'·29N 01°47'·44W UQ (2) R 1s 16m 10M; W tr, R top; vis 143°-094°.

• BOURGENAY

Ldg lts 040°: Front, 46°26'·40N 01°40'·50W QG 8M; rear, QG 8M.
Roches du Joanne buoy 46°25'·35N 01°41'·90W L Fl 10s; SWM.
Digue W hd 46°26'·37N 01°40'·59W Fl R 4s 9M.

• PLATEAU DE ROCHEBONNE (Offshore shoal)

NW buoy 46°12'·90N 02°31'·60W Q (9) 15s; WCM; *Whis.*
NE buoy 46°12'·80N 02°24'·80W Iso G 4s; SHM.
SW buoy 46°10'·15N 02°26'·90W Fl (2) R 6s; PHM.
SE buoy 46°09'·30N 02°21'·00W Q (3) 10s; ECM; *Bell.*

PERTUIS BRETON/ÎLE DE RÉ

• JARD-SUR-MER/LA TRANCHE-SUR-MER

Jard-sur-Mer S bkwtr hd 46°24'·44N 01°34'·77W; PHM.
La Tranche pier hd 46°20'·62N 01°25'·50W Fl (2) R 6s 6m 6M; R col.

Pte du Grouin-du-Cou 46°20'·73N 01°27'·75W Fl WRG 5s 29m **W20M, R16M, G16M**; W 8-sided tr, B top; vis R034°-061°, W061°-117°, G117°-138°, W138°-034°.

• L'AIGUILLON/LA FAUTE-SUR-MER

Le Lay buoy 46°16'·17N 01°16'·41W Q (6) + L Fl 15s; SCM.
No 1 buoy 46°16'·65N 01°16'·20W; SHM.

• ANSE DE L'AIGUILLON/MARANS

Pte de L'Aiguillon buoy 46°15'·40N 01°11'·42W L Fl 10s; SWM.
Port du Pavé ent 46°18'·21N 01°07'·91W Fl G 4s 9m 7M; W col, G top.

• PORT DU PLOMB

W Môle 46°12'·18N 01°12'·13W Fl R 4s 9m 7M; W col, R top.

• LA FLOTTE

La Flotte N bkwtr hd 46°11'·38N 01°19'·23W Fl WG 4s 10m W12M, G9M; W ○ tr, G top; vis G130°-205°, W205°-220°, G220°-257°; *Horn (3) 30s* (by day HW-2 to HW+2). Moiré effect Dir lt 212·5°.
Rivedoux-Plage ldg lts 200°: Front, N pier hd 46°09'·83N 01°16'·56W QG 6m 6M; W tr, G top; rear, 100m from front, QG 9m 6M; W and G chequered col; synch with front.

• ST MARTIN DE RÉ

Bkwtr West hd 46°12'·57N 01°21'·82W Fl R 2·5s 7m 4M; W post, R top.
On ramparts, E of ent 46°12'·50N 01°21'·80W Oc (2) WR 6s 18m W10M, R7M; W tr, R top; vis Wshore-245°, R245°-281°, W281°-shore.
Mole hd Iso G 4s 10m 6M; W tripod, G top; obsc by Pte de Loix when brg less than 124°.

• PORT D'ARS-EN-RÉ

Le Fier d'Ars ldg lts 265°: Front, 46°14'·12N 01°28'·65W Iso 4s 5m 11M; ■ on W hut; vis 141°-025°; **rear**, 370m from front, Dir Iso G 4s 13m **15M**; G ■ on dwelling; synch with front, intens 263°-267°.
Ldg lts 232°: Front, 46°12'·81N 01°30'·50W Q 5m 9M; W hut, R lantern; rear, 370m from front, Q 13m 11M; B stripe on W framework tr, G top; vis 142°-322°.

Les Baleines 46°14'·70N 01°33'·60W Fl (4) 15s 53m **27M**; Gy 8-sided tr, R lantern; RC.
Les Baleineaux 46°15'·87N 01°35'·12W Oc (2) 6s 23m 11M; pink tr, R top.

• ÎLE DE RÉ (SOUTH COAST)

Chanchardon 46°09'·78N 01°28'·33W Fl WR 4s 15m W11M, R9M; B 8-sided tr, W base; vis R118°-290°, W290°-118°.
Chauveau 46°08'·09N 01°16'·33W Oc (2+1) WR 12s 27m **W15M**, R11M; W ○ tr, R top; vis W057°-094°, R094°-104°, W104°-342°, R342°-057°.
Pte de Sablanceaux 46°09'·82N 01°15'·08W Q Vi 7m 1M; W mast and hut, G top.

PERTUIS D'ANTIOCHE

• PERTUIS D'ANTIOCHE/LA ROCHELLE

Chauveau buoy 46°06'·62N 01°15'·98W VQ (6) + L Fl 10s; SCM; *Whis*.
Roche du Sud buoy 46°06'·43N 01°15'·15W Q (9) 15s; WCM.
Le Lavardin 46°08'·15N 01°14'·45W Fl (2) WG 6s 14m W11M, G8M; vis G160°-169°, W169°-160°; IDM.

La Pallice, Môle d'Escale 46°09'·42N 01°14'·43W Dir lt 016°. Dir Q WRG 33m W14M, R13M, G13M; Gy tr; vis G009°-014·7°, W014·7°-017·3°, R017·3°-031°. Sig Stn.
Tour Richelieu 46°08'·95N 01°10'·27W Fl (4) R 12s 10m 9M; R tr; RC; *Siren (4) 60s* (HW–1 to HW+1).
Les Minimes buoy 46°08'·07N 01°11'·45W Q (9) 15s; WCM.
La Rochelle ldg lts 059°: Front, 46°09'·42N 01°09'·06W Dir Q 15m 13M; R ●tr, W bands; intens 056°-062°; by day Fl 4s; rear, 235m from front, Q 25m 14M; W 8-sided tr, G top; synch with front, vis 044°-074°, obsc 061°-065° by St Nicolas tr; by day Fl 4s.
SWM buoy PA, Iso 4s 8m 7M; *Whis*; Ra refl; 46°05'·69N 01°42'·37W.

• ÎLE D'AIX/PASSAGE DE L'EST

Île d'Aix 46°00'·67N 01°10'·60W Fl WR 5s 24m **W24M, R20M**; two W ○ trs, one for lt, one to screen R sector; vis R103°-118°, W118°-103°.
Fort Boyard lt tr 46°00'·03N 01°12'·78W Q (9) 15s.

• FOURAS

Port Sud bkwtr hd 45°59'·03N 01°05'·63W Fl WR 4s 6m 9/6M.
Port Nord pier hd 45°59'·88N 01°05'·75W Oc (3+1) WG 12s 9m W11M, G8M; W&G tr; vis G084°-127°, W127°-084°.

• LA CHARENTE/ROCHEFORT

Ldg lts 115°: Front, **Fort de la Pointe** 45°58'·02N 01°04'·29W Dir QR 8m **19M**; W □ tr, R top; **rear**, 600m from front, Dir QR 21m **20M**; W □ tr, R top; both intens 113°-117°. QR 21m 8M; same tr; vis 322°-067° over Port-des-Barques anchorage.
Port-des-Barques ldg lts 134·3°: Front, 45°57'·01N 01°04'·09W Iso G 4s 5m 9M; rear, 490m from front, Iso G 4s 13m 11M; synch with front; intens 125°-145°.
Rochefort No 1 Basin ent 45°56'·61N 00°57'·21W (unmarked).

ÎLE D'OLÉRON

Pte de Chassiron 46°02'·80N 01°24'·60W Fl 10s 50m, **28M**; W ○ tr, B bands; part obsc 297°-351°; Sig Stn.
Rocher d'Antioche 46°04'·00N 01°23'·70W Q 20m 11M; NCM.

• ST DENIS

E Jetty hd 46°02'·16N 01°21'·97W Fl (2) WG 6s 6m W9M G6M; □ hut; vis G205°-277°, W277°-292°, G292°-165°.
Dir lt 205° 46°01'·67N 01°21'·84W Dir Iso WRG 4s 14m W11M, R8M, G8M; vis G190°-204°, W204°-206°, R206°-220°.

• PORT DU DOUHET/PASSAGE DE L'OUEST

N ent bn 46°00'·18N 01°19'·10W; SHM.
Chan buoy 46°00'·45N 01°17'·61W Q; NCM.
Chan buoy 46°00'·29N 01°15'·26W Q; NCM.
Chan buoy 45°59'·91N 01°14'·71W Q (3) 10s; ECM.

• LE CHÂTEAU D'OLÉRON

Ldg lts 319°: Front, 45°53'·05N 01°11'·45W QR 11m 7M; R line on W tr; vis 191°-087°; rear, 240m from front, QR 24m 7M; W tr, R top; synch with front.
Tourelle Juliar 45°54'·10N 01°09'·45W Q (3) WG 10s 12m W11M; G8M; ECM; vis W147°-336°, G336°-147°.

• BOYARDVILLE (LA PÉRROTINE)

La Pérrotine buoy 45°58'·37N 01°13'·20W; SHM.
Mole hd 45°58'·30N 01°13'·76W Fl (2) R 6s 8m 5M; W tr,   R top; obsc by Pte des Saumonards when brg less than 150°.

• LA SEUDRE

Pont de la Seudre 45°48'·00N 01°08'·25W Q 20m 9M each side, vis 054°-234° and 234°-054°.
Pte de Mus de Loup 45°47'·90N 01°08'·50W Oc G 4s 8m 6M; vis 118°-147°.

• LA COTINIÈRE

Dir lt 048° 45°54'·45N 01°18'·50W Dir Oc WRG 4s 13m

18

W11M, R9M, G9M; W stripe with B border on W col; vis G033°-046°, W046°-050°, R050°-063°.
Ent ldg lts 339°. 45°54'·80N 01°19'·70W Front, Dir Oc (2) 6s 6m 13M; W tr, R top; vis 329°-349°; rear, 425m from front, Dir Oc (2) 6s 14m 12M; W tr, R bands; synch with front; intens 329°-349°.

ATT Maumusson buoy 45°47'·00N 01°17'·80W; L Fl 10s; SWM.

LA GIRONDE AND APPROACHES

• LA GIRONDE, GRANDE PASSE DE L'OUEST
BXA buoy 45°37'·60N 01°28'·60W Iso 4s 8m 7M; SWM; Ra refl; Racon (B); *Whis*.
Pte de la Coubre 45°41'·87N 01°13'·93W Fl (2) 10s 64m **28M**; W ○ tr, R top; RC; Sig Stn. F RG 42m R12M, G10M; same tr; vis R030°-043°, G043°-060°, R060°-110°.
Ldg lts 081·5°: **Front**, 1·1M from rear, Dir Iso 4s 21m **20M**; W mast on dolphin; intens 080·5°-082·5°; Q (2) 5s 10m 3M; same structure.
La Palmyre, common rear, 45°39'·77N 01°07'·15W Dir Q 57m **27M**; W radar tr; intens 080·5°-082·5°.
Dir FR 57m **17M**; same tr; intens 325·5°-328·5°.
Ldg lts 327°. **Terre-Nègre**, Front, 1·1M from rear, Oc (3) WRG 12s 39m **W18M**, R14M, G14M; W tr, R top on W side; vis R304°-319°, W319°-327°, G327°-000°, W000°-004°, G004°-097°, W097°-104°, R104°-116°.
Pointe de Grave Jetée Nord hd 45°34'·47N 01°03'·58W, Q 6m 2M; NCM.
Spur 45°34'·38N 01°03'·57W Iso G 4s 5m 2M; vis 173°-020°.

Cordouan 45°35'·25N 01°10'·34W Oc (2+1) WRG 12s 60m **22/18M**; W ▲ tr, dark Gy band and top; vis W014°-126°, G126°-178·5°, W178·5°-250°, W(unintens)250°-267°, R(unintens)267°-294·5°, R294·5°-014°; obsc in estuary when brg more than 285°.

• LA GIRONDE, PASSE SUD
Ldg lts 063°: Front, **St Nicolas**, 45°33'·80N 01°04'·93W Dir QG 22m **16M**; W □ tr; intens 061·5°-064·5°;
rear, **Pte de Grave**, 0·84M from front, Oc WRG 4s 26m **W19M**, **R15M**, **G15M**; W □ tr, B corners and top; vis W(unintens) 033°-054°, W054°-233·5°, R233·5°-303°, W303°-312°, G312°-330°, W330°- 341°, W(unintens) 341°-025°.
Ldg lts 041°: Front, **Le Chay**, 45°37'·35N 01°02'·30W Dir QR 33m **18M**; W tr, R top; intens 039·5°-042·5°;
rear, **St Pierre**, 0·97M from front, Dir QR 61m **18M**; R water tr; intens 039°-043°.

• ROYAN
Royan Jetée Sud 45°37'·08N 01°01'·72W VQ (2) R 1s 11m 12M; *Horn (2) 20s*, sounded by day from HW–2½ to HW+2.
Royan Hbr Nouvelle Jetée hd ent Oc (2) R 6s 8m 6M.

• PORT BLOC
Port Bloc ent N side 45°34'·20N 01°03'·66W Fl G 4s 9m 3M. S pier hd Iso R 4s 8m 4M.

• PAUILLAC/BLAYE
Pauillac NE bkwtr 45°12'·02N 00°44'·50W Fl G 4s 7m 5M.
Ent E side 45°11'·89N 00°44'·52W QG 7m 4M.
Blaye ent N side 45°07'·55N 00°39'·91W Q (3) R 5s 6m 3M. S side, Fl G 4s.

• BORDEAUX
Pont d'Aquitaine 44°52'·87N 00°32'·23W 4 F Vi.
Halte Nautique (yacht pontoons 200m S of bridge) is on W bank inshore of pile, Iso G 4s 5m 5M, almost in mid-stream.

LA GIRONDE TO L'ADOUR

Hourtin 45°08'·55N 01°09'·65W Fl 5s 55m **23M**; R ■ tr.

• ARCACHON
Cap Ferret 44°38'·83N 01°14'·90W Fl R 5s 53m **27M**; W ○ tr, R top; RC. Oc (3) 12s 46m 14M; same tr; vis 045°-135°.
ATT-ARC buoy 44°34'·89N 01°18'·61W L Fl 10s 8m 5M; SWM; (frequently shifted); *Whis*.
Émissaire buoy 44°30'·55N 01°17'·55W Fl (2) 6s 8m 5M; IDM. Ra refl.
La Salie Wharf hd 44°30'·90N 01°15'·60W Q (9) 15s 19m 10M; WCM.
Arcachon W bkwtr hd 44°39'·80N 01°09'·10W QG 6M.
La Vigne 44°40'·50N 01°14'·20W Iso R 4s 7m 5M; (occas.)

Contis 44°05'·70N 01°18'·90W Fl (4) 25s 50m **23M**; W ○ tr, B diagonal stripes.

• CAPBRETON
Digue Nord hd 43°39'·45N 01°26'·80W Fl (2) R 6s 13m 12M; W ○ tr, R top; *Horn 30s*.

L'ADOUR TO BAIE DE FONTARABIE

• ANGLET/BAYONNE
BA buoy 43°32'·66N 01°32'·68W L Fl 10s 8m 8M; SWM.
Digue du large hd 43°31'·96N 01°31'·92W QR 11m 8M;   W tr, R top.
Digue extérieure Sud 43°31'·60N 01°31'·68W, Q (9) 15s 6M; WCM.
Jetée Sud hd Iso G 4s 9m 10M; W □ tr, G top.
Jetée Nord hd Oc (2) R 6s 12m 8M; W pylon, R top.
Boucau ldg lts 090°: Front, 43°31'·88N 01°31'·15W Dir Q 9m **19M**; rear, 250m from front, Dir Q 15m 19M; both W trs, R tops, both intens 086·5°-093·5°.
Ent ldg lts 111·5° (moved as necessary and lit when chan practicable): Front, Dir FG 6m 14M; rear, 149m from front, Dir FG 10m 14M; W tr, G bands; both intens 109°-114°.
Marina ent W side 43°31'·64N 01°30'·44W Fl G 2s 5m 2M; W tr, G top.

• BIARRITZ
Pte Saint-Martin 43°29'·69N 01°33'·17W Fl (2) 10s 73m **29M**; W tr, B top.
Biarritz ldg lts 174° 43°29'·15N 01°33'·88W both Fl R 2s 7/19m 3M.
Guethary ldg lts 133°: Front, 43°25'·65N 01°36'·45W QR 11m 6M; W mast, R top; rear, 66m from front, QR 33m 6M; W tr.
Aero Mo (L) 43°28'·45N 01°31'·90W 7·5s 80m.

• ST JEAN DE LUZ
Passe d'Illarguita ldg lts 138·5°: Front, Socoa, Q WR 36m W12M, R8M; vis W shore-264°, R264°-282°, W282°-shore, W □ tr, B stripe; 43°23'·77N 01°41'·12W.
Rear, Bordagain, 0·77M from front, Dir Q 67m **20M**; B col, W band on W framework tr, B bands.
Ste Barbe ldg lts 101°. **Front**, 43°24'·03N 01°39'·79W Dir Oc (4) R 12s 30m **18M**; W△ on W bldg; intens 095°-107°.
Rear, 340m from front, Dir Oc (4) R 12s 47m **18M**; B ▲ on W □ tr; synch with front; intens 095°-107°.
Ent ldg lts 150·7°, **Front**, 43°23'·32N 01°40'·07W Dir QG 18m **16M**; W □ tr, R stripe; **rear**, 410m from front, Dir QG 27m **16M**; W □ tr, G stripe. Both intens 149·5°-152°.
Digue des Criquas hd 43°23'·92N 01°40'·59W Iso G 4s 11m 7M; G ■ tr; *Horn 15s*.

• HENDAYE
Cap Higuer 43°23'·59N 01°47'·44W Fl (2) 10s 63m **23M**.
Hendaye Epi Socoburu hd 43°22'·90N 01°47'·28W L Fl R 10s 7m 5M.
Marina Digue Coude Fl (2) R 6s 6m 2M; vis 294°-114°.

8.18.5 PASSAGE INFORMATION

BAY OF BISCAY (charts 1104, 20, 2664, 1102)

The *North Biscay Pilot* (Imray/ICC), South to the Gironde, and *South Biscay Pilot* (Adlard Coles), Gironde to La Coruna, are recommended; as is the Admiralty *Bay of Biscay Pilot*. Larger scale French charts are more suitable for inshore waters. For French Glossary see 8.15.9. Some Breton words are in 8.17.5.

Despite its reputation, weather in the S part of the Bay is often warm and settled in summer when the Azores high and Spanish heat low are the dominant weather features. NE'lies prevail in sea area Finisterre in summer and gales may occur twice monthly, although forecast more frequently. Atlantic lows can bring W'ly spells at any time. SE or S winds are rare, but wind direction and speed often vary from day to day. Sea and land breezes can be well developed in the summer. Off N Spain *Galernas* are dangerous squally NW winds which blow with little warning. Rainfall is moderate, increasing in the SE, where thunder is more frequent. Sea fog occurs May-Oct, but is less common in winter.

Tidal streams are weak offshore, but can be strong in estuaries and channels, and around headlands. The tidal stream chartlets at 8.18.3 are based on NP 265 (Admiralty Tidal Stream Atlas for France, W Coast) which uses data from actual observations out to 15-25M offshore. The equivalent French Atlas gives more data, but based on computer predictions.

The general direction and rate of the surface current much depends on wind: in summer it is SE, towards the SE corner of B of Biscay, where it swings W along N coast of Spain. In winter with W gales, the current runs E along N coast of Spain, sometimes at 3kn or more. When crossing B of Biscay, allow for a likely set to the E, particularly after strong W winds.

BAIE DE BOURGNEUF (charts 3216, 2646)

B de Bourgneuf is entered between Pte de St Gildas and Pte de l'Herbaudière, the NW tip of Île de Noirmoutier. Within the B the only yacht hbrs are Pornic (8.18.9) and L'Herbaudière (8.18.10). There are minor drying hbrs at La Bernerie-en-Retz, Le Collet, Port des Brochets and Bec de l'Epoids; with a good anch 5ca NE of Pte des Dames. The E and S sides of the B are encumbered with shoals, rks and oyster or mussel fisheries. The Bay is sheltered except in W winds, which can raise a heavy sea on the ebb stream.

From the NW (chart 3216) the approach is simple, but beware La Couronnée (dries 1·8m; buoyed) a rky bank about 2M WSW of Pte de St Gildas. Adjacent to it, Banc de Kerouars (least depth 1m; breaks) extends 3M further E. Approach Pornic in the W sector of Pte de Noveillard lt, ie S of Banc de Kerouars and NW of Notre Dame IDM bn tr, which lies 2M SW of Pornic and marks end of a line of rks extending ESE to La Bernerie. Pierre du Chenal is an isolated rk about 1M SSE of Notre Dame.

At the N end of Île de Noirmoutier, Chenal de la Grise, between Île du Pilier and Pte de l'Herbaudière and in the W sector of Martroger NCM bn lt, carries 3m, and gives access to L'Herbaudière marina. If heading E to Pornic, pass N of Martroger, and clear of Roches des Pères about 1M ENE. Extending 6M to seaward off the NW end of the island, beware Chaussée des Boeufs, buoyed rks, some drying on to which the tide sets. The S ent via Goulet de Fromentine (SHOM 5039; ECM 549) is difficult due to a shifting bar and 8 hrs of W-going stream; the conspic bridge has 24m clearance. Once inside, further progress to NNE is restricted to shoal draft at sp HW±1 by Route du Gois, causeway drying 3m.

ILE D'YEU TO PERTUIS BRETON (AC 2663)

Les Marguerites, rky shoals, lie SSW of Goulet de Fromentine, with the part-drying reef, Pont d'Yeu (SCM buoy), extending midway between the mainland and the Île d'Yeu; here anch is prohib due to underwater cables. The passage along the NE of the island carries 6-7m nearer to the island. The low-lying, wooded Côte de la Vendée continues 40M SE to Pte du Grouin Cou with few dangers more than 1·5M offshore, except near Les Sables-d'Olonne.

Île d'Yeu, 30m high, has the main lt ho near the NW end and on the NE coast a very conspic water tr close to Port Joinville (8.18.11), crowded in season . Pte des Courbeaux lt ho is at the low SE end of the island and a lesser lt is at the NW end. The SW coast is steep-to and rky, with a tiny drying hbr at Port de la Meule (best to anch outside) and, further E, anch at Anse des Vieilles, both only tenable in settled conditions.

14M to the E of Île d'Yeu lies St Gilles-Croix-de-Vie (8.18.12). Thence 14M further SE is Les Sables-d'Olonne (8.18.13), with Les Barges drying reef (lt) 2·5M W of the ent. Bourgenay (8.18.14) is 6M further SE. The approaches to these secure hbrs are exposed to onshore winds from SE to NW, and susceptible to swell. Jard-sur-Mer is a small drying hbr midway between Bourgenay and Pte du Grouin Cou.

PERTUIS BRETON (chart 2641)

Pertuis Breton is entered between Pte du Grouin du Cou and Pte des Baleines on Île de Ré, (both lit). Beware rky ledges (dry) extending 2·5M NW from Les Baleines. It gives access to the hbrs of Ars-en-Ré (8.18.15), St Martin (8.18.16) and La Flotte on the N shore of Île de Ré which is surrounded by shallows and drying areas. From St Martin to Pte de Sablanceaux there are extensive oyster beds.

On the mainland side, in fresh NW winds against tide a bad sea builds on the bank which extends 8M W of Pte du Grouin du Cou. 1M S of the Pte is Roche de l'Aunis (depth 0·8m). From the Pte sand dunes and mussel beds, with seaward limits marked by SPM buoys, run 8M ESE to the drying ent to Rivière Le Lay, which is fronted by a bar (dries 1m), dangerous in bad weather. The chan to L'Aiguillon/La Faute-sur-Mer (8.18.15) is marked by bns and buoys. 4M further E is entrance to Anse de l'Aiguillon, in which are extensive mussel beds. In NE corner is entrance to Sèvre Niortaise which, after 3·5M, gives access to the canal leading to the port of Marans. Further S is a sheltered route to La Rochelle and Pertuis d'Antioche via Coureau de la Pallice and the road bridge (30m clearance) from the mainland to Île de Ré.

PERTUIS D'ANTIOCHE (chart 2746)

A SWM buoy marks the W approach to Pertuis d'Antioche which runs between Île de Ré and Île d'Oléron, giving access to La Rochelle (8.18.17), Ile d'Aix, La Charente and Rochefort (8.18.19). Its shores are low-lying. Île de Ré forms the N side, fringed by rky ledges extending 2·5M SE from Pte de Chanchardon (lt) and nearly 1M from Pte de Chauveau (marked by lt tr and two bns). Off Pte de Chassiron (lt ho, Sig Stn), at the N tip of Île d'Oléron, reefs extend 5ca W, 1·5M N to Rocher d'Antioche (lit), and 1·5M E, and there is often a nasty sea.

Well offshore, 34-40M W of Île de Ré, Plateau de Rochebonne is a large rky plateau on which the sea breaks dangerously. It is steep-to on all sides, has least depth 3·3m and is buoyed.

18

ÎLE D'OLERON (charts 2746, 2663)

On the NE coast of Ile d'Oléron (8.18.18) there are marinas at Port St Denis and Le Douhet at the N end; further S are yacht and fishing hbrs at Boyardville and Le Château. All are sheltered from the prevailing W'lies.

From Pertuis d'Antioche, Grande Rade des Trousses is entered via either Passage de l'Est close to Île d'Aix (8.18.18) or Passage de l'Ouest, which run each side of La Longe le Boyard, an extensive sandbank on which stands Ft Boyard tr. From Grande Rade, where good anch is found except in fresh NW winds, the narrow and shallow Coureau d'Oléron winds between ledges, oyster beds and constantly changing shoals, with buoys moved to conform. About 2M SE of Le Chateau it is crossed by a bridge, clearance 15m; the bridge arch for the navigable chan is marked at road level by W □ boards, with G ▲ or R ■ superimposed, illuminated at night. Just N of bridge is Fort du Chapus, connected to mainland by causeway. SHOM 6335 is needed. S-going stream starts at HW Pte de Grave − 0230, N-going at HW Pte de Grave + 0500, sp rates 2kn. Up the Seudre River (8.18.20) there are anchs and yacht facilities at Marennes.

The W coast, from Pte de Chassiron 15M SSE to Pte de Gatseau, is bounded by drying rks and shoals. In bad weather the sea breaks 4 or 5M offshore. La Cotinière, the only hbr, is much used by fishing boats and is exposed to the Atlantic. Tidal streams are weak, sp rate 1kn, starting NW at HW Pte de Grave + 0300 and SE at HW Pte de Grave − 0505, but often overcome by current due to prevailing wind. The rate however increases towards Pte de Gatseau.

Here Pertuis de Maumusson separates the island from the mainland. Its ent is marked by a SWM buoy about 3M WSW of Pte de Gatseau. Banc de Gatseau and Banc des Mattes, both of which dry in places, lie N and S of the chan, and are joined by a sand bar which usually has a depth of about 1·5m. Depth and position vary, and buoys may not mark the best water. Any swell speedily forms breakers, and the chan is very dangerous then or in any onshore winds, especially on the ebb (sp rate 4kn). In calm weather with no swell, a stout craft and reliable engine, and having gained local advice, enter about HW − 1; ideally follow a local FV with deeper draught.

APPROACHES TO LA GIRONDE (chart 2910)

The Gironde (8.18.21) is formed from the Garonne and Dordogne, which join at Bec d'Ambès, 38M above Pte de Grave. BXA lt buoy is moored off the mouth of the estuary, about 11M WSW of Pte de la Coubre. Banc de la Mauvaise, the S end of which dries extends 5M seaward. Cordouan lt ho is on a large sand spit in the middle of the estuary. Grande Passe de l'Ouest starts about 4M E of BXA buoy and is dredged through Grand Banc, the outer bar of La Gironde. Enter to seaward of buoys Nos. 1 and 2, and keep in buoyed chan with ldg lts. Off Terre-Nègre lt the SE-going stream begins at HW − 0500 (sp 1·5kn), and the NW-going at HW+0130 (sp 2·5kn).

Passe Sud, a lesser chan, is entered at the SWM lt buoy, 9M SW of Pte de Grave, and runs NE past Pte de Grave. There are two sets of ldg lts; the second lead over Platin de Grave, but it is better to pass NW of this shoal. Both entrance chans are dangerous in strong onshore winds, due to breakers and also the mascaret (bore) on the outgoing stream. Westerly swell breaks on La Mauvaise and around Cordouan, and sandbanks shift constantly. In places tidal streams run 4kn or more, and with wind against tide a dangerous sea can build.

LA GIRONDE TO CAPBRETON (charts 1102, 2664)

From Pte de la Négade to Capbreton, the coast is a featureless stretch of 107M broken only by the entrance to Arcachon (8.18.24). It is bordered by sand dunes and pine trees, and is often a lee shore with no shelter from W winds. 5M offshore a current usually sets N at about 0·5kn, particularly with a S wind; in winter this may be stronger after W winds. Within 1M of the coast there may be a S'ly counter-current.

A missile range, operated by Centre d'Essais des Landes, lies between Pointe de la Négade and Capbreton and extends up to 45M offshore. For details of boundaries, activity and sources of information, see 8.18.25.

The Fosse (or Gouf) de Capbreton, a submarine canyon, runs at right angles to the coast. The 50m depth contour is 3ca W of Capbreton hbr bkwtr and the 100m line is 4ca further W. In strong W winds a dangerous sea breaks along the N and S edges of it. Strong N or W winds and swell make the ent to the large marina at Capbreton (8.18.26) impassable. Anglet/Bayonne may then be a safer option; or stay at sea.

CAPBRETON TO SPANISH BORDER (charts 1343, 1102)

There is a marina at Anglet (8.18.27), but few facilities for yachts further up the R. Adour at Bayonne. At L'Adour ent the flood runs E and SE, sp rate 2-4kn; the ebb runs W, sp rate 3-5kn. S of Pte St Martin the coast has mostly sandy beaches and rky cliffs, with offlying rky shoals and Pyrenees mountains inland. In strong W winds the sea breaks over Loutrou shoal; and on Plateau de St Jean-de-Luz, a chain of rky shoals lying 1-4M offshore.

St Jean-de-Luz (chart 1343 and 8.18.28) is best approached first time or in bad weather through Passe d'Illarguita (between Illarguita and Belhara Perdun shoals): follow the 138° transit (Le Socoa lt on with Bordagain lt) until the Ste Barbe ldg lts (101°) are in transit; thence enter by Passe de l'Ouest on the 151° transit of the inner hbr ldg lts.

Baie de Fontarabie, in Spanish Rada de Higuer, lies on the border of France and Spain, and is entered between Pte Ste Anne and Cabo Higuer (a bare, rugged cape with lt ho) 1·75M WNW. Les Briquets (dry) lie 1M N of Pte Ste Anne. Keep to W of Banc Chicharvel and Bajo Iruarri in ent to B. Entry should not be attempted with strong onshore winds or heavy swell. R La Bidassoa is entered between breakwaters in SW corner of the B, giving access to marina at Hendaye-Plage (8.18.29). In the middle of the bay is a neutral area, marked by beacons and shown on chart 1181. To seaward of this area the boundary line (approximately 01°46'·2W) runs N from a white pyramid on the S shore, about 1M SW of Pte Ste Anne.

8.18.6   DISTANCE TABLE

Approximate distances in nautical miles are by the most direct route, whilst avoiding dangers and allowing for Traffic Separation Schemes. Places in *italics* are in adjoining areas; places in **bold** are in 8.0.8, Cross-Channel Distances.

1.	*Le Conquet*	**1**																		
2.	*St Nazaire*	145	**2**																	
3.	Pornic	146	16	**3**																
4.	L'Herbaudière	144	16	10	**4**															
5.	Port Joinville	147	35	30	20	**5**														
6.	St Gilles-C-de-Vie	166	45	40	29	18	**6**													
7.	Sables d'Olonne	181	65	55	40	31	16	**7**												
8.	Bourgenay	190	74	64	49	40	25	9	**8**											
9.	St Martin (I de Ré)	208	92	75	67	55	44	27	20	**9**										
8.	La Rochelle	218	101	92	76	66	51	36	29	12	**10**									
11.	Rochefort	242	126	116	102	84	75	61	54	36	26	**11**								
12.	R La Seudre	242	125	116	100	89	71	58	52	33	24	30	**12**							
13.	Port St Denis	220	103	94	78	59	48	33	30	21	13	26	22	**13**						
14.	Port Bloc/Royan	234	122	115	107	97	85	71	60	56	52	68	27	42	**14**					
15.	Bordeaux	289	177	170	162	152	140	126	115	111	107	123	82	97	55	**15**				
16.	Cap Ferret	274	168	160	153	138	130	113	110	102	98	114	75	88	68	123	**16**			
17.	Capbreton	316	220	215	211	192	186	169	166	165	156	172	131	145	124	179	58	**17**		
18.	Anglet/Bayonne	328	232	223	223	200	195	181	178	177	168	184	143	157	132	187	70	12	**18**	
19.	*Santander*	300	243	237	229	212	210	204	204	206	202	218	184	192	180	235	133	106	103	**19**
20.	*Cabo Finisterre*	382	404	399	390	377	395	393	394	406	407	423	399	397	401	456	376	370	373	274	**20**

8.18.7 Special Notes for France: see 8.15.8
8.18.8 French Glossary: see 8.15.9

PORNIC   8-18-9

Loire Atlantique 47°06'·55N 02°06'·59W   Rtg 3-2-1

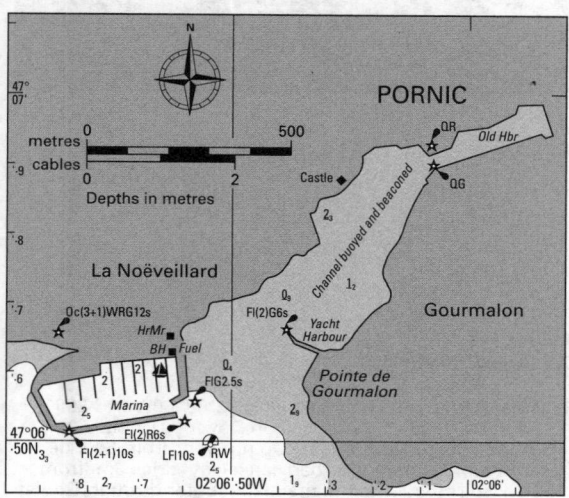

CHARTS
AC 2981, 2986, 2646; Imray C40; SHOM 7394, 7395, 7068; ECM 547, 549
TIDES
+0515 Dover; ML 3·6; Duration 0540; Zone –0100

Standard Port BREST (←—)

Times				Height (metres)			
High Water		Low Water		MHWS	MHWN	MLWN	MLWS
0500	1100	0500	1100	6·9	5·4	2·6	1·0
1700	2300	1700	2300				
Differences PORNIC							
–0050	+0030	–0010	–0010	–1·1	–0·8	–0·4	–0·2

SHELTER
Very good in large marina (2m); access HW±5. But no access LW±1 when Coeff >75, nor in winds >F7 from SE to W. Leave the SWM buoy to stbd, especially near LWS. Do not cut the corner round the S bkwtr head due to rky spur. Enter between the SHM pile and 2 PHM piles, on which the ☆s are mounted. A rky spur also extends SW from the head of the E jetty. Visitors berths are on P1 (for LOA >12m), P2 and P3 pontoons (first to stbd). Old hbr dries 1·8m; access HW±2½ via marked, lit drying chan.
NAVIGATION
WPT 47°06'·10N 02°08'·70W, 253°/073° from/to jetty hd, 1·5M. 4-6M WSW of hbr beware Banc de Kerouars, least depth 1m, on which seas break; it is unmarked, but the W sector of Pte de Noëveillard lt clears it by night. From the NW pass between this bank and the mainland. All other hazards are well marked. The S end of B de Bourgneuf is full of oyster beds, and many obstructions.
LIGHTS AND MARKS
Pte de Noëveillard Oc (3+1) WRG 12s 22m 13/9M; G shore-051°, W051°-079°, R079°-shore; the W sector lies between Notre-Dame rk, IDM bn tr, and the E end of Banc de Kerouars. Marina SW elbow Fl (2+1) 10s 4m 3M. Off the S jetty head Fl (2) R 6s 4m 2M; off E jetty head Fl G 2·5s 4m 2M. Entry sigs (simplified).
RADIO TELEPHONE
VHF Ch 09 (H24).
TELEPHONE
Hr Mr 02·40·82·05·40; Aff Mar 02·40·82·01·69; CROSS 02·97·55·35·35; ⌗ 02·40·82·03·17; SNSM 02·40·82·00·47; Auto 08·36·68·08·44; Police 02·40·82·00·29; Dr 02·40·82·01·80; Brit Consul 01·40·63·16·02.
FACILITIES
Port-la-Noëveillard Marina (754+90 **Ⓥ**) ☎ 02·40·82·05·40, FF114, P, D (on pontoon), FW, ME, AC, El, Sh, BH (50 ton), C (6 ton) CH; **CN de Pornic** ☎ 02·40·82·34·72; **Services:** ME, El, Ⓔ, Sh, CH, SM. **Town** Market Sun am. V, Gaz, R, Bar, ✉, Ⓑ, ⇌, ✈ (Nantes). Ferry: Roscoff/St Malo.

18

L'HERBAUDIÈRE   8-18-10

Vendée 47°01´·70N 02°17´·77W (Ile de Noirmoutier)
Rtg 2-2-2

CHARTS
AC 2981, 2986, 2646; Imray C40; SHOM 7394, 7395; ECM
547, 549

TIDES
+0500 Dover; ML 3·4; Zone −0100

Standard Port BREST (◀—)

Times				Height (metres)			
High Water		Low Water		MHWS	MHWN	MLWN	MLWS
0500	1100	0500	1100	6·9	5·4	2·6	1·0
1700	2300	1700	2300				
Differences L'HERBAUDIÈRE							
−0047	+0023	−0020	−0020	−1·4	−1·0	−0·5	−0·2
FROMENTINE							
−0045	+0020	−0015	+0005	−1·7	−1·3	−0·8	−0·1

SHELTER
Good in marina (E side), dredged 1·5m-2·5m; Ⓥs berth on
pontoon F. FV hbr (W side); NB early morning departures.
The ⚓ off Pte des Dames lt, Oc (3) WRG 12s, is exposed to
N and E winds.

NAVIGATION
WPT 47°03´·05N 02°17´·5W, 009°/189° from/to W jetty lt,
1·4M. There are rks and banks to the SW, NW and NE of
Pte de l'Herbaudière. Ldg lts and white sector (187·5°-
190°) of the W jetty lt both lead into ent chan, dredged to
1·3m and passing close W of two 0·8m patches; care is
needed at LWS. Two SHM buoys, both Fl G 2·5s, and a
PHM buoy, Fl R 2·5s, mark the last 2ca of the chan. W
bkwtr obscures vessels leaving.

LIGHTS AND MARKS
Visibility in summer is often poor. Conspic daymarks are
R/W radio mast 500m W of hbr and water tr about 1M SE.
Ile du Pilier, Fl (3) 20s 33m 29M, is 2·5M WNW of hbr.
Appr in any of the 3 W sectors of Basse de Martroger,
NCM bn, Dir Q WRG 11m 9/6M, G033°-055°, W055°-060°,
R060°-095°, G095°-124°, W124°-153°, R153°-201°, W201°-
240°, R240°-033°.
Ldg lts 188°, both grey masts, Q 5/26m 7M, vis 098°-278°,
lead over Banc de la Blanche (1·8m) approx 2M N of hbr.
L'Herbaudière W jetty, Oc (2+1) WG 12s 9m 10/7M,
W187·5°-190° (2½°), G elsewhere. E jetty head Fl (2) R 6s
8m 4M; inner head Fl R 2·5s 3m 1M.

RADIO TELEPHONE
Hr Mr VHF Ch 09 (HO).

TELEPHONE
Hr Mr 02·51·39·75·97; Aff Mar 02·51·39·94·01; SNSM
02·51·39·33·90; CROSS 02·97·55·35·35; Météo
02·40·84·80·19; Auto 08·36·68·08·85; ⌗ 02·51·39·06·80;
Police 02·51·39·04·36; Dr 02·51·39·05·64; Brit Consul
01·40·63·16·02.

FACILITIES
Marina (442+50 Ⓥ), ☎ 02·51·39·05·05, 🅑 02·51·39·75·97;
FF124, FW, P, D, AC, C (25 ton), Slip, ME, SM, Ⓡ, Gas, Gaz,
V, R, Bar (July, Aug), Sh, SC; **Quay** Bar, R, ME, Sh, V;
Services: El, Ⓔ, CH.

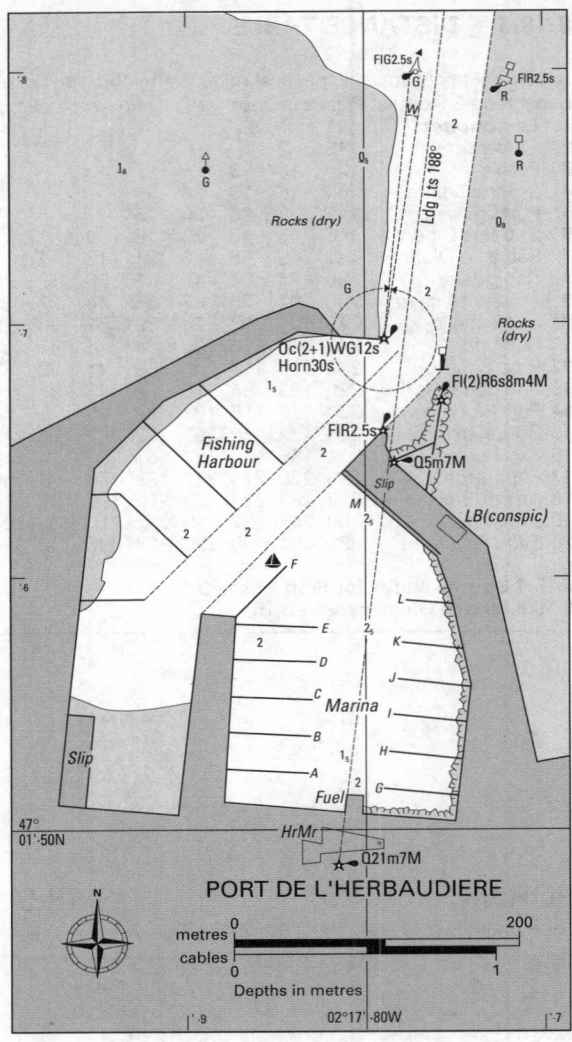

PORT DE L'HERBAUDIERE

metres   0   200
cables   0   1
Depths in metres

ADJACENT HARBOUR ON ILE DE NOIRMOUTIER

NOIRMOUTIER-EN-L'ILE 46°59´·40N 02°13´·10W. AC 2981;
SHOM 7394. Tides as above. Good shelter and AB, 4M
SE of L'Herbaudière, but FV hbr dries up to 3·0m on mud/
gravel. Appr HW±1 across extensive drying rock ledges
to the N and E of ent. The E'ly of 2 chans runs SSW from
approx 47°00´·50N 02°11´·10W, then doglegs WNW to the
ent. It is marked by 5 unlit PHM bns. An inshore chan
runs S from off Pte des Dames lt ho, Oc (3) WRG12s 34m.
It is more easily followed, keeping about 400m off 5 unlit
SHM bns along the shore. Both chans meet at the ent
where the flood tide sets S. S jetty hd has ☆ Oc (2) R 6s.
Follow the jetty on N side for about 1M to hbr. A prior
recce (3M overland from L'Herbaudière) is advised. Hr Mr
☎ 02.51.39.08.39. **Quay** AB, FW, C (4 ton); **Services:** ME,
El, Ⓔ, Sh, CH, SM. **Town** P, D, V, Gaz, R, Bar, Ⓡ, ✉, Ⓑ, ⇌
✈ at Nantes, via ferry to Pornic and bus. Ferry: Roscoff or
St Malo.

ADJACENT HARBOUR

FROMENTINE, Vendée, 46°53´·60N 02°08´·60W. AC 2981,
SHOM 7394, 6853. HW +0550 on Dover (UT); ML 3·2m;
Duration 0540. Tides above. Do not appr from Baie de
Bourgneuf as there is a road causeway, dries 3m, from
Ile de Noirmoutier to the mainland. Enter through Goulet
de Fromentine, under the bridge (clearance 27m). The
chan is buoyed, moved as necessary, but is very shallow,
so dangerous in bad weather. At sp the ebb can reach
8kn, the flood 5kn. Do not attempt night entry. ⚓ W of
pier. Coming from N, beware Les Boeufs. Tourelle Milieu
lies on the N side of Le Goulet de Fromentine, Fl (4) R 12s
6m 5M, R tr. Pte de Notre Dames-de-Monts Dir lt, Oc (2)
WRG 6s 21m 13/10M, G000°-043°, W043°-063°, R063°-
073°, W073°-094°, G094°-113°, W113°-116°, R116°-175°,
G175°-196°, R196°-230°. Fromentine SWM lt buoy, L Fl
10s+bell, 46°53´·10N 02°11´·50W, is about 1·5M WSW of
Pte du Notre Dames-de-Monts. Bridge, two x Iso 4s 32m
18M. Facilities: Aff Mar at Noirmoutier; ⌗ at Beauvois-
sur-Mer; **Quay** Slip, C (3 ton), FW; **Cercle Nautique de
Fromentine-Barfatre** (CNFB); **Services:** ME, El, Sh, CH.

PORT JOINVILLE, Ile d'Yeu

Vendée 46°43'·80N 02°20'·75W   Rtg 2-2-2   **8-18-11**

CHARTS
AC 3640, 2663; Imray C40; SHOM 6613, 6890, 6853; ECM 549, 1022

TIDES
+0550 Dover; ML 3·1; Duration 0600; Zone –0100

Standard Port BREST (◄—)

Times				Height (metres)			
High Water		Low Water		MHWS	MHWN	MLWN	MLWS
0500	1100	0500	1100	6·9	5·4	2·6	1·0
1700	2300	1700	2300				
Differences PORT JOINVILLE (Ile d'Yeu)							
–0025	+0010	–0030	–0030	–1·7	–1·3	–0·6	–0·2

SHELTER
Good in enlarged marina, but very crowded in season; best to pre-book as it is the only secure hbr on the island. The wet basin (3·7m) access HW±1½, is mainly for FVs, but possible overflow for yachts in high season; no pontoons; tfc lts R & G, just S of lock. No ⚓ in outer hbr; swell enters in N/NE winds. If the marina is full, yachts can moor between Gare Maritime and the ice factory, keeping clear of ferries to W. A grid to the W of the ice factory is marked by R paint lines on quay wall.

NAVIGATION
WPT Basse Mayence NCM, 46°44'·65N 02°19'·10W, 055°/235° from/to bkwtr lt, 1·3M. Chan dredged 1·5m, appr with care at LW. Beware Basse du Bouet (dries 0·6m) 3ca NW, La Sablaire shoal to the E and rks along the coast both sides of hbr ent.

LIGHTS AND MARKS
Very conspic high water tr brg 224° leads to hbr. Ldg lts 219°, both QR 11/16m 6M, vis 169°-269°; rear (mast) 85m from front. Conspic chimney W of hbr ent.

NW jetty head Oc (3) WG 12s 9m 11/8M; G shore-150°, W150°-232°, G232°-279°, W279°-285°, G285°-shore; horn (3) 30s, tidal sigs. Quai du Canada hd Iso G 4s 7m 6M unintens 337°-067°. Galiote jetty root Fl R 2·5s 1M.

RADIO TELEPHONE
Marina VHF Ch 09 16 (HO).

TELEPHONE
Hr Mr 02·51·58·38·11; Hbr Office 02·51·58·51·10; Aff Mar 02·51·59·42·60; ⊞ 02·51·58·37·28; CROSS 02·97·55·35·35; Météo 02·51·36·10·78; Auto 08·36·68·08·85; SNSM 02·51·58·32·01; Police 02·51·58·30·05; Dr 02·51·58·31·70; Ⓗ 02·51·68·30·23; Brit Consul 01·40·63·16·02. Note: There are phone-card telephones only.

FACILITIES
Marina (390+30 Ⓥ), ☎ 02·51·58·51·10, ⚓ 02·51.58.44.34, FF92 (FF151 in Jul/Aug), FW, AC, P, D, El, ME, Sh; **Wet Basin** Slip, FW, C (18 ton); **CN Ile d'Yeu** ☎ 02·51·58·31·50; **Services:** ME, El, Sh, CH, Ⓔ.
Town V, Gaz, R, Bar, ✉, Ⓑ, ⇌ (St Gilles-Croix-de-Vie), ✈ (Nantes). Flights from airfield 2M west of Port Joinville to Nantes and (summers only) to Les Sables d'Olonne. Ferry: Roscoff or St Malo. Local ferries to Fromentine, St Gilles and Les Sables-d'Olonne.

ADJACENT HARBOUR ON ILE D'YEU

PORT DE LA MEULE, Ile d'Yeu, Vendée, 46°41'·75N 03°20'·60W. AC 2663; SHOM 6890, 6853. –0050 sp and – 0020 nps on Brest; ML 3·0m. A small, drying fishing hbr on the S side of Ile d'Yeu, only safe in settled offshore weather; untenable in S winds. Many FVs inside hbr; best to ⚓ outside ent. Between Pte de la Père to the W and Pte de la Tranche to the SE, appr brg 034° on W chapel; then 022° towards W square patch on Gy □ lt tr, R top, Oc WRG 4s 9m 9/6/5M, vis G007°-018°, W018°-028°, R028°-042°. (Night ent not advised). Within 1ca of ent beware rks, first to port, then to stbd. Few facilities: Slips, R, Bar; V 1½ miles.

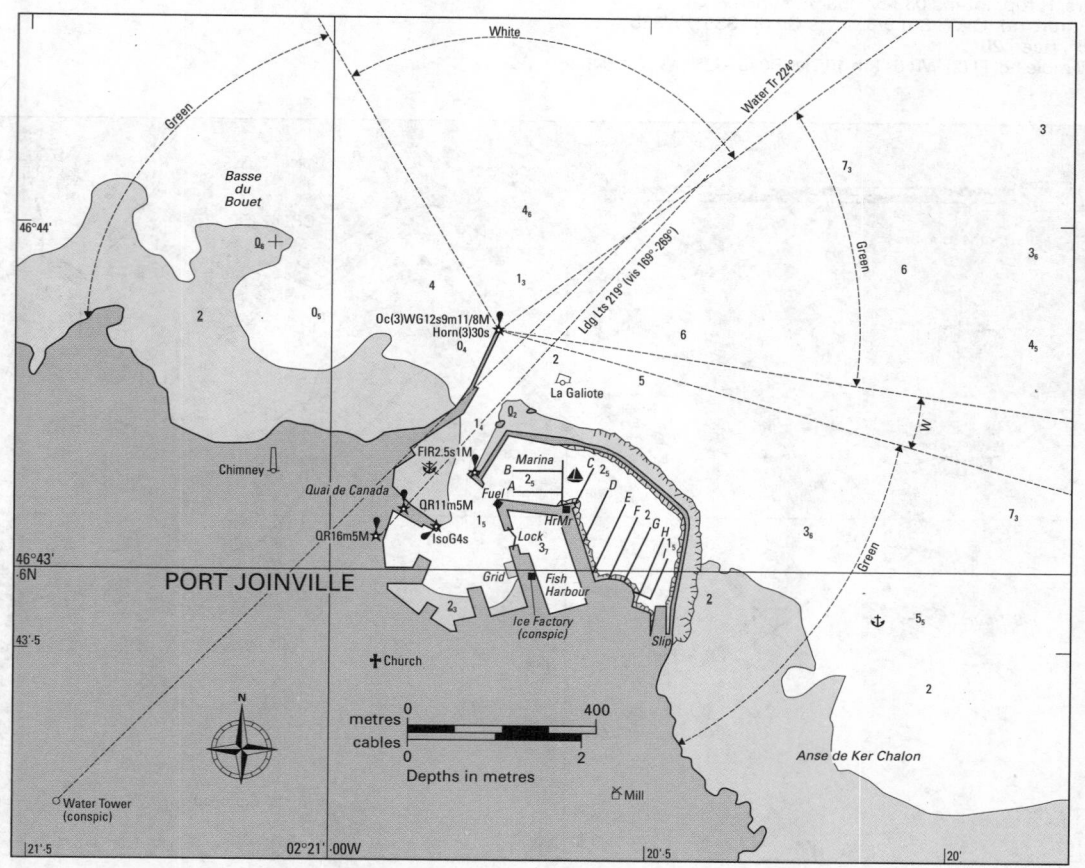

ST GILLES-CROIX-DE-VIE

Vendée 46°41'·60N 01°57'·05W   Rtg 2-1-2   **8-18-12**

CHARTS
AC 3640, 2663; Imray C40; SHOM 6613, 6853, 6523;
ECM 1022, 549

TIDES
+0500 Dover; ML 3·2; Duration 0600; Zone –0100

Standard Port BREST (←—)

Times				Height (metres)			
High Water		Low Water		MHWS	MHWN	MLWN	MLWS
0500	1100	0500	1100	6·9	5·4	2·6	1·0
1700	2300	1700	2300				
Differences ST GILLES-CROIX-DE-VIE							
–0032	+0013	–0033	–0033	–1·8	–1·3	–0·6	–0·3

SHELTER
Good shelter, and easy access except in strong SW'lies
or swell when breakers form off ent. Chan (⚓ prohib) is
dredged 1·5m, but very shallow near bkwtr hds due to
silting. Best arr/dep HW –2 to HW, to avoid strong ebb.
On N bank are: small yacht basin inside Grand Môle; two
tidal FV basins; beyond them the marina nominally
dredged to 1·5m. If full, pick up ⚓ or lie alongside quay
(dries) on E bank below bridge. In good weather ⚓ off
ent, close SE of ldg line.

NAVIGATION
WPT Pill'Hours SCM, Q (6) +L Fl 15s, Bell, 46°41'·05N
01°58'·00W, 231°/051° from/to Jetée de la Garenne lt,
0·75M. Beware Rocher Pill'Hours (2·8m) and drying
reefs extending 1ca (180m) SE. Tide runs very strongly
in ent, particularly on ebb.

LIGHTS AND MARKS
Landmarks are Pte de Grosse-Terre (rky hdland) with lt
ho, W truncated conical tr; the rear ldg lt structure; and
two spires NE of the marina.
Pte de Grosse Terre Fl (4) WR 12s 25m 17/13M, vis
W290°-125°, R125°-145°.
Ldg lts 043°: both Dir Oc (3+1) R 12s 7/28m 13M; both W
□ trs, R top; intens 033·5°-053·5°, synch.
SE mole hd, QWG 8m 9/6M, vis G045°-335°, W335°-
045°, Reed 20s.
NW mole hd, Fl (2) WR 6s 8m 10/7M, R045°-225°, W225°-045°.

RADIO TELEPHONE
VHF Ch 09 (season 0600-2200; out of season 0800-1200,
1400-1800LT).

TELEPHONE
Hr Mr Port de Plaisance 02·51·55·30·83; Aff Mar
02·51·55·10·58; ☷ 02·51·55·10·58; CROSS 02·97·55·35·35;
SNSM 02·51·55·01·19; Météo 02·51·36·10·78; Auto
08·36·68·08·85; Police 02·51·55·01·19; Dr 02·51·55·11·93;
Brit Consul 01·40·63·16·02.

FACILITIES
Port la Vie Marina (800+60 visitors) ☎ 02·51·55·30·83, ⚓
02·51·55·31·43, Access H24, P, D, FW, AC, ME, El, CH, Gaz,
SM, BH (26 ton), Slip, R, V, Bar; **Quay** Slip, FW, C (6 ton);
CN de Havre de Vie ☎ 02·51·55·87·91;
Services: ME, El, Sh, CH, Ⓔ, C (15 ton), SM, SHOM.
Town V, Gaz, R, Bar, ✉, Ⓑ, ➹. A ferry runs to Ile d'Yeu.
Ferry: Roscoff or St Malo.

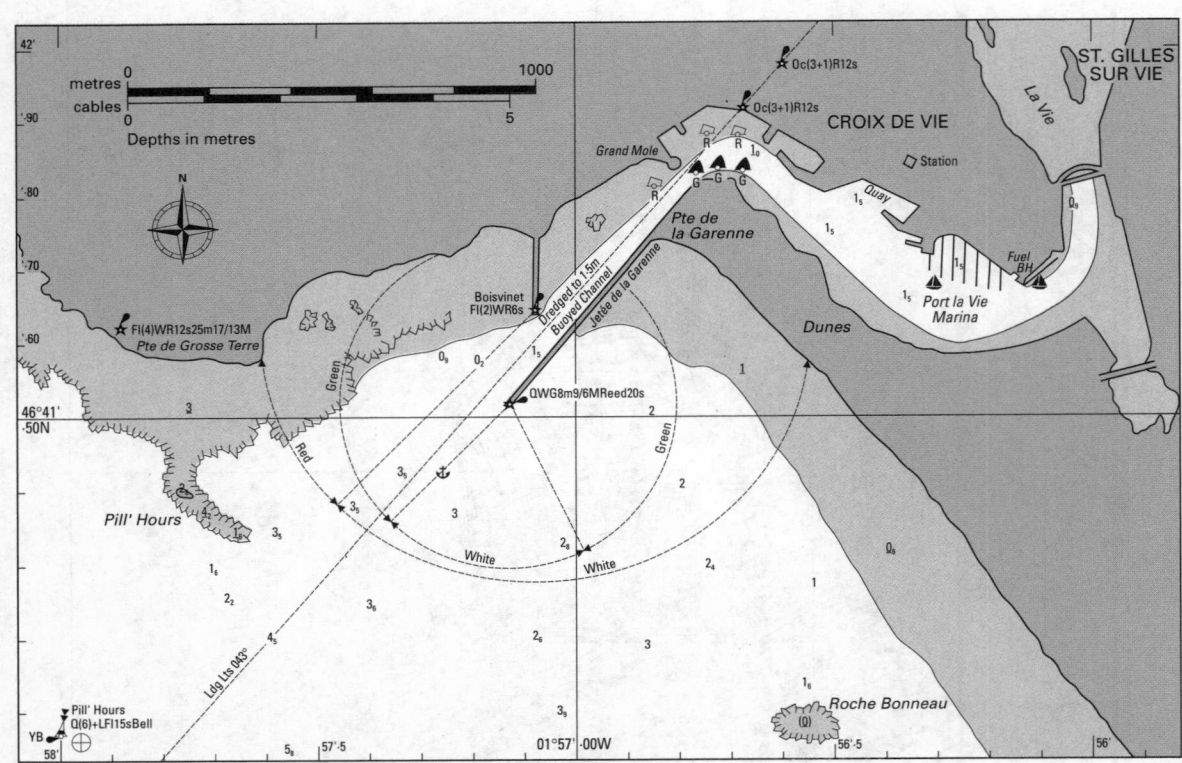

LES SABLES D'OLONNE   8-18-13

Vendée 46°29'·40N 01°47'·40W   Rtg 3-2-2

CHARTS
AC 3640, 2663; Imray C40; SHOM 6551, 6522, 6523; ECM 1022

TIDES
+0530 Dover; ML 3·2; Duration 0640; Zone −0100

Standard Port BREST (←)

Times				Height (metres)			
High Water		Low Water		MHWS	MHWN	MLWN	MLWS
0500	1100	0500	1100	6·9	5·4	2·6	1·0
1700	2300	1700	2300				
Differences LES SABLES D'OLONNE							
−0030	+0015	−0035	−0035	−1·7	−1·3	−0·6	−0·3

SHELTER
Access at all tides; entry is easy except in winds from SE to SW when apprs get rough. Sailing is prohib in the entry chan to hbr. Commercial and FV Basins prohib to yachts. Access to marina (1·5 - 3·5m) H24. Visitors check in at pontoon port side, by Capitainerie. Pontoon L, at NE end, is for visitors and multihulls; or berth as directed.

NAVIGATION
WPT Nouch Sud SCM, Q (6)+L Fl 15s, 46°28'·63N 01°47'·35W, 220°/040° from/to front ldg lt 033°, 1·2M. To the W, beware Les Barges d'Olonne, extending 3M W of Pte de Aiguille. There are 2 appr chans: the SW chan with La Potence ldg lts 033°, which lead into SE chan on ldg line 320°. In bad weather use the SE chan. Le Noura and Le Nouch are two isolated rks on shallow patches S of Jetée St Nicolas. Further SE, Barre Marine breaks, even in moderate weather. A buoyed wk (dries) lies off hbr ent, to E of 320° ldg line. At hbr ent, dredged chan (2m) initially favours the E side, then mid-chan.

LIGHTS AND MARKS
Les Barges lt ho, Fl (2) R 10s 25m 13M, gy tr, 2M W of ent. L'Armandèche lt ho, Fl (2+1) 15s 42m 24M, 6ca W of ent. SW Chan ldg lts 033°: both Iso R 4s 14/33m 16M; rear, 330m from front (both H24). SE Chan ldg lts 320°: front QG 11m 8M; rear, 465m from front, Oc (2+1) 12s 33m 13M. St Nicolas jetty hd, UQ (2) R 1s 16m 10M vis 143°-094°; Horn (2) 30s. Inner ldg lts 327°, both FR 6/9m 11M; R/W vert stripes difficult to see by day.

RADIO TELEPHONE
Port VHF Ch 12 16 (0800-1800). Marina Ch 09 16 (0600-2400LT in season; 0800-2000LT out of season).

TELEPHONE
Marina 02·51·32·51·16; Aff Mar 02·51·21·01·80; CROSS 02·97·55·35·35; Météo 02·51·36·10·78; Auto 08·36·68·08·85; ⌗ 02·51·32·02·33; SNSM 02·51·21·20·55; Police 02·51·33·69·91; Dr 02·51·95·14·47; Ⓗ 02·51·21·06·33; Brit Consul 05·56·52·28·35.

FACILITIES
Port Olona Marina (1100+110 Ⓥ), ☎ 02·51·32·51·16, ⛴ 51.32.37.13, FF90 (Jun/Sep), 130FF (Jul/Aug), Slip, P, D, FW, ME, El, AC, Sh, Ⓓ;
Services: El, Sh, CH, BH (27 ton), Ⓔ, SHOM, SM, Divers.
Town P, D, V, Gaz, R, Bar, ⊠, Ⓑ, ⇌, ✈. Ferry: Roscoff or St Malo.

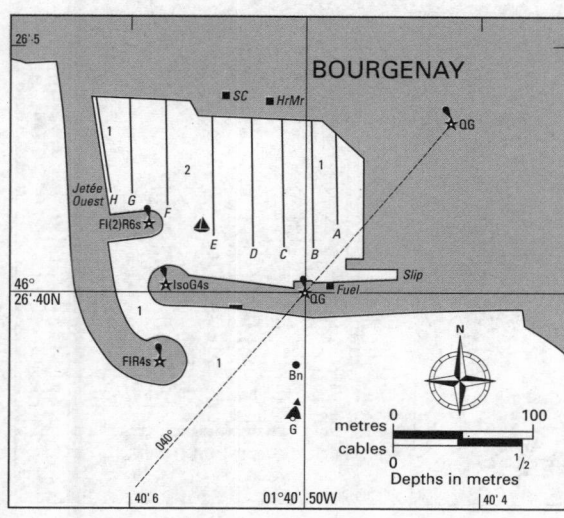

BOURGENAY   8-18-14

Vendée 46° 26'·38N 01° 40'·57W   Rtg 4-2-2

CHARTS
AC 2663; Imray C41; SHOM 6522; ECM 1022

TIDES
+0600 Dover; ML 3·1; Duration 0640; Zone −0100. Use Differences LES SABLES D'OLONNE (8.18.13), 5·5M NW.

SHELTER
Good in the marina (2m). Caution: even in moderate weather, & especially with SW winds, a big swell can break at the ent.

NAVIGATION
WPT Fairway buoy SWM, L Fl 10s, 46°25'·35N 01°41'·90W, 220°/040° from/to pier head, 1·35M. 600m ENE of WPT, beware Roches de Joanne (2·9m; dangerous in bad wx) and shoal patch to E of ent, marked by unlit SHM buoy and bn. Ent chan, dredged 1·0m, has two 90° turns marked by luminous chevrons; 3kn speed limit.

LIGHTS AND MARKS
Ldg lts 040°: both QG 8M; front W hut with G □, vis 020°-060°; rear W pylon, W □ with G border, vis 010°-070°. The Iso G 4s 5M and Fl (2) R 6s 5M are not vis from seaward.

RADIO TELEPHONE
VHF Ch 09 16 (office hrs; in summer 0800-2100LT).

TELEPHONE
Hr Mr/SNSM 02·51·22·20·36, ⛴ 02·51·22·29·45; CROSS 02·97·55·35·35; Auto 08·36·68·08·85; ⌗ 02·51·32·02·33; Aff Mar 02·51·21·81·71; Police 02·51·90·60·07; Dr 02·51·90·62·68; Ⓗ 02·51·96·00·41; Brit Consul 05·56·52·28·35.

FACILITIES
Marina (470+90 Ⓥ) ☎ 02·51·22·20·36, FF95, FW, AC, P, D, Slip; **Association Nautique de Bourgenay** (ANB) ☎ 02·51·22·02·57; **Services:** CH, C (15 ton), Gaz.
Town R, Ⓓ, V, Bar, ⊠, Ⓑ, ⇌ (Les Sables d'Olonne), ✈ (La Lande, Chateau d'Olonne). Ferry: Roscoff or St Malo.

18

MINOR HARBOURS IN PERTUIS BRETON

JARD-SUR-MER, Vendée, 46°24′·45N 01°34′·75W. Rtg 4-5-3. AC 2641, 2663; SHOM 6522. HW +0600 on Dover (UT); HW−0010 & ht −2·0m on Brest; ML 3·1m; Duration 0640. Small drying hbr, access HW±2, 4·5m max at HW. Moorings inside bkwtr, inc 7 Y ⚓s. Hr Mr's office with blue roof and adjacent bldgs are conspic from afar. W daymarks 4ca (740m) E of hbr lead 038° via narrow ent between the drying Roches de l'Islatte and Roches de la Brunette, marked by buoys. Then pick up 293° transit of RW marks on W side of hbr, ldg to ent. There are no lights. Hr Mr (occas) ☎ 02·51·33·40·17; ⌗ ☎ 02·51·95·11·33; Facilities: **Jetty** FW, C (5 ton); **Services:** CH, Divers.

L'AIGUILLON/LA-FAUTE-SUR-MER, Vendée, 46°20′·00N 01°18′·60W. Rtg 4-3-2. AC 2641, 2663; SHOM 6521. HW +0535 on Dover (UT); HW −0030, ht +0·6m on Pte de Grave (Zone −0100); ML 3·4m. Shelter good in two yacht hbrs, but avoid in strong S or W winds; ent only safe in fine weather with off-shore winds. Access HW±2½. Beware mussel beds with steel piles which cover at HW; also oyster beds. The area is very flat and, being shallow, waves build up quickly in any wind. The bar to seaward dries and is dangerous in bad weather. Ent can best be identified by a conspic transformer on a hill, La Dive, opposite side of chan to Pointe d'Arcay. Enter at Le Lay SCM buoy, Q (6) + L Fl 15s, with transformer brg 033°. ⚓ in R Lay or berth at L'Aiguillon (NE bank); or in drying tidal basin at La Faute (SW bank). Hr Mrs (L'Aiguillon) ☎ 05.51.97.06.57; (La Faute) ☎ 05.51.56.45.02; Aff Mar ☎ 05.51.56.45.35; CROSS ☎ 05.56.09.82.00; Dr ☎ 05.51.56.46.17; Facilities: **Club Nautique Aiguillonais et Fautais (CNAF)** ☎ 05.51.97.04.60; **Services:** ME, CH.

MARANS, Vendée, 46°19′·00N 01°00′·00W. AC 2641, 2663; SHOM 6521; ECM 551. Tides: see L'Aiguillon above; HW at Brault lock = HW La Rochelle + 0020. Good shelter in non-tidal hbr approx 10M from SWM buoy, L Fl 10s, (46°· 15′·40N 01°11′·42W) abeam Pte de l'Aiguillon with 10m high B bn. Buoyed chan, dries 1·0m, leads NE past Pavé jetty, Fl G 4s, thence 3½M up-river to Brault lifting bridge and 5ca to lock, open HW±2 sp, HW±1 np. Best arrival at HW. Waiting buoys before bridge; pontoon inside vast lock which has small swing bridge at far end. Straight 3M canal to stbd side pontoon. Brault lock ☎ 05.46.01.53.77; Facilities: **Quay** ☎ 05.46.01.8.36, AB (40+10 Ⓥ), FW, C (3 tons); P & D (cans); BY, ME, Sh, SM. **Town** V, R, Bar.

OTHER HARBOUR ON ILE DE RÉ

LA FLOTTE, Charente Maritime, 46°11′·35N 01°19′·25W. Rtg 3-4-2. AC 2641, 2746; SHOM 6668, 6521. HW +0535 on Dover (UT). La Flotte is 2M SE of St Martin (8.18.16). From NW keep clear of Le Couronneau; from E, keep N of bn off Pte des Barres. Appr on 215° in W sector of La Flotte lt ho, W tr with G top, Fl WG 4s 10m 12/9M; vis G130°-205°, W205°-220°, G220°-257°; horn (3) 30s by day HW±2. Moiré indicator shows vert B line when on course 215°, or chevrons to regain course. 5 waiting Bys outside; or ⚓ off in 3m, sheltered from S & W. Outer hbr sheltered by mole and dries 2·4m; access HW±3. 3 pontoons in outer hbr for 8 visitors; pre-booking advised. Inner hbr dries 2·7m. Hr Mr ☎ 46.09.67.66; ⌗ at St Martin; Facilities: **Quay** FF75, Slip, FW, Ⓥ berth on mole, Grid; **Cercle Nautique de la Flotte-en-Ré** (CNLF) (open Jul-15 Sep) ☎ 05.46.09.59.30, Bar; **Services:** P & D (cans), CH, ME, SM, ▣.

ARS-EN-RÉ,   8-18-15

Charente Maritime, 46°12′·70N 01°30′·62W   Rtg 4-3-1

CHARTS
AC 2641; Imray C41; SHOM 6521, 6333; ECM 551, 1022
TIDES
+0540 Dover; ML 3·7m; Zone −0100; See 8.18.16
SHELTER
Two sheltered marinas: (a) Bassin de la Criée (2m), is on NW side of chan approx 600m NE of town; access HW±2 over sill 2·5m CD, Ⓥ berths on pontoon H, to port. (b) Bassin Prée, at head of chan, access HW ±2 over sill, dries 2·9m; Ⓥ berths to stbd. Or AB outside on NW quay drying to mud. Note: draught, tidal coefficient and wind/barometer dictate access times.
NAVIGATION
WPT 46°14′·62N 01°20′·66W (2ca S of Rocha NCM buoy), 085°/265° from/to first SHM chan buoy, 3·65M. Beware shoal ground close S of outer ldg line. The appr chan is restricted by rky ledges drying 0·4m and 1·5m; access HW±3. Chan is marked by 2 sets of ldg lts, buoys and bns. There is ⚓ in a pool (2m) close S of Pte du Fier. Port d'Ars is at the head of a chan in the SW corner of the bay, Le Fier d'Ars, which dries to salt pans & oyster beds.
LIGHTS AND MARKS
Conspic ⛪ spire, white with black top, is in the town, about 1ca SE of the 232° ldg line. Outer ldg lts 265° (from near Le Rocha NCM buoy, Q): front, Iso 4s 5m 11M, W ☐ on hut, vis 141°-025°; rear, 370m from front, Dir Iso G 4s 13m 15M, G ☐ tr on house (synch, intens 264°-266°). Port d'Ars ldg lts, hard to see by day, lead 232° across Fiers d'Ars into hbr: front, Q 5m 9M, W ☐ with R lantern; rear, 370m from front, Q 13m 11M, B ☐ on W framework tr, G top, vis 142°-322°.
RADIO TELEPHONE
VHF Ch 09.

TELEPHONE
Hr Mr (La Criée) 05·46·29·25·10, (La Prée) 05.46.29.08.52; SNSM 05·46·34·49·84; Aff Mar 05·46·09·68·89 (at La Flotte); CROSS 05.56.09.82.00; ⌗ 05·46·09·21·78; Auto 08·36·68·08·17; Police 05·46·29·41·48; Dr 05·46·29·44·19; Brit Consul 05·56·52·28·35.
FACILITIES
Marinas FF122, Slip, FW, C (6 ton); **Cercle Nautique d'Ars -en-Ré** ☎ 05·46·29·23·04 (Apl to Nov); **Services:** ME, El, Sh.

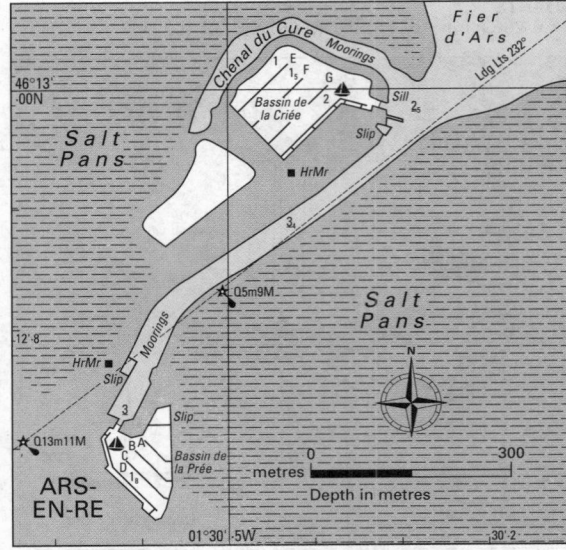

ST MARTIN, Ile de Ré   8-18-16

Charente Maritime 46°12'·56N 01°21'·84W   Rtg 3-3-1

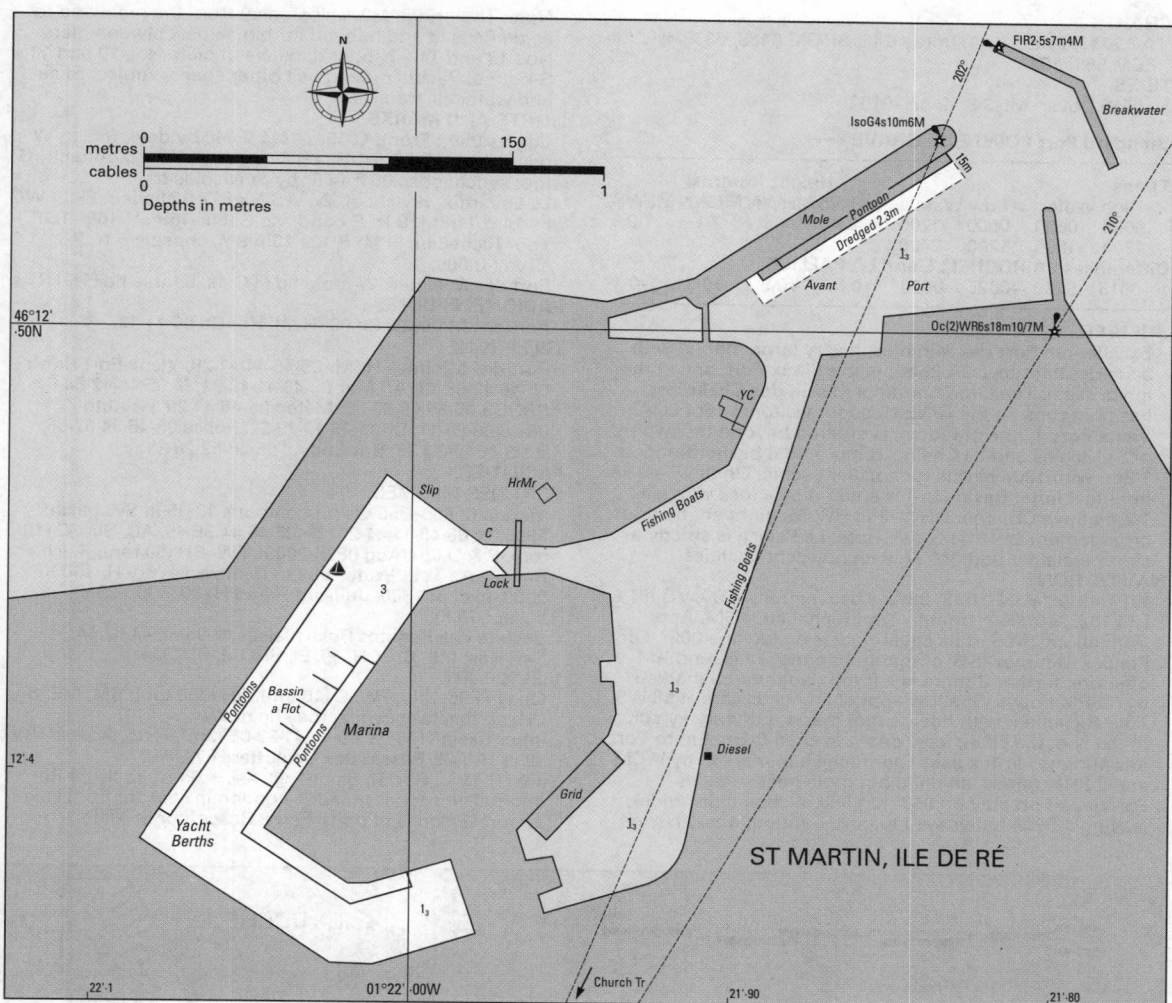

CHARTS
AC 2641, 2746; Imray C41; SHOM 6668, 6521; ECM 551, 1022
TIDES
+0535 Dover; ML 3·7; Zone –0100

Standard Port POINTE DE GRAVE (⟶)

Times				Height (metres)			
High Water		Low Water		MHWS	MHWN	MLWN	MLWS
0000	0600	0500	1200	5·4	4·4	2·1	1·0
1200	1800	1700	2400				
Differences ST MARTIN, Ile de Ré							
+0007	–0032	–0030	–0025	+0·5	+0·3	+0·2	–0·1

SHELTER
Complete shelter in non-tidal marina (depth 3m); often very crowded with queue to enter. 4 W waiting buoys off ent. Avant port is protected by bkwtr close to the NE and mole on NW side. Inside mole a waiting pontoon (season only) is dredged 2·3m; can be disturbed in fresh NW to NE winds. Access HW–3 to +2 via chan (dries 1·5m) to drying basin for FVs. Marina gates open about HW–2 and close HW+2½, depending on coefficient (sill is 0·8m above CD), 0630-2200LT May, Jun and Sept; 0500-2300 Jul and Aug. Berth as directed by Hr Mr.
NAVIGATION
WPT Rocha NCM By, Q, 46°14'·75N 01°20'·80W, 020°/200° from/to St Martin mole hd, 2·4M.
From the NW, pass N and E of Le Rocha, a rky bank

extending 2½M ENE from Pte du Grouin.
From SE, pass well N of unlit NCM bn, about ¾M NE of ent, marking Le Couronneau drying ledge in R sector (245°-281°) of St Martin lt ho Oc (2) WR 6s.
By day appr with lt ho and ⊕ □ tr in line 210°, or mole hd lt in transit 202° with ⊕ tr; the lt ho is easier to see.
LIGHTS AND MARKS
Citadelle is conspic 3ca E of hbr ent. Lt ho, Oc (2) WR 6s 18m 10/7M, vis W shore-245°, R245°-281°, W281°-shore, is on ramparts at SE side of ent. Mole hd, Iso G 4s 10m 6M, is obscured by Pte du Grouin when brg <124°.
RADIO TELEPHONE
VHF Ch 09 (0800-1900LT in summer).
TELEPHONE
Hr Mr 05·46·09·26·69; Aff Mar 05·46·09·68·89 (in La Flotte); ⌗ 05·46·09·21·78; Météo 05·46·41·29·14; Auto 08·36·68·08·17; CROSS 05·56·09·82·00; Police 05·46·09·21·17; Dr 05·46·09·20·08; Ⓗ 05·46·09·20·01; Brit Consul 05·56·52·28·35.
FACILITIES
Marina (135+50 visitors), FF90, P, D, FW, AC, ME, El, Sh;
Quay FW, C (4 ton); **YC St Martin** ☎ 05·46·09·22·07;
Services: ME, El, Ⓔ, Sh, CH, SHOM.
Town P, D, V, Gaz, R, Bar, ✉, Ⓑ, ⇌, ✈ (La Rochelle).
Ferry: Roscoff or St Malo.

18

LA ROCHELLE   8-18-17
Charente Maritime 46°09'·40N 01° 09'·15W   Rtg 3-1-1

CHARTS
AC 2743, 2746, 2641; Imray C41; SHOM 6468, 6333/4;
ECM 551, 1022
TIDES
+0515 Dover; ML 3·8; Zone −0100

Standard Port POINTE DE GRAVE (⟶)

Times				Height (metres)			
High Water		Low Water		MHWS	MHWN	MLWN	MLWS
0000	0600	0500	1200	5·4	4·4	2·1	1·0
1200	1800	1700	2400				
Differences LA ROCHELLE and LA PALLICE							
+0015	−0030	−0025	−0020	+0·6	+0·5	+0·3	−0·1

SHELTER
Excellent in **Port des Minimes**, a very large marina with
3·5m depth (max LOA 25m); in the Vieux Port, and in the
Inner Basin. The large non-tidal **Bassin des Chalutiers**
has pontoons on the N/NE sides for visitors >16m LOA.
Vieux Port, in the old town, is entered beyond the two trs
of St Nicolas and La Chaine. It has a tidal basin (dredged
1·3m) with 100+ berths for smaller yachts. On the E side a
non-tidal **Inner Basin** (3m) is entered by a lock with sill
1·2m above CD, opens HW−2 to HW+½; night ent by prior
arrangement ☎ 46.41.32.05. Note: La Pallice is strictly a
commercial/FV port 3M W, with no yacht facilities.
NAVIGATION
WPT 46°06'·63N 01°15'·98W, Chauveau SCM By, VQ (6) +
L Fl 10s, 240°/060° from/to Tour Richelieu, 4·6M. Appr
from about 1M S of Le Lavardin lt tr on ldg line 059°. Off
Pte des Minimes (SW of marina) drying rks extend ¼M
offshore; further S there is a firing danger area marked
by 5 SPM buoys. Shallow appr chan needs care at MLWS.
Tour Richelieu (with tide gauge) marks a drying rky spit
to the N of the chan; least depth in chan 0·2m. Ent to Port
des Minimes is 1ca past Tour Richelieu, marked by WCM
and 2 PHM buoys, all unlit; but mole heads are lit.
For Vieux Port stay on 059° ldg line in chan (35m wide),
leaving 4 PHM buoys well to port. Caution: many ferries.

Note: The bridge (30m clearance) from the mainland to
Ile de Ré is lit and buoyed for big ships: between piers
Nos 13 and 14 = N-bound; between piers Nos 10 and 11 =
S-bound. Yachts may transit other spans, subject to air
and water clearances.
LIGHTS AND MARKS
Ldg lts 059°: Front, Q 15m 14M (Fl 4s by day), R ○ tr, W
bands; rear, Q 25m 14M (Fl 4s by day), W octagonal tr, G
top; synch, obsc 061°-065° by St Nicolas tr.
Le Lavardin, rky shoal 3M WSW of Tr Richelieu, Fl (2) WG
6s 14m 11/8M, B tr, R band, vis G160°-169°, W169°-160°.
Tour Richelieu, Fl (4) R 12s 10m 9M, conspic R tr, RC,
siren (4) 60s.
Port des Minimes: W mole hd Fl G 4s; E mole hd Fl (2) R 6s.
RADIO TELEPHONE
Port des Minimes Ch 09 (H24). Hbr Ch 06 11 12.
TELEPHONE
Port des Minimes Hr Mr 05·46·44·41·20, Vieux Port Hr Mr
05·46·41·68·73; Aff Mar 05·46·41·43·91; ♯ 05·46·42·64·64;
CROSS 05·56·09·82·00; Météo 05·46·41·29·14; Auto
08·36·68·08·17; Dr 05·46·42·19·22; Police 05·46·34·67·55;
Ⓗ 05·46·27·33·33; Brit Consul 05·56·52·28·35.
FACILITIES
PORT DES MINIMES
Marina (2,800+250 Ⓥs on pontoons 13-15 in SW basin),
FF95, ☎ 05·46·44·41·20, 📞 05·46·44·36·49, AC, Slip, C (10
ton), P & D (Jul/Aug 0800-2000), FW, BH (50 ton), R, Ice,
Bar, Ⓑ, ✉, ♿, ▣. Water bus to the town every H, 1000-
2000, except 1300; Jul/Aug H and H+30, 0900-2330,
except 1300.
Société des Régates Rochellaises ☎ 05·46·44·62·44;
Services: ME, Sh, CH, Ⓔ, El, SHOM, SM, Gaz.
VIEUX PORT
Quay FF95, Slip, FW, C (10 ton), BH (300 ton), SM, ME, Sh,
CH, no toilets/showers, may be noisy.
Inner Basin (100) ☎ 05·46·41·32·05 (3m), FF95, Access HW
−2 to HW+½. **Bassin des Chalutiers** FW, AC.
Town P, D, V, Gaz, R, Bar, ✉, Ⓑ, ⇌, ✈. Ferry to Ile de Ré;
internal air services (and to London in season) from Laleu
airport (2½km N of port). Ferry: Roscoff or St Malo.

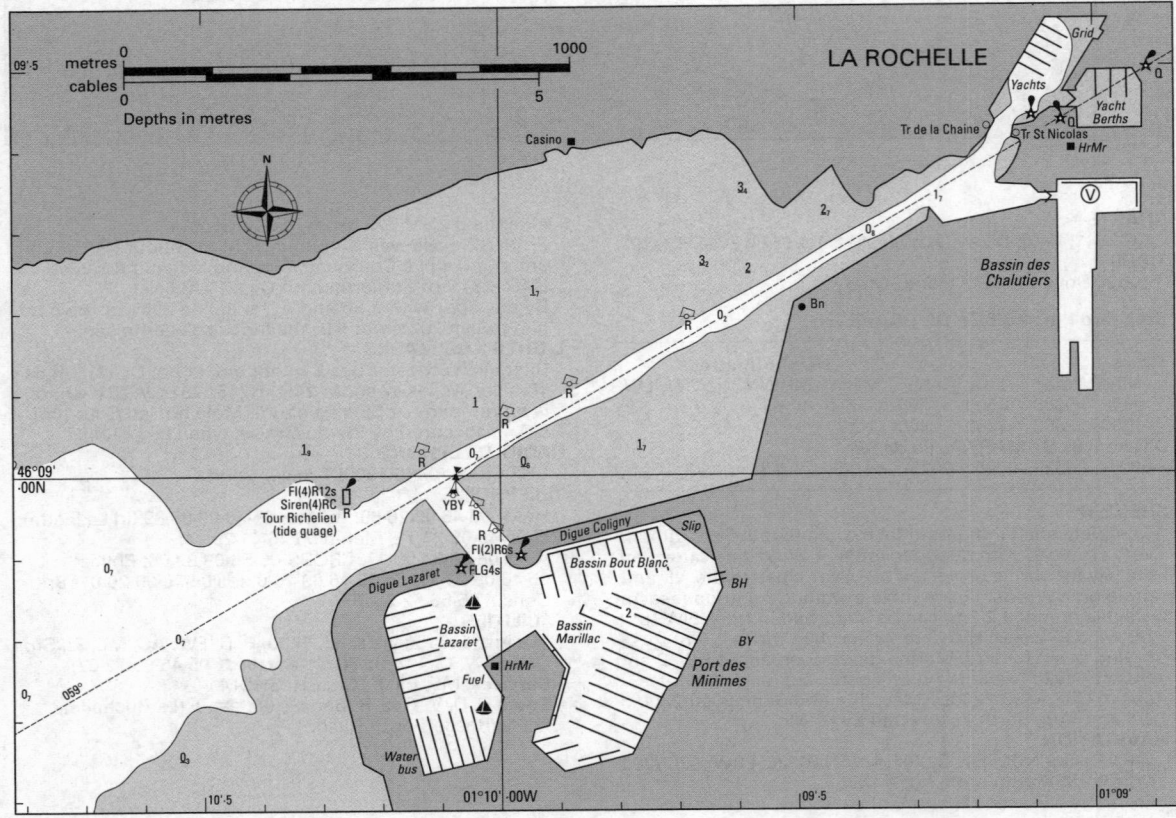

ILE D'OLÉRON   8-18-18
Charente Maritime   Rtgs: see below

CHARTS
AC 2746, 2663; SHOM 6914, 6913, 6912, 6334, 6335; ECM 552
TIDES
+0545 Dover; ML 3·9; Duration 0540; Zone –0100

Standard Port POINTE DE GRAVE (→)

Times				Height (metres)			
High Water		Low Water		MHWS	MHWN	MLWN	MLWS
0000	0600	0500	1200	5·4	4·4	2·1	1·0
1200	1800	1700	2400				
Differences LE CHAPUS							
+0015	–0040	–0025	–0015	+0·6	+0·6	+0·4	+0·2
POINTE DE GATSEAU							
+0005	–0005	–0015	–0025	–0·1	–0·1	+0·2	+0·2

HARBOURS
In the N of the island Port St Denis and Le Douhet have dedicated marinas. Beware fishing nets with very small floats especially near Port St Denis. On the E coast Boyardville, with small marina, and Le Chateau are mainly for FVs. La Cotinière, on the W coast, suffers from almost constant Atlantic swell and is much used by FVs.

PORT ST DENIS   46°02'·16N 01°21'·97W   Rtg 3-4-2

SHELTER
Very good in marina, max depth 2·5m. Access over sill 1·5m CD is approx HW±3½ for 2m draft. Depth gauge on S bkwtr. 3 W waiting buoys about 700m E of ent in 0·7 - 1m.

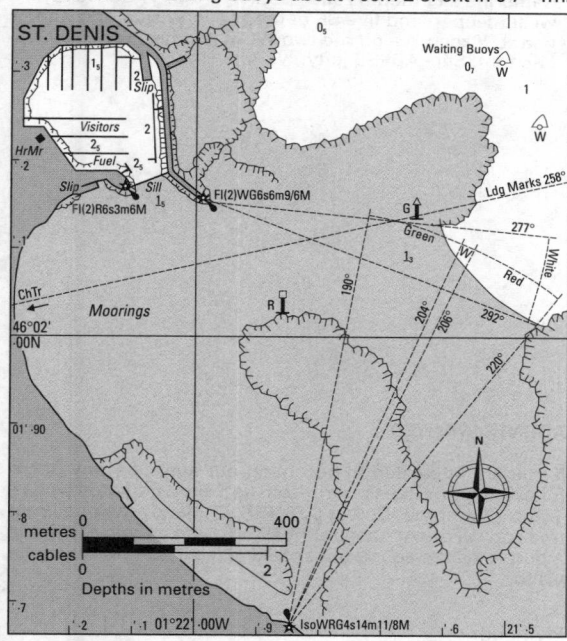

NAVIGATION
WPT 46°03'·27N 01°20'·75W, 025°/205° from/to chan ent, 1·35M. Appr chan dries about 1·1m. Daymarks lead 258° to ent. By night 2 Dir lts lead 205° and 284° in sequence.
LIGHTS AND MARKS
Pte de Chassiron, Fl 10s 50m 28M, 1·9M WNW. Rocher d'Antioche bn, Q 20m 11M, 2·2M NNW. Daymarks: SHM perch on with ✠ tr 258°. Dir lt, ½M S of hbr ent, Iso WRG 4s, W sector 204°-206°, leads 205° to pick up second Dir lt Fl (2) WG 6s on N pier; W sector 277°-292°, leads 284°.
RADIO TELEPHONE
VHF Ch 09.
TELEPHONE
Hr Mr 05·46·47·97·97; Yacht Club Océan 05·46·47·80·50; Aff Mar 05·46·47·60·01; SNSM 05·46·47·06·33; Ⓗ (12km) 05·46·47·00·86; Auto 08·36·68·08·17.
FACILITIES
Marina (600+70 Ⓥ) ☎ 05·46·47·97·97, ☎ 05·46·47·88·23, FF99, FW, AC, P, D, Slip, BH (10 ton); **YCO** ☎ 05·46·47·84·40.

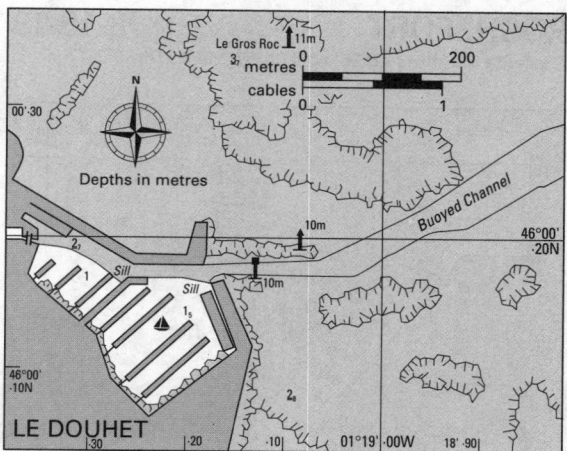

LE DOUHET   46°00'·15N 01°19'·18W   Rtg 3-4-2

SHELTER
Very good in marina on SE side of hbr; FVs use NW part. But ent is difficult in fresh NE'lies against ebb; beware swell and overfalls. Access HW –3½ to HW +3 for 1·5m draft, over sill 1·8m CD. Sill is marked by SHM bn, W of which a training wall protects pontoons. Ⓥ pontoon to port beyond sill.
NAVIGATION
WPT 46°00'·54N 01°17'·61W, NCM buoy Q, 068°/248° from/to ent 1·1M. Unlit, buoyed appr chan dries about 1·5m to approx 0·35M offshore. A fish farm 2M E of Le Douhet is marked by two NCM lt buoys, Q, and an ECM buoy, Q (3) 10s. Note: the WPT buoy is the NW'ly of the two NCM buoys. Further E, La Longe le Boyard is a rocky/sandy shoal; Fort Boyard is a conspic tr 27m, Q (9) 15s.
LIGHTS AND MARKS
No lts/ldg marks; bkwtrs marked by perches.
RADIO TELEPHONE
VHF Ch 09.
TELEPHONE.
Hr Mr 05·46·76·71·13, ☎ 05·46·76·78·26.
FACILITIES
Marina (305+45 visitors), FF70, FW, AC, Max LOA 15m; V at St Georges d'Oléron and La Brée.

OTHER HARBOURS ON ILE D'OLÉRON

BOYARDVILLE, Ile d'Oléron, Charente Maritime. Rtg 3-3-2. 45°58'·30N 01°13'·76W. AC 2746, 2663; SHOM 6913/4, 6334/5; ECM 552. HW +0545 on Dover (UT); tides as for Ile d'Aix (see 8.18.19). Fishing port, with good shelter in non-tidal marina (2m), but berths are usually taken and multiple rafting is the norm. Access HW±2 to drying appr chan and into marina to stbd via automatic lock, open approx HW±2. NB: Strong river current and awkward turn into marina; best to allow all departing boats to get clear first. From La Perrotine SHM buoy steer 265° for 4ca to S bkwtr lt, Fl (2) R 6s 8m 5M. Six W waiting buoys ½M N of chan or ⚓ in 3m. VHF Ch 09. Hr Mr ☎ 05·46·47·23·71. **Marina** (165+45 visitors) FF80, AC, FW C (10 ton), Slip, P & D; **YCB** ☎ 05·46·47·05·82. **Services:** ME, El, Sh, CH.

LE CHATEAU, Ile d'Oléron, Charente Maritime, 45°52'·95N 01°11'·30W. AC 2663; SHOM 6913, 6334, 6335; ECM 552. HW +0545 on Dover (UT); tides as for Ile d'Aix (8.18.19), ML 3·8m, duration 0540. Mainly occupied by oyster FVs; not recommended for yachts, except temporary visit. Possible drying berth on NE quay. Access HW±3. From N, appr via Chenal Est, to SCM bn marking Grand Montanne and ent to appr chan. From S, appr via Coureau d'Oléron, under mainland bridge (clnce 18m), thence 1M to ent chan. Ldg lts 319°, QR 11/24m 7M synch. Hr Mr ☎ 05·46·47·00·01. Facilities: Slip, L, FW, C (25 ton).

18

ROCHEFORT   8-18-19

Charente Maritime 45°56'·60N 00°57'·20W   Rtg 3-2-1

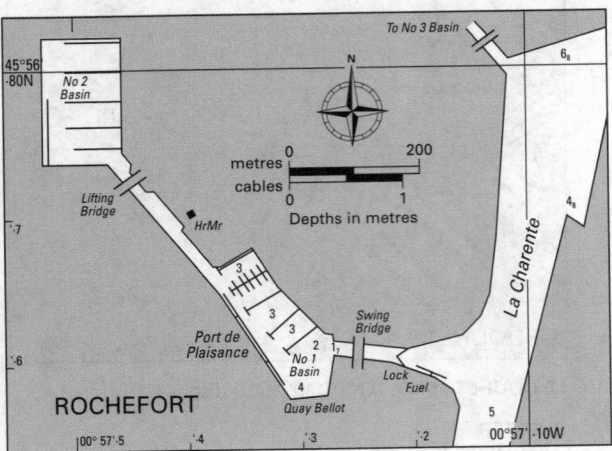

CHARTS
AC 2748, 2746; SHOM 4333, 6334; ECM 552

TIDES
+0610 Dover; Zone –0100

Standard Port POINTE DE GRAVE (→)

Times				Height (metres)			
High Water		Low Water		MHWS	MHWN	MLWN	MLWS
0000	0600	0500	1200	5·4	4·4	2·1	1·0
1200	1800	1700	2400				
Differences ROCHEFORT							
+0020	–0020	+0040	+0115	+1·0	+0·7	+0·1	+0·4
ILE D'AIX							
+0015	–0040	–0030	–0025	+0·7	+0·5	+0·3	–0·1

SHELTER
Excellent. Rochefort is on La Charente, about 10M from Port-des-Barques. Appr advised on late flood, as bar breaks on ebb. ↥ out of chan at Soubise or Martrou; or lock into Port de Plaisance on W bank, Bassin No 1; access HW La Rochelle ±1; at nps access can be only HW±¼. Waiting and fuel pontoon, just outside lock, dries to soft mud. Beware very strong currents here, other than at HW or LW. Bassin No 2 is entered from No 1, via lifting bridge. No 3 Bassin, 400m N, is for commercial craft only. The river is navigable 3·5M on to Tonnay-Charente.

NAVIGATION
WPT Les Palles NCM, Q, 45°59'·58N 01°09'·53W, 293°/113° from/to front ldg lt 115°, 4·0M. Stream in river runs about 2kn (4kn in narrows), and at sp there is a small bore. Beware wk just S of WPT. When WSW of Fouras pick up second (Port-des-Barques) ldg line (135°). The bar at Fouras carries about 0·5m. From Port-des-Barques follow the alignment of lettered pairs (RR to AA) of unlit ldg bns. Fixed bridge, 32m clearance, is 2M before Rochefort.

LIGHTS AND MARKS
Ile d'Aix Fl WR 5s 24m 24/20M; twin W trs with R tops; vis R103°-118°, W118°-103°. Ldg lts 115°, both QR, intens 113°-117°, W □ trs with R tops. Port Sud de Fouras, pier hd, Fl WR 4s 6m, 9/6M, vis R115°-177°, W177°-115°. Port-des-Barques ldg lts 135°, both Iso G 4s synch, intens 125°-145°, W □ trs; rear has B band on W side.

RADIO TELEPHONE
Port VHF Ch 12 16. Marina Ch 09 (HW±1).

TELEPHONE
Hr Mr 05·46·83·99·96; Aff Mar 05·46·84·22·67; CROSS 05·56·09·82·00; Météo 05·46·41·11·11; Auto 08.36.68.08.17; ‡ 05·46·99·03·90; Dr 05·46·99·61·11; Police 05·46·87·26·12; Brit Consul 05·56·52·28·35.

FACILITIES
Marina (280+20 visitors) in Basins 1 & 2 ☎ 05·46·83·99·96, ⚓ 05·46·99·80·56, FF63, FW, AC, ME, El, Sh, C (30 ton), D & P (outside lock), ⌧; **Port Neuf** Slip, FW; **Club Nautique Rochefortais** ☎ 05·46·87·34·61, Slip; **Services:** ME, El, Ⓔ, Sh, CH. **Town** P, D, V, Gaz, R, Bar, ⌧, Ⓑ, ⇌, ✈ (La Rochelle). Ferry: Roscoff or St Malo.

ADJACENT ANCHORAGE AT MOUTH OF LA CHARENTE

ILE D'AIX, Charente Maritime, 46°01'·00N 01°10'·00W. AC 2746, 2748; SHOM 6914, 6334. HW +0545 on Dover (UT); ML 3·9m. Tides see 8.18.19. Only a fine weather ↥ or pick up a buoy off the landing jetty at St Catherine's Pt, Fl WR 5s 24m 24/20M, the S tip of the island. Moorings E of St Catherine's Pt (depths shoal rapidly); four W buoys to west (deeper) and five SE of the Pt. On W side of island, near LW keep 3ca off the two WCM perches. **Facilities:** C (1·5 ton), Slip, AB (SE jetty), V, R.

AGENTS WANTED

If you are interested in becoming our agent for any of the following ports, please write to: The Editor, Edington House, Trent, Sherborne, Dorset DT9 4SR, England – and get your free copy of the Almanac annually. You do not have to live in a port to be the agent, but should at least be a fairly regular visitor.

Plymouth	Port Haliguen
Walton-on-the-Naze	La Trinité-sur-Mer
Hopeman	Piriac
Burghead	St Nazaire/Loire
Findhorn	Pornic
Nairn	St Gilles-Croix-de-Vie
Inverness	Les Sables d'Olonne
Loch Aline	River Seudre
Craobh	Port Bloc/Gironde
Workington	Anglet/Bayonne
Lough Swilly	St Jean-de-Luz
Portbail	Hendaye
St Malo/Dinard	Grandcamp-Maisy
Le Légué/St Brieuc	Port-en-Bessin
Lampaul	Ouistreham/Caen
L'Aberildut	Dives
Douarnenez	St Valéry-en-Caux
Lorient	Dunkerque
River Étel	Emden
Le Palais (Belle Ile)	Langeoog

SEUDRE RIVER   8-18-20

Charente Maritime 45°48'·00N 01°08'·50W

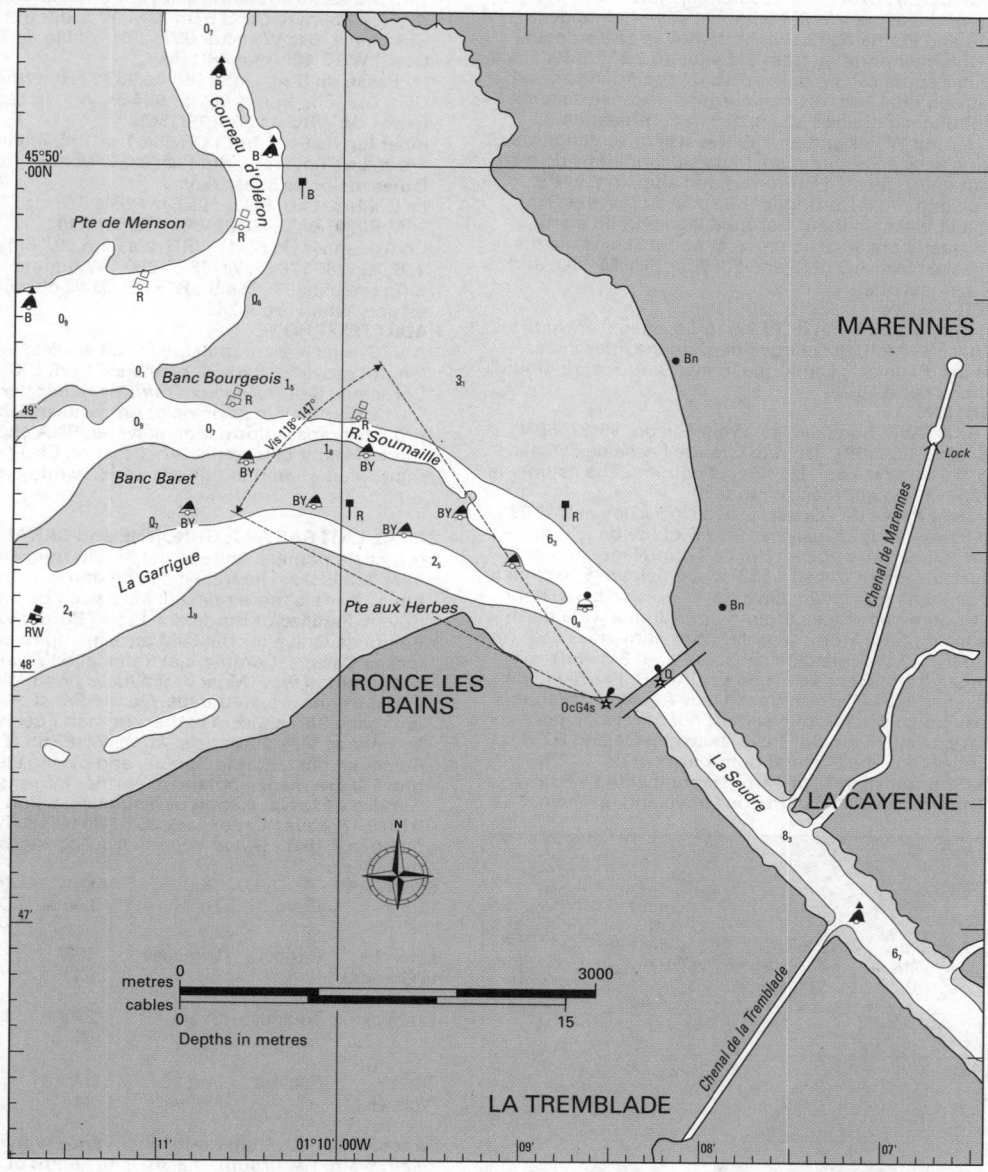

CHARTS
AC 2663; SHOM 6912, 6335; ECM 552

TIDES
+0545 Dover; ML 3·6; Duration Sp 0545, Np 0700

Standard Port POINTE DE GRAVE (⟶)

Times				Height (metres)			
High Water		Low Water		MHWS	MHWN	MLWN	MLWS
0000	0600	0500	1200	5·4	4·4	2·1	1·0
1200	1800	1700	2400				
Differences LA CAYENNE							
+0030	−0015	−0010	−0005	+0·2	+0·2	+0·3	0·0

SHELTER
Good in the yacht basin (2m) at Marennes. Lock opens about HW±2 sp, HW±1 np; or secure ⸚s at La Cayenne, La Grève (½M upstream), and at ent to Chenal de la Tremblade.

NAVIGATION
WPT 45°55'·88N 01°08'·65W, Chenal Est-Nord WCM buoy, for Chenal Est and Coureau d'Oléron. Best to appr La Seudre from N, through Coureau d'Oléron, and thence via Chenal de la Soumaille (dries about 0·7m). Chenal de la Garrigue carries slightly more water. Both are marked by bns and buoys.

Beware oyster beds. Pont de Seudre has clearance of 18m. Overhead power cables (24m) span Canal de Marennes. La Seudre is navigable to lock at Riberou. Beware: Pertuis de Maumusson is usable only in good weather, at about HW −1; see 8·18·5. In even moderate weather it is **extremely dangerous**, especially with out-going stream or any swell.

LIGHTS AND MARKS
There are no ldg lts/marks. Lights: Pte de Mus de Loup, Oc G 4s 8m 6M, vis 118°-147°. On bridge, between piers 6 and 7, Q 20m 10M, vis up/downstream. Chan marked by W boards.

RADIO TELEPHONE
VHF Ch 09.

TELEPHONE
Marennes: Hr Mr 05·46·85·02·68; Aff Mar 05·46·85·14·33; Police 05·46·85·00·19; Dr 05·46·85·23·06.
La Tremblade: Hr Mr 05·46·36·00·22; ⌗ 05·46·47·62·53; Auto 08.36.68.08.17; Dr 05·46·36·16·35; Brit Consul 05·56·36·16·35.

FACILITIES
MARENNES **Basin** ☎ 05·46·85·15·11, FW, AC, C (6 ton), ME, CH; **Services:** Sh, ME, CH. **Town** Slip, M, P, D, L, FW, V, R, Bar.
LA TREMBLADE **Quay** Slip, P, D, FW, C (5 ton); **Services:** ME, Sh, SM, CH. **Town** Slip, P, D, L, FW, Gaz, V, R, Bar, ✉, Ⓑ, ⇌, ✈ (La Rochelle). Ferry: Roscoff or St Malo.

18

LA GIRONDE & CANALS   8-18-21

LA GIRONDE ESTUARY is a substantial waterway. The mouth of the estuary is 9M wide between Pointe de la Coubre and Pointe de Grave. From Royan to Bordeaux (55M) the river narrows from 6M wide to 2.5M at Pauillac. The outer apprs can be dangerous due to Atlantic swell, very strong tidal streams and currents, extensive shoals and shifting sandbanks, see 8.18.5. A combination of swell, strong W'lies and an ebb tide will raise dangerous, breaking seas some 5m high; in these conditions do not attempt entry. Be alert for ferries and shipping. In the Gironde and the R Dordogne the sp flood reaches 3kn and the ebb 4kn. In the R Garonne the sp flood starts with a small bore and then runs at about 3kn, while the ebb reaches 5kn. AC 2910 and 2916, or SHOM 7028 and 7029, are essential.

SHELTER
Yacht hbrs from Royan (8.18.22) to Bordeaux* include Port Bloc (8.18.23), St Georges-de-Didonne, Meschers, Mortagne, Pauillac*, Lamarque, Blaye* and Port de Bourg. For *hbrs, see 8.18.22.

NAVIGATION
WPT BXA SWM buoy, Iso 4s, Whis, Racon, 45°37'·60N 01°28'·60W, 261°/081° from/to Grande Passe de l'Ouest Nos 1 & 2 buoys, 4·8M. Do not cut corners. The estuary is entered via two approach channels:
(1) **Grande Passe de l'Ouest.** Leave No 1 buoy at LW. 081° on La Palmyre ldg lts passes close S of Pte de la Coubre; thence 100° to pass abeam Pte de Terre-Nègre and enter the river on astern transit of 327° (see below). The chan is deep and well marked/lit. Give the Mauvaise bank, Banc de la Coubre and shoals around Cordouan a wide berth.
(2) **Passe du Sud.** From 'G' unlit SWM buoy track 063° on the ldg lts at St Nicolas/Pte de Grave until 3M abeam Cordouan lt ho; thence 041° on Le Chay/St Pierre ldg lts to pick up the 327° astern transit (see below). The chan carries approx 5m through shoals; not advised in poor vis or heavy swell. Platin de Grave, between G4 and G7 Bys, has only 1·8m. The 6 lateral buoys are not lit.
The astern transit 327° of Terre-Nègre lt with La Palmyre, FR 57m 17M, leads NE of Pte de Grave and up-river.

LIGHTS AND MARKS
(1) **Grande Passe de l'Ouest** ldg lts 081°, both intens 080·5°-082·5°: Front Dir Iso 4s 21m 22M, and Q (2) 5s 10m 3M same structure, W pylon on dolphin; rear, La Palmyre Dir Q 57m 27M, W radar tr. From No 9 SHM buoy, use W sector 097°- 104° of Pte de Terre-Nègre, Oc (3) WRG 12s 39m 18/14M.
(2) **Passe du Sud**, Outer ldg lts 063°: Front St Nicolas Dir QG 22m 16M, intens 061·5°-064·5°, W □ tr; rear, Pte de Grave Oc WRG 4s 26m 19/15M.
Inner ldg lts 041°, both QR 33/61m 18M, intens 039°-043°: Front, Le Chay; rear, Ste Pierre 0·97M from front.
Other major lts in estuary:
La Coubre lt ho, Fl (2) 10s 64m 28M RC, also FRG 42m 12/10M R030°-043°, G043°-060°, R060°-110°.
Courdouan lt Oc (2+1) WRG 12s 60m 22/18M, W014°-126°, G126°-178·5°, W178·5°-250°, W (unintens) 250°-267°, R (unintens) 267°-294·5°, R294·5°-014°; obscured in estuary when brg > 285°.

RADIO TELEPHONE
A VTS, which is compulsory for all vessels regardless of length, provides radar surveillance from BXA buoy to Bordeaux. Call *Bordeaux Traffic* or *Radar Verdon* on VHF Ch 12 16 (H24). In poor vis or on request *Radar Verdon* provides radar information between BXA and Verdon roads. Height of water is broadcast on Ch 17 every 5 mins, plus a weather bulletin and nav info on request.

CANAL LATÉRAL À LA GARONNE and CANAL DU MIDI
provide a popular route to the Mediterranean, despite over 130 locks. The transit can be done in about a week, but 12 days is more relaxed. Masts can be unstepped at Royan, Pauillac or Bordeaux. Leave Bordeaux at LW Pointe de Grave for the 30M passage up river to the first lock at Castets. Commercial traffic and W-bound boats have right of way. Most of the locks on the Canal Latéral à la Garonne are automatic. On the Canal du Midi there are many hire cruisers in the summer. Fuel is available by hose at Mas d'Agenais, Agen, Port Sud (Toulouse), Castelnaudary, Port la Robine, and by can elsewhere. V and FW are readily obtained. Further information from: Service de la Navigation de Toulouse, 8 Port St Etienne, 31079 Toulouse Cedex, ☎ 05·61·80·07·18. Tolls are listed in 8.15.8. *Guide Vagnon No 7* or *Navicarte No 11* are advised.

SUMMARY

Canal	From	To	Km/ Locks	Min Depth (m)	Min Height (m)
Latéral à la Garonne	Castets	Toulouse	193/ 53	2·2	3·5
Du Midi	Toulouse	Sete	240/ 65	1·6	3·0
De la Nouvelle	Salleles	Port la Nouvelle	37/ 14	1·5	3·1

Notes: Max LOA 30m; draft 1·5m (varies with season); max beam 5·5m. Headroom of 3·3m is to centre of arch; over a width of 4m, clearance is about 2·40m. Speed limit 8km/hr (about 4½kn), but 3km/hr under bridges/over aqueducts.

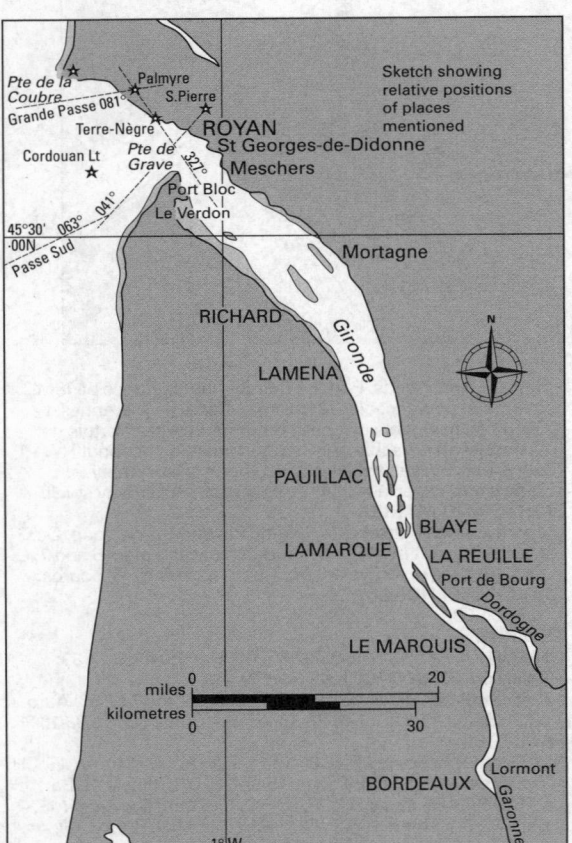

Sketch showing relative positions of places mentioned

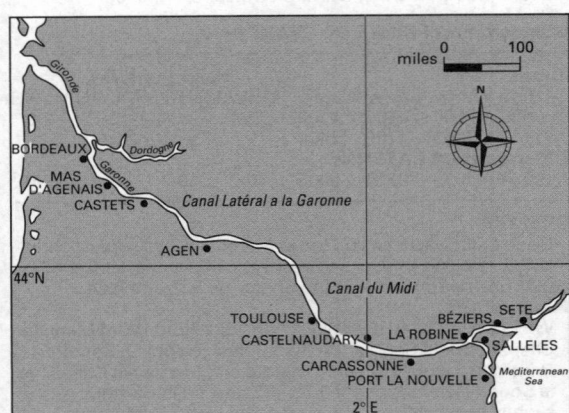

ROYAN   8-18-22

Charente Maritime 45°37'·20N 01°01'·54W   Rtg 3-1-1

CHARTS
AC 2910, 2916, 2664; Imray C41, 42; SHOM 7028, 7070; ECM 553, 554

TIDES
+0530 Dover; ML 3·2; Duration Sp 0615, Np 0655; Zone –0100

Standard Port POINTE DE GRAVE (→)

Times				Height (metres)			
High Water		Low Water		MHWS	MHWN	MLWN	MLWS
0000	0600	0500	1200	5·4	4·4	2·1	1·0
1200	1800	1700	2400				
Differences ROYAN							
0000	–0005	–0005	–0005	–0·3	–0·2	0·0	0·0

SHELTER
Good. Easy access H24 except in strong W/NW winds. Ent chan is dredged 1·5m, and basins approx 2·5m, but beware silting to 1m outside head of New Jetty. A good port of call for Canal du Midi with crane for masts.

NAVIGATION
WPT R1 SHM buoy, Iso G 4s, 45°36'·62N 01°01'·90W, 193°/013° from/to S Jetty lt, 0·47M. The Gironde apprs can be dangerous; see 8.18.5 and 8.18.21 for details; allow about 2 hrs from Pte de la Coubre to Royan. The banks off Royan shift and buoys are consequently altered. Off hbr ent, there is an eddy, running S at about 1kn on the flood and 3kn on the ebb. Beware fast ferries and FVs.

LIGHTS AND MARKS
See 8.18.21 for details of appr chans. Other lts as chartlet; the Iso 4s on end of Quai d'acceuil is a neon sign.

RADIO TELEPHONE
VHF Ch 09 16 (season 0800-2000; otherwise 0900-1800LT).

TELEPHONE
Hr Mr 05·46·38·72·22; Aff Mar 05·46·39·26·30; CROSS 05·56·73·31·31; SNSM 05·46·38·75·79; ⊞ 05·46·38·51·27; Météo 05·56·34·20·11; Auto 08.36.68.08.17; Police 05·46·38·34·22; Dr 05·46·05·68·69; Ⓗ 05·46·38·01·77; Brit Consul 05·56·52·28·35.

FACILITIES
Marina (920 + 100 Ⓥ) ☎ 05·46·38·72·22, 🛥 05·46·39·42·47, FF135, Slip, P & D (0900-1230, 1430-1900), FW, C (1·5 ton), BH (26 ton), ME, AC, El, Sh, Grid, Ice; **Les Régates de Royan** ☎ 05·46·05·44·13; **Services:** CH, Ⓔ, SM, SHOM. **Town** P, D, V, R, Bar, Gaz, ▣, ✉, Ⓑ, ⇌, ✈ (Bordeaux). Ferry: Roscoff or St Malo.

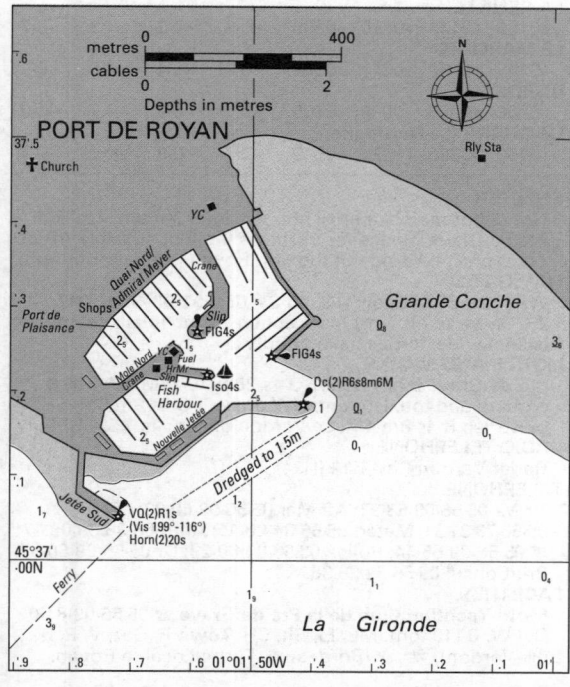

OTHER HARBOURS ON THE GIRONDE

MESCHERS-sur-GIRONDE, Charente Maritime, 45°33'·15N 00°56'·55W. AC 2910, 2916; SHOM 7028; ECM 554. Tides as for ROYAN, 5M down-river same bank. Good shelter in all weathers, but access via drying chan is HW–3 to HW. Appr close to Pte de Meschers between PHM and SHM unlit perches. Narrow chan has shore close to port and mudbank close to stbd. Ldg marks/lts 000° are 2 FW on W posts; entry to hbr is just before the front ldg mark. To stbd drying marina basin has access HW±3. Dead ahead an automatic lock gives access over sill 2m CD to a wet basin HW±2½ by day; waiting pontoons. Hr Mr ☎ 05.46.02.56.89; Auto 05.36.68.08.17. Facilities: **Marinas** (125 in drying basin, 123 in wet basin, 18 visitors), FW, AC. **Town** P & D (cans), R, Bar, V.

MORTAGNE-sur-GIRONDE (La Rive), Charente Maritime, 45°28'·25N 00°48'·75W. AC 2916; SHOM 7028, 7029. Tides, use RICHARD differences (8.18.23). Good shelter in marina on E bank of river, 14M from Royan/40M from Bordeaux (near the 75km mark). Leave the main Gironde chan at No 18 PHM buoy, Fl (2) R 6s, and head E for 4·5M to Mortagne appr chan. Ent is marked by unlit PHM and SHM bns. Enter chan, 2·5m at mean tides, on 063°, for 0·9M across drying mudbanks to lock which opens HW–2 to HW. VHF Ch 09. Hr Mr ☎ 05.46.90.63.15. Facilities: **Marina** (130+20 visitors), 6m depth, FW, AC, Slip, ME, BY, BH (10 ton), V, Ice; Fuel, Aff Mar, ⊞, and SNSM at Royan; Auto 05.36.68.08.17.

PAUILLAC, Gironde, 45°11'·88N 00°44'·53W. Rtg 4-3-1. AC 2916, 2910; SHOM 7029; HW +0620 on Dover (UT); ML 3·0m. See 8.18.23. Excellent shelter in marina on W bank, 25M from Le Verdon, and at 47km post from Bordeaux. Access at all tides (depth 1·5m), but keep very close to NE side of ent at LW, due to silting. Visitors use pontoon A at ent. Beware current in the river on ent/dep. Lts: Fl G 4s 7m 5M on NE elbow of bkwtr. Ent at S end is marked by QG and QR. Hr Mr ☎ 05·56·59·12·16, 🛥 05.56.59.25.82; VHF Ch 09 (0800–1800LT). Aff Mar 05.56.59.01.58; SNSM/CROSS 05·56·09·82·00; ⊞ 05·56·59·04·01; Météo 05·36·68·08·33. Facilities: **Marina** (200+ 50 Ⓥ), ☎ 05·56·59·12·16, FW, AC, Slip, ME, El, Sh; **Quay** FW, D, P (cans), C (14 ton); **CN de Pauillac** ☎ 05·56·59·12·58; **Services:** C for mast step/un-step, CH, Sh.

BLAYE, Charente Maritime, 45°07'·53N 00°39'·90W. AC 2916; SHOM 7029. HW +0715 on Dover (UT); HW +0145 and –0·3m on Pte de Grave; ML 2·4m. Good shelter; access good except in S to SW winds. Ent is abeam S end of of Ile Nouvelle at 37km post and close S of La Citadelle (conspic). N quay has Q (3) R 5s 6m 3M, on R mast, and Fl G 4s on S quay. Max stay 24 hours. VHF Ch 12 (0800–1800LT). Hr Mr ☎ 05·57·42·13·63, 🛥 05·57·42·28·19; Facilities: **Quay** Access HW±2½, FW, AC, P, D, C (25 ton), Slip, ME.

BORDEAUX, Gironde, 44°52'·80N 00°32'·30W. AC 2916; SHOM 7029, 7030. HW +0715 on Dover (UT); ML 2·4m. See 8.18.23. Bordeaux is about 55M up the Gironde estuary and R Garonne. Beware big ships, strong currents (up to 5kn when river in spate) and large bits of flotsam. The chan is well marked and lit. Pte du Jour marina (Halte Nautique) is 2M from city centre, on W bank close S of Pont d'Aquitaine suspension bridge (clearance 51m), with 20 visitors berths and de-masting crane, (less handy than Royan's crane). Berths may also be available, by arrangement with Hr Mr, 1½M above bridge in No 2 Basin, access HW –1 to HW+½; crane available. Or berth on wharves between No 1 Basin and Pont de Pierre, but stream is strong. VHF Ch 12. Hr Mr ☎ 05·56·52·51·04; Aff Mar ☎ 05·56·52·26·23; ⊞ ☎ 05·56·44·47·10; Météo ☎ 05·56·90·91·21; Facilities: **Marina** ☎ 05·56·50·84·14 VHF Ch 09; **Sport Nautique de la Gironde** ☎ 05·56·50·84·14; **Services:** Slip, C (5 ton), ME, El, Sh, CH, Ⓔ, SHOM.

18

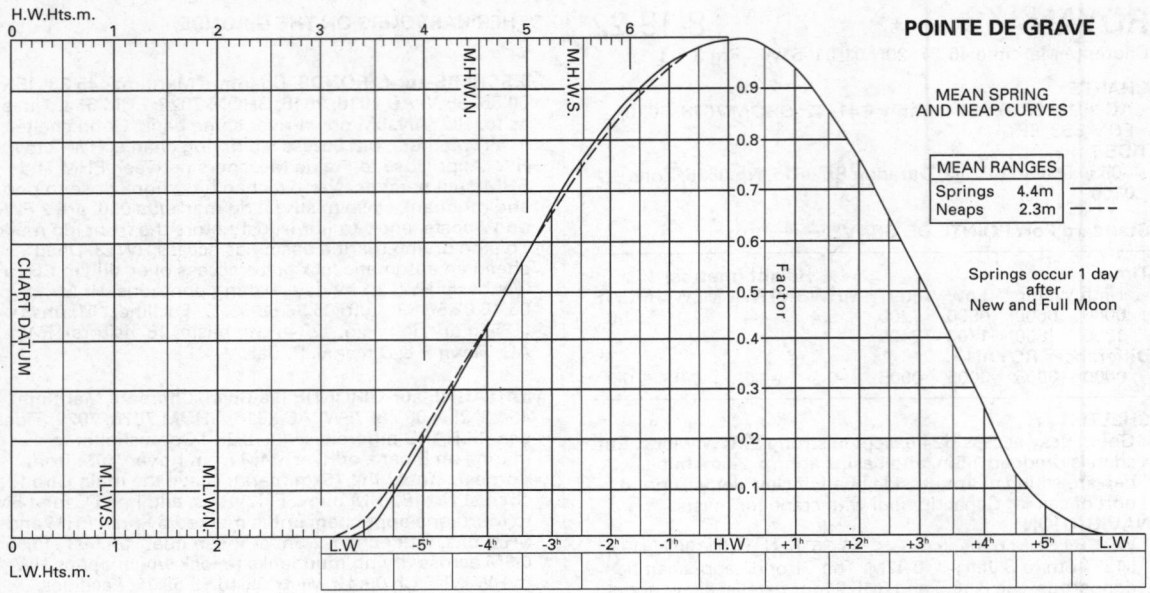

POINTE DE GRAVE

MEAN SPRING
AND NEAP CURVES

MEAN RANGES	
Springs	4.4m
Neaps	2.3m

Springs occur 1 day
after
New and Full Moon

PORT BLOC   8-18-23

Gironde 45°34'·18N 01°03'·64W   Rtg 3-4-2

CHARTS
AC 2910, 2664, 2916; Imray C42; ECM 553, 554; SHOM 7028, 6335. Note: 7029 & 7030 cover to Bordeaux/Libourne

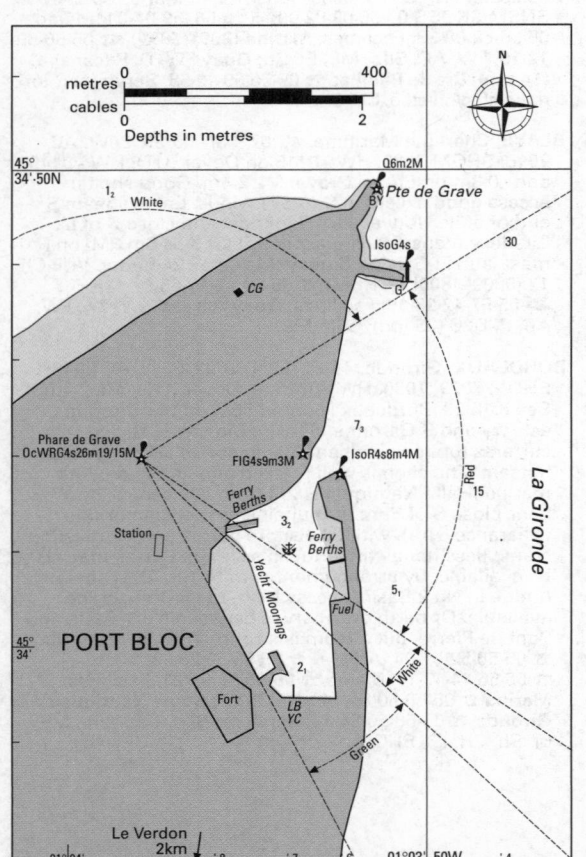

TIDES
(Pauillac) +0720 Dover; ML 3·0; Duration: Sp 0615; Np 0655; Zone –0100
NOTE: Pte de Grave is a Standard Port; tidal predictions for each day of the year are given below and apply to Port Bloc

Standard Port POINTE DE GRAVE (→)

Times				Height (metres)			
High Water		Low Water		MHWS	MHWN	MLWN	MLWS
0000	0600	0500	1200	5·4	4·4	2·1	1·0
1200	1800	1700	2400				
Differences RICHARD							
+0018	+0018	+0028	+0033	–0·1	–0·1	–0·4	–0·5
LAMENA							
+0035	+0045	+0100	+0125	+0·2	+0·1	–0·5	–0·3
PAUILLAC							
+0100	+0100	+0135	+0205	+0·1	0·0	–1·0	–0·5
LA REUILLE							
+0135	+0145	+0230	+0305	–0·2	–0·3	–1·3	–0·7
LE MARQUIS							
+0145	+0150	+0247	+0322	–0·3	–0·4	–1·5	–0·9
BORDEAUX							
+0200	+0225	+0330	+0405	–0·1	–0·2	–1·7	–1·0
LIBOURNE (La Dordogne)							
+0250	+0305	+0525	+0540	–0·7	–0·9	–2·0	–0·4

SHELTER
Good, but mainly a ferry hbr, dredged 3m and 4ca S of Pte de Grave. Space for yachts is limited; possible AB on pontoons on W side of the hbr. Royan is a better option.
NAVIGATION
WPT 13b SHM buoy, QG, 45°34'·66N 01°02'·90W, 047°/ 227° from/to hbr ent, 7ca. Caution strong tidal streams. Ent is 30m wide; ferries have priority.
LIGHTS AND MARKS
Pte de Grave lt ho, Oc WRG 4s 26m 19/15M, W □ tr, B corners and top. Hbr ent: NW quay Fl G 4s 9m 3M, SE bkwtr Iso R 4s 8m 4M. Le Verdon oil jetty is 1.5M SSE.
RADIO TELEPHONE
Radar Verdon Ch 11 12 (H24).
TELEPHONE
Hr Mr 05·56·09·63·91; Aff Mar 05·56·09·60·23; CROSS 05·56·73·31·31; Météo 05·56·34·20·11; Auto 08·36·68·08·17; ⊞ 05·56·09·65·14; Police 05·56·09·80·29; Dr 05·56·09·60·37; Brit Consul 05·56·52·28·35.
FACILITIES
Moto Yachting Club de la Pte de Grave ☎ 05·56·09·84·02, D, FW, C (10 ton), ME, El, Sh, CH. **Town** P, Gaz, V, R, ✉ & Ⓑ (Verdon), ⇌, ✈ (Bordeaux). Ferry: Local to Royan.

TIME ZONE –0100
(French Standard Time)
Subtract 1 hour for UT

For French Summer Time add ONE hour in non-shaded areas

FRANCE – POINTE DE GRAVE

LAT 45°34′N   LONG 1°04′W

TIMES AND HEIGHTS OF HIGH AND LOW WATERS

YEAR **1999**

JANUARY

Day	Time	m	Day	Time	m
1 F	0413 / 1011 / 1640 / 2232	5.5 / 1.1 / 5.5 / 1.1	**16** SA	0413 / 1014 / 1637 / 2232	5.1 / 1.5 / 5.0 / 1.5
2 SA ○	0501 / 1102 / 1729 / 2320	5.6 / 0.9 / 5.5 / 1.0	**17** SU ●	0450 / 1054 / 1713 / 2310	5.2 / 1.4 / 5.1 / 1.3
3 SU	0547 / 1150 / 1814	5.7 / 0.9 / 5.5	**18** M	0527 / 1134 / 1749 / 2349	5.4 / 1.2 / 5.2 / 1.3
4 M	0005 / 0631 / 1235 / 1858	1.1 / 5.6 / 1.0 / 5.4	**19** TU	0604 / 1213 / 1825	5.4 / 1.1 / 5.2
5 TU	0048 / 0713 / 1317 / 1939	1.2 / 5.5 / 1.1 / 5.2	**20** W	0028 / 0643 / 1251 / 1904	1.2 / 5.5 / 1.1 / 5.2
6 W	0129 / 0752 / 1358 / 2018	1.3 / 5.3 / 1.3 / 4.9	**21** TH	0107 / 0724 / 1330 / 1945	1.2 / 5.4 / 1.1 / 5.1
7 TH	0211 / 0830 / 1441 / 2058	1.5 / 5.0 / 1.6 / 4.7	**22** F	0147 / 0808 / 1412 / 2030	1.3 / 5.3 / 1.2 / 5.0
8 F	0254 / 0912 / 1526 / 2145	1.7 / 4.8 / 1.8 / 4.5	**23** SA	0231 / 0857 / 1457 / 2123	1.4 / 5.2 / 1.4 / 4.8
9 SA	0343 / 1004 / 1619 / 2247	2.0 / 4.5 / 2.0 / 4.3	**24** SU	0321 / 0954 / 1549 / 2229	1.5 / 5.0 / 1.6 / 4.6
10 SU	0439 / 1112 / 1722 / 2359	2.2 / 4.4 / 2.2 / 4.3	**25** M	0421 / 1102 / 1652 / 2347	1.7 / 4.8 / 1.7 / 4.6
11 M	0545 / 1230 / 1830	2.3 / 4.3 / 2.2	**26** TU	0531 / 1220 / 1805	1.8 / 4.7 / 1.8
12 TU	0108 / 0653 / 1340 / 1933	4.3 / 2.3 / 4.4 / 2.2	**27** W	0104 / 0646 / 1336 / 1921	4.7 / 1.8 / 4.8 / 1.8
13 W	0205 / 0754 / 1435 / 2026	4.5 / 2.2 / 4.5 / 2.0	**28** TH	0213 / 0800 / 1444 / 2031	4.9 / 1.6 / 5.0 / 1.6
14 TH	0253 / 0846 / 1521 / 2111	4.7 / 2.0 / 4.7 / 1.8	**29** F	0312 / 0906 / 1542 / 2130	5.1 / 1.4 / 5.1 / 1.4
15 F	0335 / 0932 / 1601 / 2152	4.9 / 1.7 / 4.9 / 1.6	**30** SA	0404 / 1002 / 1633 / 2222	5.3 / 1.2 / 5.3 / 1.2
			31 SU ○	0451 / 1052 / 1718 / 2308	5.5 / 1.0 / 5.4 / 1.1

FEBRUARY

Day	Time	m	Day	Time	m
1 M	0533 / 1137 / 1758 / 2351	5.6 / 0.9 / 5.4 / 1.0	**16** TU ●	0510 / 1115 / 1732 / 2333	5.5 / 1.1 / 5.3 / 1.1
2 TU	0612 / 1219 / 1836	5.6 / 0.9 / 5.4	**17** W	0548 / 1156 / 1810	5.6 / 0.9 / 5.5
3 W	0030 / 0648 / 1257 / 1909	1.1 / 5.5 / 1.0 / 5.2	**18** TH	0013 / 0628 / 1235 / 1849	0.9 / 5.7 / 0.8 / 5.5
4 TH	0107 / 0721 / 1332 / 1941	1.2 / 5.3 / 1.2 / 5.1	**19** F	0053 / 0709 / 1315 / 1928	0.9 / 5.7 / 0.9 / 5.4
5 F	0143 / 0753 / 1408 / 2013	1.3 / 5.1 / 1.4 / 4.9	**20** SA	0133 / 0751 / 1355 / 2011	1.0 / 5.5 / 1.0 / 5.2
6 SA	0219 / 0827 / 1445 / 2050	1.5 / 4.9 / 1.6 / 4.7	**21** SU	0215 / 0837 / 1437 / 2059	1.1 / 5.3 / 1.2 / 5.0
7 SU	0259 / 0908 / 1527 / 2137	1.7 / 4.6 / 1.9 / 4.4	**22** M	0302 / 0931 / 1527 / 2200	1.3 / 5.0 / 1.5 / 4.7
8 M	0344 / 1001 / 1618 / 2242	2.0 / 4.4 / 2.2 / 4.2	**23** TU	0358 / 1038 / 1627 / 2320	1.6 / 4.8 / 1.7 / 4.6
9 TU	0441 / 1117 / 1725	2.2 / 4.2 / 2.3	**24** W	0508 / 1203 / 1742	1.8 / 4.6 / 1.9
10 W	0005 / 0555 / 1327 / 1841	4.2 / 2.4 / 4.1 / 2.4	**25** TH	0047 / 0629 / 1327 / 1906	4.6 / 1.9 / 4.6 / 1.9
11 TH	0122 / 0710 / 1359 / 1947	4.3 / 2.3 / 4.3 / 2.2	**26** F	0202 / 0751 / 1438 / 2021	4.7 / 1.7 / 4.8 / 1.8
12 F	0222 / 0812 / 1454 / 2041	4.5 / 2.1 / 4.5 / 2.0	**27** SA	0304 / 0858 / 1536 / 2120	5.0 / 1.5 / 5.0 / 1.5
13 SA	0310 / 0904 / 1538 / 2128	4.8 / 1.8 / 4.8 / 1.7	**28** SU	0355 / 0951 / 1623 / 2209	5.2 / 1.2 / 5.2 / 1.3
14 SU	0352 / 0950 / 1617 / 2211	5.0 / 1.5 / 5.0 / 1.5			
15 M	0431 / 1033 / 1655 / 2252	5.3 / 1.3 / 5.2 / 1.2			

MARCH

Day	Time	m	Day	Time	m
1 M	0438 / 1038 / 1702 / 2253	5.4 / 1.1 / 5.3 / 1.1	**16** TU	0407 / 1007 / 1632 / 2229	5.3 / 1.2 / 5.3 / 1.1
2 TU ○	0515 / 1120 / 1737 / 2332	5.5 / 1.0 / 5.4 / 1.0	**17** W ●	0447 / 1051 / 1711 / 2312	5.5 / 0.9 / 5.5 / 0.9
3 W	0549 / 1157 / 1808	5.5 / 1.0 / 5.4	**18** TH	0528 / 1133 / 1750 / 2354	5.8 / 0.7 / 5.6 / 0.7
4 TH	0008 / 0621 / 1231 / 1838	1.0 / 5.5 / 1.0 / 5.3	**19** F	0609 / 1214 / 1830	5.9 / 0.7 / 5.7
5 F	0041 / 0650 / 1303 / 1906	1.1 / 5.3 / 1.1 / 5.2	**20** SA	0035 / 0651 / 1255 / 1911	0.7 / 5.8 / 0.7 / 5.6
6 SA	0113 / 0719 / 1334 / 1936	1.2 / 5.2 / 1.3 / 5.0	**21** SU	0116 / 0734 / 1336 / 1954	0.8 / 5.7 / 0.9 / 5.4
7 SU	0145 / 0750 / 1407 / 2008	1.3 / 5.0 / 1.5 / 4.8	**22** M	0158 / 0820 / 1419 / 2041	0.9 / 5.4 / 1.1 / 5.1
8 M	0219 / 0825 / 1441 / 2047	1.6 / 4.7 / 1.8 / 4.6	**23** TU	0245 / 0914 / 1508 / 2139	1.2 / 5.0 / 1.5 / 4.8
9 TU	0257 / 0908 / 1522 / 2137	1.8 / 4.4 / 2.0 / 4.3	**24** W	0340 / 1023 / 1607 / 2300	1.5 / 4.7 / 1.8 / 4.6
10 W	0345 / 1010 / 1618 / 2252	2.1 / 4.2 / 2.3 / 4.1	**25** TH	0450 / 1153 / 1724	1.8 / 4.5 / 2.0
11 TH	0453 / 1143 / 1740	2.3 / 4.0 / 2.4	**26** F	0031 / 0615 / 1319 / 1851	4.5 / 1.9 / 4.5 / 2.1
12 F	0027 / 0620 / 1316 / 1902	4.1 / 2.3 / 4.1 / 2.3	**27** SA	0149 / 0738 / 1428 / 2005	4.7 / 1.8 / 4.7 / 1.8
13 SA	0143 / 0734 / 1420 / 2006	4.3 / 2.1 / 4.4 / 2.1	**28** SU	0252 / 0843 / 1522 / 2103	4.9 / 1.6 / 4.9 / 1.6
14 SU	0238 / 0832 / 1509 / 2058	4.7 / 1.8 / 4.7 / 1.8	**29** M	0340 / 0933 / 1604 / 2150	5.1 / 1.3 / 5.1 / 1.4
15 M	0325 / 0922 / 1552 / 2145	5.0 / 1.5 / 5.0 / 1.4	**30** TU	0419 / 1017 / 1639 / 2232	5.2 / 1.2 / 5.2 / 1.2
			31 W ○	0453 / 1056 / 1710 / 2309	5.3 / 1.1 / 5.3 / 1.1

APRIL

Day	Time	m	Day	Time	m
1 TH	0523 / 1131 / 1739 / 2343	5.4 / 1.1 / 5.3 / 1.1	**16** F ●	0505 / 1107 / 1728 / 2331	5.8 / 0.7 / 5.7 / 0.7
2 F	0553 / 1203 / 1807	5.4 / 1.1 / 5.3	**17** SA	0549 / 1151 / 1811	5.9 / 0.6 / 5.8
3 SA	0014 / 0622 / 1233 / 1836	1.1 / 5.3 / 1.2 / 5.2	**18** SU	0015 / 0633 / 1234 / 1854	0.6 / 5.9 / 0.7 / 5.7
4 SU	0044 / 0650 / 1302 / 1905	1.2 / 5.2 / 1.3 / 5.1	**19** M	0058 / 0719 / 1317 / 1940	0.7 / 5.7 / 0.9 / 5.5
5 M	0115 / 0720 / 1332 / 1936	1.3 / 5.0 / 1.5 / 4.9	**20** TU	0142 / 0808 / 1402 / 2028	0.9 / 5.4 / 1.2 / 5.2
6 TU	0147 / 0753 / 1404 / 2012	1.5 / 4.7 / 1.7 / 4.7	**21** W	0230 / 0903 / 1451 / 2126	1.2 / 5.0 / 1.5 / 4.9
7 W	0222 / 0832 / 1441 / 2056	1.7 / 4.5 / 1.9 / 4.5	**22** TH	0325 / 1012 / 1551 / 2242	1.5 / 4.7 / 1.8 / 4.6
8 TH	0305 / 0925 / 1530 / 2159	1.9 / 4.4 / 2.2 / 4.3	**23** F	0433 / 1138 / 1704	1.8 / 4.5 / 2.0
9 F	0403 / 1044 / 1641 / 2325	2.2 / 4.1 / 2.4 / 4.1	**24** SA	0008 / 0554 / 1259 / 1825	4.6 / 1.9 / 4.5 / 2.1
10 SA	0526 / 1222 / 1810	2.3 / 4.1 / 2.4	**25** SU	0126 / 0713 / 1406 / 1938	4.6 / 1.8 / 4.7 / 1.9
11 SU	0052 / 0648 / 1337 / 1922	4.3 / 2.1 / 4.4 / 2.1	**26** M	0228 / 0816 / 1457 / 2035	4.8 / 1.6 / 4.8 / 1.7
12 M	0158 / 0752 / 1433 / 2021	4.6 / 1.8 / 4.7 / 1.8	**27** TU	0316 / 0906 / 1537 / 2123	4.9 / 1.5 / 5.0 / 1.5
13 TU	0250 / 0847 / 1520 / 2112	5.0 / 1.5 / 5.1 / 1.4	**28** W	0354 / 0949 / 1610 / 2205	5.1 / 1.3 / 5.1 / 1.4
14 W	0337 / 0936 / 1603 / 2200	5.3 / 1.1 / 5.4 / 1.1	**29** TH	0426 / 1027 / 1639 / 2242	5.1 / 1.2 / 5.2 / 1.3
15 TH	0421 / 1022 / 1646 / 2246	5.6 / 0.8 / 5.6 / 0.8	**30** F ○	0456 / 1101 / 1709 / 2315	5.2 / 1.2 / 5.2 / 1.2

18

Chart Datum: 2·83 metres below Lallemand System (Mean Sea Level, Marseilles)

TIME ZONE –0100
(French Standard Time)
Subtract 1 hour for UT

For French Summer Time add ONE hour in non-shaded areas

FRANCE – POINTE DE GRAVE

LAT 45°34′N   LONG 1°04′W

TIMES AND HEIGHTS OF HIGH AND LOW WATERS

YEAR **1999**

MAY

Day	Time	m	Time	m	Time	m	Time	m
1 SA	0527	5.2	1133	1.2	1739	5.2	2347	1.2
2 SU	0557	5.1	1203	1.3	1810	5.2		
3 M	0018	1.2	0626	5.1	1233	1.3	1840	5.1
4 TU	0049	1.3	0657	4.9	1303	1.5	1913	5.0
5 W	0121	1.4	0730	4.7	1336	1.6	1949	4.8
6 TH	0157	1.6	0809	4.5	1413	1.8	2032	4.6
7 F	0239	1.8	0859	4.3	1500	2.0	2129	4.4
8 SA	0332	1.9	1007	4.2	1602	2.2	2242	4.4
9 SU	0442	2.0	1131	4.2	1721	2.2		
10 M	0001	4.4	0559	2.0	1250	4.4	1835	2.0
11 TU	0112	4.7	0708	1.7	1352	4.7	1939	1.7
12 W	0212	5.0	0808	1.4	1446	5.0	2037	1.4
13 TH	0305	5.3	0902	1.1	1534	5.3	2129	1.1
14 F	0355	5.5	0953	0.9	1621	5.5	2220	0.9
15 SA ●	0443	5.7	1042	0.7	1706	5.7	2308	0.7
16 SU	0530	5.8	1129	0.7	1753	5.7	2355	0.6
17 M	0618	5.7	1215	0.8	1840	5.7		
18 TU	0042	0.7	0707	5.6	1300	0.9	1928	5.5
19 W	0128	0.9	0757	5.3	1346	1.2	2018	5.2
20 TH	0217	1.1	0852	5.0	1436	1.5	2113	5.0
21 F	0310	1.4	0955	4.7	1532	1.7	2217	4.7
22 SA	0411	1.7	1109	4.5	1637	2.0	2332	4.6
23 SU	0522	1.9	1224	4.4	1749	2.0		
24 M	0047	4.5	0636	1.9	1328	4.5	1900	2.0
25 TU	0151	4.6	0740	1.8	1420	4.6	2000	1.8
26 W	0242	4.8	0832	1.6	1502	4.8	2050	1.7
27 TH	0322	4.8	0917	1.5	1537	4.9	2134	1.6
28 F	0357	4.9	0956	1.4	1610	5.0	2212	1.5
29 SA	0430	5.0	1031	1.4	1643	5.1	2248	1.4
30 SU O	0503	5.0	1104	1.3	1716	5.1	2322	1.3
31 M	0536	5.0	1137	1.3	1748	5.1	2355	1.3

JUNE

Day	Time	m	Time	m	Time	m	Time	m
1 TU	0607	5.0	1209	1.4	1821	5.1		
2 W	0028	1.3	0639	4.9	1241	1.4	1856	5.0
3 TH	0103	1.4	0714	4.8	1316	1.5	1933	4.9
4 F	0139	1.5	0753	4.6	1354	1.7	2017	4.7
5 SA	0221	1.6	0840	4.5	1439	1.8	2109	4.6
6 SU	0309	1.7	0939	4.4	1535	1.9	2211	4.6
7 M	0409	1.8	1051	4.4	1642	2.0	2320	4.6
8 TU	0517	1.8	1206	4.5	1753	1.9		
9 W	0031	4.7	0626	1.6	1314	4.7	1900	1.7
10 TH	0136	4.9	0730	1.4	1414	4.9	2002	1.4
11 F	0236	5.1	0830	1.2	1508	5.2	2101	1.2
12 SA	0332	5.3	0927	1.0	1559	5.4	2156	0.9
13 SU ●	0424	5.5	1019	0.9	1648	5.6	2249	0.8
14 M	0516	5.6	1110	0.8	1738	5.6	2339	0.7
15 TU	0606	5.6	1158	0.8	1826	5.6		
16 W	0028	0.7	0656	5.4	1245	1.0	1915	5.5
17 TH	0115	0.9	0745	5.2	1331	1.1	2003	5.3
18 F	0202	1.1	0834	5.0	1418	1.4	2051	5.0
19 SA	0250	1.3	0925	4.7	1508	1.6	2143	4.8
20 SU	0343	1.6	1022	4.5	1603	1.8	2241	4.6
21 M	0441	1.8	1126	4.4	1706	2.0	2347	4.4
22 TU	0547	1.9	1232	4.3	1812	2.0		
23 W	0056	4.4	0653	1.9	1332	4.4	1917	2.0
24 TH	0156	4.4	0752	1.8	1421	4.5	2013	1.9
25 F	0246	4.5	0841	1.7	1504	4.7	2101	1.7
26 SA	0329	4.6	0924	1.6	1543	4.8	2143	1.5
27 SU	0407	4.8	1003	1.5	1620	4.9	2222	1.5
28 M	0443	4.8	1039	1.4	1656	5.0	2300	1.4
29 TU	0518	4.9	1115	1.4	1730	5.1	2336	1.3
30 W	0551	4.9	1150	1.4	1805	5.1		

JULY

Day	Time	m	Time	m	Time	m	Time	m
1 TH	0012	1.3	0625	4.9	1225	1.4	1841	5.1
2 F	0048	1.3	0700	4.8	1301	1.4	1919	5.0
3 SA	0125	1.3	0738	4.8	1340	1.5	2001	4.9
4 SU	0205	1.4	0822	4.7	1422	1.6	2049	4.8
5 M	0249	1.4	0914	4.6	1512	1.6	2144	4.7
6 TU	0341	1.5	1016	4.5	1611	1.7	2247	4.7
7 W	0441	1.6	1128	4.5	1717	1.7	2356	4.7
8 TH	0549	1.6	1241	4.6	1827	1.6		
9 F	0107	4.8	0658	1.5	1348	4.8	1935	1.5
10 SA	0214	4.9	0805	1.4	1448	5.0	2040	1.3
11 SU	0316	5.1	0907	1.2	1543	5.2	2140	1.1
12 M	0413	5.3	1017	1.0	1635	5.4	2236	0.9
13 TU ●	0505	5.4	1056	0.9	1725	5.5	2327	0.8
14 W	0554	5.4	1145	0.9	1812	5.6		
15 TH	0015	0.8	0641	5.3	1230	0.9	1858	5.5
16 F	0100	0.9	0725	5.2	1314	1.1	1940	5.3
17 SA	0143	1.0	0806	5.0	1356	1.2	2021	5.1
18 SU	0225	1.3	0846	4.7	1439	1.5	2101	4.8
19 M	0309	1.5	0928	4.5	1526	1.7	2146	4.6
20 TU	0358	1.7	1019	4.3	1618	1.9	2243	4.3
21 W	0454	2.0	1124	4.2	1720	2.1	2353	4.2
22 TH	0600	2.1	1236	4.2	1829	2.1		
23 F	0108	4.2	0706	2.1	1341	4.3	1933	2.1
24 SA	0211	4.3	0805	2.0	1435	4.5	2029	1.9
25 SU	0302	4.4	0854	1.8	1520	4.7	2116	1.7
26 M	0345	4.6	0937	1.6	1600	4.8	2159	1.6
27 TU	0424	4.7	1017	1.5	1637	5.0	2239	1.4
28 W	0459	4.9	1056	1.4	1713	5.1	2318	1.3
29 TH	0534	4.9	1133	1.3	1748	5.2	2356	1.2
30 F	0608	5.0	1211	1.2	1825	5.2		
31 SA	0033	1.1	0644	5.0	1248	1.2	1903	5.2

AUGUST

Day	Time	m	Time	m	Time	m	Time	m
1 SU	0110	1.1	0722	4.9	1325	1.2	1943	5.1
2 M	0148	1.2	0803	4.9	1405	1.3	2028	5.0
3 TU	0229	1.2	0849	4.7	1451	1.4	2119	4.9
4 W	0316	1.4	0946	4.6	1544	1.6	2219	4.7
5 TH	0412	1.6	1057	4.5	1649	1.7	2331	4.6
6 F	0519	1.7	1217	4.5	1802	1.7		
7 SA	0049	4.6	0634	1.7	1332	4.6	1918	1.6
8 SU	0203	4.7	0749	1.6	1437	4.9	2029	1.4
9 M	0308	4.9	0856	1.4	1521	5.1	2132	1.2
10 TU	0405	5.1	0954	1.2	1625	5.3	2226	1.0
11 W ●	0455	5.2	1044	1.0	1712	5.5	2315	0.9
12 TH	0539	5.3	1130	0.9	1755	5.5	O 2335	1.0
13 F	0000	0.8	0620	5.3	1213	0.9	1834	5.4
14 SA	0040	0.9	0657	5.2	1252	1.0	1911	5.3
15 SU	0118	1.1	0731	5.0	1329	1.2	1944	5.1
16 M	0155	1.2	0803	4.8	1406	1.4	2017	4.8
17 TU	0232	1.5	0837	4.6	1445	1.6	2055	4.6
18 W	0312	1.7	0920	4.4	1530	1.9	2145	4.3
19 TH	0400	2.0	1019	4.2	1625	2.2	2254	4.1
20 F	0502	2.2	1138	4.1	1737	2.3		
21 SA	0020	4.0	0617	2.3	1301	4.1	1853	2.3
22 SU	0137	4.1	0727	2.2	1405	4.3	1957	2.1
23 M	0235	4.3	0824	2.0	1455	4.6	2049	1.8
24 TU	0321	4.5	0912	1.8	1537	4.8	2134	1.6
25 W	0401	4.7	0954	1.5	1615	5.1	2216	1.4
26 TH	0437	4.9	1034	1.3	1651	5.2	2256	1.2
27 F O	0512	5.1	1114	1.2	1727	5.4	2335	1.0
28 SA	0548	5.2	1152	1.1	1804	5.4		
29 SU	0013	1.0	0624	5.2	1230	1.0	1843	5.4
30 M	0051	1.0	0702	5.2	1308	1.1	1923	5.4
31 TU	0129	1.0	0742	5.1	1347	1.1	2007	5.2

Chart Datum: 2·83 metres below Lallemand System (Mean Sea Level, Marseilles)

TIME ZONE –0100
(French Standard Time)
Subtract 1 hour for UT

For French Summer Time add
ONE hour in non-shaded areas

FRANCE – POINTE DE GRAVE

LAT 45°34′N   LONG 1°04′W

TIMES AND HEIGHTS OF HIGH AND LOW WATERS

YEAR **1999**

SEPTEMBER

Day	Time	m	Time	m	Time	m	Time	m
1 W	0209	1.2	0827	4.9	1431	1.3	2057	4.9
2 TH	0254	1.4	0922	4.7	1522	1.5	2159	4.7
3 F	0348	1.6	1034	4.5	1627	1.8	2318	4.5
4 SA	0458	1.9	1203	4.5	1747	1.9		
5 SU	0044	4.5	0621	1.9	1324	4.6	1912	1.8
6 M	0201	4.6	0742	1.8	1431	4.9	2026	1.5
7 TU	0304	4.9	0849	1.5	1527	5.1	2124	1.3
8 W	0356	5.1	0943	1.3	1614	5.3	2214	1.1
9 TH ●	0440	5.2	1030	1.1	1655	5.4	2258	0.9
10 F	0518	5.3	1112	1.0	1732	5.5	2338	0.9
11 SA	0553	5.3	1151	1.0	1806	5.4		
12 SU	0015	1.0	0624	5.2	1226	1.1	1837	5.3
13 M	0049	1.1	0654	5.1	1300	1.2	1906	5.1
14 TU	0121	1.3	0722	4.9	1332	1.4	1936	4.9
15 W	0154	1.5	0754	4.7	1407	1.6	2010	4.6
16 TH	0228	1.8	0832	4.5	1444	1.9	2054	4.3
17 F	0308	2.1	0922	4.3	1531	2.2	2156	4.1
18 SA	0402	2.3	1038	4.1	1638	2.4	2330	3.9
19 SU	0521	2.5	1214	4.1	1807	2.4		
20 M	0101	4.0	0645	2.4	1330	4.3	1922	2.2
21 TU	0204	4.3	0750	2.2	1424	4.5	2018	1.9
22 W	0252	4.5	0841	1.9	1509	4.9	2105	1.6
23 TH	0332	4.8	0926	1.6	1548	5.2	2148	1.3
24 F	0410	5.1	1008	1.2	1626	5.4	2229	1.1
25 SA O	0447	5.3	1049	1.1	1703	5.6	2310	0.9
26 SU	0524	5.4	1130	1.0	1742	5.7	2350	0.9
27 M	0603	5.5	1210	0.9	1822	5.7		
28 TU	0029	0.9	0724	5.4	1250	0.9	1904	5.5
29 W	0109	1.0	0724	5.3	1330	1.1	1950	5.3
30 TH	0150	1.2	0810	5.1	1415	1.3	2042	5.0

OCTOBER

Day	Time	m	Time	m	Time	m	Time	m
1 F	0236	1.5	0907	4.8	1507	1.6	2149	4.7
2 SA	0332	1.8	1023	4.6	1614	1.9	2316	4.5
3 SU	0444	2.1	1155	4.5	1739	2.0		
4 M	0043	4.5	0611	2.1	1317	4.7	1907	1.9
5 TU	0156	4.7	0732	1.9	1423	4.9	2016	1.6
6 W	0254	4.9	0835	1.7	1516	5.1	2109	1.4
7 TH	0341	5.1	0926	1.4	1559	5.3	2155	1.2
8 F	0419	5.2	1010	1.2	1635	5.4	2236	1.1
9 SA ●	0452	5.3	1050	1.1	1707	5.4	2313	1.1
10 SU	0522	5.3	1126	1.1	1737	5.4	2347	1.1
11 M	0551	5.3	1159	1.2	1806	5.3		
12 TU	0018	1.3	0620	5.2	1230	1.3	1835	5.1
13 W	0048	1.4	0649	5.0	1301	1.4	1904	4.9
14 TH	0118	1.6	0720	4.9	1333	1.6	1936	4.7
15 F	0150	1.8	0755	4.6	1408	1.9	2014	4.4
16 SA	0227	2.1	0840	4.4	1450	2.1	2108	4.1
17 SU	0313	2.3	0944	4.2	1547	2.4	2233	4.0
18 M	0422	2.5	1116	4.1	1712	2.5		
19 TU	0013	4.0	0553	2.5	1242	4.3	1836	2.3
20 W	0123	4.3	0706	2.3	1344	4.6	1938	2.0
21 TH	0215	4.6	0803	2.0	1433	4.9	2029	1.7
22 F	0259	4.9	0851	1.6	1516	5.2	2115	1.4
23 SA	0339	5.2	0937	1.2	1557	5.5	2159	1.1
24 SU O	0419	5.4	1021	1.1	1639	5.7	2242	0.9
25 M	0500	5.6	1105	0.9	1737	5.6	2325	0.8
26 TU	0542	5.6	1148	0.8	1804	5.8		
27 W	0008	0.9	0625	5.6	1232	0.9	1850	5.6
28 TH	0050	1.0	0711	5.5	1316	1.0	1939	5.4
29 F	0134	1.3	0801	5.2	1403	1.3	2035	5.1
30 SA	0223	1.6	0859	5.0	1456	1.6	2145	4.7
31 SU	0320	1.9	1014	4.7	1603	1.9	2310	4.5

NOVEMBER

Day	Time	m	Time	m	Time	m	Time	m
1 M	0431	2.1	1141	4.6	1724	2.0		
2 TU	0031	4.5	0552	2.2	1300	4.7	1847	1.9
3 W	0139	4.7	0709	2.0	1405	4.9	1953	1.7
4 TH	0234	4.9	0811	1.8	1457	5.1	2045	1.5
5 F	0318	5.0	0901	1.6	1538	5.2	2130	1.4
6 SA	0353	5.1	0945	1.4	1612	5.2	2209	1.3
7 SU	0423	5.2	1025	1.4	1642	5.3	2245	1.3
8 M ●	0453	5.3	1101	1.3	1712	5.3	2318	1.3
9 TU	0523	5.3	1133	1.3	1742	5.2	2349	1.4
10 W	0554	5.2	1205	1.4	1811	5.1		
11 TH	0019	1.5	0625	5.1	1236	1.5	1841	4.9
12 F	0050	1.6	0657	5.0	1308	1.6	1913	4.7
13 SA	0122	1.8	0732	4.8	1343	1.8	1950	4.5
14 SU	0158	2.0	0814	4.6	1423	2.0	2037	4.3
15 M	0241	2.2	0909	4.4	1513	2.2	2146	4.1
16 TU	0339	2.4	1022	4.3	1620	2.3	2313	4.1
17 W	0456	2.4	1144	4.4	1739	2.2		
18 TH	0032	4.3	0613	2.3	1254	4.6	1848	2.0
19 F	0132	4.6	0717	2.0	1352	4.9	1947	1.7
20 SA	0223	4.9	0812	1.7	1443	5.2	2039	1.4
21 SU	0309	5.2	0904	1.4	1530	5.5	2128	1.2
22 M	0354	5.5	0954	1.1	1616	5.7	2216	1.0
23 TU O	0439	5.6	1042	0.9	1703	5.8	2302	0.9
24 W	0525	5.7	1130	0.8	1751	5.8	2349	0.9
25 TH	0612	5.7	1217	0.8	1840	5.6		
26 F	0035	1.0	0701	5.6	1304	1.0	1932	5.4
27 SA	0122	1.2	0753	5.4	1353	1.2	2028	5.1
28 SU	0212	1.5	0850	5.1	1446	1.5	2132	4.8
29 M	0307	1.8	0956	4.9	1546	1.8	2246	4.6
30 TU	0409	2.0	1111	4.7	1656	2.0		

DECEMBER

Day	Time	m	Time	m	Time	m	Time	m
1 W	0000	4.6	0520	2.1	1227	4.7	1810	2.0
2 TH	0107	4.6	0633	2.1	1333	4.8	1918	1.9
3 F	0203	4.7	0737	2.0	1428	4.8	2014	1.8
4 SA	0248	4.9	0832	1.8	1512	4.9	2101	1.6
5 SU	0324	5.0	0918	1.7	1547	5.0	2142	1.5
6 M	0357	5.1	0959	1.6	1620	5.1	2219	1.5
7 TU ●	0429	5.2	1036	1.5	1652	5.1	2252	1.5
8 W	0502	5.2	1111	1.5	1724	5.1	2325	1.5
9 TH	0535	5.2	1144	1.5	1755	5.0	2357	1.5
10 F	0608	5.2	1217	1.5	1826	4.9		
11 SA	0029	1.6	0641	5.1	1251	1.5	1859	4.8
12 SU	0102	1.7	0717	5.0	1326	1.6	1934	4.7
13 M	0139	1.8	0757	4.8	1404	1.8	2017	4.5
14 TU	0220	2.0	0845	4.7	1449	1.9	2111	4.4
15 W	0310	2.1	0943	4.6	1543	2.0	2221	4.3
16 TH	0412	2.2	1052	4.5	1648	2.0	2337	4.4
17 F	0522	2.1	1204	4.6	1757	2.0		
18 SA	0048	4.6	0630	2.0	1311	4.8	1903	1.8
19 SU	0148	4.8	0734	1.7	1411	5.1	2004	1.5
20 M	0242	5.1	0833	1.5	1507	5.3	2100	1.3
21 TU	0333	5.4	0929	1.2	1600	5.5	2154	1.1
22 W O	0423	5.6	1023	1.0	1651	5.7	2245	1.0
23 TH	0512	5.7	1115	0.8	1741	5.7	2335	0.9
24 F	0602	5.8	1205	0.8	1832	5.6		
25 SA	0023	1.0	0651	5.7	1254	0.9	1922	5.5
26 SU	0110	1.1	0741	5.6	1342	1.1	2013	5.2
27 M	0157	1.3	0831	5.3	1430	1.3	2105	4.9
28 TU	0246	1.6	0924	5.1	1521	1.6	2202	4.7
29 W	0340	1.8	1023	4.8	1618	1.8	2306	4.5
30 TH	0439	2.0	1131	4.6	1722	2.0		
31 F	0014	4.5	0546	2.1	1243	4.5	1831	2.1

18

Chart Datum: 2·83 metres below Lallemand System (Mean Sea Level, Marseilles)

ARCACHON   8-18-24

Gironde 44°39'·83N 01°09'·04W   Rtg 5-1-1

TIDES
+0620 Dover; ML 2·5; Zone –0100
Standard Port POINTE DE GRAVE (⟵)

Times				Height (metres)			
High Water		Low Water		MHWS	MHWN	MLWN	MLWS
0000	0600	0500	1200	5·4	4·4	2·1	1·0
1200	1800	1700	2400				

Differences ARCACHON
+0010	+0025	0000	+0020	–1·1	–1·0	–0·8	–0·6

CAP FERRET
–0015	+0005	–0005	+0015	–1·4	–1·2	–0·8	–0·5

CHARTS
AC 2664; Imray C42; SHOM 6766, 7070; ECM 255, 1024
SHELTER
Good in marina (max LOA 15m), but it is impossible to ent Bassin d'Arcachon in strong SW-N winds or at night. Visitors' berths in the marina are very scarce in season. If marina full, there is a good ⚓ N of it, except in strong N'lies.
Around the Bassin are many small drying hbrs worth exploring by shoal draft boats:
On the W, La Vigne*, Le Canon, Piquey and Claouey; on the NE, Port de Lège, Ares, Andernos, Fontainevieille*, Lanton (Cassy) and Audenge*; and
on the S, La Teste and Gujan. *see below for notes.

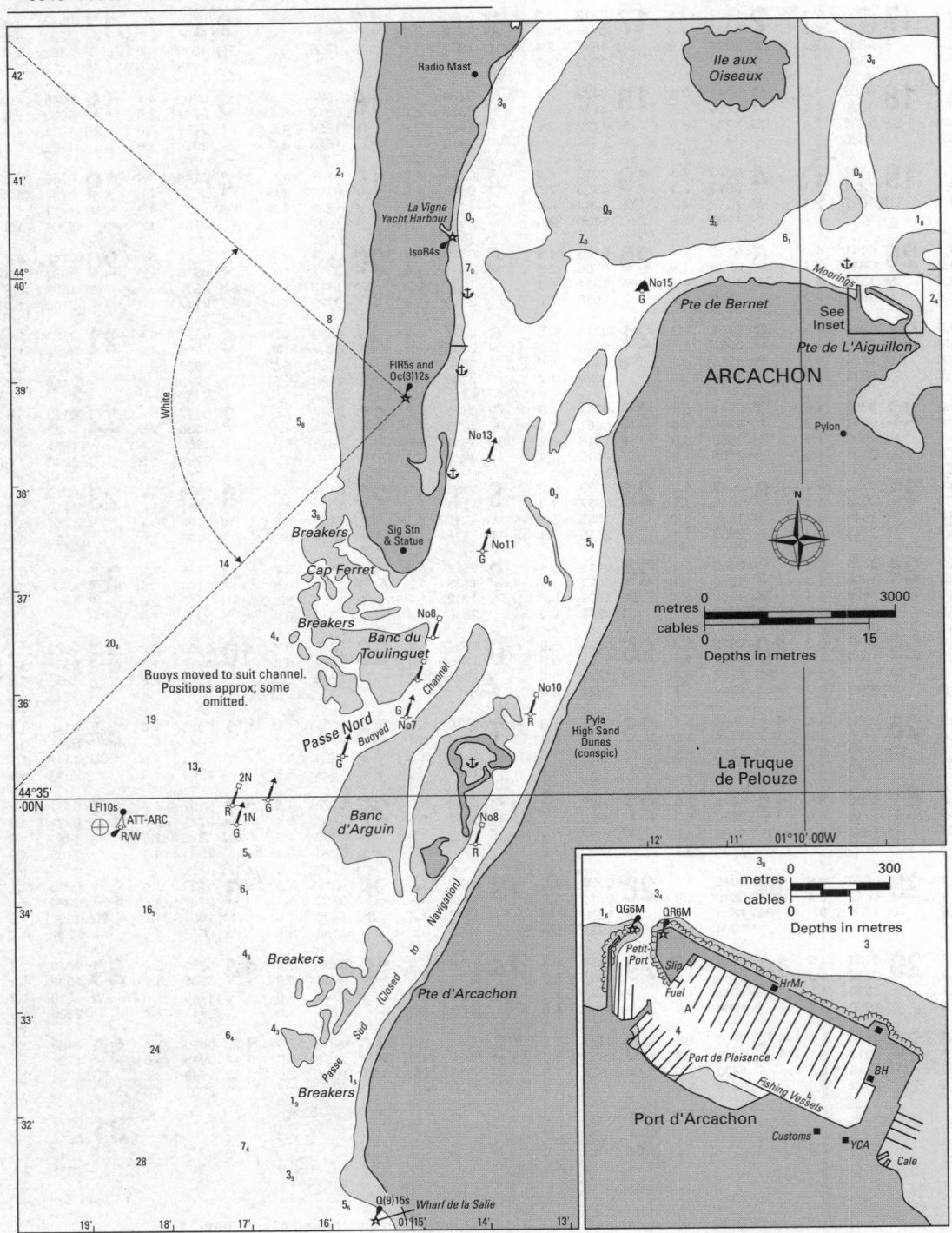

NAVIGATION

WPT 44°34'·89N 01°18'·61W, ATT ARC (SWM) buoy, 270°/090° from/to N Passe first chan buoys, 0·7M. Only appr is the well buoyed, unlit N Passe which runs E, NE then N between Banc d'Arguin and Banc du Toulinguet towards Cap Ferret where it meets the longer S Passe. The latter, although used by a few local FVs, is closed to navigation. Between Cap Ferret and Wharf de la Salie the sea breaks in any wind on the shifting sand banks; the chan can be seen between the breakers. Buoys are moved frequently; latest known positions are published in the updating Supplements to this Almanac.

Best time to start appr is HW−1 and no later than HW+1. Due to the ebb (6kn sp) the chan bar (mean depth 4·5m) is impassable from HW+1 until LW, and it is best to wait until LW+3. When swell is higher than 1m, bar may be dangerous. Best to leave on the last of the flood; wait in a convenient "lagoon" ⚓ near the Banc d'Arguin.

For navigation update call *Cap Ferret Semaphore* Ch 16 10 (HJ); or Service de la Marine Gironde ☎ 05·56·82·32·97. Beware firing ranges between Arcachon and Capbreton, out to 45M offshore; see 8.18.25, next col.

LIGHTS AND MARKS

Cap Ferret Fl R 5s 53m 27M and Oc (3) 12s 46m 14M, vis 045°-135°. The dunes (103m high) are very conspic. ATT-ARC (landfall/SWM buoy, L Fl 10s) is moved as required to indicate approach to N Passe. La Salie IDM buoy Fl (2) 6s is off chartlet, about 1·5M WSW of the Wharf de Salie WCM bn, Q (9) 15s 19m 10M.

Secondary chans in the Bassin d'Arcachon are marked by piles lettered A to K, plus pile number, clockwise from the N. **Marina**: W bkwtr QG, E bkwtr QR.

RADIO TELEPHONE

VHF Ch 09 16 (H24).

TELEPHONE

Hr Mr 05·56·22·36·75, 🛥 05·56·83·26·19; ⌗ 05·56·83·05·89; Aff Mar 05·57·52·57·07; SNSM 05·56·83·22·44; CROSS 05·56·73·31·31; Auto 08·36·68·08·33; Police 05·56·83·04·63; Dr 05·56·83·04·72; Ⓗ 05·56·83·39·50; Brit Consul 05·56·52·28·35.

FACILITIES

Marina (2192+ 57 visitors), FF154 (2nd night free), Access HW±3, FW, AC, D, Slip, C (10/20 ton), BH (45 ton); **YC du Bassin d'Arcachon** ☎ 05·56·83·22·11, P, D, FW, Slip, R, Bar; **Services**: P, D, ME, EI, Ⓔ, SHOM, Sh, CH, SM, ▣. **Town** V, R, Gaz, ✉, Ⓑ, ⇌, ✈ (Bordeaux). Ferry: Roscoff or St Malo.

MINOR HARBOURS IN THE ARCACHON BASIN

FONTAINEVIEILLE, Gironde, 44°43'·36N 01°04'·51W. AC 2664; SHOM 6766 (essential); ECM 255. Tides as 8.18.24. Drying marina on NE side of Bassin d'Arcachon, access HW±3 via Chenal de Mouchtalette. Proceed from E0 pile to E8, where fork left onto NNE for 7ca to hbr ent. No lts. Boats dry out on pontoons. Hr Mr ☎ 05.56.82.17.31; Auto 05.36.65.08.33. Facilities: **Marina** (178+ 2), FW, Fuel, Slip, ME.

LA VIGNE, Gironde, 44°40'·50N 01°14'·20W. AC 2664; SHOM 6766; ECM 255. HW time & ht approx as Cap Ferret above; ML 2·4m. Access HW±2. See 8.18.24. Good shelter, but crowded; beware strong currents across hbr ent. 2 perches mark the ent and an a lt Iso R 4s 7m 4M. A small bkwtr (unlit) protrudes into the ent from the NE side. Aff Mar ☎ 05.56·60·52.76. Facilities: **Marina** (268 + 2) Max LOA 8·5m, ☎ 05·56·60·54.36, AC, Slip, CH, C (2 ton), P, D.

AUDENGE, Gironde, 44°40'·65N 01°01'·50W. AC 2664; SHOM 6766 (essential); ECM 255. Tides as 8.18.24. Drying marina and oyster port 5·5M E of Arcachon, access sp HW−2 to HW, nps HW−1 to HW. Appr from G0 pile via drying Chenal d'Audenge to G8 pile, 5ca short of the ent. Hr Mr ☎ 05.56.26.88.97. The Old Port (84 berths) is to the N; the New Port has 130 pontoon berths, FW, AC, Fuel, Slip, YC.

ANDERNOS, Gironde, 44°44'·32N 01°06'·05W. AC 2664; SHOM 6766; ECM 255. HW time & ht approx as Arcachon 8.18.24; ML 2·4m; access about HW±2. Dredged channel to Bétey, with side chan to Andernos, is very well marked by lateral poles D0 to D14. Jetty was rebuilt (1995) with drying 'Halte Nautique' (pontoon) at outer end; only for yachts able to take the ground, max LOA 12m. Also ⚓ on flat drying fore-shore. Hr Mr ☎ 56.82.00.12. Few facilities.

LANDES RANGE   8-18-25

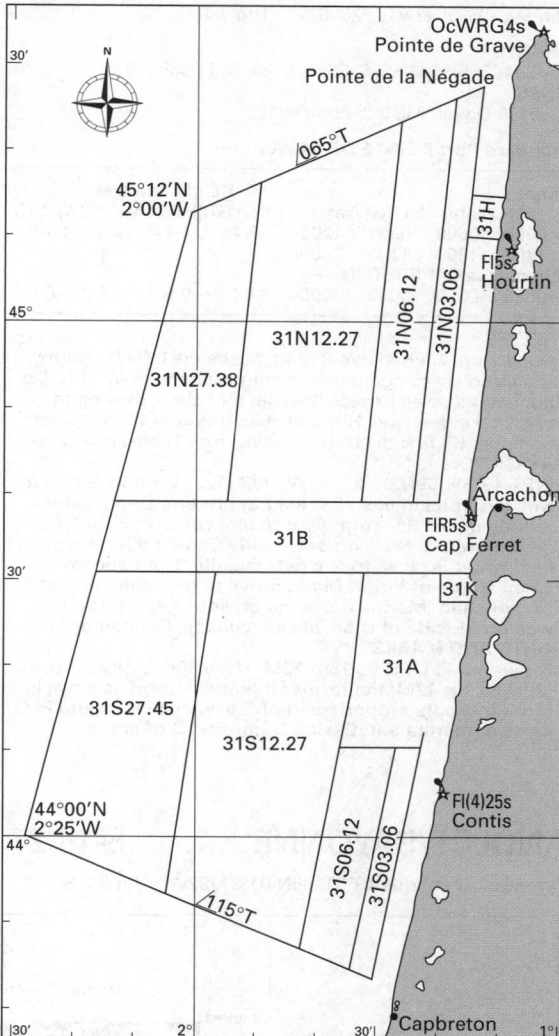

Limits: The Centre d'Essais des Landes (CEL) firing range lies between Pte de la Negade and Capbreton and extends 45M offshore. Its N boundary bears 065° from 45°12'N 02°00'W; the S boundary bears 115° from 44°N 02°25'W. The W boundary joins these two lat/long positions. The inshore limit parallels the coast 3M off, except in 3 places where it joins the coast:
a. at Sector 31H, off Hourtin, between 45°14'N and 45°09'N;
b. at Sector 31K, between 44°31'N and 44°28'N; and
c. at Sector 31A, between 44°28'N and 44°13'N, which itself extends 12M offshore. (This is the most often used sector).
Sector designations: The range is split into blocks 31N and 31S, to the N and S of a clear corridor (31B) 8M wide bearing 270° from Arcachon. 31N and 31S are sub-divided into N/S sectors delineated by distance off the coast. Thus, 31S 27.45 means the S block, in a sector 27-45M offshore.
Range activity: Various sectors are active from 0830-1800 LT Mon-Fri; but never on Sun, rarely on a Sat. The range is not active in August. Navigation through active sectors is prohib from the coast to the 12M territorial limit; beyond 12M it is strongly discouraged.
Information: Landes broadcasts range activity on VHF Ch 06, after warning on Ch 06 and 16, at 0815 & 1615LT Mon-Thurs, and at 0815 & 1030LT Fri. For more info on request (Mon-Thurs 0800-1700LT; Fri 0800-1100) call Landes VHF Ch 06 or ☎ 05.58.78.18.00 (same hrs); also recorded data H24 on ☎ 05.58.82.22.42/43. Other sources of info include: Hr Mr's, Aff Maritimes, CROSS Soulac and Sémaphores at La Coubre, Cap Ferret and Socoa; all on request Ch 16, which should be monitored on passage.
Transit options include: sailing by night or at weekends or in August; or routeing outside the 45M limit.

18

CAPBRETON   8-18-26

Landes 43°39'·42N 01°26'·82W   Rtg 4-2-1

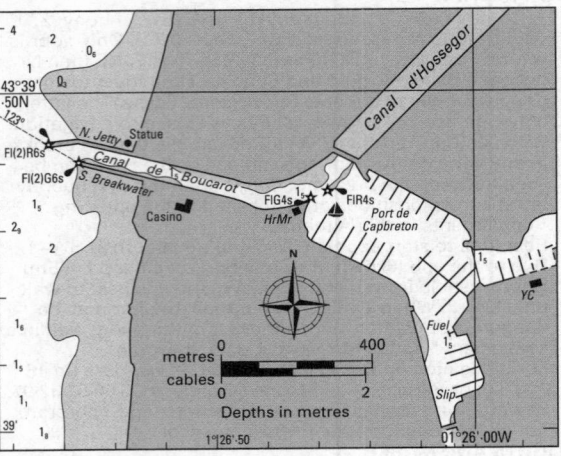

CHARTS
AC 1102; SHOM 6586, 6557, 6786; ECM 555, 1024
TIDES
+0450 Dover; ML 2·3; Zone –0100

Standard Port POINTE DE GRAVE (←)

Times				Height (metres)			
High Water		Low Water		MHWS	MHWN	MLWN	MLWS
0000	0600	0500	1200	5·4	4·4	2·1	1·0
1200	1800	1700	2400				
Differences CAPBRETON							
–0030	–0020	0000	0000	–1·4	–0·8	–0·7	–0·5

SHELTER
Good. Appr advised HW–3 to +1; not before LW+2½. Narrow canalised ent dangerous in strong winds from W to N. Do not enter if swell or seas break in mid-chan; they often break on either side. Hbr and chan dredged 1·5m. Visitors' pontoon 'B' (first to stbd of marina ent). There are 3 basins.
NAVIGATION
WPT 49°39'·69N 01°27'·41W, 303°/123° from/to N pier lt, ½M. Bkwtr lts in line 123° lead to hbr ent. Depths shoal rapidly in last 3ca from 50m to 3m; see 8.18.5 for Gouf de Capbreton. No ⚓ off ent. Inside Canal de Boucarot best water is close to N bkwtr initially; from abeam small statue of Virgin Mary, move to mid-chan or just S of mid-chan. Marina ent is via obvious gap in training wall on SE side of chan, abeam conspic Capitainerie.
LIGHTS AND MARKS
N pier hd, Fl (2) R 6s 13m 12M, Horn 30s. S bkwtr hd, Fl (2) G 6s 7m 12M; the former lt, now disused, is close E. (Silting occurs around head of S bkwtr). Fl R 4s and Fl G 4s lts at marina ent. Casino is conspic S of ent.

RADIO TELEPHONE
VHF Ch 09 (0800-1900 in season).
TELEPHONE
Hr Mr 05·58·72·21·23; Aff Mar 05·58·72·10·43; CROSS 05·56·73·31·31; ⌗ 05·59·46·68·80; SNSM 05·58·72·47·44; Auto 08.36.68.08.40; Ⓗ (Bayonne) 05·59·44·35·35; Police 05·58·72·01·18; Brit Consul 05·56·52·28·35.
FACILITIES
Marina (950+58 Ⓥ), ☎ 05·58·72·21·23, ⛟ 05·58·72·40·35, FF124, Slip, BH (28 ton), AC, P & D (0830-1200, 1400-1800 or ☎ 05.58.72.15.66), FW, ME, EI, C (1·5 ton), Sh, Ⓒ;
CN Capbreton-Hossegor-Seignosse ☎ 05·58·72·03·39;
Services: Sh, CH, SM, Ⓔ; ⇌ Bayonne (17km); ✈ Biarritz (25km).

ANGLET/BAYONNE   8-18-27

Pyrénées Atlantique 49°31'·95N 01°31'·92W   Rtg 3-2-3

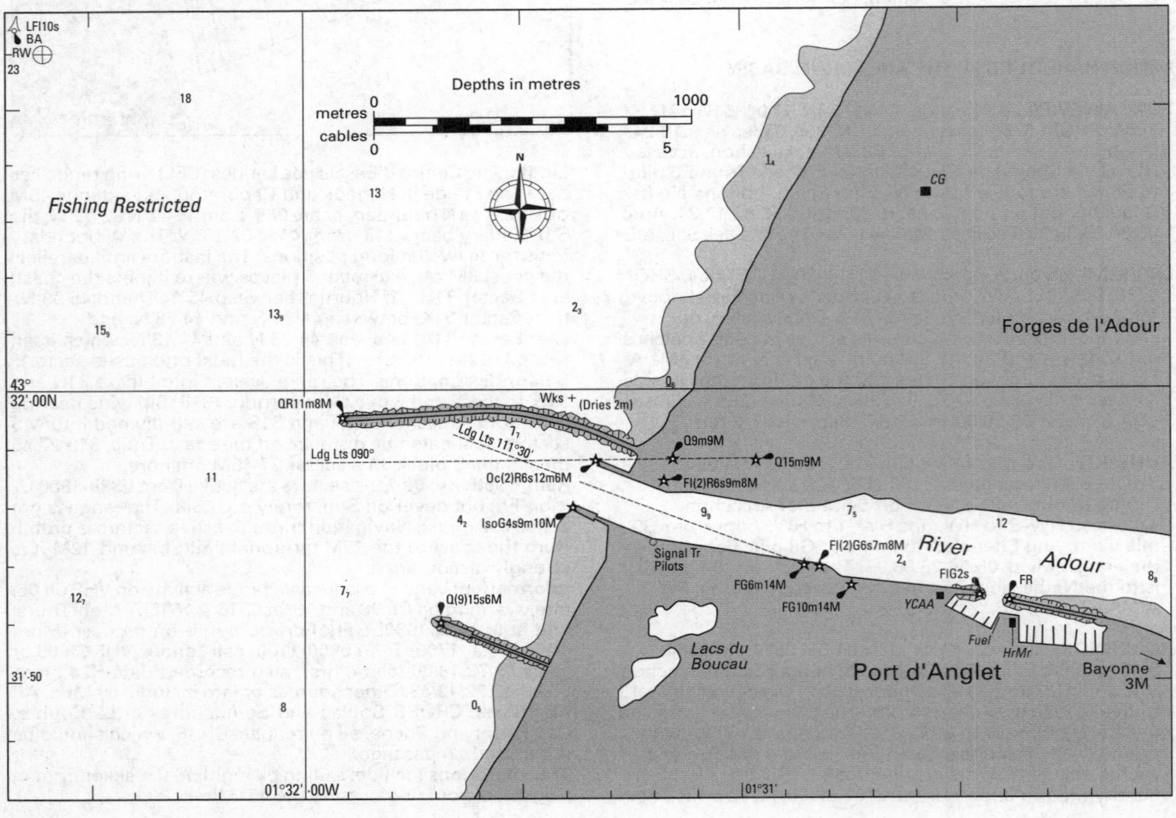

ANGLET/BAYONNE *continued*

CHARTS
AC 1343, 1102; SHOM 6536, 6557, 6786; ECM 555
TIDES
+0450 Dover (UT); ML 2·5; Zone −0100

Standard Port POINTE DE GRAVE (←)

Times				Height (metres)			
High Water		Low Water		MHWS	MHWN	MLWN	MLWS
0000	0600	0500	1200	5·4	4·4	2·1	1·0
1200	1800	1700	2400				
Differences L'ADOUR (BOUCAU)							
−0030	−0035	−0025	−0040	−1·2	−1·1	−0·4	−0·3

SHELTER
Very good in Anglet marina, 0·70M from ent, on S bank of
R Adour. (New marina planned to W of existing marina).
Possible berths at Bayonne, 3M up river, on S bank below
bridge. ‡ prohib in river which is well marked.
NAVIGATION
WPT 43°32'·66N 01°32'·68W, BA SWM buoy, 322°/142°
from/to N bkwtr lt, 0·9M. Access good except in strong W
winds. Strong tidal stream, max 5kn at sp ebb.

LIGHTS AND MARKS
BA HFP buoy, L Fl 10s (WPT), is NW of ent. Pte St Martin Fl (2)
10s 73m 29M is 2·45M SSW of hbr. Ldg Its 090°, both Q 9/
15m 14M, intens 087°-093°. Inside ent, further ldg Its 111°,
both QG, moved as required. 3 more sets of ldg Its upriver to
Bayonne. IPTS (full code) from sig tr on S side of ent.
RADIO TELEPHONE
Marina Ch 09. Port/pilots 12 16 (0800-1200; 1400-1800LT).
TELEPHONE
Marina 05·59·63·05·45; Hr Mr Bayonne 05·59·63·11·57;
CROSS 05·56·09·82·00; ⌗ 05·59·59·08·29; Aff Mar
05·59·55·06·68; SNSM 05·59·83·40·50; Ⓗ 05·59·44·35·35;
Météo 05·59·23·84·15; Auto 08·36·65·08·64.
FACILITIES
Marina (367+58 Ⓥ), ☎ 05·59·63·05·45; P, D, FW, ME, EI,
AC, C (1·3 ton), Ⓒ, BH (13 ton), Slip, Sh; **Port** C (30 ton),
Slip, FW, P, D; **YC Adour Atlantique** ☎ 05·59·63·16·22;
Services: CH, Ⓔ, SHOM.
Town ⇌, ✈ (Biarritz). Ferry: Bilboa-Portsmouth.

ST JEAN-DE-LUZ   8-18-28
Pyrénées Atlantique, 43°23'·92N 01°40'·53W   Rtg 3-3-1

CHARTS
AC 1343, 1102; SHOM 6526, 6558, 6786; ECM 555
TIDES
HW +0435 on Dover (UT); ML 2·5m; Zone −0100

Standard Port POINTE DE GRAVE (←)

Times				Height (metres)			
High Water		Low Water		MHWS	MHWN	MLWN	MLWS
0000	0600	0500	1200	5·4	4·4	2·1	1·0
1200	1800	1700	2400				
Differences ST JEAN DE LUZ (SOCOA)							
−0040	−0045	−0030	−0045	−1·1	−1·1	−0·6	−0·4

SHELTER
Except in strong NW winds, the bay can be entered at all
times and good ‡s found in approx 4m on the W and SE
sides. Beware antipollution booms off the beaches and a
submerged jetty in SE corner of bay. There are 2 hbrs:
St Jean-de-Luz in S of bay with a small marina (2·5m) at
Ciboure, close to rear QG ldg lt. Sailing is prohib in the
port. Unmasted craft may ‡ in La Nivelle River via fixed
bridge 1·9m clearance.
Socoa hbr (dries about 0·5m) on the NW side of the bay,
close S of conspic fort. Tide gauge at ent.
NAVIGATION
WPT 43°24'·16N 01°40'·71W, 331°/151° from/to W ent,
2½ca. Yachts can approach within the N quadrant direct to
hbr ent, but in heavy W'ly weather seas break on various
shoals on the Plateau de St Jean-de-Luz. 3M W of hbr ent
beware Les Briquets rks, drying 0·4m, 2M NE of Hendaye.
The 3 appr chans are defined by ldg Its: The main outer
chan leads 138° between Illarguita and Belhara Perdun
banks. Thence, or if coming from the W, the middle chan
leads 101° past the hbr breakwaters. The inner chan leads
151° through the W ent into the bay and to St Jean de Luz
hbr. The E ent to the bay is not recommended. There are
other chans but these are unlit and not advised without
local knowledge. Speed limit in the bay is 7kn.
LIGHTS AND MARKS
Outer 138° ldg Its: Front, Socoa lt, QWR 36m 12/8M, W ☐
tr, B stripe, vis W shore-264°, R264°-282°, W282°-shore; R
sector covers Socoa hbr ent. Rear Q 67m 20M, hard to see
by day, but nearby Bordagain tr, 100m, is more conspic.
Ste Barbe ldg Its 101°, both Oc (4) R 12s 30/47m 18M;
front, W bldg with △ gable; rear B ▲ on W tr. Inner 151°
ldg Its, both Dir QG 18/27m 16M intens 149·5°-152°; front,
W tr, R stripe; rear, W tr, G stripe. Digue des Criquas hd,
Iso G 4s 11m 7M. Digue d'Artha is a detached unlit bkwtr
across the middle of the bay. La Rhune, an 898m high
conical mountain, is conspic in good vis 5·5M SSE of hbr.

RADIO TELEPHONE
Marina VHF Ch 09 16.
TELEPHONE
ST JEAN-DE-LUZ: Hr Mr 05·59·47·26·81; ⌗ 05·59·47·18·61;
Aff Mar 05·59·47·14·55; CROSS 05·56·73·31·31; Météo
05·59·22·03·30; Auto 08·36·68·08·64; SNSM
05·59·47·22·98; Police 05·59·26·01·55;
SOCOA: As for St Jean de Luz.
FACILITIES
ST JEAN-DE-LUZ **Quay** FW, AC, P, C (6 ton), Slip; **Services:**
Ⓔ, ME, EI, Sh, CH.
SOCOA **Jetty** C (1 ton), FW, P, D, AC, Slip, BY; **YC Basque**
☎ 05·59·47·18·31; **Services:** ME, CH, EI, Sh.
Town V, R, Bar, Ⓒ, ✉, Ⓑ, ⇌.

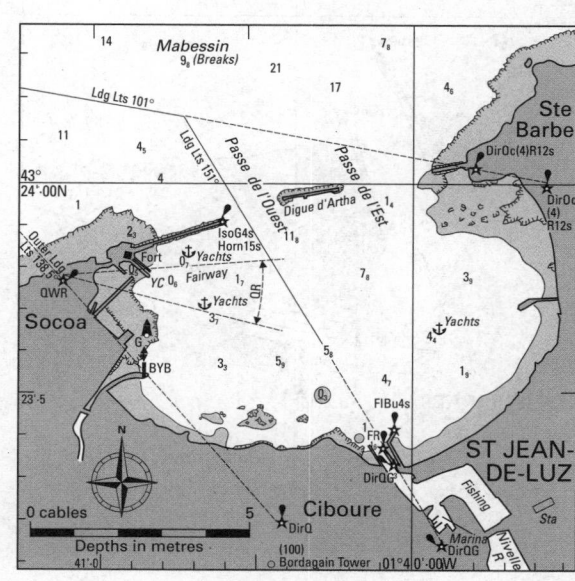

18

HENDAYE   8-18-29

Pyrénées Atlantique, 43°22'·91N 01°47'·25W   Rtg 2-2-1

CHARTS
AC 1181, 1102; SHOM 6556, 6558, 6786; ECM 555

TIDES
HW +0450 on Dover (UT); ML 2·3m; Zone −0100
Use differences **ST JEAN DE LUZ (SOCOA)** 8-18-27

SHELTER
Excellent in marina (3m); access H24. Or in Port of Refuge
(S of C Higuer) in 2-3m. Good ⚓ in river off Fuenterrabia.
Moorings in the B de Chingoudy are exposed to N/NE
and S/SW gales. NB: Hendaye is on the French bank of
the Rio Bidassoa; Fuenterrabia on the Spanish side. A
neutral area lies in the Baie de Fontarabie.

NAVIGATION
WPT 43°24'·00N 01°46'·50W, 025°/205° from/to W bkwtr hd
1·25M. Beware Les Briquets 8ca N of Pte Ste Anne at E
end of the Baie and, near centre of B, keep clear of Bajo
Iruarri. River ent is easy except in heavy N'ly swell; sp
ebb is very strong. Inshore of Pte des Dunes lt, Fl R 2·5s,
hug the E training wall for best water. A spit drying 1·3m
(SHM bn, VQ (3) G 5s) off Fuenterrabia narrows the chan
to about 100m before marina ent opens up.

LIGHTS AND MARKS
On W end of bay, Cabo Higuer lt ho , Fl (2) 10s 63m 23M.
River ent bkwtrs: East L Fl R 10s 7m 5M; West Fl (3) G 9s
9m 5M. River dredged to 2m. Marina ent between Fl (2) R
6s 6m 2M on elbow of W bkwtr (hd marked by FR strip lt)
and Fl Y 4s 5m 3M at E side; near the latter is a conspic
RW TV relay mast (40m).

RADIO TELEPHONE
Marina VHF Ch 09 (H24).

TELEPHONE
Hr Mr 05·59·48·06·10; Aff Mar 05·59·20·77·67;
⌗ 05·59·20·70·82; CROSS 05·59·09·82·00; SNSM
05·59·20·60·33; Météo 05·59·24·58·80; Auto 08·36·68·08·64;
Police 05·59·20·65·52; Ⓗ 05·59·20·08·22.

FACILITIES
Marina (600 + 120) ☎ 05·59·48·06·10, FF135, AC, FW, P, D,
BH (30 ton), Slip; Boats > 17m LOA should moor in Baie de
Chingoudy;
Club Maritime Hendayais ☎ 05·59·20·03·02, Bar;
Services: CH, Sh, El, Ⓔ, ME.
Town V, R, Bar, Gaz, ✉, Ⓑ, ⇌, ✈ (Fuenterrabia or Biarritz).
Local ferry from marina to Fuenterrabia. UK ferry from
Bilbao/Santander.

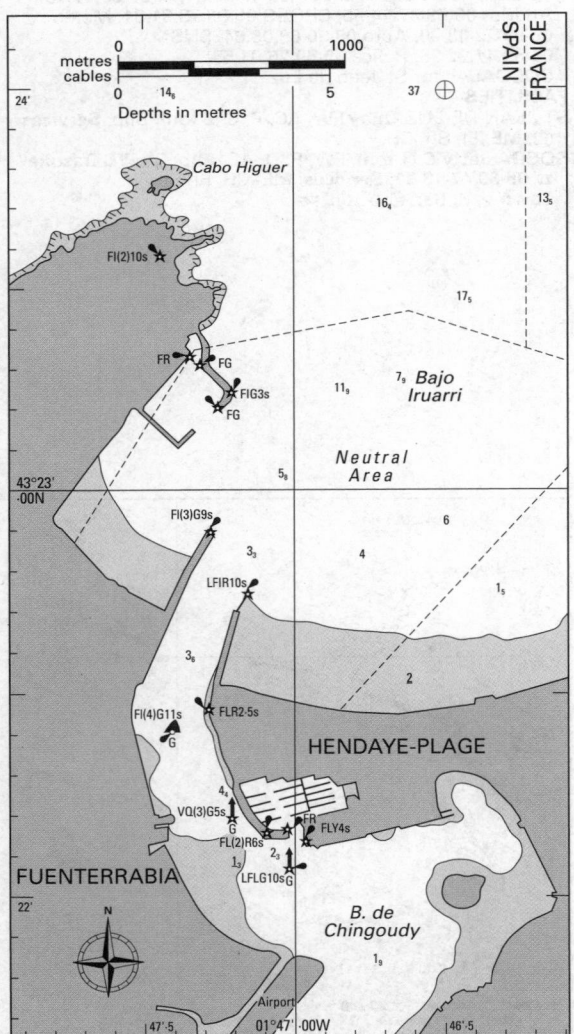

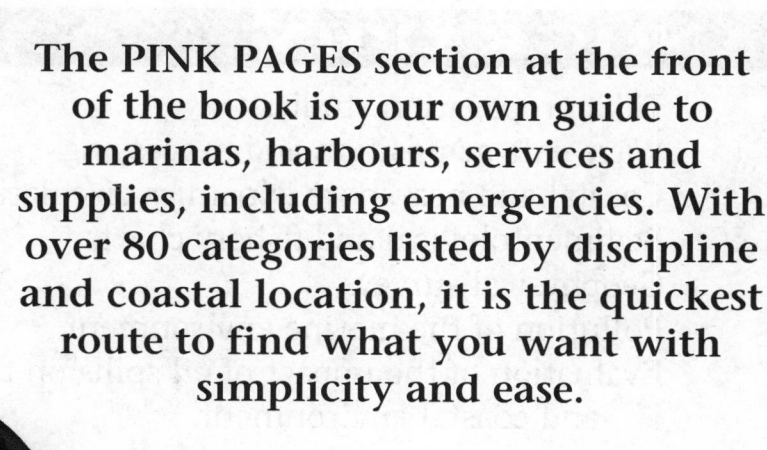

VOLVO PENTA SERVICE

Sales and service centres in area 19
Names and addresses of Volvo Penta dealers in
this area are available from:

France *Volvo Penta France* , 55 Avenue des Champs Pierreux, 92757 Cedex
Tel +33 1 55175445, Fax +33 1 55175261
Netherlands *Volvo Penta Benelux BV*, Nijverheidsweg 1, Postbus 195, 3640 AD
Mijdrecht Tel +31 2972 80111, Fax +31 2972 87364.

VOLVO PENTA

Area 19

North-East France
Barfleur to Dunkerque

8.19.1	Index	**Page 769**
8.19.2	Diagram of ports, lights, RDF bns, Coast radio and weather stns	**770**
8.19.3	Tidal stream charts	**772**
8.19.4	List of coastal lights, fog signals and waypoints	**774**
8.19.5	Passage information	**777**
8.19.6	Distance table	**778**
8.19.7	English Channel waypoints	**See 8.1.7**
8.19.8	Special notes for France	**See 8.15.8**
8.19.9	Barfleur	**779**
8.19.10	St Vaast-la-Hougue	**779**
8.19.11	Carentan and Isigny Iles St Marcouf	**780**
8.19.12	Grandcamp-Maisy Arromanches	**781**
8.19.13	Port-en-Bessin	**782**
8.19.14	Courseulles-sur-Mer	**782**
8.19.15	Ouistreham Caen	**783**
8.19.16	Dives-sur-Mer	**784**
8.19.17	Deauville and Trouville	**785**
8.19.18	Honfleur	**786**
8.19.19	Le Havre, Standard Port, tidal curves	**790**
8.19.20	River Seine Rouen Paris Canals to the Mediterranean	**791**
8.19.21	Fécamp	**792**
8.19.22	St Valéry-en-Caux	**792**
8.19.23	Dieppe, Standard Port, tidal curves	**796**
8.19.24	Le Tréport	**797**
8.19.25	St Valéry-sur-Somme/Le Crotoy	**798**
8.19.26	Le Touquet and Etaples	**798**
8.19.27	Boulogne	**799**
8.19.28	Dover Strait TSS	**800**
8.19.29	Calais	**801**
8.19.30	Dunkerque (Port Est), Standard Port, tidal curves Gravelines	**802**

19

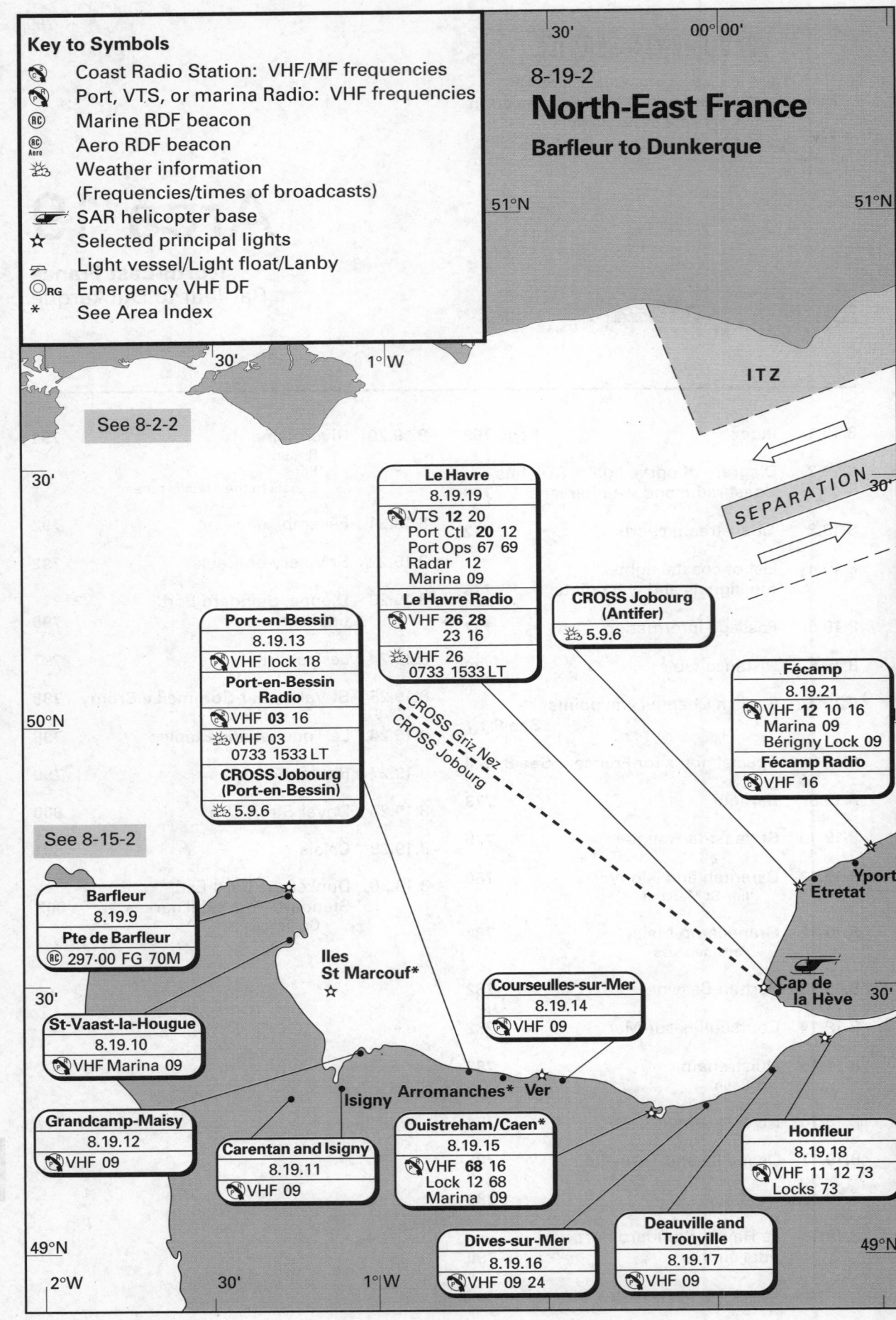

Key to Symbols

- Coast Radio Station: VHF/MF frequencies
- Port, VTS, or marina Radio: VHF frequencies
- (RC) Marine RDF beacon
- (RC) Aero RDF beacon
- Weather information (Frequencies/times of broadcasts)
- SAR helicopter base
- ☆ Selected principal lights
- Light vessel/Light float/Lanby
- (O)RG Emergency VHF DF
- * See Area Index

8-19-2
North-East France
Barfleur to Dunkerque

51°N

51°N

30'   00° 00'

30'   1° W

See 8-2-2

30'

ITZ

SEPARATION

30'

Le Havre
8.19.19
VTS **12** 20
Port Ctl **20** 12
Port Ops 67 69
Radar 12
Marina 09
Le Havre Radio
VHF **26 28** 23 16
VHF 26 0733 1533 LT

CROSS Jobourg (Antifer)
5.9.6

Port-en-Bessin
8.19.13
VHF lock 18
Port-en-Bessin Radio
VHF **03** 16
VHF 03 0733 1533 LT
CROSS Jobourg (Port-en-Bessin)
5.9.6

50°N

Fécamp
8.19.21
VHF **12** 10 16
Marina 09
Bérigny Lock 09
Fécamp Radio
VHF 16

CROSS Griz Nez
CROSS Jobourg

See 8-15-2

Yport
Etretat

Barfleur
8.19.9
Pte de Barfleur
(RC) 297·00 FG 70M

Iles St Marcouf*
☆

Cap de la Hève

Courseulles-sur-Mer
8.19.14
VHF 09

30'

30'

St-Vaast-la-Hougue
8.19.10
VHF Marina 09

Isigny
Arromanches* Ver

Grandcamp-Maisy
8.19.12
VHF 09

Carentan and Isigny
8.19.11
VHF 09

Ouistreham/Caen*
8.19.15
VHF **68** 16
Lock 12 68
Marina 09

Honfleur
8.19.18
VHF 11 12 73
Locks 73

49°N

Deauville and Trouville
8.19.17
VHF 09

49°N

Dives-sur-Mer
8.19.16
VHF 09 24

2° W

30'

1° W

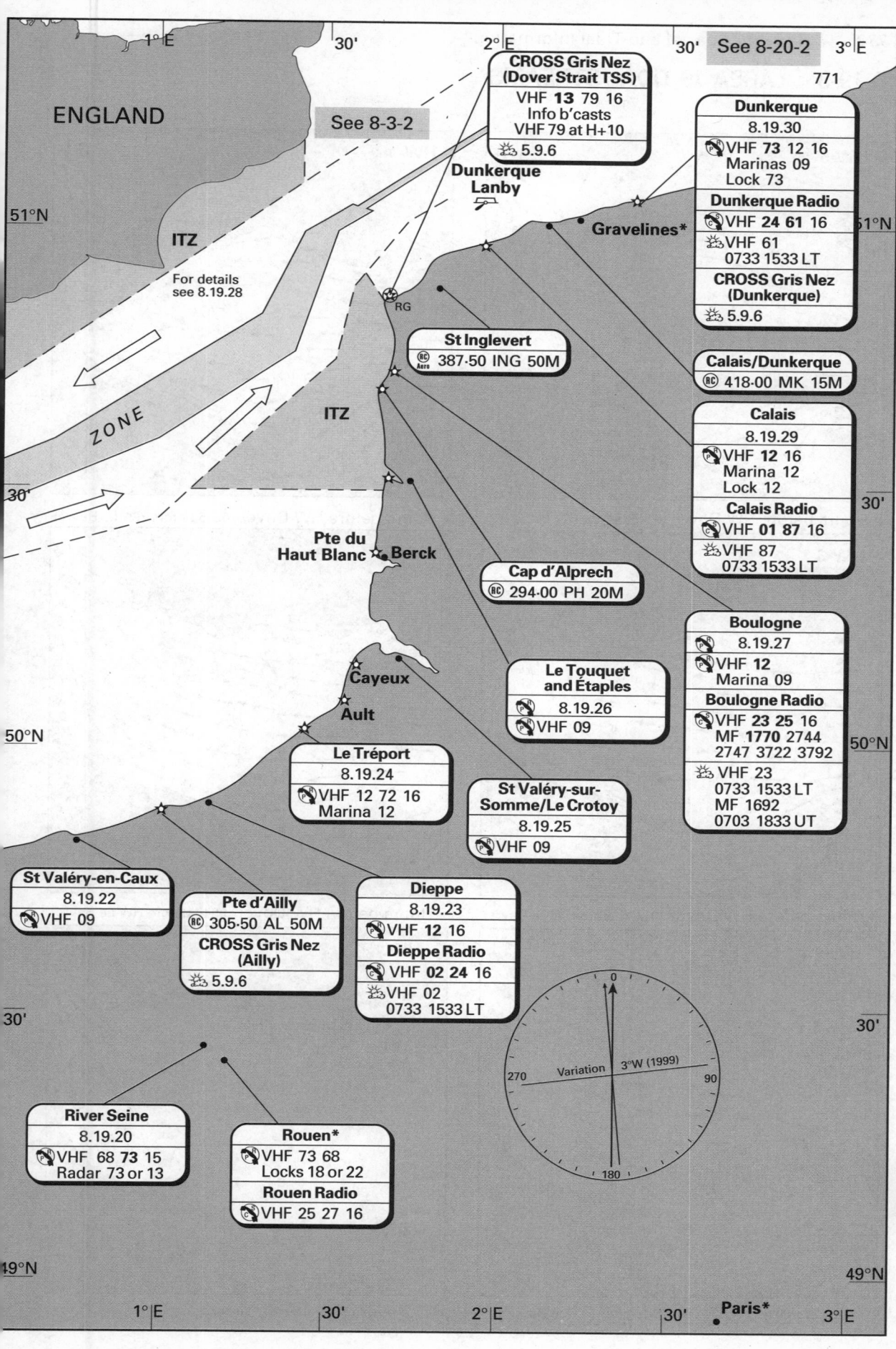

ENGLAND

51°N

1°E 30' 2°E 30' 3°E

See 8-20-2

771

ITZ

For details see 8.19.28

ZONE

ITZ

RG

30'

CROSS Gris Nez (Dover Strait TSS)
VHF **13** 79 16
Info b'casts
VHF 79 at H+10
5.9.6

Dunkerque Lanby

Gravelines*

Dunkerque
8.19.30
VHF **73** 12 16
Marinas 09
Lock 73
Dunkerque Radio
VHF **24 61** 16
VHF 61
0733 1533 LT
CROSS Gris Nez (Dunkerque)
5.9.6

51°N

St Inglevert
(RC) 387·50 ING 50M
Aero

Calais/Dunkerque
(RC) 418·00 MK 15M

Calais
8.19.29
VHF **12** 16
Marina 12
Lock 12
Calais Radio
VHF **01 87** 16
VHF 87
0733 1533 LT

30'

Pte du Haut Blanc Berck

Cap d'Alprech
(RC) 294·00 PH 20M

Le Touquet and Étaples
8.19.26
VHF 09

Cayeux

Ault

50°N

Boulogne
8.19.27
VHF **12**
Marina 09
Boulogne Radio
VHF **23 25** 16
MF **1770** 2744
2747 3722 3792
VHF 23
0733 1533 LT
MF 1692
0703 1833 UT

50°N

Le Tréport
8.19.24
VHF 12 72 16
Marina 12

St Valéry-sur-Somme/Le Crotoy
8.19.25
VHF 09

St Valéry-en-Caux
8.19.22
VHF 09

Pte d'Ailly
(RC) 305·50 AL 50M
CROSS Gris Nez (Ailly)
5.9.6

Dieppe
8.19.23
VHF **12** 16
Dieppe Radio
VHF **02 24** 16
VHF 02
0733 1533 LT

30'

30'

Variation 3°W (1999)
0
90
180
270

River Seine
8.19.20
VHF 68 **73** 15
Radar 73 or 13

Rouen*
VHF 73 68
Locks 18 or 22
Rouen Radio
VHF 25 27 16

49°N

1°E 30' 2°E 30' Paris* 3°E

49°N

19

8-19-3 AREA 19 TIDAL STREAMS

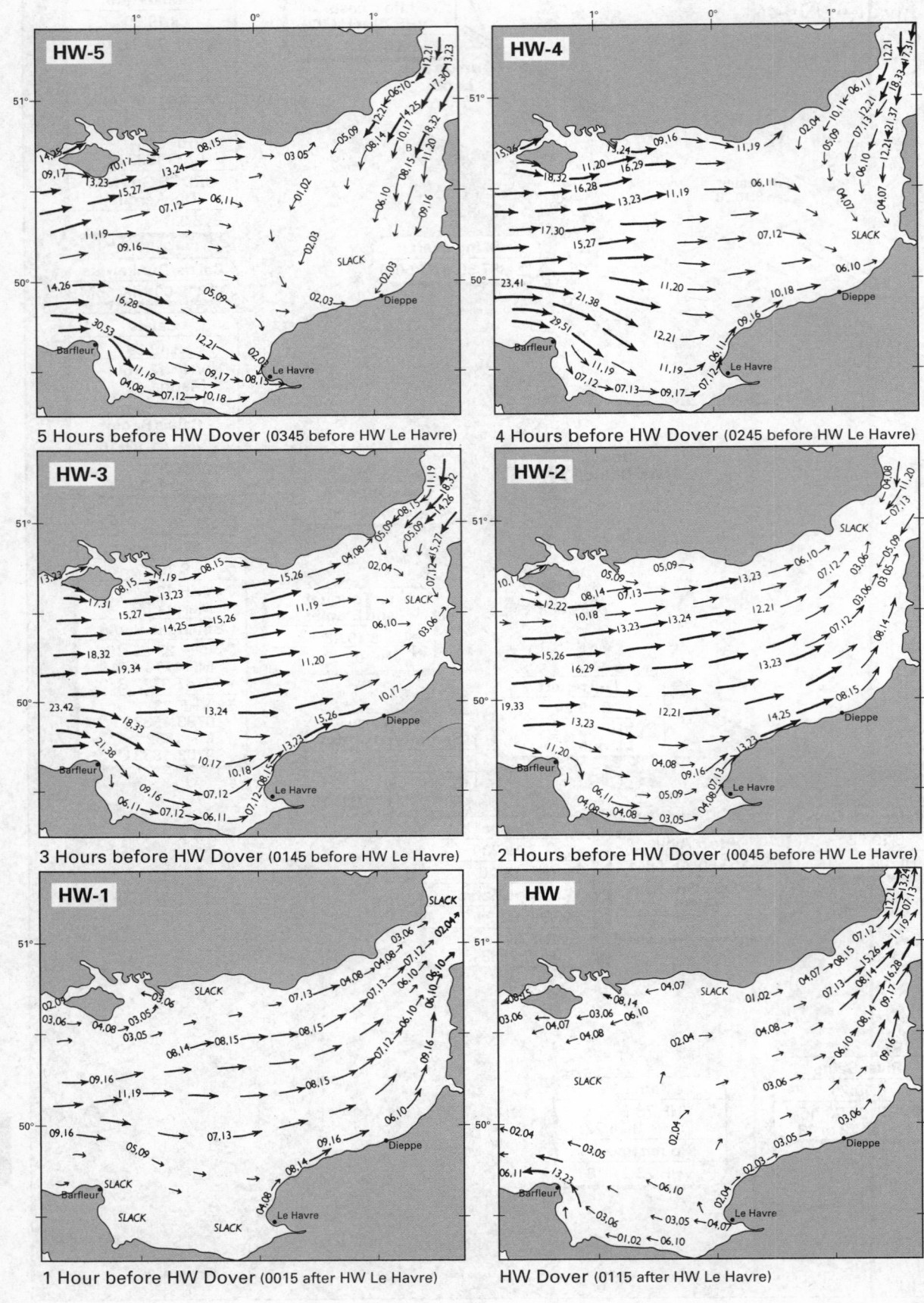

HW-5
5 Hours before HW Dover (0345 before HW Le Havre)

HW-4
4 Hours before HW Dover (0245 before HW Le Havre)

HW-3
3 Hours before HW Dover (0145 before HW Le Havre)

HW-2
2 Hours before HW Dover (0045 before HW Le Havre)

HW-1
1 Hour before HW Dover (0015 after HW Le Havre)

HW
HW Dover (0115 after HW Le Havre)

Westward 8.15.3   Northward 8.2.3   North-eastward 8.3.3   Eastward 8.20.3

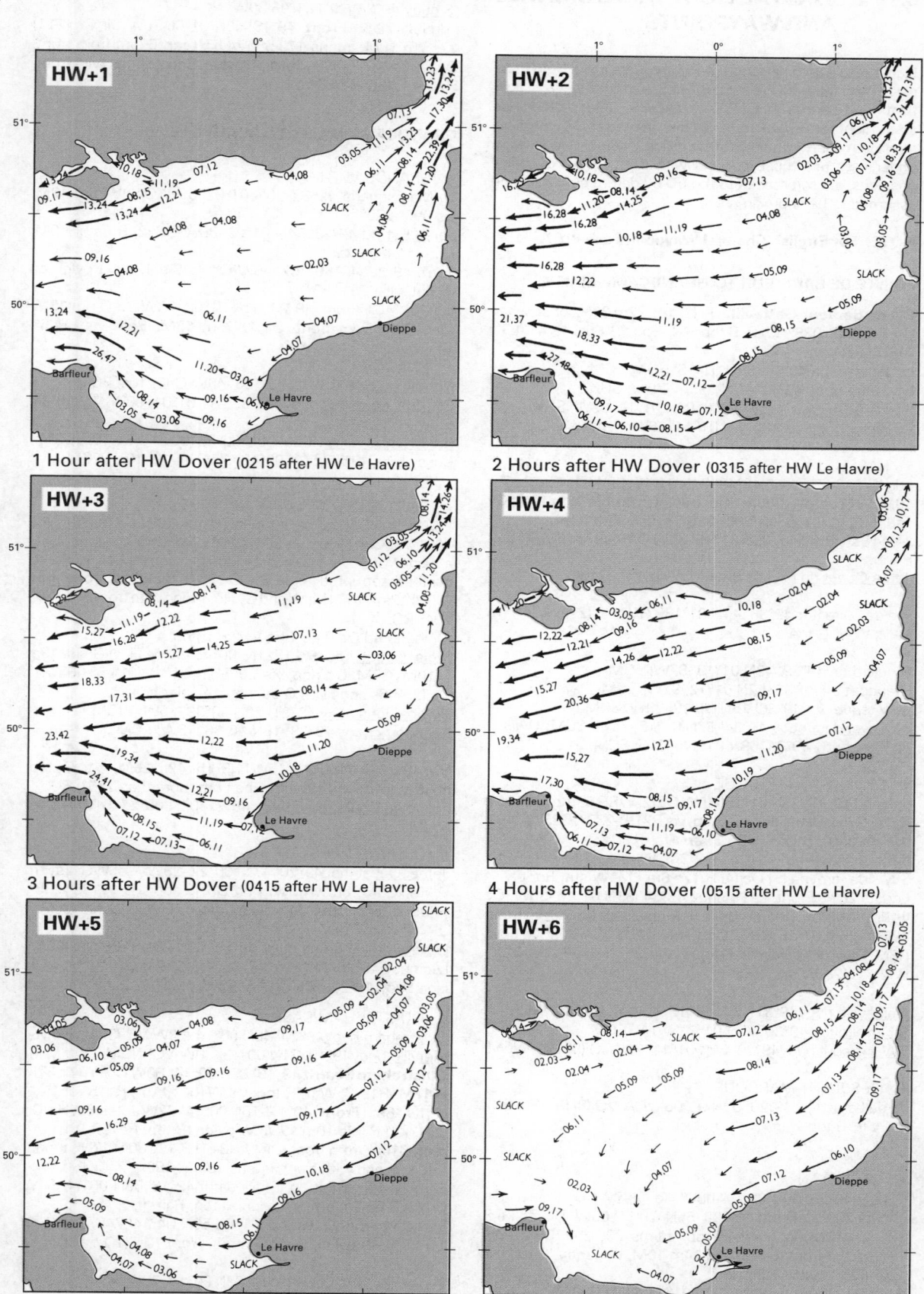

1 Hour after HW Dover (0215 after HW Le Havre)

2 Hours after HW Dover (0315 after HW Le Havre)

3 Hours after HW Dover (0415 after HW Le Havre)

4 Hours after HW Dover (0515 after HW Le Havre)

5 Hours after HW Dover (0615 after HW Le Havre)

6 Hours after HW Dover (0510 before HW Le Havre)

19

8.19.4 COASTAL LIGHTS, FOG SIGNALS AND WAYPOINTS

Lights with a nominal range of 15M or more are in **bold** print, places and features are in CAPITALS, and light-vessels, light floats and Lanbys in *CAPITAL ITALICS*. Unless otherwise stated lights are white. m = elevation in metres; M = nominal range in miles. Fog signals are in *italics*. Useful waypoints are underlined; use those on land with care. All geographical positions are referenced to the ED 50 datum but should be assumed to be approximate.

NOTE: For English Channel Waypoints see 8.1.7.

POINTE DE BARFLEUR TO GRANDCAMP-MAISY

Pte de Barfleur-Gatteville, Fl (2) 10s 72m **29M**, obsc when brg less than 088°; Gy tr, B top; RC; *Horn (2) 60s;* 49°41'·83N 01°15'·87W.
La Jamette bn 49°41'·92N 01°15'·51W; ECM.
La Grotte buoy 49°41'·12N 01°14'·78W; SHM.
Roche-à-l'Anglais buoy 49°40'·84N 01°14'·85W; SHM.
Le Hintar buoy 49°40'·75N 01°14'·76W; PHM.

- BARFLEUR
Ldg lts 219·5°. Front, 49°40'·24N 01°15'·53W Oc (3) 12s 7m 10M; W □ tr; rear, 288m from front, Oc (3) 12s 13m 10M; Gy and W □ tr, G top; vis 085°-355°; synch with front.
Jetée Est hd 49°40'·39N 01°15'·38W Oc R 4s 5m 6M; W hut, R top.
Jetée Ouest hd Fl G 4s 8m 6M; W pylon, G top.

Pte de Saire lt tr 49°36'·44N 01°13'·71W Oc (2+1) 12s 11m 10M; W tr, G top.

Moulard bn 49°39'·42N 01°13'·87W; ECM.
Dranguet bn 49°36'·82N 01°12'·92W; ECM.
Le Vitéquet bn 49°36'·15N 01°13'·29W; SCM.
Le Gavendest buoy 49°34'·67N 01°13'·74W; SCM; *Whis.*
La Dent buoy 49°34'·63N 01°14'·12W; SCM.

- ST VAAST-LA-HOUGUE
Jetty hd 49°35'·25N 01°15'·35W Oc (2) WRG 6s 12m W10M, R7M, G7M; W 8-sided tr, R top; vis R219°-237°, G237°-310°, W310°-350°, R350°-040°; *Siren Mo(N) 30s.*
NE side bkwtr hd Iso G 4s 6m 3M; W tank, G top.
SW side, groyne hd Oc (4) R 12s 6m 6M; W hut, R top.
Ldg lts 267°. Front, La Hougue 49°34'·31N 01°16'·30W, Oc 4s 9m 10M; W pylon, G top; rear, Morsalines 1·8M from front, 49°34'·25N 01°18'·95W Oc (3+1) WRG 12s 90m W11M, R8M, G8M; W 8-sided tr, G top; vis W171°-316°, G316°-321°, R321°-342°, W342°-355°.

Quineville buoy 49°31'·85N 01°12'·40W Q (9) 10s; WCM.
S Floxel buoy 49°30'·75N 01°13'·70W; ECM.
SW Marcouf buoy 49°29'·80N 01°11'·92W Q (9) 15s; WCM.

- ÎLES SAINT-MARCOUF
Île du Large lt tr 49°29'·90N 01°08'·70W VQ (3) 5s 18m 8M; ■ Gy tr, G top.

- CARENTAN
Cl buoy 49°25'·50N 01°07'·00W Iso 4s; SWM.
Ldg lts 209·5°. **Front**, 49°20'·55N 01°11'·05W Dir Oc (3) R 12s 6m **18M**; W mast, R top; intens 208·2°-210·7°; rear, 723m from front, Oc (3) 12s 14m 10M; W gantry, G top; vis 120°-005°; synch with front.
W Channel ent bn 49°22'·00N 01°09'·90W Fl (3) G 12s; G △, on G bn.

- ISIGNY-SUR-MER
IS buoy 49°24'·30N 01°06'30W; NCM.
Ldg lts 172·5°. **Front**, 49°19'·50N 01°06·70W Dir Oc (2+1) 12s 7m **18M**; intens 170·5°-174·5°; **rear**, 625m from front, Dir Oc (2+1) 12s 19m **18M**; W pylon, B top; synch with front; intens 170·5°-174·5°.

GRANDCAMP-MAISY TO DEAUVILLE

- GRANDCAMP-MAISY
La Maresquerie 49°23'·20N 01°02'·65W Oc 4s 28m 12M; vis 090°-270°.
Jetée Est hd 49°23'·54N 01°02'·88W Oc (2) R 6s 9m 9M; *Horn Mo(N) 30s.*
Perré 49°23'·40N 01°02'·40W Oc 4s 8m 12M; G pylon on W hut; vis 083°-263°.
Ldg lts 146°. Front, 49°23'·41N 01°02'·93W Dir Q 9m **15M**; rear,102m from front, Dir Q 12m **15M**. Both vis:144·5°-147·5°.

Norfalk buoy 49°28'·83N 01°03'·40W Q (3) 10s; ECM.
Est du Cardonnet buoy 49°26'·97N 01°01'·00W VQ (3) 5s; ECM.
Broadsword buoy 49°25'·39N 00°52'·90W Q (3) 10s; ECM.
Cussy buoy 49°29'·50N 00°43'·25W VQ (9) 10s; WCM.

- PORT-EN-BESSIN/ARROMANCHES
Ldg lts 204°. Front, 49°21'·00N 00°45'·56W Oc (3) 12s 25m 10M; W pylon, G top; vis 069°-339°; *Siren 20s* – sounded over a sector of 90° each side of ldg line, continuous in the W sector, interrupted in the E (TD 1997); rear, 93m from front, Oc (3) 12s 42m 11M; W and Gy Ho; synch with front; vis 114°-294° RC.
Môle Est hd Oc R 4s 14m 7M; R pylon.
Môle Ouest hd 49°21'·21N 00°45'·42W Fl WG 4s 13m W10M, G7M; G pylon; vis G065°-114·5°, W114·5°-065°.
Oc (2) R 6s and Fl (2) G 6s mark the pier hds.
Bombardons buoy 49°21'·70N 00°39'·15W; WCM.
Roseberry buoy 49°23'·15N 00°36'·15W; ECM.

Ver 49°20'·47N 00°31'·15W Fl (3) 15s 42m **26M**; W tr, Gy top; obsc by cliffs of St Aubin when brg more than 275°; RC.
Fosse de Courseulles buoy 49°21'·33N 00°27'·61W Iso 4s; SWM.

- COURSEULLES-SUR-MER
Jetée Ouest hd 49°20'·47N 00°27'·28W Iso WG 4s 7m W9M, G6M; brown pylon on Dn, G top; vis W135°-235°, G235°-135°; *Horn 30s* sounded from HW±2 hours.

Essarts de Langrune buoy 49°22'·65N 00°21'·25W; NCM.
Luc buoy 49°20'·85N 00°18'·20W; NCM.
Lion buoy 49°20'·80N 00°15'·92W; NCM.

- OUISTREHAM/CAEN
Ouistreham buoy 49°20'·48N 00°14'·73W VQ (3) 5s; ECM.
Merville buoy 49°19'·71N 00°13'·30W VQ; NCM.
Ouistreham Main lt 49°16'·85N 00°14'·80W Oc WR 4s 37m **W17M**, R13M; W tr, R top; vis W151°-115°, R115°-151°.
ldg lts 185°. **Front**, 49°17'·16N 00°14'·72W Jetée Est Hd Dir Oc (3+1) R 12s 10m **17M**; W pylon, R top; Ra refl; **rear**, 610m from front, Dir Oc (3+1) R 12s 30m **17M**; tripod, R top; synch with front; intens 183·5°-186·5°.
Enrochements Est hd (St-Médard) 49°18'·08N 00°14'·54W Oc (2) R 6s 7m 8M; W pylon, R top; Ra refl.
Enrochements Ouest hd 49°17'·50N 04°14'·74W Iso G 4s 11m 7M; W pylon, G top; Ra refl; *Horn 10s*, (TD 1992).

Viaduc de Calix, Caen 49°11'·23N 00°19'·70W Iso 4s on E and W sides; FG on N side, FR on S side.

- DIVES

D1 buoy 49°18'·78N 00°05'·67W L Fl 10s; SWM.
Dives-sur-Mer 49°17'·85N 00°05'·20W Oc (2+1) WRG 12s 6m W12M, R9M, G9M; R hut; vis G125°-157°, W157°-162°, R162°-194°.

- DEAUVILLE/TROUVILLE

Semoy buoy 49°24'·20N 00°02'·45E VQ (3) 5s; ECM.
Trouville SW buoy 49°22'·60N 00°02'·64E VQ (9) 10s; WCM.
W jetty 49°22'·44N 00°04'·17E Fl WG 4s 10m W9M, G6M; B pylon, G top; vis W005°-176°, G176°-005°.
Trouville East 49°22'·28N 00°04'·41E Fl (4) WR 12s 8m W7M, R4M; W pylon, R top; vis W131°-175°, R175°-131°.
Ldg lts 148°. Front, 49°22'·09N 00°04'·57E Oc R 4s 11m 12M; W tr, R top; vis 330°-150°; Horn (2) 30s; rear, 217m from front, Oc R 4s 17m 10M; W pylon, R top; synch with front; vis 120°-170°.

ESTUAIRE DE LA SEINE/LE HAVRE

Ratelets buoy 49°25'·35N 00°01'·80E Q (9) 15s; WCM.
Ratier S buoy 49°25'·21N 00°07'·22E VQ (6) + L Fl 10s; SCM.
Ratier NW buoy 49°26'·85N 00°02'·55E VQ G; SHM.
Ducan-L-Clinch buoy 49°27'·23N 00°02'·58E VQ (9) 10s; WCM.

- CHENAL DE ROUEN

No 4 buoy 49°27'·05N 00°02'·64E QR; PHM.
No 7 buoy 49°26'·24N 00°04'·82E QG; SHM.
Digue du Ratier Hd 'A' 49°25'·97N 00°06'·66E VQ 10m 4M; NCM; Ra refl; tide gauge.
Spillway bn 49°25'·80N 00°12'·80E VQ (9) 10s 15m 7M; WCM.

- HONFLEUR

Falaise des Fonds 49°25'·53N 00°12'·93E Fl (3) WRG 12s 15m **W17M**, R13M, G13M; W □ tr, G top; vis G040°-080°, R080°-084°, G084°-100°, W100°-109°, R109°-162°, G162°-260°.
Digue Est hd 49°25'·73N 00°14'·04E Q 9m 8M; NCM; Horn (5) 40s. (Km 356 from Paris.)

- LA SEINE MARITIME

La Risle, Digue Sud 49°26'·37N 00°22'·07E Iso G 4s 11m 6M; W pylon, G top; Ra refl; (Km 346 from Paris).
Marais-Vernier 49°27'·78N 00°26'·89E Fl G 4s 8m 5M; W Col, R top (Km 340).
Digue Nord, Tancarville 49°28'·81N 00°28'·30E QR 9m 6M; W col, R top; (Km 337).
Quillebeuf 49°28'50N 00°31'·63E QG 12m 8M (Km 332·4).
Caudebec-en-Caux 49°31'·52N 00°43'·78E VQ R (Km 310).
Duclair 49°28'·80N 00°52'·32E QR (Km 278).

- ROUEN

Feu de Rouen 49°26'·42N 01°02'·62E Oc (2) R 6s 10m (Km 245·5).

- APPROACHES TO LE HAVRE

Spoil ground buoy 49°27'·84N 00°02'·38E Q (9) 15s; WCM.
N du Mouillage buoy 49°28'·65N 00°01'·36E Fl (4) Y 15s; SPM.
RN buoy 49°28'·68N 00°01'·10W Fl (2) 6s; IDM.
RNA buoy 49°28'·70N 00°05'·45W Iso 4s; SWM.
HP buoy 49°29'·61N 00°03'·70W Fl Y 4s; SPM; Whis.

LHA Lanby 49°31'·44N 00°09'·78W Mo (A) 12s 10m 7M; W buoy, R stripes; Racon.
Ldg lts 106·8°. Front, **Quai Roger Meunier** 49°28'·97N 00°06'·58E Dir F 36m **25M**; Gy tr, G top; intens 106°-108°; (H24); rear, 0·73M from front, **Quai Joannes Couvert** Dir F 78m **25M**; Gy tr, G top; intens 106°-108° (H24); Ra refl.
Cap de la Hève 49°30'·79N 00°04'·24E Fl 5s 123m **24M**; W 8-sided tr, R top; vis 225°-196°.

- LE HAVRE

Digue Sud Hd 49°29'·11N 00°05'·46E VQ (3) G 2s 15m 11M; W tr, G top.
Digue Nord Hd 49°29'·25N 00°05'·52E Fl R 5s 15m **21M**; W tr, R top; Horn 15s.
Marina, Digue Augustin Normand 49°29'·32N 00°05'·63E Q (2) G 5s 5m 2M.

- LE HAVRE TO CAP D'ANTIFER

Octeville W buoy 49°31'·67N 00°01'·90E VQ (6) + L Fl 10s; SCM.
Port du Havre-Antifer 49°39'·59N 00°09'·28E Dir Oc WRG 4s 24m **W15M**, R13M, G13M; W pylon, B top; vis G068·5°-078·5°, W078·5°-088·5°, R088·5°-098·5°.
A17 buoy 49°41'·60N 00°01'·75E Iso G 4s; SHM.
A18 buoy 49°42'·07N 00°02'·21E QR; PHM.
Port d'Antifer ldg lts 127·5°. **Front**, 49°38'·36N 00°09'·20E Dir Oc 4s 105m **22M**; W pylon, G top vis 127°-128°; **rear**, 430m from front, Dir Oc 4s 124m **22M**; W mast, G top. buoy day both show FW lts **33M**; vis 126·5°-128·5°; (occas.)

CAP D'ANTIFER TO POINTE DU HAUT BLANC

Cap d'Antifer 49°41'·07N 00°10'·00E Fl 20s 128m **29M**; Gy 8-sided tr, G top; vis 021°-222°.
Yport ldg lts 166°. Front, 49°44'·40N 00°18'·70E Oc 4s 10m, W mast, G top; rear, 30m from front, Oc 4s 14m, W pylon, G top on house.

- FÉCAMP

Jetée Nord 49°45'·99N 00°21'·87E Fl (2) 10s 15m **16M**; Gy tr, R top; Horn (2) 30s.
Jetée Sud hd, 49°45'·95N 00°21'·89E QG 14m 9M; Gy tr, G top; vis 072°-217°.
Jetée root QR 10m 4M.

Paluel buoy 49°52'·20N 00°38'·10E Q; NCM.

- SAINT VALÉRY-EN-CAUX

Jetée Ouest 49°52'·47N 00°42'·62E Fl (2) G 6s 13m 14M; W tr, G top.
Jetée Est hd 49°52'·35N 00°42'·75E Fl (2) R 6s 8m 4M; W mast.

Roches d'Ailly buoy 49°56'·58N 00°56'·90E VQ; NCM; Whis.
Pointe d'Ailly 49°55'·13N 00°57'·56E Fl (3) 20s 95m **31M**; W □ tr, G top; RC; Horn (3) 60s. (TD 1997.)
D1 buoy 49°57'·11N 01°01'·35E VQ (3) 5s; ECM; Bell.
Daffodils wk buoy 50°02'·52N 01°04'·10E VQ (9) 10s; WCM.
Berneval wk buoy 50°03'·46N 01°06'·62E; WCM.

- DIEPPE

Jetée Est hd 49°56'·22N 01°05'·15E Iso R 4s 12m 8M; R col.
Jetée Ouest 49°56'·32N 01°05'·04E Iso G 4s 11m 8M, W tr, G top; Horn 30s.
Falaise du Pollet 49°55'·98N 01°05'·37E Q R 35m 12M; R & W structure; vis 105·5°-170·5°.

Penly No 1 buoy 49°59'·10N 01°11'·47E Fl (3) Y 12s; SPM.
Penly No 2 buoy 49°59'·50N 01°12'10E Fl Y 4s; SPM.

- LE TRÉPORT

Jetée Ouest hd 50°03'·94N 01°22'·22E Fl (2) G 10s 15m **20M**; W tr, G top; Horn Mo(N) 30s.
Jetée Est 50°03'·93N 01°22'·30E Oc R 4s 8m 6M; W col, R top. Port signals Fl (5) G 500m SE.
Ault 50°06'·32N 01°27'·31E Oc (3) WR 12s 95m **W18M**, R14M, W tr, R top; vis W040°-175°, R175°-220°.

19

- BAIE DE SOMME/LE CROTOY/ST VALÉRY-SUR-SOMME.
Cayeux-sur-Mer 50°11'·60N 01°30'·80E Fl R 5s 32m **22M**; W tr, R top.
AT-SO buoy 50°14'·29N 01°28'·65E VQ; NCM.
Pte du Hourdel lt tr 50°12'·85N 01°34'·10E Oc (3) WG 12s 19m W12M, G9M; W tr, G top; vis W053°-248°, G248°-323°; *Reed (3) 30s*.
Le Crotoy 50°12'·93N 01°37'·45E Oc (2) R 6s 19m 9M; W pylon; vis 285°-135°.
Marina, E side 50°13'·02N 01°38'·10E Fl G 2s 4m 2M.
St Valéry-sur-Somme, embankment hd 50°12'·29N 01°35'·92E Q (3) G 6s 2m 2M; G pylon; Ra refl.
W hd of embankment 50°11'·40N 01°37'·60E Iso G 4s 9m 9M; W pylon, G top; vis 347°-222°.
La Ferté môle hd 50°11'·20N 01°38'·70E Fl R 4s 9m 9M; W pylon, R top; vis 000°-250°.

- SOMME TO LE TOUQUET
FM buoy 50°20'·40N 01°31'·00E; WCM.
Pointe de Haut-Blanc (Berck-Plage) 50°23'·90N 01°33'·75E Fl 5s 44m **23M**; W tr, R bands, G top.
Vergoyer SW buoy 50°26'·90N 01°00'·10E VQ (9) 10s; WCM.
Bassurelle buoy 50°32'·70N 00°57'·80E Fl (4) R 15s 6M; Racon (B); R refl; *Whis*.

Vergoyer W buoy 50°34'·65N 01°13'·70E Fl G 4s; SHM.
Vergoyer E buoy 50°35'·75N 01°19'·80E VQ (3) 5s; ECM.
Vergoyer NW buoy 50°37'·10N 01°18'·00E Fl (2) G 6s; SHM.
Vergoyer N buoy 50°39'·65N 01°22'·30E VQ; NCM; Racon (C).

LE TOUQUET TO DUNKERQUE

- LE TOUQUET
Le Touquet (La Canche) 50°31'·40N 01°35'·60E Fl (2) 10s 54m **25M**; Or tr, brown band; W and G top.
Mérida wk buoy 50°32'·80N 01°33'·30E; WCM.
Camiers, Rivière Canche ent, N side 50°32'·80N 01°36'·40E Oc (2) WRG 6s 17m W10M, R7M, G7M; R pylon; vis G015°-090°, W090°-105°, R105°-141°.

Cap d'Alprech 50°41'·96N 01°33'·83E Fl (3) 15s 62m **23M**; W tr, B top; RC; FR lts on radio mast 600m ENE.
Ophélie buoy 50°43'·91N 01°30'·92E Fl G 4s; SHM.

- BOULOGNE
Approach buoy 50°45'·36N 01°31'·15E VQ (6) + L Fl 10s 8m 6M; SCM; Ra refl; *Whis*.
Digue (Carnot) 50°44'·48N 01°34'·13E Fl (2+1) 15s 25m **19M**; W tr, G top; *Horn (2+1) 60s*.
Digue Nord hd 50°44'·76N 01°34'·27E Fl (2) R 6s 10m 7M; R tr.
Jetée SW 50°43'·95N 01°35'·19E FG 17m 5M; W col, G top; *Horn 30s*.

ZC1 buoy 50°44'·94N 01°27'·30E Fl (4) Y 15s; SPM.
Bassure de Baas buoy 50°48'·50N 01°33'·15E VQ; NCM; *Bell*.
ZC2 buoy 50°53'·50N 01°31'·00E Fl (2+1) Y 15s; SPM.
Cap Gris-Nez 50°52'·05N 01°35'·07E Fl 5s 72m **29M**; W tr, B top; vis 005°-232°; RG; *Horn 60s*. Fog detector lt.
Buoy 50°54'·11N 01°32'·03E Fl (2) 6s; IDM.
Abbeville buoy 50°56'·05N 01°37'·70E VQ (9) 10s; WCM.
CA3 buoy 50°56'·80N 01°41'·25E Fl G 4s; SHM; *Whis*.
Sangatte 50°57'·23N 01°46'·57E Oc WG 4s 12m W8M, G6M; W pylon, B top; vis W065°-089°, W089°-152°, G152°-245°.
RCW buoy 51°01'·20N 01°45'·45E VQ; NCM.
CA2 buoy 51°00'·91N 01°48'·86E Q; NCM.
CA4 buoy 50°58'·94N 01°45'·18E VQ (9) 10s 8m 8M; WCM; R refl; *Whis*.

CA6 buoy 50°58'·30N 01°45'·70E VQ R; PHM.
CA5 buoy 50°57'·70N 01°46'·20E QG; SHM.
CA8 buoy 50°58'·43N 01°48'·72E QR; PHM; *Bell*.
CA10 buoy 50°58'·68N 01°50'·00E Fl (2) R 6s; PHM.

- CALAIS
Jetée Ouest hd 50°58'·30N 01°50'·48E Iso G 3s 12m 9M; (in fog Iso 3s); W tr, G top; *Bell (1) 5s*.
Jetée Est hd 50°58'·45N 01°50'·54E Fl (2) R 6s 12m **17M**; (in fog two Fl (2) 6s (vert); Gy tr, R top; Ra refl; *Horn (2) 40s*.
Calais 50°57'·73N 01°51'·28E Fl (4) 15s 59m **22M**; W 8-sided tr, B top; vis 073°-260°.

- OFFSHORE MARKS
MPC buoy 51°06'·09N 01°38'·36E Fl Y 2·5s 10m 6M; SPM.
SANDETTIÉ lt F 51°09'·40N 01°47'·20E Fl 5s 12m **24M**; R hull; *Horn 30s*; Racon (T).
Ruytingen SW buoy 51°04'·99N 01°46'·90E Fl (3) G 12s; SHM; *Whis*.
Ruytingen W buoy 51°06'·90N 01°50'·60E VQ; NCM.
Ruytingen NW buoy 51°09'·05N 01°57'·40E Fl G 4s; SHM.
Ruytingen N buoy 51°13'·12N 02°10'·42E VQ; NCM.
Ruytingen SE buoy 51°09'·20N 02°09'·00E VQ (3) 15s; ECM.
Dyck E buoy 51°05'·70N 02°05'·70E Q (3) 10s; ECM.
DY1 buoy 51°09'·00N 02°15'·00E Fl G 4s; SHM.
DY2 buoy 51°09'·50N 02°19'·50E Fl (2) R 6s; PHM.
DY3 buoy 51°11'·50N 02°22'·50E Q; NCM.

DUNKERQUE LANBY 51°03'·00N 01°51'·83E Fl 3s 10m **25M**; R tubular structure on circular buoy; Racon.
RCE buoy 51°02'·40N 01°53'·20E Iso G 4s; SHM.
Walde 50°59'·57N 01°55'·00E Fl (3) 12s 13m 4M; B pylon on hut.
DKA buoy 51°02'·59N 01°57'·06E L Fl 10s; SWM.
DW5 buoy 51°02'·20N 02°01'·00E QG; SHM.

- GRAVELINES
Haut-fond de Gravelines buoy 51°04'·10N 02°05'·10E VQ (9) 10s; WCM.
Jetée Ouest 51°00'·98N 02°05'·55E Fl (2) WG 6s 9m W8M, G8M; Y ○ tr, G top; vis W317°-327°, G078°-085°, W085°-244°.
Jetée Est 51°00'·98N 02°05'·69E Fl (3) R 12s 5m 4M.

- DUNKERQUE PORT OUEST
DKB buoy 51°03'·00N 02°09'·34E VQ (9) 10s; WCM.
Port Ouest ldg lts 120°. **Front**, 51°01'·72N 02°11'·99E Dir FG 16m **21M**; W col, G top; intens 119°-121°;
Rear, 600m from front, Dir FG 30m **21M**; W col, G top; intens 119°-121°. By day both show F 28M.
Jetée Clipon hd 51°02'·69N 02°09'·86E Fl (4) 12s 24m 13M; W ○ col, R top; vis 278°-243°; *Siren (4) 60s*.

- DUNKERQUE PORT EST
DW29 buoy 51°03'·88N 02°20'·32E Fl (3) G 12s; SHM.
Ldg lts 137·5°, both Oc (2) 6s 7/10m 12M, W cols + R tops.
Dunkerque 51°02'·98N 02°21'·94E Fl (2) 10s 59m **26M**; W tr, B top.
Jetée Ouest hd 51°03'·68N 02°21'·04E Oc (2+1) WG 12s 35m **W15M**, G12M; W tr, brown top; vis G252°-310°, W310°-252°; Sig stn; *Dia (2+1) 60s*.
Jetée Est hd 51°03'·63N 02°21'·28E Fl (2) R 10s 12m **16M**; R □ on W pylon, R top. *Horn (2) 20s*; Fl (2) 10s (in fog).

E1 buoy 51°04'·12N 02°23'·18E Fl (2) G 6s; SHM.
E2 buoy 51°04'·38N 02°22'·40E VQ (6) + L Fl 10s; SCM.
E4 buoy 51°04'·62N 02°24'·60E Fl R 4s; PHM.
E6 buoy 51°04'·86N 02°27'·27E QR; PHM.
E7 buoy 51°05'·20N 02°28'·60E Fl R, *Whis*; SWM.
E8 buoy 51°05'·50N 02°28'·62E Fl (3) G, SHM.
E11 buoy 51°07'·30N 02°30'·71E Fl G 4s; SHM.
E12 buoy 51°07'·95N 02°30'·78E VQ (6) + L Fl 10s; SCM.

8.19.5   PASSAGE INFORMATION

For detailed sailing directions refer to: *Normandy and Channel Islands Pilot* (Adlard Coles/Brackenbury), The *Shell Channel Pilot* (Imray/Cunliffe) and *North France Pilot* (Imray/Thompson). Also the Admiralty *Channel Pilot* and *Dover Strait Pilot*.

The coasts of Normandy and Picardy are convenient to hbrs along the S Coast of England – the distance from (say) Brighton to Fécamp being hardly more than an overnight passage. It should be noted however that many of the hbrs dry, so that a boat which can take the ground is an advantage. For details of TSS in the Dover Strait, see 8.19.28. Notes on the English Channel and on cross-Channel passages appear in 8.3.5 and 8.15.5; see 8.0.8 for cross-Channel distances. For French glossary, see 8.15.9. The coast and ports westward from Pte de Barfleur are covered in Area 15.

The inland waterways system can be entered via the Seine (8.19.20), St Valéry-sur-Somme (8.19.25), Calais, Gravelines (8.19.29), and Dunkerque (8.19.30). See 8.15.8 for tolls.

PTE DE BARFLEUR TO GRANDCAMP (chart 2135, *2613*)

Raz de Barfleur (8.15.5) must be avoided in bad weather. In calm weather it can be taken at slack water (HW Cherbourg –4½ and +2) or the inshore passage used, passing 5ca E of La Jamette ECM bn. Pte de Barfleur marks the W end of B de Seine, which stretches 55M east to C d'Antifer, 12M N of Le Havre. There are no obstructions on a direct course across the Bay, but a transhipment area for large tankers is centred about 10M ESE of Pte de Barfleur. A feature of the Baie de Seine is the stand of tide at HW. Caution: The W end of the Baie de Seine is affected by floating Sargassum weed; in hbrs from St Vaast to Grandcamp propeller fouling is commonplace.

S from Barfleur (8.19.9) the coast runs SSE 4M to Pte de Saire, with rks and shoals up to 1M offshore. 2M S of Pte de Saire is St Vaast-la-Hougue (8.19.10): approach S of Île de Tatihou, but beware drying rks: La Tourelle, Le Gavendest and La Dent, which lie near the approaches and are buoyed.

Îles St Marcouf (8.19.11) lie 7M SE of St Vaast-la-Hougue, about 4M offshore, and consist of Île du Large (lt) and Île de Terre about ¼M apart. Banc de St Marcouf, with depths of 2·4m and many wks, extends 2·5M NW from the islands, and the sea breaks on this in strong N or NE winds. The Banc du Cardonnet, with depths of 5·2m and many wks, extends for about 5M ESE from the islands.

At the head of B du Grand Vey, about 10M S of Îles St Marcouf, are the (very) tidal hbrs of Carentan and Isigny (8.19.11); entry is only possible near HW. The Carentan chan is well buoyed and adequately lit. It trends SSW across sandbanks for about 4M, beyond which it runs between two breakwaters leading to a lock gate, and thence into canal to Carentan. The Isigny chan is deeper, but the hbr dries. Neither chan should be attempted in strong onshore winds.

On E side of B du Grand Vey, Roches de Grandcamp (dry) extend more than 1M offshore, N and W of Grandcamp (8.19.12), but they are flat and can be crossed from the N in normal conditions HW±1½. Three NCM buoys mark the N edge of the shoal. Heavy kelp can give false echo soundings.

GRANDCAMP TO DEAUVILLE (chart 2136, *2613*)

Between Pte de la Percée and Port-en-Bessin (8.19.13) a bank lies offshore, with drying ledges extending 3ca. A race forms over this bank with wind against tide. Off Port-en-Bessin the E-going stream begins about HW Le Havre – 0500, and the W-going at about HW Le Havre + 0050, sp rates 1·25kn.

From Port-en-Bessin the coast runs east 4M to C Manvieux, beyond which lie remnants of the wartime hbr of Arromanches, where there is occas anch. Between C Manvieux and Langrune, 10M E, Plateau du Calvados lies offshore. Rocher du Calvados (dries 1·6m) lies on the W part of this bank. There are numerous wrecks and obstructions in the area.

Roches de Ver (dry) lie near centre of Plateau du Calvados, extending 8ca offshore about 1M W of Courseulles-sur-Mer (8.19.14). The approach to this hbr is dangerous in strong onshore winds. Les Essarts de Langrune (dry) lie E of Courseulles-sur-Mer, and extend up to 2·25M seaward of Langrune. At their E end lie Roches de Lion (dry), which reach up to 1·5M offshore in places and extend to a point 2·5M W of Ouistreham ferry hbr and marina (8.19.15). Here a canal leads 7M inland to a marina in the centre of Caen.

6M E of Ouistreham is River Dives (8.19.16) with marina. The banks dry for 1M to seaward, and entry is only possible from HW ± 2½, and not in fresh onshore wind conditions.

Deauville/Trouville (8.19.17), 8M ENE of Dives, is an important yachting hbr. The sands dry more than 5ca offshore; in strong W or N winds the entrance is dangerous and the sea breaks between the jetties. In such conditions it is best attempted within 15 mins of HW, when the stream is slack. To the NE beware Banc de Trouville (dries 2m), and shoal water to the N where Les Ratelets dries at the mouth of the Seine.

ESTUAIRE DE LA SEINE/LE HAVRE (charts 2146, 2990)

The Seine est is entered between Deauville and Le Havre, and is encumbered by shallow and shifting banks which extend seawards to Banc de Seine, 15M W of Le Havre. With wind against tide there is a heavy sea on this bank. Here the SW-going stream begins at HW Le Havre + 0400, and the NE-going at HW Le Havre – 0300, sp rates 1·5kn. Between Deauville and Le Havre the sea can be rough in W winds.

Chenal du Rouen is the main chan into R. Seine, and carries much commercial tfc. The S side of the chan is contained by Digue du Ratier, a training wall which extends E to Honfleur (8.19.18). With almost 24 hours access/exit, Honfleur is a useful starting port when bound up-river. See 8.19.20 for notes on R. Seine, Rouen and Paris; and canals to the Med.

Le Havre (8.19.19) is a large commercial port, as well as a yachting centre. From the NW, the most useful mark is the Le Havre Lanby 9M W of C de la Hève (lt). The appr chan, which runs 6M WNW from the hbr ent, is well buoyed and lit. Strong W winds cause rough water over shoal patches either side of the chan. Coming from the N or NE, there is deep water close off C de la Hève, but from here steer S to join the main ent chan. Beware Banc de l'Éclat (depth 0·1m), which lies on N side of main chan and about 1·5M from harbour ent.

9M N of C de la Hève is Port d'Antifer, a VLCC harbour. A huge breakwater extends about 1·5M seaward, and should be given a berth of about 1·5M, or more in heavy weather when there may be a race with wind against tide. Commercial vessels in the buoyed app chan have priority. Yachts should cross the app chan to the NW of A17/A18 lt buoys; at 90° to its axis; as quickly as possible, and well clear of ships in the chan. Crossing vessels should contact *Vigie Port d'Antifer* and any priority vessel on VHF Ch 16. Off Cap d'Antifer the NE-going stream begins about HW Le Havre – 0430, and the SW-going at about HW Le Havre + 0140. There are eddies close inshore E of Cap d'Antifer on both streams.

CAP D'ANTIFER TO DIEPPE (chart *2451*)

From C d'Antifer to Fécamp (8.19.21) drying rks extend up to 2½ca offshore. At Fécamp pierheads the E-going stream begins about HW Le Havre – 0500, and the W-going at about HW Le Havre + 0025, sp rates 2·75kn. Off Pte Fagnet, close NE of Fécamp, lie Les Charpentiers (rks which dry, to almost 2ca offshore).

From Fécamp to St Valéry-en-Caux (8.19.22), 15M ENE, (and beyond to Le Treport and Ault) the coast consists of chalk cliffs broken by valleys. There are rky ledges, extending 4ca offshore in places. The nuclear power station at Paluel 3M W of St Valéry-en-Caux (prohibited area marked by lt buoy) is conspic. Immediately E of St Valéry-en-Caux shallow sandbanks, Les Ridens, with a least depth of 0·6m, extend about 6ca offshore. At St Valéry-en-Caux ent the E-going

19

stream begins about HW Dieppe – 0550, and the W-going stream begins about HW Dieppe – 0015, sp rates 2·75kn. E of the ent a small eddy runs W on the E-going stream.

Between St Valéry-en-Caux and Pte d'Ailly (lt, fog sig, RC) there are drying rks 4ca offshore in places. About 1·5M E of Pte de Sotteville a rky bank (depth 4·2m) extends about 1M NNW; a strong eddy causes a race over this bank.
Drying rks extend 5ca off Pte d'Ailly, including La Galère, a rk which dries 6·8m, about 3ca N of the Pte. Dangerous wks lie between about 1·2M WNW and 1·5M NNW of the lt ho. About 6M N of Pte d'Ailly, Les Ecamias are banks with depths of 11m, dangerous in a heavy sea.
From Pte d'Ailly to Dieppe (8.19.23) the coast is fringed by a bank, drying in places, up to 4ca offshore. E of Pte d'Ailly an eddy runs W close inshore on first half of E-going stream. Off Dieppe the ENE-going stream begins about HW Dieppe – 0505, and the WSW-going at about HW Dieppe + 0030, sp rates 2kn.

DIEPPE TO BOULOGNE

Between Dieppe and Le Tréport (8.19.24), 14M NE, rky banks, drying in places, extend 5ca offshore. A prohib area extends 6ca off Penly nuclear power station and is marked by lt Bys. About 3M NW of Le Tréport, Ridens du Tréport (depth 5·1m) should be avoided in bad weather. Banc Franc-Marqué (depth 3·6m) lies 2M offshore, and about 3M N of Le Tréport.

N of Ault (lt) the coast changes from medium cliffs to low sand dunes. Offshore there are two shoals, Bassurelle de la Somme and Quémer, on parts of which the sea breaks in bad weather. 4·5M NW of Cayeux-sur-Mer the stream is rotatory anti-clockwise. The E-going stream begins about HW Dieppe –0200, and sets 070° 2·5kn at sp : the W-going stream begins about HW Dieppe + 0600, and sets 240° 1·5kn at sp.

B de Somme, between Pte du Hourdel and Pte de St Quentin, is a shallow, drying area of shifting sands. The chan, which runs close to Pte du Hourdel, is buoyed, but the whole est dries out 3M to seaward, and should not be approached in strong W or NW winds. For St Valéry-sur-Somme and Le Crotoy, see 8.19.25.

From Pte de St Quentin the coast runs 17M N to Pte du Touquet, with a shallow coastal bank which dries to about 5ca offshore, except in the approaches to the dangerous and constantly changing Embouchure de l'Authies (about 7M north), where it dries up to 2M offshore.

Le Touquet/Étaples (8.19.26) lies in the Embouchure de la Canche, entered between Pte du Touquet and Pte de Lornel, and with a drying bank which extends 1M seaward of a line joining these two points. Le Touquet-Paris-Plage lt is shown from a conspic tr, 1M S of Pte du Touquet. Off the entrance the N-going stream begins about HW Dieppe – 0335, sp rate 1·75kn; and the S-going stream begins about HW Dieppe + 0240, sp rate 1·75kn.

In the approaches to Pas de Calais a number of shoals lie offshore: La Bassurelle, Le Vergoyer, Bassure de Baas, Le Battur, Les Ridens, and The Ridge (or Le Colbart). In bad weather, and particularly with wind against tide in most cases, the sea breaks heavily on all these shoals. From Pte de Lornel to Boulogne (8.19.27; chart 438) the coast dries up to 5ca offshore. Off Digue Carnot the N-going stream begins HW Dieppe – 0130, and the S-going at HW Dieppe + 0350, sp rates 1·75kn.

BOULOGNE TO DUNKERQUE (charts 2451, 1892, 323)

Between Boulogne and C Gris Nez (lt, fog sig) the coastal bank dries about 4ca offshore. The NE-bound traffic lane of the Dover Strait TSS (8.19.28) lies only 3M off C Gris Nez. Keep a sharp lookout not only for coastal traffic in the ITZ, but also cross-Channel ferries, particularly very fast hovercraft, jetfoils and catamarans. 1M NW of C Gris Nez the NE-going stream begins at HW Dieppe – 0150, and the SW-going at HW Dieppe + 0355, sp rates 4kn.

In bad weather the sea breaks heavily on Ridens de Calais, 3M N of Calais (8.19.29 and chart 1352), and also on Ridens de la Rade about 1·5M NE of the hbr. The drying hbr of Gravelines (8.19.29), which should not be used in strong onshore winds, is about 3M SW of Dunkerque Port Ouest; this is a commercial/ferry port which yachts should not enter. The old port, Dunkerque Port Est (8.19.30), has good yacht facilities and is 7·5M further E. If E-bound, the Passe de Zuydcoote (3·3m) is an inshore link to West Diep.

Offshore a series of banks lie roughly parallel with the coast: Sandettié bank (about 14M to N), Outer Ruytingen midway between Sandettié and the coast, and the Dyck banks which extend NE'wards for 30M from a point 5M NE of Calais. There are well-buoyed channels between some of these banks, but great care is needed in poor visibility. In general the banks are steep-to on the inshore side, and slope seaward. In bad weather the sea breaks on the shallower parts.

8.19.6   DISTANCE TABLE

Approximate distances in nautical miles are by the most direct route, whilst avoiding dangers and allowing for Traffic Separation Schemes. Places in *italics* are in adjoining areas; places in **bold** are in 8.0.8, Cross-Channel Distances; places underlined are in 8.0.10, Distances across the North Sea.

1. *Cherbourg*	1																			
2. Barfleur	20	2																		
3. **St Vaast**	26	10	3																	
4. Carentan	41	26	20	4																
5. Grandcamp-Maisy	39	21	16	13	5															
6. Courseulles	54	39	35	37	25	6														
7. **Ouistreham**	66	46	46	46	35	11	7													
8. Dives-sur-Mer	69	53	49	51	38	17	8	8												
9. **Deauville/Trouville**	76	56	53	56	43	21	14	7	9											
8. **Honfleur**	82	62	69	62	50	28	24	17	10	10										
11. **Le Havre**	70	56	53	56	45	23	19	13	8	9	11									
12. **Fécamp**	80	64	63	72	64	40	39	39	32	34	25	12								
13. St Valéry-en-Caux	82	77	78	88	80	55	58	55	44	45	38	15	13							
14. **Dieppe**	108	94	95	105	94	75	68	67	61	63	54	29	16	14						
15. St Valéry-sur-Somme	130	120	120	132	125	103	103	97	95	95	85	62	45	35	15					
16. Étaples	134	124	130	140	130	110	110	117	100	100	90	70	58	50	19	16				
17. **Boulogne**	142	128	133	145	135	118	115	108	108	110	101	76	61	54	30	12	17			
18. **Calais**	160	148	157	170	168	140	138	129	128	130	121	96	81	74	50	32	20	18		
19. Dunkerque	182	170	179	192	190	162	160	151	150	152	143	118	103	96	69	51	42	22	19	
20. *Nieuwpoort*	197	185	194	207	205	177	175	166	165	165	158	133	118	111	84	66	57	37	15	20

8.19.7   English Channel Waypoints: See 8.1.7

8.19.8   Special Notes for France: See 8.15.8.

BARFLEUR   8-19-9

Manche 49°40'·40N 01°15'·40W   Rtg 3-4-1

CHARTS
AC 1349, *2135*, 1106, *2613*; SHOM 7090, 5609, 6864, 7120; ECM 528; Imray C32; Stanfords 1, 7

TIDES
−0208 Dover; ML 3·9; Duration 0550; Zone −0100

Standard Port CHERBOURG (←)

Times				Height (metres)			
High Water		Low Water		MHWS	MHWN	MLWN	MLWS
0300	1000	0400	1000	6·4	5·0	2·5	1·1
1500	2200	1600	2200				
Differences BARFLEUR							
+0110	+0055	+0052	+0052	+0·1	+0·3	0·0	0·0

SHELTER
Excellent, but ent difficult in fresh E/NE winds. Hbr dries; access HW ±2½. Yachts berth at SW end of quay, clear of FVs; limited space. Beware rks/shoals in SE of hbr. Safe to ⚓ outside hbr in off-shore winds. See Hr Mr for moorings.

NAVIGATION
WPT 49°41'·30N 01°14'·21W, 039°/219° from/to front ldg lt, 1·35M. In rough weather, esp wind against tide, keep 5M off Pte de Barfleur to clear the Race; see 8.19.5. From the N, identify La Jamette ECM bn and La Grotte SHM buoy. From the S, keep seaward of Pte Dranguet and Le Moulard, both ECM bns. Beware cross currents and Le Hintar rks (buoyed) and La Raie (bn) to E of ldg line. The chan may not be clearly identified until close in. A new spur bkwtr (55m long) is still planned from the ☆ Fl G 4s, halfway across the ent, toward the ☆ Oc R 4s.

LIGHTS AND MARKS
Pte de Barfleur lt ho is conspic 1½M NNW of hbr, Fl (2) 10s 72m 29M, grey tr, B top, Reed (2) 60s. The church tr is a conspic daymark.
Ldg Its 219°: both Oc (3) 12s 7/13m 10M, W □ trs, synch; not easy to see by day. Buoys are small. Jetée Est Oc R 4s 5m 6M. Jetée Ouest Fl G 4s 8m 6M.

RADIO TELEPHONE
None.

TELEPHONE
Hr Mr 02.33.54.08.29; Aff Mar 02.33.23.36.12; CROSS 02.33.52.72.13; SNSM 02.33.23.8.10; ⌗ 02.33.53.79.65; Météo 02.33.53.53.44; Auto 08.36.68.08.50; Police 17; SAMU 15; Dr 02.33.54.00.02; Brit Consul 02.33.44.20.13.

FACILITIES
NW Quay (125 + 20 visitors), AB 39FF, M, Slip, L, D, FW, AC (long cable needed); **SC** ☎ 02.33.43.71.93.
Town Gaz, ME (Montfarville: 1km S), V, R, Bar, ✉, ⒷB, bus to Cherbourg for ⇌, ✈, Ferry.

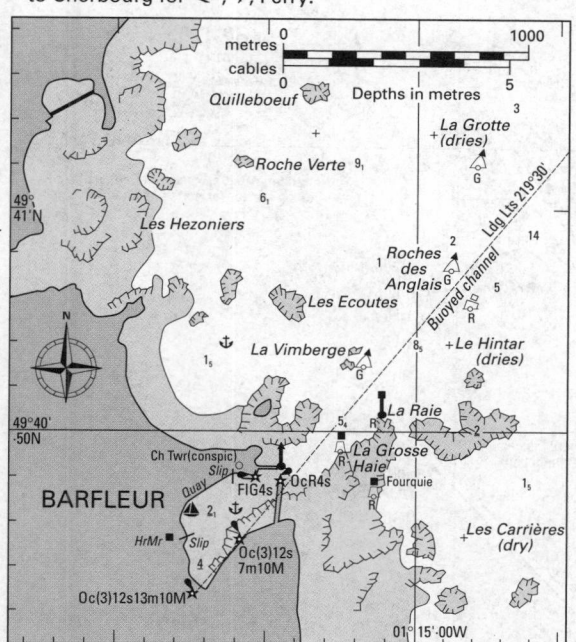

ST VAAST-LA-HOUGUE   8-19-10

Manche 49°35'·25N 01°15'·35W   Rtg 3-2-1

CHARTS
AC 1349, *2135*, *2613*; SHOM 7090, 6864, 7056, 7120; ECM 527, 528; Imray C32; Stanfords 1, 7

TIDES
−0240 Dover; ML 3·9; Duration 0530; Zone −0100

Standard Port CHERBOURG (←)

Times				Height (metres)			
High Water		Low Water		MHWS	MHWN	MLWN	MLWS
0300	1000	0400	1000	6·4	5·0	2·5	1·1
1500	2200	1600	2200				
Differences ST VAAST-LA-HOUGUE							
+0110	+0045	+0050	+0100	+0·2	+0·2	0·0	−0·1

SHELTER
Excellent in marina, 2·3m; lock open HW−2¼ to HW+3. Crowded in season. If full, or awaiting lock, ⚓ off in White sector of jetty lt between brgs of 330° and 350°, but this ⚓ becomes untenable in strong E-S winds.

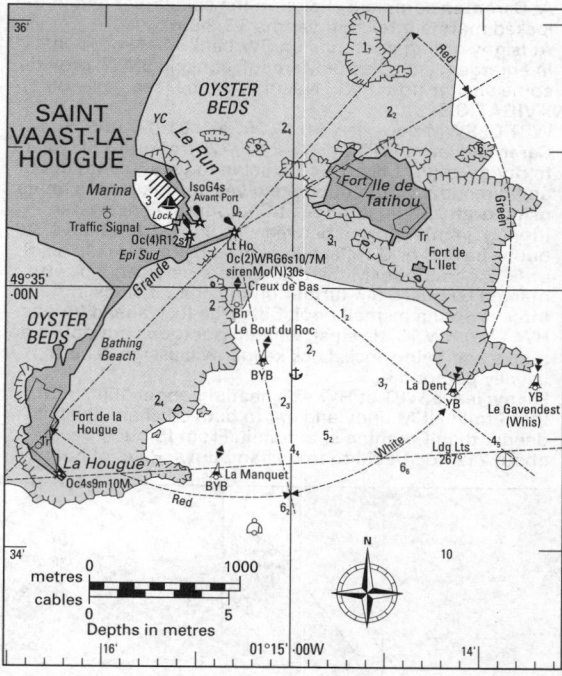

NAVIGATION
WPT 49°34'·40N 01°13'·78W, 130°/310° from/to main jetty lt (Oc 6s) 1·3M. Appr in W sector, leaving La Dent SCM By to stbd and Le Bout du Roc ECM By and Le Creux de Bas ECM bn to port. The ent is wide and well marked. Beware boats at ⚓, cross currents and oyster beds. "Le Run" appr is not advised and should not be attempted >1·2m draft.

LIGHTS AND MARKS
Do not confuse similar towers (conspic) on Ile de Tatihou and La Hougue Pte. From N, Pte de Saire Oc (2+1) 12s 11m 10M. From E, ldg lts 267°: front La Hougue Oc 4s 9m 10M; rear Morsalines Oc (3+1) WRG 12s 90m 11/8M in W sector. Main jetty hd lt, Oc (2) WRG 6s 12m 10/7M, W tr + R top, vis W310°-350°. R/G tfc sigs at lock ent.

RADIO TELEPHONE
VHF Ch 09.

TELEPHONE
Hr Mr 02.33.23.61.00, ☎ 02.33.54.09.55; ⌗ 02.33.44.16.00; Aff Mar 02.33.54.43.61; CROSS 02.33.52.72.13; SNSM 02.33.54.42.52; Météo 02.36.65.08.50; Dr 02.33.54.43.42; Police 02.33.54.12.11; Brit Consul 02.33.44.20.13.

FACILITIES
Marina (655 + 150 🅥) ☎ 02.33.23.61.00, FF102, Access HW −2¼ to +3, FW, C (25 ton), AC, D, P, BY, ME, El, Sh, Gaz, CH, Bar, R, ◎, V, Slip; **Cercle Nautique de la Hougue** ☎ 02.33.54.55.73, Bar, R, C (3 ton), P, D, CH, FW, V.
Town P, D, V, Gaz, R, Bar, ◎, ✉, ⒷB, ⇌ (bus to Valognes), Cherbourg: ✈, Ferry. Tourist Office 02.33.54.41.37.

19

CARENTAN/ISIGNY   8-19-11

Manche Rtg 4-2-1   Calvados Rtg 4-4-3

CHARTS
AC *2135, 2613*; SHOM 7056; ECM 527; Imray C32; Stan'd 1
TIDES
−0225 Dover; ML Rade de la Chapelle 4·4; Duration 0510;
Zone −0100

Standard Port CHERBOURG (←)

Use differences RADE DE LA CHAPELLE 8.19.12
HW Carentan is HW Cherbourg +0110. See tidal graph for
Carentan appr chan (facing page).

SHELTER
Temp ⊥ N of buoyed chans in winds <F5. Entry protected
from prevailing S to W winds, but is not to be attempted
in onshore winds >F5. Drying out on the hard sands of
the estuary is not advised; nor is an early approach, as a
bore (*mascaret*) may occur in the river channels between
HW−3 and HW −2½ particularly at springs.
At **Carentan** complete shelter in the canal/river and in the
locked marina (max/min depths 3·5/2·9m).
At **Isigny** drying pontoons on SW bank ¼M N of town.
In emergency the Iles St Marcouf, conspic 5M N, provide
some shelter from NNE, N and W winds (see next col).
NAVIGATION
WPT CI SWM buoy, Iso 4s, 49°25'·30N 01°07'·10W. For
Carentan: leave WPT at HW−2 to −1½, tracking 214° to ent
to drying chan, 1·6M. Chan is liable to vary in both depth
and direction. Graph opposite gives approx access times,
using draft and tidal range at Cherbourg. Least water
(drying 3·4m) reported between No 9b and 10b buoys. All
buoys have R or G reflective panels; 6 are lit, Fl (3) 12s R
or G. After about 4M the chan enters between 2 bkwtrs,
marked by bns. 3·5M further on the chan divides into
three, forming a small pool. Enter the lock ahead (opens
HW−2 to HW +3, tfc sigs); waiting pontoons are on E side
above and below lock. Lock-keeper will assign Ⓥ berth,
usually pontoon K.
Isigny: leave WPT at HW −2½ heading about 150°/1·1M
for IS unlit NCM buoy and ent to buoyed chan which is
deeper than Carentan's, but unlit. From IS buoy track
about 212° for 1·25M to first chan buoys. Pairs of buoys

are spaced at approx 3ca intervals, but between Nos 9/10
and 11/12 the interval is 6ca, with a SHM perch midway.
LIGHTS AND MARKS
Carentan: Bkwtr outer bns are lit, Fl (3)R 12s and Fl (3)G
12s. Ldg Its: Front Oc (3)R 12s 6m 17M and rear Oc (3)
12s 14m 11M, lead 209°30' for 1·6M from the ends of the
bkwtrs and immediately outside (not valid within the
buoyed chan). From front Idg It, lock is approx 3M.
Lock sigs: FG = lock open, FR = lock closed.
Isigny: Ldg Its, both Oc (2+1) 12s 7/19m 18M synch &
intens 171°-175°, lead 173° for 1·9M between bkwtrs to
front Idg It. Here turn port into R l'Aure for ½M to town.
RADIO TELEPHONE
VHF Carentan Ch 09 (0800-1800LT & in lock opening hrs).
Ch 09 also at Isigny (0900-1200 & 1400-1800LT).
TELEPHONE
Hr Mr Carentan 02.33.42.24.44; Lockmaster 02.33.71.8.85;
Hr Mr Isigny 02.31.22.8.67; Aff Mar 02.33.44.00.13; Auto
08.36.68.08.50; ⌗ 02.33.44.16.00; CROSS 02.33.52.72.13;
Police 02.33.42.00.17; Ⓗ 02.33.42.14.12; Dr 02.33.42.33.21;
Brit Consul 02.33.44.20.13.
FACILITIES
CARENTAN
Marina (220 + 50 Ⓥ) ☎ 02.33.42.24.44, ☏ 02.33.42.00.03,
FF74, Access HW −2 to HW +3, FW, AC, P & D (0900-
1000), Slip, C (50 ton), BH (16 ton);
YC Croiseurs Côtiers de Carentan ☎ 02.33.42.28.53, Bar;
Services: ME, EI, Sh, CH, BY. **Town** Bar, Ⓑ, D, P, ✉, ➔, R,
V, ✈ (Cherbourg). Ferry: Cherbourg.
ISIGNY **Quay** AB (55+5), FW, AC, P, D, C (8 ton), Slip;
Club Nautique AB, C, R, Bar; **Services:** ME, EI, Sh.
Town R, V, Bar, Ⓑ, ✉.

ADJACENT ANCHORAGE

ILES ST MARCOUF, Manche, 49°29'·70N 01°08'·70W. AC
2135, *2613*; SHOM 7056. Tides, 8.19.12. The 2 islands, Ile
de Terre and to the N, Ile du Large, look from afar like
ships at ⊥. The former is a bird sanctuary and is closed to
the public; the latter has a small dinghy hbr on the W
side. ⊥ SW or SE of Ile du Large or SE or NE of the Ile de
Terre. Holding is poor on pebbles and kelp; no shelter in
S'lies. Ile du Large It, VQ (3) 5s 18m 9M. Both islands are
surrounded by drying rks, uninhabited and lack facilities.

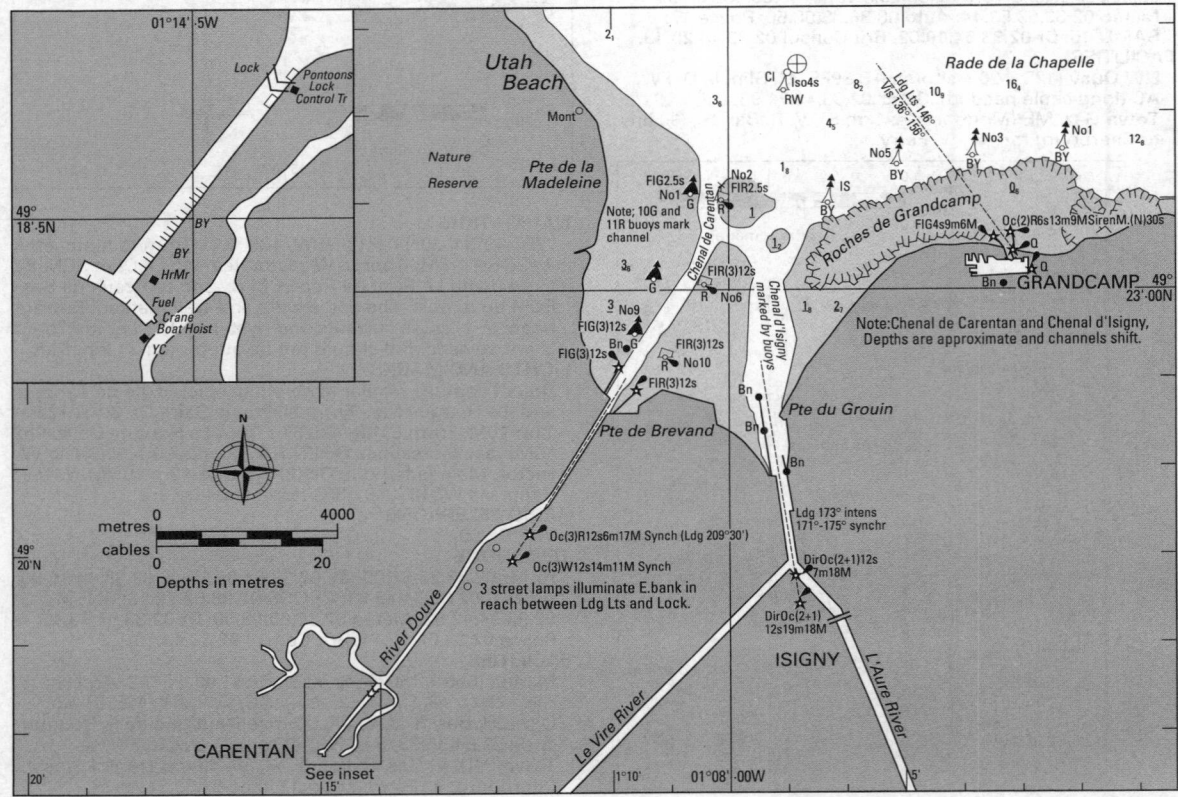

CARENTAN *continued*

CARENTAN TIDAL GRAPH

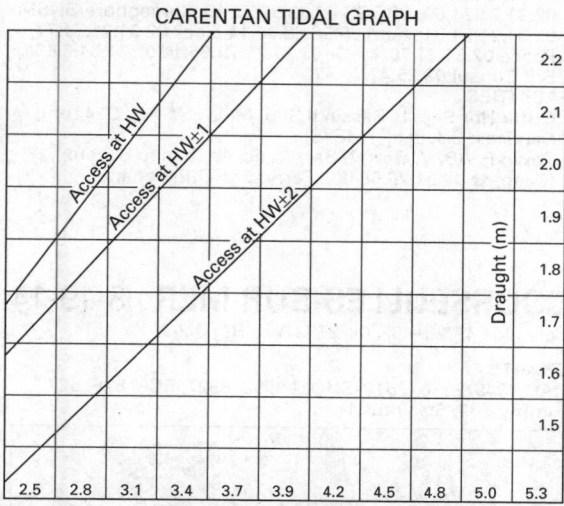

Caution: This graph, based on data from Port-Carentan, includes a safety clearance of 0·5m. Skippers may wish to add an additional margin to cater for depth variations due to shifting of the channel and/or Météorological conditions.

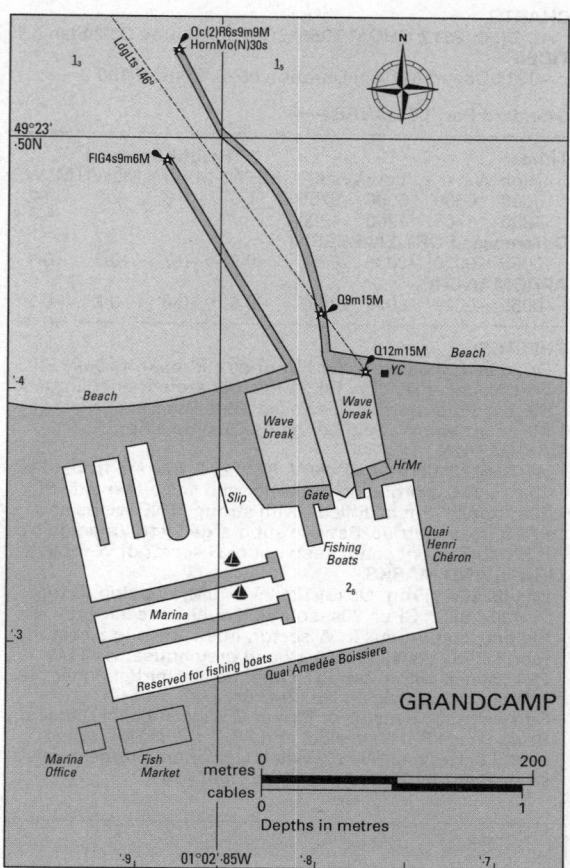

GRANDCAMP

GRANDCAMP-MAISY   8-19-12

Calvados 49°23'·50N 01°02'·87W.

CHARTS
AC *2135, 2613*; SHOM 7056; ECM 527; Imray C32; Stan'd 1

TIDES
–0220 Dover; ML Rade de la Chapelle 4·4; Duration 0510; Zone –0100

Standard Port CHERBOURG (←)

Times				Height (metres)			
High Water		Low Water		MHWS	MHWN	MLWN	MLWS
0300	1000	0400	1000	6·4	5·0	2·5	1·1
1500	2200	1600	2200				
Differences RADE DE LA CHAPELLE (3M to NW)							
+0115	+0050	+0130	+0117	+0·8	+0·9	+0·1	+0·1
ILES SAINT MARCOUF							
+0118	+0052	+0125	+0110	+0·6	+0·7	+0·1	+0·1

SHELTER
Access day & night, but difficult in NW to NE winds > F6. Safe appr sp HW ±2, nps HW ±1.5. Gate into wet basin, with marina to the W, opens at LW Dunkerque (8.19.29) and closes at HW Dunkerque, ie approx local HW ±2½. **V** on N pontoon at E end. SW corner of basin is very dirty.

NAVIGATION
WPT 49°25'·00N 01°04'·60W, 326°/146° from/to front ldg lt 2·0M. Large flat rks, Les Roches de Grandcamp, extend about 1½M out from the hbr and dry approx 1·5m; heavy kelp cover can cause echosounders to under-read.

LIGHTS AND MARKS
3 NCM Bys, numbered 1, 3 and 5, mark the seaward limit of Les Roches de Grandcamp. Appr between Nos 3 & 5. E pier hd lt, Oc (2) R 6s, on a RW col. Ldg lts 146°: both Dir Q 9/12m 15M (vis 144·5°-147·5°). Two other ldg lts: Oc 4s 8/28m 12M, to E and S of hbr, lead 221°.

RADIO TELEPHONE
VHF Ch 09.

TELEPHONE
Hr Mr 02.31.22.63.16; Aff Mar 02.31.22.60.65; CROSS 02.33.52.72.13; SNSM 02.31.22.67.12; Météo 02.21.33.25.26; Auto 08.36.68.08.14; Police 02.31.22.00.18; Dr 02.31.22.60.44; Ⓗ Bayeux 02.31.51.51.51; Brit Consul 02.35.42.27.47.

FACILITIES
Marina (268 + 25 **V**) ☎ 02.31.22.63.16, FF75, El, FW, BH (5 ton), Bar, V, AC; **Services:** ME, El, ⊠, Sh, CH, Gaz, C. **Town** P & D (cans), Gaz, ⊠, Ⓑ, ⇌ (Carentan), ✈ (Caen). Ferry: Cherbourg, Ouistreham.

ANCHORAGE BETWEEN PORT-EN-BESSIN AND COURSEULLES-SUR-MER

ARROMANCHES, Manche, 49°21'·80N 00°37'·20W. AC *2135, 2613*; SHOM 6927. HW is –0040 on Le Havre; see Port-en-Bessin (8.19.13). Strictly a fair weather ‡, with little shelter from the WW II Mulberry caissons which are conspic esp at LW. Rocher du Calvados dries 1·6m, 7ca ENE of ent. There are many wrecks offshore; 3 to the W and N are marked by a WCM and two ECM buoys. The most N'ly ECM buoy (Roseberry, 49°23'·2N 00°36'·1W) bears approx 025°/1·5M from the ent (lat/long as line 1) which is marked by a small unlit PHM and SHM buoy. Enter on about 245° for ‡ in 3m to S of the caissons, or sound closer inshore. Caution rky plateau off the beach and obstructions to SE of ent, marked by four W buoys. Facilities: **YC Port Winston** ☎ 02.31.22.31.01, 2 slips (dinghies).

19

PORT-EN-BESSIN   8-19-13

Calvados 49°21'·22N 00°45'·40W

CHARTS
AC 2136, *2613*; SHOM 7056; ECM 527; Imray C32; Stan'd 1

TIDES
−0215 Dover; ML 4·4; Duration 0520; Zone −0100

Standard Port LE HAVRE (⟶)

Times				Height (metres)			
High Water		Low Water		MHWS	MHWN	MLWN	MLWS
0000	0500	0000	0700	7·9	6·6	2·8	1·2
1200	1700	1200	1900				
Differences PORT-EN-BESSIN							
−0055	−0030	−0030	−0055	−0·7	−0·7	−0·2	−0·1
ARROMANCHES							
−0055	−0025	−0027	−0035	−0·6	−0·6	−0·2	−0·2

SHELTER
Good in 2nd basin; outer hbr dries completely. Busy FV port. Yachts may stay for 24 hrs, but are not encouraged; there is little room. Basins accessible HW ±2. Contact Hr Mr on arrival. Waiting berths on Quai de L'Epi.

NAVIGATION
WPT 49°22'·00N 00°44'·90W, 024°/204° from/to front ldg lt 204°, 1·1M. ⌕ prohib in outer hbr and 1ca either side of 204° transit. Ent is difficult with strong N/NE winds and >F8 it is dangerous. Beware submerged jetty (marked by R bn) to E of ent chan. Keep out of G sector of W mole lt.

LIGHTS AND MARKS
Ldg lts 204°: Front Oc (3) 12s 25m 10M, W pylon, G top, vis 069°-339°; Siren 20s (sounded over 90° each side of ldg line, continuous in W sector, interrupted in E sector); rear, Oc (3) 12s 42m 11M, W and grey house; vis 114°-294°, synch with front; RC. Other lts as chartlet; inner pier hds are Oc (2) R 6s and Fl (2) G 6s.
Entry sigs: Ⓡ over Ⓖ, or R over G flags = basins closed. Bridge has FR lt each side, and FR in the middle when shut. Lock opens HW ±2. When lock open, bridge opens whenever possible to suit yachts and FVs.

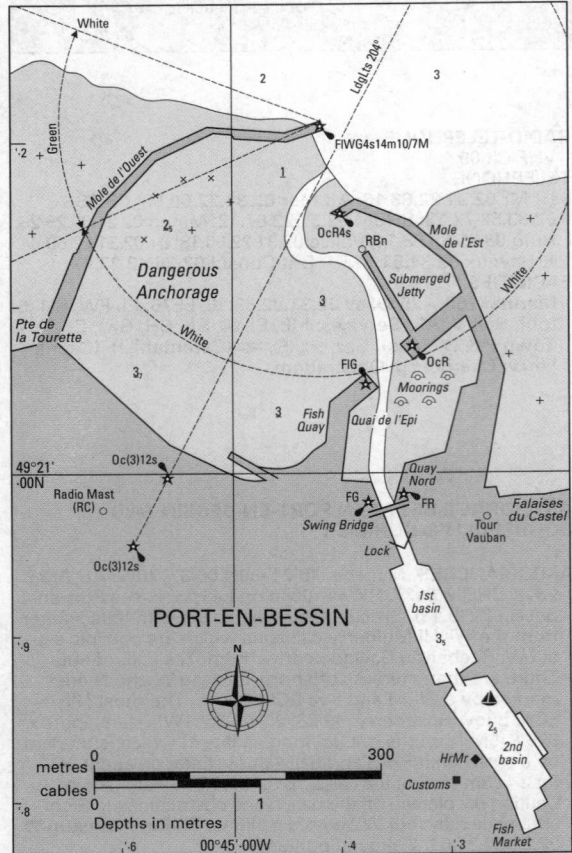

PORT-EN-BESSIN

RADIO TELEPHONE
VHF Ch 18 (HW ±2) for lock opening.
TELEPHONE
Hr Mr 02.31.21.70.49; Aff Mar 02.31.21.71.52; ⌗ 02.31.21.71.09; CROSS 02.33.52.72.13; Semaphore/SNSM 02.31.21.81.51; Auto 08.36.68.08.14; Lock 02.31.21.71.77; Police 02.31.21.70.10; Dr 02.31.21.74.26; Ⓗ 02.31.51.51.51; Brit Consul 02.35.42.27.47.
FACILITIES
Outer Hbr Slip, L; **Bassin II** Slip, M, L, FW, AB, C (4 ton); **Services:** CH, El, Ⓔ, ME, Sh.
Town P, AB, V, Gaz, R, Bar, ✉, Ⓑ, ⇌ (bus to Bayeux), ✈ (Caen, ☎ 02.31.26.58.00). Ferry: See Ouistreham.

COURSEULLES-SUR-MER 8-19-14

Calvados 49°20'·48N 00°27'·27W   Rtg 3-2-2

CHARTS
AC *1349*, 2136, *2613*; SHOM 5598, 6927; ECM 526, 527; Imray C32; Stanfords 1

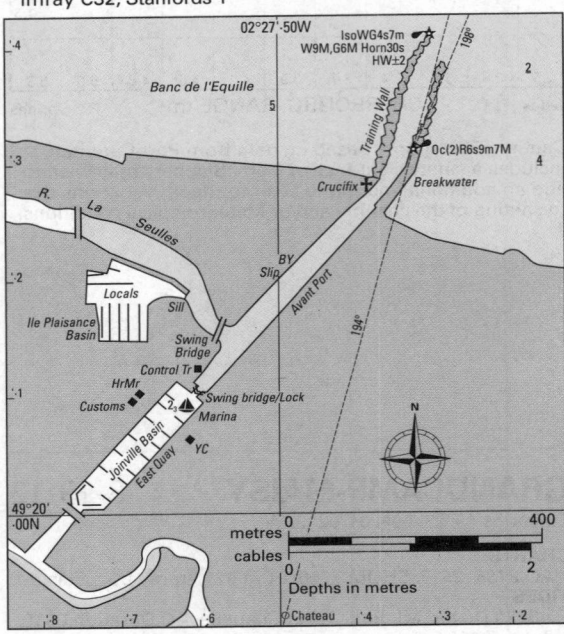

TIDES
−0300 Dover; ML 4·6; Duration No data; Zone −0100

Standard Port LE HAVRE (⟶)

Times				Height (metres)			
High Water		Low Water		MHWS	MHWN	MLWN	MLWS
0000	0500	0000	0700	7·9	6·6	2·8	1·2
1200	1700	1200	1900				
Differences COURSEULLES-SUR-MER							
−0045	−0015	−0020	−0025	−0·5	−0·5	−0·1	−0·1

SHELTER
Good in **Bassin Joinville** (3m), but appr becomes difficult in strong N to NE winds. Avant Port dries 2·5m; best ent at HW −1. Swing bridge/lock into Bassin Joinville opens on request, HW ±2. Ile Plaisance Basin only suitable for small shoal draft boats; sill (dries 3m). Access HW ±3, but swing bridge only opens HW±2. Fair weather ⌕ (3-5m) at Anneau de la Marguerite, 134°/0·4M from landfall buoy.

NAVIGATION
WPT 49° 22'·00N 00° 28'·70W, 314°/134° from/to landfall By SWM Iso 4s, 1·0M. Plateau du Calvados extends 2M seaward and banks dry for 0·6M. Outer ldg marks: front Bernières-sur-mer church tr on with La Delivrande church twin spires (partly obsc'd by trees), lead 134° close to landfall buoy. Beware rks awash at CD either side of ldg line. Maintain 134° for 0·55M until ent bears 198°.

COURSEULLES continued

LIGHTS AND MARKS
Pte de Ver lt ho, Fl (3) 15s 42m 26M, is 2·5M W of hbr and obsc'd by cliffs when brg >275°, but from the N provides useful distance-to-go bearings. W trng wall is marked by ☆, Iso WG 4s 7m 9/6M (stay in W sector), and by 2 SHM perches and conspic crucifix at root. E trng wall marked by 2 PHM perches and ☆ Oc (2) R 6s 9m 7M at root of bkwtr. This lt in transit with Chateau (conspic) leads 194° to hbr ent.

RADIO TELEPHONE
VHF Ch 09: Control Tr HW±2. Hr Mr & Office only open:

	0900-1200	1500-1800LT
Mon-Fri	May-Aug	Jul, Aug
Sat	All year	Jul, Aug
Sun + Hols	Apr-Aug	Shut

TELEPHONE
Hr Mr 02.31.37.51.69; Control tr 02.31.37.46.03; Aff Mar @ Caen 02.31.85.40.55; CROSS 02.33.52.72.13; ⌗ @ Port-en-Bessin 02.31.21.71.09; SNSM 02.31.37.45.47; Météo 08.36.68.12.34; Auto 08.36.68.08.14; Police @ Ouistreham 02.31.97.13.15; Dr 02.31.37.45.28; Ambulance 15; Fire 18; Brit Consul Cherbourg 02.33.88.65.70.

FACILITIES
Joinville Basin ☎ 02.31.37.51.69, report to pontoon X on E Quay, FF137, Slip, FW, AC, C (25 ton).
Services: P & D (cans 600m), BY, ME, El, Ⓔ, Sh, CH, SM.
Société des Régates de Courseulles ☎ 02.31.37.47.42, Bar.
Île Plaisance Basin FW, AC, no Ⓥ; local shoal draft boats.
Town V, Gaz, R, Bar, ⊠, ◎, Ⓑ, ⇌ (via bus to Caen), ✈ (Caen-Carpiquet). Taxi ☎ 02.31.37.46.00. Ferry: See Ouistreham.

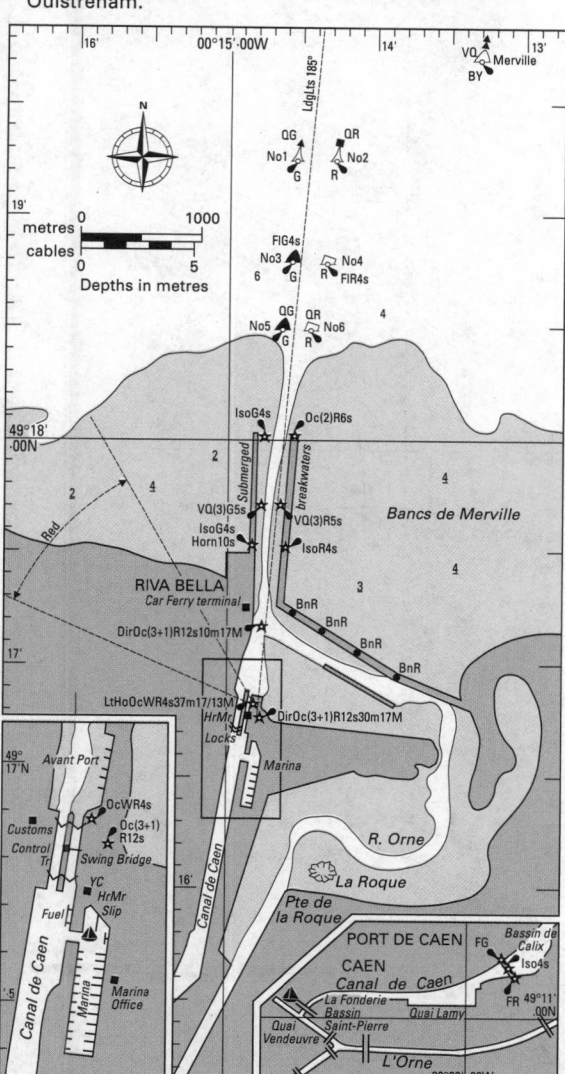

OUISTREHAM   8-19-15
Calvados 49°16'·88N 00°14'·81W (E lock)   Rtg 3-1-2

CHARTS
AC 1349, 2136, *2613*; SHOM 7055, 6927, 6928; ECM 526; Imray C32; Stanfords 1
TIDES
−0118 Dover; ML 4·6; Duration 0525; Zone −0100

Standard Port LE HAVRE (⟶)

Times				Height (metres)			
High Water		Low Water		MHWS	MHWN	MLWN	MLWS
0000	0500	0000	0700	7·9	6·6	2·8	1·2
1200	1700	1200	1900				
Differences OUISTREHAM							
−0045	−0010	−0005	0000	−0·3	−0·3	−0·2	−0·3

Note: There is a double HW at Ouistreham (also at Dives and Trouville). The HW differences, when referred to the start of the stand at Le Havre, give the time of the first HW.

SHELTER
Very good in marina (depth 3·5m and access HW±3), 1ca S of locks on E side. Waiting pontoon on E of Avant Port.
NAVIGATION
WPT ECM buoy, VQ (3) 5s, 49° 20'·48N 00° 14'·73W, 352°/172° from/to No 1 & 2 buoys, 1·26M. Ent chan is marked by training walls, with bns. Yachts normally enter canal by smaller E lock. Beware turbulence in locks. Lock opens for arrivals at HW−2½*, −1½, +2¼ and +3¼*; and for departures at HW−3, −2, +1¾ and +2¾*. * denotes extra openings (0700–2000LT) mid Jun-mid Sep; also at w/ends and public hols only, from 1 Apr-mid Jun and mid Sep-31 Oct. Detailed timings, which may vary, posted at SRCO.
LIGHTS AND MARKS
From WPT, pick up ldg lts 185°, both Dir Oc (3+1) R 12s 10/30m 17M, synch, intens 183·5°–186·5°. Chan has lt bys. Main lt ho, W + R top, conspic, Oc WR 4s 37m 17/13M. IPTS (full code) shown from control tr. Yachts may only enter when Ⓦ shows to port or stbd of lowest main tfc lt, indicating E or W lock. Waiting pontoon is no longer lit.
RADIO TELEPHONE
Call *Ouistreham Port* VHF Ch 68 16; Lock Ch 12 68 (HW −2 to HW +3). Sté des Régates Ch 09 (office hours).
TELEPHONE
Hr Mr/Lock 02.31.97.14.43; Marina 02.31.97.13.05; Aff Mar 02.31.97.18.65; ⌗ 02.31.86.61.50; CROSS 02.33.52.72.13; SNSM 02.31.97.14.43; Ferry terminal 02.31.96.80.80; Météo 02.31.26.68.11; Auto 08.36.68.08.14; Police 02.31.97.13.15; Dr 02.31.97.18.45; Brit Consul 02.35.42.27.47; Taxi 02.31.97.35.67.
FACILITIES
Marina (600 + 65 Ⓥ) ☎ 02.31.97.13.05, FF130, Slip, FW, ME, El, Sh, CH, AC, BH (8 ton), Gas, Gaz, Kos, SM, Bar, P, D, (Fuel pumps open ½hr before outbound lock opening);
Société des Régates de Caen-Ouistreham (SRCO) ☎ 02.31.97.13.05, FW, ME, El, Sh, CH, V, Bar;
Services: BY, Sh, El, Ⓔ, ME, CH, SM, SHOM.
Town V, Gaz, R, Bar, ⊠, Ⓑ, ⇌ (bus to Caen), ✈ (Caen). Ferry: to Portsmouth. (May-Sept, also to Poole).

CAEN 49°11'·03N 00°21'·13W. Charts: AC *1349*, SHOM 7055.

Passage and Facilities:
The 8M canal passage is simple and takes approx 1¾hrs. Bridges will open free for yachts which transit at the posted times; at other times fees (at least FF81) are due. Daily transit times are posted at the SRCO YC: S-bound is usually pm and N-bound am. It is important to be *at the first bridge* (Pegasus) at/before the posted transit time; allow ½hr from Ouistreham to Pegasus bridge. Depths 2·5m to 10m; max speed 7kn; transit only permitted by day; no overtaking. Outbound vessels have right of way. Keep listening watch on Ch 68. There are 3 moving bridges, at: Bénouville (Pegasus) (2½M from locks), Colombelles (5M) and La Fonderie (8M). Tfc lts no longer used. Calix (6½M) is now a fixed 33m high viaduct. Turn stbd after La Fonderie bridge for marina at Bassin St Pierre in city centre. VHF *Caen Port* Ch 12 68. Hr Mr ☎ 02.31.52.12.88; Aff Mar ☎ 02.31.85.40.55; ⌗ ☎ 02.31.86.61.50; **Marina** (64 visitors) ☎ 02.31.95.24.47, FF80, P & D (cans), ME, Sh, El, AB, FW; **Services:** ME, El, Sh, SM, CH. **City** Ⓑ, Bar, Ⓗ, ⊠, R, V, ⇌, ✈ (Carpiquet).

19

DIVES-SUR-MER   8-19-16

Calvados 49°17'·86N 00°05'·13W   Rtg 3-2-2

CHARTS
AC 2146; SHOM 6928; ECM 526; Imray C32; Stanfords 1
TIDES
–0135 Dover; ML 5·1m; Duration; Zone –0100

Standard Port LE HAVRE (⟶)

Times				Height (metres)			
High Water		Low Water		MHWS	MHWN	MLWN	MLWS
0000	0500	0000	0700	7·9	6·6	2·8	1·2
1200	1700	1200	1900				
Differences DIVES-SUR-MER							
–0100	–0010	0000	0000	+0·3	+0·2	+0·2	+0·1

Note: There is a double HW at Dives (also at Ouistreham and Trouville). The HW differences, when referred to the start of the stand at Le Havre, give the time of the first HW.

SHELTER
Good, but appr dries to 1M offshore and can be difficult in NW/NE > F5. Marina ent 400m W of Dir lt, off shallow R La Dives. Access HW±3 (HW±2½ for draft >1·5m) via single gate. Sill below gate is 2·5m above CD; gate opens when tide 4·5m above CD. Or follow river chan to berth on YC pontoon (2 ⓥ) below footbridge (max draft 1·5m).
NAVIGATION
WPT 49°18'·78N 00°05'·67W, Landfall buoy "DI", L Fl 10s, 339°/159° from/to No 1 and 2 Bys, 4ca. (Note: buoy "DI" is off chartlet). Two waiting Bys (untenable in WNW F4) are reported close to WPT in 3m. Beware sandbanks (drying 4·2m) each side of buoyed chan; keep well clear of two large SHM bns on W side. After last chan buoys, hug the shore to G (R horiz band) Division buoy and 4 G perches marking submerged training wall leading to marina ent.
LIGHTS AND MARKS
By day ent is seen at W end of densely wooded hills behind Houlgate.
Dir lt 159° Oc (2+1) WRG 12s 7m 12/9M, R hut opposite Pte de Cabourg, vis G125°-157°, W157°-162°, R162°-194°. W sector covers chan only up to Nos 3/4 marks; thence follow the chan buoys/bns. 4 PHM and 2 SHM buoys, all unlit, are moved to suit shifting chan; Nos 3 and 5 SHMs are bns, lit QG 12m 4M and Fl G 4s 13m 4M respectively. Close E of marina ent a Division buoy, IQG (2+1), indicates preferred chan to port and marks shoals to N. Caution: Buoys/bns may not be numbered; positions are approximate due to the lack of large-scale charts.
RADIO TELEPHONE
VHF Ch 09, H24.
TELEPHONE
Hr Mr 02.31.24.48.00; CROSS 02.35.52.72.13; Météo = via Hr Mr; Auto 08.36.68.08.14; Police 02.31.24.85.00; Dr 02.31.91.05.44.

FACILITIES
Marina (Port Guillaume) (545+55 ⓥ) ☎ 02.31.24.48.00, ⚓ 02.31.24.73.02, AC, FW, P, D, ▣, Slip, BH (30 ton), C (1·5 ton); **Cabourg YC** ☎ 02.31.91.23.55, Bar; **Services:** BY, ME, EI, CH, Sh.
Town V, R, Bar, Ⓑ, ✉, ✈ (Deauville). Ferry: Ouistreham.

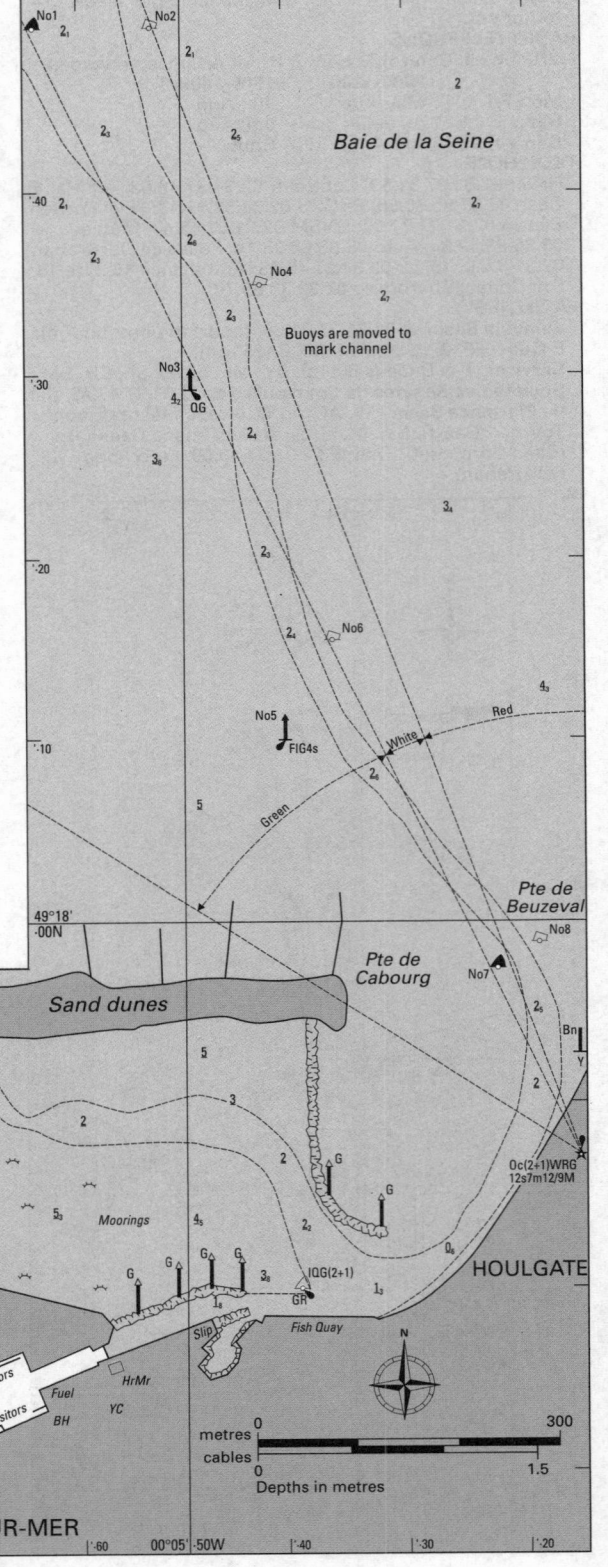

DEAUVILLE/TROUVILLE   8-19-17

Calvados 49°22'·44N 00°04'·23E   Rtg 3-1-1

CHARTS

AC *1349*, 2146, *2613*; SHOM 6928, 6736; ECM 526, 1012;
Imray C32; Stanfords 1

TIDES

−0130 Dover; ML 5·1; Duration 0510; Zone −0100

Standard Port LE HAVRE (⟶)

Times				Height (metres)			
High Water		Low Water		MHWS	MHWN	MLWN	MLWS
0000	0500	0000	0700	7·9	6·6	2·8	1·2
1200	1700	1200	1900				
Differences TROUVILLE							
−0100	−0010	0000	+0005	+0·4	+0·3	+0·3	+0·1

Note: There is a double HW at Trouville (also at Ouistreham and Dives). The HW differences, when referred to the start of the stand at Le Havre, give the time of the first HW.

SHELTER

Good in marina and Yacht Hbr, but ent to chan difficult in NW/N winds > force 6. Chan and river dry 2·4m; no access LW±2½, for 2m draft. Marina lock opens H24, if enough water outside. Yacht Hbr gate open HW −2 to HW +2½.

NAVIGATION

WPT 49°23'·00N 00°03'·70E, 328°/148° from/to W bkwtr lt Fl WG 4s, 0·65M. Semoy ECM, VQ (3) 5s, marks wreck 2·2M from ent, on ldg line. Do not appr from E of N due to Les Ratelets and Banc de Trouville. Trouville SW buoy, WCM, VQ (9) 10s, is 1M WNW of ent.

LIGHTS AND MARKS

Casino is conspic on Trouville side. Ldg lts 148°, both Oc R 4s synch. Yacht Hbr ent sigs (vert): 3 Ⓡ = closed; 3 Ⓖ = passage one way; 2 Ⓖ over Ⓦ = passage both ways.

RADIO TELEPHONE

Marina and Yacht Hbr VHF Ch 09.

TELEPHONE

Hr Mr Marina 02.31.98.30.01; Marina lock 02.31.88.95.66; Hr Mr Yacht Hbr 02.31.98.50.40; Yacht Hbr lock 02.31.88.36.21; Aff Mar 02.31.88.36.21; ⊞ 02.31.88.35.29; SNSM 02.31.88.31.70; CROSS 02.33.52.72.13; Auto (local) 08.36.68.08.14; Auto (regional) 08.36.68.08.76; Police 02.31.88.13.07; Dr 02.31.88.23.57; Ⓗ 02.31.14.33.33; Brit Consul 02.35.42.27.47.

FACILITIES

Port Deauville (Marina) (800 + 100 Ⓥ) ☎ 02.31.98.30.01, ⚓ 02.31.81.98.92, FF111, D, AC, FW, ME, EI, Sh, C (6 ton), BH (45 ton), Slip, CH, SM, R, Bar; **Deauville Marina Club**.
Yacht Hbr (320+80 Ⓥ) ☎ 02.31.98.50.40, FF97, FW, AC, Slip, D (pump S end of Bassin Morny), P (cans, 20m);
Deauville YC ☎ 02.31.88.38.19, FW, C (8 ton), CH, Bar; **Services:** CH, ME, EI, Sh.
Both towns P (cans), V, Gaz, R, Bar, ✉, Ⓑ, BY, CH, Slip, Sh, ME, EI, Ⓔ, ⇌, ✈ Deauville. Ferry: See Le Havre and Ouistreham.

19

HONFLEUR   8-19-18

Calvados   49° 25'·75N 00° 13'·93E   Rtg 1-2-1

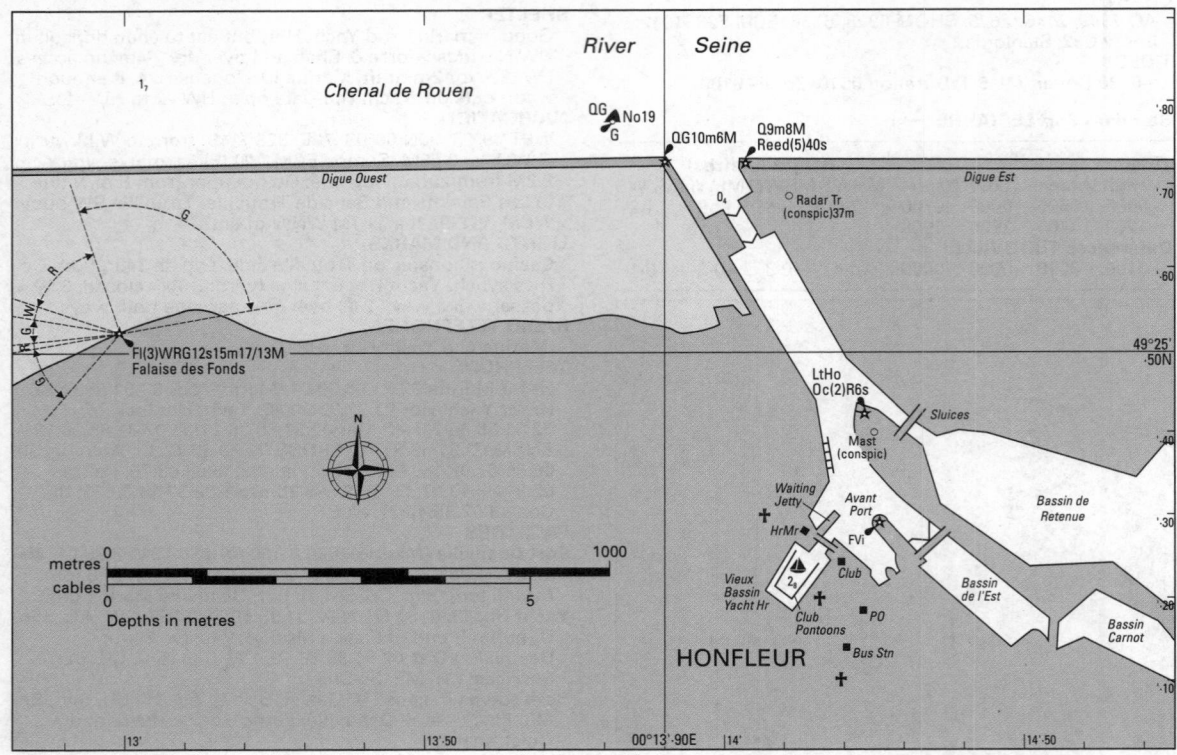

CHARTS
AC 2994, 2146, *2613*; SHOM 6796, 6683; ECM 1012; Imray
C31; Stanfords 1
TIDES
−0135 Dover; ML 5·0; Duration 0540; Zone −0100

Standard Port LE HAVRE (→)

Times				Height (metres)			
High Water		Low Water		MHWS	MHWN	MLWN	MLW
0000	0500	0000	0700	7·9	6·6	2·8	1·2
1200	1700	1200	1900				
Differences HONFLEUR							
−0135	−0135	+0015	+0040	+0·1	+0·1	+0·1	+0·3
ANTIFER							
+0025	+0015	+0005	−0007	+0·1	0·0		0·0

In the Seine there is a HW stand of about 2hrs 50 mins. The
HW time differences refer to the beginning of the stand.

SHELTER
Excellent in the Vieux Bassin where visitors raft up on a
pontoon on NW side. Or ask YC for possible vacant berth
on YC finger pontoons. Yachts can wait on E side of the
jetty immediately outside the Vieux Bassin. There are
also berths for 24 hrs max on the W side of Avant Port,
close N of the waiting jetty. Yachts may not berth
anywhere else in the Avant Port. Larger yachts can enter
Bassin de l'Est; see Hr Mr.
NAVIGATION
WPT Ratier NW SHM buoy, VQG, 49°26'·63N, 00°03'·41E,
at ent to well buoyed Chenal de Rouen. Appr at HW ±3,
keeping between the Digue Nord, marked by posts, and
the PHM chan buoys to avoid shipping. Ent between No
19 SHM buoy and very conspic radar tr. Beware strong
currents across ent.
The **outer lock** (fitted with recessed bollards and ladders,
but no pontoons) operates H24, but NOT LW±2 due to
silting. It opens at H, every hour for arrivals; and every
H+30 for departures. IPTS are in force.

At the Vieux Bassin the old lock gate is permanently open.
The **road bridge** lifts as shown below (LT).
Yachts leaving have priority over arrivals.
Mid season (1 Mar-31 May; 16 Sept-31 Oct)
Weekdays: 0730, 1030, 1530, 1830.
Sat/Sun/Hols: 0730, 0830, 0930, 1030, 1730, 1830, 1930, 2030.
High Season (1 Jun-15 Sept)
Every day: same as Sat/Sun/National holidays in mid-season.
Low season (1 Nov-28 Feb)
Weekdays: as mid season.
Sat/Sun/Hols: 0730, 0830, 0930, 1030, 1530, 1630, 1730, 1830.
LIGHTS AND MARKS
Falaise des Fonds lt, 0·75M W of ent Fl (3) WRG 12s 15m,
17/13M, W □ tr, vis G040°-080°, R080°-084°, G0084°-100°,
W100°-109°, R109°-162°, G162°-260°. E mole Q 9m 9M, Y
metal framework tr with B top, Reed (5) 40s. W mole QG
10m 6M, G framework tr.
IPTS are in force at the lock.
Note: The Pont de Normandie, 1·7M E of Honfleur ent,
has 52m clearance and a pile lt, Fl Y 2·5s 3m, on N side of
chan.
RADIO TELEPHONE
Hr Mr VHF Ch 09 16; Lock 09 16 (H24); Radar tower Ch **73**
16 (H24).
TELEPHONE
Hr Mr 02.31.14.61.09, ☎ 02.31.89.42.10; Lock 02.31.98.72.82;
CROSS 02.33.52.72.13; Aff Mar 02.31.89.20.67;
⚓ 02.31.89.12.13; SNSM 02.31.89.16.49; Auto (regional)
08.36.68.08.76; Auto (offshore) 08.36.68.08.08; Police
02.31.89.11.26; Dr 02.31.89.34.05; Ⓗ 02.31.89.04.74; Cercle
Nautique ☎/☎ 02.31.98.87.13; Brit Consul 02.35.42.27.47.
FACILITIES
Vieux Bassin Yacht Hbr (120 + 30 Ⓥ, max LOA 20m), FF95
AB, FW, AC; **Cercle Nautique d'Honfleur** ☎ & ☎
02.31.89.87.13, M; **Services:** BY, Sh, Ⓔ, C (10 ton), Slip.
Town P & D (cans), V, R, Bar, ▢, Gaz, ✉, Ⓑ, ⭢, ✈
Deauville. Ferry: Le Havre.

TIME ZONE –0100
(French Standard Time)
Subtract 1 hour for UT
For French Summer Time add ONE hour in non-shaded areas

FRANCE – LE HAVRE

LAT 49°29′N   LONG 0°07′E

TIMES AND HEIGHTS OF HIGH AND LOW WATERS

YEAR **1999**

JANUARY

Time	m	Time	m
1 0433 1.4 / 0951 7.9 / F 1705 1.2 / 2220 7.9		**16** 0438 2.1 / 0954 7.4 / SA 1701 1.8 / 2219 7.3	
2 0528 1.3 / 1040 8.0 / SA 1758 1.0 / O 2309 8.0		**17** 0519 1.9 / 1032 7.6 / SU 1742 1.6 / ● 2257 7.5	
3 0618 1.2 / 1126 8.1 / SU 1846 0.9 / 2356 8.0		**18** 0559 1.7 / 1110 7.7 / M 1822 1.4 / 2335 7.6	
4 0703 1.2 / 1210 8.0 / M 1929 1.0		**19** 0639 1.5 / 1148 7.8 / TU 1901 1.2	
5 0040 7.9 / 0744 1.4 / TU 1252 7.9 / 2008 1.2		**20** 0013 7.7 / 0719 1.4 / W 1227 7.8 / 1941 1.2	
6 0122 7.7 / 0822 1.6 / W 1332 7.6 / 2044 1.5		**21** 0054 7.7 / 0759 1.5 / TH 1308 7.8 / 2020 1.3	
7 0203 7.4 / 0857 2.0 / TH 1412 7.4 / 2119 1.9		**22** 0135 7.6 / 0838 1.6 / F 1351 7.6 / 2058 1.5	
8 0243 7.2 / 0933 2.4 / F 1454 7.0 / 2154 2.3		**23** 0218 7.5 / 0918 1.8 / SA 1436 7.5 / 2138 1.7	
9 0327 6.9 / 1012 2.7 / SA 1540 6.7 / 2235 2.7		**24** 0305 7.3 / 1002 2.1 / SU 1525 7.2 / 2224 2.0	
10 0419 6.6 / 1059 3.0 / SU 1639 6.4 / 2326 3.0		**25** 0359 7.1 / 1054 2.3 / M 1628 7.0 / 2321 2.3	
11 0523 6.5 / 1158 3.2 / M 1750 6.3		**26** 0510 6.9 / 1200 2.5 / TU 1747 6.9	
12 0031 3.1 / 0633 6.5 / TU 1312 3.2 / 1905 6.3		**27** 0035 2.5 / 0628 6.9 / W 1323 2.5 / 1906 6.9	
13 0148 3.1 / 0738 6.6 / W 1428 2.9 / 2008 6.6		**28** 0200 2.4 / 0741 7.1 / TH 1444 2.2 / 2019 7.2	
14 0257 2.8 / 0831 6.9 / TH 1528 2.5 / 2058 6.8		**29** 0314 2.1 / 0846 7.4 / F 1552 1.8 / 2120 7.5	
15 0351 2.4 / 0915 7.1 / F 1618 2.2 / 2140 7.1		**30** 0419 1.8 / 0941 7.6 / SA 1654 1.4 / 2212 7.7	
		31 0518 1.5 / 1029 7.8 / SU 1749 1.2 / O 2258 7.8	

FEBRUARY

Time	m	Time	m
1 0608 1.3 / 1113 7.9 / M 1834 1.0 / 2341 7.9		**16** 0545 1.5 / 1052 7.8 / TU 1808 1.1 / ● 2318 7.7	
2 0650 1.2 / 1153 8.0 / TU 1913 1.0		**17** 0627 1.2 / 1132 7.9 / W 1850 0.9 / 2357 7.9	
3 0020 7.9 / 0726 1.3 / W 1231 7.9 / 1947 1.1		**18** 0708 1.0 / 1213 8.0 / TH 1930 0.8	
4 0057 7.8 / 0759 1.4 / TH 1307 7.8 / 2019 1.3		**19** 0038 7.9 / 0748 1.0 / F 1254 8.0 / 2008 0.8	
5 0133 7.6 / 0829 1.7 / F 1342 7.5 / 2047 1.7		**20** 0119 7.9 / 0826 1.1 / SA 1336 7.9 / 2045 1.0	
6 0207 7.3 / 0858 2.0 / SA 1416 7.3 / 2115 2.1		**21** 0200 7.7 / 0904 1.3 / SU 1419 7.7 / 2122 1.4	
7 0240 7.1 / 0926 2.4 / SU 1450 6.9 / 2144 2.5		**22** 0243 7.5 / 0944 1.7 / M 1506 7.4 / 2203 1.9	
8 0316 6.8 / 1001 2.8 / M 1530 6.6 / 2223 2.9		**23** 0332 7.2 / 1031 2.1 / TU 1604 7.0 / 2256 2.3	
9 0404 6.5 / 1049 3.1 / TU 1630 6.3 / 2318 3.2		**24** 0440 6.9 / 1132 2.5 / W 1725 6.7	
10 0517 6.3 / 1155 3.3 / W 1801 6.1		**25** 0008 2.7 / 0605 6.7 / TH 1258 2.6 / 1854 6.7	
11 0034 3.4 / 0646 6.3 / TH 1322 3.2 / 1927 6.2		**26** 0140 2.6 / 0729 6.9 / F 1428 2.4 / 2013 7.0	
12 0206 3.2 / 0755 6.5 / F 1445 2.8 / 2029 6.6		**27** 0303 2.4 / 0838 7.1 / SA 1544 2.0 / 2113 7.3	
13 0317 2.7 / 0848 6.9 / SA 1546 2.3 / 2117 7.0		**28** 0415 1.9 / 0931 7.4 / SU 1649 1.5 / 2201 7.5	
14 0412 2.2 / 0932 7.2 / SU 1638 1.9 / 2159 7.3			
15 0500 1.8 / 1013 7.5 / M 1724 1.5 / 2238 7.5			

MARCH

Time	m	Time	m
1 0512 1.6 / 1015 7.6 / M 1739 1.2 / 2242 7.7		**16** 0435 1.7 / 0949 7.5 / TU 1700 1.4 / 2215 7.6	
2 0556 1.3 / 1055 7.8 / TU 1818 1.1 / O 2320 7.8		**17** 0524 1.3 / 1031 7.8 / W 1748 1.0 / ● 2256 7.9	
3 0632 1.2 / 1132 7.9 / W 1851 1.0 / 2355 7.8		**18** 0609 0.9 / 1112 8.0 / TH 1831 0.7 / 2337 8.0	
4 0703 1.2 / 1206 7.9 / TH 1921 1.1		**19** 0652 0.7 / 1154 8.2 / F 1912 0.5	
5 0029 7.8 / 0733 1.3 / F 1240 7.8 / 1950 1.2		**20** 0018 8.1 / 0732 0.6 / SA 1237 8.2 / 1952 0.6	
6 0101 7.6 / 0800 1.5 / SA 1312 7.6 / 2016 1.5		**21** 0100 8.1 / 0811 0.7 / SU 1320 8.1 / 2029 0.8	
7 0132 7.4 / 0825 1.8 / SU 1342 7.4 / 2039 1.9		**22** 0141 7.9 / 0849 1.1 / M 1403 7.8 / 2106 1.3	
8 0201 7.2 / 0850 2.1 / M 1411 7.1 / 2104 2.3		**23** 0224 7.5 / 0928 1.5 / TU 1451 7.4 / 2146 1.8	
9 0230 6.9 / 0918 2.5 / TU 1445 6.7 / 2136 2.7		**24** 0312 7.2 / 1013 2.0 / W 1549 7.0 / 2237 2.4	
10 0308 6.6 / 0959 2.9 / W 1533 6.3 / 2224 3.1		**25** 0418 6.8 / 1114 2.5 / TH 1711 6.6 / 2350 2.8	
11 0405 6.3 / 1057 3.2 / TH 1648 6.1 / 2334 3.4		**26** 0547 6.6 / 1241 2.7 / F 1843 6.6	
12 0537 6.1 / 1221 3.3 / F 1841 6.1		**27** 0126 2.8 / 0715 6.7 / SA 1414 2.5 / 2001 6.8	
13 0112 3.4 / 0714 6.3 / SA 1357 3.0 / 1955 6.4		**28** 0253 2.5 / 0824 6.9 / SU 1534 2.0 / 2058 7.1	
14 0239 2.9 / 0816 6.7 / SU 1510 2.4 / 2049 6.9		**29** 0405 2.0 / 0914 7.2 / M 1634 1.6 / 2142 7.4	
15 0341 2.3 / 0905 7.1 / M 1608 1.9 / 2133 7.3		**30** 0456 1.7 / 0956 7.5 / TU 1718 1.4 / 2221 7.6	
		31 0534 1.4 / 1033 7.6 / W 1753 1.2 / O 2255 7.7	

APRIL

Time	m	Time	m
1 0607 1.3 / 1107 7.7 / TH 1823 1.2 / 2327 7.7		**16** 0545 0.8 / 1049 8.0 / F 1807 0.6 / ● 2313 8.1	
2 0636 1.3 / 1140 7.7 / F 1853 1.2 / 2359 7.7		**17** 0630 0.6 / 1133 8.2 / SA 1851 0.5 / 2356 8.2	
3 0705 1.3 / 1212 7.7 / SA 1920 1.3		**18** 0714 0.5 / 1218 8.2 / SU 1933 0.6	
4 0030 7.6 / 0732 1.4 / SU 1244 7.5 / 1945 1.5		**19** 0040 8.1 / 0755 0.6 / M 1304 8.1 / 2012 0.9	
5 0100 7.5 / 0757 1.6 / M 1314 7.3 / 2010 1.8		**20** 0123 7.9 / 0835 0.9 / TU 1350 7.8 / 2052 1.3	
6 0128 7.3 / 0821 1.9 / TU 1343 7.1 / 2034 2.2		**21** 0207 7.6 / 0916 1.4 / W 1439 7.4 / 2133 1.9	
7 0157 7.0 / 0849 2.3 / W 1417 6.8 / 2105 2.6		**22** 0257 7.2 / 1002 1.9 / TH 1538 6.9 / 2225 2.4	
8 0235 6.7 / 0925 2.6 / TH 1503 6.4 / 2147 3.0		**23** 0401 6.8 / 1102 2.4 / F 1656 6.6 / 2338 2.8	
9 0327 6.4 / 1017 3.0 / F 1607 6.2 / 2250 3.3		**24** 0524 6.5 / 1223 2.6 / SA 1821 6.6	
10 0441 6.1 / 1134 3.2 / SA 1747 6.1		**25** 0104 2.8 / 0648 6.6 / SU 1345 2.5 / 1936 6.8	
11 0026 3.3 / 0625 6.2 / SU 1311 2.9 / 1914 6.4		**26** 0223 2.5 / 0757 6.8 / M 1458 2.2 / 2032 7.0	
12 0157 2.9 / 0737 6.6 / M 1428 2.4 / 2013 6.9		**27** 0331 2.2 / 0849 7.0 / TU 1558 1.9 / 2116 7.3	
13 0304 2.3 / 0832 7.0 / TU 1531 1.8 / 2102 7.3		**28** 0422 1.9 / 0931 7.3 / W 1642 1.7 / 2153 7.5	
14 0402 1.7 / 0919 7.5 / W 1628 1.3 / 2146 7.7		**29** 0501 1.6 / 1007 7.4 / TH 1718 1.5 / 2226 7.6	
15 0455 1.2 / 1004 7.8 / TH 1720 0.9 / 2230 7.9		**30** 0535 1.5 / 1041 7.5 / F 1751 1.4 / O 2258 7.6	

19

Chart Datum: 4·38 metres below Lallemand System (Mean Sea Level, Marseilles)

TIME ZONE –0100
(French Standard Time)
Subtract 1 hour for UT

For French Summer Time add
ONE hour in non-shaded areas

FRANCE – LE HAVRE

LAT 49°29'N   LONG 0°07'E

TIMES AND HEIGHTS OF HIGH AND LOW WATERS

YEAR 1999

MAY

Day	Time	m	Day	Time	m
1 SA	0607 / 1113 / 1822 / 2329	1.4 / 7.5 / 1.4 / 7.6	16 SU	0608 / 1114 / 1829 / 2335	0.7 / 8.1 / 0.7 / 8.1
2 SU	0637 / 1146 / 1851	1.4 / 7.5 / 1.5	17 M	0655 / 1202 / 1914	0.6 / 8.1 / 0.7
3 M	0001 / 0705 / 1219 / 1918	7.6 / 1.5 / 7.4 / 1.6	18 TU	0021 / 0740 / 1249 / 1957	8.1 / 0.7 / 8.0 / 1.0
4 TU	0032 / 0732 / 1251 / 1945	7.5 / 1.6 / 7.3 / 1.9	19 W	0107 / 0823 / 1338 / 2040	7.9 / 0.9 / 7.7 / 1.4
5 W	0102 / 0800 / 1323 / 2013	7.3 / 1.8 / 7.1 / 2.1	20 TH	0153 / 0906 / 1428 / 2124	7.6 / 1.3 / 7.4 / 1.9
6 TH	0135 / 0830 / 1400 / 2045	7.1 / 2.1 / 6.9 / 2.5	21 F	0243 / 0953 / 1525 / 2216	7.2 / 1.8 / 7.0 / 2.3
7 F	0215 / 0905 / 1445 / 2126	6.8 / 2.4 / 6.6 / 2.8	22 SA	0342 / 1048 / 1631 / 2318	6.9 / 2.2 / 6.7 / 2.7
8 SA	0304 / 0952 / 1542 / 2223	6.6 / 2.7 / 6.4 / 3.1	23 SU	0452 / 1154 / 1743	6.6 / 2.5 / 6.6
9 SU	0408 / 1100 / 1701 / 2347	6.4 / 2.9 / 6.3 / 3.1	24 M	0028 / 0606 / 1301 / 1854	2.7 / 6.5 / 2.5 / 6.7
10 M	0533 / 1227 / 1828	6.4 / 2.7 / 6.5	25 TU	0135 / 0718 / 1405 / 1955	2.6 / 6.6 / 2.4 / 6.9
11 TU	0113 / 0653 / 1345 / 1932	2.8 / 6.6 / 2.3 / 6.9	26 W	0237 / 0815 / 1504 / 2042	2.4 / 6.8 / 2.2 / 7.1
12 W	0223 / 0753 / 1451 / 2026	2.3 / 7.0 / 1.8 / 7.3	27 TH	0333 / 0901 / 1555 / 2122	2.1 / 7.0 / 2.0 / 7.3
13 TH	0326 / 0847 / 1552 / 2115	1.7 / 7.4 / 1.4 / 7.7	28 F	0420 / 0940 / 1638 / 2156	1.9 / 7.2 / 1.8 / 7.4
14 F	0424 / 0937 / 1649 / 2203	1.3 / 7.7 / 1.0 / 7.9	29 SA	0501 / 1015 / 1717 / 2230	1.7 / 7.3 / 1.7 / 7.5
15 SA ●	0518 / 1025 / 1741 / 2249	0.9 / 8.0 / 0.8 / 8.1	30 SU ○	0537 / 1049 / 1752 / 2303	1.6 / 7.4 / 1.7 / 7.5
			31 M	0611 / 1123 / 1824 / 2336	1.6 / 7.4 / 1.7 / 7.5

JUNE

Day	Time	m	Day	Time	m
1 TU	0641 / 1158 / 1855	1.6 / 7.3 / 1.8	16 W	0006 / 0726 / 1237 / 1945	8.0 / 0.7 / 7.9 / 1.1
2 W	0009 / 0712 / 1232 / 1926	7.5 / 1.6 / 7.3 / 1.9	17 TH	0053 / 0811 / 1325 / 2029	7.9 / 0.9 / 7.8 / 1.4
3 TH	0043 / 0855 / 1308 / 1959	7.4 / 1.7 / 7.2 / 2.0	18 F	0139 / 0855 / 1413 / 2112	7.6 / 1.2 / 7.5 / 1.8
4 F	0120 / 0818 / 1347 / 2034	7.2 / 1.9 / 7.0 / 2.3	19 SA	0226 / 0938 / 1502 / 2157	7.3 / 1.6 / 7.2 / 2.1
5 SA	0201 / 0855 / 1431 / 2115	7.0 / 2.1 / 6.9 / 2.5	20 SU	0315 / 1023 / 1555 / 2246	7.0 / 2.0 / 6.9 / 2.5
6 SU	0248 / 0939 / 1522 / 2207	6.8 / 2.3 / 6.7 / 2.7	21 M	0411 / 1113 / 1653 / 2341	6.7 / 2.4 / 6.7 / 2.7
7 M	0343 / 1037 / 1625 / 2315	6.7 / 2.5 / 6.6 / 2.8	22 TU	0514 / 1209 / 1757	6.5 / 2.6 / 6.6
8 TU	0451 / 1148 / 1741	6.6 / 2.5 / 6.7	23 W	0042 / 0623 / 1311 / 1903	2.6 / 6.5 / 2.7 / 6.7
9 W	0031 / 0609 / 1303 / 1851	2.6 / 6.7 / 2.3 / 6.9	24 TH	0145 / 0731 / 1412 / 2001	2.7 / 6.6 / 2.6 / 6.9
10 TH	0143 / 0716 / 1413 / 1951	2.3 / 7.0 / 1.9 / 7.3	25 F	0245 / 0827 / 1510 / 2048	2.5 / 6.8 / 2.4 / 7.0
11 F	0251 / 0816 / 1519 / 2046	1.8 / 7.3 / 1.6 / 7.6	26 SA	0340 / 0912 / 1601 / 2128	2.2 / 6.9 / 2.2 / 7.2
12 SA	0354 / 0912 / 1620 / 2138	1.4 / 7.6 / 1.3 / 7.8	27 SU	0427 / 0951 / 1646 / 2205	2.0 / 7.1 / 2.0 / 7.3
13 SU ●	0452 / 1006 / 1717 / 2229	1.1 / 7.8 / 1.1 / 8.0	28 M	0509 / 1028 / 1726 / 2240	1.8 / 7.2 / 1.9 / 7.4
14 M	0547 / 1058 / 1809 / 2318	0.8 / 8.0 / 0.9 / 8.1	29 TU	0547 / 1104 / 1802 / 2316	1.7 / 7.3 / 1.8 / 7.5
15 TU	0638 / 1148 / 1858	0.7 / 8.0 / 0.8	30 W	0622 / 1140 / 1837 / 2351	1.6 / 7.4 / 1.8 / 7.5

JULY

Day	Time	m	Day	Time	m
1 TH	0657 / 1216 / 1913	1.5 / 7.4 / 1.8	16 F	0037 / 0757 / 1307 / 2013	7.9 / 0.9 / 7.8 / 1.3
2 F	0027 / 0733 / 1253 / 1950	7.5 / 1.5 / 7.3 / 1.8	17 SA	0119 / 0837 / 1350 / 2051	7.7 / 1.1 / 7.6 / 1.6
3 SA	0106 / 0810 / 1333 / 2028	7.4 / 1.6 / 7.3 / 1.9	18 SU	0201 / 0913 / 1432 / 2127	7.5 / 1.5 / 7.3 / 2.0
4 SU	0147 / 0848 / 1416 / 2108	7.3 / 1.8 / 7.2 / 2.1	19 M	0243 / 0948 / 1514 / 2204	7.2 / 1.9 / 7.0 / 2.3
5 M	0231 / 0929 / 1502 / 2153	7.2 / 2.0 / 7.0 / 2.3	20 TU	0327 / 1026 / 1601 / 2247	6.9 / 2.4 / 6.8 / 2.7
6 TU	0320 / 1017 / 1554 / 2248	7.0 / 2.1 / 6.9 / 2.4	21 W	0419 / 1111 / 1657 / 2341	6.6 / 2.7 / 6.6 / 2.9
7 W	0418 / 1115 / 1659 / 2353	6.9 / 2.3 / 6.9 / 2.5	22 TH	0524 / 1209 / 1804	6.4 / 3.0 / 6.5
8 TH	0530 / 1224 / 1813	6.8 / 2.3 / 7.0	23 F	0048 / 0639 / 1320 / 1914	3.0 / 6.3 / 3.0 / 6.5
9 F	0107 / 0645 / 1340 / 1921	2.3 / 6.9 / 2.1 / 7.2	24 SA	0201 / 0750 / 1430 / 2014	2.9 / 6.5 / 2.8 / 6.7
10 SA	0222 / 0753 / 1452 / 2023	2.0 / 7.2 / 1.9 / 7.4	25 SU	0304 / 0845 / 1529 / 2102	2.6 / 6.7 / 2.5 / 7.0
11 SU	0329 / 0856 / 1556 / 2121	1.6 / 7.5 / 1.6 / 7.7	26 M	0357 / 0929 / 1619 / 2142	2.2 / 7.0 / 2.2 / 7.2
12 M	0431 / 0954 / 1657 / 2215	1.3 / 7.7 / 1.3 / 7.9	27 TU	0444 / 1008 / 1704 / 2220	1.9 / 7.2 / 2.0 / 7.4
13 TU ●	0530 / 1046 / 1754 / 2304	1.0 / 7.9 / 1.2 / 8.0	28 W	0527 / 1046 / 1744 / 2257	1.7 / 7.3 / 1.8 / 7.5
14 W	0625 / 1136 / 1845 / 2351	0.9 / 7.9 / 1.1 / 8.0	29 TH	0606 / 1122 / 1823 / 2334	1.5 / 7.5 / 1.7 / 7.6
15 TH	0713 / 1223 / 1932	0.8 / 7.9 / 1.2	30 F	0645 / 1159 / 1902	1.3 / 7.5 / 1.5
			31 SA	0012 / 0723 / 1238 / 1940	7.7 / 1.3 / 7.6 / 1.5

AUGUST

Day	Time	m	Day	Time	m
1 SU	0051 / 0801 / 1317 / 2019	7.7 / 1.3 / 7.5 / 1.6	16 M	0132 / 0841 / 1357 / 2052	7.6 / 1.5 / 7.5 / 1.8
2 M	0132 / 0838 / 1358 / 2057	7.6 / 1.4 / 7.5 / 1.7	17 TU	0208 / 0909 / 1433 / 2120	7.3 / 1.9 / 7.2 / 2.2
3 TU	0214 / 0916 / 1440 / 2137	7.4 / 1.6 / 7.3 / 1.9	18 W	0244 / 0937 / 1509 / 2152	7.0 / 2.3 / 6.9 / 2.6
4 W	0259 / 0957 / 1527 / 2224	7.2 / 1.9 / 7.1 / 2.2	19 TH	0324 / 1012 / 1554 / 2236	6.6 / 2.8 / 6.6 / 3.0
5 TH	0351 / 1047 / 1626 / 2322	7.0 / 2.2 / 7.0 / 2.4	20 F	0420 / 1102 / 1659 / 2340	6.3 / 3.2 / 6.3 / 3.3
6 F	0501 / 1152 / 1743	6.8 / 2.4 / 6.9	21 SA	0545 / 1217 / 1825	6.1 / 3.4 / 6.2
7 SA	0037 / 0624 / 1314 / 1901	2.5 / 6.8 / 2.4 / 7.0	22 SU	0108 / 0713 / 1349 / 1940	3.3 / 6.2 / 3.2 / 6.4
8 SU	0201 / 0741 / 1434 / 2011	2.3 / 7.0 / 2.2 / 7.3	23 M	0229 / 0817 / 1500 / 2035	2.9 / 6.5 / 2.8 / 6.8
9 M	0313 / 0849 / 1541 / 2112	1.9 / 7.3 / 1.9 / 7.6	24 TU	0328 / 0906 / 1554 / 2119	2.4 / 6.9 / 2.4 / 7.1
10 TU	0418 / 0947 / 1645 / 2205	1.5 / 7.6 / 1.6 / 7.8	25 W	0419 / 0946 / 1642 / 2159	2.0 / 7.2 / 2.0 / 7.4
11 W ●	0520 / 1036 / 1744 / 2252	1.2 / 7.8 / 1.3 / 7.9	26 TH	0505 / 1024 / 1726 / 2237	1.6 / 7.5 / 1.7 / 7.7
12 TH	0614 / 1122 / 1833 / 2335	1.0 / 7.9 / 1.2 / 8.0	27 F ○	0548 / 1101 / 1807 / 2314	1.3 / 7.6 / 1.4 / 7.8
13 F	0659 / 1204 / 1914	0.9 / 7.9 / 1.2	28 SA	0629 / 1139 / 1847 / 2353	1.1 / 7.8 / 1.3 / 7.9
14 SA	0016 / 0737 / 1244 / 1950	8.0 / 0.9 / 7.8 / 1.3	29 SU	0708 / 1218 / 1926	1.0 / 7.8 / 1.2
15 SU	0055 / 0811 / 1321 / 2022	7.9 / 1.2 / 7.7 / 1.5	30 M	0032 / 0746 / 1257 / 2004	7.9 / 1.2 / 7.8 / 1.2
			31 TU	0113 / 0822 / 1337 / 2041	7.9 / 1.1 / 7.7 / 1.4

Chart Datum: 4·38 metres below Lallemand System (Mean Sea Level, Marseilles)

TIME ZONE –0100
(French Standard Time)
Subtract 1 hour for UT

For French Summer Time add
ONE hour in non-shaded areas

FRANCE – LE HAVRE

LAT 49°29′N   LONG   0°07′E

TIMES AND HEIGHTS OF HIGH AND LOW WATERS

YEAR **1999**

SEPTEMBER

	Time	m		Time	m
1 W	0155 0858 1419 2119	7.7 1.4 7.5 1.7	**16** TH	0204 0855 1423 2108	7.1 2.3 7.0 2.6
2 TH	0239 0937 1504 2202	7.4 1.8 7.2 2.1	**17** F	0237 0924 1459 2146	6.7 2.8 6.6 3.0
3 F	0332 1024 1602 2258	7.1 2.3 7.0 2.5	**18** SA	0323 1008 1553 2241	6.3 3.2 6.3 3.3
4 SA	0444 1129 1724	6.8 2.7 6.8	**19** SU	0439 1117 1726	6.0 3.6 6.1
5 SU	0017 0615 1259 1850	2.7 6.7 2.7 6.8	**20** M	0009 0632 1301 1902	3.5 6.0 3.5 6.2
6 M	0150 0738 1425 2005	2.5 6.9 2.4 7.1	**21** TU	0148 0744 1427 2004	3.1 6.4 3.0 6.6
7 TU	0306 0845 1536 2105	2.0 7.3 2.0 7.5	**22** W	0256 0837 1526 2052	2.6 6.9 2.5 7.1
8 W	0414 0937 1642 2153	1.6 7.6 1.7 7.7	**23** TH	0350 0919 1616 2133	2.0 7.3 2.0 7.5
9 TH ●	0512 1022 1734 2235	1.2 7.8 1.4 7.9	**24** F	0438 0958 1702 2212	1.6 7.6 1.6 7.8
10 F	0559 1102 1815 2315	1.0 7.9 1.2 8.0	**25** SA ○	0524 1036 1745 2251	1.2 7.8 1.2 8.0
11 SA	0637 1140 1850 2351	1.0 7.9 1.2 8.0	**26** SU	0606 1115 1827 2331	1.0 8.0 1.0 8.1
12 SU	0709 1215 1921	1.1 7.9 1.3	**27** M	0647 1155 1907	0.8 8.0 0.9
13 M	0026 0739 1249 1950	7.9 1.2 7.9 1.5	**28** TU	0012 0726 1235 1946	8.1 0.8 8.0 1.0
14 TU	0100 0806 1322 2017	7.7 1.5 7.5 1.8	**29** W	0054 0804 1316 2025	8.0 1.0 7.9 1.2
15 W	0133 0831 1353 2041	7.4 1.9 7.3 2.2	**30** TH	0138 0841 1358 2103	7.8 1.4 7.6 1.6

OCTOBER

	Time	m		Time	m
1 F	0224 0920 1445 2146	7.5 1.9 7.3 2.1	**16** SA	0203 0851 1419 2110	6.8 2.8 6.7 2.9
2 SA	0319 1007 1545 2242	7.1 2.4 6.9 2.5	**17** SU	0247 0931 1509 2159	6.4 3.2 6.4 3.2
3 SU	0436 1030 1711	6.7 2.9 6.9	**18** M	0350 1030 1622 2314	6.1 3.6 6.1 3.4
4 M	0006 0609 1253 1841	2.8 6.7 2.9 6.7	**19** TU	0537 1207 1812	6.1 3.6 6.2
5 TU	0144 0731 1420 1955	2.5 6.9 2.6 7.0	**20** W	0057 0702 1343 1923	3.3 6.4 3.2 6.5
6 W	0259 0833 1530 2051	2.1 7.3 2.1 7.6	**21** TH	0214 0759 1448 2016	2.7 6.8 2.6 7.0
7 TH	0403 0921 1629 2136	1.7 7.6 1.7 7.6	**22** F	0313 0845 1541 2101	2.1 7.3 2.0 7.4
8 F	0454 1001 1714 2215	1.4 7.8 1.5 7.8	**23** SA	0405 0927 1631 2143	1.6 7.7 1.5 7.8
9 SA	0534 1038 1750 2251	1.2 7.9 1.4 7.9	**24** SU ○	0454 1007 1718 2226	1.2 7.9 1.2 8.0
10 SU	0607 1112 1821 2325	1.0 7.9 1.3 7.9	**25** M	0540 1049 1803 2308	0.9 8.1 0.9 7.9
11 M	0638 1144 1851 2358	1.3 7.9 1.4 7.8	**26** TU	0624 1131 1847 2352	0.8 8.2 0.8 8.2
12 TU	0707 1216 1920	1.4 7.7 1.5	**27** W	0706 1213 1929	0.8 8.1 0.9
13 W	0031 0734 1248 1946	7.6 1.7 7.6 1.8	**28** TH	0037 0746 1257 2010	8.1 1.0 8.0 1.1
14 TH	0102 0758 1317 2010	7.4 2.0 7.3 2.1	**29** F	0123 0826 1341 2051	7.9 1.4 7.7 1.5
15 F	0132 0823 1345 2037	7.1 2.4 7.1 2.5	**30** SA	0212 0908 1430 2135	7.5 2.0 7.3 2.0
			31 SU	0310 0958 1532 2233	7.1 2.5 7.0 2.5

NOVEMBER

	Time	m		Time	m
1 M	0426 1108 1654 2356	6.8 2.9 6.7 2.7	**16** TU	0319 0959 1542 2233	6.4 3.3 6.4 3.2
2 TU	0552 1240 1818	6.7 2.9 6.7	**17** W	0433 1117 1705 2359	6.3 3.4 6.3 3.1
3 W	0124 0709 1359 1932	2.5 6.9 2.6 6.9	**18** TH	0607 1247 1831	6.5 3.2 6.5
4 TH	0235 0810 1505 2028	2.2 7.2 2.2 7.2	**19** F	0121 0712 1400 1933	2.8 6.8 2.7 6.9
5 F	0334 0856 1600 2113	1.9 7.5 1.9 7.4	**20** SA	0228 0805 1502 2025	2.3 7.2 2.1 7.3
6 SA	0422 0936 1643 2152	1.7 7.6 1.7 7.6	**21** SU	0327 0852 1558 2113	1.8 7.6 1.6 7.7
7 SU	0501 1011 1719 2227	1.6 7.7 1.6 7.7	**22** M	0422 0938 1650 2200	1.4 7.9 1.2 7.9
8 M ●	0534 1044 1751 2300	1.5 7.8 1.5 7.7	**23** TU ○	0513 1023 1740 2247	1.1 8.1 1.0 8.1
9 TU	0606 1115 1823 2332	1.5 7.8 1.5 7.6	**24** W	0601 1108 1828 2335	0.9 8.2 0.8 8.2
10 W	0637 1147 1853	1.6 7.7 1.6	**25** TH	0647 1154 1914	0.9 8.2 0.8
11 TH	0005 0705 1218 1920	7.5 1.8 7.6 1.8	**26** F	0023 0732 1241 1958	8.1 1.1 8.0 1.0
12 F	0037 0733 1248 1947	7.4 2.1 7.4 2.0	**27** SA	0112 0816 1328 2043	7.9 1.4 7.8 1.4
13 SA	0108 0800 1318 2016	7.1 2.4 7.2 2.3	**28** SU	0203 0901 1418 2130	7.6 1.9 7.4 1.8
14 SU	0142 0830 1355 2048	6.9 2.7 6.9 2.6	**29** M	0259 0952 1516 2225	7.2 2.3 7.1 2.2
15 M	0224 0907 1442 2131	6.6 3.0 6.6 2.9	**30** TU	0404 1053 1625 2330	6.9 2.7 6.8 2.5

DECEMBER

	Time	m		Time	m
1 W	0516 1205 1739	6.8 2.8 6.7	**16** TH	0351 1040 1615 2311	6.6 3.0 6.6 2.8
2 TH	0042 0629 1317 1853	2.6 6.8 2.8 6.7	**17** F	0503 1152 1731	6.6 3.0 6.6
3 F	0150 0733 1422 1956	2.5 7.0 2.5 6.9	**18** SA	0025 0620 1307 1846	2.7 6.8 2.7 6.8
4 SA	0250 0825 1519 2046	2.3 7.2 2.3 7.1	**19** SU	0140 0723 1420 1949	2.4 7.1 2.3 7.1
5 SU	0341 0907 1606 2127	2.1 7.4 2.0 7.3	**20** M	0250 0819 1526 2046	2.0 7.4 1.8 7.5
6 M	0424 0944 1646 2204	2.0 7.5 1.9 7.4	**21** TU	0352 0912 1625 2140	1.6 7.7 1.4 7.8
7 TU	0503 1018 1723 2238	1.9 7.6 1.7 7.5	**22** W ○	0449 1002 1720 2232	1.3 8.0 1.1 8.0
8 W	0538 1050 1758 2311	1.8 7.6 1.7 7.5	**23** TH	0542 1052 1812 2322	1.1 8.1 0.8 8.1
9 TH	0612 1123 1830 2345	1.8 7.6 1.7 7.4	**24** F	0633 1140 1902	1.0 8.2 0.8
10 F	0643 1155 1900	1.8 7.6 1.7	**25** SA	0012 0721 1229 1949	8.1 1.1 8.1 0.9
11 SA	0018 0713 1227 1931	7.4 1.9 7.5 1.9	**26** SU	0101 0808 1316 2035	8.0 1.3 7.9 1.1
12 SU	0051 0745 1301 2002	7.3 2.2 7.4 2.1	**27** M	0150 0853 1403 2119	7.7 1.6 7.6 1.5
13 M	0127 0817 1339 2037	7.1 2.4 7.1 2.3	**28** TU	0239 0937 1452 2203	7.4 2.0 7.3 1.9
14 TU	0207 0854 1422 2116	6.9 2.7 6.9 2.5	**29** W	0330 1024 1546 2251	7.1 2.4 7.0 2.3
15 W	0255 0940 1513 2206	6.7 2.9 6.7 2.7	**30** TH	0427 1116 1647 2345	6.8 2.7 6.7 2.7
			31 F	0531 1217 1756	6.7 2.9 6.6

Chart Datum: 4·38 metres below Lallemand System (Mean Sea Level, Marseilles)

19

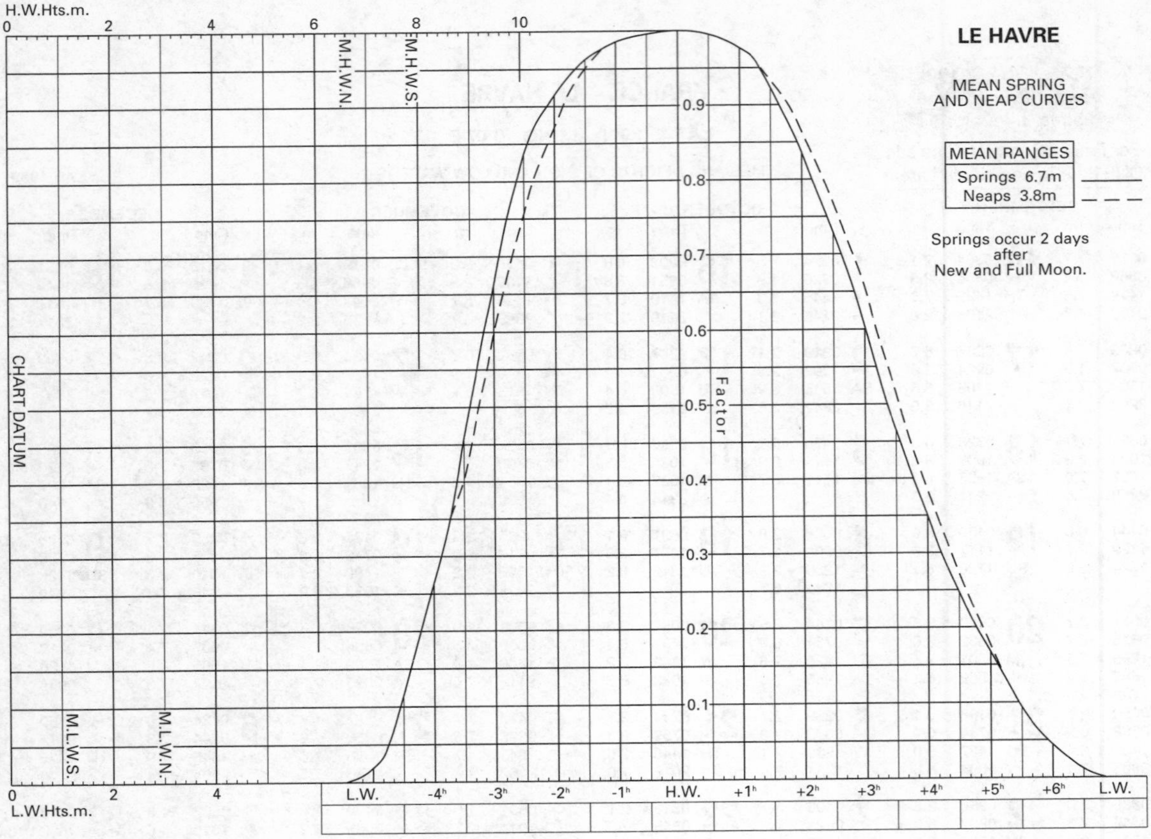

LE HAVRE

MEAN SPRING
AND NEAP CURVES

MEAN RANGES
Springs 6.7m
Neaps 3.8m

Springs occur 2 days
after
New and Full Moon.

H.W.Hts.m.

CHART DATUM

M.H.W.N. M.H.W.S.

M.L.W.S. M.L.W.N.

Factor

L.W.Hts.m.

L.W. -4ʰ -3ʰ -2ʰ -1ʰ H.W. +1ʰ +2ʰ +3ʰ +4ʰ +5ʰ +6ʰ L.W.

LE HAVRE   8-19-19

Seine Maritime 49°29'·18N 00°05·51E   Rtg 1-1-2

CHARTS
AC 2990, 2146, *2613*; SHOM 6683, 6796, 6736; ECM 526, 1012; Imray C31; Stanfords 1

TIDES
−0103 Dover; ML 4·9; Duration 0543; Zone −0100.
Le Havre is a Standard Port; tidal predictions are given above. There is a stand at HW of about 3 hours.

SHELTER
Excellent in the marina, access H24. ♥ berth pontoon O. Or request Hr Mr for long stay in Bassin du Commerce.

NAVIGATION
WPT 49°31'·05N 00°04'·00W, 287°/107° from/to bkwtrs, 6·4M. ⚓ prohib in and to the N of the fairway; it is also prohib to cross the fairway E of buoys LH7 and LH8. Banc de l'Éclat, awash at LW, lies N of appr chan and lobster pots close each side. Obey IPTS at end of Digue Nord.

LIGHTS AND MARKS
Ldg lts 107° both Dir FW 36/78m 25M; grey trs, G tops; intens 106°-108° (H24). 2 chys, RW conspic, on ldg line.

RADIO TELEPHONE
Call: *Havre Port* Control tr VHF Ch 12 20 (or 2182 kHz). Port Ops Ch 67 69 (H24). Radar Ch 12. Marina Ch 09.

TELEPHONE
Hr Mr 02.32.74.74.00; Marina 02.35.21.23.95; Aff Mar 02.35.19.29.99; CROSS 02.33.52.72.23; ⌗ 02.35.41.33.51; SNSM 02.35.22.41.03; Météo 02.35.42.21.06; Auto 08.36.68.08.76; Dr 02.35.41.23.61; Ⓗ 02.35.73.32.32; Brit Consul 02.35.42.27.47.

FACILITIES
Marina (973 + 41 Ⓥ) ☎ 02.35.21.23.95, 🚤 02.35.22.72.72, FF104, AC, BH (16 ton), C (6 ton), CH, Slip, P & D (cash in HO; credit card OT), El, FW, Gas, Gaz, R, Ⓞ, &, V;
YC Sport Nautique (SNH) ☎ 02.35.21.01.41, Bar;
Sté des Régates du Havre (SRH) ☎ 02.35.42.41.21, R, Bar;
Services: Ⓔ, ME, El, Sh, CH, SHOM, ACA.
City All needs. Ferry: Portsmouth.

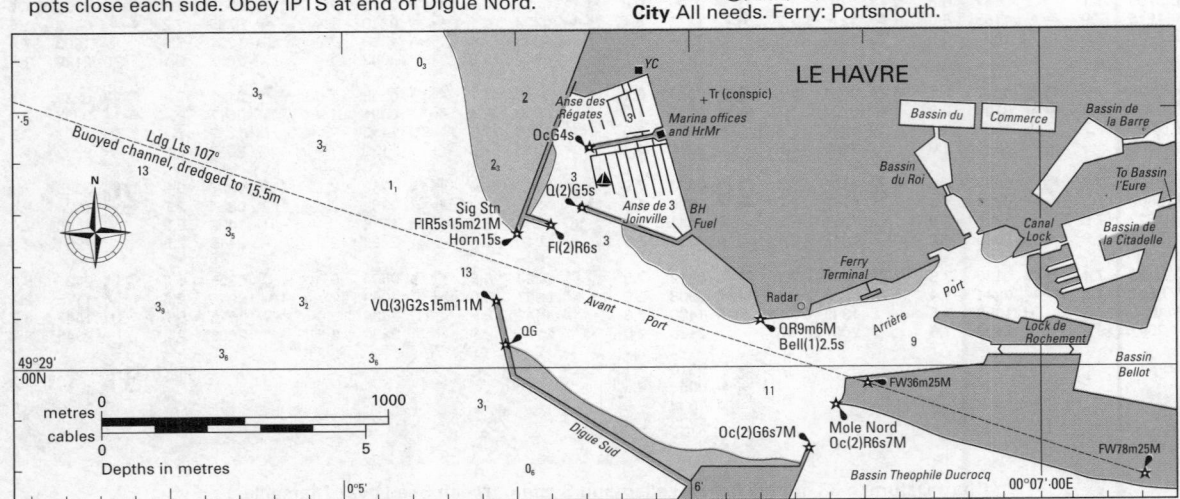

RIVER SEINE   8-19-20

CHARTS

AC 2880, 2994, 2146, *2613*; SHOM 6796, 6117; Imray C31

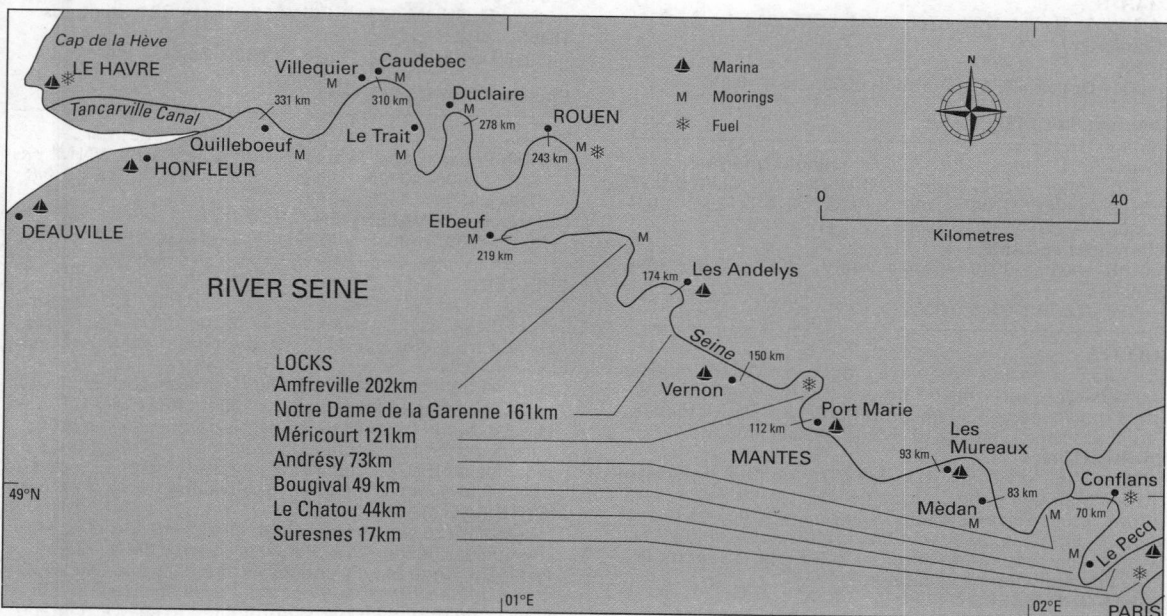

TIDES

Standard Port LE HAVRE (⟵) Zone –0100

Times				Height (metres)			
High Water		Low Water		MHWS	MHWN	MLWN	MLWS
0000	0500	0000	0700	7·9	6·6	2·8	1·2
1200	1700	1200	1900				

Differences TANCARVILLE*

–0105	–0100	+0105	+0140	–0·1	–0·1	0·0	+1·0

QUILLEBOEUF*

–0045	–0050	+0120	+0200	0·0	0·0	+0·2	+1·4

VATTEVILLE*

+0005	–0020	+0225	+0250	0·0	–0·1	+0·8	+2·3

CAUDEBEC*

+0020	–0015	+0230	+0300	–0·3	–0·2	+0·9	+2·4

ROUEN

+0440	+0415	+0525	+0525	–0·2	–0·1	+1·6	+3·6

*HW differences refer to the start of the stand, which lasts about 2¾ hrs up to Vatteville and about 1¾hrs at Duclair.

It is important to study the tides. The flood stream starts progressively later as a boat proceeds upriver. So even a 4kn boat leaving the estuary at LW can carry the flood for the 78M (123km) to Rouen. But going down river on the ebb a boat will meet the flood. Rather than ⚓ for about 4 hrs, in a fast boat it is worth continuing, because the ebb starts sooner the further downstream one gets. Between Quilleboeuf (335km) and La Mailleraye (303km) the Seine bore (*mascaret*) still runs at HWS if the river is in flood.

NAVIGATION: The Seine gives access to Paris and central France, and to the Mediterranean via the canals (below). But there is a constant traffic of barges (*péniches*), and in the tidal section (below Amfreville) the strong stream and ships' wash make it dangerous to moor alongside and uncomfortable to ⚓. Masts can be lowered at Deauville, Le Havre (marina) and Rouen. Yacht navigation is prohib at night, and ⚓s are scarce. A good ⚓ ⓦ light is needed, and it is useful to have a radar reflector and a VHF aerial, even with the mast lowered. Listen on Ch 73.

ENTRY is usually via the dredged/buoyed Chenal de Rouen, which can be rough in a strong W'ly wind and ebb tide. Care is needed, especially near the mouth where there are shifting banks and often morning fog.

ENTRY VIA THE CANAL DE TANCARVILLE may be preferred if sea conditions are bad, but with 3 locks and 9 bridges delays must be expected. To enter the Canal at Le Havre transit the lock Quinette de Rochemont (E of the front ldg lt) into Bassin Bellot. At the E end transit the Vétillart lock; thence via 3 bridges through Garage de Graville, Bassin de Despujols, and across the N end of Bassin de Lancement, which leads into the canal proper with 3 more bridges. Exit into the Seine (at 338km) via locks close E of Tancarville suspension bridge (50m).

LOCKS: Locks are as shown above. Call VHF Ch 18† or 22. Above Amfreville the current is about 1kn in summer, but more in winter.

FACILITIES: The most likely places for mooring and fuel are shown above. For Rouen and Paris see below.

REFERENCE: For detailed information see *A Cruising Guide to the Lower Seine* (Imray).

ROUEN, Seine Maritime, 49°26'·63N 01°03'·00E. AC 2880, 2994; SHOM 6117. HW +0330 on Dover (UT); ML 6·2m; Duration 0400. Yacht navigation prohib SS+½ to SR–½. Use pontoon SE side Bassin St Gervais (N bank) for mast unstep/restep (max stay 48 hrs); or mast step at Darse des Docks 250km. Berth in La Halte de Plaisance NE side of Ile Lacroix. VHF call *Rouen Port* Ch 73 68; 82 for height of water. Hr Mr 02.35.52.54.56; Aff Mar 02.35.98.53.98; ⌗ 02.35.98.27.60; Météo 02.35.80.11.44; Facilities: **Bassin St Gervais** C (3 to 25 ton), FW; **La Halte de Plaisance** (50) ☎ 02.35.88.00.00, FW, AC, Slip, C (30 ton), BH (4 ton); **Rouen YC** ☎ 02.35.66.52.52; **Services**: ME, El, Sh, P, D, CH, Ⓔ.

PARIS. The Touring Club de France ☎ 01.42.65.90.70, ⛴ 01.42.65.11.31, has AB, AC, FW on the N bank near Place de la Concorde, but noise and wash intrude. The **Port de Paris-Arsenal**, the first basin of the Canal St Martin, has complete shelter for 112 + 65 visitors; depth 1·9m. Ent is on the NE bank 170m before Pont d'Austerlitz at lock 9, which, with air clearance of 5·2m, is remotely controlled by Hr Mr (0800-2345LT); waiting pontoon (with intercom to Hr Mr) upstream. VHF Ch 09. Caution strong current if river in flood. Hr Mr ☎ 01.43.41.39.32, ⛴ 01.44.74.02.66; AC, FW, C (7 ton), D & P (cans), Ⓞ, plus city amenities; Aff Mar ☎ 01.42.73.55.05; River Police 01.47.07.17.17; Metro stns: Quai de la Rapée and Bastille (lines 1, 5), RER, ⇌, ✈.

CANALS TO THE MEDITERRANEAN

The quickest route is Le Havre/Paris/St Mammes/canal du Loing/canal du Briare/canal Latéral à la Loire/canal du Centre/Saône/Rhône, approx 1318km (824M), 182 locks. Max dimensions: LOA 38·5m, beam 5m, draft 1·8m, air draft 3·5m. Further info and dates of closures (*chomages*) are available every March from the French Tourist Office, 178 Piccadilly, London, W1V OAL, ☎ 0171 629-2869, ⛴ 0171 493-6594. Tolls are due; see 8.15.8.

19

FÉCAMP   8-19-21

Seine Maritime 49°45'·97N 00°21'·85E   Rtg 3-1-2

CHARTS
AC 1352; SHOM 7207, 6765, 6824; ECM 1012; Imray C31; Stanfords 1

TIDES
–0044 Dover; ML 4·9; Duration 0550; Zone –0100

Standard Port DIEPPE (→)

Times				Height (metres)			
High Water		Low Water		MHWS	MHWN	MLWN	MLWS
0100	0600	0100	0700	9·3	7·4	2·5	0·8
1300	1800	1300	1900				
Differences FÉCAMP							
–0015	–0010	–0030	–0040	–1·0	–0·6	+0·3	+0·4
ETRETAT							
–0020	–0020	–0045	–0050	–1·2	–0·8	+0·3	+0·4

SHELTER
Excellent in basins, but in even moderate W/NW winds a considerable surf runs off the ent and the Avant Port (Ⓥ at 'V' pontoon) can be uncomfortable. Bassin Bérigny is entered via lock, HW –2 to HW; pontoons at E end.

NAVIGATION
WPT 49°46'·10N 00°21'·12E, 282°/102° from/to Jetée Nord lt, 0·50M. Beware the Charpentier Rks off Pte Fagnet and strong cross currents, depending on tides. Access best at HW +1. Ent chan dredged 1·5m, but prone to silting; best water is close to N jetty. Boats < 1·2m draft can enter at any tide and in most weathers.

LIGHTS AND MARKS
Ent lies SSW of conspic ⌘, sig stn and TV mast on Pte Fagnet cliff. N jetty Fl (2) 10s 15m 16M, grey tr, R top; horn (2) 30s sounded HW –2½ to HW +2; root QR 10m 4M. Jetée Sud hd, QG 14m 9M; obscd by cliff when brg more than 217°. QR and QG in transit 082° lead towards hbr ent. IPTS on tr by Avant Port show when Bassin Bérigny lock is open.

RADIO TELEPHONE
VHF Ch 12 10 16 (HW –3 to HW + 1). Ch 09 Marina and Écluse Bérigny (0800-1200; 1400-2000LT).

TELEPHONE
Hr Mr 02.35.28.25.53; Aff Mar 02.35.28.16.35; CROSS 03.21.87.21.87; SNSM 02.35.28.00.91; ⌗ 02.35.28.19.40; Auto 08.36.68.08.76; Police 02.35.28.16.69; Ⓗ 02.35.28.05.13; Brit Consul 02.35.42.27.47.

FACILITIES
Marina (580 + 30 Ⓥ) ☎ 02.35.28.13.58, FF113, FW, AC, D, C (mobile 36 ton), 🅖; **Bassin Bérigny lock** ☎ 02.35.28.23.76, AB, M, D, FW, Slip; **Sté des Régates de Fécamp** ☎ 02.35.28.08.44, AB, FW; **Services:** Slip, M, ME, El, Ⓔ, Sh, CH, Gaz, C (30 ton). **Town** EC Mon; P, D, V, Gaz, R, Bar, ✉, Ⓑ, ⇌, ✈ (Le Havre).

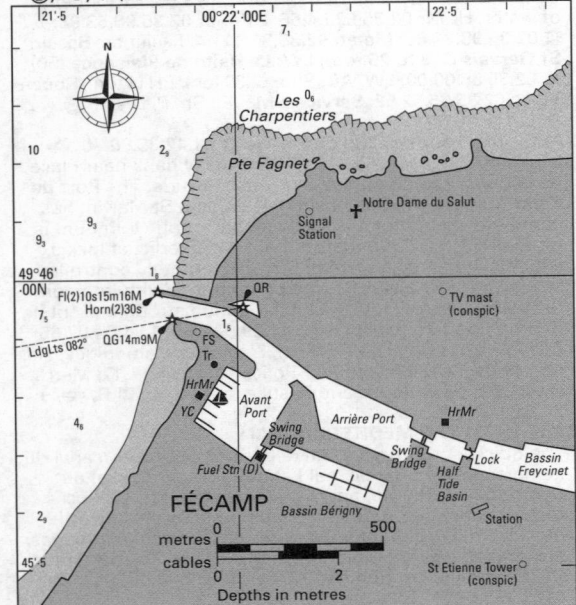

FÉCAMP

ST VALÉRY-EN-CAUX   8-19-22

Seine Maritime 49°52'·44N 00°42'·54E   Rtg 3-2-2

CHARTS
AC 2451; SHOM 6794; ECM 1012; Imray C31; Stanfords 1

TIDES
–0044 Dover; ML 4·6; Duration 0530; Zone –0100

Standard Port DIEPPE (→)

Times				Height (metres)			
High Water		Low Water		MHWS	MHWN	MLWN	MLWS
0100	0600	0100	0700	9·3	7·4	2·5	0·8
1300	1800	1300	1900				
Differences ST VALÉRY-EN-CAUX							
–0007	–0007	–0015	–0025	–0·8	–0·6	–0·2	–0·1

SHELTER
Good. Avant Port dries 3m; access from HW –3. Lock opens HW ±2¼ by day; by night, at HW±½ (bridge opens H and H+30 during these periods). Ⓥ pontoon to stbd, past lock.

NAVIGATION
WPT 49°53'·00N 00°42'·50E, 000°/180° from/to Jetée Ouest lt, 0·50M. Coast dries to approx 150m off the pier hds. Ent is easy, but in fresh W to NE winds confused seas break across ent. Shingle builds up against W wall; hug the E side. Inside the pier hds, wave-breaks (marked by posts each side) dampen the swell. 6 W waiting buoys N of lock.

LIGHTS AND MARKS
Hbr is hard to see between high chalk cliffs. From N or W the nuclear power stn at Paluel is conspic 3M W of ent. From E a white bldg is conspic E of ent, as is a vert white stripe in the cliffs close W of ent. Lts as on chartlet. Tfc sigs at the bridge/lock are coordinated to seaward/inland: Ⓖ = ent/exit; Ⓡ = no ent/ exit; Ⓡ + Ⓖ = no movements.

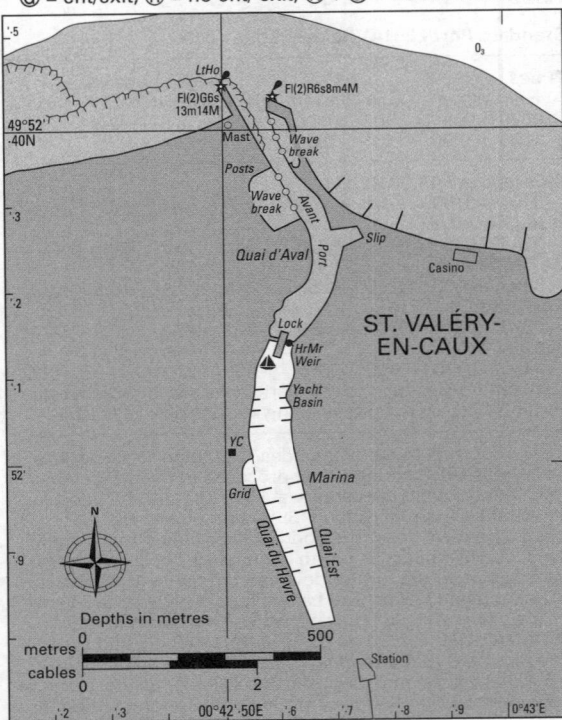

ST. VALÉRY-EN-CAUX

RADIO TELEPHONE
VHF Ch 09 (French only).

TELEPHONE
Hr Mr 02.35.97.01.30; Aff Mar 02.35.28.16.35; CROSS 03.21.87.21.89; SNSM 02.35.97.09.03; ⌗ 02.35.82.24.47; Météo 03.21.31.52.23; Auto 08.36.68.08.76; Police 02.35.97.05.27; Dr 02.35.97.05.99; Ⓗ 02.35.97.06.21; Brit Consul 02.35.42.27.47.

FACILITIES
Marina (580 + 20 Ⓥ) ☎ 02.35.97.01.30, ⛴ 02.35.97.90.73, FF102, AC, FW, C (5/10 ton), CH, El, Gaz, ME, Sh, V, Bar; **Club Nautique Valeriquais** ☎ 02.35.97.25.49, C (8 ton), Bar; **Services:** Ⓔ. **Town** EC Mon (all day); P, D, CH, V, Gaz, R, Bar, ✉, Ⓑ, bus to ⇌ at Yvetot; ✈ & Ferry Dieppe.

TIME ZONE –0100
(French Standard Time)
Subtract 1 hour for UT

For French Summer Time add
ONE hour in non-shaded areas

FRANCE – DIEPPE

LAT 49°56′N   LONG 1°05′E

TIMES AND HEIGHTS OF HIGH AND LOW WATERS

YEAR **1999**

JANUARY

Day	Time	m	Time	m	Time	m	Time	m
1 F	0521	1.1	1049	9.2	1752	0.8	2317	9.2
16 SA	0526	1.7	1055	8.5	1750	1.4	2317	8.5
2 SA O	0615	0.9	1139	9.4	1845	0.6		
17 SU ●	0608	1.5	1134	8.8	1831	1.2	2356	8.8
3 SU	0006	9.4	0705	0.8	1225	9.5	1933	0.6
18 M	0648	1.3	1212	9.0	1911	1.0		
4 M	0052	9.4	0751	0.8	1310	9.5	2017	0.7
19 TU	0034	9.0	0728	1.1	1250	9.1	1951	0.9
5 TU	0135	9.3	0832	1.0	1352	9.3	2057	0.9
20 W	0112	9.1	0807	1.1	1329	9.2	2030	0.8
6 W	0217	9.1	0911	1.3	1433	9.0	2134	1.2
21 TH	0152	9.1	0847	1.1	1409	9.1	2109	0.9
7 TH	0257	8.7	0947	1.6	1513	8.5	2208	1.6
22 F	0232	9.0	0926	1.2	1451	8.9	2147	1.1
8 F	0337	8.3	1022	2.0	1554	8.1	2243	2.0
23 SA	0313	8.8	1006	1.4	1534	8.6	2228	1.3
9 SA	0419	7.8	1103	2.4	1639	7.6	2325	2.4
24 SU	0358	8.5	1051	1.7	1623	8.3	2314	1.7
10 SU	0508	7.4	1153	2.7	1733	7.1		
25 M	0451	8.1	1145	1.9	1723	7.9		
11 M	0019	2.7	0608	7.1	1255	2.9	1842	6.9
26 TU	0012	2.0	0559	7.9	1252	2.1	1839	7.7
12 TU	0126	2.9	0721	7.1	1408	2.8	1957	7.0
27 W	0126	2.1	0718	7.8	1415	2.1	1959	7.8
13 W	0240	2.8	0831	7.3	1519	2.5	2101	7.3
28 TH	0250	2.0	0835	8.0	1533	1.8	2112	8.1
14 TH	0347	2.4	0927	7.7	1617	2.1	2152	7.8
29 F	0403	1.7	0942	8.4	1641	1.4	2215	8.6
15 F	0440	2.1	1013	8.1	1706	1.8	2237	8.2
30 SA	0507	1.4	1040	8.9	1741	1.0	2309	8.9
31 SU O	0603	1.1	1130	9.2	1834	0.8	2356	9.2

FEBRUARY

Day	Time	m	Time	m	Time	m	Time	m
1 M	0652	0.9	1214	9.4	1920	0.6		
16 TU ●	0631	1.1	1155	9.1	1856	0.8		
2 TU	0038	9.3	0736	0.8	1255	9.4	2000	0.6
17 W O	0017	9.2	0715	0.8	1235	9.4	1939	0.5
3 W	0118	9.3	0814	0.9	1333	9.4	2036	0.7
18 TH	0056	9.4	0756	0.7	1315	9.5	2019	0.7
4 TH	0154	9.3	0848	1.0	1409	9.1	2108	1.0
19 F	0136	9.5	0836	0.6	1355	9.5	2057	0.4
5 F	0229	9.0	0918	1.3	1444	8.8	2136	1.3
20 SA	0216	9.4	0915	0.7	1436	9.4	2134	0.6
6 SA	0303	8.6	0946	1.6	1517	8.4	2203	1.7
21 SU	0256	9.2	0953	0.9	1518	9.0	2212	1.0
7 SU	0336	8.2	1017	2.0	1551	7.9	2235	2.1
22 M	0338	8.8	1034	1.3	1603	8.5	2254	1.5
8 M	0411	7.7	1056	2.4	1631	7.3	2317	2.6
23 TU	0426	8.3	1123	1.7	1659	8.0	2348	2.0
9 TU	0456	7.2	1147	2.8	1727	6.9		
24 W	0530	7.8	1227	2.1	1815	7.5		
10 W	0013	3.0	0604	6.8	1255	3.1	1851	6.6
25 TH	0101	2.3	0655	7.5	1353	2.3	1944	7.5
11 TH	0130	3.1	0735	6.8	1421	2.9	2019	6.9
26 F	0231	2.3	0823	7.7	1520	2.0	2105	7.8
12 F	0258	2.9	0850	7.2	1538	2.5	2122	7.4
27 SA	0352	2.0	0936	8.1	1633	1.5	2209	8.4
13 SA	0406	2.4	0946	7.8	1636	1.9	2212	8.0
28 SU	0500	1.5	1032	8.6	1733	1.1	2259	8.8
14 SU	0459	1.9	1032	8.3	1726	1.5	2256	8.5
15 M	0546	1.4	1114	8.8	1812	1.1	2337	8.9

MARCH

Day	Time	m	Time	m	Time	m	Time	m
1 M	0555	1.2	1119	9.0	1822	0.8	2342	9.1
16 TU ●	0520	1.4	1050	8.8	1748	1.0	2313	9.0
2 TU O	0639	1.0	1159	9.2	1903	0.7		
17 W ●	0610	0.9	1133	9.2	1836	0.6	2355	9.4
3 W	0020	9.3	0717	0.8	1236	9.3	1939	0.7
18 TH	0656	0.6	1215	9.6	1920	0.3		
4 TH	0055	9.3	0751	0.8	1310	9.3	2010	0.7
19 F	0036	9.6	0740	0.4	1256	9.8	2002	0.2
5 F	0128	9.2	0822	0.9	1342	9.2	2039	0.9
20 SA	0116	9.8	0821	0.3	1337	9.8	2041	0.2
6 SA	0159	9.1	0849	1.1	1413	8.9	2104	1.1
21 SU	0157	9.7	0900	0.4	1419	9.6	2118	0.4
7 SU	0229	8.8	0914	1.4	1443	8.6	2128	1.5
22 M	0237	9.4	0938	0.7	1501	9.2	2155	0.9
8 M	0258	8.4	0941	1.7	1512	8.1	2156	1.9
23 TU	0319	9.0	1019	1.1	1547	8.6	2237	1.4
9 TU	0327	7.9	1014	2.1	1545	7.6	2232	2.4
24 W	0407	8.3	1107	1.6	1643	8.0	2331	2.0
10 W	0404	7.4	1057	2.6	1631	7.0	2320	2.9
25 TH	0511	7.7	1210	2.1	1759	7.4		
11 TH	0457	6.9	1156	3.0	1741	6.6		
26 F	0045	2.5	0638	7.3	1337	2.3	1931	7.3
12 F	0029	3.2	0625	6.6	1318	3.1	1928	6.6
27 SA	0217	2.5	0810	7.4	1506	2.1	2054	7.7
13 SA	0202	3.1	0808	6.9	1451	2.7	2047	7.2
28 SU	0340	2.1	0923	8.0	1620	1.6	2154	8.3
14 SU	0326	2.6	0914	7.5	1600	2.1	2143	7.8
29 M	0447	1.6	1016	8.5	1717	1.2	2241	8.7
15 M	0428	1.9	1005	8.2	1657	1.5	2230	8.5
30 TU	0538	1.3	1100	8.8	1802	1.0	2321	9.0
31 W O	0618	1.1	1138	9.1	1839	0.9	2356	9.1

APRIL

Day	Time	m	Time	m	Time	m	Time	m
1 TH	0653	0.9	1212	9.1	1911	0.8		
16 F	0632	0.5	1151	9.6	1856	0.3		
2 F	0028	9.2	0724	0.9	1243	9.2	1941	0.8
17 SA	0012	9.7	0719	0.3	1234	9.8	1940	0.1
3 SA	0059	9.1	0753	0.9	1314	9.1	2009	0.9
18 SU	0054	9.8	0803	0.2	1318	9.9	2021	0.2
4 SU	0129	9.0	0821	1.1	1345	8.9	2035	1.1
19 M	0137	9.8	0844	0.3	1401	9.7	2101	0.5
5 M	0158	8.8	0847	1.3	1414	8.6	2059	1.5
20 TU	0219	9.5	0924	0.6	1446	9.3	2140	0.9
6 TU	0225	8.5	0913	1.6	1442	8.2	2126	1.8
21 W	0304	9.0	1006	1.0	1534	8.7	2224	1.5
7 W	0254	8.1	0943	2.0	1515	7.8	2200	2.3
22 TH	0353	8.3	1055	1.6	1630	8.0	2318	2.1
8 TH	0330	7.6	1023	2.4	1557	7.3	2245	2.7
23 F	0456	7.7	1157	2.1	1743	7.5		
9 F	0418	7.1	1118	2.8	1658	6.8	2348	3.1
24 SA	0030	2.4	0616	7.3	1316	2.3	1907	7.4
10 SA	0531	6.7	1231	2.9	1832	6.7		
25 SU	0154	2.5	0744	7.4	1438	2.1	2027	7.7
11 SU	0113	3.1	0715	6.8	1402	2.7	2003	7.1
26 M	0312	2.1	0856	7.8	1549	1.8	2127	8.1
12 M	0242	2.6	0833	7.4	1519	2.1	2106	7.8
27 TU	0416	1.7	0950	8.2	1645	1.4	2214	8.5
13 TU	0350	1.9	0931	8.1	1621	1.4	2158	8.5
28 W	0507	1.4	1034	8.6	1730	1.2	2253	8.8
14 W	0448	1.3	1020	8.8	1717	0.9	2244	9.1
29 TH	0547	1.3	1111	8.8	1806	1.1	2328	8.9
15 TH	0542	0.9	1106	9.3	1809	0.5	2329	9.5
30 F O	0621	1.3	1144	8.9	1839	1.1	2359	9.0

19

Chart Datum: 4·43 metres below Lallemand System (Mean Sea Level, Marseilles)

TIME ZONE –0100
(French Standard Time)
Subtract 1 hour for UT
For French Summer Time add ONE hour in non-shaded areas

FRANCE – DIEPPE

LAT 49°56′N   LONG 1°05′E

TIMES AND HEIGHTS OF HIGH AND LOW WATERS   YEAR **1999**

MAY

Day	Time 1	Time 2	Time 3	Time 4
1 SA	0654 1.1	1216 8.9	1910 1.0	
16 SU	0656 0.4	1213 9.7	1918 0.3	
2 SU	0030 9.0	0725 1.1	1247 8.9	1941 1.1
17 M	0033 9.8	0743 0.3	1300 9.7	2003 0.4
3 M	0100 8.9	0755 1.1	1318 8.8	2009 1.3
18 TU	0119 9.7	0828 0.3	1346 9.6	2045 0.6
4 TU	0130 8.8	0823 1.3	1349 8.6	2036 1.5
19 W	0204 9.4	0912 0.6	1433 9.2	2128 1.0
5 W	0200 8.5	0852 1.5	1420 8.3	2105 1.8
20 TH	0251 9.0	0956 1.0	1522 8.7	2213 1.5
6 TH	0232 8.2	0924 1.8	1455 7.9	2139 2.1
21 F	0341 8.4	1044 1.5	1616 8.2	2305 1.9
7 F	0309 7.8	1003 2.1	1537 7.5	2223 2.5
22 SA	0439 7.9	1133 1.9	1719 7.7	
8 SA	0356 7.4	1053 2.5	1632 7.2	2321 2.8
23 SU	0008 2.3	0546 7.5	1246 2.2	1829 7.5
9 SU	0459 7.0	1159 2.6	1749 7.0	
24 M	0118 2.4	0701 7.3	1355 2.2	1943 7.5
10 M	0035 2.8	0626 7.0	1318 2.5	1915 7.3
25 TU	0227 2.3	0814 7.5	1501 2.0	2047 7.8
11 TU	0157 2.5	0747 7.5	1436 2.0	2024 7.9
26 W	0330 2.0	0913 7.8	1559 1.8	2138 8.1
12 W	0310 1.9	0851 8.1	1543 1.5	2121 8.5
27 TH	0424 1.7	1000 8.1	1648 1.6	2220 8.4
13 TH	0413 1.3	0947 8.7	1643 1.0	2213 9.0
28 F	0509 1.5	1040 8.4	1729 1.4	2256 8.6
14 F	0511 0.9	1038 9.2	1739 0.6	2301 9.4
29 SA	0548 1.4	1116 8.5	1806 1.3	2330 8.7
15 SA	0605 0.6	1126 9.5	1830 0.4	● 2348 9.7
30 SU	0625 1.3	1150 8.6	1842 1.3	O
31 M	0003 8.8	0659 1.2	1223 8.7	1915 1.3

JUNE

Day	Time 1	Time 2	Time 3	Time 4
1 TU	0036 8.8	0733 1.2	1257 8.7	1947 1.4
16 W	0104 9.6	0814 0.4	1333 9.5	2032 0.7
2 W	0108 8.7	0804 1.3	1330 8.6	2018 1.5
17 TH	0151 9.4	0900 0.6	1420 9.2	2116 1.0
3 TH	0142 8.6	0836 1.4	1404 8.4	2050 1.7
18 F	0237 9.0	0944 0.9	1507 8.9	2200 1.4
4 F	0217 8.3	0911 1.6	1442 8.2	2127 1.9
19 SA	0324 8.6	1028 1.3	1555 8.4	2245 1.8
5 SA	0256 8.0	0950 1.8	1524 7.9	2209 2.2
20 SU	0414 8.1	1114 1.7	1646 8.0	2335 2.1
6 SU	0341 7.7	1037 2.1	1614 7.6	2301 2.4
21 M	0508 7.7	1205 2.1	1742 7.6	
7 M	0437 7.5	1133 2.2	1716 7.5	
22 TU	0031 2.4	0609 7.3	1303 2.3	1846 7.4
8 TU	0004 2.4	0546 7.4	1241 2.2	1830 7.6
23 W	0133 2.4	0717 7.2	1405 2.3	1953 7.5
9 W	0117 2.2	0702 7.6	1354 1.9	1941 7.9
24 TH	0236 2.3	0825 7.4	1507 2.2	2054 7.7
10 TH	0231 1.9	0813 8.0	1505 1.6	2045 8.4
25 F	0337 2.1	0922 7.6	1604 2.0	2144 8.0
11 F	0339 1.4	0915 8.5	1610 1.2	2143 8.9
26 SA	0430 1.9	1008 7.9	1653 1.8	2226 8.2
12 SA	0441 1.0	1049 8.2	1709 0.9	2236 9.2
27 SU	0516 1.6	1049 8.2	1737 1.6	2304 8.4
13 SU	0539 0.7	1105 9.3	1805 0.7	● 2327 9.5
28 M	0558 1.5	1127 8.4	1816 1.5	O 2341 8.6
14 M	0634 0.5	1156 9.5	1857 0.6	
29 TU	0637 1.3	1203 8.5	1853 1.4	
15 TU	0016 9.6	0726 0.4	1245 9.6	1946 0.6
30 W	0016 8.7	0713 1.2	1239 8.6	1928 1.4

JULY

Day	Time 1	Time 2	Time 3	Time 4
1 TH	0052 8.7	0749 1.2	1315 8.7	2003 1.4
16 F	0136 9.4	0846 0.6	1404 9.3	2101 0.9
2 F	0128 8.7	0825 1.2	1352 8.6	2040 1.5
17 SA	0219 9.2	0926 0.8	1446 9.0	2140 1.2
3 SA	0205 8.6	0902 1.3	1430 8.5	2118 1.6
18 SU	0301 8.8	1003 1.2	1527 8.6	2216 1.6
4 SU	0245 8.4	0941 1.5	1511 8.3	2158 1.8
19 M	0343 8.4	1039 1.6	1609 8.2	2254 2.0
5 M	0328 8.2	1023 1.6	1556 8.1	2244 1.9
20 TU	0426 7.9	1118 2.0	1654 7.8	2338 2.3
6 TU	0416 8.0	1111 1.8	1647 7.9	2337 2.1
21 W	0515 7.4	1205 2.4	1747 7.4	
7 W	0514 7.8	1208 1.9	1750 7.8	
22 TH	0034 2.6	0616 7.0	1305 2.7	1853 7.1
8 TH	0041 2.1	0623 7.8	1316 1.9	1903 7.9
23 F	0141 2.7	0730 7.0	1415 2.7	2005 7.2
9 F	0155 1.9	0739 7.9	1431 1.8	2014 8.2
24 SA	0252 2.6	0842 7.2	1524 2.5	2108 7.5
10 SA	0310 1.6	0849 8.3	1542 1.5	2119 8.6
25 SU	0355 2.2	0938 7.6	1622 2.2	2158 7.9
11 SU	0417 1.3	0952 8.7	1646 1.2	2218 8.9
26 M	0448 1.9	1025 8.0	1711 1.8	2241 8.2
12 M	0519 0.9	1050 9.0	1745 0.9	2312 9.2
27 TU	0534 1.6	1106 8.3	1754 1.6	2321 8.5
13 TU	0617 0.7	1143 9.3	1841 0.8 ●	
28 W	0616 1.4	1145 8.6	1834 1.4	O 2359 8.7
14 W	0003 9.4	0712 0.5	1233 9.4	1932 0.7
29 TH	0656 1.2	1222 8.8	1913 1.3	
15 TH	0051 9.5	0801 0.5	1320 9.4	2019 0.8
30 F	0036 8.9	0736 1.0	1259 8.9	1951 1.2
31 SA	0113 9.0	0814 0.9	1337 9.0	2029 1.2

AUGUST

Day	Time 1	Time 2	Time 3	Time 4
1 SU	0151 9.0	0852 1.0	1415 8.9	2107 1.2
16 M	0232 9.0	0931 1.2	1454 8.8	2141 1.5
2 M	0231 8.9	0929 1.1	1454 8.8	2145 1.4
17 TU	0308 8.5	0959 1.6	1529 8.4	2210 1.9
3 TU	0311 8.7	1007 1.3	1535 8.5	2226 1.6
18 W	0343 8.0	1029 2.1	1604 7.9	2246 2.3
4 W	0355 8.4	1049 1.5	1621 8.3	2313 1.8
19 TH	0421 7.5	1108 2.5	1647 7.4	2333 2.7
5 TH	0447 8.0	1140 1.8	1718 8.0	
20 F	0513 7.0	1202 2.9	1747 6.9	
6 F	0012 2.0	0553 7.8	1245 2.1	1832 7.8
21 SA	0038 3.0	0630 6.6	1316 3.2	1913 6.8
7 SA	0127 2.1	0715 7.7	1406 2.1	1952 7.9
22 SU	0202 3.0	0801 6.8	1444 3.0	2033 7.1
8 SU	0250 1.9	0833 7.9	1524 1.8	2105 8.2
23 M	0320 2.6	0909 7.2	1552 2.5	2131 7.6
9 M	0402 1.5	0943 8.4	1632 1.5	2209 8.7
24 TU	0419 2.1	1000 7.8	1645 2.0	2218 8.1
10 TU	0508 1.1	1043 8.8	1734 1.2	2304 9.1
25 W	0509 1.7	1043 8.3	1731 1.6	2300 8.6
11 W	0607 0.6	1135 9.2	1829 0.9	● 2353 9.3
26 TH	0554 1.3	1123 8.7	1814 1.3	2339 8.9
12 TH	0700 0.6	1221 9.4	1918 0.8	
27 F	0638 1.0	1202 9.0	1856 1.1	O
13 F	0037 9.4	0745 0.6	1303 9.4	2001 0.8
28 SA	0017 9.2	0719 0.8	1239 9.2	1936 0.9
14 SA	0118 9.4	0825 0.6	1342 9.4	2039 0.9
29 SU	0055 9.3	0758 0.7	1317 9.3	2015 0.8
15 SU	0156 9.3	0901 0.8	1419 9.1	2112 1.2
30 M	0133 9.4	0836 0.8	1355 9.3	2052 0.9
31 TU	0212 9.3	0912 0.8	1433 9.2	2129 1.1

Chart Datum: 4·43 metres below Lallemand System (Mean Sea Level, Marseilles)

TIME ZONE –0100
(French Standard Time)
Subtract 1 hour for UT

For French Summer Time add
ONE hour in non-shaded areas

FRANCE – DIEPPE

LAT 49°56'N   LONG 1°05'E

TIMES AND HEIGHTS OF HIGH AND LOW WATERS

YEAR **1999**

SEPTEMBER

Day	Time	m	Day	Time	m
1 W	0252 / 0949 / 1513 / 2208	9.0 / 1.1 / 8.9 / 1.3	**16** TH	0303 / 0947 / 1520 / 2202	8.2 / 2.0 / 8.0 / 2.3
2 TH	0335 / 1029 / 1558 / 2253	8.6 / 1.5 / 8.4 / 1.7	**17** F	0335 / 1020 / 1554 / 2242	7.6 / 2.5 / 7.5 / 2.7
3 F	0425 / 1118 / 1653 / 2350	8.1 / 1.9 / 7.9 / 2.1	**18** SA	0417 / 1107 / 1644 / 2339	7.0 / 3.0 / 6.9 / 3.1
4 SA	0532 / 1223 / 1811	7.6 / 2.3 / 7.6	**19** SU	0524 / 1215 / 1809	6.6 / 3.4 / 6.5
5 SU	0109 / 0702 / 1352 / 1941	2.3 / 7.5 / 2.4 / 7.6	**20** M	0102 / 0713 / 1353 / 1953	3.3 / 6.5 / 3.3 / 6.8
6 M	0239 / 0829 / 1516 / 2101	2.1 / 7.8 / 2.1 / 8.0	**21** TU	0238 / 0835 / 1517 / 2059	2.9 / 7.1 / 2.8 / 7.4
7 TU	0356 / 0940 / 1627 / 2204	1.7 / 8.3 / 1.6 / 8.6	**22** W	0346 / 0930 / 1614 / 2150	2.3 / 7.8 / 2.1 / 8.1
8 W	0502 / 1035 / 1727 / 2255	1.2 / 8.8 / 1.2 / 9.0	**23** TH	0439 / 1015 / 1703 / 2233	1.7 / 8.4 / 1.6 / 8.6
9 TH	0557 / 1122 / 1818 / ● 2339	0.9 / 9.2 / 1.0 / 9.3	**24** F	0527 / 1057 / 1749 / 2314	1.2 / 8.9 / 1.2 / 9.1
10 F	0644 / 1203 / 1901	0.7 / 9.4 / 0.9	**25** SA	0613 / 1136 / 1833 / O 2354	0.9 / 9.2 / 0.9 / 9.4
11 SA	0018 / 0724 / 1241 / 1938	9.4 / 0.7 / 9.4 / 0.8	**26** SU	0656 / 1215 / 1916	0.6 / 9.5 / 0.7
12 SU	0054 / 0758 / 1315 / 2010	9.4 / 0.8 / 9.4 / 0.9	**27** M	0033 / 0737 / 1254 / 1956	9.6 / 0.5 / 9.6 / 0.6
13 M	0129 / 0829 / 1348 / 2040	9.3 / 0.9 / 9.2 / 1.2	**28** TU	0112 / 0816 / 1333 / 2035	9.6 / 0.5 / 9.6 / 0.7
14 TU	0201 / 0856 / 1420 / 2106	9.0 / 1.2 / 8.9 / 1.5	**29** W	0152 / 0816 / 1413 / 2113	9.5 / 0.7 / 9.4 / 0.9
15 W	0232 / 0921 / 1450 / 2131	8.6 / 1.6 / 8.5 / 1.8	**30** TH	0234 / 0930 / 1454 / 2152	9.2 / 1.0 / 9.0 / 1.2

OCTOBER

Day	Time	m	Day	Time	m
1 F	0318 / 1011 / 1539 / 2238	8.7 / 1.5 / 8.5 / 1.7	**16** SA	0300 / 0944 / 1516 / 2205	7.8 / 2.5 / 7.6 / 2.6
2 SA	0410 / 1102 / 1637 / 2336	8.1 / 2.1 / 7.9 / 2.2	**17** SU	0340 / 1027 / 1602 / 2256	7.3 / 3.0 / 7.1 / 3.0
3 SU	0521 / 1211 / 1759	7.5 / 2.5 / 7.4	**18** M	0437 / 1129 / 1712	6.8 / 3.4 / 6.6
4 M	0059 / 0654 / 1344 / 1933	2.5 / 7.4 / 2.6 / 7.5	**19** TU	0009 / 0612 / 1256 / 1859	3.3 / 6.6 / 3.4 / 6.7
5 TU	0232 / 0821 / 1509 / 2052	2.2 / 7.7 / 2.2 / 8.0	**20** W	0143 / 0748 / 1430 / 2017	3.1 / 7.0 / 2.9 / 7.2
6 W	0348 / 0928 / 1618 / 2151	1.7 / 8.3 / 1.6 / 8.5	**21** TH	0302 / 0850 / 1535 / 2113	2.5 / 7.7 / 2.2 / 8.0
7 TH	0450 / 1019 / 1713 / 2238	1.3 / 8.9 / 1.2 / 9.0	**22** F	0402 / 0940 / 1629 / 2200	1.8 / 8.4 / 1.6 / 8.6
8 F	0540 / 1102 / 1758 / 2319	1.0 / 9.2 / 1.0 / 9.2	**23** SA	0454 / 1025 / 1719 / 2244	1.2 / 9.0 / 1.1 / 9.1
9 SA	0621 / 1140 / 1836 / ● 2355	0.9 / 9.3 / 1.0 / 9.3	**24** SU	0543 / 1107 / 1807 / O 2327	0.8 / 9.4 / 0.8 / 9.5
10 SU	0656 / 1214 / 1909	0.9 / 9.3 / 1.0	**25** M	0629 / 1149 / 1852	0.6 / 9.6 / 0.6
11 M	0028 / 0727 / 1246 / 1940	9.3 / 1.0 / 9.3 / 1.0	**26** TU	0009 / 0714 / 1230 / 1936	9.7 / 0.5 / 9.8 / 0.5
12 TU	0100 / 0756 / 1316 / 2009	9.2 / 1.1 / 9.1 / 1.2	**27** W	0051 / 0755 / 1311 / 2017	9.8 / 0.6 / 9.8 / 0.6
13 W	0131 / 0823 / 1346 / 2035	9.0 / 1.3 / 8.9 / 1.5	**28** TH	0134 / 0835 / 1354 / 2058	9.7 / 0.7 / 9.5 / 0.8
14 TH	0201 / 0848 / 1415 / 2100	8.7 / 1.7 / 8.5 / 1.8	**29** F	0218 / 0915 / 1438 / 2140	9.3 / 1.1 / 9.1 / 1.1
15 F	0230 / 0913 / 1444 / 2128	8.2 / 2.1 / 8.1 / 2.2	**30** SA	0305 / 0959 / 1527 / 2227	8.8 / 1.6 / 8.5 / 1.7
			31 SU	0400 / 1052 / 1627 / 2327	8.2 / 2.1 / 7.9 / 2.1

NOVEMBER

Day	Time	m	Day	Time	m
1 M	0511 / 1202 / 1745	7.6 / 2.5 / 7.5	**16** TU	0408 / 1057 / 1635 / 2330	7.2 / 3.1 / 7.0 / 2.9
2 TU	0046 / 0635 / 1328 / 1910	2.4 / 7.5 / 2.6 / 7.5	**17** W	0520 / 1209 / 1758	6.9 / 3.2 / 6.9
3 W	0211 / 0757 / 1447 / 2027	2.3 / 7.7 / 2.2 / 7.8	**18** TH	0048 / 0648 / 1333 / 1923	2.9 / 7.1 / 2.9 / 7.2
4 TH	0323 / 0902 / 1553 / 2126	1.9 / 8.2 / 1.8 / 8.3	**19** F	0210 / 0801 / 1449 / 2028	2.5 / 7.6 / 2.3 / 7.8
5 F	0423 / 0953 / 1647 / 2213	1.5 / 8.7 / 1.4 / 8.7	**20** SA	0318 / 0859 / 1550 / 2123	1.9 / 8.3 / 1.7 / 8.5
6 SA	0511 / 1035 / 1730 / 2253	1.3 / 9.0 / 1.3 / 8.9	**21** SU	0417 / 0949 / 1646 / 2213	1.4 / 8.9 / 1.2 / 9.0
7 SU	0550 / 1113 / 1807 / 2329	1.2 / 9.1 / 1.2 / 9.0	**22** M	0511 / 1037 / 1738 / 2300	1.0 / 9.3 / 0.8 / 9.4
8 M	0624 / 1146 / 1839 / ●	1.2 / 9.1 / 1.2	**23** TU	0602 / 1123 / 1828 / O 2347	0.7 / 9.6 / 0.6 / 9.7
9 TU	0001 / 0655 / 1217 / 1911	9.0 / 1.2 / 9.1 / 1.2	**24** W	0650 / 1208 / 1916	0.6 / 9.8 / 0.5
10 W	0032 / 0726 / 1247 / 1942	9.0 / 1.3 / 9.0 / 1.3	**25** TH	0033 / 0736 / 1253 / 2002	9.8 / 0.6 / 9.8 / 0.5
11 TH	0104 / 0756 / 1318 / 2011	8.9 / 1.4 / 8.9 / 1.4	**26** F	0119 / 0820 / 1339 / 2046	9.7 / 0.7 / 9.6 / 0.7
12 F	0135 / 0823 / 1348 / 2038	8.6 / 1.7 / 8.6 / 1.7	**27** SA	0207 / 0904 / 1427 / 2131	9.4 / 1.1 / 9.2 / 1.0
13 SA	0205 / 0850 / 1418 / 2107	8.3 / 2.0 / 8.2 / 2.0	**28** SU	0256 / 0950 / 1517 / 2219	8.9 / 1.5 / 8.7 / 1.5
14 SU	0238 / 0922 / 1452 / 2142	8.0 / 2.4 / 7.8 / 2.4	**29** M	0350 / 1042 / 1614 / 2314	8.4 / 2.0 / 8.1 / 1.9
15 M	0316 / 1002 / 1536 / 2229	7.6 / 2.8 / 7.4 / 2.7	**30** TU	0451 / 1144 / 1719	7.9 / 2.3 / 7.7

DECEMBER

Day	Time	m	Day	Time	m
1 W	0020 / 0600 / 1255 / 1831	2.3 / 7.6 / 2.5 / 7.5	**16** TH	0442 / 1133 / 1712	7.4 / 2.7 / 7.3
2 TH	0131 / 0714 / 1406 / 1946	2.3 / 7.6 / 2.4 / 7.6	**17** F	0004 / 0552 / 1242 / 1826	2.7 / 7.4 / 2.7 / 7.4
3 F	0240 / 0823 / 1512 / 2051	2.2 / 7.9 / 2.1 / 7.9	**18** SA	0116 / 0708 / 1358 / 1941	2.4 / 7.6 / 2.4 / 7.7
4 SA	0342 / 0919 / 1609 / 2142	2.0 / 8.2 / 1.8 / 8.2	**19** SU	0231 / 0816 / 1510 / 2046	2.1 / 8.1 / 1.9 / 8.2
5 SU	0433 / 1005 / 1656 / 2225	1.7 / 8.5 / 1.6 / 8.4	**20** M	0339 / 0916 / 1614 / 2144	1.6 / 8.6 / 1.4 / 8.7
6 M	0515 / 1044 / 1736 / 2302	1.6 / 8.7 / 1.5 / 8.6	**21** TU	0440 / 1010 / 1712 / 2238	1.2 / 9.1 / 1.0 / 9.2
7 TU	0553 / 1119 / 1812 / ● 2336	1.5 / 8.8 / 1.4 / 8.7	**22** W	0536 / 1101 / 1807 / O 2329	0.9 / 9.4 / 0.7 / 9.5
8 W	0627 / 1151 / 1847	1.4 / 8.9 / 1.3	**23** TH	0630 / 1151 / 1859	0.7 / 9.7 / 0.5
9 TH	0010 / 0701 / 1224 / 1920	8.7 / 1.4 / 8.9 / 1.3	**24** F	0019 / 0721 / 1240 / 1949	9.6 / 0.6 / 9.7 / 0.4
10 F	0043 / 0734 / 1256 / 1952	8.7 / 1.5 / 8.8 / 1.4	**25** SA	0108 / 0809 / 1328 / 2037	9.6 / 0.7 / 9.6 / 0.5
11 SA	0115 / 0804 / 1329 / 2022	8.7 / 1.7 / 8.7 / 1.5	**26** SU	0156 / 0856 / 1416 / 2123	9.5 / 0.9 / 9.4 / 0.8
12 SU	0148 / 0835 / 1402 / 2054	8.5 / 1.8 / 8.4 / 1.7	**27** M	0244 / 0941 / 1503 / 2207	9.1 / 1.2 / 9.0 / 1.2
13 M	0223 / 0908 / 1438 / 2129	8.2 / 2.1 / 8.1 / 2.0	**28** TU	0332 / 1026 / 1552 / 2252	8.7 / 1.6 / 8.5 / 1.5
14 TU	0301 / 0947 / 1519 / 2211	7.9 / 2.3 / 7.8 / 2.2	**29** W	0422 / 1114 / 1644 / 2341	8.2 / 2.0 / 8.0 / 2.0
15 W	0346 / 1034 / 1609 / 2302	7.6 / 2.6 / 7.5 / 2.4	**30** TH	0516 / 1208 / 1743	7.8 / 2.3 / 7.5
			31 F	0037 / 0618 / 1310 / 1850	2.4 / 7.5 / 2.5 / 7.3

Chart Datum: 4·43 metres below Lallemand System (Mean Sea Level, Marseilles)

19

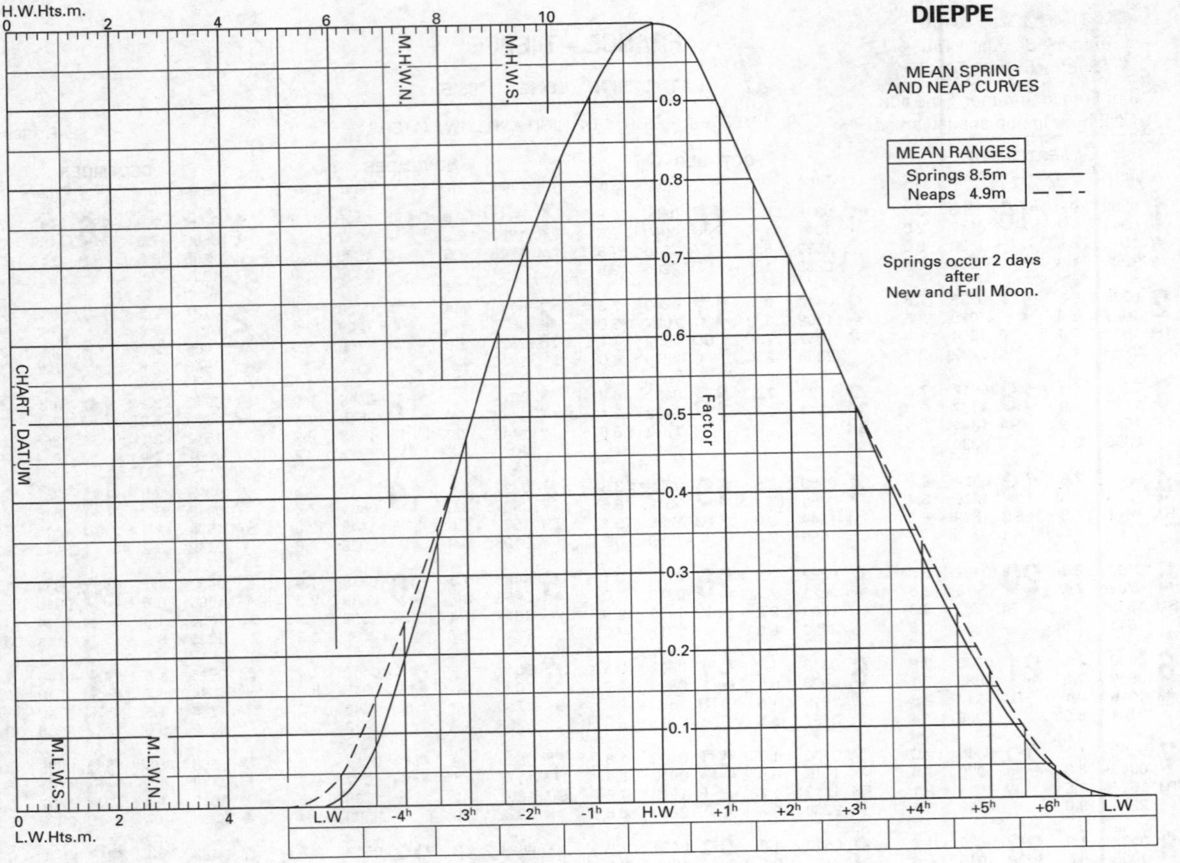

DIEPPE

MEAN SPRING
AND NEAP CURVES

MEAN RANGES	
Springs	8.5m
Neaps	4.9m

Springs occur 2 days
after
New and Full Moon.

H.W.Hts.m.

CHART DATUM

M.H.W.N. M.H.W.S.

M.L.W.S. M.L.W.N.

L.W.Hts.m.

Factor

L.W -4h -3h -2h -1h H.W +1h +2h +3h +4h +5h +6h L.W

DIEPPE

8-19-23

Seine Maritime 49°56'·36N 01°05'·08E   Rtg 1-1-1

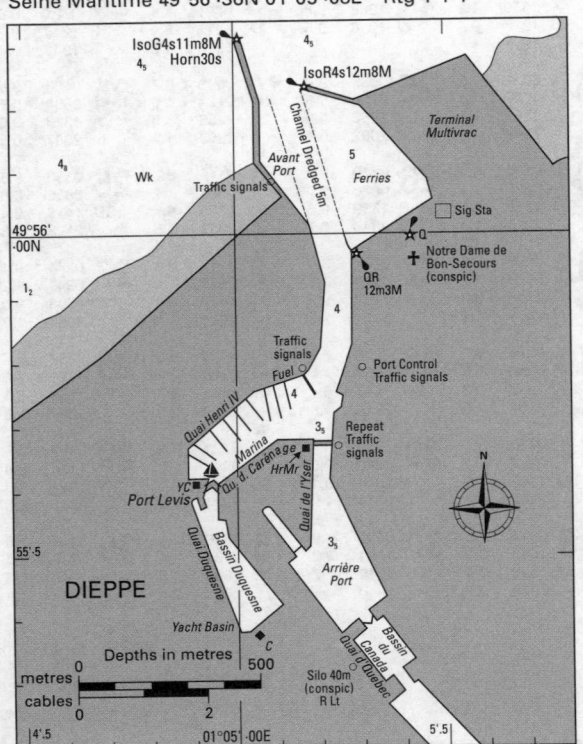

DIEPPE

CHARTS
AC 2147, *2451*; SHOM 7317, 7083, 6824; ECM 1011, 1012;
Imray C31; Stanfords 1

TIDES
−0011 Dover; ML 4·9; Duration 0535; Zone −0100
NOTE: Dieppe is a Standard Port. Tidal predictions for
each day of the year are given above.

SHELTER
Very good. Access all tides, but ent is exposed to winds
from NW to NE, causing a heavy scend. An effective
fixed wavebreak across the narrowest part of the chan
protects and gives access (about 30m wide) at its E end
to marina Jehan Ango (9 pontoons) in the Avant Port at
Quai Henri IV. Or yachts can lock into Bassin Duquesne
HW −2 to +1; bridge opens H and H+30 during each
period; berth in NW corner. The new ferry terminal is at
the E side of port ent. Yachts prohib in Arrière Port.

NAVIGATION
WPT 49°56'·48N 01°04'·60E, 298°/118° from/to W jetty
extension, 0·35M. Ent to hbr is simple, but beware strong
stream across ent. ‡ is prohib in a zone 5ca off pierhead.
Ent chan and Avant Port are dredged 5m. Entry/exit are
controlled during ferry movements. Due to restricted
visibility, yachts **must** request entry on Ch 12, 2M before
hbr ent; also 10 mins before leaving.

LIGHTS AND MARKS
Dieppe lies in a gap between high chalk cliffs, identified
by a castle with pinnacle roofs on the W side of the gap
and the conspic ch spire on the E cliff. ECM buoy (DI), VQ
(3) 5s, bell, is 2·5M WNW of hbr ent. W jetty head, Iso G
4s 11m 8M, Horn 30s. E jetty head, Iso R 4s 12m 8M. Fl
Vio 4s at SW corner of ferry berths.

IPTS (full code) shown from stns at root of W jetty and on
W side of hbr; repeated (simplified code) where shown
on chartlet.

DIEPPE *continued*

Extra sigs combined with IPTS:
Ⓖ to right = Ferry entering; Ⓡ to right = Ferry leaving.
Ⓦ to left = Bassin Duquesne lock gates open.
ⓇⓇ (hor) to right = Dredger in chan.
Lock sigs at Bassin Duquesne: 2 Ⓖ (vert) = closed.
Request bridge & lock to open = Sound 2 blasts; request will not be met unil H or H+30 within period HW−2 to +1.
Ⓖ = Enter, no exit; Ⓡ = No exit (shown only into Bassin Duquesne).

RADIO TELEPHONE
Dieppe Port VHF Ch **12** (HO) 16 (H24) for entry/depart; see NAVIGATION. Ch 09 for marina which also monitors Ch 12.

TELEPHONE
Hr Mr 02.35.84.8.55; Marina 02.35.40.19.79; Aff Mar 02.35.06.96.70; CROSS 03.21.87.21.87; ⌗ 02.35.82.24.47; SNSM 02.35.84.8.55; Météo 03.21.31.52.23; Auto 08.36.68.08.76; Police 02.35.06.96.74; Ⓗ 02.35.06.76.76; Brit Consul 02.35.42.27.47.

FACILITIES
Port de Plaisance (Jehan Ango) ☎ 02.35.40.19.79 (380 inc 50 Ⓥ) FF130, FW, AC, D by credit card-operated pumps H24 (P by cans), C (12 ton);
Bassin Duquesne (80 inc 50 Ⓥ, but mostly now used by locals) ☎ 02.35.84.22.99, FW, AC, C (30 & 3 ton); **Cercle de la Voile de Dieppe** ☎ 02.35.84.22.99, FW, R, Bar;
Services: ME, El, Ⓔ, Sh, CH, Sh. **Town** P, D, FW, V, Gaz, R, Bar, ✉, ▣, Ⓑ, ⇌, ✈. Ferry: Dieppe - Newhaven.

LE TRÉPORT   8-19-24

Seine Maritime 50°03'·95N 01°22'·24E   Rtg 3-2-2

CHARTS
AC 1352, 2147, 2612, *2451*; SHOM 7207, 7083, 6824; ECM 1011; Imray C31; Stanfords 1

TIDES
−0025 Dover; ML 5·0; Duration 0530; Zone −0100

Standard Port DIEPPE (⟵)

Times				Height (metres)			
High Water		Low Water		MHWS	MHWN	MLWN	MLWS
0100	0600	0100	0700	9·3	7·4	2·5	0·8
1300	1800	1300	1900				
Differences LE TRÉPORT							
+0005	0000	+0007	+0007	+0·1	+0·1	0·0	+0·1
CAYEUX							
0000	+0005	+0015	+0010	+0·5	+0·6	+0·4	+0·4

SHELTER
Good in marina at S side of first S Basin (3·7m), E of FVs. But ent chan and most of Avant Port dry; S side is dredged 1·5m, but prone to silting. Lock opens HW±4 1 Mar-1 Dec; other months HW ±3. E of the marina a lifting bridge gives access to extra berths in 2nd basin dredged 2m. Port de Commerce is only used by yachts as an overflow.

NAVIGATION
WPT 50°04'·30N 01°21'·70E, 315°/135° from/to ent, 0·52M. Coast dries to approx 300m off the pier hds. Shingle spit extends NW from E pier hd; keep well to the W. Entry difficult in strong on-shore winds which cause scend in Avant Port.

LIGHTS AND MARKS
Le Tréport is identified between high chalk cliffs, with crucifix (lit) above town and conspic church S of hbr. No ldg lts/marks. IPTS were installed 1996, as shown. W jetty Fl (2) G 10s 15m 20M. E jetty Oc R 4s 8m 6M.
Lock sigs shown from head of dredged/piled chan to S Basin: Ⓖ = enter lock; Ⓡ = no entry.

RADIO TELEPHONE
Call: *Capitainerie Le Tréport* VHF Ch 12 16 (HW ±3).

TELEPHONE
Hr Mr 02.35.86.17.91, ⚓ 02.35.86.60.11; Lock (to marina) 02.35.50.63.06; Aff Mar 02.35.06.96.70; SNSM 02.35.86.8.91; Auto 08.36.68.08.76; CROSS 03.21.87.21.87; ⌗ 02.35.86.15.34; Police 02.35.86.12.11; Dr 02.35.86.16.23; Brit Consul 03.21.96.33.76.

FACILITIES
Marina (130+10) FF105.48, AC, FW; **Avant Port** M;
Port de Commerce C (10 ton);
YC de la Bresle ☎ 02.35.86.19.93, C, Bar; **Services:** ME, CH, El, Ⓔ, P, D, Gaz.
Town P, D, V, Gaz, R, Bar, ✉, Ⓑ, ⇌, ✈ (Dieppe). Ferry: Dieppe.

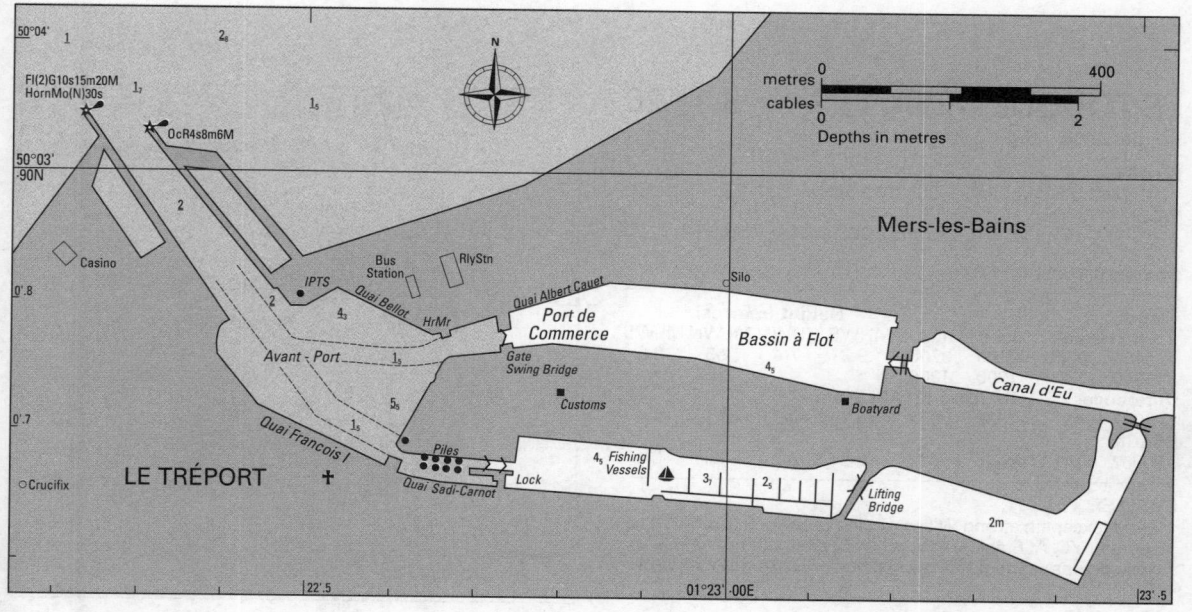

ST VALÉRY-SUR-SOMME/ LE CROTOY 8-19-25

Somme Rtg 3-3-2

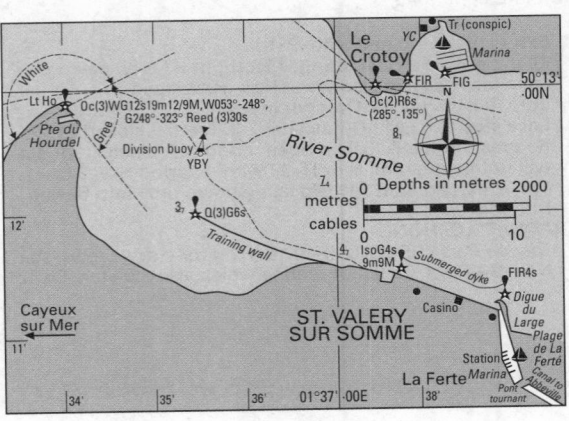

CHARTS
AC *2451*; SHOM 7416; ECM 1011; Imray C31; Stanfords 1
TIDES
LE HOURDEL −0010 Dover; ML —; Zone −0100

Standard Port DIEPPE (◄—)

Times				Height (metres)			
High Water		Low Water		MHWS	MHWN	MLWN	MLWS
0100	0600	0100	0700	9·3	7·4	2·5	0·8
1300	1800	1300	1900				
Differences ST VALÉRY-SUR-SOMME							
+0035	+0035	No data		+0·9	+0·7	No data	
LE HOURDEL							
+0020	+0020	No data		+0·8	+0·6	No data	

SHELTER
The B de Somme is open to W and can be dangerous in onshore winds >F6. Silting is a major problem. All 3 very well sheltered hbrs (ie Le Hourdel, Le Crotoy and St Valéry-sur-Somme) are FV ports; small cargo vessels very occasionally berth at St Valéry town quay. Options:
(1) dry out on hard sand at Le Hourdel; access HW±1½.
(2) enter Le Crotoy marina when tidal range at Dover >4·4m (approx Coefficient 85) with max. draft 1·5m.
(3) enter (HW ±1) St Valéry marina (max. draft 2·5m).
(4) enter Abbeville Canal at St Valéry (max. draft 3m up to Abbeville) by prior arrangement and daylight only.
NAVIGATION
WPT 'ATSO' NCM By, VQ, 50°14'·29N 01°28'·65E, about 1M W of buoyed chan (shifts). From N, beware being set by the flood onto shoals off Pte St Quentin. The whole estuary dries up to 3M seaward of Le Hourdel. The sands build up in ridges offshore, but inside Pte du Hourdel are generally flat, except where R Somme and minor streams scour their way to the sea. If Dover tidal range >4·4m, at HW ±1 there is sufficient water over the sands inside Pte du Hourdel for vessels <1·5m draft.
Start appr from 'ATSO' at HW St Valéry −2. Buoys are moved to suit ever-shifting chans. Follow chan with lateral buoys numbered S1 to S50 (some lit), in strict order (no corner-cutting!) to small unlit WCM Division buoy, in variable position E of Pte du Hourdel; then see below. Departure from Le Hourdel/Le Crotoy is not possible before HW −2; St Valéry HW−2, for a fair tide if N-bound.
LIGHTS AND MARKS
Only landmark is Cayeux-sur-Mer lt ho (W with R top) Fl R 5s 32m 22M (off chartlet to SSW). Pte du Hourdel lt ho Oc (3) WG 12s 19m 12/9M. Le Crotoy Oc (2) R 6s 19m 9M.

LE HOURDEL: Chan unmarked; follow 'S' buoys, then head SW toward end of shingle spit; hug the shingle.
LE CROTOY: From Division By chan runs N & E with lateral Bys C1 to C8. Enter hbr very close to FV stages (port-side). Secure at last FV stage and ask YC for berth. Tidal hbr badly silted, with 2 drying pontoons.
ST VALÉRY-SUR-SOMME: From Division buoy, buoyed chan continues with SHMs becoming bns on submerged training wall, the seaward end of which is lit, Q (3) G 6s 2m 2M; then four bns on end of groynes. Iso G 4s 9m 9M marks beginning of tree-lined promenade; submerged dyke opposite marked with PHM bns. W tr on head of Digue du Large, Fl R 4s 9m 9M, leads into marina, dredged 2m, and town quay.
RADIO TELEPHONE
VHF Ch 09 (St Valéry HW ±2; Le Crotoy YC Jul/Aug only).
TELEPHONE
St Valéry Hr Mr 03.22.26.91.64; Le Crotoy (Port de plaisance) 03.22.27.83.11; Aff Mar 03.22.27.81.44; ∰ 03.22.24.04.75; Lock (canal) 03.22.60.80.23; CROSS 03.21.87.21.87; Auto 08.36.68.08.80; Police 03.22.60.82.08; Dr 03.22.26.92.25; Brit Consul 03.21.96.33.76.
FACILITIES
ST VALÉRY
Marina and YC Sport Nautique Valéricain (250 + 30 Ⓥ) ☎ 03.22.26.91.64, FF82, FW, AC, C (6 ton), Slip, R, ▣, Bar; Access HW±1; **Services:** ME, El, CH, Ⓔ, charts.
Town EC Mon; P, D, CH, V, Gaz, R, Bar, ✉, Ⓑ, ⇌ and ✈ (Abbeville). Ferry: See Boulogne.
LE CROTOY
Marina (280) ☎ 03.22.27.83.11, FW, C (6 ton), Slip; **YC Nautique de la Baie de Somme** ☎ 03.22.27.83.11, Bar.
Town EC Mon; Ⓑ, Bar, D, P, ✉, R, ⇌, V.

LE TOUQUET/ÉTAPLES 8-19-26

Pas de Calais Rtg 4-3-2

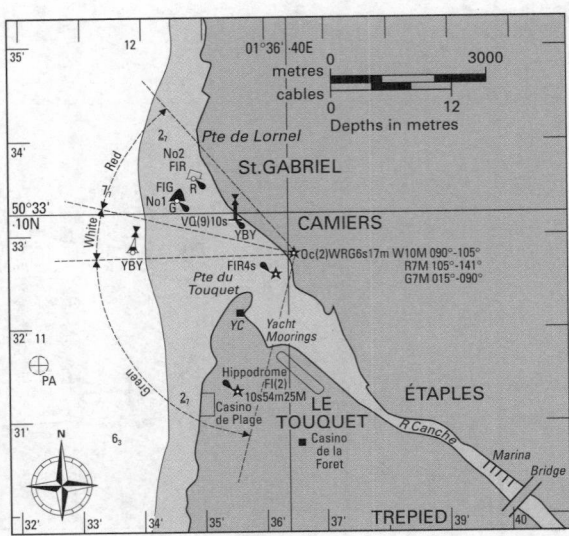

CHARTS
AC *2451*; SHOM 7416; ECM 1011; Imray C31; Stanfords 1, 9
TIDES
−0010 Dover; ML 5·3; Duration 0520; Zone −0100

Standard Port DIEPPE (◄—)

Times				Height (metres)			
High Water		Low Water		MHWS	MHWN	MLWN	MLWS
0100	0600	0100	0700	9·3	7·4	2·5	0·8
1300	1800	1300	1900				
Differences LE TOUQUET (ÉTAPLES)							
+0007	+0017	+0032	+0032	+0·2	+0·3	+0·4	+0·4
BERCK							
+0007	+0017	+0028	+0028	+0·5	+0·5	+0·4	+0·4

SHELTER
Good, except in strong W'lies. Drying moorings to stbd off Le Touquet YC. At Étaples, access HW±2 to small marina (1.2m) close downstream of low bridge; beware strong 5kn current.

LE TOUQUET/ÉTAPLES continued

NAVIGATION

WPT 50°35'.00N 01°31'.80E, 308°/128° from/to Camiers lt, 3·8M. Appr & ent are not easy; estuary dries 2M offshore. In even moderate SW/W winds seas break heavily a long way out and entry should not be attempted. Best app is at HW −1 to reach Étaples marina at slack water. The chan is always shifting and buoys, some lit, are moved accordingly; prior info advised. Drying wreck 2M NW of Le Touquet lt ho, is marked by unlit WCM Mérida buoy.

LIGHTS AND MARKS

Le Touquet is at the S end of the Terres de Tourmont, a conspic range 175m high, visible for 25M.
Appr between Pte de Lornel and Pte du Touquet, where La Canche lt ho is conspic Or tr, brown band, W & G top, Fl (2) 10s 54m 25M.
Camiers lt Oc (2) WRG 6s 17m 9/6M (R pylon hard to see by day) is on NE side of estuary. Chan ent usually lies in It's R sector (105°-141°), but may lie in G sector, (015°-090°) ie S of the WCM wreck buoy, which is itself within the W sector (090°-105°).
Canche No 2 PHM buoy, Fl (2) R 6s, is first lateral chan buoy; essential to follow the buoys; do not cut corners.

Bn, Fl R 4s 8m 2M, approx 4ca SW of Camiers Lt, marks the seaward end of sunken training wall defining NE side of River Canche to marina; wall also marked by posts.

RADIO TELEPHONE

VHF Ch 09 (both hbrs), 77 (Le Touquet only).

TELEPHONE

Hr Mr Le Touquet 03.21.05.12.77; Hr Mr Étaples 03.21.84.54.33, 🕭 03.21.09.76.96; Aff Mar Étaples 03.21.94.61.50; Auto 08.36.68.08.62; ⌗ 03.21.05.01.72; CROSS 03.21.87.21.87; Police 03.21.94.60.17; Dr 03.21.05.14.42; Brit Consul 03.21.96.33.76.

FACILITIES

LE TOUQUET
Cercle Nautique du Touquet ☎ 03.21.05.12.77, M, P, Slip, ME, D, FW, C, CH, R, Bar; **Services:** BY, Sh, SM.
Town P, D, V, Gaz, R, Bar, ⊠, Ⓑ, ⇌, ✈.
ÉTAPLES
Marina (115 + 15 visitors), FF85, FW, C (8 ton), AC, P, D;
Quay BH (130 ton), FW, Slip; **Centre Nautique de la Canche** ☎ 03.21.94.74.26, Bar, Slip;
Services: CH, El, Ⓔ, M, ME, Sh, D.
Town Ⓑ, Bar, D, P, ⊠, R, ⇌, V. ✈ Le Touquet. Ferry: Boulogne-Folkestone.

BOULOGNE-SUR-MER   8-19-27

Pas de Calais 50°44'.56N 01°34'.13E   Rtg 2-2-2

CHARTS

AC 438, *1892, 2451*; SHOM 7247,7323, 7416; ECM 1010, 1011; Imray C31, C8; Stanfords 1, 9, 20

TIDES

0000 Dover; ML 4·9; Duration 0515; Zone −0100

Standard Port DUNKERQUE (→)

Times				Height (metres)			
High Water		Low Water		MHWS	MHWN	MLWN	MLWS
0200	0800	0200	0900	6·0	5·0	1·5	0·6
1400	2000	1400	2100				
Differences BOULOGNE							
−0045	−0100	−0045	−0025	+2·8	+2·2	+1·1	+0·5

SHELTER

Good, except in strong NW'lies. Ent possible at all tides and in most weather. Very busy ferry and FV port; beware wash from FVs. Marina pontoons (2·9m) are on SW side of tidal basin alongside Quai Chanzy; max LOA 10m. If >10m, pre-arrange. No yacht berths on Quai Gambetta; FVs only. When R Liane in spate beware turbulent water.

NAVIGATION

WPT 50°44'.50N 01°33'.00E, 270°/090° from/to S bkwtr (Digue Carnot) lt, 0·72M. Fairway buoy SCM, VQ (6) + L Fl 10s, is 295°/2·1M from S bkwtr lt. Cap d'Alprech lt ho, Fl (3) 15s 62m 23M, is 2·5M S of hbr ent. E side of hbr dries. Obey IPTS from SW jetty (see below). No navigational dangers and ent is easily identified and well marked, but keep W and S of Digue Nord lt tr, Fl (2) R 6s, as outer half of bkwtr covers at HW.

LIGHTS AND MARKS

Monument tr is conspic 2M E of hbr ent. Cathedral dome is conspic, 0·62M E of marina. St Nicolas Ch spire leads 123° through Avant Port. Ldg lts 123°: front 3 FG in ▽; rear Dir FR, intens 113°-133°, lead towards marina. 2 Bu lts (hor) upriver of marina = sluicing from R Liane.
IPTS are shown from SW jetty hd (FG ☆), and from Quai Gambetta, opposite ☆ 3FG ▽ (chartlet), visible from marina. One Ⓡ (below IPTS) = dredger working (this does not prohibit movements).

RADIO TELEPHONE

VHF Ch **12** (H24). Marina Ch 09. Forecasts by CROSS Gris Nez Ch 79 at H+10 (078-1910LT).

TELEPHONE

Hr Mr 03.21.80.72.00; Hr Mr Plaisance 03.21.31.70.01; Control Tr 03.21.31.52.43; Aff Mar 03.21.30.53.23; CROSS 03.21.87.21.87; Météo03. 21.83.53.71; Auto 08.36.65.08.08; Police 03.21.31.75.17; Emergency 17; Ⓗ 03.21.99.33.33; Brit Consul 03.21.96.33.76.

FACILITIES

Marina (114 + 17 Ⓥ, at least) ☎ 03.21.31.70.01, FF102, FW, AC, D, Slip, C (20 ton); **Quai Gambetta** FVs only; **YC Boulonnais** ☎ 03.21.31.80.67, C, R, Bar;
Services: Ⓔ, ME, El, Sh, M, Divers, SHOM;
Town P (cans), V, Gas, Gaz, R, Bar, ⊠, Ⓑ, ⇌, ✈ (Le Touquet). SeaCat to Folkestone.

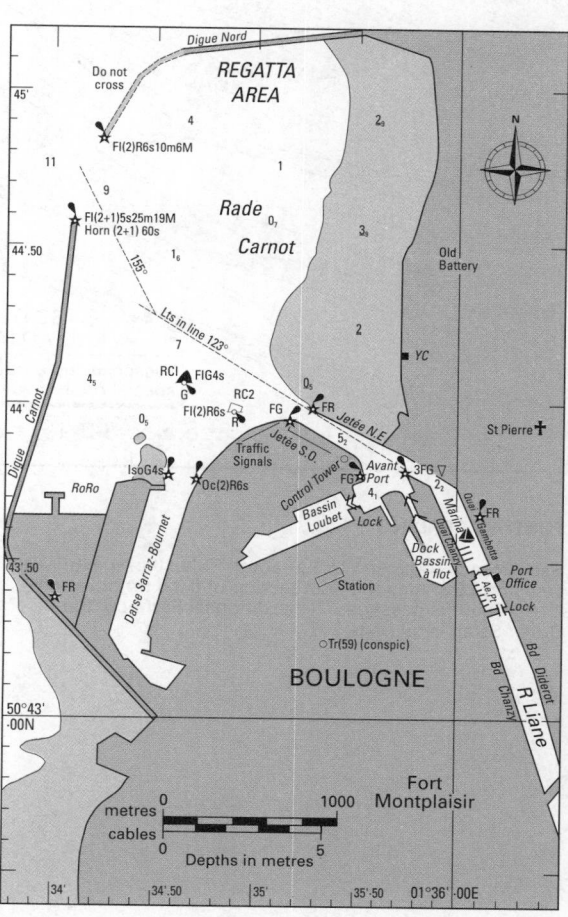

19

DOVER STRAIT TRAFFIC SEPARATION SCHEME

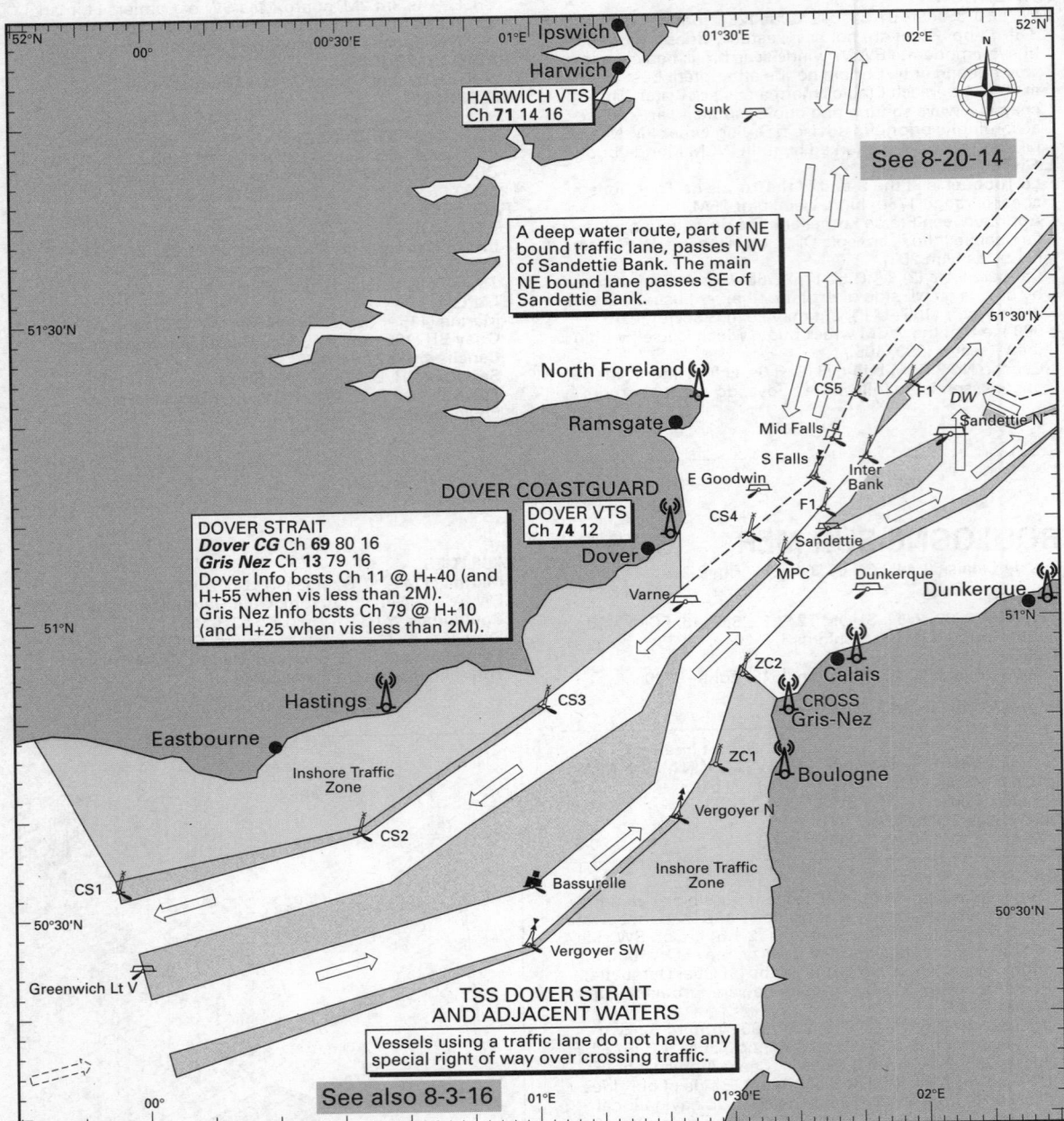

See 8-20-14

A deep water route, part of NE bound traffic lane, passes NW of Sandettie Bank. The main NE bound lane passes SE of Sandettie Bank.

HARWICH VTS
Ch 71 14 16

DOVER COASTGUARD

DOVER VTS
Ch 74 12

DOVER STRAIT
Dover CG Ch 69 80 16
Gris Nez Ch 13 79 16
Dover Info bcsts Ch 11 @ H+40 (and H+55 when vis less than 2M).
Gris Nez Info bcsts Ch 79 @ H+10 (and H+25 when vis less than 2M).

Inshore Traffic Zone

Inshore Traffic Zone

TSS DOVER STRAIT
AND ADJACENT WATERS

Vessels using a traffic lane do not have any special right of way over crossing traffic.

See also 8-3-16

FURTHER READING

See notes in Chapter 1 (1.1.2) about Rule 10 of the IRPCS, crossing TSS. Also the final section of 8.3.5 for notes on cross-Channel passages. An additional chartlet of the Dover Strait is on page 267.

CALAIS   8-19-29

Pas de Calais 50°58'·34N 01°50'·50E   Rtg 3-3-2

CHARTS
AC 1352, *1892, 323*; SHOM 7258, 6651; ECM 1010; Imray C8; Stanfords 1, 20

TIDES
+0048 Dover; ML 4·0; Duration 0525; Zone –0100

Standard Port DUNKERQUE (⟶)

Times				Height (metres)			
High Water		Low Water		MHWS	MHWN	MLWN	MLWS
0200	0800	0200	0900	6·0	5·0	1·5	0·6
1400	2000	1400	2100				
Differences CALAIS							
–0020	–0030	–0015	–0005	+1·2	+0·9	+0·6	+0·3

SHELTER
Very good, especially in the marina at Bassin de l'Ouest (3-6m). R waiting buoys outside lock (times below). Ent is rough with heavy swell in strong NW to NE winds; access H24. Enter Bassin Carnot only if bound for the canals.

NAVIGATION
WPT 50°58'·50N 01°49'·90E, 298°/118° from/to Jetée Ouest lt, 0·43M. Beware the Ridens de la Rade, about 4ca N of ent, a partly drying (0·6m) sandbank on which seas break. From the E it may be best to keep seaward of this bank until able to round CA8 PHM lt buoy and appr from 1M W of hbr. Byelaws require yachts to have engine running (even if sailing) and not to impede commercial vessels/ferries. Ent is relatively easy and well marked but there is much shipping. Keep a good lookout.

LIGHTS AND MARKS
Cap Blanc-Nez and Dover Patrol monument are conspic 5·5M WSW of hbr ent. Several churches and bldgs in the town are conspic. From a position ¼M SE of CA 10 PHM buoy, Fl (2) R 6s, the main lt ho (conspic), Fl (4) 15s, leads 141° through ent. The intens sector (115·5°-121·5°) of Dir FR 14m 14M at Gare Maritime leads close past the W jetty Iso G 3s. Hbr Control is conspic, pyramidal bldg on port-side as Arrière Port is entered.

IPTS (full code), shown from Hbr Control, to be obeyed. If no sigs are shown (ie no ferries under way), yachts may enter/leave. Or they may follow a ferry entering/leaving, keeping to the stbd side of the fairway. Supplementary traffic sigs, shown alongside the top IPTS lt, are:
Ⓡ = ferry leaving; no movements.
Ⓖ = ferry entering; no movements.
One Ⓡ (alongside lower IPTS lt) = dredger working, (this does not prohibit movements).
Bassin de l'Ouest: Lock gates and bridge open HW –1½, HW and HW +½. (Sat and Sun HW –2, HW and HW +1).
Ⓨ   = 10 mins before lock opens.
Ⓡ   = All movements prohib.
Ⓖ   = Movement authorised.
4 blasts   = Request permission to enter.
Prior to leaving, best to tell bridge operator your ETD.
Bassin Carnot: Gates open HW –1½ to HW +¾. Lock sigs:
ⓖⓖ (hor) = Enter.
ⓡⓡ (hor) = Do not enter.
Ⓖ   = Exit from basin permitted.
Ⓡ   = Do not exit from basin.
2 blasts   = Request permission to enter.

RADIO TELEPHONE
Whilst underway in appr's and hbr, keep a close listening watch on Ch **12** 16 (H24) *Calais Port Traffic* and marina. Carnot lock Ch 12 (occas). Hoverport Ch 20 (occas). Cap Gris Nez, Channel Navigation Info Service (CNIS), call: *Gris Nez Traffic* Ch **13** 79 16 (H24). Info broadcasts in English and French on Ch 79, at H + 10, and also at H + 25 when vis is < 2M. *CROSS Gris Nez* Ch 15, 67, **68**, 73.

TELEPHONE
Hr Mr (Marina) 03.21.34.55.23; Hr Mr (Port) 03.21.96.31.20; Aff Mar 03.21.34.52.70; CROSS 03.21.87.21.87; SNSM 03.21.96.31.20; ⌗ 03.21.34.75.40; Météo 03.21.33.24.25; Auto 08.36.68.08.62; Police 03.21.96.74.17; Ⓗ 03.21.46.33.33; Brit Consul 03.21.96.33.76.

FACILITIES
Marina (350 + 400 Ⓥ) ☎ 03.21.34.55.23, ⛽ 03.21.96.10.78. AB pontoon: 52FF summer; AB quay: 26FF summer. D, P (cans), FW, BH (3 ton), AC, CH, Gaz, R, Ⓞ, Sh, SM, V, Bar; Access HW –1½ to HW +½; **YC de Calais** ☎ 03.21.97.02.34, M, P, Bar; **Town** CH, SM, ME, V, Gaz, R, Bar, ✉, Ⓑ, ⇌, ✈. Ferry: Dover.

CALAIS

19

MINOR HARBOUR (10M W of Dunkerque Est)

GRAVELINES, Nord, 51°00'·90N 02°05'·75E, AC 1350, *323;*
SHOM 7057, 6651. HW +0045 on Dover (UT); ML 3·3m;
Duration 0520. See 8.19.30. Good shelter, but chan dries
1·5m. Safest entry HW −1; do not attempt it in strong
onshore winds. Appr to bkwtrs, with old lt ho (unlit,
conspic B/W spiral) in transit with wtr tr 142°. Nuclear
power stn 1M NE. Beware strong E-going stream across
ent at HW.
Keep to W on entry and to E when inside. Hbr dries (soft
mud). Yachts may take the ground or enter Bassin
Vauban via lock open HW ±1½; waiting pontoon outside.
Lts: W bkwtr, Fl (2) WG 6s 9m 8M, vis G078°-085° (very
close inshore from W), W085°-244° (seaward arc), W317°-
327° (within ent chan); E bkwtr, Fl (3) R 12s 5m 6M; 130m
N of this lt is a NCM bn, VQ 6m 4M.
VHF Ch 09 (HO). Aff Mar ☎ 03.28.23.06.12. Facilities: **Bassin
Vauban** (410+40) ☎ 03.28.23.13.42, FW, AC, BH (12 ton),
C (3 ton); **YC Gravelines** ☎ 03.28.23.14.68, M, C (10 ton);
Services: CH, El, M, ME, Sh.
Town Ⓑ, Bar, D, P, ✉, R, ⇌, V, ▣.

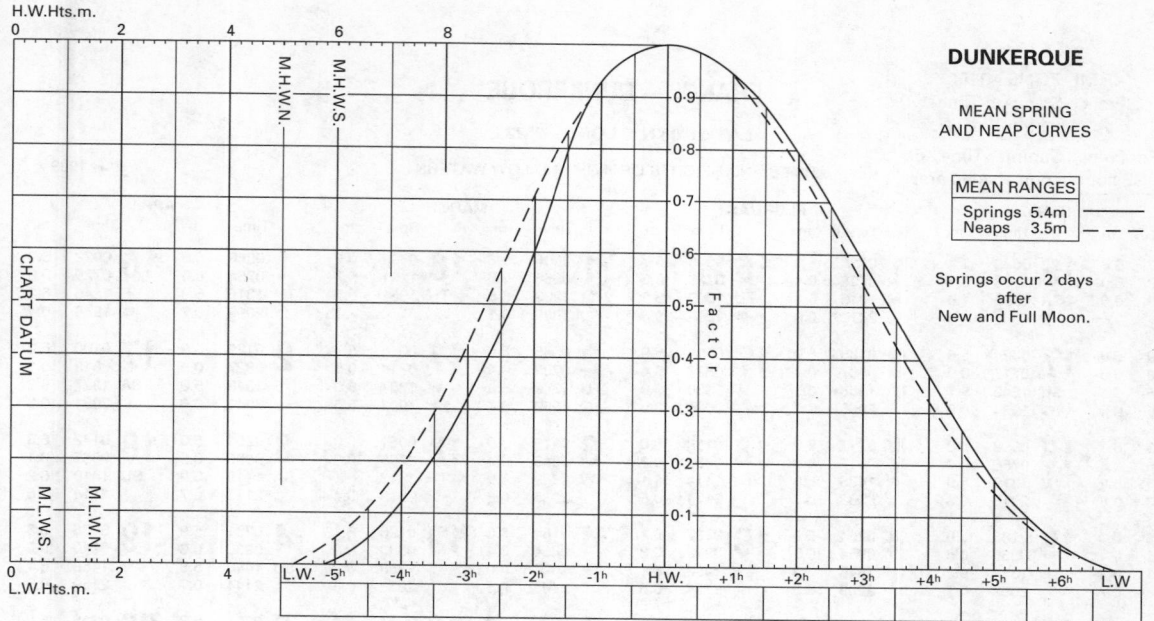

H.W.Hts.m.

DUNKERQUE

MEAN SPRING
AND NEAP CURVES

MEAN RANGES	
Springs	5.4m
Neaps	3.5m

Springs occur 2 days
after
New and Full Moon.

L.W.Hts.m.

DUNKERQUE (Port Est)   8-19-30
Nord 51°03'·67N 02°21'·10E

CHARTS
AC 1350, *323*, 1872; SHOM 7057, 6651; ECM 1010; Imray
C30; Stanfords 1, 20
TIDES
+0050 Dover; ML 3·2; Duration 0530; Zone –0100

Standard Port DUNKERQUE (→)

Times				Height (metres)			
High Water		Low Water		MHWS	MHWN	MLWN	MLWS
0200	0800	0200	0900	6·0	5·0	1·5	0·6
1400	2000	1400	2100				
Differences WISSANT (8M WSW of Calais)							
–0035	–0050	–0030	–0010	+2·0	+1·5	+0·8	+0·4
SANDETTIE BANK (11M N of Calais)							
–0015	–0025	–0020	–0005	+0·1	–0·1	–0·1	–0·1
GRAVELINES (10M ENE of Calais)							
–0005	–0015	–0005	+0005	+0·3	+0·1	–0·1	–0·1

SHELTER
Good; hbr accessible at all tides/weather, but fresh NW–
NE winds cause heavy seas at ent and scend in hbr. Yachts
must use E Port (a busy commercial port), **not** the W Port
(ferry). Choice of 2 tidal marinas ¾M down E side of hbr:
Port du Grand Large or YCMN, almost ; or enter non-tidal
marinas in Bassin du Commerce and Bassin de la Marine
via Ecluse Trystram or Watier and three swing bridges.
NAVIGATION
WPT (E Port) 51°03'·90N 02°21'·00E, 355°/175° from/to
Jetée Ouest lt, 0·20M. From the W, fetch the Dunkerque
Lanby (Fl 3s), 5M N of Calais, thence to DKA SWM buoy
(L Fl 10s), and then via series of DW lt buoys past W Port
to DW 29 SHM buoy, ½M WNW of ent. From the E, via
Nieuwpoort Bank WCM buoy, Q (9) 15s, the E1-12 buoys
(8.19.4) lead S of Banc Hills. Streams reach about 3½kn.
LIGHTS AND MARKS
Two power stn chimneys (113m) are conspic 1M WSW of
hbr ent. Main lt ho Fl (2) 10s 59m 28M, W tr with B top.
Ldg lts: Outer (both F Vi) lead 179° through ent. A second
pair, with common rear, lead 185°. (Both pairs are "Big
Ship").
Inner, both Oc (2) 6s, lead 137° toward marinas. The East
jetty is also illuminated by 6 bright sodium lights.

IPTS (full) shown from head of Jetée Ouest.
Lock sigs (H24), shown at Ecluse Watier, consist of three
horiz pairs disposed vertically. Middle pair refer to Ecluse
Watier and lowest pair to Ecluse Trystram:

Ⓖ Ⓖ	=	lock open.
Ⓡ Ⓡ	=	lock closed.

Lock sigs at each lock:

Ⓖ Ⓖ	=	lock ready.
Ⓖ + Fl Ⓖ	=	enter and secure on side of Fl Ⓖ.
Ⓦ	=	enter lock; slack water, both gates
Ⓖ Ⓖ		open.
Ⓡ Ⓡ	=	lock in use, no entry.

RADIO TELEPHONE
Call *Dunkerque Port* VHF Ch 12 16 **73** (H24) for traffic info
(English spoken). Locks Ch 73. Marinas Ch 09.
TELEPHONE
Hr Mr 03.28.29.72.61, ☎ 03.28.29.72.75; ⌗ 03.28.64.78.16;
Port Control 03.28.29.72.87; Aff Mar 03.28.26.73.00;
CROSS 03.21.87.21.87; SNSM 03.28.66.86.14; Météo
03.28.66.45.25; Auto 08.36.68.08.59; Police 03.28.59.13.22;
Ⓗ 03.28.66.70.01; Brit Consul 03.28.66.33.33.
FACILITIES
Port du Grand Large (185+25 Ⓥ) ☎ 03.28.63.23.00,
☎ 03.28.66.66.62, FF65, H24 access (3m), FW, AC, BH (30
ton), YC, Bar, ▣;
YC Mer du Nord Marina (180+40 Ⓥ) ☎ 03.28.66.79.90,
☎ 03.28.66.36.62, FF95, approx 2m, Slip, D, P, FW, C (7½
ton), AC, ME, SM, R, Bar;
Access H24 via Ecluse Trystram, or Watier (unlikely), to
non-tidal marinas:
Bassin du Commerce (120+13 Ⓥ) YC de Dunkerque (YCD)
marina (4m) ☎/☎ 03.28.21.13.77, FF58, M, D, L, FW, CH;
and to:
Port du Bassin de la Marine (250), FW, AC, YC.
Services: SHOM, P, D, M, ME, El, Ⓔ, Sh, CH. **Town** P, D,
V, Gaz, R, Bar, ✉, Ⓑ, ⇌, ✈ (Lille). Ferry: Ramsgate.

19

TIME ZONE –0100
(French Standard Time)
Subtract 1 hour for UT
For French Summer Time add
ONE hour in non-shaded areas

FRANCE – DUNKERQUE

LAT 51°03′N LONG 2°22′E

TIMES AND HEIGHTS OF HIGH AND LOW WATERS

YEAR 1999

JANUARY

Day	Time	m	Day	Time	m
1 F	0629 / 1149 / 1858	0.8 / 6.0 / 0.6	16 SA	0639 / 1208 / 1855	1.1 / 5.5 / 1.0
2 SA O	0019 / 0720 / 1236 / 1945	6.0 / 0.6 / 6.1 / 0.6	17 SU ●	0024 / 0717 / 1243 / 1934	5.6 / 0.9 / 5.7 / 0.9
3 SU	0105 / 0806 / 1324 / 2030	6.1 / 0.5 / 6.2 / 0.6	18 M	0058 / 0756 / 1318 / 2013	5.8 / 0.7 / 5.9 / 0.8
4 M	0149 / 0851 / 1411 / 2113	6.1 / 0.4 / 6.2 / 0.7	19 TU	0133 / 0835 / 1354 / 2052	5.9 / 0.6 / 6.0 / 0.7
5 TU	0234 / 0935 / 1457 / 2155	6.0 / 0.5 / 6.0 / 0.8	20 W	0210 / 0915 / 1432 / 2132	5.9 / 0.5 / 6.0 / 0.7
6 W	0317 / 1016 / 1541 / 2235	5.9 / 0.6 / 5.9 / 1.0	21 TH	0247 / 0955 / 1512 / 2211	5.9 / 0.5 / 6.0 / 0.8
7 TH	0358 / 1057 / 1623 / 2314	5.7 / 0.8 / 5.6 / 1.2	22 F	0326 / 1035 / 1554 / 2251	5.8 / 0.6 / 5.8 / 0.9
8 F	0439 / 1138 / 1707 / 2356	5.5 / 1.0 / 5.4 / 1.4	23 SA	0408 / 1117 / 1640 / 2335	5.7 / 0.7 / 5.7 / 1.0
9 SA	0525 / 1224 / 1757	5.2 / 1.2 / 5.1	24 SU	0458 / 1204 / 1736	5.6 / 0.8 / 5.5
10 SU	0045 / 0619 / 1319 / 1858	1.6 / 5.0 / 1.4 / 4.9	25 M	0026 / 0557 / 1303 / 1840	1.2 / 5.4 / 1.0 / 5.3
11 M	0148 / 0727 / 1424 / 2011	1.8 / 4.8 / 1.6 / 4.8	26 TU	0132 / 0705 / 1416 / 1954	1.3 / 5.3 / 1.1 / 5.2
12 TU	0258 / 0842 / 1532 / 2119	1.8 / 4.8 / 1.6 / 4.8	27 W	0249 / 0824 / 1532 / 2117	1.4 / 5.2 / 1.2 / 5.2
13 W	0406 / 0946 / 1635 / 2216	1.7 / 4.9 / 1.5 / 5.0	28 TH	0406 / 0946 / 1648 / 2231	1.3 / 5.3 / 1.1 / 5.4
14 TH	0507 / 1044 / 1730 / 2306	1.5 / 5.1 / 1.3 / 5.2	29 F	0520 / 1051 / 1755 / 2329	1.1 / 5.6 / 0.9 / 5.6
15 F	0558 / 1128 / 1815 / 2348	1.3 / 5.3 / 1.1 / 5.4	30 SA	0621 / 1146 / 1849	0.8 / 5.8 / 0.7
			31 SU O	0017 / 0711 / 1233 / 1935	5.8 / 0.6 / 6.0 / 0.7

FEBRUARY

Day	Time	m	Day	Time	m
1 M	0059 / 0756 / 1316 / 2017	5.9 / 0.4 / 6.1 / 0.6	16 TU ●	0040 / 0737 / 1300 / 1954	5.7 / 0.6 / 5.9 / 0.6
2 TU	0138 / 0837 / 1358 / 2056	6.0 / 0.4 / 6.1 / 0.7	17 W	0114 / 0817 / 1336 / 2034	5.9 / 0.4 / 6.0 / 0.5
3 W	0217 / 0917 / 1438 / 2133	6.0 / 0.4 / 6.0 / 0.7	18 TH	0150 / 0857 / 1414 / 2114	6.0 / 0.3 / 6.1 / 0.5
4 TH	0254 / 0954 / 1516 / 2209	5.9 / 0.5 / 5.9 / 0.8	19 F	0227 / 0938 / 1452 / 2154	6.1 / 0.3 / 6.1 / 0.5
5 F	0330 / 1029 / 1552 / 2242	5.8 / 0.6 / 5.7 / 1.0	20 SA	0306 / 1018 / 1533 / 2234	6.0 / 0.3 / 6.0 / 0.6
6 SA	0405 / 1103 / 1627 / 2317	5.6 / 0.8 / 5.5 / 1.2	21 SU	0347 / 1100 / 1619 / 2316	5.8 / 0.5 / 5.8 / 0.8
7 SU	0442 / 1139 / 1707 / 2354	5.4 / 1.0 / 5.3 / 1.4	22 M	0436 / 1145 / 1713	5.8 / 0.7 / 5.6
8 M	0526 / 1220 / 1756	5.2 / 1.3 / 5.0	23 TU	0004 / 0534 / 1240 / 1816	1.0 / 5.6 / 0.9 / 5.3
9 TU	0041 / 0621 / 1316 / 1858	1.6 / 4.9 / 1.6 / 4.7	24 W	0107 / 0642 / 1352 / 1932	1.2 / 5.3 / 1.2 / 5.0
10 W	0147 / 0732 / 1429 / 2014	1.8 / 4.7 / 1.7 / 4.6	25 TH	0226 / 0808 / 1513 / 2103	1.4 / 5.1 / 1.3 / 5.0
11 TH	0307 / 0853 / 1544 / 2131	1.9 / 4.6 / 1.7 / 4.7	26 F	0350 / 0937 / 1637 / 2220	1.3 / 5.2 / 1.2 / 5.2
12 F	0422 / 1004 / 1653 / 2234	1.7 / 4.8 / 1.5 / 4.9	27 SA	0510 / 1045 / 1746 / 2319	1.1 / 5.4 / 1.0 / 5.4
13 SA	0526 / 1101 / 1749 / 2323	1.4 / 5.1 / 1.2 / 5.2	28 SU	0610 / 1139 / 1837	0.8 / 5.7 / 0.8
14 SU	0616 / 1146 / 1834	1.1 / 5.4 / 1.0			
15 M	0004 / 0657 / 1225 / 1914	5.5 / 0.8 / 5.7 / 0.8			

MARCH

Day	Time	m	Day	Time	m
1 M	0006 / 0658 / 1223 / 1920	5.6 / 0.6 / 5.8 / 0.7	16 TU	0632 / 1201 / 1851	0.7 / 5.7 / 0.7
2 TU O	0045 / 0739 / 1302 / 1959	5.8 / 0.4 / 5.9 / 0.7	17 W ●	0016 / 0714 / 1237 / 1932	5.7 / 0.5 / 6.0 / 0.5
3 W	0119 / 0818 / 1339 / 2035	5.9 / 0.4 / 6.0 / 0.6	18 TH	0051 / 0755 / 1313 / 2012	6.0 / 0.3 / 6.1 / 0.4
4 TH	0154 / 0854 / 1414 / 2108	6.0 / 0.4 / 6.0 / 0.6	19 F	0126 / 0836 / 1350 / 2053	6.1 / 0.2 / 6.2 / 0.3
5 F	0228 / 0928 / 1448 / 2141	5.9 / 0.4 / 5.9 / 0.7	20 SA	0204 / 0918 / 1431 / 2134	6.2 / 0.1 / 6.2 / 0.3
6 SA	0300 / 0959 / 1519 / 2212	5.9 / 0.6 / 5.8 / 0.8	21 SU	0245 / 0959 / 1514 / 2216	6.2 / 0.2 / 6.1 / 0.4
7 SU	0331 / 1030 / 1551 / 2243	5.7 / 0.7 / 5.6 / 1.0	22 M	0329 / 1042 / 1601 / 2259	6.1 / 0.4 / 5.9 / 0.6
8 M	0405 / 1101 / 1625 / 2314	5.6 / 0.9 / 5.4 / 1.2	23 TU	0419 / 1128 / 1655 / 2348	5.9 / 0.6 / 5.6 / 0.9
9 TU	0443 / 1135 / 1707 / 2352	5.3 / 1.2 / 5.1 / 1.4	24 W	0518 / 1223 / 1758	5.6 / 1.0 / 5.3
10 W	0531 / 1220 / 1804	5.0 / 1.5 / 4.7	25 TH	0051 / 0627 / 1336 / 1916	1.2 / 5.3 / 1.3 / 4.9
11 TH	0044 / 0639 / 1323 / 1919	1.7 / 4.7 / 1.7 / 4.5	26 F	0210 / 0756 / 1500 / 2053	1.3 / 5.0 / 1.4 / 4.9
12 F	0201 / 0800 / 1449 / 2041	1.9 / 4.5 / 1.8 / 4.5	27 SA	0336 / 0925 / 1625 / 2205	1.3 / 5.1 / 1.3 / 5.2
13 SA	0332 / 0922 / 1613 / 2157	1.8 / 4.7 / 1.6 / 4.8	28 SU	0455 / 1033 / 1731 / 2302	1.1 / 5.3 / 1.1 / 5.3
14 SU	0449 / 1029 / 1719 / 2255	1.5 / 5.0 / 1.3 / 5.1	29 M	0553 / 1125 / 1819 / 2347	0.8 / 5.6 / 0.9 / 5.5
15 M	0547 / 1120 / 1809 / 2339	1.1 / 5.4 / 1.0 / 5.5	30 TU	0639 / 1206 / 1900	0.6 / 5.7 / 0.8
			31 W O	0023 / 0718 / 1241 / 1936	5.7 / 0.5 / 5.8 / 0.7

APRIL

Day	Time	m	Day	Time	m
1 TH	0056 / 0754 / 1315 / 2009	5.8 / 0.5 / 5.9 / 0.7	16 F ●	0022 / 0729 / 1246 / 1948	6.0 / 0.2 / 6.2 / 0.4
2 F	0129 / 0827 / 1348 / 2041	5.9 / 0.5 / 5.9 / 0.6	17 SA	0100 / 0812 / 1327 / 2031	6.2 / 0.1 / 6.2 / 0.3
3 SA	0201 / 0859 / 1419 / 2113	5.9 / 0.5 / 5.9 / 0.7	18 SU	0142 / 0855 / 1410 / 2114	6.3 / 0.1 / 6.2 / 0.3
4 SU	0231 / 0930 / 1448 / 2144	5.9 / 0.6 / 5.8 / 0.7	19 M	0226 / 0940 / 1456 / 2159	6.3 / 0.2 / 6.1 / 0.3
5 M	0301 / 1000 / 1518 / 2214	5.8 / 0.7 / 5.6 / 0.9	20 TU	0315 / 1025 / 1547 / 2245	6.2 / 0.4 / 5.9 / 0.5
6 TU	0333 / 1029 / 1551 / 2244	5.6 / 0.9 / 5.4 / 1.1	21 W	0407 / 1114 / 1642 / 2336	6.0 / 0.7 / 5.6 / 0.8
7 W	0408 / 1102 / 1627 / 2319	5.4 / 1.1 / 5.2 / 1.3	22 TH	0507 / 1210 / 1744	5.6 / 1.0 / 5.3
8 TH	0449 / 1143 / 1718	5.1 / 1.4 / 4.8	23 F	0038 / 0615 / 1321 / 1858	1.0 / 5.3 / 1.3 / 5.0
9 F	0007 / 0558 / 1240 / 1838	1.5 / 4.8 / 1.6 / 4.6	24 SA	0154 / 0740 / 1441 / 2029	1.2 / 5.0 / 1.5 / 4.9
10 SA	0112 / 0718 / 1357 / 1955	1.7 / 4.6 / 1.8 / 4.5	25 SU	0315 / 0904 / 1600 / 2138	1.2 / 5.1 / 1.4 / 5.0
11 SU	0239 / 0837 / 1527 / 2113	1.7 / 4.7 / 1.6 / 4.7	26 M	0430 / 1008 / 1705 / 2234	1.1 / 5.3 / 1.2 / 5.3
12 M	0405 / 0951 / 1641 / 2218	1.4 / 5.0 / 1.3 / 5.1	27 TU	0528 / 1059 / 1754 / 2318	0.8 / 5.4 / 1.0 / 5.4
13 TU	0510 / 1047 / 1737 / 2306	1.0 / 5.4 / 0.9 / 5.4	28 W	0613 / 1140 / 1834 / 2356	0.7 / 5.6 / 0.9 / 5.6
14 W	0602 / 1131 / 1823 / 2345	0.7 / 5.8 / 0.7 / 5.7	29 TH	0652 / 1215 / 1909	0.7 / 5.7 / 0.8
15 TH	0646 / 1209 / 1906	0.4 / 6.0 / 0.5	30 F O	0030 / 0725 / 1249 / 1941	5.7 / 0.6 / 5.8 / 0.7

Chart Datum: 2·69 metres below Lallemand System (Mean Sea Level, Marseilles)

TIME ZONE –0100
(French Standard Time)
Subtract 1 hour for UT

For French Summer Time add
ONE hour in non-shaded areas

FRANCE – DUNKERQUE

LAT 51°03′N   LONG   2°22′E

TIMES AND HEIGHTS OF HIGH AND LOW WATERS

YEAR **1999**

MAY

Day	Time	m	Time	m	Time	m	Time	m
1 SA	0104	5.8	0757	0.6	1321	5.8	2014	0.7
2 SU	0135	5.8	0830	0.6	1351	5.8	2047	0.7
3 M	0205	5.8	0902	0.7	1420	5.7	2119	0.7
4 TU	0236	5.7	0934	0.8	1452	5.6	2151	0.8
5 W	0310	5.6	1005	0.9	1526	5.5	2222	1.0
6 TH	0346	5.4	1038	1.1	1603	5.2	2259	1.1
7 F	0427	5.2	1120	1.3	1650	5.0	2344	1.3
8 SA	0531	4.9	1213	1.5	1804	4.8		
9 SU	0043	1.5	0643	4.8	1320	1.6	1914	4.7
10 M	0157	1.5	0753	4.9	1442	1.5	2025	4.8
11 TU	0320	1.3	0905	5.1	1559	1.3	2133	5.1
12 W	0431	1.0	1007	5.4	1701	1.0	2228	5.4
13 TH	0528	0.7	1057	5.7	1752	0.7	2312	5.7
14 F	0618	0.4	1139	6.0	1839	0.5	2354	6.0
15 SA ●	0704	0.3	1222	6.1	1925	0.4		
16 SU	0037	6.2	0750	0.2	1305	6.2	2010	0.3
17 M	0123	6.3	0836	0.2	1353	6.2	2057	0.3
18 TU	0212	6.3	0922	0.3	1443	6.1	2144	0.3
19 W	0304	6.2	1010	0.5	1536	5.9	2233	0.4
20 TH	0359	6.0	1100	0.8	1630	5.6	2324	0.7
21 F	0455	5.7	1155	1.0	1727	5.3		
22 SA	0022	0.9	0558	5.4	1259	1.3	1833	5.1
23 SU	0129	1.1	0714	5.1	1410	1.4	1952	4.9
24 M	0242	1.2	0831	5.1	1521	1.4	2101	5.0
25 TU	0351	1.1	0933	5.1	1626	1.3	2156	5.1
26 W	0452	1.0	1024	5.3	1720	1.1	2243	5.3
27 TH	0541	0.9	1108	5.4	1804	1.0	2327	5.5
28 F	0621	0.8	1148	5.5	1841	0.9		
29 SA	0005	5.6	0656	0.6	1224	5.6	1914	0.9
30 SU ○	0040	5.6	0729	0.8	1257	5.7	1948	0.8
31 M	0113	5.7	0803	0.8	1327	5.7	2023	0.8

JUNE

Day	Time	m	Time	m	Time	m	Time	m
1 TU	0143	5.7	0838	0.8	1358	5.7	2059	0.8
2 W	0217	5.7	0913	0.9	1433	5.6	2133	0.8
3 TH	0255	5.6	0947	0.9	1511	5.5	2207	0.9
4 F	0334	5.5	1023	1.1	1551	5.3	2245	1.0
5 SA	0418	5.3	1104	1.2	1636	5.2	2329	1.1
6 SU	0511	5.2	1153	1.3	1734	5.0		
7 M	0021	1.2	0611	5.1	1251	1.4	1836	5.0
8 TU	0125	1.2	0713	5.1	1402	1.4	1940	5.0
9 W	0240	1.1	0819	5.2	1517	1.2	2046	5.2
10 TH	0352	0.9	0926	5.4	1624	1.0	2149	5.4
11 F	0455	0.7	1024	5.7	1723	0.8	2243	5.7
12 SA	0551	0.5	1115	5.9	1816	0.6	2333	5.9
13 SU ●	0643	0.4	1203	6.0	1906	0.5		
14 M	0021	6.1	0732	0.4	1251	6.1	1955	0.4
15 TU	0111	6.2	0820	0.4	1341	6.1	2043	0.3
16 W	0202	6.2	0908	0.4	1433	6.0	2131	0.3
17 TH	0255	6.1	0956	0.6	1524	5.9	2219	0.4
18 F	0347	6.0	1044	0.8	1614	5.7	2308	0.6
19 SA	0438	5.7	1133	1.0	1703	5.5	2359	0.8
20 SU	0532	5.4	1226	1.2	1758	5.2		
21 M	0054	1.0	0633	5.2	1325	1.4	1903	5.1
22 TU	0156	1.1	0743	5.0	1429	1.5	2011	5.0
23 W	0300	1.2	0847	5.0	1534	1.5	2115	5.0
24 TH	0403	1.2	0944	5.1	1635	1.4	2208	5.1
25 F	0500	1.1	1034	5.2	1729	1.2	2257	5.3
26 SA	0548	1.1	1119	5.3	1813	1.1	2341	5.4
27 SU	0628	1.0	1200	5.4	1851	1.0		
28 M ○	0019	5.5	0704	1.0	1236	5.5	1927	0.9
29 TU	0054	5.6	0741	0.9	1308	5.6	1955	0.8
30 W	0127	5.7	0818	0.9	1341	5.7	2043	0.3

JULY

Day	Time	m	Time	m	Time	m	Time	m
1 TH	0202	5.7	0856	0.8	1418	5.7	2118	0.7
2 F	0240	5.7	0933	0.9	1457	5.6	2155	0.7
3 SA	0320	5.7	1010	0.9	1535	5.5	2233	0.8
4 SU	0401	5.5	1049	1.0	1615	5.4	2314	0.9
5 M	0445	5.4	1133	1.1	1702	5.3		
6 TU	0000	0.9	0538	5.3	1224	1.2	1759	5.2
7 W	0056	1.0	0637	5.3	1326	1.3	1901	5.2
8 TH	0204	1.0	0741	5.3	1440	1.3	2008	5.3
9 F	0318	1.0	0852	5.3	1552	1.1	2119	5.4
10 SA	0426	0.9	1051	5.1	1658	1.0	2225	5.6
11 SU	0531	0.7	1103	5.7	1759	0.8	2322	5.8
12 M	0629	0.6	1156	5.9	1854	0.6		
13 TU ●	0014	6.0	0721	0.5	1245	6.0	1944	0.4
14 W	0104	6.1	0809	0.5	1333	6.1	2032	0.3
15 TH	0153	6.2	0855	0.5	1420	6.0	2118	0.3
16 F	0242	6.1	0940	0.6	1506	5.9	2202	0.4
17 SA	0329	6.0	1023	0.8	1549	5.6	2246	0.5
18 SU	0413	5.8	1105	1.0	1632	5.6	2328	0.7
19 M	0458	5.5	1147	1.2	1716	5.4		
20 TU	0013	0.9	0545	5.3	1234	1.4	1807	5.2
21 W	0103	1.2	0641	5.0	1331	1.5	1909	5.0
22 TH	0203	1.4	0748	4.9	1436	1.6	2020	4.9
23 F	0307	1.5	0856	4.8	1544	1.6	2126	4.9
24 SA	0413	1.5	0957	4.9	1650	1.5	2229	5.0
25 SU	0514	1.3	1051	5.1	1746	1.3	2319	5.2
26 M	0603	1.2	1137	5.3	1830	1.1	2359	5.4
27 TU	0644	1.1	1216	5.5	1907	0.9		
28 W ○	0036	5.6	0721	1.0	1250	5.6	1944	0.4
29 TH	0110	5.7	0759	0.9	1324	5.7	2022	0.6
30 F	0144	5.8	0837	0.8	1359	5.8	2100	0.6
31 SA	0221	5.9	0916	0.8	1435	5.8	2139	0.5

AUGUST

Day	Time	m	Time	m	Time	m	Time	m
1 SU	0258	5.9	0954	0.8	1511	5.8	2217	0.6
2 M	0336	5.8	1032	0.8	1549	5.7	2256	0.7
3 TU	0417	5.7	1112	0.9	1632	5.6	2339	0.8
4 W	0507	5.5	1158	1.1	1726	5.5		
5 TH	0029	0.9	0606	5.4	1255	1.2	1830	5.4
6 F	0134	1.1	0713	5.3	1409	1.3	1941	5.3
7 SA	0251	1.2	0830	5.2	1528	1.3	2104	5.3
8 SU	0407	1.1	0953	5.3	1643	1.1	2220	5.5
9 M	0520	1.0	1101	5.5	1751	0.8	2320	5.8
10 TU	0621	0.8	1154	5.8	1846	0.8		
11 W ●	0011	6.0	0712	0.7	1239	5.9	1934	0.4
12 TH	0056	6.1	0757	0.6	1321	6.0	2018	0.3
13 F	0139	6.1	0839	0.6	1401	6.0	2100	0.3
14 SA	0222	6.1	0918	0.7	1440	6.0	2140	0.4
15 SU	0303	6.0	0956	0.8	1519	5.9	2218	0.5
16 M	0341	5.8	1032	0.9	1556	5.8	2254	0.7
17 TU	0418	5.6	1108	1.1	1633	5.6	2330	0.9
18 W	0457	5.4	1146	1.3	1716	5.3		
19 TH	0011	1.2	0543	5.1	1233	1.5	1809	5.0
20 F	0103	1.5	0641	4.8	1335	1.8	1917	4.8
21 SA	0210	1.7	0756	4.6	1451	1.9	2037	4.7
22 SU	0326	1.8	0914	4.7	1609	1.7	2155	4.8
23 M	0439	1.6	1020	4.9	1716	1.5	2255	5.1
24 TU	0538	1.4	1112	5.2	1806	1.2	2339	5.4
25 W	0622	1.1	1154	5.5	1846	1.0		
26 TH	0015	5.7	0700	0.9	1229	5.7	1923	0.7
27 F ○	0049	5.8	0738	0.8	1301	5.8	2000	0.5
28 SA	0122	6.0	0816	0.7	1334	6.0	2039	0.4
29 SU	0156	6.1	0854	0.7	1408	6.0	2118	0.4
30 M	0232	6.1	0933	0.6	1444	6.0	2156	0.5
31 TU	0309	6.0	1011	0.7	1522	5.9	2235	0.5

19

Chart Datum: 2·69 metres below Lallemand System (Mean Sea Level, Marseilles)

TIME ZONE –0100
(French Standard Time)
Subtract 1 hour for UT

For French Summer Time add ONE hour in non-shaded areas

FRANCE – DUNKERQUE

LAT 51°03′N   LONG 2°22′E

TIMES AND HEIGHTS OF HIGH AND LOW WATERS   YEAR **1999**

SEPTEMBER

Day	Time m	Day	Time m
1 W	0350 5.9 / 1051 0.8 / 1607 5.8 / 2317 0.7	**16** TH	0412 5.5 / 1105 1.3 / 1631 5.4 / 2325 1.3
2 TH	0440 5.7 / 1135 1.0 / 1701 5.6	**17** F	0453 5.2 / 1143 1.5 / 1719 5.1
3 F	0005 1.0 / 0541 5.4 / 1231 1.3 / 1808 5.4	**18** SA	0008 1.6 / 0547 4.8 / 1233 1.8 / 1825 4.7
4 SA	0111 1.2 / 0652 5.2 / 1347 1.4 / 1926 5.2	**19** SU	0108 1.9 / 0700 4.6 / 1348 2.0 / 1945 4.6
5 SU	0233 1.4 / 0819 5.0 / 1512 1.4 / 2100 5.2	**20** M	0232 2.0 / 0823 4.5 / 1521 1.9 / 2108 4.7
6 M	0357 1.3 / 0951 5.2 / 1635 1.2 / 2217 5.5	**21** TU	0359 1.8 / 0942 4.8 / 1639 1.6 / 2226 5.0
7 TU	0514 1.1 / 1052 5.5 / 1742 0.9 / 2315 5.7	**22** W	0506 1.5 / 1041 5.1 / 1735 1.2 / 2314 5.4
8 W	0612 0.9 / 1143 5.7 / 1834 0.6	**23** TH	0555 1.2 / 1126 5.5 / 1819 0.9 / 2349 5.7
9 TH ●	0002 6.0 / 0658 0.8 / 1225 5.9 / 1919 0.4	**24** F	0635 0.9 / 1202 5.7 / 1857 0.7
10 F	0042 6.1 / 0739 0.7 / 1301 6.0 / 1959 0.4	**25** SA ○	0023 6.0 / 0713 0.8 / 1234 5.9 / 1935 0.5
11 SA	0119 6.1 / 0817 0.7 / 1336 6.1 / 2037 0.4	**26** SU	0055 6.1 / 0751 0.6 / 1306 6.1 / 2014 0.4
12 SU	0156 6.1 / 0853 0.7 / 1411 6.0 / 2113 0.5	**27** M	0128 6.2 / 0830 0.6 / 1340 6.2 / 2054 0.3
13 M	0232 6.0 / 0927 0.8 / 1446 6.0 / 2146 0.6	**28** TU	0205 6.2 / 0910 0.6 / 1418 6.2 / 2134 0.4
14 TU	0306 5.9 / 1000 0.9 / 1519 5.8 / 2219 0.8	**29** W	0244 6.1 / 0950 0.6 / 1500 6.1 / 2215 0.5
15 W	0338 5.7 / 1032 1.1 / 1553 5.7 / 2250 1.0	**30** TH	0329 6.0 / 1032 0.8 / 1547 6.0 / 2258 0.8

OCTOBER

Day	Time m	Day	Time m
1 F	0421 5.7 / 1118 1.0 / 1645 5.7 / 2349 1.1	**16** SA	0411 5.3 / 1106 1.5 / 1636 5.1 / 2327 1.6
2 SA	0524 5.4 / 1216 1.3 / 1754 5.4	**17** SU	0459 4.9 / 1151 1.7 / 1742 4.8
3 SU	0056 1.4 / 0638 5.1 / 1334 1.5 / 1916 5.2	**18** M	0021 1.9 / 0615 4.6 / 1253 1.9 / 1900 4.6
4 M	0223 1.6 / 0809 4.9 / 1502 1.5 / 2053 5.2	**19** TU	0134 2.0 / 0734 4.5 / 1420 2.0 / 2019 4.7
5 TU	0349 1.5 / 0936 5.1 / 1624 1.2 / 2206 5.4	**20** W	0308 1.9 / 0853 4.7 / 1551 1.7 / 2135 5.0
6 W	0503 1.2 / 1038 5.4 / 1729 0.9 / 2302 5.7	**21** TH	0425 1.6 / 1001 5.1 / 1656 1.3 / 2232 5.4
7 TH	0557 1.0 / 1126 5.7 / 1817 0.6 / 2347 5.9	**22** F	0520 1.2 / 1050 5.4 / 1745 0.9 / 2315 5.7
8 F	0640 0.9 / 1203 5.9 / 1859 0.5	**23** SA	0604 1.0 / 1128 5.8 / 1827 0.7 / 2351 6.0
9 SA ○	0023 6.0 / 0717 0.8 / 1237 6.0 / 1936 0.5	**24** SU ○	0645 0.8 / 1202 6.0 / 1908 0.6
10 SU	0056 6.1 / 0752 0.8 / 1310 6.0 / 2011 0.6	**25** M	0025 6.2 / 0725 0.6 / 1237 6.2 / 1949 0.4
11 M	0129 6.1 / 0825 0.8 / 1343 6.0 / 2044 0.6	**26** TU	0101 6.3 / 0806 0.5 / 1316 6.3 / 2030 0.4
12 TU	0201 6.0 / 0858 0.8 / 1415 6.0 / 2115 0.7	**27** W	0142 6.2 / 0848 0.5 / 1358 6.3 / 2113 0.4
13 W	0232 5.9 / 0930 0.9 / 1446 5.9 / 2146 0.9	**28** TH	0225 6.2 / 0930 0.6 / 1444 6.3 / 2157 0.6
14 TH	0302 5.7 / 1001 1.1 / 1518 5.7 / 2216 1.1	**29** F	0314 6.0 / 1017 0.7 / 1536 6.1 / 2244 0.8
15 F	0335 5.5 / 1032 1.3 / 1554 5.5 / 2248 1.3	**30** SA	0408 5.8 / 1107 0.9 / 1635 5.8 / 2338 1.2
		31 SU	0510 5.4 / 1206 1.2 / 1742 5.5

NOVEMBER

Day	Time m	Day	Time m
1 M	0046 1.5 / 0621 5.1 / 1321 1.4 / 1903 5.2	**16** TU	0533 4.8 / 1218 1.7 / 1820 4.8
2 TU	0207 1.6 / 0751 5.0 / 1444 1.4 / 2035 5.2	**17** W	0051 1.9 / 0648 4.7 / 1327 1.8 / 1929 4.8
3 W	0329 1.6 / 0912 5.1 / 1603 1.2 / 2145 5.4	**18** TH	0209 1.8 / 0758 4.8 / 1453 1.6 / 2041 5.0
4 TH	0440 1.4 / 1012 5.3 / 1706 1.0 / 2239 5.6	**19** F	0333 1.6 / 0908 5.0 / 1608 1.3 / 2145 5.3
5 F	0534 1.1 / 1059 5.6 / 1755 0.8 / 2322 5.8	**20** SA	0437 1.3 / 1005 5.4 / 1706 1.0 / 2236 5.7
6 SA	0616 1.0 / 1137 5.7 / 1835 0.7 / 2358 5.9	**21** SU	0529 1.0 / 1050 5.7 / 1755 0.7 / 2318 5.9
7 SU	0653 1.0 / 1212 5.9 / 1911 0.7	**22** M	0616 0.8 / 1131 6.0 / 1841 0.5 / 2358 6.1
8 M ●	0031 5.9 / 0727 0.9 / 1246 5.9 / 1944 0.7	**23** TU ○	0700 0.7 / 1213 6.2 / 1925 0.4
9 TU	0104 5.9 / 0759 0.9 / 1318 6.0 / 2015 0.8	**24** W	0040 6.3 / 0745 0.5 / 1256 6.3 / 2010 0.4
10 W	0134 5.9 / 0832 0.9 / 1349 5.9 / 2048 0.9	**25** TH	0124 6.3 / 0831 0.5 / 1344 6.4 / 2056 0.5
11 TH	0204 5.9 / 0905 0.9 / 1420 5.8 / 2119 1.0	**26** F	0212 6.2 / 0918 0.5 / 1434 6.3 / 2144 0.6
12 F	0235 5.8 / 0936 1.1 / 1453 5.7 / 2150 1.2	**27** SA	0303 6.0 / 1006 0.6 / 1528 6.1 / 2233 0.9
13 SA	0308 5.6 / 1008 1.2 / 1529 5.5 / 2222 1.3	**28** SU	0357 5.8 / 1057 0.8 / 1625 5.8 / 2327 1.2
14 SU	0344 5.4 / 1042 1.4 / 1610 5.3 / 2301 1.5	**29** M	0454 5.5 / 1154 1.0 / 1726 5.5
15 M	0426 5.1 / 1124 1.6 / 1706 5.0 / 2349 1.7	**30** TU	0028 1.4 / 0557 5.2 / 1300 1.2 / 1839 5.3

DECEMBER

Day	Time m	Day	Time m
1 W	0138 1.6 / 0716 5.0 / 1413 1.3 / 2002 5.1	**16** TH	0018 1.6 / 0559 5.0 / 1250 1.5 / 1842 5.0
2 TH	0252 1.6 / 0835 5.1 / 1526 1.3 / 2110 5.2	**17** F	0121 1.7 / 0705 5.0 / 1400 1.4 / 1947 5.1
3 F	0402 1.5 / 0934 5.2 / 1631 1.1 / 2205 5.3	**18** SA	0238 1.6 / 0812 5.1 / 1518 1.3 / 2054 5.3
4 SA	0501 1.3 / 1025 5.4 / 1725 1.0 / 2252 5.5	**19** SU	0352 1.4 / 0917 5.3 / 1626 1.1 / 2156 5.5
5 SU	0549 1.2 / 1108 5.5 / 1809 1.0 / 2332 5.6	**20** M	0454 1.1 / 1015 5.6 / 1725 1.0 / 2250 5.8
6 M	0628 1.1 / 1149 5.7 / 1846 0.9	**21** TU	0550 0.9 / 1107 5.9 / 1818 0.9 / 2339 6.0
7 TU ○	0009 5.7 / 0703 1.0 / 1225 5.7 / 1919 0.9	**22** W	0641 0.7 / 1156 6.1 / 1908 0.5
8 W	0043 5.7 / 0736 0.9 / 1259 5.8 / 1951 0.9	**23** TH	0026 6.1 / 0730 0.5 / 1245 6.3 / 1956 0.5
9 TH	0114 5.8 / 0810 0.9 / 1330 5.8 / 2025 0.9	**24** F	0115 6.2 / 0819 0.4 / 1335 6.3 / 2044 0.5
10 F	0143 5.8 / 0845 0.9 / 1402 5.8 / 2059 1.0	**25** SA	0204 6.2 / 0907 0.4 / 1427 6.3 / 2132 0.6
11 SA	0216 5.7 / 0918 1.0 / 1437 5.7 / 2132 1.1	**26** SU	0254 6.0 / 0956 0.4 / 1518 6.1 / 2220 0.8
12 SU	0251 5.6 / 0951 1.1 / 1514 5.6 / 2206 1.2	**27** M	0343 5.9 / 1044 0.6 / 1610 5.9 / 2309 1.0
13 M	0328 5.5 / 1026 1.2 / 1554 5.4 / 2243 1.4	**28** TU	0432 5.7 / 1135 0.8 / 1702 5.6 / 2359 1.3
14 TU	0407 5.3 / 1106 1.3 / 1639 5.2 / 2326 1.5	**29** W	0524 5.4 / 1228 1.0 / 1801 5.3
15 W	0455 5.1 / 1153 1.4 / 1738 5.1	**30** TH	0055 1.5 / 0626 5.2 / 1328 1.2 / 1911 5.1
		31 F	0158 1.6 / 0739 5.0 / 1433 1.3 / 2021 5.0

Chart Datum: 2·69 metres below Lallemand System (Mean Sea Level, Marseilles)

Area 20

Belgium and the Netherlands
Nieuwpoort to Delfzijl

8.20.1	Index	**Page 807**
8.20.2	Diagram of ports, lights, RDF bns, Coast radio and weather stns	**808**
8.20.3	Tidal stream charts	**810**
8.20.4	List of coastal lights, fog signals and waypoints	**812**
8.20.5	Dutch glossary	**817**
8.20.6	Passage information	**820**
8.20.7	Distance table	**821**
8.20.8	Special notes for Belgium and the Netherlands	**822**
8.20.9	Nieuwpoort (Nieuport)	**823**
8.20.10	Oostende (Ostend)	**824**
8.20.11	Blankenberge	**824**
8.20.12	Zeebrugge	**825**
8.20.13	Breskens	**825**
8.20.14	TSS off the Belgian and Dutch coasts	**826**
8.20.15	Westerschelde Walsoorden Paal Doel Ellewoutsdijk	**827**
8.20.16	Terneuzen	**828**
8.20.17	Antwerpen (Antwerp)	**828**
8.20.18	Vlissingen (Flushing), Standard Port, tidal curves	**829**
8.20.19	Oosterschelde	**833**
8.20.20	Stellendam & Hellevoetsluis	**835**
8.20.21	VTS in the Maas area & TSS	**839**
8.20.22	Hoek van Holland Standard Port, tidal curves	**840**
8.20.23	Rotterdam	**840**
8.20.24	Scheveningen	**841**
8.20.25	IJmuiden	**842**
8.20.26	Amsterdam	**843**
8.20.27	IJsselmeer	**843**
8.20.28	Den Helder	**845**
8.20.29	Oudeschild	**846**
8.20.30	Harlingen Nes (Ameland)	**846**
8.20.31	Vlieland	**847**
8.20.32	West Terschelling	**847**
8.20.33	Zeegat van Terschelling	**848**
8.20.34	Lauwersoog Oostmahorn Zoutkamp	**848**
8.20.35	Delfzijl Schiermonnikoog Eemshaven Termunterzijl	**849**
8.20.36	TSS off the Dutch coast	**850**
8.20.37	TSS off the Dutch and German coasts	**851**
8.20.38	Southern North Sea waypoints	**852**

20

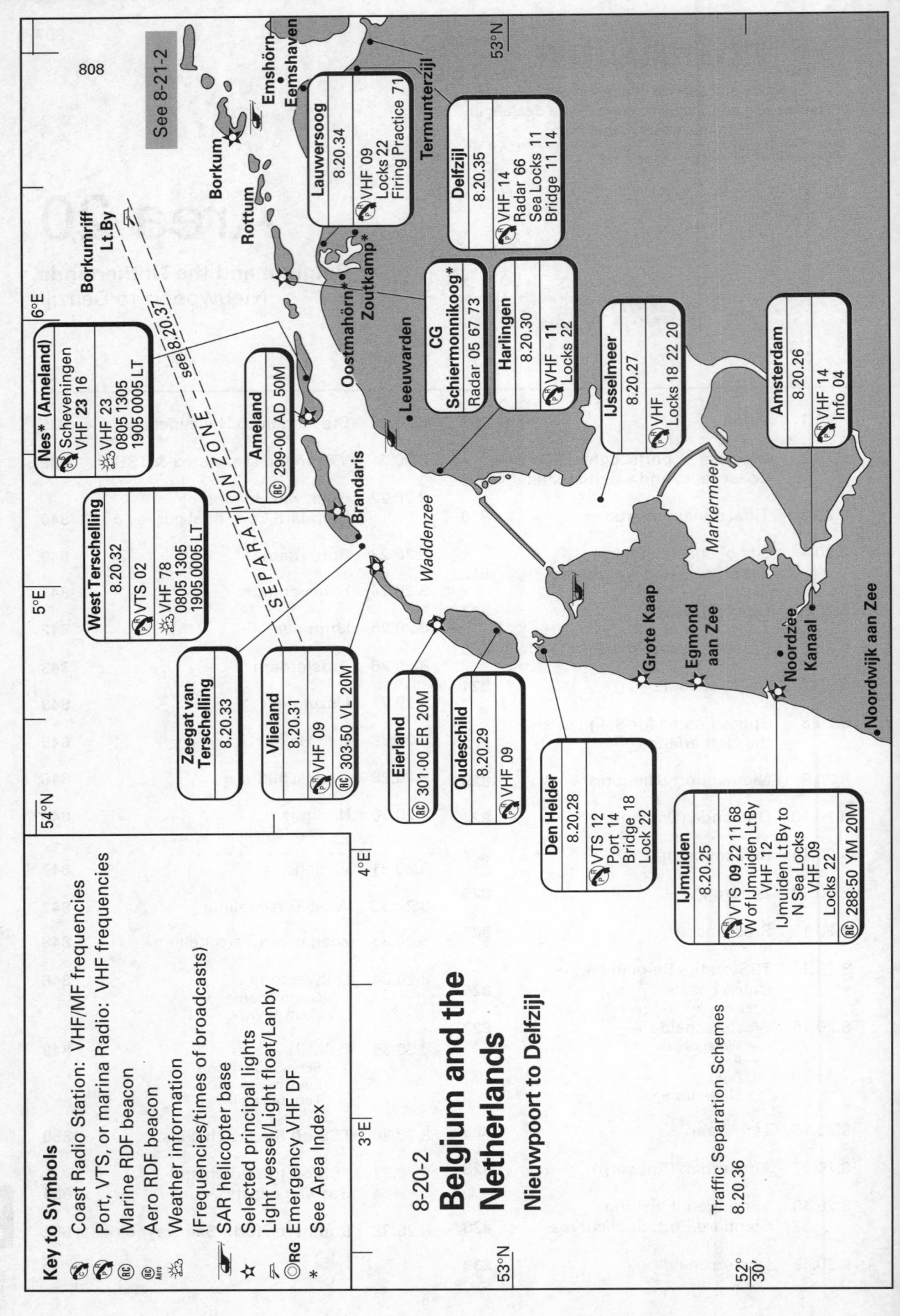

Key to Symbols

- Coast Radio Station: VHF/MF frequencies
- Port, VTS, or marina Radio: VHF frequencies
- RC Marine RDF beacon
- RC Aero Aero RDF beacon
- Weather information (Frequencies/times of broadcasts)
- ☆ Selected principal lights
- ▭ Light vessel/Light float/Lanby
- ORG Emergency VHF DF
- ⦿ SAR helicopter base
- * See Area Index

8-20-2
Belgium and the Netherlands
Nieuwpoort to Delfzijl

Traffic Separation Schemes
8.20.36

808

See 8-21-2

Borkumriff Lt.By

Borkum

Rottum

Emshörn
Eemshaven

Termunterzijl

Lauwersoog
8.20.34
VHF 09
Locks 22
Firing Practice 71

Delfzijl
8.20.35
VHF 14
Radar 66
Sea Locks 11
Bridge 11 14

Oostmahörn*
Zoutkamp*

CG Schiermonnikoog*
Radar 05 67 73

Harlingen
8.20.30
VHF 11
Locks 22

Leeuwarden

Nes* (Ameland)
Scheveningen
VHF 23 16
VHF 23
0805 1305
1905 0005 LT

Ameland
RC 299·00 AD 50M

Brandaris

Waddenzee

West Terschelling
8.20.32
VTS 02
VHF 78
0805 1305
1905 0005 LT

IJsselmeer
8.20.27
VHF
Locks 18 22 20

Markermeer

Amsterdam
8.20.26
VHF 14
Info 04

Zeegat van Terschelling
8.20.33

Vlieland
8.20.31
VHF 09
RC 303·50 VL 20M

Eierland
RC 301·00 ER 20M

Oudeschild
8.20.29
VHF 09

Grote Kaap

Egmond aan Zee

Noordzee Kanaal

Noordwijk aan Zee

Den Helder
8.20.28
VTS 12
Port 14
Bridge 18
Lock 22

IJmuiden
8.20.25
VTS 09 22 11 68
W of IJmuiden Lt By
VHF 12
IJmuiden Lt By to
N Sea Locks
VHF 09
Locks 22
RC 288·50 YM 20M

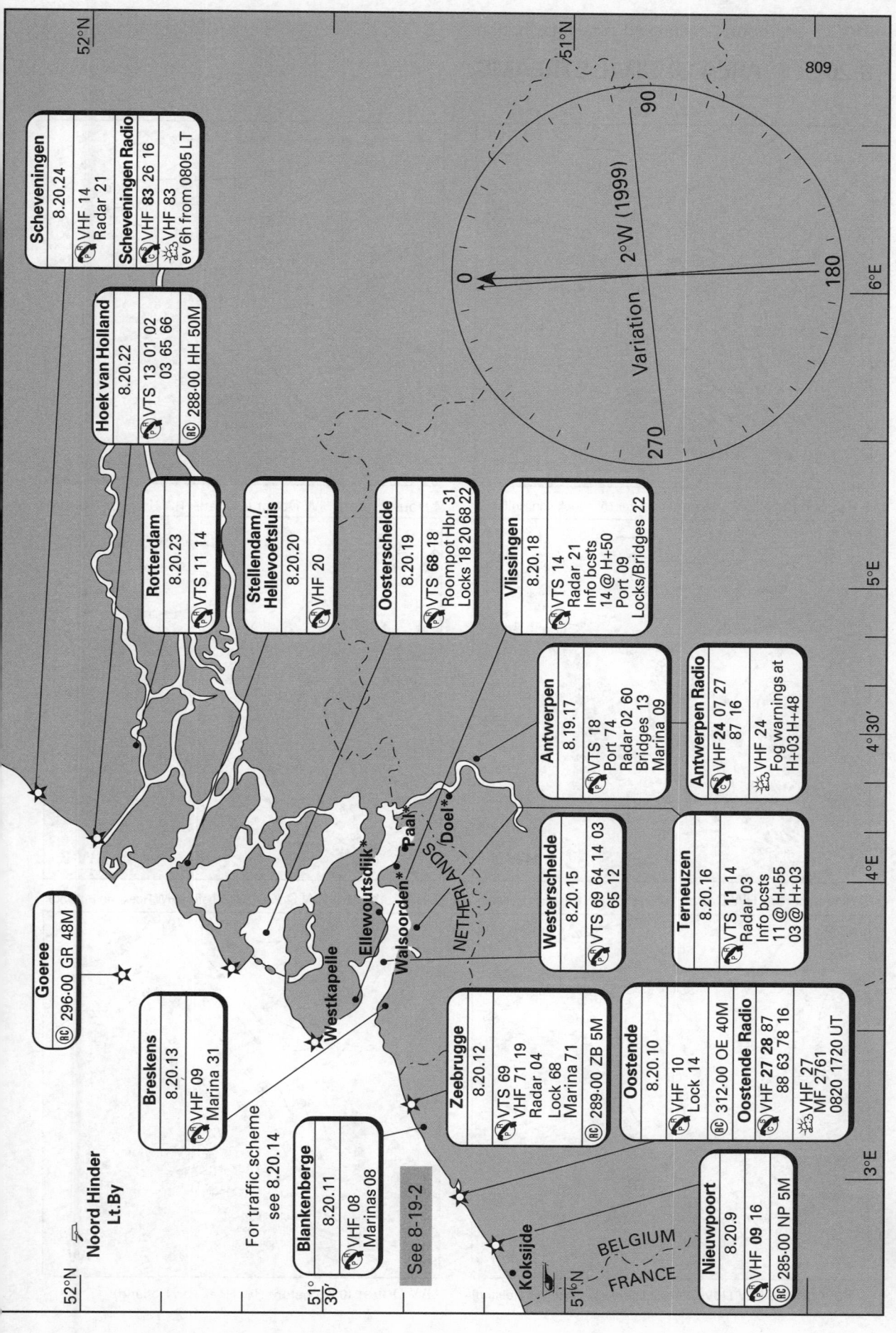

809

Scheveningen
8.20.24

📻 VHF 14
Radar 21

Scheveningen Radio

📻 VHF 83 26 16

📡 VHF 83
ev 6h from 0805 LT

Hoek van Holland
8.20.22

📻 VTS 13 01 02
03 65 66

(RC) 288·00 HH 50M

Rotterdam
8.20.23

📻 VTS 11 14

**Stellendam/
Hellevoetsluis**
8.20.20

📻 VHF 20

Oosterschelde
8.20.19

📻 VTS 68 18
Roompot Hbr 31
Locks 18 20 68 22

Vlissingen
8.20.18

📻 VTS 14
Radar 21
Info bcsts
14 @ H+50
Port 09
Locks/Bridges 22

Antwerpen
8.19.17

📻 VTS 18
Port 74
Radar 02 60
Bridges 13
Marina 09

Antwerpen Radio

📻 VHF 24 07 27
87 16

📡 VHF 24
Fog warnings at
H+03 H+48

Westerschelde
8.20.15

📻 VTS 69 64 14 03
65 12

Terneuzen
8.20.16

📻 VTS 11 14
Radar 03
Info bcsts
11 @ H+55
03 @ H+03

Goeree

(RC) 296·00 GR 48M

Breskens
8.20.13

📻 VHF 09
Marina 31

Westkapelle

Ellewoutsdijk*

Walsoorden*

Paal*

Doel*

NETHERLANDS

For traffic scheme
see 8.20.14

**Noord Hinder
Lt.By**

Blankenberge
8.20.11

📻 VHF 08
Marinas 08

See 8-19-2

Zeebrugge
8.20.12

📻 VTS 69
VHF 71 19
Radar 04
Lock 68
Marina 71

(RC) 289·00 ZB 5M

Oostende
8.20.10

📻 VHF 10
Lock 14

(RC) 312·00 OE 40M

Oostende Radio

📻 VHF 27 28 87
88 63 78 16

📡 VHF 27
MF 2761
0820 1720 UT

Nieuwpoort
8.20.9

📻 VHF 09 16

(RC) 285·00 NP 5M

BELGIUM

FRANCE

Koksijde

Variation

2°W (1999)

0

90

180

270

52°N

51°N

52°N

6°E

5°E

4°30'

4°E

3°E

51°
30'

51°N

20

8-20-3   AREA 20 TIDAL STREAMS

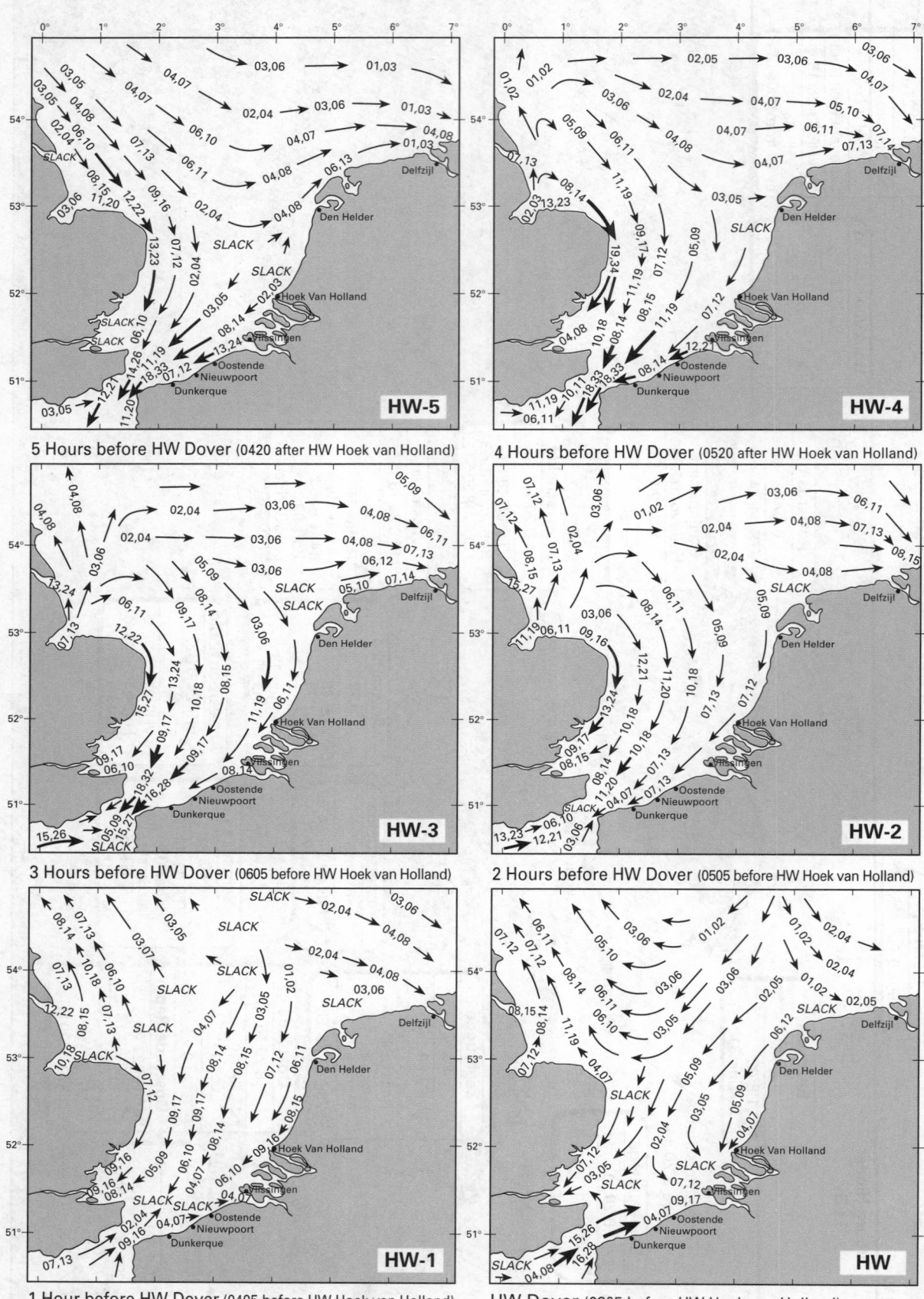

HW-5

5 Hours before HW Dover (0420 after HW Hoek van Holland)

HW-4

4 Hours before HW Dover (0520 after HW Hoek van Holland)

HW-3

3 Hours before HW Dover (0605 before HW Hoek van Holland)

HW-2

2 Hours before HW Dover (0505 before HW Hoek van Holland)

HW-1

1 Hour before HW Dover (0405 before HW Hoek van Holland)

HW

HW Dover (0305 before HW Hoek van Holland)

South-westward 8.19.3   North-westward 8.4.3   North-eastward 8.21.3

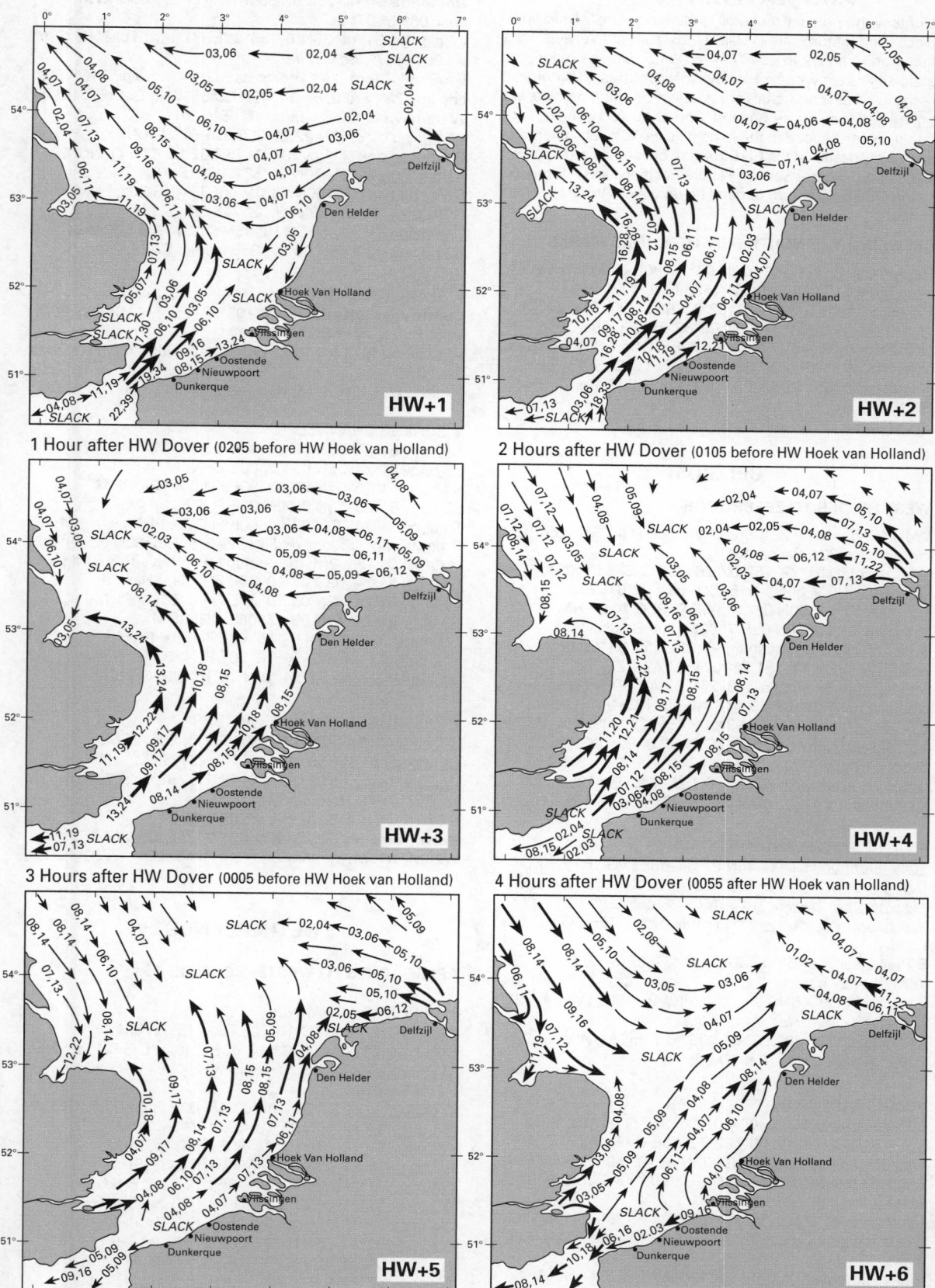

1 Hour after HW Dover (0205 before HW Hoek van Holland)

2 Hours after HW Dover (0105 before HW Hoek van Holland)

3 Hours after HW Dover (0005 before HW Hoek van Holland)

4 Hours after HW Dover (0055 after HW Hoek van Holland)

5 Hours after HW Dover (0155 after HW Hoek van Holland)

6 Hours after HW Dover (0255 after HW Hoek van Holland)

20

8.20.4   COASTAL LIGHTS, FOG SIGNALS AND WAYPOINTS

Lights with a nominal range of 15M or more are in **bold** print, places and features are in CAPITALS, and light-vessels, light floats and Lanbys in *CAPITAL ITALICS*. Unless otherwise stated lights are white. m = elevation in metres; M = nominal range in miles. Fog signals are in *italics*. Useful waypoints are underlined; use those on land with care. All positions are generally referenced to the largest scale Admiralty chart and are mainly based on the ED 50 datum but should be assumed to be approximate. Some offshore positions are referenced to the OSGB 36 datum depending on which Admiralty chart is used.

CROSSING THE NORTH SEA: OFFSHORE MARKS

Garden City buoy 51°29'·20N 02°17'·90E Q (9) 15s; WCM.
Twin buoy 51°32'·10N 02°22'·62E Fl (3) Y 9s; SPM.
Birkenfels buoy 51°39'·05N 02°32'·05E Q (9) 15s; WCM.
Track Ferry buoy 51°33'·80N 02°36'·50E Fl Y 5s; SPM.
NHR-SE buoy 51°45'·50N 02°40'·00E Fl G 5s; SHM; Racon (N).
NHR-S buoy 51°51'·40N 02°28'·75E Fl Y 10s; SPM; *Bell.*
Noordhinder buoy 52°00'·20N 02°51'·50E Fl (2) 10s; Racon (T); SWM.
NHR-N buoy 52°10'·90N 03°05'·00E L Fl 8s; Racon (K); SWM.

BELGIUM

WEST HINDER TO ZEEBRUGGE

West Hinder lt 51°23'·36N 02°26'·36E Fl (4) 30s 23m 13M; *Horn Mo(U) 30s*; Racon (W).
WH Zuid buoy 51°22'·75N 02°26'·36E Q (6) + L Fl 15s; SCM.
Oost-Dyck NCM buoy, Q, 51°21'·55N 02°31'·20E.
A-Z buoy 51°21'·50N 02°37'·00E Fl (3) G 10s; SHM.
A-N buoy 51°23'·50N 02°37'·00E Fl (4) R 20s; PHM.
KB NCM buoy, Q, Racon (K), 51°20'·95N 02°43'·00E.
KB2 NCM buoy, VQ, 51°21'·02N 02°42'·22E.
Middelkerke Bk buoy 51°18'·25N 02°42'·80E Fl G 5s; SHM.
MBN buoy 51°20'·87N 02°46'·40E Q; NCM.
SW Akkaert buoy 51°22'·33N 02°46'·42E Q (9) 15s; WCM.
Mid Akkaert buoy 51°24'·80N 02°54'·00E VQ (3) 5s; ECM.
Scheur 1 buoy 51°23'·18N 03°02'·00E Fl G 5s; SHM.
Goote Bank buoy 51°26'·98N 02°52'·72E Q (3)10s; ECM.
BT Ratel buoy 51°11'·62N 02°28'·00E Fl (4) R 15s; PHM.

• NIEUWPOORT AND APPROACHES

Trapegeer buoy 51°08'·46N 02°34'·45E Fl G 10s; SHM.
Den Oever wreck buoy 51°09'·20N 02°39'·50E Q; NCM.
Nieuwpoort Bk buoy 51°10'·21N 02°36'·16E Q (9) 15s; WCM.
Weststroombank buoy 51°11'·39N 02°43'·15E Fl (4) R 20s; PHM.
E Pier, near root 51°09'·32N 02°43'·89E Fl (2) R 14s 26m **16M**; R tr, W bands.
E pier hd 51°09'·46N 02°43'·17E FR 11m 10M; W tr; vis 025°-250°, 307°-347°; *Horn Mo (K) 30s*.
W pier hd 51°09'·40N 02°43'·09E FG 11m 9M; W tr; vis 025°-250°, 284°-324°; RC; *Bell (2) 10s.*

• OOSTENDE AND APPROACHES

D1 wreck buoy 51°14'·00N 02°38'·65E Q (3) 10s; ECM.
LST 420 buoy 51°15'·50N 02°40'·70E Q (9) 15s; WCM.
Zuidstroombank buoy 51°12'·33N 02°47'·50E Fl R 5s; PHM.
Middelkerkebank S buoy 51°14'·78N 02°42'·00E Q (9) R 15s; PHM.
Oostendebank W buoy 51°16'·25N 02°44'·85E Q (9) 15s; WCM.
Oostendebank E buoy 51°17'·36N 02°52'·00E Fl (4) R 20s; PHM.
Nautica Ena wreck buoy 51°18'·12N 02°52'·85E Q; NCM.
Wenduinebank W buoy 51°17'·28N 02°52'·87E Q (9) 15s; WCM.

Buitenstroombank buoy 51°15'·20N 02°51'·80E Q; NCM.
Binnenstroombank buoy 51°14'·50N 02°53'·73E Q (3) 10s; ECM.
Oostende 51°14'·23N 02°55'·91E Fl (3) 10s 65m **27M**; W tr; obsc 069·5°-071°.
W pier hd 51°14'·36N 02°55'·12E FG 14m 10M; W ○ tr; vis 057°-327°; *Bell (1) 4s.*
E pier hd FR 15m 12M; W ○ tr; vis 333°-243°; *Horn Mo(OE) 30s.*
Ldg lts 128°, Front, 51°14'·18N 02°55'·62E. Both FR 4M on W framework trs, R bands; vis 051°-201°.
A1 buoy 51°22'·42N 02°53'·42E Iso 8s; SWM.
Oostendebank N buoy 51°21'·25N 02°53'·00E Q; NCM.
A1 bis buoy 51°21'·70N 02°58'·10E L Fl 10s; SWM.
SWW buoy 51°22'·00N 03°01'·00E Fl (4) R 20s; PHM.
WBN buoy 51°21'·50N 03°02'·71E QG; SHM.
Wenduine Bk E buoy 51°18'·85N 03°01'·70E QR; PHM.
A2 buoy 51°22'·50N 03°07'·05E Iso 8s; SWM.

• BLANKENBERGE

Comte Jean jetty 51°18'·78N 03°06'·95E Fl (2) 8s 30m **20M**; W tr, B top; vis 065°-245°.
W mole hd FG 14m 11M; W tr; intens 065°-290°, unintens 290°-335°.
E pier hd FR 12m 11M; W tr; vis 290°-245°; *Bell (2) 15s.*

• SCHEUR CHANNEL

S2 buoy 51°23'·40N 02°58'·17E QR; PHM.
S3 buoy 51°24'·35N 03°03'·00E Q; NCM.
S4 buoy 51°25'·07N 03°02'·93E Fl (4) R 10s; PHM.
S5 buoy 51°23'·73N 03°05'·90E Fl G 5s; SHM.
S6 buoy 51°24'·25N 03°06'·00E Fl R 5s; PHM.
Droogte van Schooneveld (MOW 5) 51°25'·50N 03°09'·00E Fl (5) Y 20s 12m 2M; measuring bn with platform; Ra refl.
S7 buoy 51°24'·02N 03°10'·40E Fl G 5s; SHM.
S8 buoy 51°24'·48N 03°10'·50E Fl (4) R 10s; PHM.
S9 buoy 51°24'·47N 03°15'·06E QG; SHM.
S10 buoy 51°24'·92N 03°15'·07E Fl R 5s; PHM.
S12 buoy 51°24'·67N 03°18'·30E Fl (4) R 10s; PHM.
Scheur-Wiel buoy 51°24'·26N 03°18'·00E Q; NCM.

• ZEEBRUGGE AND APPROACHES

S-Z buoy 51°23'·72N 03°07'·67E Q (3) 10s; ECM.
Zand buoy 51°22'·56N 03°10'·16E QG; SHM.
W Outer bkwtr hd 51°21'·79N 03°11'·25E Oc G 7s 31m 7M; vis 057°-267°; *Horn (3) 30s.*
E bkwtr Oc R 7s 31m 7M; vis 087°-281°.
Heist, mole hd 51°20'·90N 03°12'·25E Oc WR 15s 22m, **W20M**, **R18M**; vis W068°-145°, R145°-201°, W201°-296°; tfc sigs.

NETHERLANDS

APPROACHES TO WESTERSCHELDE

• WIELINGEN CHANNEL

Z buoy 51°22'·60N 03°10'·80E Q (9) 15s; WCM.
BVH buoy 51°23'·15N 03°12'·05E Q (6) + L Fl R 15s; PHM.
MOW3 tide gauge 51°23'·45N 03°12'·00E Fl (5) Y 20s; Racon (H); SPM; *Whis.*
Wielingen buoy 51°23'·30N 03°15'·00E Fl (3) G 15s; SHM.
W1 buoy 51°23'·50N 03°18'·00E Fl G 5s; SHM.
W2 buoy 51°24'·64N 03°21'·58E Iso R 8s; PHM.
W3 buoy 51°24'·03N 03°21'·58E Iso G 8s; SHM.
W4 buoy 51°24'·92N 03°24'·48E L Fl R 5s; PHM.
W5 buoy 51°24'·33N 03°24'·48E L Fl G 5s; SHM.
W6 buoy 51°25'·15N 03°27'·25E L Fl R 8s; PHM.
W7 buoy 51°24'·65N 03°27'·30E L Fl G 8s; SHM.
W8 buoy 51°25'·48N 03°30'·15E L Fl R 5s; PHM.
W9 buoy 51°24'·97N 03°30'·13E L Fl G 5s; SHM.
W10 buoy 51°25'·80N 03°33'·00E QR; PHM.

Wave observation post 51°22'·84N 03°22'·82E Fl (5) Y 20s.
Kruishoofd 51°23'·73N 03°28'·36E Iso WRG 8s 14m W8M, R6M, G5M; W □ tr, B post; vis R074°-091°, W091°-100°, G100°-118°, W118°-153°, R153°-179°, W179°-198°, G198°-205°, W205°-074°.
Nieuwe Sluis 51°24'·48N 03°31'·38E Oc WRG 10s 27m W14M, R11M, G10M; B 8-sided tr, W bands; vis R055°-086°, W086°-091·5°, G091·5°-134°, W134-140·5°, G140·5°-144·5°, W144·5°-236·5°, G236·5°-243°, R243°-260°, G260°-263·5, R263·5-292°, W292°-055°; *Horn (3) 30s.*

• APPROACHES TO BRESKENS
Songa buoy 51°25'·34N 03°33'·78E QG; SHM.
SS-VH buoy 51°24'·75N 03°34'·00E Q; NCM.

• BRESKENS FERRY HARBOUR
W mole hd 51°24'·40N 03°33'·23E FG 8m 4M; B & W mast; in fog FY; Ra refl; Fog Det lt.

• BRESKENS
W mole hd 51°24'·09N 03°34'·12E F WRG 6m; Gy mast; vis R090°-128°, W128°-157°, G157°-169·5°, W169·5°-173°, R173°-194°, W194°-296°, W296°-300°, R300°-320°, G320°-090°; in fog FY; *Horn Mo (U) 30s.*

WESTKAPELLE TO VLISSINGEN

Noorderhoofd ldg lts 149·5°, NW Hd of dyke. Front, 0·73M from rear, Oc WRG 10s 20m W13M, R10M, G10M; R tr, W band; vis R353°-008°, G008°-029°, W029°-169°.
Westkapelle, Common rear, 51°31'·80N 03°26'·90E Fl 3s 50m **28M**; tr, R top; obsc on certain brgs.
Zoutelande ldg lts 326°, Front, 1·8M from rear, FR 21m 12M; R ■ tr; vis 321°-352°.
Molenhoofd 51°31'·61N 03°26'·07E Oc WRG 6s 9m; W mast R bands; vis R306°-329°, W329°-349°, R349°-008°, G008°-034·5°, W034·5°-036·5°, G036·5°-144°, W144°-169°, R169°-198°.
Kaapduinen, ldg lts 130°. Front, 51°28'·52N 03°31'·05E Oc 5s 26m 13M; Y ■ tr, R bands; vis 115°-145°. Rear, 220m from front, Oc 5s 35m 13M; Y ■ tr, R bands; synch with front; vis 107·5°-152·5°.
Fort de Nolle 51°27'·00N 03°33'·20E Fl WRG 2·5s 11m W6M, R4M, G4M; W col, R bands; vis R293°-309°, W309°-324·5°, G324·5°-336·5°, R336·5°-027°, G027°-044°, R044°-090°, G090°-110·5°, W110·5°-114·5°, G114·5°-119°, R119-130°.

• VLISSINGEN (FOR KANAAL DOOR WALCHEREN)
Ldg lts 117°. Leugenaar causeway, Front, 51°26'·47N 03°34'·22E Oc R 5s 5m 7M; W&R pile; intens 108°-126°.
Sardijngeul rear, 550m from front, Oc WRG 5s 8m W12M, R9M, G8M; R △ with W bands on R & W mast; synch; vis R245°-271°, G271°-285°, W285°-123°, R123°-147°.
Koopmanshaven, W Mole root 51°26'·42N 03°34'·61E Iso WRG 3s 15m W12M, R10M, G9M; R pylon; vis R253°-270°, W270°-059°, G059°-071°, W071°-077°, R077°-101°, G101°-110°, W110°-114°.
Buitenhaven E mole-hd 51°26'·37N 03°34'·75E FG 4M.
Buitenhaven W mole hd 51°26'·44N 03°36'·12E FR 10m 5M; also Iso WRG 4s; B mast; vis W072°-021°, G021°-042°, W042°-056°, R056°-072°; Tfc sigs; *Horn 15s.*
Schone Waardin 51°26'·60N 03°37'·95E Oc WRG 9s 10m W13M, R10M, G9M; R mast, W bands; vis: R248°-260·5°, G260·5°-269°, W269°-287·5°, G287·5°-326°, R326°-341°, G341°-023°, W023°-024°, G024°-054°, R054°-065°, W065°-075·5°, G075·5°-079°5°, R079·5°-083°.

• VLISSINGEN OOST
W mole hd 51°26'·94N 03°40'·17E FR 8m 5M; W col; in fog FY; *Horn (2) 20s.*

Ldg lts 023°. Front, 51°27'·91N 03°04'·07E Oc R 8s 7m 8M; G post. Rear, 100m from front, Oc R 8s 12m 8M; G mast; synch with front, both vis 015°-031°.
E Hbr Dir lt 305° 51°27'·93N 03°40'·62E Dir F WRG; vis 303·5°-304·9°; W304·9°-305·1°, G305·1°-306·5°.

WESTERSCHELDE

• BORSSELE-NOORDNOL
Pier hd 51°25'·55N 03°42'·80E Oc WRG 5s; 9m; R mast, W bands; vis R305°-331°, W331°-341°, G341°-000°, W000°-007°, R007°-023°, G023°-054°, W054°-057°, G057°-113°, W113°-128°, R128°-155°, W155°-305°.
Borssele, Total jetty, NW end 51°24'·85N 03°43'·61E Iso WR 10s; vis R133°-141·5°, W141·5°-133°.
Borssele-Everingen 51°24'·73N 03°44'·20E Iso WRG 4s 9m; W structure, R band; vis R021°-026°, G026°-080°, W080°-100°, R100°-137°, W137°-293°, R293°-308°, W308°-344°, G344°-357°, W357°-021°.

• ELLEWOUTSDIJK
W pier hd (unlit) 51°23'·14N 03°49'·12E.

• TERNEUZEN (FOR GENT)
Nieuw Neuzenpolder ldg lts 125°. Front, 51°21'·10N 03°47'·23E Oc 5s 18m 13M; W col, B bands; intens 117°-133°. Rear, 365m from front, Oc 5s 18m 13M; B&W tr; synch with front; intens 117°-133°.
Dow Chemical jetty, 4 dolphins, Fl 3s and Fl R 3s; *Horn 15s.*
West Buitenhaven E mole hd (for Westsluis and Middensluis) 51°20'·61N 03°48'·93E FR 5M; tfc sigs.
Oost Buitenhaven E mole hd (Oostsluis) 51°20'·60N 03°49'·81E FR 5M; Tfc sigs.
Jacht Haven W Jetty 51°20'·59N 03°49'·68E Oc WRG 5s 14m W9M, R7M, G6M; B&W tr; vis R090°-115°, W115°-238·5°, G238·5°-248°, W248°-279°, R279°-004°.
W mole hd 51°20'·62N 03°49'·72E FG 6m; Gy mast; in fog FY.

• HANSWEERT (FOR KANAAL DOOR ZUID BEVELAND)
W mole hd 51°26'·45N 04°00'·50E Oc WRG 10s 9m W9M, R7M, G6M; R tr, W band; vis R288°-310°, W310°-334°, G334°-356·5°, W356·5°-042·5°, R042·5°-061·5°, W061·5°-082·5°, G082·5°-102·5°, W102·5°-114·5°, R114·5°-127·5°, W127·5°-288°; in fog FY.

• WALSOORDEN
S mole hd Ent 51°22'·96N 04°02'·18E FR 5m; Gy col.

• PAAL APPROACHES
Speelmansgat lt bn 51°22'·03N 04°06'·26E Fl (5) Y 20s.

• ZANDVLIET
Ldg lts 118°. Front, 51°20'·70N 04°16'·40E Oc WRG 5s 11m W9M, R7M, G6M; vis R shore-350°, W350°-017°, G017°-019°, W019°-088°, G088°-109°, W109°-125°, R125°-shore. Rear, 200m from front, Oc 5s 18m 9M.

• DOEL/LILLO/ANTWERPEN (Belgium)
Ldg lts 185·5°. Front, 51°18'·51N 04°16'·25E Fl WRG 3s 5m W9M, R7M, G6M; vis Rshore-175°, W175°-202°, G202°-306·5°, W306·5°-330·9°, R330·9°-shore. Rear, 260m from front, Fl 3s 14m 9M; synch with front. By day vis 183°-185°.
Doel jetty hd 51°18'·72N 04°16'·18E Oc WR 5s 9m W9M, R7M; Y □, B stripes on tr; vis R downstream-185°, W185°-334°, R334°-upstream shore.
Lillo Pier SE end 51°18'·20N 04°17'·28E Oc WRG 10s 5m W9M, R7M, G6M; R □ W band on B bn; vis R shore-303·1°, W303·1°-308·2°, G308·2°-096·5°, W096·5°-148°, R148°-shore.
No. 109 buoy 51°14'·04N 04°23'·80E Iso G 8s; SHM.
Antwerp Marina 51°14'·15N 04°23'·77E F WR 9m 3M; vis Wshore-283°-R283°-shore.

20

OOSTERSCHELDE AND APPROACHES

- **OUTER APPROACHES**

Wave observation post VR 51°30'·35N 03°14'·53E Fl Y 5s.
SW Thornton buoy 51°31'·01N 02°51'·00E Iso 8s; SWM.
TB buoy 51°34'·45N 02°59'·15E Q; NCM.
ZSB buoy 51·36'·64N 03°15'·77E VQ (9) 10s; WCM.
Westpit buoy 51°33'·70N 03°10'·00E Iso 8s; SWM.
Rabsbank buoy 51°38'·30N 03°10'·00E Iso 4s; SWM.
Middelbank buoy 51°40'·90N 03°18'·30E Iso 8s; SWM.
MD 3 buoy 51°42'·75N 03°27'·06E Fl G5s; SHM.
Schouwenbank buoy 51°45'·00N 03°14'·40E Mo (A) 8s;
SWM; Racon (O).

- **WESTGAT/OUDE ROOMPOT** (selected marks)

OG-WG buoy 51°37'·23N 03°23'·87E VQ (9) 10s; WCM.
WG1 buoy 51°38'·05N 03°26'·30E L Fl G 5s; SHM.
WG4 lt bn 51°38'·60N 03°28'·80E L Fl R 8s; PHM.
WG7 buoy 51°39'·45N 03°32'·75E L Fl G 5s; SHM.
WG-GB buoy 51°39'·75N 03°32'·75E VQ (6) + L Fl 10s; SCM.
OR2 By 51°39'·53N 03°33'·78E; PHM.
OR5 buoy 51°38'·60N 03°35'·45E L Fl G 8s; SHM.
OR 6 buoy 51°38'·78N 03°36'·39E L Fl R 8s; PHM.
OR8 By 51°38'·28N 03°37'·40E; PHM.
OR11 buoy 51°37'·03N 03°38'·48E L Fl G 5s; SHM.
OR12 buoy 51°37'·35N 03°39'·30E L Fl R 5s; PHM.
Roompotsluis ldg lts 073·5°. Front, 51°37'·38N 03°40'·80E
Oc G 5s. Rear, 280m from front, Oc G 5s; synch.
N bkwtr hd 51°37'·34N 03°40'·17E FR 6m; *Horn(2) 30s.*

- **SOPHIAHAVEN/COLIJNSPLAAT**

Roompot Marina N mole hd 51°35'·78N 03°43'·27E FR.
Colijnsplaat E jetty hd 51°36'·28N 03°51'·15E FR 3m 3M; *Horn.*
Zeeland Bridge. N and S passages marked by FY lts, 14m.

- **KATS/GOESSCHE SAS (GOES)/WEMELDINGE**

Kats S jetty hd 51°34'·44N 03°53'·72E Oc WRG 8s 5m 5M;
vis W344°-153°, R153°-165°, G165°-200°, W200°-214°,
G214°-258°, W258°-260°, G260°-313°, W313°-331°.
Goessche Sas S mole hd 51°32'·28N 03°55'·92E FR.
Wemeldinge W jetty hd 51°31'·34N 04°00'·25E FG.
W Hd new ent 51°31'·20N 04°00'·90E Oc WRG 5s 7m W9M,
R7M, G7M; vis R105·5°-114°, W114°-124°, G124°-140·5°,
W140·5°-144°, G144°-192°, W192°-205°, R205°-233·5°,
W233·5°-258·5°. R & G lts mark canal.

- **YERSEKE/THOLENSCHE GAT/GORISHOEK**

O25/Sv 12 buoy 51°31'·40N 04°02'·42E QG; SHM.
Ldg lts 155° (through Schaar van Yerseke). Front, 51°30'·07N
04°03'·46E Iso 4s 8m; in fog FY. Rear, 180m from front, Iso
4s 13m; synch; in fog 2 FY. FG and FR mark mole Hds.
Tholensche Gat. Strijenham 51°31'·40N 04°08'·91E Oc WRG
5s 9m W8M, R5M, G5M; R □, W bands, on mast; vis
Wshore-268°, R268°-281·5°, W281·5°-297°, G297°-310°,
R310°-060·5°, G060·5°-068°, W068°-082°. R082°-115°,
W 115°-shore.

Werkhaven W mole hd 51°30'·93N 04°09'·75W FG.
Gorishoek 51°31'·57N 04°04'·68E Iso WRG 8s 7m W6M,
R4M, G4M; R pedestal, W bands; vis R260°-278°, W278°-
021°, G021°-025°, W025°- 071°, G071°-085°, W085°-103°,
R103°-120°, W120°-260°.
Galgeplaat buoy 51°32'·67N 03°59'·04E Q (6) + L Fl 15s; SCM.

- **STAVENISSE/ST ANNALAND**

Hoek Van Ouwerkerk ldg lts 009·2° Front, 51°36'·92N
03°58'·27E Iso WRG 6s; viz R267°-306°, W306°-314°, G314°-
007·5°, W007·5°-011·5°, G011·5°-067°, W067°-068·5°,
G068·5°-085°, W085°-102·°5, G102·5°-112·5°, R112·5°-
121·5°. Rear, 300m from front, Iso 6s.
Keeten B buoy 51°36'·41N 03°58'·15E Mo (A) 8s; SWM;
Racon (K).

Stavenisse E mole hd 51°35'·73N 04°00'·35E Oc WRG 5s
10m W12M, R9M, G8M; B pylon; W075°-090°, R090°-105·5°,
W105·5°-108°, G108°-118·5°, W118·5°-124°, G124°-155°,
W155°-158°, G158°-231°, W231°-238·5°, R238·5°-253°,
W253°-350°.
St Annaland entrance W side 51°36'·32N 04°06'·60E FG.

- **ZIJPE/ANNA JACOBAPOLDER**

Veerhaven N mole hd 51°38'·63N 04°06'·02E Iso G 4s.
St Philipsland, on dyke 51°39'·17N 04°07'·16E Oc WRG 4s
9m W8M, R5M, G4M; pylon on B ● col; vis W051°-100°,
R100°-144°, W144°-146°, G146°-173°.
Zijpsche Bout 51°38'·83N 04°05'·78E Oc WRG 10s 9m
W12M, R9M, G8M; mast on R col; vis R208°-211°, W211°-
025°, G025°-030°, W030°-040°, R040°-066°.
Tramweghaven S mole 51°38'·90N 04°05'·87E Iso R 4s 7m.

- **KRAMMER/BRUINISSE/KRAMMERSLUIZEN**

Stoofpolder 51°39'·52N 04°06'·39E Iso WRG 4s 10m W12M,
R9M, G8M; B tr, W bands; vis W147°-154°, R154°-226·5°,
G226·5°-243°, W243°-253°, G253°-259°, W259°-263°, G263°-
270°, R270°-283°, W283°-008°.
Bruinisse N mole hd 51°39'·94N 04°06'·03E FR 4M; Gy Bn.
Krammersluizen N bkwtr hd 51°39'·78N 04°08'·35E FR.

- **DE VAL/ZIERIKZEE**

Engelsche Vaarwater ldg lts 019°. Front, 51°37'·75N
03°55'·60E Iso WRG 3s 7m W6M, R4M, G4M; R pedestal, W
band; vis R290°-306°, W306°-317·5°, G317·5°-334°, W334°-
336·5°, G336·5°-017·5°, W017·5°-026°, G026°-090°, R090°-
108°, W108°-290°. Rear, 300m from front, Iso 3s 15m 6M;
R ■ on W mast, R bands.
Zierikzee W jetty hd 51°37'·95N 03°53'·45E Oc WRG 6s 10m
W6M, R4M, G4M; R pedestal, W band; vis G063°-100°,
W100°-133°, R133°-156°, W156°-278°, R278°-306°, G306°-
314°, W314°-333°, R333°-350°, W350°-063°.

- **FLAUWERSPOLDER/SCHELPHOEK/BURGHSLUIS**

Flauwerspolder W mole hd 51°40'·70N 03°50'·86E Iso WRG
4s 7m W6M, R4M, G4M; W daymark, B band on pylon; vis
R303°-344°, W344°-347°, G347°-083°, W083°-086°, G086°-
103°, W103°-110°, R110°-128°, W128°-303°.
Schelphoek E bkwtr hd 51°41'·28N 03°48'·79E Fl (2) 10s 8m.
Hammen. Burghsluis S mole hd 51°40'·59N 03°45'·56E
F WRG 9m W8M, R5M, G4M; mast on R col; vis W218°-230°,
R230°-245°, W245°-253·5°, G253·5°-293°, W293°-000°,
G000°-025·5°, W025·5°-032°, G032°-041°, R041°-070°,
W070°-095°.

HARINGVLIET AND APPROACHES

Buitenbank buoy 51°51'·20N 03°25'·80E Iso 4s; SWM.
Bollen buoy 51°50'·00N 03°33'·00E VQ (9) 10s; WCM.
MW buoy 51°44'·30N 03°23'·75E Q (9) 15s; WCM.
MN buoy 51°47'·70N 03°30'·00E Q; NCM.
BG2 51°46'·10N 03°37'·20E Fl Y 5s; Y pile.
West Schouwen 51°42'·58N 03°41'·60E Fl (2+1)15s 58m
30M; Gy tr, R diagonal stripes on upper part.
Ooster buoy 51°47'·97N 03°41'·32E Q (9) 15s; WCM.
SH buoy 51°49'·50N 03°45'·90E VQ (9) 10s; WCM.
Ha10 51°51'·80N 03°51'·80E Fl Y 5s; Y pile.
SG buoy 51°52'·00N 03°51'·50E Iso 4s; SWM.
SG 2 buoy 51°51'·80N 03°53'·50E Iso R 2s; PHM.
SG 5 buoy 51°50'·97N 03°55'·45E L Fl G 8s; SHM.
SG 9 buoy 51°50'·81N 03°57'·41E L Fl G 8s; SHM.
SG 19 By 51°51'·24N 04°00'·20E; SHM.
G1 buoy 51°50'·23N 04°02'48E L Fl G 8s; SHM.

- **STELLENDAM**

N mole hd 51°49'·93N 04°02'·09E FG; *Horn (2) 15s.*

• HELLEVOETSLUIS/HELIUSHAVEN

Haven W side 51°49'·23N 04°07'·74E Iso WRG 10s 16m W11M, R8M, G7M; W tr, R cupola; vis G shore-275°, W275°-294°, R294°-316°, W316°-036°, G036°-058°, W058°-095°, R095°-shore.

Tramhaven E mole hd 51°49'·23N 04°08'·00E FG 6m.

Heliushaven W jetty 51°49'·29N 04°07'·23E FR 7m 4M.

Hoornsche Hoofden, watchhouse on dyke 51°48'·32N 04°11'·05E Oc WRG 5s 7m W7M, R5M, G4M; vis W288°-297°, G297°-313°, W313°-325°, R325°-335°, G335°-344·5°, W344·5°-045°, G045°-055°, W055°-131°, R131°-shore.

• MIDDELHARNIS/NIEUWENDIJK

Middelharnis W pier hd 51°46'·65N 04°11'·81E F WRG 5m W8M, R5M, G4M; vis W144°-164·5°, R164·5°-176·5°, G176·5°-144°.

Nieuwendijk ldg lts 303·5°. Front, 51°45'·10N 04°19'·48E Iso WRG 6s 8m W9M, R7M, G6M; B framework tr; vis G093°-100°, W100°-103·5°, R103·5°-113°, W113°-093°. Rear, 450m from front, F 11m 9M; B framework tr.

• VOLKERAKSLUIZEN/WILLEMSTAD

Jachtensluis W side, S ent 51°41'·50N 04°23'·20E FG (sport).

Jachtensluis E side, E ent 51°41'·97N 04°25'·52E FR.

Noorder Voorhaven, W mole hd 51°42'·08N 04°25'·88E FG 6m 4M; R lantern on pedestal; in fog FY.

Willemstad HD 9A buoy 51°41'·84N 04°26'·75E Iso G 4s; SHM.

HOEK VAN HOLLAND AND APPROACHES

Noord Hinder buoy 52°00'·15N 02° 51'·50E Fl (2) 10s: Racon (T); Horn (2) 30s; SWM.

Euro Platform 51°59'·99N 03°16'·55E Mo (U) 15s; W structure, R bands; helicopter platform; Horn Mo(U) 30s.

Goeree 51°55'·53N 03°40'·18E Fl (4) 20s 32m 28M; R and W chequered tr on platform; RC; helicopter platform; Racon (T); Horn (4) 30s.

Westhoofd 51°48'·83N 03°51'·90E Fl (3) 15s 56m 30M; R ■ tr.

Kwade Hoek 51°50'·25N 03°59'·07E Iso WRG 4s 10m W12M, R9M, G8M; B mast, W bands; vis W 235°-068°, R068°-088°, G088°-107°, W107°-113°, R113°-142°, W142°-228°, R228°-235°; FR on radio mast 4·2M NE.

MC buoy 52°01'·18N 03°53'·57E Iso 4s; SWM; Racon (M).

Hinder buoy 51°54'·60N 03°55'·50E Q (9) 15s; WCM.

MV buoy 51°57'·50N 03°58'·50E Q (9) 15s; WCM.

MVN buoy 51°59'·66N 04°00'·29E VQ; NCM.

Indusbank N buoy 52°02'·92N 04°03'·73E Q; NCM.

• HOEK VAN HOLLAND

Maasvlakte 51°58'·25N 04°00'·94E Fl (5) 20s 67m 28M; B 8-sided tr, W bands; vis 340°-267°.

Nieuwe Noorderdam hd 51°59'·71N 04°02'·92E FR 25m 10M; Or tr, B bands; helicopter platform; in fog Al Fl WR 6s; vis 278°-255°.

Nieuwe Zuiderdam hd 51°59'·19N 04°02'·58E FG 25m 10M; Y tr, B bands; helicopter platform; in fog Al Fl WG 6s; vis 330°-307°; Horn 10s.

Maasmond ldg lts 107° Front, 51°58'·60N 04°07'·58E Iso 4s 30m 21M; R tr, W bands. Rear, 0·6M from front, Iso 4s 47m 21M; both vis 101°-123°, synch.

Maassluis Buitenhaven E ent 51°54'·99N 04°14'·89E FG.

• ROTTERDAM

Vlaardingen Buitenhaven E ent 51°54'·04N 04°21'·02E FG.

Spuihaven W ent 51°54'·03N 04°24'·06E FR.

Veerhaven E ent 51°54'·45N 04°28'·82E FG.

HOEK VAN HOLLAND TO DEN HELDER

• SCHEVENINGEN

SCH buoy 52°07'·80N 04°14'·20E Iso 4s; SWM.

Scheveningen 52°06'·30N 04°16'·17E Fl (2) 10s 49m 29M; brown tr; vis 014°-244°.

Ldg lts 156°. Front, 52°05'·82N 04°15'·68E Iso 4s 17m 14M. Rear, 100m from front, Iso 4s 21m 14M; synch with front.

SW mole hd 52°06'·28N 04°15'·22E FG 11m 9M; G 6-sided tr, W bands, R lantern; Horn (3) 30s.

Noordwijk-aan-Zee 52°15'·00N 04°26'·10E Oc (3) 20s 32m 18M; W □ tr.

Survey platform 52°16'·40N 04°17'·90E FR and Mo (U) 15s; Horn Mo (U) 20s.

Eveline buoy 52°25'·55N 04°25'·15E VQ (9) 10s; WCM.

• IJMUIDEN

A-NE buoy 52°27'·95N 03°48'·70E L Fl Y 10s; SPM.

IJ 3 buoy 52°29'·80N 04°12'·10E Fl (3) Y 10s; SPM.

IJmuiden buoy (IJM) 52°28'·50N 04°23'·87E Mo (A) 8s; SWM; Racon (Y); (also known as Verkenningston.)

Ldg lts 100·5°. Front, F WR 30m W16M, R13M; dark R tr; vis W050°-122°, R122°-145°, W145°-160°; RC. By day F 4m vis 090·5°-110·5°. Rear, 570m from front, Fl 5s 52m 29M; dark R tr; vis 019°-199°.

S bkwtr hd 52°27'·86N 04°32'·00E FG 14m 10M; in fog Fl 3s; Horn (2) 30s.

• NOORDZEE KANAAL/AMSTERDAM/IJSSELMEER

Ø Km mark 52°27'·86N 04°35'·64E.

20 Km mark 52°25'·21N 04°51'·94E.

Sixhaven yacht hbr 52°23'·02N 04°53'·77E F & FR.

Oranjesluizen (to IJsselmeer) 52°22'·98N 04°57'·70E.

• IJMUIDEN TO TEXEL

BSP buoy 52°30'·80N 04°30'·00E Fl (4) Y 12s; SPM.

CP-Q8-A platform 52°35'·75N 04°31'·80E Mo (U) 15s.

Egmond-aan-Zee 52°37'·20N 04°37'·40E Iso WR 10s 36m W18M, R14M; W tr; vis W010°-175°, R175°-188°.

Petten buoy 52°47'·38N 04°36'·80E VQ (9) 10s; WCM.

• ZEEGAT VAN TEXEL

Vinca G buoy 52°46'·10N 04°12'·00E Q (9) 15s; WCM; Racon (D).

TX1 buoy 52°48'·17N 04°15'·60E Fl G 5s; SHM.

ZH buoy 52°54'·70N 04°34'·84E VQ (6) + L Fl 10s; SCM.

MR buoy 52°56'·80N 04°33'·90E Q (9) 15s; WCM.

NH buoy 53°00'·30N 04°35'·45E VQ; NCM.

Grote Kaap 52°52'·90N 04°42'·98E Oc WRG 10s 31m W11M, R8M, G8M; vis G041°-088°, W088°-094°, R094°-131°.

• SCHULPENGAT

Schulpengat. Ldg lts 026·5°. Front, 53°00'·88N 04°44'·52E Iso 4s 18M; vis 024·5°-028·5°. Rear, Den Hoorn 0·83M from front, Oc 8s 18M; church spire; vis 024°-028°.

Huisduinen 52°57'·20N 04°43'·37E F WR 27m W14M, R11M; ■ tr; vis W070°-113°, R113°-158°, W158°-208°.

Kijkduin, Rear, 52°57'·35N 04°43'·60E Fl (4) 20s 56m 30M; brown tr; vis except where obsc by dunes on Texel.

SG buoy 52°52'·95N 04°38'·00E Mo (A) 8s; Racon (Z); SWM.

S1 buoy 52°53'·57N 04°38'·88E Iso G 4s; SHM.

S2 buoy 52°53'·87N 04°38'·02E Iso R 4s; PHM.

S3 buoy 52°54'·48N 04°39'·62E Iso G 8s; SHM.

S4 buoy 52°54'·65N 04°39'·53E Iso R 8s; PHM.

S5 buoy 52°55'·40N 04°40'·30E Iso G 4s; SHM.

S6 buoy 52°55'·55N 04°39'·78E Iso R 4s; PHM.

S7 buoy 52°56'·30N 04°40'·99E Iso G 8s; SHM.

S6A buoy 52°56'·57N 04°40'·60E QR; PHM.

S8 buoy 52°57'·12N 04°41'·10E; PHM.

S9 buoy 52°56'·90N 04°42'·15E; SHM.

20

S10 buoy 52°57'·65N 04°41'·65E Iso R 8s; PHM.
S11 buoy 52°57'·60N 04°43'·35E Iso G 4s; SHM.
S14/MG17 buoy 52°58'·42N 04°43'·40E VQ (6) + L Fl 10s; SCM.

● MOLENGAT
Verkenningston MG buoy 53°03'·95N 04°39'·45E Mo (A) 8s; SWM.
MG 1 buoy 53°02'·05N 04°41'·46E Iso G 4s; SHM.
MG 2 buoy 53°02'·18N 04°41'·87E Iso R 4s; PHM.
MG 6 buoy 53°01'·08N 04°41'·83E Iso R 4s; PHM.
MG 5 buoy 53°01'·08N 04°41'·52E Iso G 4s; SHM.
MG 9 buoy 53°00'·07N 04°41'·50E QG; SHM.
MG 10 buoy 53°00'·25N 04°41'·90E; QR, PHM.
MG 13 buoy 52°59'·17N 04°42'·30E Iso G 8s; SHM.
MG 16 buoy 52°59'·10N 04°42'·86E QR; PHM.
MG 18 buoy 52°58'·67N 04°43'·70E; PHM.
MG 20 buoy 52°58'·77N 04°44'·40E Iso R 8s; PHM.

● MARSDIEP/DEN HELDER
T3 buoy 52°58'·12N 04°46'·49E Iso G 8s; SHM.
Marinehaven, W bkwtr hd (Harssens I) 52°58'·00N 04°46'·84E QG 12m 8M; *Horn 20s.*
MH6, E side of ent 52°57'·97N 04°47'·51E Iso R 4s 9m 4M; R pile; Ra refl.
Ent W side, Fl G 5s 9m 4M; vis 180°-067° (H24).
Ent E side, QR 9m 4M; (H24.)
Ldg lts 191°. Front, 52°57'·42N 04°47'·17E Oc G 5s 16m 14M; B △ on bldg; vis 161°-221°. Rear, 275m from front, Oc G 5s 25m 14M; B ▽ on bldg; vis 161°-247°, synch.

Schilbolsnol 53°00'·56N 04°45'·78E F WRG 27m **W15M**, R12M, G11M; G tr; vis W338°-002°, G002°-035°, W035°-038° (leading sector for Schulpengat), R038°-051°, W051°-068°.

Mok 53°00'·25N 04°46'·85E Oc WRG 10s 10m W10M, R7M, G6M; vis R229°-317°, W317°-337°, G337°-112°.

WADDENZEE

● DEN OEVER/STEVINSLUIZEN
M13 buoy 52°59'·36N 04°52'·62E Iso G 8s; SHM.
LW buoy 52°59'55N 04°56'·00E L Fl 10s; SWM.
W1 buoy 52°59'·01N 04°56'·82E Iso G 4s; SHM.
W9 buoy 52°57'·30N 04°57'·61E Iso G 8s; SHM.
O5 buoy 52°56'·89N 05°01'·98E Iso G 4s; SHM.
Ldg lts 131° 52°56'·37N 05°03'·04E Front and Rear both Oc 10s 7M; vis 127°-137°.
Detached bkwtr N hd 52°56'·80N 05°02'·38E L Fl R 10s.
Stevinsluizen W wall, 80m from Hd 52°56'·27N 05°02'·23E Iso WRG 2s; vis G195°-213°, W213°-227°, R227°-245°.

● TEXELSTROOM/OUDESCHILD
T17 buoy 53°01'·20N 04°51'·50E Iso G 8s; SHM.
T14 buoy 53°02·28N 04°51'·56E Iso R 8s; PHM.
Oudeschild S mole hd 53°02'·37N 04°51'·26E FR 7m; *Horn (2) 30s* (sounded 0600-2300).
Oc 6s 7m lt seen between FR and FG leads into hbr.
T23 buoy 53°03'·55N 04°55'·70E QG; SHM.
T27 buoy 53°03'·52N 04°59'·25E Iso G 8s; SHM.

● DOOVE BALG/KORNWERDERZAND/LORENTZ-SLUIZEN
D4 buoy 53°02'·61N 05°03'·74E Iso R 8s; PHM.
D3A/J2 buoy 53°01'·98N 05°07'·84E Fl (2+1) G 10s; G post, R band.
D16 buoy 53°02'·84N 05°10'·79E Iso R 8s; PHM.
D24 buoy 53°03'·83N 05°15'·65E Iso R 8s; PHM.

Kornwerderzand Buitenhaven, W mole hd 53°04'·82N 05°20'·13E FG 9m 7M; *Horn Mo(N) 30s.*
Spuihaven Noord, W mole hd 53°04'·81N 05°19'·69E L Fl G 10s 7m 7M.

● BOONTJES/APPROACHES TO HARLINGEN
BO11/KZ/2 53°05'·00N 05°20'·31E Q; NCM.
BO15 buoy 53°05'·75N 05°22'·14E Fl G 2s; SHM.
BO28 buoy 53°07'·85N 05°22'·65E Iso R 8s; PHM.
BO34 buoy 53°08'·90N 05°23'·05E Iso R 2s; PHM.
BO40 buoy 53°09'·90N 05°23'·40E Iso R 4s; PHM.

● VLIESTROOM (selected marks)
VL1 buoy 53°18'·97N 05°08'·80E QG; SHM.
VL 8 buoy 53°18'·57N 05°10'·95E L Fl R 8s; PHM.
VL9 buoy 53°17'·85N 05°10'·00E Iso G 4s; SHM.
VL12/WM1 buoy 53°17'·15N 05°11'·24E VQ (9) 10s; WCM.
VL16 buoy 53°16'·90N 05°10'·72E L Fl R 8s; PHM.
VL15 buoy 53°15'·95N 05°09'·80E L Fl G 8s; SHM.

● APPR TO HARLINGEN/BLAUWE SLENK/POLLENDAM (selected marks)
BS1/IN2 buoy 53°15'·22N 05°10'·00E VQ; NCM.
BS3 buoy 53°14'·82N 05°10'·43E L Fl G 5s; SHM.
BS7 buoy 53°14'·14N 05°11'·25E L Fl G 8s; SHM.
BS11 buoy 53°13'·68N 05°13'·08E Iso G 4s; SHM.
BS19 buoy 53°13'·35N 05°17'·20E QG; SHM.
BS27 buoy 53°11'·95N 05°18'·40E QG; SHM.
BS31 buoy 53°11'·62N 05°19'·77E L Fl G 8s; SHM.
BS 33 buoy 53°10'·73N 05°23'·51E VQ G; SHM.

● HARLINGEN
Ldg lts 112°. Front, 53°10'·56N 05°24'·42E Iso 6s 8m 13M; vis 097°-127°; and FG 9m 7. Rear, 500m from front, Iso 6s 19m 13M; both on B masts, W bands; vis 104·5°-119·5° (H24).
N mole hd 53°10'·57N 05°24'·42E Iso R 5s 8m 4M; R pedestal.

TEXEL TO AMELAND

● APPROACHES TO EIERLANDSE GAT
Eierland, N point of Texel 53°10'·97N 04°51'·40E Fl (2) 10s 52m **29M**; R tr; RC.
TX 3 buoy 52°58'·61N 04°22'·50E Fl (3) G 10s; SHM.
VL South buoy 53°08'·95N 04°26'·63E L Fl Y 10s; SPM.
VL1 buoy 53°11'·00N 04°35'·40E Fl (2) G 10s; SHM.
Baden buoy 53°13'·62N 04°41'·35E Q (9) 15s; WCM.
EG buoy 53°13'·39N 04°47'·15E VQ (9) 10s; WCM.

● ZEEGAT VAN TERSCHELLING AND APPROACHES
VL CENTER LANBY 53°27'·00N 04°40'·00E Fl 5s 12M; Racon (C); *Horn (2) 30s.*
Vlieland 53°17'·79N 05°03'·58E Iso 4s 53m **20M**; RC.
VL3 buoy 53°16'·98N 04°39'·68E Fl (3) G 9s; SHM.
VL5 buoy 53°22'·90N 04°44'·00E QG; SHM.
VL7 buoy 53°25'·53N 04°54'·01E Fl (3) G 9s; SHM.
SM buoy 53°19'·29N 04°55'·71E Iso 4s; SWM.

● ZUIDER STORTEMELK (selected marks)
ZS-Bank buoy 53°18'·98N 04°57'·98E VQ; NCM.
ZS1 buoy 53°18'·85N 04°59'·62E Fl G 5s; SHM.
ZS13/VS2 buoy 53°18'·80N 05°05'·93E Fl (2+1) G 12s; leave to port for Vlieland and to stbd for Terschelling and Harlingen.

● VLIELAND
VS3 buoy 53°18'·37N 05°06'·25E QG; SHM.
VS5 buoy 53°18'·08N 05°06'·20E L Fl G 5s; SHM.
VS14 buoy 53°17'·62N 05°05'70E L Fl R 8s; PHM.
E mole hd 53°17'·73N 05°05'·59E FG.
W mole hd 53°17'·72N 05°05'·57E FR.

● WEST TERSCHELLING
SG 17 buoy 53°21'·20N 05°13'·37E L Fl G 8s; SHM.
Brandaris tr 53°21'·67N 05°12'·99E Fl 5s 55m **29M**; Y ■ tr; vis except where obsc by dunes on Vlieland and Terschelling. Ldg lts 053·5°, W hbr mole hd, Front, 53°21'·30N 05°13'·18E FR 5m 5M; R post, W bands; *Horn 15s.* **Rear**, on dyke, 1·1M

from front Iso 5s 14m **19M**; vis 045°-061°.
<u>W Terschelling E pier hd</u> 53°21'·31N 05°13'·27E FG 5m 4M.

AMELAND TO DELFZIJL

● ZEEGAT VAN AMELAND AND APPROACHES
<u>TG buoy</u> 53°24'·22N 05°02'·40E Q (9) 15s; WCM.
<u>Otto buoy</u> 53°24'·70N 05°06'·60E VQ (3) 5s; ECM.
<u>VL 11 buoy</u> 53°28'·13N 05°04'·03E L Fl G 10s; SHM.
<u>TE 1 buoy</u> 53°30'·02N 05°13'·60E Fl (3) G 9s; SHM.
<u>TE 3 buoy</u> 53°31'·86N 05°23'·00E L Fl G 10s; SHM.
<u>TE 5 buoy</u> 53°33'·70N 05°32'·63E Fl (3) G 10s; SHM.
<u>TS buoy</u> 53°28'·20N 05°21'·60E VQ; NCM.

Ameland, W end 53°27'·02N 05°37'·60E Fl (3) 15s 57m **30M**;
brown tr, W bands; RC.
<u>BR buoy</u> 53°30'·70N 05°33'·62E Q; NCM.
Ballumerbocht 53°25'·90N 05°44'·2E Iso R 4s 5m 4M.

● NES
<u>Nieuwe Veerdam mole hd</u> 53°26'·02N 05°46'·53E Iso 6s 2m 8M.
Reegeul R3 53°28'·80N 05°46'·0E Iso G 4s.

● AMELAND TO SCHIERMONNIKOOG
<u>TE 9 buoy</u> 53°37'·45N 05°51'·85E Fl (3) G 9s; SHM.
<u>TE 13 buoy</u> 53°41'·15N 06°11'·15E QG; SHM.
<u>AM buoy</u> 53°31'·00N 05°44'·80E VQ; NCM.
<u>NAM 21 buoy</u> 53°31'·20N 05°55'·50E Fl Y; SPM.
<u>WRG buoy</u> 53°32'·90N 06°03'·30E Q; NCM.
<u>WG buoy</u> 53°32'·25N 06°06'·11E Iso 8s; SWM.

Schiermonnikoog 53°29'·20N 06°08'·90E Fl (4) 20s 43m
28M; ● tr, dark R tr. F WR 29m **W15M**, R12M; (same tr); vis
W210°-221°, R221°-230°.
Ferry pier hd 53°28'·17N 06°12'·21E 2 F.

● LAUWERSOOG/OOSTMAHORN/ZOUTKAMP
Lauwersoog E mole hd 53°24'·72N 06°12'·14E FR 4M.
<u>Lauwersoog W mole hd</u> 53°24'·73N 06°12'·09E FG 3M; in
fog FY; Horn (2) 30s.
Oostmahorn ent 53°23'·01N 06°09'·72E FG.
Zoutkamp ent (unlit) 53°20'·42N 06°17'·66E.

● EEMSHAVEN
<u>W Pier</u> 53°27'·80N 06°50·15E FG 8m 3M.

● DELFZIJL
<u>W mole hd</u> 53°19'·05N 07°00'·38E FG; Ra refl.
E mole hd FR, in fog FY; Horn 15s.
Ldg lts 203°: Front, 53°18'·56N 07°00'·25E Iso 4s; rear, 310m
from front, Iso 4s.
Zeehavenkanaal, N side (odd numbered posts: three QG, four
Fl G 2s, six Fl G 5s; R Refl.
Zeehavenkanaal, S side, even numbered posts: one Fl (2) R
6s; one Fl R 2s, five Fl R 5s, one QR; R Refl.
E side ent No. 21 (marina ent) 53°19'·83N 06°56'·12E QG; W
post on dolphin.

● TERMUNTERZIJL
<u>BW 13 buoy</u> 53°18'·70N 07°02'·37E; Fl G 5s SHM.

**For lights and marks on the German bank of River Ems
see 8.21.4.**

8.20.5 GLOSSARY WOORDENLIJST

English	Nederlands
A. NAVIGATION	**NAVIGATIE**

Marks, Buoys, Beacons — **Merken, Tonnen, Bakens**

Beacon (Bn)	Baken
Buoy	Boei
Can (PHM buoy)	Stompe ton
Chequered	Geblokt
Column	Zuil, kolom
Cone, conical (SHM buoy)	Spitse ton
Diamond (◇ shape)	Ruit (◇ vorm)
Dividers	Steekpasser
Framework Tower	Traliemast
Isolated danger (IDM buoy)	Losliggend gevaar
Landfall (SWM buoy)	Verkenningston
Landmark	Oriëntatiepunt
Leading line, transit	Geleidelijn
Log Book	Journaal
Perch	Prik
Pilot Station	Loodsstation
Port (side)	Bakboord
Radio beacon	Radiobaken
Signal station	Seinstation, semafoor
Special mark (SPM buoy)	Bijzondere betonning
Square (□)	Vierkant
Starboard (Stbd)	Stuurboord
Topmark	Topteken
Tower (Tr)	Toren
Watch Tr, lookout	Uitkijk

Colours **Kleuren**

Black (B)	Zwart (Z)
Blue (Bu)	Blauw (B)
Green (G)	Groen (Gn)
Grey	Grijs
Red, (R)	Rood (r)
Stripe	Streep
White (W)	Wit (W)
Yellow (Y)	Geel (gl)

Lights **Lichten**

Alternating (Al)	Alternerend (Alt)
Extinguished (Lt)	Gedoofd
Fixed (F)	Vast licht (V)
Fixed and Flashing (F Fl)	Vast en schitterend (V & S)
Flashing	Schitterlicht (S)
Interrupted quick flashing (IQ)	Onderbroken flikkerlicht
Isophase (Iso)	Isofase (Iso)
Leading Light	Geleidelicht
Lighthouse	Vuurtoren
Lightship	Lichtschip
Obscured	Verduisterd
Occulting (Oc)	Onderbroken (Oc)
Quick flashing (Q)	Flikkerlicht (Fl)
Temporary	Tijdelijk
Very quick flashing (VQ)	Snelflikkerlicht

Fog Signals **Mistseinen**

Bell	Bel/klok
Explosive (fog)	Knalmistsein
Foghorn	Misthoorn
Reed (horn)	Hoorn
Siren	Sirene
Whistle	Fluit

Compass **Kompa**

Compass, hand-bearing	Handpeilkompas
East (E)	Oost
North (N)	Noord

20

South (S)	Zuid
West (W)	West

Tides/Depths — Getij/Diepten

Bay	Baai, inham
Beach, sandy	Zandstrand
Channel	Kanaal, geul, vaarwater
Chart Datum	Reductievlak
Cliff	Klip, krijtrots
Coastline	Kustlijn
Draught	Diepgang
Echosounder	Dieptemeter
Estuary	Riviermond
Flood/ebb stream	Vloed/eb stroom
Gulf	Golf
Height, headroom, clearance	Doorvaarthoogte
High Water (HW)	Hoogwater
Island	Eiland
Knots (kn)	Knopen
Low Water (LW)	Laagwater
Peninsula	Schiereiland
Point, headland	Punt
Mean Sea level	Middenstandsvlak (ML)
Mean (tide)	Gemiddeld
Narrows	Zeeëngte
Neaps (np)	Doodtij
Range	Verval
Rate (tide)	Snelheid
River	Rivier
Sandhill, dunes	Duinen
Slack water, stand	Kentering (hoog of laag)
Springs (sp)	Springtij
Strait(s)	Straat
Tidal stream al as	Stroomatlas
Tide Tables	Getijtafel

Features — Kenmerken

Bridge	Brug
Castle	Kasteel
Conspicuous (conspic)	Opvallend
Railway	Spoorweg
Steeple, spire	Toren, spits
Water tower	Watertoren
Windmill	Windmolen

Dangers/Seabed — Gevaren/Zeebodem

Aground	Aan de grond
Bank	Bank
Breakers	Branding
Clay	Klei
Mud (M)	Modder (M)
Prohibited area	Verboden gebied
Sand (S)	Zand (Z)
Seaweed, kelp	Zeewier
Shoal	Droogte
Stony, shingly	Grind of kiezel
Reef	Rif
Rock, stone	Rots, steen
Wreck	Wrak

Ports/Harbours — Havens

Alongside berth (AB)	Aanlegplaats
Anchorage (⚓)	Ankerplaats
Basin	Bassin, dok
Breakwater, mole	Havendam
Breakwater, wave-break	Golfbreker
Concrete	Beton
Dolphin	Dukdalf
Downstream	Stroomafwaarts
Dredged	Gebaggerd
Drying berth	Droogvallende ligplaats
Ferry	Veer
Finger berth/pontoon	Box/Ponton
Fishing harbour	Vissershaven
Fixed bridge	Vaste brug
Harbour dues	Havengeld
Harbour Master	Havenmeester
Inner harbour	Binnenhaven
Jetty	Pier
Landing (L)	Haventrap
Lifeboat (LB)	Reddingsboot
Lifting bridge	Beweegbare brug
Lock	Sluis
Mooring buoy	Meerboei
Mooring	Ligplaats
Outer harbour	Buitenhaven
Post, pile (mooring)	Paal, meerpaal
Roadstead	Rede
Slipway (slip)	Scheepshelling
Stone	Steen
Swing bridge	Draaibrug
Upstream	Stroomopwaarts
Yacht harbour, marina	Jachthaven

B. METEOROLOGY — METEOROLOGIE

Pressure — Drukgebied

Forecast	Weervoorspelling
Front, warm/cold	Front, warm/koud
High pressure	Hogedrukgebied
Low pressure	Depressie
Ridge (high)	Rug
Rise/fall	Rijzen/vallen
Settled	Vast
To deepen	Dieper worden
To fill	Opvullen
Trough (low)	Trog

Wind — Wind

Calm (F0)	Windstil
Light airs (F1)	Flauw en stil
Light breeze (F2)	Zwakke wind
Gentle breeze (F3)	Matige wind
Moderate breeze (F4)	Matige wind
Fresh breeze (F5)	Vrij krachtige wind
Strong breeze (F6)	Krachtige wind
Near gale (F7)	Harde wind
Gale (F8)	Stormachtig
Severe gale (F9)	Storm
Storm (F10)	Zware storm
Back	Krimpen
Freshening	Toenemend
Gust	Windvlaag
Lull	Luwte
Moderating	Afnemend
Squall	Bui
Veer	Ruimen

Precipitation — Neerslag

Drizzle	Motregen
Hail	Hagel
Rain	Regen
Shower	Stortbui
Sleet	Natte sneeuw
Thunderstorm	Onweer

Cloud & Visibility — Hemel en Zicht

Clearing up	Opklarend
Cloudy	Bewolkt
Mist	Nevel
Fog	Mist
Overcast	Betrokken

Sea state — Zee

Choppy	Kort
Moderate	Aanschietende zee

Overfalls (tide race)	Stroomrafeling	Oil, lubricating	Smeerolie
Rough	Ruw	Propeller	Schroef
Smooth	Vlak	Sea-cock	Buitenboordkraan
Swell	Deining	Spark plug	Bougie
		Split pin	Splitpen

C THE BOAT

Sails/Spars/Rigging

Backstay	Achterstag
Batten (sail)	Zeillat
Boom	Giek
Bosun's chair	Bootsmanstoel
Ensign	Scheepsvlag
Forestay	Voorstag
Genoa	Genua
Halyard	Val
Mainsail	Grootzeil
Mast	Mast
Mast, to step/unstep	Mast plaatsen/verwijderen
Shackle	Sluiting
Sheet	Schoot
Spinnaker boom	Spinnakerboom
Splice	Splits
Stainless steel	Roestvast staal (RVS)
Staysail	Stagfok
Topping lift	Kraanlijn
Turnbuckle, bottle-screw	Wantspanner
Whipping twine	Garen

HET JACHT

Zeilen/Masten/Tuigage

Starter motor	Startmotor
To bleed (air)	Ontluchten
Washer	Vulring

Tools

Feeler gauge	Voelermaat
File (wood/metal)	Vijl
Hacksaw	Metaalzaag
Hammer	Hamer
Pliers	Buigtang
Screwdriver	Schroevedraaier
Spanner, adjustable	Sleutel, Engelse sleutel
Vice	Bankschroef

Gereedschappen

D. ASHORE

Nautical

Boat hoist (BH)	Botenlift
Boatyard (BY)	Jachtwerf
Chandlery (CH)	Scheepsleverancier
Coastguard (CG)	Kustwacht
Crane (C)	Hijskraan
Customs (⌗)	Douane
Diesel (D)	Dieselolie
Dustbin	Vuilniscontainer
Engineer (ME)	Werktuigkundige
Fresh water (FW)	Drinkwater
Fuel	Brandstof
Methylated spirits	Spiritus
Paraffin	Petroleum
Petrol (P)	Benzine
Power point (AC)	Stopcontact
Shipwright (Sh)	Scheepsbouwer
Sailmaker (SM)	Zeilmaker

AAN LAND

Nautisch

On deck

Anchor	Anker
Beam, breadth	Breedte
Bilge pump	Lenspomp
Boat hook	Pikhaak
Bucket	Emmer, puts
Fender	Stootkussen
Glass fibre (GRP)	Fiberglas, glasvezel
Life jacket	Reddingvest
Oar	Riem
Pulpit/pushpit	Preekstoel/Hekstoel
Rudder	Roer
Tender	Bijboot
Tiller	Helmstok
Varnish	Lak, vernis
Winch handle	Lier-handle

Aan dek

Non-nautical, Shopping

Airport (✈)	Vliegveld
Bakery	Bakker
Butcher	Slager
Chemist	Apotheek
Dentist	Tandarts
Doctor	Dokter, huisarts
Hospital (Ⓗ)	Ziekenhuis
Ironmonger	Yzerwarenwinkel
Launderette (▣)	Wasserette
Market, food (V)	Supermarkt
Off licence	Slijter
Post Office (✉)	Postkantoor
Railway station (⇌)	Spoorwegstation
Stamps	Postzegels

Niet nautisch, winkelen

Below deck

Corkscrew	Kurketrekker
Galley	Kombuis
Gas cooker	Gastoestel
Matches	Lucifers
Plug	Stop
Saucepan	Steelpan
Tap	Kraan

Onderdeks

E. FIRST AID

Acute infection	Acute infectie
Appendicitis	Blindedarmontsteking
Burn	Brandwond
Coma	Coma
Coughing blood	Bloed ophoesten
Delirium	Delirium, geest-verwarring
Drowning	Verdrinken
Fracture	Breuk
Head injury	Hoofdwond
Haemorrhage	Bloeding
Laceration	Scheuring
Perforated ulcer	Opengebarsten zweer
Poisoning	Vergiftiging
Vomiting blood	Bloed braken
Sting (insect, jellyfish)	Steek (insect, kwal)

Electrics

Battery (ships)	Accu
Bulb, lamp	Lamp
Distilled water	Gedestilleerd water
Fuse	Zekering
Insulating tape	Isolatieband
Navigation lights	Navigatielichten
Solder	Soldeer
Switch	Schakelaar

Elektrisch

EERSTE HULP

Engine

Alternator	Wisselstroom-dynamo
Drive-belt	V-snaar
Fuel filter	Brandstoffilter
Gasket	Pakking
Grease	Vet
Injector	Verstuiver
Impeller	Impeller, Waaier
Nut and bolt	Moer en bout

Motor

20

8.20.6 PASSAGE INFORMATION

North Sea Passage Pilot (Imray/Navin) covers the North Sea and Belgian/Dutch coasts to Den Helder. *Cruising Guide to the Netherlands* (Imray/Navin) continues to the Ems. Refer also to *Havengids Nederland* (Vetus) in Dutch, well illustrated.

BELGIUM (chart 1872)

Features of this coast are the long shoals lying roughly parallel to it. Mostly the deeper, buoyed chans run within 3M of shore, where the outer shoals can give some protection from strong W or SW winds. Strong W to NE winds can equally create dangerous conditions especially in wind against tide situations. Approaching from seaward it is essential to fix position from one of the many marks, so that the required chan is correctly identified before shoal water is reached. Shipping is a hazard, but it helps to identify the main routes.

From the SW/W, the natural entry to the buoyed chans is at Dunkerque Lanby. From the Thames, bound for Oostende (8.20.10) or the Westerchelde (8.20.15), identify W Hinder lt. From the N, route via NHR-S and NHR-SE buoys or the N Hinder lt buoy. For TSS at W and S Hinder, see 8.20.14.

Off the Belgian coast the E-going stream begins at HW Vlissingen – 0320 (HW Dover – 0120), and the W-going at HW Vlissingen + 0240 (HW Dover + 0440), sp rates 2kn. Mostly the streams run parallel with the coast. Nieuwpoort (8.20.9) is 8M from the French border. From the W, approach through Passe de Zuydcoote (buoyed with least depth 3·3m) and West Diep. From ENE app through Kleine Rede, the inner road off Oostende which carries a depth of 6m. There are other apprs through the chans and over the banks offshore, but they need care in bad weather.

Sailing E from Oostende, leave about HW Vlissingen – 0300 to carry the E-going stream. If bound for Blankenberge (8.20.11) it is only necessary to keep a mile or two offshore, but if heading E of Zeebrugge (8.20.12) it is advisable to clear the hbr extension by 1M or more. The main route to Zeebrugge for commercial shipping is through Scheur (the deep water chan of the Westerschelde) as far as Scheur-Zand lt buoy, about 3M NW of hbr ent. There is much commercial traffic, and yachts should keep clear (S of) the buoyed chan so far as possible. Beware strong tidal stream and possibly dangerous seas in approaches to Zeebrugge.

NETHERLANDS (charts 325, 110, 2322)

While British Admiralty charts are adequate for through passages, coastal navigation, and entry to the main ports, larger scale Dutch charts are essential for any yacht exploring the cruising grounds along this coast or using any of the smaller hbrs. For Dutch Glossary, see 8.20.5.

Numerous wrecks and obstructions lie offshore and in coastal areas; those that could be hazardous are marked. The Off Texel TSS extends NNE from the TX 1 lt buoy, see 8.20.36: the separation zone incorporates the Helder gas field. Some 20–30M N lie the Placid and Petroland fields with production platforms. For general notes on N Sea oil and gas installations, see 8.5.5. The shoals of the North Sea coast and Waddenzee are liable to change due to gales and tidal streams. Sea level may also be affected by barometic pressure; wise to take advice from the Coastguard.

WESTERSCHELDE TO DEN HELDER

The main approach chans to Westerschelde are Scheur/ Wielingen and Oostgat, but yachts are required to keep clear of these. From Zeebrugge keep close to S side of estuary until past Breskens (8.20.13) when, if proceeding to Vlissingen (8.20.18), cross close W of By H-SS. From N, use Deurloo/ Spleet chans to S side of estuary. The tide runs hard in the estuary, causing a bad sea in chans and overfalls on some banks in strong winds. Vessels under 20m must give way to larger craft; and yachts under 12m are requested to stay just outside the main buoyed chans, including those between Walsoorden and Antwerpen (8.20.17) if navigation permits.

The Oosterschelde (8.20.19 and chart 192) is entered via the Roompotsluis, in the South half of the barrage. Coming from the S, Oostgat runs close to the Walcheren shore. Westkapelle l t ho is conspic near the W end of Walcheren. There are two lesser lts nearby: Molenhoofd 5ca WSW and Noorderhoofd 7ca NNW. Having passed the latter the coast runs NE past Domburg but becomes shallower as the Roompot is approached, so it is necessary to keep near the Roompot chan which here is marked by unlit buoys. It is important to have updated information on the buoyage and the chans.

The Schaar, Schouwenbank, Middelbank and Steenbanken lie off the W approaches to Oosterschelde. Westgat and Oude Roompot are the main channels, both well marked. From the north, Geul van de Banjaard (unlit) leads to Oude Roompot. Further north, the Slijkgat (lit) is the approach chan to Stellendam (8.20.20 and entry to the Haringvliet).

Shipping is very concentrated off Hoek van Holland (8.20.22) at the ent to Europoort and Rotterdam (8.20.23). Maas TSS must be noted and regulations for yachts obeyed, see 8.20.21.

The coast N to Den Helder is low, and not easily visible from seaward, like most of the Dutch coast. Conspic landmarks include: Scheveningen light house and big hotels, Noordwijk aan Zee light, big hotels and breakwaters at Zandvoort, and two lt ho's at IJmuiden, chys of steelworks N of IJmuiden, Egmond aan Zee lt, and chys of nuclear power station 1·5M NNE of Petten. For TSS see 8.20.36. 3M W of IJmuiden (8.20.25) the N-going stream begins at HW Hoek van Holland – 0120, and the S-going at HW Hoek van Holland + 0430, sp rates about 1·5kn. Off ent to IJmuiden the stream turns about 1h earlier and is stronger, and in heavy weather there may be a dangerous sea. At IJmuiden (8.20.25) the Noordzeekanaal leads to Amsterdam (8.20.26) and the IJsselmeer (8.20.27).

THE WEST FRISIAN ISLANDS (charts 2593)

N from Den Helder (8.20.28), thence E for nearly 150M along the Dutch and German coasts, lies the chain of Frisian Is. They have similar characteristics – being low, long and narrow, with the major axis parallel to the coast. Texel is the largest and, with Vlieland and Terschelling, lies further offshore.

Between the islands, narrow chans (*zeegat* in Dutch, *Seegat* in German) give access to/from the North Sea. Most of these chans are shallow for at least part of their length, and in these shoal areas a dangerous sea builds up in a strong onshore wind against the outgoing (ebb) tide. The zeegaten between Den Helder and Texel, between Vlieland and Terschelling and the zeegat of the Ems are safe for yachts up to force 8 winds between SW and NE. All the others are unsafe in strong onshore winds.

The flood stream along this coast is E-going, so it starts to run in through the zeegaten progressively from W to E. Where the tide meets behind each island, as it flows in first at the W end and a little later at the E end, is formed a bank called a *wad* (Dutch) or *Watt* (German). These banks between the islands and the coast are major obstacles to E/W progress inside the islands. The chans are narrow and winding, marked by buoys and/or withies (⚓ ⚓) in the shallower parts, and they mostly dry; so that it is essential to time the tide correctly.

This is an area most suited to shallow-draft yachts, particularly flat bottomed or with bilge keels, centreboards or legs, that can take the ground easily. Whilst the zeegaten are described briefly below, the many chans inside the islands and across the Waddenzee are mentioned only for orientation.

TEXEL TO TERSCHELLING

Zeegat van Texel (chart 191) lies between Den Helder and the Is of Texel, and gives access to the Waddenzee, the tidal part of the former Zuider Zee. Haaksgronden shoals extend 5M seaward, with three chans: Schulpengat on S side, leading into Breewijd; Westgat through centre of shoals, where the stream sets across the chan, is only suitable for passage in good weather and in daylight; and Molengat near the Texel shore. Schulpengat is the well marked main chan, buoys being prefixed with letter 'S'; but strong SW winds cause rough sea against the SW-going (ebb) stream which begins at HW Helgoland – 0330, while the NE-going (flood) stream begins at HW Helgoland + 0325, sp rates 1·5kn. Molengat is marked by buoys prefixed by letters 'MG', but strong winds between W and N cause a bad sea. When coming from the NW or NE the Molengat is always the best route unless the weather is exceptionally bad. Routeing via the Schulpengat involves a southerly deviation of approx 15M and leads W of the very dangerous Zuider Haaks which should be avoided in bad weather. In Molengat the N-going (ebb) stream begins at HW Helgoland – 0145, and the S-going (flood) stream at HW Helgoland + 0425, sp rates 1·25kn. For Oudeschild, see 8.20.29.

E of Den Helder and the **Marsdiep**, the flood makes in three main directions through the SW Waddenzee:
(a) to E and SE through Malzwin and Wierbalg to Den Oever (where the lock into IJsselmeer is only available during daylight hours on working days); thence NE along the Afsluitdijk, and then N towards Harlingen (8.20.30).
(b) to NE and E through Texelstroom and Doove Balg towards the Pollen flats; and (c) from Texelstroom, NE and N through Scheurrak, Omdraai and Oude Vlie, where it meets the flood stream from Zeegat van Terschelling. The ebb runs in reverse. The Kornwerderzand locks (available H24), near NE end of Afsluitdijk, also give access to the IJsselmeer (8.20.27).
Eierlandsche Gat, between Texel and Vlieland, consists of dangerous shoals between which run very shallow and unmarked chans, only used by fishermen.

Zeegat van Terschelling (chart 112 and 8.20.33), between Vlieland (8.20.31) and Terschelling, gives access to the hbrs of Vlieland, West Terschelling (8.20.32) and Harlingen (8.20.30); also to the locks at Kornwerderzand. Shallow banks extend more than 5M seaward; the main chan (buoyed) through them is Zuider Stortemelk passing close N of Vlieland. In this chan the buoys are prefixed by letters 'ZS', and the E-going (flood) stream begins at HW Helgoland + 0325, while the W-going (ebb) stream begins at HW Helgoland – 0230, sp rates 2·5kn. Vliesloot leads to Oost Vlieland hbr. Approach West Terschelling via West Meep and Slenk. From Zuider Stortemelk the Vliestroom, a deep well buoyed chan (buoys prefixed by letters 'VL'), runs S about 4M until its junction with Blauwe Slenk and Inschot. Blauwe Slenk runs ESE to Harlingen; and Inschot SE to Kornwerderzand.

AMELAND TO DELFZIJL (charts 2593, 3509, 3510)

Zeegat van Ameland, between Terschelling and Ameland, is fronted by the sandbank of Bornrif extending 3M seaward. Westgat is the main entrance, with buoys prefixed by letters 'WG'. The chan runs close N of Terschelling, and divides into

Boschgat and Borndiep. For Nes (Ameland), see 8.20.30. In Westgat the flood stream begins at HW Helgoland + 0425, and the ebb stream at HW Helgoland – 0150, sp rates 2kn. A dangerous sea develops in strong onshore winds.

Friesche Zeegat, between Ameland and Schiermonnikoog (8.20.35), has a main chan also called Westgat and buoys marked 'WG'. In strong winds the sea breaks across the whole passage. Westgat leads S through Wierumer Gronden, past Engelsmanplaat (a prominent sandbank) and into Zoutkamperlaag which is the main chan (marked by buoys prefixed 'Z') to Lauwersoog (8.20.34), where locks give access to the Lauwersmeer and inland waterways.

Further E, the estuary of R Ems (chart 3509) runs seaward past the SW side of the German island of Borkum (8.21.11). It leads to Delfzijl and Termunterzijl (8.20.35), or Emden (8.21.9), see 8.21.5. Hubertgat, which runs parallel to and S of the main Westerems chan, is slightly more direct when bound to/from the W, but in both these well lit chans there is a dangerous sea in strong NW winds over the ebb. The E-going (flood) stream begins at HW Helgoland + 0530, and the W-going (ebb) stream begins at HW Helgoland –0030, sp rates 1·5kn.

CROSSING NORTH SEA FROM BELGIUM AND SCHELDE (charts 1406, 323)

Avoid major traffic areas and cross TSS (8.20.14) at 90° to take departure from either Dunkerque Lanby or W Hinder lt depending on destination. From Dunkerque Lanby make good Ruytingen SW buoy, thence CS4 buoy and S Goodwin lt F (on W-going stream) or E Goodwin lt F (on N-going stream). From W Hinder lt for N Thames Estuary, make good Garden City buoy (on E-going stream) or Twin buoy (on W-going stream) in order to make N or S Galloper buoys and thence Long Sand Head buoy. Avoid shallower patches over W Hinder, Fairy, N Falls and Galloper Banks, particularly in rough weather when under-keel clearance may be reduced. For distances across the North Sea, see 8.0.10.

CROSSING NORTH SEA FROM THE NETHERLANDS Charts 1406, 1408, 1872, 2449, 3371)

From ports S of Hoek van Holland proceed westward across banks avoiding shallower patches to pick up Birkenfels buoy, across N Hinder W TSS (8.20.14) and thence to N Galloper buoy (for N Thames estuary) or Outer Gabbard buoy (for Lowestoft and North). For ports N of Hoek van Holland passages can be made from coast to coast avoiding TSS areas and crossing DW routes (8.20.36/37) with care.

8.20.7   DISTANCE TABLE

Approximate distances in nautical miles are by the most direct route, whilst avoiding dangers and allowing for Traffic Separation Schemes. Places in *italics* are in adjoining areas; places in **bold** are in 8.0.10, Distances across the North Sea.

	1	2	3	4	5	6	7	8	9	10	11	12	13	14	15	16	17	18	19	20
1. *Dunkerque*	1																			
2. **Nieuwpoort**	15	2																		
3. **Oostende**	26	9	3																	
4. Blankenberge	35	18	9	4																
5. **Zeebrugge**	40	23	13	5	5															
6. **Vlissingen**	55	39	29	21	16	6														
7. **Roompotsluis**	68	51	40	33	28	24	7													
8. **Stellendam**	90	83	72	55	50	45	32	8												
9. Hook of Holland	92	77	67	59	54	47	48	16	9											
8. Rotterdam	112	97	87	79	74	67	68	36	20	10										
11. Scheveningen	106	91	81	73	68	61	50	30	14	34	11									
12. IJmuiden	131	116	106	98	93	86	87	55	39	59	25	12								
13. Amsterdam	144	129	110	111	106	99	100	68	52	72	38	13	13							
14. **Den Helder**	169	154	131	136	131	120	125	93	77	97	63	38	51	14						
15. Den Oever	180	165	142	147	142	131	136	104	88	108	74	49	*62	11	15					
16. Harlingen	199	184	161	166	161	150	155	123	107	127	93	68	81	30	21	16				
17. **Vlieland**	202	187	164	169	164	153	158	126	110	130	96	71	84	33	33	18	17			
18. **Terschelling**	201	186	163	168	163	152	157	125	109	129	95	70	83	39	34	19	7	18		
19. **Delfzijl**	277	262	239	244	239	228	233	201	185	205	171	146	159	115	110	102	92	85	19	
20. *Borkum*	257	242	219	224	219	208	213	181	165	185	151	126	139	95	90	80	72	65	22	20

*Amsterdam to Den Oever via IJmuiden and Den Helder = 62M; but via the IJsselmeer = 45M.

20

SPECIAL NOTES FOR BELGIUM AND THE NETHERLANDS   8-20-8

BELGIUM

PROVINCES are given for ports in lieu of UK 'counties'.

CHARTS Those most widely used are the '*Vlaamse Banken*' issued by the Hydrografische Dienst der Kust. Imray C30 is also popular amongst Belgian yachtsmen.

TIME ZONE is –0100, which is allowed for in tidal predictions but no provision is made for daylight saving schemes shown by the non-shaded areas on the tide tables (see 9.1.2).

HARBOURS: Although the Hr Mr ☎ is given for Belgian hbrs, he is not the key figure for yachtsmen that he is in UK hbrs. Berths and moorings are administered by the local YCs. The prefix VVW = *Vlaamse Vereniging voor Watersport* ≅ Association of Flemish Watersports.

SIGNALS IPTS (see colour plate 9) are used at Nieuwpoort, Oostende and Zeebrugge, which are the Ports of entry. In season (early April to late Sept) Blankenberge is also a Port of entry with Customs.
Small craft wind warnings (onshore wind >F3; offshore wind >F4) apply to craft <6m LOA and are shown at these 3 ports and Blankenberge as follows:
Day: 2 black ▼s, points together. By night: Lt Fl Bu.

TELEPHONE To call UK from Belgium, dial 00-44 then the UK area code minus the prefix 0, followed by the number required. To call Belgium from UK, dial 00-32 then the code and number. Dialling codes are 3 digits, followed by a 6 digit subscriber No.

Emergencies: Police 101; Fire, Ambulance and Marine 100. 112 (EC emergency number) is not yet available in Belgium.

MRCC Oostende, ☎ (059) 70.10.00, coordinates SAR operations; see 6.11.3. In emergency call *Oostende Radio* VHF Ch 16 (☎ 70.24.38) or ☎ 100. For medical advice call *Radiomédical Oostende* on Ch 16.

PUBLIC HOLIDAYS New Year's Day, Easter Mon, Labour Day (1 May), Ascension Day, Whit Mon, National Day (21 July), Feast of the Assumption (15 Aug), All Saints' Day (1 Nov), Armistice Day (11 Nov), King's Birthday or Fete de la Dynastie (15 Nov), Christmas Day.

RULES: Hbr police are strict about yachts using their engines entering hbr. If sails are used as well, hoist a ▼. Yachts may not navigate within 200m of shore (MLWS).

INLAND WATERWAYS: *Immatriculatieplaat* (licence plates) are required for all yachts on the Flemish waterways. These plates cost 1100Bef (1998) and are obtainable from: 2000 ANTWERPEN, Markgravestraat 16. ☎ 03/232.98.05; or from offices in Brussels and other cities. Boats should fly the 'drapeau de navigation', a R flag with W □ in centre. Belgian Competence requirements for helmsmen are the same as the Dutch (RH col).
Note: More info from Belgian Tourist Office, 29 Princes St, London W1R 7RG, ☎ 0171-6290230, ✎ 6290454; or Federation Royale Belge du Yachting, FRYB/KBJV, PB 241 Bouchoutlaan, 1020 Brussels, Belgium.

NETHERLANDS

PROVINCES are given in lieu of 'counties' in the UK.

CHARTS The following Dutch charts are quoted:
a. Zeekaarten (equivalent to AC); issued by the Royal Netherlands Navy Hydrographer, and updated by Dutch Notices to Mariners; available from chart agents.
b. Dutch Yacht Charts (DYC) "Kaarten voor Kust-en Binnenwateren"; issued every March by the Hydrographer in 8 sets, booklet format (54 x 38cm), covering coastal and inland waters.
c. ANWB Waterkaarten (ANWB); 18 charts of inland waterways (lettered A to S, excluding Q) .

TIME ZONE is –0100, which is allowed for in tidal predictions, but no provision is made for daylight saving schemes as indicated by the non-shaded areas (see 7.1.2).

HARBOURS The term marina is little used; most yacht hbrs are private clubs or Watersport Associations (WSV or WV): *Gem (Gemeentelijke)* = municipal. Sometimes (in Belgium also) berth-holders show a green tally if a berth is free, or a red tally if returning same day; but best to check with Hr Mr. Duty-free fuel (coloured red) is not available for pleasure craft. A tourist tax of f1.00/person/night is often levied.

CUSTOMS Main customs/ports of entry are Breskens, Vlissingen, Roompotsluis*, Hoek van Holland, Maassluis, Vlaardingen, Schiedam, Rotterdam, Scheveningen, IJmuiden, Den Helder, Harlingen, Vlieland*, West Terschelling, Lauwersoog and Delfzijl. No entry/customs at Stellendam, Den Oever or Kornwerderzand. *Summer only.

BUOYAGE Buoys are often named by the abbreviations of the banks or chans which they mark (e.g. VL = Vliestroom). A division buoy has the abbreviations of both chans meeting there, eg VL2-SG2 = as above, plus Schuitengat. Some chans are marked by withies: SHM bound ‡; PHM unbound ⸸. On tidal flats (e.g. Friesland) where the direction of main flood stream is uncertain, bound withies are on the S side of a chan and unbound on the N side. In minor chans the buoyage may be moved without notice to accommodate changes.
The SIGNI buoyage system is used on some inland waters, including the IJsselmeer (see 8.20.27), but not on the Westerschelde, Waddenzee, Eems and Dollard.

SIGNALS Traffic signals The standard French/Belgian system is not used in the Netherlands. Where possible the local system is given.

Sluicing signals The following signals may be shown:
By day: A blue board, with the word 'SPUIEN' on it; often in addition to the night signal of 3 ⓡin a △.

Visual storm signals Lt sigs only are shown day and night, as per the International System (see 8.15.8), at Vlissingen, Hoek van Holland, Amsterdam, IJmuiden, Den Helder, West Terschelling, Harlingen, Eierland, Ameland, Oostmahorn, Schiermonnikoog, Zoutkamp and Delfzijl.

Inland waterways (Most bridges and locks work VHF Ch 18)
Bridge signals (shown on each side):
To request bridges to open sound 'K' (—·—).
Ⓖ = Bridge open.   Ⓨ = You may pass under this arch.
Ⓡ = Bridge closed (opens on request).
Ⓡ over Ⓖ = Bridge about to open.
2 Ⓡ (vert) = Bridge out of use.
2 Ⓖ (vert) = Bridge open but not in use (you may pass).

Railway bridges
Opening times of railway bridges are in a free annual leaflet '*Openingstijden Spoorwegbruggen*' available from ANWB, L & A/Wat, Postbus 93200, 2509 BA, Den Haag; (send A5 SAE with international reply coupon).

RADIO TELEPHONE Use low power setting (1 watt), except for emergencies and public correspondence. Monitor TSS info broadcasts and make contact on VTS sector channels. Note: Do not use Ch M in Dutch waters, where it is a salvage frequency; Ch 31 is for Dutch marinas (little used).

TELEPHONE To call UK from the Netherlands, dial 00-44; then the UK area code minus the prefix 0, followed by the number required. To call the Netherlands from the UK dial 00-31 then the area code minus the prefix 0, plus number.
Emergencies: Fire, Police, Ambulance, dial 112.

MARINE RESCUE CO-ORDINATION is the task of the Coast Guard Centre at IJmuiden which keeps watch H24 on VHF Ch 16, 2182Khz and 500Khz; ☎ (0255) 546546; ✎ 546548. See also 6.11.4 for notes on SAR operations.

PUBLIC HOLIDAYS New Year's Day, Easter Mon, Queen's Birthday (30 April), Liberation Day (5 May), Ascension Day, Whit Mon, Christmas and Boxing Days.

INLAND WATERWAYS: All craft must carry a copy of the waterway regulations, *Binnenvaart Politiereglement (BPR)*, as given in the current ANWB publication *Almanak voor Watertoerisme, Vol 1* (written in Dutch). At present craft >15m LOA or capable of more than 20kph (11kn) must be commanded by the holder of a Certificate of Competence. On lakes, rivers and canals this may be the International or Helmsman's Overseas Certificate of Competence, but the RYA Coastal Skipper (or higher) Certificate of Competence is required for navigation on the Schelde, Waddensee and IJsselmeer.

INFORMATION: A useful document 'Watersports Paradise', is obtainable from the Dutch Tourism Board, 25 Buckingham Gate, London, SW1E 6LD, ☎ 0891 717777; or the Royal Netherland Embassy, 12a Kensington Palace Gdns, London W8 4QU ☎ 0171-581 9615.

NIEUWPOORT (NIEUPORT)

Belgium, West Flanders 51°09'·40N 02°43'·23E   Rtg 2-1-2

8-20-9

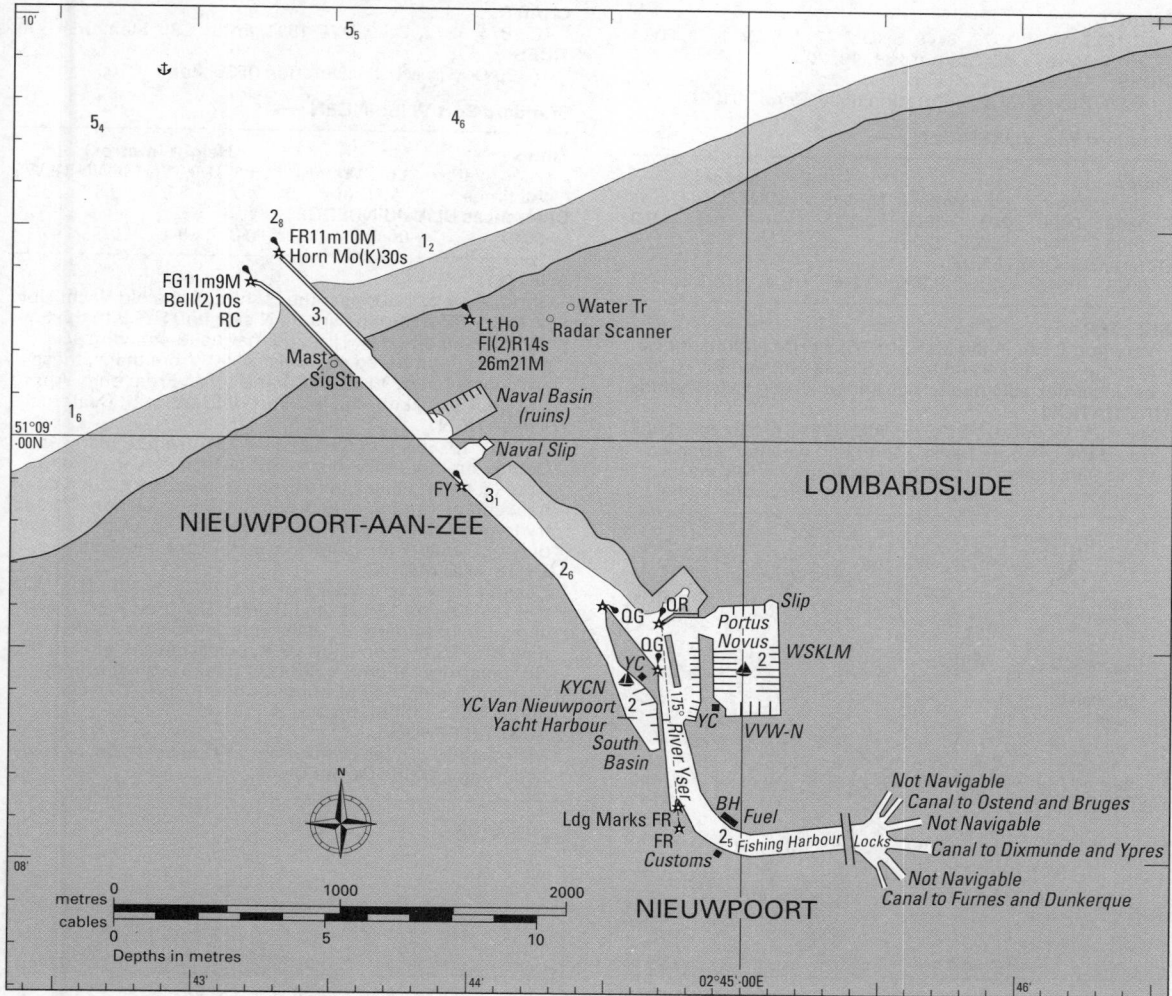

CHARTS
AC 1873, 1872, *2449*; Belgian 101, D11; DYC 1801; SHOM 7214; ECM 1010; Imray C30; Stanfords 1, 19, 20

TIDES
+0105 Dover; ML 2·7; Duration 0515; Zone –0100

Standard Port VLISSINGEN (⟶)

Times				Height (metres)			
High Water		Low Water		MHWS	MHWN	MLWN	MLWS
0300	0900	0400	1000	4·7	3·9	0·8	0·3
1500	2100	1600	2200				
Differences NIEUWPOORT							
–0110	–0050	–0035	–0045	+0·6	+0·5	+0·4	+0·1

SHELTER
Good except in strong NW'lies. There are two yacht hbrs, access H24, run by three YCs: Royal YC of Nieuwpoort (**KYCN**) to the SW gets very full; but there is always room in the Portus Novus, run by the Air Force YC (**WSKLM**) at the N and E side; and **VVW-N**ieuwpoort to the S and centre.

NAVIGATION
WPT 51°10'·00N 02°42'·00E, 308°/128° from/to ent, 0·90M. The bar (1·5m) is liable to silt up but there is usually sufficient water for yachts. At sp the stream reaches 2kn across the ent. The 1M long ent chan to both yacht hbrs is dredged, although levels can drop to about 2m. Note: For activity at firing range E of Nieuwpoort, call range officer on Ch 67; range is not used mid-June to end Sept.

LIGHTS AND MARKS
Lt ho Fl (2) R 14s 26m 21M; conspic R tr, W bands. E pier head FR 11m 10M, W tr, vis 025°-250°, 307°-347°, Horn Mo (K) 30s. W pier head, FG 11m 9M, W tr, vis 025°-250°, 284°-324°, Bell (2) 10s, RC.
IPTS from root of W pier, plus: 2 cones, points together or Fl Bu lt = No departure for craft < 6m LOA. Watch out for other tfc sigs, especially STOP sign near exit from Novus Portus, shown in conjunction with IPTS.

RADIO TELEPHONE
VHF Ch 09 16 (H24).

TELEPHONE (Dial code 058)
Hr Mr/Pilots 233000, ☎ 231575; Lock 233050; CG/Marine Police 233045; Marine Rescue Helicopter 311714; ☷ 233451; Duty Free Store 233433; Ⓗ (Oostende) 707631; Dr 233089; Brit Consul (02) 2179000; Police 234246.

FACILITIES
KYCN (420 + 80 Ⓥ) ☎ 234413, 600BeF, M, FW, C (10 ton), Slip, CH, Gas, ME, El, Sh, V, D, ⊡, R, Bar;
WSKLM (500 + Ⓥ) ☎ 233641, ☎ 239845, 350BeF, M, L, FW, C (2 ton mobile), CH, R, Bar;
VVW-N (950 + Ⓥ) ☎ 235232, ☎ 234058, 550BeF, Slip, FW, El, Ⓔ, ⊡, BH (45 & 10 ton), AC (meters), CH, P, D, ⏚, Sh, SM, R, Bar, Free bicycles for shopping;
Services: D, L, ME, El, Sh, C (15 ton), Gaz, CH, SM.
Town P, D, V, R, Bar, ✉, Ⓑ, ⇌, ✈ (Ostende). Ferry: See Ostende. (Fuel can be bought at the hbr by arrangement).

20

OOSTENDE (OSTEND)   8-20-10

Belgium, West Flanders 51°14'·30N 02°55'·18E   Rtg 1-1-1

CHARTS
AC 1873, 1874, 1872, *2449*; SHOM 7214; ECM 1010; DYC 1801.2; Imray C30; Stanfords 1, 19, 20

TIDES
+0120 Dover; ML 2·6; Duration 0530; Zone –0100

Standard Port VLISSINGEN (→)

Times				Height (metres)			
High Water		Low Water		MHWS	MHWN	MLWN	MLWS
0300	0900	0400	1000	4·7	3·9	0·8	0·3
1500	2100	1600	2200				
Differences OOSTENDE							
–0055	–0040	–0030	–0045	+0·4	+0·4	+0·3	+0·1

SHELTER
Very good, esp in the Mercator Yacht Hbr (1·2m); ent via Montgomery Dock and lock. NSYC (2·7m) and ROYC may be uncomfortable due ferries and/or strong W/NW winds.

NAVIGATION
WPT 51°15'·00N 02°53'·97E, 308°/128° from/to ent, 0·98M. Avoid the offshore banks esp in bad weather; appr via West Diep inside Stroombank or from the NW via Kwintebank and buoyed chan. Busy ferry/commercial hbr.

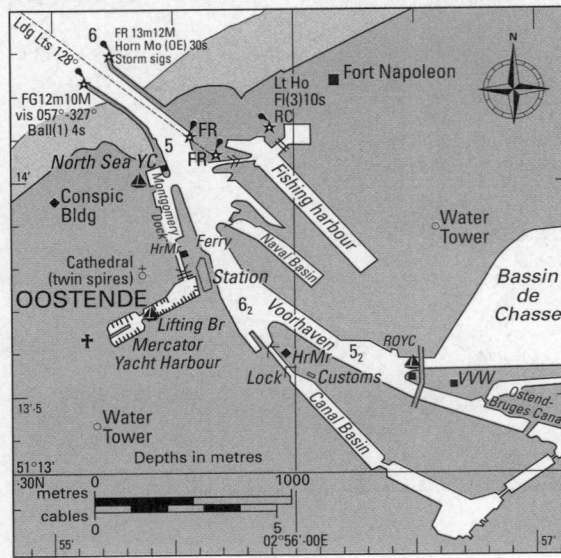

LIGHTS AND MARKS
Europa Centrum bldg (105m) is conspic 3ca SSW of ent. Lt ho Fl (3) 10s 63m 27M, conspic W tr with 2 sinusoidal blue bands, RC. Ldg lts 128°, both FR 12/18m 4M, both X on W pylons, R bands, vis 051°-201°. W pier, FG 12m 10M, W tr, vis 057°-327°, Bell 4s.
E pier FR 13m 12M, W tr, vis 333°-243°, horn Mo (OE) 30s. IPTS shown from E pier, plus QY lts = keep clear of ent and chan, for ferry arrival/departure.
2 ▼, points together or Fl Bu lt = No departure for craft < 6m LOA; (shown at ent to Montgomery dock).

RADIO TELEPHONE
Port VHF Ch 10 16 (H24). All vessels inc yachts, call *Signal Post* Ch 09 to ent/dep. Mercator lock/yacht hbr Ch 14 (H24).

TELEPHONE (Dial code 059)
Hr Mr 330905, ☎ 330387; Life Saving 701100; ⌗ 322009; Police 500925; Ⓗ 707637; Weather (no code needed): 1603 (Dutch), 1703 (French); Brit Consul (02) 2179000.

FACILITIES
Berthing fees: See 8.20.9. **Montgomery Dock** (70 + 50 Ⓥ) YC, Bar, R, FW, Slip; **North Sea YC** (N end of Montgomery Dock) ☎ 702754, FW, AB, R, Bar; **Mercator Yacht Hbr** (450+50 Ⓥ) ☎ 705762, FW, D, AC, C, Slip; **Royal Oostende YC** (1M SE up Voorhaven, 160 + 40 Ⓥ) ☎ 321452, Slip, M, FW, AB, C (½ ton), R, Bar; Access via Achterhaven to the Belgian, Dutch and French canals. **Services:** ME, CH, Sh, El, SM. D at FV hbr or by tanker ☎ 500874. **Town** All amenities, ⇌, ✈. Ferry: Ramsgate.

BLANKENBERGE   8-20-11

Belgium, West Flanders 51°18'·95N 03°06'·60E   Rtg 3-1-2

CHARTS
AC 1874, 1872, *2449*; DYC 1801; Imray C30; Stanfords 1, 19

TIDES
+0130 Dover; ML 2·5; Duration 0535; Zone –0100

Standard Port VLISSINGEN (→)

Times		Height (metres)			
High Water	Low Water	MHWS	MHWN	MLWN	MLWS
All times	All times	4·7	3·9	0·8	0·3
Differences BLANKENBERGE					
–0040	–0040	–0·3	–0·1	+0·3	+0·1

SHELTER
Good. Keep to port, past the FV hbr, to the old Yacht Hbr (2·4m); VNZ pontoons are on N side and SYCB to the E. Or turn stbd into new Hbr and marina (2·4m) with 15 pontoons, numbered clockwise I - XV from the N; these are controlled by VNZ, SYCB and VVW. From early Apr to late Sept Blankenberge is a Port of Entry, with Customs.

NAVIGATION
WPT 51°19'·60N 03°05'·40E, 314°/134° from/to piers, 1M. Do not attempt entry in strong NW'lies. Beware strong tides (& fishing lines) across ent. Access HW ±2; ent chan between piers silts, only dredged 1·5m in season. Do not try to enter/depart LW±1½, especially at sp. Oct-end May, only ent/leave HW±1, unless depth is pre-checked.

LIGHTS AND MARKS
Conspic high-rise blocks E of lt ho, Fl (2) 8s 30m 20M, W tr B top. Ldg lts 134°, both FR 5/8m 3M, (Red X on mast) show the best water. A Water tr is conspic on E side of new Hbr. FS by lt ho shows 2 ▼, points inward, or Fl Bu lt = No departure for craft < 6m LOA (small craft warning). Caution: 3 unlit Y SPM buoys and one Fl (4) Y 20s lie about 400m off hbr ent and to E and W.

RADIO TELEPHONE
Marinas VHF Ch 08. *Blankenberge Rescue* Ch 08; or relay Zeebrugge Traffic Centre Ch 69.

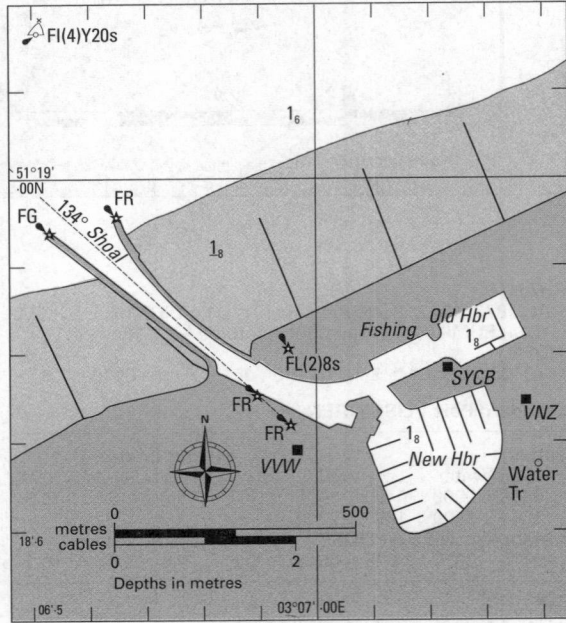

TELEPHONE (Dial code 050)
Hr Mr: use VNZ, SYCB or VVW Tel Nos; ⌗ 544223; Police 429842; Dr 333668; Ⓗ 413701; Brit Consul (02) 2179000.

FACILITIES
Fees: Based on beam, <3m = 400BeF; <3.5m = 500 BeF; <4m = 600 BeF; plus 100BeF for every additional 0·25m.
Old Yacht Hbr (mainly locals): **YC Vrije Noordzeezeilers (VNZ)** ☎ 429150, AC, FW, Bar, R; **Scarphout YC (SYCB)** ☎ 411420, C (10/2½ ton), CH, FW, AC, Slip, Bar, R, Ⓔ;
Marina (VVW) ☎ 417536, AC, FW, Bar, Ⓞ, Slip, P, D (hose, duty free), ME, Sh, Ⓔ, El, SM, CH, C (20 ton). **Town** Gaz, R, Bar, ⊠, Ⓑ, ⇌, ✈ Ostend.

ZEEBRUGGE   8-20-12

Belgium, West Flanders 51°21'·80N 03°11'·60E   Rtg 1-1-2

CHARTS
AC 1874, 1872, *2449*; Zeekaart 1441; DYC 1801.3, 1803; Imray C30; Stanfords 1, 19

TIDES
+0110 Dover; ML 2·4; Duration 0535; Zone –0100

Standard Port VLISSINGEN (→)

Times				Height (metres)			
High Water		Low Water		MHWS	MHWN	MLWN	MLWS
0300	0900	0400	1000	4·7	3·9	0·8	0·3
1500	2100	1600	2200				
Differences ZEEBRUGGE							
–0035	–0015	–0020	–0035	+0·1	+0·1	+0·3	+0·1

SHELTER
Very good in the Yacht Hbr, access H24. Caution on ent/dep due to limited vis and fast FVs; give all jetties a wide berth. Brugge is 6M inland by canal.

NAVIGATION
WPT Scheur-Zand ECM By, Q (3) 10s, 51°23'·70N 03°07'·68E, 309°/129° from/to ent, 3·1M. Beware strong currents in hbr apprs (up to 4kn at HW –1) and major WIP on container terminal in outer hbr N of Leopold Dam. Zeebrugge is the main Belgian fishing port and a ferry terminal, so keep clear of FVs and ferries.

LIGHTS AND MARKS
Heist (W inner bkwtr hd) Oc WR 15s 22m 20/18M, Gy ○ tr. Ldg lts toward Vissershaven for marina at W end:
(1) 136°: Oc 5s 22/45m 8M, vis 131°-141° synch (H24).
(2) 154°: Front Oc WR 6s 20m 3M, R △, W bands; rear Oc 6s 34m 3M, R ▽, W bands, synch (H24).
(3) 220°: Front 2FW neon (vert) 30/22m; rear FW neon 30m. Both W concrete columns, B bands.
(4) 193°: Front 2FR (vert) 30/22; rear FR 29m. Both W concrete columns, R bands.
IPTS are shown at hds of W outer and inner bkwtrs. When LNG-Gas tanker is under way, 3 FY (vert) lts next to IPTS Nos 2 and 5 prohibit all movements in hbr/apprs unless special permission to move has been given. At S side of Visserhaven a QY lt prohibits ent/dep Visserhaven.

RADIO TELEPHONE
Port Control VHF Ch 71 (H24). Marina Ch 71. Locks Ch 68.

TELEPHONE (Dial code 050)
Hr Mr 543241; Port Control 546867; Lock Mr 543231; CG 545072; Sea Saving Service 544007; ⊞ 54.54.55; Police 544148; Dr 544590; Ⓗ 320832; Brit Consul (02) 2179000.

FACILITIES
Berthing fees: See 8.20.9. **Yacht Hbr** (100 + 70) ☎ 544903, FW, Slip, Sh, CH, D; **Royal Belgian SC** ☎ 544903, M, AB f450; **Alberta** (R, Bar of RBSC) ☎ 544197; **Services:** ME, El, CH. **Town** P, D, Sh, Gaz, V, R, Bar, ⊠, Ⓑ, ≋ 15 mins to Brugge, tram to Oostende, ✈ (Ostend). Ferry: Zeebrugge-Felixstowe/Hull.

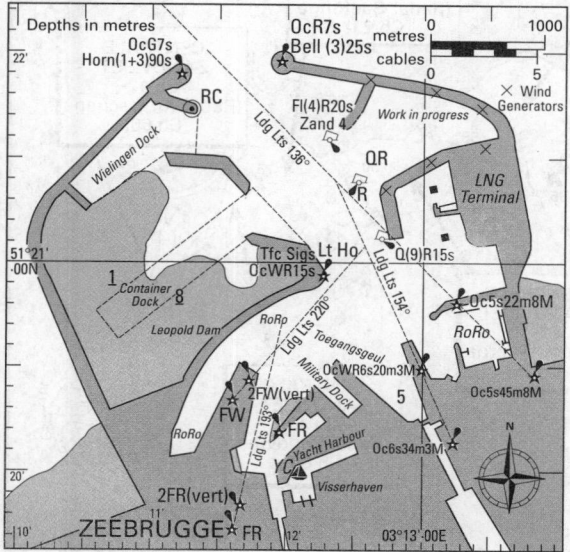

BRESKENS   8-20-13

Zeeland 51°24'·02N 03°34'·15E   Rtg 1-1-1

CHARTS
AC 120, 1874, 1872; Zeekaart 120, 101; DYC 1801.4, 1803; Imray C30; Stanfords 1, 19

TIDES
+0210 Dover; ML no data; Duration 0600; Zone –0100

Standard Port VLISSINGEN (→)

Times				Height (metres)			
High Water		Low Water		MHWS	MHWN	MLWN	MLWS
0300	0900	0400	1000	4·7	3·9	0·8	0·3
1500	2100	1600	2200				
Differences BRESKENS: Use VLISSINGEN figures							
CADZAND (7M WSW)							
–0030	–0025	–0020	–0025	–0·2	–0·2	–0·2	–0·1

SHELTER
Good in all winds; access H24, 5m at ent. ⓥ berth on the N finger (4m). ⚓ off Plaat van Breskens, in fine weather, not in commercial/fishing hbr. Beware fast ferries.

NAVIGATION
WPT SS-VH NCM By, Q, 51°24'·75N 03°34'·00E, 353°/173° from/to W mole lt (within W sector), 0·69M. Beware strong tides across the ent. Do not confuse the ent with the ferry port ent, 0·7M WNW, where yachts are prohib.

LIGHTS AND MARKS
Large bldg/silo on centre pier in hbr and two apartment blocks (30m) SE of marina are conspic. W mole hd F WRG 6m; vis R090°-128°, W128°-157°, G157°-169·5°, W169·5°-173°, R173°-194°, G194°-296°, W296°-300°, R300°-320°, G320°-090°; Horn Mo (U) 30s. E mole hd FR 5m.
Nieuwe Sluis lt, Oc WRG 10s 28m 14/10M, B 8-sided tr, W bands, is 1·2M W of ferry hbr.

RADIO TELEPHONE
Marina VHF Ch 31.

TELEPHONE (Dial code 0117)
Hr Mr 381902; ⊞ 382610; Police (0117) 453156; Dr 381566/389284; Ⓗ (0117) 459000; Brit Embassy (070) 3645800.

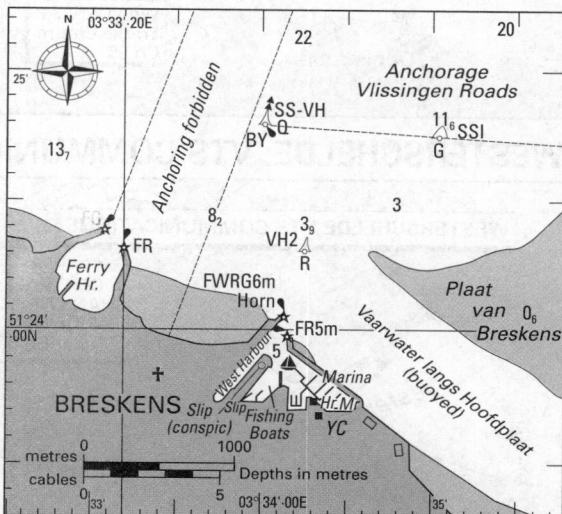

FACILITIES
Marina (Jachthaven Breskens) ☎ 381902, f30, FW, ☉, AC; **YC Breskens** ☎ 383278, R, Bar;
Services: SM, CH, D & P (fuel pontoon is in FV hbr), Gaz, chart agent, BY, C (20 ton), El, Ⓔ, ME, Sh, Slip, 🅳.
Town V, R, Bar, ⊠, Ⓑ, Gas, ≋ (Flushing), ✈ (Ostend or Brussels). Ferry: local to Vlissingen.

20

TSS OFF THE BELGIAN AND DUTCH COASTS

8-20-14

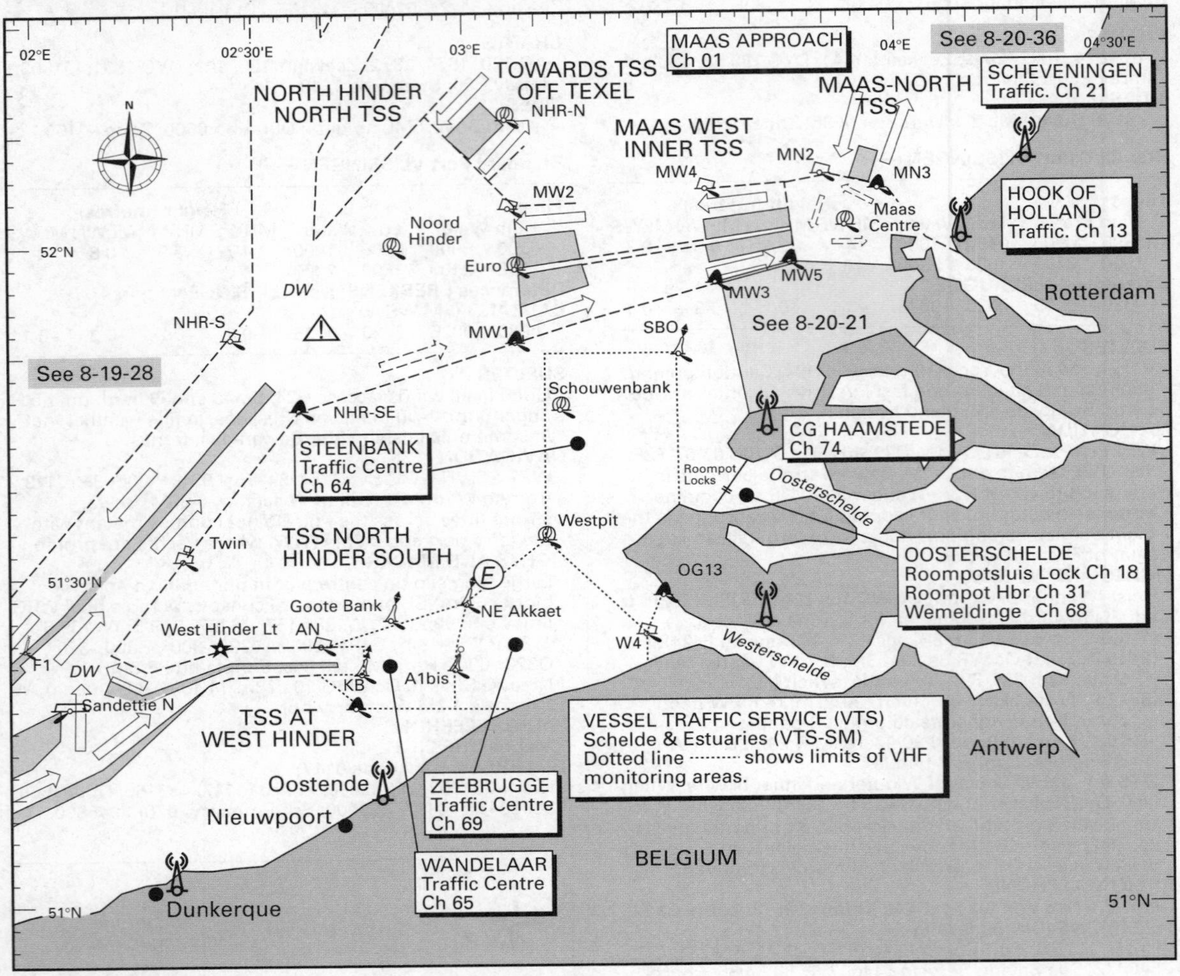

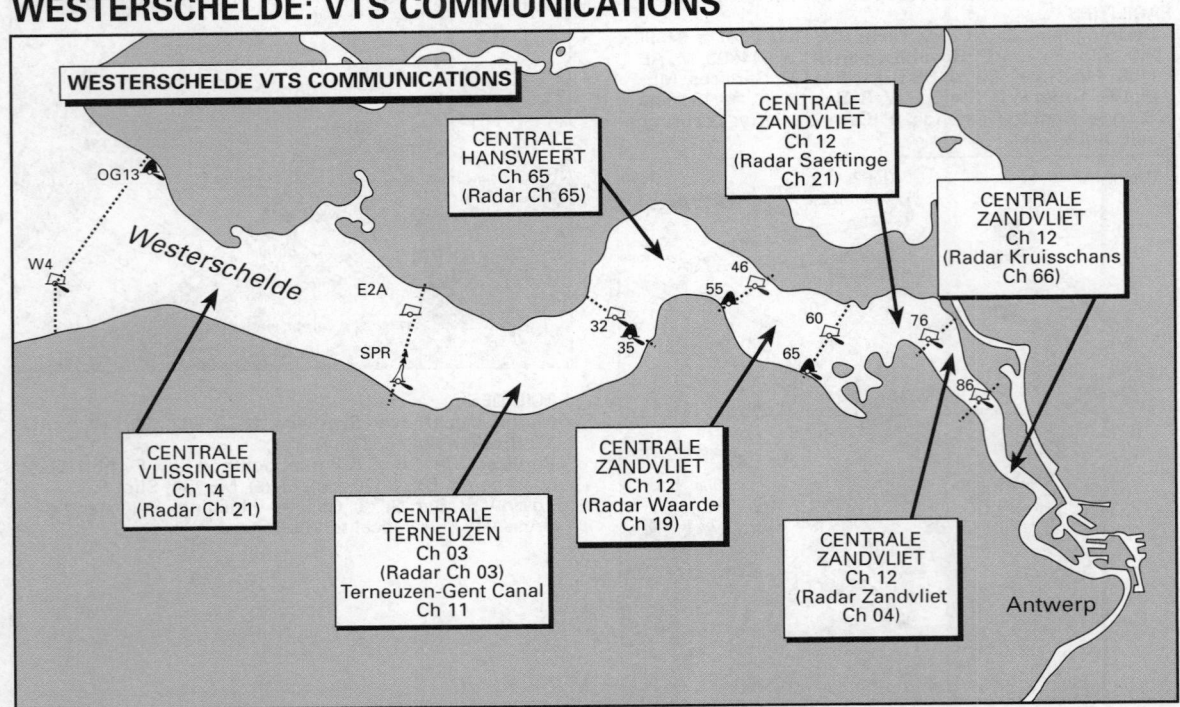

WESTERSCHELDE: VTS COMMUNICATIONS

WESTERSCHELDE   8-20-15
Zeeland

CHARTS
AC 1874, 120, 139; Zeekaart 1443; DYC 1803; Imray C30

TIDES
+0200 Dover; ML Hansweert 2·6, Westkapelle 2·0, Bath 2·8; Duration 0555; Zone –0100

Standard Port VLISSINGEN (→)

Times				Height (metres)			
High Water		Low Water		MHWS	MHWN	MLWN	MLWS
0300	0900	0400	1000	4·7	3·9	0·8	0·3
1500	2100	1600	2200				
Differences WESTKAPELLE							
–0025	–0015	–0010	–0025	–0·5	–0·5	0·0	0·0
HANSWEERT							
+0100	+0050	+0040	+0100	+0·7	+0·6	+0·1	0·0
BATH							
+0125	+0115	+0115	+0140	+1·1	+0·9	+0·1	0·0

SHELTER AND FACILITIES
Some hbrs for yachts between Terneuzen and Antwerpen (38M) are listed below in sequence from seaward:
ELLEWOUTSDIJK, 51°23'·00N 03°49'·00E. DYC 1803.2. HW +0200 and +0·3m on Vlissingen; ML 2·6m. Small, safe hbr; unlit. Dries, easy access HW ±3; 1·5m at MLWS. Hr Mr ☎ (0113) 548248 FW, D, Gaz; **YC Ellewoutsdijk** ☎ 548446.
HOEDEKENSKERKE, 51°25'·25N 03·55'·00E. DYC 1803.3. Disused ferry hbr (dries) on N bank, abeam ✦ Iso WRG 2s R □ tr, W band. Access HW–2½ to +3 for 1m draft. **YC WV Hoedekenskerke** ☎ (0113) 63x259; Ⓥ berths, P, D, Gaz, FW, ME. **Town** ✉, Ⓑ, ⇌ (Goes).
HANSWEERT, 51°26'·40N 04°00'·75E. DYC 1803.3. Tidal differences above. Can be used temporarily, but it is the busy ent to Zuid Beveland canal. Lt Oc WRG 10s, R lattice tr, W band, at ent. Waiting berths outside lock on E side. Ⓥ berths in inner hbr, W side; **Services:** ME, BY, P, D, C (17 ton), CH, R. **Town** ✉, Ⓑ, ⇌ (Kruiningen-Yerseke).
WALSOORDEN, 51°23'·00N 04°02'·00E. DYC 1803.3. HW is +0110 and +0·7m on Vlissingen; ML 2·6m. Prone to swell. SHM buoy 57A, L Fl G 8s, is 1ca N of ent. Ldg lts 220° both Oc 3s. Hbr ent marked with FG and FR. Yacht basin dead ahead on ent to hbr, depths 2 to 2·8m. *Zandvliet Radio* VHF Ch 12. Hr Mr ☎ (0114) 681235, FW, Slip; **Services:** Gas, P, D, BY, ME, El. **Town** R, Bar, ✉.
PAAL, 51°21'·30N 04°06'·70E. DYC 1803.3. HW +0120 and +0·8m on Vlissingen; ML 2·7m. Unlit, drying yacht hbr on W side of river mouth, ent marked by withy. Appr from No. 63 SHM buoy, L Fl G 8s, and Tide gauge, Fl (5) Y 20s across drying Speelmansgat. *Zandvliet Radio* VHF Ch 12. Hr Mr ☎ (0114) 315548; **Jachthaven** AC, FW; **Services:** V, P, D, Gaz, ME, El, R.

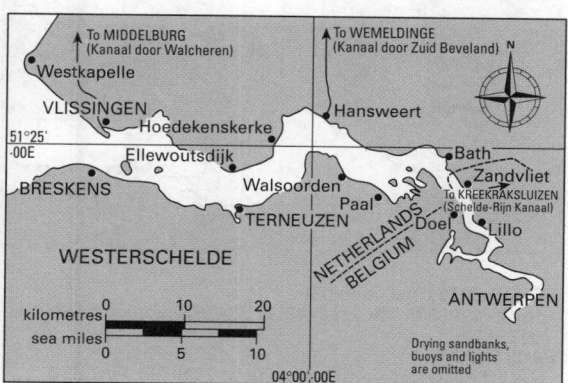

DOEL, Antwerpen, 51°18'·70N 04°16'·15E. DYC 1803.5. HW +0100 and +0·7m on Vlissingen. Small drying hbr on W bank. Ldg lts 185·5°: front Fl WRG 3s; rear Fl 3s, synch. N pier hd lt, Oc WR 5s. Hr Mr ☎ (03) 7733072; **YC de Noord** ☎ 7733669, R, Bar, FW.
LILLO, Antwerpen, 51°18'·24N 04°17'·40E. DYC 1803.5. 1M SE of Doel on opp bank; small drying hbr for shoal-draft only; HW±3. Landing stage in river has Oc WRG 10s. Hr Mr (035) 686456; **YC Scaldis.**

NAVIGATION
WPTs: See Breskens (8.20.13), Terneuzen (8.20.16) and Vlissingen (8.20.18). The approaches into the estuary from seaward are described in detail under 8.20.18; also the busy junction area between Vlissingen and Breskens. The Westerschelde chan winds through a mass of well marked sand-banks. It is the waterway to Antwerpen and Gent (via canal), very full of shipping and barges (Beware unforeseen reactions). It is necessary to work the tides, which average 2½kn, more at springs. Yachts should keep to the edge of main chan. Alternative chans must be used with caution, particular going downstream on the ebb.

LIGHTS AND MARKS
The apprs to Westerschelde are well lit by lt ho's: on the S shore at Kruishoofd and Nieuwe Sluis, and on the N shore at Westkapelle. See 8.20.4. The main fairways are, for the most part, defined by ldg lts and by the W sectors of the many Dir lts.

COMMUNICATIONS AND CONTROL (VTS)
Commercial traffic in the Westerschelde must comply with a comprehensive VTS which covers from the North Sea Outer Approaches up-river to Antwerp. See the TSS and VTS diagrams on the facing page and continuation diagrams at 8.20.36 and 8.20.37.
7 TRAFFIC CENTRES control the following areas:
In offshore approaches:
(1) *Wandelaar* Ch 65 (NW of Oostende);
(2) *Zeebrugge* Ch 69 (W, N and E of Zeebrugge);
(3) *Steenbank* Ch 64 (NW of Vlissingen).
Within the Westerschelde:
(4) *Vlissingen* Ch 14 (Vlissingen to E2A/PvN SPR buoys at approx 51°24'N 03°44'E);
(5) *Terneuzen* Ch 03 (thence to Nos 32/35 buoys at approx 51°23'N 03°57'E);
Also *Terneuzen* Ch 11 covers the Terneuzen-Gent Canal.
(6) *Hansweert* Ch 65 (thence to Nos 46/55 buoys at approx 51°24'N 04°02'E);
(7) *Zandvliet* Ch 12 (thence to Antwerpen).

Radar: In addition, within the 7 Traffic areas above, 16 unmanned Radar stns, as shown in brackets in the diagram opposite, provide radar, weather and hbr info on separate VHF Channels.
Broadcast reports of visibility, met, tidal data and ship movements are made in Dutch and English at:
Every H+55 on Ch 14 by *Vlissingen*;
Every H+00 on Ch 11 by *Terneuzen*;
Every H+35 on Ch 12 by *Zandvliet*.
Yachts should listen at all times on the VHF Ch for the area in which they are, so as to be aware of other shipping and to be contactable if required. Do not transmit, unless called. If you have a problem and need help, state vessel's name, position and the nature of the problem. Dutch is the primary language, English secondary.
If you have an **emergency**, call initially on the working/ channel in use; you may then be switched to *Schelde Cordination Centre* (SCC at Vlissingen) Ch 67.

TERNEUZEN　　　　　　　8-20-16

Zeeland 51°20'·62N 03°49'·75E　Rtg 1-1-2

CHARTS
AC 120; Zeekaart 1443; DYC 1803.2; Imray C30

TIDES
+0230 Dover; ML 2·5; Duration 0555; Zone –0100

Standard Port VLISSINGEN (⟶)

Times				Height (metres)			
High Water		Low Water		MHWS	MHWN	MLWN	MLWS
0300	0900	0400	1000	4·7	3·9	0·8	0·3
1500	2100	1600	220				
Differences TERNEUZEN							
+0020	+0020	+0020	+0030	+0·4	+0·3	+0·1	0·0

SHELTER
Very good except in strong NW winds. Marina in the Veerhaven is tidal and exposed to NE. Or enter the E lock (Oostsluis) and see Lockmaster for berth as on chartlet. Yachts are prohib in W Hbr and lock (Westsluis).

NAVIGATION
WPT No 18 PHM Buoy, Iso R 8s, 51°20'·95N 03°48'·83E, 299°/119° from/to Veerhaven ent, 0·65M. The Terneuzen-Gent canal is 17M long with 3 bridges, min clearance 6·5m when closed.

LIGHTS AND MARKS
The Dow Chemical works and storage tanks are conspic 2M W of hbr. For the Veerhaven, the water tr to SE and the Oc WRG lt on W mole are conspic. When entry prohib, a second R lt is shown below FR on E mole. Sigs for Oostsluis: R lts = entry prohib; G lts = entry permitted.

RADIO TELEPHONE
Call: *Havendienst Terneuzen* VHF Ch 11 (H24); also info broadcasts every H+00 for vessels in the basins & canal. East lock Ch 18. For Terneuzen-Gent canal call on Ch 11 and keep watch during transit. Contact Zelzate Bridge (call: *Uitkijk Zelzate*) direct on Ch 11, other bridges through Terneuzen or, at the S end, *Havendienst Gent* Ch 05 11 (H24). See also 8.20.15.

TELEPHONE (Dial code 0115)
Hr Mr 612161; CG (0255) 534344 (H24); ⌗ 612377; Police 613017; Ⓗ 688000; Dr 112; Brit Consul (020) 6764343.

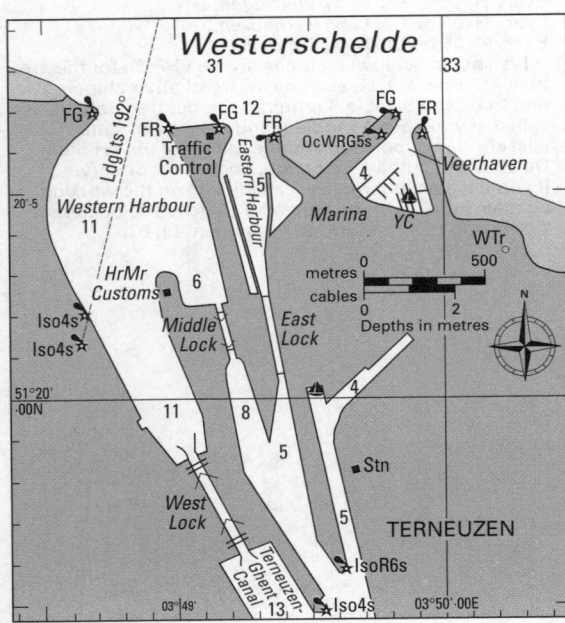

FACILITIES
Yacht Hbr (120) ☎ 697089, Slip, ME, El, Sh, BH (15 ton), FW; **WSV de Honte YC** ☎ 617633, AB f21.84, L, FW, Ⓒ; **Neuzen YC** ☎ 614411, AB f16.70, M, L, FW;
Services: ME, El, BY, P, D, L, FW, C (40 ton), AB, Sh, Gaz.
Town P, D, CH, V, R, Bar, ⌧, Ⓑ, ✈ (Ghent). Ferry: local to Vlissingen.

ANTWERPEN　　8-20-17
(ANTWERP)

Antwerpen 51°13'·85N 04°23'·77E　Rtg 3-1-1

CHARTS
AC 139; Zeekaart 1443; DYC 1803.5

TIDES
+0342 Dover; ML 2·9; Duration 0605; Zone –0100

Standard Port VLISSINGEN (⟶)

Times				Height (metres)			
High Water		Low Water		MHWS	MHWN	MLWN	MLWS
0300	0900	0400	1000	4·7	3·9	0·8	0·3
1500	2100	1600	2200				
Differences ANTWERPEN							
+0128	+0116	+0121	+0144	+1·1	+0·9	0·0	0·0

SHELTER
Excellent in Jachthaven Antwerpen (marina) on W bank, 4ca SW of Kattendijksluis and ½M from city centre (via two tunnels). Access by lock HW ±1 (H24, 1 Apr-31 Oct)). In winter lock opens only by arrangement. A T-shaped ferry pontoon is 2½ca N of ent, with waiting berths on the inshore side; also a waiting buoy (IMALSO) is off the ent.

NAVIGATION
For Westerschelde see 8.20.13/14/15/17. It is advised to check off the buoys coming up-river. After No 116 PHM buoy, Iso R 8s, there is a gap of 1.5M before reaching No. 107 SHM buoy, Iso G 8s, which marks a 90° bend in the river onto S and is close to the pontoon (see SHELTER). No 109 SHM buoy, Iso G 8s, is 250m NE of marina ent.

LIGHTS AND MARKS
The marina is marked by a concrete pile, black topmark and lt, F WR 9m 3M, (W shore-283°, R 283°-shore). Lock entry and depth signals are no longer used

RADIO TELEPHONE
Call *Jachthaven Antwerpen* VHF Ch 09 (HW±1). Call Port Operations *Antwerpen Havendienst* Ch 74 (H24) and for Safety; VTS Ch 18; Radar Ch 02 60; Bridges Ch 13.

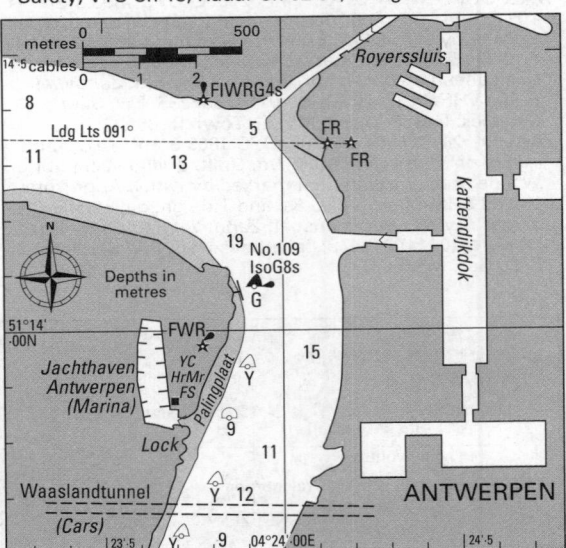

TELEPHONE (Dial code 03)
Hr Mr 2190895, ☎ 2196748; ⌗ 2340840; Police 321840; Ⓗ 2177111.

FACILITIES
Jachthaven Antwerpen Marina ☎ 2190895, FW, D, R, V, Gaz, El, Sh, AC, C (1·5 ton), Slip; **Royal YC van België** ☎ 2192682, Bar, R, M, C (5 ton), D, P, CH, FW, L, Slip; **Kon. Liberty YC** ☎ 2191147; Services: BY, ME, BH, ACA, DYC Agent.
City All facilities, ⌧, Ⓑ, ⇌, ✈. Ferry: Ostend-Ramsgate.

VLISSINGEN (FLUSHING) 8-20-18

Zeeland 51°26'·36N 03°34'·70E (Koopmanshaven). Rtg 1-2-1

CHARTS

AC 120, 1872, 1874; Zeekaart 1442, 1443, 1533; DYC 1801.3, 1803.8; Imray C30; Stanfords 1, 19

TIDES

+0215 Dover; ML 2·3; Duration 0555; Zone –0100
NOTE: Vlissingen is a Standard Port. Tidal predictions for each day of the year are given on the next 3 pages.

SHELTER

Very good in both yacht hbrs:
1. **Michiel de Ruyter** marina (2·9m) in the Vissershaven has 6m wide ent, approached from the Koopmanshaven. Storm barrier is open 1 Apr-1 Nov. Sill with 1·0m water at MLWS; check depth gauge on barrier wall. Small swing bridge (pedestrian) is operated by Hr Mr 0800-2000LT, with R/G tfc lts. The bridge is open 2000-0800LT, but only for yachts to leave; Ⓡ Ⓡ (vert) tfc lts prohibit arrival from sea, because the marina is not lit.
2. **VVW Schelde** (3m) is near the ent to the Walcheren Canal. Entering the Buitenhaven beware ferries. Keep to port and S of ferry terminal for the locks, which operate H24; yachts use smallest, most N'ly lock. Waiting possible on piles to SE. Marina is to NW, past both Binnenhaven.

NAVIGATION

WPT H-SS NCM buoy, Q, 51°25'·97N 03°37'·54E, 125°/305° from/to Buitenhaven ent, 0·95M.
Commercial Shipping: Yachts should keep clear of the busy shipping chans, ie Wielingen from the SW, Scheur from the W, and Oostgat from the NW. To the E of where Wielingen and Scheur merge (NCM buoy S-W), be aware of the major ship anchorages: Wielingen Noord and Zuid either side of the fairway as defined by buoys W6, 7, 9, 10 and Songa. Close to the E, Vlissingen Roads are also a major anchorage (N of buoys SS-VH to SS7, and SW of H-SS). There is a precautionary TSS area between this anch and Vlissingen itself. Yachts are forbidden to sail in the TSS fairways. Ocean-going ships often manoeuvre off the town to transfer pilots. Fast ferries frequently enter/leave the Buitenhaven terminal.
Recommended Yacht routes: From the SW there are few dangers. After Zeebrugge, keep S of the Wielingen chan buoys (W1-9). Off Breskens be aware of the fast ferries to/from Vlissingen; continue E to SS3 buoy, then cross to Vlissingen on a N'ly track, keeping W of H-SS buoy.

From the W, keep clear of the Scheur chan by crossing to the S of Wielingen as soon as practicable.
From N, by day, in vicinity of Kaloo or DR1 buoys, follow the Geul van de Rassen, Deurloo and Spleet chans to SP4 buoy. Turn S to cross Wielingen at 90° between buoys W6 and W8; thence via W9 as per the SW approach.
A variation after Deurloo is to use the Nollegeul channel (NG1-15), crossing quickly to the Vlissingen shore as and when traffic in Oostgat permits.
Another route, slightly further offshore, is to skirt the NW side of Kaloo bank to Botkil-W buoy, thence SE via Geul van de Walvischstaart to SP5 and 4 buoys.
None of these N'ly routes is lit. By night the Oostgat can be used with caution keeping outside the SW edge of the buoyed chan.

LIGHTS AND MARKS

From NW, Oostgat ldg lts 117°: Front Leugenaar, Oc R 5s 5m 7M; rear Sardijngeul, 550m from front, Oc WRG 5s 10m 12/8M, R △, W bands on R and W mast.
Note: Conspic Radar Tr (close NW of Koopmanshaven) shows a Fl Y lt to warn if ships are approaching from the NW, ie around the blind arc from Oostgat/Sardijngeul.
The lt ho at the root of the W bkwtr of Koopmanshaven is brown metal framework tr, Iso WRG 3s 15m 12/9M. On S side of de Ruyter marina is a conspic W metal framework tr (50m), floodlit.
Buitenhaven tfc sigs from mole W side of ent:
R flag or extra Ⓡ near FR on W mole hd = Entry prohib.

RADIO TELEPHONE

Zeeland Seaports Ch 09. Lock & bridge info Ch 22.
See also Westerschelde (8.20.15) for VTS.

TELEPHONE (Dial code 0118)

Hr Mr 468080; East Hbr Port Authority 478741; Schelde Tfc Coordination Centre 424790; Buitenhaven Lock 412372; ⌗ 484600; Police 415050; Ⓗ 425000; Dr 412233; Brit Consul (020) 6764343.

FACILITIES

Michiel de Ruyter (100 + 40 visitors) ☎ 414498, f27.42, D, FW, AC, Bar, R, YC, ▣;
Jachthaven 'VVW Schelde' (90 + 50 visitors) ☎ 465912, f13.50, AC, Bar, C (10 ton), CH, D, FW, R, ▣, ⛴, M, Slip, (Access H24 via lock), approx 1km by road from ferry terminal; **Services:** BY, Sh, ME, Sh, SM, bikes for hire..
Town P, D, CH, V, R, Bar, ✉, Ⓑ, ⇌, ✈ (Antwerpen).
Ferry: local to Breskens/Terneuzen.

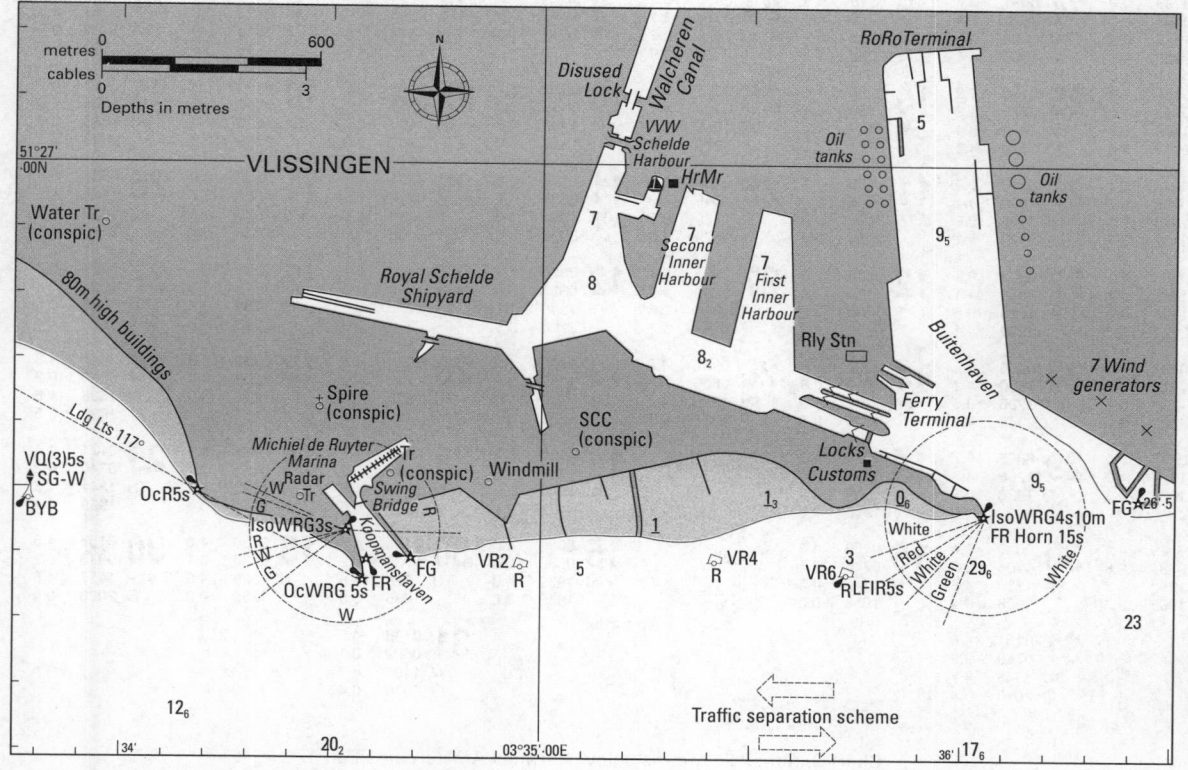

TIME ZONE –0100
(Dutch Standard Time)
Subtract 1 hour for UT

For Dutch Summer Time add
ONE hour in non-shaded areas

NETHERLANDS – VLISSINGEN (FLUSHING)

LAT 51°27′N   LONG 3°36′E

TIMES AND HEIGHTS OF HIGH AND LOW WATERS

YEAR **1999**

JANUARY

Day	Time	m	Day	Time	m
1 F	0047 / 0719 / 1307 / 1940	4.6 / 0.5 / 4.7 / 0.3	16 SA	0112 / 0726 / 1326 / 1940	4.3 / 0.6 / 4.4 / 0.6
2 SA O	0136 / 0807 / 1356 / 2027	4.7 / 0.3 / 4.9 / 0.3	17 SU ●	0148 / 0806 / 1406 / 2015	4.5 / 0.5 / 4.5 / 0.6
3 SU	0226 / 0856 / 1445 / 2110	4.7 / 0.2 / 4.9 / 0.3	18 M	0226 / 0842 / 1439 / 2055	4.6 / 0.4 / 4.7 / 0.5
4 M	0312 / 0940 / 1530 / 2153	4.8 / 0.2 / 4.9 / 0.4	19 TU	0259 / 0922 / 1517 / 2138	4.7 / 0.3 / 4.8 / 0.5
5 TU	0356 / 1022 / 1615 / 2231	4.7 / 0.2 / 4.9 / 0.5	20 W	0336 / 1008 / 1555 / 2221	4.7 / 0.2 / 4.8 / 0.5
6 W	0441 / 1108 / 1705 / 2315	4.6 / 0.2 / 4.7 / 0.6	21 TH	0415 / 1056 / 1633 / 2300	4.7 / 0.2 / 4.8 / 0.5
7 TH	0526 / 1146 / 1747 / 2352	4.5 / 0.3 / 4.5 / 0.8	22 F	0457 / 1136 / 1716 / 2346	4.6 / 0.2 / 4.7 / 0.6
8 F	0609 / 1230 / 1838	4.3 / 0.5 / 4.3	23 SA	0542 / 1215 / 1805	4.5 / 0.2 / 4.5
9 SA	0035 / 0655 / 1315 / 1928	0.9 / 4.1 / 0.6 / 4.1	24 SU	0031 / 0628 / 1308 / 1905	0.7 / 4.4 / 0.3 / 4.4
10 SU	0130 / 0745 / 1409 / 2026	1.0 / 3.9 / 0.6 / 3.8	25 M	0120 / 0729 / 1406 / 2010	0.8 / 4.2 / 0.4 / 4.2
11 M	0240 / 0856 / 1515 / 2136	1.1 / 3.7 / 0.9 / 3.7	26 TU	0226 / 0840 / 1505 / 2120	0.9 / 4.1 / 0.6 / 4.1
12 TU	0356 / 1005 / 1625 / 2251	1.1 / 3.7 / 0.9 / 3.8	27 W	0325 / 0950 / 1616 / 2232	0.9 / 4.1 / 0.6 / 4.1
13 W	0456 / 1116 / 1730 / 2347	1.0 / 3.8 / 0.9 / 3.9	28 TH	0456 / 1059 / 1736 / 2342	0.9 / 4.2 / 0.6 / 4.2
14 TH	0544 / 1205 / 1820	0.9 / 4.0 / 0.8	29 F	0606 / 1206 / 1836	0.7 / 4.3 / 0.5
15 F	0029 / 0634 / 1250 / 1905	4.1 / 0.8 / 4.2 / 0.7	30 SA	0037 / 0705 / 1258 / 1928	4.4 / 0.5 / 4.6 / 0.4
			31 SU O	0131 / 0755 / 1348 / 2013	4.5 / 0.3 / 4.7 / 0.4

FEBRUARY

Day	Time	m	Day	Time	m
1 M	0216 / 0843 / 1436 / 2056	4.6 / 0.2 / 4.8 / 0.4	16 TU ●	0206 / 0826 / 1419 / 2038	4.5 / 0.3 / 4.8 / 0.4
2 TU	0257 / 0927 / 1516 / 2135	4.7 / 0.1 / 4.9 / 0.4	17 W O	0239 / 0906 / 1456 / 2120	4.7 / 0.1 / 4.9 / 0.4
3 W	0339 / 1008 / 1559 / 2211	4.7 / 0.1 / 4.8 / 0.5	18 TH	0316 / 0952 / 1536 / 2202	4.8 / 0.0 / 4.9 / 0.3
4 TH	0417 / 1045 / 1637 / 2250	4.7 / 0.2 / 4.7 / 0.6	19 F	0356 / 1035 / 1616 / 2246	4.8 / 0.0 / 4.9 / 0.4
5 F	0457 / 1126 / 1717 / 2325	4.6 / 0.3 / 4.6 / 0.6	20 SA	0436 / 1118 / 1658 / 2328	4.8 / 0.0 / 4.8 / 0.4
6 SA	0536 / 1158 / 1756	4.5 / 0.4 / 4.4	21 SU	0519 / 1200 / 1745	4.7 / 0.1 / 4.6
7 SU	0006 / 0615 / 1230 / 1840	0.7 / 4.3 / 0.5 / 4.1	22 M	0009 / 0607 / 1246 / 1839	0.5 / 4.5 / 0.2 / 4.4
8 M	0036 / 0701 / 1310 / 1926	0.8 / 4.1 / 0.7 / 3.9	23 TU	0100 / 0706 / 1336 / 1946	0.6 / 4.3 / 0.4 / 4.1
9 TU	0115 / 0750 / 1405 / 2026	0.9 / 3.8 / 0.9 / 3.7	24 W	0206 / 0816 / 1435 / 2056	0.7 / 4.1 / 0.6 / 3.9
10 W	0256 / 0856 / 1524 / 2129	1.1 / 3.6 / 1.0 / 3.6	25 TH	0310 / 0930 / 1556 / 2215	0.8 / 4.0 / 0.7 / 3.8
11 TH	0405 / 1016 / 1639 / 2255	1.1 / 3.6 / 1.0 / 3.6	26 F	0436 / 1045 / 1720 / 2329	0.8 / 4.0 / 0.7 / 4.0
12 F	0516 / 1130 / 1746	1.0 / 3.8 / 0.9	27 SA	0601 / 1159 / 1826	0.7 / 4.2 / 0.6
13 SA	0000 / 0615 / 1221 / 1835	3.9 / 0.8 / 4.0 / 0.8	28 SU	0031 / 0655 / 1256 / 1918	4.2 / 0.4 / 4.5 / 0.5
14 SU	0048 / 0705 / 1305 / 1918	4.1 / 0.6 / 4.3 / 0.6			
15 M	0126 / 0746 / 1346 / 1958	4.4 / 0.5 / 4.5 / 0.5			

MARCH

Day	Time	m	Day	Time	m
1 M	0126 / 0746 / 1340 / 1959	4.4 / 0.2 / 4.7 / 0.4	16 TU	0059 / 0719 / 1320 / 1936	4.3 / 0.4 / 4.6 / 0.5
2 TU O	0205 / 0830 / 1422 / 2040	4.6 / 0.1 / 4.7 / 0.4	17 W ●	0137 / 0805 / 1441 / 2015	4.6 / 0.2 / 4.8 / 0.3
3 W	0240 / 0908 / 1501 / 2115	4.7 / 0.1 / 4.8 / 0.4	18 TH	0215 / 0846 / 1433 / 2100	4.8 / 0.0 / 5.0 / 0.3
4 TH	0317 / 0947 / 1535 / 2149	4.7 / 0.1 / 4.8 / 0.4	19 F	0255 / 0930 / 1513 / 2143	4.9 / -0.1 / 5.0 / 0.2
5 F	0355 / 1022 / 1616 / 2225	4.7 / 0.2 / 4.7 / 0.5	20 SA	0335 / 1013 / 1555 / 2226	4.9 / -0.1 / 5.0 / 0.3
6 SA	0428 / 1056 / 1647 / 2258	4.6 / 0.3 / 4.6 / 0.5	21 SU	0416 / 1056 / 1638 / 2310	4.9 / -0.1 / 4.9 / 0.3
7 SU	0502 / 1122 / 1722 / 2328	4.5 / 0.4 / 4.4 / 0.6	22 M	0458 / 1138 / 1725 / 2355	4.8 / 0.0 / 4.6 / 0.3
8 M	0535 / 1150 / 1755 / 2355	4.4 / 0.5 / 4.2 / 0.6	23 TU	0547 / 1226 / 1817	4.6 / 0.2 / 4.4
9 TU	0615 / 1215 / 1836	4.2 / 0.6 / 4.0	24 W	0045 / 0645 / 1312 / 1925	0.4 / 4.4 / 0.4 / 4.1
10 W	0029 / 0655 / 1259 / 1926	0.7 / 3.9 / 0.8 / 3.8	25 TH	0139 / 0755 / 1416 / 2036	0.6 / 4.1 / 0.6 / 3.8
11 TH	0125 / 0805 / 1354 / 2035	0.9 / 3.7 / 1.0 / 3.7	26 F	0301 / 0916 / 1546 / 2205	0.7 / 3.9 / 0.8 / 3.7
12 F	0326 / 0925 / 1606 / 2200	1.1 / 3.5 / 1.1 / 3.5	27 SA	0426 / 1040 / 1715 / 2319	0.8 / 4.0 / 0.8 / 3.9
13 SA	0435 / 1050 / 1710 / 2325	1.0 / 3.7 / 1.0 / 3.7	28 SU	0556 / 1149 / 1820	0.6 / 4.2 / 0.6
14 SU	0540 / 1156 / 1805	0.8 / 4.0 / 0.8	29 M	0025 / 0655 / 1246 / 1905	4.1 / 0.3 / 4.5 / 0.5
15 M	0020 / 0636 / 1239 / 1856	4.0 / 0.6 / 4.3 / 0.6	30 TU	0108 / 0732 / 1328 / 1945	4.4 / 0.2 / 4.6 / 0.4
			31 W O	0146 / 0809 / 1406 / 2019	4.5 / 0.1 / 4.7 / 0.4

APRIL

Day	Time	m	Day	Time	m
1 TH	0221 / 0845 / 1439 / 2053	4.6 / 0.1 / 4.7 / 0.4	16 F ●	0148 / 0822 / 1408 / 2037	4.8 / -0.1 / 5.0 / 0.2
2 F	0255 / 0919 / 1516 / 2128	4.7 / 0.1 / 4.7 / 0.3	17 SA	0228 / 0906 / 1451 / 2122	4.9 / -0.1 / 5.1 / 0.1
3 SA	0327 / 0956 / 1545 / 2202	4.7 / 0.2 / 4.7 / 0.4	18 SU	0310 / 0951 / 1535 / 2205	5.0 / -0.1 / 5.0 / 0.1
4 SU	0402 / 1026 / 1620 / 2236	4.6 / 0.3 / 4.5 / 0.4	19 M	0353 / 1035 / 1618 / 2249	5.0 / -0.1 / 4.8 / 0.2
5 M	0430 / 1057 / 1650 / 2300	4.5 / 0.4 / 4.4 / 0.5	20 TU	0438 / 1116 / 1706 / 2335	4.9 / 0.1 / 4.6 / 0.2
6 TU	0506 / 1126 / 1719 / 2326	4.4 / 0.5 / 4.3 / 0.5	21 W	0528 / 1159 / 1759	4.7 / 0.2 / 4.3
7 W	0535 / 1146 / 1756	4.3 / 0.6 / 4.1	22 TH	0025 / 0626 / 1256 / 1905	0.3 / 4.4 / 0.5 / 4.0
8 TH	0000 / 0615 / 1226 / 1836	0.6 / 4.1 / 0.7 / 3.9	23 F	0125 / 0745 / 1355 / 2015	0.5 / 4.2 / 0.7 / 3.8
9 F	0045 / 0705 / 1319 / 1946	0.6 / 3.8 / 0.9 / 3.6	24 SA	0245 / 0900 / 1520 / 2146	0.6 / 4.0 / 0.8 / 3.7
10 SA	0154 / 0840 / 1510 / 2109	0.9 / 3.6 / 1.1 / 3.5	25 SU	0410 / 1026 / 1655 / 2300	0.6 / 4.0 / 0.8 / 3.9
11 SU	0356 / 1005 / 1636 / 2236	0.9 / 3.7 / 1.0 / 3.7	26 M	0531 / 1129 / 1800 / 2355	0.5 / 4.2 / 0.7 / 4.1
12 M	0505 / 1115 / 1736 / 2346	0.7 / 4.0 / 0.8 / 4.0	27 TU	0627 / 1221 / 1846	0.3 / 4.4 / 0.5
13 TU	0559 / 1208 / 1826	0.5 / 4.2 / 0.6	28 W	0041 / 0710 / 1306 / 1926	4.3 / 0.2 / 4.6 / 0.5
14 W	0025 / 0655 / 1248 / 1911	4.3 / 0.3 / 4.7 / 0.4	29 TH	0121 / 0746 / 1341 / 1959	4.4 / 0.2 / 4.6 / 0.4
15 TH	0106 / 0738 / 1328 / 1952	4.6 / 0.1 / 4.9 / 0.3	30 F O	0157 / 0818 / 1417 / 2028	4.5 / 0.2 / 4.6 / 0.4

Chart Datum: 2·32 metres below Normaal Amsterdams Peil

TIME ZONE –0100
(Dutch Standard Time)
Subtract 1 hour for UT

For Dutch Summer Time add
ONE hour in non-shaded areas

NETHERLANDS – VLISSINGEN (FLUSHING)

LAT 51°27′N   LONG 3°36′E

TIMES AND HEIGHTS OF HIGH AND LOW WATERS

YEAR 1999

MAY

Day	Time	m		Day	Time	m
1 SA	0228 / 0852 / 1447 / 2106	4.6 / 0.2 / 4.6 / 0.3		16 SU	0205 / 0842 / 1430 / 2102	4.9 / -0.1 / 5.0 / 0.1
2 SU	0301 / 0925 / 1519 / 2140	4.6 / 0.3 / 4.5 / 0.3		17 M	0249 / 0925 / 1516 / 2148	5.0 / 0.0 / 4.9 / 0.1
3 M	0336 / 0958 / 1551 / 2216	4.6 / 0.3 / 4.5 / 0.4		18 TU	0336 / 1012 / 1602 / 2235	5.0 / 0.1 / 4.8 / 0.1
4 TU	0406 / 1031 / 1622 / 2240	4.5 / 0.5 / 4.4 / 0.4		19 W	0423 / 1056 / 1650 / 2326	4.9 / 0.2 / 4.6 / 0.1
5 W	0437 / 1056 / 1656 / 2310	4.4 / 0.6 / 4.3 / 0.5		20 TH	0515 / 1146 / 1748	4.7 / 0.4 / 4.4
6 TH	0510 / 1126 / 1728 / 2346	4.3 / 0.6 / 4.2 / 0.5		21 F	0016 / 0615 / 1229 / 1850	0.2 / 4.5 / 0.5 / 4.1
7 F	0548 / 1205 / 1804	4.2 / 0.7 / 4.0		22 SA	0115 / 0722 / 1336 / 1955	0.3 / 4.3 / 0.7 / 3.9
8 SA	0030 / 0635 / 1255 / 1909	0.6 / 4.0 / 0.9 / 3.8		23 SU	0214 / 0831 / 1444 / 2105	0.4 / 4.1 / 0.8 / 3.8
9 SU	0135 / 0800 / 1405 / 2036	0.7 / 3.8 / 1.0 / 3.7		24 M	0335 / 0955 / 1615 / 2222	0.5 / 4.1 / 0.8 / 3.9
10 M	0305 / 0920 / 1545 / 2155	0.7 / 3.9 / 0.9 / 3.8		25 TU	0456 / 1100 / 1726 / 2325	0.5 / 4.2 / 0.7 / 4.0
11 TU	0420 / 1029 / 1649 / 2256	0.6 / 4.1 / 0.8 / 4.0		26 W	0556 / 1156 / 1816	0.4 / 4.3 / 0.6
12 W	0522 / 1132 / 1756 / 2351	0.4 / 4.4 / 0.6 / 4.3		27 TH	0016 / 0636 / 1236 / 1855	4.2 / 0.4 / 4.4 / 0.5
13 TH	0626 / 1217 / 1840	0.2 / 4.7 / 0.4		28 F	0055 / 0748 / 1316 / 1931	4.3 / 0.4 / 4.5 / 0.5
14 F	0037 / 0710 / 1302 / 1931	4.6 / 0.1 / 4.9 / 0.3		29 SA	0132 / 0748 / 1348 / 2002	4.4 / 0.4 / 4.5 / 0.4
15 SA ●	0123 / 0757 / 1346 / 2016	4.8 / 0.0 / 5.0 / 0.2		30 SU O	0202 / 0822 / 1422 / 2035	4.5 / 0.4 / 4.5 / 0.3
				31 M	0237 / 0856 / 1456 / 2115	4.5 / 0.4 / 4.5 / 0.3

JUNE

Day	Time	m		Day	Time	m
1 TU	0309 / 0932 / 1529 / 2149	4.6 / 0.4 / 4.5 / 0.3		16 W	0320 / 0956 / 1549 / 2222	4.9 / 0.2 / 4.7 / 0.1
2 W	0345 / 1006 / 1602 / 2226	4.5 / 0.5 / 4.4 / 0.4		17 TH	0411 / 1038 / 1639 / 2310	4.9 / 0.3 / 4.6 / 0.1
3 TH	0415 / 1036 / 1636 / 2255	4.4 / 0.6 / 4.3 / 0.4		18 F	0506 / 1122 / 1728 / 2358	4.7 / 0.5 / 4.5 / 0.1
4 F	0451 / 1110 / 1712 / 2336	4.4 / 0.7 / 4.2 / 0.4		19 SA	0556 / 1210 / 1822	4.6 / 0.6 / 4.3
5 SA	0532 / 1150 / 1752	4.3 / 0.7 / 4.1		20 SU	0050 / 0658 / 1306 / 1919	0.2 / 4.4 / 0.7 / 4.1
6 SU	0014 / 0619 / 1234 / 1850	0.5 / 4.2 / 0.8 / 4.0		21 M	0146 / 0758 / 1405 / 2025	0.4 / 4.2 / 0.8 / 3.9
7 M	0115 / 0731 / 1346 / 2006	0.5 / 4.1 / 0.9 / 3.9		22 TU	0245 / 0906 / 1504 / 2136	0.5 / 4.0 / 0.9 / 3.9
8 TU	0236 / 0845 / 1455 / 2116	0.5 / 4.1 / 0.9 / 3.9		23 W	0400 / 1018 / 1625 / 2239	0.6 / 4.0 / 0.9 / 3.9
9 W	0336 / 0949 / 1616 / 2221	0.5 / 4.2 / 0.8 / 4.1		24 TH	0506 / 1115 / 1725 / 2338	0.6 / 4.1 / 0.8 / 4.0
10 TH	0446 / 1055 / 1716 / 2318	0.4 / 4.4 / 0.6 / 4.3		25 F	0555 / 1206 / 1820	0.6 / 4.2 / 0.7
11 F	0545 / 1150 / 1816	0.3 / 4.6 / 0.4		26 SA	0025 / 0645 / 1250 / 1906	4.2 / 0.5 / 4.3 / 0.6
12 SA	0009 / 0645 / 1239 / 1909	4.6 / 0.2 / 4.8 / 0.2		27 SU	0105 / 0721 / 1326 / 1946	4.3 / 0.5 / 4.4 / 0.5
13 SU ●	0059 / 0736 / 1326 / 1958	4.8 / 0.1 / 4.9 / 0.2		28 M O	0141 / 0756 / 1358 / 2018	4.4 / 0.5 / 4.4 / 0.4
14 M	0146 / 0820 / 1415 / 2045	4.9 / 0.1 / 4.9 / 0.1		29 TU	0215 / 0830 / 1436 / 2056	4.5 / 0.5 / 4.5 / 0.4
15 TU	0235 / 0908 / 1501 / 2136	4.9 / 0.1 / 4.8 / 0.1		30 W	0251 / 0909 / 1507 / 2136	4.5 / 0.5 / 4.5 / 0.3

JULY

Day	Time	m		Day	Time	m
1 TH	0326 / 0946 / 1546 / 2209	4.6 / 0.5 / 4.5 / 0.3		16 F	0356 / 1018 / 1626 / 2256	4.9 / 0.4 / 4.7 / 0.1
2 F	0357 / 1020 / 1619 / 2244	4.6 / 0.6 / 4.4 / 0.3		17 SA	0443 / 1102 / 1707 / 2335	4.8 / 0.5 / 4.6 / 0.2
3 SA	0435 / 1058 / 1658 / 2330	4.6 / 0.6 / 4.4 / 0.3		18 SU	0531 / 1142 / 1755	4.7 / 0.6 / 4.5
4 SU	0515 / 1135 / 1737	4.5 / 0.7 / 4.3		19 M	0015 / 0619 / 1226 / 1841	0.3 / 4.5 / 0.7 / 4.3
5 M	0016 / 0601 / 1226 / 1828	0.3 / 4.4 / 0.7 / 4.2		20 TU	0105 / 0716 / 1315 / 1931	0.4 / 4.2 / 0.8 / 4.1
6 TU	0105 / 0700 / 1315 / 1928	0.4 / 4.3 / 0.8 / 4.1		21 W	0156 / 0810 / 1414 / 2036	0.6 / 4.0 / 0.9 / 3.9
7 W	0155 / 0806 / 1420 / 2035	0.4 / 4.2 / 0.8 / 4.1		22 TH	0253 / 0916 / 1536 / 2146	0.7 / 3.8 / 1.0 / 3.8
8 TH	0306 / 0915 / 1525 / 2141	0.4 / 4.2 / 0.8 / 4.1		23 F	0406 / 1030 / 1636 / 2256	0.8 / 3.8 / 0.9 / 3.8
9 F	0410 / 1022 / 1640 / 2250	0.4 / 4.3 / 0.7 / 4.3		24 SA	0504 / 1129 / 1733 / 2356	0.8 / 3.9 / 0.8 / 4.0
10 SA	0515 / 1126 / 1751 / 2347	0.4 / 4.4 / 0.6 / 4.5		25 SU	0606 / 1219 / 1825	0.8 / 4.1 / 0.7
11 SU	0619 / 1221 / 1851	0.3 / 4.6 / 0.4		26 M	0042 / 0650 / 1306 / 1918	4.1 / 0.7 / 4.2 / 0.6
12 M	0043 / 0716 / 1313 / 1946	4.7 / 0.3 / 4.7 / 0.5		27 TU	0126 / 0730 / 1342 / 1956	4.3 / 0.7 / 4.4 / 0.5
13 TU ●	0135 / 0806 / 1402 / 2032	4.8 / 0.2 / 4.7 / 0.1		28 W O	0158 / 0806 / 1416 / 2036	4.5 / 0.6 / 4.5 / 0.4
14 W	0222 / 0849 / 1449 / 2122	4.9 / 0.3 / 4.8 / 0.1		29 TH	0231 / 0846 / 1449 / 2112	4.6 / 0.6 / 4.6 / 0.1
15 TH	0309 / 0935 / 1536 / 2206	4.9 / 0.3 / 4.7 / 0.1		30 F	0305 / 0926 / 1526 / 2155	4.7 / 0.5 / 4.6 / 0.2
				31 SA	0342 / 1005 / 1600 / 2236	4.7 / 0.5 / 4.6 / 0.2

AUGUST

Day	Time	m		Day	Time	m
1 SU	0417 / 1046 / 1638 / 2315	4.7 / 0.6 / 4.6 / 0.2		16 M	0506 / 1116 / 1721 / 2345	4.7 / 0.6 / 4.6 / 0.3
2 M	0456 / 1125 / 1717	4.7 / 0.6 / 4.5		17 TU	0546 / 1150 / 1801	4.5 / 0.7 / 4.4
3 TU	0001 / 0541 / 1206 / 1802	0.2 / 4.6 / 0.7 / 4.4		18 W	0019 / 0628 / 1236 / 1845	0.5 / 4.3 / 0.8 / 4.2
4 W	0046 / 0636 / 1256 / 1855	0.3 / 4.4 / 0.7 / 4.3		19 TH	0105 / 0709 / 1314 / 1935	0.7 / 4.0 / 0.9 / 4.0
5 TH	0136 / 0736 / 1344 / 2002	0.4 / 4.3 / 0.8 / 4.2		20 F	0206 / 0806 / 1447 / 2035	0.9 / 3.8 / 1.1 / 3.7
6 F	0230 / 0845 / 1506 / 2116	0.5 / 4.2 / 0.8 / 4.1		21 SA	0316 / 0916 / 1556 / 2200	1.0 / 3.6 / 1.1 / 3.6
7 SA	0340 / 0956 / 1616 / 2226	0.5 / 4.1 / 0.8 / 4.2		22 SU	0430 / 1051 / 1700 / 2320	1.0 / 3.7 / 1.0 / 3.8
8 SU	0456 / 1105 / 1730 / 2335	0.5 / 4.2 / 0.7 / 4.3		23 M	0536 / 1149 / 1754	1.0 / 3.9 / 0.8
9 M	0605 / 1208 / 1835	0.5 / 4.4 / 0.5		24 TU	0015 / 0625 / 1240 / 1855	4.0 / 0.9 / 4.1 / 0.7
10 TU	0032 / 0702 / 1305 / 1931	4.6 / 0.4 / 4.5 / 0.3		25 W	0100 / 0705 / 1316 / 1935	4.3 / 0.7 / 4.3 / 0.5
11 W	0127 / 0749 / 1352 / 2018	4.8 / 0.4 / 4.7 / 0.2		26 TH	0136 / 0746 / 1351 / 2009	4.5 / 0.6 / 4.5 / 0.4
12 TH	0212 / 0836 / 1435 / 2105	4.9 / 0.4 / 4.8 / 0.1		27 F O	0207 / 0819 / 1425 / 2049	4.7 / 0.6 / 4.7 / 0.2
13 F	0255 / 0918 / 1519 / 2150	5.0 / 0.4 / 4.8 / 0.1		28 SA	0242 / 0902 / 1501 / 2132	4.9 / 0.5 / 4.8 / 0.1
14 SA	0339 / 0958 / 1559 / 2230	4.9 / 0.5 / 4.8 / 0.1		29 SU	0316 / 0946 / 1536 / 2211	4.9 / 0.5 / 4.8 / 0.1
15 SU	0421 / 1035 / 1641 / 2305	4.8 / 0.6 / 4.7 / 0.2		30 M	0355 / 1026 / 1615 / 2255	4.9 / 0.5 / 4.8 / 0.1
				31 TU	0435 / 1106 / 1655 / 2338	4.9 / 0.5 / 4.7 / 0.2

20

Chart Datum: 2·32 metres below Normaal Amsterdams Peil

TIME ZONE –0100
(Dutch Standard Time)
Subtract 1 hour for UT

For Dutch Summer Time add ONE hour in non-shaded areas

NETHERLANDS – VLISSINGEN (FLUSHING)

LAT 51°27'N LONG 3°36'E

TIMES AND HEIGHTS OF HIGH AND LOW WATERS   YEAR 1999

SEPTEMBER

Day	Time / m
1 W	0516 4.7 · 1151 0.6 · 1736 4.6
16 TH	0545 4.3 · 1145 0.8 · 1759 4.3
2 TH	0020 0.3 · 0607 4.5 · 1236 0.7 · 1829 4.4
17 F	0010 0.8 · 0625 4.1 · 1220 0.9 · 1845 4.0
3 F	0106 0.4 · 0706 4.3 · 1325 0.8 · 1936 4.2
18 SA	0045 1.0 · 0710 3.9 · 1310 1.1 · 1946 3.8
4 SA	0206 0.6 · 0818 4.1 · 1440 0.9 · 2052 4.1
19 SU	0150 1.2 · 0815 3.6 · 1516 1.2 · 2059 3.6
5 SU	0315 0.8 · 0935 3.9 · 1555 0.9 · 2209 4.1
20 M	0356 1.2 · 0935 3.5 · 1626 1.1 · 2246 3.7
6 M	0440 0.8 · 1055 4.0 · 1715 0.8 · 2328 4.3
21 TU	0456 1.1 · 1116 3.7 · 1731 0.9 · 2346 4.0
7 TU	0555 0.7 · 1205 4.2 · 1836 0.5
22 W	0556 1.0 · 1205 4.0 · 1819 0.7
8 W	0027 4.5 · 0656 0.6 · 1256 4.5 · 1926 0.3
23 TH	0031 4.3 · 0640 0.8 · 1248 4.3 · 1906 0.5
9 TH	0117 4.8 · 0738 0.5 · 1337 4.7 · ● 2008 0.2
24 F	0106 4.6 · 0715 0.6 · 1325 4.6 · 1946 0.3
10 F	0156 4.9 · 0820 0.5 · 1419 4.8 · 2050 0.1
25 SA	0141 4.9 · 0755 0.5 · 1356 4.8 · O 2023 0.2
11 SA	0239 4.9 · 0855 0.5 · 1456 4.8 · 2128 0.1
26 SU	0215 5.0 · 0836 0.4 · 1433 4.9 · 2105 0.2
12 SU	0316 4.9 · 0936 0.5 · 1535 4.8 · 2205 0.2
27 M	0256 5.1 · 0921 0.4 · 1511 5.0 · 2147 0.1
13 M	0355 4.8 · 1009 0.5 · 1612 4.8 · 2238 0.3
28 TU	0333 5.1 · 1002 0.4 · 1551 5.0 · 2230 0.1
14 TU	0430 4.7 · 1046 0.6 · 1647 4.7 · 2312 0.5
29 W	0413 5.0 · 1046 0.4 · 1632 4.9 · 2312 0.2
15 W	0507 4.5 · 1116 0.7 · 1726 4.5 · 2340 0.6
30 TH	0456 4.8 · 1128 0.5 · 1716 4.8 · 2357 0.3

OCTOBER

Day	Time / m
1 F	0546 4.5 · 1215 0.6 · 1807 4.5
16 SA	0539 4.2 · 1146 0.8 · 1755 4.1
2 SA	0046 0.5 · 0642 4.2 · 1309 0.7 · 1915 4.3
17 SU	0008 1.0 · 0620 4.0 · 1230 0.9 · 1845 3.9
3 SU	0139 0.8 · 0801 4.0 · 1414 0.8 · 2036 4.1
18 M	0055 1.1 · 0727 3.7 · 1330 1.1 · 2010 3.7
4 M	0255 0.9 · 0839 3.8 · 1546 0.9 · 2200 4.1
19 TU	0230 1.3 · 0839 3.6 · 1547 1.1 · 2146 3.7
5 TU	0424 1.0 · 1041 3.9 · 1716 0.7 · 2315 4.3
20 W	0416 1.2 · 1004 3.7 · 1646 0.9 · 2256 4.0
6 W	0550 0.8 · 1149 4.2 · 1820 0.5
21 TH	0515 1.0 · 1125 4.0 · 1745 0.7 · 2349 4.3
7 TH	0015 4.5 · 0646 0.7 · 1238 4.4 · 1910 0.3
22 F	0606 0.8 · 1210 4.3 · 1829 0.5
8 F	0106 4.7 · 0726 0.6 · 1321 4.6 · 1948 0.2
23 SA	0031 4.7 · 0645 0.6 · 1247 4.6 · 1916 0.3
9 SA	0142 4.9 · 0802 0.5 · 1357 4.7 · ● 2027 0.2
24 SU	0109 4.9 · 0728 0.5 · 1326 4.9 · O 1959 0.2
10 SU	0219 4.9 · 0835 0.5 · 1436 4.8 · 2102 0.2
25 M	0148 5.1 · 0812 0.4 · 1406 5.0 · 2040 0.1
11 M	0256 4.9 · 0909 0.5 · 1509 4.8 · 2135 0.3
26 TU	0228 5.2 · 0855 0.3 · 1445 5.1 · 2123 0.1
12 TU	0327 4.8 · 0940 0.5 · 1546 4.8 · 2210 0.4
27 W	0310 5.1 · 0940 0.3 · 1528 5.1 · 2205 0.1
13 W	0402 4.7 · 1015 0.6 · 1617 4.7 · 2240 0.6
28 TH	0354 5.0 · 1026 0.3 · 1614 5.0 · 2251 0.2
14 TH	0436 4.5 · 1045 0.6 · 1648 4.5 · 2308 0.7
29 F	0438 4.8 · 1112 0.4 · 1658 4.9 · 2336 0.4
15 F	0507 4.4 · 1115 0.7 · 1726 4.3 · 2336 0.8
30 SA	0527 4.5 · 1200 0.5 · 1752 4.6
31 SU	0022 0.6 · 0625 4.2 · 1256 0.6 · 1906 4.3

NOVEMBER

Day	Time / m
1 M	0119 0.8 · 0740 4.0 · 1408 0.7 · 2020 4.1
16 TU	0025 1.0 · 0639 3.9 · 1254 0.9 · 1926 3.9
2 TU	0246 1.0 · 0901 3.8 · 1536 0.8 · 2139 4.1
17 W	0130 1.2 · 0806 3.8 · 1414 0.9 · 2045 3.9
3 W	0410 1.0 · 1020 3.9 · 1701 0.7 · 2255 4.3
18 TH	0255 1.2 · 0918 3.8 · 1550 0.8 · 2159 4.0
4 TH	0537 0.9 · 1125 4.1 · 1801 0.5 · 2355 4.5
19 F	0415 1.1 · 1030 4.0 · 1656 0.7 · 2306 4.3
5 F	0619 0.8 · 1218 4.4 · 1845 0.4
20 SA	0526 0.9 · 1127 4.3 · 1756 0.5 · 2357 4.7
6 SA	0046 4.6 · 0706 0.7 · 1257 4.5 · 1926 0.3
21 SU	0616 0.7 · 1215 4.6 · 1845 0.3
7 SU	0121 4.7 · 0741 0.6 · 1335 4.6 · 1959 0.3
22 M	0039 4.9 · 0700 0.5 · 1258 4.9 · 1931 0.2
8 M	0157 4.8 · 0812 0.5 · 1411 4.7 · ● 2036 0.4
23 TU	0123 5.0 · 0748 0.4 · 1341 5.0 · O 2016 0.1
9 TU	0231 4.8 · 0846 0.5 · 1445 4.8 · 2108 0.4
24 W	0208 5.1 · 0836 0.3 · 1425 5.1 · 2100 0.1
10 W	0305 4.7 · 0926 0.5 · 1517 4.7 · 2139 0.5
25 TH	0251 5.1 · 0922 0.3 · 1510 5.1 · 2146 0.2
11 TH	0337 4.7 · 0956 0.5 · 1552 4.7 · 2212 0.6
26 F	0336 4.9 · 1008 0.2 · 1556 5.0 · 2230 0.3
12 F	0410 4.5 · 1025 0.6 · 1626 4.5 · 2240 0.7
27 SA	0426 4.8 · 1056 0.3 · 1646 4.9 · 2316 0.5
13 SA	0442 4.4 · 1055 0.7 · 1658 4.4 · 2306 0.8
28 SU	0517 4.6 · 1146 0.3 · 1741 4.7
14 SU	0516 4.3 · 1125 0.7 · 1736 4.3 · 2340 0.9
29 M	0001 0.6 · 0612 4.3 · 1240 0.4 · 1845 4.4
15 M	0552 0.8 · 1206 0.8 · 1815 4.1
30 TU	0055 0.8 · 0718 4.1 · 1339 0.6 · 1955 4.2

DECEMBER

Day	Time / m
1 W	0205 1.0 · 0826 4.0 · 1444 0.7 · 2110 4.1
16 TH	0055 1.0 · 0720 4.0 · 1334 0.7 · 2000 4.1
2 TH	0325 1.1 · 0946 3.9 · 1627 0.7 · 2226 4.2
17 F	0205 1.0 · 0832 4.0 · 1456 0.7 · 2112 4.1
3 F	0444 1.0 · 1056 4.0 · 1725 0.6 · 2325 4.3
18 SA	0326 1.0 · 0946 4.1 · 1606 0.6 · 2219 4.3
4 SA	0555 0.9 · 1145 4.2 · 1818 0.5
19 SU	0424 0.9 · 1048 4.3 · 1710 0.5 · 2318 4.5
5 SU	0015 4.4 · 0636 0.8 · 1235 4.4 · 1858 0.5
20 M	0535 0.7 · 1142 4.5 · 1816 0.4
6 M	0058 4.5 · 0716 0.7 · 1310 4.5 · 1935 0.5
21 TU	0016 4.7 · 0639 0.6 · 1236 4.7 · 1907 0.3
7 TU	0135 4.6 · 0750 0.6 · 1349 4.6 · ● 2008 0.5
22 W	0103 4.8 · 0731 0.4 · 1323 4.9 · O 1956 0.2
8 W	0208 4.6 · 0826 0.5 · 1425 4.6 · 2039 0.5
23 TH	0148 4.9 · 0820 0.3 · 1409 5.0 · 2042 0.2
9 TH	0246 4.6 · 0859 0.5 · 1500 4.6 · 2116 0.6
24 F	0236 4.9 · 0908 0.2 · 1456 5.0 · 2126 0.3
10 F	0317 4.6 · 0936 0.5 · 1531 4.6 · 2151 0.6
25 SA	0325 4.9 · 0956 0.2 · 1545 5.0 · 2213 0.4
11 SA	0349 4.5 · 1016 0.5 · 1606 4.6 · 2215 0.7
26 SU	0412 4.8 · 1043 0.1 · 1633 4.9 · 2255 0.5
12 SU	0421 4.5 · 1046 0.5 · 1637 4.5 · 2250 0.8
27 M	0502 4.6 · 1129 0.2 · 1726 4.8 · 2342 0.6
13 M	0456 4.4 · 1115 0.6 · 1711 4.4 · 2325 0.8
28 TU	0555 4.5 · 1220 0.3 · 1821 4.6
14 TU	0535 4.3 · 1145 0.6 · 1755 4.3
29 W	0029 0.7 · 0648 4.3 · 1304 0.4 · 1919 4.3
15 W	0008 0.9 · 0620 4.1 · 1240 0.6 · 1845 4.2
30 TH	0126 0.9 · 0751 4.2 · 1410 0.6 · 2026 4.1
31 F	0224 1.0 · 0855 3.9 · 1515 0.7 · 2134 4.0

Chart Datum: 2·32 metres below Normaal Amsterdams Peil

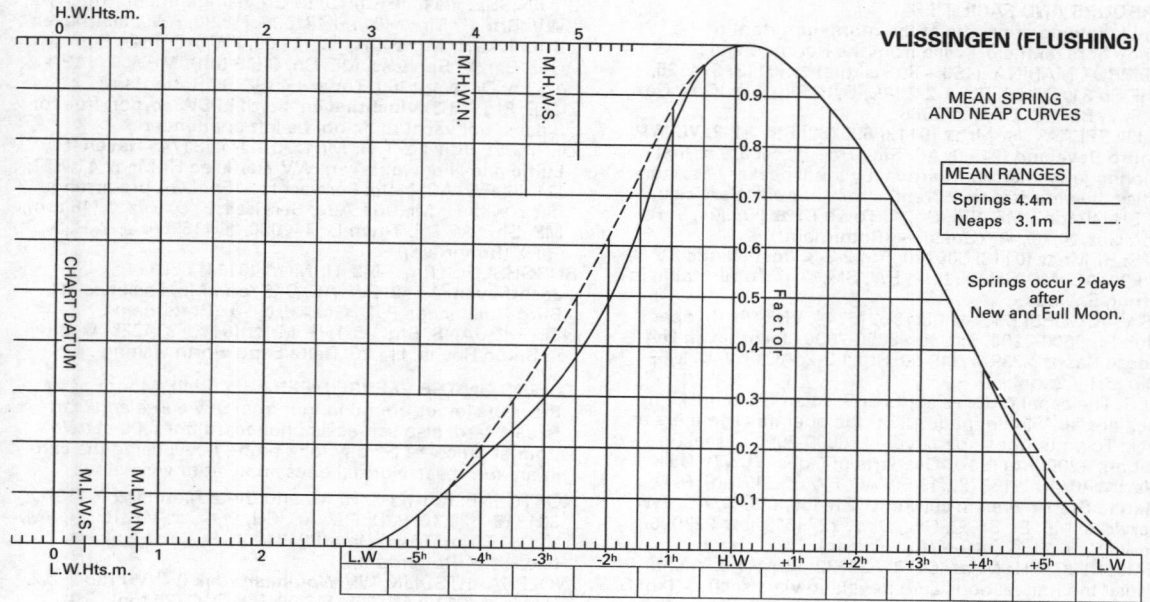

VLISSINGEN (FLUSHING)

MEAN SPRING AND NEAP CURVES

MEAN RANGES	
Springs	4.4m
Neaps	3.1m

Springs occur 2 days after New and Full Moon.

OOSTERSCHELDE   8-20-19

Zeeland 51°37'·30N 03°40'·20E (Roompotsluis)

CHARTS
AC 110, 120, 3371; Zeekaart 1448; DYCs 1805, 1801; Imray C30; Stanfords 19

TIDES
+0230 Dover Zone –0100; ML Sas van Goes 2·0, Zierikzee 1·8; Duration Sas van Goes 0615, Zierikzee 0640

Standard Port VLISSINGEN (←)

Times				Height (metres)			
High Water		Low Water		MHWS	MHWN	MLWN	MLWS
0300	0900	0400	1000	4·7	3·9	0·8	0·3
1500	2100	1600	2200				
Differences ROOMPOTSLUIS (outside)							
–0005	+0015	+0020	–0005	–1·1	–1·0	–0·2	0·0
ROOMPOTSLUIS (inside)							
+0115	+0105	+0045	+0105	–1·4	–1·1	–0·1	+0·1
WEMELDINGE							
+0150	+0120	+0055	+0115	–0·9	–0·6	–0·3	–0·1
KRAMMER LOCKS							
+0215	+0125	+0100	+0110	–1·0	–0·9	–0·3	–0·1
BERGSEDIEP LOCK							
+0145	+0125	+0105	+0115	–0·6	–0·4	–0·2	0·0

SHELTER
Good shelter in many hbrs at any tide; see facing page. Veerse Meer is a non-tidal waterway with moorings; enter from Oosterschelde via Zandkreekdam lock. The Schelde-Rijn Canal can be entered at Bergsediepsluis near Tholen; and the S Beveland Canal at Wemeldinge.

NAVIGATION
WPT WG1 SHM buoy, QG, 51°38'·05N 03°26'·30E at ent to Westgat/Oude Roompot buoyed chan. There are several offshore banks, see 8.20.5. Not advised to enter in strong W/NW'lies, and only from HW –6 to HW +1½ Zierikzee. All vessels must use the Roompotsluis (lock). The areas each side of the barrier are very dangerous due to strong tidal streams and many obstructions. Passage is prohib W of Roggenplaat.
Zeelandbrug has 12·2m clearance at centre of arch in buoyed chans. Clearance (m) is indicated on some of bridge supports. If wind < F 7, bascule bridge near N end lifts at H & H+30, Mon-Fri 0700-2130; Sat/Sun from 0900.

LIGHTS AND MARKS
See 8.20.4. Roompotsluis ldg lts 073·5° both Oc G 5s; Ent: N side FR, S side FG; depth 5m.

RADIO TELEPHONE
VHF-fitted craft must monitor Ch 68 in the Oosterschelde. Ch 68 broadcast local forecasts at H+15. *Verkeerspost Wemeldinge* Ch 68 MUST be called if entering canal; also for radar guidance in poor vis. Call *Zeelandbrug* Ch 18 for opening times and clearance. Locks: *Roompotsluis* Ch 18. *Krammersluizen* Ch 22 (H24). Zandreek *Sluis Kats* Ch 18; *Sluis Grevelingen* Ch 20; Bergse Diepsluis Ch 18.

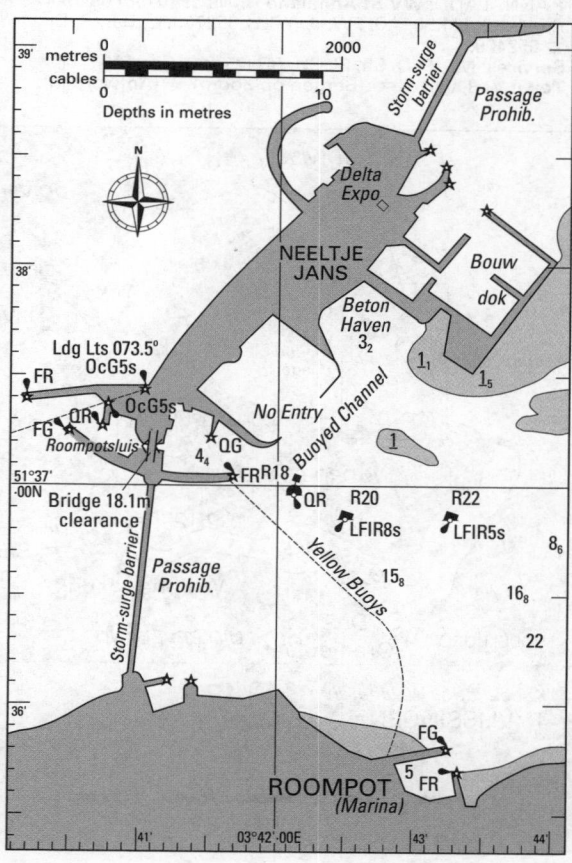

20

HARBOURS AND FACILITIES

The following are some of the more important of the many hbrs (anti-clockwise from the Roompotsluis):

ROOMPOT MARINA: (150 + 80 visitors) ☎ (0113) 374125, VHF Ch 31, f34.50, Rtg 1-2-2, AC, D, P, Slip, FW, Gas, Gaz, ▣, R, V, Bar, Ⓑ, Dr ☎ 372565.

COLIJNSPLAAT: Hr Mr ☎ (0113) 695762; Rtg 1-2-2, **YC WV Noord Beveland** f21.80, AC, Slip, FW, ▣; secure at first floating jetty and report arrival by loudspeaker or at hbr office; beware strong current across hbr ent; **Services:** P, D, BH (40 ton), ME, SM, Sh, ⚓. **Town** Dr ☎ 695304, V, R, Bar, Gaz, ✉, Ⓑ, ⇌ (Goes), ✈ (Rotterdam).

KATS: Hr Mr ☎ (0113) 600270; Rtg 2-3-3, **Rest Nautic BV** f20.00, AC, ME, BH (35 ton), FW, SM, ▣; uncomfortable in strong E winds.

SAS VAN GOES: Lock ☎ (0113) 216744, VHF Ch 18; opens Mon-Fri 0600-2200, Sat/Sun 0800-2000. **Jachthaven Het Goese Sas** 223944, f19.50, Rtg 1-3-2, AC, FW, D, ME, Slip, BH (12 ton), ▣.

GOES: The canal to Goes starts at Sas van Goes (lock); no facilities at Wilhelminadorp; bridge operates same hrs as lock. Town bridges open every H 0800-2000 in season, but not 1200. Rtg 1-4-1. Outskirts of Goes: **YC WV De Werf** ☎ (0113) 216372, f19.50, AC, FW, C (3½ ton), P, D; **Marina Stadshaven** in centre ☎ 216136, f19.50, AC, FW; **Services:** ME, El, Sh, ▣, Gaz, Dr ☎ 227451, Ⓗ ☎ 227000. **Town** V, R, ✉, Ⓑ, ⇌, ✈ (Antwerpen).

WEMELDINGE: Hr Mr ☎ (0113) 622022. Rtg 1-4-3. Yachts transit the Kanaal door Zuid Beveland via a section 1km E of the town. Use the former ent (via R/G tfc lts) to berth at the yacht hbrs in the Voorhaven or Binnenhaven. SHM buoy O21 to N of the E mole marks a shoal. **Services:** f26.20, ME, SM, AC, C (6·5 ton) ME, FW, P, D, ⚓, Dr 6227451, Ⓗ ☎ 6227000. **Town** V, R, ✉, Ⓑ, ⇌ (Goes), ✈ (Antwerpen).

YERSEKE: Leave to port the preferred chan buoy at hbr ent. Rtg 1-4-2. Hr Mr VHF Ch 09. Both marinas are S of the outer FV hbr: **Prinses Beatrix Haven** ☎ (0113) 571726, f24.10, 1·6m, FW, D, BH (10 ton); **Services:** SM, Sh, El, Dr ☎ 571444. **Town** V, R, ✉, Ⓑ, ⇌ (Kruiningen-Yerseke), ✈.

STAVENISSE: Hr Mr ☎ (0166) 692815. Rtg 3-4-3. **Marina** at end of hbr canal (access HW±3 for 1·8m draft), f12.10, Slip, FW, P & D (cans), Sh, C (4·5 ton), V, Gaz.

ST ANNALAND: **WV St Annaland** Hr Mr ☎ (0166) 652624, Rtg 1-2-2, f21.50, AC, FW, ⚓; **YC** ☎ 652783, ▣, Bar, R; Dr ☎ 652400.
Services: ME, P, D, Sh, El, CH, BH (25 ton), Gaz, BY.
Town V, R, Ⓑ, ✉, ⇌ (Bergen op Zoom), ✈ (Antwerpen).

BRUINISSE: via lock (Ch 20) to Grevelingenmeer. Rtg 1-1-2. **WV 'Bru'** Hr Mr ☎ (0111) 481506, f18.90, FW; **Jachthaven Bruinisse** Hr Mr ☎ 481485, f21.00, FW, AC, P, D, Slip, ▣, Gaz, Bar, V; **Services:** ME, Sh, SM, C (16 ton). MHW = NAP + 1.53m; Dr ☎ 481280. **Town** ✉, Ⓑ, ✈ (Rotterdam).

ZIJPE: Rtg 1-5-3. **Vluchthaven**, berth in SW corner; free for 3 days, but yacht must not be left unattended.

ZIERIKZEE: Rtg 1-2-1. Hr Mr ☎ (0111) 413174; **Haven 't Luitje** and **Nieuwe Haven: WV Zierikzee** Hr Mr ☎ 414877, f21.80, FW, AC; Note: For yachts >15m LOA pre-arrange berth with Hr Mr, Jun-Aug; **Services:** P, D, Gaz, C (18 ton), ME, Sh, SM, CH. **Town** Dr 412080, Ⓗ 416900, ▣, V, R, ✉, Ⓑ, ✈ (Rotterdam).

BURGHSLUIS: Rtg 1-5-3. Hr Mr ☎ (0111) 653114; **Jachthaven** f15.40, FW, AC, C (6 ton), ME. Facilities at Burg-Haamstede P, D, Gaz, ✉, Ⓑ, ✈ (Rotterdam).

NEELTJE JANS: Rtg 1-5-1. Hr Mr ☎ (0113) 374225. Ⓥ jetty in Beton Haven, f14.00. **Delta Expo** worth visiting.

TOWNS ON THE VEERSE MEER

(non-tidal). Moorings at the islets/jetties are no longer free. Buy a *Zeelandkaart* (smart card; also serves as phonecard) for f100 at a VVV (tourist office) or ✉; pay for a night, f7.50, using the card in an *automaat*. Normal dues apply at towns below:

KORTGENE: Rtg 1-1-2. Hr Mr and **Delta Marina** ☎ (0113) 301315, f29.40, P, D, FW, AC, CH, El, ▣, ⚓, ME, R, Sh, SM, V, C (16 ton). **Town** Dr ☎ 301319, V, R, Bar, ✉, Ⓑ, ⇌ (Goes), ✈ (Rotterdam).

WOLPHAARTSDIJK: **WV Wolphaartsdijk (WVW)** Rtg 1-2-2. Hr Mr ☎ (0113) 581565, f13.90, P & D, C (20 ton), ▣, ⚓; **Royal YC Belgique (RYCB)** ☎ 581496, f11.40, P & D, Sh.

DE PIET: Rtg 1-5-1. There are 72m of pontoons for small craft; 4 other little havens around De Omloop. Use card.

ARNEMUIDEN: Rtg 1-5-2. **Jachthaven Oranjeplaat** Hr Mr ☎ (0118) 501248, f14.70, Slip, P & D, C (12 ton), ⇌.

VEERE: Rtg 1-2-1. Yacht berths at: **Jachtclub Veere** in the Stadshaven, very busy, ☎ (0118) 501246, f22.00, FW, AC; **Marina Veere** on canal side, ☎ 501553, f22.00, FW, AC; **Jachtwerf Oostwatering** ☎ 501665, f20.00, FW, AC, ▣; **WV Arne**, at Oostwatering – report at Ⓥ jetty, ☎ 501484, f14.00, FW, AC. **Town** Dr ☎ 501271, V, R, Bar, ✉, Ⓑ, ⇌ (Middelburg), ✈ (Rotterdam).

MIDDELBURG: (This town is about 3M S of Veere on the Walcheren canal to Vlissingen). Rtg 1-4-1. No mooring in Kanaal door Walcheren. All bridges & Veere lock: Ch 22. **WV Arne** in the Dockhaven, ☎ (0118) 627180, f19.50, FW, AC, ME, El, Sh, SM, ▣; **Services:** D, Gaz, CH, BY, AC, Sh, Slip. **Town** Dr ☎ 612637; Ⓗ ☎ 625555; V, R, Bar, ✉, Ⓑ, ⇌, ✈ (Rotterdam).

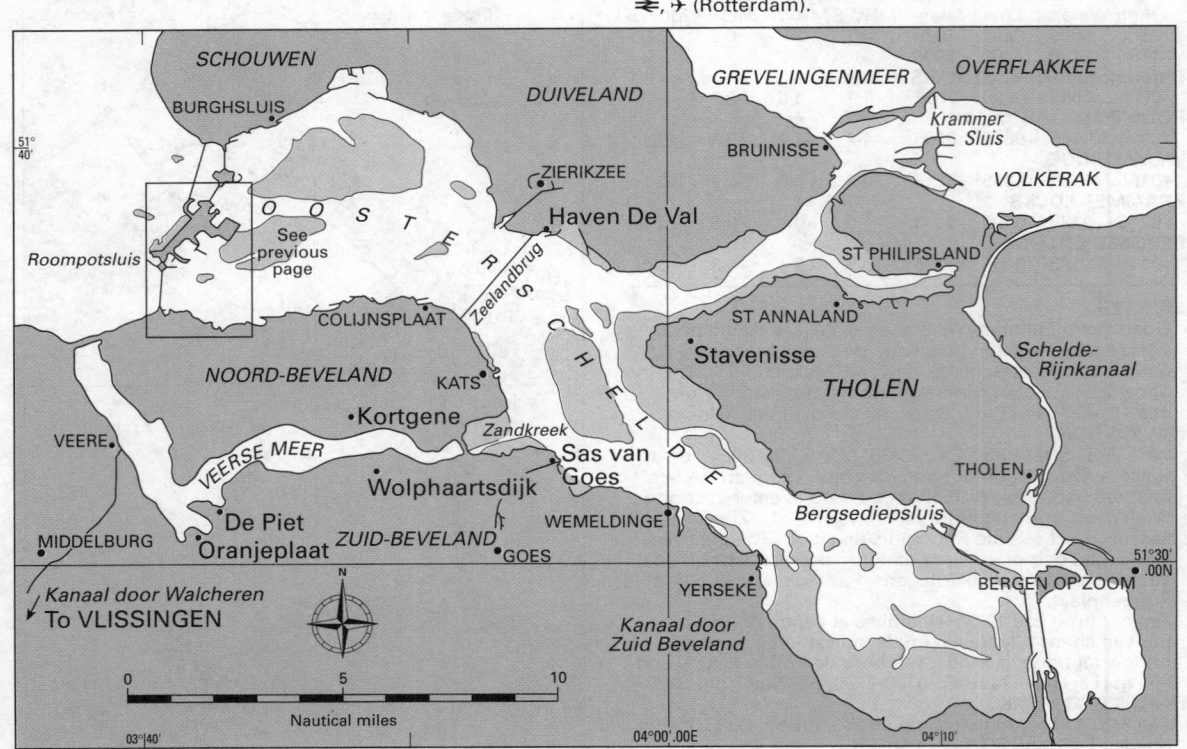

STELLENDAM & HELLEVOETSLUIS

8-20-20

Zuid Holland 51°49'·88N 04°02'·10E   Rtgs: (Stellendam) 4-5-3; (Hellevoetsluis) 1-2-1.

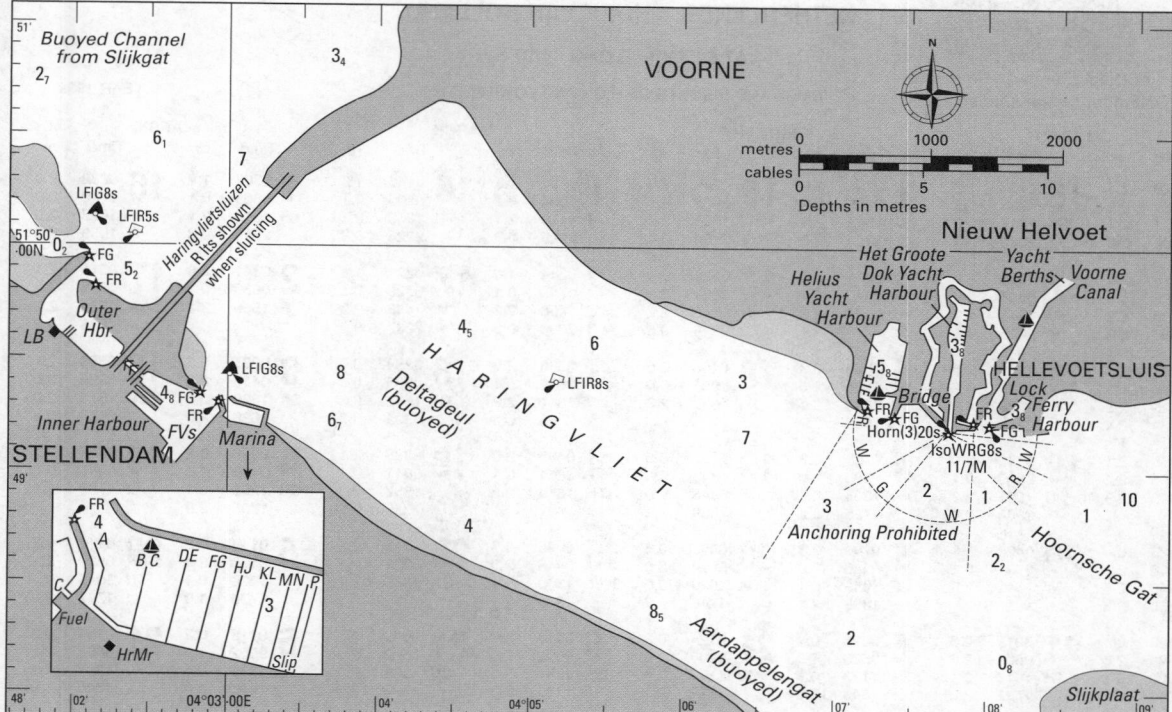

CHARTS
AC 2322; Zeekaart 1447, 1448; DYC 1801.6, 1807.6; Imray
C30; Stanfords 19

TIDES
+0300 Dover; ML 1·2; Duration 0510; Zone −0100

Standard Port VLISSINGEN (←)

Times				Height (metres)			
High Water		Low Water		MHWS	MHWN	MLWN	MLWS
0300	0900	0400	1000	4·7	3·9	0·8	0·3
1500	2100	1600	2200				

Differences HARINGVLIETSLUIZEN

+0015	+0015	+0015	−0020	−1·7	−1·6	−0·4	0·0

NOTE: Double LWs occur. The rise after the 1st LW is called
the Agger. Water levels on this coast are much affected by
weather. Prolonged NW gales can raise levels by up to 3m.

SHELTER
Good in Stellendam marina, beyond the lock and the
Inner hbr; or go 3M to Hellevoetsluis for one of the 3
yacht hbrs: Heliushaven (1·9-5m); via swing bridge into
Het Groote Dok (2-4m); and via lock into the Voorne canal
(2·8-4·8m).
In the Haringvliet there are about 6 large pontoons (*vlot*
on the DYC) equipped for barbecue picnics; but they are
prone to wash and only useable in calm conditions.
Within 10M upstream of Hellevoetsluis there are good
yacht facilities on the S bank at Middelharnis, Stad aan't
Haringvliet and Den Bommel; on the N bank at YC De Put
(Vuile Gat) and Hitsertse Kade. If bound for Rotterdam,
proceed via Spui or Dordrecht.

NAVIGATION
WPT Slijkgat SG SWM buoy, Iso 4s, 51°52'·00N 03°51'·50E,
290°/110° from/to Kwade Hoek lt, 5·0M. From the N, the
Gat van de Hawk chan to Stellendam lock is no longer
buoyed and is dangerous due to long-term WIP south of
Maasvlakte. It is therefore best to take the well buoyed/lit
Slijkgat chan along the Goeree shore, but it is dangerous
to enter Slijkgat in strong W/NW winds.
Beware a shoal about 5ca from the lock, marked by SHM
buoys. Keep clear of dam during sluicing.
Lock and lifting bridge operate H24 throughout the year.

Within the Haringvliet the 3M leg to Hellevoetsluis is well
marked by 10 PHM buoys (DG2 to DG18 and HV2); only
DG16 is lit as on chartlet. The SW side of the Haringvliet
has 6 SHM buoys (DG1-11) leading to the well buoyed,
but unlit Aardappelengat chan (S of Slijkplaat) and the
ent to Middelharnis.

LIGHTS AND MARKS
Haringvlietsluizen sluicing sigs: 3 Ⓡ in △, shown from
pier heads on dam; danger area marked by small Y buoys.
Hellevoetsluis lt Iso WRG 8s 16m 11/7M, W stone tr, R
cupola. G shore-275°, W275°-294°, R294°-316°, W316°-
036°, G036°-058°, W058°-095°, R096°-shore.

RADIO TELEPHONE
For lock call: *Goereese Sluis* VHF Ch 20. Hellevoetsluis Hr
Mr and Middelharnis Hr Mr: Ch 74.

TELEPHONE (Dial codes: 0187 Stellendam; 0181
Hellevoetsluis)
Hr Mr Stellendam 491000, Hellevoetsluis 330911;
☵ Rotterdam (010) 4298088 or Vlissingen (0118) 484600;
Police, Fire, Ambulance 112; Brit Consul (020) 6764343.

FACILITIES
STELLENDAM (0187)
Stellendam Marina ☎ 493769, ⛴ 493807, f30.00 (70/175
berths inc Ⓥ, eventually 400). FW, AC, Fuel, Slip, C, Bar,
R, V.
Town V, R, Bar, ✉ (2½ km), ✈ (Rotterdam).
HELLEVOETSLUIS (0181)
Marina, Het Groote Dok ☎ 312166, f20.00, swing bridge
opens every H in daylight from 0800 in summer; waiting
pontoons are downstream. El, Gaz, FW, ME, CH;
Helius Haven YC ☎ 315868, AB f18, P, D, FW;
Voorne Canal YC ☎ 315476, AB f18, P, D, FW;
Services: CH, El, ME.
Town P, D, V, R, Bar, ✉, Ⓑ, ✈ (Rotterdam).
Ferry: Hook of Holland-Harwich; or Rotterdam-Hull.

20

TIME ZONE –0100
(Dutch Standard Time) Subtract 1 hour for UT
For Dutch Summer Time add ONE hour in non-shaded areas

NETHERLANDS – HOEK VAN HOLLAND

LAT 51°59′N   LONG 4°07′E

TIMES AND HEIGHTS OF HIGH AND LOW WATERS   YEAR 1999

JANUARY

Day	Time	m	Day	Time	m
1 F	0128 / 0650 / 1351 / 1909	2.1 / 0.4 / 2.1 / 0.3	16 SA	0155 / 0735 / 1416 / 2030	1.9 / 0.3 / 2.0 / 0.4
2 SA O	0218 / 0729 / 1438 / 1956	2.1 / 0.3 / 2.2 / 0.3	17 SU ●	0236 / 0804 / 1445 / 2015	2.0 / 0.2 / 2.1 / 0.4
3 SU	0307 / 0815 / 1525 / 2324	2.1 / 0.2 / 2.3 / 0.4	18 M	0309 / 0829 / 1528 / 2250	2.0 / 0.2 / 2.2 / 0.4
4 M	0355 / 0855 / 1609	2.1 / 0.2 / 2.3	19 TU	0346 / 0859 / 1601 / 2334	2.0 / 0.1 / 2.2 / 0.4
5 TU	0025 / 0438 / 0946 / 1655	0.4 / 2.0 / 0.1 / 2.3	20 W	0425 / 0931 / 1641	2.0 / 0.1 / 2.2
6 W	0126 / 0525 / 1029 / 1741	0.4 / 2.0 / 0.1 / 2.2	21 TH	0015 / 0501 / 1016 / 1722	0.3 / 2.0 / 0.1 / 2.2
7 TH	0205 / 0609 / 1119 / 1829	0.4 / 1.9 / 0.1 / 2.1	22 F	0104 / 0541 / 1055 / 1801	0.3 / 1.9 / 0.0 / 2.2
8 F	0255 / 0656 / 1215 / 1919	0.4 / 1.9 / 0.1 / 2.0	23 SA	0144 / 0628 / 1139 / 1851	0.4 / 1.9 / 0.0 / 2.1
9 SA	0115 / 0746 / 1315 / 2016	0.4 / 1.8 / 0.1 / 1.9	24 SU	0227 / 0718 / 1235 / 1950	0.4 / 1.9 / 0.0 / 2.0
10 SU	0215 / 0835 / 1420 / 2115	0.4 / 1.7 / 0.2 / 1.8	25 M	0240 / 0820 / 1355 / 2056	0.4 / 1.8 / 0.0 / 1.9
11 M	0335 / 0940 / 1600 / 2225	0.4 / 1.6 / 0.2 / 1.7	26 TU	0255 / 0925 / 1506 / 2206	0.4 / 1.8 / 0.1 / 1.9
12 TU	0446 / 1054 / 1710 / 2346	0.4 / 1.6 / 0.3 / 1.7	27 W	0345 / 1035 / 1603 / 2320	0.4 / 1.8 / 0.2 / 1.8
13 W	0524 / 1206 / 1805	0.4 / 1.7 / 0.3	28 TH	0445 / 1148 / 1715	0.4 / 1.8 / 0.2
14 TH	0036 / 0624 / 1245 / 1910	1.8 / 0.3 / 1.8 / 0.3	29 F	0026 / 0549 / 1248 / 2050	1.9 / 0.4 / 1.9 / 0.3
15 F	0120 / 0704 / 1335 / 2000	1.8 / 0.3 / 1.9 / 0.4	30 SA	0125 / 0639 / 1338 / 2140	1.9 / 0.3 / 2.1 / 0.3
			31 SU O	0215 / 0725 / 1428 / 2236	2.0 / 0.2 / 2.1 / 0.3

FEBRUARY

Day	Time	m	Day	Time	m
1 M	0258 / 0805 / 1516 / 2320	2.0 / 0.2 / 2.2 / 0.3	16 TU ●	0249 / 0805 / 1505 / 2250	2.0 / 0.1 / 2.2 / 0.4
2 TU	0346 / 0846 / 1557	2.0 / 0.1 / 2.2	17 W	0325 / 0831 / 1545 / 2315	2.0 / 0.1 / 2.2 / 0.3
3 W	0005 / 0425 / 0919 / 1638	0.3 / 2.0 / 0.1 / 2.2	18 TH	0406 / 0905 / 1617	2.0 / 0.0 / 2.3
4 TH	0105 / 0505 / 1005 / 1725	0.3 / 2.0 / 0.1 / 2.2	19 F	0005 / 0445 / 0945 / 1659	0.3 / 2.0 / 0.0 / 2.2
5 F	0140 / 0546 / 1049 / 1806	0.3 / 2.0 / 0.1 / 2.1	20 SA	0055 / 0522 / 1029 / 1746	0.3 / 2.0 / 0.0 / 2.2
6 SA	0225 / 0626 / 1133 / 1846	0.4 / 1.9 / 0.1 / 2.0	21 SU	0124 / 0606 / 1119 / 1832	0.3 / 2.0 / 0.0 / 2.1
7 SU	0040 / 0705 / 1235 / 1936	0.4 / 1.9 / 0.1 / 1.9	22 M	0216 / 0655 / 1214 / 1926	0.3 / 1.9 / 0.1 / 2.0
8 M	0130 / 0750 / 1324 / 2020	0.3 / 1.8 / 0.1 / 1.8	23 TU	0207 / 0745 / 1345 / 2025	0.3 / 1.9 / 0.1 / 1.8
9 TU	0204 / 0845 / 1415 / 2115	0.3 / 1.7 / 0.2 / 1.7	24 W	0246 / 0900 / 1445 / 2140	0.3 / 1.8 / 0.1 / 1.7
10 W	0400 / 0950 / 1645 / 2215	0.3 / 1.6 / 0.3 / 1.6	25 TH	0324 / 1015 / 1605 / 2306	0.3 / 1.8 / 0.2 / 1.6
11 TH	0516 / 1105 / 1750 / 2344	0.3 / 1.6 / 0.3 / 1.6	26 F	0434 / 1135 / 1930	0.3 / 1.8 / 0.2
12 F	0605 / 1220 / 1850	0.3 / 1.7 / 0.3	27 SA	0014 / 0534 / 1245 / 2100	1.7 / 0.3 / 1.8 / 0.2
13 SA	0050 / 0656 / 1304 / 2010	1.7 / 0.2 / 1.8 / 0.3	28 SU	0119 / 0925 / 1336 / 2150	1.8 / 0.2 / 2.0 / 0.3
14 SU	0146 / 0720 / 1349 / 2147	1.8 / 0.2 / 1.9 / 0.3			
15 M	0209 / 0734 / 1425 / 2227	1.9 / 0.2 / 2.1 / 0.4			

MARCH

Day	Time	m	Day	Time	m
1 M	0204 / 1004 / 1418 / 2225	1.9 / 0.2 / 2.1 / 0.3	16 TU	0146 / 0705 / 1358 / 2225	1.8 / 0.1 / 2.1 / 0.3
2 TU O	0244 / 0745 / 1458 / 2306	1.9 / 0.1 / 2.2 / 0.3	17 W ●	0221 / 0729 / 1438 / 2237	1.9 / 0.1 / 2.2 / 0.3
3 W	0328 / 0821 / 1541 / 2345	2.0 / 0.1 / 2.2 / 0.3	18 TH	0258 / 0805 / 1517 / 2305	2.0 / 0.0 / 2.3 / 0.3
4 TH	0405 / 0854 / 1619	2.0 / 0.1 / 2.3	19 F	0338 / 0841 / 1557 / 2355	2.1 / -0.1 / 2.3 / 0.3
5 F	0035 / 0445 / 1300 / 1655	0.3 / 2.0 / 0.1 / 2.1	20 SA	0418 / 0921 / 1639	2.1 / -0.1 / 2.2
6 SA	0115 / 0515 / 1341 / 1735	0.3 / 2.0 / 0.1 / 2.0	21 SU	0035 / 0502 / 1005 / 1720	0.3 / 2.1 / 0.0 / 2.1
7 SU	0156 / 0549 / 1105 / 1809	0.3 / 2.0 / 0.1 / 1.9	22 M	0120 / 0542 / 1055 / 1807	0.2 / 2.1 / 0.0 / 2.0
8 M	0125 / 0626 / 1145 / 1846	0.3 / 1.9 / 0.1 / 1.9	23 TU	0156 / 0629 / 1310 / 1905	0.2 / 2.0 / 0.1 / 1.9
9 TU	0040 / 0706 / 1244 / 1926	0.2 / 1.9 / 0.1 / 1.8	24 W	0140 / 0721 / 1345 / 2005	0.2 / 1.9 / 0.0 / 1.7
10 W	0114 / 0744 / 1335 / 2026	0.2 / 1.8 / 0.2 / 1.7	25 TH	0205 / 0836 / 1456 / 2125	0.2 / 1.8 / 0.1 / 1.6
11 TH	0215 / 0905 / 1445 / 2130	0.2 / 1.6 / 0.3 / 1.6	26 F	0326 / 1000 / 1545 / 2245	0.2 / 1.7 / 0.2 / 1.5
12 F	0445 / 1020 / 1720 / 2245	0.2 / 1.6 / 0.3 / 1.5	27 SA	0425 / 1130 / 1920	0.2 / 1.8 / 0.2
13 SA	0546 / 1140 / 1820	0.2 / 1.6 / 0.3	28 SU	0010 / 0524 / 1235 / 2044	1.6 / 0.2 / 1.9 / 0.2
14 SU	0010 / 0615 / 1240 / 2007	1.6 / 0.2 / 1.8 / 0.3	29 M	0110 / 0911 / 1325 / 2140	1.7 / 0.1 / 2.0 / 0.2
15 M	0105 / 0645 / 1325 / 2135	1.7 / 0.2 / 1.9 / 0.3	30 TU	0153 / 0954 / 1400 / 2204	1.8 / 0.1 / 2.1 / 0.2
			31 W O	0235 / 1025 / 1445 / 2246	1.9 / 0.1 / 2.1 / 0.3

APRIL

Day	Time	m	Day	Time	m
1 TH	0308 / 0805 / 1519 / 2315	1.9 / 0.1 / 2.1 / 0.3	16 F ●	0232 / 0740 / 1452 / 1959	2.0 / 0.0 / 2.3 / 0.3
2 F	0341 / 0839 / 1556	2.0 / 0.1 / 2.1	17 SA	0315 / 0818 / 1533 / 2038	2.1 / -0.1 / 2.3 / 0.2
3 SA	0001 / 0415 / 1220 / 1628	0.2 / 2.0 / 0.1 / 2.0	18 SU	0356 / 0859 / 1615 / 2125	2.1 / 0.0 / 2.2 / 0.2
4 SU	0025 / 0449 / 1255 / 1705	0.2 / 2.0 / 0.1 / 2.0	19 M	0436 / 0946 / 1703	2.1 / 0.0 / 2.1
5 M	0116 / 0526 / 1320 / 1736	0.2 / 2.0 / 0.1 / 1.9	20 TU	0116 / 0520 / 1045 / 1747	0.2 / 2.1 / 0.1 / 2.0
6 TU	0115 / 0552 / 1330 / 1806	0.2 / 1.9 / 0.2 / 1.8	21 W	0155 / 0608 / 1307 / 1846	0.2 / 2.1 / 0.1 / 1.8
7 W	0145 / 0626 / 1224 / 1835	0.2 / 1.9 / 0.2 / 1.8	22 TH	0040 / 0705 / 1340 / 1943	0.1 / 2.0 / 0.1 / 1.7
8 TH	0040 / 0659 / 1330 / 1920	0.1 / 1.8 / 0.2 / 1.7	23 F	0144 / 0813 / 1425 / 2115	0.1 / 1.9 / 0.1 / 1.5
9 F	0135 / 0744 / 1414 / 2045	0.1 / 1.7 / 0.2 / 1.6	24 SA	0244 / 0950 / 1534 / 2240	0.1 / 1.8 / 0.2 / 1.5
10 SA	0234 / 0941 / 1650 / 2206	0.2 / 1.6 / 0.3 / 1.5	25 SU	0354 / 1116 / 1854 / 2344	0.1 / 1.8 / 0.2 / 1.6
11 SU	0505 / 1044 / 1800 / 2326	0.1 / 1.7 / 0.3 / 1.5	26 M	0459 / 1215 / 2005	0.1 / 1.9 / 0.2
12 M	0557 / 1159 / 1944	0.1 / 1.8 / 0.2	27 TU	0046 / 0825 / 1306 / 2115	1.7 / 0.1 / 2.0 / 0.1
13 TU	0025 / 0600 / 1244 / 2105	1.6 / 0.1 / 2.0 / 0.2	28 W	0135 / 0930 / 1345 / 2135	1.8 / 0.1 / 2.0 / 0.2
14 W	0116 / 0630 / 1335 / 2201	1.8 / 0.1 / 2.1 / 0.2	29 TH	0204 / 0714 / 1426 / 2226	1.9 / 0.1 / 2.0 / 0.2
15 TH	0156 / 0659 / 1411 / 2225	1.9 / 0.0 / 2.2 / 0.3	30 F O	0245 / 0755 / 1458 / 2256	1.9 / 0.1 / 2.0 / 0.2

Chart Datum: 0·84 metres below Normaal Amsterdams Peil

TIME ZONE –0100
(Dutch Standard Time)
Subtract 1 hour for UT

For Dutch Summer Time add ONE hour in non-shaded areas

NETHERLANDS – HOEK VAN HOLLAND

LAT 51°59′N   LONG 4°07′E

TIMES AND HEIGHTS OF HIGH AND LOW WATERS

YEAR **1999**

MAY

Day	Time	m	Day	Time	m
1 SA	0315 / 0824 / 1531 / 2317	2.0 / 0.2 / 2.0 / 0.2	16 SU	0249 / 0756 / 1512 / 2020	2.1 / 0.0 / 2.2 / 0.2
2 SU	0349 / 1120 / 1606 / 2357	2.0 / 0.2 / 2.0 / 0.1	17 M	0333 / 0839 / 1557 / 2101	2.2 / 0.1 / 2.1 / 0.1
3 M	0426 / 1155 / 1635	2.0 / 0.2 / 1.9	18 TU	0418 / 0925 / 1642 / 2149	2.2 / 0.1 / 2.0 / 0.1
4 TU	0027 / 0455 / 1235 / 1705	0.1 / 2.0 / 0.2 / 1.9	19 W	0503 / 1324 / 1736	2.2 / 0.1 / 1.9
5 W	0110 / 0521 / 1305 / 1740	0.1 / 2.0 / 0.2 / 1.8	20 TH	0150 / 0615 / 1414 / 1829	0.1 / 2.1 / 0.2 / 1.8
6 TH	0140 / 0556 / 1350 / 1809	0.1 / 1.9 / 0.2 / 1.8	21 F	0000 / 0648 / 1325 / 1946	0.0 / 2.0 / 0.2 / 1.7
7 F	0000 / 0636 / 1400 / 1851	0.1 / 1.9 / 0.3 / 1.7	22 SA	0104 / 0754 / 1404 / 2044	0.0 / 1.9 / 0.2 / 1.6
8 SA	0055 / 0715 / 1417 / 1954	0.1 / 1.8 / 0.3 / 1.6	23 SU	0214 / 0915 / 1715 / 2216	0.0 / 1.8 / 0.2 / 1.5
9 SU	0155 / 0855 / 1625 / 2136	0.1 / 1.7 / 0.3 / 1.5	24 M	0324 / 1034 / 1826 / 2320	0.0 / 1.8 / 0.2 / 1.6
10 M	0304 / 1005 / 1730 / 2235	0.1 / 1.8 / 0.3 / 1.6	25 TU	0434 / 1146 / 1924	0.1 / 1.9 / 0.3
11 TU	0404 / 1114 / 1857 / 2346	0.1 / 1.9 / 0.2 / 1.7	26 W	0015 / 0524 / 1236 / 2030	1.7 / 0.1 / 1.9 / 0.2
12 W	0505 / 1215 / 2035	0.1 / 2.0 / 0.2	27 TH	0059 / 0615 / 1315 / 2114	1.8 / 0.1 / 2.0 / 0.2
13 TH	0038 / 0549 / 1259 / 2125	1.8 / 0.0 / 2.1 / 0.2	28 F	0139 / 0704 / 1355 / 2200	1.8 / 0.2 / 2.0 / 0.2
14 F	0122 / 0636 / 1345 / 1859	1.9 / 0.0 / 2.2 / 0.2	29 SA	0214 / 0800 / 1435 / 2010	1.9 / 0.2 / 2.0 / 0.2
15 SA ●	0207 / 0711 / 1428 / 1940	2.0 / 0.0 / 2.2 / 0.2	30 SU O	0255 / 0920 / 1505 / 2100	1.9 / 0.2 / 2.0 / 0.2
			31 M	0325 / 1030 / 1546 / 2334	2.0 / 0.2 / 1.9 / 0.1

JUNE

Day	Time	m	Day	Time	m
1 TU	0359 / 1124 / 1615	2.0 / 0.2 / 1.9	16 W	0400 / 1220 / 1631 / 2136	2.2 / 0.2 / 1.9 / 0.1
2 W	0004 / 0436 / 1210 / 1645	0.1 / 2.0 / 0.2 / 1.9	17 TH	0448 / 1304 / 1718 / 2230	2.2 / 0.2 / 1.9 / 0.0
3 TH	0035 / 0505 / 1255 / 1715	0.1 / 2.0 / 0.2 / 1.8	18 F	0538 / 1410 / 1816 / 2330	2.1 / 0.2 / 1.8 / 0.0
4 F	0114 / 0538 / 1341 / 1755	0.0 / 2.0 / 0.3 / 1.8	19 SA	0635 / 1500 / 1905	2.1 / 0.3 / 1.7
5 SA	0205 / 0615 / 1405 / 1840	0.0 / 1.9 / 0.3 / 1.7	20 SU	0029 / 0735 / 1556 / 2010	0.0 / 2.0 / 0.3 / 1.7
6 SU	0020 / 0658 / 1505 / 1929	0.0 / 1.9 / 0.3 / 1.7	21 M	0134 / 0840 / 1645 / 2126	0.0 / 1.9 / 0.3 / 1.6
7 M	0124 / 0805 / 1550 / 2045	0.0 / 1.9 / 0.3 / 1.6	22 TU	0244 / 0955 / 1746 / 2225	0.0 / 1.8 / 0.3 / 1.6
8 TU	0225 / 0937 / 1700 / 2200	0.0 / 1.9 / 0.3 / 1.6	23 W	0354 / 1115 / 1650 / 2336	0.1 / 1.8 / 0.3 / 1.7
9 W	0325 / 1040 / 1820 / 2306	0.0 / 1.9 / 0.3 / 1.7	24 TH	0504 / 1205 / 1740	0.1 / 1.8 / 0.3
10 TH	0425 / 1135 / 1937	0.0 / 2.0 / 0.3	25 F	0025 / 0555 / 1244 / 1836	1.7 / 0.2 / 1.9 / 0.2
11 F	0005 / 0514 / 1236 / 2050	1.8 / 0.0 / 2.1 / 0.2	26 SA	0115 / 0654 / 1336 / 1904	1.8 / 0.2 / 1.9 / 0.2
12 SA	0055 / 0610 / 1321 / 1839	1.9 / 0.0 / 2.1 / 0.2	27 SU	0156 / 0750 / 1416 / 1950	1.8 / 0.3 / 1.9 / 0.2
13 SU ●	0142 / 0655 / 1409 / 1919	2.0 / 0.1 / 2.1 / 0.2	28 M O	0225 / 0840 / 1445 / 2020	1.9 / 0.3 / 1.9 / 0.1
14 M	0232 / 0745 / 1456 / 2001	2.1 / 0.1 / 2.1 / 0.1	29 TU	0306 / 0944 / 1519 / 2035	2.0 / 0.3 / 1.9 / 0.1
15 TU	0315 / 0830 / 1545 / 2045	2.2 / 0.2 / 2.0 / 0.1	30 W	0335 / 1050 / 1551 / 2104	2.0 / 0.3 / 1.9 / 0.1

JULY

Day	Time	m	Day	Time	m
1 TH	0408 / 1135 / 1625 / 2145	2.0 / 0.3 / 1.9 / 0.1	16 F	0436 / 1255 / 1706 / 2205	2.2 / 0.3 / 1.9 / 0.0
2 F	0445 / 1235 / 1705 / 2224	2.0 / 0.3 / 1.9 / 0.1	17 SA	0525 / 1344 / 1755 / 2255	2.2 / 0.3 / 1.9 / 0.0
3 SA	0518 / 1315 / 1739 / 2253	2.0 / 0.3 / 1.8 / 0.0	18 SU	0616 / 1434 / 1840 / 2344	2.1 / 0.3 / 1.8 / 0.0
4 SU	0559 / 1406 / 1826 / 2339	2.0 / 0.3 / 1.8 / 0.0	19 M	0705 / 1525 / 1925	2.0 / 0.4 / 1.8
5 M	0645 / 1445 / 1909	2.0 / 0.3 / 1.7	20 TU	0055 / 0756 / 1355 / 2020	0.0 / 1.9 / 0.4 / 1.7
6 TU	0034 / 0745 / 1530 / 2016	0.0 / 2.0 / 0.3 / 1.7	21 W	0154 / 0856 / 1455 / 2115	0.1 / 1.8 / 0.3 / 1.7
7 W	0145 / 0855 / 1520 / 2114	0.0 / 2.0 / 0.4 / 1.7	22 TH	0320 / 0954 / 1605 / 2234	0.1 / 1.7 / 0.3 / 1.6
8 TH	0244 / 1006 / 1545 / 2224	0.0 / 2.0 / 0.3 / 1.8	23 F	0435 / 1126 / 1715 / 2345	0.2 / 1.7 / 0.3 / 1.7
9 F	0344 / 1108 / 1656 / 2335	0.0 / 2.0 / 0.3 / 1.8	24 SA	0534 / 1213 / 1755	0.2 / 1.7 / 0.2
10 SA	0455 / 1211 / 1734	0.1 / 2.0 / 0.3	25 SU	0046 / 0635 / 1304 / 1844	1.7 / 0.3 / 1.8 / 0.2
11 SU	0035 / 0555 / 1305 / 1825	1.9 / 0.1 / 2.0 / 0.2	26 M	0136 / 0724 / 1344 / 1936	1.8 / 0.3 / 1.8 / 0.2
12 M	0126 / 0646 / 1355 / 1909	2.0 / 0.2 / 2.0 / 0.2	27 TU	0210 / 0800 / 1425 / 1954	1.9 / 0.4 / 1.9 / 0.2
13 TU ●	0215 / 0729 / 1446 / 2014	2.1 / 0.2 / 2.0 / 0.1	28 W O	0239 / 0830 / 1454 / 2100	2.0 / 0.4 / 1.9 / 0.1
14 W	0305 / 1115 / 1531 / 2036	2.2 / 0.3 / 2.0 / 0.1	29 TH	0315 / 0834 / 1536 / 2043	2.1 / 0.4 / 2.0 / 0.1
15 TH	0347 / 1205 / 1617 / 2115	2.2 / 0.3 / 2.0 / 0.1	30 F	0348 / 1126 / 1609 / 2115	2.1 / 0.4 / 2.0 / 0.1
			31 SA	0425 / 1216 / 1645 / 2155	2.2 / 0.4 / 1.9 / 0.1

AUGUST

Day	Time	m	Day	Time	m
1 SU	0505 / 1256 / 1726 / 2224	2.1 / 0.3 / 1.9 / 0.0	16 M	0546 / 1416 / 1806 / 2316	2.1 / 0.4 / 1.9 / 0.1
2 M	0541 / 1346 / 1806 / 2316	2.1 / 0.3 / 1.9 / 0.0	17 TU	0625 / 1455 / 1845	2.0 / 0.4 / 1.9
3 TU	0625 / 1426 / 1848	2.1 / 0.4 / 1.9	18 W	0010 / 0709 / 1310 / 1936	0.1 / 1.9 / 0.4 / 1.8
4 W	0006 / 0715 / 1500 / 1934	0.0 / 2.0 / 0.4 / 1.8	19 TH	0104 / 0805 / 1400 / 2036	0.2 / 1.8 / 0.3 / 1.7
5 TH	0104 / 0815 / 1447 / 2056	0.0 / 2.0 / 0.4 / 1.8	20 F	0205 / 0855 / 1540 / 2125	0.2 / 1.7 / 0.3 / 1.7
6 F	0235 / 0926 / 1536 / 2206	0.1 / 1.9 / 0.4 / 1.8	21 SA	0407 / 0954 / 1656 / 2244	0.3 / 1.6 / 0.3 / 1.6
7 SA	0334 / 1035 / 1630 / 2316	0.1 / 1.9 / 0.4 / 1.8	22 SU	0526 / 1146 / 1735	0.3 / 1.6 / 0.3
8 SU	0444 / 1156 / 1724	0.2 / 1.8 / 0.3	23 M	0016 / 0620 / 1240 / 1830	1.7 / 0.4 / 1.7 / 0.2
9 M	0015 / 0543 / 1255 / 1815	1.9 / 0.3 / 1.9 / 0.2	24 TU	0106 / 0710 / 1325 / 1910	1.8 / 0.4 / 1.8 / 0.2
10 TU	0112 / 0920 / 1346 / 1900	2.0 / 0.3 / 1.9 / 0.2	25 W	0146 / 0830 / 1406 / 1924	1.9 / 0.4 / 1.9 / 0.2
11 W ●	0206 / 1010 / 1435 / 1935	2.1 / 0.4 / 2.0 / 0.2	26 TH	0219 / 0750 / 1435 / 1944	2.1 / 0.5 / 2.0 / 0.2
12 TH	0251 / 1106 / 1518 / 2020	2.2 / 0.4 / 2.0 / 0.1	27 F O	0248 / 0803 / 1509 / 2020	2.2 / 0.5 / 2.0 / 0.1
13 F	0336 / 1145 / 1605 / 2100	2.2 / 0.4 / 2.0 / 0.1	28 SA	0325 / 0840 / 1545 / 2050	2.2 / 0.5 / 2.1 / 0.1
14 SA	0415 / 1235 / 1645 / 2139	2.2 / 0.4 / 2.0 / 0.1	29 SU	0400 / 1145 / 1621 / 2125	2.3 / 0.4 / 2.1 / 0.1
15 SU	0458 / 1325 / 1725 / 2225	2.2 / 0.4 / 2.0 / 0.1	30 M	0439 / 1230 / 1701 / 2205	2.3 / 0.4 / 2.0 / 0.1
			31 TU	0522 / 1316 / 1738 / 2245	2.2 / 0.4 / 2.0 / 0.1

20

Chart Datum: 0·84 metres below Normaal Amsterdams Peil

TIME ZONE –0100
(Dutch Standard Time)
Subtract 1 hour for UT

For Dutch Summer Time add
ONE hour in non-shaded areas

NETHERLANDS – HOEK VAN HOLLAND

LAT 51°59′N LONG 4°07′E

TIMES AND HEIGHTS OF HIGH AND LOW WATERS

YEAR **1999**

SEPTEMBER

Day	Time	m	Day	Time	m
1 W	0605 / 1355 / 1825 / 2339	2.2 / 0.4 / 2.0 / 0.1	16 TH	0629 / 1155 / 1845	1.9 / 0.4 / 1.9
2 TH	0649 / 1420 / 1916	2.1 / 0.4 / 2.0	17 F	0036 / 0703 / 1255 / 1935	0.3 / 1.8 / 0.3 / 1.8
3 F	0054 / 0750 / 1417 / 2015	0.1 / 1.9 / 0.4 / 1.9	18 SA	0114 / 0800 / 1400 / 2046	0.3 / 1.7 / 0.3 / 1.7
4 SA	0214 / 0900 / 1454 / 2129	0.2 / 1.8 / 0.4 / 1.8	19 SU	0225 / 0911 / 1625 / 2156	0.4 / 1.6 / 0.3 / 1.6
5 SU	0330 / 1013 / 1610 / 2256	0.2 / 1.7 / 0.4 / 1.8	20 M	0445 / 1014 / 1714 / 2314	0.4 / 1.6 / 0.3 / 1.7
6 M	0434 / 1146 / 1704	0.3 / 1.7 / 0.4	21 TU	0545 / 1155 / 1816	0.4 / 1.6 / 0.3
7 TU	0004 / 0826 / 1245 / 2035	1.9 / 0.3 / 1.8 / 0.3	22 W	0036 / 0700 / 1245 / 1834	1.8 / 0.4 / 1.7 / 0.3
8 W	0105 / 0926 / 1339 / 1841	2.1 / 0.3 / 1.9 / 0.2	23 TH	0115 / 0910 / 1335 / 1855	2.0 / 0.4 / 1.9 / 0.2
9 TH ●	0157 / 1006 / 1425 / 1921	2.2 / 0.4 / 2.0 / 0.2	24 F	0149 / 0957 / 1408 / 1913	2.1 / 0.4 / 2.0 / 0.2
10 F	0236 / 1025 / 1500 / 1955	2.2 / 0.4 / 2.0 / 0.2	25 SA O	0221 / 0739 / 1441 / 1945	2.3 / 0.5 / 2.1 / 0.1
11 SA	0315 / 1126 / 1545 / 2036	2.3 / 0.5 / 2.1 / 0.1	26 SU	0257 / 0809 / 1517 / 2022	2.4 / 0.4 / 2.2 / 0.1
12 SU	0355 / 1155 / 1618 / 2115	2.3 / 0.5 / 2.1 / 0.2	27 M	0337 / 0846 / 1555 / 2100	2.4 / 0.4 / 2.2 / 0.1
13 M	0436 / 1245 / 1655 / 2156	2.2 / 0.4 / 2.1 / 0.2	28 TU	0415 / 0920 / 1635 / 2139	2.4 / 0.4 / 2.2 / 0.1
14 TU	0515 / 1340 / 1735 / 2234	2.1 / 0.4 / 2.0 / 0.2	29 W	0456 / 0959 / 1717 / 2228	2.3 / 0.4 / 2.2 / 0.1
15 W	0556 / 1054 / 1809 / 2324	2.0 / 0.4 / 2.0 / 0.3	30 TH	0541 / 1045 / 1802 / 2326	2.2 / 0.4 / 2.1 / 0.2

OCTOBER

Day	Time	m	Day	Time	m
1 F	0627 / 1144 / 1849	2.0 / 0.4 / 2.1	16 SA	0625 / 1216 / 1846	1.9 / 0.3 / 1.9
2 SA	0130 / 0725 / 1344 / 1955	0.2 / 1.9 / 0.4 / 2.0	17 SU	0100 / 0655 / 1316 / 1923	0.4 / 1.8 / 0.3 / 1.8
3 SU	0226 / 0833 / 1446 / 2104	0.3 / 1.7 / 0.4 / 1.8	18 M	0144 / 0755 / 1404 / 2110	0.5 / 1.7 / 0.3 / 1.7
4 M	0326 / 1005 / 1545 / 2245	0.4 / 1.6 / 0.4 / 1.8	19 TU	0417 / 0936 / 1644 / 2236	0.4 / 1.6 / 0.3 / 1.7
5 TU	0635 / 1135 / 1654 / 2359	0.4 / 1.7 / 0.3 / 2.0	20 W	0524 / 1044 / 1735 / 2346	0.5 / 1.6 / 0.3 / 1.9
6 W	0815 / 1233 / 2030	0.3 / 1.8 / 0.3	21 TH	0640 / 1205 / 1820	0.5 / 1.7 / 0.3
7 TH	0053 / 0916 / 1325 / 2124	2.1 / 0.3 / 1.9 / 0.2	22 F	0036 / 0825 / 1251 / 1815	2.0 / 0.4 / 1.9 / 0.3
8 F	0139 / 0935 / 1405 / 1908	2.2 / 0.4 / 2.0 / 0.2	23 SA	0115 / 0945 / 1331 / 1845	2.2 / 0.4 / 2.0 / 0.2
9 SA ●	0215 / 1015 / 1445 / 1938	2.2 / 0.4 / 2.1 / 0.2	24 SU O	0151 / 0704 / 1411 / 1920	2.3 / 0.4 / 2.1 / 0.1
10 SU	0257 / 1056 / 1521 / 2014	2.3 / 0.5 / 2.1 / 0.2	25 M	0230 / 0741 / 1450 / 1956	2.4 / 0.4 / 2.2 / 0.1
11 M	0335 / 1124 / 1558 / 2055	2.2 / 0.5 / 2.1 / 0.3	26 TU	0313 / 0815 / 1533 / 2038	2.4 / 0.4 / 2.3 / 0.1
12 TU	0411 / 1226 / 1628 / 2124	2.2 / 0.4 / 2.1 / 0.3	27 W	0356 / 0900 / 1613 / 2119	2.4 / 0.4 / 2.3 / 0.1
13 W	0450 / 1306 / 1706 / 2205	2.1 / 0.4 / 2.1 / 0.3	28 TH	0437 / 0939 / 1655 / 2209	2.3 / 0.3 / 2.3 / 0.2
14 TH	0522 / 1030 / 1738 / 2255	2.0 / 0.4 / 2.1 / 0.4	29 F	0521 / 1029 / 1743 / 2303	2.1 / 0.3 / 2.2 / 0.3
15 F	0555 / 1115 / 1809 / 2350	2.0 / 0.3 / 2.0 / 0.4	30 SA	0608 / 1124 / 1831	2.0 / 0.3 / 2.1
			31 SU	0105 / 0704 / 1244 / 1935	0.3 / 1.8 / 0.3 / 2.0

NOVEMBER

Day	Time	m	Day	Time	m
1 M	0154 / 0825 / 1355 / 2055	0.4 / 1.7 / 0.3 / 1.9	16 TU	0134 / 0725 / 1336 / 1955	0.5 / 1.8 / 0.2 / 1.8
2 TU	0259 / 0955 / 1515 / 2224	0.4 / 1.6 / 0.3 / 1.9	17 W	0240 / 0850 / 1435 / 2146	0.5 / 1.7 / 0.3 / 1.8
3 W	0615 / 1104 / 1845 / 2345	0.4 / 1.7 / 0.3 / 2.0	18 TH	0454 / 1006 / 1534 / 2244	0.5 / 1.7 / 0.3 / 1.9
4 TH	0756 / 1215 / 1955	0.4 / 1.8 / 0.2	19 F	0610 / 1116 / 1634 / 2344	0.5 / 1.7 / 0.3 / 2.1
5 F	0033 / 0835 / 1306 / 2105	2.1 / 0.3 / 1.9 / 0.2	20 SA	0806 / 1249 / 1730	0.4 / 1.9 / 0.3
6 SA	0119 / 0936 / 1345 / 1849	2.2 / 0.4 / 2.0 / 0.3	21 SU	0040 / 0905 / 1259 / 1816	2.2 / 0.4 / 2.0 / 0.3
7 SU	0159 / 0945 / 1425 / 1924	2.2 / 0.4 / 2.1 / 0.3	22 M	0125 / 0646 / 1345 / 1851	2.3 / 0.4 / 2.2 / 0.1
8 M ●	0235 / 1024 / 1459 / 2004	2.2 / 0.4 / 2.1 / 0.3	23 TU O	0207 / 0719 / 1427 / 1935	2.4 / 0.4 / 2.3 / 0.1
9 TU	0315 / 1116 / 1531 / 2035	2.2 / 0.4 / 2.2 / 0.4	24 W	0252 / 0755 / 1512 / 2018	2.3 / 0.3 / 2.3 / 0.2
10 W	0349 / 1150 / 1605 / 2330	2.1 / 0.3 / 2.2 / 0.4	25 TH	0333 / 0839 / 1553 / 2105	2.3 / 0.3 / 2.3 / 0.2
11 TH	0425 / 1215 / 1639	2.1 / 0.3 / 2.1	26 F	0419 / 0926 / 1639 / 2156	2.2 / 0.2 / 2.3 / 0.3
12 F	0014 / 0456 / 1010 / 1708	0.4 / 2.0 / 0.3 / 2.1	27 SA	0505 / 1015 / 1725 / 2255	2.1 / 0.2 / 2.3 / 0.4
13 SA	0056 / 0525 / 1044 / 1746	0.4 / 2.0 / 0.3 / 2.1	28 SU	0555 / 1115 / 1819	2.0 / 0.2 / 2.2
14 SU	0115 / 0555 / 1124 / 1815	0.5 / 1.9 / 0.2 / 2.0	29 M	0100 / 0615 / 1225 / 1919	0.4 / 1.9 / 0.2 / 2.1
15 M	0040 / 0636 / 1230 / 1855	0.5 / 1.9 / 0.2 / 1.9	30 TU	0135 / 0805 / 1329 / 2035	0.4 / 1.8 / 0.2 / 2.0

DECEMBER

Day	Time	m	Day	Time	m
1 W	0234 / 0915 / 1445 / 2155	0.5 / 1.7 / 0.2 / 1.9	16 TH	0220 / 0810 / 1344 / 2050	0.5 / 1.8 / 0.1 / 1.9
2 TH	0544 / 1046 / 1815 / 2304	0.4 / 1.7 / 0.2 / 2.0	17 F	0310 / 0915 / 1444 / 2205	0.5 / 1.7 / 0.2 / 2.0
3 F	0655 / 1146 / 1905	0.4 / 1.8 / 0.2	18 SA	0355 / 1036 / 1556 / 2305	0.5 / 1.8 / 0.2 / 2.0
4 SA	0004 / 0810 / 1235 / 2014	2.0 / 0.4 / 1.9 / 0.3	19 SU	0450 / 1136 / 1644	0.5 / 1.9 / 0.2
5 SU	0055 / 0835 / 1319 / 1845	2.1 / 0.4 / 2.0 / 0.3	20 M	0005 / 0535 / 1236 / 1745	2.1 / 0.4 / 2.0 / 0.3
6 M	0139 / 0945 / 1359 / 1940	2.1 / 0.4 / 2.0 / 0.3	21 TU	0056 / 0614 / 1318 / 1831	2.2 / 0.4 / 2.1 / 0.2
7 TU ●	0219 / 0750 / 1435 / 2030	2.1 / 0.4 / 2.1 / 0.4	22 W O	0146 / 0659 / 1407 / 1919	2.2 / 0.3 / 2.2 / 0.2
8 W	0255 / 0825 / 1508 / 2150	2.1 / 0.3 / 2.1 / 0.4	23 TH	0235 / 0746 / 1456 / 2005	2.2 / 0.3 / 2.3 / 0.3
9 TH	0329 / 0844 / 1545 / 2250	2.1 / 0.3 / 2.1 / 0.4	24 F	0319 / 0825 / 1537 / 2048	2.2 / 0.2 / 2.3 / 0.3
10 F	0406 / 0914 / 1614 / 2340	2.1 / 0.3 / 2.1 / 0.4	25 SA	0407 / 0916 / 1625	2.1 / 0.2 / 2.3
11 SA	0435 / 0949 / 1656	2.0 / 0.2 / 2.1	26 SU	0046 / 0455 / 0959 / 1712	0.4 / 2.0 / 0.1 / 2.3
12 SU	0015 / 0510 / 1030 / 1726	0.4 / 2.0 / 0.2 / 2.1	27 M	0125 / 0546 / 1056 / 1806	0.4 / 2.0 / 0.1 / 2.2
13 M	0105 / 0534 / 1105 / 1759	0.4 / 1.9 / 0.2 / 2.1	28 TU	0215 / 0635 / 1156 / 1854	0.4 / 1.9 / 0.1 / 2.1
14 TU	0135 / 0615 / 1155 / 1839	0.5 / 1.9 / 0.1 / 2.0	29 W	0325 / 0735 / 1306 / 1959	0.4 / 1.8 / 0.1 / 2.0
15 W	0210 / 0706 / 1245 / 1936	0.5 / 1.8 / 0.1 / 2.0	30 TH	0154 / 0835 / 1355 / 2110	0.4 / 1.8 / 0.1 / 1.9
			31 F	0305 / 0950 / 1520 / 2225	0.4 / 1.7 / 0.2 / 1.9

Chart Datum: 0·84 metres below Normaal Amsterdams Peil

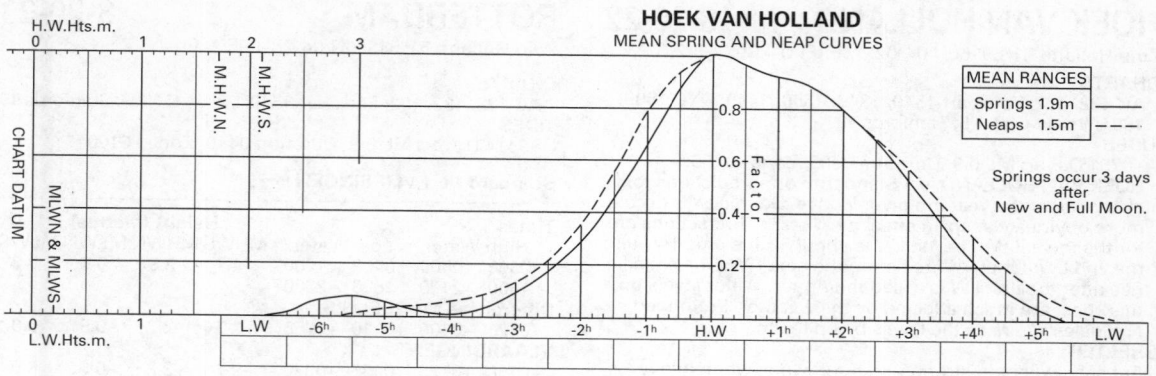

HOEK VAN HOLLAND
MEAN SPRING AND NEAP CURVES

MEAN RANGES	
Springs 1.9m	——
Neaps 1.5m	- - - -

Springs occur 3 days
after
New and Full Moon.

VTS IN THE MAAS PRECAUTIONARY AREA AND TSS   8-20-21

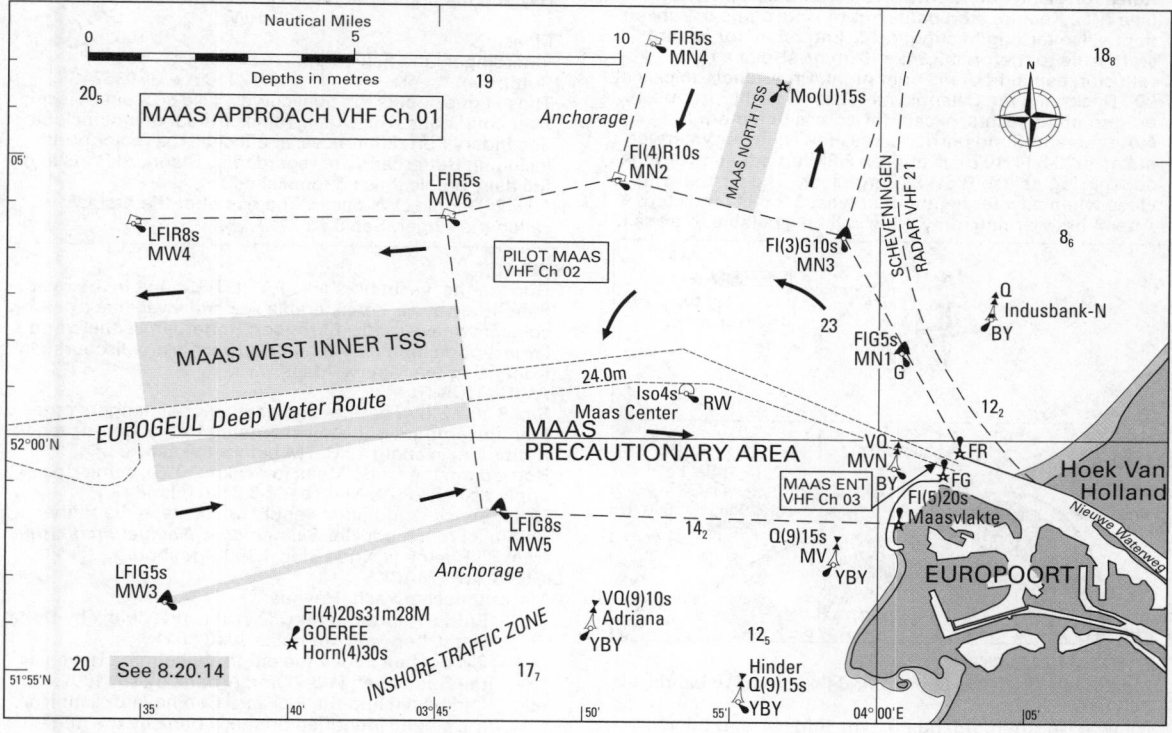

THE MAAS-ROTTERDAM VTS (H24) covers from approx 38M W of the Hook up to central Rotterdam; see the schematic diagram above and that on page 826.
3 main **Traffic Centres**, each on Ch 13, with their radar stn sub-sectors (*italics*) on a dedicated VHF Ch, are as follows:
(1)   **Traffic Centre Hoek van Holland (VCH)**
Maas Approach Ch 01, (Outer apps, from 38M W of Hook);
Pilot Maas Ch 02, (from approx 11M in to 4M W of Hook);
Maas Ent (Maasmond) Ch 03, (from 4M in to km 1031);
Rozenburg Ch 65, (Nieuwe Waterweg to km 1023);
Note: **English** language spoken on Ch 01, 02 and 03.
(2)   **Traffic Centre Botlek (VCB)**
Maassluis Ch 80, (km 1023 to km 1017);
Botlek Ch 61, (km 1017 to km 1011);
(3)   **Traffic Centre Stad (VCS)**
Eemhaven Ch 63, (km 1011 to km 1007);
Waalhaven Ch 60, (km 1007 to km 1003);
Note: Hartel and Maasboulevard Tfc Centres, and their radar sectors, have been omitted because yachts would not usually enter their areas. The Hbr Coordination Centre (HCC) administers Rotterdam port on Ch 11 14.
Yachts should **first report** to *Maas Approach* or *Pilot Maas* (or to *Maas Ent* if using the ITZ), stating name/type of vessel, position & destination; then obey instructions,

listening on the appropriate VHF Ch's as shown by W □ signboards on the river banks. (Km signs are similar).
Info broadcasts (weather, vis, tfc and tidal) are made by Traffic Centres and radar stns on request.
Other stations: Oude Maas Ch 62; Spijkenisserbrug and Botlekbrug Ch 18; Brienenoordbrug Ch 20; Bridge at Alblasserdam Ch 22; Dordrecht Ch 19 04 71 (H24).

NAVIGATING INTO THE NEUWE WATERWEG
WPTs From S: MV-N NCM lt By, Q, 51°59'·65N 04°00'·30E, 288°/108° from/to Nieuwe Zuiderdam lt, 1·5M. From N: Indusbank NCM lt By, Q, 52°02'·93N 04°03'·72E, 010°/190° from/to Nieuwe Noorderdam lt, 3·2M. There are no real navigational dangers but it is a very busy waterway with a constant stream of ocean-going and local ships. Keep clear of ships manoeuvering whilst transferring pilots.
Crossing the Entrance: To cross the Maasgeul (seaward of the bkwtrs), yachts should call *Maas Ent* Ch 03, with position and course, and keep watch on Ch 03. Cross under power on a track, 030°/210°, close W of line joining buoys MV (51°57'·50N 03°58'·50E), MV-N (51°59'·65N 04°00'·30E) and Indusbank N (52°02'·93N 04°03'·72E). Beware the strong tidal set across the ent.

20

HOEK VAN HOLLAND 8-20-22

Zuid Holland 51°59'·50N 04°02'·78E (Ent)   Rtg 1-3-2

CHARTS
AC 132, 122; Zeekaart 1540, 1349, 1350, 1449; DYC 1809, 1801; Imray C30, Y5; Stanfords 19

TIDES
+0251 Dover; ML 0·9; Duration 0505; Zone –0100.
HOEK VAN HOLLAND is a Standard Port; predictions for every day of the year are given above. Double LWs occur, more obviously at sp; in effect a LW stand. Predictions are for the *lower* LW. The 1st LW is about 5½ hrs after HW and the 2nd LW about 4¼ hrs before the next HW. The slight rise after the first LW is called the Agger. Water levels on this coast are much affected by the weather. Prolonged NW gales can raise the levels by up to 3m.

SHELTER
Ent safe except in strong on-shore winds when heavy seas/swell develop. Berghaven hbr is closed to yachts; better shelter at Maassluis (3m), 6M up river (km 1019).

NAVIGATION
See previous page for entry Waypoints and advice on crossing to seaward of the entrance (Maasgeul).
Rules for Yachts (in Nieuwe Waterweg): Comply with VTS (see R/T). Keep to stbd bank, not too close due to sunken debris. No tacking/beating; no ⚓. Eng ready for instant start. Able to motor at 3.24kn (6km/hr). Hoist a radar reflector, esp in poor vis or at night. Cross chan quickly at 90°. Docks, inc the Calandkanaal/Beerkanaal (Europoort), are prohib to yachts, except for access to a marina.
Note: An anti-flood barrier across the Nieuwe Waterweg at km 1026·5 (4°10'E), is approx 2·5M up-stream from the conspic ldg lts (Iso R 6s) at Berghaven. The barrier will close when a water height of at least 3·2m is predicted. After 4 hrs warning, only 2 hrs will be available to transit.

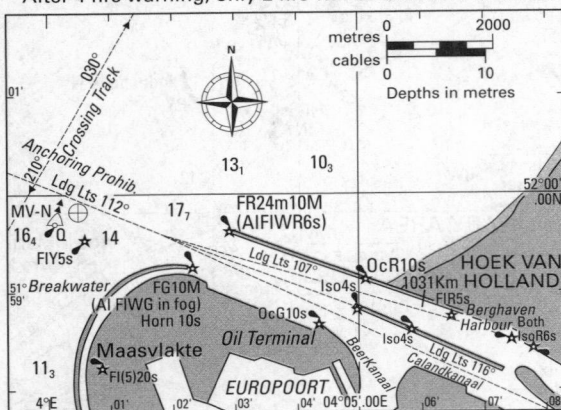

LIGHTS AND MARKS
Maasvlakte Fl (5) 20s 66m 28M; B 8-sided tr, W bands; vis 340°-267° (H24).
Nieuwe Noorderdam, hd FR 24m 10M; Or tr, B bands, helipad; in fog Al Fl WR 6s.
Nieuwe Zuiderdam, hd FG 24m 10M; Or tr, B bands, helipad; in fog Al Fl WG 6s; Horn 10s.
Ldg lts 107° (for Nieuwe Waterweg): Both Iso R 6s 29/43m 18M; R trs, W bands; vis 100°-114° (H24); synch.
Traffic Sigs from Pilot/Sig Stn, which has RDF bn HH 288, (N side of Nieuwe Waterweg, close W of Berghaven):
ⓇⓇⓇ
　Ⓦ　= No entry to, or exit from, Maas Estuary
ⓇⓇⓇ
Nieuwe Waterweg:
ⓇⓇ　　　　　　　ⓇⓇ
　Ⓦ　= No entry.　Ⓦ　= No exit
ⓇⓇ　　　　　　　ⓇⓇ
Patrol vessels show a Fl Bu lt. If such vessels show a Fl R lt, it means 'Stop'.

RADIO TELEPHONE
See previous page for details of VTS procedures

TELEPHONE (Dial code 010)
Port Authority (HCC) 4251400; Pilot (Hook) 4251422; Police 4141414; ⊞ 4112800; Brit Consul (020) 6764343.

FACILITIES
Maassluis ☎ 5912277, AB, CH, EI, FW, BY, ME, Sh.
Town P, D, V, R, Bar, ⊠, Ⓑ, ≠, ✈ (Rotterdam).
Ferry: Hook-Harwich (HSS); Rotterdam Europoort-Hull.

ROTTERDAM 8-20-23

Zuid Holland 51°54'·00N 04°28'·00E   Rtg 1-1-2

CHARTS
AC 133, 132, 122; Zeekaart 1540/1/2; DYC 1809; Stanfords 19

TIDES
+0414 Dover; ML 0·9; Duration 0440; Zone –0100

Standard Port VLISSINGEN (←)

Times				Height (metres)			
High Water		Low Water		MHWS	MHWN	MLWN	MLWS
0300	0900	0400	1000	4·7	3·9	0·8	0·3
1500	2100	1600	2200				
Differences MAASSLUIS							
+0125	+0100	+0110	+0255	–2·7	–2·2	–0·5	0·0
VLAARDINGEN							
+0150	+0125	+0135	+0320	–2·7	–2·2	–0·5	0·0

NOTE 1: Maassluis and Vlaardingen are both referenced to Vlissingen, as shown above, in British Admiralty Tables. The Dutch *Guide to the Netherlands and Belgian coasts* (HP11) shows the following time differences relative to HW and the first LW at Hoek van Holland:

	HW	LW
Maassluis	+0113	+0038
Vlaardingen and Schiedam	+0114	+0112
Rotterdam	+0123	+0352

These figures, plus the tidal curves, take account of local river conditions. The Dutch Tables (HP33) do not include Secondary Port differences; in effect all the major ports, including Rotterdam, are regarded as Standard Ports and full daily predictions are published.
NOTE 2: Double LWs occur. The rise after the first LW is called the Agger. See 8.20.22.

SHELTER
Good in the yacht hbrs (see FACILITIES), but in the river there is always a considerable sea and swell due to constant heavy traffic; Europoort/Rotterdam is the world's largest port complex. All but local yachts are discouraged from using the Nieuwe Maas.

NAVIGATION
See 8.20.21/22. There are no navigational dangers other than the amount of heavy sea-going traffic. Berghaven to Rotterdam is about 19M. 7M before the centre of Rotterdam, the Oude Maas joins (km 1013); same rules apply as in 8.20.21. Min speed 3.24kn (6km/hr).
Note: Special regulations apply to yachts in the Rhine; obtain a French booklet *Service de la Navigation du Rhin* from 25 Rue de la Nuée Bleu, 6700 Strasbourg.

LIGHTS AND MARKS
Marks to locate Yacht Havens:
(1)　Ent to Vlaardingen YC (2·7m) is on N bank by Delta Hotel, between km posts 1010-1011.
(2)　2M on, just above the ent to Wilhelmina Haven is the Spuihaven (1·8-2·3m); N bank by km 1007.
(3)　Parkhaven and the lock into Coolhaven Yacht Hbr are clearly identified on the N bank by the huge Euromast in the park (km 1002·5).
(4)　The Royal Maas YC at the Veerhaven (3·3m), a centre for traditional yachts, is on the N bank (km 1001·5).
(5)　City Marina (4·0m) is between Noordereiland and S bank; km post 1000 is on NW bank. Transit the eye-catching Erasmus bridge (11m clearance below fixed span; lifting section at SE end through which ldg lts, both Iso 2s, lead 056·7°); then 2nd ent to stbd, via lifting bridge.

RADIO TELEPHONE
The VTS Ch's for central Rotterdam are 63, 60, 81 and 21; see 8.20.20 and related diagram. The Hbr Coordination Centre (HCC) administers Rotterdam port on Ch 11 14. Call HCC Ch 11 for emergencies. English is official second language. Erasmus bridge Ch 18.

TELEPHONE (Dial code 010)
Hbr Coordination Centre (HCC) 4251400, also Emergency; ⌗ 4298088; Police 4141414; ⊞ 4112800; Brit Consul (020) 6764343.

FACILITIES
Vlaardingen YC (Oude Haven via lock/bridge), M, BY, ME, SM, FW, P, D, Gaz, ≠; Hr Mr ☎ 4346786.
Schiedam YC (Spuihaven) ☎ 4267765, D, L, FW, ME, EI, Sh, CH, AB, ≠;　*continued*

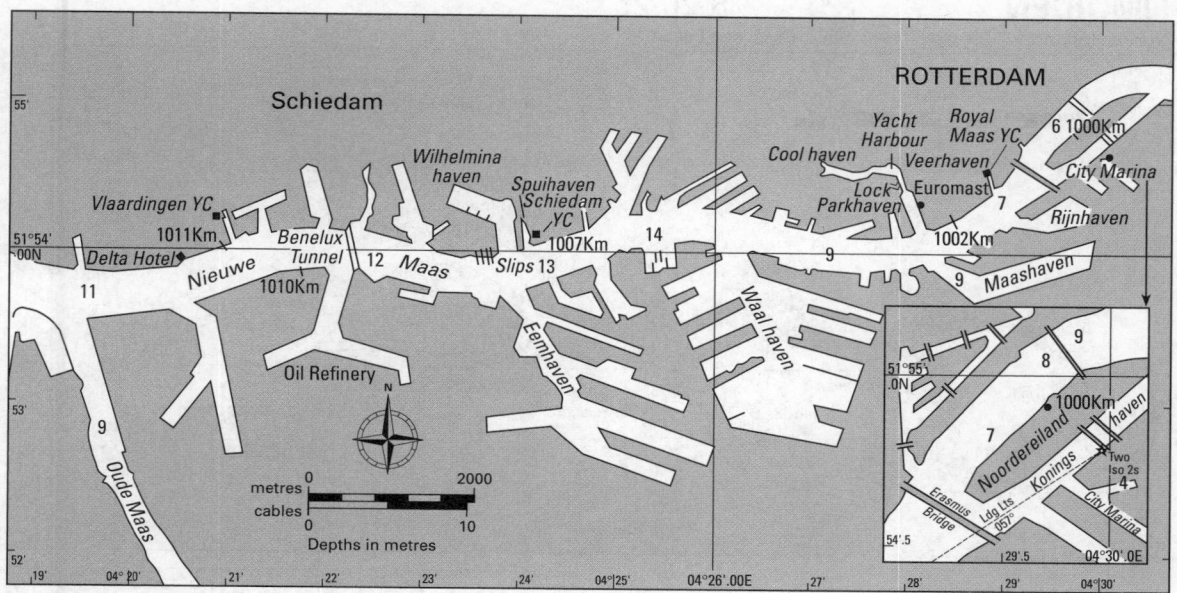

ROTTERDAM *continued*
Coolhaven Yacht Hbr ☎ 4738614, Slip, M, P, D, L, FW, ME, El, Sh, C, CH, AB, V, R, Bar;
Royal Maas YC ☎ 4137681, D, L, FW, ME, El, SH, CH, AB; home of the "Brown Fleet", traditional Dutch barges.
City Marina (51°54'·68N 04°29'·82E, S bank close to Noordereiland). ☎ via (0187) 493769, 🛥 493807, 110 AB in 4m, FW, AC, YC, Water taxi.

YC IJsselmonde ☎ 482833, AB (1·2-1·8m), AC, FW; on S bank at km 994, opposite the Hollandsche IJssel fork (off chartlet).
Services: P, D, ME; Gaz, ACA, DYC Agent.
City all facilities, ✉, Ⓑ, ⇌, ✈, Ferry: Rotterdam - Hull, also Hook-Harwich (HSS).

SCHEVENINGEN   8-20-24
Zuid Holland 52°06'·28N 04°15'·35E   Rtg 2-1-1

CHARTS
AC 122, 2322; Zeekaart 1035, 1349, 1350, 1449; DYC 1801; ANWB H/J; Imray Y5; Stanfords 19

TIDES
+0320 Dover; ML 0·9; Duration 0445; Zone –0100

Standard Port VLISSINGEN (←)

Times				Height (metres)			
High Water		Low Water		MHWS	MHWN	MLWN	MLWS
0300	0900	0400	1000	4·7	3·9	0·8	0·3
1500	2100	1600	2200				
Differences SCHEVENINGEN							
+0105	+0100	+0220	+0245	–2·5	–2·1	–0·5	–0·1

NOTE: Double LWs occur. The rise after the 1st LW is called the Agger. Water levels on this coast can be much affected by winds: Prolonged NW gales can raise levels by up to 3m, whilst strong E winds can lower levels by 1m.

SHELTER
Very good at marina in the Second Hbr; access H24. The chan from 1st to 2nd Hbrs is narrow with limited vis.

NAVIGATION
WPT SCH (SWM) buoy, Iso 4s, 52°07'·80N 04°14'·20E, 336°/156° from/to ent, 1·6M. Strong tidal streams setting NE/SW across the ent can cause problems. Winds >F6 from SW to N cause scend in the outer hbr, when ent can be difficult. Beware large ships entering and leaving.

LIGHTS AND MARKS
Outer ldg lts, both Iso 4s, 156°; Inner, both Oc G 5s, 131°.
Tfc signals (from Semaphore mast):
Ⓡ over Ⓦ = Entry prohib.   Ⓦ over Ⓡ = Exit prohib.
Fl Ⓨ = entry difficult due to vessels leaving.
Q Ⓨ is shown by ent to First Hbr (W side) when vessels are entering or leaving port.
Tide signals:
Ⓖ over Ⓦ = tide rising.   Ⓦ over Ⓖ = tide falling.
Ⓡ = less than 5m in entry chan.

RADIO TELEPHONE
Call: *Scheveningen Haven* VHF Ch 21 (H24) prior to entry/dep to de-conflict from ferries and FVs. Radar also Ch 21.

TELEPHONE (Dial code 070)
Marina Hr Mr 3520017, mobile 06-52727153; Port Hr Mr 3527701; Traffic Centre 3527721; ⌗ 3514481; Police 3104911; Dr 3455300; Ambulance 3222111; Brit Consul (020) 6764343.

FACILITIES
YC Scheveningen (223 + 100 visitors) ☎ 3520017, f27.00, AC, Bar, C (15 ton), CH, D, El, FW, ME, R, Ⓡ, Sh, SM;
Clubhouse ☎ 3520308; **Hbr** Slip, FW, ME, Sh, C (60 ton), CH, R, Bar; **Services:** ME, El, Sh, CH, SM, DYC Agent.
Town P, D, V, R, Bar, ✉, Ⓑ, ⇌, ✈ Rotterdam/Amsterdam. Ferry: See Rotterdam or Hoek van Holland.

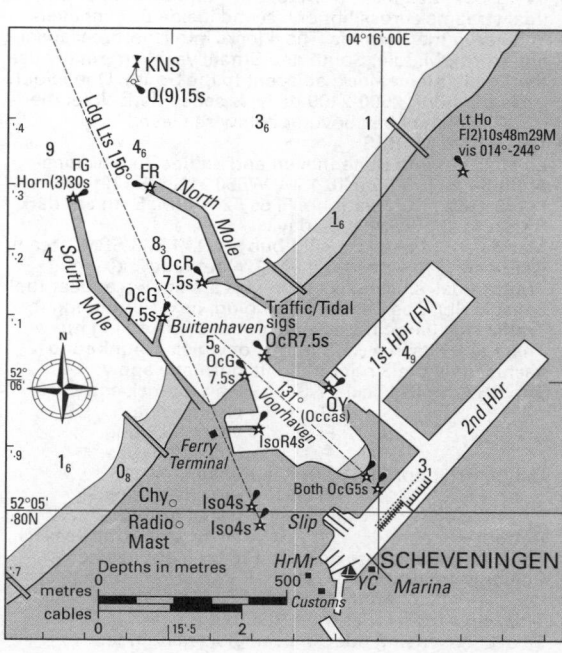

IJMUIDEN   8-20-25
Noord Holland 52°28'·03N 04°32'·00E   Rtgs: see Facilities

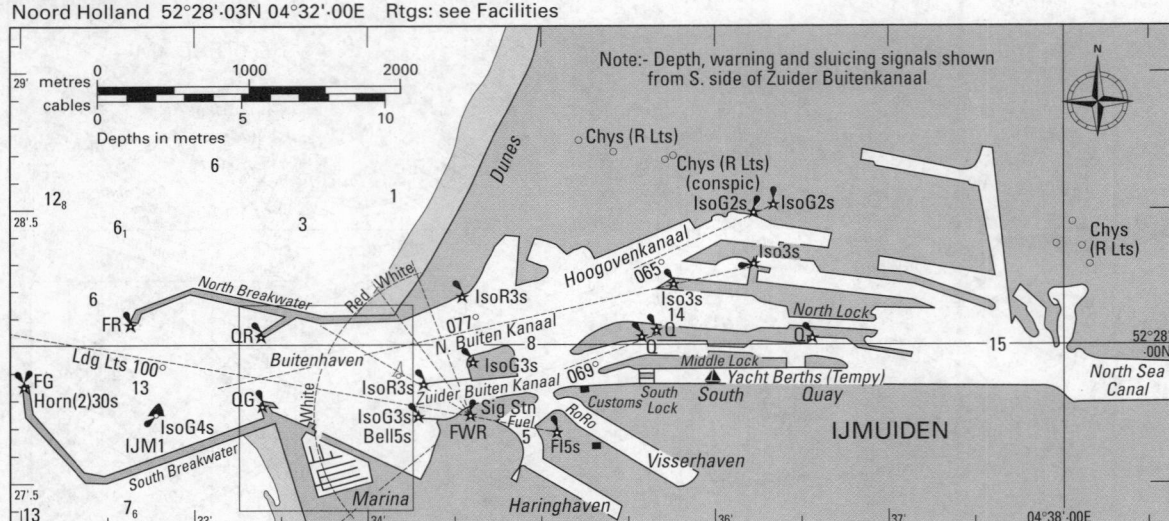

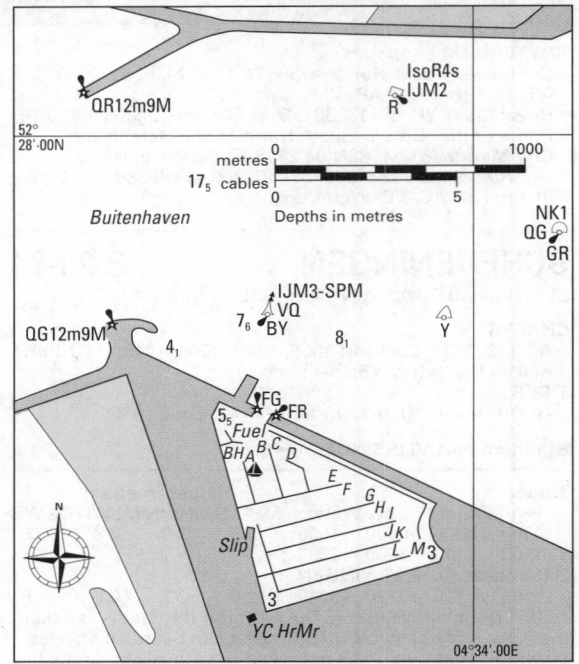

CHARTS
AC 2322, 124; Zeekaart 1450, 1543, 1035, 1350; DYC 1801;
Imray Y5; Stanfords 19

TIDES
+0400 Dover; ML 1·0; Zone –0100

Standard Port VLISSINGEN (←)

Times				Height (metres)			
High Water		Low Water		MHWS	MHWN	MLWN	MLWS
0300	0900	0400	1000	4·7	3·9	0·8	0·3
1500	2100	1600	2200				
Differences IJMUIDEN							
+0145	+0140	+0305	+0325	–2·6	–2·2	–0·5	–0·1

SHELTER
Very good at SPM marina (5·5m - 3m depths) on S side of
Buitenhaven (see chartlet). There are also temp (24hrs)
berths at canal locks. There are small marinas at IJmond
under lift-bridge (VHF Ch 18) in Zijkanaal C, km 10; and at
Nauwerna (Zijkanaal D, km 12).

NAVIGATION
WPT IJM (SWM) buoy, Mo (A) 8s, Racon, 52°28'·70N
04°23'·93E, 275°/095° from/to ent, 5·0M. Beware strong
tidal streams across hbr ent, scend inside Buitenhaven
and heavy merchant tfc. The 4 locks into Noordzeekanaal
are: North, Middle, South and Small; yachts normally use
the Small (Kleine) lock, adjacent to the South. One in/out
cycle per hour, 0600-2100 daily, is scheduled. Note: the
canal level may be above or below sea level.

LIGHTS AND MARKS
Ldg lts 100° into Buitenhaven and Zuider Buitenkanaal:
Front lt ho FWR 30m 16/13M, W050°-122°, R122°-145°,
W145°-160°, RC; rear lt ho, Fl 5s 52m 29M. Both are dark
R trs and show a Ⓦ lt by day.
Marina ent marked by SPM buoy, VQ, "IJM3-SPM", 1ca to
N. Ent sigs: Ⓡ = no entry; Ⓡ+Ⓖ = get ready; Ⓖ = go.
Traffic, tidal, sluicing & storm sigs are shown at/near the
conspic Hbr Ops Centre (HOC) bldg, next to front ldg lt.
Traffic sigs (large frame adjacent to the front ldg lt):
There are 9 lts in a 3 x 3 frame, of which, for **inbound**
yachts, only the 3 right-hand lts normally apply:
Top RH lt (for S Lock) Fl Ⓖ = wait for lock entry.
　　　　　　　　　Ⓖ = clear to enter.
　　　　　　　Fl Ⓡ = vessels exiting.
　　　　　　　　　Ⓡ = lock not in use.
Centre RH lt (for Zuider Buiten Kanaal)
　　　　　　　Fl Ⓡ = vessels exiting.
　　　　　　　　　Ⓡ = traffic prohib.
Bottom RH lt　　　Ⓡ = entry prohib, all vessels.
For **outbound yachts** only the top LH lt applies (for
Zuider Buitenkanaal) Fl Ⓡ = vessels entering.
　　　　　　　　　Ⓡ = traffic prohib.
Tidal sigs, from radar tr on HOC bldg:
Ⓖ over Ⓦ = rising tide; Ⓦ over Ⓖ = falling tide.

RADIO TELEPHONE
Call the following VTS stns (H24) in sequence for entry:
Traffic Centre IJmuiden　　Ch 88 (W of IJM buoy).
IJmuiden Hbr Control (HOC)　Ch 61 (IJM buoy to locks).
(Seaport Marina　　　　　**Ch 74; call SPM).**
IJmuiden Locks　　　　　　Ch 22.
Traffic Centre Noordzeekanaal Ch 03 (Lock to km 11·2).
Amsterdam Port Control　　Ch 04 (Km 11·2 to A'dam).
Yachts should monitor the appropriate Ch for tfc info.
Radar assistance is available on request Ch 88 and 61.
Visibility reports are broadcast on all Chans every H+00
when vis <1000m.

TELEPHONE (Dial code 0255)
Traffic Centre IJmuiden 534542; Hbr Ops (HOC) 519027;
Pilot 564503; ⌗ 560800; CG 537644; Police 535035; Ⓗ
565100; Brit Consul (020) 6764343; Emergencies 112.

FACILITIES
Seaport Marina (SPM) ☎ 560300/🖅 560301. Rtg 3-1-1.
(600 inc Ⓥ), f34.80, AC, FW, D & P, BH (70 ton), El, Ⓔ, CH,
Gas, Slip, SM, Sh, ME, R, Bar, ▣, in summer, bus/🚃 to
Amsterdam and Haarlem; **WV IJmond** Rtg 1-4-1. Hr Mr ☎
(023) 5375003, AB f8.80 inc AC, D, BY, C (20 ton), ▣, Bar,
V, R. **Town** P, D, Gaz, V, R, Bar, ✉, Ⓑ, 🚃 (bus to
Beverwijk), ✈ Amsterdam. Ferry: IJmuiden-Newcastle.

AMSTERDAM   8-20-26

Noord Holland 52°23'·00N 04°54'·00E   Rtgs: see Facilities

CHARTS
AC 124; Zeekaart 1543; DYC 1801, 1810; ANWB G, I

TIDES
Amsterdam is between the Noordzeekanaal and the IJsselmeer, both of which are non-tidal; Zone –0100.

SHELTER
Complete in any of 5 yacht hbrs/marinas (see chartlet & Facilities). The main one is Sixhaven, on the N bank, NE of the ⤳ (conspic); it is small, pleasant and well located, so mostly full by 1800. WV Aeolus is a good alternative. Twellega is more for the larger yacht; bus to city centre. Gem. Haven on the S bank, close NW of the Hbr bldg (conspic), is prone to wash from passing ships and not recommended. There is a small marina, WV Zuiderzee, on N bank immediately E of Oranjesluizen.

NAVIGATION
See 8.20.25. The 13·5M transit of the Noordzeekanaal is simple, apart from the volume of commercial traffic. The speed limit is 9kn. Schellingwoude bridge (9m), at 500m E of Oranjesluizen, opens: all year Mon-Fri 0600-0700, 0900-1600, 1800-2200. Sat 0600-2200. Sun & Public hols from 1 Apr to 1 Nov: 0900-2100; 1 Nov to 1 Apr: closed. There are waiting pontoons both sides of Oranjesluizen. Amsterdam gives access to canals running to N & S and also, via the Oranjesluizen (H24), into the IJsselmeer.

LIGHTS AND MARKS
Both banks of the canal and the ents to branch canals and basins are lit. The chan E towards the Oranjesluizen and the Amsterdam-Rijn canal is lit/buoyed.

RADIO TELEPHONE
VHF Ch 04. See also 8.20.25. Oranjesluizen Ch 18.

TELEPHONE (Dial code 020)
Port Control 6221201; ⌗ 5867511; Emergency 112; Police 5599111; Dr 5555555; Brit Consul 6764343.

FACILITIES
Marinas: Sixhaven (60 + some ⓥ) ☎ 6370892, Rtg 1-4-1, f12.00 inc AC, FW, Bar (weekends);
ZV Aeolus ☎ 6360791, Rtg 1-4-1, f8.00 inc AC, YC, FW;
Twellega ☎ 6320616, Rtg 1-2-2, f18.00, AC, FW, Sh, P, C (30 ton); **WV Zuiderzee** No ☎, Rtg 1-5-2, f10, YC, AC, FW;
Gem. Haven Amsterdam (min 3 days), f34.50.
City: All facilities, Gaz, Ⓔ, ACA, DYC Agent, Ⓑ, ✉, ⤳, ✈.
Ferries: IJmuiden-Newcastle. See also Hoek van Holland.

IJSSELMEER   8-20-27

CHARTS
AC 1408, 2593; Zeekaart 1351, 1454; DYC 1810: up to date copy is essential to avoid live firing ranges, fishing areas and other hazards; it also has many hbr chartlets.

TIDES
The IJsselmeer is non-tidal. Tides at locks at Den Oever and Kornwerderzand: –0230 Dover; ML 1·2; Zone –0100

Standard Port HELGOLAND (⟶)

Times				Height (metres)			
High Water		Low Water		MHWS	MHWN	MLWN	MLWS
0200	0700	0200	0800	2·7	2·3	0·4	0·0
1400	1900	1400	2000				
Differences KORNWERDERZAND							
–0210	–0315	–0300	–0215	–0·5	–0·4	–0·1	+0·2
DEN OEVER							
–0245	–0410	–0400	–0305	–0·8	–0·6	0·0	+0·2

SHELTER
Excellent in the many marinas, some of which are listed below. Most berths are bows on to a pontoon, stern lines to piles; there are few ⚓s.

NAVIGATION
The IJsselmeer is the un-reclaimed part of the former Zuiderzee; it is separated from the Waddenzee by the 20M long Afsluitdijk, completed in 1932. It is divided into two parts by the Houtribdijk, with locks at Enkhuizen to the NW and Lelystad in the SE. The SW part is the Markermeer (20M x 15M, 2-4·5m deep); the rest of the IJsselmeer is 30M x 20M, 7m max. Three ents via locks:
(1) IJmuiden, Noordzeekanaal to Oranjesluizen (8.20.24).
(2) Den Oever (SW end of the Afsluitdijk): Appr from Waddenzee via well marked/lit chan; Idg Its 132°, both Oc 10s to ent, thence follow Dir Iso WRG 2s, 220° to wait in Buitenhaven. 2 bridges and locks operate in unison HO. From IJsselmeer, wait in Binnenhaven; FR/G at ent.
(3) Kornwerderzand lock (NE end of the Afsluitdijk) H24. From Waddenzee, via W, NW or NE chans. Ent has FR/G and Iso G 6s. Wait in Buitenhaven; yachts use the smaller E lock. From IJsselmeer, Idg Its Iso 4s 348° to FR/G at ent; wait in Binnenhaven (3·8m).
Standard lock sigs (vert): Ⓡ Ⓡ = not in service; Ⓡ = no entry; Ⓡ Ⓖ = stand by; Ⓖ = enter.

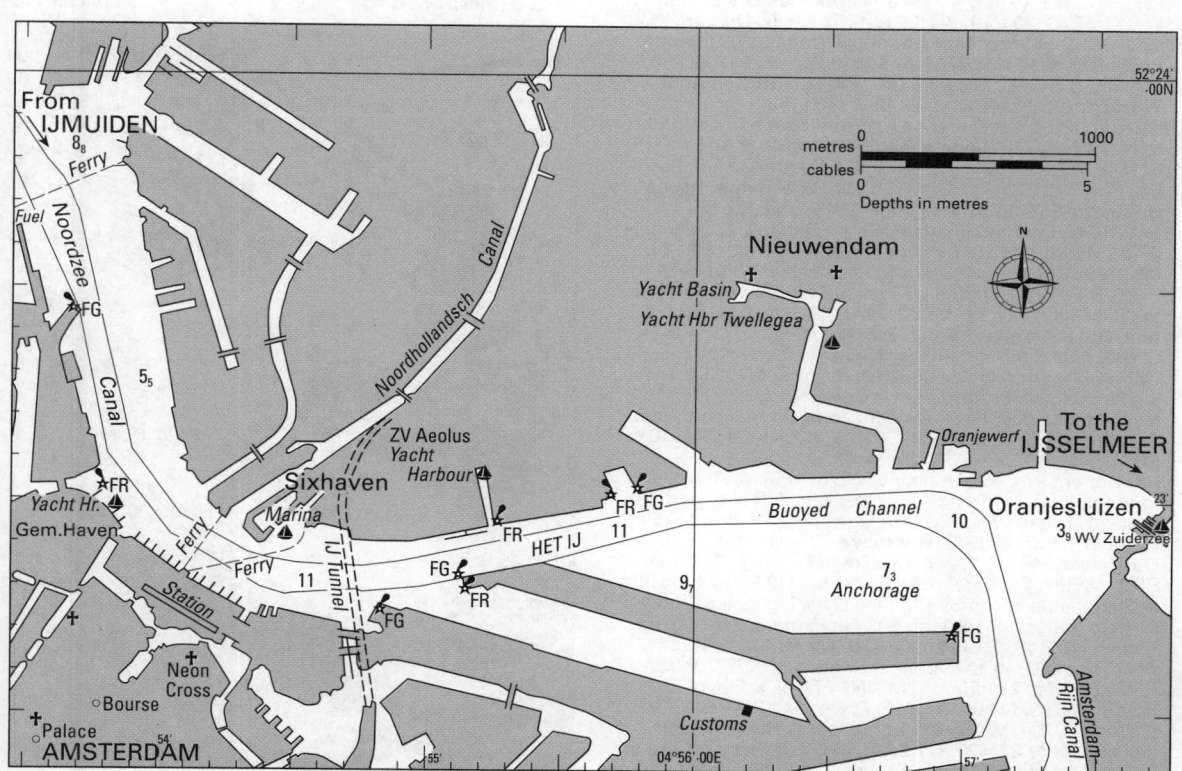

IJSSELMEER continued

Speed limits: in buoyed chans and <250m from shore 10·5kn. Hbr limits vary; see ANWB Almanak Vol 2. Strong winds get up very quickly and often cause short seas; they can also raise the water level on a lee shore, or lower it on a weather shore, by 1m or more. Most hbrs have water level gauges which should be checked in bad weather. In non-tidal waters CD usually refers to the level at which the water is kept. In the Netherlands, this may be Kanaalpeil, which is related to Normaal Amsterdams Peil (NAP), which in turn is approx Mean Sea Level.
A firing range, operational Tues to Thurs 1000 - 1900LT, extends S from Breezanddijk (53°01'·0N 05°12'·5E) to 3M N of Medemblik then NNW to Den Oever (DYC 188.3). Call the range control on Ch 71 *Schietterrein Breezanddijk*. Scheveningen Radio broadcasts firing times on the day of firing after Dutch forecasts, at even hours; also at 1900 the previous day in English Ch 25, 27, 83 after the weather.

BUOYAGE The SIGNI buoyage system is used in the whole of the IJsselmeer. The main features are:
(1) Lateral buoyage as for IALA (Region A).
(2) Supplementary PHM & SHM buoys may be R/W or G/ W respectively; they also indicate a least depth of 2m.
(3) At division of chan, a spherical buoy as follows:
a. Chans of equal importance = R & G bands; topmark R and G sphere;
b. Main chan to port = G above R bands; topmark G △ or G △ above a G ○;
c. Main chan to stbd = R above G bands; topmark R □ or R □ above a R ○.

RADIO TELEPHONE
VHF Ch's at locks are: Oranjesluizen 18; Enkhuizen 22; Den Oever 20; Kornwerderzand 18; Lelystad 20.

HARBOURS AND FACILITIES
A useful guide, one of the few in English, is *IJsselmeer Harbours* by Hilary Keatinge (Barnacle Marine 1988). It is essential to have the *Almanac voor Watertoerisme*, Vol I onboard; it contains the BPR (Waterway Code). Some of the many hbrs are listed below (clockwise from the NW):
DEN OEVER: Jachthaven (3m) to port of ent; Hr Mr ☎ (0227) 511798, f17.50, D, P, FW, ◪.
MAKKUM: Approx 1M SE of Kornwerderzand, a SHM buoy MA5, Iso G4s, marks the 4·1M buoyed chan. FR/FG lts lead 092° into Makkum, Hr Mr ☎ (0515) 231450. To stbd, **Marina Makkum** (2·5m) ☎ (0515) 232828, f21.50, P, D, AC, FW, SM, Gaz, V, Bar, R, ◪. 4 other marinas/YCs are further E; BY, ME, C (30 ton); BH (30 ton). **Town** ⓑ, Dr, V, R.
WORKUM: 2·5M N of Hindeloopen; FW ldg lts 081° along buoyed chan to **It Soal Marina** ☎ (0515) 542937, f21.50, BY, ME, C, FW, D, P (cans), Gaz, BH; **Jachthaven Anne Wever** ☎ (0515) 542361, f17.10, C (40 ton).
HINDELOOPEN: has 2 marinas, one in town and one 180m to N. **Jachthaven Hindeloopen** (500) Hr Mr ☎ (0514) 521856, f23.70, P, D, FW, AC, ◪, BH (30 ton); CH, R, Bar; **Old Hbr** f11.20, D, P, FW, ME, EI, Sh; **W.V Hylper Haven** Hr Mr ☎ (0514) 522019, f9.00, P, D, FW, ME, EI, Sh.
STAVOREN: Ent Buitenhaven 048° on Dir lt Iso 4s between FR/G. Marina, f15.50, E of ent in Oudehaven, ☎ (0514) 681216, VHF Ch 74. Or, 1km S, ent Nieuwe Voorhaven (FR/G & Fl 5s Dir lt) then via lock to **Stavoren Marina** (3m) ☎ 681566, f22.50, BY, ME, C, FW, P, D, SM, Gaz, BH (20 ton); **Outer Marina** (3·5m) close S of Nieuwe Voorhaven, f24.00. Also 3 other marinas. **Town** ⓑ, Dr, V, R, ⇌.
LEMMER: Appr on ldg lts 038°, Iso 8s, to KL5/VL2 By; then ldg lts 083°, Iso 8s, through Lemstergeul. Lastly FG and Iso G 4s lead 065° into town and some 14 marinas. **Gem. Jachthaven** Hr Mr ☎ (0514) 561331, f17.50; **Services:** BY, ME, C, FW, P, D, Gaz, SM. **Town** ⓑ, Dr, V, R, ⊠.
URK: Hbr ent ½M SE of lt ho, Fl 5s 27m 18M. Dir lt Iso G 4s to hbr ent, FR/G. Hbr has 4 basins; keep NNW to berth in Nieuwe Haven, Westhaven or Oosthaven (3·3m), f14.50. Hr Mr ☎ (0527) 689970. **Westhaven** P & D (cans), SM; **Oosthaven** ME, EI, Sh, Ⓔ, CH. **Town** EC Tues; ⓑ, ⊠, Dr.
KETELHAVEN: Ent Ketelmeer via bridge (12·9m) which lifts at S end; after 4M to By WK1 Iso G 4s, ldg lts Iso 8s 101°/ 0·7M in buoyed chan. Turn S for unlit marina ent (2·2m). **Marina** (200) f16.50, FW, AC, R. Hr Mr ☎ (0321) 312271. W ent has FG/R lts to Ketelsluis: Hr Mr ☎ 318237 D, P (cans).
LELYSTAD: has 2 marinas: 2M NNE of lock is **Flevo** (550) ☎ (0320) 279803, f24.00, BY, ME, C, FW, AC, P, D, Gaz, ◪, BH (50 ton), R, Bar, V. Close N of the lock is **Houtribhaven** (560) Hr Mr ☎ 271421, f17.20, D, CH, V, R, Bar, C (12 ton). Radio mast, R lts, (140m) is conspic; marinas are lit.

MARKERMEER

MUIDERZAND: Ent 1M N of Hollandsebrug at buoys IJM5-JH2/IJM3. **Marina** ☎ (036) 5365151, f24.00, FW, AC, D, P.
NAARDEN: 1M SE of Hollandsebrug (12·9m), ent at GM54 buoy. **Gem Jachthaven** (1000) ☎ (036) 6942106, f17.50, D, P, AC, FW, EI, BH, C, CH, V, R, Bar, ⇌ (Naarden-Bussum).
MUIDEN: Ldg lts Q 181° into **KNZ & RV Marina** (2·6m), W of ent; home of Royal Netherlands YC (150 berths). Hr Mr ☎ (0294) 261450, f28.50, D, P (cans), CH, FW, Bar, R. On E bank **Stichting Jachthaven** (70) ☎ 261223, f22.50, D, P.
DURGERDAM: Convenient for Oranjesluizen. Ldg lts 337°, both FR. Keep strictly to chan which is ½M E of overhead power lines. Berth to stbd of ent (1·8m), f15.20. ☎ (020) 4904717.
MARKEN (picturesque show piece): Ent Gouwzee from N, abeam Volendam, thence via buoyed chan; Dir FW lt 116° between FR/G at hbr (2·2m). Lt ho, conspic, Oc 8s 16m 9M, on E end of island. Hr Mr ☎ (0299) 734967, f12.50, FW, AC, V, R, ⒷⒷ, P & D (cans).
MONNICKENDAM: Appr as for Marken, then W to MO10 Iso R 8s and ldg lts FR at 236°. Hr Mr ☎ (0299) 658585. 4 marinas & facilities: f16.20, ME, C, FW, P (cans), D, Gaz, AC, CH.
VOLENDAM: Berth to stbd (2·4m). Dir lt Fl 5s 313°. FR/FG at ent. ☎ (0299) 369620, f14.60, ME, FW, C, P, D, Gaz, SM.
EDAM: Appr via unlit chan keeping Iso W 8s between FG /R at narrow ent; beware commercial traffic. **Jachthaven Galgenveld** (2·5m) S side pf outer hbr, f15.20. Or lock into the Oorgat and via S canal to Nieuwe Haven. Hr Mr ☎ (0299) 371092, f11.60, ME, EI, Sh. **Town** Bar, ◪, ⊠, Gaz, Ⓑ.
HOORN: Radio tr (80m) 1·5M ENE of hbr. Iso 4s 15m 10M and FR/G at W Hbr ent. Four options: to port **Stichting Jachthaven Hoorn** (700) Hr Mr ☎ (0299) 215208, f16.20, FW, AC, ◪, CH, V, ME, EI, Sh, C; to stbd ⚓ in **Buitenhaven** (2m); ahead & to stbd **Vluchthaven Marina** f17.50, (100) ☎ 213540 FW; ahead to **Binnenhaven** (2·7m) via narrow lock (open H24) AB f16.20, P, FW.
Town V, CH, ⊠, R, Dr, P & D (cans), Ⓑ, Gaz, ⇌.
ENKHUIZEN: From SW, appr via buoyed chan and ldg lts Iso 4s at 039°; from NE, ldg lts Iso 8s at 230° and FR /G at bkwtrs lead to Krabbersgat lock and hbr. Call lock Ch 22. The 2 marinas and Buitenhaven are NE of the lock: **Compagnieshaven** (500) Hr Mr ☎ (0228) 313353 f20.00, P, D, FW, AC, CH, BH (12), Gaz; **Buyshaven** (195) ☎ 315660, f17.60, FW, AC; **Buitenhaven** ☎ 312444 f14.75, FW. **Town** EC Mon; Market Wed; C, Slip, CH, SM, ME, EI, Sh, Ⓑ, Bar, P & D (cans), Dr, ⊠, ⇌.
Continued

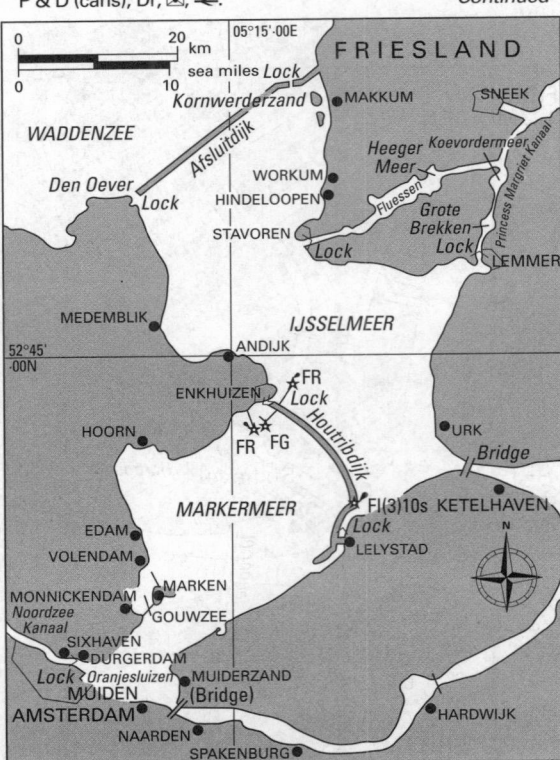

IJSSELMEER (WEST) *Continued*

ANDIJK: Visitors use **Stichting Jachthaven Andijk,** the first of 2 marinas; (600) ☎ (0228) 593085, f16.20, narrow ent with tight turn between FR/G lts. ME, C (20), SM, Gaz, ◙, D, CH.

MEDEMBLIK: Ent on Dir lt Oc 4s 232° between FR/G. Go via Oosterhaven (P & D) into Middenhaven (short stay), then via bridge to Westerhaven. **Pekelharinghaven** (120) Hr Mr ☎ (0227) 542175, f16.50; ent is to port by Castle, CH, Bar, R; **Middenhaven** Hr Mr ☎ 541686, f13.75, FW; **Stichting Jachthaven** Hr Mr ☎ 541681 in Westerhaven, f16.20, FW, AC, ◙, C. **Town** Ⓑ, CH, ME, El, SM, Sh, ✉, Dr, Bar, ◙, R, V.

INLAND ROUTE TO RIVER EMS (DELFZIJL 8.20.35)

As an alternative to the shallow tidal route inshore of the Frisian Islands, or as a bad weather option, masted yachts can transit the canals/lakes from the IJsselmeer to Delfzijl without lowering masts. From Lemmer to Delfzijl is about 100M/180km, via Prinses Margrietkanaal, Leeuwarden, Dokkumer Ee, Dokkum, Lauwersmeer, Zoutkamp, Reit Diep, Groningen and Eemskanaal. Leeuwarden can also be reached from Harlingen via the Van Harinxma Kanaal or from Stavoren via the Johan Frisco Kanaal. Minimum depths approx 1·8m. ANWB charts A and B are needed.

DEN HELDER   8-20-28

Noord Holland 52°58'·00N 04°47'·35E

CHARTS
AC 191, 2322, 2593; Zeekaart 1454, 1546; DYC 1811.2, 1801; ANWB F; Imray Y5; Stanfords 19

TIDES
–0430 Dover; ML 1·1; Duration No data; Zone –0100

Standard Port HELGOLAND(→)

Times				Height (metres)			
High Water		Low Water		MHWS	MHWN	MLWN	MLWS
0200	0700	0200	0800	2·7	2·3	0·4	0·0
1400	1900	1400	2000				
Differences DEN HELDER							
–0410	–0520	–0520	–0430	–0·9	–0·7	0·0	+0·2

SHELTER
Good in the Naval Hbr, the yacht hbr (KMYC) being hard to stbd on entering. Den Helder is the main base of the Royal Netherlands Navy which owns and runs the KMYC and the Marinehaven Willemsoord. Caution: many FVs, ferries and off-shore service vessels. 2 other YCs/marinas both of which can only be reached via the Rijkszeehaven, Moorman bridge, Nieuwe Diep and lock, offer AB in or near the Binnenhaven: MWV and YC Den Helder; see below under FACILITIES for details.

NAVIGATION
WPT Schulpengat SG (SWM) buoy, Mo (A) 8s, 52°52'·95N 04°38'·00E, 206·5°/026·5° from/to Kaap Hoofd, 6·0M. Two chans lead via the Marsdiep to the hbr ent:
(1) From N, the Molengat is good except in strong NW winds when seas break heavily.
(2) From S, the Schulpengat is well marked and lit. Beware fast ferries to/from Texel and strong tidal streams across the hbr ent.

LIGHTS AND MARKS
Schulpengat: Ldg lts 026·5° on Texel; front Iso 4s 18M; rear Oc 8s 18M, Ch spire, both vis 025°-028°. Kijkduin lt ho Fl (4) 20s 56m 30M, R tr, is conspic 2·3M WSW of hbr. Molengat: ldg lts 141·5°; front Iso 5s 13m 8M; rear, 650m from front, FW 22m 8M; tr on Ⓗ; both vis 124°-157°. Hbr ldg lts 191°. Both Oc G 5s 16/25m 14M (synch); front B ▲ on bldg; rear B ▼ on B framework tr.
A 60m radar tower is conspic on the E side of hbr ent.
Entry sigs, from Harssens hbr office on W side of ent: ⓇⓇ (vert) = No entry/exit; no traffic allowed within hbr.
Bridges: Moorman bridge operates 7 days a week H24. Access to the North Holland Canal via the Nieuwe Diep and Koopvaardersschutsluis.Van Kinsbergen bridge operated by Hr Mr, 0500-2300 Mon-Fri; 0700-1400 Sat. All bridges remain closed 0715-0810, 1200-1215, 1245-1300, Mon-Fri. Also 0830-0910 Mon and 1545-1645 Fri. All LT.

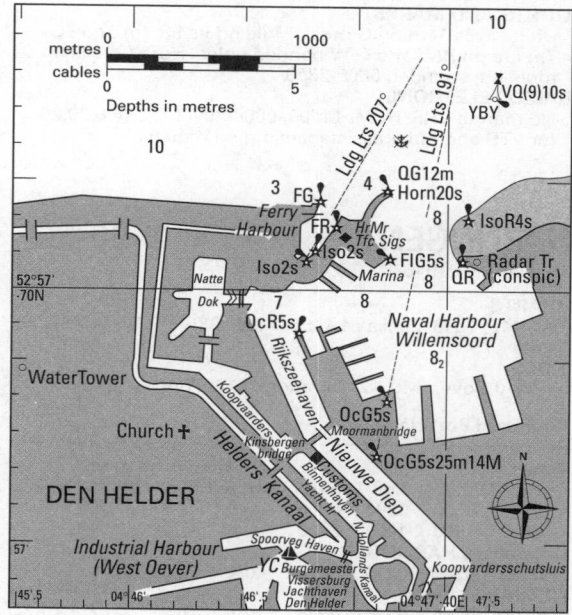

RADIO TELEPHONE
Monitor VTS Ch 12 *Den Helder Traffic* in the Schulpengat, Molengat and Marsdiep; weather forecast available on request. Port Ch 14 (H24); also Ch 14 for van Kinsbergen bridge (remote control). Koopvaardersschutsluis Ch 22 (H24), which also operates Burgemeester Vissersbrug by remote control. Moormanbridge Ch 18 (H24).

TELEPHONE (Dial code 0223)
Municipal Hr Mr 613955, 🖷 627780, mobile ☎ 0652 97 94 80; Hr Mr (Yacht Haven) 637444; Pilot 617424; Vessel Traffic Centre 652770; Naval Base Commander 656822; ⚓ 615182; Emergency 112; Police 655700; Ⓗ 611414; Water Police 616767; Immigration 657515; Brit Consul (020) 6764343.

FACILITIES
In naval hbr: **KMYC** ☎ 652645, f13.80, FW, D, Bar, R;
In or near Binnenhaven:
MWV YC ☎ 617076, f11.50, P (at garage), D, L, FW, AB;
Yacht Haven Den Helder ☎ 637444, f15.65, ME, El, Sh, C, CH, Slip, FW, R, Bar; **YC WSOV** ☎ 652173; **YC HWN** ☎ 624422;
Services: CH, SM, Floating dock, Gaz.
Town P, CH, V, R, Bar, ✉, Ⓑ, ⇌, ✈ (Amsterdam).
Ferry: Hook of Holland-Harwich; Rotterdam-Hull.

20

OUDESCHILD   8-20-29

Texel, 53°02'·39N 04°51'·26E   Rtg 1-2-2

CHARTS
AC 191, 2593; Zeekaart 1546, 1454; DYC 1811·3
TIDES
–0355 Dover; ML 1·1m; Duration 0625; Zone –0100

Standard Port HELGOLAND (⟶)

Times				Height (metres)			
High Water		Low Water		MHWS	MHWN	MLWN	MLWS
0200	0700	0200	0800	2·7	2·3	0·4	0·0
1400	1900	1400	2000				
Differences OUDESCHILD							
–0310	–0420	–0445	–0400	–0·9	–0·7	0·0	+0·2

SHELTER
Good in marina (2·1m) in NE basin. A Port of Entry in summer. Yachts are advised not to ent/dep Mon and Fri mornings when all FVs sail/return.
NAVIGATION
WPT 53°02'·28N 04°51'·72E, 111°/291° from/to hbr ent, 3ca. From seaward, app via Schulpengat or Molengat into Marsdiep (see 8.20.26). Thence from abeam ferry hbr of 't Horntje (Texel) steer NE via Texelstroom for 3·5M to hbr ent, marked by PHM buoy (T14), Iso R 8s. Enter on course 291° with dir lt, Oc 6s, midway between S mole hd FR and N mole hd FG. Speed limit 5kn (9kph).
LIGHTS AND MARKS
Dir lt Oc 6s 14m on G mast. Mole hd lts FR 7m and FG 7m are on R/W and G/W banded poles. Horn (2) 30s on S mole hd, sounded 0600-2300.
RADIO TELEPHONE
No marina VHF. Hr Mr Ch 09, 0800-2000LT. See 8.20.26 for VTS and radar assistance/info on request.

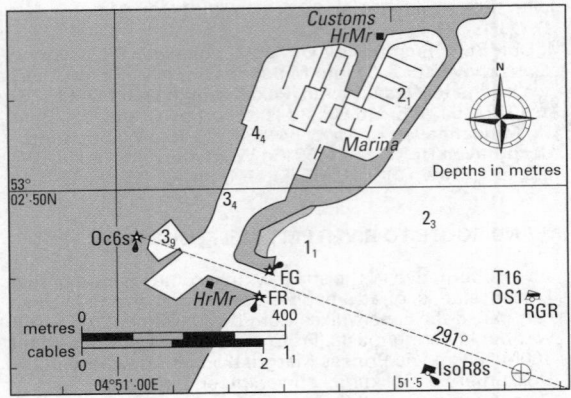

TELEPHONE (Dial code 0222)
Hr Mr (marina) ☎ 313608 (1100-1130; 1800-1930LT); Port Hr Mr 312710/home 313538; CG 316270; Police 322188 (in season); Ambulance 312323 (H24) or 112; Taxi 312323.
FACILITIES
Marina (Passanten-haven; 200 berths) ☎ 313608, f22.50, D, FW, AC, Slip, ⊡, Bar, R, &; **YC WV Texel**, C;
Services: ME, BY, Sh, ⚓, Dry dock, C, SM, V by mobile shop in season.
Village (walking distance), CH, P, Gaz, V (supermarket), ⑧, ✉, R. Ferry from 't Horntje to Den Helder. UK ferries from Hook/Rotterdam. ✈ Amsterdam.

HARLINGEN   8-20-30

Friesland 53°10'·63N 05°24'·22E

CHARTS
AC 112, 2593; Zeekaart 1454, 1456; DYC 1811·5; ANWB B; Imray Y5
TIDES
–0210 Dover; ML 1·2; Duration 0520; Zone –0100

Standard Port Helgoland (⟶)

Times				Height (metres)			
High Water		Low Water		MHWS	MHWN	MLWN	MLWS
0200	0700	0200	0800	2·7	2·3	0·4	0·0
1400	1900	1400	2000				
Differences HARLINGEN							
–0155	–0245	–0210	–0130	–0·4	–0·3	–0·1	+0·2
NES (AMELAND)							
–0135	–0150	–0245	–0225	+0·1	+0·2	+0·2	+0·2

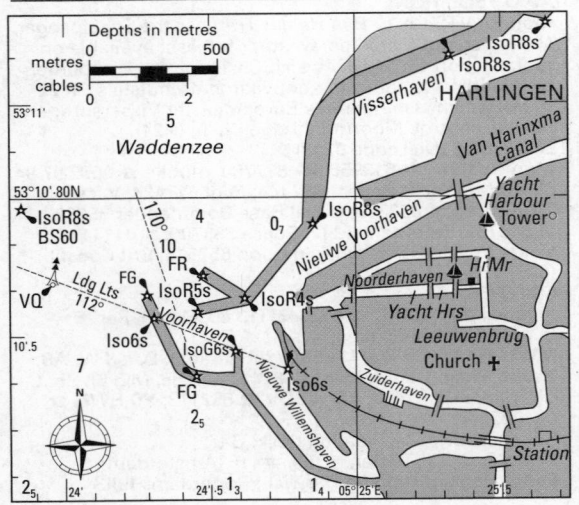

SHELTER
Very good in Noorderhaven, but ent can be rough at HW with W/NW winds. Entering on the flood, beware strong stream across ent. Note: Access to/from Noorderhaven is restricted by the two N/S bridges either end of the Oude Buitenhaven; these open in unison 2 x per hr 0600-2200 in season (on request in winter) and are shut at times of boat trains/ferries. Some berths at Van Harinxma yacht hbr; but only advised if going via the canal on to the lakes.
NAVIGATION
WPT SM buoy from seaward (see 8.20.29). Then follow the buoyed Vliestroom and Blauwe Slenk chans which narrow for the last 2½M. Pleasure craft should use the Hanerak, a buoyed (Nos HR1-23) chan, parallel about 600m S of the Pollendam which is used by ferries. Caution: When training wall is covered, tidal stream sweeps across the Pollendam, marked by lateral lt bns.
LIGHTS AND MARKS
Ldg lts 112°, both Iso 6s.
RADIO TELEPHONE
VHF Ch 11 (Mon 0000 to Sat 2200LT). Harinxma Canal locks Ch 22.
TELEPHONE (Dial code 0517)
Hr Mr 413041; CG (Brandaris) (0562) 442341; ⌗ 418750; Police 413333; Ⓗ 499999; Brit Consul (020) 6764343.
FACILITIES
Noorderhaven Yacht Hbr ☎ 415666, FW, EI, CH, V, R, Bar, ⊡; **Yacht Hbr Van Harinxma Canal** ☎ 416898, FW, ⊡, C (6 ton); **Services:** CH, EI, E, Gaz, Diving/salvage, EI, ME (by arrangement), D, P. **Town** EC Mon; LB, D, P, V, R, Bar, SM, ✉, ⑧, ⇌, ✈ (Amsterdam). Ferry: See Hook.

NES, AMELAND, Friesland, 53°26'·28N 05°46'·62E. AC 2593, Zeekaart 1458, DYC 1811.6, 1812.2. HW –0055 on Dover; ML 1·6m; Duration 0625. See 8.20.30. Shelter from all but E/S winds. Yacht pontoons at N end of hbr (0·8m) beyond ferry terminal; W side dries to soft mud. Beware sandbanks in the Zeegat van Ameland. Enter from Molengat at MG28-R1 SCM By, VQ(6) + L Fl 10s. Lts: Ameland (W end), Fl (3) 15s 57m 30M, RC. Ferry pier hd Iso 6s 2m 8M. L Fl R 8s and L Fl G 8s piles at ent to yacht hbr ('t Leye Gat, 140 berths), f15.00. Facilities: Gaz, YC. Hr Mr ☎ (0515) 32159.

VLIELAND   8-20-31

WEST FRISIAN ISLANDS
Friesland 53°17'·73N 05°05'·57E   Rtg 2-3-2

CHARTS
AC 112, 2593; Zeekaart 1456; DYC 1811.4/.5; Imray Y5

TIDES
−0300 Dover; ML 1·4; Duration 0610; Zone −0100

Standard Port HELGOLAND (→)

Times				Height (metres)			
High Water		Low Water		MHWS	MHWN	MLWN	MLWS
0200	0700	0200	0800	2·7	2·3	0·4	0·0
1400	1900	1400	2000				
Differences VLIELAND-HAVEN							
−0250	−0320	−0355	−0330	−0·3	−0·2	+0·1	+0·2

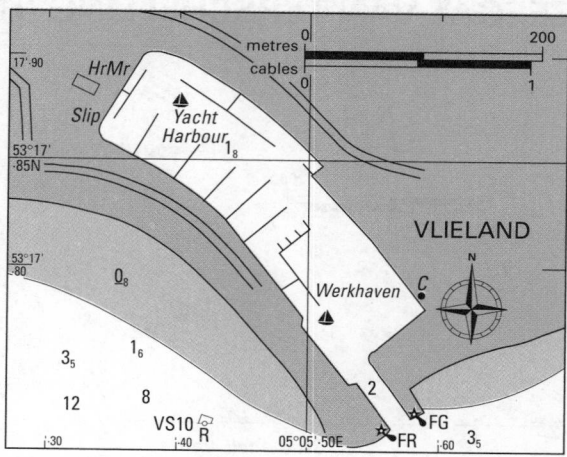

SHELTER
Good; yacht hbr (2m) is very/over-crowded in season. ⚓ in 4-9m, about 0·5M W of the hbr (and nearer the village), except in SE/SW winds; but do not ⚓ in buoyed chan between hbr and ferry pier (no berthing). From the S a safe ⚓ is in Fransche Gaatje, SE of Richel, 6M from hbr.

NAVIGATION
WPT SM (SWM) By, Iso 4s, 53°19'·05N 04°55'·73E, 274°/094° from/to ZS1 and ZS2 Bys, 2·3M (via ZS Bank NCM). See 8.20.33. In fresh W/NW winds a heavy ground swell can raise dangerous seas from the WPT to ZS1/2 Bys. The Zuider Stortemelk is deep, well marked/lit and leads to the Vliestroom. Vliesloot, which forks off to the S, is narrow and in places has only 2·5m at LW sp; keep in mid-chan.

LIGHTS AND MARKS
Main lt ho Iso 4s 53m 20M; R tr, W lantern, R top; RC. Tfc sigs: R Flag or ⓇⓇ at ent = hbr closed (full).

RADIO TELEPHONE
Hr Mr Ch 09; CG Ch 02 (Brandaris, W. Terschelling). All vessels in the Zeegat van Terschelling and N Waddenzee must monitor Ch 02 for the *Brandaris Traffic Centre VTS.*

TELEPHONE (Dial code 0562)
Hr Mr 451729; CG (0562) 442341; ⌗ 451522; Police 451312; Dr 451307; Brit Consul (020) 6764343.

FACILITIES
Yacht Hbr (250) ☎ 451729, f19.50, FW, dinghy slip, ▢; **Hbr** C (10 ton), P & D (cans), D by hose at Harlingen. **Village** El, CH, Ⓔ, Gaz, V, R, ⊠, Ⓑ, ⇌ (ferry to Harlingen), ✈ (Amsterdam). Ferry: Hook of Holland-Harwich.

WEST TERSCHELLING   8-20-32

WEST FRISIAN ISLANDS
Friesland 53°21'·40N 05°13'·23E

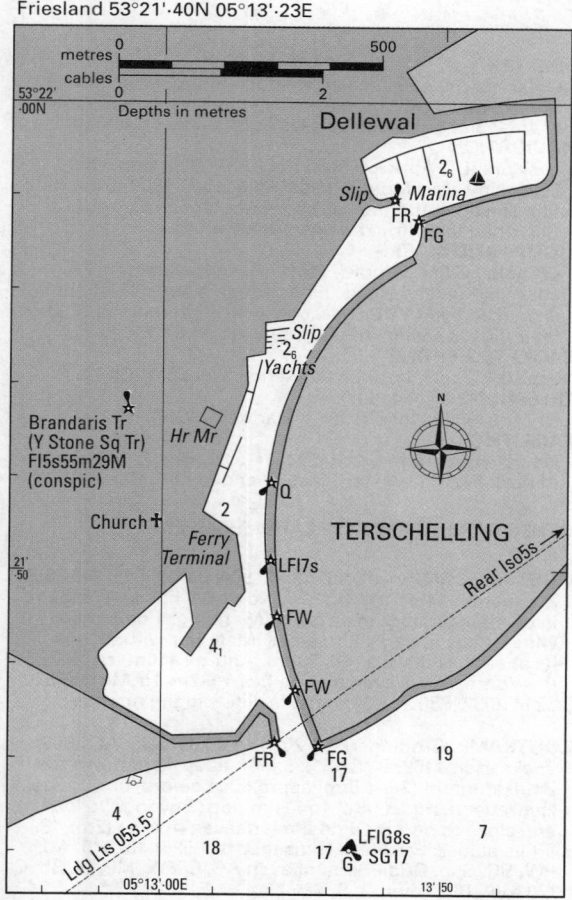

CHARTS
AC 112, 2593; Zeekaart 1456; DYC 1811.4/.5; Imray Y5

TIDES
−0300 Dover; ML 1·4; Duration No data; Zone −0100

Standard Port HELGOLAND (→)

Times				Height (metres)			
High Water		Low Water		MHWS	MHWN	MLWN	MLWS
0200	0700	0200	0800	2·7	2·3	0·4	0·0
1400	1900	1400	2000				
Differences WEST TERSCHELLING							
−0220	−0250	−0335	−0310	−0·4	−0·2	+0·1	+0·2

SHELTER
Good, especially in marina in NE corner of hbr beyond ferry and FV quays. Very crowded in season; considerable commercial traffic and ferries in confined waters.

NAVIGATION
WPT: SM buoy from all directions (see 8.20.31 and .33). Thence via Stortemelk, but first call *Brandaris* for the latest nav/tidal info before deciding the better route:
(a) Vliestroom into West Meep. At NOM4-S13 ECM buoy, VQ (3) 5s, 53°19'·15N 05°15'·65E, enter Slenk chan ldg WNW into the Schuitengat. Best timing = HW±2 .
(b) the shorter Schuitengat, but the ent is narrow/shallow (2·2m). Buoys SG1 and SG2 have been removed. Inside the ent follow the chan buoys and ldg lts 053° to hbr ent.

LIGHTS AND MARKS
Brandaris tr (conspic Y ▢ tr), Fl 5s 55m 29M, storm sigs. Ldg lts 053°: front (W mole) FR, R post, W bands; rear (on dyke 1·1M from front, off chartlet) Iso 5s. See 8.20.4.

RADIO TELEPHONE
Hr Mr Ch 09. CG Ch 02 04 16 67. *Brandaris* (VTS) Ch 02 broadcasts wx, vis, tfc, tidal info at odd H+30 in Dutch and English on request. Yachts in the area must monitor Ch 02 (see 8.20.31); visitors can get update on nav/chans.

TELEPHONE (Dial code 0562)
Hr Mr 442910/442919; CG 442341; ⌗ 442884.

FACILITIES
Marina: Stichting Passantenhaven (500) ☎ 443337, f24.00 (f2.15/metre + f1.00 per head + f1.00) max 3 nights, C, FW; **Hbr** Slip; **Services:** Gaz, ME, SM, Chart agent. **Village** EC Wed; CH, V, R, Bar, ⊠, P & D (cans, see Hr Mr; nearest D by hose is at Harlingen), Ⓑ, ⇌ (ferry to Harlingen), ✈ (Amsterdam). Ferry: Hook-Harwich; Europoort-Hull.

20

ZEEGAT VAN TERSCHELLING (Het Vlie)

[Chart: Zeegat van Terschelling]

Labels on chart:
- 2₈
- N 4
- Engelschhoek
- Boomkensdiep (not used)
- TERSCHELLING
- West-Terschelling Fl5s
- Brandaris
- metres 0 ... 2000
- cables 0 ... 10
- Depths in metres
- 21'
- 1₈
- 1
- 0₉
- 0₁₅
- 0₁
- 0₅
- 0₇
- 7
- 1₄
- 12
- 0₃
- SG9-S2
- YBY
- Q(9)15s
- Schuitengat (buoyed) 8
- 5
- Slenk
- 15
- Shoals
- 53°20'·00N
- 9
- Stortemelk Banks
- 9
- 9
- LFlR5s ZS18
- 9
- 0₅
- Jacobs
- QR VL4
- 1₅
- 0₄
- Ruggen
- 19'
- 6
- VL1 QG
- 34
- 0₄
- LFlR8s VL8
- (buoyed) Zuider Stortemelk
- ZS13-VS2 Fl(2+1)G10s
- Vliesloot Buoyed
- 2₄
- 0₃
- 15
- Vliestroom Buoyed
- WM2
- VLIELAND
- VILLAGE
- 18' Iso4s
- Ferry
- No Landing
- RICHEL
- Often Covers
- Fransche Gaatje
- 0₃
- 8
- 0₄
- 0₃
- 1₄
- 05' 05°10'·00E
- Harlingen
- 11
- West Meep
- 12'

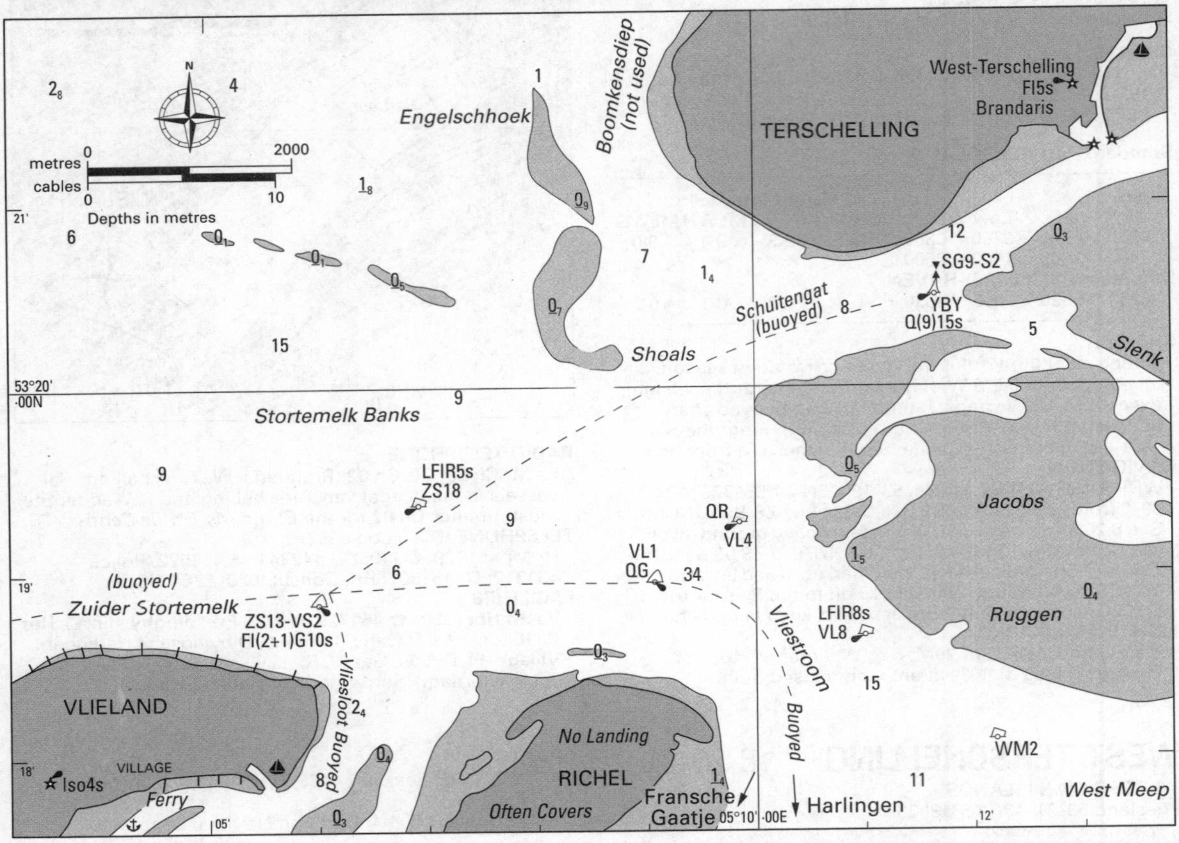

LAUWERSOOG

Friesland, 53°24'·72N 06°12'·10E

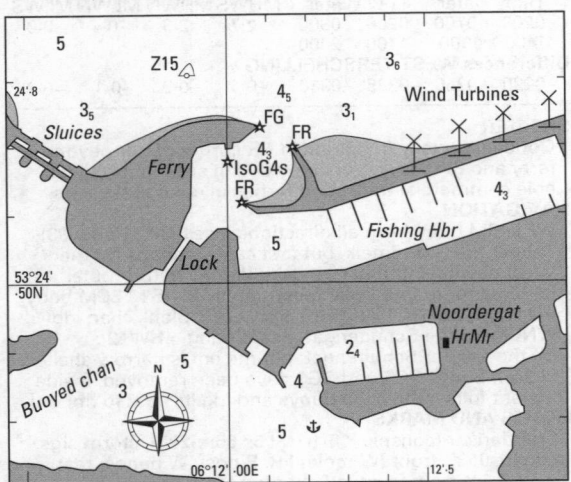

Labels on chart:
- 5
- Z15
- 3₆
- 24'·8
- 3₅
- 4₅
- 3₁
- Wind Turbines
- Sluices
- FG
- FR
- Ferry
- 4₃
- Iso G 4s
- FR
- Fishing Hbr
- 4₃
- 5
- 53°24'·50N
- Lock
- 5
- Noordergat
- HrMr
- 2₄
- Buoyed chan
- 3
- N
- 5
- 4
- 5
- 06°12'·00E
- 12'·5

CHARTS
AC 3509, 3761, Zeekaart 1458, DYC 1812.3

TIDES
HW −0150 on Dover; ML 1·7m; Zone −0100

Standard Port HELGOLAND (→)

Times				Height (metres)			
High Water		Low Water		MHWS	MHWN	MLWN	MLWS
0200	0700	0200	0800	2·7	2·3	0·4	0·0
1400	1900	1400	2000				

Differences LAUWERSOOG

−0130	−0145	−0235	−0220	+0·2	+0·3	+0·3	+0·3

SHELTER
Outer hbr has swell in bad weather. Pontoons in inner FV hbr to await lock. Complete shelter in Noordergat marina (2·4m-2·8m) 3ca SE of lock; **V**s berth on first pontoon.

NAVIGATION
Lock hrs (LT) **Apr-Oct:** Mon-Sat 0700-1900; Sun 0900-2000. **Nov-Mar:** Mon-Fri 0700-1200, 1300-1800 (Sat 1700); Sun closed. Enter the Lauwersmeer for canals from Harlingen to Delfzijl; no need to lower mast.

LIGHTS AND MARKS
W mole FG 3M. E mole FR 4M. Visserhaven mole FR. Lock lead-in jetty Iso 4s. Firing range 1·5m ENE of hbr ent is marked by Fl Y 10s beacons, which alternate W/R when the range is active; info is broadcast on Ch 71.

RADIO TELEPHONE
Hbr VHF Ch 09; Lock Ch 22; Range broadcast Ch 71.

TELEPHONE (Dial code 0519)
Hr Mr 349023; Lock 349043; Marina 349040.

FACILITIES
Noordergat marina, ☎ 349040, f15.00, Gaz, BY, D (E end of hbr), FW; P (ferry terminal, W end of hbr), Bar, R, V, YC.

OTHER HARBOURS IN THE LAUWERSMEER

OOSTMAHORN, Friesland, 53°22'·90N 06°09'·71E. AC 3509, Zeekaarten 1458, DYC 1812.3. Non-tidal hbr on W side of Lauwersmeer; lock in as for Lauwersoog. Floating bns with Y flags mark fishing areas. Main hbr with FR and FG lts at ent has marina (2·2-3·0m). Approx 450m to the SSE the Voorm Veerhaven marina has 1·5-2m. Hr Mr ☎ (0519) 321445/321880; f13.50, most facilities in the marinas.

ZOUTKAMP, Groningen, 53°20'·43N 06°17'·63E. AC 3509, Zeekaarten 1458, DYC 1812.3; non-tidal. Appr down the Zoutkamperril (2·6-4·5m); approx 2ca before lock/bridge, Hunzegat marina (1·5-2·1m) is to port. Beyond the lock and close to port is Oude Binnenhaven marina (2m), f8. FR lts at lock. Facilities: **Hunzegat** ☎ (0595) 402875, AC, FW, SC, Slip. **Oude-Binnenhaven** AC, C, FW, ME, El, Sh, C (20 ton), BH. **Town** D, P, SM, Gaz, ✉, R, V, Dr.

DELFZIJL   8-20-35

Groningen 53°19'·00N 07°00'·50E   Rtg 1-3-2

CHARTS
AC 3510, 3509; Zeekaart 1555; DYC 1812.6; ANWB A

TIDES
−0025 Dover; ML 2·1; Duration 0605; Zone −0100

Standard Port HELGOLAND (→)

Times				Height (metres)			
High Water		Low Water		MHWS	MHWN	MLWN	MLWS
0200	0700	0200	0800	2·7	2·3	0·4	0·0
1400	1900	1400	2000				
Differences DELFZIJL							
+0020	−0005	−0040	0000	+0·9	+0·9	+0·3	+0·3
SCHIERMONNIKOOG							
−0120	−0130	−0240	−0220	+0·2	+0·3	+0·3	+0·3
KNOCK (R. Ems)							
+0018	+0005	−0028	+0004	+0·6	+0·6	0·0	0·0

SHELTER
Good in Neptunus Marina (3·5m) on W of Handelshaven. The Floating Jetty acts as a wavebreak. Berthing (4·5m) also in Farmsumerhaven (24hr only) via the Eemskanaal lock; or at the N end of the Old Eemskanaal in Yacht Hbr 't Dok (4m).

NAVIGATION
WPT Huibertgat SWM buoy, Iso 8s, Whis, 53°34'·90N 06°14'·32E, 270°/090° from/to Borkum Kleiner lt, 15·5M, in W sector. Chan buoys unlit for first 10M.
WPT Westereems SWM buoy, Iso 4s, Racon, 53°36'·97N, 06°19'·48E, 272°/092° from/to Nos 1 and 2 Westereems chan buoys, 1·6M.
WPT from N & E: Riffgat SWM buoy, Iso 8s, 53° 38'·90N 06° 27'·10E, 312°/132° from/to Westereems chan buoys, 3·2M; and 8·75M to Borkum Kleiner lt (See 8.21.10). Thence via Randzelgat and Doekegat (well buoyed/lit) to enter 3M ESE of the city of Delfzijl. Beware strong cross tides at the ent.
INLAND ROUTE TO IJSSELMEER: See 8.20.27.

LIGHTS AND MARKS
From the river, appr ldg lts 203°, both Iso 4s. Hbr ent, FG on W arm and FR on E arm (in fog, Horn 15s and FY). Zeehavenkanaal has Fl G lts to N and Fl R to S. Entry sigs on both piers: 2 (R) = No entry, unless cleared by Hbr office on VHF Ch 14.

RADIO TELEPHONE
All vessels, except recreational craft, must call *Delfzijl Radar* VHF Ch 66 (H24) for VTS, co-ordinated with Ems Traffic. *Port Control* is Ch 14; Sea Locks Ch 11. Traffic, wx and tidal info is broadcast every even H+10 on Ch 14 in Dutch and English on request. *Ems Traffic* Ch 15 18 20 21 (H24) broadcasts every H + 50 weather and tidal info in German, including gale warnings for coastal waters between Die Ems and Die Weser.

TELEPHONE (Dial code 0596)
Hr Mr (Delfzijl Port Authority) 640400, 🖅 630424; Neptunus Hr Mr 615004; Hr Mr 't Dok 616560; Sea locks 613293; CG (Police) 613831; ⌗ 615060; Police 112; Ⓗ 644444; Brit Consul (020) 6764343.

FACILITIES
Neptunus Yacht Hbr ☎ 615004, f15.00, D, Bar, M, L, FW; **Yacht Hbr 't Dok** AB f8.00, D, FW; **Ems Canal** L, FW, AB; **Motor Boat Club Abel Tasman** ☎ 616560 Bar, M, D, FW, L, ◎, V. **Services:** CH, ACA, DYC Agent, ME, El, Gaz. **Town** P, D, V, R, Bar, ✉, Ⓑ, ⇌, ✈ (Groningen/Eelde). Ferry: See Hook of Holland.

OTHER HARBOUR ON THE WEST FRISIAN ISLANDS

SCHIERMONNIKOOG, Friesland, 53°28'·12N 06°10'·10E. AC3509, 3761, Zeekaart 1458, DYC 1812.3. HW −0150 on Dover. See 8.20.35. Appr via Westgat, buoyed/lit, but in bad weather dangerous due to shoals (3·8m) at seaward end. Leave Zoutkamperlaag via Glinder chan (1·5m) to enter Gat van Schiermonnikoog (buoyed). From GVS16-R1 buoy a drying chan, marked by perches/withies, runs 1M N to small yacht hbr (1·3-1·5m) about 1M W of the ferry pier. Access HW −2 to +1, with 1·5m max depth at HW in apprs. Picturesque, but very full in high season; not cheap, ie f27.00. Lts: at W end of island, lt ho Fl (4) 20s 43m 28M, R tr; Ferry pier hd lt FW and Fl (5) Y 20s tide gauge. Hr Mr ☎ (0519) 51544 (May-Sept); Facilities: FW, AC. Note: The CG station at the lt ho provides radar surveillance of the Terschelling/German Bight TSS out to 48M radius and coordinates local SAR operations. It keeps watch on VHF Ch 00, 05, 16, 67 and 73 (all H24); ☎ 0519 531247, 🖅 0519 531000.

ADJACENT HARBOUR AT MOUTH OF THE EMS

EEMSHAVEN, Groningen, 53°27'·75N 06°50'·40E. AC 3509, 3510, Zeekaart 1555, DYC 1812.5/.6. HW −0100 (approx) on Dover. Tides as for Borkum 8.21.11. Eemshaven is a modern commercial port, but may be used by yachts as a port of refuge. Easy appr via Randzelgat and Doekegat or via the buoyed/lit Oude Westereems (Alte Ems), passing the outer anchorage for merchant ships. The last buoy, 1·5M before the hbr ent, is A16 PHM Fl (4) R.
Call *Eemshaven Radar* Ch 19 (H24) for VTS info; and *Eemshaven Port Control* Ch 14 for clearance to enter. There are many wind turbines to the NW and N of the port. A large power stn and chy (128m) are 2M ESE of the port. White roofed bldgs at the port are conspic. Enter on Iso 4s ldg lts 175°, between mole hds, FG and FR. Inner ldg lts, both Iso R 4s, leads 195° to S end of port. Yachts turn stbd here into Emmahaven, marked by FG and FR, and berth on floating jetty on the S bank. Hr Mr ☎ (Delfzijl Port Authority) 640400, 🖅 630424; other ☎ numbers see Delfzijl. Facilities: No special facilities for yachts.

ADJACENT HARBOURS

TERMUNTERZIJL Groningen, 53°18'·21N 07°02'·30E. AC 3510; Zeekaart 1555; DYC 1812. HW −0025 on Dover (UT); use Differences Delfzijl. Ent (1·3M ESE of Delfzijl ent) is close to BW13 SHM buoy Fl G 5s (53°18'·70N 07°02'·40E); thence chan marked by 7 R and 7 G unlit bns. Yachts berth in Vissershaven (0·9m), stbd of ent, or on pontoons (1m) to port of ent, f8.00. Hr Mr ☎ (0596) 601891 (Apr-Sept), VHF Ch 09, FW, AC, Bar, R.

EMDEN see 8.21.9

20

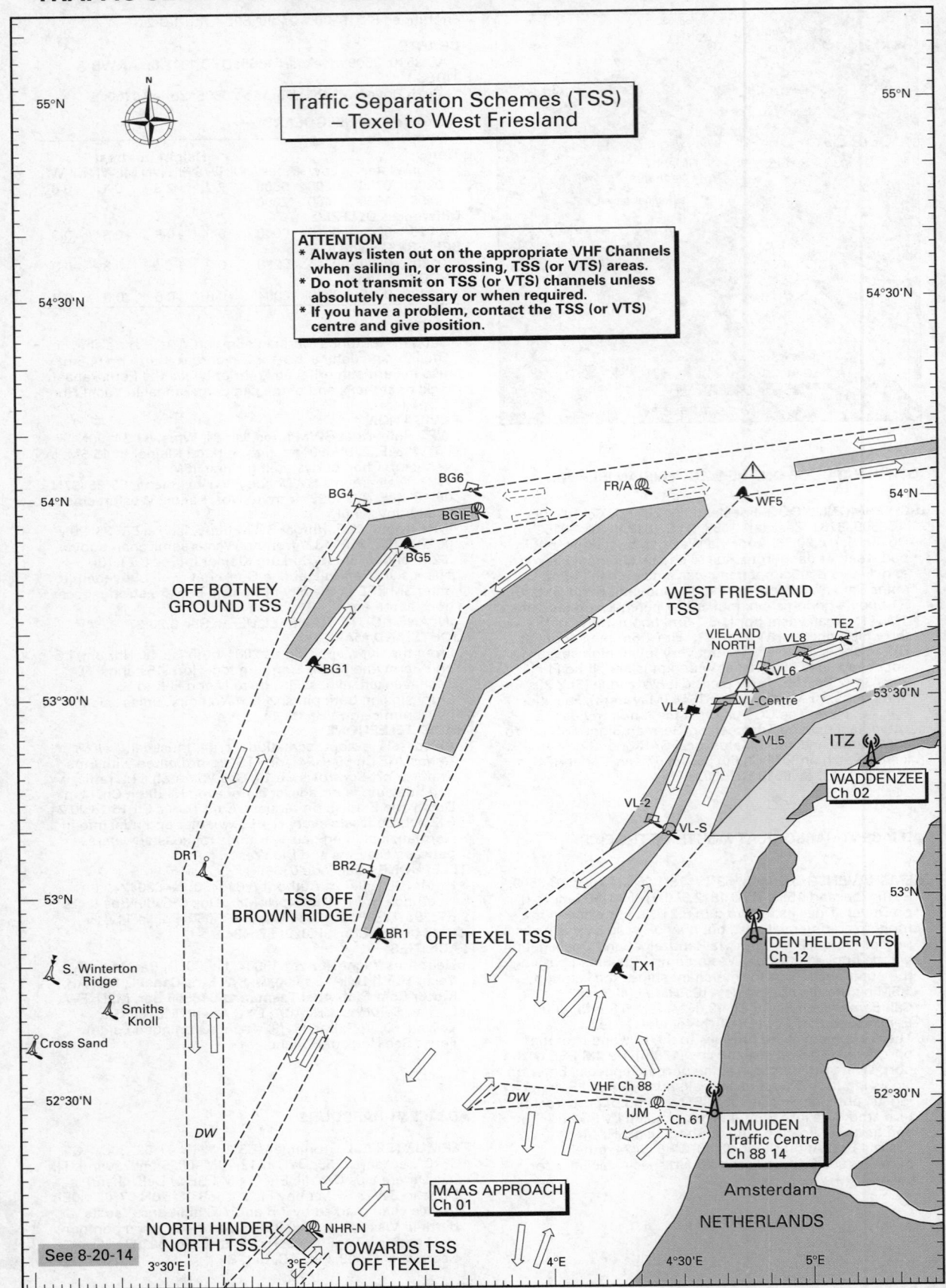

Traffic Separation Schemes (TSS)
– Texel to West Friesland

ATTENTION
* Always listen out on the appropriate VHF Channels when sailing in, or crossing, TSS (or VTS) areas.
* Do not transmit on TSS (or VTS) channels unless absolutely necessary or when required.
* If you have a problem, contact the TSS (or VTS) centre and give position.

OFF BOTNEY GROUND TSS

WEST FRIESLAND TSS

VIELAND NORTH

WADDENZEE Ch 02

ITZ

TSS OFF BROWN RIDGE

OFF TEXEL TSS

DEN HELDER VTS Ch 12

S. Winterton Ridge

Smiths Knoll

Cross Sand

VHF Ch 88

IJM   Ch 61

IJMUIDEN Traffic Centre Ch 88 14

Amsterdam

NETHERLANDS

MAAS APPROACH Ch 01

NORTH HINDER NORTH TSS

NHR-N

TOWARDS TSS OFF TEXEL

See 8-20-14

TSS OFF THE DUTCH AND GERMAN COASTS

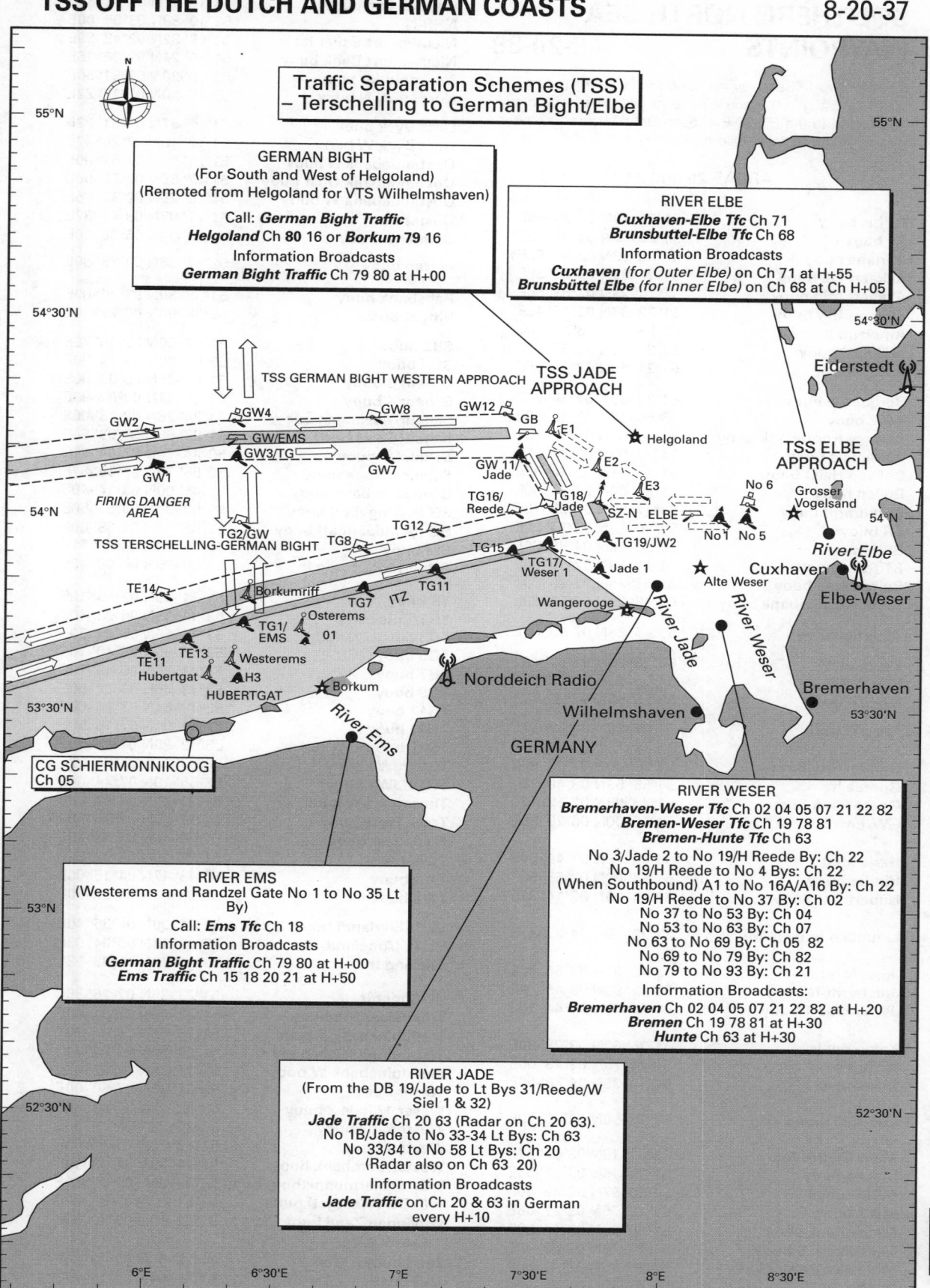

Traffic Separation Schemes (TSS)
– Terschelling to German Bight/Elbe

GERMAN BIGHT
(For South and West of Helgoland)
(Remoted from Helgoland for VTS Wilhelmshaven)

Call: *German Bight Traffic*
Helgoland Ch **80** 16 or *Borkum* 79 16
Information Broadcasts
German Bight Traffic Ch 79 80 at H+00

RIVER ELBE
Cuxhaven-Elbe Tfc Ch 71
Brunsbuttel-Elbe Tfc Ch 68
Information Broadcasts
Cuxhaven (for Outer Elbe) on Ch 71 at H+55
Brunsbüttel Elbe (for Inner Elbe) on Ch 68 at Ch H+05

CG SCHIERMONNIKOOG
Ch 05

RIVER EMS
(Westerems and Randzel Gate No 1 to No 35 Lt
By)

Call: *Ems Tfc* Ch 18
Information Broadcasts
German Bight Traffic Ch 79 80 at H+00
Ems Traffic Ch 15 18 20 21 at H+50

RIVER WESER
Bremerhaven-Weser Tfc Ch 02 04 05 07 21 22 82
Bremen-Weser Tfc Ch 19 78 81
Bremen-Hunte Tfc Ch 63

No 3/Jade 2 to No 19/H Reede By: Ch 22
No 19/H Reede to No 4 Bys: Ch 22
(When Southbound) A1 to No 16A/A16 By: Ch 22
No 19/H Reede to No 37 By: Ch 02
No 37 to No 53 By: Ch 04
No 53 to No 63 By: Ch 07
No 63 to No 69 By: Ch 05 82
No 69 to No 79 By: Ch 82
No 79 to No 93 By: Ch 21
Information Broadcasts:
Bremerhaven Ch 02 04 05 07 21 22 82 at H+20
Bremen Ch 19 78 81 at H+30
Hunte Ch 63 at H+30

RIVER JADE
(From the DB 19/Jade to Lt Bys 31/Reede/W
Siel 1 & 32)
Jade Traffic Ch 20 63 (Radar on Ch 20 63).
No 1B/Jade to No 33-34 Lt Bys: Ch 63
No 33/34 to No 58 Lt Bys: Ch 20
(Radar also on Ch 63 20)
Information Broadcasts
Jade Traffic on Ch 20 & 63 in German
every H+10

55°N   55°N
54°30'N   54°30'N
54°N   54°N
53°30'N   53°30'N
53°N
52°30'N   52°30'N

TSS GERMAN BIGHT WESTERN APPROACH
TSS JADE APPROACH
TSS ELBE APPROACH
TSS TERSCHELLING-GERMAN BIGHT

GW2   GW4   GW8   GW12   GB   E1
GW/EMS   Helgoland   E2
GW3/TG   E3
GW1   GW7   GW 11/   No 6   Grosser
FIRING DANGER   Jade   SZ-N   ELBE   Vogelsand
AREA   TG16/   TG18/   No 1 No 5   River Elbe
TG2/GW   Reede   Jade   No 1
TG12   TG19/JW2
TG8   TG15   Alte Weser   Cuxhaven
TE14   TG17/   Jade 1   Elbe-Weser
Borkumriff   Weser 1
TG7   ITZ   TG11   Wangerooge   River Jade   River Weser
TG1/   Osterems
EMS   01   Norddeich Radio   Bremerhaven
TE11   TE13   Westerems   Wilhelmshaven
Hubertgat   H3   GERMANY
HUBERTGAT   River Ems
Borkum

Eiderstedt

SOUTHERN NORTH SEA WAYPOINTS

8-20-38

Southern North Sea waypoints and principal light positions south of 54°N are listed alphabetically. They are mainly referenced to the ED 50 European Datum, or to the datum shown on the largest scale Admiralty chart.

AREAS 20 and 21

A1 bis buoy	51°21'·70N 02°58'·10E
A2 buoy	51°22'·50N 03°07'·05E
Adriana buoy	51°56'·13N 03°50'·63E
Akkaert NE buoy	51°27'·31N 02°59'·38E
Akkaert Mid buoy	51°24'·23N 02°53'·50E
Akkaert SW buoy	51°22'·33N 02°46'·42E
Ameland lt	53°27'·02N 05°37'·60E
A-Noord buoy	51°23'·50N 02°37'·00E
A-Zuid buoy	51°21'·50N 02°37'·00E
Bergues N buoy	51°20'·00N 02°24'·62E
BG 2 buoy	53°58'·42N 03°17'·50E
Binnenstroombank buoy	51°14'·50N 02°53'·73E
Birkenfels buoy	51°39'·05N 02°32'·05E
Bol van Heist buoy	51°23'·15N 03°12'·05E
Bollen buoy	51°50'·00N 03°33'·00E
Borkumriff buoy	53°47'·50N 06°22'·13E
BR buoy	53°30'·70N 05°33'·62E
BSP buoy	53°30'·80N 04°30'·00E
BT Ratel buoy	51°11'·62N 02°28'·00E
Buitenbank buoy	51°51'·20N 03°25'·80E
Buitenstroombank buoy	51°15'·20N 02°51'·80E
Dovetief buoy	53°45'·38N 07°09'·80E
Eierland lt	53°10'·97N 04°51'·40E
Elbe 1 lt F	54°00'·00N 08°06'·58E
Eveline buoy	52°25'·55N 04°25'·15E
Fairy W buoy	51°23'·90N 02°09'·44E
Garden City buoy	51°29'·20N 02°17'·90E
Goeree lt	51°55'·53N 03°40'·18E
Goote Bank buoy	51°26'·98N 02°52'·72E
GW/Ems lt F	54°10'·00N 06°20'·80E
Harle buoy	53°49'·28N 07°49'·00E
Hinder buoy	51°54'·60N 03°55'·50E
Hubert Gat buoy	53°34'·90N 06°14'·32E
IJmuiden buoy (IJM)	52°28'·50N 04°23'·87E
Juist-N buoy	53°43'·90N 06°55'·40E
Juisterriff-N buoy	53°42'·90N 06°45'·82E
JW 5/Jade 1 buoy	53°52'·47N 07°44'·10E
Kaloo buoy	51°35'·60N 03°23'·30E
KB buoy	51°21'·75N 02°43'·00E
Kijkduin lt	52°57'·35N 04°43'·60E
LST '420' buoy	51°15'·50N 02°40'·70E
Maas Centre buoy	52°01'·18N 03°53'·57E
Magne buoy	51°39'·15N 03°19'·60E
MBN buoy	51°20'·87N 02°46'·40E
MD 3 buoy	51°42'·75N 03°27'·06E
Middelbank buoy	51°40'·90N 03°18'·30E
Middelkerk S buoy	51°14'·78N 02°42'·00E
Middelkerk Bank buoy	51°18'·25N 02°42'·80E
MV buoy	51°57'·50N 03°58'·50E
MW 1 buoy	51°51'·25N 03°09'·40E

Nautica Ena buoy	51°18'·12N 02°52'·85E
NHR-N	52°10'·90N 03°05'·00E
Nieuwpoort E pier lt	51°09'·32N 02°43'·89E
Nieuwpoort Bank buoy	51°10'·21N 02°36'·16E
Noordhinder buoy	52°00'·20N 02°51'·50E
Norderney N buoy	53°46'·10N 07°17'·22E
Oost Dyck buoy	51°21'·57N 02°31'·23E
Oost Dyck W buoy	51°17'·18N 02°26'·42E
Oostendebank N buoy	51°21'·25N 02°53'·00E
Oostendebank Oost buoy	51°17'·36N 02°52'·00E
Oostendebank W buoy	51°16'·25N 02°44'·85E
Ooster buoy	51°47'·97N 03°41'·32E
Osterems buoy	53°41'·94N 06°36'·20E
Petten buoy	52°47'·38N 04°36'·80E
Rabsbank buoy	51°38'·30N 03°10'·00E
Riffgat buoy	53°38'·90N 06°27'·10E
SBZ buoy	51°42'·50N 03°16'·70E
SCH buoy	52°07'·80N 04°14'·20E
Scheur 3 buoy	51°24'·35N 03°03'·00E
Scheur 4 buoy	51°25'·07N 03°02'·93E
Scheur-Wielingen buoy	51°24'·26N 03°18'·00E
Scheur-Zand buoy	51°23'·68N 03°07'·68E
Schlucter buoy	53°44'·70N 07°04'·22E
Schlusseltone buoy	53°56'·30N 07°54'·87E
Schouwenbank buoy	51°45'·00N 03°14'·40E
SG (Haringvliet) buoy	51°52'·00N 03°51'·50E
SG (Schulpengat) buoy	52°52'·95N 04°38'·00E
SM buoy	53°19'·29N 04°55'·71E
Schiermonnikoog lt	53°29'·20N 06°08'·90E
TB buoy	51°34'·45N 02°59'·15E
TG1/Ems buoy	53°43'·38N 06°22'·40E
TG3 buoy	53°44'·65N 06°31'·20E
TG5 buoy	53°45'·90N 06°40'·10E
TG7 buoy	53°47'·35N 06°49'·78E
TG9 buoy	53°48'·45N 06°57'·80E
TG11 buoy	53°49'·64N 07°06'·60E
TG13 buoy	53°51'·00N 07°15'·50E
TG15 buoy	53°52'·20N 07°24'·35E
TG17/JW1 buoy	53°53'·47N 07°33'·22E
TG19/JW2 buoy	53°55'·10N 07°44'·60E
Thornton SW buoy	51°31'·01N 02°51'·00E
Track Ferry buoy	51°33'·80N 02°36'·50E
Trapegeer buoy	51°08'·46N 02°34'·45E
Twin buoy	51°32'·10N 02°22'·62E
TX 1 buoy	52°48'·17N 04°15'·60E
TX 3 buoy	52°58'·61N 04°22'·50E
VL 1 (Eierland) buoy	53°11'·00N 04°35'·40E
VL 11 (Ameland)	53°28'·13N 05°04'·03E
Vlieland lt	53°17'·79N 05°03'·58E
W Hinder lt	51°23'·36N 02°26'·36E
Wandelaar SW buoy	51°22'·00N 03°01'·00E
Wenduinebank E buoy	51°18'·85N 03°01'·70E
Wenduinebank N buoy	51°21'·50N 03°02'·71E
Wenduinebank W buoy	51°17'·28N 02°52'·87E
Weser buoy	53°54'·25N 07°50'·00E
Weser 1/Jade 2 buoy	53°52'·13N 07°47'·36E
Westerems buoy	53°36'·98N 06°19'·50E
Westpit buoy	51°33'·70N 03°10'·00E
Weststroombank buoy	51°11'·39N 02°43'·15E
WG (Schiermonnikoog) buoy	53°32'·25N 06°06'·11E
WG-OG (Westgat) buoy	51°37'·23N 03°28'·87E
Wielingen Zand buoy	51°22'·60N 03°10'·80E
Zand buoy	51°22'·56N 03°10'·16E
ZSB buoy	51°36'·64N 03°15'·77E
Zuidstroombank buoy	51°12'·33N 02°47'·50E

VOLVO PENTA SERVICE

**Sales and service centres in area 21
Names and addresses of Volvo Penta dealers in
this area are available from:**
Germany *Volvo Penta Central Europe GmbH*, Redderkoppel 5, Postfach 9013,
D-24151 Kiel Tel +49 431 39940, Fax +49 431 396774

Area 21

Germany
Emden to Danish border

**VOLVO
PENTA**

8.21.1	Index	**Page 853**
8.21.2	Diagram of ports, lts, RDF bns, Coast radio and weather stns	**854**
8.21.3	Tidal stream charts	**856**
8.21.4	List of coastal lights, fog signals and waypoints	**858**
8.21.5	German glossary	**862**
8.21.6	Passage information	**865**
8.21.7	Distance table	**866**
8.21.8	Special notes for Germany	**867**
8.21.9	Emden Greetsiel Norddeich Nessmersiel	**868**
8.21.10	East Frisian Islands Juist Baltrum Spiekeroog	**869**
8.21.11	Borkum	**870**
8.21.12	Norderney	**870**
8.21.13	Dornumer-Accumersiel	**871**
8.21.14	Langeoog	**871**
8.21.15	Wangerooge Bensersiel Neuharlingersiel Harlesiel	**872**
8.21.16	Hooksiel Wangersiel Rüstersiel	**873**
8.21.17	Wilhelmshaven, Standard Port, tidal curves Dangast	**877**
8.21.18	Bremerhaven	**878**
8.21.19	Cuxhaven, Standard Port, tidal curves	**879**
8.21.20	River Elbe and Hamburg	**883**
8.21.21	Brunsbüttel Otterndorf	**884**
8.21.22	Nord-Ostsee Kanal	**885**
8.21.23	Helgoland, Standard Port, tidal curves	**886**
8.21.24	Büsum Tönning Husum Pellworm Wittdün (Amrum) Wyk (Föhr)	**890**
8.21.25	Sylt	**890**
8.21.26	Tidal differences for the west coast of Denmark	**891**

21

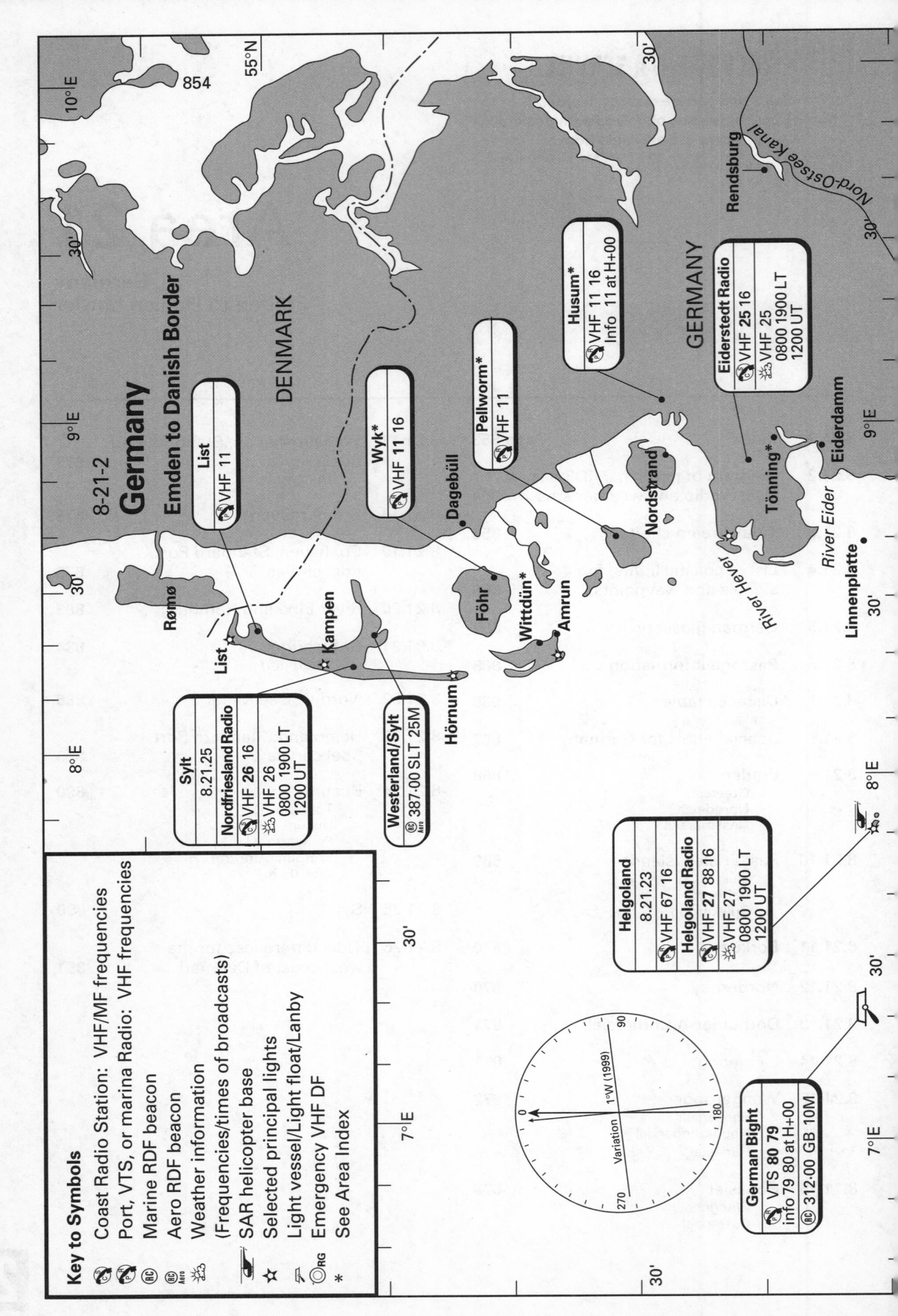

Key to Symbols

	Coast Radio Station: VHF/MF frequencies
	Port, VTS, or marina Radio: VHF frequencies
	Marine RDF beacon
	Aero RDF beacon
	Weather information (Frequencies/times of broadcasts)
	SAR helicopter base
☆	Selected principal lights
	Light vessel/Light float/Lanby
RG	Emergency VHF DF
*	See Area Index

8-21-2

Germany
Emden to Danish Border

854

List
VHF 11

Wyk*
VHF 11 16

Pellworm*
VHF 11

Husum*
VHF 11 16
Info 11 at H+00

Eiderstedt Radio
VHF 25 16
VHF 25
0800 1900 LT
1200 UT

Sylt
8.21.25
Nordfriesland Radio
VHF 26 16
VHF 26
0800 1900 LT
1200 UT

Westerland/Sylt
387·00 SLT 25M

Helgoland
8.21.23
Helgoland Radio
VHF 67 16
VHF 27 88 16
VHF 27
0800 1900 LT
1200 UT

German Bight
VTS 80 79
info 79 80 at H+00
312·00 GB 10M

Variation 1°W (1999)

DENMARK

GERMANY

Rømø

List

Kampen

Hörnum

Föhr

Wittdün*

Amrun

Dagebüll

Nordstrand

River Hever

Tönning*

River Eider

Linnenplatte

Eiderdamm

Rendsburg

Nord-Ostsee Kanal

55°N

10°E

9°E

8°E

7°E

9°E

8°E

7°E

30'

30'

30'

30'

30'

30'

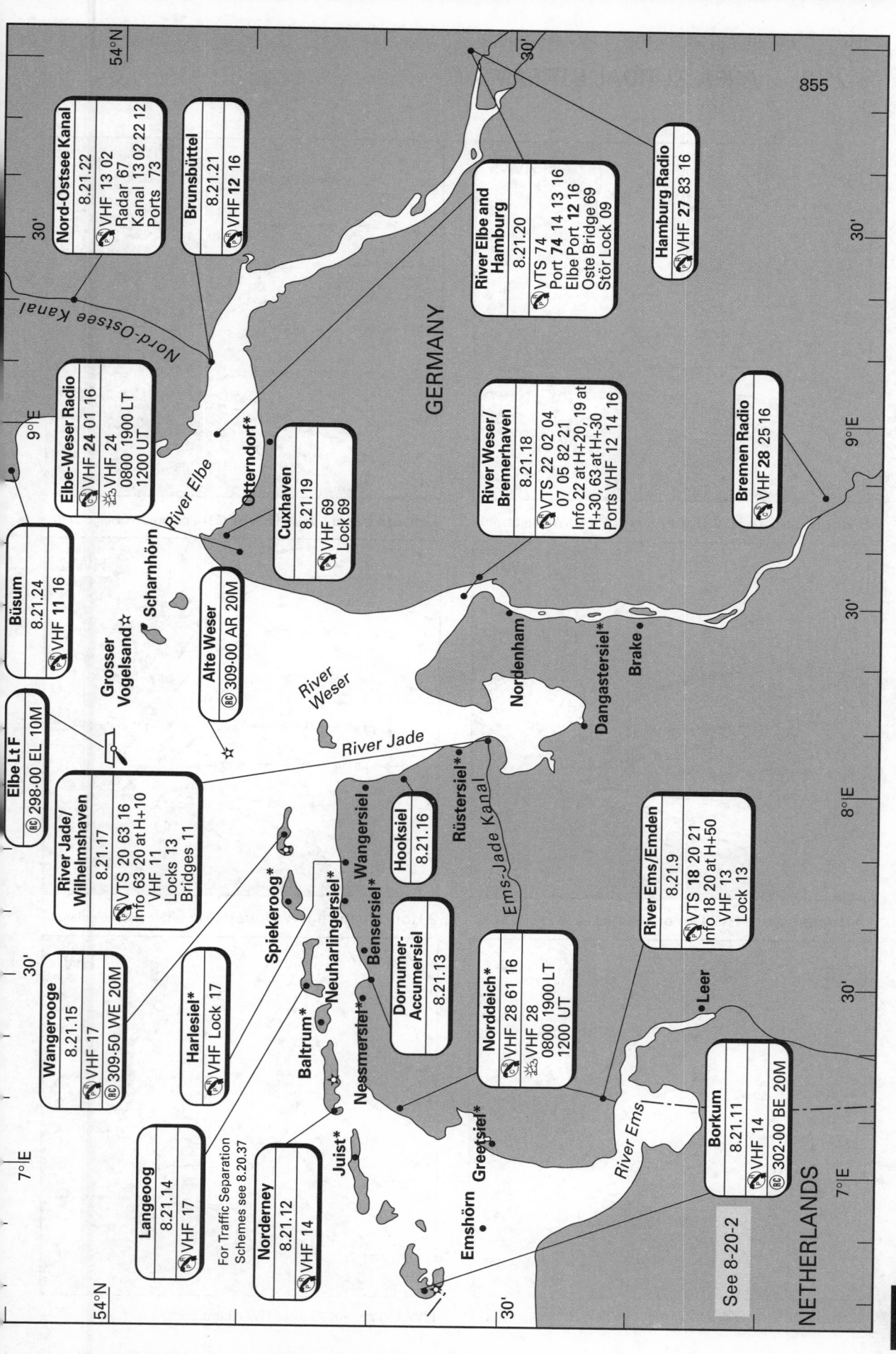

855

Nord-Ostsee Kanal
8.21.22
📻 VHF 13 02
Radar 67
Kanal 13 02 22 12
Ports 73

Brunsbüttel
8.21.21
📻 VHF **12** 16

Hamburg Radio
📻 VHF **27** 83 16

River Elbe and Hamburg
8.21.20
📻 VTS 74
Port **74** 14 13 16
Elbe Port **12** 16
Oste Bridge 69
Stör Lock 09

Elbe-Weser Radio
📻 VHF **24** 01 16
📡 VHF 24
0800 1900 LT
1200 UT

Büsum
8.21.24
📻 VHF **11** 16

Cuxhaven
8.21.19
📻 VHF 69
Lock 69

River Weser/Bremerhaven
8.21.18
📻 VTS 22 02 04
07 05 82 21
Info 22 at H+20, 19 at
H+30, 63 at H+30
Ports VHF 12 14 16

Bremen Radio
📻 VHF **28** 25 16

GERMANY

Otterndorf*

River Elbe

Scharnhörn

Grosser Vogelsand ☆

Alte Weser
📻 309·00 AR 20M

Elbe Lt F
📻 298·00 EL 10M

River Jade/Wilhelmshaven
8.21.17
📻 VTS 20 63 16
Info 63 20 at H+10
Locks 13
Bridges 11

River Weser

River Jade

Nordenham

Dangastersiel*

Brake •

Hooksiel
8.21.16

Rüstersiel*•

Wangersiel*

Ems-Jade Kanal

River Ems/Emden
8.21.9
📻 VTS **18** 20 21
Info 18 20 at H+50
VHF 13
Lock 13

Wangerooge
8.21.15
📻 VHF 17
📻 309·50 WE 20M

Harlesiel*
📻 VHF Lock 17

Spiekeroog*

Neuharlingersiel*

Bensersiel*

Dornumer-Accumersiel
8.21.13

Norddeich*
📻 VHF 28 61 16
📡 VHF 28
0800 1900 LT
1200 UT

Leer •

Langeoog
8.21.14
📻 VHF 17

Norderney
8.21.12
📻 VHF 14

For Traffic Separation
Schemes see 8.20.37

Baltrum*

Nessmersiel*•

Juist*

Greetsiel*•

Emshörn

River Ems

Borkum
8.21.11
📻 VHF 14
📻 302·00 BE 20M

See 8-20-2

NETHERLANDS

Nord-Ostsee Kanal

54°N

9°E

8°E

7°E

30'

30'

30'

30'

30'

21

8-21-3   AREA 21 TIDAL STREAMS

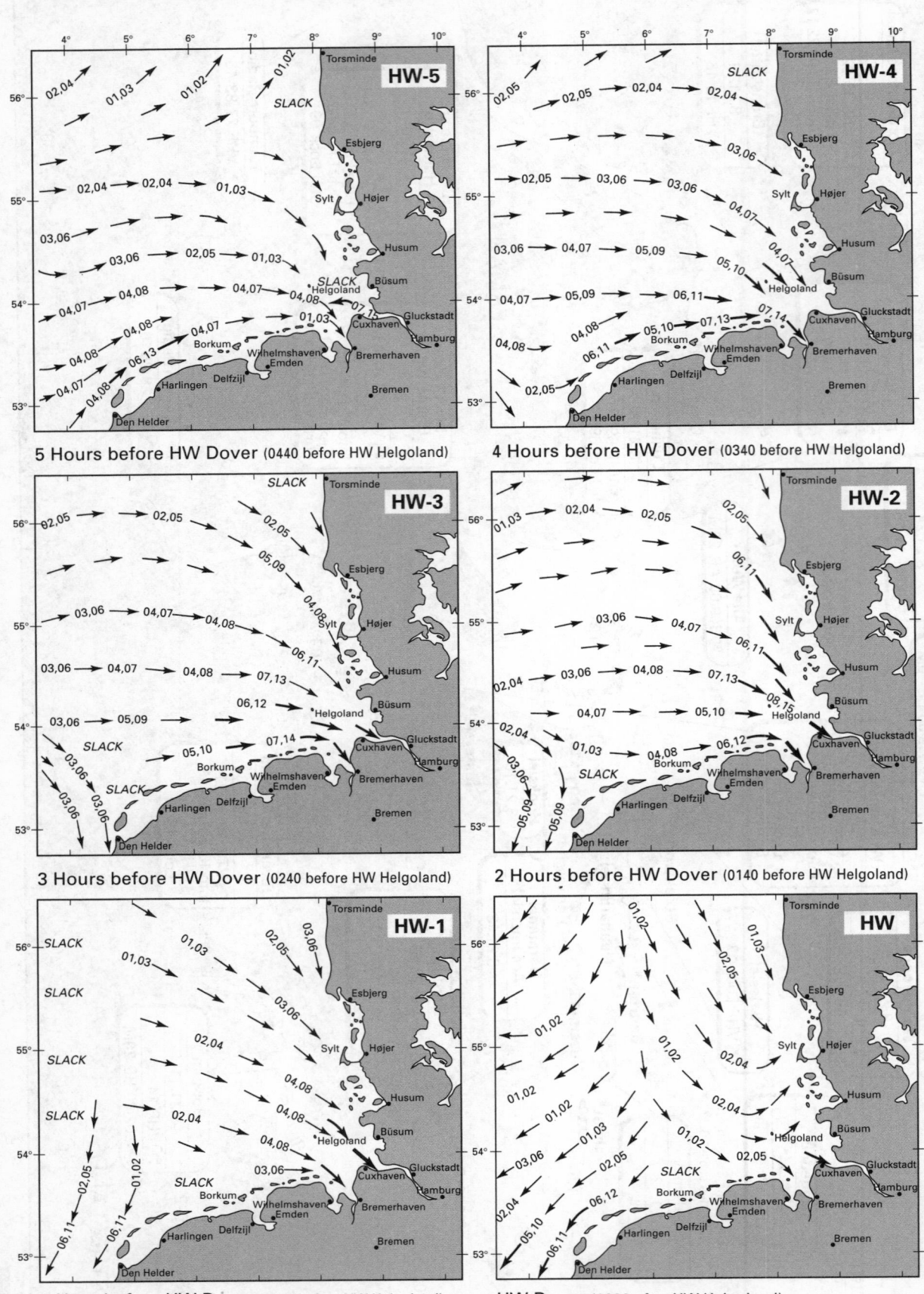

5 Hours before HW Dover (0440 before HW Helgoland)

4 Hours before HW Dover (0340 before HW Helgoland)

3 Hours before HW Dover (0240 before HW Helgoland)

2 Hours before HW Dover (0140 before HW Helgoland)

1 Hour before HW Dover (0040 before HW Helgoland)

HW Dover (0020 after HW Helgoland)

South-westward 8.20.3

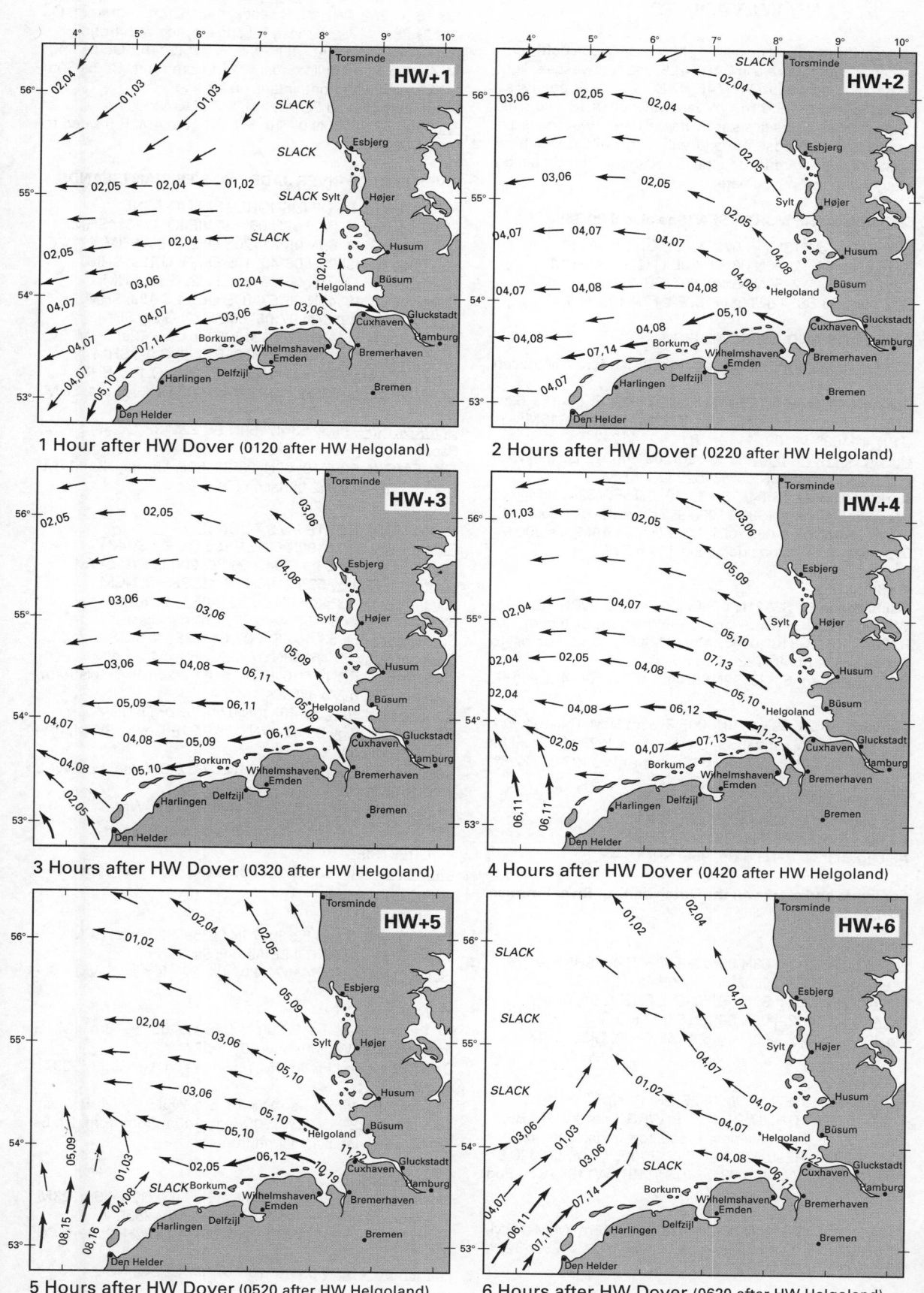

1 Hour after HW Dover (0120 after HW Helgoland)

2 Hours after HW Dover (0220 after HW Helgoland)

3 Hours after HW Dover (0320 after HW Helgoland)

4 Hours after HW Dover (0420 after HW Helgoland)

5 Hours after HW Dover (0520 after HW Helgoland)

6 Hours after HW Dover (0620 after HW Helgoland)

21

8.21.4 COASTAL LIGHTS, FOG SIGNALS AND WAYPOINTS

Lights with a nominal range of 15M or more are in **bold** print, places and features are in CAPITALS, and light-vessels, light floats and Lanbys in *CAPITAL ITALICS*. Unless otherwise stated lights are white. m = elevation in metres; M = nominal range in miles. Fog signals are *italics*. Useful waypoints are underlined; use those on land with care. All geographical positions are referenced to the ED 50 datum but should be assumed to be approximate.

CROSSING THE NORTH SEA (See also 8.20.38)

GW12 buoy 54°13'·30N 07°22'·40E QR; PHM.
GW8 buoy 54°12'·90N 06°51'·20E Fl (2) R 9s; PHM.
GW4 buoy 54°12'·50N 06°20'·60E QR; PHM.
BG2 buoy 53°58'·42N 03°17'·50E L Fl R 10s; PHM.

RIVER EMS AND APPROACHES

Westerems buoy 53°36'·98N 06°19'·50E Iso 4s; SWM; Racon (T).
Borkum Grosser 53°35'·38N 06°39'·82E Fl (2) 12s 63m **24M**; brown tr. F WRG 46m **W19M, R15M, G15M**; vis G107·4°-109°, W109°-111·2°, R111·2°-112·6°.
Hubert Gat SWM buoy 53°34'·90N 06°14'·32E Iso 8s; *Whis.*
H11 buoy 53°34'·65N 06°33'·62E QG; SHM.
Borkum Kleiner 53°34'·78N 06°40'·08E FW 32m **30M**; R tr, W bands; FW (intens) 089·9°-090·9° (Ldg sector for Hubertgat); RC; Fl 3s **16M**; vis 088°-089·9°; Q (4) 10s **16M**; vis 090·9°-093°; RC; Iso Y 4s on tide gauge 420m SW.

- BORKUM
Fischerbalje 53°33'·21N 06°43'·00E Oc (2) WRG 16s 15m **W16M**, R12M, G11M; W l tr, R top and lantern, on tripod; vis R260°-313°, G313°-014°, W014°-068°, (Ldg sector to Fischerbalje); R068°-123°. Fog det lt.
Schutzhafen ent 53°33'·52N 06°45'·11E FG 10m 4M, and FR 8m 4M.

Campen 53°24'·39N 07°01'·00E F 62m **30M**; R framework tr, 2 galleries, W central col, G cupola; vis 127°-127·3°. Fl 5s (same tr); vis 126·5°-127°. Fl (4) 15s (same tr) vis 127·3°-127·8°.

- ALTE EMS
A2a buoy 53°32'·93N 06°39'·53E; PHM.
A3 buoy 53°32'·85N 06°39'·25E; SHM.
A5 buoy 53°31'·81N 06°39'·95E; SHM.

For lights and marks on the Dutch bank of River Ems see 8.20.4

- DUKE GAT
No 35 buoy 53°27'·08N 06°52'·88E Fl G 4s; SHM.
No 37 buoy 53°26'·00N 06°55'·00E QG; SHM.
No 41 buoy 53°24'·32N 06°56'·80E Fl (2) G 9s; SHM.
No 45 buoy 53°22'·05N 06°58'·57E; SHM.
No 49 buoy 53°20'·02N 06°59'·75E Oc (2) G 9s; SHM.

- KNOCK
K4 buoy 53°19'·87N 07°00'·82E QR; PHM.
Knock 53°20'·37N 07°01'·50E F WRG 28m W12M, R9M, G8M; Gy tr, four galleries, broad top, radar antenna; vis W270°-299°, R299°-008·3°, G008·3°-023°, W023°-026·8°, R026·8°-039°, W039°-073°, R073°-119°, W119°-154°; Fog det lt.

Wybelsum 53°20'·20N 07°06'·57E F WR 16m W6M, R5M; W framework tr, R bands; radar antenna; vis W295°-320°, R320°-024°, W024°-049°; Fog Det lt.

- EMDEN
Logum ldg lts 075·2°. Front, 53°20'·17N 07°08'·05E Oc (2) 12s 16m 12M; W mast, R bands; rear, 630m from front, Oc (2) 12s 28m 12M; W mast, R bands; synch with front.
Ldg lts 087·6°. Front, 53°20'·07N 07°12'·15E Oc 5s 14m 14M; intens on ldg line; rear, 0·8M from front, Oc 5s 30m 14M; synch with front, intens on ldg line.
Outer hbr E pier hd FG 7m 5M; R ○ tr, B band.
W pierhd 53°20'·10N 07°10'·57E FR 10m 4M; R 8-sided tr; *Horn Mo (ED) 30s.*

RIVER EMS TO RIVER JADE, INC E FRISIAN ISLANDS.

- OUTER LIMIT OF INSHORE TRAFFIC ZONE
TG1/Ems buoy 53°43'·38N 06°22'·40E IQ. G 13s; SHM.
TG3 buoy 53°44'·65N 06°31'·20E Fl (2) G 9s; SHM.
TG5 buoy 53°45'·90N 06°40'·10E Oc (3) G 12s; SHM.
TG7 buoy 53°47'·35N 06°49'·78E Fl (2) G 9s; SHM.
TG9 buoy 53°48'·45N 06°57'·80E Oc (3) G 12s; SHM.
TG11 buoy 53°49'·64N 07°06'·60E Fl (2) G 9s; SHM.
TG13 buoy 53°51'·00N 07°15'·50E Oc (3) G 12s; SHM.
TG15 buoy 53°52'·20N 07°24'·35E Fl (2) G 9s; SHM.
TG17/JW 1 buoy 53°53'·47N 07°33'·22E IQ 13s; SHM.
TG19/JW 2 buoy 53°55'·10N 07°44'·60E Oc (3) G 12s; SHM.

BORKUMRIFF buoy 53°47'·50N 06°22'·13E Oc 4s; SWM; Racon (T).
GW/EMS lt F 54°10'·00N 06°20'·80E Iso 8s 12m **17M**; *Horn Mo (R) 30s (H24)*; Racon (T).

- INSHORE ROUTE EMS TO JADE
Riffgat buoy 53°38'·90N 06°27'·10E Iso 8s; SWM.
Oosterems buoy 53°41'·94N 06°36'·20E Iso 4s; SWM.
Juisterriff -N buoy 53°42'·90N 06°45'·82E Q; NCM.
Juist - N buoy 53°43'·90N 06°55'·40E VQ; NCM.
53°40'·95N 07°03'·50E Aero Fl 5s 14m (occas).
Schluchter buoy 53°44'·70N 07°04'·22E Iso 8s; SWM.
Dovetief buoy 53°45'·38N 07°09'·80E Iso 4s; SWM.
Platform 54°42'·1N 07°10'·0E; Mo (U) 15s 24m 9M; R platform, Y stripes; *Horn Mo (U) 30s.*
Norderney N buoy 53°46'·10N 07°17'·22E Q; NCM.
Accumer Ee buoy 53°47'·27N 07°28'·37E Iso 8s; SWM; (frequently moved.)
Otzumer Balje buoy 53°48'·01N 07°37'·38E Iso 4s; SWM; (frequently moved.)
Harle buoy 53°49'·28N 07°49'·00E Iso 8s; SWM.

- GREETSIEL
Meßstation lt bn 53°32'·97N 07°02'·22E Fl Y 4s 15m 3M.

- JUIST
Training wall, S end 53°39'·70N 06°59'·92E; pile; SCM.
Juist 53°41'·9N 07°03'·5E Aero Fl 5s 14m.
Schluchter buoy 53°44'·70N 07°04'·22E Iso 8s; SWM.

- NORDDEICH
W training wall, hd 53°38'·7N 07°09'·0E FG 8m 4M; G framework tr, W lantern; vis 021°-327°.
E training wall hd FR 8m 4M; R & W △s on R tr; vis 327°-237°; Fog lt.
Ldg lts 144°. Front, Iso WR 6s 6m W6M, R4M; B mast; vis R078°-122°, W122°-150°; rear, 140m from front, Iso 6s 9m 6M; B mast; synch with front.

- NORDERNEY
Norderney 53°42'·6N 07°13'·8E Fl (3) 12s 59m **23M**; R 8 sided tr; unintens 067°-077° and 270°-280°.
Fish h br W mole hd 53°41'·9N 07°09'·9E Oc (2) R 9s 13m 4M; R & W tr.
Norderney N buoy 53°46'·10N 07°17'·22E Q; NCM.

• BALTRUM
Baltrum groyne hd 53°43'·3N 07°21'·7E Oc WRG 6s 7m W6M,
R4M, G3M; vis G074·5°-090°, W090°-095°, R095°-074·5°.

• NESSMERSIEL
Mole N hd 53°41'·9N 07°21'·7E Oc 4s 6m 5M; G mast.
Accumer Ee buoy 53°47·27N 07°28'·37E Iso 8s; SWM;
(frequently moved.)

• LANGEOOG
W mole hd 53°43'·42N 07°30'·13E Oc WRG 6s 8m W7M,
R5M, G4M; R basket on R mast; vis G064°-070°, W070°-
074°, R074°-326°, W326°-330°, G330°-335°, R335°-064°;
Horn Mo (L) 30s (0730-1800LT).

• DORNUMER-ACCUMERSIEL
W bkwtr hd 53°41'·25N 07°29'·40E.

• BENSERSIEL
E training wall hd 53° 41'·84N 07°32'·90E Oc WRG 6s 6m
W5M, R3M, G2M; vis G110°-119°, W119°-121°, R121°-
110°.
Ldg lts 138°: Front, Iso 6s 7m 9M; rear, 167m from front,
Iso 6s 11m 9M. Both intens on ldg line.

Otzumer Balje buoy 53°48'·01N 07°37'·38E Iso 4s SWM;
(frequently moved.)

• SPIEKEROOG
Spiekeroog 53°45'·0N 07°41'·3E FR 6m 4M; R mast;
vis 197°-114°.

• NEUHARLINGERSIEL
Training wall hd 53°43'·22N 07°42'·30E Oc 6s 6m 5M; G
mast.

• HARLESIEL
Harle buoy 53°49'·28N 07°49'·00E Iso 8s; SWM.
Carolinensieler Balje, Leitdamm 53°44'·13N 07°50'·10E L Fl
8s 7m 6M; G mast.
N mole hd 53°42'·63N 07°48'·70E Iso R 4s 6m 7M.

• WANGEROOGE
Wangerooge, W end 53°47'·45N 07°51'·52E Fl R 5s 60m
23M; R ○ tr, 2 W bands; same tr; F WRG 24m **W22M, W15M,
R17M**, R11M, **G18M**, G10M; vis R358·5°-008°, W008°-
018·5°, G018·5°-055°, W055°-060·5°, R060·5°-065·5°,
W065·5°–071°, G(18M) 119·4°-138·8°, W(22M) 138·8°-152·2°,
Ldg sector, R(17M) 152·2°-159·9°; RC.
E mole hd 53°46'·50N 07°52'·17E FG 3m 5M.

RIVER JADE AND APPROACHES

JW5/Jade 1 buoy 53°52'·47N 07°44'·10E Oc G 4s; SHM.
Weser 1/Jade 2 buoy 53°52'·13N 07°47'·36E Fl (2+1) G 15s;
Racon (T); SHM.
Mellumplate 53°46'·35N 08°05'·60E F 27m **24M**; R □ tr, W
band; vis 116·1°-116·4°; Ldg sector for outer part of
Wangerooger Fahrwasser. The following lts are shown from
the same tr over sectors indicated. Fl 4s **23M**; vis 114°-
115·2°. Fl (4) 15s; vis 117·2°-118·4°. Oc WRG 29m W14M,
R11M, G10M; vis R000°-006°, W006°-037·6°, G037·6°-114°,
R118·4°-168°, W168°-183·5°, R183·5°-212°, W212°-266°,
R266°-280°, W280°-000°. Mo (A) 7·5s; vis 115·2°-116·1°.
Ldg sector. Mo (N) 7·5s; vis116·4°-117·2°; Ldg sector.
Helicopter platform.
No 7 buoy 53°50'·30N 07°51'·24E Oc (3) G 12s; SHM.
No 11 buoy 53°49'·23N 07°55'·08E Fl G 4s; SHM.
No 15 buoy 53°48'·13N 07°58'·88E IQ. G 13s; SHM.

No 19 buoy 53°47'·02N 08°01'·97E QG; SHM.
No 23 buoy 53°45'·21N 08°02'·81E Oc (3) G 12s; SHM.
Minsener Oog, Buhne A N end 53°47'·30N 08°00'·45E
F WRG 16m W13M, R10M, G9M; □ tr; vis R050°-055°,
W055°-134·8°, R134·8°-146·7°, W146·7-156·6°, G156·6°-
211·3°, W211·3°-255·2°, G255·2°-290·2°, W290·2°-050°.
Oldoog, Buhne C 53°45'·40N 08°01'·35E Oc WRG 4s 25m
W13M, R10M, G9M; B col, W bands, Radar tr (55m);   vis
W176·5°-184·2°, G184·2°-200·3°, W200·3°-210, R210°-274°,
W274°-033°; Fog Det lt.
Schillig 53°41'·85N 08°01'·78E Oc WR 6s 15m **W15M**,
R12M; B pylon, W band; vis W195·8°-221°, R221°-254·5°,
W254·5°-278.3°.
Hooksielplate Cross lt 53°40'·20N 08°09'·00E Oc WRG 3s
25m W7M, R5M, G4M, Radar tr (55m), R bands; vis R345°-
359·3°, W359·3°-002·1°, G002·1°-011·8°, W011·8°-018·5°,
R018·5°-098·7°, W098·7°-104·6°, G104·6°-115·3°, W115·3°-
119·8°, R119·8°-129·2°; Fog Det lt.
No 31/Reede/W Siel 1 buoy 53°41'·59N 08°04'·50E Oc (3) G
12s; SHM.

• WANGERSIEL
No 37/Hooksiel buoy 53°39'·38N 08°06'·63E IQ G 13s; SHM.

• HOOKSIEL
H3 buoy 53°38'·68N 08°05'·42E; SHM.
Voslapp ldg lts 164·5°. **Front**, 53°37'·19N 08°06'·88E Iso 6s
15m **24M**; R tr, W bands, R lantern; R Refl; intens on ldg line;
rear, 2·35M from front Iso 6s 60m **27M**; W tr, R bands. Same
structure, Cross light F RWG 20m W9M, R6M, G5M; vis
W200°-228°, G228°-248°, W248°-269°, R269°-310°.
Tossens Ldg lts 146°. **Front**, 53°34'·56N 08°12'·42E Oc 6s
15m **20M**; W tr, R band, R lantern; **rear**, 2M from front, Oc 6s
51m **20M;** R ○ tr, W stripes, 3 galleries.

• WILHELMSHAVEN
Eckwarden ldg lts 154°. **Front, Solthörner Watt** 53°32'·45N
08°13'·09E Iso WRG 3s 15m **W19M**, W12M, R9M, G8M;
R tr, W bands; vis R346°-348°, W348°-028°, R028°-052°;
W (intens) 052°-054° ldg sector, G054°-067·5°, W067·5°-
110°, G110°-152·6°; W (intens) 152·6° across fairway, with
undefined limit on E side of Ldg line; **rear**, 1·27M from front,
Iso 3s 41m **21M**; R tr & lantern; synch with front.
Neuer Vorhaven ldg lts 207·8°. Front, Iso 4s 17m 11M; B
mast, R lantern; rear, 180m from front, Iso 4s 23m 11M; Y
bldg; intens on ldg line.
W mole hd Oc G 6s 15m 4M.
E mole hd Oc R 6s 5M.
Fluthaffen N mole hd 53°30'·91N 08°09'·40E F WG 9m W6M,
G3M; G tr; vis W216°-280°, G280°-010°, W010°-020°, G020°-
130°.
Flutmole hd FR 6m 5M.
Arngast Dir lt 53°28'·91N 08°10'·97E F WRG 30m **W21M**,
W10, **R16M, G17M**, G7M; R l tr, W bands; vis: W135°-142°,
G142°-150°, W150°-152°, G152°-174·6°, R180·5°-191°,
W191°-213°, R213°-225°, W(10M) 286°-303°, G(7M) 303°-
314°. Same structure Fl WG 3s **W20M**, vis: G174·6°-175·5°,
W175·5°-176·4°. Same structure Fl (2) W 9s; vis: 177·4°-
180·5°. Same structure Oc 6s **20M**; vis: 176·4°-177·4°.

• DANGAST
Lock 53°26'·85N 08°06'·60E.

• VARELER SIEL
Lock 53°24'·65N 08°11'·40E.

RIVER WESER AND APPROACHES

Weser buoy 53°54'·25N 07°50'·00E Iso 5s 12m **17M**; SWM;
Racon.
Schlüsseltonne buoy 53°56'·30N 07°54'·87E Iso 8s; SWM.

Alte Weser 53°51'·85N 08°07'·72E F WRG 33m **W22M, R19M, G17M**; R ○ tr, 2 W bands, B base, floodlit; vis W288°-352°, R352°-003°, W003°-017°, ldg sector for Alte Weser, G017°-045°, W045°-074°, G074°-118°, W118°-123°, Ldg sector for Alte Weser, R123°-140°, G140°-175°, W175°-183°, R183°-196°, W196°-238°; Fog det lt; RC; *Horn Mo (AL) 60s.*

Tegeler Plate, N end 53°47'·90N 08°11'·50E Oc (3) WRG 21m **W21M, R17M, G16M**; R tr, gallery, W lantern, R roof; vis W329°-340°, R340°-014°, W014°-100°, G100°-116°, W116°-119°; ldg sector for Neue Weser, R119°-123°, G123°-144°, W144°-147°; ldg sector for Neue Weser R147°-264°; Fog det lt.

Hohe Weg, NE part 53°42'·80N 08°14'·65E F WRG 29m **W19M, R16M, G15M**; R 8-sided tr, 2 galleries, G lantern; vis W102°-138·5°, G138·5°-142·5°, W142·5°-145·5°, R145·5°-184°, W184°-278·5°; Fog det lt.

Robbennordsteert 53°42'·20N 08°20'·45E F WR 11m W10M, R7M; R col; vis W324°-004°, R004°-090°, W090°-121°.
Robbenplate ldg lts 122·3°. **Front**, 53°40'·92N 08°23'·06E Oc 6s 15m **17M**; R tripod; intens on ldg line; **rear**, 0·54M from front, Oc 6s 37m **18M**; R tr, 3 galleries, G lantern; vis 116°-125·5°; synch with front; Fog det lt.
Wremerloch ldg lts 140·1°. Front, 53°38'·41N 08°25'·10E Iso 6s 15m13M; rear, 0·57M from front, Iso 6s 31m 14M; synch with front; Ra Refl.
Dwarsgat ldg lts 320·1°. Front, 53°43'·15N 08°18'·55E   Iso 6s 16m **15M**; rear, 0·75M from front, Iso 6s 31m 17m **17M;** synch with front (same ldg Line as Wremer Loch).
Langlütjen ldg lts 305·2°. Front, 53°39'·50N 08°23'·07E Oc 6s 15m 13M; B mast, B & W gallery; vis 288°-310°; Ra Refl; rear, 0·5M from front, Oc 6s 31m 14M; synch with front.
Imsum ldg lts 125·2°. Front 53°36'·42N 08°30'·59E Oc 6s 15m 13M; R tripod with gallery; **Rear**, 1·02M from front, Oc 6s 39m **16M**; synch with front.
Solthorn ldg lts 320·6°. Front 53°38'·34N 08°27'·39E Iso 4s 15m 13M; R&W mast; rear, 700m from front, Iso 4s 31m **17M**; synch with front.
Fischeriehafen ldg lts 150·8°. **Common front**, 53°31'·93N 08°34'·60E Oc 6s 17m **18M**, R ▽ on W mast; **rear**, 0·68M from front, Oc 6s 45m **18M** 2 R ▽s on W mast, R bands; synch with front.
No 61 buoy 53°32'·28N 08°34'·04E QG; SHM; Km 66·0.

- BREMERHAVEN
Vorhafen N pier hd 53°32'·19N 08°34'·57E FR 15m 5M.
S pier hd 53°32'·14N 08°34'·57E FG 15m 5M.
Nordenham Hafen N ent 53°28'·10N 08°29'·14E FG; Km 56·0.
Hafen von Brake Dir lt 53°18'·88N 08°29'·27E Dir Iso WRG 4s 15m W9M, R7M, G7M; vis W345°-352·5°, W(intens) 352·5°-356°, G356°-360°; Km 40·5.
Hunte 1 buoy 53°15'·50N 08°28'·95E IQG; SHM; Km 32·7.
BREMEN
Hasenbüren Sporthafen 53°07'·51N 08°40'·02E 2 FY (vert); Km 11·6.

GERMAN BIGHT

GERMAN BIGHT lt F 54°10'·70N 07°26'·01E Iso 8s 12m **17M**; R hull marked D-B; RC; Racon; *Horn Mo (DB) 30s.*
D-B Weser buoy 54°02'·42N 07°43'·05E Oc (3) R 12s; PHM; Racon.

- HELGOLAND
Restricted area Helgoland-W buoy 54°10'·65N 07°48'·29E; WCM.
Helgoland-O buoy 54°09'·00N 07°53'·57E Q (3) 10s; ECM; *Whis.*

Helgoland 54°10'·96N 07°53'·01E Fl 5s 82m **28M**; brown ■ tr, B lantern, W balcony. FR on radio masts 180m SSE and 740m NNW.

Vorhafen. Ostmole, S elbow Oc WG 6s 5m W7M, G4M; G post; vis W203°-250°, G250°-109°; Fog det lt.
Ostmole hd FG 7m 4M; vis 289°-180°; *Horn (3) 30s.*
Sudmole hd Oc (2) R 12s 7m 4M; Gy post, R lantern; vis 101°-334°.
Binnenhafen ldg lts 302·2° W Pier, Front, Oc R 6s 8m 7M; rear, 50m from front, Oc R 6s 10m 7M; synch with front.

- DÜNE
Düne -S buoy 54°09'·57N 07°56'·04E Q (6) + L Fl 15s; SCM.
Ldg lts 020°. Front, Iso 4s 11m 8M; intens on ldg line; rear, 120m from front, Iso WRG 17m W11M, R10M, G10M; synch with front; vis G010°-018·5°, W018·5°-021°, R201°-030°, G106°-125°, W125°-130°, R130°-144°.
Sellebrunn W buoy 54°14'·43N 07°49'·83E Q (9) 15s; WCM; *Whis.*
Nathurn-N buoy 54°13'·40N 07°49'·05E; NCM.

RIVER WESER TO RIVER ELBE

Nordergründe N buoy 53°57'·08N 08°00'·17W VQ; NCM.
Westertill N buoy 53°58'·18N 08°06'·82E Q; NCM.
Scharnhörnriff W buoy 53°58'·53N 08°08'·80E Q (9) 15s; WCM.
Scharnhörnriff N buoy 53°58'·99N 08°11'·25E Q; NCM.

RIVER ELBE AND APPROACHES

ELBE 1 lt F 54°00'·00N 08°06'·58E Iso 10s 12m **17M**; R hull and lt tr; RC; Racon (T); *Horn Mo (R) 30s* (H24).
Grosser Vogelsand 53°59'·78N 08°28'·68E Fl (3) 12s 39m **25M**; helicopter platform on R ● tr, W bands; vis 085·1°-087·1°; Fog det lt. Same tr, Iso 3s **26M**; vis 087·1°-091·1°. Oc 6s **26M**; vis 091·1°-095·1°. Fl (4) 15s **19M**; vis 095·1°-101·9°. Fl (4) R 15s 12M; vis 101·9°-105·1°. Fl R 3s **15M**; vis 113°-270°. Oc (4) R 18s 9M; vis 322·5°-012°; Fog det lt; *Horn Mo (VS) 30s.*
Neuwerk, S side 53°54'·95N 08°29'·85E L Fl (3) WRG 20s 39m **W16M**, R12M, G11M; vis G165·3°-215·3°, W215·3°-238·8°, R238·8°-321°, R343°-100°.
No 1 buoy 53°59'·27N 08°13'·30E QG; SHM.
No 5 buoy 53°59'·35N 08°19'·08E QG; SHM.
No 19 buoy 53°57'·83N 08°34'·48E QG; SHM.
No 25 buoy 53°56'·67N 08°38'·32E QG; SHM.

- CUXHAVEN
Ldg lts 151·2°. **Baumrönne**, front, 53°51'·25N 08°44'·24E 1·55M from rear, Fl 3s 25m **17M**; W tr, B band on gallery; 143·8°-149·2°. Same tr, Iso 4s **17M**; vis 149·2°-154·2°. Fl (2) 9s **17M**; vis 154·2°-156·7°. **Altenbruch, common rear**, 53°49'·83N 08°45'·50E Iso 4s 58m **21M**; intens on ldg line; synch with front. Same structure, Iso 8s 51m **22M**; synch with front.
Altenbruch ldg lts 261°. **Common front**, 53°50'·08N 08°47'·75E Iso 8s 19m **19M**; W tr, B bands. Same structure, Iso WRG 8s W8M, R9M, G8M; vis G117·5°-124°, W124°-135°, R135°-140°; rear, Wehldorf Iso 8s 31m 11M; W tr, B bands; synch with front.
No 35 buoy 53°50'·73N 08°45'·86E Oc (2) G 9s; SHM.
No 43 buoy 53°50'·27N 08°52'·30E Oc (2) G 9s; SHM.

- OTTERNDORF
Medem, Hadelner Kanal ent 53°50'·20N 08°53'·93E Fl (3) 12s 6m 5M; B △, on B col.

Balje ldg lts 130·8°. **Front**, 53°51'·33N 09°02'·70E Iso 8s 24m **17M**; W tr, R bands; **rear**, 1·35M from front, Iso 8s 54m **21M**; W tr, R bands; intens on ldg line; synch with front.
Zweidorf 53°53'·42N 09°05'·69E Oc R 5s 9m 3M; R □ on W pylon; vis 287°-107°.
No 51 buoy 53°51'·07N 09°00'·22E QG; SHM.
No 57 buoy 53°52'·55N 09°06'·38E QG SHM.

- BRUNSBÜTTEL

Ldg lts 065·5°. Front, **Schleuseninsel** Iso 3s 24m **16M**; R tr, W bands; vis North of 063·3°; rear, **Industriegebiet**, 0·9M from front, Iso 3s 46m **21M**; R tr, W bands; synch with front.
Alterhaven N mole (mole 4) hd 53°53'·29N 09°07'·59E F WR (vert) 15m W10M, R8M; vis R275·5°-079°, W079°-084°.

- NORD-OSTSEE KANAL (KIEL CANAL), RENDSBURG/ KIEL-HOLTENAU

No 2/Obereider 1 buoy 54°18'·95N 09°42'·71E Fl (2+1) R 15s; PHM.
Kiel Nordmole 54°21'·83N 10°09'·18E Oc (2) WR 9s 23m.
Tiessenkal Oc (3) WG 12s 22m.

- FRIEBURG

Entrance bn (unlit) 53°50'·25N 09°18'·90E; SHM.
Rhinplatte Nord 53°48'·09N 09°23'·36E Oc WRG 6s 11m W6M, R4M, G3M; vis: G122°-144°, W144°-150°, R150°-177°, W177°-122°; Ra refl.

- STÖRLOCH/BORSFLETH, STÖR/BEIDENFLETH

Stör ldg lts 093·8°. Front, 53°49'·29N 09°23'·91E Fl 3s 7m 6M; △ on R ● tr; rear, 200m from front, Fl 3s 12m 6M; synch with front.

- GLÜCKSTADT

Glückstadt ldg lts 131·8° **Front**, Iso 8s 15m **19M**; W tr, R bands; intens on ldg line; **rear**, 0·68M from front, Iso 8s 30m **21M**; W tr, R bands; intens on ldg line.
N mole Oc WRG 6s 9m W9M R6M, G6M; W tr with gallery; vis R330°-343°, W343°-346°, G346°008°, G123°-145°, W145°-150°, R150°-170°.
N pierhd 53°47'·15N 09°24'·58E FR 5m 4M.
South mole hd, FG.
Pagensand ldg lts 135° 53°42'·15N 09°30'·30E. Front, Iso 4s 20m 13M; W tr, R bands; rear, 880m from front, Iso 4s 32m 13M.

- STADE

Stadersand 53°37'·74N 09°31'·72E Iso 8s 20m 14M.

HAMBURG

- HAMBURGER YACHT HAFEN, WEDEL

No 122 buoy 53°34'·20N 09°40'·68E Oc (2) R 9s; PHM.
E ent E pier hd 53°34'·30N 09°40'·87E FG 3M.
(Both ent show FR & FG May to Oct.)

- SCHULAU

No 123 buoy 53°33'·90N 09°42'·05E Fl G 4s; SHM.
E ent E pier hd 53°34'·14N 09°42'·05E FG.

- NEUENSCHLEUSE

119/HN1 buoy 53°34'·08N 09°39'·49E QG; SHM.

- MÜHLENBERG

Ent E pierhd 53°33'·22N 09°49'·48E (unmarked).

- TEUFELSBRÜCK

Ent bkwtr hd 53°32'·88N 09°52'·12E (unmarked).

- RÜSCHKANAL

East ent 53°32'·63N 09°51'·10E FR 8m 5M.

- CITY SPORTHAFEN

Brandenburger Hafen ent 53°32'·56N 09°58'·88E Iso Or 2s.

RIVER ELBE TO DANISH BORDER

- INSHORE ROUTE RIVER ELBE TO SYLT

Süderpiep buoy 54°06'·00N 08°21'·90E Iso 8s; SWM; *Whis.*
Eider buoy 54°14'·04N 08°18'·21E Iso 4s; SWM.
Rütergat buoy 54°31'·02N 08°12'·00E Iso 8s; SWM.
Amrum Bank S buoy 54°32'·00N 08°04'·95E Q (6) + L Fl 15s; SCM.
Vortrapptief buoy 54°35'·00N 08°12'·20E Iso 4s; SWM.
Amrum Bank W buoy 54°38'·00N 07°55'·40E Q (9) 15s; WCM.
Threeknobs W buoy 54°43'·52N 08°09'·95E Q (9)15s; WCM.
Amrum Bank N buoy 54°45'·00N 08°07'·00E Q; NCM.
Lister Tief buoy 55°05'·38N 08°16'·88E Iso 8s; SWM *Whis.*

- BÜSUM

Süderpiep buoy 54°06'·00N 08°21'·90E Iso 8s; SWM; *Whis.*
Büsum 54°07'·65N 08°51'·55E Iso WRG 16s 22m **W17M**, R14M, G13M; vis W248°-317°, R317°-024°, W024°-084°, G084°-092·5°, W092·5°-094·5° ldg sector for Süder Piep, R094·5°-097°, W097°-148°.
W mole hd Oc (3) R 12s 10m 4M; R tr; FW Fog Det lt.
E mole hd 54°07'·21N 08°51'·70E Oc (3) G 12s 10m 4M; G tr; vis 260°-168°.
Ldg lts 355·1°. Front, 54°07'·53N 08°51'·58E Iso 4s 9m 13M; B mast, W bands; rear, 110m from front, Iso 4s 12m 13M; synch with front.

- RIVER EIDER

St Peter 54°17'·30N 08°39'·15E L Fl (2) WR 15s 23m **W15M**, R13M; R tr, B lantern; vis R271°-294°, W294°-325°, R325°-344°, W344°-035°, R035°-055°, W055°-068°, R068°-091°, W091°-120°.
Eiderdamm lock, N mole, W end Oc (2) R 12s 8m 5M; W tr.
S mole, W end Oc G 6s 8m 5M: W tr, Gy top.

- TÖNNING

W mole hd 54°16'·01N 08°57'·12E FR 5m 4M; R col.
Quay 54°18'·95N 08°57'·12E FG 5m 4M; G col.

- RIVER HEVER

Hever buoy 54°20'·45N 08°18'·80E Iso 4s; SWM; *Whis.*
No 3 buoy 54°20'·69N 08°23'·12E Fl G 4s; SHM.
No 8 buoy 54°21'·39N 08°27'·11E Fl R 4s; PHM.
Norderhever buoy 54°22'·52N 08°30'·80E Fl (2+1) R 15s; PHM.
Westerheversand 54°22'·45N 08°38'·50E Oc (3) WRG 15s 41m **W21M**, **R17M**, **G16M**; R tr, W bands; vis W012·2°-069°, G069°-079·5°°, W079·5°-080·5°; Ldg sector for Hever, R080·5°-107°, W107°-157°, R157°-169°, W169°-206·5°, R206·5°-218·5°, W218·5°-233°, R233°-248°.

- HUSUM

Husumer Au outer ldg lts 106·5°. Front, 54°28'·57N 09°00'·78E Iso R 8s 8m 5M; R mast, W bands; intens on ldg line; rear, 0·52M from front, Iso R 8s 17m 6M; Y mast; synch with front.
Inner ldg lts 090°. Front, 54°28'·79N 09°00'·32E Iso G 8s 7m 3M; R mast, W bands; intens on ldg line; rear, 40m from front, Iso G 8s 9m 3M; intens on ldg line; synch with front.

- NORDSTRAND

Strucklahnungshörn, W mole hd 54°30'·00N 08°48'·5E Oc G 6s 8m 2M.

- PELLWORM

Pellworm S side ldg lts 041°. **Front**, 54°29'·82N 08°40'·05E Oc WR 5s 14m **W20M**, W11M, R8M. Intens on ldg line;   vis W303°-313·5°, R313·5°-316·5°; **rear**, 0·8M from front, Oc 5s 38m **20M**; R tr, W band; synch with front. Same tr as rear lt, Cross light Oc WR 5s 38m W14M, W9M, R11M, R6M; vis R11M 122·6°-140°, W14M 140°-161·5°, R11M 161·5°-179·5°, W14M 179·5°-210·2°, R6M 255°-265·5°, W9M 265·5°-276°, R6M 276°-297°, W9M 297°-307°.

21

- WITTDÜN, AMRUM

Rütergat buoy 54°31'·02N 08°12'·00E Iso 8s; SWM.
Amrum Hafen ldg lts 272°. Front, 54°37'·88N 08°22'·92E Iso
R 4s 11m 10M; W mast, R stripe; intens on ldg line; **r**ear,
0·9M from front, Iso R 4s 33m **15M**.
Amrum 54°37'·90N 08°21'·36E Fl 7·5s 63m **23M**; R tr, W
bands.
Wriakhorn Cross lt 54°37'·62N 08°21'·22E L Fl (2) WR 15s
26m W9M, R7M; vis W297·5°-319·5°, R319·5°-330°, W330°-
005·5°, R055·5°-034°.
Nebel 54°38'·75N 08°21'·75E Oc WRG 5s 16m **W20M**,
R15M, G15M; R tr, W band; vis R255·5°-258·5°, W258·5°-
260·5°, G260·5°-263·5°.
Norddorf 54°40'·19N 08°18'·60E Oc WRG 6s 22m **W15M**,
R12M, G11M; W tr, R lantern; vis W009°-032°, G032°-034°,
W034°-036·8°; ldg sector, R036·8°-099°, W099°-146°, R146°-
176·5°, W176·5-178·5°, G178·5°-188°, G(unintens) 188°-202°,
W(partially obscd) 202°-230°.

- LANGENESS

Nordmarsch 54°37'·58N 08°31'·85E L Fl (3) WR 20s 13m
W14M, R11M; dark brown tr; vis W268°-279°, R279°-306°,
W306°-045°, R045°-070°, W070°-218°.

- OLAND

Near W Pt 54°40'·51N 08°41'·28E F WRG 7m W13M, R10M,
G9M; R tr; G086°-093°, W093°-160°, R160°-172°.

- SCHLÜTTSIEL

Schl No 20 buoy 54°40'·83N 08°44'·60E; PHM.
Harbour ent, S side 54°40'·89N 08°45'·10E; SHM.

- WYK, FÖHR

Nieblum 54°41'·10N 08°29'·20E Oc (2) WRG 10s 11m
W19M, R15M, G15M; R tr, W band; vis G028°-031°, W031°-
032·5°, R032·5°-035·5°.

- DAGEBÜLL

Dagebüllhaven 53°43'·82N 08°41'·43E Iso WRG 8s 23m
W18M, R15M, G15M; G mast; vis G042°-043°, W043°-
044·5°, R044·5°-047°.
FW lts shown on N and S mole hd.

- SYLT

Threeknobs-W buoy 54°43'·52N 08°09'·95E Q (9) 15s; WCM.
Hörnum Odde buoy 54°44'·20N 08°18'·00E QR; PHM.
Hörnum ldg lts 012·5°. Front, 54°44'·82N 08°17'·45E Iso 8s
20m 14M; R tr, W band; intens on ldg line; **rear**, **Hörnum**
54°45'·29N 08°17'·60E Iso 8s 45m **15M**; R tr, W band; synch
with front; intens on ldg line. Same tr Fl (2) 9s 48m **20M**.
N pierhd FG 6m 3M; vis 024°-260°.
South mole hd 54°45'·57N 08°17'·97E FR 7m 4M; R mast.
Kampen, Rote Kliff 54°56'·87N 08°20'·50E Oc (4) WR 15s
62m **W20M**, R16M; W tr, B band; vis W193°-260°, W(unintens)
260°-339°, W339°-165°, R165°-193°.
Lister Tief buoy 55°05'·38N 08°16'·88E Iso 8s; SWM; *Whis*.

Ellenbogen N end, List West 55°03'·25N 08°24'·19E
Oc WRG 6s 19m W14M, R11M, G10M; W tr, R lantern; vis
R040°-133°, W133°-227°, R227°-266·4°, W266·4°-268°,
G268°-285°, W285°-310°, W(unintens) 310°-040°.
N side, List Ost 55°03'·00N 08°26'·70E Iso WRG 6s 22m
W14M, R11M, G10M; W tr, R band; vis W(unintens) 010·5°-
098°, W098°-262°, R262°-278°, W278°-296°, R296°-323·3°,
W323·3°-324·5°, G324·5°-350°, W350°-010·5°, Q 4M on tr
9·4M NNE, shown when firing takes place.

List Land 55°01'·07N 08°26'·47E Oc WRG 3s 13m W12M,
R9M, G8M; W mast, R band; vis W170°-203°, G203°-212°,
W212°-215·5°, R215·5°-232·5°, W232·5°-234°, G234°-243°,
W243°-050°.

8.21.5 GLOSSARY   GLOSSAR

English	Deutsch

A. NAVIGATION   NAVIGATION

Marks, Buoys, Beacons	Tonnen, Baken
Beacon (bn)	Bake
Buoy	Tonne
Can (PHM buoy)	Stumpftonne
Chequered	gewürfelt
Column	Laternenträger
Cone, conical (SHM buoy)	Kegel, kegelförmig
Diamond (◇ shape)	Raute (◇ Rautenförmig)
Dividers	Kartenzirkel, Stechzirkel
Framework Tower	Gittermast
Isolated danger (IDM buoy)	Einzelgefahr
Landfall (SWM buoy)	Ansteuerungstonne
Landmark	Landmarke
Leading line, transit	Leitlinie
Log Book	Logbuch, Schiffstagebuch
Perch	Pricke
Port (side)	Backbord
Radio beacon	Funkfeuer
Signal station	Signalstelle
Special mark (SPM buoy)	Sonderzeichen
Square (□)	Viereck
Starboard (Stbd)	Steuerbord
Topmark	Toppzeichen
Tower (Tr)	Turm

Colours	Farben
Black (B)	schwarz (B)
Blue (Bu)	blau (Bl)
Green (G)	grün (Gn)
Grey	grau (Gr)
Red, (R)	rot (R)
Stripe	Steifen
White (W)	weiß (W)
Yellow (Y)	gel

Lights	Leuchtfeuer
Alternating (Al)	Wechselfeuer (Wchs)
Extinguished (lt)	velöscht
Fixed (F)	Festfeuer (F)
Fixed and Flashing (F Fl)	Mischfeuer (FFl)
Flashing	Blitzfeuer (Fl)
Interrupted quick flashing (IQ)	Unterbrochenes Funkelfeuer
Isophase (Iso)	Gleichtaktfeuer (Iso)
Leading Light	Richtfeuer
Lighthouse	Leuchtturm
Lightship	Feuerschiff
Obscured	verdunkelt
Occulting (Oc)	Unterbrochenes Feuer (Oc)
Quick flashing (Q)	Funkelfeuer mitdauerndem
Temporary	zeitweilig
Very quick flashing (VQ)	Schnelles Funkelfeuer

Fog Signals	Nebelsignale
Bell	Glocke
Explosive (fog)	Knall
Foghorn	Nebelhorn
Reed (horn)	Mundnebelhorn
Siren	Sirene
Whistle	Heuler/Nebelhorn

Compass	Kompaß
Compass, hand-bearing	Handpeilkompaß
East (E)	Ost
North (N)	Nord
South (S)	Süd
West (W)	West

Tides/Depths	Gezeiten/Tiefen
Bay	Bucht
Beach, sandy	Strand
Channel	Fahrwasser
Chart Datum (CD)	Kartennull
Cliff	Kliff
Coastline	Küstenlinien
Draught	Tiefgang
Echosounder	Echolot
Estuary	Flußmündung
Flood/ebb stream	Flutstrom/Ebbstrom
Gulf	Golf, Haff
Height, headroom, clearance	Durchfahrtshöhe
High Water (HW)	Hochwasser
Island	Insel
Knots (kn)	Knoten
Low Water (LW)	Niedrigwasser
Peninsula	Halbinsel
Point, headland	Huk, Landspitze
Mean Sea level	Wasserstand
Mean (tide)	Mittelwasser
Narrows	Enge
Neaps (np)	Nipptide
Range	Tidenhub
Rate (tide)	Geschwindigkeit
River	Fluß
Sandhill, dunes	Sandhügel, Dünen
Slack water, stand	Stauwasser
Springs (sp)	Springtide
Strait(s)	Straße
Tidal stream al as	Gezeitenstromatlas
Tide Tables	Gezeitentafeln

Features	Merkmale
Bridge	Brücke
Castle	Schloß
Conspicuous (conspic)	auffällig
Railway	Eisenbahn
Steeple, spire	Kirchturm
Water tower	Wasserturm
Windmill	Windmühle

Dangers/Seabed	Gefahren/Meeresboden
Aground	Auf Grund sitzen
Bank	Bank
Breakers	Brandung
Clay	Lehm/Ton (Cy)
Mud (M)	Schlick (M)
Prohibited area	Sperrgebiet
Sand (S)	Sand (S)
Seaweed, kelp	Seetang
Shoal	Untiefe
Stony, shingly	Steine (St)
Reef	Riff
Rock, stone	Fels
Wreck	Wrack

Ports/Harbours	Häfen
Alongside berth (AB)	Liegeplatz, Anleger
Anchorage (⚓)	Ankerplatz
Basin	Becken
Breakwater, mole	mole
Breakwater, wave-break	Wellenbrecher
Concrete	Beton
Dolphin	Dalben
Downstream	Stromab
Dredged	Gebaggert
Drying berth	Trockenplatz
Ferry	Fähre
Finger berth/pontoon	Liegeplatz/Ponton
Fishing harbour	Fischereihafen

Fixed bridge	Feste Brücke
Harbour dues	Hafengebühr
Harbour Master	Hafenmeister
Inner harbour	Innerer Hafen
Jetty	Anlegestelle
Landing (L)	Landungstreppe
Lifeboat (LB)	Rettungsboot
Lifting bridge	Hubbrücke
Lock	Schleuse
Mooring buoy	Festmachetonne
Mooring	Ligeplatz
Outer harbour	Aussenhafen
Post, pile (mooring)	Pfosten, Pfahl, Pfeiler
Roadstead	Reede
Slipway (slip)	Slip/Aufschleppe
Stone	Stein
Swing bridge	Drehbrücke
Upstream	Stromauf
Yacht harbour, marina	Yachthafen, Marina

B. METEOROLOGY	METEOROLOGIE
Pressure	**Druck**
Forecast	Wettervorhersage
Front, warm/cold	Front, warm/kalt
High pressure	Hochdruck
Low pressure	Tiefdruck
Ridge (high)	Rücken
Rise/fall	steigen/fallen
Settled	beständig
To deepen	sich vertiefen
To fill	auffüllen
Trough (low)	Trog

Wind	**Wind**
Calm (F0)	Ruhig
Light airs (F1)	Leiser Zug
Light breeze (F2)	Leichte Brise
Gentle breeze (F3)	Schwache Brise
Moderate breeze (F4)	Mäßige Brise
Fresh breeze (F5)	Frische Brise
Strong breeze (F6)	Starker Wind
Near gale (F7)	Steifer Wind
Gale (F8)	Stürmischer Wind
Severe gale (F9)	Sturm
Storm (F10)	Schwerer Sturm
Back	zurückdrehen
Freshening	zunehmend
Gust	Windstoß
Lull	Vorübergehende Abflauen
Moderating	abnehmend
Squall	Bö
Veer	rechtsdrehen

Precipitation	**Niederschlag**
Drizzle	Sprühregen
Hail	Hagel
Rain	Regen
Shower	Schauer
Sleet	Schneeregen
Thunderstorm	Gewitter

Cloud & Visibility	**Himmel und Sichtweite**
Clearing up	aufklarend
Cloudy	bewölkt
Mist	Feuchter Dunst
Fog	Nebel
Overcast	bedeckt

Sea state	**See (-gaug)**
Choppy	kabbelig
Moderate	bewegt

21

Overfalls (tide race)	Stromkabbelung
Rough	grob
Smooth	glatt
Swell	Dünung

C THE BOAT
DAS BOOT

Sails/Spars/Rigging
Segel/Spieren/Rigg

Backstay	Achterstag
Batten (sail)	Segellatten
Boom	Baum
Bosun's chair	Bootsmannsstuhl
Ensign	Nationalflagge
Forestay	Vorstag
Genoa	Genua
Halyard	Fall
Mainsail	Grossegel
Mast	Mast
Mast, to step/unstep	Mast setzen/legen
Shackle	Schäkel
Sheet	Schot
Spinnaker boom	Spinnakerbaum
Splice	Spleiß
Stainless steel	Rostfreier Stahl
Staysail	Fock
Topping lift	Dirk
Turnbuckle, bottle-screw	Wantenspanner
Whipping twine	Takelgarn

On deck
An deck

Anchor	Anker
Beam, breadth	Breite
Bilge pump	Lenzpumpe
Boat hook	Peekhaken
Bucket	Pütz
Fender	Fender
Glass fibre (GRP)	Fiberglas (GFK)
Life jacket	Rettungsweste
Oar	Riemen
Pulpit/pushpit	Bugkorb/Heckkorb
Rudder	Ruder
Tender	Beiboot, Schlauchboot
Tiller	Ruderpinne
Varnish	Lack
Winch handle	Winschkurbel

Below deck
Unter Deck

Corkscrew	Korkenzieher
Galley	Kombüse
Gas cooker	Gasherd
Matches	Streichhölzer
Plug	Stöpsel
Saucepan	Kochtopf
Tap	Hahn

Electrics
Elektrik

Battery (ships)	Batterie
Bulb, lamp	Glühlampe
Distilled water	Destilliertes Wasser
Fuse	Sicherung
Insulating tape	Isolierband
Navigation lights	Positionslaternen
Solder	Lötmetall
Switch	Schalter

Engine
Motor

Alternator	Lichtmaschine
Drive-belt	Keilriemen
Fuel filter	Brennstofffilter
Gasket	Dichtung, Packungsring
Grease	Fett
Injector	Einspritzdüse
Impeller	Impeller

Nut and bolt	Mutter und Schraube
Oil, lubricating	Schmieröl
Propeller	Schraube/Propeller
Sea-cock	Seeventil
Spark plug	Zündkerze
Split pin	Splint
Starter motor	Anlasser
To bleed (air)	entlüften
Washer	Unterlegscheibe

Tools
Werkzeug

Feeler gauge	Fühlerlehre (Spion)
File (wood/metal)	Feile
Hacksaw	Metallsäge, Bügelsäge
Hammer	Hammer
Pliers	Kneifzange
Screwdriver	Schraubenzieher
Spanner, adjustable	Schlüssel, (Engländer)
Vice	Schraubstock, Feilkolben

D. ASHORE
AN LAND
Nautical
Nautisch

Boat hoist (BH)	Bootswinde, Bootskran
Boatyard (BY)	Yachtwerft
Chandlery (CH)	Jachtausrüster
Coastguard (CG)	Küstenwache
Crane (C)	Kran
Customs (#)	Zoll
Diesel (D)	Dieselöl
Dustbin	Mülltonne
Engineer (ME)	Mechaniker
Fresh water (FW)	Trinkwasser
Fuel	Kraftstoff
Methylated spirits	Brennspiritus
Paraffin	Petroleum
Petrol (P)	Benzin
Power point (AC)	Steckdose
Shipwright (Sh)	Bootsbauer
Sailmaker (SM)	Segelmacher

Non-nautical, Shopping
Einkaufen/Shopping

Airport (✈)	Flughafen
Bakery	Bäcker
Butcher	Schlachter/Fleischer
Chemist	Apotheke
Dentist	Zahnarzt
Doctor	Arzt
Hospital (H)	Krankenhaus
Ironmonger	Eisenwarenhändler
Launderette	Wäscherei
Market, food (V)	Markt
Off licence	Wein-u. Spririuosenhändler
Post Office (✉)	Postamt
Railway station (⇌)	Bahnhof
Stamps	Briefmarken

E. FIRST AID
ERSTE-HILFE

Acute infection	akute Infektion
Appendicitis	Blinddarmentzündung
Burn	Brandwunde
Coma	Koma
Coughing blood	Bluthusten
Delirium	Delirium
Drowning	Ertrinkend
Fracture	Fraktur
Head injury	Kopfverletzung
Haemorrhage	Blutung
Laceration	Schürfwunde, Verletzung
Perforated ulcer	Geschwürdurchbruch
Poisoning	Vergiftung
Vomiting blood	Bluterbrechen
Sting (insect, jellyfish)	Stich, Stachel (Insekt)

8.21.6 PASSAGE INFORMATION

Refer to: Admiralty Pilot *North Sea (East)*; *Cruising Guide to Germany and Denmark* (Imray/Navin) and *Frisian Pilot* (Adlard Coles/Brackenbury). For German Glossary, see 8.21.5.

RIVER EMS (charts 3509, 3510)

The River Ems forms the boundary between Netherlands and Germany, and is a major waterway leading to Eemshaven, Delfzijl (8.20.35), Emden (8.21.9), Leer and Papenburg. Approach through Hubertgat or Westerems, which join W of Borkum; the latter is advised at night. Both are well buoyed but can be dangerous with an ebb stream and a strong W or NW wind. The flood begins at HW Helgoland + 0530, and the ebb at HW Helgoland – 0030, sp rates 1·5kn.

From close SW of Borkum the chan divides: Randzel Gat to the N and Alte Ems running parallel to it to the S – as far as Eemshaven on the S bank. About 3M further on the chan again divides. Bocht van Watum is always varying so keep in main chan, Ostfriesisches Gatje, for Delfzijl and beyond. Off Eemshaven the stream runs 2-3kn.

Osterems is the E branch of the estuary of R. Ems, passing between Borkum and Memmert. It is poorly marked, unlit and much shallower than Westerems. It also gives access to the Ley chan, leading to the hbr of Greetsiel (8.21.9). But it is not advised except with local knowledge and in ideal weather.

RIVER EMS TO RIVER JADE (chart 3761)

The route to seaward of the Frisian Is from abeam Borkum to the E end of Wangerooge is about 50 miles. This is via the ITZ, S of the Terschellinger-German Bight TSS, 8.20.37, the E-going lane of which is marked on its S side by SHM buoys lettered DB1, DB3, DB5 etc. About 4M S of this line of buoys the landward side of the ITZ is marked by landfall buoys showing the apprs to the eight main seegaten between the East Frisian Is. There are major lts on Borkum, Norderney and Wangerooge. Near the TSS the E-going stream begins at HW Helgoland – 0500, and the W-going at HW Helgoland + 0100, sp rates 1·2kn. Inshore the stream is influenced by the flow through the seegaten.

THE EAST FRISIAN ISLANDS (8.21.10 and chart 3761)

The East Frisian Islands have fewer facilities for yachtsmen than the Dutch Islands to the W, and most of them are closer to the mainland. For general notes, see 8.20.5 and 8.21.8. For navigating inside the islands, in the so-called watt chans, it is essential to have the large scale pleasure craft charts and to understand the system of channel marking. Withies, unbound (with twigs pointing up) are used as PHMs, and withies which are bound (with twigs pointing down) as SHMs. Inshore of the islands the *conventional direction of buoyage is always from West to East*, even though this may conflict with the actual direction of the flood stream in places.

Borkum (8.21.11 and chart 3509) lies between Westerems and Osterems, with high dunes each end so that at a distance it looks like two separate islands. Round the W end of Borkum are unmarked groynes, some extending 2¾ca offshore. Conspic landmarks include Grosse bn and Neue bn, a water tr, Borkum Grosser lt ho, Borkum Kleiner lt ho, and a disused lt ho; all of which are near the W end of the island.

Memmert on the E side of Osterems is a bird sanctuary, and landing is prohibited. There are Nature Reserves (entry prohibited) inshore of Baltrum, Langeoog and the W end of Spiekeroog (chart 1875). **Juist** (8.21.10) is the first of the chain of similar, long, narrow and low-lying islands. Most have groynes and sea defences on their W and NW sides. Their bare sand dunes are not easy to identify, so the few conspic landmarks must be carefully selected. Shoals extend seaward for 2M or more in places. The seegaten between the islands vary in position and depth, and all of them are dangerous on the ebb tide, even in a moderate onshore wind. Norderneyer Seegat is a deep chan close W of **Norderney**, but it is approached across dangerous offshore shoals, through

which lead two shallow buoyed channels, Dovetief and Schluchter. Dovetief is the main chan, but Schluchter is more protected from the NE. Depths vary considerably and at times the chans silt up. Neither should be used in strong winds. Further inshore, Norderneyer Seegat leads round the W end of the island to the harbour of Norderney (8.21.12). Beware groynes and other obstructions along the shore.

SW of Norderney, Busetief leads in a general S direction to the tidal hbr of Norddeich (8.21.9), which can also be approached with sufficient rise of tide from Osterems through the Norddeich Wattfahrwasser with a depth of about 2m at HW. Busetief is deeper than Dovetief and Schluchter, and is buoyed. The flood begins at HW Helgoland – 0605, and the ebb at HW Helgoland – 0040, sp rates 1kn.

Baltrum (8.21.10) is about 2·5M long, very low in the E and rising in the W to dunes only about 15m high. With local knowledge and only in good weather it could be approached through Wichter Ee, a narrow unmarked channel between Norderney and Baltrum; but it is obstructed by drying shoals and a bar and is not advised. A small pier and groyne extend about 2ca from the SW corner of Baltrum. The little hbr dries, and is exposed to the S and SW. Southwards from Wichter Ee, the Nessmersiel Balje, with buoys on its W side prefixed by 'N', leads to the sheltered hbr of Nessmersiel (8.21.9).

Proceeding E, the next major chan through the islands is Acummer Ee between Baltrum and **Langeoog**. Shoals extend 2M offshore, depths in chan vary considerably and it is prone to silting; it is marked by buoys prefixed with 'A', moved as necessary. In onshore winds the sea breaks on the bar and the chan should not be used. Apart from Langeoog (8.21.14), Accumer Ee gives access to the mainland hbrs of Dornumer-Accumersiel (8.21.13) and Bensersiel (8.21.15).

Between Langeoog and **Spiekeroog**, the buoyed Westerbalje and Otzumer Balje chans lead inward. The latter is normally the deeper (0·7m–2·0m) but both chans may silt up and should be used only in good weather and on a rising tide.

Harle chan (buoys prefixed by 'H') leads W of **Wangerooge** (8.21.15), but beware Buhne H groyne which extends 7½ca WSW from end of island to edge of fairway. Dove Harle (buoys prefixed by 'D') leads to the hbr. In bad weather Harlesiel, 4M S on the mainland, is a more comfortable berth.

Blau Balje leads between the E end of Wangerooge and **Minsener Oog**. Although marked by buoys (prefixed 'B' and moved as necessary) this chan is dangerous in N winds and there is a prohib area (15 May–31 Aug) S of the E end of Wangerooge for the protection of seals.

RIVER JADE (charts 3368, 3369)

To the E of Wangerooge and Minsener Oog lie the estuaries of R. Jade and R. Weser. Although not so hazardous as R. Elbe, the outer parts of both rivers can become very rough with wind against tide, and are dangerous on the ebb in strong NW winds. The Jade is entered from Jade 1 buoy via the Wangerooger Fahrwasser (buoyed) which leads SSE past Wangersiel and the yachting centre of Hooksiel (8.21.16) to Wilhelmshaven (8.21.17). To the S of Wilhelmshaven, the Jadebusen is a large, shallow area of water, through which chans run to the small hbrs of Dangastersiel and Vareler Siel.

RIVER WESER (charts 3368, 3405, 3406, 3407)

The River Weser is an important waterway leading to the ports of Bremerhaven, Nordenham, Brake and Bremen which in turn connect with the inland waterways. The upper reaches, *Unterweser*, run from Bremen to Bremerhaven (8.21.18) and below Bremerhaven the *Aussenweser* flows into a wide estuary split by two main chans, Neue Weser and Alte Weser. The position and extent of sandbanks vary: on the W side they tend to be steep-to, but on the E side there are extensive shoals (e.g. Tegeler Plate).

Weser lt buoy marks the approach from NW to Neue Weser (the main fairway) and Alte Weser which are separated by Roter Sand and Roter Grund, marked by the disused Roter Sand lt tr (conspic). Both chans are well marked and they join

21

about 3M S of Alte Weser lt tr (conspic). From this junction Hohewegrinne (buoyed) leads inward in a SE direction past Tegeler Plate lt tr (conspic) on the NE side and Hohe Weg lt tr (conspic) to the SW; here it is constrained by training walls. In the Aussenweser the stream, which runs over 3kn at sp, often sets towards the banks and the branch chans which traverse them.

The Weser-Elbe Wattfahrwasser is a demanding, but useful inshore passage between R. Weser and R. Elbe. It leads NNE from the Wurster Arm (E of Hohe Weg), keeping about 3M offshore; SE of Neuwerk and around Cuxhaven training wall. It normally requires two tides, but there are suitable anchs.

RIVER ELBE (charts 3261, 3262, 3266, 3268)

Yachts entering the Elbe are probably bound for the Nord-Ostsee Kanal ent at Brunsbüttel (8.21.21). See 8.21.19 for Cuxhaven and 8.21.20 for the River Elbe and Hamburg. From E end of TSS the chan is well marked by buoys and beacon trs. Commercial traffic is very heavy. At Elbe 1 lt Float the E-going (flood) stream begins at HW Helgoland – 0500, and the W-going (ebb) stream at HW Helgoland + 0500, sp rates 2kn. The stream runs harder N of Scharnhörn, up to 3·5kn on the ebb, when the Elbe estuary is dangerous in strong W or NW winds.

ELBE TO NORTH FRISIAN ISLANDS (charts 1875, 3767)

The W coast of Schleswig-Holstein is flat and marshy, with partly-drying banks extending 5 - 10M offshore. Between the banks and islands, the chans change frequently. Süderpiep and Norderpiep lead to Büsum (8.21.24) and Meldorfer Hafen, joining S of Blauort. Norderpiep has a bar (depth 3m) and is unlit; Süderpiep is deeper and preferable in W'lies. Landmarks from seaward are Tertius bn and Blauortsand bn, and a conspic silo at Büsum.

Approaching R. Eider from seaward, find the Ausseneider lt buoy, about 6M W of the buoyed ent chan. The ent can be rough in W winds, and dangerous in onshore gales. St Peter lt ho is conspic on N shore. Here the estuary winds up to the Eiderdamm, a storm barrage with a lock (H24) and sluices. Tönning is about 5M up-river. The upper Eider parallels the Nord-Ostsee Kanal which it joins at Gieselau.

The R. Hever consists of several chans on the N side of Eiderstedt Peninsula, and S of the North Frisian Islands of **Süderoogsand** and **Pellworm**. Mittelhever is the most important of the three buoyed chans through the outer grounds, all of which meet SE of Süderoogsand before they separate once more into Heverstrom leading to Husum (8.21.24), and Norderhever which runs NE between Pellworm and Nordstrand into a number of watt channels. Schmaltief and Rütergat give access to **Amrum** (hbr on SE side), to Wyk on the E side of **Fohr** and to Dagebüll.

Sylt (8.21.26) is the largest of the N Frisian Islands, almost 20M long from S to N. It has a straight seaward coast, and a peninsula on its E side connects by Hindenburgdamm to the mainland. Vortrapptief is the chan inward between Amrum and Sylt, leading to Hörnum Hafen. It has a depth of about 4m (subject to frequent change) and is buoyed and lit. The area should not be approached in strong W winds. The flood (ESE-going) stream begins at HW Helgoland – 0350, and the ebb (WNW-going) at HW Helgoland + 0110, sp rates 2·5kn.

Lister Tief is the chan between the N end of Sylt and the Danish island of **Rømø**; it gives access to List Roads and hbr as well as to Danish hbrs. Lister Tief is well buoyed, with a least depth over the bar of about 4m. In relative terms it is the safest chan on this coast (after Süderpiep), available for yachts seeking anch under the lee of Sylt in strong W winds (when however there would be a big swell over the bar on the ebb). Beware buoyed obstructions (ODAS), 18M WSW of List West lt ho.

FROM GERMAN BIGHT TO UK (charts 2182A, 1405, 3761, 2593, 1505)

From the Elbe, Weser and Jade estuaries, skirt the E ends of TSS to take departure from Helgoland (8.21.23). Thence parallel the N side of TSS, 8.20.37, towards Botney Ground (BG2 buoy) if heading to ports north of the Humber. If bound for the Thames Estuary or down Channel, it is advisable to follow the ITZ westwards until well S of Texel (TX 1 lt buoy); thence take departure westward from the Netherlands (see 8.20.5). The edges of the TSS are well marked by lt buoys. Avoid areas of offshore industrial activity (8.5.5). West of German Bight streams run approx E/W, spring rates under 1kn. For distances across the North Sea, see 8.0.10.

8.21.7   DISTANCE TABLE

Approximate distances in nautical miles are by the most direct route, whilst avoiding dangers and allowing for Traffic Separation Schemes. Places in *italics* are in adjoining areas; places in **bold** are in 8.0.10, Distances across the North Sea.

Place	1	2	3	4	5	6	7	8	9	10	11	12	13	14	15	16	17	18	19	20
1. *Den Helder*	1																			
2. *Delfzijl*	115	2																		
3. Borkum	95	22	3																	
4. Emden	125	10	32	4																
5. Norderney	115	41	31	47	5															
6. Langeoog	130	56	46	63	18	6														
7. Wangerooge	148	65	55	80	29	21	7													
8. **Helgoland**	153	81	67	85	44	35	24	8												
9. Hooksiel	150	83	71	97	44	34	19	35	9											
8. **Wilhelmshaven**	159	89	80	106	53	43	27	43	9	10										
11. **Bremerhaven**	180	100	88	115	62	47	38	44	36	45	11									
12. Cuxhaven	175	105	95	120	69	60	42	38	47	56	58	12								
13. **Brunsbüttel**	192	120	110	137	84	77	55	64	70	78	17	15	13							
14. Kiel/Holtenau	245	173	163	190	137	130	108	104	117	123	131	70	53	14						
15. Hamburg	229	159	104	174	81	114	61	88	101	110	81	54	37	90	15					
16. Husum	198	127	105	137	85	77	52	47	73	82	82	66	76	129	113	16				
17. **Hörnum Lt (Sylt)**	192	119	97	129	77	72	60	38	69	78	80	63	75	128	112	48	17			
18. **Esbjerg**	187	155	133	165	123	119	109	83	116	125	127	110	126	179	163	95	47	18		
19. *Thyboron*	322	222	200	232	186	204	178	154	301	310	201	200	196	249	233	163	120	90	19	
20. *Skagen*	378	327	305	337	291	308	283	259	405	414	306	304	301	231	338	268	225	195	104	20

SPECIAL NOTES FOR GERMANY
8-21-8

LANDS are given in place of the 'counties' in the UK.

CHARTS: German charts are issued by the Bundesamt für Seeschiffahrt und Hydrographie (BSH), Hamburg. In this Almanac those prefixed 'D' are standard German nautical charts. The BSH prefix refers to the 3000 Series of charts for pleasure craft. These are a convenient size (42 x 59cm) and are stowed in a clear polythene envelope; each set has up to 16 sheets at medium/large scale. All charts are corrected by Nachrichten für Seefahrer (NfS) = Notices to Mariners. Where possible the AC, Imray and Dutch chart numbers are also quoted.

TIME ZONE is –0100, which is allowed for in the tidal predictions, but no provision is made for daylight saving schemes which are indicated by the non-shaded areas on the tide tables (see 7.1.2).

LIGHTS: In coastal waters particular use is made of light sectors. A ldg or Dir sector (usually W, and often intens) may be flanked by warning sectors to show the side on which the vessel has deviated: If to port, a FR lt or a Gp Fl W lt with an even number of flashes; if to stbd, a FG lt or a Gp Fl W lt with an odd number of flashes. Crossing lts with R, W and G sectors may indicate the limits of roadsteads, turning points in chans etc.

SIGNALS: Local port, tidal, distress and traffic signals are given where possible:

Traffic signals

(R)(R)	= Passage/entry prohib.
(R)	= Be prepared to pass or enter.
(W) (R)(R)	= Bridge closed or down; vessels which can pass under the available clearance may proceed, but beware of oncoming tfc which has right of way.
(W)(W) (R)(R)	= Lift bridge will remain at first step; vessels which can pass under the available vertical clearance may proceed.
(G)(G)	= Passage/entry permitted; oncoming tfc stopped.
(W) (G)(G)	= Passage permitted, but beware of oncoming traffic which may have right of way.
(R) (R)	= Bridge, lock or barrage closed to navigation.
(R)	= Exit from lock prohib.
(G)	= Exit from lock permitted.

Visual storm signals in accordance with the International System (see 8.15.8) are shown at: Borkum, Norderney, Norddeich, Accumersiel, Bensersiel, Bremerhaven, Brunsbüttel, Die Oste, Glückstadt, Stadersand, Hamburg, Büsum, Tönning, Husum, Wyk, List and Helgoland.

Signals hoisted at masts

By day	By night	Meaning
R cylinder	(W) (R) (W) (R)	= Reduce speed to minimize wash.
● ● ▼	(R) (R) (G)	= Fairway obstructed.
● ▼ ▲ (or R board with W band)	(R) (G) (W)	= Chan permanently closed.

When motoring under sail, always display a motoring ▼. Rule 25e is strictly enforced and non-compliance will incur a fine.

HARBOURS: There are no commercially run marinas. Most yacht hbrs are owned by the state or community and run by a local Yacht Club (as in Belgium and the Netherlands).

TRAFFIC SEPARATION SCHEMES: The extensive TSS (off Terschelling, in the German Bight and in the approaches to the Rivers Jade and Elbe) are depicted in 8.20.37 since they link up with the various Dutch TSS. Information broadcasts by VTS centres and their associated communications are also shown in 8.20.37, as well as in Area 21.

Caution: When in the ITZ to the south of the E-bound lane of the Terschelling-German Bight TSS, it is forbidden to cross the TSS between the Rivers Ems and Jade. Nor should the S edge of the E-bound lane (well marked by buoys TG 1 - TG 17) be approached closer than 1M, except in emergency or stress of weather. The German Water Police can impose on-the-spot fines or confiscate equipment to the value of DM2000, pending payment of the fine.

HIGH SPEED CRAFT: High Speed Craft (see 8.0.5) operate from Emden to Borkum; and from Hamburg to Stadersand, Cuxhaven and Helgoland. Keep a good lookout.

TELEPHONES: To call UK from Germany, dial 00 44; then the UK area code, but omitting the prefix 0, followed by the number required. To call Germany from UK, dial 00-49, and area code minus initial zero, then desired number.

EMERGENCIES: Police: dial 18. Fire, Ambulance: dial 112.

MARINE RESCUE CO-ORDINATION CENTRES: Coast station, Elbe-Weser Radio ☎ (04721) 22066. Kiel Radio, ☎ (0431) 39011. Norddeich Radio, ☎ (04931) 1831. See also 6.11.5 for notes on SAR.

WEATHER FORECASTS: Similar to the British Marinecall; from 1 April –30 Sept, forecast and outlook are available by dialling 0190 1160 plus two digits for the following areas:

-40 = Inland pleasure craft;
-45 = North Frisian Islands and Helgoland;
-46 = R Elbe from Elbe 1/Cuxhaven to Hamburg;
-47 = Weser Estuary and Jade Bay;
-48 = East Frisian Islands and Ems Estuary;
-53 = For foreign pleasure craft;
-54 = Denmark;
-55 = Netherlands.

For year round weather synopsis, forecast and outlook, dial 0190 1169 plus two digits as follows:
-20 = General information;
-21 = North Sea and Baltic;
-22 = German Bight and SW North Sea;
-31 = 5 day bulletin for North Sea and Baltic, containing an outlook and forecasts of wind, sea state, air and water temperature, plus warnings of fog, thunderstorms etc.

Strong wind (>F6) and storm warnings for the German North Sea coast may be obtained from ☎ 040 3 196628 (H24); if no warnings are in force, a wind forecast is given.

PUBLIC HOLIDAYS: New Year's Day, Good Friday, Easter Monday, Labour Day (1 May), Ascension Day, Whit Monday, Day of German Unity (3 Oct), Christmas Day and Boxing Day.

NATIONAL WATER PARKS exist in the Wadden Sea areas (tidal mud flats) of Lower Saxony, (excluding the Jade and Weser rivers and the Ems-Dollart estuary), and along the west coast of Schleswig-Holstein. Conservation of the ecology is the prime aim. The Parks (shown on AC & BSH charts) are divided into 3 zones with certain rules:
Zone 1 comprises the most sensitive areas (about 30%) where yachts must keep to buoyed chans, except HW±3. Speed limit 8kn.
Zone 2 is a buffer zone.
Zone 3 is the remainder. No special constraints exist in Zones 2 and 3.

CUSTOMS: Entry hbrs are Borkum, Norderney, Norddeich, Wilhelmshaven, Bremerhaven, Cuxhaven. Not Helgoland.

GAS: Sometimes Calor gas bottles can be re-filled. German 'Flussig' gas can be used with Calor regulators.

CURRENCY: 1 Deutsche Mark = 100 Pfennig.

USEFUL ADDRESSES: German National Tourist Office, 65 Curzon St, London W1Y 7PE; ☎ 0891 600100 (recorded info); 📠 0171-495 6129. German Embassy, 23 Belgrave Sq, Chesham Place, London SW1X 8PX (☎ 0171-235 5033).

GERMAN GLOSSARY: See 8.21.5. Best wishes *und immer eine Handbreit Wasser unter dem Kiel!*

21

EMDEN   8-21-9

Niedersachsen, Ostfriesland, 53°20'·10N 07°10'·80E

CHARTS
AC 3510; BSH 90, 91, 3012 sheets 5 & 6
TIDES
HW +0022 on Dover (UT); ML 1·9m; Zone −0100

Standard Port HELGOLAND (→)

Times				Height (metres)			
High Water		Low Water		MHWS	MHWN	MLWN	MLWS
0200	0700	0200	0800	2·7	2·3	0·4	0·0
1400	1900	1400	2000				
Differences EMDEN							
+0041	+0028	−0011	+0022	+0·8	+0·8	0·0	0·0
EMSHÖRN							
−0037	−0041	−0108	−0047	+0·1	+0·2	0·0	0·0
KNOCK (R. Ems)							
+0018	+0005	−0028	+0004	+0·6	+0·6	0·0	0·0

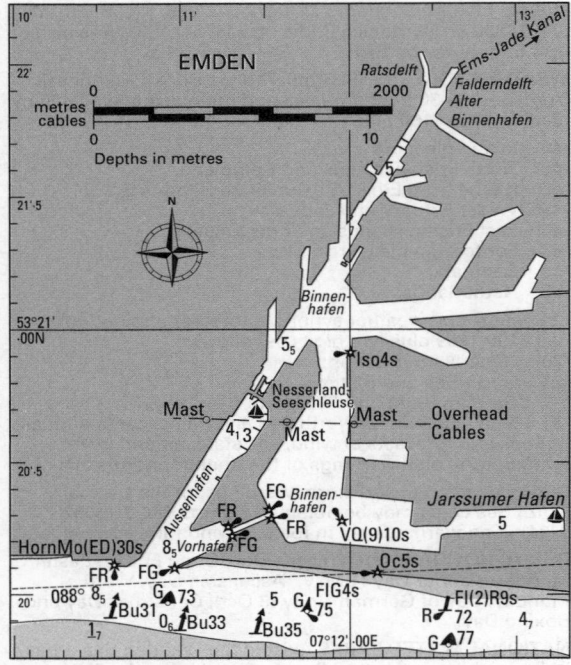

SHELTER
Good shelter, except in SW winds, in Außenhafen (3m) at yacht hbr on E side just before Nesserlander Lock. If full, lock into Binnenhafen, sheltered in all winds; Jarßumer Hafen (5m) in SE corner is mainly for locals and far from city. Possible AB at Alter Binnenhafen (4·5m), Ratsdelft (3m) and Falderndelft (3m) in city centre, if requested to lock-keeper. Lock hrs 0700-1900LT (0700-1530 Sun). For opening sound M (− −). Exceptionally, Binnenhafen can be entered via Vorhafen and Grosse Seeschleuse (H24).
NAVIGATION
See Delfzijl (8.20.33) and Borkum (8.21.11) for outer approaches via well buoyed/lit R Ems to abeam Knock lt ho. Thence 6M via Emder Fahrwasser which has drying banks and training walls close outboard of chan buoys. 3 conspic HT pylons (101m) help identify Außenhafen.
LIGHTS AND MARKS
Fahrwasser ldg lts 075°, both Oc (2) 12s 16/28m 12M (off chartlet). Ldg lts 088°, both Oc 5s 14/30m 12M, lead to hbr ent, marked by FR and FG lts. City centre bears 030°/2M.
RADIO TELEPHONE
Radar cover of the Ems is as follows:
Borkum Radar   Ch 18   Buoys 1 - 35;
Knock Radar   Ch 20   Buoys 35 - 57;
Wybelsum Radar   Ch 21   Buoys 57 - Emden Hbr ent;
Ems Traffic broadcasts safety & weather info in German H+50 on Ch 15, 18, 20 and 21. Emden locks Ch 13 (H24).

TELEPHONE (Dial code 04921)
Hr Mr ☎ 897260/897265 (H24); Nesserlander lock ☎ 897-270; Weather ☎ 21458; Tourist Info 20094; Police 110; Fire/Ambulance 112.
FACILITIES
Yacht Club ☎ 26020 FW, AC, AB 11DM; all amenities in city (1M). Ferry to Borkum.
Note: The Ems-Jade canal, 39M to Wilhelmshaven, can be used by yachts with lowering masts & max draft 1·7m. Min bridge clearance 3·75m. It has 6 locks. Speed limit 4kn.

OTHER MAINLAND HARBOURS BETWEEN RIVERS EMS AND JADE

GREETSIEL, Niedersachsen, 53°32'·90N 07°02'·15E. AC 3509, 3761; BSH 89, 3012, 3015.5 & .2. HW −0400 on Dover (UT), −0010 on Helgoland (zone −0100); ML 2·6m. Buoyed chan leads from Osterems 3M SE, then NE to Ley bn, Fl Y 4s, tide gauge. Dir lt 165°, F WRG 10m 8M, leads between 1M long bkwtrs to lock; access HW−4 to +3. Yachts berth on marina pontoons (3m). A canal connects Greetsiel to Emden. There are a few facilities: Hr Mr ☎ (04926) 760; ⊞ ☎ (04931) 2764. **Village** R, V, ⇌.

NORDDEICH, Niedersachsen, 53°38'·75N 07°08'·98E. AC 3761, BSH 3012.1, 3015.5. HW −0030 on Dover (UT); See 8.21.12. Very good shelter in hbr, reached by chan 50m wide, 2m deep and over 1M long between two training walls which cover at HW and are marked by stakes. Hr divided by central mole; yachts berth in W hbr. Lts on W training wall hd FG 8m 4M, vis 021°-327°. On E training wall hd FR 8m 4M, vis 327°-237°. Ldg lts 144°: front, Iso WR 6s 6m 6/4M; rear, 140m from front, Iso W 6s 9m 6M synch. Ldg lts 350°: front Iso WR 3s 5m 6/4M; rear, 95m from front, Iso W 3s 8m 6M. Ldg lts 170°: front Iso W 3s 12m 10M; rear, 420m from front, Iso W 3s 23m 10M, synch. Hr Mr VHF Ch 17, ☎ (04931) 81317; ⊞ ☎ 2735; YC ☎ 3560; Facilities: AB, C (5 ton), D ☎ 2721, FW, Slip, CH, BSH agent. **Town** ⑧, Bar, Dr, ⊠, R, ⇌, V, Gaz. Ferry to Juist and Norderney.

NESSMERSIEL, Niedersachsen, 53°41'·80N 07°21'·73E. AC 1875, 3761; BSH 3015.6, D89; HW −0040 on Dover (UT); −0020 on Helgoland (zone −0100); HW ht −0·2m on Helgoland. Good shelter in all weathers. Appr down the Nessmersieler Balje, chan marked by SHM buoys and bns leading to end of Leitdamm. Here, a lt bn, Oc 4s 5M, together with unlit bns mark the course of the Leitdamm on W; ⵜ mark the E side of chan. Leitdamm covers at HW. Beyond ferry berth is a Yachthafen (1½M); secure to pontoons S of Ferry Quay. Hbr dries (2m at HW). Hr Mr ☎ 2981; ⊞ ☎ 2735. Facilities: **Nordsee YC Nessmersiel**; no supplies except FW. **Village** (1M to S) has limited facilities. Ferry to Baltrum.

EAST FRISIAN ISLANDS   8-21-10

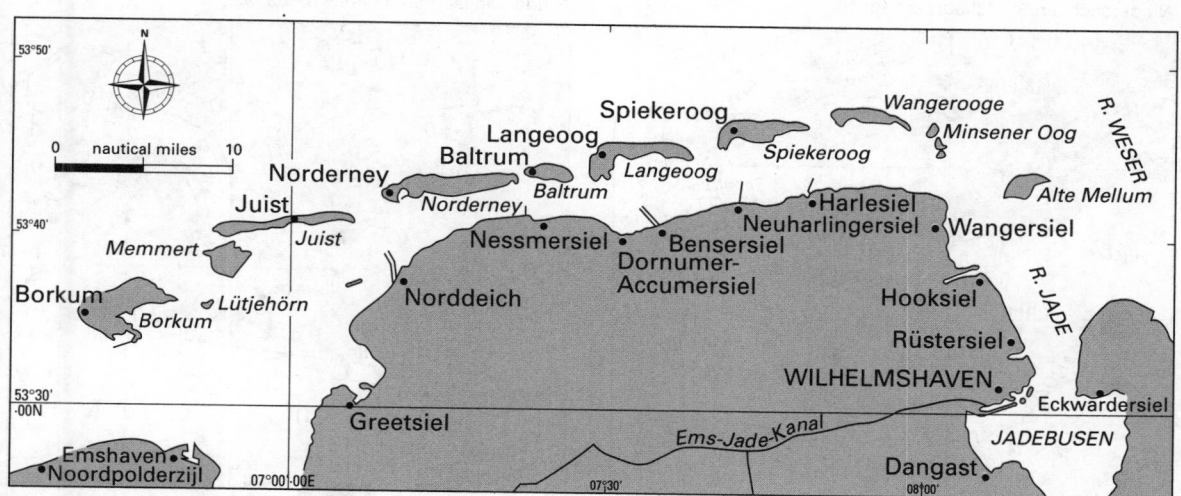

THE EAST FRISIAN ISLANDS off the North Sea coast of Germany and the North Frisian Islands off Schleswig-Holstein and Denmark together comprise the German Frisian Islands. The East Frisian Islands run from the Ems estuary to the Jade Bay with two small islands in the Elbe estuary. They lie between 3 and 20M off-shore and were, at one time, the north coast. The area between the low-lying islands and the present coastline which is now flooded by the sea is called the Watten. The islands are known locally as the Ostfriesischen and the inhabitants speak a patois known as Fries, a language with a close resemblance to English.

TIDES: The gaps between the islands are known as *Seegats* and the watersheds (where the tide meets having swept both ways round the island, usually about ⅓ of the way from the E end of the S side) are known as *Watts*. Tidal streams are very slack over the watts but very strong in the Seegats, especially on the sp ebb. Persistent strong W/NW winds may raise the sea level by over 0.25m (exceptionally by 3m); against the ebb they cause steep dangerous seas over the bars near the entrance to the Seegats. Strong E/SE winds can lower sea level by more than 0.25m, dangerously reducing clearances. All the Seegats are dangerous in winds >F4 with any N in them.

BUOYAGE: Deep water chans are buoyed, but shoal chans are marked by withies (*pricken* in German). Withies the natural way up ⪤ are to be taken as PHMs and withies bound or inverted thus ⪥ are to be taken as SHMs. As stated in 8.21.5, the conventional direction of buoyage is always from West to East inside the islands, so leave PHMs to the N whichever way the stream is flowing.

BRIEF NOTES:
BORKUM (14 sq miles): The largest island, see 8.21.11.
LUTJEHORN: Bird sanctuary; landing prohib.
MEMMERT: Bird sanctuary; landing prohib. Lt on stone tr with G cupola, Oc (2) WRG 14s 15m 17/12M.
JUIST (6½ sq miles): No yacht hbr. See next column.
NORDERNEY (10 sq miles): Lt on R octagonal tr, Fl (3) W 12s 9M 23M. See 8.21.12.
BALTRUM (3 sq miles): Pretty island with small town and hbr at W end. See next column.
LANGEOOG (7 sq miles): See 8.21.14.
SPIEKEROOG (5 sq miles): See next column.
WANGEROOGE (2 sq miles): See 8.21.15.
MINSENER OOG: Large bn. Beware groynes and overfalls in strong NW winds.
ALTE MELLUM: Bird sanctuary; landing prohib.
SCHARHÖRN (2 sq miles): Between Alte Mellum and Neuwerk; (off chartlet, in Elbe estuary). Uninhabited.
GROSSES KNECHTSAND: Between Alte Mellum and Neu Werk; Bird sanctuary; landing prohib; (off chartlet).
NEUWERK (off chartlet, in Elbe estuary): Island only inhabited by LB crew and lt ho men. Lt in ☐ brick tr with B cupola, L Fl (3) WRG 20s 38m 16/12M. On W side there is a conspic W radar tr and landing stage. Ferry to Cuxhaven.

OTHER HARBOURS IN THE EAST FRISIAN ISLANDS

JUIST, Niedersachsen, 53°39'·70N 07°00'·00E. AC 3509; BSH 90, 3015.4. HW −0105 on Dover (UT); −0035 on Helgoland (zone −0100); HW ht +0·1 on Helgoland (both differences valid at Memmert). Ent through narrow chan running N in the centre of the S side of island, marked by withies to port. To the W of these is the long (5ca) landing pier. Conspic marks are: West bn, on Haakdünen at W end of island, Juist water tr in centre and East bn, 1M from E end of island. Aero lt Fl W 5s 14m (occas) at the airfield. There is no yacht hbr, but yachts can dry out on soft mud alongside quay in ferry hbr. ⌀ 1ca S of W part of town ½M E of steamer pier or at E end of island. Hr Mr ☎ 724; ⌗ ☎ 351. Facilities: FW, Slip, C; villages of Oosdorp, Westdorp and Loog in centre have limited facilities, V, R, Bar, Gaz. Ferry to Norddeich.

BALTRUM, Niedersachsen, 53°43'·30N 07°21'·80E. AC 1875, 3761; BSH 3015.6/7. HW −0040 on Dover (UT); Use differences Langeoog 8.21.14. Shelter is good except in SW winds. Without detailed local knowledge and ideal conditions, the appr via the unmarked, drying Wichter Ee Seegat is not recommended. Better appr is at HW via the Norderneyer Wattfahrwasser running S of Norderney (which also gives access to Neßmersiel). Hbr partly dries. Yacht moorings in the Bootshafen at the E end of hbr. Lt at the groyne head Oc WRG 6s 7m 6/3M G082·5°-098°, W098°-103°, R103°-082·5°. Hr Mr ☎ (04939) 448. Facilities: Hbr AB, FW; **Baltrumer Bootsclub YC**. **Village** (¼M NNE) V, R, Bar. No fuel. Ferry from Neßmersiel.

SPIEKEROOG, Niedersachsen, 53°45'·00N 07°40'·40E. AC 3368, 1875, 3761; BSH 89, 3015.8. HW −0008 on Dover (UT); ML 1·3m; Duration 0555. See differences 8.21.14. Good shelter except in S/SW winds which cause heavy swell. Small ferry hbr (1.6m) on S side of Spiekeroog with yacht pontoons is reached by marked chan, dredged 1·2m. Lt on R mast, FR 6m 4M, vis 197°-114°. Hr Mr ☎ (04976) 235. Facilities: 60+40 visitors, 14DM, C (15 ton), town is ½M from hbr. Ferry from Nieuharlingersiel.

21

BORKUM   8-21-11

EAST FRISIAN ISLANDS
Niedersachsen 53°33'·50N 06°45'·10E

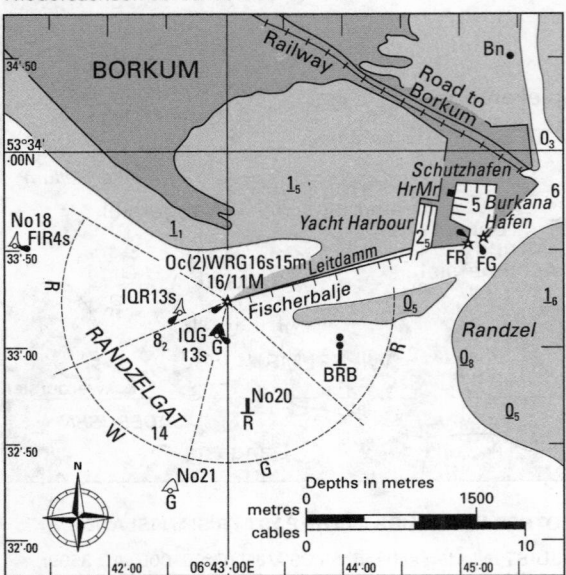

CHARTS
AC 3509, 3761; BSH 3015/2, D90; DYC 1812; ANWB A
TIDES
–0105 Dover; ML 1·4; Duration 0610; Zone –0100

Standard Port HELGOLAND (→)

Times				Height (metres)			
High Water		Low Water		MHWS	MHWN	MLWN	MLWS
0200	0700	0200	0800	2·7	2·3	0·4	0·0
1400	1900	1400	2000				
Differences BORKUM (FISCHERBALJE)							
–0048	–0052	–0124	–0105	0·0	0·0	0·0	0·0
EMSHÖRN							
–0037	–0041	–0108	–0047	+0·1	+0·2	0·0	0·0

SHELTER
Good in both yacht hbr (2 - 2·5m) and at Burkana Hafen in the NE part of the Schutzhafen (5 - 7·5m); access to both H24. The tiny ferry hbr is prohib to yachts.
NAVIGATION
WPT Riffgat (SWM) buoy, Iso 8s, 53°38'·90N 06°27'·10E, 302°/122° from/to Fischerbalje lt, 11M. See also 8.20.35. There are many groynes extending up to 2¾ca (500m) off shore. From any direction, pick up the Fischerbalje lt at the end of the Leitdamm, covers at HW. Beware strong currents across the buoyed Fischerbalje chan. Speed limit in hbrs is 5kn.
LIGHTS AND MARKS
Landmarks: Water tr, Grosse and Kleine lt ho's at Borkum town; 2 wind turbines 3ca NNE of yacht hbr ent. From the Fischerbalje lt the chan up to the hbr is well buoyed/lit. Yacht hbr ent is abeam F7 SHM buoy, Oc (3) G 12s. Schutzhafen ent shows FR on W and FG on E moles. Fischerbalje lt, Oc (2) WRG 16s 15m 16/11M, W tr with R top and lamp on tripod; R260°-313°, G313°-014°, W014°-068°. Initial app in sector R068°-123° until abm. Fog det lt.
RADIO TELEPHONE
Hr Mr VHF Ch 14 (In season Mon-Fri 0700-2200; Sat 0800-2100; Sun 0700-2000). See also Delfzijl, 8.20.30.
TELEPHONE (Dial code 04922)
Hr Mr 3440; CG Borkum Kleiner Lt Tr; ☷ 2287; Police 3950; Ⓗ 813; Brit Consul (040) 446071.
FACILITIES
Yacht Hbr (50 + 200 visitors) ☎ 7333, AB, FW, Slip, D, R, Bar, AC, C (6 ton), V, R; **Burkana Hafen** (80) ☎ 7877, ⛴ 7646; FW, AC, D (cans, limited; or ☎ 2483).
Town (7km NW) P, ME, El, Gaz, V, R, Bar, ✉, Ⓑ, ⛴ (ferry to Emden), ✈ (Emden and Bremen). Ferry: Hamburg-Harwich. The S part of the island is a Nature Reserve.

NORDERNEY   8-21-12

EAST FRISIAN ISLANDS
Niedersachsen 53°41'·94N 07°09'·93E

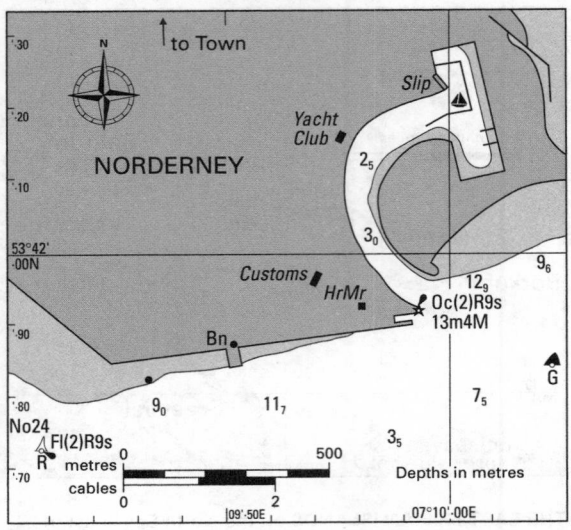

CHARTS
AC 3761; DYC 1812; Zeekarten 1353; BSH 3015, 3012, D89
TIDES
–0042 Dover; ML 1·4; Duration 0605; Zone –0100

Standard Port HELGOLAND (→)

Times				Height (metres)			
High Water		Low Water		MHWS	MHWN	MLWN	MLWS
0200	0700	0200	0800	2·7	2·3	0·4	0·0
1400	1900	1400	2000				
Differences NORDERNEY (RIFFGAT)							
–0024	–0030	–0056	–0045	+0·1	+0·1	0·0	0·0
NORDDEICH HAFEN							
–0018	–0017	–0029	–0012	+0·2	+0·2	0·0	0·0
MEMMERT							
	No data		No data	+0·1	+0·1	0·0	0·0

SHELTER
Good; the hbr is accessible H24. Yacht hbr is at the NE of the hbr, where yachts lie bow to pontoon, stern to posts; or AB on W wall of hbr, as crowded in Jul/Aug. Hbr speed limit 3kn.
NAVIGATION
WPT Dovetief SWM buoy, Iso 4s, 53°45'·35N 07°09'·83E, 013°/193° from/to D8 PHM buoy, Oc (2) R 9s, 1·63M. Ent through the Dovetief (see 8.21.5) is well buoyed but the bar can be dangerous in on-shore winds and following seas which break on it, especially on an ebb tide. Follow the buoyed chan closely around W tip of island. Ent via the Schlucter is no longer advised as it has less water (1997). Ent at night is dangerous. Note: Tidal streams run across the Schlucter and Dovetief, not along it. Beware merchant shipping.
LIGHTS AND MARKS
Land marks: in centre of island Norderney lt ho, 8-sided R brick tr, Fl (3) 12s 59m 23M. Water tr in town (conspic). W mole head Oc (2) R 9s 13m 4M, RW ○ tr.
RADIO TELEPHONE
VHF Ch 17 (Mon 0700-1200, 1230-1730; Tues 0900-1200, 1230-1900; Wed – Sun 0700-1200, 1230-1900).
TELEPHONE (Dial code 04932)
Hr Mr 82826; CG 2293; ☷ 2386; Weather 549; Police 788; Ⓗ 477 and 416; Brit Consul (040) 446071.
FACILITIES
M, L, FW, C (10 ton), V, R, CH, SM, Slip, ME, El, Sh, P, D, Gaz; **Yacht Club** Bar.
Town V, R, Bar, ✉, Ⓑ, ⛴ (ferry to Norddeich), ✈ (to Bremen). Ferry: Hamburg-Harwich.

DORNUMER-ACCUMERSIEL

Niedersachsen 53°41'·40N 07°29'·40E   **8-21-13**

CHARTS
AC 1875, 3761; BSH 3015, Sheet 7, D89
TIDES
–0040 Dover; ML 1·4; Duration 0600; Zone –0100

Standard Port HELGOLAND (→)

Use Differences LANGEOOG (8.21.14)

SHELTER
The marina provides complete shelter in all winds; depth 3m, access HW ±4. Ent is narrow; keep to W of chan on entering. Marina is fenced so obtain a key before leaving.
NAVIGATION
Appr through Accumer Ee (see 8.21.5 and 8.21.14) leading into Accumersieler Balje and to AB3 SHM buoy, IQ G 13s. From here keep four withies ‡ to stbd, clear of the Leitdamm. Note warnings on German chart D89.

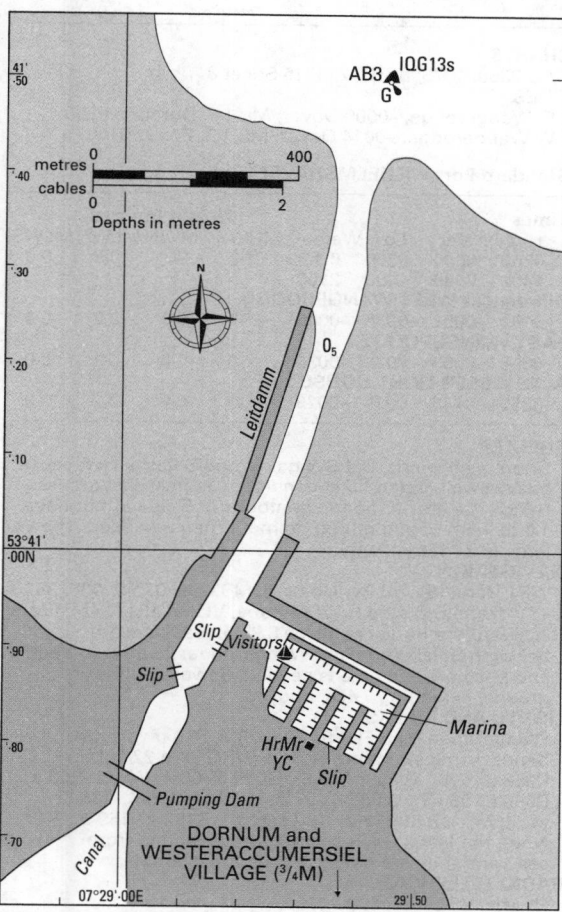

LIGHTS AND MARKS
None.
RADIO TELEPHONE
None.
TELEPHONE (Dial code 04933)
Hr Mr 2510; Deputy Hr Mr 441; ⌗ (04971) 7184; Lifeboat (04972) 247; Weather 0190 116048; Police 2218; Ⓗ 04941-940; Brit Consul (040) 446071.
FACILITIES
Dornumer Yacht Haven (250) **YC** ☎ 2240; All facilities; FW, R, Slip, Gaz, D, ME, El, Sh; pontoons are lifted out of season.
Town V, R, Bar, ✉, Ⓑ, ⇌ (Harlesiel), ✈ (Bremen or Hamburg). Ferry: Hamburg-Harwich.

LANGEOOG

EAST FRISIAN ISLANDS
Niedersachsen 53°43'·42N 07°30'·20E   **8-21-14**

CHARTS
AC 1875, 3761; ANWB A; BSH 3015, Sheet 7, D89
TIDES
–0010 Dover; ML No data; Duration 0600; Zone –0100

Standard Port HELGOLAND (→)

Times				Height (metres)			
High Water		Low Water		MHWS	MHWN	MLWN	MLWS
0200	0700	0200	0800	2·7	2·3	0·4	0·0
1400	1900	1400	2000				
Differences LANGEOOG							
+0003	–0001	–0034	–0018	+0·3	+0·3	0·0	0·0
SPIEKEROOG							
+0003	–0003	–0031	–0012	+0·4	+0·4	+0·1	+0·1
NEUHARLINGERSIEL							
No data		No data		+0·5	+0·5	0·0	0·0

SHELTER
Hbr is well sheltered by 20m high sand dunes, but it is open to the S. The E side of hbr dries; chan to yacht pontoons is marked by ‡ withies.
NAVIGATION
WPT Accumer Ee (see 8.21.5) SWM buoy, Iso 8s, 53°47'·27N 07°28'·37E, 045°/225° from/to A1 chan buoy, SHM, Oc (2) G 9s, 1·40M; thence via buoyed chan to A9/B26 SHM lt buoy. W sector of W mole lt leads 072° to ent. Ice protectors extend about 40m E of E mole, awash at HW, marked by withies.

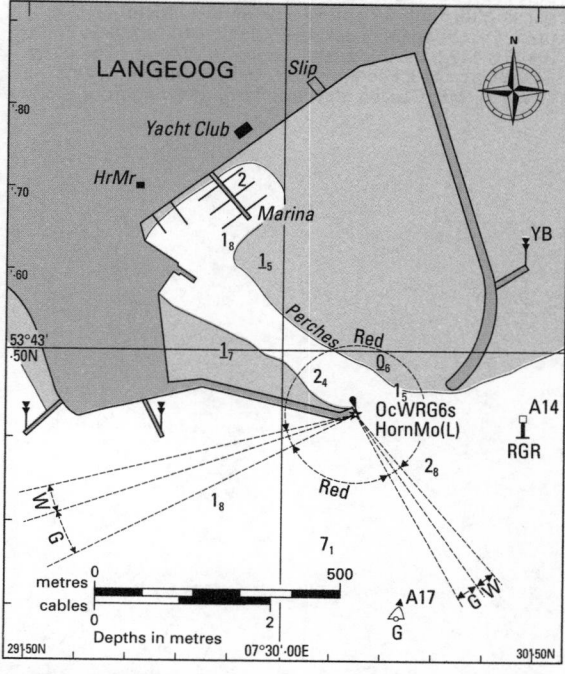

LIGHTS AND MARKS
Lt bn on W mole, Oc WRG 6s 8m 7/4M; G064°-070°, W070°-074°, R074°-326°, W326°-330°, G330°-335°, R335°-064°, Horn Mo (L) 30s (sounded 0730-1800LT). Daymarks: Langeoog ch and water tr 1·5M to NNW.
RADIO TELEPHONE
Hr Mr VHF Ch 17, 0700-1700.
TELEPHONE (Dial code 04972)
Hr Mr 502; Lifeboat CG 247; ⌗ 275; Weather Emden 21458; Police 810; Dr 589; Brit Consul (040) 446071.
FACILITIES
Langeoog Marina (70 + 130 visitors) ☎ 552, Slip, FW, C, (12 ton), El, Bar, R; **Segelverein Langeoog YC.**
Village (1½ M) P, D, V, R, Gaz, Bar, ✉, Ⓑ, ⇌ (ferry to Norddeich), ✈ (to Bremen). Ferry: Hamburg-Harwich.
NOTE: Motor vehicles are prohib on the island. Village is 1½M away; go by foot, pony and trap or train. Train connects with ferries to Bensersiel.

21

OTHER MAINLAND HARBOURS BETWEEN RIVERS EMS AND JADE

BENSERSIEL, Niedersachsen, 53°41'·80N 07°32'·90E. AC 1875, 3761; BSH 3015.7. HW −0024 on Dover (UT); +0005 on Helgoland (zone −0100); HW ht +0·4m on Helgoland. Very good shelter in the yacht hbr (dries). Ent chan from Rute 1·5M between training walls with depth of 1·5m. Walls cover at HW. Yacht hbr to SW just before hbr ent (2m); also berths on the SW side of main hbr.
Lights: E training wall hd Oc WRG 6s 6m 5/2M, G110°-119°, W119°-121°, R121°-110°. W mole hd FG; E mole hd FR. Ldg lts 138°, both Iso W 6s 7/11m 9M (intens on line), synch. Hr Mr VHF Ch 17, ☎ (04971) 2502; ⌗ ☎ (04421) 42031; Facilities: FW, C (8 ton), D (on E pier), P (cans), El, Slip, ME, Sh.
Town Ⓑ, Bar, ✉, R, ⇌, V, Gaz. Ferry to Langeoog.

NEUHARLINGERSIEL, Niedersachsen, 53°43'·20N 07°42'·40E. AC 3368, 1875, 3761; BSH 3015.8. HW 0000 on Dover (UT); see differences under 8.21.14. Appr chan well marked from Bakledge N end of Leitdamm, Oc 6s. Beware strong tidal streams across the ent. Chan runs close E of Leitdamm which is marked by stakes with ⊥. It covers at HW. Yachts lie in NE corner of hbr; where there are many poles. Visitors berths very limited. Hr Mr ☎ (04974) 289.
Facilities: **Quay** FW, D.
Village (picturesque) V, R, Bar. Ferry to Spiekeroog (35 mins).

HARLESIEL, Niedersachsen, 53°44'·10N 07°50'·10E. AC 3369, 3368; BSH 3015.8. HW −0100 on Dover (UT); HW (zone −0100) −0005 and ht +0·5m on Helgoland. Excellent shelter S of lock which opens approx HW ±1. 120 yacht berths on pontoons to W by village or at BY to E after passing through lock on W side of dyke. River navigable up to Carolinensiel. Lock, VHF Ch 17, 0700-2100. Hr Mr ☎ (04464) 1472, berthing fees similar to Wangerooge; ⌗ ☎ 249; YC ☎ 1473; Facilities: BY, C, V, R, Slip, P, D, FW.
Town El, ME, Gaz, ✉, V, ✈ and ferry to Wangerooge.

WANGEROOGE   8-21-15
EAST FRISIAN ISLANDS
Niedersachsen 53° 46'·50N 07° 52'·18E

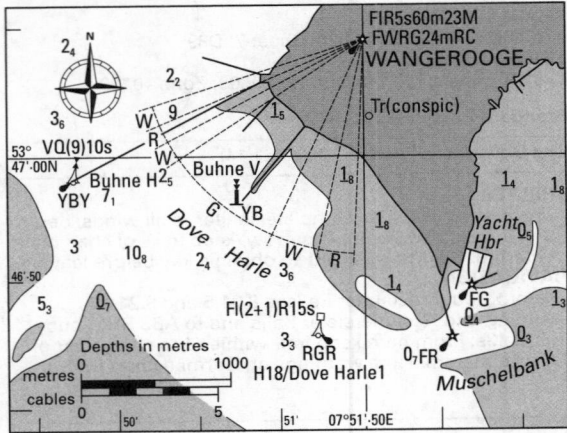

CHARTS
AC 3368, 1875; BSH D2, 3015 Sheet 8
TIDES
E Wangerooge, −0009 Dover; ML 1·9. Duration 0600
W Wangerooge, −0014 Dover; ML 1·5. Zone −0100

Standard Port WILHELMSHAVEN(→)

Times				Height (metres)			
High Water		Low Water		MHWS	MHWN	MLWN	MLWS
0200	0800	0200	0900	4·3	3·7	0·6	0·0
1400	2000	1400	2100				
Differences WEST WANGEROOGE							
−0101	−0058	−0035	−0045	−1·1	−0·9	−0·2	0·0
EAST WANGEROOGE							
−0058	−0053	−0024	−0034	−1·0	−0·8	−0·1	· 0·0
ALTE WESER LIGHT HOUSE							
−0055	−0048	−0015	−0029	−1·0	−0·9	−0·2	0·0

SHELTER
Good in all winds, but SW gales, and S'lies at HW, cause heavy swell and difficult conditions in hbr. Best access HW±2. Yachts on marina pontoons at E side of hbr have 1·3 to 1·8m depth; rafting no more than two deep. The W jetty is for ferries only.
NAVIGATION
WPT Harle (SWM) By, Iso 8s, 53°49'·28N 07°49'·00E, 351°/171° from/to Buhne H WCM buoy, VQ (9) 10s, 2·4M. From seaward the Harle chan (see 8.21.5) leads inward between Spiekeroog and Wangerooge; it varies in depth and position, and care is needed. Beware Buhne H groyne, extending 7½ca, buoyed.
LIGHTS AND MARKS
Wangerooge Lt ho Fl R 5s 60m 23M; R ○ tr with two W bands; same structure: Dir lt, F WRG 24m 22/10M, R358·5°-008°, W008°-018·5°, G018·5°-055°, W055°-060·5°, R060·5°-065·5°, W065·5°-071°, G (18M) 119·4°-138·8°, W (22M) 138·8°-152·2° (ldg sector), R152·2°-159·9°, RC. Note: the last 3 GWR sectors above lead in from seaward; they are not shown on the chartlet.
RADIO TELEPHONE
Hr Mr VHF Ch 17, 0700-1700.
TELEPHONE (Dial code 04469)
Hr Mr 630; ⌗ 223; Weather Bremerhaven 72220; Police 205; Ambulance 588; Brit Consul (040) 446071.
FACILITIES
Wangerooge YC ☎ 364, 14.10DM, FW, L, El, M, Gaz.
Village El, V, P and D (cans), CH, ▣, Ⓑ, ⇌ (ferry to Harlesiel), ✈ (to Harle and Helgoland). Ferry: Hamburg-Harwich.

HOOKSIEL

8-21-16

Niedersachsen 53°38'·85N 08°05'40E

CHARTS
AC 3369; BSH 3015 Sheet 10, D7

TIDES
+0034 Dover; ML no data; Duration 0605; Zone –0100

Standard Port WILHELMSHAVEN (➡)

Times				Height (metres)			
High Water		Low Water		MHWS	MHWN	MLWN	MLWS
0200	0800	0200	0900	4·3	3·7	0·6	0·0
1400	2000	1400	2100				
Differences HOOKSIEL							
–0023	–0022	–0008	–0012	–0.5	–0.4	–0.1	0.0
SCHILLIG							
–0031	–0025	–0006	–0014	–0.7	–0.6	–0.1	0.0

SHELTER
Temp AB in the Vorhafen (approx 1m at MLWS) but it is very commercial and uncomfortable in E winds. Beyond the lock there is complete shelter in the Binnentief, 2M long and approx 2·8m deep. Best berths for visitors in Alter Hafen Yacht Hbr in the town. Max draught 2m; bigger yachts go to YCs; see lockmaster.

NAVIGATION
WPT No 37/Hooksiel 1 SHM buoy, IQ G 13s, 53°39'·38N 08°06'·63E 227°/047° from/to ent 1·1M. See also 8.21.17 for outer appr's. Ent is marked by small H3 SHM buoy, approx 350m E, and by withies. Caution: strong cross tide, tanker pier and restricted area to SE of ent. Appr to lock through Vorhafen, enclosed by two moles. Depth in chan 2·5m. Lock hrs Mon - Fri 0800-1900, Sat/Sun 0900-2000 (LT); exact times on noticeboard. Secure well in lock. Do not enter Watersports Area due to water-ski cables.

LIGHTS AND MARKS
Ldg Its 164·5°, both Iso 6s 15/24m 24/27M, synch/intens, lead W of the WPT. Conspic chys of oil refinery 1·7M S of lock, which is in the W047°-062° sector of Hooksielplate Cross It, Oc WRG 3s. ☆ L Fl R 6s on dayglo R pile on S mole and a street lamp on N mole. R/G tfc sigs at lock.

RADIO TELEPHONE
Port VHF Ch 63. VTS Centre, *German Bight Traffic* broadcasts safety and weather info Ch 80 every H in German/English; *Jade Traffic* broadcasts info in German every H+10 Ch 20 63.
Radar cover of the Jade is as follows:
Jade Radar I   Ch 63   Buoys 1 - 33;
Jade Radar II   Ch 20   Buoys 33 - 58.

TELEPHONE (Dial code 04425)
Hr Admin 958012; Lockmaster 430; ⌗ 1302; CG (0421) 5550555; Weather (0190) 116047; Police 269; Ⓗ (04421) 2080; Dr 1080; Brit Consul (040) 446071.

FACILITIES
Visitors Yacht Hr (50) AB, 9DM (at 1DM/metre LOA). AC, FW, Bar; **Whf** (Werft BY) ☎ 95850, BH (25 ton), Slip; **Alter Hafen** AB, FW, V, R, Bar; **Wilhelmshaven YC** ☎ 285. **Town** BY, SM, ME, El, CH, P, D, Gaz, V, R, Bar, Ⓑ, ✉, ⇌ (Wilhelmshaven), ✈ (Wilhelmshaven or Bremen).

ADJACENT HARBOURS ON THE RIVER JADE

WANGERSIEL, Niedersachsen, 53°41'·00N 08°01'·60E. AC 3369; BSH 3015.9/8. HW –0100 on Dover (UT); use SCHILLIG differences 8.21.16; ML 3·3m. From spar buoy W2 (PHM) besom perches mark the N side of the chan to the hbr. Best water 10 to 20m from perches. Depth at ent, 1·3m. Chan keeps shifting especially at E end. Boats drawing 1·5m can cross the bar HW ±2½. Most of hbr dries. Berth on N quay. YC and FW are in the NW corner. Hr Mr ☎ 238. Facilities: No fuel. At Horumersiel (¼M) V, R, Bar.

RÜSTERSIEL, Niedersachsen, 53°33'·74N 08°09'·33E. AC 3369; BSH 3015.12. Tides approx as Wilhelmshaven, 3M to the S. Appr from No 47 SHM buoy, IQ G 13s; SW for 9ca to Maadesiel, close N of NWO oil pier and tanks. A conspic factory chy (275m) is 4ca S of ent. The outer hbr dries; access HW±2 via sluice gate. The small marina (3m) is 8ca up the Maade river; or continue 1M, via opening bridge (0700-1700 Mon-Fri), to berth on N quay at Rüstersiel.

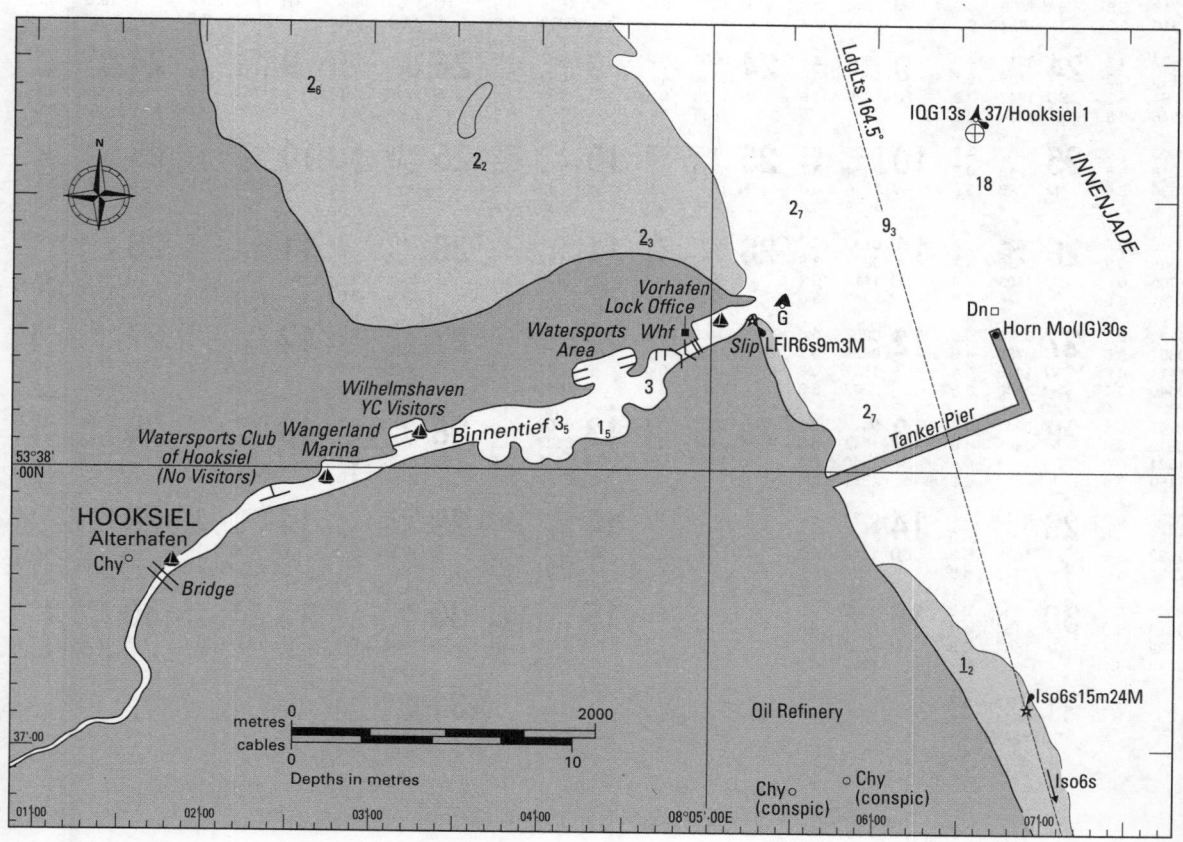

TIME ZONE –0100
(German Standard Time)
Subtract 1 hour for UT

For German Summer Time add
ONE hour in non-shaded areas

GERMANY – WILHELMSHAVEN

LAT 53°31′N   LONG 8°09′E

TIMES AND HEIGHTS OF HIGH AND LOW WATERS

YEAR 1999

JANUARY

Day	Time	m	Day	Time	m
1 F	0545 / 1159 / 1817	0.2 / 4.2 / 0.2	**16** SA	0555 / 1209 / 1816	0.3 / 4.1 / 0.3
2 SA O	0028 / 0645 / 1255 / 1909	4.2 / 0.1 / 4.3 / 0.2	**17** SU ●	0028 / 0641 / 1252 / 1859	4.2 / 0.2 / 4.1 / 0.2
3 SU	0115 / 0735 / 1344 / 1954	4.3 / 0.1 / 4.3 / 0.3	**18** M	0109 / 0724 / 1334 / 1940	4.3 / 0.1 / 4.1 / 0.1
4 M	0159 / 0823 / 1431 / 2038	4.4 / 0.1 / 4.2 / 0.3	**19** TU	0147 / 0805 / 1415 / 2021	4.3 / 0.1 / 4.1 / 0.1
5 TU	0245 / 0910 / 1518 / 2123	4.5 / 0.1 / 4.1 / 0.3	**20** W	0224 / 0845 / 1454 / 2058	4.3 / 0.0 / 4.1 / 0.1
6 W	0329 / 0954 / 1601 / 2202	4.4 / 0.1 / 4.0 / 0.2	**21** TH	0300 / 0922 / 1531 / 2132	4.3 / 0.0 / 4.0 / 0.1
7 TH	0410 / 1032 / 1640 / 2236	4.4 / 0.2 / 3.9 / 0.3	**22** F	0339 / 0959 / 1611 / 2210	4.3 / 0.0 / 4.0 / 0.1
8 F	0448 / 1106 / 1716 / 2310	4.3 / 0.2 / 3.8 / 0.3	**23** SA	0424 / 1042 / 1656 / 2254	4.3 / 0.0 / 4.0 / 0.2
9 SA	0527 / 1140 / 1754 / 2346	4.2 / 0.3 / 3.7 / 0.5	**24** SU	0511 / 1128 / 1742 / 2338	4.3 / 0.1 / 3.9 / 0.2
10 SU	0609 / 1218 / 1836	4.0 / 0.5 / 3.6	**25** M	0557 / 1213 / 1828	4.2 / 0.2 / 3.9
11 M	0030 / 0658 / 1306 / 1931	0.6 / 3.9 / 0.6 / 3.6	**26** TU	0025 / 0650 / 1305 / 1926	0.4 / 4.1 / 0.4 / 3.8
12 TU	0130 / 0801 / 1411 / 2040	0.8 / 3.8 / 0.7 / 3.7	**27** W	0128 / 0759 / 1415 / 2040	0.5 / 4.0 / 0.4 / 3.8
13 W	0243 / 0912 / 1524 / 2150	0.8 / 3.8 / 0.6 / 3.8	**28** TH	0247 / 0921 / 1536 / 2201	0.5 / 4.0 / 0.4 / 3.9
14 TH	0357 / 1021 / 1632 / 2252	0.7 / 3.9 / 0.5 / 4.0	**29** F	0413 / 1042 / 1655 / 2315	0.4 / 4.0 / 0.3 / 4.0
15 F	0502 / 1120 / 1729 / 2343	0.5 / 4.0 / 0.4 / 4.1	**30** SA	0530 / 1151 / 1802	0.2 / 4.1 / 0.3
			31 SU O	0015 / 0634 / 1247 / 1856	4.2 / 0.1 / 4.1 / 0.2

FEBRUARY

Day	Time	m	Day	Time	m
1 M	0103 / 0725 / 1335 / 1942	4.3 / 0.1 / 4.2 / 0.2	**16** TU ●	0047 / 0703 / 1317 / 1923	4.2 / 0.0 / 4.1 / 0.1
2 TU	0147 / 0811 / 1418 / 2025	4.4 / 0.1 / 4.1 / 0.2	**17** W	0128 / 0746 / 1400 / 2005	4.3 / -0.1 / 4.1 / 0.0
3 W	0229 / 0854 / 1459 / 2105	4.5 / 0.1 / 4.1 / 0.2	**18** TH	0208 / 0829 / 1440 / 2045	4.3 / -0.2 / 4.1 / -0.1
4 TH	0310 / 0933 / 1536 / 2140	4.4 / 0.1 / 4.1 / 0.1	**19** F	0247 / 0909 / 1519 / 2122	4.4 / -0.2 / 4.1 / -0.1
5 F	0347 / 1007 / 1610 / 2210	4.4 / 0.1 / 4.0 / 0.1	**20** SA	0328 / 0949 / 1600 / 2202	4.3 / -0.2 / 4.0 / -0.1
6 SA	0421 / 1037 / 1642 / 2240	4.3 / 0.1 / 3.9 / 0.1	**21** SU	0413 / 1031 / 1642 / 2245	4.3 / -0.1 / 4.0 / 0.0
7 SU	0455 / 1106 / 1713 / 2309	4.1 / 0.2 / 3.8 / 0.2	**22** M	0459 / 1113 / 1724 / 2324	4.3 / 0.0 / 4.0 / 0.1
8 M	0527 / 1132 / 1744 / 2341	4.0 / 0.3 / 3.7 / 0.4	**23** TU	0542 / 1152 / 1805	4.2 / 0.2 / 3.9
9 TU	0603 / 1203 / 1826	3.8 / 0.5 / 3.6	**24** W	0004 / 0638 / 1238 / 1859	0.2 / 4.0 / 0.3 / 3.8
10 W	0025 / 0654 / 1256 / 1929	0.6 / 3.7 / 0.6 / 3.6	**25** TH	0102 / 0739 / 1347 / 2016	0.3 / 3.9 / 0.5 / 3.8
11 TH	0133 / 0807 / 1412 / 2049	0.7 / 3.6 / 0.7 / 3.6	**26** F	0225 / 0908 / 1516 / 2145	0.4 / 3.8 / 0.5 / 3.9
12 F	0257 / 0929 / 1537 / 2207	0.6 / 3.7 / 0.6 / 3.8	**27** SA	0400 / 1036 / 1642 / 2305	0.4 / 3.8 / 0.4 / 4.0
13 SA	0417 / 1043 / 1650 / 2311	0.5 / 3.8 / 0.5 / 4.0	**28** SU	0521 / 1146 / 1750	0.1 / 3.9 / 0.3
14 SU	0522 / 1142 / 1749	0.3 / 4.0 / 0.3			
15 M	0002 / 0616 / 1232 / 1838	4.1 / 0.1 / 4.1 / 0.2			

MARCH

Day	Time	m	Day	Time	m
1 M	0005 / 0623 / 1239 / 1843	4.2 / 0.1 / 4.0 / 0.2	**16** TU	0546 / 1208 / 1811	0.0 / 4.0 / 0.1
2 TU O	0051 / 0711 / 1322 / 1927	4.3 / 0.0 / 4.1 / 0.2	**17** W ●	0022 / 0637 / 1255 / 1859	4.2 / -0.1 / 4.1 / 0.0
3 W	0132 / 0752 / 1401 / 2006	4.4 / 0.0 / 4.1 / 0.1	**18** TH	0106 / 0723 / 1340 / 1943	4.3 / -0.2 / 4.1 / -0.2
4 TH	0210 / 0831 / 1436 / 2042	4.4 / 0.0 / 4.1 / 0.0	**19** F	0148 / 0807 / 1422 / 2026	4.3 / -0.2 / 4.1 / -0.2
5 F	0247 / 0906 / 1508 / 2114	4.4 / 0.0 / 4.1 / 0.0	**20** SA	0231 / 0851 / 1503 / 2107	4.4 / -0.3 / 4.1 / -0.2
6 SA	0322 / 0936 / 1539 / 2143	4.3 / 0.0 / 4.0 / -0.1	**21** SU	0315 / 0933 / 1544 / 2148	4.4 / -0.3 / 4.1 / -0.1
7 SU	0354 / 1005 / 1610 / 2211	4.2 / 0.0 / 3.9 / 0.0	**22** M	0400 / 1014 / 1624 / 2230	4.3 / -0.1 / 4.1 / -0.1
8 M	0425 / 1032 / 1638 / 2238	4.1 / 0.0 / 3.9 / 0.0	**23** TU	0445 / 1053 / 1704 / 2308	4.3 / 0.0 / 4.1 / 0.0
9 TU	0453 / 1053 / 1703 / 2302	3.9 / 0.1 / 3.8 / 0.2	**24** W	0529 / 1131 / 1746 / 2349	4.1 / 0.2 / 4.0 / 0.1
10 W	0520 / 1114 / 1735 / 2335	3.8 / 0.3 / 3.7 / 0.4	**25** TH	0620 / 1218 / 1842	3.9 / 0.3 / 3.9
11 TH	0601 / 1153 / 1830	3.6 / 0.5 / 3.6	**26** F	0047 / 0730 / 1328 / 2001	0.2 / 3.7 / 0.5 / 3.8
12 F	0033 / 0710 / 1307 / 1951	0.6 / 3.5 / 0.7 / 3.6	**27** SA	0212 / 0900 / 1500 / 2134	0.3 / 3.7 / 0.5 / 3.9
13 SA	0159 / 0838 / 1441 / 2120	0.6 / 3.5 / 0.6 / 3.7	**28** SU	0349 / 1029 / 1628 / 2254	0.2 / 3.7 / 0.4 / 4.0
14 SU	0330 / 1004 / 1608 / 2236	0.4 / 3.7 / 0.5 / 3.9	**29** M	0509 / 1137 / 1734 / 2351	0.1 / 3.8 / 0.2 / 4.1
15 M	0446 / 1113 / 1717 / 2333	0.2 / 3.9 / 0.3 / 4.1	**30** TU	0604 / 1222 / 1820	0.0 / 4.0 / 0.1
			31 W O	0033 / 0646 / 1300 / 1901	4.2 / 0.0 / 4.0 / 0.1

APRIL

Day	Time	m	Day	Time	m
1 TH	0111 / 0725 / 1337 / 1941	4.2 / 0.0 / 4.1 / 0.0	**16** F ●	0041 / 0657 / 1317 / 1919	4.3 / -0.3 / 4.1 / -0.2
2 F	0149 / 0803 / 1411 / 2017	4.3 / 0.0 / 4.1 / 0.0	**17** SA	0128 / 0743 / 1400 / 2003	4.4 / -0.4 / 4.2 / -0.3
3 SA	0224 / 0836 / 1442 / 2047	4.3 / 0.0 / 4.1 / -0.1	**18** SU	0213 / 0828 / 1442 / 2047	4.4 / -0.3 / 4.2 / -0.3
4 SU	0257 / 0905 / 1510 / 2115	4.2 / 0.0 / 4.1 / -0.1	**19** M	0259 / 0912 / 1524 / 2131	4.4 / -0.3 / 4.2 / -0.3
5 M	0328 / 0932 / 1540 / 2143	4.1 / -0.1 / 4.0 / -0.1	**20** TU	0346 / 0954 / 1606 / 2213	4.3 / -0.1 / 4.2 / -0.2
6 TU	0357 / 0958 / 1608 / 2209	4.0 / 0.0 / 4.0 / -0.1	**21** W	0433 / 1033 / 1648 / 2255	4.2 / 0.0 / 4.1 / -0.1
7 W	0425 / 1020 / 1633 / 2234	3.9 / 0.0 / 3.9 / 0.0	**22** TH	0521 / 1115 / 1733 / 2341	4.0 / 0.2 / 4.1 / 0.0
8 TH	0451 / 1040 / 1703 / 2303	3.8 / 0.2 / 3.8 / 0.2	**23** F	0615 / 1205 / 1832	3.8 / 0.3 / 4.0
9 F	0528 / 1114 / 1750 / 2353	3.6 / 0.4 / 3.6 / 0.4	**24** SA	0040 / 0723 / 1313 / 1948	0.1 / 3.7 / 0.3 / 3.9
10 SA	0630 / 1220 / 1905	3.5 / 0.6 / 3.6	**25** SU	0200 / 0846 / 1437 / 2115	0.2 / 3.6 / 0.5 / 3.9
11 SU	0112 / 0755 / 1352 / 2034	0.5 / 3.5 / 0.6 / 3.7	**26** M	0328 / 1008 / 1601 / 2231	0.2 / 3.7 / 0.4 / 4.0
12 M	0244 / 0924 / 1523 / 2156	0.3 / 3.6 / 0.5 / 3.9	**27** TU	0443 / 1112 / 1704 / 2326	0.0 / 3.8 / 0.2 / 4.1
13 TU	0405 / 1039 / 1638 / 2300	0.1 / 3.8 / 0.3 / 4.0	**28** W	0534 / 1155 / 1748	0.0 / 3.9 / 0.1
14 W	0510 / 1139 / 1738 / 2352	-0.1 / 3.9 / 0.1 / 4.2	**29** TH	0007 / 0613 / 1231 / 1830	4.1 / 0.0 / 4.0 / 0.1
15 TH	0606 / 1231 / 1831	-0.2 / 4.0 / -0.1	**30** F O	0046 / 0653 / 1309 / 1912	4.2 / 0.0 / 4.1 / 0.0

Chart Datum: 2·26 metres below Normal Null (German reference level)

TIME ZONE –0100
(German Standard Time)
Subtract 1 hour for UT
For German Summer Time add
ONE hour in non-shaded areas

GERMANY – WILHELMSHAVEN

LAT 53°31′N   LONG 8°09′E

TIMES AND HEIGHTS OF HIGH AND LOW WATERS

YEAR **1999**

MAY

Day	Time	m		Day	Time	m
1 SA	0125 / 0733 / 1346 / 1950	4.2 / 0.0 / 4.2 / 0.0		**16** SU	0107 / 0720 / 1337 / 1941	4.4 / –0.3 / 4.2 / –0.3
2 SU	0201 / 0806 / 1417 / 2020	4.2 / 0.0 / 4.2 / –0.1		**17** M	0155 / 0804 / 1420 / 2027	4.4 / –0.3 / 4.3 / –0.3
3 M	0232 / 0834 / 1445 / 2049	4.2 / –0.1 / 4.2 / –0.1		**18** TU	0243 / 0849 / 1505 / 2114	4.4 / –0.2 / 4.3 / –0.3
4 TU	0302 / 0901 / 1513 / 2117	4.1 / –0.1 / 4.1 / –0.2		**19** W	0334 / 0935 / 1551 / 2201	4.2 / –0.1 / 4.3 / –0.2
5 W	0333 / 0928 / 1543 / 2146	4.0 / –0.1 / 4.1 / –0.1		**20** TH	0424 / 1019 / 1636 / 2247	4.1 / 0.0 / 4.3 / –0.1
6 TH	0403 / 0954 / 1613 / 2216	3.9 / 0.0 / 4.0 / 0.0		**21** F	0514 / 1103 / 1723 / 2335	3.9 / 0.2 / 4.2 / 0.0
7 F	0434 / 1021 / 1646 / 2249	3.8 / 0.1 / 3.9 / 0.1		**22** SA	0607 / 1152 / 1819	3.8 / 0.3 / 4.1
8 SA	0513 / 1057 / 1730 / 2334	3.7 / 0.3 / 3.8 / 0.2		**23** SU	0030 / 0707 / 1251 / 1925	0.1 / 3.7 / 0.4 / 4.0
9 SU	0608 / 1154 / 1834	3.6 / 0.4 / 3.7		**24** M	0136 / 0815 / 1401 / 2039	0.2 / 3.6 / 0.4 / 4.0
10 M	0041 / 0722 / 1313 / 1954	0.3 / 3.6 / 0.5 / 3.8		**25** TU	0250 / 0927 / 1515 / 2150	0.2 / 3.7 / 0.4 / 4.0
11 TU	0203 / 0844 / 1439 / 2114	0.2 / 3.6 / 0.4 / 3.9		**26** W	0359 / 1030 / 1620 / 2248	0.1 / 3.8 / 0.3 / 4.1
12 W	0323 / 1000 / 1555 / 2222	0.0 / 3.8 / 0.2 / 4.1		**27** TH	0453 / 1118 / 1711 / 2335	0.0 / 3.9 / 0.2 / 4.1
13 TH	0432 / 1105 / 1700 / 2321	–0.1 / 3.9 / 0.0 / 4.2		**28** F	0537 / 1159 / 1756	0.0 / 4.0 / 0.1
14 F	0534 / 1202 / 1800	–0.2 / 4.0 / –0.1		**29** SA	0017 / 0621 / 1239 / 1841	4.1 / 0.0 / 4.1 / 0.0
15 SA ●	0016 / 0630 / 1253 / 1854	4.3 / –0.3 / 4.1 / –0.2		**30** SU O	0059 / 0702 / 1318 / 1921	4.1 / 0.0 / 4.2 / 0.0
				31 M	0136 / 0737 / 1352 / 1954	4.2 / 0.0 / 4.2 / –0.1

JUNE

Day	Time	m		Day	Time	m
1 TU	0209 / 0808 / 1422 / 2026	4.2 / –0.1 / 4.2 / –0.1		**16** W	0230 / 0832 / 1449 / 2103	4.3 / –0.1 / 4.4 / –0.2
2 W	0242 / 0838 / 1453 / 2058	4.1 / –0.1 / 4.2 / –0.1		**17** TH	0323 / 0921 / 1537 / 2153	4.2 / 0.0 / 4.4 / –0.2
3 TH	0315 / 0908 / 1524 / 2131	4.0 / –0.1 / 4.2 / 0.0		**18** F	0414 / 1008 / 1623 / 2239	4.1 / 0.0 / 4.4 / –0.1
4 F	0348 / 0938 / 1558 / 2205	4.0 / 0.0 / 4.1 / 0.0		**19** SA	0501 / 1050 / 1708 / 2324	3.9 / 0.1 / 4.3 / 0.0
5 SA	0424 / 1012 / 1636 / 2243	3.9 / 0.1 / 4.1 / 0.1		**20** SU	0548 / 1133 / 1757	3.8 / 0.2 / 4.2
6 SU	0506 / 1052 / 1721 / 2328	3.8 / 0.2 / 4.0 / 0.1		**21** M	0010 / 0636 / 1221 / 1850	0.1 / 3.7 / 0.3 / 4.1
7 M	0556 / 1142 / 1815	3.7 / 0.3 / 3.9		**22** TU	0100 / 0729 / 1314 / 1950	0.2 / 3.7 / 0.4 / 4.0
8 TU	0023 / 0657 / 1246 / 1921	0.1 / 3.7 / 0.3 / 4.0		**23** W	0158 / 0828 / 1417 / 2054	0.3 / 3.7 / 0.4 / 4.0
9 W	0130 / 0807 / 1400 / 2034	0.1 / 3.7 / 0.3 / 4.0		**24** TH	0301 / 0932 / 1525 / 2158	0.3 / 3.8 / 0.4 / 4.0
10 TH	0244 / 0920 / 1514 / 2145	0.0 / 3.8 / 0.2 / 4.1		**25** F	0404 / 1032 / 1629 / 2256	0.2 / 3.9 / 0.3 / 4.1
11 F	0356 / 1029 / 1624 / 2250	–0.1 / 3.9 / 0.1 / 4.2		**26** SA	0459 / 1122 / 1723 / 2346	0.2 / 4.0 / 0.2 / 4.1
12 SA	0503 / 1131 / 1730 / 2351	–0.1 / 4.0 / 0.0 / 4.3		**27** SU	0548 / 1207 / 1811	0.1 / 4.1 / 0.1
13 SU ●	0605 / 1227 / 1830	–0.2 / 4.2 / –0.1		**28** M O	0031 / 0632 / 1249 / 1854	4.1 / 0.0 / 4.2 / 0.0
14 M	0048 / 0658 / 1315 / 1923	4.3 / –0.2 / 4.3 / –0.2		**29** TU	0110 / 0711 / 1327 / 1932	4.1 / 0.0 / 4.2 / 0.0
15 TU	0139 / 0745 / 1401 / 2012	4.4 / –0.1 / 4.4 / –0.2		**30** W	0148 / 0747 / 1402 / 2009	4.1 / 0.0 / 4.3 / 0.0

JULY

Day	Time	m		Day	Time	m
1 TH	0225 / 0823 / 1436 / 2045	4.2 / 0.0 / 4.3 / 0.0		**16** F	0309 / 0909 / 1521 / 2142	4.2 / 0.0 / 4.5 / –0.1
2 F	0300 / 0856 / 1509 / 2120	4.1 / 0.0 / 4.3 / 0.0		**17** SA	0356 / 0953 / 1605 / 2224	4.1 / 0.0 / 4.4 / –0.1
3 SA	0335 / 0928 / 1544 / 2156	4.0 / 0.0 / 4.2 / 0.0		**18** SU	0438 / 1031 / 1645 / 2302	4.0 / 0.1 / 4.4 / 0.0
4 SU	0413 / 1004 / 1625 / 2237	4.0 / 0.1 / 4.2 / 0.0		**19** M	0517 / 1106 / 1726 / 2340	3.9 / 0.1 / 4.3 / 0.1
5 M	0458 / 1048 / 1712 / 2323	3.9 / 0.1 / 4.2 / 0.0		**20** TU	0555 / 1144 / 1808	3.8 / 0.2 / 4.1
6 TU	0545 / 1135 / 1800	3.8 / 0.1 / 4.1		**21** W	0017 / 0635 / 1225 / 1854	0.3 / 3.8 / 0.4 / 4.0
7 W	0010 / 0635 / 1226 / 1853	0.0 / 3.8 / 0.2 / 4.1		**22** TH	0059 / 0723 / 1316 / 1950	0.4 / 3.7 / 0.5 / 3.9
8 TH	0104 / 0732 / 1327 / 1957	0.1 / 3.8 / 0.3 / 4.1		**23** F	0155 / 0825 / 1424 / 2059	0.5 / 3.7 / 0.6 / 3.9
9 F	0209 / 0839 / 1438 / 2110	0.1 / 3.8 / 0.3 / 4.1		**24** SA	0305 / 0936 / 1539 / 2210	0.5 / 3.8 / 0.5 / 3.9
10 SA	0323 / 0952 / 1553 / 2224	0.1 / 3.9 / 0.2 / 4.2		**25** SU	0415 / 1041 / 1647 / 2311	0.4 / 4.0 / 0.3 / 4.0
11 SU	0436 / 1102 / 1707 / 2332	0.1 / 4.0 / 0.1 / 4.2		**26** M	0515 / 1134 / 1742	0.3 / 4.1 / 0.2
12 M	0544 / 1204 / 1813	0.0 / 4.2 / 0.0		**27** TU	0002 / 0605 / 1220 / 1829	4.1 / 0.2 / 4.2 / 0.1
13 TU ●	0034 / 0643 / 1258 / 1911	4.3 / 0.0 / 4.3 / –0.1		**28** W O	0046 / 0649 / 1302 / 1912	4.1 / 0.1 / 4.2 / 0.0
14 W	0129 / 0734 / 1346 / 2003	4.3 / 0.0 / 4.4 / –0.2		**29** TH	0127 / 0730 / 1342 / 1952	4.1 / 0.0 / 4.3 / 0.0
15 TH	0220 / 0821 / 1434 / 2054	4.2 / 0.0 / 4.5 / –0.1		**30** F	0207 / 0810 / 1418 / 2032	4.2 / 0.0 / 4.3 / 0.0
				31 SA	0245 / 0846 / 1452 / 2108	4.2 / 0.0 / 4.3 / –0.1

AUGUST

Day	Time	m		Day	Time	m
1 SU	0320 / 0918 / 1528 / 2144	4.1 / 0.0 / 4.3 / –0.1		**16** M	0405 / 1005 / 1615 / 2232	4.1 / 0.0 / 4.4 / 0.1
2 M	0358 / 0955 / 1610 / 2226	4.0 / 0.0 / 4.3 / 0.0		**17** TU	0439 / 1036 / 1650 / 2303	4.0 / 0.1 / 4.2 / 0.2
3 TU	0442 / 1039 / 1657 / 2312	4.0 / 0.1 / 4.3 / 0.0		**18** W	0510 / 1107 / 1724 / 2332	3.9 / 0.2 / 4.1 / 0.3
4 W	0527 / 1124 / 1741 / 2354	3.9 / 0.1 / 4.3 / 0.1		**19** TH	0542 / 1139 / 1759	3.8 / 0.4 / 3.9
5 TH	0609 / 1206 / 1827	3.9 / 0.2 / 4.2		**20** F	0002 / 0619 / 1219 / 1846	0.5 / 3.8 / 0.5 / 3.8
6 F	0038 / 0658 / 1258 / 1926	0.2 / 3.9 / 0.3 / 4.1		**21** SA	0048 / 0716 / 1320 / 1954	0.7 / 3.7 / 0.7 / 3.7
7 SA	0138 / 0803 / 1410 / 2044	0.2 / 3.9 / 0.4 / 4.1		**22** SU	0159 / 0833 / 1443 / 2116	0.7 / 3.7 / 0.7 / 3.8
8 SU	0256 / 0923 / 1534 / 2208	0.4 / 3.9 / 0.3 / 4.1		**23** M	0323 / 0953 / 1605 / 2232	0.7 / 3.9 / 0.5 / 3.9
9 M	0419 / 1042 / 1656 / 2323	0.3 / 4.1 / 0.2 / 4.1		**24** TU	0439 / 1059 / 1712 / 2332	0.5 / 4.0 / 0.3 / 4.0
10 TU	0533 / 1149 / 1805	0.2 / 4.2 / 0.2		**25** W	0539 / 1151 / 1804	0.4 / 4.2 / 0.2
11 W ●	0025 / 0634 / 1244 / 1904	4.2 / 0.2 / 4.3 / 0.0		**26** TH	0020 / 0627 / 1235 / 1849	4.1 / 0.2 / 4.2 / 0.1
12 TH	0118 / 0725 / 1332 / 1954	4.2 / 0.1 / 4.4 / –0.1		**27** F O	0104 / 0711 / 1317 / 1931	4.1 / 0.1 / 4.3 / 0.0
13 F	0206 / 0810 / 1417 / 2041	4.2 / 0.1 / 4.5 / 0.0		**28** SA	0145 / 0752 / 1355 / 2012	4.2 / 0.1 / 4.3 / 0.0
14 SA	0249 / 0853 / 1500 / 2124	4.2 / 0.1 / 4.5 / 0.0		**29** SU	0224 / 0831 / 1432 / 2051	4.2 / 0.0 / 4.4 / –0.1
15 SU	0330 / 0932 / 1539 / 2200	4.1 / 0.0 / 4.4 / 0.0		**30** M	0301 / 0906 / 1510 / 2130	4.2 / 0.0 / 4.4 / –0.1
				31 TU	0338 / 0942 / 1551 / 2210	4.1 / 0.0 / 4.4 / 0.0

Chart Datum: 2·26 metres below Normal Null (German reference level)

21

TIME ZONE –0100
(German Standard Time)
Subtract 1 hour for UT

For German Summer Time add
ONE hour in non-shaded areas

GERMANY – WILHELMSHAVEN

LAT 53°31′N   LONG 8°09′E

TIMES AND HEIGHTS OF HIGH AND LOW WATERS

YEAR **1999**

SEPTEMBER

	Time	m		Time	m
1 W	0419 1023 1636 2252	4.1 0.1 4.4 0.1	**16** TH	0427 1030 1642 2248	4.0 0.2 4.0 0.3
2 TH	0501 1105 1719 2331	4.1 0.2 4.3	**17** F	0454 1058 1711 2311	3.9 0.4 3.9 0.5
3 F	0540 1144 1804	4.0 0.3 4.1	**18** SA	0525 1130 1750 2348	3.8 0.6 3.7 0.7
4 SA	0013 0628 1235 1905	0.4 3.9 0.4 4.0	**19** SU	0615 1224 1854	3.7 0.8 3.6
5 SU	0113 0737 1351 2029	0.6 3.9 0.5 3.9	**20** M	0055 0731 1346 2020	0.9 3.7 0.8 3.6
6 M	0239 0905 1526 2201	0.7 3.9 0.5 3.9	**21** TU	0228 0900 1518 2147	0.9 3.8 0.7 3.8
7 TU	0411 1031 1653 2319	0.6 4.1 0.3 4.0	**22** W	0357 1019 1636 2256	0.8 4.0 0.4 3.9
8 W	0527 1138 1800	0.4 4.2 0.1	**23** TH	0506 1117 1733 2350	0.5 4.1 0.2 4.0
9 TH ●	0016 0623 1229 1851	4.1 0.3 4.3 0.1	**24** F	0559 1203 1821	0.4 4.2 0.1
10 F	0102 0710 1313 1937	4.1 0.2 4.4 0.1	**25** SA O	0036 0644 1247 1905	4.1 0.2 4.3 0.0
11 SA	0144 0752 1354 2019	4.2 0.2 4.5 0.1	**26** SU	0119 0728 1328 1948	4.2 0.1 4.4 -0.1
12 SU	0223 0831 1433 2057	4.2 0.2 4.5 0.1	**27** M	0159 0809 1408 2029	4.2 0.0 4.4 -0.1
13 M	0258 0906 1509 2130	4.2 0.1 4.4 0.1	**28** TU	0237 0848 1449 2110	4.2 0.0 4.4 0.0
14 TU	0329 0936 1542 2158	4.2 0.1 4.3 0.2	**29** W	0316 0926 1531 2150	4.2 0.0 4.4 0.1
15 W	0359 1003 1613 2224	4.1 0.1 4.2 0.2	**30** TH	0354 1004 1614 2228	4.2 0.1 4.3 0.2

OCTOBER

	Time	m		Time	m
1 F	0434 1043 1658 2306	4.2 0.2 4.2 0.4	**16** SA	0416 1024 1634 2231	4.0 0.4 3.9 0.5
2 SA	0515 1124 1748 2352	4.1 0.3 4.0 0.6	**17** SU	0446 1055 1710 2304	3.9 0.6 3.7 0.8
3 SU	0607 1219 1853	4.0 0.5 3.8	**18** M	0530 1142 1807	3.8 0.8 3.6
4 M	0056 0720 1340 2019	0.8 3.9 0.6 3.7	**19** TU	0005 0639 1255 1928	1.0 3.7 0.9 3.6
5 TU	0225 0851 1518 2152	0.8 4.0 0.5 3.8	**20** W	0133 0806 1425 2056	1.1 3.8 0.8 3.7
6 W	0359 1018 1646 2308	0.7 4.1 0.4 3.9	**21** TH	0306 0930 1549 2213	0.9 3.9 0.5 3.8
7 TH	0513 1123 1747	0.5 4.3 0.2	**22** F	0423 1036 1654 2313	0.7 4.1 0.3 4.0
8 F	0000 0604 1209 1830	0.4 4.4 0.3 4.3	**23** SA	0522 1128 1747	0.4 4.2 0.1
9 SA ●	0039 0646 1249 1910	4.1 0.3 4.4 0.2	**24** SU O	0004 0613 1215 1836	4.1 0.3 4.3 0.0
10 SU	0117 0727 1329 1951	4.2 0.2 4.4 0.2	**25** M	0050 0700 1300 1922	4.2 0.1 4.4 0.0
11 M	0153 0805 1406 2027	4.2 0.2 4.4 0.2	**26** TU	0132 0743 1343 2004	4.3 0.1 4.4 0.0
12 TU	0225 0837 1439 2057	4.3 0.2 4.4 0.3	**27** W	0211 0825 1427 2047	4.3 0.1 4.5 0.1
13 W	0254 0905 1509 2122	4.3 0.1 4.2 0.2	**28** TH	0252 0907 1512 2128	4.3 0.1 4.4 0.1
14 TH	0322 0931 1538 2146	4.2 0.1 4.1 0.3	**29** F	0333 0947 1558 2207	4.3 0.1 4.3 0.3
15 F	0349 0957 1606 2208	4.1 0.2 4.0 0.4	**30** SA	0413 1028 1646 2248	4.1 0.2 4.1 0.5
31 SU	0458 1113 1739 2337	4.2 0.3 3.9 0.6			

NOVEMBER

	Time	m		Time	m
1 M	0553 1211 1844	4.1 0.5 3.8	**16** TU	0503 1117 1737 2331	3.9 0.6 3.7 0.8
2 TU	0042 0705 1327 2003	0.8 4.0 0.6 3.7	**17** W	0600 1217 1845	3.8 0.7 3.6
3 W	0203 0830 1457 2129	0.8 4.0 0.6 3.7	**18** TH	0044 0716 1334 2005	1.0 3.8 0.6 3.7
4 TH	0330 0952 1619 2241	0.8 4.1 0.5 3.8	**19** F	0210 0837 1456 2124	0.9 4.0 0.5 3.8
5 F	0442 1056 1718 2332	0.6 4.2 0.3 4.0	**20** SA	0331 0949 1608 2232	0.7 4.1 0.3 3.9
6 SA	0533 1142 1800	0.4 4.3 0.3	**21** SU	0438 1049 1710 2329	0.5 4.2 0.2 4.1
7 SU	0009 0616 1222 1840	4.1 0.4 4.3 0.3	**22** M	0537 1143 1806	0.3 4.3 0.1
8 M ●	0046 0658 1302 1920	4.2 0.4 4.3 0.3	**23** TU O	0020 0630 1233 1855	4.2 0.3 4.4 0.1
9 TU	0123 0738 1339 1955	4.2 0.3 4.3 0.3	**24** W	0104 0717 1320 1939	4.3 0.2 4.4 0.1
10 W	0155 0809 1411 2024	4.3 0.3 4.3 0.3	**25** TH	0146 0802 1407 2023	4.4 0.2 4.4 0.1
11 TH	0223 0836 1440 2050	4.3 0.2 4.2 0.3	**26** F	0230 0849 1458 2110	4.4 0.1 4.3 0.2
12 F	0251 0904 1510 2115	4.3 0.2 4.1 0.3	**27** SA	0317 0937 1549 2155	4.4 0.1 4.2 0.3
13 SA	0320 0932 1539 2140	4.2 0.2 4.0 0.4	**28** SU	0402 1022 1639 2238	4.4 0.1 4.0 0.4
14 SU	0349 1001 1610 2206	4.1 0.3 3.9 0.5	**29** M	0448 1109 1730 2325	4.3 0.3 3.9 0.6
15 M	0421 1034 1647 2240	4.0 0.5 3.8 0.7	**30** TU	0540 1201 1828	4.2 0.4 3.7

DECEMBER

	Time	m		Time	m
1 W	0021 0643 1303 1933	0.7 4.1 0.5 3.6	**16** TH	0535 1150 1813	4.0 0.4 3.7
2 TH	0127 0755 1416 2045	0.7 4.0 0.5 3.6	**17** F	0007 0635 1251 1919	0.7 3.9 0.4 3.7
3 F	0241 0909 1530 2154	0.7 4.0 0.5 3.8	**18** SA	0118 0745 1403 2032	0.7 4.0 0.4 3.7
4 SA	0353 1016 1634 2252	0.7 4.1 0.5 3.9	**19** SU	0235 0900 1518 2145	0.7 4.1 0.4 3.8
5 SU	0453 1109 1725 2336	0.6 4.1 0.4 4.1	**20** M	0350 1010 1629 2252	0.5 4.2 0.3 4.0
6 M	0542 1155 1809	0.5 4.2 0.4	**21** TU	0459 1113 1734 2349	0.4 4.3 0.2 4.1
7 TU ●	0016 0628 1236 1850	4.2 0.4 4.2 0.4	**22** W O	0600 1210 1830	0.2 4.3 0.1
8 W	0054 0709 1313 1925	4.3 0.3 4.2 0.3	**23** TH	0039 0654 1303 1919	4.3 0.1 4.3 0.1
9 TH	0128 0743 1347 1955	4.3 0.2 4.2 0.3	**24** F	0126 0745 1355 2007	4.4 0.1 4.3 0.2
10 F	0158 0813 1419 2026	4.3 0.2 4.2 0.3	**25** SA	0215 0837 1448 2057	4.4 0.0 4.2 0.2
11 SA	0229 0845 1452 2055	4.3 0.2 4.1 0.3	**26** SU	0305 0930 1541 2146	4.4 0.0 4.1 0.2
12 SU	0300 0916 1524 2123	4.2 0.2 4.0 0.3	**27** M	0353 1017 1630 2228	4.4 0.0 4.0 0.2
13 M	0332 0947 1556 2153	4.2 0.3 3.9 0.4	**28** TU	0437 1101 1716 2309	4.4 0.1 3.9 0.3
14 TU	0407 1022 1634 2227	4.1 0.4 3.8 0.5	**29** W	0523 1144 1802 2354	4.3 0.2 3.8 0.4
15 W	0447 1102 1719 2311	4.0 0.4 3.8 0.6	**30** TH	0614 1230 1851	4.2 0.4 3.7
31 F	0043 0710 1323 1948	0.5 4.0 0.5 3.6			

Chart Datum: 2·26 metres below Normal Null (German reference level)

WILHELMSHAVEN
MEAN SPRING AND NEAP CURVES

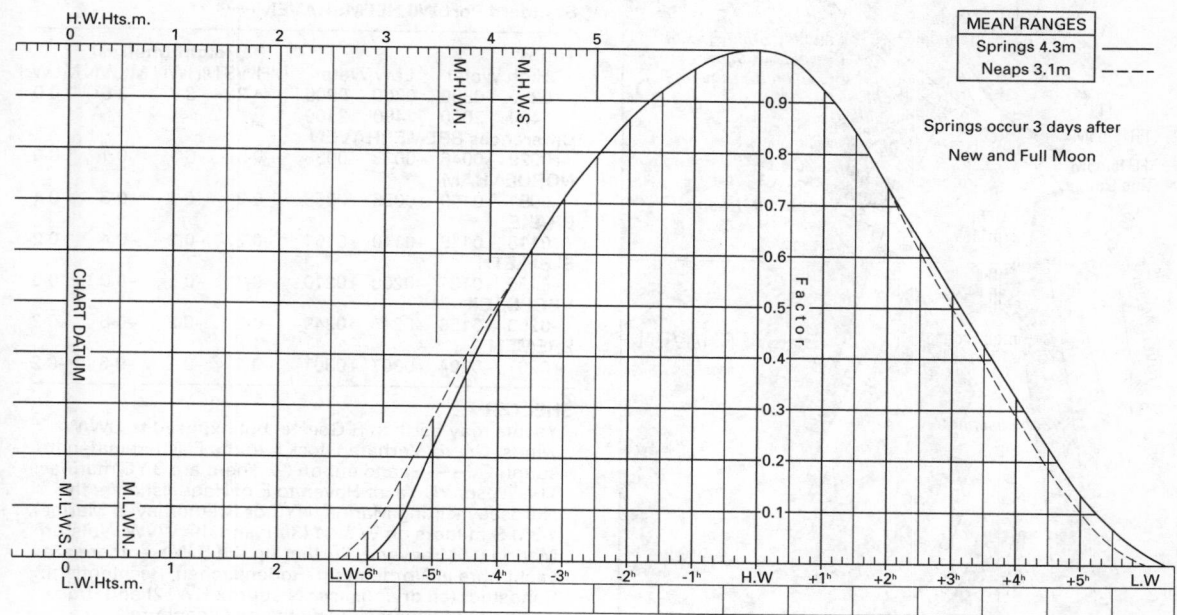

WILHELMSHAVEN   8-21-17

Niedersachsen 53°31'·00N 08°09'·00E

CHARTS
AC 3369; BSH 3015 Sheet 12, D7

TIDES
+0050 Dover; ML 2·3; Duration 0615; Zone –0100
WILHELMSHAVEN is a Standard Port. Predictions above.

SHELTER
Good in the yacht hbrs at Großer Hafen and Nordhafen,
inside the sea lock, the latter rather remote. Sea lock
operates Mon-Thur: 0600-1830; Fri: 0600-1700; Sat, Sun
and hols: 0800-1600 (all LT). Nassauhafen in the tidal hbr
(*Fluthafen*) has yacht pontoons in about 1·7m.

NAVIGATION
WPT 1b/Jade 1 SHM buoy, Oc G 4s, 53°52'·42N 07°44'·10E,
296°/116° from/to Mellumplate lt, 14·2M. From abeam this
lt, it is approx 15M to Wilhelmshaven, a busy commercial
port, via the deep, wide and well marked fairway.
Note: The Ems-Jade canal, 39M to Emden, is usable by
yachts with lowering masts and max draft 1·7m. Min
bridge clearance 3·75m. It has 6 locks. Speed limit 4kn.

LIGHTS AND MARKS
R Jade is well marked/lit; for principal lts see 8.21.4. Ldg
lts 208° into Neuer Vorhafen both Iso 4s. Fluthafen N mole
FWG 9m 6/3M (sectors on chartlet); S arm, hd FR.

RADIO TELEPHONE
Port Ch 11 16 (H24). Sea lock Ch 13. Bridge opening Ch 11.
See 8.21.16 for VTS, broadcast info and radar assistance.

TELEPHONE (Dial code 04421)
Hr Mr 291256; Port Authority 48000; Naval base/Port
Captain 308 71 (operator); Sea Lock 186480; VTS 489381;
⌗ 480723; Weather Bremerhaven 72220; Water Police
942358; Ⓗ 8011; Brit Consul (040) 446071.

FACILITIES
Nassauhafen Marina (28 + 100 Ⓥ) ☎ 41439, 12DM, AC, P,
D, BY, Slip, ME, Bar, FW, SM, R; **Wiking Sportsboothafen**
(30) ☎ 41301 AC, Bar, CH, EI, FW, Gaz, ME, R, SM, V, Sh;
Hochsee YC Germania ☎ 44121. There are 16 YCs in the
area. **City** BY, SM, ME, CH, EI, P, D, Gaz, V, ✉, Ⓑ, ⇌, ✈.
Ferry: Hamburg-Harwich.

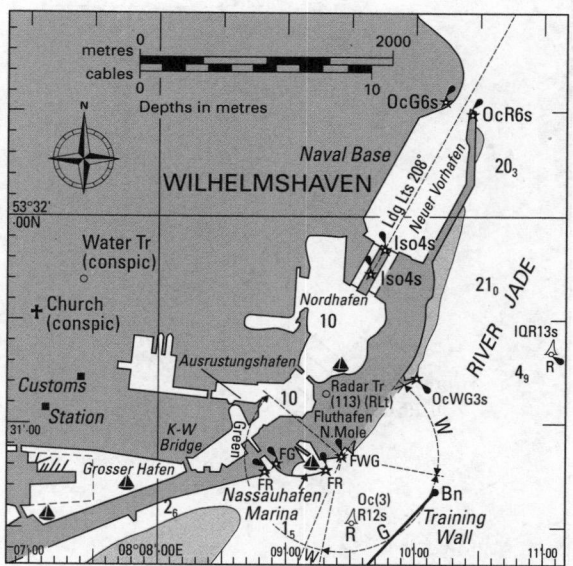

ADJACENT HARBOUR IN JADEBUSEN

DANGAST, Niedersachsen, 53°27'·00N 08°07'·00E. AC
3369; BSH 3015.13. HW +0055 on Dover (UT); –0007 on
Helgoland (zone –0100). 4M S of Wilhelmshaven, drying
hbr in the wide bay of Jadebusen, which mostly dries.
Appr via Stenkentief, marked on NW side by stakes,
thence SW into Dangaster Aussentief (0·5m at LWS).
Unlit, other than Arngast lt, F WRG (not visible from SW),
R tr, W bands, in the middle of Jadebusen. Yacht hbr
(dries) on W side just before lock into Dangaster Tief,
access HW ±2. Facilities: usual amenities can be found in
the seaside town of Dangast.

21

BREMERHAVEN 8-21-18

Federal State of Bremen 53°32'·16N 08°34'·57E

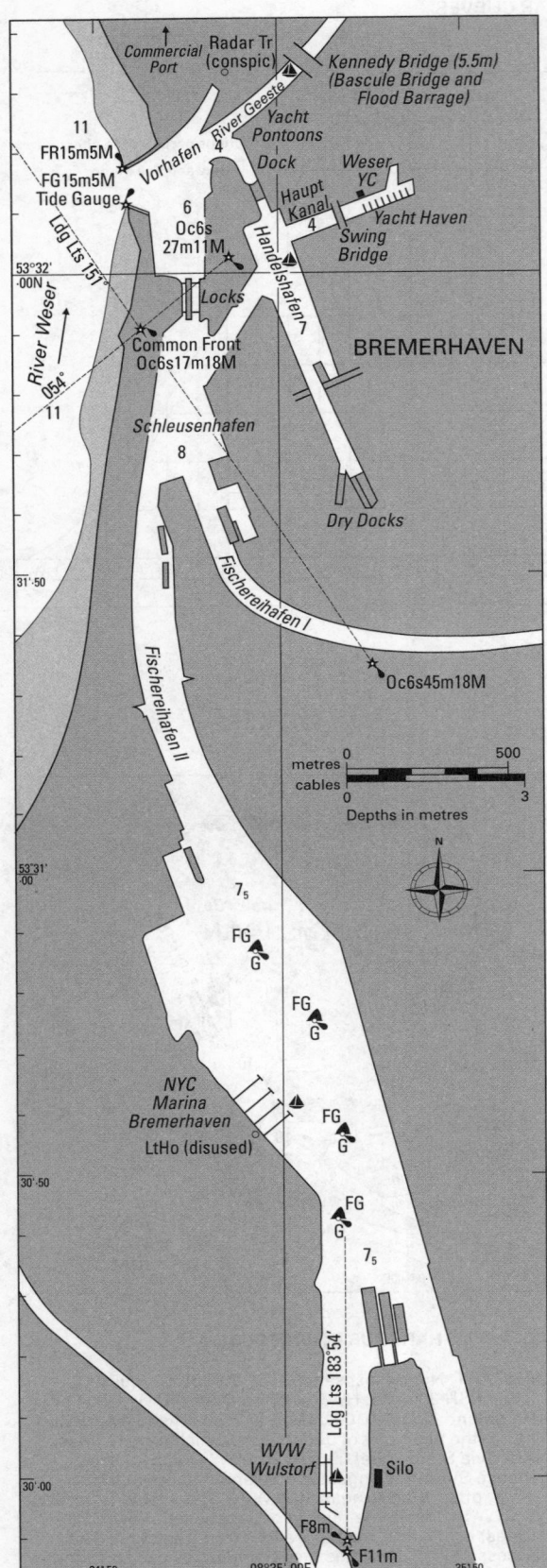

CHARTS
AC 3406, 3405; BSH 3011 Sheets 7, 8 & 10, D4
TIDES
+0051 Dover; ML 2·0; Duration 0600; Zone –0100

Standard Port WILHELMSHAVEN (←)

Times				Height (metres)			
High Water		Low Water		MHWS	MHWN	MLWN	MLWS
0200	0800	0200	0900	4·3	3·7	0·6	0·0
1400	2000	1400	2100				
Differences BREMERHAVEN							
+0029	+0046	+0033	+0038	–0·3	–0·1	–0·1	0·0
NORDENHAM							
+0051	+0109	+0055	+0058	–0·2	–0·1	–0·3	–0·1
BRAKE							
+0118	+0119	+0140	+0151	–0·2	–0·2	–0·4	–0·2
ELSFLETH							
+0130	+0131	+0200	+0210	–0·1	–0·1	–0·3	0·0
VEGESACK							
+0200	+0156	+0245	+0249	–0·2	–0·2	–0·6	–0·2
BREMEN							
+0207	+0204	+0307	+0307	–0·1	–0·1	–0·6	–0·2

SHELTER
Yachts may berth in R Geeste, but exposed to SW/W winds. Or, via Vorhafen, lock into the Fischereihafen II; sound Q (— — · —) and ent on ⑤. There are 3 YC/marinas: The Weser YC Yacht Haven to E of Handelshafen; the Nordseeyachting Marina (NYC or Bremerhaven Marina), 1·3M S of locks on W side (3m); and the WVW Wulstorf Marina 0·5M beyond. Further up the R Weser there are yacht hbrs at Nordenham, Rodenkirchen, Rechtenfleth, Sandstedt (all drying; access approx HW±2) and Brake; and on the R Hunte at Elsfleth and Oldenburg.
NAVIGATION
WPT Alte Weser: Schlüsseltonne (SWM) buoy, Iso 8s, 53°56'·30N 07°54'·87E, 300°/120° from/to Alte Weser lt, 9M. For R Weser (very well marked) see 8.21.5. Leave R Weser at SHM lt buoy 61. Beware much commercial shipping; also ferries using R Geeste.
Note: The Geeste and Hadelner Kanals (1·5m depth; air draft 2·7m) link Bremerhaven to Otterndorf (32M).
LIGHTS AND MARKS
Ldg lts, both Oc 6s 17/45m 18M, synch, lead 151° down main chan (R Weser). Vorhafen ent, FR & FG 15m 5M, is close SW of conspic 112m radar tr.
RADIO TELEPHONE
Radar cover and info in the outer Weser is as follows:

Alte Weser Radar	Ch 22	Neue Weser: buoys 3a -19H;
ditto	ditto	Alte Weser: buoys A1 - 16a;
Hohe Weg Radar I & II	Ch 02	Buoys 21 - 37;
Robbenplate Rdr I & II	Ch 04	Buoys 37 - 53;
Blexen Radar	Ch 07	Buoys 53 - 63;
Luneplate Radar I	Ch 05	Buoys 63 - 58;

Bremerhaven Weser Traffic broadcasts info in German at H+20 on all the above chans. Bremerhaven Port & locks Ch 12 16 (H24). Brake Lock Ch 10 (H24). Bremen-Weser Traffic broadcasts at H+30 on Ch 19 78 81; Oslebshausen Lock Radio Ch 12. Bremen Port Radio Ch 03 14 16 (H24). Hunte Traffic broadcasts at H+30 on Ch 17. Hunte Bridge Radio Ch 10 (HJ). Oldenburg Bridge Radio Ch 69 (H24).
TELEPHONE (Dial code 0471)
Hr Mr 9474625; Fischereihafen Lock 9474628; Weather 72220; Police 94667; Ⓗ 2991; Brit Consul (040) 4480320.
FACILITIES
Weser YC ☎ 23531 C, AC, FW, R, Bar; **NYC Marina** ☎ 77555 P, D, C, Slip, AC, FW; **WVW Marina** ☎ 73268, FW, Slip, C, El, P, D; **City** all facilities: ACA, Gaz, ⇌, ✈.

The yacht lay with a very slight heel (thanks to a pair of small bilge-keels on her bottom) in a sort of trough she had dug for herself, so that she was still ringed with a few inches of water, as it were with a moat.

For miles in every direction lay a desert of sand. To the north it touched the horizon, and was only broken by the blue dot of Neuwerk Island and its lighthouse. To the east it seemed also to stretch to infinity, but the smoke of a steamer showed where it was pierced by the stream of the Elbe. To the south it ran up to the pencil-line of the Hanover shore. Only to the west was it broken by any vestiges of the sea it had arisen from.

Riddle of the Sands: Erskine Childers

CUXHAVEN
MEAN SPRING AND NEAP CURVES

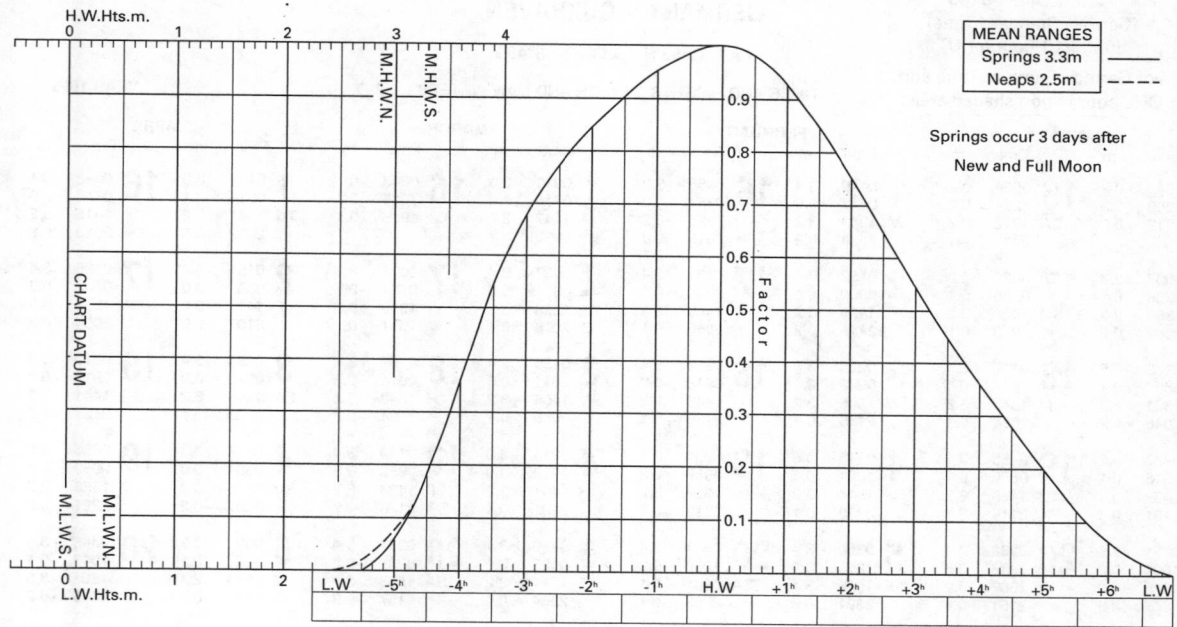

MEAN RANGES	
Springs 3.3m	——
Neaps 2.5m	- - - -

Springs occur 3 days after
New and Full Moon

CUXHAVEN   8-21-19
Niedersachsen 53°52'·48N 08°42'·56E (Marina ent). Rtg 1-1-1

CHARTS
AC 3261; BSH 3010 Sheet 1
TIDES
+0103 Dover; ML 1·7; Duration 0535; Zone –0100
CUXHAVEN is a Standard Port; predictions are below

Standard Port CUXHAVEN (→)

Times				Height (metres)			
High Water		Low Water		MHWS	MHWN	MLWN	MLWS
0200	0800	0200	0900	3·3	2·9	0·4	0·0
1400	2000	1400	2100				
Differences SCHARHÖRN (11M to NW)							
–0045	–0047	–0057	–0059	0·0	0·0	0·0	0·0

SHELTER
Good in the YC marina (4m; closed in winter). Marina
Cuxhaven, close S of radio mast, is entered from Alter
Hafen via bridge which opens H and H+30, requested by 2
long blasts. Yachts > 20m LOA may berth in the Alter
Hafen or Alter Fischereihafen. See 8.21.22 for Otterndorf.
NAVIGATION
WPT No 31 SHM buoy, Fl G 4s, 53°53'·97N 08°41'·27E,
332°/152° from/to marina ent, 1·7M. From No 23 SHM
buoy, appr is in W sector (144°-149°) of Baumrönne ldg lt
Fl 3s. Chan well marked/lit, see 8.21.4, and .20. Ebb runs
up to 5kn off Cuxhaven. Much commercial shipping.
LIGHTS AND MARKS
Ent to YC Marina is close NW of conspic radar tr, and N
of main lt ho (dark R with copper cupola) FWR, Fl (4) 12s,
Oc 6s and Fl (5) 12s (for sectors see chartlet). YC marina
ent, N side FWG; S side FWR, shown 1 Apr-31 Oct.
RADIO TELEPHONE
Radar cover of the outer Elbe is as follows:

Elbe West Radar	Ch 65	G. Bight lt float - buoy 1;
Elbe East Radar	Ch 19	Elbe lt float - buoy 5;
Scharhörn Radar	Ch 18	Buoys 3 - 15;
Neuwerk Radar	Ch 05	Buoys 13 - 29;
Cuxhaven Radar	Ch 21	Buoys 27 - 41;
Belum Radar	Ch 03	Buoys 39 - 53.

Cuxhaven Elbe Traffic broadcasts nav/weather info for
the outer Elbe on Ch 71 in German & English every H + 55.
CG & LB: Ch 16. *Cuxhaven Elbe Port* Ch **12** 16 (H24). Port/
lock work Ch 69.

TELEPHONE (Dial code 04721)
Hr Mr 34111 (Apr-Oct); CG 38011; LB 34622 and Ch 16;
Weather 36400; Port Authority 501450; ☰ 21085; British
Cruising Ass'n and Little Ship Club 57270, ☎ 572757;
Police 110; Dr & Fire 112; Brit Consul (040) 446071.
FACILITIES
Cuxhaven YC Marina (Segler-Vereinigung) ☎ 34111
(summer only), 20DM, Slip, FW, P & D (cans), C (10 ton),
AC (free up to 500 watts, then 0·70DM/kilowatt), BY, ME,
El, Sh, CH, SM, Gaz, chart agent, Ⓔ, R, Bar, ☒, ☰;
Cuxhaven Marina ☎ 37363, open all year, 90 berths inc
approx 45 for Ⓥ, 20DM, usual facilities. Swing bridge
opens every H and H+30 during daytime.
City All facilities, ⇌, ✈ (Bremen, Hamburg, Hanover).
Ferry: Hamburg -Harwich.

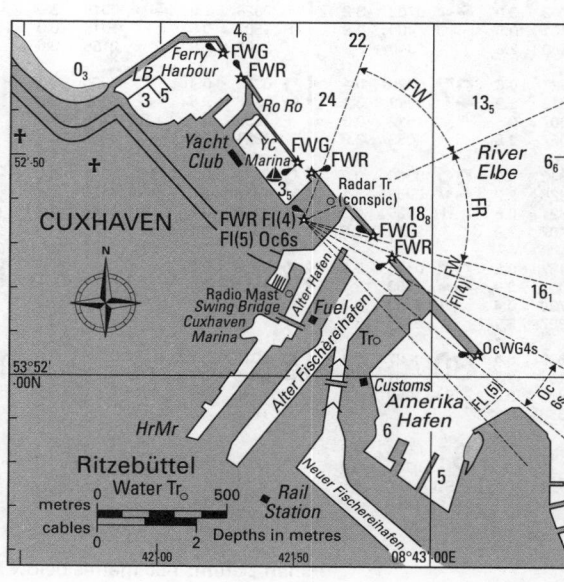

TIME ZONE –0100
(German Standard Time)
Subtract 1 hour for UT

For German Summer Time add
ONE hour in non-shaded areas

GERMANY – CUXHAVEN

LAT 53°52′N   LONG 8°43′E

TIMES AND HEIGHTS OF HIGH AND LOW WATERS

YEAR **1999**

JANUARY

Day	Time	m	Day	Time	m
1 F	0642 / 1209 / 1912	0.2 / 3.3 / 0.2	**16** SA	0654 / 1221 / 1912	0.2 / 3.2 / 0.2
2 SA O	0037 / 0739 / 1303 / 2002	3.3 / 0.1 / 3.3 / 0.2	**17** SU ●	0038 / 0738 / 1302 / 1953	3.3 / 0.1 / 3.2 / 0.1
3 SU	0123 / 0827 / 1351 / 2046	3.5 / 0.1 / 3.3 / 0.2	**18** M	0117 / 0817 / 1343 / 2034	3.3 / 0.1 / 3.2 / 0.1
4 M	0207 / 0913 / 1439 / 2131	3.6 / 0.1 / 3.3 / 0.3	**19** TU	0155 / 0857 / 1423 / 2114	3.4 / 0.1 / 3.2 / 0.1
5 TU	0251 / 1001 / 1526 / 2215	3.6 / 0.2 / 3.3 / 0.3	**20** W	0232 / 0936 / 1502 / 2151	3.4 / 0.0 / 3.2 / 0.1
6 W	0335 / 1044 / 1611 / 2253	3.6 / 0.2 / 3.2 / 0.2	**21** TH	0308 / 1013 / 1538 / 2225	3.4 / 0.0 / 3.2 / 0.1
7 TH	0415 / 1121 / 1651 / 2328	3.5 / 0.2 / 3.0 / 0.3	**22** F	0346 / 1051 / 1619 / 2303	3.4 / 0.1 / 3.1 / 0.1
8 F	0455 / 1156 / 1730	3.4 / 0.2 / 3.0	**23** SA	0430 / 1136 / 1706 / 2348	3.4 / 0.0 / 3.1 / 0.1
9 SA	0003 / 0536 / 1231 / 1810	0.3 / 3.3 / 0.3 / 2.9	**24** SU	0518 / 1221 / 1753	3.4 / 0.1 / 3.0
10 SU	0041 / 0620 / 1311 / 1855	0.4 / 3.1 / 0.4 / 2.8	**25** M	0034 / 0607 / 1306 / 1841	0.2 / 3.3 / 0.2 / 3.0
11 M	0126 / 0712 / 1401 / 1950	0.5 / 3.0 / 0.5 / 2.8	**26** TU	0124 / 0702 / 1400 / 1940	0.3 / 3.2 / 0.3 / 2.9
12 TU	0227 / 0816 / 1507 / 2057	0.6 / 2.9 / 0.5 / 2.8	**27** W	0229 / 0812 / 1512 / 2053	0.4 / 3.1 / 0.3 / 2.9
13 W	0342 / 0928 / 1621 / 2207	0.6 / 2.9 / 0.5 / 2.9	**28** TH	0350 / 0933 / 1635 / 2213	0.3 / 3.1 / 0.3 / 3.0
14 TH	0457 / 1037 / 1729 / 2307	0.5 / 3.0 / 0.4 / 3.1	**29** F	0513 / 1053 / 1753 / 2325	0.2 / 3.1 / 0.2 / 3.1
15 F	0602 / 1134 / 1825 / 2356	0.4 / 3.1 / 0.3 / 3.2	**30** SA	0627 / 1201 / 1858	0.1 / 3.2 / 0.2
			31 SU O	0024 / 0727 / 1256 / 1950	3.3 / 0.1 / 3.2 / 0.2

FEBRUARY

Day	Time	m	Day	Time	m
1 M	0110 / 0817 / 1343 / 2034	3.4 / 0.0 / 3.2 / 0.2	**16** TU ●	0055 / 0757 / 1323 / 2015	3.3 / 0.0 / 3.2 / 0.0
2 TU	0152 / 0900 / 1425 / 2115	3.5 / 0.1 / 3.2 / 0.2	**17** W	0134 / 0838 / 1405 / 2056	3.4 / -0.1 / 3.2 / -0.1
3 W	0233 / 0942 / 1506 / 2155	3.6 / 0.1 / 3.2 / 0.2	**18** TH	0212 / 0918 / 1445 / 2136	3.4 / -0.2 / 3.2 / -0.1
4 TH	0313 / 1021 / 1544 / 2230	3.5 / 0.1 / 3.2 / 0.1	**19** F	0251 / 0959 / 1522 / 2213	3.4 / -0.2 / 3.2 / -0.1
5 F	0350 / 1055 / 1619 / 2301	3.4 / 0.1 / 3.1 / 0.0	**20** SA	0331 / 1039 / 1604 / 2253	3.4 / -0.2 / 3.1 / -0.1
6 SA	0426 / 1125 / 1653 / 2332	3.3 / 0.1 / 3.0 / 0.1	**21** SU	0416 / 1122 / 1648 / 2337	3.4 / -0.1 / 3.2 / 0.0
7 SU	0502 / 1155 / 1727	3.2 / 0.1 / 2.9	**22** M	0503 / 1205 / 1732	3.4 / 0.0 / 3.1
8 M	0002 / 0536 / 1223 / 1801	0.2 / 3.1 / 0.2 / 2.9	**23** TU	0019 / 0550 / 1244 / 1815	0.1 / 3.3 / 0.2 / 3.1
9 TU	0034 / 0615 / 1256 / 1843	0.3 / 3.0 / 0.4 / 2.8	**24** W	0101 / 0641 / 1332 / 1910	0.2 / 3.1 / 0.3 / 3.0
10 W	0119 / 0709 / 1350 / 1946	0.4 / 2.8 / 0.5 / 2.8	**25** TH	0201 / 0751 / 1444 / 2027	0.2 / 3.0 / 0.3 / 2.9
11 TH	0231 / 0824 / 1509 / 2105	0.5 / 2.8 / 0.5 / 2.8	**26** F	0326 / 0919 / 1615 / 2156	0.2 / 2.9 / 0.3 / 3.0
12 F	0358 / 0946 / 1635 / 2221	0.4 / 2.8 / 0.4 / 2.9	**27** SA	0500 / 1046 / 1740 / 2315	0.1 / 2.9 / 0.2 / 3.1
13 SA	0519 / 1058 / 1748 / 2323	0.3 / 3.0 / 0.3 / 3.1	**28** SU	0618 / 1156 / 1846	0.1 / 3.0 / 0.2
14 SU	0623 / 1154 / 1845	0.2 / 3.1 / 0.2			
15 M	0012 / 0713 / 1240 / 1932	3.2 / 0.1 / 3.1 / 0.1			

MARCH

Day	Time	m	Day	Time	m
1 M	0013 / 0716 / 1247 / 1936	3.3 / 0.0 / 3.1 / 0.1	**16** TU	0643 / 1215 / 1906	-0.1 / 3.1 / 0.1
2 TU O	0057 / 0801 / 1328 / 2018	3.4 / 0.0 / 3.2 / 0.1	**17** W ●	0027 / 0731 / 1300 / 1951	3.3 / -0.2 / 3.2 / -0.1
3 W	0135 / 0841 / 1406 / 2056	3.4 / 0.0 / 3.2 / 0.1	**18** TH	0109 / 0814 / 1342 / 2034	3.4 / -0.3 / 3.2 / -0.2
4 TH	0213 / 0919 / 1441 / 2131	3.5 / 0.0 / 3.2 / 0.0	**19** F	0149 / 0856 / 1423 / 2116	3.4 / -0.3 / 3.2 / -0.2
5 F	0250 / 0953 / 1514 / 2204	3.4 / 0.0 / 3.2 / 0.0	**20** SA	0231 / 0939 / 1503 / 2157	3.4 / -0.3 / 3.2 / -0.2
6 SA	0324 / 1025 / 1546 / 2234	3.3 / 0.0 / 3.1 / -0.1	**21** SU	0314 / 1021 / 1544 / 2239	3.4 / -0.2 / 3.2 / -0.2
7 SU	0357 / 1054 / 1617 / 2303	3.2 / 0.0 / 3.0 / -0.1	**22** M	0400 / 1103 / 1628 / 2321	3.4 / -0.1 / 3.2 / -0.1
8 M	0431 / 1121 / 1648 / 2330	3.1 / 0.0 / 3.0 / 0.0	**23** TU	0447 / 1144 / 1710	3.3 / 0.0 / 3.2
9 TU	0501 / 1143 / 1716 / 2354	3.1 / 0.1 / 2.9 / 0.1	**24** W	0002 / 0535 / 1224 / 1754	0.0 / 3.2 / 0.2 / 3.1
10 W	0531 / 1205 / 1750	2.9 / 0.2 / 2.8	**25** TH	0044 / 0628 / 1313 / 1851	0.1 / 3.0 / 0.3 / 3.0
11 TH	0028 / 0615 / 1248 / 1845	0.3 / 2.8 / 0.4 / 2.7	**26** F	0145 / 0740 / 1425 / 2011	0.1 / 2.8 / 0.3 / 2.9
12 F	0130 / 0725 / 1405 / 2006	0.4 / 2.7 / 0.4 / 2.7	**27** SA	0311 / 0910 / 1558 / 2143	0.0 / 2.8 / 0.3 / 3.0
13 SA	0300 / 0854 / 1541 / 2133	0.4 / 2.7 / 0.4 / 2.8	**28** SU	0448 / 1038 / 1726 / 2302	0.1 / 2.8 / 0.3 / 3.1
14 SU	0432 / 1017 / 1708 / 2246	0.2 / 2.8 / 0.3 / 3.0	**29** M	0606 / 1145 / 1830 / 2357	0.0 / 3.0 / 0.2 / 3.3
15 M	0547 / 1123 / 1814 / 2342	0.1 / 3.0 / 0.2 / 3.2	**30** TU	0657 / 1229 / 1914	-0.1 / 3.1 / 0.1
			31 W O	0037 / 0736 / 1305 / 1954	3.3 / -0.1 / 3.2 / 0.1

APRIL

Day	Time	m	Day	Time	m
1 TH	0113 / 0814 / 1341 / 2032	3.3 / -0.1 / 3.2 / 0.0	**16** F ●	0042 / 0748 / 1318 / 2010	3.4 / -0.3 / 3.2 / -0.2
2 F	0151 / 0852 / 1415 / 2107	3.4 / 0.0 / 3.2 / 0.0	**17** SA	0126 / 0832 / 1359 / 2054	3.4 / -0.3 / 3.3 / -0.3
3 SA	0226 / 0925 / 1446 / 2138	3.4 / 0.0 / 3.2 / -0.1	**18** SU	0210 / 0915 / 1441 / 2137	3.5 / -0.3 / 3.3 / -0.3
4 SU	0258 / 0954 / 1515 / 2207	3.3 / 0.0 / 3.2 / -0.2	**19** M	0256 / 0959 / 1523 / 2221	3.4 / -0.2 / 3.3 / -0.3
5 M	0329 / 1022 / 1544 / 2235	3.2 / -0.1 / 3.1 / -0.2	**20** TU	0345 / 1043 / 1607 / 2305	3.4 / -0.1 / 3.3 / -0.2
6 TU	0401 / 1048 / 1614 / 2302	3.1 / -0.1 / 3.1 / -0.1	**21** W	0434 / 1125 / 1652 / 2348	3.3 / 0.0 / 3.3 / -0.1
7 W	0432 / 1111 / 1643 / 2327	3.0 / 0.0 / 3.0 / 0.0	**22** TH	0525 / 1208 / 1739	3.1 / 0.2 / 3.2
8 TH	0501 / 1133 / 1715 / 2357	2.9 / 0.1 / 2.9 / 0.1	**23** F	0035 / 0622 / 1300 / 1839	0.0 / 3.0 / 0.3 / 3.1
9 F	0540 / 1210 / 1804	2.8 / 0.3 / 2.8	**24** SA	0136 / 0732 / 1409 / 1956	0.1 / 2.8 / 0.3 / 3.0
10 SA	0050 / 0643 / 1319 / 1918	0.2 / 2.7 / 0.4 / 2.8	**25** SU	0256 / 0855 / 1535 / 2122	0.1 / 2.7 / 0.3 / 3.1
11 SU	0212 / 0808 / 1452 / 2046	0.3 / 2.7 / 0.4 / 2.8	**26** M	0425 / 1017 / 1659 / 2237	0.1 / 2.8 / 0.3 / 3.2
12 M	0345 / 0935 / 1624 / 2205	0.2 / 2.7 / 0.3 / 3.0	**27** TU	0539 / 1119 / 1800 / 2330	0.0 / 3.0 / 0.2 / 3.2
13 TU	0505 / 1048 / 1736 / 2306	0.0 / 2.9 / 0.1 / 3.1	**28** W	0627 / 1200 / 1843	-0.1 / 3.1 / 0.1
14 W	0608 / 1144 / 1833 / 2356	-0.1 / 3.0 / 0.0 / 3.3	**29** TH	0009 / 0704 / 1235 / 1923	3.3 / 0.0 / 3.2 / 0.0
15 TH	0701 / 1233 / 1924	-0.3 / 3.1 / -0.1	**30** F O	0048 / 0744 / 1313 / 2004	3.3 / 0.0 / 3.2 / 0.0

Chart Datum: 1·66 metres below Normal Null (German reference level)

TIME ZONE –0100
(German Standard Time)
Subtract 1 hour for UT
For German Summer Time add ONE hour in non-shaded areas

GERMANY – CUXHAVEN

LAT 53°52′N   LONG 8°43′E

TIMES AND HEIGHTS OF HIGH AND LOW WATERS

YEAR **1999**

MAY

#	Time	m	#	Time	m
1 SA	0127 0823 1349 2041	3.3 0.0 3.3 0.0	**16** SU	0104 0808 1336 2031	3.5 -0.3 3.3 -0.2
2 SU	0202 0857 1419 2112	3.3 0.0 3.3 -0.1	**17** M	0151 0852 1419 2116	3.5 -0.2 3.4 -0.2
3 M	0233 0925 1446 2141	3.3 0.0 3.3 -0.1	**18** TU	0240 0938 1504 2204	3.4 -0.2 3.4 -0.2
4 TU	0303 0952 1515 2210	3.2 -0.1 3.2 -0.2	**19** W	0333 1025 1550 2252	3.3 -0.1 3.4 -0.2
5 W	0336 1019 1547 2239	3.1 -0.1 3.1 -0.1	**20** TH	0425 1110 1637 2339	3.2 0.0 3.4 -0.1
6 TH	0409 1047 1619 2309	3.0 0.0 3.1 0.0	**21** F	0517 1156 1727	3.1 0.2 3.3
7 F	0444 1116 1655 2343	2.9 0.1 3.0 0.1	**22** SA	0028 0613 1246 1824	0.0 3.0 0.3 3.2
8 SA	0523 1154 1741	2.8 0.2 2.9	**23** SU	0123 0715 1346 1932	0.1 2.8 0.3 3.1
9 SU	0030 0619 1252 1845	0.1 2.7 0.3 2.9	**24** M	0229 0825 1458 2046	0.1 2.8 0.3 3.1
10 M	0139 0733 1412 2004	0.1 2.7 0.3 2.9	**25** TU	0344 0935 1613 2156	0.1 2.8 0.3 3.1
11 TU	0302 0854 1538 2121	0.1 2.8 0.3 3.0	**26** W	0454 1036 1717 2252	0.1 2.9 0.2 3.2
12 W	0422 1008 1654 2227	-0.1 2.9 0.1 3.2	**27** TH	0547 1123 1806 2338	0.0 3.1 0.1 3.2
13 TH	0529 1110 1757 2323	-0.2 3.0 0.0 3.3	**28** F	0630 1203 1850	0.0 3.2 0.1
14 F	0628 1204 1855	-0.2 3.1 -0.1	**29** SA	0021 0712 1243 1935	3.2 0.0 3.3 0.0
15 SA ●	0015 0721 1252 1946	3.4 -0.3 3.2 -0.2	**30** SU ○	0101 0753 1321 2014	3.2 0.0 3.3 0.0
			31 M	0138 0828 1353 2047	3.3 0.0 3.3 -0.1

JUNE

#	Time	m	#	Time	m
1 TU	0211 0859 1423 2118	3.3 0.0 3.3 -0.1	**16** W	0229 0922 1449 2151	3.4 0.0 3.5 -0.1
2 W	0243 0929 1454 2150	3.2 0.0 3.3 -0.1	**17** TH	0323 1011 1537 2242	3.3 0.1 3.5 -0.1
3 TH	0317 1000 1527 2222	3.1 0.0 3.3 0.0	**18** F	0415 1058 1623 2328	3.2 0.1 3.5 -0.1
4 F	0354 1032 1602 2257	3.1 0.0 3.2 0.0	**19** SA	0505 1141 1711	3.1 0.2 3.4
5 SA	0432 1107 1642 2337	3.0 0.1 3.2 0.0	**20** SU	0013 0554 1225 1802	0.0 3.0 0.2 3.3
6 SU	0516 1148 1728	2.9 0.2 3.1	**21** M	0100 0645 1314 1857	0.1 2.9 0.3 3.2
7 M	0022 0606 1238 1823	0.0 2.8 0.2 3.1	**22** TU	0151 0740 1409 1957	0.2 2.8 0.3 3.1
8 TU	0118 0707 1343 1929	0.0 2.8 0.3 3.1	**23** W	0249 0839 1513 2102	0.2 2.8 0.4 3.1
9 W	0226 0817 1458 2041	0.0 2.8 0.2 3.1	**24** TH	0354 0941 1621 2205	0.2 2.9 0.3 3.1
10 TH	0340 0928 1613 2150	0.0 2.9 0.1 3.2	**25** F	0458 1039 1724 2303	0.2 3.0 0.2 3.1
11 F	0451 1035 1722 2252	-0.1 3.0 0.0 3.3	**26** SA	0552 1129 1817 2353	0.1 3.1 0.1 3.2
12 SA	0556 1135 1826 2351	-0.1 3.2 0.0 3.4	**27** SU	0639 1213 1905	0.1 3.3 0.0
13 SU ●	0656 1228 1923	-0.1 3.3 -0.1	**28** M ○	0036 0723 1253 1947	3.2 0.1 3.3 0.0
14 M	0046 0747 1315 2012	3.4 -0.1 3.4 -0.2	**29** TU	0115 0802 1330 2024	3.3 0.0 3.4 -0.1
15 TU	0138 0834 1401 2100	3.4 -0.1 3.5 -0.2	**30** W	0152 0838 1404 2100	3.3 0.0 3.4 0.0

JULY

#	Time	m	#	Time	m
1 TH	0228 0914 1438 2135	3.3 0.0 3.4 0.0	**16** F	0312 0958 1522 2229	3.3 0.1 3.6 0.0
2 F	0305 0948 1512 2209	3.2 0.0 3.4 0.0	**17** SA	0359 1041 1605 2310	3.2 0.1 3.5 0.0
3 SA	0341 1021 1547 2246	3.1 0.1 3.3 0.0	**18** SU	0442 1119 1647 2349	3.1 0.1 3.5 0.1
4 SU	0420 1057 1629 2329	3.1 0.1 3.3 0.0	**19** M	0524 1157 1731	3.0 0.2 3.4
5 M	0506 1141 1716	3.0 0.1 3.3	**20** TU	0027 0605 1236 1816	0.2 3.0 0.3 3.2
6 TU	0015 0555 1229 1807	0.0 3.0 0.1 3.2	**21** W	0106 0648 1318 1904	0.3 2.9 0.3 3.1
7 W	0103 0646 1321 1902	0.0 2.9 0.2 3.2	**22** TH	0150 0737 1410 2002	0.4 2.9 0.4 3.0
8 TH	0157 0744 1424 2006	0.1 2.9 0.3 3.2	**23** F	0247 0838 1519 2111	0.4 2.9 0.5 3.0
9 F	0304 0850 1536 2118	0.1 3.0 0.2 3.2	**24** SA	0357 0947 1634 2222	0.4 3.0 0.4 3.0
10 SA	0417 1001 1652 2229	0.1 3.1 0.2 3.3	**25** SU	0508 1051 1742 2323	0.3 3.1 0.3 3.1
11 SU	0530 1109 1802 2335	0.1 3.2 0.1 3.3	**26** M	0607 1144 1837	0.3 3.2 0.2
12 M	0636 1209 1906	0.0 3.3 0.0	**27** TU	0012 0656 1228 1923	3.2 0.3 3.3 0.1
13 TU ●	0036 0733 1301 2001	3.4 0.0 3.4 -0.1	**28** W ○	0053 0740 1308 2003	3.2 0.1 3.4 0.1
14 W	0130 0822 1348 2051	3.4 0.0 3.5 -0.1	**29** TH	0134 0821 1346 2042	3.3 0.1 3.4 0.1
15 TH	0221 0910 1435 2141	3.3 0.0 3.6 0.0	**30** F	0214 0900 1422 2120	3.3 0.1 3.4 0.0
			31 SA	0251 0936 1456 2156	3.3 0.1 3.5 0.0

AUGUST

#	Time	m	#	Time	m
1 SU	0326 1009 1531 2233	3.2 0.1 3.4 0.0	**16** M	0412 1053 1619 2318	3.2 0.1 3.4 0.1
2 M	0405 1045 1613 2316	3.2 0.1 3.4 0.0	**17** TU	0447 1125 1657 2350	3.1 0.1 3.3 0.2
3 TU	0450 1130 1701	3.1 0.1 3.4	**18** W	0522 1158 1735	3.0 0.2 3.2
4 W	0002 0537 1217 1749	0.0 3.1 0.2 3.4	**19** TH	0021 0557 1230 1813	0.3 3.0 0.4 3.1
5 TH	0045 0622 1301 1838	0.1 3.1 0.3 3.3	**20** F	0052 0637 1311 1903	0.5 2.9 0.5 3.0
6 F	0130 0712 1355 1939	0.2 3.0 0.3 3.2	**21** SA	0139 0734 1415 2013	0.6 2.9 0.6 2.9
7 SA	0233 0817 1508 2056	0.3 3.0 0.4 3.2	**22** SU	0252 0850 1540 2134	0.6 2.9 0.6 2.9
8 SU	0353 0936 1633 2217	0.3 3.1 0.3 3.2	**23** M	0418 1008 1703 2249	0.6 3.0 0.4 3.0
9 M	0515 1053 1752 2330	0.3 3.2 0.1 3.2	**24** TU	0535 1113 1809 2346	0.4 3.2 0.3 3.1
10 TU	0626 1158 1858	0.2 3.3 0.1	**25** W	0632 1202 1859	0.3 3.3 0.2
11 W ●	0031 0724 1250 1953	3.3 0.2 3.5 0.0	**26** TH	0031 0719 1244 1941	3.2 0.3 3.4 0.1
12 TH	0123 0813 1336 2041	3.3 0.2 3.6 0.1	**27** F ○	0113 0801 1323 2021	3.3 0.2 3.4 0.1
13 F ○	0210 0857 1420 2126	3.3 0.2 3.6 0.1	**28** SA	0154 0841 1401 2101	3.3 0.1 3.5 0.1
14 SA	0254 0940 1503 2208	3.3 0.2 3.6 0.1	**29** SU	0232 0919 1437 2139	3.3 0.1 3.5 0.1
15 SU	0335 1020 1542 2245	3.3 0.1 3.5 0.1	**30** M	0308 0955 1514 2217	3.3 0.1 3.5 0.0
			31 TU	0345 1033 1555 2258	3.3 0.1 3.5 0.1

Chart Datum: 1·66 metres below Normal Null (German reference level)

21

TIME ZONE –0100
(German Standard Time)
Subtract 1 hour for UT
For German Summer Time add ONE hour in non-shaded areas

GERMANY – CUXHAVEN

LAT 53°52′N   LONG 8°43′E

TIMES AND HEIGHTS OF HIGH AND LOW WATERS   YEAR **1999**

SEPTEMBER

Day	Time	m	Day	Time	m
1 W	0428 / 1115 / 1642 / 2341	3.2 / 0.1 / 3.5 / 0.2	16 TH	0440 / 1122 / 1655 / 2338	3.1 / 0.2 / 3.2 / 0.4
2 TH	0512 / 1158 / 1729	3.2 / 0.2 / 3.4	17 F	0510 / 1150 / 1728	3.1 / 0.4 / 3.1
3 F	0021 / 0554 / 1240 / 1817	0.3 / 3.2 / 0.3 / 3.3	18 SA	0002 / 0545 / 1223 / 1810	0.5 / 3.0 / 0.5 / 2.9
4 SA	0105 / 0644 / 1332 / 1920	0.4 / 3.1 / 0.4 / 3.1	19 SU	0042 / 0636 / 1320 / 1917	0.7 / 2.9 / 0.7 / 2.8
5 SU	0209 / 0754 / 1450 / 2045	0.5 / 3.0 / 0.4 / 3.0	20 M	0152 / 0752 / 1445 / 2043	0.8 / 2.9 / 0.7 / 2.8
6 M	0337 / 0922 / 1625 / 2215	0.6 / 3.1 / 0.4 / 3.1	21 TU	0326 / 0920 / 1618 / 2208	0.8 / 3.0 / 0.6 / 2.9
7 TU	0508 / 1046 / 1751 / 2331	0.5 / 3.2 / 0.2 / 3.1	22 W	0456 / 1036 / 1734 / 2314	0.6 / 3.1 / 0.4 / 3.1
8 W	0621 / 1151 / 1854	0.4 / 3.4 / 0.1	23 TH	0603 / 1132 / 1829	0.5 / 3.2 / 0.2
9 TH	0026 / 0715 / 1239 / ●1942	3.2 / 0.3 / 3.5 / 0.1	24 F	0004 / 0652 / 1215 / 1914	3.2 / 0.3 / 3.4 / 0.1
10 F	0110 / 0759 / 1320 / 2024	3.3 / 0.3 / 3.5 / 0.1	25 SA	0047 / 0736 / 1255 / O1957	3.2 / 0.2 / 3.4 / 0.0
11 SA	0151 / 0840 / 1401 / 2105	3.3 / 0.2 / 3.6 / 0.1	26 SU	0129 / 0818 / 1335 / 2038	3.3 / 0.1 / 3.5 / 0.0
12 SU	0230 / 0918 / 1440 / 2142	3.3 / 0.2 / 3.6 / 0.2	27 M	0208 / 0859 / 1414 / 2118	3.4 / 0.1 / 3.5 / 0.0
13 M	0306 / 0953 / 1516 / 2215	3.4 / 0.2 / 3.5 / 0.2	28 TU	0246 / 0938 / 1454 / 2158	3.4 / 0.1 / 3.6 / 0.1
14 TU	0339 / 1024 / 1549 / 2245	3.3 / 0.1 / 3.4 / 0.2	29 W	0323 / 1017 / 1537 / 2238	3.4 / 0.1 / 3.5 / 0.2
15 W	0410 / 1054 / 1622 / 2312	3.2 / 0.2 / 3.3 / 0.3	30 TH	0403 / 1056 / 1622 / 2317	3.4 / 0.2 / 3.5 / 0.3

OCTOBER

Day	Time	m	Day	Time	m
1 F	0446 / 1137 / 1710 / 2358	3.4 / 0.3 / 3.4 / 0.4	16 SA	0432 / 1118 / 1652 / 2326	3.2 / 0.4 / 3.0 / 0.6
2 SA	0529 / 1221 / 1803	3.3 / 0.4 / 3.2	17 SU	0506 / 1150 / 1732	3.1 / 0.6 / 2.9
3 SU	0046 / 0624 / 1318 / 1911	0.6 / 3.1 / 0.4 / 3.0	18 M	0002 / 0552 / 1239 / 1831	0.7 / 3.0 / 0.7 / 2.8
4 M	0153 / 0739 / 1440 / 2038	0.7 / 3.1 / 0.5 / 2.9	19 TU	0105 / 0702 / 1356 / 1952	0.9 / 2.9 / 0.7 / 2.8
5 TU	0324 / 0910 / 1618 / 2210	0.7 / 3.1 / 0.4 / 3.0	20 W	0234 / 0828 / 1527 / 2119	0.9 / 3.0 / 0.6 / 2.8
6 W	0459 / 1036 / 1744 / 2324	0.6 / 3.3 / 0.3 / 3.1	21 TH	0407 / 0949 / 1650 / 2233	0.8 / 3.1 / 0.4 / 3.0
7 TH	0611 / 1138 / 1842	0.5 / 3.4 / 0.2	22 F	0522 / 1052 / 1752 / 2330	0.6 / 3.2 / 0.2 / 3.1
8 F	0013 / 0658 / 1221 / 1922	3.2 / 0.4 / 3.5 / 0.2	23 SA	0618 / 1141 / 1843	0.4 / 3.4 / 0.1
9 SA	0049 / 0737 / 1259 / ●2000	3.3 / 0.3 / 3.5 / 0.2	24 SU	0017 / 0707 / 1225 / O1929	3.2 / 0.3 / 3.5 / 0.1
10 SU	0126 / 0817 / 1338 / 2039	3.3 / 0.3 / 3.5 / 0.2	25 M	0100 / 0753 / 1308 / 2012	3.3 / 0.2 / 3.5 / 0.1
11 M	0203 / 0854 / 1415 / 2115	3.4 / 0.3 / 3.5 / 0.3	26 TU	0141 / 0835 / 1349 / 2053	3.4 / 0.1 / 3.6 / 0.2
12 TU	0236 / 0926 / 1448 / 2145	3.4 / 0.3 / 3.5 / 0.3	27 W	0220 / 0917 / 1433 / 2136	3.4 / 0.2 / 3.6 / 0.2
13 W	0305 / 0956 / 1519 / 2212	3.4 / 0.2 / 3.4 / 0.3	28 TH	0300 / 0959 / 1519 / 2218	3.5 / 0.1 / 3.5 / 0.2
14 TH	0334 / 1024 / 1549 / 2236	3.3 / 0.2 / 3.3 / 0.3	29 F	0342 / 1041 / 1607 / 2259	3.5 / 0.2 / 3.4 / 0.3
15 F	0402 / 1051 / 1620 / 2300	3.2 / 0.3 / 3.2 / 0.4	30 SA	0425 / 1123 / 1658 / 2342	3.3 / 0.3 / 3.3 / 0.5
			31 SU	0512 / 1210 / 1754	3.4 / 0.4 / 3.1

NOVEMBER

Day	Time	m	Day	Time	m
1 M	0033 / 0609 / 1309 / 1902	0.6 / 3.2 / 0.4 / 3.0	16 TU	0522 / 1214 / 1758	3.1 / 0.6 / 2.9
2 TU	0139 / 0722 / 1426 / 2023	0.7 / 3.2 / 0.5 / 2.8	17 W	0032 / 0621 / 1316 / 1907	0.7 / 3.0 / 0.6 / 2.8
3 W	0303 / 0848 / 1556 / 2148	0.8 / 3.2 / 0.5 / 2.9	18 TH	0146 / 0736 / 1435 / 2027	0.8 / 3.0 / 0.5 / 2.8
4 TH	0431 / 1010 / 1718 / 2259	0.7 / 3.3 / 0.4 / 3.0	19 F	0312 / 0856 / 1557 / 2144	0.7 / 3.1 / 0.4 / 2.9
5 F	0543 / 1112 / 1815 / 2347	0.6 / 3.4 / 0.3 / 3.2	20 SA	0432 / 1006 / 1707 / 2249	0.6 / 3.2 / 0.3 / 3.1
6 SA	0632 / 1156 / 1855	0.5 / 3.4 / 0.3	21 SU	0538 / 1103 / 1806 / 2343	0.4 / 3.4 / 0.2 / 3.2
7 SU	0022 / 0711 / 1234 / 1933	3.3 / 0.4 / 3.4 / 0.3	22 M	0635 / 1154 / 1900	0.3 / 3.5 / 0.1
8 M	0059 / 0751 / 1313 / ●2012	3.4 / 0.4 / 3.4 / 0.3	23 TU	0030 / 0726 / 1241 / O1947	3.3 / 0.2 / 3.5 / 0.1
9 TU	0135 / 0829 / 1350 / 2047	3.4 / 0.4 / 3.5 / 0.4	24 W	0113 / 0810 / 1326 / 2029	3.4 / 0.1 / 3.5 / 0.1
10 W	0206 / 0900 / 1421 / 2115	3.5 / 0.3 / 3.5 / 0.4	25 TH	0155 / 0854 / 1414 / 2114	3.5 / 0.1 / 3.5 / 0.2
11 TH	0234 / 0929 / 1451 / 2142	3.5 / 0.2 / 3.4 / 0.4	26 F	0239 / 0942 / 1506 / 2202	3.5 / 0.1 / 3.4 / 0.2
12 F	0303 / 0958 / 1521 / 2208	3.4 / 0.2 / 3.2 / 0.3	27 SA	0325 / 1031 / 1559 / 2248	3.5 / 0.1 / 3.3 / 0.3
13 SA	0333 / 1026 / 1554 / 2234	3.3 / 0.3 / 3.1 / 0.4	28 SU	0411 / 1117 / 1650 / 2332	3.5 / 0.2 / 3.2 / 0.4
14 SU	0404 / 1056 / 1628 / 2303	3.2 / 0.4 / 3.0 / 0.5	29 M	0459 / 1204 / 1744	3.5 / 0.3 / 3.1
15 M	0439 / 1130 / 1707 / 2339	3.2 / 0.5 / 2.9 / 0.6	30 TU	0020 / 0553 / 1257 / 1844	0.6 / 3.4 / 0.4 / 3.0

DECEMBER

Day	Time	m	Day	Time	m
1 W	0118 / 0657 / 1400 / 1952	0.6 / 3.2 / 0.4 / 2.8	16 TH	0011 / 0551 / 1248 / 1832	0.5 / 3.1 / 0.4 / 2.9
2 TH	0226 / 0810 / 1514 / 2104	0.7 / 3.2 / 0.5 / 2.8	17 F	0108 / 0652 / 1350 / 1938	0.6 / 3.1 / 0.4 / 2.8
3 F	0343 / 0925 / 1629 / 2212	0.6 / 3.2 / 0.5 / 3.0	18 SA	0220 / 0803 / 1502 / 2051	0.6 / 3.1 / 0.4 / 2.9
4 SA	0455 / 1030 / 1733 / 2307	0.6 / 3.3 / 0.4 / 3.1	19 SU	0338 / 0916 / 1617 / 2201	0.5 / 3.2 / 0.3 / 3.0
5 SU	0554 / 1123 / 1822 / 2351	0.5 / 3.3 / 0.4 / 3.2	20 M	0453 / 1023 / 1727 / 2305	0.4 / 3.3 / 0.2 / 3.2
6 M	0641 / 1208 / 1904	0.4 / 3.3 / 0.4	21 TU	0559 / 1124 / 1830	0.3 / 3.4 / 0.2
7 TU	0030 / 0724 / 1249 / ●1944	3.3 / 0.4 / 3.4 / 0.4	22 W	0000 / 0658 / 1219 / O1924	3.3 / 0.2 / 3.5 / 0.1
8 W	0107 / 0803 / 1325 / 2018	3.4 / 0.3 / 3.4 / 0.3	23 TH	0048 / 0749 / 1310 / 2011	3.4 / 0.1 / 3.4 / 0.1
9 TH	0140 / 0836 / 1357 / 2049	3.5 / 0.3 / 3.4 / 0.3	24 F	0134 / 0838 / 1402 / 2059	3.5 / 0.0 / 3.4 / 0.2
10 F	0209 / 0907 / 1429 / 2119	3.5 / 0.2 / 3.3 / 0.3	25 SA	0222 / 0930 / 1456 / 2150	3.5 / 0.0 / 3.3 / 0.2
11 SA	0240 / 0938 / 1502 / 2150	3.4 / 0.2 / 3.2 / 0.3	26 SU	0312 / 1023 / 1550 / 2238	3.6 / 0.1 / 3.3 / 0.2
12 SU	0312 / 1009 / 1536 / 2219	3.4 / 0.2 / 3.1 / 0.3	27 M	0359 / 1110 / 1640 / 2321	3.6 / 0.1 / 3.1 / 0.3
13 M	0345 / 1041 / 1611 / 2250	3.3 / 0.3 / 3.1 / 0.4	28 TU	0444 / 1153 / 1727	3.5 / 0.1 / 3.1
14 TU	0420 / 1118 / 1651 / 2326	3.2 / 0.3 / 3.0 / 0.4	29 W	0003 / 0532 / 1236 / 1816	0.4 / 3.4 / 0.2 / 3.0
15 W	0502 / 1159 / 1736	3.2 / 0.4 / 2.9	30 TH	0049 / 0624 / 1324 / 1908	0.4 / 3.3 / 0.3 / 2.9
			31 F	0140 / 0721 / 1419 / 2005	0.5 / 3.1 / 0.4 / 2.8

Chart Datum: 1·66 metres below Normal Null (German reference level)

RIVER ELBE/HAMBURG   8-21-20

Niedersachsen/Schleswig-Holstein   Rtg 1·1·2

CHARTS

AC 3262, 3266, 3268; BSH 3010 Sheets 1 to 12 (as shown below), D46, D47, D48

TIDES

Glückstadt	ML 1·2	Duration 0515	Zone -0100
Brunshausen	ML 1·1	Duration 0510	
Hamburg	ML 1·3	Duration 0435	

Standard Port CUXHAVEN (←)

High Water		Low Water		MHWS	MHWN	MLWN	MLWS
0200	0800	0200	0900	3·3	2·9	0·4	0·0
1400	2000	1400	2100				

Differences GLÜCKSTADT

+0205	+0214	+0220	+0213	−0·2	−0·2	−0·1	+0·1

STADERSAND

+0241	+0245	+0300	+0254	−0·1	0·0	−0·1	+0·1

SCHULAU

+0304	+0315	+0337	+0321	+0·1	+0·1	−0·2	+0·1

HAMBURG

+0338	+0346	+0421	+0406	+0·3	+0·3	−0·3	0·0

NAVIGATION

Distances: Elbe lt float to Cuxhaven = 24M; Cuxhaven to Wedel Yacht Haven = 45M; Wedel to City Sport Hafen = 11·5M. The river has 13m up to Hamburg and is tidal to Geesthacht, 24M above Hamburg. Strong W winds can raise the level by as much as 4m. Entry should not be attempted with strong W/NW winds against the ebb. It is a very busy waterway and at night the many lights can be confusing. Yachts should keep to stbd, preferably just outside the marked chan. Elbe VTS (not mandatory for yachts) offers radar guidance and broadcasts met, nav & tidal info; see 8.21.19 & .21 and R/TELEPHONE below.

SHELTER AND FACILITIES

Some of the better hbrs are listed below, but it is not a particularly salubrious yachting area:

FREIBURG: 7M above Brunsbüttel on the SW bank. Small vessels can enter at HW and there is excellent shelter at Freiburg Reede. ML 2·2m. Hr Mr ☎ (04779) 8314. Facilities: ME, EI, Sh, C, FW, YC; **Jugendheim & YC Klubheim** V, R, Bar. (Sheet 4).

STÖRLOCH/BORSFLETH: Ent approx 600m above locks on E bank. ML 2·8m. Hr Mr ☎ (04124) 71437. Facilities: FW, YC. Stör Bridge VHF Ch 09, 16. (Sheet 4).

STÖR/BEIDENFLETH: ML 2·8m (Sheet 4). **Langes Rack YC**.

GLÜCKSTADT: on the NE bank, 2½M above mouth of R Stör. Good shelter; inner and outer hbrs have 2m depth. Lock into inner hbr opens HW −2 to +½. VHF Ch 11. Hr Mr ☎ (04124) 2087; ⌗ ☎ 2171. YC, FW, C, D, V, R, ◎, Bar. (Sheet 5).

WISCHHAFEN: Hr Mr ☎ (04770) 334; ⌗ 3014 FW, M, Slip, P, D, ML 2·7m. (Sheet 5).

RUTHENSTROM: Ldg marks into hbr, two bns with △ topmarks on 197°. ML 2·6m. Hr Mr ☎ (04143) 5282; C, Slip, FW, M, ME, EI, Sh. (Sheet 6).

KRÜCKAUMÜNDUNG JACHTHAFEN: ☎ (04125) 1521 Slip, FW. ML 2·7m. ⌗ ☎ 20551. (Sheet 6).

PINNAUMÜNDUNG JACHTHAFEN: Ent via lock gate on N bank after passing through main locks. ML 2·5m. Hr Mr ☎ (04101) 22447 Slip, M, FW, YC, C. (Sheet 6).

PINNAU-NEUENDEICH: Marina 1½M up the Pinnau from main locks and another at approx 2M. (Sheet 6).

ABBENFLETH: Ent marked by two bns in line 221° with △ topmarks. (Sheets 6/7).

HASELDORF Hafen: Hr Mr ☎ (04129) 268 Slip, FW, V, YC.

R.SCHWINGE on SW bank, 12M up-river from Glückstadt:
  BRUNSHAUSEN (04141) 3085
  HÖRNE/WÖHRDEN ML 2·8m
  STADE (04141) 101275 C, YC, V; Access HW ±2.
Very good shelter in scenic town. ⌗ ☎ 3014. (Sheets 7/8).

LÜHE: Hafen in town of Lühe. (Sheet 8).

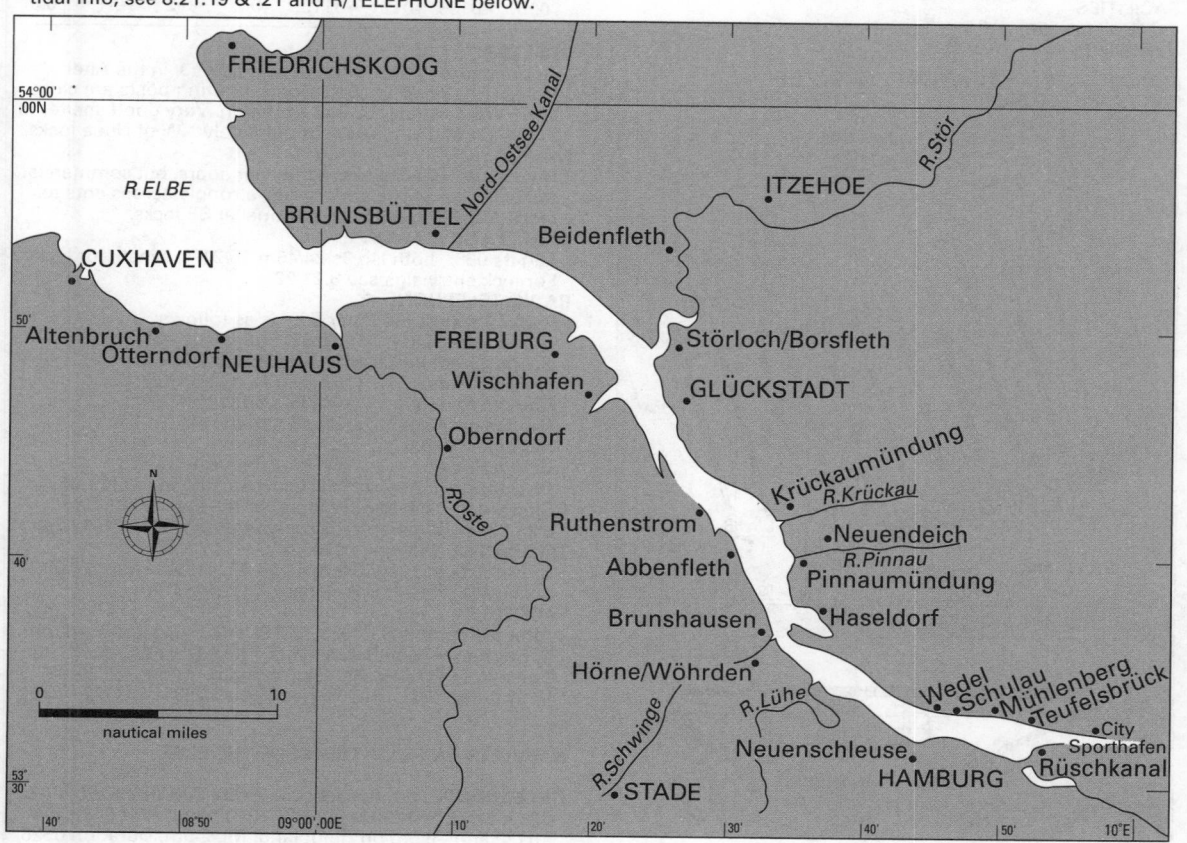

HAMBURG

A busy commercial port with several marinas. Visitors berth at Wedel in Hamburger Yachthafen or in the City Sporthafen, in city centre esp for visitors (see below).
WEDEL: on N bank, 12M downstream from Hamburg, very good shelter H24; **Hamburger Yachthafen**, 14DM, (1800 berths + 300 being added) with 2 ents marked by FR and FG lts. A conspic 20m tall radar tr is at W corner of hbr. Hr Mr ☎ (04103) 4438 (office), 5632 (Hr Mr east), 88608 (Hr Mr west); ⌗ ☎ 0171-2766300; D & P, Bar, BH (16 ton), BY, C, CH, EI, Ⓔ, FW, ME, SC, Sh, Slip, SM. (Sheets 8/9).
SCHULAU: Good shelter, 7ca E of Wedel. Beware strong tidal streams across ent, marked by FR and FG lts. Hr Mr ☎ 2422, Slip, C, P, D, ME, Ⓗ, CH, SC. (Sheet 8/9).
NEUENSCHLEUSE: opposite Wedel. (Sheet 9).
MÜHLENBERG: N bank, (250), Slip, FW, SC. Small boats only; 0·6m above CD. (Sheets 9/10).
TEUFELSBRÜCK: small hbr on N bank. Good shelter, sandbar at ent. Bar, FW, SC. (Sheets 9/10).
RÜSCHKANAL: on S bank in Finkenwerder, C, CH, EI, FW, ME, Slip, Sh, with 4 SCs and nearby resort area.
CITY SPORTHAFEN: (80+50) ☎ 364297, 20DM, D, P, FW, AC; Ent on N bank beyond St Pauli-Landungsbrücken.

RADIO TELEPHONE

Elbe VTS: see 8.21.19 for radar cover up to buoy No 53. See 8.21.21 for buoys 51 - 125. Then *Hamburg Radar:*
Ch 19 Buoys 123 - 129;
Ch 03 Buoys 129 - Seemanshöft;
Ch 63 Seemanshöft - Vorhafen (outer hbr);
Ch 07 Parkhafen - Kuhwerder Vorhafen;
Ch 05 Kuhwerder Vorhafen - Norderelbbrücke;
Ch 80 Köhlbrand - Hamburger Häfen.
Hamburg Port Traffic and Hbr Control vessel Ch 13 14 **73** (H24). Süderelbe: Rethe and Kattwyk bridges and Harburg lock Ch 13 (H24). All stns monitor Ch 16.

TELEPHONE (Dial code 040)

Met 3190 8826/7; Auto 0190 116456; Brit Consul 446071.

FACILITIES

City all facilities, ACA, ✉, Ⓑ, ≋, ✈. Ferry: Hamburg-Harwich.

HAMBURGER YACHTHAFEN, WEDEL

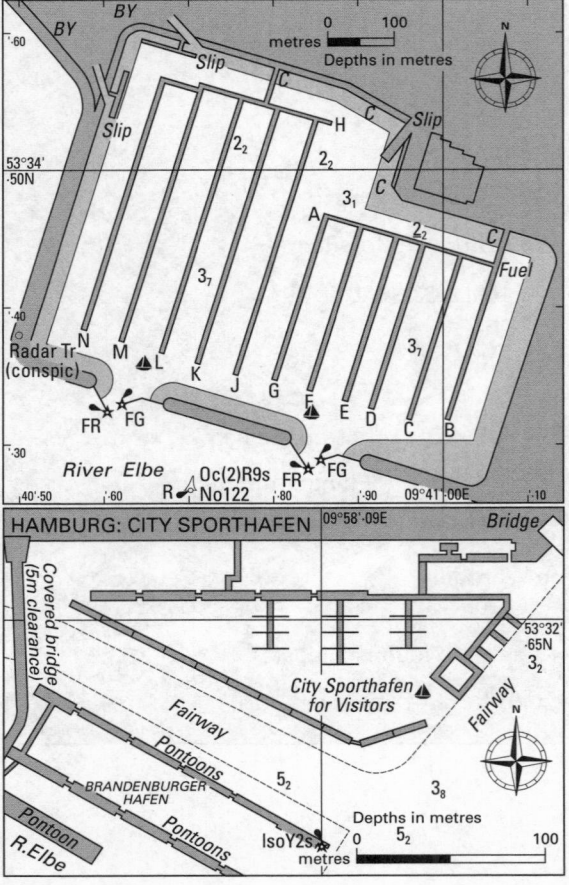

BRUNSBÜTTEL   8-21-21

Schleswig-Holstein 53°53'·28N 09°07'·85E   Rtg 1*-3-2

CHARTS

AC 2469, 3262; BSH 3010 Sheet 3

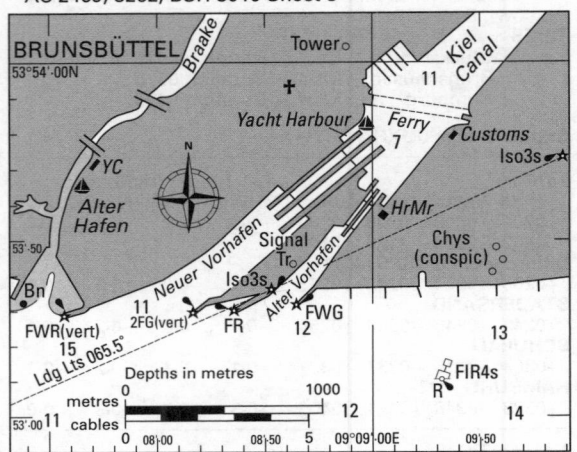

TIDES

+0203 Dover; ML 1·4; Duration 0520; Zone –0100

Standard Port CUXHAVEN (←—)

Times				Height (metres)			
High Water		Low Water		MHWS	MHWN	MLWN	MLWS
0200	0800	0200	0900	3·3	2·9	0·4	0·0
1400	2000	1400	2100				
Differences BRUNSBÜTTEL							
+0057	+0105	+0121	+0112	–0·2	–0·2	–0·1	0·0

SHELTER

Good in drying yacht hbr, access HW ±3, in the Alter Hafen (Rtg 3-3-2) W of the locks. Waiting posts are close E of FWG ☆ at ent to Alter Vorhafen. Very good shelter in Kanal-Yachthafen inside, immediately NW of Neue locks.

NAVIGATION

No navigational dangers in the near apprs, but commercial traffic is heavy. The stream sets strongly across ents to locks. Yachts usually use the smaller SE locks.

LIGHTS AND MARKS

Ldg lts 065°, both Iso 3s 24/46m 16/21M, synch, for locks. For lock entry sigs see 8.21.22.

RADIO TELEPHONE

Radar cover of the inner Elbe is as follows:
Brunsbüttel Radar I	Ch 62	Buoys 51 - 59;
S. Margarethen Radar	Ch 18	Buoys 57a - 65;
Freiburg Radar	Ch 61	Buoys 63 - 77;
Rhinplatte Radar	Ch 05	Buoys 75 - 89;
Pagensand Radar	Ch 66	Buoys 87 - 103;
Hetlingen Radar	Ch 21	Buoys 101 - 115;
Wedel Radar	Ch 60	Buoys 113 - 125.

Brunsbüttel Elbe Traffic broadcasts info every H + 05 on Ch 68 in English and German for the inner Elbe. See 8.21.22 for Kanal entry. *Brunsbüttel Elbe Port* Ch 12 16.

TELEPHONE (Dial code 04852)

Hr Mr 8011 ext 360; CG 8444; ⌗ 87241; Weather 36400; Police 112; Ⓗ 601; Brit Consul (040) 446071.

FACILITIES

Alter Hafen ☎ 04855-629, DM15, AC, FW, Slip, C (20 ton), R, SC; **Kanal-Yachthafen*** ☎ 8011, DM15, FW, AC, ⌗, Bar. **Town** P, D, EI, ME, Sh, Gaz, V, R, LB, Ⓗ, Bar, ✉, Ⓑ, ≋, ✈ (Hamburg). **KIEL**: Nautischer Dienst (0431) 331772 ACA.

HARBOUR ON SOUTH BANK OF THE ELBE

OTTERNDORF, Niedersachsen, 53°50'·20N 08°54'·00E. AC 3261, 3262; BSH 3014.11. HW +0100 on Dover (UT); HW +0120 and +0·5m on Helgoland; ML 2·9m; Duration 0525. Ent marked by Medem lt bn Fl (3) 12s 6m 5M & perches. Chan (0·6m) from Elbe divides and yachts can take the W branch to Kutterhafen (0·9m) or the canal to E, through lock then turn sharp stbd to yacht hbr. Lockmaster ☎ (04751) 2190; Yacht hbr ☎ 13131 C, AC, FW, Bar. **Town** (3km) ME, Gaz, V, ✉.

NORD-OSTSEE KANAL
(Kiel Canal)
Schleswig-Holstein

8-21-22

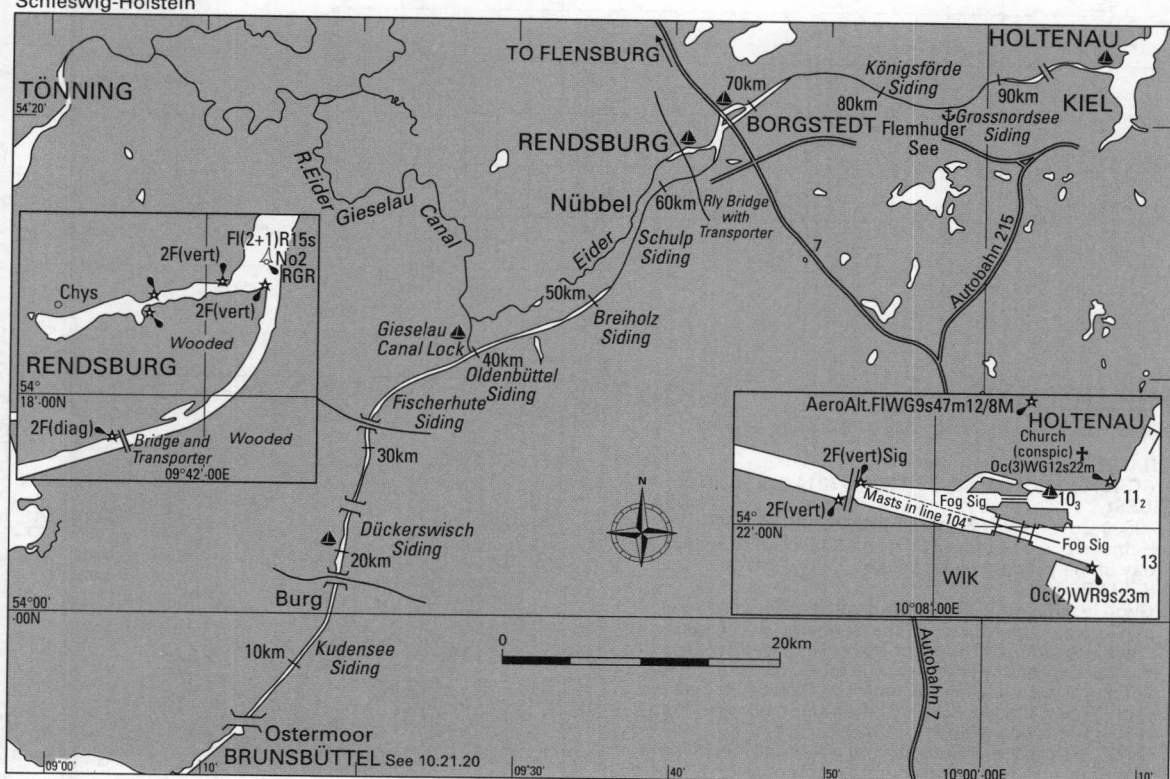

CHARTS
AC 2469, 696 (Kieler Förde); BSH 3009, Sheets 1-4

NAVIGATION
The Canal runs from Brunsbüttel (8.21.21) to Kiel-Holtenau, 53·3M (98·7 km). Km posts start from Brunsbüttel. Width is 103 to 162m on the surface, and depth 11m. Yachts may only use the Canal and its ents by day and good vis. (This does not apply to craft going to the Inner or Old Hbrs at Brunsbüttel, or to the yacht berths at Holtenau). Speed limit is 8kn. All 6 bridges have 40m clearance. Fly flag 'N' (no pilot). Sailing, except motor sailing is prohib; yachts must then display a B ▼, or a B pennant. Canal dues are paid at the Holtenau locks at the 'Dues Office' (N bank). Yachts purely in transit are not usually troubled by the Customs Authority; they should fly the third substitute of the International Code.

SHELTER
The principal port along the canal is Rensburg, between km posts 60 and 67, with all facilities including 3 yacht hbrs in the Obereidersee. Rensburg is linked to Tönning (see under 8.21.24) by the R Eider and Gieselau Canal. There are 9 passing places (sidings or *weichen*). Yachts are to regulate their passage so as to reach their planned berthing places during daylight. These may be at:
1) Brunsbüttel (km 0);
2) Kudensee siding (km 9·5);
3) Dückerswisch siding (km 20·7);
4) Fischerhütte siding (km 35);
5) Oldenbüttel siding (km 40), at ent to Gieselau Canal;
6) Breiholz siding (km 48);
7) Schülp siding (km 57);
8) The Obereidersee (Rendsburg), ent at km 66;
9) The Borgstedter See, ent at km 70;
10) Königsförde siding (km 80);
11) Grossnordsee siding (km 85), or ⚓ in Flemhuder See;
12) Schwartenbek siding (km 92);
13) Kiel-Holtenau (km 98·7).
Kiel-Holtenau, at the Baltic end of the canal, is a major port with a Yacht Hbr on the N bank (E of locks); all usual facilities. Two pairs of locks (yachts usually use the N pair) lead into the Kieler Förde which is practically tideless and at almost the same level as the canal.

SIGNALS
Lock signals (shown at signal tr and centre pier of lock):

Ⓡ	= no entry.
Ⓦ over Ⓡ	= prepare to enter.
Ⓦ	= yachts may enter (berth on pontoons).
Ⓦ over Ⓖ	= enter without pilot (yachts follow ships flying Flag N); secure to middle wall.
Ⓖ	= enter with pilot; secure to middle wall.
Ⓦ over Ⓦ and Ⓖ	= enter with pilot and secure by Ⓦ lt.

In the canal, the only traffic sig applicable to yachts is :

3 Ⓡ (vert) = STOP. Keep to stbd; give way to large vessel approaching.

RADIO TELEPHONE
Before entering/leaving, yachts should request a lock:
at Brunsbüttel to *Kiel Kanal I* on Ch 13;
or at Holtenau to *Kiel Kanal IV* on Ch 12.
Ports: Ostermoor (Brunsbüttel to Burg) Ch 73;
Breiholz (Breiholz to Audorf) Ch 73.
Canal. Maintain listening watch as follows:
Kiel Kanal I   Ch 13   Brunsbüttel ent and locks;
Kiel Kanal II   Ch 02   Brunsbüttel to Breiholz;
Kiel Traffic   Ch 22   Breiholz to Holtenau;
Kiel Kanal IV   Ch 12   Holtenau ent and locks.
Info broadcasts by *Kiel Kanal II* on Ch 02 at H+15, H+45; and by *Kiel Kanal III* on Ch 03 at H+20, H+50. Vessels should monitor these broadcasts and not call the station if this can be avoided.

FACILITIES
A BP fuel barge is on the N bank, close E of the Holtenau locks. At Wik (S side of locks) **Nautischer Dienst** (Kapt Stegmann & Co) ☎ 0431 331772 are ACA & BSH Agents. The **British Kiel YC** is 5ca NNW of Stickenhörn ECM buoy, Q (3) 10s, 1M NNE of the locks. It is part of a military centre with no commercial facilities; but AB (about 20DM) may be available for visitors to whom a friendly welcome is extended. Call *Sailtrain* VHF Ch 67 or ☎ (0431) 398833, 📠 397172.

21

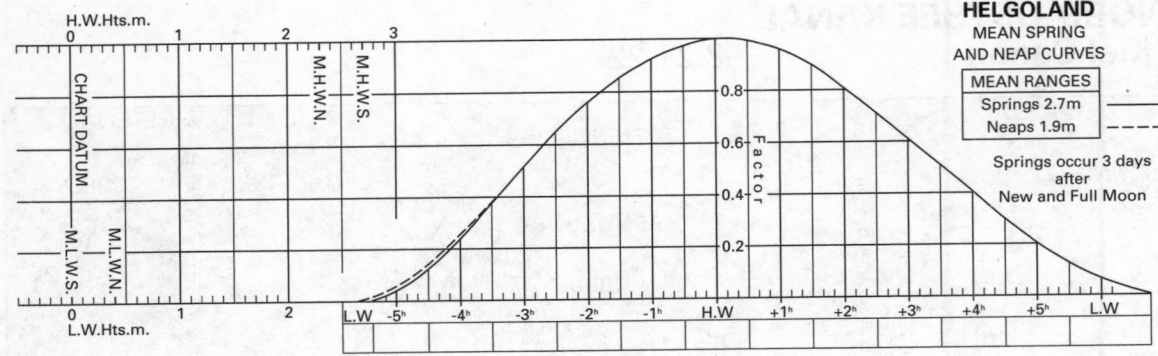

HELGOLAND
MEAN SPRING
AND NEAP CURVES

MEAN RANGES
Springs 2.7m
Neaps 1.9m

Springs occur 3 days
after
New and Full Moon

HELGOLAND   8-21-23

Schleswig-Holstein 54°10'·30N 07°54'·00E   Rtg 1-2-1

CHARTS
AC 1875, 3761; D3, 88; BSH 3013, 3014.2 & .3, 3015
TIDES
–0030 Dover; ML 1·4; Duration 0540; Zone –0100
Helgoland is a Standard Port and tidal predictions for each
day of the year are given below.
SHELTER
Good in safe artificial hbr (5m); yachts should berth on
pontoons on the NE side of the Südhafen which gets very
crowded, rafting 10 deep; or in the Binnenhafen. Or ⚓ in
the SW part of the Vorhafen, sheltered except in SE'lies;
get permission from Port Control VHF Ch 67. Yachts are
prohib from the Nordost hbr, the Dünen hbr and from
landing on Düne Island.
NOTE: Helgoland is not a port of entry into Germany.
Customs in Helgoland are for passport control. Duty free
goods are obtainable; hence many day-trippers by ferry.
NAVIGATION
WPT Helgoland ECM buoy, Q (3) 10s, Whis, 55°09'·00N
07°53'·57E, 202°/022° from/to Düne front ldg lt, 2·1M.
Beware the Hogstean shoal, 4ca S of Sudmole head lt, and
other rky shoals either side of chan. The S chan and ent
are used by ferries. Beware lobster pots around Düne Is.
Caution: Entry is prohib at all times into Nature Reserves
close either side of the appr chans from SSW and NW.
These Reserves extend about 2M NE and SW of Helgoland;
their limits are marked by Cardinal buoys. Marine police
are active in this respect. A smaller Reserve, lying to the
N, E and S of Düne, is a prohib ⚓, with other restrictions.
See BSH 3014.2 and AC 126, 3761 and 1875 for limits.
LIGHTS AND MARKS
Helgoland lt ho, Fl 5s 82m 28M; brown □ tr, B lantern, W
balcony.
Düne ldg lts 020°: front Iso 4s 11m 8M; rear Dir Iso WRG
4s 17m 11/10M synch, W sector 018·5°-021°.
Binnenhafen ldg lts 302°: both Oc R 6s, synch.
RADIO TELEPHONE
Helgoland Port Radio Ch 67 16 (**1/5-31/8**. Mon-Thur:
0700-1200,1300-2000; Fri/Sat 0700-2000; Sun 0700-1200LT.
1/9-30/4. Mon-Thur 0700-1200, 1300-1600; Fri 0700-1200).
Coast Radio Ch 03 16 27 88 (H24). *German Bight Traffic*
(Traffic Centre, at Helgoland lt ho) broadcasts weather
and safety info in **English** and German every H on Ch 80
for 26M radius of Helgoland.
TELEPHONE (Dial code 04725)
Hr Mr 504; CG 210; ⌗ 304; Met 606; Police 607; Dr 7345; Ⓗ
8030; LB 210; SAR 524; Brit Consul (040) 446071.
FACILITIES
Vorhafen L, ⚓; **Südhafen** ☎ 504, AB 22DM, D, FW, ME,
CH, C (mobile 12 ton), V, R, Bar; **Binnenhafen** ☎ 504, P, D,
⛽, AB, FW, ME, CH, V, R, Bar; **Wasser Sport Club** ☎ 585
Bar, R, M, C (12 ton), D, P, CH, ME, El, Sh, FW, ▣, V.
Town Gaz, V, R, Bar, ✉, Ⓑ, ⇌ (ferry Cuxhaven), ✈ (to
Bremen, Hamburg and Cuxhaven). Ferry: Hamburg-
Harwich.

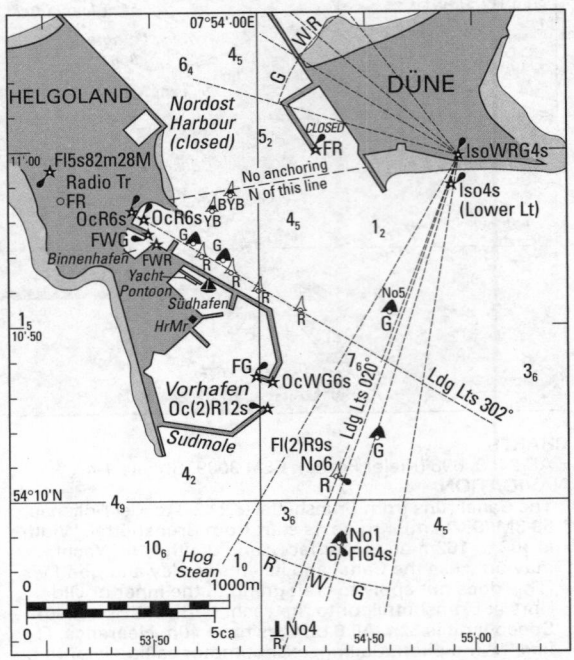

AGENTS WANTED

If you are interested in becoming our agent for any of the
following ports, please write to: The Editor, Edington House,
Trent, Sherborne, Dorset DT9 4SR, England – and get your
free copy of the Almanac annually. You do not have to live in
a port to be the agent, but should at least be a fairly regular
visitor.

Plymouth	Port Haliguen
Walton-on-the-Naze	La Trinité-sur-Mer
Hopeman	Piriac
Burghead	St Nazaire/Loire
Findhorn	Pornic
Nairn	St Gilles-Croix-de-Vie
Inverness	Les Sables d'Olonne
Loch Aline	River Seudre
Craobh	Port Bloc/Gironde
Workington	Anglet/Bayonne
Lough Swilly	St Jean-de-Luz
Portbail	Hendaye
St Malo/Dinard	Grandcamp-Maisy
Le Légué/St Brieuc	Port-en-Bessin
Lampaul	Ouistreham/Caen
L'Aberildut	Dives
Douarnenez	St Valéry-en-Caux
Lorient	Dunkerque
River Étel	Emden
Le Palais (Belle Ile)	Langeoog

TIME ZONE –0100
(German Standard Time)
Subtract 1 hour for UT

For German Summer Time add
ONE hour in non-shaded areas

GERMANY – HELGOLAND

LAT 54°11′N   LONG   7°53′E

TIMES AND HEIGHTS OF HIGH AND LOW WATERS

YEAR **1999**

JANUARY

	Time	m		Time	m
1 F	0516 / 1056 / 1743 / 2322	0.1 / 2.7 / 0.1 / 2.7	**16** SA	0530 / 1108 / 1747 / 2326	0.2 / 2.6 / 0.2 / 2.7
2 SA O	0611 / 1150 / 1832	0.1 / 2.8 / 0.1	**17** SU ●	0615 / 1148 / 1827	0.1 / 2.6 / 0.1
3 SU	0009 / 0659 / 1238 / 1916	2.8 / 0.0 / 2.8 / 0.2	**18** M	0005 / 0654 / 1227 / 1907	2.7 / 0.1 / 2.7 / 0.1
4 M	0054 / 0745 / 1323 / 2000	2.9 / 0.1 / 2.7 / 0.2	**19** TU	0043 / 0732 / 1307 / 1946	2.7 / 0.0 / 2.7 / 0.1
5 TU	0141 / 0832 / 1410 / 2045	2.9 / 0.1 / 2.7 / 0.2	**20** W	0120 / 0810 / 1346 / 2022	2.8 / 0.0 / 2.6 / 0.1
6 W	0226 / 0917 / 1455 / 2126	2.9 / 0.1 / 2.6 / 0.2	**21** TH	0157 / 0848 / 1423 / 2058	2.8 / –0.1 / 2.6 / 0.0
7 TH	0306 / 0957 / 1537 / 2203	2.8 / 0.1 / 2.5 / 0.2	**22** F	0235 / 0928 / 1503 / 2138	2.8 / –0.1 / 2.5 / 0.1
8 F	0345 / 1034 / 1617 / 2241	2.8 / 0.2 / 2.4 / 0.3	**23** SA	0319 / 1013 / 1549 / 2224	2.8 / 0.0 / 2.5 / 0.1
9 SA	0425 / 1111 / 1658 / 2322	2.7 / 0.3 / 2.4 / 0.4	**24** SU	0407 / 1058 / 1638 / 2310	2.8 / 0.1 / 2.5 / 0.2
10 SU	0510 / 1152 / 1745	2.6 / 0.4 / 2.3	**25** M	0457 / 1143 / 1727	2.7 / 0.2 / 2.4
11 M	0010 / 0603 / 1245 / 1841	0.5 / 2.5 / 0.5 / 2.3	**26** TU	0002 / 0551 / 1240 / 1826	0.2 / 2.6 / 0.3 / 2.4
12 TU	0113 / 0708 / 1353 / 1948	0.5 / 2.4 / 0.5 / 2.3	**27** W	0110 / 0700 / 1354 / 1939	0.3 / 2.6 / 0.3 / 2.4
13 W	0227 / 0820 / 1506 / 2056	0.5 / 2.4 / 0.4 / 2.4	**28** TH	0233 / 0820 / 1516 / 2058	0.3 / 2.5 / 0.3 / 2.4
14 TH	0339 / 0927 / 1610 / 2155	0.5 / 2.5 / 0.3 / 2.5	**29** F	0355 / 0940 / 1630 / 2211	0.2 / 2.5 / 0.2 / 2.6
15 F	0439 / 1023 / 1702 / 2243	0.3 / 2.6 / 0.3 / 2.6	**30** SA	0505 / 1048 / 1731 / 2311	0.1 / 2.6 / 0.2 / 2.7
			31 SU O	0602 / 1143 / 1822 / 2359	0.0 / 2.6 / 0.1 / 2.8

FEBRUARY

	Time	m		Time	m
1 M	0650 / 1229 / 1905	0.0 / 2.6 / 0.2	**16** TU ●	0636 / 1206 / 1850	0.0 / 2.6 / 0.0
2 TU	0042 / 0734 / 1310 / 1946	2.9 / 0.0 / 2.6 / 0.2	**17** W O	0022 / 0715 / 1247 / 1930	2.7 / –0.1 / 2.6 / –0.1
3 W	0124 / 0816 / 1350 / 2027	2.9 / 0.1 / 2.6 / 0.1	**18** TH	0101 / 0754 / 1328 / 2008	2.7 / –0.2 / 2.6 / –0.1
4 TH	0205 / 0855 / 1430 / 2104	2.9 / 0.1 / 2.6 / 0.1	**19** F	0140 / 0834 / 1407 / 2046	2.8 / –0.2 / 2.5 / –0.1
5 F	0242 / 0930 / 1507 / 2137	2.8 / 0.0 / 2.5 / 0.0	**20** SA	0221 / 0915 / 1448 / 2128	2.8 / –0.2 / 2.5 / –0.1
6 SA	0317 / 1001 / 1541 / 2210	2.7 / 0.1 / 2.4 / 0.1	**21** SU	0305 / 0958 / 1532 / 2212	2.8 / –0.1 / 2.5 / 0.0
7 SU	0352 / 1032 / 1615 / 2242	2.6 / 0.1 / 2.4 / 0.2	**22** M	0351 / 1040 / 1617 / 2255	2.8 / 0.0 / 2.5 / 0.0
8 M	0426 / 1102 / 1650 / 2317	2.5 / 0.2 / 2.3 / 0.3	**23** TU	0437 / 1121 / 1701 / 2342	2.7 / 0.1 / 2.5 / 0.1
9 TU	0504 / 1140 / 1733	2.4 / 0.3 / 2.3	**24** W	0529 / 1212 / 1757	2.6 / 0.2 / 2.4
10 W	0007 / 0559 / 1239 / 1836	0.4 / 2.3 / 0.4 / 2.2	**25** TH	0048 / 0639 / 1328 / 1914	0.2 / 2.4 / 0.3 / 2.4
11 TH	0120 / 0714 / 1359 / 1953	0.5 / 2.2 / 0.4 / 2.3	**26** F	0216 / 0805 / 1500 / 2042	0.2 / 2.4 / 0.3 / 2.4
12 F	0245 / 0836 / 1521 / 2108	0.4 / 2.3 / 0.2 / 2.4	**27** SA	0347 / 0932 / 1621 / 2201	0.1 / 2.4 / 0.2 / 2.5
13 SA	0401 / 0947 / 1629 / 2210	0.3 / 2.4 / 0.3 / 2.5	**28** SU	0500 / 1041 / 1723 / 2301	0.0 / 2.4 / 0.0 / 2.7
14 SU	0502 / 1041 / 1722 / 2300	0.2 / 2.5 / 0.2 / 2.6			
15 M	0552 / 1125 / 1808 / 2343	0.0 / 2.6 / 0.1 / 2.7			

MARCH

	Time	m		Time	m
1 M	0553 / 1132 / 1810 / 2346	0.0 / 2.5 / 0.1 / 2.7	**16** TU	0524 / 1059 / 1744 / 2315	–0.1 / 2.5 / 0.0 / 2.7
2 TU O	0637 / 1214 / 1851	0.0 / 2.6 / 0.1	**17** W ●	0611 / 1142 / 1828 / 2357	–0.2 / 2.5 / –0.1 / 2.7
3 W	0026 / 0717 / 1252 / 1930	2.8 / 0.0 / 2.6 / 0.1	**18** TH	0653 / 1223 / 1909	–0.3 / 2.6 / 0.0
4 TH	0105 / 0754 / 1327 / 2006	2.8 / 0.0 / 2.6 / 0.0	**19** F	0038 / 0734 / 1305 / 1950	2.8 / –0.3 / 2.6 / –0.2
5 F	0141 / 0828 / 1401 / 2040	2.8 / 0.0 / 2.6 / 0.0	**20** SA	0120 / 0816 / 1347 / 2032	2.8 / –0.3 / 2.6 / –0.2
6 SA	0216 / 0900 / 1434 / 2111	2.7 / 0.0 / 2.5 / –0.1	**21** SU	0204 / 0858 / 1429 / 2114	2.8 / –0.2 / 2.6 / –0.2
7 SU	0248 / 0929 / 1505 / 2141	2.6 / 0.0 / 2.5 / –0.1	**22** M	0248 / 0939 / 1512 / 2157	2.7 / –0.1 / 2.6 / –0.1
8 M	0320 / 0956 / 1535 / 2209	2.6 / 0.0 / 2.4 / 0.0	**23** TU	0333 / 1019 / 1555 / 2240	2.7 / 0.0 / 2.6 / –0.1
9 TU	0349 / 1020 / 1604 / 2237	2.5 / 0.1 / 2.4 / 0.1	**24** W	0420 / 1101 / 1640 / 2329	2.6 / 0.1 / 2.5 / 0.0
10 W	0418 / 1048 / 1639 / 2315	2.4 / 0.2 / 2.3 / 0.2	**25** TH	0515 / 1154 / 1738	2.4 / 0.2 / 2.4
11 TH	0502 / 1137 / 1734	2.2 / 0.4 / 2.2	**26** F	0037 / 0627 / 1311 / 1858	0.1 / 2.3 / 0.3 / 2.4
12 F	0021 / 0614 / 1256 / 1853	0.4 / 2.1 / 0.4 / 2.2	**27** SA	0206 / 0755 / 1445 / 2029	0.1 / 2.2 / 0.3 / 2.4
13 SA	0150 / 0743 / 1429 / 2019	0.4 / 2.1 / 0.4 / 2.3	**28** SU	0338 / 0921 / 1610 / 2148	0.0 / 2.3 / 0.1 / 2.5
14 SU	0319 / 0907 / 1552 / 2133	0.2 / 2.2 / 0.3 / 2.4	**29** M	0450 / 1027 / 1708 / 2245	0.0 / 2.4 / 0.1 / 2.6
15 M	0430 / 1011 / 1654 / 2229	0.1 / 2.4 / 0.2 / 2.6	**30** TU	0536 / 1113 / 1750 / 2326	–0.1 / 2.5 / 0.1 / 2.7
			31 W O	0614 / 1151 / 1830	–0.1 / 2.5 / 0.0

APRIL

	Time	m		Time	m
1 TH	0004 / 0652 / 1228 / 1908	2.7 / –0.1 / 2.6 / 0.0	**16** F ●	0628 / 1159 / 1846	–0.3 / 2.6 / –0.2
2 F	0042 / 0729 / 1302 / 1943	2.8 / 0.0 / 2.6 / 0.0	**17** SA	0014 / 0710 / 1241 / 1929	2.8 / –0.3 / 2.6 / –0.3
3 SA	0117 / 0801 / 1333 / 2014	2.7 / 0.0 / 2.6 / –0.1	**18** SU	0057 / 0753 / 1324 / 2013	2.8 / –0.3 / 2.6 / –0.3
4 SU	0149 / 0830 / 1403 / 2044	2.6 / –0.1 / 2.6 / –0.2	**19** M	0143 / 0836 / 1408 / 2058	2.8 / –0.2 / 2.6 / –0.3
5 M	0220 / 0857 / 1432 / 2113	2.5 / –0.1 / 2.5 / –0.2	**20** TU	0230 / 0919 / 1452 / 2142	2.7 / –0.1 / 2.6 / –0.2
6 TU	0250 / 0923 / 1501 / 2141	2.5 / –0.1 / 2.5 / –0.1	**21** W	0318 / 1000 / 1537 / 2229	2.6 / 0.0 / 2.6 / –0.1
7 W	0319 / 0947 / 1529 / 2208	2.4 / 0.0 / 2.4 / 0.0	**22** TH	0408 / 1046 / 1626 / 2322	2.5 / 0.1 / 2.6 / 0.0
8 TH	0347 / 1013 / 1602 / 2242	2.3 / 0.1 / 2.3 / 0.1	**23** F	0506 / 1142 / 1726	2.3 / 0.2 / 2.5
9 F	0426 / 1056 / 1651 / 2339	2.2 / 0.3 / 2.2 / 0.2	**24** SA	0029 / 0616 / 1256 / 1843	0.0 / 2.2 / 0.3 / 2.4
10 SA	0530 / 1208 / 1804	2.1 / 0.4 / 2.2	**25** SU	0151 / 0738 / 1423 / 2008	0.1 / 2.2 / 0.3 / 2.5
11 SU	0103 / 0656 / 1342 / 1931	0.3 / 2.1 / 0.4 / 2.3	**26** M	0316 / 0858 / 1544 / 2123	0.0 / 2.2 / 0.2 / 2.5
12 M	0235 / 0823 / 1510 / 2050	0.1 / 2.2 / 0.3 / 2.4	**27** TU	0423 / 1001 / 1642 / 2218	0.0 / 2.3 / 0.1 / 2.6
13 TU	0351 / 0934 / 1619 / 2153	0.0 / 2.3 / 0.1 / 2.5	**28** W	0508 / 1045 / 1722 / 2258	–0.1 / 2.4 / 0.0 / 2.6
14 W	0450 / 1029 / 1713 / 2244	–0.2 / 2.4 / 0.0 / 2.6	**29** TH	0544 / 1122 / 1802 / 2338	–0.1 / 2.5 / 0.0 / 2.6
15 TH	0541 / 1115 / 1802 / 2330	–0.3 / 2.5 / –0.1 / 2.7	**30** F O	0623 / 1200 / 1842	0.0 / 2.6 / 0.0

Chart Datum: 1·68 metres below Normal Null (German reference level)

TIME ZONE –0100
(German Standard Time)
Subtract 1 hour for UT

For German Summer Time add ONE hour in non-shaded areas

GERMANY – HELGOLAND

LAT 54°11′N   LONG 7°53′E

TIMES AND HEIGHTS OF HIGH AND LOW WATERS

YEAR 1999

MAY

Day	Time	m		Day	Time	m
1 SA	0018 / 0701 / 1236 / 1918	2.6 / -0.1 / 2.6 / -0.1		**16** SU	0646 / 1217 / 1908	-0.3 / 2.7 / -0.3
2 SU	0052 / 0733 / 1306 / 1949	2.6 / -0.1 / 2.6 / -0.1		**17** M	0037 / 0729 / 1301 / 1954	2.8 / -0.2 / 2.7 / -0.3
3 M	0123 / 0801 / 1335 / 2018	2.6 / -0.1 / 2.6 / -0.2		**18** TU	0124 / 0815 / 1348 / 2042	2.7 / -0.2 / 2.7 / -0.3
4 TU	0152 / 0828 / 1404 / 2048	2.5 / -0.1 / 2.6 / -0.2		**19** W	0215 / 0901 / 1436 / 2131	2.7 / -0.1 / 2.7 / -0.2
5 W	0223 / 0856 / 1434 / 2118	2.5 / -0.1 / 2.5 / -0.1		**20** TH	0307 / 0946 / 1524 / 2220	2.5 / 0.0 / 2.7 / -0.1
6 TH	0255 / 0924 / 1505 / 2150	2.4 / 0.0 / 2.5 / 0.0		**21** F	0359 / 1034 / 1615 / 2314	2.4 / 0.1 / 2.6 / 0.0
7 F	0329 / 0955 / 1541 / 2227	2.3 / 0.1 / 2.4 / 0.1		**22** SA	0455 / 1128 / 1712	2.3 / 0.2 / 2.6
8 SA	0409 / 1037 / 1627 / 2317	2.2 / 0.2 / 2.3 / 0.1		**23** SU	0014 / 0558 / 1232 / 1819	0.0 / 2.2 / 0.3 / 2.5
9 SU	0504 / 1139 / 1730	2.2 / 0.3 / 2.3		**24** M	0122 / 0707 / 1345 / 1933	0.1 / 2.2 / 0.3 / 2.5
10 M	0028 / 0619 / 1301 / 1848	0.1 / 2.2 / 0.3 / 2.3		**25** TU	0234 / 0818 / 1459 / 2043	0.1 / 2.2 / 0.2 / 2.5
11 TU	0152 / 0740 / 1425 / 2006	0.0 / 2.2 / 0.2 / 2.4		**26** W	0339 / 0920 / 1601 / 2140	0.1 / 2.3 / 0.2 / 2.5
12 W	0309 / 0853 / 1538 / 2113	-0.1 / 2.3 / 0.1 / 2.5		**27** TH	0429 / 1009 / 1648 / 2226	0.0 / 2.4 / 0.1 / 2.6
13 TH	0413 / 0954 / 1638 / 2210	-0.2 / 2.4 / 0.0 / 2.6		**28** F	0511 / 1049 / 1730 / 2310	0.0 / 2.5 / 0.1 / 2.6
14 F	0509 / 1046 / 1733 / 2303	-0.3 / 2.5 / -0.1 / 2.7		**29** SA	0552 / 1129 / 1813 / 2351	0.0 / 2.6 / 0.0 / 2.6
15 SA ●	0600 / 1134 / 1823 / 2351	-0.3 / 2.6 / -0.2 / 2.8		**30** SU O	0632 / 1207 / 1852	0.0 / 2.6 / -0.1
				31 M	0026 / 0706 / 1241 / 1925	2.6 / -0.1 / 2.6 / -0.1

JUNE

Day	Time	m		Day	Time	m
1 TU	0058 / 0736 / 1311 / 1956	2.6 / -0.1 / 2.6 / -0.1		**16** W	0111 / 0758 / 1333 / 2029	2.7 / -0.1 / 2.8 / -0.2
2 W	0130 / 0806 / 1342 / 2028	2.6 / -0.1 / 2.6 / -0.1		**17** TH	0203 / 0847 / 1423 / 2120	2.6 / 0.0 / 2.8 / -0.2
3 TH	0203 / 0836 / 1414 / 2101	2.6 / 0.0 / 2.6 / -0.1		**18** F	0256 / 0934 / 1511 / 2209	2.5 / 0.0 / 2.8 / -0.1
4 F	0238 / 0908 / 1448 / 2138	2.5 / 0.0 / 2.6 / 0.0		**19** SA	0346 / 1019 / 1558 / 2257	2.4 / 0.1 / 2.7 / 0.0
5 SA	0316 / 0945 / 1527 / 2219	2.4 / 0.1 / 2.5 / 0.0		**20** SU	0435 / 1106 / 1649 / 2346	2.3 / 0.2 / 2.7 / 0.1
6 SU	0359 / 1029 / 1613 / 2306	2.3 / 0.1 / 2.5 / 0.0		**21** M	0528 / 1157 / 1744	2.3 / 0.2 / 2.6
7 M	0450 / 1122 / 1708	2.3 / 0.2 / 2.5		**22** TU	0038 / 0623 / 1255 / 1844	0.1 / 2.2 / 0.3 / 2.5
8 TU	0004 / 0551 / 1227 / 1813	0.0 / 2.2 / 0.2 / 2.5		**23** W	0136 / 0723 / 1400 / 1949	0.2 / 2.3 / 0.3 / 2.5
9 W	0113 / 0700 / 1342 / 1924	0.0 / 2.2 / 0.2 / 2.5		**24** TH	0240 / 0826 / 1507 / 2053	0.2 / 2.3 / 0.3 / 2.5
10 TH	0227 / 0811 / 1455 / 2033	-0.1 / 2.3 / 0.1 / 2.6		**25** F	0342 / 0924 / 1607 / 2150	0.2 / 2.4 / 0.2 / 2.5
11 F	0334 / 0916 / 1603 / 2137	-0.1 / 2.4 / 0.0 / 2.6		**26** SA	0435 / 1014 / 1658 / 2239	0.1 / 2.5 / 0.1 / 2.6
12 SA	0436 / 1016 / 1705 / 2237	-0.2 / 2.5 / -0.1 / 2.7		**27** SU	0520 / 1058 / 1744 / 2323	0.1 / 2.6 / 0.0 / 2.6
13 SU ●	0533 / 1110 / 1801 / 2332	-0.2 / 2.6 / -0.1 / 2.7		**28** M O	0602 / 1138 / 1826	0.0 / 2.6 / 0.0
14 M	0624 / 1157 / 1850	-0.2 / 2.7 / -0.2		**29** TU	0000 / 0640 / 1216 / 1903	2.6 / 0.0 / 2.6 / 0.0
15 TU	0022 / 0710 / 1244 / 1938	2.7 / -0.1 / 2.8 / -0.2		**30** W	0036 / 0715 / 1251 / 1938	2.6 / 0.0 / 2.7 / 0.0

JULY

Day	Time	m		Day	Time	m
1 TH	0111 / 0750 / 1325 / 2013	2.6 / 0.0 / 2.7 / 0.0		**16** F	0150 / 0832 / 1408 / 2105	2.6 / 0.0 / 2.9 / -0.1
2 F	0147 / 0823 / 1359 / 2048	2.6 / 0.0 / 2.7 / 0.0		**17** SA	0239 / 0916 / 1452 / 2148	2.6 / 0.0 / 2.8 / -0.1
3 SA	0223 / 0856 / 1433 / 2125	2.5 / 0.0 / 2.7 / 0.0		**18** SU	0324 / 0956 / 1534 / 2229	2.5 / 0.1 / 2.8 / 0.0
4 SU	0302 / 0935 / 1514 / 2210	2.5 / 0.0 / 2.7 / 0.0		**19** M	0406 / 1036 / 1617 / 2308	2.4 / 0.1 / 2.7 / 0.1
5 M	0347 / 1020 / 1601 / 2257	2.4 / 0.1 / 2.6 / 0.0		**20** TU	0448 / 1117 / 1703 / 2348	2.4 / 0.2 / 2.6 / 0.2
6 TU	0436 / 1108 / 1651 / 2344	2.4 / 0.1 / 2.6 / 0.0		**21** W	0532 / 1201 / 1751	2.3 / 0.3 / 2.5
7 W	0527 / 1200 / 1745	2.4 / 0.2 / 2.6		**22** TH	0033 / 0622 / 1256 / 1849	0.3 / 2.3 / 0.4 / 2.4
8 TH	0039 / 0625 / 1304 / 1848	0.1 / 2.3 / 0.2 / 2.6		**23** F	0133 / 0723 / 1406 / 1957	0.4 / 2.3 / 0.4 / 2.4
9 F	0146 / 0731 / 1418 / 2000	0.1 / 2.4 / 0.2 / 2.6		**24** SA	0244 / 0831 / 1520 / 2106	0.3 / 2.4 / 0.3 / 2.4
10 SA	0259 / 0841 / 1533 / 2112	0.1 / 2.4 / 0.1 / 2.6		**25** SU	0352 / 0934 / 1624 / 2207	0.3 / 2.5 / 0.2 / 2.5
11 SU	0409 / 0950 / 1643 / 2220	0.0 / 2.5 / 0.0 / 2.6		**26** M	0448 / 1026 / 1716 / 2256	0.2 / 2.6 / 0.1 / 2.6
12 M	0512 / 1051 / 1744 / 2321	0.0 / 2.6 / -0.1 / 2.7		**27** TU	0535 / 1111 / 1802 / 2336	0.1 / 2.7 / 0.1 / 2.6
13 TU ●	0608 / 1144 / 1838	0.0 / 2.7 / -0.1		**28** W O	0617 / 1152 / 1843	0.1 / 2.7 / 0.0
14 W	0014 / 0657 / 1232 / 1928	2.7 / 0.0 / 2.8 / -0.1		**29** TH	0015 / 0656 / 1231 / 1920	2.6 / 0.0 / 2.7 / 0.0
15 TH	0102 / 0744 / 1320 / 2017	2.7 / 0.0 / 2.9 / -0.1		**30** F	0053 / 0734 / 1307 / 1956	2.7 / 0.0 / 2.8 / 0.0
				31 SA	0130 / 0809 / 1342 / 2032	2.6 / 0.0 / 2.8 / -0.1

AUGUST

Day	Time	m		Day	Time	m
1 SU	0206 / 0843 / 1418 / 2111	2.6 / 0.0 / 2.8 / -0.1		**16** M	0254 / 0928 / 1505 / 2154	2.6 / 0.1 / 2.8 / 0.1
2 M	0244 / 0922 / 1459 / 2155	2.5 / 0.0 / 2.8 / 0.0		**17** TU	0331 / 1002 / 1542 / 2227	2.5 / 0.1 / 2.7 / 0.2
3 TU	0329 / 1007 / 1545 / 2240	2.5 / 0.0 / 2.8 / 0.0		**18** W	0406 / 1036 / 1620 / 2258	2.5 / 0.2 / 2.6 / 0.3
4 W	0417 / 1052 / 1632 / 2322	2.5 / 0.1 / 2.7 / 0.1		**19** TH	0441 / 1111 / 1659 / 2333	2.4 / 0.3 / 2.5 / 0.4
5 TH	0503 / 1137 / 1721	2.5 / 0.2 / 2.7		**20** F	0522 / 1155 / 1748	2.4 / 0.4 / 2.4
6 F	0008 / 0553 / 1234 / 1821	0.2 / 2.5 / 0.3 / 2.6		**21** SA	0025 / 0619 / 1302 / 1857	0.5 / 2.3 / 0.5 / 2.3
7 SA	0112 / 0658 / 1351 / 1937	0.3 / 2.4 / 0.3 / 2.6		**22** SU	0140 / 0733 / 1426 / 2018	0.5 / 2.4 / 0.5 / 2.3
8 SU	0233 / 0816 / 1516 / 2059	0.2 / 2.5 / 0.2 / 2.6		**23** M	0303 / 0850 / 1546 / 2132	0.5 / 2.4 / 0.4 / 2.4
9 M	0353 / 0933 / 1632 / 2213	0.2 / 2.6 / 0.1 / 2.6		**24** TU	0414 / 0954 / 1648 / 2229	0.4 / 2.6 / 0.2 / 2.5
10 TU	0500 / 1040 / 1736 / 2314	0.2 / 2.7 / 0.0 / 2.6		**25** W	0509 / 1044 / 1736 / 2312	0.3 / 2.7 / 0.1 / 2.6
11 W ●	0557 / 1135 / 1829	0.1 / 2.8 / 0.0		**26** TH	0554 / 1126 / 1819 / 2352	0.2 / 2.7 / 0.0 / 2.6
12 TH	0005 / 0645 / 1221 / 1916	2.7 / 0.1 / 2.9 / 0.0		**27** F O	0635 / 1206 / 1858	0.1 / 2.8 / 0.0
13 F	0050 / 0730 / 1305 / 2001	2.7 / 0.1 / 2.9 / 0.0		**28** SA	0031 / 0714 / 1245 / 1935	2.7 / 0.1 / 2.8 / 0.0
14 SA	0133 / 0813 / 1348 / 2043	2.7 / 0.1 / 2.9 / 0.0		**29** SU	0110 / 0751 / 1322 / 2013	2.7 / 0.0 / 2.8 / -0.1
15 SU	0215 / 0853 / 1427 / 2120	2.6 / 0.1 / 2.9 / 0.0		**30** M	0146 / 0827 / 1401 / 2052	2.7 / 0.0 / 2.9 / 0.0
				31 TU	0224 / 0906 / 1442 / 2133	2.6 / 0.0 / 2.8 / 0.0

Chart Datum: 1·68 metres below Normal Null (German reference level)

TIME ZONE –0100
(German Standard Time)
Subtract 1 hour for UT

For German Summer Time add ONE hour in non-shaded areas

GERMANY – HELGOLAND

LAT 54°11′N LONG 7°53′E

TIMES AND HEIGHTS OF HIGH AND LOW WATERS

YEAR **1999**

SEPTEMBER

Day	Times · m
1 W	0307 2.6 · 0948 0.1 · 1525 2.8 · 2216 0.1
2 TH	0352 2.6 · 1031 0.1 · 1611 2.8 · 2256 0.2
3 F	0436 2.6 · 1116 0.2 · 1700 2.7 · 2341 0.4
4 SA	0526 2.5 · 1214 0.3 · 1803 2.5
5 SU	0048 0.5 · 0636 2.5 · 1336 0.4 · 1926 2.5
6 M	0217 0.5 · 0803 2.5 · 1510 0.3 · 2056 2.5
7 TU	0346 0.4 · 0927 2.6 · 1631 0.2 · 2211 2.5
8 W	0454 0.3 · 1033 2.8 · 1730 0.1 · 2307 2.6
9 TH ●	0545 0.2 · 1123 2.9 · 1816 0.1 · 2352 2.7
10 F	0629 0.2 · 1206 2.9 · 1858 0.1
11 SA	0032 2.7 · 0711 0.2 · 1247 2.9 · 1938 0.1
12 SU	0110 2.7 · 0750 0.2 · 1325 2.9 · 2015 0.2
13 M	0147 2.7 · 0826 0.1 · 1401 2.9 · 2048 0.2
14 TU	0221 2.7 · 0858 0.1 · 1434 2.8 · 2117 0.2
15 W	0254 2.6 · 0928 0.1 · 1507 2.7 · 2145 0.2
16 TH	0324 2.6 · 0957 0.2 · 1540 2.6 · 2212 0.3
17 F	0354 2.5 · 1027 0.3 · 1613 2.5 · 2240 0.5
18 SA	0430 2.5 · 1105 0.5 · 1656 2.4 · 2325 0.6
19 SU	0522 2.4 · 1205 0.6 · 1801 2.3
20 M	0038 0.7 · 0637 2.4 · 1330 0.6 · 1927 2.3
21 TU	0210 0.7 · 0802 2.4 · 1501 0.5 · 2052 2.4
22 W	0335 0.6 · 0917 2.5 · 1613 0.3 · 2157 2.5
23 TH	0438 0.4 · 1013 2.7 · 1706 0.2 · 2245 2.6
24 F	0526 0.3 · 1058 2.8 · 1751 0.0 · 2326 2.6
25 SA O	0609 0.2 · 1139 2.8 · 1832 0.0
26 SU	0006 2.7 · 0649 0.1 · 1219 2.8 · 1910 0.0
27 M	0045 2.7 · 0729 0.1 · 1300 2.9 · 1949 0.0
28 TU	0124 2.7 · 0808 0.1 · 1341 2.9 · 2030 0.0
29 W	0203 2.7 · 0848 0.1 · 1423 2.9 · 2109 0.1
30 TH	0243 2.8 · 0929 0.1 · 1506 2.8 · 2149 0.2

OCTOBER

Day	Times · m
1 F	0326 2.7 · 1011 0.2 · 1552 2.8 · 2231 0.4
2 SA	0412 2.7 · 1059 0.3 · 1646 2.6 · 2322 0.5
3 SU	0508 2.6 · 1203 0.4 · 1754 2.5
4 M	0033 0.6 · 0623 2.5 · 1328 0.4 · 1920 2.4
5 TU	0204 0.6 · 0753 2.6 · 1504 0.4 · 2050 2.4
6 W	0336 0.5 · 0918 2.7 · 1623 0.3 · 2203 2.5
7 TH	0443 0.4 · 1021 2.8 · 1716 0.2 · 2253 2.6
8 F	0528 0.3 · 1106 2.9 · 1754 0.2 · 2331 2.7
9 SA ●	0607 0.3 · 1145 2.9 · 1832 0.2
10 SU	0009 2.7 · 0648 0.3 · 1225 2.9 · 1910 0.2
11 M	0046 2.8 · 0725 0.2 · 1302 2.9 · 1945 0.3
12 TU	0119 2.8 · 0758 0.2 · 1335 2.9 · 2015 0.3
13 W	0149 2.8 · 0827 0.1 · 1405 2.8 · 2042 0.3
14 TH	0219 2.7 · 0856 0.1 · 1434 2.7 · 2107 0.3
15 F	0248 2.6 · 0924 0.2 · 1505 2.6 · 2132 0.4
16 SA	0318 2.6 · 0954 0.3 · 1537 2.5 · 2201 0.5
17 SU	0352 2.5 · 1029 0.5 · 1617 2.4 · 2241 0.6
18 M	0440 2.5 · 1121 0.6 · 1717 2.3 · 2348 0.8
19 TU	0548 2.4 · 1239 0.7 · 1838 2.3
20 W	0117 0.8 · 1410 0.6 · 2005 2.3
21 TH	0247 0.7 · 0832 2.5 · 1530 0.4 · 2117 2.5
22 F	0358 0.5 · 0936 2.7 · 1629 0.2 · 2212 2.6
23 SA	0452 0.3 · 1025 2.8 · 1718 0.1 · 2257 2.6
24 SU O	0538 0.2 · 1110 2.8 · 1802 0.0 · 2339 2.7
25 M	0622 0.1 · 1153 2.9 · 1844 0.0
26 TU	0019 2.8 · 0704 0.1 · 1235 2.9 · 1924 0.0
27 W	0100 2.8 · 0746 0.1 · 1319 2.9 · 2006 0.1
28 TH	0142 2.8 · 0830 0.1 · 1405 2.9 · 2048 0.2
29 F	0224 2.8 · 0913 0.1 · 1451 2.7 · 2129 0.3
30 SA	0308 2.8 · 0958 0.2 · 1540 2.7 · 2215 0.4
31 SU	0356 2.8 · 1050 0.3 · 1637 2.6 · 2309 0.6

NOVEMBER

Day	Times · m
1 M	0455 2.7 · 1155 0.4 · 1746 2.4
2 TU	0019 0.6 · 0609 2.6 · 1314 0.4 · 1906 2.3
3 W	0143 0.7 · 0734 2.6 · 1441 0.4 · 2029 2.4
4 TH	0310 0.6 · 0855 2.7 · 1557 0.3 · 2139 2.5
5 F	0417 0.5 · 0957 2.7 · 1649 0.3 · 2229 2.6
6 SA	0503 0.4 · 1042 2.8 · 1726 0.3 · 2307 2.7
7 SU	0541 0.3 · 1122 2.8 · 1803 0.3 · 2344 2.8
8 M ●	0622 0.3 · 1202 2.8 · 1842 0.3
9 TU	0021 2.8 · 0700 0.3 · 1238 2.8 · 1916 0.3
10 W	0052 2.8 · 0731 0.2 · 1309 2.8 · 1944 0.3
11 TH	0121 2.8 · 0800 0.2 · 1338 2.7 · 2011 0.3
12 F	0150 2.8 · 0829 0.2 · 1408 2.6 · 2037 0.3
13 SA	0221 2.7 · 0859 0.2 · 1439 2.6 · 2105 0.3
14 SU	0252 2.7 · 0931 0.2 · 1513 2.5 · 2136 0.5
15 M	0327 2.6 · 1007 0.4 · 1553 2.4 · 2216 0.6
16 TU	0411 2.6 · 1054 0.5 · 1645 2.3 · 2312 0.7
17 W	0509 2.5 · 1158 0.5 · 1754 2.3
18 TH	0028 0.7 · 0623 2.5 · 1319 0.5 · 1914 2.3
19 F	0153 0.7 · 0741 2.6 · 1439 0.3 · 2029 2.4
20 SA	0309 0.5 · 0851 2.7 · 1546 0.2 · 2132 2.5
21 SU	0411 0.4 · 0949 2.8 · 1641 0.1 · 2224 2.6
22 M	0505 0.3 · 1040 2.8 · 1732 0.1 · 2311 2.7
23 TU O	0555 0.2 · 1128 2.8 · 1817 0.1 · 2354 2.8
24 W	0640 0.1 · 1213 2.9 · 1900 0.1
25 TH	0037 2.8 · 0725 0.1 · 1300 2.9 · 1944 0.1
26 F	0123 2.9 · 0814 0.1 · 1351 2.8 · 2032 0.2
27 SA	0211 2.9 · 0903 0.1 · 1442 2.7 · 2118 0.3
28 SU	0258 2.9 · 0951 0.1 · 1534 2.6 · 2204 0.4
29 M	0346 2.8 · 1043 0.2 · 1628 2.5 · 2257 0.5
30 TU	0440 2.8 · 1141 0.3 · 1729 2.4 · 2358 0.5

DECEMBER

Day	Times · m
1 W	0545 2.7 · 1246 0.4 · 1837 2.3
2 TH	0108 0.6 · 0659 2.6 · 1358 0.4 · 1949 2.3
3 F	0224 0.6 · 0814 2.6 · 1509 0.4 · 2057 2.4
4 SA	0334 0.5 · 0919 2.6 · 1608 0.3 · 2153 2.5
5 SU	0429 0.4 · 1012 2.7 · 1655 0.3 · 2238 2.6
6 M	0513 0.4 · 1057 2.8 · 1736 0.3 · 2318 2.7
7 TU ●	0556 0.3 · 1138 2.8 · 1815 0.3 · 2355 2.8
8 W	0635 0.3 · 1214 2.8 · 1849 0.3
9 TH	0028 2.8 · 0708 0.2 · 1246 2.8 · 1919 0.3
10 F	0059 2.8 · 0739 0.2 · 1317 2.7 · 1949 0.2
11 SA	0130 2.8 · 0811 0.2 · 1350 2.6 · 2019 0.2
12 SU	0202 2.7 · 0843 0.2 · 1422 2.6 · 2049 0.3
13 M	0234 2.7 · 0916 0.2 · 1456 2.5 · 2122 0.3
14 TU	0309 2.7 · 0954 0.3 · 1536 2.4 · 2201 0.4
15 W	0351 2.6 · 1038 0.3 · 1622 2.4 · 2249 0.5
16 TH	0441 2.6 · 1129 0.3 · 1718 2.3 · 2348 0.5
17 F	0541 2.6 · 1232 0.3 · 1825 2.3
18 SA	0059 0.5 · 0650 2.6 · 1346 0.3 · 1937 2.3
19 SU	0216 0.5 · 0802 2.6 · 1458 0.3 · 2046 2.4
20 M	0328 0.4 · 0910 2.7 · 1604 0.2 · 2148 2.6
21 TU	0432 0.2 · 1011 2.8 · 1703 0.1 · 2243 2.7
22 W O	0530 0.1 · 1107 2.8 · 1755 0.1 · 2332 2.8
23 TH	0621 0.0 · 1158 2.8 · 1842 0.1
24 F	0019 2.8 · 0711 0.0 · 1248 2.8 · 1929 0.1
25 SA	0109 2.9 · 0802 0.0 · 1340 2.7 · 2020 0.1
26 SU	0201 2.9 · 0855 0.0 · 1433 2.6 · 2109 0.2
27 M	0249 2.9 · 0944 0.0 · 1524 2.5 · 2154 0.2
28 TU	0333 2.9 · 1030 0.1 · 1612 2.5 · 2239 0.3
29 W	0420 2.8 · 1117 0.2 · 1702 2.4 · 2328 0.4
30 TH	0513 2.7 · 1206 0.3 · 1755 2.3
31 F	0022 0.4 · 0612 2.6 · 1302 0.4 · 1853 2.3

Chart Datum: 1·68 metres below Normal Null (German reference level)

21

BÜSUM   8-21-24

Schleswig-Holstein, 54°07'·20N 08°51'·60E   Rtg 2-2-2

CHARTS
AC 1875, 3767; BSH 44, 105, 3014.4
TIDES
HW +0036 on Dover (UT); ML 1·8m; Duration 0625

Standard Port HELGOLAND (←)

Times				Height (metres)			
High Water		Low Water		MHWS	MHWN	MLWN	MLWS
0100	0600	0100	0800	2·7	2·3	0·4	0·0
1300	1800	1300	2000				
Differences BÜSUM							
+0054	+0049	−0001	+0027	+0·9	+0·9	+0·1	0·0
LINNENPLATE							
+0047	+0046	+0034	+0046	+0·7	+0·6	+0·1	0·0
SÜDERHÖFT							
+0103	+0056	+0051	+0112	+0·8	+0·7	+0·1	0·0

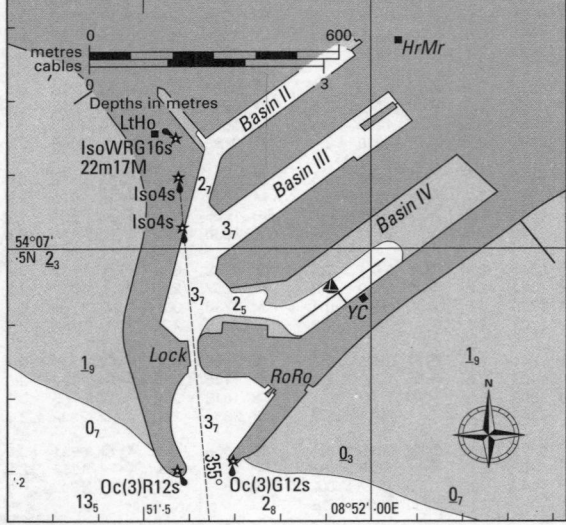

SHELTER
Very good. For lock opening (H24), call VHF Ch 11 or give 1 long blast in appr chan; 2 long blasts on reaching lock if not already open; obey R/G lts. Turn 90° stbd into yacht hbr (1·8m LW) Basin IV. Basin II is deeper; berth on FVs.
NAVIGATION
WPT 54°06'·50N 08°19'·10E, SWM buoy Iso 8s, 270°/090° from/to Süderpiep No 2 PHM buoy, 5M. Süderpiep or Norderpiep (unlit; beware bar if wind-over-tide) are well-buoyed chans, approx 15M long; night appr not advised. Beware strong cross-tides and sudden winds over moles.
LIGHTS AND MARKS
Lt ho Iso WRG 6s; W092·5°-094·5° leads 093·5° for last 4M of Süderpiep. Hbr lts as chartlet. A high bldg is conspic 9ca NW of hbr; silo is conspic in hbr.
RADIO TELEPHONE
VHF call Büsum Port Ch 11 16.
TELEPHONE (Dial code 04834)
Hr Mr 2183; CG 2246; ⌗ 2376; Dr 2088; YC 2997.
FACILITIES
Yacht hbr AB 18.00DM, AC, FW, M, BY, EI, ME, C, P, D, ⌨.
Town CH, V, R, Bar, ✉, ⑬, ≋, Ⓗ, ✈ (Hamburg).
Note: Meldorf yacht hbr is 4M ESE; full yacht facilities.

OTHER HBRS ON W COAST OF SCHLESWIG-HOLSTEIN

TÖNNING, Schleswig-Holstein, 54°18'·92N 08°57'·11E. AC 3767; BSH104, 3014.8. HW +0246 and +0·5m on Helgoland; ML 2·7m. Eiderdamm lock, 5·5M seawards, operates H24. VHF Ch 14 16. Lock N mole Oc (2) R 12s; S mole Oc G 6s. R Eider with the Gieselau Kanal links Tönning to the Kiel Canal (8.21.22). Above the dam, R Eider is tidal, when sluices are operated HW +3 to HW+½, (beware strong currents). Berth in middle of S quay, 3m at MHW. If heading E up river, bridge (clnce 5·6m) opens on request Mon-Sat 0600-SS. Hr Mr ☎ (04861) 1400; Dr ☎ 389; Ⓗ ☎ 706; Facilities: **Quay** 13.50DM, FW, P, D, BY, C (5 ton), Slip; **YC** ☎ 754 (all welcome). **Town** ⑬, ✉, ≋, Gaz.

HUSUM, Schleswig-Holstein, 54°28'·78N 09°00'·00E. AC 3767; BSH 105, 3013.12. HW + 0036 on Dover (UT); ML 1·9m; Duration 0555. See 8.21.25. A sluice/lock, 7ca W of rly bridge, is shut when level > 0·3m over MHW, as shown by ⑬. Beware the canal effect when passing big ships in the narrow appr chan. In the outer hbr yachts should turn stbd just before rly bridge for pontoons on S bank, or pass through bridge (clnce 5m when shut) to inner hbr by SC Nordsee; both dry. VHF call Husum Port Ch 11. Tfc reports broadcast on Ch 11 every H +00 from HW −4 to HW +2. Outer ldg lts 106° both Iso R 8s, synch & intens on ldg line. Inner ldg lts 090° both Iso G 8s, synch & intens on ldg line. Night entry not advised. Hr Mr ☎ (04841) 667218; Sluice ☎ 2565; **Husum YC** ☎ 65670; **SC Nordsee** ☎ 3436; ⌗ ☎ 61759. AB 13.50DM, P, D, at hbr.

HARBOURS IN THE NORTH FRISIAN ISLANDS

PELLWORM, 54°31'·31N 08°41'·24E. AC 3767; BSH 3013.11. Tides: see Suderoogsand/Husum, 8.21.25. Outer appr via Norderhever; ldg lts 041° Oc 5s. Ent chan from NH18 PHM buoy, Fl (2+1) R 15s, has 0·2m; access near HW. VHF Ch 11. Small yacht hbr 2·8m at MHW; drying on soft mud.

WITTDÜN, Amrum, 54°37'·85N 08°24'·65E. AC 3767; BSH107, 3013.6. HW +0107 on Dover (UT); +0137 on Helgoland (zone −0100); ML 2·7m; Duration 0540. See 8.21.25. Wittdün is the main hbr of Amrum. Yachts berth S of stone quay, lying bows to pontoon, stern to posts. Good shelter except in E winds. The quay 800m to the E is reserved for ferries only. Chan has 2m and is marked by PHM withies ⌘; Ldg lts 272°: Both Iso R 4s 11/33m 10/15M; W masts, R bands; intens on ldg line. Lt ho Fl 7·5s 63m 23M; R tr, W bands; same location as rear ldg lt. It is not advisable to enter at night. Wriakhörn, Cross lt, is 1M WSW of hbr, L Fl (2) WR 15s 26m 9/7M; W297·5°-319·5°, R319·5°-330°, W330°-005·5°, R005·5°-034°. Hr Mr ☎ (04682) 2294; ⌗ ☎ 2026; Dr ☎ 2612; Facilities: AB 18DM, P & D (cans) at Nebel; **Amrum YC** ☎ 2054.

WYK, Island of Föhr, 54°41'·70N 08°34'·80E. AC 3767; BSH107, 3013.6. HW +0107 on Dover (UT); +0137 on Helgoland (zone −0100); ML 2·8. Good yacht hbr (1·5m) to N of ent, sheltered in all winds; visitors berth W side of pontoon 1. Access H24. Also berths on E quay of inner hbr. Ferry hbr (4m). Lts: Oldenhorn (SE point of Föhr), R tr, Oc (4) WR 15s 10m 13/10M; W208°-245°, R245°-298°, W298°-333°, R333°-080°. S mole, FR 9m 4M, R mast. E mole, FG 7m 4M, G mast.. Port VHF Ch 11 16. Yacht hbr Hr Mr ☎ (04681) 3030; Commercial Hr Mr ☎ 2852; **YC** ☎ 1280; Dr ☎ 8998; ⌗ ☎ 2594; Facilities: **Hbr road** (500m), CH, ⌨, P & D (cans); **Yacht Hbr** 18DM, R, V; **W Quay** D.

SYLT   8-21-25

Schleswig-Holstein 54°45'·54N 08°17'·86E (Hörnum)
Rtgs: Hörnum 3-3-1; List 3-3-1

CHARTS
AC 3767/8; BSH D107, D108, 3013.3 List, 3013.5 Hörnum
TIDES
+0110 Dover; ML 1·8; Duration 0540; Zone −0100

Standard Port HELGOLAND (←)

Times				Height (metres)			
High Water		Low Water		MHWS	MHWN	MLWN	MLWS
0100	0600	0100	0800	2·7	2·3	0·4	0·0
1300	1800	1300	2000				
Differences LIST							
+0252	+0240	+0201	+0210	−0·7	−0·6	−0·2	0·0
HÖRNUM							
+0223	+0218	+0131	+0137	−0·5	−0·3	−0·2	0·0
AMRUM-HAFEN							
+0138	+0137	+0128	+0134	+0·2	+0·2	+0·1	0·0
DAGEBÜLL							
+0226	+0217	+0211	+0225	+0·6	+0·6	−0·1	0·0
SUDEROOGSAND							
+0116	+0102	+0038	+0122	+0·3	+0·4	+0·1	0·0
HUSUM							
+0205	+0152	+0118	+0200	+1·2	+1·1	+0·1	0·0

SHELTER

The island of Sylt, about 20M long, has Westerland (the capital) in the centre, List in the N and Hörnum in the S. The Hindenburgdamm connects it to the mainland.

LIST: The small hbr is sheltered except in NE/E winds. Ent is 25m wide and hbr 3m deep.

HÖRNUM: Good in the small hbr, approx 370m x 90m, protected by outer mole on SE side and by 2 inner moles. Yacht haven at the N end. Good ⚓ in Hörnum Reede in W and N winds and in Hörnumtief in E and S winds.

There are two other hbrs; Rantum (9DM) and Munkmarsch (13.50DM) which both dry; access HW ±3. Large areas of Sylt are nature reserves; landing prohib.

NAVIGATION

LIST WPT: Lister Tief SWM buoy, Iso 8s, 55°05'·37N 08°16'·87E, 292°/112° from/to List Ost lt, 6·1M. Lister Tief (see 8.21.5) is well marked. In strong W/NW winds expect a big swell on the bar (depth 4m) on the ebb, which sets on to Salzsand. NE quay is open construction, unsuitable for yachts. Chan buoys through roadstead lead to hbr. Access at all tides, but beware strong cross streams.

HÖRNUM WPT: Vortrapptief (SWM) buoy, Oc 4s, 54°35'·00N 08°12'·20E, 215°/035° from/to Norddorf lt (Amrum), 6·35M. Appr through Vortrapptief buoyed chan (see below) inside drying banks. In strong W winds the sea breaks on off-lying banks and in the chan. Final appr from NE, keeping mid-chan in hbr ent. Access at all tides.

LIGHTS AND MARKS

LIST: See 8.21.4 for List West lt Oc WRG 6s, List Ost Iso WRG 6s, List Land Oc WRG 3s and Kampen L Fl WR 10s. Rømø church is conspic. N mole hd FG, vis 218°-038°. S mole hd FR, vis 218°-353°.

HÖRNUM: Conspic radio mast (5 Fl R lts) 3M N of hbr. Follow W034°-036·8° leading sector of Norddorf lt (Oc WRG 6s) until Hörnum lt, Fl (2) 9s, bears 012°. N pier hd FG, vis 024°-260°. Outer mole hd FR (mole floodlit).

RADIO TELEPHONE

List VHF Ch 11 (0800-1200, 1600-1800).

TELEPHONE (Dial code 04651)

LIST: Hr Mr 870374; Police 870510; Ⓗ 870841; ⌗ 870413, CG 870365; Dr 870350.

HÖRNUM: Hr Mr 881027; Dr 881016; Police 881510; CG 881256.

FACILITIES

LIST: **Hbr** AB 14DM, FW, ⌗, C (35 ton), Slip, SC. **Village** V, R, Bar, P & D (cans), Ferry to Römö (Denmark).

WESTERLAND: CG 85199; Police 7047. **Town** V, R, Bar, P & D (cans), Gaz, ⌗, ✉, Ⓑ, ⇌, ✈.

HÖRNUM: Sylter YC ☎ 880274, AB 20DM, Bar, AC, FW, ▣. **Town** V, R, Bar, ME, ✉, Ⓑ.

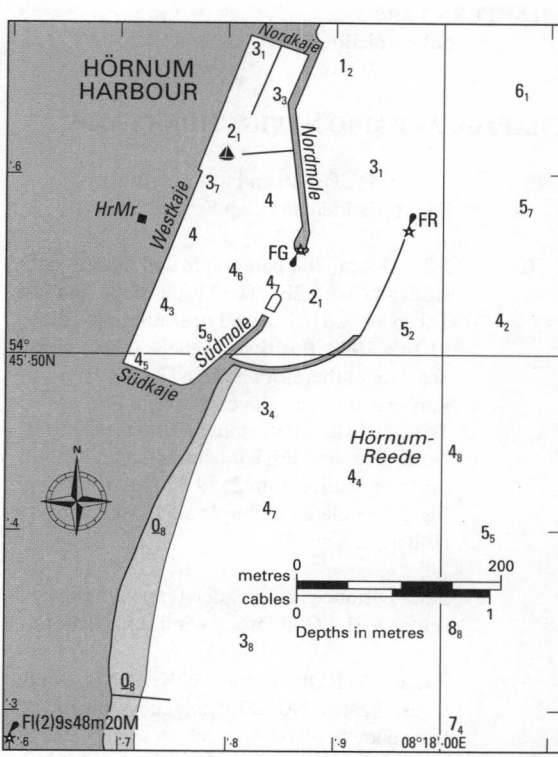

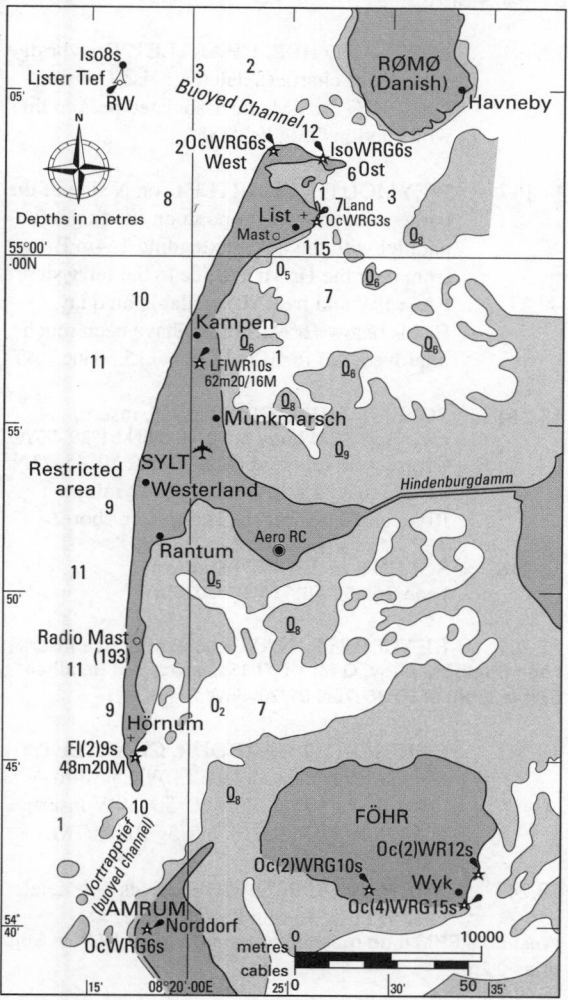

TIDAL DIFFERENCES FOR WEST COAST OF DENMARK   8-21-26

These figures are mean values, to be used with caution.

Standard Port HELGOLAND (←)

Times				Height (metres)			
High Water		Low Water		MHWS	MHWN	MLWN	MLWS
0300	0700	0100	0800	2·7	2·3	0·4	0·0
1500	1900	1300	2000				
Differences HØJER							
+0247	+0322	No data		−0·3	−0·2	0·0	0·0
RØMØ HAVN							
+0227	+0302	+0221	+0201	−0·8	−0·7	−0·1	0·0
GRADYB BAR							
+0137	+0152	No data		−1·2	−1·1	−0·1	0·0
ESBJERG							
+0307	+0307	+0221	+0221	−1·1	−0·9	−0·2	−0·1
BLAVANDSHUK							
+0147	+0157	+0131	+0121	−0·9	−0·9	−0·1	0·0
TORSMINDE							
+0337	+0357	+0301	+0231	−1·8	−1·6	−0·3	0·0
THYBORON							
+0427	+0537	+0631	+0431	−2·3	−2·0	−0·3	0·0
HANSTHOLM							
+0407	+0647	+0601	+0351	−2·4	−2·0	−0·3	0·0
HIRTSHALS							
+0402	+0627	+0601	+0321	−2·4	−2·0	−0·3	0·0

21

Late Corrections

Information in the preceding pages of the Almanac is corrected to Weekly Edition 17/98 of *Admiralty Notices to Mariners*.
Late Corrections continue the process up to and including Weekly Edition 23/98.

CHAPTERS 1 and 2
Nil corrections

CHAPTER 3 – RADIO NAVIGATIONAL AIDS

1.49   3.2.5.1, DGPS, amend to ‡ (on trial): Pte St Mathieu and Cap Ferret lt ho's.

2.50   3.3.1 Decca, 2nd paragraph, add margin note: Holland Chain 2E: The Purple slave station at Thorpeness, UK, ceased operating wef 2359 31 July 1998. Positions in the southern North Sea cannot therefore be fixed using the Purple and Green slaves of Chain 2E.
The other Chain 2E stations (for the central North Sea) and Frisian Islands Chain 9B will cease operating from 2359 31 Dec 1999.
Fig 3(3), delete the Purple slave station of Holland Chain 2E.

3.53   3.5.5 Distance finding, delete: penultimate sentence (La Corbière ... wind information).

4.55   Table 3(1) RDF beacons, ENGLAND, South Coast, beacon No 147, Dungeness, amend frequency to 301·5.
ENGLAND, East coast, beacon No 127, Cromer, amend frequency to 314·5.

5.57   Ibid, WALES, beacon No 034D, Point Lynas, amend frequency to 304·50.

6.61   Table 3(3), RACONS, No 226 amend position: **East Goodwin lt float** 51°13'·23N 01°36'·48E.

CHAPTER 4
Nil corrections

CHAPTER 5 – WEATHER

7.90   5.3.3.1, insert at 0400 and 1545: Northwood Surface analysis.
Ibid, 5.5.1 Weather Centres, RH col, Ireland Central Forecast Office, Dublin, amend: (01) 8424655.

CHAPTERS 6 and 7
Nil corrections

CHAPTER 8 – HARBOUR, COASTAL AND TIDAL INFORMATION

AREA 1 – SOUTH WEST ENGLAND

8.148   ENGLISH CHAN WPTS, AREA 3, amend: E Goodwin lt F   51°13'·23N 01°36'·48E.

9.151   ST MARY'S, L & M, pierhead lt Fl RWG 2s, line 2, amend: G129°-070° (301°).

10.175   DARTMOUTH, Up-river to Dittisham and Totnes, Berthing, delete: lines 3-4 (Steamer Quay .... planned). Substitute:
Drying AB on E bank for about 15 yachts, clear of ferries using Steamer Quay.

AREA 2 – CENTRAL SOUTHERN ENGLAND

11.187   CLFSW, LH col, after BEAULIEU RIVER entry, insert under SOLENT MARKS: Lepe Spit SCM buoy, Q (6) + L Fl 15s, 50°46'.75W 01°20'·55W.

12.190   PASSAGE INFO, LH col, line 5 after Stone Pt, amend: marked by Lepe Spit SCM buoy and where a bn marks cable area.

13.191   PORTLAND HBR, CHARTLET, Ferrybridge (W edge of chartlet), delete: Iso G4s 5m 2m,   QG 3m 2M and associated pecked line with caption "Ldg lts 288°".

14.197   WEYMOUTH, CHARTLET, on N side of the harbour insert: a yacht pontoon (no fingers) parallel with the quay, extending 144m E from near the Hr Mr's office to the ferry steps. FAC: FW and free AC available on quay. Heads below Hr Mr's office have been much improved. AB for 10m LOA = £15.50 inc VAT.

15.214   SOLENT AREA, CHARTLET, insert: Lepe Spit SCM buoy at 50°46'.75N 01°20'·55W. Obstruction reported (May '98) at 50°45'·21N 01°27'·46W, 2m ENE of ent to Lymington River and 4 ca off the Hampshire shore.

16.216   SOLENT AREA WPTS, insert: Lepe Spit 50°46'.75N 01°20'·55W.

17.221   BEAULIEU R, NAV, line 2, after 4ca insert: Lepe Spit SCM buoy, Q (6) + L Fl 15s, is 7ca E of Beaulieu Spit dolphin at 50°46'.75N 01°20'·55W.

18.242   CHICHESTER HARBOUR, CHARTLET, Chichester Bar bn, delete: Fl WR 5s 14m 7/5M &. At 50°45'·70N 00°56'·39W insert: West Pole PHM bn, Fl WR 5s 10m 5/7M.

19.243   Ibid, NAV, APPROACHES, lines 5-8, delete: CHI SPIT .... Bar bn lt. Substitute:
West Pole PHM lt bn must be rounded to clear W Pole Spit, dries 0·2m.

L & M, lines 1-3, Bar Bn, after topmark, amend:
Fl (2) R 10s 7m 2M; tide gauge.
Insert:
West Pole PHM bn, Fl WR 5s 10m 7/5M, vis W321°-081°,
R081°-321°, 50°45´.70N 00°56´.39W. 3 SHM Bys .....

In summary: West Pole spit is marked by new PHM bn, lit as above. The seasonal CHI SPIT PHM buoy is removed. Chichester Bar bn lt is amended to a 360° lt, Fl (2) R 10s 7m 2M.

AREA 3 – SOUTH EAST ENGLAND

20.252   CLFSW, LH col, DOVER, amend:
E GOODWIN lt F, 51°13´.23N 01°36´.48E.

21.259   BRIGHTON, NAV, lines 2-3, amend:
Ent chan dredged 2·0m, but after gales shoaling occurs especially on E side; craft drawing >1·5m should keep to the W side of chan until past the first SHM buoy.
        L & M, line 3 after ...leads to ent, amend:
Five Y spar lt buoys, anti-clockwise from the W, with brg/dist from W bkwtr hd, are as follows: Fl Y 10s (257°/3·1M); Fl Y 6s (237°/1·5M); Fl Y 3s (193°/1·95M); Fl Y 4s (180°/2ca); and Fl Y 2s (152°/2·1M).
A sewer outfall can buoy, Fl Y 5s, (123°/3·3M) is 1·1M off the coast.

AREA 4 – EAST ENGLAND

22.288   RIVER MEDWAY, CHARTLET, correction to AC 1835: Delete 5 mooring buoys (Nos 54-58) in the stream approx 3 ca SSW of Hoo Marina, just off SW corner of inset.

AREA 5 – NORTH EAST ENGLAND

23.333   Distance Table, Hull to Whitby (97M) amend: 88M.

AREA 6 – SOUTH EAST SCOTLAND

24.361   CLFSW, RH col, FIRTH OF FORTH - N SHORE, KIRKCALDY, lines 4 & 5, delete: W and E Rockheads SHM buoys.

AREA 7 – NORTH EAST SCOTLAND

Nil corrections

AREA 8 – NORTH WEST SCOTLAND

25.420   CLFSW, LH col, LOCH INCHARD/LOCH LAXFORD, lines 2-4, delete and substitute:
Kinlochbervie Dir lt 327° WRG 15m **16M**, dayglow Y framework tr (floodlit), 58°27´.52N 05°03´.01W; sectors FG 326°-326·5°, Al GW 326·5°-326·75°, FW 326·75°-327·25°, Al RW 327·25°-327·5°, FR 327·5°-328°.

26.430   ST KILDA, 4th & 3rd lines from end, amend:
Call *Kilda Radio* VHF Ch 16 **12** 73 (HJ) for permission to land;   (01870) 604406 (HO), 604612 (OT);   604601.

27.431   KINLOCHBERVIE, CHARTLET, delete rear ldg lt and pecked ldg line joining it to front ldg lt. Front ldg lt, substitute: Dir WRG. Pecked ldg line 327°, delete: Ldg lts.
        L & M, lines 6-8, delete: Ldg lts 327° ... white . Substitute:
Dir   WRG 327°into hbr, 15m **16M**, dayglow Y framework tr (floodlit); see 8.8.4 for vis sectors.

28.432   LOCH GAIRLOCH, penultimate line, after
Hr Mr   (01445) 712140 insert: 710184.

AREA 9 – SOUTH WEST SCOTLAND

29.467   GREAT CUMBRAE ISLAND, add footnote:
A dangerous rock   is reported at 55°46'.82N 03°53'.78W, close inshore off the NE end of the island near Down Craig Water sports centre (290°/1·28M from Largs Yacht Haven).

30.476   GIRVAN, penultimate line, Hr Mr   , amend:
Hr Mr   (01465) 713648,   714454.

AREA 10 – NW ENGLAND, IoM and N WALES

31.486   CLFSW, LH col, HOLYHEAD, line 1,
amend: *Bkwtr hd*, Fl (3) G 10s ....

32.504   HOLYHEAD, CHARTLET, W bkwtr hd,
amend: Fl (3) G 10s ...

AREA 11 – SOUTH WALES AND BRISTOL CHANNEL

33.520   PWLLHELI, FAC, lines 1-2, amend:
Marina (400)   701219 (H24),   701443, £13.90, FW, P, D, LPG, AC, BH (40 ton), C, Slip,   ,   .

34.525   MILFORD HAVEN, CHARTLET, Neyland inset, at 51°41'·995N 04°57'·040W insert: SCM buoy *Traynor*, Q(6) + L Fl 15s.

35.539   BRISTOL (CITY DOCKS), FAC, Bristol Marina, line 1, amend: 921 3198,   929 7672, £8.68.

36.540   PORTISHEAD, TEL, add:
Police 818181 or 01179 27777; Health centre 847474;
    (Bristol) 01179 230000.

AREA 12 – SOUTH IRELAND

37.573   CORK HARBOUR, CHARTLET, insert   Fl (2) R 5s on C2 PHM perch at 51°48'·67N 08°17'·30W (mouth of the Owenboy River).

38.580   VALENTIA HBR, last line , add:
Marina (80 AB) at Cahersiveenplanned for 1999.

THIS PAGE IS INTENTIONALLY BLANK, FOR CUT-AND-PASTE CORRECTING

AREA 13 – NORTH IRELAND

39.596   STRANGFORD LOUGH, SHELTER, line 5, the boatpark (marina) became operational in June 1998, with AC and FW on pontoons.

AREA 14 – CHANNEL ISLANDS

40.628   BEAUCETTE, CHARTLET, insert unlit SCM bn on drying patch close NE of marina ent. Note: This bn 'replaces' the SHM bn, shown on AC 808 (Beaucette inset), which was never actually in place!

41.638   LA CORBIÈRE lt. Delete Wind information (lines 6-19). Add footnote:
From May 1998 wind direction, speed and gust info, using sensors at La Collette tanker basin, was being broadcast in English on VHF Ch 18 every 2 minutes on a trial basis.
La Corbière light, fog horn, RDF bcn and associated distance finding capability are unchanged. Plans to instal a DGPS bcn are under discussion.

AREA 15 – CENTRAL NORTH FRANCE

42.649   CLFSW, LH col, ST MALO, Chenal de la Petite Porte, line 4, Bassé NE buoy, amend:
Vieux Banc-Est NCM buoy, Q, Bell, 48°42'·49N 02°09'·06W.

43.674   TIDES. For the Standard Port of ST MALO, amend mean Heights of tides as follows:

Times				Height (metres)			
High Water		Low Water		MHWS	MHWN	MLWN	MLWS
0100	0800	0300	0800	12·2	9·3	4·2	1·5
1300	2000	1500	2000				

44.668   ST MALO, TIDAL CURVES, MEAN RANGES BOX, amend: Springs 10·7m; Neaps 5·1m.

45.669   ST MALO, NAV, line 5, Chenal de la Petite Porte, correction to AC 2700: Move NCM buoy, Q, marking Basse NE du Vieux-Banc, 2ca E to 48°42'·49N 02°09'·06W. The buoy and shoal are approx 100m SW of the 130° ldg line for Ch de la Petite Porte, but off the chartlet, 3·5M NW of Le Grand Jardin lt ho.

46.670   RIVER RANCE/DINAN, FAC, after Mordreuc delete: P, V. Line 3, delete word Villages. Line 4, amend La Pommeraie to La Cale de Plouër.

AREA 16 – NORTH BRITTANY

47.681   CLFSW, LH col, TRÉGASTEL, line 7, Le Crapaud WCM lt buoy, amend Lat/Long:
48°46'·75N 03°40'·52W.

48.686 –   PAIMPOL to PLOUMANC'H, TIDES. For
.690   the Standard Port of ST MALO, amend mean Heights of tides as follows:

Times				Height (metres)			
High Water		Low Water		MHWS	MHWN	MLWN	MLWS
0100	0800	0300	0800	12·2	9·3	4·2	1·5
1300	2000	1500	2000				

AREA 17 – SOUTH BRITTANY

49.715   CLFSW, LHcol, ÎLE DE HÖEDIC, line 2, Les Sœurs bn amend longitude: 02°55'·10W.

AREA 18 – SOUTH BISCAY

50.767   ANGLET/BAYONNE, SHELTER, line 4, after bridge insert: (5·2m clearance).

AREA 19 – NORTH EAST FRANCE

51.784   DIVES-SUR-MER, CHARTLET, training wall at 49°17'·80N 00°05'·50W: delete the first and last SHM bns and straighten the kink in the training wall. FAC, line 2 after   No, insert FF65.

52.791   RIVER SEINE, NAV, line 6 before Deauville insert: Dives (FF310 for 30 mins); line 7 after Le Havre (marina) insert: FF340 for 30 mins; delete: and Rouen (where masting facilities are reported to be poor and expensive).
RH col, ROUEN, lines 5/6 delete: or mast ... 250km.

AREA 20 – BELGIUM AND THE NETHERLANDS

53.813   CLFSW, RH col, ZANDVLIET, lines 1-4, amend (noting that these are no longer ldg lts):
Oc 5s 17m 9M, 51°20'·70N 04°16'·40E.
Oc 5s 17m 9M, R col, W bands, on R mast.

54.822 –   NIEUWPOORT to IJMUIDEN, TIDES. For
.842   the Standard Port of VLISSINGEN, amend mean Heights of tides as follows:

Times				Height (metres)			
High Water		Low Water		MHWS	MHWN	MLWN	MLWS
0300	0900	0400	1000	4·8	3·9	0·9	0·3

55.833   VLISSINGEN, TIDAL CURVES, MEAN RANGES BOX, amend: Springs 4·5m; Neaps 3·0m.

AREA 21 – GERMANY

Nil corrections

THIS PAGE IS INTENTIONALLY BLANK, FOR CUT-AND-PASTE CORRECTING

Index

Explanation

Abbreviations are entered under the full word and not the abbreviation.

For example St Abb's comes under Saint not St.

The prefix C before a page number indicates a Coast Radio Station.

The prefix L before a page number indicates an entry in the lists of Coastal Lights, Fog Signals and Waylights.

The prefix R before a page number indicates a Radio Navigational Aid.

Bold names/page numbers indicate ports/harbours with chartlet.

A

A1/A2 buoy, 812
A17/A18 buoy, L775
Abandon ship, 113
Abbenfleth, 883
Abbeville, Canal, 798
Abbeville buoy, L776
Abbreviations and symbols, 3-6
Aberaeron, 522
Aberbenoit, Lí, L682, **695**
Aberdaron, 520
Aberdeen, R61, L362, 364, **377**
Aberdeen tides, 378-380
Aberdour, 368
Aberdovey, L514, **522**
Aberildut, Lí, L682, **696**
Abermenai Point, 488
Aberporth, R57, 522
Abersoch, 520
Abertay, R61, L362, 364
Aberwracíh, Lí, L681, 684, **695**
Aberystwyth, L514, **522**
A'Bhraige, Loch, L421, 436
Acairseid Mhór, 426
Accumer Ee, 871
Achilbeg Island, L591
Achill Sound, L590, 593
Acknowledgements, 1
Adjusting compass, 26
Admiralty Chart symbols, 16-17
Admiralty Notices to Mariners, 2
Admiralty tidal stream atlases, 123
Adour, L' (Boucau), L744, 746, 766
Adrigole, 578
AE buoy, L468
Aero radiobeacons, 55
Agger, The, 840
Aground, vessels, 10, 18-19
Aigle, Pointe a l', L649, 673
Aiguillon, L', L716, 745, 752
Ailly, Pointe d', R59, L775, 778
Ailsa Craig, L458
Aircraft directing signals/procedures, 112
Airds Pt, L422
Air traffic control centres, SAR, 107
Aix, Ile d', L743, 756
Alarm signal, radiotelephone, 106
Albert Bridge, 294
Alde/Ore, River, 316
Aldeburgh, L280, 317
Alderney, R55, 148, L 622, 627
    anchorages around, 627
Alderney Race, 624, 650
Aline, Loch, L422, **440**
Alligande, L622
Allington Lock, 289
Alloa, 367

Almanak voor Watertoerisme (ANWB), 844
Alprech, Cap d', R59, L776, 799
Alsh, Kyle of Loch, L421, 424, 436
Alsh, Loch, 437
Alt, River, 495
Alte Ems, L858
Alte Mellum, 869
Altenbruch, L860
Alterhaven, L861
Alte Weser, R59, L860, 872
Althorne, 304
Alum Bay, 213
Amble, L330, 332, **351**
Ameland, R59, L817, 821, 846
Amendments, record of, 2
Amlwch, L486, 505
Amrum, L861, L862, 866, 890
Amsterdam, **843**
Anchor lights, 11, 18-19
Ancresse Bay, L', 629
Andernos, 765
Andijk, 845
Anglesey, 488, 502
Anglesey Radio, C73
Anglet, L744, **766**
Anglia Field Platform A48/19, R61
Annalong Harbour, L588, 595
Annan Waterfoot, 489
Annat buoy, L362
Anstruther, L361, **373**
Antifer, Cap d', R59, 149, L 775, 777
Antwerpen (Antwerp), L813, 820, **828**
Anvil Point, L186, 189
Appin, Port, 441
Appingedam, C78
Appledore, 542-543
Approaches to St Helier, 636
Aran Islands, 593, 612
Aranmore, L590
Arbroath, L362, **375**
Arcachon, L744, 746, **764**
Arcachon Radio, C76
Ardfern, 449
Ardglass, L588, **596**
Ardgowan outfall buoy, L468
Ardgroom Harbour, 579
Ardinamar, 448
Ardminish Bay, 461
Ardmore buoys, L468
Ardmore Pt, L422
Ardnakinna Point, L552
Ardnamurchan Point, L422, 423, 424
Ardnave Point, 461
Ardrishaig, L456, 460, **463**
Ardrossan, L458, **475**
Ardyne buoy,, L468
Area indexes, Area 1, 137
    Area 2, 181
    Area 3, 245
    Area 4, 269

Area 5, 323
Area 6, 355
Area 7, 383
Area 8, 415
Area 9, 451
Area 10, 479
Area 11, 509
Area 12, 545
Area 13, 583
Area 14, 617
Area 15, 643
Area 16, 675
Area 17, 707
Area 18, 737
Area 19, 769
Area 20, 807
Area 21, 853
Area of Concern, Solent, 215
Area planning forecasts, 88
Areas, Map of (Ch 8), 128
Areas, shipping forecasts, 82
Argenton, 699
Arinagour, L422, 439
Arisaig, L422, 438
Arklow, L550, **563**
Armadale Bay, 438, L422
Armandéche, L', L742
Arnemuiden, 834
Arngast, L859
Arnish Point, L420
Arnside, 492
Aromen, 683
Arradon, 729
Arran, Isle of, L458, 460, 466
Arrochar, 470
Arromanches, L774, 781, 782
Ars-en-RÈ, L743, **752**
Arundel, 254
Arzal, 671, 731
Ashlett Creek, 229
Askaig, Port (Islay), 461
ATT-ARC buoy, L744
ATT Maumusson buoy, L744
Audenge, 764
Audierne, L712, 717, **719**
August Rock Buoy, L142
August Rock By, 153
Aulne, L' River, 671, 700-701
Ault, L776
Auray, 729
Auskerry, L389, 407
Autolink R/T, 69
Aven, River, L713, 717, 723
Avoch, 398
Avonmouth, L516, 519, **538**
Avonmouth tides, 535-537
Avon River (Devon), 169
Axmouth/Beer, 179
Ayr, L458, 476
Ayr, Point of (N Wales), 487
Ayre, Point of (IoM), R62, L485, 487

B

B.1 D Platform Amethyst, R61
B.1 D Platform Dowsing, L329
BA buoy, L744
Backaland Bay, 406
Badcall Bay, 431
Baginbun Head, 566
Bagi Stack, L391
Baie (Bay), see proper name
Baily, R57, L550
Balbriggan, 594, 595
Baleines, Les, R58, L743
Balivanich, 425
Balje, L860
Ballinskelligs Bay, 579
Ballybunnion Lt By, R62
Ballycastle, 604
Ballycotton, 572
Ballycrovane Harbour, L552, 579
Ballyholme Bay, 598-599
Ballynacourty, L551
Ballynacourty Point, 572
Ballynakill, 611
Ballysadare Bay, 610
Ballywater, L588
Balta Sound, L391, 413, 414
Baltimore, 576
Baltrum, 859, 865, 869
Balue, La, L649, 668
Bamburgh, L330, 352
Banc de Guérande, L716
Banche, La, L716
Banff, 394
Bangor (N Ireland), L588, **598-599**
Bangor (Wales), L486, 503
Bann, River, L589, **606**
Bantry Bay, L551, 554, **578**
Bantry Radio, C75
Barcaldine Pier (Loch Creran), 441
Bardsey Island, L486, 488, 505
Barfleur, L774, **779**
Barfleur, Pointe de, R59, 149, L 648,
    650, 777
Barfleur Race, 779
Barges, Les, L742
Bar Lanby, R Mersey, R62, L485
Barloge Creek, 575
Barmouth, L514, **521**
Barnouic, L680
Barnstaple, 542-543
Barometer conversion scale, 85
Barra, R56, R111
Barra (Hebrides), L421, 423
Barra (N Bay), 425
Barra Head (Berneray), 425
Barrel of Butter, L389
Barrow-in-Furness, L484, 487, 492
Barrow/Walney Island, R57
Barrow Deep, L275
Barrow No. 3 Lt By, R61
Barry, L515, **532**
Bartholomew Ledge Buoy, L142, 147
Bartlett Creek, 289
Bas-Sablons, Les, L649, **669**
Basse Bréfort, 148
Basse du Lis Lanby, L683
Basse du Milieu Lanby, L714
Basse du Renier buoy, L648
Basse du Renier Lt By, 148
Basse Hergo, L715
Basse Pérennès buoy, L713
Basse Vieille buoy, L683

Bassin Vauban, 669
Bassotière, L742
Bass Rock, L360, 363
Bassurelle buoy, L776
Bassurelle Lt By, R63
Basta Voe, 412
Bath, 827
Battlesbridge, 304
Batz, Île de, 148, L681, 684, 694
Baule, La, 733
Baumrönne, L861
Bawdsey, R111, 316
Bawdsey Bank, L277
Bayonne, L744, **766**
Bayonne Radio, C76
BBC, general forecasts, 86
    Radio 4 shipping forecasts, 86
BBC Radio Guernsey, 638
BBC Radio Jersey, 638
Beachley/Aust, 534
Beachy Head, L250, 252
Beadnell Bay, 351
Beag, Loch, 449
Beamer Rock buoy, L361
Bearhaven, L551, 578
Bearing of sun, rising and setting, 32
Beat frequency oscillator (BFO), 53
Beaucette (Guernsey), L622, **628**
Beaufort scale, 84
Beaulieu River, L187, **221**
Beaumaris, 502, 503
Bec de l'Epoids, L742
Becquet, Le, L648, 657
Bee Ness, 289
Beer, 179
Beg-ar-Vechen, Pointe de, L713
Beg-Léguer, L681
Belcroute Bay, 638
Belfast City, R57
Belfast Lough, L588, 592, **598-599**
Belfast tides, 600-602
Belgian coast radio stations, 78
Belgium
    Inland waterways, 822
    Maritime Rescue Centres, 822
    Passage Information, 820
    Public Holidays, 822
    SAR, 116
    Special notes for, 822
    Storm signals, 822
    Weather information, 98
Belgium and Netherlands, TSS, 826
Belle Île, 726
Belle Île, Goulphar Lt, L714
Belle Île, Le Palais, L714
Belle Île Radio, C76
Belmullet Radio, C75
Bell Rock, R61, L362
Bélon, River, L713, 717, 723
Belvoir Bay (Herm), 631
Bembridge, R55, L188, **234**
Bembridge Ledge Buoy, 216-217
Benbecula, 423
Benodet, L713, 717, **720**
Bensersiel, L859, 865, 872
Berck, 798
Bergsediep Lock, 833
Berkeley, 534
Berneray, L420, 423
Bernerie-en-Retz, La, L742
Berry Head, R55, R111, L 143, 147
Berthaume, Anse de, 700-701
Bervie, Loch, 431
Berwick-upon-Tweed, L330, 332, **353**,
    363

Beuzec, L713
Bhraige, Loch a', L421, 436
Biarritz, R58, L744
Bibliography for each Area, see first
    paragraph of Passage Information
Bideford, L517, 542-543
Big Russel, 624, 630
Bill of Portland, 147, L186, 191
Binic, L649, **673**
Birkenfels buoy, L812
Birvideaux, Plateau des, L714
Biscay, Bay of, 745
Bishop Rock, R61, L142, 147
Bishops, The, 518
Black Ball Harbour, 578
Black Deep, L275
Black Head (Antrim), R57
Black Head (Belfast Lough), 598-599
Black Head (Galway), L591
Black Head (Killantringan), L458
Black Nore Point, L516
Blackpool, R57, L484, 493
Black Rock (Aranmore), L590
Black Rock (Falmouth), L142
Blacksod Quay/Bay, L590, 611
Blacktoft, 340
Blackwater, River, L276, **308**
Blakeney, L328, **334**
Blankenberge, L812, 820, **824**
Blasket Islands, 554
Blåvandshuk, 891
Blavet, R, 724
Blaye, L744, 759
Bloody Foreland, L590, 592, 593
Bloscon, R58, L681, 694
Blue Mull Sound, 412, 413
Blyth, L330, **350**
Boddam, 381
Bodic (Le Trieux), L680
Bognor Regis, L250, 254
Boisdale, Loch, L421, 425, 426
Bol van Heist Lt MOW 3, R63
Bonawe, 446
Bo'ness buoy, L361
Boniface Down, R111
Bonne Nuit Bay, L623, 638
Bordagain, L744
Bordeaux, 758, 759, 760
Bordeaux-Arcachon Radio, C76
Bordeaux/Merignac, R58
Bordeaux Harbour (Guernsey), 629
Borkum, L858, 865, 869, **870**
Borkumriff buoy, L858
Borsfleth, 883
Borssele-Noordnol, L813
Boscastle, 544
Bosham, 243
Boston, L329, **336**
Boston Lower Road, 328
Bouley Bay, 638-639
Boulmer, 113, 351
Boulogne, L776, 778, **799**
Boulogne-sur-Mer Radio, C76
Bourgenay, L742, **751**
Bourgneuf, Baie de, 745
Bournemouth, 212
Bournemouth/Hurn, R55
Bovisand Pier, 162-163
Bowling, 471
Boyardville, L743, 755
Boyne, River, L588, 595
Braakman, L813
Braakman/Braakmanhaven, L813
Bradwell, 308

Braefoot Bay, L361
Brake (Looe Channel), 252
Brake (R. Weser), 878
Brancaster Staithe, L328, 335
Brandaris Tower, L816, 847
Brandon Bay, L552, 580
Braye (Alderney), L622, 624, **627**
Breaksea Lt F, R62, L515
Brecqhou, 635
BrÈhat, Œlede, R58, L680, 684, **686**
Brehon, L622, 628
Bremen, L860, 878
Bremen Radio, C78
Bremerhaven, L860, **878**
Breskens, L813, **825**
Bressay, L390
Brest, L683, 685, **700-701**
Brest-le-Conquet Radio, C76
Brest, Le Rade de, 700-701
Brest, tidal coefficients, 698
Brest tides, 702-704
Breton words, 717
Bridges, vertical clearance under, 122
Bridgwater, 540
Bridlington, L329, **342**
Bridport, L143, **180**
Brightlingsea, L276, **309**
Brighton, R55, L250, **259**
Brigneau, L713, 723
Brigognan, 694
Bristol (City Docks), L517, 519, **538**
Bristol Channel, 518
Bristol Deep, L516
British Kiel YC, 885
British Summer Time, 118
British Telecom Coast Radio Stations,
     67, 72
Brittany, North, 684
Brittany, South, 717
Brittany inland waterways, 671
Brixham, L143, **176**
Broadhaven, L590, 611
Broadstairs, L251
Brodick, 466
Brough Haven, 341
Brough of Birsay, L390
Broughty Castle, L362
Bruckless Harbour, 609
Brugge, 825
Bruichladdich (Islay), 461
Bruinisse, 834
Brunsb.ttel, L861, **884**
Brunshausen, 883
BS1 to BS 32 buoys (Blauwe Slenk),
     L816
Buchan Ness, R61
Buckie, L388, **395**
Buckler's Hard, 221
Bude, 544
Bull Lt F, L329
Bullock Bank, 147
Bull Point, L517
Bull Rock, L552
Bull Sand Fort, 340
Bunbeg, L590, 609
Buncrana, L589
Bunessan, 440
Bunowen Bay, 612
Buoyage, IALA Region A, 15, 27
Buoyage, SIGNI, 844
Burgee, 24
Burghead, L388, **397**
Burghsluis, L815, 834
Burhou, 627
Burnham-on-Crouch, L275, **304**

Burnham-on-Crouch tides, 305-307
Burnham-on-Sea, L517, **540**
Burnham Flats, L280, L328
Burnham Overy Staithe, 335
Burnham Radio, C72
Burnmouth, L360, 365
Burntisland, L361, **372**
Burnt Islands, 466
Buron, Le, L649
Burra Voe, 413
Burray/Burrayness, 406, 407
Burry Inlet/Port, L515, **530**
Bursledon, 228
Burtonport, L590, 609
Burton Stather, 340
Bur Wick, 407
B. sum, L861, **890**
Bute, Isle of, 466
Bute, Kyles of, L457, 460
Butec, L421
Butt of Lewis, R56, L420
BXA buoy, R63, L744, 746, 758

C

CA 3, CA 4, Lt By, 149
Cadgwith, 153
Cadzand, 825
Caen, 783
Caernarfon, L486, 488, **502**
Cailleach Head, L420
Cairndhu Lt By, L457
Caister, R111
Caister-on-Sea, 322
Caladh Harbour, 466
Caledonian Canal, 399
Calais, R59, L776, **801**
Calais, Pas de, 778
Calais Radio, C76
Calculators, coastal navigation, 31
Caldey Island, L515, 518, 529
Caledonian Canal, 398, L422, **441**
Calf of Man (IoM), L485, 487
Calf Sound, 500
Calf Sound (Orkney), 406
Calshot Castle/Spit, L187, 216-217, 228
Calvados, Plateau du, 777, 782
Camaret, L683, **705**
Camel, River, 544
Camiers, L776, 799
Camoel, 731
Campbeltown, L456, **464**
Campen, L858
Canal d'Île et Rance, 671
Canal du Midi, 758
Canal Latérale à la Garonne, 758
Canals to the Mediterranean, 791
Cancale, L649, 664, 669
Canche, R, 799
Canger Rock buoy, L623
Canna, L422, 424, 438
Cannis Rock Lt By, 147
Cantick Head, L389
Cap (Cape), see proper name
Capbreton, L744, 746, **766**
Cappagh, 582
Carantec, 693
Cardiff, R57, L515, 518
Cardiff (Penarth), 532
Cardigan, 523
Cardigan Bay, L514, 518
Cardigan Bay Radio, C73

Cardinal marks, 15, 27
Carentan/Isigny, L774, **780-781**
Cargreen, 162-163
Carlingford Lough, L588, **594**
Carloway, 425
Carmarthen, 530
Carmarthen Bay, 518
Carnan, Loch, L420, 425
Carnane, R57
Carnlough Harbour, L589, 604
Carnmore/Galway, R57
Carnsore Point, 553, 566
Carradale Bay, 464
Carrickarory, 607
Carrickfergus, L589, **598-599**
Carrigaholt, 581
Carron, Loch, L421, 437
Carsaig Bay (Mull), 440-441
Carsaig Bay (Sound of Jura), 462
Carteret, L648, **662**
Carteret Radio, C76
Cashla Bay, L591, 593, 612
Casquets, The, 24, R61, 148, L 622
Casquets TSS, 627
Castlebay, 425, 426
Castlebay S By, R62
Castle Breakwater, St Peter Port, R55
Castle Buoy, L142
Castle Cornet, 630
Castle Haven, 575
Castle Lt By, 147
Castlemartin firing range, 530
Castletown (Bearhaven), 578
Castletown (IoM), L485, 499
Castletownshend, 575
Cat Firth (Shetland), 412
Caudebec, 791
Cava Lt, L389
Cayenne, La, 757
Cayeux-sur-Mer, L776, 778, 797
Cazaux, R58
Celsius (Centigrade) to Fahrenheit, 85
Celtic Radio, C72
Celtic Sea, 592
Cemaes Bay, 505
Centre d'Essais des Landes (firing
     range), 746
Certificate of Competence,
     International, 12
Cézon, Île, 695
CH 1 buoy, L648
CH 1 Lt By, 148
Chaine Tower (Larne), L589
Chanchardon, L743
Channel Islands, special notes for, 626
     weather sources, 91
Channel Lt F, R61, 148, L 622
Channels, VHF radio, 67
Chanonry, L388, 398
Chapelle, Rade de la, 781
Chapel Rock (R Severn, L516
Chapman's Pool, 199
Chapus, Le, 755
Charles Martel buoy, L683
Charlestown, 160
Chart corrections, 2
Chart Datum, 49
Chart datum, 118
Charted depth, 118
Charts, 129
     France, 652-653
     Germany, 867
     Netherlands, 822
Chart symbols, 16-17
Chassiron, Pointe de, L743, 746

Château Costaeres, 690
Château d'Oléron, Le, L743, 755
Château du Taureau, 693
Châteaulin, 700-701
Chatham, 289
Chats, Pointe des, L713
Chausey, Iles, 664
Chaussée de Beg-Meil buoy, L713
Chaussée de Sein, R63, 683, L 712
Chauveau Lt Ho/buoy, L743
Checkstone Buoy, L143, 147
Cheek Point, 567
Chelsea Harbour, 298
Chenal d'Erquy, L649
Chenal de la Grande Porte, L649, 668
Chenal de la Helle, L682, 685, 697
Chenal de la Petite Porte, L649, 668
Chenal de Rouen, L775
Chenal du Four, 685, 697
Chepstow, 532
Cherbourg, R59, 148, L 648, 650, 656
Cherbourg Radio, C76
Cherbourg tides, 658-660
Chesil Beach/Cove, 180
Chester, 494
Chester Flat buoy, L486
Chichester Harbour, 190, 216-217, 242
Chivenor, 113
Ch M, radiotelephone, VHF, 67
Christchurch, 212
Christchurch Bay, L189
Church Ope Cove, 199
City Sporthafen, L861, 884
Clacton-on-Sea, L276, 308
Clare Island, L591, 611
Cleanderry Harbour, 579
Clear Island (North Harbour), 576
Cleavel Point, 208-211
Clestran Sound, L389
Clevedon, 540
Clew Bay, L591, 611
Clifden Bay, 611
Clifden Radio, C75
Cloch Point, R56, L457
Clonakilty Bay, 575
Clovelly, 542-543
Clyde, Firth of, L457, 460
        Area chart, 469
        Area waypoints, 468
Clyde, River, 471
Clythness, L388, 392
Coastguard, Solent, 215
Coastguard, HM, 108-109
        Weather information, 90
Coast radio stations, UK, map of, 71
Coast radio stations, Dutch, 78
        introduction, 67
        search and rescue, CRS, 105
        UK, 67
        weather bulletins, 91
Cobh, 572-573
Cobh tides, 569-571
Cobo Bay, 629
Cochon, Le, L713
Cockenzie, L360, 367
Cockle buoy, L280, L328
Code flags, International Code of
        Signals, 20-21
Codling Lanby, R62, L550
Coefficients, tidal, 118, 699
Cognac/Châteaubernard, R58
Colchester, 309
Coleraine, L589, 607
Colijnsplaat, L814, 834
Coll, L422, 424, 439

Collette, La Basin, 636
Collision, action to avoid, 8
Collision avoidance, radar, 60
Collision regulations, 8
Colne, River, L276, 278, L 280, 309
Colombier, Le, L680
Colonsay, L456, 459, 461
Columbine Spit buoy, L274
Colwyn Bay, 494
Combrit, Pointe de, L713
Commercial tidal prediction, 123
Compass, deviation and variation, 26
Compass Head, R111
Competence, Certificate of,
        International, 12
Computation of rates graph, 125
Comte Jean, L812
Concarneau, L713, 722
Conduct of vessels in sight of one
        another, 9
Cone, motor sailing, 10
Coningbeg Lt V, R62
Connah's Quay, 494
Connel (Oban), 446
Connemara, 593
Conquet, Le, L682, 699
Conquet, Le Radio, C76
Contis, L744
Control of distress traffic, 104
Convergency, half, 32
Conversion factors, 46
Conwy, L486, 487, 501
Copinsay, L389
Coq, Pointe du, L713
Coquet Island, L330, 332, 351
Corbeaux, Pointe des (Île d'Yeu), L742
Corbière, La, R55, 148, L 623, 625, 638
Corblet Bay, 627
Cordemais, 735
Cordouan, L744
Cordovan Lt ho, 758
Cork, L551, 553
Cork buoy (Harwich), L276
Cork Harbour, 572-573
Cork Hole (The Wash), L328
Cork Lt By (Ireland), R62
Cork Radio, C75
Cork Sand/Rough Shoals, L276, 278, L
        280
Corne, La, L680, 689
Corniguel, 720
Cornwall, Cape, 519, 544
Cornwall, North, 144, 519
Corpach, L422, 441
Corran Narrows, L422, 441
Corryvreckan, Gulf of, 459
Corsewall Point, L458
Corton buoy, L277, L280
Coryton, 302
Cospas/Sarsat, SAR satellites, 106
Cotehele Quay, 162-163
Cotentin peninsular, W Coast, 651
Cotinière, La, L744, 755
Coubee de Nez, L623
Coubre, Pointe de la, R58, L744, 758
Coulport, 470
Couronnée buoy, La, L716
Courseulles-sur-Mer, L774, 782
Courtesy ensign, 24
Courtesy flags, 627
Courtmacsherry, L551, 553, 574
Courtown, 563
Cove, The (Scilly), 151
Coverack, 153
Covesea Skerries, L388

Cowes, L187, 216-217, **222-223**
Coz, Cap, L713, 721
Crac'h, Rivière de, L715
Craighouse (Sound of Jura), 461
Craignish, Loch, L422, 449
Craignure, 440
Craigton Point, L388, 398
Crail, L362, 368
Crammag Head, L458
Cramond, L360, 368
Cranfield Point, 595
Craobh Marina, L422, 449
Craster, 351
Creac'h, Pointe de, R63, R110, L 682,
        696
Creran, Loch, 441
Creux Harbour, 635
Crevichon, 631
Criccieth, 520
Crinan Canal, 459, 462
Croisic, Le, 718, 733
Croix, La (Le Trieux), L680, 687
Cromarty Firth, R61, L388, 392, 398,
        400
Cromer, R55, R61, L 328, 334
Cromwell Pt, L552
Crookhaven, L551, 577
Crosby Lt F, L485
CROSS, Corsen, 115
        Étel, 115
        Gris Nez, 115
        Jobourg, 115
Cross Channel distances, 134
Cross Channel passages, 253
Crosshaven, 572-573
Crossing, UK to Cherbourg/Alderney,
        650
Crossing the Irish Sea, 592
Crossing the North Sea
        from Belgium and Schelde, 821
        from German Bight to UK, 866
        from the Netherlands, 821
        Thames Estuary to Belgium /
                Netherlands, 279
Crossing to Scotland, 592
Crosslaw, R111
Cross references, Navetex, 70
        Safety, 70
        weather, 70
Cross Sand buoy, R61, L280, L 328
CROSS stations, 115
Crotoy, Le, L776, 798
Crouch, River, L275, L280, 304
Crouesty, L715, 718, 727
Crowlin Islands, L421, 436
Cruising formalities, 12
CS1, CS2, CS3, CS4 Lt Bys, 148
Cuan Sound, 448
Culag Harbour, L420
Culdrose, 113
Cullen, 395
Cullercoats, L330, 346
Cullercoats Radio, C72
Culmore Bay, 607
Cultra, 598-599
Cumberland Basin, 516, 538
Currents, ocean, 124
Cushendun Bay, 603
Customs
        HM, telephone numbers, 13
Cutler buoy, L280
Cuxhaven, L860, 879
Cuxhaven tides, 880-882

D

Dagebüll, L862, 890
Dahouet, L649, **672**
Dale Roads, 524-525
Dames, Pointe des, L742
Dangast, 877
Darnett Ness, 289
Darrynane, L552, 579
Dartmouth, L143, 146, **174**
Dartmouth tides, 171-173
Davaar Island (Campbeltown), L456, 464
Deal, L251, 262
Deauville (Trouville), L775, 777, **785**
Deben, River, L277, L280, **314, 316**
Decca, 50
Decca warnings, 72
Declination of Sun, 40
Dee, River, L485, 494
Dee Estuary, 487
Deer Sound (Orkney), 406, 408
Definitions, tides, 118
Definitions and terms, Depth, 26
    Direction, 26
    Distance, 26
    Position, 26
    Speed, 26
    Time, 26
Delfzijl, L817, 821, **849**
Dell Quay, 243
Demie de Pas, L623
Den Helder, L816, 820, **845**
Denmark (West), tidal differences, 891
Den Oever, L816, 843, 844
Derby Haven, L485
Derrible Bay, 636
Desormes buoy, 148, L623
de Val, L814
Deviation, card, 26
Devin, Pte de, L742
Devonport, 162-163
Devonport tides, 165-167
DGPS beacons in NW Europe, 49
DiÈlette, L648, **662**
Dieppe, L775, 778, **796**
Dieppe Radio, C76
Dieppe Tides, 793-795
Differential GPS, 49
Digital selective calling (DSC), 106
Digue Carnot, L776
Dinan, 670
Dinard, L649, 668, 669
Dingle, L552, 554, **580**
Dingwall, 398
Directing signals by aircraft, 112
Disabled people, facilities for, 131
Distance for a given speed and time, 36-37
Distance off, vertical sextant angle, 32, 34-35
Distance of lights, rising-dipping, 33
Distance of the horizon, 32, 33
Distance table, 132
    across Channel, 134
    across Irish Sea, 135
    across North Sea, 136
    Area 1, 146
    Area 2, 190
    Area 3, 253
    Area 4, 279
    Area 5, 333
    Area 6, 365

Area 7, 393
Area 8, 424
Area 9, 460
Area 10, 488
Area 11, 519
Area 12, 555
Area 13, 594
Area 14, 625
Area 15, 651
Area 16, 685
Area 17, 718
Area 18, 747
Area 19, 778
Area 20, 821
Area 21, 866
Distress
    alerting, 106
    signals, 11, 103
    urgency and safety traffic by RT, 70
Dittisham, 175
Divers, signals, 18-19
Dives-sur-Mer, L775, **784**
Dixcart Bay, 636
DKA buoy, L776
Documentation, of yachts, 12
    personal, 12
Dodman Point Gunnery Range, 160
Doel, L813, 827
Doëlan, L713, 717, 723
Donaghadee Sound, L588, 592, 598-599
Donegal Bay, 593
Donegal Harbour, 609
Donges, L716, 735
Doove Balg, L816
Dornie Bridge, 436
Dornoch Firth, L388, 392, 400
Dornumer-Accumersiel, L859, 865, **871**
Douarnenez, L683, 685, **706**
Douglas (IoM), L485, **500**
Douhet, Le, 755
Dover, 252, **262-263**
Dover Strait, R61, L251, 252, **267**
Dover Strait TSS, 800
Dover tides, 264-266
Downies Bay, 608
Dowsing B1D Platform, L329
Dredgers, lights, 18-19
Dressing ship, 24
Dreswick Point, 499
Drogheda, L588
Drugs, smuggling, 13
Druimyeon Bay, 461
Drummore, 487, 489
Drying heights, 118
Duart Point, L422
Dubh Artach, L422
Dubh Sgeir (Luing), L422
Dublin, L550, **558-559**
Dublin (North Wall) tides, 560-562
Dublin/Rush, R57
Dublin Radio, C75
Duddon Bar, 491
Dudgeon Lt By, R61, L329
Duke Gat, L858
Dumbarton, 471
Dumet, Île, L715, 732
Dunany Point, 595
Dunbar, L360, **366**
Dunbeacon Harbour, 577
Duncannon, 567
Duncansby Head, R56, R62, L 389, 400
Duncansby Race, 392

Dundalk, L588, 595
Dundee, R56, 374
Dundrum Bay, L588, 595
Düne, L860
Dungarvan Bay, L551, 568
    Hbr, 568, 572
Dungeness, R55, 147, L 250, 252, 262-263
Dunkerque, R59, L776, 778
Dunkerque (Port Est), **803**
Dunkerque Lanby, R63, 149, L 776
Dunkerque Radio, C76
Dunkerque Tides, 804-806
Dunkerron Harbour, 579
Dun Laoghaire, L550, **558-559**
Dunmanus Harbour, 577
Dunmore East, L551, **568**
Dunnet Head, R111, L389, 392
Dunoon, 468
Dunstaffnage Bay, L422, **446**
Dunvegan, Loch, L422, 436
Duquesne, Bassin, 796
Duration, 118
Durdle Door, L199
Durgerdam, 844
Durness, Kyle of, 405
Dursey Sound, 554
Dury Voe, 413
Dutch Glossary, 817-819
Dwarsgat, L860
DW Route Lt By EF, R63

E

E-mail, 80
Eagle Island, R57, L590, 593, 611
Earwig buoy, L486
Easington, R111
East Anglian Waypoints, L280
Eastbourne, L250, **260**
East Channel Lt By, R61, 148, L 622
East coast Radio, 558-559
East Ferry, 572-573
East Goodwin Lt F, L251
East Gunnet buoy, L360
Eastham, 494
East Lepe buoy, L187, 216-217
East Loch Roag, L421
East Loch Tarbert (Harris), L420, 425, 426
East Loch Tarbert (Mull of Kintyre), L456, 463
East Maiden, R62
East Rock buoy, L623
East Swin, L275
East Usk, L515
East Weddel Sound, 406
East Yell, L391
Eatharna, Loch (Coll), 439
EC1, EC2 and EC3 Lt Bys, R61, 148, L 622
Eckmühl (Pointe de Penmarc'h), R58, L712
Eclipse notes, 40
Écrehou, Les, L623, 625, 638-639
Ecrevière Lt By, 148, L648
Edam, 844
Eday, L390, 406
Eddystone, R61, L143, 147, 162-163
Edinburgh, R56, 367
Eeragh (Galway Bay), L591
Egilsay, L390

Eglinton/Londonderry, R57
Egmond-aan-Zee, L815
Eider River/Eiderdamm, L861, 866
Eiderstedt Radio, C78
Eierland, R59, L816
Eierlandsche Gat, 821
Eigg, 424, 438
Eil, Loch, 441
Eilean Ban, L421
Eilean Glas (Scalpay), R62, L420
Eilean Trodday, L421
Elbe No 1 Lt F, R59, R63, L 860
Elbe River, 866, **883**
Elbe Weser Radio, C78
Electronic calculators, 31
Elie, 368
Elie Ness, L361
Elizabeth Castle/St Helier, R55
Ellewoutsdijk, L813, 827
Élorn, L', River, 700-701
Elsfleth, 878
Emden, 849, L858, **868**
Emergency, definitions, 103
Emergency Position Indicating, Radio
    Beacons (EPIRBs), 106
Emergency signals and procedures.
    (RT), 103
Emergency VHF DF (Direction Finding),
    emergency DF service, 111
    emergency DF service map, 111
Ems, River, 821, L858, 865
Ems-Jade Canal, 868, 877
Emshörn, 868, 870
Emsworth, 243
English and Welsh Grounds Lt, R62,
    L515, 540
English Channel (East), 252
English Channel waypoints, 147-149
Enkhuizen, 844
Ennis, R57
Ensigns, 23, 24
Environmental guidance, 131
Epney, 534
Eport, Loch, 426
Eriboll, Loch, L389, 393, 405-406
Eriskay, L421
Erisort, Loch, L420, 423
Erme, River, 169
Erquy, L649, 672
Error in radio bearings, 53
Errors, notification of, 2
Esbjerg, 890
Esha Ness, L391
...taples, 798
...tel, River, R110, 717, **725**
Étel, Rivièra d', 714
Etive, Loch, 446
Etretat, 792
Europoort, 820, 840
Ewe, Loch, L420, 423, 432
Exe, River, L143, 146, **178**
Exercise Areas, Naval (S coast), 244
Exeter, R55
Exmouth Dock, 179
Eyemouth, L360, **365**
Eynort, Loch, 426

F

Facilities, 131
Facilities for disabled people, 131
Facsimile broadcasts, 89

Factors, tidal, 122
Fagbury buoy, L277
Fagnet, Pointe, 792
Fahan Creek, 608
Fahrenheit to celsius (centigrade), 85
Fair Head, 592
Fair Isle, L390, 393, 413, **414**
Fairlie, L458
Fairlight, R111
Fairway, Needles, 147, L186, 189, 213,
    216-217
Faix, Le, L682
Fal, River, 154
Falconet Tower, L421
Falmouth, L142, 154
Falmouth (Pendennis), C72, R111
Falmouth tides, 156-158
Fanad Head, L589, 608
Fareham, 238-240
Farne Islands, L330, 332, 352
Faslane, 470
Fastnet, R62, L551, 553, 592
Fastnet TSS, 576
Fathoms and feet to metres, 46
Faute-sur-Mer, La, 745, 752
Fawley/Hythe, L187, 226-228
Fearnach Bay Pier, 448
FÈcamp, L775, **792**
Fécamp Radio, C76
Feet to metres, metres to feet, 46
Felixstowe, L277, 279, 315, 316
Fenit Pier/Harbour, L552, 554, **580-581**
Feochan, Loch, 448
Ferlas Channel, 687
Fermain Bay, 629
Ferret, Cap, R58, L744, 765
Ferris Point, 603
Ferry services, 133
Ferryside, 530
Fersness Bay, 406
Fethaland, Point of, L391, 412
Fiddler's Ferry, 494
Fidra, R56, L360, 366
Fife Ness, R56, R111, L 362, 364
Filey, L329, 342
Findhorn, 397
Findochty, 395
Finner Camp, 114
Firth of Clyde, Area chart, 467
Firth of Forth, 366
Fischerbalje, L858, 870
Fishbourne, 243
Fisherrow, 368
Fishguard, L514, **523**
Fishing vessels, lights, 18-19
Fladda, L422
Flag etiquette, 24
Flags, International Code, 20-21
Flag signalling, International Code of
    Signals, 20-21, 66
Flamanville, 662
Flamborough, R55, R111, L 329
Flamborough Head, 332
Flannan Islands, L421, 430
Flat Holm, L515, 519, 532
Flauwerspolder, L814
Fleetwood, L484, **493**
Flotilla reporting schemes, 69
Flotta, 406
Flotte, La, L743, 752
Flushing (Falmouth), 155
Flushing (Vlissingen), L813, 820, 829
Fog signals, 11
Föhr, L862, 866, 890

Folkestone, L251, **262-263**
Folly Inn/Reach, 222-223
Fontaines Bay, Les, 636
Fontainevieille, 764
Fontarabie, Baie de, L744, 746, 768
Fontenelle Bay, 629
Foraine, La, L648
Forecaster direct, METCALL direct, 90
Forecasts
    by telephone call, 88
    coast radio stations, 91
    HM Coastguard, VHF, 90
    inshore waters, 86
    local radio, 92-93
    shipping, 86
Foreign customs procedures, 13
Foreland, 234
Fôret, Port La, L713, 721
Formby Lt F, L485, 494
Fort Belan, 502
Fort Cromwell Pt, L552
Fort de Nolle, L813
Forth, Firth of, L360, 363, **367**
Forth, North Channel buoy, R61, L360
Fortrose, 398
Fort William, L422, **441**
Foula, L391, 412, 413, **414**
Four, Chenal du, L682, 685, 697
Four, Plâteau du, L716, 718, 732
Fouras, L743
Fours, Les buoy, L623
Fowey, L142, **160**
Foyle, Lough, L589, 592, **607**
Foynes, R57, L552, 581
France, CROSS, 114
    Emergency VHF DF, 116
    Medical, 116
    Semaphore stations, 116
    SNSM, 116
    weather sources, 96-97
France, Special notes for
    Affaires Maritimes, 652-653
    Charts, 652-653
    Facilities, 652-653
    Meteo, 652-653
    Public Holidays, 652-653
    Storm signals, 652-653
    Tidal signals, 652-653
    Tourist Office, French, 652-653
    Traffic signals, 652-653
    Waterways, Inland, 652-653
Fraserburgh, L388, **394**
Freeman Channel, L328
Fréhel, Cap, L649
Freiburg, L861, 883
Fremington, 542-543
French coast radio stations, 76
French forecast areas, 97
French Glossary, 653-655
Frequencies, radio, 66
Freshwater Bay, 212
Friesche Gat, 821
Frisian Islands
    East, 865, **869**
    North, 866, 890
    West, 820, 847
Fromentine, L742, 748
Fromveur, Passage du, 696
Fuenterrabia, 768
Fugla Ness, L391
Fyne, Loch, L456, 460

G

Gaelic words, 459
Gaine, Passe de la, 689
Gairloch, Loch, L420, 423, 432
Gale warnings, 85
Galley Head, L551
Gallions Point Marina, 296
Galloper (S) Lt By, R61
Galloway, Mull of, L458, 460
Galway, Carnmore, R57
Galway Bay, 612
Galway Bay FM, 612
Galway Harbour, L591, 593, **613**
Galway tides, 614-616
Gantocks Beacon, L457, 468
Garden City buoy, L812
Gardenstown, 394
Gareloch/Rhu, L457, **470**
Garelochead, 470
Garlieston, L484, 489
Garnish Bay, 579
Garonne La, L744, 758
Garraunbaun Point, L552
Garth Pier, L391
Gas systems, 102
Gatseau, Pointe de, 755
General information, 129
German Bight Lt F, R59, R63, L 860
German coast radio stations, 78
German glossary, 862-864
Germany, SAR, 116
    weather sources, 100
Germany, Special notes for, 867
    Charts, 867
    Maritime Rescue Centres, 867
    National Water Parks, 867
    Public Holidays, 867
    Storm signals, 867
    Tourist Office, 867
    Traffic Separation Schemes, 867
    Traffic signals, 867
    Weather forecasts, 867
Gigha Island/Sound, 459, 461
Gill's Bay, 405
Gillingham, 289
Girdle Ness, R56, R61, L 362
Gironde, La, L744, 746, **758**
Girvan, L458, 476
Gladstone Dock, 494
Glandore, L551, 553, **575**
Glas, Eilean (Scalpay), R62, L420
Glasgow, L458, 471, L 484
Glasson Dock, 492
Glénan, Îles de, L713, 717, 723
Glenelg Bay, 436
Glengariff, 578
Glengarrisdale Bay, 461
Glen Head Radio, C75
Global maritime distress and safety
    system (GMDSS), 106
Global Positioning System (GPS), 48
Glossary, Dutch, 817-819
    French, 653-655
    German, 862-864
Gloucester & Sharpness Canal, 534
Glückstadt, R59, L861, 883
Gluss Isle (Sullom Voe), L391
GMDSS implementation, 105
Goeree, R59, R63, L 815
Goes, C78, L814, 834
Goil, Loch, L457, 471
Goldmer Gat/Wallet, L276, 278

Goleen, 577
Golspie, 400
Gometra, 441
Goodwin Sands, L251, 252
Goole, 340
Gore Channel, 274
Gorey (Jersey), L623, **639**
Gorleston, 322
Gorran Haven, 159
Gosport, 238-240
Gott Bay (Tiree), 439
Goulet de Brest, L683
Goulphar (Belle ële), L714
Gourdon, 376
Gourmalon, Pte de, L742
Gourock, L457, **471**
Goury, 661
GPS, 48
    differential, 49
    dilution of precision, 49
    integrity monitoring, 49
    Precise Positioning System, 48
    Standard Positioning System, 48
Gradyb Bar, 891
Graemsay Island, L389
Grandcamp-Maisy, L774, 777, **781**
Grand Charpentier, Le, L716, 733, 735
Grande Amfroque, 628
Grande Bassee de Portsall buoy, L682
Grande Fauconniere, 631
Grande Grève, La, 636
Grande Havre, 629
Grande Île (Chausey), L648, 664
Grande Vinotière, La, L682, 699
Grand Jardin, Le (St Malo), R58, 669
Grand Lejon, L649, 673
Grands Cardinaux, Les, L715
Grangemouth, L361
Granton, L360, 367
Granville, R58, L649, 651, **664**
Grassholm, 518
Grave, Pointe de, L744, 758
Grave, Pointe de, tides, 761-763
Gravelines, L776, 802
Gravesend, 294
Great Cumbrae, 467
Greatman Bay, 612
Great Ormes Head, R111
Great Saltee, 566
Great Yarmouth, R55, L277, **322**
Greencastle, 607
Green Isle, L468
Greenock, L457, 471
Greenock tides, 472-474
Greenway Quay (Dittisham), 174
Greenwich Lt V, R61, 147, L 250
Greetsiel, L858, 868
Gremista Marina, L390, 413
Grève au Lancon (Plemont), 638
Grève d'Azette, La, L623
Grève de la Ville, 636
Grève de Lecq, 638
Greystones, 558-559
Gribbin Head, 145
Grimsay, L420
Grimsby, 331, 340
Grimsby Radio, C72
Gris Nez, Cap, R110, L776, 801
Groix, Île de, R58, L713, 717, 723
Groomsport, 598-599
Grosnez Point, L623, L623, 625
Grosser Vogelsand, L860
Grosses Knechtsand, 869
Grosse Terre, Pointe de, L742
Grote Kaap, L815

Grouin-du-Cou, Pointe du, L743, 745
Grovehurst jetty, 286
Grove Point, R111
Gruney Island, R62, L391
Grunna Voe (Shetland), 412
Gruting Voe (Shetland), 412
Grutness Voe (Shetland), 412
Guernsey, R55, R111, L 622, 624
    anchorages around, 629
Guethary, L744
Guilvinec, Le, L712, 717, 719
Gunfacts, 114, 244
    Plymouth, 114
    Ship, 114
Gut buoy, L484
GW/Ems Lt F, R63, L858
Gweedore Harbour/Bunbeg, 609
Gwennap Head, 146
Gwineas, L142, 144

H

Haarlem, C78
Hague, Cap de la, R110, L648, 650
Haile Sand Fort, L329
Hale Head, 494
Hamble, River, L187, 216-217, **228**
Hamburg, 883
Hamburg, City Sporthafen, L861, **884**
Hamburg Radio, C78
Hammen, L815
Hammersmith Bridge, 294
Hamna Voe, 412
Hannaine Bay, 627
Hanois, Les, 148, L622
Hansholm, 891
Hansweert, L813, 827
Harbour information, 129
Harbour ratings, 129
Haringvliet, L814, 835
Harlesiel, L859, 865, 872
Harlingen, L816, 821, **846**
Harport, Loch, L422, 436
Harrington, 490
Harris, 423
Harris, Sound of, 426
Hartland, R111
Hartland Point, 519
Hartlepool, R111, L330, 332, **344**
Harwich, R61, L276, 278, L 280, 315
Haseldorf, 883
Hastings, 261
Hastings Radio, C72
Haulbowline, L588, 594
Haut-Blanc, Pointe du, 149, L776
Havelet Bay, 629
Havengore, 303
Haverfordwest, 524-525
Havre, Le, R59, R63, L 775, 777, **790**
Havre, Le, tides, 787-789
Havre, Le Radio, C76
Havre Gosselin, 636
Hayle, L517, 544
Hayling Island, 243
Hazards, 113
Héaux de Bréhat, Les, 148, L680, 686
Hebrides, Outer, L421, 423, 425, 426
Hebrides Radio, C73
Height of eye and distance of horizon,
    31, 33
Height of tide, 118
Heights of tide in Poole Harbour, 204

Heist, L812
Helensburgh, 470
Helford River, 153
Helgoland, L860, **886**
Helgoland Radio, C78
Helgoland tides, 887-889
Helicopter rescue, 113
Helle, Chenal de la, L682, 685, **697**
Hellevoetsluis, L815, **835**
Helmsdale, L389, **401**
Helston Buoy, L142, 147
Hendaye, L744, 746, **768**
Hengistbury Head, R111, 212
Hennebont, 725
HerbaudiЁre, Lì, L742, 745, **748**
Herm, L622, 625, **631**
Herne Bay, 285
Hestan Island, L484, 489
Heugh, The (Hartlepool), 344
Heugh, The (Holy Island), 352
Hève, Cap de la, 149, L775
Hever, River, L861, 866
Heybridge Basin, 308
Heysham, L484, 492
HF calls, Portishead Radio, 68
HF radio, 67
HIE moorings, 423, 426
High Speed Craft, 132
Higuer, Cabo, L744, 768
Hilbre Island, 494
Hillhead, 229
Hillswick, 413
Hindeloopen, 844
Hinder, Noord buoy, R63, L815
Hinkley Point, L517
Hirtshals, 891
Historic Wrecks, 130
HM Coastguard, 108-109
    MRCC's and MRSC's, 108-109
    VHF (Ch 67), 90, 108-109
    VHF DF, 111
    weather broadcasts, 108-109
HM Customs, 12
Hoedekenskerke, 827
Hoëdic, Île de, L715, 718, 726
Hoek van Holland (Hook of Holland),
    R59, L815, **840**
Hoek van Holland tides, 836-838
Hoek van Ouwerkerk, L814
Hog Island, 582
Hohe Weg, L860, 866
Højer, 891
Holburn Head, L389
Holehaven, 294
Holidays, National Public
    Belgium, 822
    France, 652-653
    Germany, 867
    Netherlands, 822
    UK, 132
Holland, see Netherlands
Holliwell Point, 304
Holm Middle Lt By, L515
Holtenau, 885
Holyhead, L486, 488, **504**
Holyhead tides, 506-508
Holy Island (Arran), L457, 466
Holy Island (Northumberland), L330,
    332, **352**
Holy Loch, L457, 471
Holywood, 598-599
Honfleur, L775, 777, **786**
Hoo, 289
Hook Head, R62, L550, 553
Hooksiel, L859, 865, **873**

Hooksielplate Cross, L859
Hook Spit, L274
Hoorn, 844
Hoo Stack, L390
Hope Cove, 169
Hopeman, L388, **396**
Horaine, La, L680, 684, 687
Horizon, distance of, 33
Hörne/Wöhrden, 883
Hörnum, L862, 891
Horse Sand Fort, L188, 238-240
Horseshoe Harbour, 576
Hoswick, L390
Houat, Île, L715, 718, 726-727
Houle-sous-Cancale, La, L649
Hourdel, Le, 798
Hourdel, Pointe du, L776, 778
Hourn, Loch, 436, 438
Hourtin, L744
House flag, 24
Houton Bay, 406, 407
Howth, L550, 553, **557**
Hoy Sound, 406, 407
Hugh Town (Scilly), 151
Huisduinen, L815
Hull, Kingston-upon-, 331, 340
Hullbridge, 304
Humber, River, R61, L329, 331, **340**
Humber Radio, C72
Hunda Sound (Orkney), 406
Hunstanton, R111, 335
Hunterston, L468, L468
Hurd Deep, 624
Hurn/Bournemouth, R55
Hurst Point, L186, 189, 212
Husum, L861, 890
Hyperbolic systems, 50
Hyskeir (Oigh Sgeir), L422
Hythe (Southampton), L187, 226-228
Hythe Range, 262-263

I

IALA Buoyage, Region A, 15
Icart Bay, 629
IJmuiden, R59, R63, L 815, **842**
IJsselmeer, 843
IJsselmeer to R. Ems, inland route, 845
Île (Island), see proper name
Île Harbour, L649, 674
Ilfracombe, L517, **542-543**
Ilfracombe Radio, C72
Immigration, arrivals from a non-EC
    country, 13
Immingham, 340
Immingham tides, 337-339
Improvements, suggestions, 2
Inchard, Loch, L420, 423, 431
Inchcolm, L360, 363, 368
Inchkeith, R56, R61, L 360, L 362, 367
Indaal, Loch, L456
Indexes, by area
    Area 1, 137
    Area 2, 181
    Area 3, 245
    Area 4, 269
    Area 5, 323
    Area 6, 355
    Area 7, 383
    Area 8, 415
    Area 9, 451
    Area 10, 479

    Area 11, 509
    Area 12, 545
    Area 13, 583
    Area 14, 617
    Area 15, 643
    Area 16, 675
    Area 17, 707
    Area 18, 737
    Area 19, 769
    Area 20, 807
    Area 21, 853
Information, general, 129
Inishbofin, L590, L591, 611
Inisheer, L591, 612
Inishgort, L591
Inishmaan, 612
Inishmore, 612
Inishnee, L591
Inishowen, L589
Inishraher Island, 611
Inishtearaght, L552
Inishtrahull, R62, L589, 607
Inmarsat, 69, 106
Inner Dowsing, R61, L329, 336
Inner Sound, 423
Inogen Lights, 315
Inshore waters forecasts, 86
Instow, L517, 542-543
Insurance, 12
Inter Bank Lt By, R61
International Certificate of Competence,
    12
International Code, 20-21, 66
    Flag signalling, 66
    Flags, 20-21
    Morse code, 20-21
    Single letter signals, 20-21
International Port Traffic Signals, 22, 23
International Regulations for Preventing
    Collisions at Sea, (1972), 8
Internet, 80
Interval, tidal, 118
Inver, Loch, L420, 431
Inveraray, L456, 463
Inverbervie, R111
Invergordon, L388, 392, 398
Inverie Bay, 438
Inverkip, L457, 468
Inverness, L388, **398**
Inverness Firth, 392
Inward Rocks, 534
Iona (Mull), 424
Iona, Sound of, 440-441
Ipswich, L277, 315
Ireland, weather sources, 92
    West Coast, 554
Ireland, Special notes for, 555
    Coast Radio Stations, 74
    Coast Rescue Service, 555
    Gaelic words, 555
    Irish Customs, 555
    Kosan gas, 555
    Marine Emergency Service, 555
    Northern Ireland Coastguard, 555
    Northern Ireland Customs, 555
    Ordnance Survey, 555
    Salmon drift nets, 555
Ireland to Scotland, crossing, 592
Irish Coast Radio Stations, 74
Irish Cruising Club, Sailing Directions,
    553, 592
Irish Sea, crossing, 592
Irish Sea distances, 135
Iroise, L', 685
Ironotter, L468

Irvine, L458, 475, 476
Isigny/Carentan, L774, **780-781**
Island FM, 638
Islay, 461
Islay, Sound of, R56, L456, 459
Islay Radio, C73
Isle of, see under proper name
Isolated danger marks, 15, 27
Itchenor, L188, 243
Itchen River, 226-228

J

Jack Sound, 518
Jade, River, L859, 865, 877
Jadebusen, 877
Jaonnet, 629
Jard-sur-Mer, L743, 752
Jaune de Glénan buoy, L713
Jersey, R111, L623, 625, 636
Jersey harbours and anchorages
    around, 638
Jersey Radio, C73, 638
Jersey West, R55
Jethou, 625, 631
Jever, R59
Jobourg, 651
Jobourg, CROSS, R110
Joburg Radio, C76
Johnshaven, L362, 376
Juist, L858, 865, 869
Jument, La (La Rance), L649
Jument, La (Ouessant), L682
Jument de Glénan, L713
Jupiter Point, 162-163
Jura, Sound of, 423, 424, L 456, 459,
    461
Jurby, L485, 487

K

Kames Bay, 466
Kampen, Rote Kliff, L862
Kats, L814, 834
Keadby, 340
Keeten B Lt By, R63
Kenmare River, 554, **579**
Kéréon (Men-Tensel), L682
Kerity, L712
Kerjean, L680, 690
Kermorvan, L682
Kernevel, 724
Kerprigent, L680, 690
Kerrera Sound, L422, 446
Ketelhaven, 844
Kettletoft Bay/Pier, 406, 408
Kew Bridge, 294
Keyhaven, 212
Kiel, Holtenau, L861, 885
Kiel Canal (Nord-Ostsee Kanal), L861,
    885
Kiggaul Bay, 612
Kijkduin, L816
Kilbaha, 581
Kilchattan Bay, 466
Kilchiaran, R111
Kilcredaune Point, L552, 554
Kilcreggan, L468
Kilkeel, L588, 595-596, 596

Kilkieran Cove, 612
Killala Bay (Inishcrone), 610
Killantringan, L458, 477
Killard Point, 596
Killary Harbour, 593, 611
Killeany Bay (Aran Islands), 612
Killiney/Dublin, R57
Killough Harbour, 596
Killybegs, L590, **609**
Killyleagh, 596
Kilmakilloge Harbour, 579
Kilmokea Point, 567
Kilmore Quay, **566**
Kilronan, 612
Kilrush, 552, 554, **582**
Kincardine, L361, 363, 367
Kingís Lynn, L328, **335**
Kingsbridge, 170
Kingston-upon-Hull, 340
Kingswear, L143, 174
Kinlochbervie, 431
Kinloss, R56
Kinnairds Head, R56, L388
Kinsale, L551, **574**
Kintyre, Mull of, L456, 459
Kip Marina, 468
Kippford, L484, 489
Kircubbin, 596
Kirkabister Ness, L390
Kirkcaldy, L361, 363, 373
Kirkcudbright, L484, 487, **489**
Kirk Sound (Orkney), 406
Kirkwall, R56, L389, **408**
Kish Bank, R62, L550
Knock John Channel, L275, 278
Knock (R Ems), 849, L858, 868
Kornwerderzand, L816, 843, 844
Kortgene, 834
Krammer Locks, 833
Krückaumündung, 883
Kruishoofd, L813
Kyle Akin (Eilean Ban), L421
Kyle of Durness, 405
Kyle of Loch Alsh, L421, 424
Kyle of Tongue, 393, 405
Kyle Rhea, L421
Kyles of Bute, L457, 460, 466

L

Laches, Les, 631
Lady Isle, L458
Laig (Eigg), Bay of, 438
Lambay Island, 592
Lamena, 760
Lamlash, **466**, L468
Lampaul (Ouessant), L682, **696**
Lancaster, 492
Land's End, R111, L142, 144, 519
Land's End, tides stream chartlets, L144
Land's End Radio, C72
Lande, La, L681, 693
Landes, missile range, 746, 765
Landguard buoy, L276
Landing signals, boats, 112
Landivisiau, R58
Langdon Battery, R111
Langeness (Nordmarsch), L862
Langeoog, L859, 865, 869, **871**
Langness Point, L485, 499
Langoz, Pte de, L712
Langstone Harbour, L188, **241**

Lann-Bihoué/Lorient, R58
Lannion, R58, L681, **692**
Lanvéoc/Poulmic, R58
Largs, L458, **467**
Larne, L589, **603**
Lateral marks, 15, 27
Lathaich, Loch/Port, 441
Lauwersmeer, 848
Lauwersoog, L817, 821, **848**
Lavernock Spit Lt By, L515
Law Hill, R111
Lawrence's Cove, 578
Lawrenny, 524-525
Laxey (IoM), L485, 499
Laxfirth, L390
Laxford, Loch, L420, 423, 431
Leconfield, 113
Lee-on-Solent, 113, 238-240
Leeds & Liverpool Canal, 495
Legal requirements for safety
    equipment, 102
LÈguÈ, Le (St Brieuc), L649, **672**
Léguer, River, L681, 692
Leigh-on-Sea, **302**
Leith, L360, 367
Leith tides, 369-371
Lelystad, C78, 844
Lemmer, 844
Lerwick, L390, **413**
Lerwick/Tingwall, R56
Lerwick tides, 409-411
Lesconil, L712, 719
Leven, Loch, 441
Leverburgh, 425
Leverets Island, 613
Lévi, Cap, 148, L648, 650
Lévi, Port de, 657
Levington, 315
Lewis, L420, 423
Lewis Radio, C73
LÈzardrieux, L680, 684, **687**
LHA Lanby, 149, L775
Libenter buoy, 148, L681, 695
Libourne, 760
Licences, radiotelephone, 66
Lightning Knoll buoy, L484
Lights, abbreviations, 28
    and shapes, 10, 18-19
    characteristics, 28
    distance off rising and dipping, 31,
        33
    navigation, 10, 18-19
    sectors, arcs of visibility, 29
    visibility, 10
Lihou Island, 629
Lillo, L813, 827
Limehouse Basin, 297
Limerick, L552, 581
Ling Hill, L329
Link calls, MF, 67
    to a yacht, 68
    VHF, 67
Linklet Bay, 406
Linnenplate, 890
Linnhe, Loch, L422, 441
Lion-sur-Mer, L774
Liscannor Bay, 554, 593, 612
Lismore, L422
List/Lister Tief, L862, 866, 891
Little Bernera, 425
Little Cumbrae, L458
Littlehampton, L250, **254**
Little Haven, 523
Little Ross, L484
Little Russel, L622, 624, **628**

Little Samphire Island, L552, 554
Liverpool, L485, 487, **494**
Liverpool tides, 496-498
Lizard Point, R55, L142, 145, 147, 152
Llanddulas, L486
Llanddwyn, Island, L486, 502
Llandudno, L485, 487, 494
Llanelli, 530
Llangwm (Black Tar), 524-525
Llanthony, 534
Lleyn Peninsula, 488, 505
Local radio stations, forecasts, 92-93
Loch, see proper name
Lochgoilhead, 470
Lochrist, L682
Locmaria, L713, 723
Locmiquélic, 724
Locquemeau, L681, 692
Locquirec, 692
Loctudy, L712, 717, **720**
Logeo, Le, 729
Logger Platform, R63
Loire, River, L716, 718, **735**
Loire Approach buoys SN1/SN2, L716
London Bridge, 278, 294
London Bridge tides, 299-301
Londonderry, R57, L589, 607
Lonehort Harbour, 578
Long, Loch, L457, 460, 471
Long Hope, 406
Longman Point, L388
Longman Yacht Haven, 398
Long Sand, L275, 278, L 280
Longships, L142, 144, 519
Longstone, L330, 332
Longy Bay, 627
Looe, L142, 145, **161**
Looe Channel (Selsey), 252
Lookout, 8, 215
Loop Head, R57, L552, 554, 581
Loran-C, 52
Lorient, 671, L714, 717, **724**
Lorient/Lann-Bihoué, R58
Lornel, Pointe de, 778
Lossiemouth, 113, L388, **396**
Lost Moan, L712
Lostwithiel, 160
Loth Bay, 406, 408
Lother Rock, R62, L389
Louet, Île, L681, 684, 693
Lower Road, L328
Lowestoft, L277, 279, L 280, **318**
Lowestoft tides, 319-321
Lowlandman's Bay, 461
Low Lee Buoy, L142, 152
Luce Bay, 487, 489
Ludaig, L421
Lühe, 883
Luing, Sound of, 424, 459
Lulworth Cove, 191, 199
Lulworth Ranges, 198
Lundy Island, L517, 519, 542-543
Lune Deep, 487
Lune River, R62, L484, 492
Lutjehorn, 869
Lybster, L389, 392, 401
Lydd, R55
Lydd Range, 261
Lydney, L516
Lyme Bay, 146
Lyme Regis, L143, **180**
Lymington, L187, **219**
Lynas, Point, R57, L486, 488
Lyness, 406
Lynher, River, 164

Lynmouth, 541
Lynmouth Foreland, R57, L517
Lynn of Lorn, L422, 441
Lyvet, 670

M

Maas, River, L815, 840
Maas, TSS/VTS, 839
Maas Center buoy, R63, L815
Maassluis, 840
Macduff/Banff, L388, **394**
Machrihanish, 461
Maddy, Loch, L420, 425, 426
Magilligan Point, 607
Magnetic variation and deviation, 26
Maidens, The, L589, 592
Mainland (Orkney), 406
Mainland (Shetland), 412
Makkum, 844
Malahide, 553, **556**
Maldon, 308
Malin Head, 593
Malin Head Radio, C75
Mallaig, L422, **438**
Malpas, 155
Man, Calf of, L485, 487
Man, Isle of, L485, 487, 499, 592
Manacles, L142, 147
Manchester Ship Canal, 495
Manech, Port, L713, 723
Manorbier, firing range, 530
Map of Areas (Ch 8), 128
Marans, 752
Marcouf, Îles St, L774, 780-781, 781
Marennes, 757
Margate, L274, 285
Marina frequency, VHF Ch M, 67
Marinecall select, 88
Marine radiobeacons, 55
Marino Point, 572-573
Maritime Safety Information, 106
Marken, 844
Markermeer, 844
Markham Field J6A, R63
Marquis, Le, 760
Marsdiep, L816, 821
Martin's Haven, 523
Maryport, L484, 487, **490**
Maseline Pier, 635
Maughold Head, L485, 487
Maumusson, Pertuis de, 746
May, Isle of, L362, 363, 368
MAYDAY, 104
Maylandsea, 308
McDermott Base, 398
Mean high and low water springs/neaps, 118
Meanings of terms, use in weather bulletins, 85
Mean level, 118
Mean Ruz, 690
Measured mile table, 38
Medemblik, 845
Medical help by radiotelephone, 69, 104
Medina, River, 222-223
Medusa Channel, 276
Medway, River, L274, **288**
Meikle Ferry, 400
Melfort, Loch, L422, **449**
Mellumplate, L859
Memmert, 865, 869, 870

Men-Joliguet, L680, 687
Men-Korn, L682
Menai Bridge, 502, 503
Menai Strait, L486, 487, **502**
Mengam, Roche, L683
Men Ruz, L681
Merrien, L713, 717, 723
Merry Men of Mey, 392
Mersea Quarters, 308
Mersey, River, L485, 487, 494
Merville buoy, L774
Meschers-sur-Gironde, 759
Mesquer, L715
METCALL Direct, 90
Meteorology, 81
MetFAX marine, 88
Methil, 373
Metres to feet, feet to metres, 46
Meule, Porte de la, L742, 749
Mevagissey, 159
Mew Island, R62, L588, 592
Mewstone, 169
MF calls to/from UK coast stations, 68
MF Radio, 67
Middelharnis, L815
Middleburg, 834
Middlesbrough, 343, 344
Mid Yell Voe, 412
Milford Haven, L514, 518, **524-525**
Milford Haven tides, 526-528
Miliau, Île, 691
Millier, Pointe de, L683
Millport, L458, 467
Mindin, Pte de, L716
Mine Head (Eire), L551, 553
Mine Head Radio, C75
Minehead (Somerset), L517, 541
Minimes, Port des, 754
Minquiers, Les, 148, L623, 625, 638-639
Minsener Oog, L859, 865, 869
Minsmere, 317
Minsterworth, 534
Mistley, 315
Mizen Head, R57, R62, L 551, 553
Mochras, 520
Moclett, Bay of, 406
Moelfre, 505
Mogueriec, L681, 693
Moidart, Loch, 438
Moines, Île-aux- (Les Sept Îles), L681, 684, 692
Mok, L816
Molène, Île de, L682, 696, 699
Molengat, L816, 821, 845
Molenhoofd, L813
Monach Islands, 425-430, 425
Monach Lt Ho, R62
Monnickendam, 844
Montoir/St Nazaire, R58
Montrose, L362, 364, **375**
Moon, Phases of, 40
Moonrise/set, 44-45
Moray Firth, 392
Morbihan, Golfe du, L715, 718, **728**
Morecambe, L484, 487, 492
Morgat, L683, **705**
Morlaix, L681, 684, **693**
Morsalines, L774, 779
Morse code, 20-21
Mortagne-sur-Gironde, 759
Mortimers Deep, L360
Mostyn Quay, L485, 494
Moulin Blanc, 700-701
Moulin Huet Bay, 629
Moul of Eswick, L390

Mount's Bay, 144
Mousehole, L142, 144, 152
Moutons, Île-aux-, L713, 717, 723
Moville, L589, 607
Moving Prohibited Zone, 215
MPC Lt By, 148, L776
Muck, 424, 438
Muckle Flugga, L391
Muckle Holm, L391
Muckle Skerry (Orkney), 407
Muckle Skerry (Shetland), L390
Muglin's Sound, L550, 553
Mühlenberg, L861, 884
Muiden, 844
Muiderzand, 844
Mull, L422, 424, 440
Mull, Ross of, 424
Mull, Sound of, L422, 424, 440
Mullaghmore, 610
Mullion Cove, 153
Mull of Galloway, L458
Mull of Kintyre, L456, 459, 592
   tidal streams, 465
Mulroy Bay, L589, 593, 608, 609
Mumbles Head, L515, 518, 531
Mupe Bay (Worbarrow Bay), 191
Mussel Bank buoy, L486
MWR FM, 608
Mylor, 155

N

Naarden, 844
Nab Tower, 147, L188, 190, 216-217, 241
Naburn, 341
Nairn, L388, **398**
Na Keal, Loch, 441
NAM Field Platform K14-FA-1, R63
Nantes, 671, 735
Narlwood Rocks, 534
Narrow channels, 8, 10
Nash Point, R57, L515, 518
National Coastwatch Institution, 112
National ensigns, 22
Naval Exercise Areas (S coast), 244
Navigational warnings, 70
Navigation by calculator, 31
Navigation lights, 10, 18-19
NAVTEX, 86
   areas, 87
   message categories, 87
   stations, 87
Neath, River, L515, 531
Nebel, L862
Nedd, Loch, 431
Needles Channel, L186, 189, **213**, 216-217
Neeltje Jans, 834
Neist Point, L422
Nene, River, L328, 335
Nes (Ameland), C78, L817, 846
Nessmersiel, L859, 865, 868
Netherlands, Passage Info, 820
   SAR, 116
   weather sources, 99
Netherlands, map of, 79
Netherlands, Special notes for, 822
   Inland waterways, 822
   Maritime Rescue Coordination, 822
   Public Holidays, 822

Storm signals, 822
   Traffic signals, 822
Neuenschleuse, L861, 884
Neuharlingersiel, L859, 871, 872
Neuwerk, L860, 869
Neuwe Waterweg, 839
Nevis, Loch, 438
Newarp Lt F, R61, L281, L 328
Newbiggin, 350
Newburgh, 374
Newcastle (Co. Down), 595-596, 596
Newcastle-upon-Tyne, 346
Newcome buoy, L277
New Galloway, R56
New Grimsby, 151
New Harbour (Galway), 613
Newhaven, R111, L250, **260**
New Hythe, 289
Newlyn, **152**
Newport (Gwent), L516, 532
Newport (IoW), **222-223**
Newquay (Cornwall), L517, 544
New Quay (Dyfed), L514, 522
New Ross, 567
Newry (Victoria Lock), 595
Newton, R111
Newton Ferrers, 169
Newton Haven, 351
Newtown River, **220**
Neyland, 524-525
NHR-S buoy, L812
NHR-SE buoy, L812
Nieblum, L862
Nieuwe Sluis (Westerschelde), L813
Nieuwpoort (Nieuport), R59, L812, 820, **823**
Nigg Sands buoy, L388
Niton Radio, C72
Nividic (An-Ividig), L682, 696
Noëveillard, Pte de, L742, 747
Noirmont Point, L623, L623
Noirmoutier, Île de, L742, 745, 748
No Man's Land Fort, L188, 216-217, 238-240
Noorderhoofd (Walcheren), L813
Noord Hinder Lt, R63, L815
Noordwijk-aan-Zee, L815
Nord-Ostsee Kanal (Kiel Canal), L861, 885
Norddeich, L858, 865, 868, 870
Norddeich Radio, C78
Norddorf, L862
Nordenham, 878
Norderney, L858, 865, 869, **870**
Nordfriesland Radio, C78
Nordholz, R59
Nordmarsch, L862
Nordstrand, L861, 866
Nordzee Kanaal, L815, 842
Norfolk, North, L328, 331
Norfolk Broads, 279, 318, 322
North Bay, 406, 426
North Berwlck, 363, 368
North Carr buoy, L362
North Channel (Needles), L186, 213
North Channel TSS, 592, 604
North Connel (Oban), R56
North Cornwall, 144
North Denes/Gt Yarmouth, R55
NE Goodwin Lt By, R61, L251
North Edinburgh/Knob Channels, L274
North Fambridge, 304
North Foreland, R55, R111, L 251, 252, 267, 278, 284
North Foreland Radio, C72

North Haisbro Lt By, R61
North Havra, L391
North Head buoy, L186, 216-217
Northney, 243
North Rhyl buoy, L486
North Rona, L389
North Ronaldsay, R62, 406
North Scroby buoy, L281, L328
North Sea
   common shipping forecast areas, 99
   distances, 136
   Passages, Forth to Norway and Baltic, 364
   Hartlepool to German Bight, 333
   Hartlepool to South Netherlands, 333
North Sea (S), Wpts, 852
North Shields, L330, 346
North Sunderland (Seahouses), L330, 332, 352
North Unst (Muckle Flugga), L391, 412
North Well buoy, R61, L328
Norwick, C72
Noss Mayo, 169
Notice of departure, 13
Not under command, vessels, 10, 18-19
NP 159 harmonic method, 123
Numbering system, 1

O

Oaze Deep, L274, 278
Oban, **446**
Oban Radio, C73
Oban tides, 443-445
Octeville/Le Havre, R59
Odet, R, 720
Offshore marks, 250
Oigh Sgeir (Hyskeir), L422
Oil and gas installations, 333
Oland, L862
Old Grimsby, 151
Old Head of Kinsale, R57, L551, 553
OlÈron, Œedi, L743, 746, **755**
Olna Firth, 412
Omonville-la-Rogue, L648, 650, **661**
Oostende (Ostend), R59, L812, 820, **824**
Oostende (Ostend) Radio, C78
Oosterschelde, L814, 820, **833**
Oostmahorn, L817, 848
Oranjeplaat, 834
Oranjesluizen, 843
Ore/Alde, River, L277, **316**
Orford Haven/Quay, 316
Orford Ness, L277, 279, L 281, 317
Orford Ness Radio, C72
Orkney Islands, L389, 393, **406**
Orlock Head, R111
Ormond's Harbour, 579
Ornsay, L421
Oronsay, 459
Orsay (Rhinns of Islay), R56, L456, 461
Ortac Rock, 624
Orwell, River, L277, **314**
Osea Island, 308
Ost Pic, L', 651, L680, L 681, 686
Otterndorf, 884
Otterswlck, 406
Oudeschild, L816, 821, **846**
Ouessant, Île d' (Ushant), R58, R63,

148, 684, 696
Ouessant, Île d' (Ushant) Radio, C76
Ouessant NE Lt By, R63, 148, L 682
Ouessant SW Lanby, R58, R63, 148, L 682
Ouistreham, L774, 777, **783**
Ouse, River, 331
Outer Crouch, 304
Outer Gabbard buoy, R61, L277, L 281
Outer Tongue Lt By, R61
Out Skerries (Shetland), L390, L391, 412
Overtaking, 9
Owenboy River, 572-573
Owers, The, L250, 252
Oxcars, 367
Oyster Haven, L551, 574
Oyster Island, 610

P

Paal, L813, 827
Padstow, L517, 519, **544**
Pagham, 254
Paignton, L143, 176
Paimboeuf, L716
Paimpol, L680, 684, **686**
Paimpol Radio, C76
Palais, Le, L714, **726**
Pallice, La, L743, 754
Palmyre, La, L744, 758
Paluden, 695
PAN-PAN, 104
PAN-PAN medico, 104
Paon, Le, L680
Papa Sound (Stronsay), L390, 393, 408
Papa Westray, 406
Par, 160
Paris, 791
Parquette, La, L683
Passage Information, 129
    Area 1, 144
    Area 2, 189
    Area 3, 252
    Area 4, 278
    Area 5, 331
    Area 6, 363
    Area 7, 392
    Area 8, 423
    Area 9, 459
    Area 10, 487
    Area 11, 518
    Area 12, 553
    Area 13, 592
    Area 14, 623
    Area 15, 650
    Area 16, 684
    Area 17, 717
    Area 18, 745
    Area 19, 777
    Area 20, 820
    Area 21, 865
Passage planning, check list, 30
    proforma, 30
Pauillac, L744, 759, 760
Peel, L485, **499**
Pegal Bay, 406
Pellerin, Le, 735
Pellworm, L861, 866, 890
Pembrey firing range, 530
Penally Range, 530
Penarth, L515, **532**

Pendeen, L517, 519
Pendennis, R111, 155
Pendennis Radio, C72
Pendine firing range, 530
Pénerf, L715, 718, 731
Penfret (Îles de Glénan), L713, 717, 722
Peninnis Head, L142
Penlan, L715, 731
Penlee Point, 162-163
Penmarc'h, Pointe de, R58, L712, 717
Pen Men (Île de Groix), R58, L713, 717, 723
Pennan Cove, 394
Penryn/Flushing, 155
Pentland Firth, L389, 392
Pentland Skerries, L389, 392
Penzance, R55, L142, **152**
Penzé, River, 693
Percelle Bay, 629
Perdrix, Les (Lézardrieux), L680
Perdrix, Les (Loctudy), L712
Perranporth, 544
Perros-Guirec, L680, 684, **690**
Personal safety equipment, 102
Perth, 374
Pertuis Breton, 745, 752
Pertuis d'Antioche, 745
Peterhead, L362, 364, **381**
Petit Bot Bay, 629
Petite-Muette, La (Dahouet), L649, 672
Petite Barge buoy, La, L742
Petite Canupe, L622, 628
Petite Foule, L742
Petit-Minou, Pointe du, L683, 700-701
Petit Port, 629
Petits Impairs, Les, L716
Petroland Platform F15-A, R63
Phases of the Moon, 40
Phonetic alphabet, 20-21
Pierowall, L390, 406, 407, 408
Pierre-Moine, La, L742
Pierre Noire buoy, La, L648
Piet, De, 834
Pilier, Île du, L742, 748
Pillar Rock Pt, L458
Pilot vessels, lights, 18-19
Pin Mill, 315
Pinnau-Neuendeich, 883
Pinnaumündung, 883
Piriac-sur-Mer, L715, **732**
Pittenweem, 368
Placid Field Platform PL-K9C-PA, R63
Pladda, L458
Plate, La, L683, L712
Plateau de la Lambarde, L716
Plateau de la Recherche, L715
Plateau des Minquiers, L623, 638-639
Plateau de St Jacques, L715
Plateau du Four, L716
Plateau du Grand Mont, L715
Platform L7, C78
Platresses, Les, L682
Platte (Guernsey), L622
Platte Fougère, R61, 148, L 622, 628
Platte Rock (Jersey), L623
Platte Sallne Bay, 627
Pléneuf-Val-André, L649
Plockton, **437**
Plouër, 670
Plougasnou Radio, C76
Ploumanacíh, L681, 684, **690**
Plymouth, R55, L143, 145, **162-163**
Point, see proper name
Pointe (Point), see proper name
Pollendam, L816, 846

Polperro, L142, 161
Pont Aven, 723
Pont l'Abbé, 720
Pont l'Abbé Radio, C76
Pontrieux, **688**
Pontusval, L681, 693
Poole Bay, 189
Poole Fairway Lt By, 147
Poole Harbour, L186, **208-211**, 216-217
Poole Harbour, heights of tide, 204
Poole Harbour Entrance, 199
Poole tides, 205-207
Porlock Bay/Weir, 541
Pornic, L742, 745, **747**
Pornichet, L716, 718, **734**
Pors Poulhan, L712
Portaferry, 596
Port à la Jument (Sark), 636
Port Askaig (Islay), 459, 461
Portavogie, L588, 596
Portbail, L648, 651, **663**
Port Beni, 689
Port Blanc (Côtes d'Armor), L680, 689
Port Blanc (Morbihan), 728
Port Bloc, L744, **760**
Port Cardigan, L514, 523
Portcé, L716
Port Clos, 686
Port d' Étel, 724
Port de Comberge, L716, 735
Port de la Gravette, L716, 735
Port de la Meule, 749
Port de Lévi, L648, 657
Port de Pavé de Charron, L743
Port de Rosmeur, 706, L716
Port-des-Barques, L743, 756
Port Dinlaen, L486
Port Dinorwic, 488, 502
Port du Becquet, 657
Port du Plomb, L743
Port Edgar, L361, **367**
Portelet Bay, 629, 638
Port Ellen (Islay), R56, L456, 459, **461**
Port-en-Bessin, R59, L774, **782**
Port-en-Bessin Radio, C76
Port Erin (IoM), L485, 499
Port és Saies, 636
Port Glasgow, L458, 471
Port Gorey (Sark), 636
Port Guillaume (Dives), 784
Port Haliguen, L714, 718, **726**
Porthcawl, 518, 531
Porth Dinllaen, 488, 505
Porthgain, 523
Porthleven, L142, 144, 153
Porthmadog, L514, **521**
Porth Trecastell, 505
Porth Ysgaden, 505
Portishead, L516, **540**
Portishead Radio, C73
Port Joinville, L742, **749**
Portknockie, 395
Port La Fûret, **721**
Portland, R55, 113
Portland, tidal streams, 192-193
Portland, Tides, 194-196
Portland Bill, 191
Portland Harbour, **191**
Portland Race, 189
Port Làthaich, L422
Port Launay, 700-701
Port Louis, 724
Portmagee, L552, 580
Portmahomack, 392, **400**
Port Manech, L713, 723

Port Maria, L714, 718, 726
Portmellon, 159
Portmore, 607
Portnafrankagh, 611
Port Navalo, L715, 727, 729
Port Nord de Fouras, L743
Port operations, radiotelephone, 69
Portpatrick, L458, **477**
Portpatrick Radio, C73
Port Racine, 661
Portree, L421, **436**
Portrieux, 674
Portrieux (St Quay), 651
Portrush, L589, 592, **606**
Portsall, L682, 695, 699
Portscatho, 159
Portsmouth, L188, 190, 216-217, **238-240**
Portsmouth tides, 235-237
Port Solent, 240
Portsoy, L388, 395
Port St Denis, 755
Portstewart, L589, 606
Port St Mary, L485, **500**
Port Talbot, 531
Port Traffic signals, 22
Port Tudy, L713, 717, **723**
Port William, L484
Portzic, Pointe de, L683, 700-701
Porz-Don, Pointe de, L680, 686
Position fixing systems, 48
Pottery Pier, 208-211
Poulains, Pointe de, L714, 717
Pouldohan, Baie de, L713
Pouldu, Le, 723
Pouliguen, Le, L716, **733**
Poulmic/Lanvéoc, R58, 700-701
Prawle, R111
Precautions, 102
Precautions using waypoints, 53, 130
Present weather reports, 91
    Map, 94
Press forecasts, 90
Preston marina, 493, 494
Prestwick, 113
Primel, Anse de, 693
Primel-TrÈgastel, L681, **693**
Prince's Channel, L274, 284
Procedures, radiotelephones, 66
Prowords, radiotelephones, 66
Publications associated, 1
Puffin Island, 488, 503
Puilladobhrain, 448
Pund, Point of the, L391
Pwllheli, L514, **520**

Quadrantal error, 53
Quai Joannes Couvert, L775
Quai Roger Meunier, L775
Q flag, quarantine, 13
Quarantine regulations, 13
Queen's Channel/Four Fathoms
    Channel, L274, 284
Queenborough, 287
Queen Elizabeth II Marina, L622
Quiberon, Baie de, L715, 717, 718, 727
Quillebeuf, 791
Quimper/Pluguffan, R58
Quineville buoy, L774
Quoile Barrier, 596

R

Raasay, Sound of, L421, 423
Racons (Radar beacons), 60, R61
Radar, 60
    as a navigation aid, 60
    for collision avoidance, 60
    in yachts, 60
    reflectors, 102
Radar beacons (Racons), 60, 61
Rade de Brest, Le, 700-701
Rade de la Chapelle, 780-781, 781
Radio communication, 66
Radio direction finding, marine, 55
Radio distress signals, 103
Radio Kerry, 566
Radio, port operations and VTS, 69
Radio Solent, 215
Radiotelephone, 130
    licences, 66
    link calls, 68
    regulations, 66
Radiotelephony, 66
Radio time signals, 80
Ramark, 60
Rame Head, R111, 145, 162-163
Ramelton, 608
Ramsey (IoM), L486, **501**
Ramsey Sound, 518, 523
Ramsgate, L251, **268**
Rams Head, L391
Ramsholt, 316
Rance, River, L649, 651, **670**
Range, of tide, 118
Ranza, Loch, 466
Rapness, 406, 408
Rathlin Island, tidal streams, 605
Rathlin Island/Sound, L590, 592, 604
Rathlin O'Birne, L590
Rathmullan, L589, 608
Ratings, harbour, 129
Rattray Head, R61, L362, 364, L 388, 392
Ravenglass, L484, 491
Raz de Sein, 683, L712
RDF (Radio direction finding) beacons, 53
RDF and DGPS beacons, map, 54
Ré, Île de, L743, 745, 753
Ré, Île de Radio, C76
Record of amendments, 2
Red Bay, L589, 592, 603, 604
Redbridge, 226-228
Redcar, L329, 332
Redkirk, 489
Reflée buoy, L622
Registration, 12
Regnéville, L648, 664
Regulations, radiotelephone, 66
Regulations for Prevention of Collisions
    at Sea, 8
Rendsburg, L861, 885
Renfrew, 471
Reports of present weather, 89, 106
Response to a distress call, 106
Restricted visibility, conduct in, 10
    sound signals, 11
Restronguet, 155
Reuille, La, 760
Rhea, Kyle, 424
Rhinns of Islay, R56, L456
Rhiw, R111
Rhoose/Cardiff, R57

Rhubha' a' Mhail, L456
Rhubha' Cadail, L420
Rhum, L422, 424, 438
Rhu Narrows, L456, 470
Rhyl, L485
Ribble, River, L484, 487, **494**
Richard, 760
Richborough, 268
Richelieu, Tour (La Rochelle), R58, L743, 754
Richmond Lock, 294
Riddon, Loch, 466
Riffgat, 870
Rijn Field Platform P15-B, R63
Rinealon Point, L552
Ringaskiddy, 572-573
Ringstead Bay, 199
Rise/Fall of tides, 118
Risk of collision, 8, 10
Rivedoux-Plage, L743
RNLI, 107
Roach, River, 303
Roancarrigmore, L551
Roaring Middle Lt F, L328
Roaring Water Bay, 576
Robbennordsteert, L860
Robert, Point, L623, 636
Roberts Cove, 572-573
Roc, Pointe du, L649
Roche Bernard, La, 718, 731
Rochebonne, L649, 668
Rochebonne, Plateau de, L742, 745
Rochefort, L743, **756**
Rochelle, La, R58, L743, **754**
Rocher d'Antioche, L743
Rochers Déan, 674
Roches Douvres, Les, 148, L680, 684
Roches du Joanne buoy, L742
Roches Gautier buoy, L622
Roche's Point, L551, 572-573
Rochester, 288, 289
Rochford, 303
Rockabill, 582, L588
Rockall, L420, 430
Rocque, La, 638
Rodel, R111
Rohein, Le, L649, 672
Roker Pier, L330, 345
Rømø Havn, 866, 891
Rona, 405
Rona, South, L421, 424, 436
Ronaldsway (IoM), R57
Roompotsluis, L814, **833**, 834
Roscoff, L681, 684, **694**
Rosédo (Île de Bréhat), R58, L680, 688
Rosehearty, 394
Rose Ness, L389
Rosière Steps, 631
Rosneath, L457, L468, 470
Rosslare Harbour, L550, **565**
Rosslare Radio, C75
Rosyth, L361, L361, 367
Rote Kliff (Kampen), L862
Rotheneuf, L649, 669
Rothesay, 457, **467**
Rotten Island, L590, 609
Rotterdam, C78, 815, **840**
Rouen, 791
Rouen Radio, C76
Rouge de Glénan buoy, L713
Rouge Terrier, 636
Round Island, R55, L142, 150
Roundstone Bay, 612
Rousay, 406
Roustel Tr, L622, 628

Route du Gois Causeway, L742
Rova Head, L389
Royal Air Force, SAR, 107
Royal Navy, SAR, 107
Royal Quays marina, 346
Royal Sovereign, 147, L250, 252, 260
Royan, L744, 759
Royan Radio, C76
Rozel Bay, L623, 638
RTE Radio 1, 608
R/T procedures, 66
Rubha A'Bhodaich, 467
Rubha A'Mhail, 461
Rubha Na Leacaig, L420
Rubha nan Gall, L422
Rubha Reidh, L420
Rule of the road, 8
Rule of Twelfths, 122
Rumble Rock, R62
Runnaneun Point, L458
Runnel Stone Lt By, 147
Runswick Bay, 343
Rüschkanal, L861, 884
Rush/Dublin, R57
Russel, Big, L622, 624, 628
Russel, Little, L622, 624, 628
Rüstersiel, 873
Ruthenstrom, 883
Rutland North Channel, L590
Ryan, Loch, L458, 476
Ryde (IoW), L188, 216-217, 233
Rye, L250, 252, 261

S

Sablanceaux, Pte de, L743
Sables DíOlonne, Les, L742, 751
Safe speed, 8
Safety, 101
Safety equipment, 102
Safety philosophy, 102
Safety Scheme, Yacht & Boat, 112
Safety signal, 104, 105
Safe water marks, 15, 27
Saignie Bay, 636
Sailing vessels, rule of the road, 9
Saint's Bay, 629
St Abb's Head, 365
St Abbs, 366
St Alban's Head, 189, 199
St Andrews, 374
St Ann's Head, R111, L514, 524-525
St Annaland, L814, 834
St Anthony Head, L142, 147, 154
St Aubin (Jersey), L623, 638
St Barbe, L742
St Bees Head, L484
St Brelade Bay, 638
St Briac, L649
St Brides Bay, 518, 523
St Brieuc, L649, 672
St Cast, L649, 672
St Catherine's Point, R55, 147, L 188, 190
St Catherine Bay, 638-639
St Denis d'Oléron, L743, 755
Ste Anne, Pte, 746
Ste Evette, 719
St George's Channel, 518
St Germain-sur-Ay, 663
St Germans, 162-163, 164
St Gildas, Pointe de, R58, 716, 718,

735, L 742
St Gilles-Croix-de-Vie, L742, 750
St Gowan Lt By, R62, L515
St Guénolé, L712, 719
St Helen's Fort, L188, 234
St Helen's Pool, 151
St Helier, R55, L623, 625, 636
St Helier tides, 640-642
St Herblain Radio, C76
St Hilaire-de-Riez Radio, C76
St Inglevert, R59
St Ives, L517, 519, 544
St Jacques-en-Sarzeau, L715
St Jean-de-Luz, L744, 746, 767
St Jean de Monts, L742
St John's Point, L588
St Katharine Haven, 297
St Kilda, R56, L421, 430
St Malo, 148, L649, 651, 668
St Malo Radio, C76
St Malo tides, 665-667
St Marcouf, Îles, L774, 780-781, 781
St Margaret's Hope, 406
St Martin's Pt, L622, 624
St Martin, Anse de, 650
St Martin, Œle de RÈ, L743, 753
St Martin, Pointe, L744, 746
St Mary's (Orkney), 406, 407
St Maryís (Scilly), R111, 144, 150, 151
St Mathieu, Pointe de, R58, L682
St Mawes, 155
St Mawgan, R57
St Michael's Mount, 145, 152
St Monans, L361, 368
St Nazaire, R58, R63, L 716, 718, 735
St Nazaire Radio, C76
St Nicolas, 758
St Ninian's Bay, 466
St Patrick's Causeway, 518
St Peter (River Eider), L861
St Peter Port, R55, L622, 624, 630
St Peter Port Radio, C73
St Peter Port tides, 632-634
St Philipsland, L814, 834
St Quay Portrieux, L649, 651, 674
St Sampson (Guernsey), L622, 629
St Servan, 669
St Thomas Head, 540
St Tudwal's, L514, 518, 520
St Vaast-la-Hougue, L774, 777, 779
St ValÈry-en-Caux, L775, 792
St ValÈry-sur-Somme, L776, 798
Saire, Pointe de, L774, 777, 779
Salcombe, L143, 170
Salen (Loch Sunart), 439
Salen (Mull), 440
Saltash, 162-163
Saltee Sound, 553
Salt Scar buoy, L329
Salutes, 24
Sanda Island, R62, L456
Sanday (Orkney), L390, 406
Sandend Bay, 395
Sandettié Bank, 778
Sandettié Lt F, R61, 147, L 776
Sandown, 234
Sandwich, 268
Sandwick, R111
Sandwick Bay, L420, 425
Sangatte, L776
SAR, Belgium, 116
    France, 114
    Germany, 116
    Ireland, 114
    Netherlands, 116

Sark, L623, 625, 635
Sark, anchorages around, 636
Sarn-y-Bwch, 518
Sarn Badrig Causeway (St Patrick's), L514, 518
Sas van Goes, L814, 834
Satcom, 69
Satellite communication, 69
Satellite systems, 48
Saundersfoot, L515, 518, 529
Sauzon, 726
Saye Bay, 627
Scalasaig (Colonsay), L456, 461
Scalloway, L391, 413, 414
Scapa Bay, 406
Scapa Flow, 393
Scarborough, L329, 332, 342
Scarinish, L422
Scatsa Ness, R56, L391
Scattery Island, 582
Scharhörn, 869, 879
Schelde, River, L813, 820, 827, 833
Scheur-Zand buoy, L812
Scheveningen, L815, 841
Scheveningen Radio, C78
Schiermonnikoog, L817, 821, 849
Schilbolsnol, L816
Schillig, L859, 873
Schleuseninsel, L861
Schlucter, 870
Schlüttsiel, L862
Schone Waardin, L813
Schouwenbank buoy, R63, L814
Schulau, L861, 883, 884
Schull, L551, 553, 577
Schulpengat, L815, 821, 845
Schwinge, River, 883
Scilly, Isles of, R55, L142, 144, 150
Scolpaig, 425
Scotland, SW, 487
Scotstown Head, R56
Scrabster, L389, 405
Scurdie Ness, R61, L362, 364, 375
Sea areas, shipping forecasts, 82
Seaham, L330, 345
Seahouses (North Sunderland), L330, 352
Seal Mills, 538
Seaport Marina, 842
Search and rescue (SAR)
    Aircraft signals, 112
    Organisation, 108-109
    Search procedures, aircraft, 112
Sea Reach buoy, R61, L275
SE Chequer Lt F, L329
Secondary ports, 119
Second Severn crossing, L516
Securité, 104, 105
Seil Sound, 448
Sein, Chaussée de, R63, L712, 717, 719
Sein, Île de, R58, L712, 717, 719
Sein, Raz de, 712, 717
Seine, Estuaire de la, 777
Seine, River, 791
Sella Ness, L391
Selsey Bill, R111, 243, 252
Sénéquet, Le, L648, 663
Sept Îles, Les, L681, 684, 692
Seudre, River, L743, 757
Seven Stones Lt V, R61, L142, 144
Severn, River/Estuary, L516, 519, 534
Severn Bridges, The, 534
Sèvre Niortaise, L743
Sextant angles, horizontal, 32

Sextant angles, vertical, 32, 34-35
Shaldon Bridge, 177
Shambles, The, 147, L186, 189
Shannon, 114
Shannon, Estuary, 554, **581**
Shannon, River, L552, 581
Shannon Radio, C75
Shapes, 10, 18-19
Shapinsay (Orkney), 407
Sharpness, L516, L516, 519, **534**
Sheephaven, 589
Sheep Haven, 593, 608, 609
Sheep's Head, L551, 554
Sheerness, L274, 288
Sheerness tides, 290-292
Shell, Loch, L420, 425, 426
Shell Bay, 631
Shell Island (Mochras), L514, 520
Sherkin Island, 576
Shetland Islands, L390, 393, **412**
Shiant Islands, 426
Shieldaig, 436
Shillay, 425
Shipping forecasts, 86, 91
Shipping forecasts record, 83
Ships Radio Licence, 66
Shirehampton, 538
Shivering Sands Tower, L274
Shoeburyness, R111, 278
Shoots, The, L516, 519, 534
Shoreham, R55, L250, 252, **255**
Shoreham tides, 256-258
Shornmead, L275
Shotley, L276, 315
Shuna, Loch, 449
Signals
    aircraft on SAR operations, 113
    shore lifesaving equipment, 112
    single letter, 20-21
    standing into danger, 112
    when towing, 10, 18-19
Signals, local, 238-240
SIGNI, buoyage, 844
Silloth, L484, 487, 490
Skadan (Fair Isle), L390, 414
Skegness, L329, 336
Skeld Voe, L391
Skellig Rocks, 554
Skelmorlie, L468
Skerries, Out (Shetland), L390
Skerries, The (Anglesey), R62, L486, 488
Skerries, The (Dublin), 594
Skerries, Ve (Shetland), R62, L390
Skerries Bank (Start Bay), 146
Skerries Bay (Meath), L588, 592
Skerries TSS, 505
Skerry, Outer (Yell Sound), L391
Skerry, Sule, L389
Skerry of Ness, L389
Skerryvore, L422
Sketrick Island, 596
Skilligs Rock, L552
Skipport, Loch, 425, 426
Skokholm Island, L514, 518
Skomer Island, 518, 523
Skroo (Fair Isle), L390, 414
Skye, Isle of, L422, 423, 436
Skye Radio, C73
Slaughden Quay, 316
Sleat, Sound of, L421, 424, 438
Sligachan, Loch, L421
Sligo, R57, R62, L 590, **610**
Slyne Head, L591, 593, 611
Small Craft Edition, Admiralty Notices to

Mariners, 2
Small Craft Warning Service (strong winds), 92-93
Small Isles, L422, 424
Smalls, The, R62, L514, 518
Small Ships Register, 12
Smalls TSS, 524-525
Smerwick Harbour, 580
Smiths Knoll Lt By, R61
Snaefell, R111
Snape, 316
Sneem, 579
Snizort, Loch, 423, 436
Soay, 436
Socoa, 767
Soldian Rock buoy, L390
Soldier's Bay, 629
Soldiers Point (Dundalk), 595
Solent, The, 189, 190
Solent area, diagram, **214**
Solent Bank, 220
Solent Coastguard, 215
Solent waypoints, 216-217
Solthörner Watt, L859
Solva, 523
Solway Firth, L484, 487
Somme, Baie de, 778, 798
Sorel Point, L623
Sound of Harris, L420
Sound signals, for distress purposes, 103
    International Regulations for
        Preventing Collisions at Sea, 11
Sources of weather information, 86
Sous CROSS Soulac, 115
Souter Point, R56
Southampton, L187, **226-228**
Southampton tides, 230-232
Southampton VTS, 215
Southampton Water, 190
South Bay, 406
South Bishop, R55, L514, 518
South Dock Marina, **296**
Southend (Kintyre), 466
Southend-on-Sea, R55, L275, **302**
Southerness Point, 489
South Ferriby, 341
South Gare (River Tees), L330
South Goodwin Lt F, L251, 268
Southport, 494
South Queensferry, 367
South Rock, 596
South Rock Lt F, R57, R62, L 588, 592
South Ronaldsay, 406
Southsea Marina, 241
South Stack, L486, 488
SW Shingles buoy, L186, 216-217
South Wick, 406
Southwold, L277, 279, **317**
Spanish Ledge Lt By, 151
Special ensigns, 24
Special marks, 15, 27
Special tidal problems, Swanage to
    Selsey, 200-202
Spelve, Loch, 441
Spiekeroog, L859, 865, 869, 871
Spit Sand Fort, 238-240
Spring tides, 118
Spurn Head/Lt F, R61, L329, 340
Stackpole Quay, 529
Stade, L861, 883
Stadersand, 883
Staffa, 441
Standard tidal ports, 119, 126
Standard times, 80, 118

Stansore Pt, 221
Staosnaig, Loch (Colonsay), 461
Starcross, 179
Start Point, L143, 145, 170
Start Point (Sanday), L390
Start Point Radio, C72
Stavenisse, L814, 834
Stavoren, 844
Steep Holm, 532
Stellendam, 814, 820, **835**
Stiff, Baie du, 696
Stiff, Le (Ouessant), L682
Stirling, 367
Stoer Head, L420
Stoer, Point of, 423
Stonehaven, L362, 364, **376**
Stonehaven Radio, C72
Stör/Beidenfleth, L861, 883
Stores, 13
Störloch/Borsfleth, L861, 883
Storm signals, visual, 91
Storm tide warning service, 126
Stornoway, R56, 113, L 420, **425**
Stornoway tides, 427-429
Stour, River, L276, **314**
Straight Point, 146, 179
Strangford Lough, L588, **596-597**
Stranraer, L458, 476
Strathy Point, L389
Straw Island, L591
Streams, in rivers, 124
    rates, 124
Stroma (Swilkie Point), L389, 392, 405
Stromness, L389, **407**
Strong wind warnings, 106
Stronsay, L390, **408**
Strontian, 439
Strumble Head, L514
Studland Bay, 208-211
Subfacts, 114, 244
Subfacts (NW Scotland), 423
Submarine exercise areas
    NW Scotland, 450
    SW Scotland/Irish Sea, 477-478
    W English Channel, **168**
Submarine hazard, 114
Sudbrook, 534
Süderhöft, 890
Süderoogsand, 866, 890
Süderpiep, L861, 866, 890
Suggestions for improvements, 2
Sule Skerry, R62, L389, 405
Sullom Voe, L391, 412, 413
Sumburgh, 113, 412, 413
Sumburgh Head, R56, L390, 393
Summer Islands (Tanera Mor), L420, 423, 432
Sun, bearing, rising and setting, 32
Sun & Moon, Rising, setting and
    twilights, 41
Sun & Moon Tables, 40
Sun's declination, 40
Sunart, Loch, L422, **439**
Sunderland, L330, 332, **345**
Sunk Head, 308
Sunk Lt F, R55, R61, 279
Sunrise, sunset and twilights, 42-43
Supplements, 2
Swale, The, L274, **286**
Swanage, L186, **199**
Swanage to Nab Tower, Tidal heights, 203
Swanage to Selsey, special tidal
    problems, 200-202
Swansea, R57, L515, 518, **531**

Swarbacks Minn, L389, 412
Sween, Loch, 460, 461
Swellies, The, 487, 503
Swilkie Point Race, 392
Swilly, Lough, L589, 592, **608**
Swinge, The, 624, 627
Sylt, L862, 866, **890**
Symbols, Admiralty chart, 16-17
Synchronised beacons, 53

T

Tabs Head, 336
Tamar, River, 164
Tancarville, 791
Tanera Mor (Summer Islands), L420, 423
Tann Spit No 38, L468
Tarbat Ness, R61, L388, 392, 399
Tarbert (Shannon), 581
Tarbert, Loch (Jura), 461
Tarbert, Loch Fyne, 463
   see also East Loch Tarbert
Tarbert, West Loch (Kintyre), 461
Tarn Point, 491
Tater-du, L142, 147
Tautenay Lt Bn, L622, 628
Tavy, River, 164
Taw, River, 542-543
Tawe River, barrage, 531
Tay, River, 374
Tayport, L361, L362, 364, 374
Tayvallich (Loch Sween), 460, 461
Tchue, La, 627
Tean Sound, 151
Teelin Harbour, 609
Tees, River, R61, L330, 332, 343
Teesside, R55
Tegeler Plate, L860
Teignmouth, L143, 146, **177**
Teignouse, Passage de la, L714, 718, 726
Telegraph Bay, 627
Telephone, Dialling codes, 131
   International calls, 131
Telephone, weather forecasts, 88
Telephones, mobile, 103
Telephoning, UK to/from, Belgium, 822
   France, 652-653
   Germany, 867
   Ireland, 555
   Netherlands, 822
Television forecasts, Ceefax and Teletext, 91
Temperature conversion, 85
Temporary importation of vessels, 13
Tenby, L515, 518, **529**
Terms used in weather bulletins, 85
Termunterzijl, L817, 849
Terneuzen, L813, **828**
Terre-Nègre, L744, 758
Terschelling, C78, 821
Terschelling, West, L816, 821, 847
Terschelling, Zeegat van, 848
Terschelling Bank, Platform L8-G, R63
Test, River, 226-228
Teufelsbrück, L861, 884
Texel, L816, 820, 846
Thames, Estuary, L275
   Estuary, 278
   Estuary diagram, **284**
   River, 278

River diagrams, **293**
Thames Barrier, 294
Thames Estuary tidal streams, 282-283
Thames Radio, C72
Thermometer conversion scale, 85
Tholen, 834
Thorney Channel, 243
Threeknobs-W buoy, L861
Thrumster, R111
Thurso, L389, 405
Thyborön, 891
Tidal, calculations of times and heights, 119
   coefficients, Brest, 698, 699
   curves, 121
   diamonds, 124
   differences, West Denmark, 891
   information, 117
   prediction by computer, 122
   predictions, 130
   stream atlases, 123
   in rivers, 124
   rates, 124
   terms, French, 699
Tidal coefficients, 118
Tidal stream charts
   Area 1, 140-141
   Area 2, 184-185
   Area 3, 248-249
   Area 4, 272-273
   Area 5, 326-327
   Area 6, 358-359
   Area 7, 386-387
   Area 8, 418-419
   Area 9, 454-455
   Area 10, 482-483
   Area 11, 512-513
   Area 12, 549-549
   Area 13, 586-587
   Area 14, 620-621
   Area 15, 646-647
   Area 16, 678-679
   Area 17, 710-711
   Area 18, 740-741
   Area 19, 772-773
   Area 20, 810-811
   Area 21, 856-857
   Isle of Wight, 224-225
   Land's End, 144
   Mull of Kintyre, 465
   Portland, 192-193
   Rathlin Island, 605
   Thames Estuary, 282-283
Tidal streams, Channel Islands, 623
Tidecalc, 122
Tide Mill Yacht Harbour, 316
Tides, 117
   calculating intermediate times and heights of tide, 121
   graphical method of interpolating, 120
   meteorological conditions, 124
   time and height differences, 120
Tighnabruaich, 466-467
Tilbury, 294
Time, BBC Radio time signals, 80
   Standard Times, 80
Times, 80, 118
Time signals, 80
Time zones, 80, 118
Tingwall, 408
Tinker's Hole, 441
Tiree, R111, L422, 424, 439
Tiumpan Head, L420
Tjerkgaast, C78

Tobermory, L422, 424, **440**
Tod Head, L361, 364
Tollesbury, 308
Tomé, Île, 690
Tönning, L861, 890
Topsham, 146, 179
Torbay, 146
Torduff Point, 489
Torquay, L143, **176**
Torridge, River, 542-543
Torridon, Loch, 423, 436
Torsminde, 891
Tor Sound, 592
Tory Island, R57, L589
Tory Sound, 593
Tossens, L859
Totland Bay, 212
Totnes, 174, 175
Toulinguet, Chenal de, 685
Toulinguet, Pointe de, 683
Touquet, Le, R59, L776, 778, **798**
Tourist Office, National
   Belgium, 822
   France, 652-653, 791
   Germany, 867
   Netherlands, 822
Toward Point, L457
Tower Race, 568
Towing and pushing, 10
Towing signals, 10, 18-19
Track Ferry buoy, L812
Traffic Centre, Botlek, 839
   Hansweert, 827
   Hoek van Holland, 839
   Stad, 839
   Steenbank, 827
   Terneuzen, 827
   Vlissingen, 827
   Wandelaar, 827
   Zandvliet, 827
   Zeebrugge, 827
Traffic separation schemes (TSS), 8, 132
Tralee Bay, L552, 580
Tranche-sur-Mer, La, L743
Trawbreaga Bay, 607
Trearddur Bay, 505
TrÈbeurden, L681, **691**
Tréboul, 706
Trefor, 505
Trégastel, L681, 691
Tréguier, L680, 689
Tréhiguier, 731
Tremblade, La, 757
TrÈport, Le, L775, 778, **797**
Treshnish Isles, 441
Trévignon, L713, 717
Trevose Head, R111, L517, 519
Trézien, L682
Triagoz, Les, L681, 684
Trieux, Le, L680, 684, 687
Trimingham, R111
Trinité-sur-Mer, La, L715, 718, 726
Tristan, Île, L683, 706
Trois Pierres, Les (Chenal de la Helle), L682
Trois Pierres, Les (Lorient), L714, 724
Troon, L458, 460, **476**
Trouville, L775, 777, **785**
True bearing of Sun at sunrise/sunset, 39
Truro, 155
Trwyn-du, L486
Trwyn Dinmor, 505
TSS, Dover Strait, 800

Elbe, 851
German Bight, 851
Jade, 851
Maas, 839
North Channel, 604
North Hinder, 850
off Belgium and Netherlands, 826
off Botney Ground, 850
off Brown Ridge, 850
off Fastnet Rock, 576
off Germany, 851
off Netherlands, 850
off Skerries, 504
off Smalls, 524-525
off Texel, 850
off Tuskar Rock, 566
Terschelling, 851
West Friesland, 850
Tuckton Bridge, 212
Turballe, La, L715, **732**
Turnberry, R56
Turnchapel, 162-163
Tuskar Rock, R57, R62, L 550, 553, 592
Tuskar Rock TSS, 565
Twelfths, rule of, 122
Twin buoy, L812
Tyne, River (North Shields), L330,
    332, **346**
Tyne, River, tides, 347-349
Tynemouth, R111
Types of emission (RDF), 53
Types of position fixing system, 48

U

Uig Bay (Loch Snizort), L422, 436
Uist, North and South, L420, 423
UK, weather sources, 91
UK Coast Radio Stations, 72
UK Public Holidays, 132
Ullapool, L420, 423, **432**
Ullapool tides, 433-435
Ulva Sound, 440
Ulverston, L492
Universal Time, 118
Unst, R56, L391, 412
Upnor, 289
Ura Firth, 412
Urgency, 104
Urk, 844
Useful addresses, 14
Ushant (Île d'Ouessant), R58, R63, L
    682, 684, 696
Ushant (Île d'Ouessant) Radio, C76
Ushenish, L420
Using the International Code, 66
Usk, River, L515, 533

V

Vaila Sound, L391, 414
Val-André, 672
Valentia, L552, 579, 580
Valentia Radio, C75
Valley, 113
Vannes, 729, **730**
Variation, 26
Varne Lanby, R61, 147, L 251, 252, 267
VAT and the single market, 13

Vatersay Sound, L421, 426
Vatteville, 791
Vazon Bay, 629
Veere, 834
Veerse Meer, 834, 834
Vegesack, 878
Ventnor, L188, 234
Ventry, 580
Vent Solaire, 717
Ver, L774
Verclut breakwater, L623, 638
Vergoyer buoy, R63, 149, L 776
Ver, Pointe de, R59
Vertical clearance under bridges, 122
Vertical sextant angles, 32
Ve Skerries, R62, L391, 412
Vessels aground lights, 10, 18-19
Vessels constrained by their draught,
    lights, 18-19
Vessels not under command, 10, 18-19
Vessel Traffic Services, 69
VHF
    calls to UK Coast Radio Stations,
        68
    frequencies, 67
    link calls, radiotelephone, 68
    R/T, 215
    radio, 67
Victoria Marina, 630
Vieille, La, L683
Vieille, La (Raz de Sein), L712
Vierge, Île, R58, L681, 695
Vigne, La, 765
Vilaine, La, River, 671, L715, 718, **731**
Village Bay, 430
Ville-es-Martin, L716
Violet Channel, 625
Visitors, cost of berth, 131
Visual signals between UK shore
    stations and ships in distress, 112
Vlaardingen, 840
Vlieland, R59, R63, L 816, **847**
Vlissingen (Flushing), L813, 820, **829**
Vlissingen tides, 830-832
Volendam, 844
Volkerak, L815
Volmet, 91
Vortrapptief buoy, L861, 891
Voslapp, L859
VTS, 69
VTS, Westerschelde, 826
VTS Maas, 839

W

Waddenzee, L816, 820
Wadebridge, 544
Wainfleet, L329, 336
Waldringfield, 316
Wallasea, 304
Wallet, L276, 278, L 281
Walls, 414
Walney Island, R57, R111, L 484, 487,
    492
Walsoorden, L813, 827
Walton-on-the-Naze, L276
Walton-on-the-Naze tides, 311-313
Walton Backwaters, 310
Wandelaar, R63
Wangerooge, R59, L859, 865, 869, **872**
Wangersiel, L859, 873
Wareham, 208-211

Warkworth Harbour, L330, 332, 351
Warning signals (Rule 34), 11
Warrenpoint (Newry River), L589, 595
Warsash, L187, 228-229
Warton, R57
Wash, The, L328, 331, 335
Watchet, L517, **541**
Waterford, R57, L550, **567**
Watermill Cove, 151
Watermouth, 541
Waternish Point, L422
Waterways, Inland
    Belgium, 822
    Brittany, **671**
    France, 791
    Netherlands, 822
Wattisham, 113
Waypoints, 130
    Area 1, 142
    Area 2, 186
    Area 3, 250
    Area 4, 272-273
    Area 5, 328
    Area 6, 360
    Area 7, 388
    Area 8, 420
    Area 9, 456
    Area 10, 484
    Area 11, 514
    Area 12, 550
    Area 13, 586-587
    Area 14, 622
    Area 15, 648
    Area 16, 680
    Area 17, 712
    Area 18, 742
    Area 19, 774
    Area 20, 812
    Area 21, 858-862
    Clyde Area, L468
    displays, 52
    East Anglian, 281
    English Channel, 147-149
    loading, 52
    navigation, 52
    North Sea (S), 852
    Solent Area, 216-217
Weather, 81
Weather bulletins, BT coast radio
    stations, 91
Weather forecasts by telephone call, 88
Weather sources, BBC inshore waters
    forecast, 86
    BBC Radio 4, 86
    Belgium, 98
    Coastguard broadcasts, 106
    CROSS broadcasts, 98
    CRS weather broadcasts Channel
        Islands, 91
    CRS weather broadcasts Ireland,
        92
    CRS weather broadcasts UK, 91
    fax broadcasts, 90
    general forecasts, 86
    Germany, 100
    Marinecall, 88
    MetFAX, 88
    Netherlands, 99
    R/T weather broadcasts France,
        96-97
    R/T, 70
    RTE weather broadcasts Ireland,
        92
    Volmet, 91
    weather centres, 90

Websites, C80
Wedel, 884
Welland, River, 336
Wellhouse Rock, 534
Wells-next-the-Sea, L281, L328, **334**
Welsh words, 518
Wembury Range, 164
Wemeldinge, 833, 834
Wemyss Bay, 468
Weser River, R63, L859, 865, 878
West Bramble Lt By, R61
West Cove (Kerry), 579
Westerems, R63, 865
Westerheversand, L861
Westerland, 891
Westerland/Sylt, R59
Westerschelde, L812, L813, 820, **827**
Westerschelde VTS, 826
West Frisian Islands, 847
West Hinder Lt, L812
Westhoofd, L815
Westkapelle, C78, L813, 820, 827
West Kyle, 466
West Lepe buoy, L187, 216-217
West Loch Tarbert, L456
West Loch Tarbert (Harris), 425
West Mersea, 308
Weston-super-Mare, L517, 540
Westport (Clew Bay), L591, **611**
Westray, L390, 406
W Scar Lt By, R62
West Schouwen, L815
West Stones, 335
West Swin, L275
West Terschelling, 847
Wexford, L550, **564**
Weymass Bay, L457
Weymouth, L186, 189, **197**
Whalsay, L390, 412
Whitaker Beacon, 304
Whitaker Channel, L275
Whitburn Firing Range, L330
Whitby, R111, **343**
Whitehaven, L484, **491**
Whitehill (Shetland), L391
Whitehills, 394
White House, 534
Whithorn Bay, Isle of, L484, 487, 489
Whitsand Bay, 161
Whitstable, L274, **285**
Wick, R56, L389, 392, **401**
Wicklow, L550, **563**
Wicklow Head Radio, C75
Wick Radio, C72
Wick Tides, 402-404
Wide Firth, L390
Wideford Hill, R111
Widewall Bay, 406, 407
Widnes, 494
Wielingen buoy, L812
Wierengermeer, C78
Wight, Isle of, L187, L188, 190
    tidal streams, 224-225
Wigtown, 487
Wilhelmshaven, L859, **877**
Wilhelmshaven tides, 874-876
William, Port, 489
Windyhead, R111
Winteringham, 341
Winterton-on-Sea, R61, 322
Winterton Ridge buoy, L328
Wisbech, L328, 335
Wischafen, 883
Witham, River, L329, 336
Wittdün, 890

Wivenhoe, 309
WLR FM, 566
Wolf Rock, R61, L142, 147, 151
Wolphaartsdijk, 834
Woodbridge Haven, L277, 316
Woolpack buoy, L328
Woolverstone, 315
Woolwich, 294
Wootton Creek, L188, **233**
Worbarrow Bay, 199
Workington, L484, 487, **490**
Workum, 844
Worthing, 255
Wouldham, 289
Wrabness, 315
Wrath, Cape, 392, L420, 423
Wrecks, Historic, 130
Wye, River, 515, L516
Wyk, L862, 890
Wyre Dock, 493
Wyre Lt ho, L493
Wyre Sound, 406

Y

Yacht and boat safety schemes, 112
Yacht routes, recommended, 829
Yarmouth (IoW), L187, **218**
Yarmouth, Great, L277, 279, 322, L 328
Yealm, River, 169
Yelland Marsh, 542-543
Yell Sound, L390, 412
Yerseke, L814, 834
Yeu, Île d', L742, 745, 749
Youghal, L551, **568**

Z

Zandvliet, L813
Zeebrugge, R59, L812, 820, **825**
Zeegaten, 820
Zeegat van Ameland, 821
Zeegat van Terschelling, 821, **848**
Zeegat van Texel, L815, 821
Zeelandbrug, 833
ZH (Zuider Haaks) buoy, L816
Zierikzee, L814, 834
Zijpe, L814, 834
Zone time, 118, 130
Zoutkamp, L817, 848
ZS buoy, L816
Zuider Stortemelk, 847
Zuid Vlije Lt By ZV11/SRK 4, R63